D1362433

HANDBOOK FOR TEXAS TEACHERS

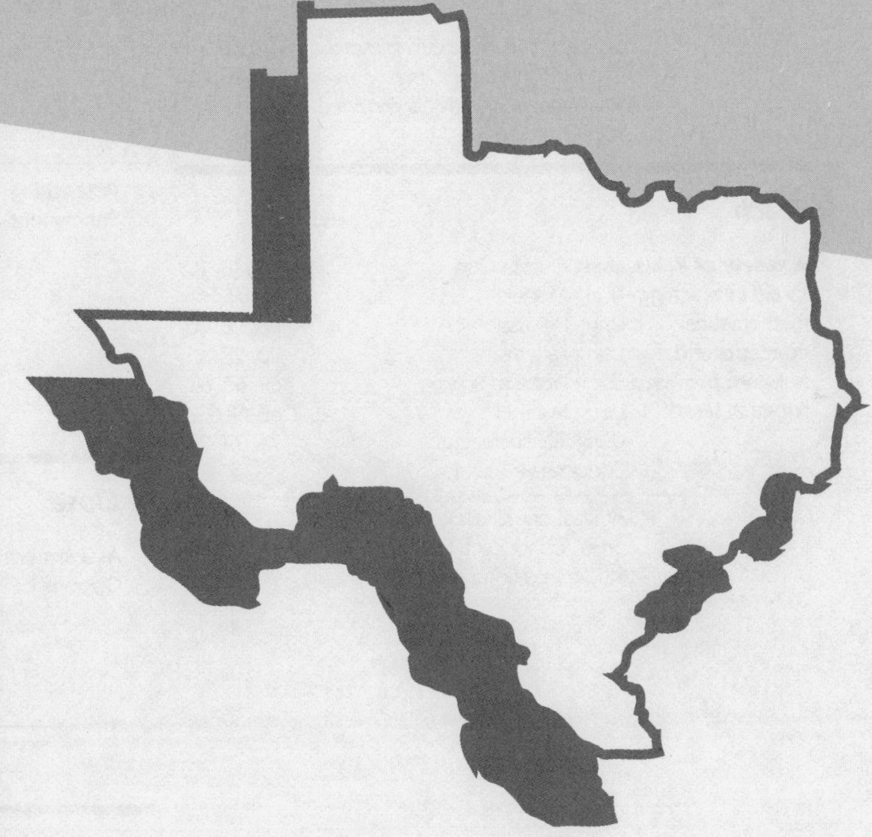

GLENCOE

Macmillan/McGraw-Hill

TTAS and Four-Step Lessons

Pre-Algebra Teacher Margin	Description	TTAS Indicators
1 Focus		
Objectives	Objectives are stated with each lesson in the Student Edition. The purpose of the lesson is stated in the margin of the Teacher's Wraparound Edition.	2A, 6B, 6D, 6E, 6F
Vocabulary	New terms are listed in the margin of each lesson in the Student Edition and are clearly defined in the lesson.	6B, 6D, 6E, 7B
Motivating the Lesson	Various strategies are suggested for most lessons. Each lesson in the Student Edition opens with a real-world situation to motivate the concept and skill that is presented. The Bell Ringer is another motivational idea that is provided for each lesson.	1A, 1B, 1C, 3A, 3B, 3G, 3E, 4B, 4E, 6A, 6B, 6C, 6G, 8A, 8B, 8D
2 Teach		
A variety of ideas to aid in teaching mathematical concepts and skills are provided for each lesson	Using Questioning Using Models Using Discussion Using Patterns Using Problem Solving Using Manipulatives Using Transparencies Cooperative Learning	1A, 1B, 1C, 1D, 1E, 2A, 2B, 2C, 2D, 2E, 3, 6B, 6C, 6D, 6E, 6F, 6G, 7A, 7B, 7C
	At least one Chalkboard Example is provided for each Example in the Student Edition	7D, 7E, 8A, 8B, 9A, 9B

Pre-Algebra Teacher Margin	Description	TTAS Indicators
3 Practice/Apply		
Checking the Concept	Suggestions for using the **Guided Practice** Exercises are provided.	1B, 1F, 2B, 2C, 2E, 7B, 7C, 7E
Error Analysis	This helps the teacher to monitor and adjust speaking and writing errors that students often make when learning skills and concepts. Suggestions for preventing these errors are provided.	2B, 2D, 2E, 3B, 4B, 6E, 7A, 7D, 7E
Independent Practice	A **Homework Assignment Guide** is provided for three levels of ability: Basic, Average, Honors. Practice Masters are provided for all lessons in the Teacher's Resource Package. Extra Practice Sets for all skill and concept lessons are included in the Student Edition.	1B, 1C, 1F, 2B, 2C, 2D, 2E
Reteaching/ Enrichment	Alternate strategies for reteaching and extending the lesson are provided in the margin for many lessons. These often include using small groups, working cooperatively. Reteaching and Enrichment Masters are also provided for all skill and concept lessons in the Teacher's Resource Package.	1A, 1B, 1D, 1F, 2E, 2F, 3B, 3D, 3E, 4E
4 Close		
Assessment Options	The suggested method for closing a lesson uses one of the following strategies: Writing Speaking Modeling An Alternate Assessment option is provided for each chapter in the teacher margin of the Chapter Review.	1B, 1C, 1F, 2B, 2C, 2D, 2E, 2F, 6G, 6H, 7D, 7E, 7F, 8C, 9D
***Special Features** (Student Edition)*		
Explorations, Algebra in Action, History, Biography, Careers, Connections	Features within every chapter provide opportunities for exploration extension, variation, and connections to real world situations.	1A, 3A, 3D, 3E, 4C, 4D, 4E, 5B, 5C, 5E, 7C, 8C, 9D

Essential Elements

1 Problem Solving

A Communicate an understanding of a problem by describing and discussing the problem and recording the relevant information

B Select appropriate strategies from a variety of approaches such as: act it out; make a model; draw a picture; systematically guess and check; make a diagram, chart, or graph; simplify the problem; find a pattern; or work backwards

C Select appropriate methods and materials for solving problems including concrete manipulatives, models, mental computation, paper and pencil, and calculator and/or computer

D Solve a problem, evaluate the outcome for reasonableness (including appropriateness of units), make revisions as needed, describe and discuss the process and solution, and make a decision based on the solution

E Generate, extend, and generalize problems and solutions

2 Number and numeration concepts

A Use scientific notation and extend to applications with calculators

B Find factors, prime factors, and multiples using divisibility rules

C Understand and apply concepts involving least common multiple and greatest common factor to fractions and algebraic monomials

D Identify and use the properties and characteristics of subsystems of the real number system

E Simplify polynomials by combining like terms and using the distributive property

F Write symbolic expressions for word phrases

3 Operations and computation

A Use basic operations and properties of integers, decimals, and fractions to solve relevant problems, using mental techniques, pencil/paper, and a calculator, as appropriate

B Use the order of operations to simplify expressions and solve multi-step problems

C Evaluate an expression that contains absolute values

D Use the laws of exponents and their applications including zero and negative integral exponents

E Simplify and estimate numeric radical expressions involving square roots using a calculator when appropriate

F Solve simple linear equations and inequalities involving rational numbers

G Estimate and solve application problems by writing and solving simple two-step equations

H Evaluate expressions and formulas containing variables, using a calculator when appropriate

I Estimate and solve problems using ratios, proportions, and percent and check the reasonableness of the result

4 Geometry and measurement

A Identify and classify geometric figures, solids, and their characteristics

B Use metric and customary units to find distance, perimeter, circumference, area, surface area, and volume in problem situations

C Use indirect measurement with similar figures

D Solve right triangle problems using the Pythagorean theorem and its converse

E Apply algebraic techniques to geometric situations

5 Probability, statistics, and graphing

A Construct a sample space by listing, using a tree diagram, etc.

B Investigate various ways to determine the number of possible outcomes for a given situation

C Find the probability of independent and dependent events

D Collect, organize, and graph data relevant to pre-algebra problems

E Interpret graphs and analyze data to solve relevant problems

F Determine measures of central tendency and their uses in relevant problem situations

6 Graphing

A Graph solution sets of equations and inequalities on a number line, using computer graphics when appropriate

B Graph linear equations and inequalities on a coordinate plane, and explore the characteristics of these graphs with computer graphics

C Find the slope and intercepts of the graph of a linear equation

D Solve systems of linear equations by graphing

Correlation of Merrill Pre-Algebra to the Texas Essential Elements and TAAS

A Preview Pre-Algebra

	Student Edition			Teacher Resource Package	
Lesson Title	**Pages**	**Essential Elements**	**TAAS Objectives**	**Pages**	
Featuring 4 Steps to Problem Solving	2-3	1A, 1D, 1E	11	P13, R12, E12	
In Your Estimation	4-5	1A, 1D, 1E	10	P6	
Choosing the Method of Computation	6-7	1A, 1B, 1C, 1D, 1E	10	P9, R8, E8	
Let's Be Reasonable	8-9	1A, 1B, 1C, 1D, 1E	13	P19, R17, E17, A32	
Getting Good at Graphs	10-11	5E	12	P7, R6, E6, A16, A61, T16	

Chapter 1
The Language of Algebra

	Student Edition			Teacher Resource Package	Other Components
Lesson Title	**Pages**	**Essential Elements**	**TAAS Objectives**	**Pages**	**Pages**
EXPL: Naming Numbers	14	1A, 1C, 1E, 3B	2	LM 27	
Order of Operations	15-17	3A, 3B		P1, R1, E1, A31	TT1-1, C1-1, TG
EXPL. Algebraic Expressions	18	1A, 1C, 1E, 3B		LM 28	
Variables & Expressions	19-21	3A, 3B, 3H	2	P2, R2, E2, T1	TT1-2, C1-2, TG
Properties	22-24	2D, 3A, 3B, 3H	2	P3, R3, E3	TT1-3, C1-3, TG
The Distributive Property	25-28	2D, 2E, 3A, 3B, 3H, 4E	2, 11	P4, R4, E4	TT1-4, C1-4, TG
EXPL: Distributive Property	29	1A, 1C, 1E, 2E		LM 29	
Variables & Equations	30-31	3F, 4B, 4E	2, 4, 11	P5, R5, E5	TT1-5, C1-5, TG
PSS: Guess & Check	33-34	1A, 1B, 1C, 1D, 1E	10, 13	P6, A46	TT1-6, C1-6, TG
Using Inverse Operations	35-38	3A, 3F, 4E, 5F	2, 11, 12	P7, R6, E6, A16, A61, T16	TT1-7, C1-7, TG
Writing Expressions	39-42	2F, 3A, 5E	12	P8, R7, E7, A1	TT1-8, C1-8, TG
PS: Use an Equation	43-45	1D, 1E, 3A	10, 12, 13	P9, R8, E8	TT1-9, C1-9, TG
Inequalities	46-47	2F, 3A, 3F, 3H	2, 12	P10, R9, E9, T31	TT1-10, C1-10, TG

Chapter 2
Integers

	Student Edition			Teacher Resource Package	Other Components
Lesson Title	**Pages**	**Essential Elements**	**TAAS Objectives**	**Pages**	**Pages**
Integers & Absolute Value	54-56	2D, 3A, 3C		P11, R10, E10, T32	TT2-1, C2-1, TG
Comparing & Ordering	57-58	2D, 2F, 5E	1, 12	P12, R11, E11	TT2-2, C2-2, TG
EXPL: Adding Integers	59	1A, 1C, 1E, 2D		LM 30	
Adding Integers	60-62	2D, 2F, 3A, 3C, 3H	2, 6, 12	P13, R12, E12, A62	TT2-3, C2-3, TG
More on Adding Integers	63-64	2D, 2E, 3A	2, 6, 12	P14, R13, E13, A17	TT2-4, C2-4, TG
EXPL: Subtract Integers	65	1A, 1C, 1E, 2D		LM 31	
Subtracting Integers	66-68	2D, 2E, 3A, 3H	2, 7	P15, R14, E14, A47, T2, T17	TT2-5, C2-5, TG
L: Statements & Negations	70-71	1A, 1E		P16	TT2-6, C2-6, TG
EXPL: Multiplying Integers	72	1A, 1C, 1E, 2D		LM 32	
Multiplying Integers	73-75	2D, 3A, 3H	2, 8	P17, R15, E15, A2	TT2-7, C2-7, TG
Dividing Integers	76-78	2D, 3A, 3H, 5F	2, 5, 9, 11	P18, R16, E16, A63	TT2-8, C2-8, TG
PS: Using Integers	79-81	1D, 1E, 3A	6, 7, 8, 9, 10, 13	P19, R17, E17, A32	TT2-9, C2-9, TG

Key to Lesson Title Abbreviations: ***EXPL*** (Exploration); ***PS*** (Problem Solving); ***PSS*** (Problem Solving Strategy); ***A*** (Application); ***L*** (Logic)

Key to copy master booklets in *Teacher Resource Package:* *P* (Practice); ***R*** (Reteaching); ***E*** (Enrichment); ***T*** (Technology); ***A*** (Activities); ***LM*** (Lab Manual)
Key to *Other Components:* *TT* (Teaching Transparencies); ***C*** (Group Activity Cards); ***TG*** (Test Generator)

Correlation of Merrill Pre-Algebra to the Texas Essential Elements and TAAS

Chapter 3
Solving One-Step Equations

Lesson Title	Student Edition Pages	Student Edition Essential Elements	Student Edition TAAS Objectives	Teacher Resource Package Pages	Other Components Pages
EXPL: Solving Equations	88	1A, 1C, 1E, 3F		LM 33	
Solving Equations: $x+a=b$	89-91	1E, 2F, 2A, 3F	2, 7, 12	P20, R18, E18	TT3-1, C3-1, TG
Solving Equations: $x-b=c$	92-94	1E, 2F, 3A, 3F	2, 6, 10, 12	P21, R19, E19, T18	TT3-2, C3-2, TG
Solving Equations: $ax=c$	95-97	1E, 2F, 3A, 3F, 4B, 5F	2, 4, 5, 9, 12	P22, R20, E20	TT3-3, C3-3, TG
Solving Equations: $\frac{x}{a}=b$	98-100	1E, 3A, 3F	2, 8	P23, R21, E21, T3, A48	TT3-4, C3-4, TG
A: Formulas	101-103	1E, 3A, 3F, 3H	2, 6, 7, 8, 9	P24, R22, E22, A3, A18	TT3-5, C3-5, TG
A: Perimeter & Area	105-108	1E, 3A, 3F, 3H, 4B, 4E	2, 4, 11	P25, R23, E23, LM35, T33, A33	TT3-6, C3-6, TG
EXPL: Perimeter & Area	109	1A, 1C, 1E, 4B, 4E		LM 34	
Solving Inequalities: $+/-$	110-112	1E, 2F, 3A, 3F, 5E	12	P26, R24, E24	TT3-7, C3-7, TG
Solving Inequalities: $\times/\div$	113-115	1E, 2F, 3A, 3F	12	P27, R25, E25	TT3-8, C3-8, TG
L: Compound Statements	116-118	1A, 1E		P28, A64	TT3-9, C3-9, TG
PS: Using Equations & Inequalities	119-121	1D, 1E, 3A, 3F	10, 12, 13	P29, R26, E26	TT3-10, C3-10, TG

Chapter 4
Factors and Fractions

Lesson Title	Student Edition Pages	Student Edition Essential Elements	Student Edition TAAS Objectives	Teacher Resource Package Pages	Other Components Pages
Factors & Monomials	128-130	1E, 2B, 3A		P30, R27, E27, T34, A49	TT4-1, C4-1, TG
Powers & Exponents	131-133	1E, 2F, 3A, 3B, 3D, 3H, 4B	1, 2, 12	P31, R28, E28, T4	TT4-2, C4-2, TG
PSS: Draw a Diagram	134-135	1A, 1B, 1C, 1D, 1E	10, 13	P32	TT4-3, C4-3, TG
Prime Factorization	136-138	1E, 2B, 3A, 4B	1, 2, 4	P33, R29, E29, A65	TT4-4, C4-4, TG
EXPL: Factor Patterns	139	1A, 1C, 1E, 2B		LM 36	
Greatest Common Factor	140-142	1E, 2B, 2C, 3A	1, 2	P34, R30, E30, T19	TT4-5, C4-5, TG
Simplifying Fractions	143-145	1E, 2C, 3A	1, 2, 11	P35, R31, E31, A4	TT4-6, C4-6, TG
Least Common Multiple	146-148	1E, 2C, 3A	1, 2	P36, R32, E32, LM37, LM38	TT4-7, C4-7, TG
Comparing Fractions	149-151	1E, 2B, 2C, 3A, 5E	1, 2, 12	P37, R33, E33, A34	TT4-8, C4-8, TG
Multiplying Powers	152-154	1E, 2F, 3A, 3D	1, 2, 12	P38, R34, E34, A19	TT4-9, C4-9, TG
Dividing Powers	155-158	1E, 2C, 3A, 3D	1, 2	P39, R35, E35	TT4-10, C4-10, TG

Key to Lesson Title Abbreviations: ***EXPL*** (Exploration); ***PS*** (Problem Solving); ***PSS*** (Problem Solving Strategy); ***A*** (Application); ***L*** (Logic)

Key to copy master booklets in *Teacher Resource Package:* *P* (Practice); ***R*** (Reteaching); ***E*** (Enrichment); ***T*** (Technology); ***A*** (Activities); ***LM*** (Lab Manual)
Key to *Other Components:* *TT* (Teaching Transparencies); ***C*** (Group Activity Cards); ***TG*** (Test Generator)

Correlation of Merrill Pre-Algebra to the Texas Essential Elements and TAAS

Chapter 5
Rationals: Adding and Subtracting Patterns

	Lesson Title	Student Edition Pages	Student Edition Essential Elements	Student Edition TAAS Objectives	Teacher Resource Package Pages	Other Components Pages
5.1	Rational Numbers	166-168	1E, 2D, 3A	4, 11	P40, R36, E36	TT5-1, C5-1, TG
5.2	Writing Decimals as Fractions	169-171	1E, 2D, 3A	1, 4, 11	P41, R37, E37	TT5-2, C5-2, TG
5.3	Estimating Sums and Differences	172-173	1B, 1C, 3A	1, 10, 13	P42, R38, E38	TT5-3, C5-3, TG
5.4	Rationals: +/− Decimals	174-176	1E, 2D, 3A, 3H	2, 6, 7, 10, 13	P43, R39, E39, T5, A20	TT5-4, C5-4, TG
5.5	Rationals: +/− Like Fractions	177-179	1E, 3A	4, 6, 7, 11	P44, R49, E40, A5	TT5-5, C5-5, TG
5.6	Rationals: +/− Unlike Fractions	180-182	1E, 3A	4, 6, 7, 10, 11, 13	P45, R41, E41, T20	TT5-6, C5-6, TG
5.7	Solving Equations & Inequalities	184-187	1E, 2F, 3A, 3F, 4E, 5E	2, 4, 6, 7, 11, 12	P46, R42, E42	TT5-7, C5-7, TG
5.8	PSS: Look for a Pattern	188-189	1A, 1B, 1C, 1D, 1E	2, 10, 13	P47, A50, A66	TT5-8, C5-8, TG
5.9	Arithmetic Sequences (Ch 9)	190-193	1E, 2F, 3A, 3H	2, 6, 7, 12	P48, R43, E43, T35, A35, A67, LM 40, LM41	TT5-9, C5-9, TG
	EXPL: Fibonacci Sequence	194	1A, 1C, 1E, 2A		LM 39	
	A: Adding & Subtracting Measures	195-197	1E, 4B	4, 11	P49, R44, E44	TT5-10, C5-10, TG

Chapter 6
Rationals: Multiplying and Dividing Patterns

	Lesson Title	Student Edition Pages	Student Edition Essential Elements	Student Edition TAAS Objectives	Teacher Resource Package Pages	Other Components Pages
6.1	Write Fractions as Decimals	204-207	1E, 2D, 3A	1	P50, R45, E45, T21, A68	TT6-1, C6-1, TG
	EXPL: Decimal Patterns	208	1A, 1C, 1E, 2D		LM 42	
6.2	Est. Products & Quotients	209-210	1E, 2D, 3A, 4B	1, 8, 9, 10	P51, R46, E46	TT6-2, C6-2, TG
6.3	Rationals: Multiplying Fractions	211-214	1E, 2D, 3A, 3D, 3H	2, 8, 10, 13	P52, R47, E47, A21, LM43	TT6-3, C6-3, TG
6.4	Rationals: Multiplying Decimals	215-218	1E, 2D, 3A, 3D, 3H	2, 8, 10, 13	P53, R48, E48	TT6-4, C6-4, TG
6.5	Multiplicative Inverses	219-221	1E, 2D, 3A	2	P54, R49, E49	TT6-5, C6-5, TG
6.6	Rationals: Dividing Fractions	222-224	1E, 2D, 3A, 3D, 3H	2, 9	P55, R50, E50	TT6-6, C6-6, TG
6.7	Rationals: Dividing Decimals	225-227	1E, 2D, 3A, 5E	9, 10, 12, 13	P56, R51, E51, A6	TT6-7, C6-7, TG
6.8	Solving Equations & Inequalities	228-230	1E, 2D, 3A, 3F	2, 8, 9	P57, R52, E52, T6, LM44	TT6-8, C6-8, TG
6.9	L: Inductive & Deductive Reasoning	231-232	1A, 1E		P58	TT6-9, C6-9, TG
6.10	Geometric Sequences – Ch 9	233-235	1E, 2F, 3A, 3H	2, 8, 9, 12	P59, R53, E53, T36	TT6-10, C6-10, TG
6.11	Scientific Notation	237-239	1E, 2A, 2D, 3A	1	P60, R54, E54, A36	TT6-11, C6-11, TG
6.12	Comparing Rational Number	240-242	1E, 2A, 2D, 3A	1	P61, R55, E55	TT6-12, C6-12, TG
6.13	A: Circles & Circumference	243-245	1E, 3A, 4A, 4B, 4E	4, 11	P62, R56, E56, A51	TT6-13, C6-13, TG

Key to Lesson Title Abbreviations: ***EXPL*** (Exploration); ***PS*** (Problem Solving); ***PSS*** (Problem Solving Strategy); ***A*** (Application); ***L*** (Logic)

Key to copy master booklets in *Teacher Resource Package:* ***P*** (Practice); ***R*** (Reteaching); ***E*** (Enrichment); ***T*** (Technology); ***A*** (Activities); ***LM*** (Lab Manual)
Key to *Other Components:* ***TT*** (Teaching Transparencies); ***C*** (Group Activity Cards); ***TG*** (Test Generator)

Chapter 7
Solving Equations and Inequalities

Lesson Title	Student Edition: Pages	Student Edition: Essential Elements	Student Edition: TAAS Objectives	Teacher Resource Package: Pages	Other Components: Pages
PSS: Work Backwards	252-253	1A, 1B, 1C, 1D, 1E	2, 10, 13	P63, A7, A37, A69	TT7-1, C7-1, TG
EXPL: 2-Step Equations	254	1A, 1C, 1E, 3F		LM45	
Solving 2-Step Equations	255-258	1E, 2F, 3A, 3F, 3G, 3H, 4E	2, 4, 11, 12	P64, R57, E57	TT7-2, C7-2, TG
PS: Writing 2-Step Equations	259-261	1D, 1E, 2F, 3A, 3F, 3G	2, 10, 12, 13	P65, R58, E58, LM47	TT7-3, C7-3, TG
EXPL: More Equations	262	1A, 1C, 1E, 3F		LM46	
Variables on Each Side	263-266	1E, 3A, 3F	2, 12	P66, R59, E59, T37	TT7-4, C7-4, TG
Solving Multi-Step Equations	267-268	1E, 3A, 3F, 5E	2, 12	P67, R60, E60	TT7-5, C7-5, TG
Solving Multi-Step Inequalities	270-271	1E, 2F, 3A, 3F	2, 12	P68, R61, E61, T7, T22, A52	TT7-6, C7-6, TG
PS: Writing Inequalities	272-274	1D, 1E, 3A, 3F	10, 12, 13	P69, R62, E62	TT7-7, C7-7, TG
A: Using the Metric System	275-277	1E, 3A, 4B	4, 11	P70, R63, E63, A22	TT7-8, C7-8, TG

Chapter 8
Graphing Equations and Inequalities

Lesson Title	Student Edition: Pages	Student Edition: Essential Elements	Student Edition: TAAS Objectives	Teacher Resource Package: Pages	Other Components: Pages
Equations & the Number Line	284-285	1E, 3A, 3F, 6A	2	P71, R64, E64	TT8-1, C8-1, TG
Inequalities & the Number Line	286-288	1E, 3A, 3F, 6A	2	P72, R65, E65, A8	TT8-2, C8-2, TG
Ordered Pairs	290-292	1E, 3A, 3F, 4E	2, 11	P73, R66, E66	TT8-3, C8-3, TG
The Coordinate System	293-295	1E, 3A, 3F, 4E	2, 11	P74, R67, E67, A70, A71	TT8-4, C8-4, TG
Equations with Two Variables	296-298	1E, 2F, 3A, 4E, 6B	2, 11, 12	P75, R68, E68	TT8-5, C8-5, TG
Graphing Equations	299-301	1E, 2F, 3A, 6B	2, 12	P76, R69, E69, A53	TT8-6, C8-6, TG
PSS: Draw a Graph	302-304	1A, 1B, 1C, 1D, 1E, 6B	2, 10, 13	P77, A23	TT8-7, C8-7, TG
Slope	305-307	1E, 3A, 5E, 6B, 6C		P78, R70, E70	TT8-8, C8-8, TG
Intercepts	308-309	1E, 3A, 6B, 6C		P79, R71, E71, T8, T23	TT8-9, C8-9, TG
EXPL: Slope	310	1A, 1C, 1E, 6C		LM48	
Systems of Equations	311-313	1E, 3A, 6B, 6C, 6D	2	P80, R72, E72, T38, LM50	TT8-10, C8-10, TG
EXPL: Graphing Inequalities	314	1A, 1C, 1E, 6B		LM49	
Graphing Inequalities	315-317	1E, 3A, 6B	2	P81, R73, E73, A38	TT8-11, C8-11, TG

Key to Lesson Title Abbreviations: ***EXPL*** (Exploration); ***PS*** (Problem Solving); ***PSS*** (Problem Solving Strategy); ***A*** (Application); ***L*** (Logic)

Key to copy master booklets in *Teacher Resource Package:* *P* (Practice); ***R*** (Reteaching); ***E*** (Enrichment); ***T*** (Technology); ***A*** (Activities); ***LM*** (Lab Manual)
Key to *Other Components:* *TT* (Teaching Transparencies); ***C*** (Group Activity Cards); ***TG*** (Test Generator)

Correlation of Merrill Pre-Algebra to the Texas Essential Elements and TAAS

Chapter 9
Proportion and Percent

Lesson Title	Student Edition			Teacher Resource Package	Other Components
	Pages	Essential Elements	TAAS Objectives	Pages	Pages
Ratios & Rates	324-325	1E, 3A, 3I	2, 11	P82, R74, E74	TT9-1, C9-1, TG
Proportions	327-329	1E, 3A, 3I	2-11	P83, R75, E75, A24	TT9-2, C9-2, TG
EXPL: Capture-Recapture	330	1A, 1C, 1E, 3I		LM51	
A: Using Proportions	331-333	1E, 3A, 3I	2, 10, 11, 13	P84, R76, E76	TT9-3, C9-3, TG
Using the Percent Proportion	334-337	1E, 3A, 3I	2, 11	P85, R77, E77, A9, A39	TT9-4, C9-4, TG
Fractions, Decimals, & Percents	338-341	1E, 3A, 3I, 5E	1, 2, 11, 12	P86, R78, E78, A72, LM52-53	TT9-5, C9-5, TG
Percent & Estimation	342-345	1E, 3A, 3I, 5E	2, 10, 11, 12	P87, R79, E79, A54	TT9-6, C9-6, TG
Solve Percent Equations	346-348	1E, 3A, 3F, 3I	2, 11	P88, R80, E80, T9	TT9-7, C9-7, TG
A: Discount & Interest	349-351	1E, 3A, 3F, 3I	2, 10, 11, 13	P89, R81, E81, T24	TT9-8, C9-8, TG
PSS: Make a Table	352-353	1A, 1B, 1C, 1E	10, 13	P90, T39	TT9-9, C9-9, TG
A: Percent of Change	354-355	1E, 3A, 3I	2, 10, 11, 13	P91, R82, E82	TT9-10, C9-10, TG

Chapter 10
Statistics and Graphs

Lesson Title	Student Edition			Teacher Resource Package	Other Components
	Pages	Essential Elements	TAAS Objectives	Pages	Pages
EXPL: Gathering Data	362	1A, 1C, 1E, 5D, 5E		LM54	
Gathering & Recording Data	363-365	1E, 3A, 5D, 5E	5, 11, 12	P92, R83, E83, A73	TT10-1, C10-1, TG
Measures of Central Tendency	367-370	1E, 3A, 5D, 5E, 5F	5, 11, 12	P93, R84, E84, T10, T25, A25	TT10-2, C10-2, TG
Stem-and-Leaf Plots	371-373	1E, 3A, 5D, 5E, 5F	5, 11, 12	P94, R85, E85	TT10-3, C10-3, TG
Measures of Variation	374-377	1E, 3A, 5D, 5E, 5F	5, 11, 12	P95, R86, E86	TT10-4, C10-4, TG
Box-and-Whisker Plots	378-381	1E, 3A, 5D, 5E, 5F	5, 11, 12	P96, R87, E87	TT10-5, C10-5, TG
EXPL: Scatter Plots	382	1A, 1C, 1E, 5D, 5E		LM55	
Scatter Plots	383-385	1E, 3A, 5D, 5E	11, 12	P97, R88, E88, T40	TT10-6, C10-6, TG
PSS: Simplify the Problem	386-387	1A, 1B, 1C, 1D, 1E	10, 11, 13	P98	TT10-7, C10-7, TG
A: Use Statistics to Predict	388-390	1A, 3A, 3I, 5D, 5E	2, 10, 11, 12, 13	P99, R89, E89, A10	TT10-8, C10-8, TG
Misleading Statistics	391-393	1A, 3A, 5D, 5E, 5F	5, 11, 12	P100, R90, E90, A40, A55, LM56	TT10-9, C10-9, TG

Key to Lesson Title Abbreviations: ***EXPL*** (Exploration); ***PS*** (Problem Solving); ***PSS*** (Problem Solving Strategy); ***A*** (Application); ***L*** (Logic)

Key to copy master booklets in *Teacher Resource Package:* *P* (Practice); ***R*** (Reteaching); ***E*** (Enrichment); ***T*** (Technology); ***A*** (Activities); ***LM*** (Lab Manual)
Key to *Other Components:* *TT* (Teaching Transparencies); ***C*** (Group Activity Cards); ***TG*** (Test Generator)

Chapter 11 *Probability*

Lesson Title	Student Edition Pages	Student Edition Essential Elements	Student Edition TAAS Objectives	Teacher Resource Package Pages	Other Components Pages
Counting . . . Using Tree Diagrams	400-402	1E, 3A, 5A, 5B	5, 11, 12	P101, R91, E91	TT11-1, C11-1, TG
Counting . . . Using Multiplication	403-405	1E, 3A, 5A, 5B	5, 11, 12	P102, R92, E92	TT11-2, C11-2, TG
Permutations & Combinations	407-409	1E, 3A, 5B	5, 11	P103, R93, E93, T11, T41, A74	TT11-3, C11-3, TG
EXPL: Games	410	1A, 1C, 1E, 5A, 5D, 5E		LM57	
Probability	411-414	1E, 3A, 5C	5, 11	P104, R94, E94, T26, A41, A75	TT11-4, C11-4, TG
PS: Make a Table	415-416	1D, 1E, 3A, 5A, 5B, 5C	5, 10, 11, 12, 13	P105, R95, E95, A11	TT11-5, C11-5, TG
EXPL: Making Predictions	417	1A, 1C, 1E, 5C, 5D, 5E		LM58	
Probability of Independent Events	418-420	1E, 3A, 5C	5, 8, 11	P106, R96, E96	TT11-6, C11-6, TG
Probability of Dependent Events	421-423	1E, 3A, 5C	5, 8, 11	P107, R97, E97	TT11-7, C11-7, TG
Adding Probabilities	424-427	1E, 3A, 5C	5, 6, 7, 11	P108, R98, E98	TT11-8, C11-8, TG
EXPL: Computer Simulation	428	1A, 1C, 1E, 5A, 5C, 5D, 5E		LM59	
PSS: Use a Simulation	429-431	1A, 1B, 1C, 1D, 1E, 5A, 5D, 5E	5, 11, 12	P109, A26, A56	TT11-9, C11-9, TG

Chapter 12 *Applying Algebra to Geometry*

Lesson Title	Student Edition Pages	Student Edition Essential Elements	Student Edition TAAS Objectives	Teacher Resource Package Pages	Other Components Pages
The Language of Geometry	438-441	1E, 3A, 4A	3, 11	P110, R99, E99	TT12-1, C12-1, TG
A: Making Circle Graphs	442-444	1E, 3A, 4A, 4E, 5D, 5E	11, 12	P111, R100, E100, T12, A12	TT12-2, C12-2, TG
Angle Relationships	446-448	1E, 3A, 4A, 4E	2, 3, 11	P112, R101, E101	TT12-3, C12-3, TG
Parallel Lines	449-451	1E, 3A, 4A, 4E	2, 3, 11	P113, R102, E102, A27	TT12-4, C12-4, TG
Constructing Segments & Angles	452-455	1E, 3A, 4A	3, 11	P114, R103, E103	TT12-5, C12-5, TG
Triangles	456-458	1E, 3A, 4A, 4E	2, 3, 11	P115, R104, E104	TT12-6, C12-6, TG
L: Conditional Statements	459-460	1A, 1E		P116	TT12-7, C12-7, TG
Congruent Triangles	461-463	1E, 3A, 4A, 4E	3, 11	P117, R105, E105, A42	TT12-8, C12-8, TG
EXPL: Transformations	464	1A, 1C, 1E, 4A		LM60	
Similar Triangles	465-467	1E, 3A, 4A, 4C, 4E	2, 3, 11	P118, R106, E106	TT12-9, C12-9, TG
A: Indirect Measurement	468-470	1D, 1E, 3A, 4A, 4C, 4E	2, 3, 11	P119, R107, E107, LM62	TT12-10, C12-10, TG
Quadrilaterals	471-473	1E, 3A, 4A, 4E	2, 3, 11	P120, R108, E108, A57	TT12-11, C12-11, TG
Polygons	474-476	1E, 3A, 4A, 4E	2, 3, 11	P121, R109, E109, T27, T42, A76	TT12-12, C12-12, TG
EXPL: Tessellations	477	1A, 1C, 1E, 4A		LM61	

Key to Lesson Title Abbreviations: ***EXPL*** (Exploration); ***PS*** (Problem Solving); ***PSS*** (Problem Solving Strategy); ***A*** (Application); ***L*** (Logic)

Key to copy master booklets in *Teacher Resource Package:* *P* (Practice); ***R*** (Reteaching); ***E*** (Enrichment); ***T*** (Technology); ***A*** (Activities); ***LM*** (Lab Manual)

Key to *Other Components:* *TT* (Teaching Transparencies); ***C*** (Group Activity Cards); ***TG*** (Test Generator)

Correlation of Merrill Pre-Algebra to the Texas Essential Elements and TAAS

Chapter 13
Measuring Area and Volume

	Student Edition			Teacher Resource Package	Other Components
Lesson Title	**Pages**	**Essential Elements**	**TAAS Objectives**	**Pages**	**Pages**
13.1 Area: Parallelograms & Triangles	484-487	1E, 3A, 3H, 4A, 4B, 4E	2, 3, 4, 10, 11, 13	P122, R110, E110, T28, A77	TT13-1, C13-1, TG
13.2 Area: Trapezoids	488-490	1E, 3A, 3H, 4A, 4B, 4E	2, 3, 4, 11	P123, R111, E111, LM65	TT13-2, C13-2, TG
13.3 Area: Circles	492-493	1E, 3A, 3H, 4A, 4B, 4E	2, 3, 4, 10, 11, 13	P124, R112, E112, A28, A43	TT13-3, C13-3, TG
EXPL: Area & Probability	494	1A, 1C, 1E, 4B, 5A, 5D		LM63	
13.4 Surface Area: Prisms	495-497	1E, 3A, 3H, 4A, 4B, 4E	2, 3, 4, 10, 11, 13	P125, R113, E113	TT13-4, C13-4, TG
13.5 Surface Area: Cylinders	498-500	1E, 3A, 3H, 4A, 4B, 4E	2, 3, 4, 10, 11, 13	P126, R114, E114	TT13-5, C13-5, TG
13.6 Surface Area: Pyramids & Cones	501-504	1E, 3A, 3H, 4A, 4B, 4E	2, 3, 4, 10, 11, 13	P127, R115, E115	TT13-6, C13-6, TG
EXPL: Volume	505	1A, 1C, 1E, 4B		LM64	
13.7 Volume: Prisms	506-508	1E, 3A, 3H, 4A, 4B, 4E	2, 3, 4, 10, 11, 13	P128, R116, E116, T43	TT13-7, C13-7, TG
13.8 Volume: Cylinders	509-510	1E, 3A, 3H, 4A, 4B, 4E	2, 3, 4, 10, 11, 13	P129, R117, E117, A58	TT13-8, C13-8, TG
13.9 Volume: Pyramids & Cones	511-514	1E, 3A, 3H, 4A, 4B, 4E	2, 3, 4, 10, 11, 13	P130, R118, E118, T13, A13	TT13-9, C13-9, TG
13.10 A: Precision & Significant Digits	515-517	1E, 3A, 4B	4	P131, R119, E119	TT13-10, C13-10, TG
13.11 PSS: Make a Model or Drawing	518-519	1A, 1B, 1C, 1D, 1E, 4B	10, 11, 13	P132	TT13-11, C13-11, TG

Chapter 14
Applying Algebra to Right Triangles

	Student Edition			Teacher Resource Package	Other Components
Lesson Title	**Pages**	**Essential Elements**	**TAAS Objectives**	**Pages**	**Pages**
14.1 Squares & Square Roots	526-528	1E, 3A, 3E, 4E	2	P133, R120, E120	TT14-1, C14-1, TG
14.2 Approximate Square Roots	529-530	1E, 3A, 3E	10, 13	P134, R121, E121, A78	TT14-2, C14-2, TG
14.3 PSS: Use Venn Diagrams	531-532	1A, 1B, 1C, 1E, 2D		P135, A44	TT14-3, C14-3, TG
14.4 The Real Number System	533-536	1E, 2D, 3A, 3E	10, 13	P136, R122, E122	TT14-4, C14-4, TG
14.5 The Pythagorean Theorem	537-540	1E, 3A, 3E, 4A, 4D	3, 11, 12	P137, R123, E123, T29, T44, A14, A79, LM67	TT14-5, C14-5, TG
EXPL: Graphing Irrationals	541	1A, 1C, 1E, 4D		LM66	
14.6 PS: Using the Pythagorean Theorem	542-544	1D, 1E, 3A, 3E, 4D, 4E	3, 10, 11, 12, 13	P138, R124, E124, LM68	TT14-6, C14-6, TG
14.7 Special Right Triangles	545-547	1E, 3A, 3E, 4A, 4D, 4E	3, 11, 12	P139, R125, E125, T14	TT14-7, C14-7, TG
14.8 The Tangent Ratio	548-549	1E, 3A, 3I, 4A, 4E	3, 11, 12	P140, R126, E126	TT14-8, C14-8, TG
14.9 Sine & Cosine Ratios	550-552	1E, 3A, 3I, 4A, 4E	3, 11, 12	P141, R127, E127	TT14-9, C14-9, TG
14.10 A: Using Trigonometric Ratios	554-557	1D, 1E, 3A, 3I, 4A, 4E	3, 10, 11, 12, 13	P142, R128, E128, A29, A59	TT14-10, C14-10, TG

Chapter 15
Polynomials

	Student Edition			Teacher Resource Package	Other Components
Lesson Title	**Pages**	**Essential Elements**	**TAAS Objectives**	**Pages**	**Pages**
Polynomials	564-567	1E, 3A	2	P143, R129, E129	TT15-1, C15-1, TG
Adding Polynomials	568-570	1C, 1E, 2E, 3A, 4B	2, 4	P144, R130, E130	TT15-2, C15-2, TG
Subtracting Polynomials	571-573	1C, 1E, 2E, 3A	2	P145, R131, E131	TT15-3, C15-3, TG
Powers of Monomials	574-576	1E, 3A, 3D, 4B	2, 4	P146, R132, E132, T15, A60, A80	TT15-4, C15-4, TG
EXPL: Multiplying Polynomials	577	1A, 1C, 1E, 2E		LM69	
Polynomial x Monomial	578-579	1C, 1E, 2E, 3A, 4B	2, 4	P147, R133, E133, T45, A15, LM71	TT15-5, C15-5, TG
Multiplying Binomials	581-582	1C, 1E, 3A	2	P148, R134, E134, T30, A30, A45	TT15-6, C15-6, TG
EXPL: Factoring	583	1A, 1C, 1E, 2E		LM70	
PSS: Eliminate Possibilities	584-585	1A, 1B, 1C, 1D, 1E		P149	TT15-7, C15-7, TG

Key to Lesson Title Abbreviations: ***EXPL*** (Exploration); ***PS*** (Problem Solving); ***PSS*** (Problem Solving Strategy); ***A*** (Application); ***L*** (Logic)

Key to copy master booklets in *Teacher Resource Package:* *P* (Practice); ***R*** (Reteaching); ***E*** (Enrichment); ***T*** (Technology); ***A*** (Activities); ***LM*** (Lab Manual)

Key to *Other Components:* *TT* (Teaching Transparencies); ***C*** (Group Activity Cards); ***TG*** (Test Generator)

Texas Assessment of Academic Skills

Mathematics Objectives	*Student Edition Pages*
1 Demonstrate an understanding of number concepts	57-58, 131-133, 136-138, 140-142, 143-145, 146-148, 149-151, 152-154, 155-158, 169-171, 172-173, 204-207, 209-210, 237-239, 240-242, 338-341
2 Demonstrate an understanding of mathematical relationships, functions, and other algebraic concepts	14, 19-21, 22-24, 25-28, 30-31, 35-38, 46-47, 60-62, 63-64, 66-68, 73-75, 76-78, 89-91, 92-94, 95-97, 98-100, 101-103, 105-108, 131-133, 136-138, 140-142, 143-145, 146-148, 149-151, 152-154, 155-158, 174-176, 184-187, 188, 190-193, 211-214, 215-218, 219-221, 222-224, 228-230, 233-235, 252-253, 255-258, 259-261, 263-266, 267-268, 270-271, 284-285, 286-288, 290-292, 293-295, 296-298, 299-301, 302-304, 311-313, 315-317, 324-325, 327-329, 331-333, 334-337, 338-341, 342-345, 346-348, 349-351, 354-355, 446-447, 449-451, 456-458, 465-467, 468-470, 471-473, 474-476, 484-487, 488-490, 492-493, 495-497, 498-500, 501-504, 506-508, 509-510, 511-514, 526-528, 564-567, 568-570, 571-573, 574-576, 578-579, 581-582
3 Demonstrate an understanding of geometric properties and relationships	438-441, 446-447, 449-451, 452-455, 456-458, 461-463, 465-467, 468-470, 471-473, 474-476, 484-487, 488-490, 492-493, 495-497, 498-500, 501-504, 506-508, 509-510, 511-514, 537-540, 542-544, 545-547, 548-549, 550-552, 554-557

Mathematics Objectives	*Student Edition Pages*
4 Demonstrate an understanding of measurement concepts using metric and customary units	30-31, 95-97, 105-108, 136-138, 166-168, 169-171, 177-179, 180-182, 184-187, 195-197, 243-245, 255-258, 275-287, 484-487, 488-490, 492-493, 495-497, 498-500, 501-504, 506-508, 509-510, 511-514, 515-517, 568-570, 574-576, 578-579
5 Demonstrate an understanding of probability and statistics	76-78, 95-97, 400-402, 403-405, 407-409, 411-414, 415-416, 418-420, 421-423, 424-427, 429-431
6 Use the operation of addition to solve problems	60-62, 63-64, 79-81, 92-94, 101-103, 174-176, 177-179, 180-182, 184-187, 190-193, 424-427
7 Use the operation of subtraction to solve problems	66-68, 79-81, 89-91, 101-103, 174-176, 177-179, 180-182, 184-187, 190-193, 424-427
8 Use the operation of multiplication to solve problems	73-75, 79-81, 98-100, 101-103, 174-176, 177-179, 180-182, 184-187, 190-193, 424-427
9 Use the operation of division to solve problems	76-78, 79-81, 95-97, 101-103, 209-210, 222-224, 225-227, 228-230, 233-235

over

Texas Assessment of Academic Skills (con't.)

Mathematics Objectives	Student Edition Pages
10 Estimate solutions to problem situations	4-7, 33-34, 43-45, 79-81, 92-94, 119-121, 134-135, 172-173, 174-176, 180-182, 188, 209-210, 211-214, 215-218, 225-227, 252-253, 259-261, 272-274, 302-304, 331-333, 342-345, 349-351, 351-353, 354-355, 415-416, 484-487, 492-493, 495-497, 498-500, 501-504, 506-508, 509-510, 511-514, 518-519, 529-530, 533-536, 542-544, 554-557
11 Determine solution strategies and will analyze or solve problems	2-3, 25-28, 30-31, 35-38, 76-78, 105-108, 143-145, 166-168, 169-171, 177-179, 180-182, 184-187, 195-197, 243-245, 255-258, 275-287, 290-292, 293-295, 296-298, 324-325, 327-329, 331-333, 334-337, 338-341, 342-345, 346-348, 349-351, 354-355, 400-402, 403-405, 407-409, 411-414, 415-416, 418-420, 421-423, 424-427, 429-431, 438-441, 442-444, 446-447, 449-451, 452-455, 456-458, 461-463, 465-467, 468-470, 471-473, 474-476, 484-487, 488-490, 492-493, 495-497, 498-500, 501-504, 506-508, 509-510, 511-514, 518-519, 537-540, 542-544, 545-547, 548-549, 550-552, 554-557

Mathematics Objectives	Student Edition Pages
12 Express or solve problems using mathematical representation	10-11, 35-38, 39-42, 43-45, 46-47, 57-58, 60-62, 63-64, 89-91, 92-94, 95-97, 110-112, 113-115, 119-121, 131-115, 119-121, 131-133, 149-151, 152-154, 184-187, 190-193, 225-227, 233-235, 255-258, 259-261, 263-266, 267-268, 270-271, 272-274, 296-298, 299-301, 338-341, 342-345, 400-402, 403-405, 415-416, 429-431, 442-444, 537-540, 542-544, 545-547, 548-549, 550-552, 554-557
13 Evaluate the reasonableness of a solution to a problem situation	8-9, 33-34, 43-45, 79-81, 119-121, 134-135, 172-173, 174-176, 180-182, 188, 211-214, 215-218, 225-227, 252-253, 259-261, 272-274, 302-304, 331-333, 349-351, 352-353, 354-355, 415-416, 484-487, 492-493, 495-497, 498-500, 501-504, 506-508, 509-510, 511-514, 518-519, 529-530, 533-536, 542-544, 554-557

GLENCOE

Macmillan/McGraw-Hill

P.O. Box 508 Columbus, Ohio 43216

BUILDING BRIDGES TO MATHEMATICAL EXCELLENCE.

TEXAS EDITION

This exciting new text will equip your students with relevant, flexible, and powerful skills for making a successful transition to algebra.

An educational program from

GLENCOE

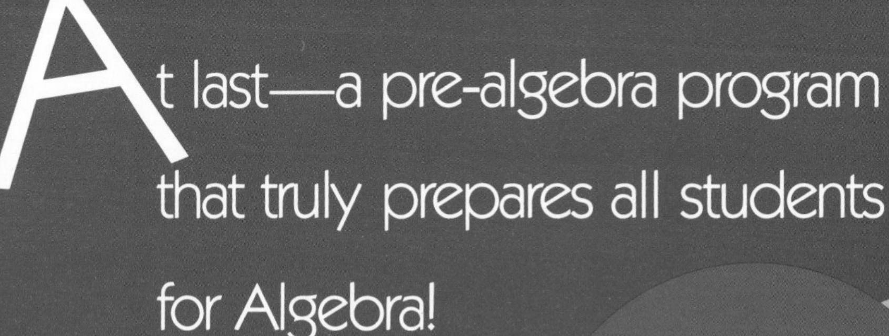

At last—a pre-algebra program
that truly prepares all students
for Algebra!

Problem-solving, applications, and communication skills are essential and interrelated components of every lesson.

Merrill Pre-Algebra features content to motivate and excite your students. It connects new concepts to other mathematical topics, other subject areas, and to real life situations. Supplemental activities—such as reteaching pages, practice and enrichment pages, and computer and lab pages—support and enhance content, making this the best algebra preparation for students of all ability levels.

In each lesson students:

Practice critical thinking as they learn how to select appropriate problem-solving strategies.

Solve problems by implementing strategies they have selected.

Communicate by generalizing and extending what they've learned to other problems and situations.

2-3 Adding Integers

Objective:
Add integers.

At night the average temperature on the surface of the planet Saturn is -150° Celsius. During the day the temperature rises 27°C. What is the average temperature on the planet's surface during the day?

Using counters to solve a problem like this would be inconvenient. Study the patterns in the following examples so that you can learn a rule for adding integers.

If you know that -3 + (-4) = -7, what property allows you to say that -4 + (-3) = -7?

Example

1 Find -3 + (-4).

-8 -7 -6 -5 -4 -3 -2 -1 0 1 (number line: -3, then -4)

Start at zero. Move 3 units to the left. From there, move 4 more units to the left. The sum is -7.

$-3 + (-4) = -7$

This example suggests the following rule.

Adding Integers with the Same Signs: To add integers with the same sign, add their absolute values. Give the result the same sign as the integers.

Study the following examples to see if you can discover a rule for adding integers that have different signs.

Examples

2 Find -5 + 2.

-7 -6 -5 -4 -3 -2 -1 0 1 2 (number line: -5, then 2)

Start at zero. Move 5 units to the left. From there, move 2 units to the right. The sum is -3.

$-5 + 2 = -3$

3 Find 7 + (-3).

-1 0 1 2 3 4 5 6 7 8 (number line: 7, then -3)

Start at zero. Move 7 units to the right. From there, move 3 units to the left. The sum is 4.

$7 + (-3) = 4$

FYI
The highest surface temperature on record in the United States is 57°C (134°F), measured in Death Valley, California. The lowest surface temperature on record in the United States is -62°C (-80°F), measured in Alaska.

60 *Integers*

Hints for Success

Helps students choose the method of computation.

Gives practical suggestions for using the calculator, estimation, and mental math.

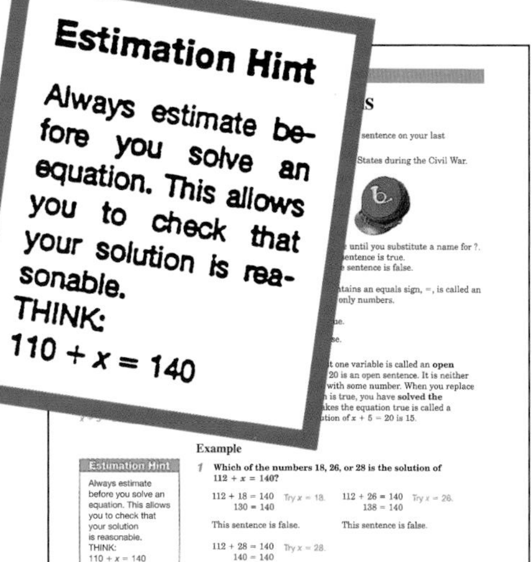

Estimation Hint
Always estimate before you solve an equation. This allows you to check that your solution is reasonable.
THINK:
110 + x = 140

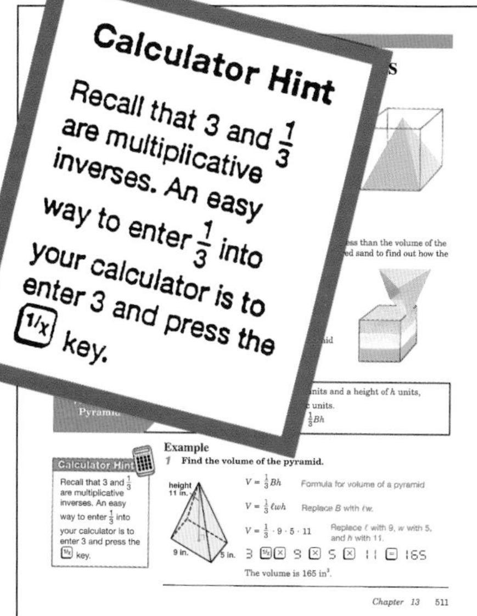

Calculator Hint
Recall that 3 and 1/3 are multiplicative inverses. An easy way to enter 1/3 into your calculator is to enter 3 and press the 1/x key.

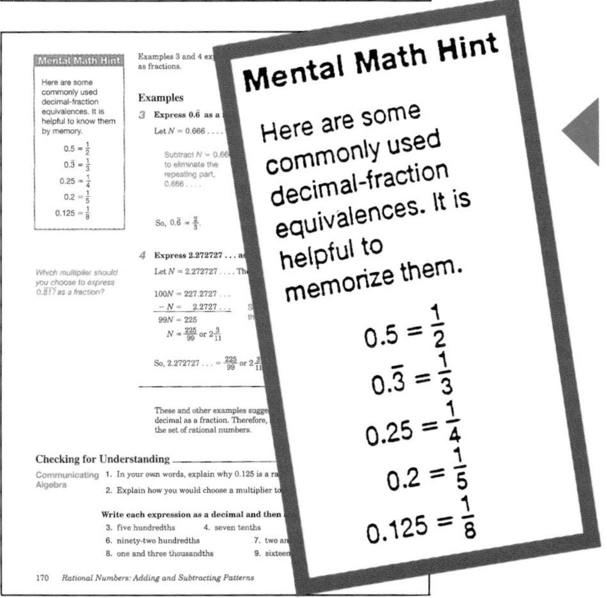

Mental Math Hint
Here are some commonly used decimal-fraction equivalences. It is helpful to memorize them.
0.5 = 1/2
0.3̄ = 1/3
0.25 = 1/4
0.2 = 1/5
0.125 = 1/8

Unequaled teacher support enables you t… systematically preview, organize, present, and enhance content.

Each lesson features:

A Four-step Teaching Model tied directly to content supports the Texas Teaching Model and the Texas Teacher Appraisal System. The model shows exactly how to focus, teach, practice/apply, and close each lesson.

A correlation to the Essential Elements and The Texas Assessment of Academic Skills.

A 5-Minute Check makes a bridge from previous lessons.

Chalkboard Examples offer additional examples.

Bellringer questions provide activities for the last few minutes of class.

Error Analysis provides ways to monitor and adjust student learning.

Alternate Strategies help you reteach and extend the lessons.

Reduced Facsimiles from the Teacher Resource Book, with answers, show precisely how to further enhance each lesson.

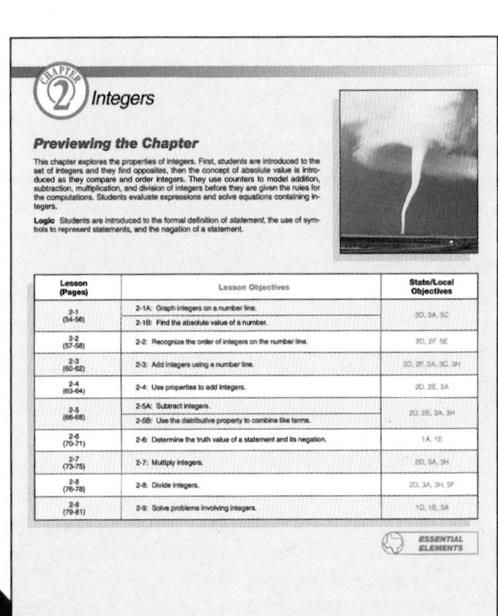

Chapter 2 Integers

Previewing the Chapter

This chapter explores the properties of integers. First, students are introduced to the set of integers and they find opposites, then the concept of absolute value is introduced as they compare and order integers. They use counters to model addition, subtraction, multiplication, and division of integers before they are given the rules for the computations. Students evaluate expressions and solve equations containing integers.

Logic Students are introduced to the formal definition of *statement*, the use of symbols to represent statements, and the negation of a statement.

Lesson (Pages)	Lesson Objectives	State/Local Objectives
2-1 (54-56)	2-1A: Graph integers on a number line.	2D, 3A, 3C
	2-1B: Find the absolute value of a number.	
2-2 (57-58)	2-2: Recognize the order of integers on the number line.	2D, 2F, 5E
2-3 (60-62)	2-3: Add integers using a number line.	2D, 2F, 3A, 3C, 3H
2-4 (63-64)	2-4: Use properties to add integers.	2D, 2E, 3A
2-5 (66-68)	2-5A: Subtract integers.	2D, 2E, 3A, 3H
	2-5B: Use the distributive property to combine like terms.	
2-6 (70-71)	2-6: Determine the truth value of a statement and its negation.	1A, 1E
2-7 (73-75)	2-7: Multiply integers.	2D, 3A, 3H
2-8 (76-78)	2-8: Divide integers.	2D, 3A, 3H, 5F
2-9 (79-81)	2-9: Solve problems involving integers.	1D, 1E, 3A

ESSENTIAL ELEMENTS

52A Chapter 2

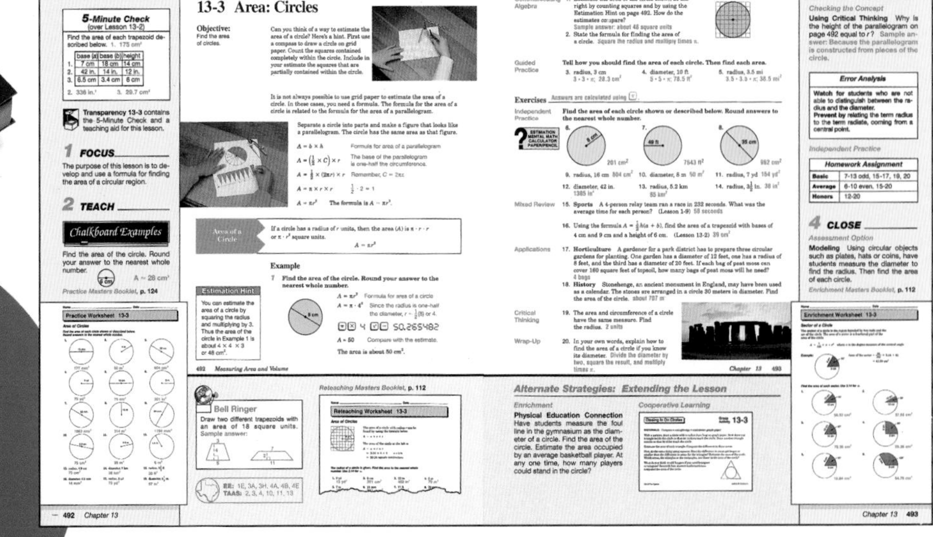

Lesson Notes 13-3

5-Minute Check (over Lesson 13-2)

Transparency 13-3 contains the 5-Minute Check and a teaching aid for this lesson.

1 FOCUS

The purpose of this lesson is to develop and use a formula for finding the area of a circular region.

2 TEACH

Chalkboard Examples

Find the area of the circle. Round your answer to the nearest whole number.

Practice Masters Booklet, p. 124

13-3 Area: Circles

Estimation Hint

Checking for Understanding

Exercises

3 PRACTICE/APPLY

Error Analysis

Homework Assignment

4 CLOSE

Enrichment Masters Booklet, p. 112

Bell Ringer

Reteaching Masters Booklet, p. 112

Alternate Strategies: Extending the Lesson

Enrichment

Cooperative Learning

492 Chapter 13

Chapter 13 493

A comprehensive 4 step Teaching Model helps you effectively organize all lessons:

1 Focus
2 Teach
3 Practice/Apply
4 Close

Support

Resources

Correlations

Each chapter features:

A **Chapter Preview Chart** that correlates with the Essential Elements.

An Academic Skills Test in the Student Edition that correlates with the Texas Assessment of Academic Skills Test.

A Two-page Enhancement Section that provides additional ways for you to help students make connections between mathematics content and real-world applications.

Enhancement activities include:

Models and Manipulatives use home-made or store-bought models and manipulatives to extend student mastery.

Cooperative Problem Solving activities present a problem or mini-project for group work.

Interactive Bulletin Board facsimiles and instructions provide further individual practice of concepts.

Multicultural Activities and Limited English Proficiency Activities relate the lessons to culturally diverse situations.

Outside Resources provide lists of books, periodicals, films, videotapes, and software.

Technology Resource ties in technology with the concepts covered.

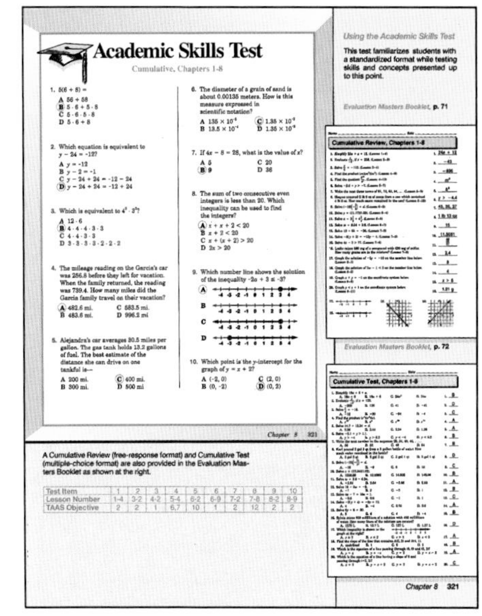

Academic Skills Test

Cumulative, Chapters 1-8

Using the Academic Skills Test

This test familiarizes students with a standardized format while testing skills and concepts presented up to this point.

Evaluation Masters Booklet, **p. 71**

Evaluation Masters Booklet, **p. 72**

A Cumulative Review (free-response format) and Cumulative Test (multiple-choice format) are also provided in the Evaluation Masters Booklet as shown at the right.

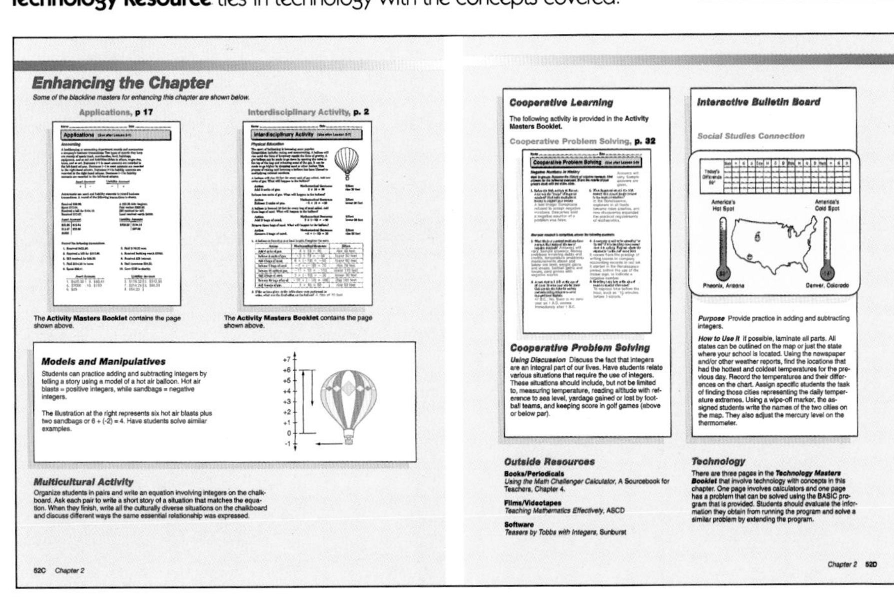

Enhancing the Chapter

Some of the blackline masters for enhancing this chapter are shown below.

Applications, p 17

Interdisciplinary Activity, p. 2

The **Activity Masters Booklet** contains the page shown above.

The **Activity Masters Booklet** contains the page shown above.

Models and Manipulatives

Students can practice adding and subtracting integers by telling a story using a model of a hot air balloon. Hot air blasts = positive integers, while sandbags = negative integers.

The illustration at the right represents six hot air blasts plus two sandbags or 6 + (-2) = 4. Have students solve similar examples.

Multicultural Activity

Organize students in pairs and write an equation involving integers on the chalkboard. Ask each pair to write a short story of a situation that matches the equation. When they finish, write all the culturally diverse situations on the chalkboard and discuss different ways the same essential relationship was expressed.

Cooperative Learning

The following activity is provided in the Activity Masters Booklet.

Cooperative Problem Solving, p. 32

Cooperative Problem Solving

Using Discussion Discuss the fact that integers are an integral part of our lives. Have students relate various situations that require the use of integers. These situations should include, but not be limited to, measuring temperature, reading altitude with reference to sea level, yardage gained or lost by football teams, and keeping score in golf games (above or below par).

Interactive Bulletin Board

Social Studies Connection

Purpose Provide practice in adding and subtracting integers.

How to Use It If possible, laminate all parts. All states can be outlined on the map or just the state where your school is located. Using the newspaper and/or other weather reports, find the locations that had the hottest and coldest temperatures for the previous day. Record the temperatures and their differences on the chart. Assign specific students the task of finding those cities representing the daily temperature extremes. Using a wipe-off marker, the assigned students write the names of the two cities on the map. They also adjust the mercury level on the thermometer.

Outside Resources

Books/Periodicals

Using the Math Challenger Calculator, A Sourcebook for Teachers, Chapter 4.

Films/Videotapes

Teaching Mathematics Effectively, ASCD

Software

Teasers by Tobbs with Integers, Sunburst

Technology

There are three pages in the **Technology Masters Booklet** that involve technology with concepts in this chapter. One page involves calculators and one page has a problem that can be solved using the BASIC program that is provided. Students should evaluate the information they obtain from running the program and solve a similar problem by extending the program.

52C Chapter 2

Chapter 2 52D

An outstanding Teacher Resource Package provides you with an abundance of first-rate materials to help teach, reteach, practice, and enhance the lessons.

Supplementary materials include:

Transparencies

A 3-Ring Transparency Binder filled with 168 color transparencies—1 for each lesson, another for each chapter opener—provides 5-Minute Check, important concepts, and more examples.

A Transparency Teacher Guide with pictures of transparencies, objectives, teaching suggestions, and extension activities.

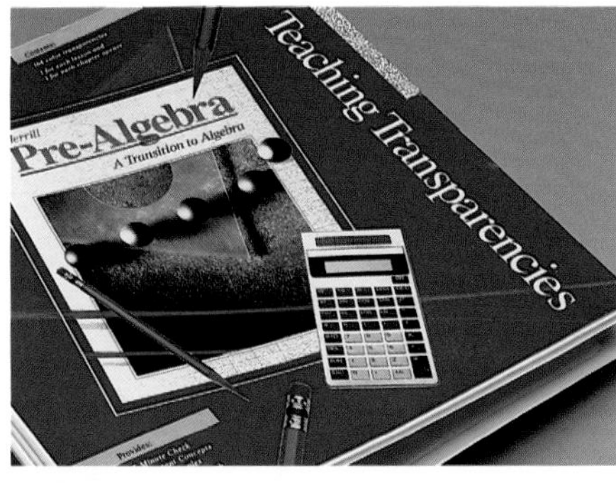

Software

A Test Generator for both Apple and IBM computers.

Teacher Resource Package

Evaluation Masters for each chapter feature multiple choice, free-response, quizzes, cumulative review, cumulative, semester, and final tests. Answers are provided full-size.

Practice Masters for each lesson, with full-size answers for easy checking.

Reteaching Masters for every skill and concept lesson, with full-size answers for easy checking.

A Lab Manual containing blackline masters of worksheets to enhance each Exploration lesson, independent lab activities for investigating mathematical concepts, and directions and patterns for algebra tiles, integer counters, and easy-to-make manipulatives.

Technology Masters for each chapter feature a calculator activity and a computer activity. Other masters provide activities on spreadsheets, graphing calculator, and computer software.

Activity Masters for each chapter feature quick activities for shortened classes, and interdisciplinary applications, cooperative problem-solving, and multicultural activities.

Enrichment Masters to extend every skill and concept lesson.

Solutions Manual

A Solutions Manual provides a complete solution for every problem in the Student Edition.

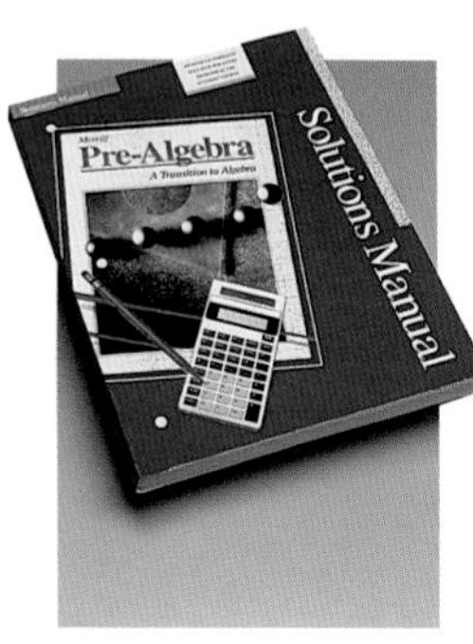

Lesson Plans

Reproducible Masters help you plan your daily lesson by making it easy for you to make the best of the learning materials for your class.

English-Spanish Glossary

Reproducible Masters provide a Spanish translation of the English-language glossary in the student edition. Also, the key chapter objectives are provided in Spanish.

Texas Assessment and Appraisal Guide

TAAS Sample Questions for each objective.

TAAS Practice Tests to help students prepare. Contains three condensed practice tests and one actual length test.

Correlations between Merrill Pre-Algebra and the TAAS objectives and the Essential Elements.

Texas Teacher Assessment System (TTAS) Correlations

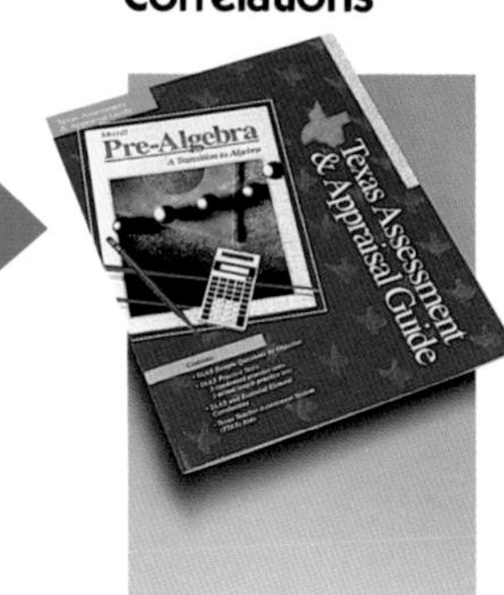

Extra special fun features! Cooperative activities that make learning pre-algebra enjoyable.

Group Activity Cards

Featuring cooperative group activities such as puzzles and games to enhance your classroom.

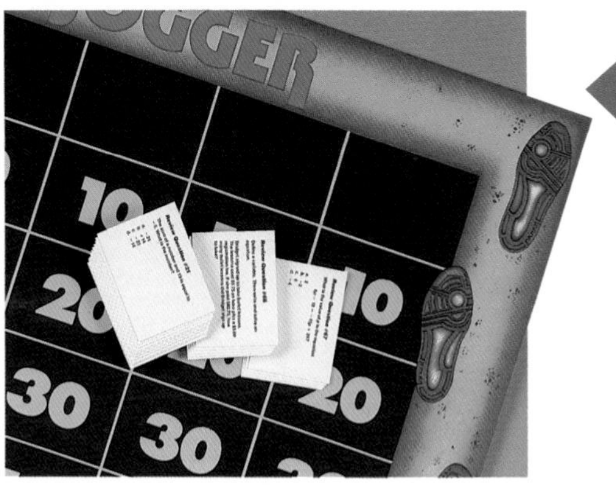

Class Review Game

Gameboard and 180 review cards—to help students review and prepare for cumulative, and final tests.

Correlation of Merrill Pre-Algebra to the NCTM Standards

Standard 1: Mathematics as Problem Solving

In grades 5-8, the mathematics curriculum should include numerous and varied experiences with problem solving as a method of inquiry and application so that students can –

- use problem-solving approaches to investigate and understand mathematical content;
- formulate problems from situations within and outside mathematics;
- develop and apply a variety of strategies to solve problems, with emphasis on multistep and nonroutine problems;
- verify and interpret results with respect to the original problem situation;
- generalize solutions and strategies to new problem situations;
- acquire confidence in using mathematics meaningfully.

SE: 2, 3, 33, 34, 43, 44, 45, 79, 80, 81, 119, 120, 121, 134, 135, 188, 189, 252, 253, 259, 260, 261, 272, 273, 274, 302, 303, 304, 352, 353, 386, 387, 415, 416, 429, 430, 431, 518, 519, 531, 532, 542, 543, 544, 584, 585

Standard 2: Mathematics as Communication

In grades 5-8, the study of mathematics should include opportunities to communicate so that students can –

- model situations using oral, written, concrete, pictorial, graphical, and algebraic methods;
- reflect on and clarify their own thinking about mathematical ideas and situations;
- develop common understandings of mathematical ideas, including the role of definitions;
- use the skills of reading, listening, and viewing to interpret and evaluate mathematical ideas;
- discuss mathematical ideas and make conjectures and convincing arguments;
- appreciate the value of mathematical notation and its role in the development of mathematical ideas.

SE: 14, 18, 19, 20, 21, 39, 131, 132, 133, 194, 237, 238, 239, 330, 438, 439, 440, 441, 518, 519, 531, 532, 580, 590

Standard 3: Mathematics as Reasoning

In grades 5-8, reasoning shall permeate the mathematics curriculum so that students can –

- recognize and apply deductive and inductive reasoning;
- understand and apply reasoning processes, with special attention to spatial reasoning and reasoning with proportions and graphs;
- make and evaluate mathematical conjectures and arguments;
- validate their own thinking;
- appreciate the pervasive use and power of reasoning as a part of mathematics.

SE: 2, 3, 4, 5, 8, 9, 10, 11, 33, 70, 71, 79, 116, 117, 118, 188, 231, 232, 239, 247, 248, 303, 386, 459, 460, 542, 584, 585

SE = Student Edition

Standard 4: Mathematical Connections

In grades 5-8, the mathematics curriculum should include the investigation of mathematical connections so that students can –

- see mathematics as an integrated whole;
- explore problems and describe results using graphical, numerical, physical, algebraic, and verbal mathematical models or representations;
- use a mathematical idea to further their understanding of other mathematical ideas;
- apply mathematical thinking and modeling to solve problems that arise in other disciplines, such as art, music, psychology, science, and business;
- value the role of mathematics in our culture and society.

SE: 13, 32, 38, 39, 53, 54, 69, 87, 89, 94, 97, 101, 102, 103, 104, 105, 127, 133, 143, 155, 159, 165, 169, 183, 187, 194, 195, 196, 197, 203, 209, 218, 236, 243, 244, 245, 251, 260, 269, 275, 277, 283, 289, 293, 323, 326, 329, 334, 349, 350, 351, 353, 354, 355, 361, 366, 368, 388, 389, 390, 399, 406, 411, 437, 438, 442, 443, 444, 445, 468, 469, 470, 483, 484, 491, 514, 515, 516, 517, 525, 534, 553, 554, 555, 556, 557, 563, 564, 580

Standard 5: Number and Number Relationships

In grades 5-8, the mathematics curriculum should include the continued development of number and number relationships so that students can –

- understand, represent, and use numbers in a variety of equivalent forms (integer, fraction, decimal, percent, exponential, and scientific notation) in real-world and mathematical problem situations;
- develop number sense for whole numbers, fractions, decimals, integers, and rational numbers;
- understand and apply ratios, proportions, and percents in a wide variety of situations;
- investigate relationships among fractions, decimals, and percents;
- represent numerical relationships in one- and two-dimensional graphs.

SE: 166, 167, 168, 169, 170, 171, 204, 205, 206, 207, 208, 237, 238, 239, 284, 285, 286, 287, 288, 289, 290, 291, 292, 293, 294, 295, 296, 297, 298, 299, 300, 301, 302, 303, 304, 305, 306, 307, 308, 309, 310, 311, 312, 313, 314, 315, 324, 325, 326, 327, 328, 329, 330, 331, 332, 333, 334, 335, 336, 337, 338, 339, 340, 341, 342, 343, 344, 345, 346, 347, 348, 349, 350, 351, 352, 353, 354, 355, 442, 443, 444

Standard 6: Number Systems and Number Theory

In grades 5-8, the mathematics curriculum should include the study of number systems and number theory so that students can –

- understand and appreciate the need for numbers beyond the whole numbers;
- develop and use order relations for whole numbers, fractions, decimals, integers, and rational numbers;
- extend their understanding of whole number operations to fractions, decimals, integers, and rational numbers;
- understand how the basic arithmetic operations are related to one another;
- develop and apply number theory concepts (e.g., primes, factors, and multiples) in real-world and mathematical problem situations.

SE: 54, 55, 56, 57, 58, 59, 60, 61, 62, 63, 64, 65, 66, 67, 68, 69, 70, 71, 72, 73, 74, 75, 76, 77, 78, 79, 80, 81, 128, 129, 130, 131, 132, 133, 134, 135, 136, 137, 138, 139, 140, 141, 142, 143, 144, 145, 146, 147, 148, 149, 150, 151, 166, 167, 168, 169, 170, 171, 174, 175, 176, 177, 178, 179, 180, 181, 182, 204, 205, 206, 207, 208, 209, 210, 211, 212, 213, 214, 215, 216, 217, 218, 219, 220, 221, 222, 223, 224, 225, 226, 227, 324, 325, 326, 327, 328, 329, 330, 331, 332, 333, 334, 335, 336, 337, 338, 339, 340, 341, 342, 343, 344, 345, 346, 347, 348, 349, 350, 351, 352, 353, 354, 355, 535, 583

Correlation of Merrill Pre-Algebra to the NCTM Standards

Standard 7: Computation and Estimation

In grades 5-8, the mathematics curriculum should develop the concepts underlying computation and estimation in various contexts so that students can –

- compute with whole numbers, fractions, decimals, integers, and rational numbers;
- develop, analyze, and explain procedures for computation and techniques for estimation;
- develop, analyze, and explain methods for solving proportions;
- select and use an appropriate method for computing from among mental arithmetic, paper-and-pencil, calculator, and computer methods;
- use computation, estimation, and proportions to solve problems;
- use estimation to check the reasonableness of results.

SE: 4, 5, 6, 7, 8, 9, 43, 44, 59, 60, 61, 62, 63, 64, 65, 66, 67, 68, 72, 73, 74, 75, 76, 77, 78, 79, 80, 81, 119, 120, 172, 173, 174, 175, 176, 177, 178, 179, 180, 181, 182, 188, 211, 212, 213, 214, 215, 216, 217, 218, 219, 220, 221, 222, 223, 224, 225, 226, 227, 327, 328, 329, 330, 331, 332, 333, 334, 335, 336, 337, 338, 339, 340, 341, 342, 343, 344, 345, 346, 347, 348, 349, 350, 351, 352, 353, 354, 355

Standard 8: Patterns and Functions

In grades 5-8, the mathematics curriculum should include explorations of patterns and functions so that students can –

- describe, extend, analyze, and create a wide variety of patterns;
- describe and represent relationships with tables, graphs, and rules;
- analyze functional relationships to explain how a change in one quantity results in a change in another;
- use patterns and functions to represent and solve problems.

SE: 101, 102, 103, 104, 105, 106, 107, 108, 188, 189, 190, 191, 192, 193, 194, 199, 200, 233, 234, 235, 352, 353, 371, 372, 373, 374, 375, 376, 377, 378, 379, 380, 381, 382, 383, 384, 385, 386, 387, 388, 389, 390, 391, 392, 393, 415, 416, 442, 443, 444

Standard 9: Algebra

In grades 5-8, the mathematics curriculum should include explorations of algebraic concepts and processes so that students can –

- understand the concepts of variable, expression, and equation;
- represent situations and number patterns with tables, graphs, verbal rules, and equations and explore the interrelationships of these representations;
- analyze tables and graphs to identify properties and relationships;
- develop confidence in solving linear equations using concrete, informal, and formal methods;
- investigate inequalities and nonlinear equations informally;
- apply algebraic methods to solve a variety of real-world and mathematical problems.

SE: 18, 19, 20, 21, 22, 23, 24, 25, 26, 27, 28, 29, 30, 31, 32, 33, 34, 35, 36, 37, 38, 39, 40, 41, 42, 43, 44, 45, 46, 47, 88, 89, 90, 91, 92, 93, 94, 95, 96, 97, 98, 99, 100, 101, 102, 103, 104, 105, 106, 107, 108, 109, 110, 111, 112, 113, 114, 115, 116, 117, 118, 119, 120, 121, 128, 129, 130, 131, 132, 133, 134, 135, 136, 137, 138, 139, 140, 141, 142, 143, 144, 145, 146, 147, 148, 149, 150, 151, 152, 153, 154, 155, 156, 157, 158, 159, 184, 185, 186, 187, 228, 229, 230, 254, 255, 256, 257, 258, 259, 260, 261, 262, 263, 264, 265, 266, 267, 268, 269, 270, 271, 272, 273, 274, 284, 285, 286, 287, 288, 289, 290, 291, 292, 293, 294, 295, 296, 297, 298, 299, 300, 301, 302, 303, 304, 305, 306, 307, 308, 309, 310, 311, 312, 313, 314, 315, 316, 317, 564, 565, 566, 567, 568, 569, 570, 571, 572, 573, 574, 575, 576, 577, 578, 579, 580, 581, 582, 583, 584, 585

SE = Student Edition

Standard 10: Statistics

In grades 5-8, the mathematics curriculum should include exploration of statistics in real-world situations so that students can –

- systematically collect, organize, and describe data;
- construct, read, and interpret tables, charts, and graphs;
- make inferences and convincing arguments that are based on data analysis;
- evaluate arguments that are based on data analysis;
- develop an appreciation for statistical methods as powerful means for decision making.

SE: 362, 363, 364, 365, 366, 367, 368, 369, 370, 371, 372, 373, 374, 375, 376, 377, 378, 379, 380, 381, 382, 383, 384, 385, 386, 387, 388, 389, 390, 391, 392, 393, 441, 444, 455, 476, 481, 508, 528, 561, 609, 610

Standard 11: Probability

In grades 5-8, the mathematics curriculum should include explorations of probability in real-world situations so that students can –

- model situations by devising and carrying out experiments or simulations to determine probabilities;
- model situations by constructing a sample space to determine probabilities;
- appreciate the power of using a probability model by comparing experimental results with mathematical expectations;
- make predictions that are based on experimental or theoretical probabilities;
- develop an appreciation for the pervasive use of probability in the real world.

SE: 400, 401, 402, 403, 404, 405, 406, 407, 408, 409, 410, 411, 412, 413, 414, 415, 416, 417, 418, 419, 420, 421, 422, 423, 424, 425, 426, 427, 428, 429, 430, 431, 441, 451, 457, 463, 476, 487, 494, 497, 513, 523, 561, 579, 580, 611, 612

Standard 12: Geometry

In grades 5-8, the mathematics curriculum should include the study of the geometry of one, two, and three dimensions in a variety of situations so that students can –

- identify, describe, compare, and classify geometric figures;
- visualize and represent geometric figures with special attention to developing spatial sense;
- explore transformations of geometric figures;
- represent and solve problems using geometric models;
- understand and apply geometric properties and relationships;
- develop an appreciation of geometry as a means of describing the physical world.

SE: 438, 439, 440, 441, 442, 443, 444, 445, 446, 447, 448, 449, 450, 451, 452, 453, 454, 455, 456, 457, 458, 459, 460, 461, 462, 463, 464, 465, 466, 467, 468, 469, 470, 471, 472, 473, 474, 475, 476, 477, 484, 485, 486, 487, 488, 489, 490, 491, 492, 493, 494, 495, 496, 497, 498, 499, 500, 501, 502, 503, 504, 505, 506, 507, 508, 509, 510, 511, 512, 513, 514, 515, 516, 517, 526, 527, 528, 529, 530, 531, 532, 533, 534, 535, 536, 537, 538, 539, 540, 541, 542, 543, 544, 545, 546, 547, 548, 549, 550, 551, 552, 553, 554, 555, 556, 557, 612, 613, 614, 615, 616, 617, 618

Standard 13: Measurement

In grades 5-8, the mathematics curriculum should include extensive concrete experiences using measurement so that students can –

- extend their understanding of the process of measurement;
- estimate, make and use measurements to describe and compare phenomena;
- select appropriate units and tools to measure to the degree of accuracy required in a particular situation;
- understand the structure and use of systems of measurement;
- extend their understanding of the concepts of perimeter, area, volume, angle measure, capacity, and weight and mass;
- develop the concepts of rates and other derived and indirect measurements;
- develop formulas and procedures for determining measures to solve problems.

SE: 101, 102, 103, 104, 105, 106, 107, 108, 109, 195, 196, 197, 218, 243, 244, 245, 260, 275, 276, 277, 439, 440, 441, 442, 443, 484, 485, 486, 487, 488, 489, 490, 491, 492, 493, 494, 495, 496, 497, 498, 499, 500, 501, 502, 503, 504, 505, 506, 507, 508, 509, 510, 511, 512, 513, 514, 515, 516, 517, 518, 519, 590

MERRILL PRE-ALGEBRA HAS IT ALL!

Stronger Content . . . Exciting Enhancements and Extensions . . . Incredible Teacher Support!

Students are introduced to algebra and integers early. Problem solving, applications, and communication skills are essential and interrelated elements of each chapter. Algebra, geometry, and other mathematical topics are carefully integrated in a format that clearly connects mathematics to students' lives and the world of work.

The student text is supported by an outstanding Teacher Wraparound Edition and Teacher Resource Package that together provide what is the most exciting, comprehensive, and detailed approach available for teaching pre-algebra.

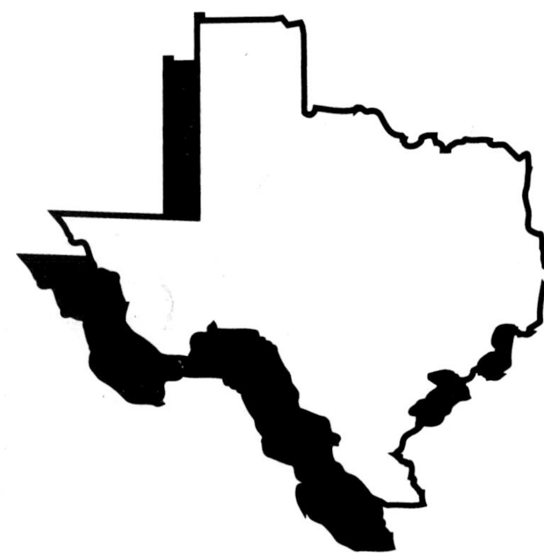

GLENCOE
Texas Regional Office
320 Westway Place, Suite 550
Arlington, TX 76018
817/784-2100
800/828-5096

Texas Regional Sales Representatives

(Central)
Cheryl Barrett
9100 Caira Cove
Austin, TX 78750
512/335-3054

(Vocational, Southwest)
Henry Evans
P.O. Box 50131
Denton, TX 76206
817/566-0307

(Dallas)
Brett L. Hicks
800 Shady Lake Drive
Bedford, TX 76021
817/268-5917

(Houston)
Elizabeth Phelps
12123 Fawnview
Houston, TX 77070
713/370-1243

(Ft. Worth)
Robert Cox
7313 Savoya Drive, #908
Ft. Worth, TX 76133
817/346-1602

(South)
Ysau Flores
13318 Rock Hampton
San Antonio, TX 78232
512/496-6582

(New Mexico, West)
Mary LyBrand
617 Acequia Madre
Sante Fe, NM 87501
505/986-9245

(East)
Gene Smith
5811 Thoreau Lane
Arlington, TX 76016
817/429-3773

GLENCOE

Macmillan/McGraw-Hill

P.O. Box 508 Columbus, Ohio 43216

90157-X

Texas Teacher's Wraparound Edition

Merrill

Pre-Algebra

A Transition to Algebra

GLENCOE

Macmillan/McGraw-Hill

Lake Forest, Illinois • Columbus, Ohio • Mission Hills, California • Peoria, Illinois

Send all inquiries to:
Glencoe Division, Macmillan/McGraw-Hill
936 Eastwind Drive
Westerville, OH 43081

ISBN: 0-675-13105-7 (Teacher Edition)

1 2 3 4 5 6 7 8 9 10 VH 00 99 98 97 96 95 94 93 92 91 2 91

Authors

Jack Price taught mathematics and science for 13 years in the Detroit Public Schools, where he served for three years as mathematics department head. After receiving his Ed.D. in Mathematics Education from Wayne State University, he became coordinator of mathematics/science for the San Diego County (California) Department of Education. Dr. Price is a past director of the National Council of Teachers of Mathematics, a former member of the National Advisory Committee on Mathematical Education, and a founding member of the Mathematical Sciences Education Board of the National Research Council. He is presently assistant director of the Center for Science and Mathematics Education at California Polytechnic University at Pomona, California, where he teaches mathematics and methods courses for preservice teachers and consults with school districts on curriculum change.

James N. Rath is former chairperson of the mathematics department at Darien High School, Darien, Connecticut. He has taught mathematics at every level of the high school curriculum and has over 30 years of classroom teaching experience. Mr. Rath received his B.A. from Catholic University of America and his M.Ed. and M.A. in mathematics from Boston College. Mr. Rath is co-author of the *Merrill Algebra* program, and is an active member of several local, state, and national professional organizations.

William Leschensky teaches mathematics at Glenbard South High School in Glen Ellyn, Illinois. He has served as mathematics department chairperson in four schools and is a former textbook editor and editorial director. Mr. Leschensky received his B.A. in mathematics from Cornell College and his M.A. in mathematics from the University of Northern Iowa. He has participated in special institutes in mathematics and physics as well as several computer workshops.

Contributing Authors

Olene H. Brame, Ph.D.
Dallas Independent School District
Dallas, Texas

David D. Molina, Ph.D.
Department of Education
Trinity University
San Antonio, Texas

Consultant

Donald W. Collins
Department of Mathematics and Informational Sciences
Sam Houston State University
Huntsville, Texas

Reviewers

Robinette Bowden
Central Davis Junior High School
Layton, Utah

Nevin Engle
Cumberland Valley High School
Mechanicsburg, Pennsylvania

Mary Faso
Ellicottville Central High School
Ellicottville, New York

Richard D. Hammann
Carlisle Area School District
Carlisle, Pennsylvania

Anne Hathaway
Wingate College
Wingate, North Carolina

Gary D. Hawsey
Fulton County Schools
Atlanta, Georgia

Lucy Koors
Emmerich Manual High School
Indianapolis, Indiana

Betty Kreutzer
Pleasanton Middle School
Pleasanton, California

Sue Meagher
High School for Law Enforcement and Criminal Justice
Houston, Texas

Barbara Smith
Unionville-Chadds Ford School District
Unionville, Pennsylvania

Peter Smith
Omaha Public Schools
Omaha, Nebraska

Karen Steele
Northeast Junior High School
Charlotte, North Carolina

Larry Stott
Bryant Intermediate School
Salt Lake City, Utah

Nick Vincequerra
Gettysburg Junior High School
Gettysburg, Pennsylvania

Deborah Volpe
Westerville South High School
Westerville, Ohio

Jan Wilson
Arsenal Technical High School
Indianapolis, Indiana

Hazel Wright
University of North Carolina
Charlotte, North Carolina

Table of Contents

CHAPTER 1 The Language of Algebra

Integers

Hints for Success
Chapters 1 and 2

Calculator	15, 80
Estimation	30, 43
Mental Math	25, 74

Solving One-Step Equations

Factors and Fractions

Hints for Success
Chapters 3 and 4

Explorations

Did you know there is a method to estimate how many fish are in a certain lake? It is called the capture-recapture method and you may use this method in the **Exploration** on page 330. There are 28 such **Explorations** in your textbook. You may investigate how to solve equations, make predictions, and discover many mathematical patterns. **Explorations** let you *do* mathematics and use your knowledge of arithmetic to find success in algebra.

Rationals: Adding and Subtracting Patterns

Rationals: Multiplying and Dividing Patterns

Hints for Success
Chapters 5 and 6

Calculator	172, 175, 206, 244
Estimation	181, 185, 196, 212, 225
Mental Math	170, 177, 216, 238, 240

Algebra in Action

What does the Mona Lisa have in common with the Great Pyramid of Egypt? Read the **Algebra in Action** feature on page 326 to find out. In each chapter you will have an opportunity to *use* mathematics in real-world situations.

Solving Equations and Inequalities

Hints for Success
Chapters 7 and 8

Graphing Equations and Inequalities

History, Biography, Careers

Why is this part of mathematics called *algebra*? Read the **Biography** feature on page 21 to find out. These features contain information about mathematics in the *past* and about career opportunities for the *future*. You may be surprised by what you read.

Proportion and Percent

Hints for Success
Chapters 9 and 10
Calculator 342
Estimation 346, 349, 354
Mental Math 328, 339, 340, 375

Statistics and Graphs

Connections

"When am I ever going to use this stuff?" It may be sooner than you think. You'll find mathematics in most of the subjects you study in school. In the **Music Connection** on page 127 you'll see that mathematics and music are related. The **Geography Connection** on page 293 relates latitude and longitude lines to mathematics. These and other **Connections** will help you *see* mathematics in your life.

Probability

Hints for Success
Chapters 11 and 12

Applying Algebra to Geometry

Measuring Area and Volume

Applying Algebra to Right Triangles

Hints for Success
Chapters 13 and 14
Calculator 511, 529
Estimation 486, 492, 502, 512, 538

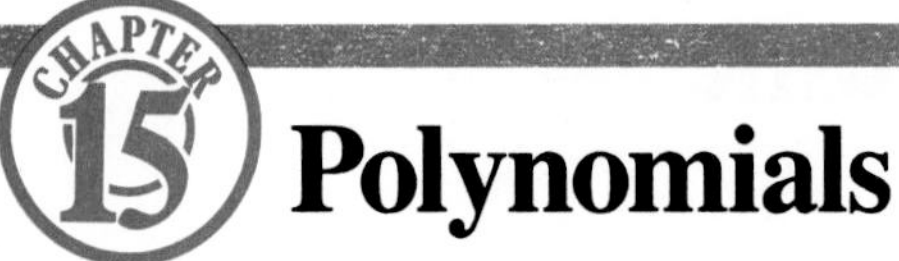

Polynomials

Hints for Success
Chapter 15
Calculator 575

To The Teacher

The purpose of this 20-page *Teacher's Guide* is to provide an introduction to the format and philosophy of the ***Merrill Pre-Algebra Teacher's Wraparound Edition.*** It is also intended to relate some background information on several contemporary issues facing mathematics educators in the 1990s, such as the use of technology and alternative assessment strategies. Suggested time schedules for six-week and nine-week grading periods, as well as lists of suggested professional references, resources of supplementary instructional materials, and clearly-defined instructional objectives are included to further make the transition to algebra a smooth one for both students and teachers.

Teacher's Guide Table of Contents

How to Use the Four-Step Teaching Plan in *Merrill Pre-Algebra*

What do you search for when making a new textbook selection? You may search for a total program that is easy to teach. Your ***Merrill Pre-Algebra Teacher's Wraparound Edition*** delivers the collective teaching experience of its authors, consultants, and reviewers so that you will have the wealth of reliable information you search for. By furnishing you with an effective teaching model, this book saves you preparation time and energy. You, in turn, are free to spend that time and energy on your most important responsibility — your students.

As a professional, you will be pleased to find this program provides you with readily available activities to engage your students throughout the entire class period.

Each chapter begins with two easy to use features. The first of these are **Connections** on how to relate the chapter opening photograph to other subject areas and provides a suggestion on how to initiate the *Class Project* that is intended to be on-going throughout the chapter. These photographs have been carefully selected to help you focus students' attention on the chapter and get them into the material immediately. Second, **Looking Ahead** provides you with a list of materials that are needed in the *Exploration* activities in the chapter.

Every lesson contains two pre-lesson activities to engage your students. The **5-Minute Check** includes one to five questions from the previous lesson. This allows you to check retention of skills and concepts. A second option is the **Bell Ringer** — a problem or activity that is also connected to the previous lesson.

Each lesson and Exploration includes a comprehensive four-part teaching plan that, when utilized consistently, makes it easy for you to teach and easy for your students to learn.

...a comprehensive four-part teaching plan that makes it easy for you to teach and easy for your students to learn.

1 FOCUS

FOCUS, or the anticipatory set as it is sometimes called, is the first step of the ***Merrill Pre-Algebra*** teaching plan. FOCUS helps prepare students for learning the day's lesson by piquing their interest. It is intended to help focus the attention of the class so the lesson can begin.

A FOCUS item may also provide time for students to interact with you, thus enabling you to modify the lesson to fit what students already know. The FOCUS activity usually can be completed within the first five minutes of class and should be a direct lead-in to the concepts that will be presented. By focusing your students, you will provide the structural framework for what is to come.

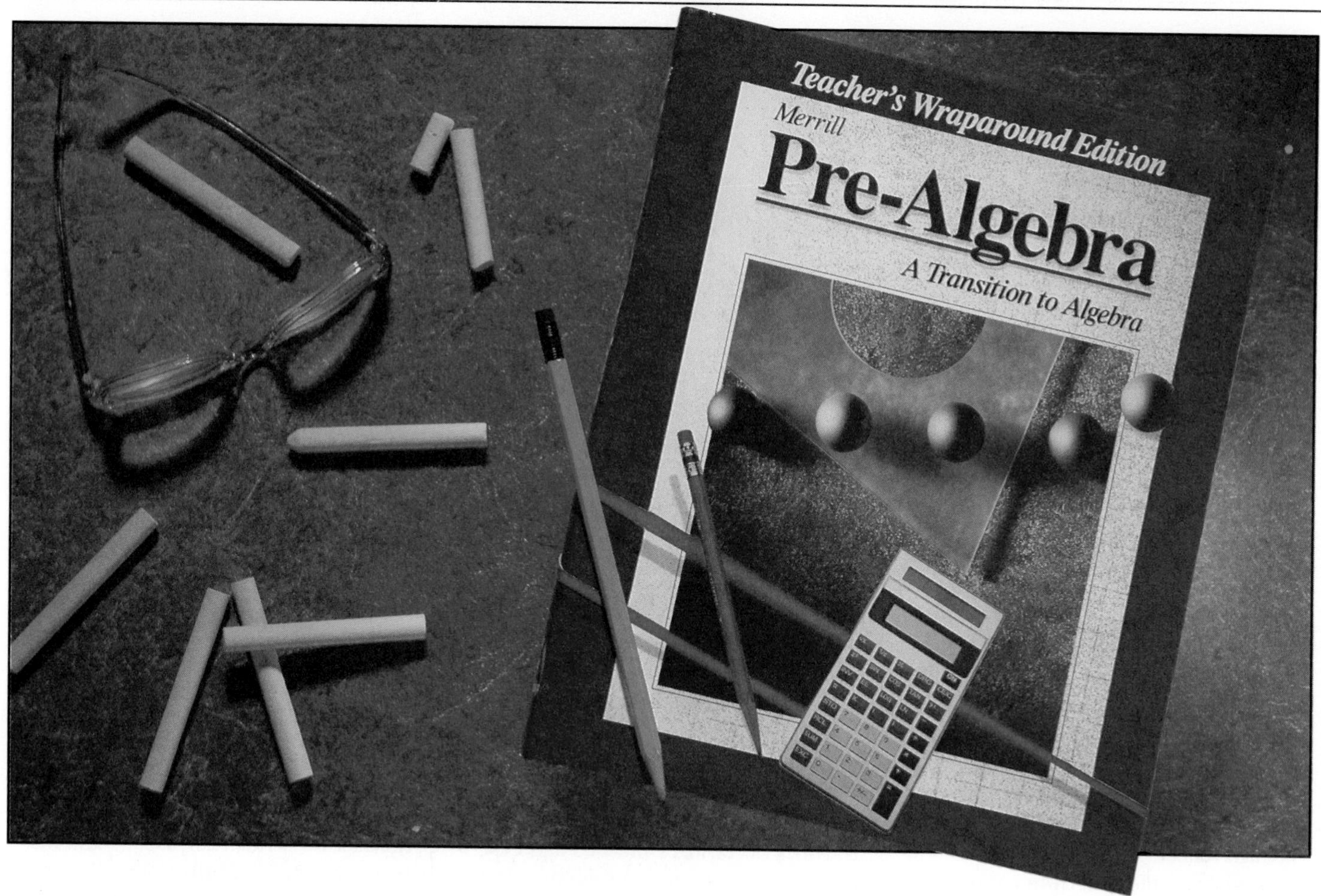

2 TEACH

TEACH, the second step of the teaching plan, is the heart of any lesson. The primary aim of the ***Merrill Pre-Algebra*** teaching plan is to give you the tools to accomplish the admittedly difficult task of enabling your students to learn algebraic concepts. Effective teaching strategies as well as **Chalkboard Examples** are provided in this part of the teaching cycle.

No matter how thoroughly a subject is covered in the classroom, there usually will be students who do not understand the lesson the first time it is taught. A **Reteaching Activity** is provided for every lesson. Reteaching is a way to teach the same concepts or facts differently so they will be more amenable to students' individual learning styles. Cooperative learning activities lend themselves well to reteaching and are periodically offered as reteaching hints. With the materials presented in the TEACH step of the four-part teaching plan, your efficiency and productivity as a teacher will increase. The TEACH step brings together the major elements that form a sound teaching approach.

3 PRACTICE/APPLY

The authors of the ***Merrill Pre-Algebra Teacher's Wraparound Edition*** view teaching as a creative art. As you are aware, teachers work at making the transfer of knowledge as efficient and productive as it can be. One finding of educational researchers is that teachers who closely guide their students during a lesson are more effective. To this end, **Checking the Concept** ideas are provided. Also, in the PRACTICE/APPLY step you will find an *Error Analysis* to assist you in identifying and correcting common student errors and a *Homework Assignment.*

You should be able to accomplish the goals of your curriculum with a minimum of time and effort.

4 CLOSE

CLOSE is the final step in the teaching plan. It provides you with a quick way of determining if students have mastered the objectives of the lesson and gives students an opportunity for direct communication in written, spoken, or modeled form.

As you review the ***Teacher's Wraparound Edition*** to ***Merrill Pre-Algebra,*** you will discover that you and your students are considered very important. With the enormous number of teaching strategies provided by the ***Teacher's Wraparound Edition,*** you should be able to accomplish the goals of your curriculum with a minimum of time and effort. This is true whether you are teaching pre-algebra for the first time, or whether you are a veteran teacher. The materials allow adaptability and flexibility so that student and curricular needs can be met.

Pre-Algebra: A Transition From Arithmetic to Algebra

"Put down six and carry two... Gee but this is hard to do... I don't care what teacher says, I can't do the sum!" This catchy little song from the musical *Babes in Toyland* frequently and sadly describes the plight of a goodly number of students who are today being abruptly "graduated" from the arithmetic of the elementary school to the algebra of the high school. All too often a student is plunged from the descriptive, concrete, number-oriented arithmetic class of the elementary school to the abstract, conceptual, symbol-centered algebra course of the high school with little or no preparation or experience in courses that bridge this gap. To remedy this deficiency, it is imperative that attention be focused on providing a prealegebra course to facilitate this transition.

The pre-algebra course cannot be woven into the existing mathematics curriculum as just another separate course offering in and of itself. It must be a means to an end. Its purpose must be to pave the way for a progressive mastery of more difficult and complex skills prerequisite for understanding algebraic concepts. Students must "explore algebraic concepts in an informal way to build a foundation for subsequent formal study of algebra."[1]

Building on their earlier (K-4) experiences with patterns, students should continue to explore concrete situations using charts, graphs, tables of data, and physical models. These explorations allow them to determine patterns in number sequences, to relate models to one another, to make generalizations about patterns and regularities in mathematics, to make predictions, and to derive their own algorithms.

With emphasis placed more on students working through problems independently or in small group endeavors, rather than on teacher direction, the teacher's role now is more that of an enabler. In a sense the mathematics classroom is transformed into a mathematics laboratory where students are encouraged to explore, examine, question, discuss, and solve. Competency in these activities necessitates practice and experience. A major purpose of the pre-algebra course is to afford the student more opportunities and time for engaging in such activities thereby facilitating the transition to more abstract ways of thinking. The task of the teacher now is to translate the every-day descriptive conversation of the student into the desired technical language and concepts of mathematics. Algebra has a language all its own—it is very technical and symbolic. To succeed in algebra, it is imperative that students learn to correctly interpret, or translate, this unique language. Students must learn to use symbols to express their ideas before they get to algebra.

Its purpose must be to pave the way for a progressive mastery of more difficult and complex skills prerequisite for understanding algebraic concepts.

"Students should be required to explain some of the typical conflicts between the language of arithmetic, with which they are familiar, and the more technical language of algebra, which they will need to master. In algebra we see that: a x b means the same as ab, but in arithmetic, 3 x 5 $\neq$ 35; and $ab = ba$, but 35 $\neq$ 53."[2] It is essential that prior to algebra the student learn how to translate the written language of arithmetic into proper symbolic statements of mathematics.

Traditionally, arithmetic in the elementary school has fallen largely in to the category of rote learning, or what we call "instrumental understanding." Being basically a collection of rules and routines without reasons, "instrumental understanding" has little need of discussion. "The common conceptualization of mathematics as the quick attainment of an exact answer by some acquired routine conflicts with a desire for discussion. The content usually demands product questions, which do not require discussion, rather than process questions."[3] Not so with algebra which is based on "relational understanding," for it is very much a part of the reasoning process and demands process questions in order to solve problems.

Discussion also demands that a student put into words his or her understanding of the problem at hand. It thus provides the teacher with a measuring stick of sorts whereby he or she can assess the degree of comprehension on the part of the student.

When students are encouraged to express their generalizations, predictions, solutions, and such about any given situation, they are necessarily required to verbalize such information in their own words and are thus prohibited from minicking or "mouthing" the stereotypical language of the teacher; it forces the gradual development and use of the vocabulary of mathematics.

A pre-algebra experience does not guarantee, of course, that all students will exhibit superior mathematical skills. That, after all, is not its intent and purpose. We must allow for individual differences and abilities in mathematics, as in all other areas of learning. We must recognize that some students in a mathematics class will, by virtue of their innate ability, naturally outshine their classmates. For them, a pre-algebra course affords the opportunity to pursue their interests and talents more fully.

Students must learn to use symbols to express their ideas before they get to algebra.

For those students who find mathematics to be "an obstacle course," it grants additional time and opportunities to learn and master basics in an effort to reach their maximum potential.

Through the implementation of a pre-algebra course whose purpose and goal is to enable students to successfully bridge the transition from the arithmetic of the elementary school to the algebra of the high school, we should begin to see more students evidencing confidence in their ability to succeed in their experiences with algebra.

With a solid foundation in a pre-algebra course, students will no longer ask the question "Why algebra for me?" — but rather, "Why not?"

1. National Council of Teachers of Mathematics, Commission on Standards for School Mathematics, *Curriculum and Evaluation Standards for School Mathematics,* (Reston, VA: The Council, 1989), p. 102.
2. Lodholz, Richard, "The Transition from Arithmetic to Algebra," *Algebra for Everyone,* (Reston, VA: NCTM, 1990), p. 27.
3. Ibid., p. 27.

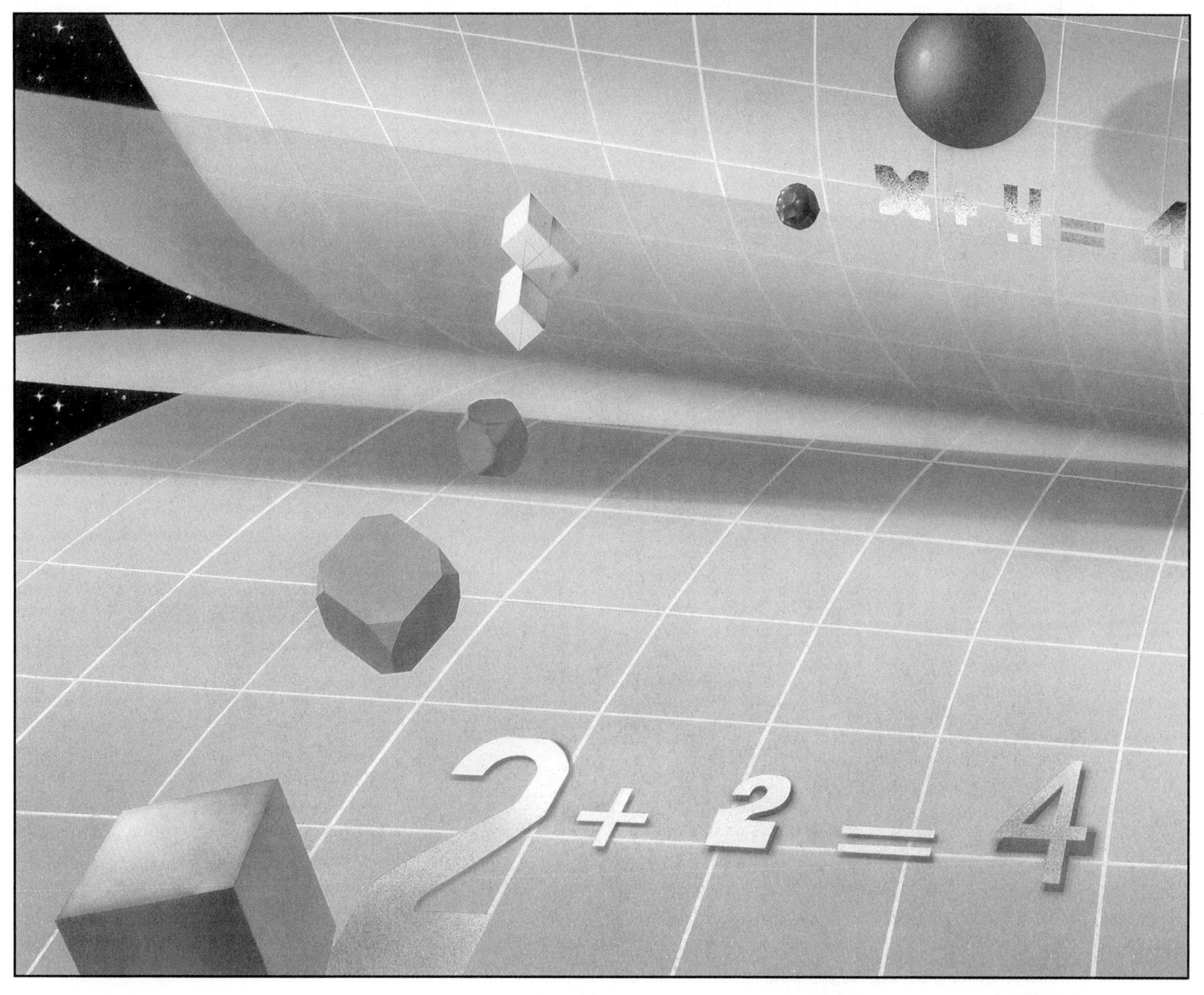

Using Manipulatives in Your Pre-Algebra Classroom

Most teachers agree that the use of manipulative materials helps students build a solid understanding of mathematical concepts and enhances students' achievement in mathematics. The universal anxiety today about achievement in mathematics should prompt educators in this field to heed results from recent studies which indicate that by using manipulative materials at every level, test scores are dramatically improved.

Whereas teachers in primary mathematics employ manipulatives quite frequently and extensively, the use of manipulatives gradually decreases in succeeding grade levels. Recent studies, however, firmly dispel the popular misconception that using manipulatives in the pre-algebra and algebra classes is a waste of precious teaching time, an activity just for little kids or, worse yet, for "dummies."

Subjects such as science, art, home economics, typing, and industrial technology actively engage students' energies and restlessness. Mathematics in the upper grades, on the other hand, has been traditionally reluctant to use this kind of hands-on approach. Based on extensive research, a similar activity-oriented approach to mathematics is now recommended for mathematics students as well.

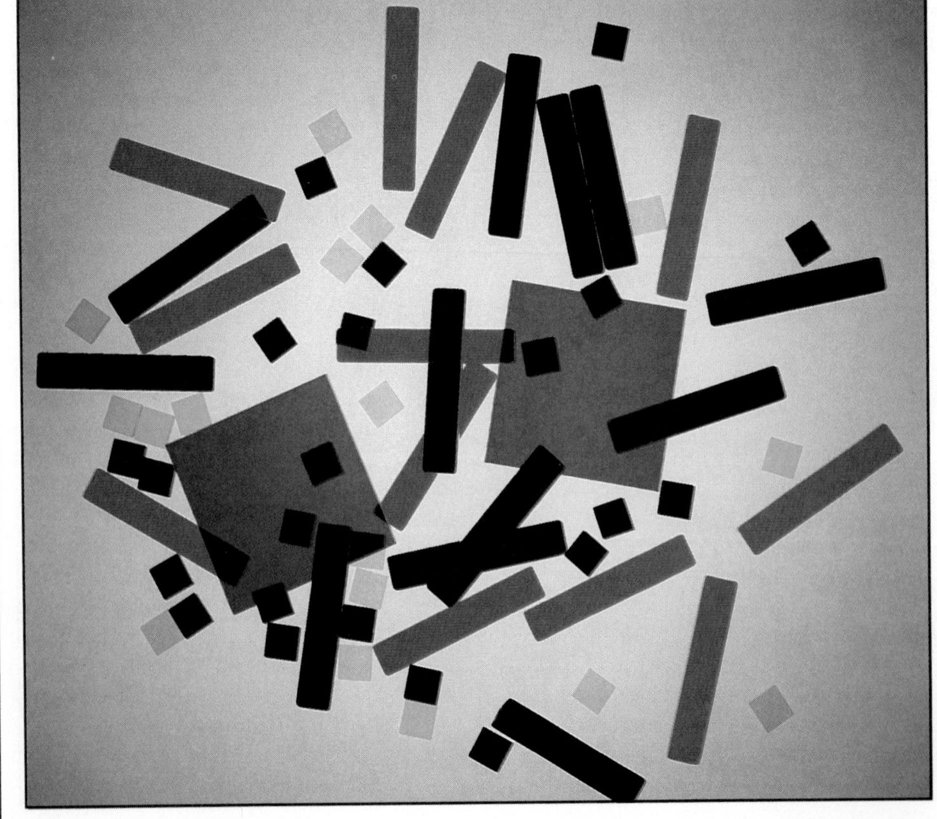

"It is as necessary to involve students physically in active learning experiences in an algebra class as it is in a first-grade classroom."[1]

Manipulative materials are the key to understanding operations and algorithms.

A major barrier to using manipulative materials in teaching mathematics at the upper level is attitude. Students' attitudes have been conditioned by the traditional view of mathematics as a body of technical algorithms. By the time students enter middle school they believe that in mathematics there is always a rule to follow. They want to be told the rule and resist the original and creative thinking required by an activity-oriented program.

Another factor contributing to the meager use of manipulatives in upper level mathematics programs is a common belief that "achievement is measured by how well students *do* the algorithms, not how well they understand them, and children must have adequate mastery of facts and algorithms if they are to be successful in later grades."[2]

In the computer age of tomorrow, however, simply knowing how to apply rote, mechanical rules for deriving correct answers will not suffice; understanding the "why" and "wherefore" behind each step of the mathematical process will become increasingly important.

"Manipulative materials are the key to understanding operations and algorithms."[3] Because abstractions are an integral part of algebra and because students derive their abstract ideas primarily from their experience, it is imperative that they experiment with a variety of manipulative materials on the concrete level to develop an understanding of algebraic symbols and concepts.

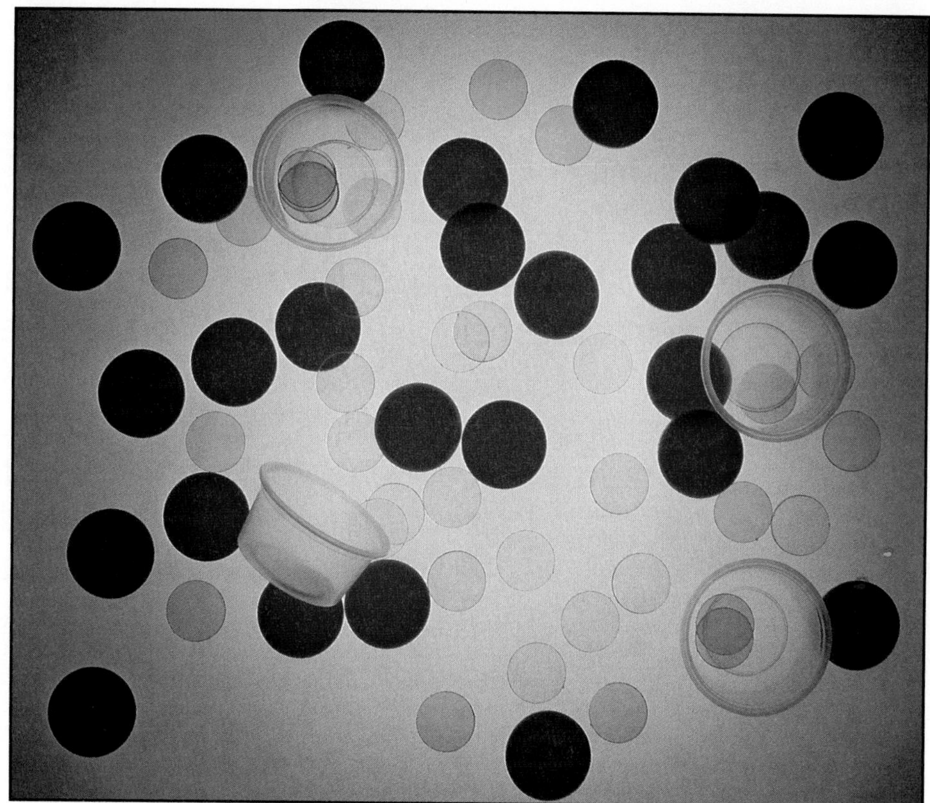

The purpose of using manipulatives is to assist students in bridging the gap from concrete to abstract.

Many teachers find that demonstrations on an overhead projector ease students with little experience in hands-on learning into working with manipulatives. Simply observing such a demonstration, however, is not enough. Follow-up activities that involve the students in the act of physically manipulating such aids are essential if students are to experience the patterns and relations inherent in mathematics.

"The purpose of using manipulatives is to assist students in bridging the gap from their own concrete environment to the abstract level."[4] Affording students the opportunity for meaningful practice through modeling algorithms with manipulatives not only results in greater understanding of the concepts and skills in question but also provides a fun alternative to everyday, routine problem-solving exercises as well.

Merrill Pre-Algebra contains many opportunities for students to use manipulatives to discover and explore algebraic concepts. The *Exploration* lessons — 28 in all — guide students to actually *do* mathematics by using counters, algebra tiles, and measuring cups just to name a few. Students are also encouraged to make conjectures based on their observations. In lessons following the *Explorations,* teachers are encouraged to allow the continued use of the manipulatives as necessary.

To make sure that students understand what is expected of each activity, the teacher must discuss its goal and model how the manipulative is to be used to achieve it. Encouraging students to suggest ways in which manipulatives can be used helps them to relate concepts and to develop mathematical insights.

The important thing to keep in mind is that most students do not automatically abstract the concepts they explore with materials; they must be led to see how the concepts relate to traditional algorithms. Summarizing and recording group activity results helps to focus on such relationships and algebraic concepts. Used in this way, manipulative materials are a justifiable means to a desirable end.

No presentation advocating the use of manipulative materials in the pre-algebra classroom would be totally complete without interjecting a note of caution. Despite the fact that manipulative materials are highly touted, and rightly so, they can, if used incorrectly, undo much of the good for which they are intended. Through careless or erroneous use of manipulatives, students might conclude that there are two distinct mathematical worlds — one of manipulatives and another of symbols — and that each has its own rules.

Teachers must, therefore, direct students to see the need for precise and exact connection between the symbols and the manipulatives; otherwise they cannot possibly develop proper mathematical understanding. The point that must be stressed repeatedly in teaching with manipulatives in the pre-algebra classroom is that "symbols and manipulatives must always reflect the same concept."[5]

If mathematics educators sincerely want to challenge their students in the pre-algebra classroom, perhaps they must first endorse the fact that the use of manipulative materials holds the promise of increasing students' understanding of and achievement in mathematics, and then translate that belief into classroom practice.

---

1. Williams, David E., "Activities for Algebra," *Arithmetic Teacher,* February 1986, p. 42.
2. Beattie, Ian D., "Modeling Operations and Algorithms," *Arithmetic Teacher,* February 1986, p. 23.
3. Ibid., p. 24.
4. Hynes, Michael C., "Selection Criteria," *Arithmetic Teacher,* February 1986, p. 11.
5. Bright, George W., "One Point of View: Using Manipulatives," *Arithmetic Teacher,* February 1986, p. 4.

Cooperative Learning

"The best answer to the question, 'What is the most effective method of teaching?' is that it depends on the goal, the student, the content, and the teacher. But the next best answer is, 'Students teaching other students.' There is a wealth of evidence that peer teaching is extremely effective for a wide range of goals, content, and students of different levels and personalities."

Wilbert McKeachie, et al, 1986

Cooperative learning groups *learn* things together, not just do things together. Studies show that cooperative learning promotes more learning than competitive or individual learning experiences regardless of student age, subject matter, or learning activity. More difficult learning tasks, such as problem solving, critical thinking, and conceptual learning, come out far ahead when cooperative strategies are used. Studies also show that in classroom settings, adolescents learn more from each other about subject matter than from the teacher.

The basic elements of a cooperative learning group are as follows:

(1) Students must perceive that they "sink or swim together."

(2) Students are responsible for everyone else in the group, as well as themselves, in learning the assigned material.

(3) Students must see that they all have the same goal, that they need to divide up the tasks and share the responsibility equally, and that they will be given one evaluation or reward that will apply to all members of the group.

Preparation and Social Skills

1. Arrange your room. Students in groups should face each other as they work together. It is helpful to number the tables so you can refer to groups by number, or have groups choose a name.

2. Decide on the size of the group. Groups work best when teams are composed of two to five students. The materials available might dictate the size of the group.

3. Assign students to groups. Each group should be mixed socially, racially, ethnically, sexually, and by learning abilities. Occasionally a student may insist on working alone. This student usually changes his or her mind when seeing that everyone else's grades are better, and the groups are having more fun.

More difficult learning tasks, such as problem solving and critical thinking, come out far ahead when cooperative strategies are used.

4. Change groups. Some teachers keep their groups together for a quarter, a semester, or for a teaching unit. Have groups stay together long enough to experience success as a group. Changing groups allows students more opportunities to deal with a variety of classmates.

5. Prepare students for cooperation. This is a critical step. Tell students about the rationale, procedures, and expected outcomes of this method of instruction. Students need to know that you are not forcing them to be friends, but asking them to work together as they will later on in life with people who come together for a specific purpose.

6. Start small. You do not have to incorporate all of this information into your planning for your first cooperative groups. You can use cooperative groups for a portion of the class period and it may not be feasible to use every day. Some ideas will be easy to adapt to your style while others may be more difficult.

7. Explain group tasks. For more activities, each group will need someone to take notes, someone to summarize as the group progresses, and someone to make sure everyone is involved. Classes that have less experience using these methods may need these roles assigned to group members at the beginning of each activity. These jobs should be done by different students each time, so that one student does not feel burdened doing the same job all the time.

8. Explain the day's lesson. On the chalkboard or overhead, write the following headings:

- ***Form Groups:*** list the number of students in each group.
- ***Topic of the Day:*** general academic topic.

▸ *Task:* title of activity. At this time, go over instructions and relate the work to previous learning.

▸ ***Goal:*** indicate whether students will all do individual work of which you will select one person's paper or product to grade, or whether they will produce only one product per group. Student signatures on all the work indicates that they will accept the collected work for their grade.

▸ ***Cooperative Skills:*** list the specific group skills you will be checking. Start with one or two basic skills. The following skills start from basic and move to more advanced.

a. Use quiet voices.

b. Encourage each other to participate.

c. Use each other's names. Use eye contact.

d. Ask your teacher for help only after you have decided as a group that you all need help.

e. Stress that all student contributions are valuable.

After students have some experience working in cooperative groups, you can expect group members to exhibit some or all of the following higher level cooperative skills.

a. Express support and acceptance, both verbal and nonverbal, through eye contact, enthusiasm, and praise.

b. Ask for help or clarification about what is happening.

c. Suggest new ideas.

d. Use appropriate humor that stays on task.

e. Describe feelings using "I messages," such as, "I like the way you praised my idea."

f. Summarize and elaborate on what others have contributed.

g. Develop memory aids and analogies that are clever ways of remembering important points.

h. Criticize ideas, not people.

i. Go beyond the first answer to a question.

Teacher Responsibilities During Cooperative Group Work

1. *Monitor student behavior.* Use a formal observation sheet to count the number of times you observe the behavior expected on that particular assignment for each group. Start with a few behaviors at the beginning and move up to many different behaviors when you feel comfortable doing so. Share your observations with each group.

2. *Provide assistance with the task.* Clarify instructions, review concepts, or answer questions. You will find students who see you nearby will automatically start asking questions. Your first response should be, "Have you asked everyone in the group?"

Your role will be supportive supervisor rather than direct supervisor, you will help a group that has gotten stuck and is experiencing a high level of frustration. You might do this by asking a few open-ended questions. In a conflict situation, you might ask the group to identify the reason for the difficulty and ask them to come up with some strategies for handling the conflict.

Cooperative learning takes teachers from center stage of the classroom and makes them a facilitator within the process.

3. *Intervene to teach cooperative skills.* As you observe that some groups have more problems than others with cooperative skills, you may wish to intervene by asking the group to think about why they are not being effective and have them work toward a solution.

4. *Provide closure for the lesson.* Students should be asked to summarize what they have learned and be able to relate it to what they have previously studied. You may want to review the main points and ask students to give examples. You should also answer any final questions.

5. *Evaluate the group process.* In order for groups to be aware of their progress in learning to work together, they must be given time to evaluate or process how they are working together. Allow a few minutes at the end of the lesson for groups to decide if they achieved the criterion you set up. Have them rate themselves on a scale of one to ten and write down specific ways they could improve.

6. *Evaluate student learning.* Evaluation tools may include traditional tests and quizzes, group quizzes, and extra points for groups achieving overall high marks.

Keep in mind that cooperative learning does not just "happen." The first few days may seem like bedlam, with some students upset, others mistrustful, and others off task. Both you and your students will make mistakes. Be patient and keep at it.

Integrating Technology Into Your Pre-Algebra Classroom

"Students today can't prepare bark to calculate their problems. They depend upon their slates which are more expensive. What will they do when their slate is dropped and it breaks? They will be unable to write!"

Teachers Conference, 1703

The above quote seems ridiculous today, but in 1703 it was not. Many people may ask, "Couldn't they see enough into the future to know that slates would be required?"; but as the old adage goes, hindsight is twenty-twenty. The difficulty lies in foreseeing the future.

The argument nowadays is in regard to computers and calculators; and while most people agree that technology should be used in the mathematics classroom, few are offering ideas on incorporation, testing, appropriate use, and other areas where teachers have questions. Some use this as an argument against using technology, but that is not the answer to the problem. Instead we must be able to recognize a good idea when we see one and adopt it for our classrooms.

Appropriate Use of Technology

There are many different ideas and definitions of "appropriate use of technology," and rightly so. Every class and every teacher is different. What is appropriate and works for one may not be appropriate or work for another. However, there are some classifications and generalizations that can be made for different grade levels. For pre-algebra, keep in mind that many of your students are just learning the technology. You should refrain from getting "high-tech" with them. Give them opportunities for success early so that they can begin to feel comfortable with technology.

Have your students complete an easy calculation for their first encounter. For the students new to technology, this will give them a sense of accomplishment because they can see something they have done; for the more technologically experienced students, this will give them a sense of confidence because they already know what is being done.

At any level of teaching, try to get students to make generalizations about what they see or do with technology.

Using Technology in Your Classroom

Technology opens up many new ideas and opportunities. It is up to you to decide how to present and use technology in your classroom. Many of the standard teaching techniques are appropriate, such as using cooperative groups, or having students work in pairs, but there are also new ways of teaching that are appropriate when using technology in your classroom. For example, you can assign lab partners in each class. Each pair of students would then work together whenever technology is used. This can also be used if you have a limited supply of equipment.

Try to get students to make generalizations about what they see or do with technology.

Teaching Aids

There are many technological teaching aids as well as numerous products to assist in the teaching of technology. One of them is a projection panel for the overhead projector. This can be used in conjunction with a demonstration computer and can project the image from the computer onto a screen or wall.

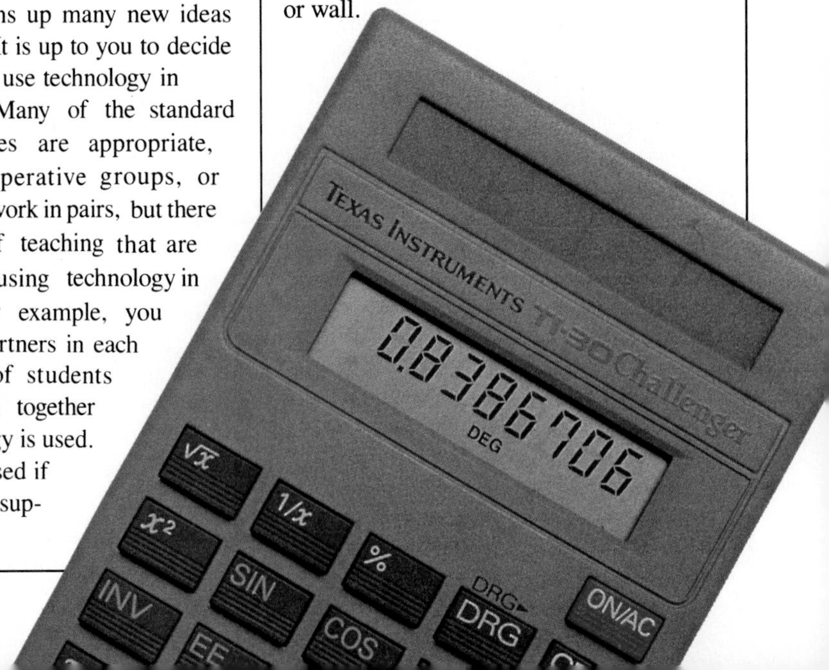

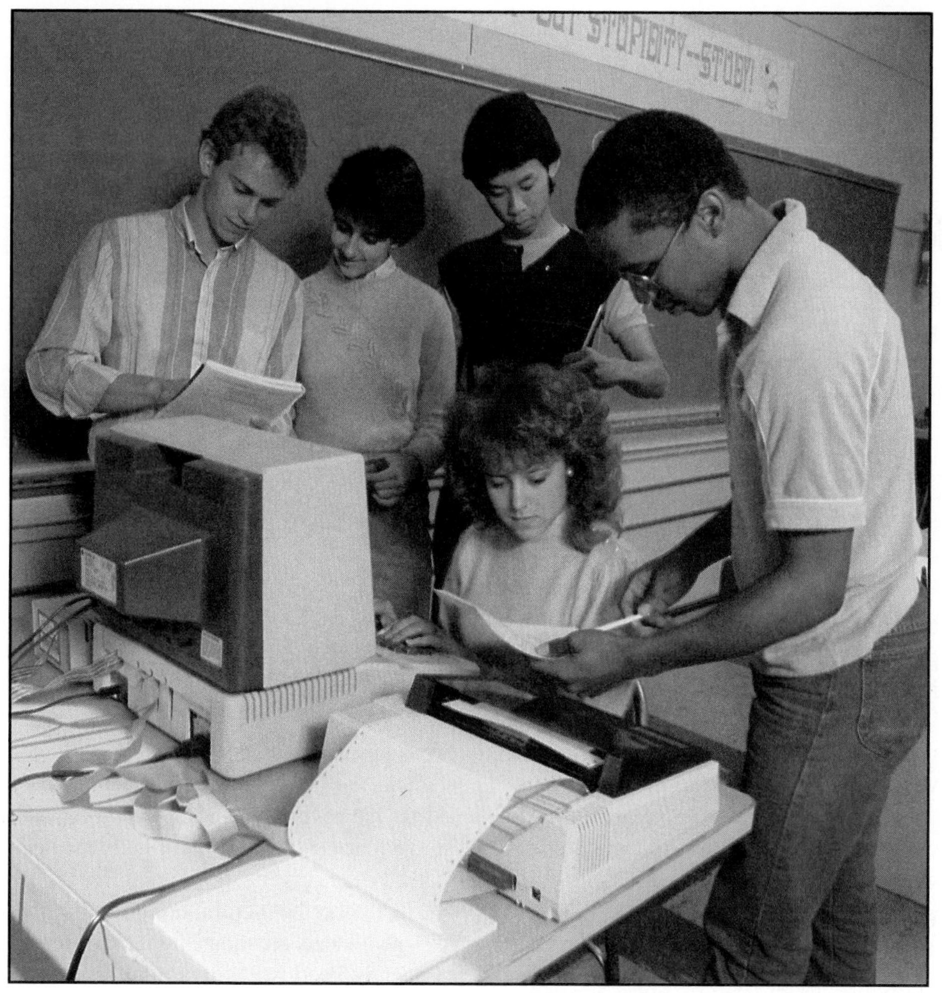

Probably the biggest advantage of technology is the amount of time it can save you.

Overhead projector calculators are also available for most models. They can serve the same purpose as a projection panel and demonstration computer.

Another teaching aid is a template of the computer or calculator keyboard that can be used on the overhead or put on the bulletin board for easy reference. (Masters for the TI-30 and TI-81 calculators are provided on pages 25 and 26 in the *Merrill Pre-Algebra Lab Manual.)* This can help in conveying the location of keys, especially second function keys on graphing calculators.

Changes in the Classroom

There will be some changes in your classroom with the onset of technology. One will be your role. It most likely will change from leader to guide. Students will begin to do things on their own and it will be up to you to keep them headed in the right direction. Students will also begin to ask more questions, including more higher-order questions, than before. You may not have all the answers, but the investigation can be enjoyable and enlightening for both you and your students.

Advantages of Technology

Probably the biggest advantage of technology is the amount of time it can save you. The ease of editing errors, the number of graphs and pictures that can be drawn in a short amount of time, the speed of calculating; all these and other time-saving advantages make technology a major plus for the mathematics classroom.

There are numerous other advantages. One is that students will have a deeper understanding of the concepts being taught. As we develop toward a more pictorial society, students are becoming visual learners. Technology teaches them in a way that piques their interest and leads to questions that show a desire to learn.

Another advantage of technology is the cooperative efforts that develop among students. Since students will most likely need to work with others when they become members of the work force, it is best for them to learn to work with others while they are in school. With technology, you can teach your students to work cooperatively, which will benefit them in college and in their careers.

Technology Fears

Perhaps the biggest fear, and certainly one that is most often expressed, is that of the technology taking the place of the teacher. *This will never happen.* There is no way that a computer can do what a teacher does, and in particular, sense what a teacher can. For example, no computer can sense uncertainty of an answer in a student's tone of voice. Few students will be able to turn on a calculator or computer and teach themselves with it. They need teachers to explain the technology and to help make connections.

You can also see the evidence of needing the teacher when you relate the use of technology in education to its use in the business world. Computers have been in the mainstream of business for quite some time now, and there has not been a reduction in the number of persons needed. Yet a large number of business executives will tell you they would not want to do their job without the use of a computer. Many teachers who have incorporated technology into their classrooms are saying the same thing.

Computers and calculators are excellent tools for teaching mathematics concepts. Though there are still some who argue their use in the classroom, none can argue their educational advantage. Technology can teach students in ways that were never before possible. In the past, teachers could only dream of being able to do some of the things that they can now do with ease, thanks to technology. While incorporating technology into your mathematical classroom can be difficult at first, in the long run, it will definitely pay off for both you and your students.

Alternate Assessment Strategies

Most students today will agree that the test is seen as the bottom line of the educational enterprise. Most of them will also agree that the present tests used to determine a student's accomplishment often fall short of the goal of measuring a student's understanding of ideas.

The vast array of testing devices today which, for the most part, center around multiple choice answers, true/false responses, and objective one-word answers, may be little more than mechanical ways of evaluating that focus on a student's ability to cough up answers on cue. They may reveal little to either the student or the teacher of the student's capabilities.

"Mathematics teachers are participating in a major restructuring of the goals and practices of mathematics education. It is essential that assessment strategies be found that can adequately reflect this new conception of the subject."[1]

Many formal assessment strategies may be rooted in informal assessment: that is, the garnering of information concomitant with instruction. Informal assessments are invaluable in the sense that they provide a realistic picture of student ability in a context where such ability is put to immediate use.

When educational goals are confined to the duplication of mathematical procedures, then conventional paper-and-pencil tests are adequate for assessing a learner's level of performance. But as our educational objectives broaden in scope, assessment should go beyond this. Assessments should now be extended for the purpose of guiding the actions of not just the student but of all those persons involved in the learning experience.

Informal assessments provide a realistic picture of student ability in a context where such ability is put to immediate use.

What Are the Alternatives?

There is a plethora of devices whereby the teacher of mathematics may expand his or her repertoire of assessment strategies. These include the use of questioning, observation, and journals.

Open-ended Questions Perhaps one of the easiest strategies to employ is that of open-ended questions which will permit students to more fully elaborate their knowledge of mathematical concepts and principles. In an assessment of this nature, students are forced to think for themselves and to express mathematical ideas in language that corresponds with their mathematical development.

The teacher has several options for scoring open-ended questions but the two most frequently used methods are analytic and holistic. Holistic scoring seems to be favored because judgement is based on the response as a whole, as opposed to analytic scoring, which evaluates answers on the basis of specific points that have been addressed in the student's responses.

Classroom Observation Documenting classroom observations is another strategic device for assessing student achievement. During the course of the instructional process, most teachers are quite adept at forming rather accurate opinions concerning the capabilities of their students which, in many instances, a later formal assessment will bear out or validate. Such observations, however, are very often not accorded the status of a test because they have not been formally structured and systematically recorded. Yet the quality of such informal assessment is in many cases superior to that obtained by formal testing. By simply implementing some structure into such observations, teachers can capitalize on this information for assessment purposes and at the same time dispense with other time-consuming and often unproductive forms of evaluation.

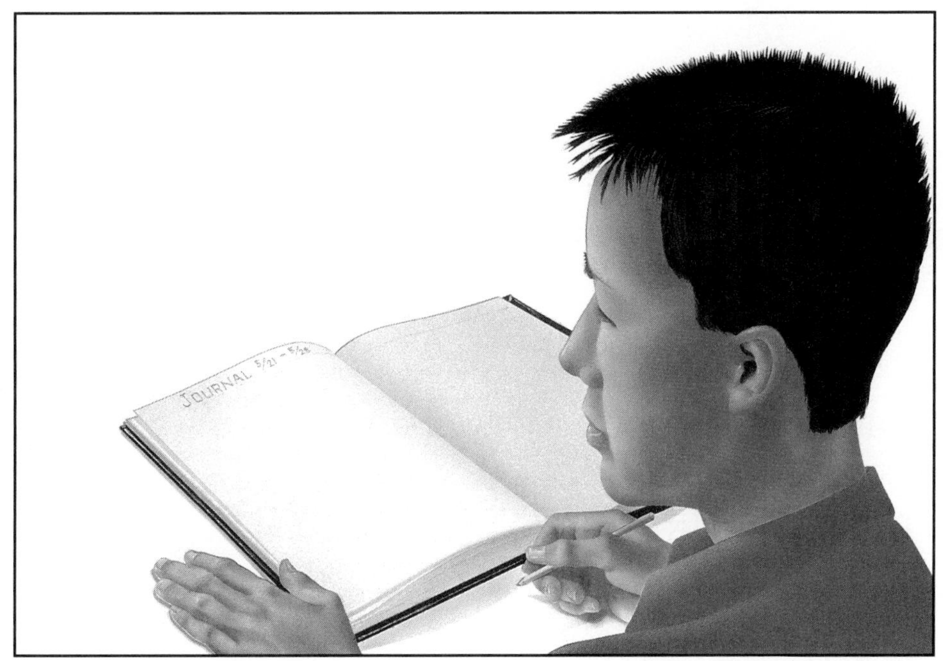

Questioning provides an excellent tool for assessing the competence of students as well as for monitoring the development of meaningful understanding. Dialogue of this nature between teacher and student is most beneficial in identifying errors in comprehension (reading and otherwise), in transformation, and in the use of process skills. "Research has indicated that at least 40% of students' errors on written mathematical problems occur before they even get to use the process skills their teachers have so laboriously stressed."[2]

Student understanding can be evaluated through writing, modeling, or speaking.

Self-evaluation One of the most valuable strategies we might implement is that of enabling students to monitor their own progress. This procedure calls for the student to write confidential answers to teacher questions regarding the way he or she feels in the class, what he or she would most like help with, and how mathematics class might be changed with an eye toward improving his or her skills.

Along the same lines, utilizing tests to which students have contributed questions not only makes for an effective revision strategy, it also provides students with a sense of ownership in the assessment process.

Portfolios and Journals Yet another means to assess student progress is to require students to periodically submit samples of their work in portfolios. Again, students might be asked to keep a daily journal in which they describe what they have learned and reflect on the material covered. Regular perusal of the journal can guide teaching procedures and serve as the basis for individual student-teacher conferences.

Daily Assessment Lastly, the mathematics class lends itself quite easily to carrying out practical tests — demonstrating skills in a practice situation. Your ***Merrill Pre-Algebra Teacher's Wraparound Edition*** contains an assessment option in each lesson plan. Student understanding can be evaluated through writing, modeling, or speaking activities. Since the skills are assessed in practice, they provide immediate feedback as well as enhanced motivation, for students who are usually most eager to show off, (correctly or not!), what they can do.

Although there are undoubtedly situations when the written test is effective, we must guard against using it to the exclusion of other forms of assessment. The examiner must select from among the many strategic techniques available, that one which will best indicate what his or her students can do.

---

1. Clarke, David J., Doug M. Clarke, and Charles J. Lovitt, "Changes in Mathematics Teaching Call for Assessment Alternatives," *Teaching and Learning Mathematics in the 1990s,* (1990 Yearbook, Reston VA: NCTM, 1990), p. 118.
2. Ibid., p. 123.

Meeting Individual Needs

"We cannot afford to have the majority of our population mathematically illiterate: Equity has become an economic necessity."

NCTM Standards (1989, p. 4)

Multicultural Perspective

There is no doubt that the United States is a multicultural society. Changing demographics, and changing economic and social orders are having a tremendous impact on the schools in this country. But, the term *multicultural* represents more than just *many cultures*. There is a multicultural basis to all knowledge, even mathematics.

From the ancient Egyptians, who used the "Pythagorean" theorem fifteen hundred years *before* Pythagoras, to the ancient Chinese, who calculated the value of π to ten places twelve hundred years *before* the Europeans, mathematics as we know it today has been shaped by many cultures. Even the term *algebra* was contributed by an Arabian mathematician, Al-Khowarizmi.

What is the role of the mathematics educator in all this? Students should have the opportunity to learn about persons from all cultures who have contributed to the development of mathematics. In addition, students should learn about persons from all cultures who have been successful in their respective careers. To this end, the *Merrill Pre-Algebra Activities Masters Booklet* contains one multicultural worksheet for each chapter. The ***Merrill Pre-Algebra Teacher's Wraparound Edition*** also contains suggestions for meeting the needs of all students in the interleaf pages that precede the chapters.

As educators, we also must prepare all students for the new jobs of the future that will require mathematical literacy. The mathematics teacher must be in the vanguard of those who demand that *all* students be given the opportunity to study the more advanced forms of mathematics. It is our responsibility as educators to make every effort to prepare the students of today to participate in the complex world of tomorrow.

Limited English Proficiency Needs

One of the greatest factors contributing to the under-achievement in mathematics education for the language-minority student is his or her failure to understand the language of instruction. There are, however, strategies which the mathematics teacher can employ to help overcome the obstacles that beset language-minority students.

Ideally, these students would be afforded the opportunity of having new concepts and skills reinforced by discussing them in their native tongue. It may be that a bilingual teacher could meet this need, or perhaps a tutor proficient in the language could be procured to provide such service.

If the student is proficient in his or her native language, perhaps materials written in that language could be provided to supplement classroom instruction.

If the student is not especially literate in his or her own language, perhaps an oral approach using pictorial materials and/or manipulative devices would be feasible.

When a student does not respond to the prescribed expectations of the school, the teacher needs to substitute developmentally equivalent tasks to shape development. If, for example, the student does not participate in classroom discussion, the wise teacher will observe his or her verbal interaction with other students in informal, less structured environments.

Because students coming from diverse cultural backgrounds lack common educational experiences, the teacher soon recognizes that the only way to establish a basis for communication is to begin instruction with content that is familiar to one and all.

"The challenge is to find personally interesting and culturally relevant ways of creating new contexts for children, contexts in which the mastery of school skills can be meaningful and rewarding."[1]

By integrating the development of language in such new contexts, we may be able to open the door to the challenging and exciting world of mathematics for the language-minority student.

1. Bowman, Barbara T., "Educating Language-Minority Children: Challenges and Opportunities," *Phi Delta Kappan*, October 1989, p. 120.

Planning Your Pre-Algebra Course

The charts below give suggested time schedules for three types of courses: minimum, standard, and accelerated, and for two types of grading periods: 9-weeks and 6-weeks.

The minimum course covers Chapters 1-10, 12, and 13. It allows for extra time for longer sessions and for reteaching and review. The standard course covers Chapters 1-14. Generally, one day is allotted for each lesson, the Chapter Review, and the Chapter Test. The accelerated course covers Chapter 1-15. This course is intended for students who master concepts quickly and retain skills well.

Nine Weeks Grading Period	TYPE OF COURSE					
	Minimum		**Standard**		**Accelerated**	
	Chapter	Days	Chapter	Days	Chapter	Days
1	1	14	1	12	1	11
	2	12	2	11	2	10
	3	13	3	12	3	11
			4 (Lessons 4-1 to 4-6)	6	4	11
2	4	13	4 (Lessons 4-7 to end)	6	5	11
	5	13	5	12	6	14
	6	17	6	15	7	8
			7	10	8	12
3	7	12	8	13	9	11
	8	14	9	12	10	11
	9	14	10	11	11	11
			11 (Lessons 11-1 to 11-6)	6	12 (Lessons 12-1 to 12-7)	7
4	10	13	11 (Lessons 11-7 to end)	5	12 (Lessons 12-8 to end)	7
	12	16	12	14	13	12
	13	15	13	13	14	11
			14	12	15	8
Total Days		166		170		166

Six Weeks Grading Period	TYPE OF COURSE					
	Minimum		**Standard**		**Accelerated**	
	Chapter	Days	Chapter	Days	Chapter	Days
1	1	14	1	12	1	10
	2	12	2	11	2	9
			3 (Lessons 3-1 to 3-6)	6	3	11
2	3	13	3 (Lessons 3-7 to end)	6	4	11
	4	13	4	12	5	11
			5	12	6 (Lessons 6-1 to 6-8)	7
3	5	13	6	15	6 (Lessons 6-9 to end)	7
	6	17	7	10	7	9
					8	12
4	7	12	8	13	9	10
	8	14	9	12	10	10
					11	10
5	9	14	10	11	12	14
	10	13	11	11	13	12
			12 (Lessons 12-1 to 12-8)	8		
6	12	15	12 (Lessons 12-9 to end)	6	14	11
	13	15	13	13	15	8
			14	11		
Total Days		165		169		162

Bibliography

Publications

Artzt, Alice, and Claire M. Newman, *How to Use Cooperative Learning in the Mathematics Classroom,* Reston, VA: NCTM, 1990.

Azzolino, Agnes, *How to Use Writing to Teach Mathematics,* Keyport, NJ: Mathematical Concepts, 1987.

Bolt, Brian, *More Mathematical Activities,* New York, NY: Cambridge University Press, 1985.

Burns, Marilyn, *The Book of Think,* Covelo, CA: Yolla Bolly Press, 1976.

Charles, Randall I., and Edward A. Silver, *The Teaching and Assessing of Mathematical Problem Solving,* Reston, VA: NCTM, 1988.

Coburn, Terrence, *How to Teach Mathematics Using a Calculator,* Reston, VA: NCTM, 1987.

Cooney, Thomas, ed., *Teaching and Learning Mathematics in the 1990s,* 1990 Yearbook, Reston, VA: NCTM, 1990.

Crandall, JoAnn, Teresa Corasiniti Dale, Nancy Rhodes, and George Spanos, *English Language Skills for Basic Algebra,* Washington, DC: Center for Applied Linguistics, 1986.

Cuevas, Gilbert J., "Mathematics Learning in English as a Second Language," *Journal for Research in Mathematics Education,* XV (March 1984) 134-144.

Curcio, Frances, *Developing Graph Comprehension: Elementary and Middle School Activities,* Reston, VA: NCTM, 1989.

Easterly, Kenneth E., Loren L. Henry and F. Morgan Simpson, *Activities for Junior High School and Middle School Mathematics,* Reston, VA: NCTM, 1981.

Ecker, Michael W., *Getting Started in Problem Solving and Math Contests,* New Nork, NY: Franklin Watts, 1987.

Edwards, Edgar L., ed., *Algebra for Everyone,* Reston, VA: NCTM, 1990.

Farrell, Margaret A., ed., *Imaginative Ideas for the Teacher of Mathematics, Grades K-12: Ranucci's Reservoir,* Reston, VA: NCTM, 1988.

Fuys, David, Dorothy Geddes, and Rosamond Tischler, *The van Heile Model of Thinking in Geometry among Adolescents,* Reston, VA: NCTM, 1988.

Gardner, Martin, *Codes, Ciphers, and Secret Writing,* New York, NY: Dover Publications, Inc., 1984.

Grouws, Douglas A., Thomas J. Cooney, and Douglas Jones, *Effective Mathematics Teaching,* Reston, VA: NCTM, 1988.

Harnadek, Anita, *Algebra Word Problems,* Pacific Grove, CA: Midwest Publications, 1989.

Hiebert, James, and Merlyn Behr, *Number Concepts and Operations in the Middle Grades,* Reston, VA: NCTM, 1988.

Jaffe, A.J., and Herbert F. Spirer, *Misused Statistics: Straight Talk for Twisted Numbers,* New York, NY: Marcel Dekker, Inc., 1987.

Jamski, William D., ed., *Mathematical Challenges for the Middle Grades,* Reston, VA: NCTM, 1990.

Johnson, David W. and Roger T. Johnson, *Cooperation and Competition, Theory and Research,* Edina, MN: Interaction Book Co., 1989.

Kagan, Spencer, *Cooperative Learning, Resources for Teachers,* Laguna Niguel, CA: Resources for Teachers, 1989.

Krause, Marina C., *Multicultural Mathematics Materials,* Reston, VA: NCTM, 1983.

Krulik, Stephen, and Jesse A. Rudnick, *A Sourcebook for Teaching Problem Solving,* Newton, MA: Allyn and Bacon, Inc., 1984.

Linn, Charles F., *Probability,* New York, NY: Thomas Y. Crowell Co., 1972.

Maletsky, Evan M., ed., *Teaching with Student Math Notes,* Reston, VA: NCTM, 1987.

Mathematical Sciences Education Board and National Research Council, *Everybody Counts: A Report to the Nation on the Future of Mathematics Education,* Washington, DC: National Academy Press, 1989.

________, *A Workbook for Teachers,* Boston, MA: Allyn and Bacon, Inc., 1980.

Marcy, Steve, and Janis Marcy, *Pre-Algebra with Pizzazz,* Palo Alto, CA: Creative Publications, 1978.

National Council of Teachers of Mathematics, *Curriculum and Evaluation Standards for School Mathematics,* Reston, VA: NCTM, 1989.

________, *Estimation and Mental Computation,* 1986 Yearbook, Reston, VA: NCTM, 1986.

________, *Historical Topics for the Mathematical Classroom,* Reston, VA: NCTM, 1989.

________, *The Ideas of Algebra, K-12,* 1988 Yearbook, Reston, VA: NCTM, 1988.

________, *Learning and Teaching Geometry, K-12,* 1987 Yearbook, Reston, VA: NCTM, 1987.

________ *Mathematics for the Middle Grades (5-9),* 1982 Yearbook, Reston, VA: NCTM, 1982.

________, *Professional Standards for Teaching Mathematics,* Reston, VA: NCTM, 1991.

________, *Teaching Statistics and Probability,* 1981 Yearbook, Reston, VA: NCTM, 1981.

Paulos, John A., *Innumeracy: Mathematical Illiteracy and Its Consequences,* New York, NY: 1988.

Phillips, Hubert, *My Best Puzzles in Logic and Reasoning,* New York, NY: Dover Publications, Inc., 1961.

Posamentier, Alfred S., and Jay Stepelman, *Teaching Secondary School Mathematics,* Columbus, OH: Charles E. Merrill, 1981.

Sachs, Leroy, ed., *Projects to Enrich School Mathematics,* Reston, VA: NCTM, 1988.

Seattle Public Schools, *Multicultural Mathematics Posters and Activities,* Reston, VA: NCTM, 1984.

Slavin, Robert, *Cooperative Learning, Student Teams, 2nd ed.,* Washington, DC: National Education Association, 1987.

Sowder, Judith T., *Setting a Research Agenda,* Reston, VA: NCTM, 1989.

Stenmark, J.K., *Assessment Alternatives in Mathematics,* Berkeley, CA: EQUALS, Lawrence Hall of Science, 1989.

Swienciki, Lawrence W., *Adventures in Pre-Algebra,* San Jose, CA: A.R. Davis, 1976.

Wagner, Sigrid, and Carolyn Kieran, *Research Issues in the Learning and Teaching of Algebra,* Reston, VA: NCTM, 1989.

Weiss, Malcolm E., *666 Jelly Beans! All that? An Introduction to Algebra,* New York, NY: Crowell, 1976.

Willoughby, Stephen S., *Mathematics Education for a Changing World,* Alexandria, VA: ASCD, 1990.

Wylie, C.R., *101 Puzzles in Thought and Logic,* New York, NY: Dover Publications, Inc., 1957.

Computer Software

You may wish to contact the publisher for the latest version.

Cappo, Marge, and Mike Fish, *The Factory,* Pleasantville, NY: Sunburst Communications.

Conquering Fractions (+,-), St. Paul, MN: MECC.

Conquering Percents, St. Paul, MN: MECC.

Conquering Ratios and Proportions, St. Paul, MN: MECC.

Dugdale, Sharon, and David Kibbey, *Green Globs and Graphing Equations,* Pleasantville, NY: Sunburst Communications.

———, *Interpreting Graphs,* Pleasantville, NY: Sunburst Communications.

Fraction Practice Unlimited, St. Paul, MN: MECC.

Horn, Marcia, and Stephen Edwards, *Keep Your Balance!,* Pleasantville, NY: Sunburst Communications.

Koetke, Walter, *Survival Math,* Pleasantville, NY: Sunburst Communications.

O'Brien, Thomas C., *More Teasers from Tobbs,* Pleasantville, NY: Sunburst Communications.

———, *Safari Search,* Pleasantville, NY: Sunburst Communications.

———, *Teasers by Tobbs with Integers,* Pleasantville, NY: Sunburst Communications.

———, *Teasers by Tobbs with Whole Numbers,* Pleasantville, NY: Sunburst Communications.

Perimeter, Area, and Volume, Big Spring, TX: Gamco Industries, Inc.

Schwartz, Judah L., and Michael Yerushalmy, *The Geometric preSupposer,* Pleasantville, NY: Sunburst Communications.

———, *The Geometric Supposer: Triangles,* Pleasantville, NY: Sunburst Communications.

Smith, Scott, *Geometric Connectors: Transformations,* Pleasantville, NY: Sunburst Communications.

Superplot, Berkeley, CA: Edusoft.

Films/Videotapes

Adventures in Perception, Dallas, TX: Association Films, Inc., 1970.

Approximating and Estimating, Wilmette IL: Films Incorporated, 1971.

Between Rational Numbers, Summit, NJ: Silver Burdett, 1970.

Classic Antics in Mathematics, Glendale, CA: AIMS Insturctional Media, 1976.

Dividing with Fractions – Reciprocals, Summit, NJ: 1970.

Donald in Mathmagic Land, Burbank, CA: Walt Disney Educational Media Co., 1959.

Equations In Algebra, Chicago, IL: International Film Bureau, Inc., 1963.

Geometry – What's That?, San Rafael, CA: Coronet Media, 1975.

The Golden Section, Mt. Vernon, NY: Macmillan Films, Inc., 1968.

Graphing Inequalities, Summit, NJ: Silver Burdett, 1970.

Mathematics of the Honeycomb, Whittier, CA: Moody Institute of Science, 1964.

Multiplying Options and Subtracting Bias, Reston, VA: NCTM, 1981.

Possibly So, Pythagoras, Chicago, IL: International Film Bureau, Inc., 1963.

Probability, Wilmette, IL: Films Incorporated, 1970.

Probability, An Introduction, Santa Monica, CA: BFA Educational Media, 1968.

Proportion at Work, Middleton, CT: Xerox Films, 1960.

The Story of Pi, Reston, VA: NCTM, 1989.

Teaching Mathematics Effectively, Alexandria VA: ASCD, 1982.

The Theory of Pythagoras, Reston, VA: NCTM, 1988.

The Weird Number, Middleton, CT: Xerox Films, 1971.

Lesson Objectives

1 The Language of Algebra

1-1: Use the order of operations to evaluate numeric expressions.
1-2: Use variables to evaluate algebraic expressions.
1-3: Recognize and apply the properties of addition and subtraction.
1-4: Use the distributive property to simplify algebraic expressions.
1-5: Differentiate between an equation and an open sentence and solve an open sentence.
1-6: Solve a problem using the guess-and-check strategy.
1-7: Use inverse operations to solve equations.
1-8: Write verbal phrases as algebraic expressions.
1-9: Solve a problem by using an equation.
1-10: Evaluate inequalities.

2 Integers

2-1: Graph integers on a number line. Find the absolute value of a number.
2-2: Recognize the order of integers on the number line.
2-3: Add integers on the number line.
2-4: Use properties to add integers.
2-5: Subtract integers and use the distributive property to combine like terms.
2-6: Determine the truth value of a statement and its negation.
2-7: Multiply integers.
2-8: Divide integers.
2-9: Solve problems involving integers.

3 Solving One-Step Equations

3-1: Use the subtraction property of equality to solve one-step equations.
3-2: Use the addition property of equality to solve one-step equations.
3-3: Use the division property of equality to solve one-step equations.
3-4: Use the multiplication property of equality to solve one-step equations.
3-5: Apply the properties of equality to solve problems involving formulas.
3-6: Find the perimeter and area of squares and rectangles.
3-7: Use the addition and subtraction properties of equality to solve inequalities.
3-8: Use the multiplication and division properties of equality to solve inequalities.
3-9: Determine the truth value of compound statements.
3-10: Solve verbal problems by translating them into equations and inequalities.

4 Factors and Fractions

4-1: Use divisibility rules to determine if a number is a factor of another number. Determine whether an expression is a monomial.
4-2: Evaluate expressions containing exponents.
4-3: Solve a problem by drawing a diagram.
4-4: Indentify prime and composite numbers. Write numbers and monomials as products of prime numbers.
4-5: Find the greatest common factor (GCF) of two or more integers or monomials.
4-6: Use the GCF to simplify fractions.
4-7: Find the lowest common multiple (LCM) of two or more numbers.
4-8: Compare fractions with unlike denominators by writing equivalent fractions with the LCM as the denominator. Find the least common denominator of algebraic fractions.
4-9: Multiply powers.
4-10: Divide powers.

5 Rational Numbers: Adding and Subtracting Patterns

5-1: Identify and compare rational numbers.
5-2: Rename decimals as fractions.
5-3: Round decimals and use rounding to estimate sums and differences of decimals.
5-4: Add and subtract decimals.
5-5: Add and subtract fractions with like denominators.
5-6: Add and subtract fractions with unlike denominators.
5-7: Solve equations and inequalities involving rational numbers.
5-8: Solve a problem by looking for a pattern.
5-9: Identify and extend an arithmetic sequence. Represent a sequence algebraically.
5-10: Convert measures within the customary system and add and subtract customary measures.

6 Rational Numbers: Multiplying and Dividing Patterns

6-1: Write fractions as terminating or repeating decimals.
6-2: Estimate products and quotients of rational numbers.
6-3: Multiply fractions.
6-4: Multiply decimals.
6-5: Identify and use the properties of multiplication.
6-6: Divide fractions.
6-7: Divide decimals.
6-8: Solve equations and inequalities containing rational numbers.
6-9: Identify examples of deductive and inductive reasoning.
6-10: Recognize and extend geometric sequences. Represent a geometric sequence algebraically.
6-11: Write numbers in scientific notation.
6-12: Compare rational numbers.
6-13: Find the circumference of a circle.

7 Solving Equations and Inequalities

7-1: Solve a problem by working backwards.
7-2: Solve equations that involve two operations.
7-3: Solve verbal problems by translating them into two-step equations.
7-4: Solve equations with variables on each side.
7-5: Solve equations that involve more than one operation.
7-6: Solve inequalities that involve more than one operation.
7-7: Solve verbal problems involving rational numbers by translating them into inequalities.
7-8: Convert measures within the metric system.

8 Graphing Equations and Inequalities

8-1: Graph the solution of an equation on a number line.
8-2: Graph the solution of an inequality on a number line.
8-3: Identify the ordered pair of numbers associated with a point on a grid.
8-4: Graph points in a coordinate system.
8-5: Find solutions for equations with two variables.
8-6: Graph linear equation on a coordinate system.
8-7: Solve a problem by using a graph.
8-8: Find the slope of a line.
8-9: Graph a linear equation by using the x- and y-intercept.
8-10: Solve systems of equations by graphing.
8-11: Graph linear inequalities on a coordinate system.

9 Proportions and Percent

9-1: Write ratios as fraction in simplest form and determine unit rates.
9-2: Determine if a pair of ratios form a proportion and solve proportions.
9-3: Use proportions to solve verbal problems.
9-4: Use the percent proportion to write fractions as percents. Solve a problem using the percent proportion.
9-5: Express decimals as percents and express percents as fractions and decimals.
9-6: Use percents to estimate.
9-7: Solve percent problems by translating them into equations.
9-8: Use percents to solve problems involving discount and interest.
9-9: Solve a problem by making a list.
9-10: Find the percent of increase and decrease.

10 Statistics and Graphs

10-1: Gather and record data using a frequency table or histogram.
10-2: Find the mean, median, and mode of a set of data.
10-3: Make a stem-and-leaf plot of a set of data and make conclusions based on the data displayed in a stem-and-leaf plot.
10-4: Use meaures of variation to compare data.
10-5: Make a box-and whisker plot of a set of data.
10-6: Interpret data displayed in a scatter plot.
10-7: Solve a problem by first solving a simpler problem.
10-8: Use a sample to predict actions of a larger group.
10-9: Recognize misleading statistics.

11 Probability

11-1: Use a tree diagram to count outcomes.
11-2: Use the fundamental counting principle to count outcomes.
11-3: Find permutations and combinations.
11-4: Find the probability of a simple event.
11-5: Solve a problem by first making a table.
11-6: Find the probability of independent events.
11-7: Find the probability of dependent events.
11-8: Find the probability of mutually exclusive events.
11-9: Investigate problems using simulation.

12 Applying Algebra to Geometry

12-1: Identify points, lines, planes, rays, segments and angles. Classify angles as acute, right or obtuse.
12-2: Construct a circle graph based on raw data.
12-3: Identify angle relationships.
12-4: Identify the relationship of angles formed by two parallel lines and a transversal.
12-5: Construct congruent segments and angles using a compass and a straightedge. Bisect segments and angles.
12-6: Find the missing angle measure of a triangle and classify triangles.
12-7: Identify a conditional and its parts and write the converse of the conditional.
12-8: Identify congruent triangles and corresponding parts of congruent triangles.
12-9: Identify corresponding parts of similar triangles and find missing measures by using lengths of corresponding sides.
12-10: Use proportions to solve problems involving similar triangles.
12-11: Find the missing angle of a quadrilateral and classify quadrilaterals.
12-12: Classify polygons.

13 Measuring Area and Volume

13-1: Find the area of parallelograms and triangles.
13-2: Find the area of a trapezoid.
13-3: Find the area of circles.
13-4: Find the surface area of triangular and rectangular prisms.
13-5: Find the surface area of circular cylinders.
13-6: Identify pyramids and find the area of pyramids and cones.
13-7: Find the area of prisms.
13-8: Find the volume of circular cylinders.
13-9: Find the volume of pyramids and cones.
13-10: Use precision and significant digits to describe a measurement.
13-11: Solve a problem by making a model or drawing.

14 Applying Algebra to Right Triangles

14-1: Find square roots of squares.
14-2: Approximate square roots.
14-3: Use a Venn diagram to solve a problem.
14-4: Identify types of numbers. Solve equations by finding square roots. Simplify square roots.
14-5: Use the Pythagorean Theorem to find the length of the side of a right triangle.
14-6: Solve problems using the Pythagorean Theorem.
14-7: Find the missing measures in 30°-60° and 45°-45° triangles.
14-8: Find the tangent of an angle and find the measure of an angle using the tangent ratio.
14-9: Find the sine and cosine of a number and find the measure of an angle using the sine and cosine ratio.
14-10: Solve problems by using the trigonometric ratios.

15 Polynomials

15-1: Identify and classify polynomials and find the degree of a polynomial.
15-2: Add polynomials.
15-3: Subtract polynomials.
15-4: Find powers of monomials.
15-5: Multiply a polynomial by a monomial.
15-6: Multiply binomials.
15-7: Solve a problem by eliminating possibilities.

As you gear up to study pre-algebra, you probably have two big questions on your mind: How is pre-algebra different from other mathematics courses I've already taken? How will it prepare me to learn algebra and geometry?

A good way to explain pre-algebra is to describe it as a bridge between arithmetic and algebra. As you cross this bridge, you will move from working problems that are mostly numerical to solving those that require more advanced reasoning skills that require working with variables, or unknowns. You will be introduced to a variety of practical and exciting reasoning skills. These reasoning skills are practical because you will use them in other classes and outside of school. They are exciting because you will find them useful throughout your life.

Here are just two of your "tickets to success."

- ***You will learn to solve particular kinds of problems called equations.*** Once you master basic algebra problem-solving methods, you can use them in your daily life. Using formulas in science, deciding how to spend your money, and keeping sports statistics are among the many practical uses for algebra.

- ***You will learn to use percent.*** Sometimes an estimate will do in figuring percentages — for example, determining roughly what percent of your day is spent in school. In other situations, such as determining the interest your money can earn in a savings account, an exact answer will be required.

A Preview of Pre-Algebra

The purpose of this 11-page section is to provide a foundation for the strategies that students will use throughout the text. It also introduces you to the four-step teaching model used throughout the text.

Pages 2 and 3 introduce the four-step plan for solving problems. Each problem-solving lesson in the text focuses on one or more problem-solving strategies. Encourage students to draw upon any or all strategies each time they encounter a problem situation.

The dimension of mathematics presented on pages 4 and 5 is estimation. It is intended to help students develop proficiency with estimation.

The material found on pages 6 and 7 is intended to make students aware of the choices of methods of computation and allows them to apply estimation procedures.

Estimation is taken one step further in pages 8 and 9 where students are asked to judge the reasonableness of their results.

The final lesson of this section, found on pages 10 and 11, focuses on a brief introduction to reading and interpreting the various forms of graphic information.

Previewing Pre-Algebra

Lesson Notes

Objective

Examine and apply the four steps for problem solving that are used throughout the book.

1 FOCUS

The purpose of this lesson is to familiarize students with the four-step plan for problem solving. Students will learn how the steps can be applied to both mathematical and nonmathematical problems.

2 TEACH

Using Discussion List each step on the chalkboard. As each step is listed, apply the step to the example contained in the lesson.

Featuring 4 Simple Steps to Problem Solving

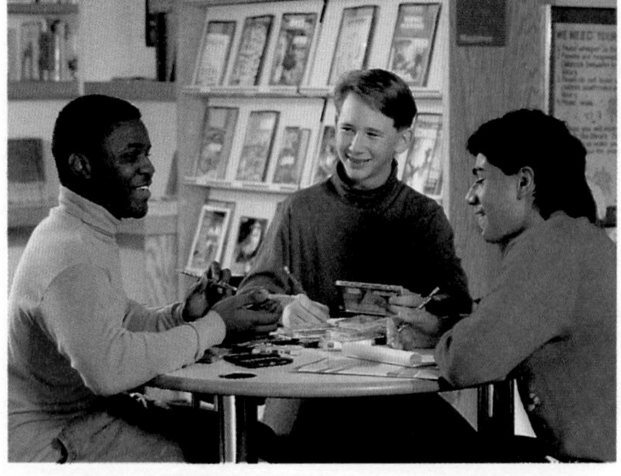

The Steps in Action

You can use these four simple steps to solve real-life problems as well as mathematical problems. For example, suppose you and some classmates are on the entertainment committee in charge of organizing a school dance. None of you has ever served on this type of committee. Together you must decide whether to provide a deejay or a live band at the dance, and then hire one. Here is how you could apply the four steps to this hypothetical real-life situation.

The Steps in Brief

Step 1 Explore
- Identify the problem to be solved.
- Ask yourself these questions:
  "What do I *already know* that can help me solve this problem?"
  "What do I *need to find out* to solve this problem?"

Step 2 Plan
- Figure out how all the facts are related.
- Choose the most practical method for solving the problem.
- Make an estimate of the answer.

Step 3 Solve
- Use the method you have chosen to actually solve the problem.

Step 4 Examine
- Examine each step you have taken to solve the problem.
- Ask yourself these questions:
  "Based on the facts, does this answer seem reasonable?"
  "If not, where is my reasoning faulty?"
  "Is there a faster or better way to solve the problem?"

Step 1 Explore

Identify the problem to be solved.
"Should we hire a deejay or a live band for the school dance?"

What do we already know that can help us solve this problem?
"A lot of kids said the deejay used at the last dance was boring."
"Live bands cost more than deejays."
"We don't have much money to spend on entertainment."

Step 2 Plan

Figure out how all the facts are related.
"Let's brainstorm a list of live bands and find out how much each costs."
"Let's do the same to come up with a list of deejays."
"No matter how cheap the boring deejay is, let's agree not to make that mistake again."

Choose the most practical method for solving the problem.
"It would be nice to take a survey of other students' opinions, but this would not be practical because we must make a decision soon."
"Instead, let's narrow our lists of live bands and deejays to ones we can afford."

Make an estimate of the answer.
"Let's take a preliminary, informal vote to see which of the affordable bands and deejays we like."

Step 3 Solve

Use the method you have chosen to actually solve the problem.
"After discussing the reasons for our choices, let's vote again and agree to let the majority rule. We will hire the band or deejay that gets the most votes."

Step 4 Examine

Examine your solution. Is it reasonable? Is there a better way to solve the problem?
"Our committee has several representatives from each grade. So, our vote gave us a good idea of what most students like."
"Since we didn't have much time, a committee decision was better than letting all the students vote on entertainment for the dance."
"The band we voted for will be within our budget since they were on our list."

It's Your Turn

Follow the same problem-solving process used by the entertainment committee to explain how a group of students on the refreshments committee would decide what to serve at the dance.

3 PRACTICE/APPLY

Have the students work in cooperative groups to solve the problem presented in **It's Your Turn**. Have students verbalize each step of the solution.

4 CLOSE

Ask students to describe real-life situations in which they need to solve a problem. Have students choose one of these situations and apply the four steps of the plan to solve it.

Lesson Notes

Objective

Develop estimation skills that will be used before, during, and after solving problems throughout the book.

1 FOCUS

The purpose of this lesson is to determine when an estimate can be used instead of an exact answer and to use rounding and reasoning to estimate answers.

2 TEACH

Using Questioning Ask students what they think the term **estimation** means and use the responses to develop a working definition of the term. Use student-generated situations to show when rounding can be used to estimate.

In Your Estimation

Estimation is a skill you use nearly every day. Suppose you plan to be home all evening and invite a friend to come over after she eats dinner. She correctly interprets this to mean that she does not need to arrive at a precise time. You can probably expect her to arrive anytime between 5:30 and 7:30 P.M

You and a friend are going to a movie. You need to find out exactly when it begins. Then you must be in your seats by 7:15 P.M., for example, so you don't miss anything on the screen.

In the first situation, you can safely estimate—or calculate approximately—when your friend will arrive. In the second, it would be foolish to make an estimate rather than to find out exactly when the movie begins.

In pre-algebra, you will develop your estimating skills to solve some problems and to check others. After you explore the problem to be solved (step 1, remember?), always estimate your answer (step 2) before solving the problem (step 3).

When Is It Safe to Estimate?

Use your reasoning skills, along with some good old-fashioned common sense, to determine whether the following situations require an exact answer or an estimate.

1. Your mother agrees to give you an advance on your allowance to buy stereo speakers, but says you must pay her back that amount plus 8 percent interest.

2. Michael wants to figure out how much his store discount coupon is worth on the sweater he plans to buy.

3. Angela needs to figure out how many sequins she needs to buy to sew on her costume for the school play.

4. Tanya's father asks her teacher to give him a general idea of where Tanya's grades rank her in a class of 187 students.

5. When they receive their $6 dinner check, Jessica and Andrea decide to reward their friendly waiter by giving him a 20% tip.

6. John asks his mom how many hours it will take them to drive from North Carolina to Florida on their family vacation.

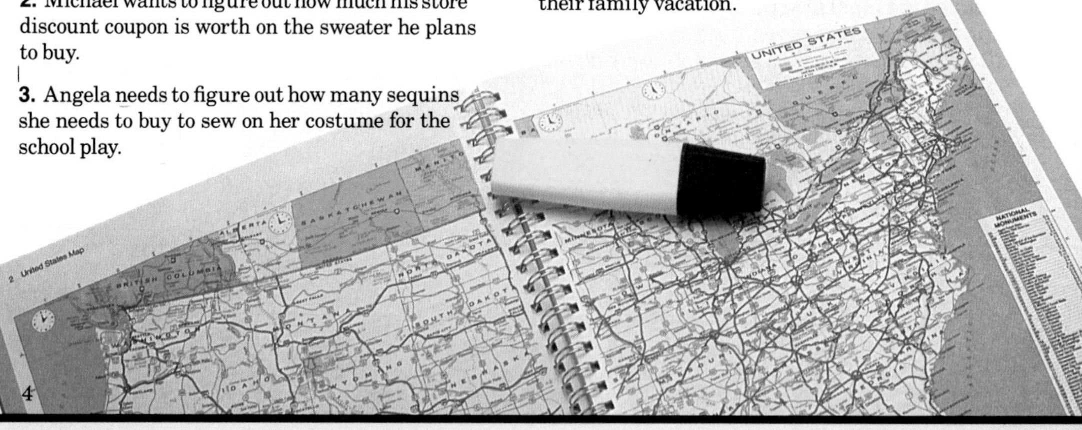

Answers: Accept reasonable answers.
1. exact
2. exact
3. estimate
4. estimate
5. exact
6. estimate

Putting Your Estimating Skills to Work

Estimating skills are especially handy when you find yourself without a pencil and paper or calculator and you must literally "use your head." To make estimating easier, you can round numbers.

For example, let's say Karen works 12 hours a week at a part-time job and earns $4.08 an hour. No taxes are withheld from her small paychecks. She is saving for a mountain bike that costs $279. She wants to estimate her weekly pay to see how long she needs to save to buy the bike. Because it ends in 0, it is easier to multiply by 10 than by 12. So, to make her estimate, Karen will use 10 for the number of hours she works.

1. Which number would be reasonably accurate and easier to use for Karen's hourly pay?

A. $4.00 B. $4.10 C. $4.15 D. $4.25

2. Multiply the number of estimated hours Karen works each week by her estimated hourly pay. Choose the most accurate estimate of how much Karen will earn in one week.

A. $40 B.$48 C. $49 D. $50

3. About how long will Karen need to work to save enough money to buy the $279 bike?

A. 4 weeks B. 7 weeks C. 10 weeks D. 12 weeks

3 *PRACTICE/APPLY*

Have students answer the lesson exercises individually. Then have students discuss their results in cooperative groups.

4 *CLOSE*

Have each student write in his or her own words how estimation can be used before solving a problem, during problem solving, and after solving a problem.

Answers

1. A
2. A
3. B

Lesson Notes

Objective

Determine and apply the best method for computing the solution to mathematical problems.

1 FOCUS

The purpose of this lesson is to analyze a problem to determine whether or not an exact answer is needed, and then choose estimation, using a calculator, mental computation, or paper-and-pencil as the best method of computation.

2 TEACH

Point out the difference between mental computation and estimation. In mental computation, the student computes an *exact* answer. For example, 1225 × 10 = 12,250. In estimation, the student *approximates* an answer. For example, 1225 × 11 is close to 1200 × 10 or 12,000.

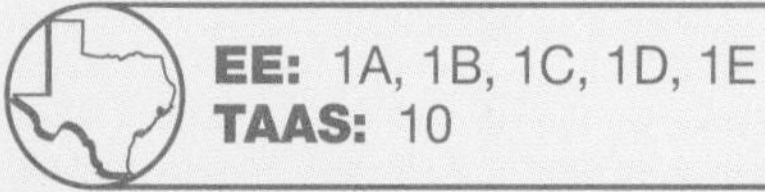

Choosing the Method of Computation

One of the most important steps in problem solving is deciding what method you will use to find the answer. This process is also called "choosing the method of computation." Sometimes, as with Karen saving to buy a bike, estimating is the best method for finding the answer.

Rely on your estimating skills whenever an *approximate* answer is appropriate to the situation. When an exact answer is required, you will need to use mental math, pencil and paper, or a calculator to carry out the computation. Use this handy chart to help you decide which method to use to solve the problems on page 7.

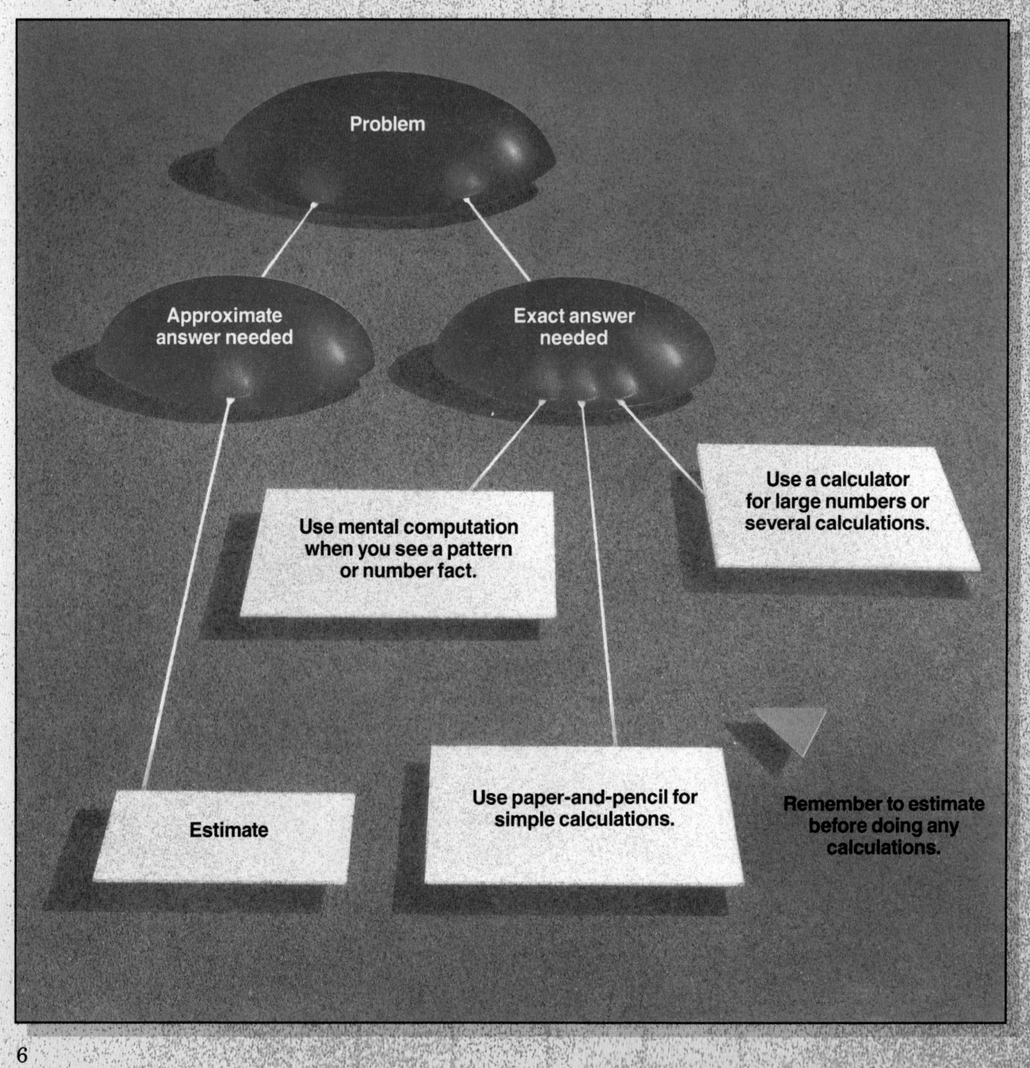

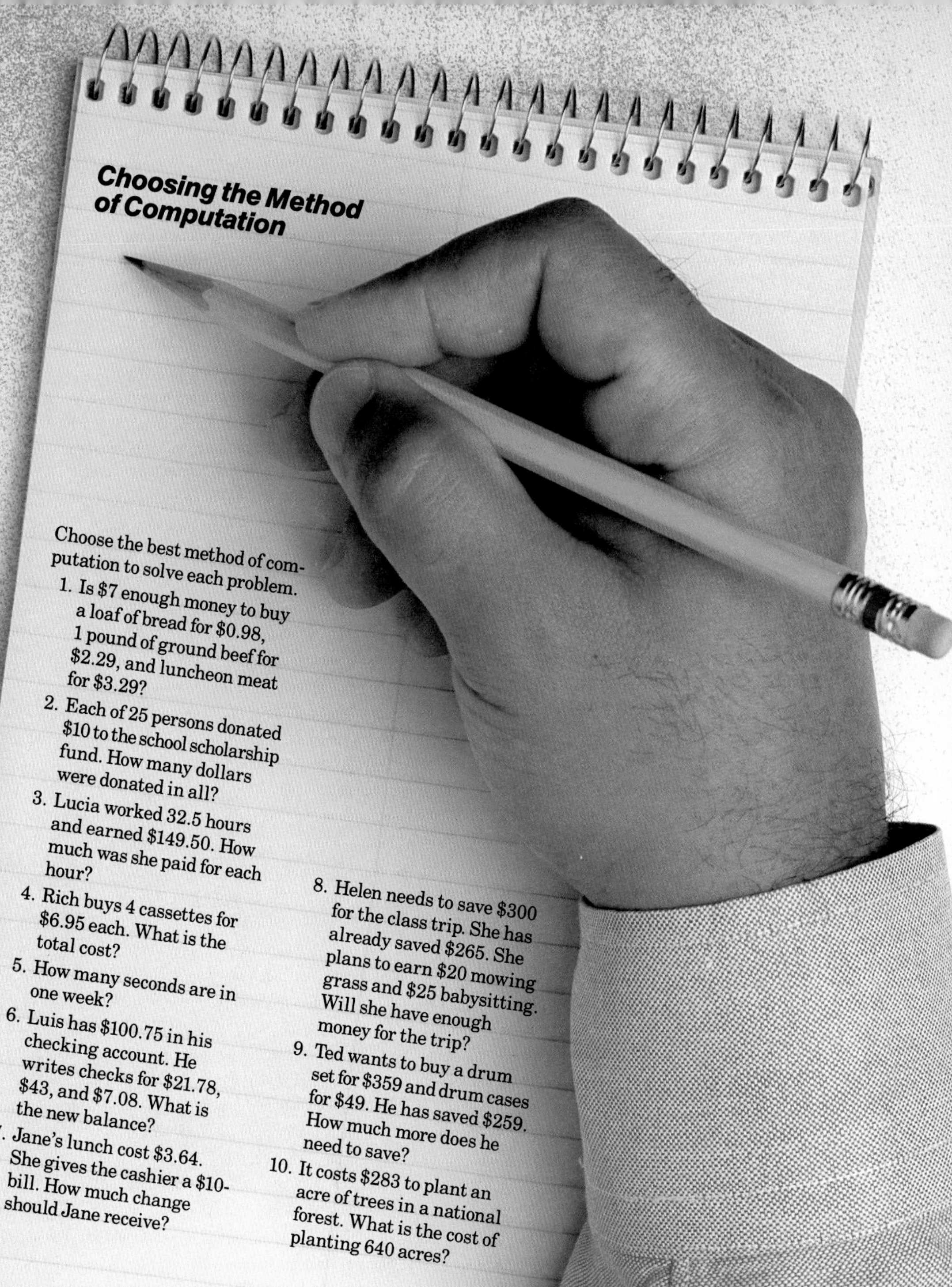

Choosing the Method of Computation
Choose the best method of computation to solve each problem.
1. Is $7 enough money to buy a loaf of bread for $0.98, 1 pound of ground beef for $2.29, and luncheon meat for $3.29?
2. Each of 25 persons donated $10 to the school scholarship fund. How many dollars were donated in all?
3. Lucia worked 32.5 hours and earned $149.50. How much was she paid for each hour?
4. Rich buys 4 cassettes for $6.95 each. What is the total cost?
5. How many seconds are in one week?
6. Luis has $100.75 in his checking account. He writes checks for $21.78, $43, and $7.08. What is the new balance?
7. Jane's lunch cost $3.64. She gives the cashier a $10-bill. How much change should Jane receive?
8. Helen needs to save $300 for the class trip. She has already saved $265. She plans to earn $20 mowing grass and $25 babysitting. Will she have enough money for the trip?
9. Ted wants to buy a drum set for $359 and drum cases for $49. He has saved $259. How much more does he need to save?
10. It costs $283 to plant an acre of trees in a national forest. What is the cost of planting 640 acres?
7

3 PRACTICE/APPLY

Have students solve the lesson exercises individually. Compare solutions. Where there are differences in solution, have each student verbalize his or her reasons for choosing that particular method of computation.

4 CLOSE

Have students work in cooperative groups to write one verbal problem that would best be solved by using estimation. Write other problems best solved by a calculator, mental computation, and paper and pencil. Trade with another group; solve.

Answers: Accept reasonable answers.

1. estimate
2. mental computation
3. calculator or paper-and-pencil
4. mental computation, calculator, or paper-and-pencil
5. calculator
6. calculator or paper-and-pencil
7. calculator or paper-and-pencil
8. estimation
9. mental computation, calculator, or paper-and-pencil
10. calculator

Lesson Notes

Objective

Develop skills to determine whether a solution to any problem is reasonable. These skills will be reinforced throughout the book.

1 FOCUS

The purpose of this lesson is to use estimation and logical reasoning to determine whether the solution to a problem is reasonable.

2 TEACH

Consumer Connection Discuss criteria for when a solution is reasonable. Have students discuss and determine the reasonableness of each of the following answers.

1. Sue wants to buy three blouses that cost $18.95 each. She hopes to have enough change from $50.00 to buy lunch.
2. Ayani is buying refreshments for 17 people. He buys snack cakes that are on sale for 3 for $1.00. He wants to use the change from a ten-dollar bill to buy lemonade.

EE: 1A, 1B, 1C, 1D, 1E
TAAS: 13

Let's Be Reasonable

In an ideal world, there would be time to re-think and re-work every problem you encounter. In real life, this usually isn't possible. Instead, you will need to use your reasoning skills to determine if your answer seems reasonable. Sometimes your estimating skills will help you determine if an answer is reasonable. Sometimes your common sense will be your guide. Often, you will rely on a combination of these two skills to quickly judge whether an answer is reasonable or unreasonable.

Practice your reasoning skills by determining whether the answers to the following situations or problems are reasonable or unreasonable. The first one is done for you.

1. Marty measures his room. He found that one wall was 43 meters long. *Oops! Measure again, Marty! A meter is a little longer than a yard, or 3 feet. Multiply 3 by 43. Marty's wall can't possibly be 43 meters long because that figure is about 129 feet.*

2. Elizabeth asked her mother for $5 for school supplies and lunch. She plans to buy 5 markers for art class that cost 55 cents each. Will she have enough left to buy the standard school lunch?

3. Jonathan is in charge of ordering 40 folders, one for each member of the science club. The catalog showed the total price for the folders to be $12. He calculates that each club member needed to give him 3 cents to pay for his or her folder.

4. Alison wants to save enough money to buy a compact disc player that costs $129.95 plus 5 percent sales tax. She plans to save $12 a week from her allowance and her regular babysitting job. She tells her friend Jessica that in three months she'll have enough to buy the CD player.

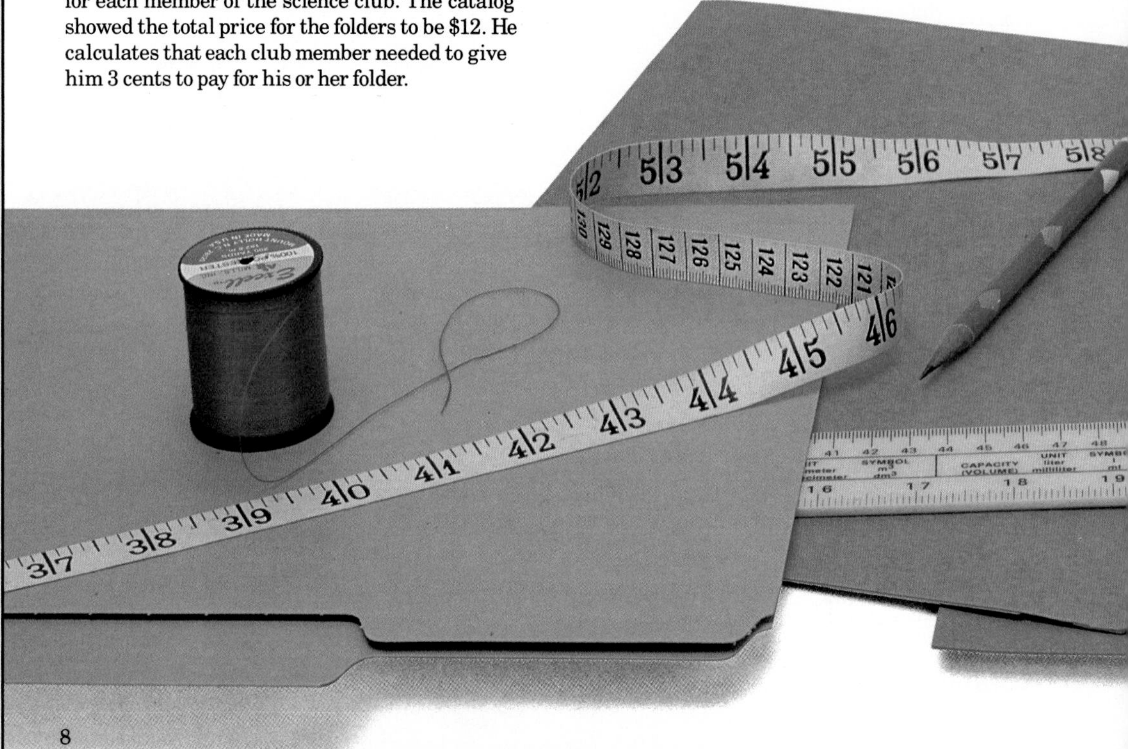

Organizing the Chapter

*You may want to refer to the **Course Planning Calendar** on Page T31.*

Planning Guide

Lesson (Pages)	Pacing Chart (in days) MINIMUM	STANDARD	ACCELERATED	Extra Practice (Student Edition)	Blackline Masters Booklets: Reteaching	Practice	Enrichment	Other Resources
1-1 (15-17)	1	1	1	p. 590, Set 1A	p. 1	p. 1	p. 1	Transparency 1-1 Group Activity Card 1-1
1-2 (19-21)	1	1	1	p. 590, Set 1A	p. 2	p. 2	p. 2	Transparency 1-2 Group Activity Card 1-2
1-3 (22-24)	1	1	1	p. 590, Set 1B	p. 3	p. 3	p. 3	Transparency 1-3 Group Activity Card 1-3
1-4 (25-28)	1	1	1	p. 590, Set 1B	p. 4	p. 4	p. 4	Transparency 1-4 Group Activity Card 1-4
1-5 (30-31)	1	1	0.5	p. 591, Set 1C	p. 5	p. 5	p. 5	Transparency 1-5 Group Activity Card 1-5
1-6 (33-34)	1	1	0.5			p. 6		Transparency 1-6 Group Activity Card 1-6
1-7 (35-38)	1.5	1	1	p. 591, Set 1C	p. 6	p. 7	p. 6	Transparency 1-7 Group Activity Card 1-7
1-8 (39-42)	1.5	1	1	p. 591, Set 1D	p. 7	p. 8	p. 7	Transparency 1-8 Group Activity Card 1-8
1-9 (43-45)	1	1	1	p. 591, Set 1D	p. 8	p. 9	p. 8	Transparency 1-9 Group Activity Card 1-9
1-10 (46-47)	1	1	0.5	p. 591, Set 1C	p. 9	p. 10	p. 9	Transparency 1-10 Group Activity Card 1-10
Review (48-49)	1.5	1	1					Test Generator
Test (50)	1	1	1		Evaluation Masters, pp. 1-6			

Other Chapter Resources

Student Edition
Exploration, pp. 14, 18, 29
Biography, p. 21
Team Problem Solving, p. 28
Algebra in Action, p. 32
Mid-Chapter Quiz, p. 34
Reading Algebra, p. 38
Academic Skills Test, p. 51

Teacher Resource Package
Interdisciplinary Activity, p. 1
Application Worksheet, p. 16
Cooperative Problem Solving, p. 31
Multicultural Activity, p. 46
Fun Activities, p. 61
Technology Worksheets, pp. 1, 16, 31
Lab Manual, pp. 27-29
Quizzes(2), p. 7
Class Review Game

Software
Test Generator

available for Apple and IBM

Enhancing the Chapter

Some of the blackline masters for enhancing this chapter are shown below.

Applications, p. 16

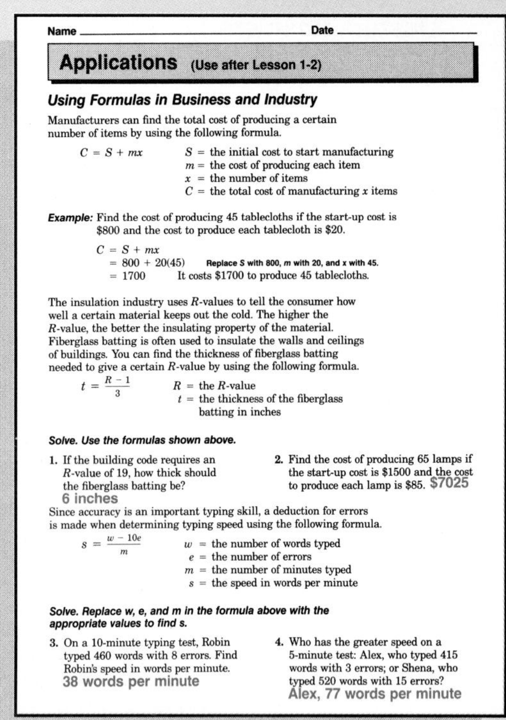

Name ______________________ Date ______________

Applications (Use after Lesson 1-2)

Using Formulas in Business and Industry

Manufacturers can find the total cost of producing a certain number of items by using the following formula.

$C = S + mx$

S = the initial cost to start manufacturing
m = the cost of producing each item
x = the number of items
C = the total cost of manufacturing x items

Example: Find the cost of producing 45 tablecloths if the start-up cost is $800 and the cost to produce each tablecloth is $20.

$C = S + mx$
$= 800 + 20(45)$ Replace S with 800, m with 20, and x with 45.
$= 1700$ It costs $1700 to produce 45 tablecloths.

The insulation industry uses R-values to tell the consumer how well a certain material keeps out the cold. The higher the R-value, the better the insulating property of the material. Fiberglass batting is often used to insulate the walls and ceilings of buildings. You can find the thickness of fiberglass batting needed to give a certain R-value by using the following formula.

$t = \frac{R - 1}{3}$

R = the R-value
t = the thickness of the fiberglass batting in inches

Solve. Use the formulas shown above.

1. If the building code requires an R-value of 19, how thick should the fiberglass batting be? 6 inches
2. Find the cost of producing 65 lamps if the start-up cost is $1500 and the cost to produce each lamp is $85. $7025

Since accuracy is an important typing skill, a deduction for errors is made when determining typing speed using the following formula.

$s = \frac{w - 10e}{m}$

w = the number of words typed
e = the number of errors
m = the number of minutes typed
s = the speed in words per minute

Solve. Replace w, e, and m in the formula above with the appropriate values to find s.

3. On a 10-minute typing test, Robin typed 460 words with 8 errors. Find Robin's speed in words per minute. 38 words per minute
4. Who has the greater speed on a 5-minute test: Alex, who typed 415 words with 3 errors; or Shena, who typed 520 words with 15 errors? Alex, 77 words per minute

The **Activity Masters Booklet** contains the page shown above.

Interdisciplinary Activity, p. 1

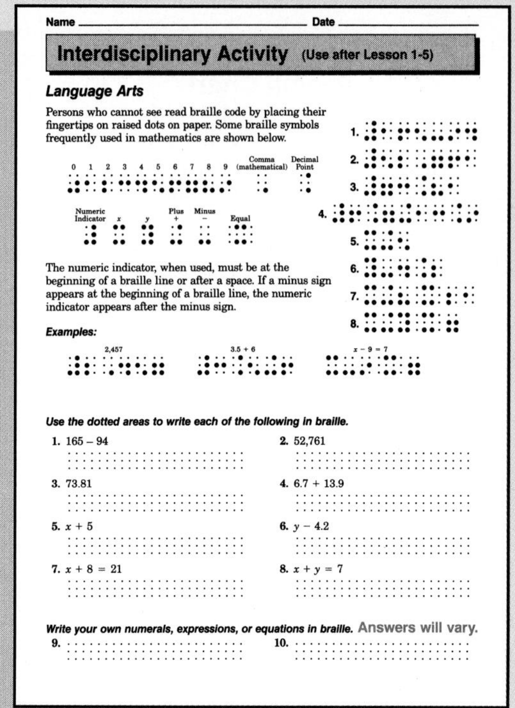

Name ______________________ Date ______________

Interdisciplinary Activity (Use after Lesson 1-5)

Language Arts

Persons who cannot see read braille code by placing their fingertips on raised dots on paper. Some braille symbols frequently used in mathematics are shown below.

0 1 2 3 4 5 6 7 8 9 Comma (mathematical) Decimal Point

Numeric Indicator x y Plus + Minus − Equal

The numeric indicator, when used, must be at the beginning of a braille line or after a space. If a minus sign appears at the beginning of a braille line, the numeric indicator appears after the minus sign.

Examples:

2,457 3.5 + 6 $x - 9 = 7$

1.
2.
3.
4.
5.
6.
7.
8.

Use the dotted areas to write each of the following in braille.

1. 165 – 94
2. 52,761
3. 73.81
4. 6.7 + 13.9
5. $x + 5$
6. $y - 4.2$
7. $x + 8 = 21$
8. $x + y = 7$

Write your own numerals, expressions, or equations in braille. Answers will vary.

9.
10.

The **Activity Masters Booklet** contains the page shown above.

Models and Manipulatives

Students have been doing algebra, but are unaware of it. The concept of a variable can be introduced by using boxes to leave numbers out of equations. This will be familiar to them and take out some of the fear of the word *algebra* that is prevalent in the minds of many students.

Have students solve the examples at the right and other similar examples.

$\square + 2 = 5$	How could you use the numbers 5 and 2 to fill in the box?
$\square - 3 = 7$	How could you use the numbers 7 and 3 to fill in the box?
$3 \times \square = 12$	How could you use the numbers 12 and 3 to fill in the box?
$\frac{\square}{4} = 2$	How could you use the numbers 2 and 4 to fill in the box?

Limited English Proficiency (LEP) Activity

Compare the translation of a foreign language (Spanish or French, etc.) with the translation of a phrase in algebraic terms. Ask students for foreign language expressions.Write the expressions on the chalkboard, showing a comparison or equivalent expression in English. Expand this comparison of languages to the comparison of English and the language of algebra. Begin with algebraic terms and extend the comparison to algebraic equations.

Cooperative Learning

The following activity is provided in the **Activity Masters Booklet.**

Cooperative Problem Solving, p. 31

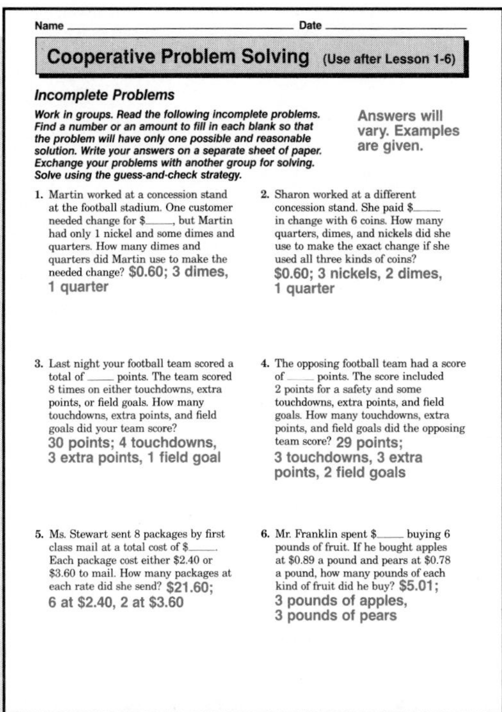

Name ____________ Date ____________

Cooperative Problem Solving (Use after Lesson 1-6)

Incomplete Problems

Work in groups. Read the following incomplete problems. Find a number or an amount to fill in each blank so that the problem will have only one possible and reasonable solution. Write your answers on a separate sheet of paper. Exchange your problems with another group for solving. Solve using the guess-and-check strategy.

Answers will vary. Examples are given.

1. Martin worked at a concession stand at the football stadium. One customer needed change for $____, but Martin had only 1 nickel and some dimes and quarters. How many dimes and quarters did Martin use to make the needed change? $0.60; 3 dimes, 1 quarter

2. Sharon worked at a different concession stand. She paid $____ in change with 6 coins. How many quarters, dimes, and nickels did she use to make the exact change if she used all three kinds of coins? $0.60; 3 nickels, 2 dimes, 1 quarter

3. Last night your football team scored a total of ____ points. The team scored 8 times on either touchdowns, extra points, or field goals. How many touchdowns, extra points, and field goals did your team score? 30 points; 4 touchdowns, 3 extra points, 1 field goal

4. The opposing football team had a score of ____ points. The score included 2 points for a safety and some touchdowns, extra points, and field goals. How many touchdowns, extra points, and field goals did the opposing team score? 29 points; 3 touchdowns, 3 extra points, 2 field goals

5. Ms. Stewart sent 8 packages by first class mail at a total cost of $____. Each package cost either $2.40 or $3.60 to mail. How many packages at each rate did she send? $21.60; 6 at $2.40, 2 at $3.60

6. Mr. Franklin spent $____ buying 6 pounds of fruit. If he bought apples at $0.89 a pound and pears at $0.78 a pound, how many pounds of each kind of fruit did he buy? $5.01; 3 pounds of apples, 3 pounds of pears

Cooperative Problem Solving

Using Modeling A box of candy contains several of the same pieces. If one person eats $1/5$ of the pieces, a second person eats $1/4$ of the remaining pieces, and a third person eats $1/3$ of those remaining pieces, there are 8 pieces left over. How many pieces of candy were there in the box? 20

Each group will be responsible for the solution and a written explanation of their solution. This is a good problem to be solved with the guess-and-check strategy.

Interactive Bulletin Board

Social Studies Connection

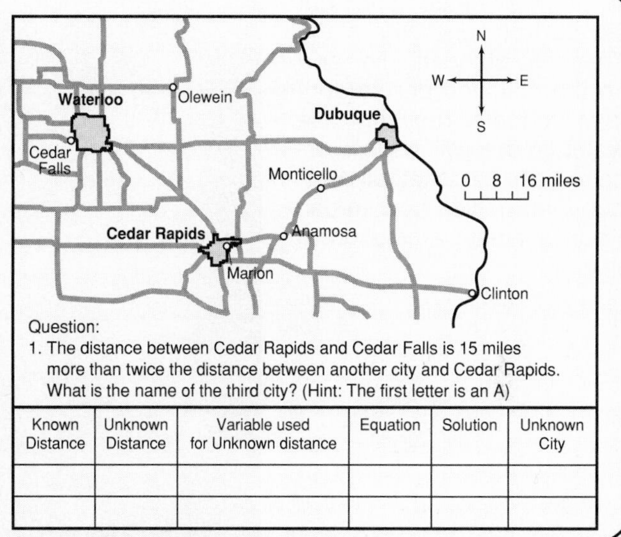

Question:

1. The distance between Cedar Rapids and Cedar Falls is 15 miles more than twice the distance between another city and Cedar Rapids. What is the name of the third city? (Hint: The first letter is an A)

Known Distance	Unknown Distance	Variable used for Unknown distance	Equation	Solution	Unknown City

Purpose Provide practice in writing equations and solving the equations.

How to Use It Use laminated paper and wipe-off markers. Use a state highway map showing the distances between cities or a state map that has a scale of miles. Have students work in groups of two or three.

Create one problem for all students or one problem for each group. Have students translate each sentence or problem into an equation. Solve the equation to determine to which city the sentence is referring.

Change the problems daily or have students create their own.

Outside Resources

Books/Periodicals
Codes, Ciphers, and Secret Writing, Dover.

Films/Videotapes
Donald in Mathemagic Land, Walt Disney Educational Media Co.

Software
Teasers by Tobbs with Whole Numbers, Sunburst.

Technology

There are three pages in the ***Technology Masters Booklet*** that involve technology with concepts in this chapter. One page involves calculators and one page has a problem that can be solved using the BASIC program that is provided. Students should evaluate the information they obtain from running the program and solve a similar problem by extending the program.

Using the Chapter Opener

Transparency 1-0 is available in the Transparency Package. It provides a full-color visual and motivational activity that you can use to engage students in the mathematical content of the chapter.

Using Problem Solving

- Ask students to determine an approach to the problem. They may use an atlas or map to find out the distance from one city to the other. They may stand in a line and measure the distance per student for several students. They may use a stopwatch to determine the average time to pass a basketball. Students can then decide how to use this data to estimate a solution to the problem.

The distance from Washington, D.C. to San Francisco, CA is approximately 2882 miles. If people in the line are spaced 20 feet apart and if it takes 3 seconds for each person to pass the ball to the next person in line, it would take 634 hours (over 26 days) to pass the ball from Washington to San Francisco.

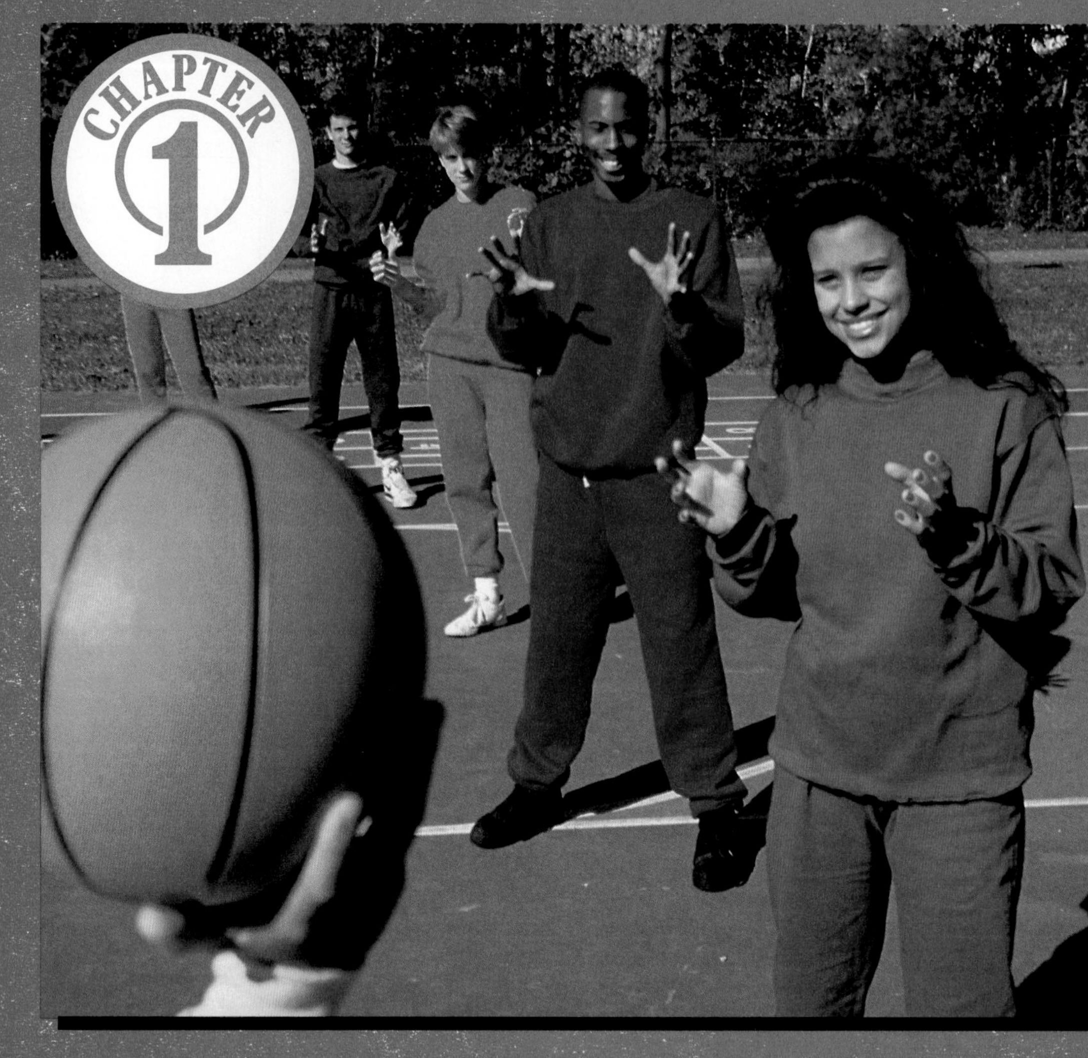

CHAPTER OBJECTIVES

In this chapter you will learn to:

- evaluate expressions using order of operations
- use properties of whole numbers to simplify expressions
- solve equations and inequalities mentally
- translate verbal phrases into algebraic expressions
- solve problems using the guess-and-check strategy

The Language of Algebra

Picture yourself standing in an endless line of people. The line stretches from Washington, D.C., to San Francisco, CA. Your challenge: determine how long it will take to pass a basketball from one end to the other.

What information do you need to solve this problem? Here are some hints:

How far is it from Washington, D.C., to San Francisco?

How many people are in line?

How many seconds, on average, does it take for one person to pass a basketball to the next person in line?

The answers to these questions may *vary.* In algebra, you use *variables* to stand for unknown quantities. Variables are the muscles of algebra! In this chapter and throughout this book you'll work with variables. Let's get started!

Estimate how long it will take to pass a basketball from Washington, D.C., to San Francisco.

Geography Connection

Class Project

Suppose the population of your state was evenly scattered throughout the state. About how many people would be standing in each square mile?

Discuss the meaning of the phrase *population density* with a classmate. Compute the population density for two other states. Display your data in a bar graph.

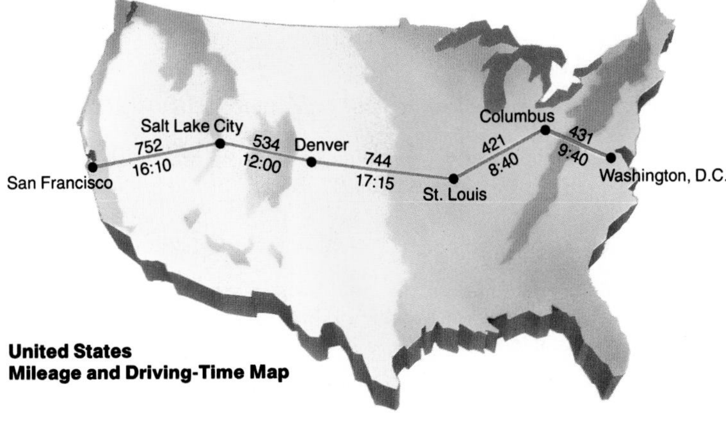

United States
Mileage and Driving-Time Map

Geography Connection

Information on population and area is available from a current atlas or World Almanac. Current census reports are also available in the library.

The phrase *population density* refers to the number of people per unit of area. When determining population densities of other states, encourage students to choose states that are geographically removed from their state and from each other.

Looking Ahead

You may want to have the following materials available to use in this chapter.

Exploration, p. 14
calculators

Exploration, p. 18
cups
counters*

Exploration, p. 29
algebra tiles**

Algebra in Action, p. 32
newspapers

* You can use the Easy-to-Make Manipulative provided on page 4 of the Lab Manual.

** You can use the Easy-to-Make Manipulative provided on page 1 of the Lab Manual.

EXPLORATION
Naming Numbers

Objective Students will develop some intuitive ideas about the order of operations. They will become familiar with the necessity for agreements prior to formal work with order of operations.

1 FOCUS

Motivating the Exploration

Give students a word sentence such as, *"The football team won the last game"*. Ask them to reword the sentence so that it says the same thing, but in a different way. Introduce the concept that number sentences can also be expressed in different ways.

2 TEACH

Using Discussion

Discussing obvious differences will be helpful in determining whether the differences are operation related or simply two different ways of naming the same number. Be certain students are aware of what operations and numbers may be used.

3 PRACTICE/APPLY

Using Cooperative Groups

Divide the class into small groups. After several problems are done by the group, have students work individually within the group and compare results.

4 CLOSE

Using Questioning

Ask students to individually rename the number formed by the last two digits of the year they were born by using only 2s, 5s, and 9s.

Exploration

Naming Numbers

Materials: calculator

Every number can be renamed as the sum, difference, product, or quotient of two or more other numbers. For example, 7 can be renamed as the sum $4 + 3$; 15 can be renamed as the quotient $30 \div 2$. In this Exploration, you will try to rename numbers using only 2s, 5s, and 9s.

Explore: Suppose that these are the only keys that work on your calculator.

[2] [5] [9] [+] [−] [×] [÷] [=]

Can you rename every number from 1 to 25 in two different ways using only these keys?

Here are some examples:

- One way to rename 15 is 9 [+] 2 [+] 2 [+] 2 [=].
- One way to rename 19 is 2 [×] 5 [+] 9 [=].

Your Turn: Try to rename every number from 1 to 25 in two different ways. Keep track of your results in a chart.

Analysis

1. Were you able to rename every number in two different ways? See Solutions Manual.
2. Explain how you can rename numbers greater than 25 using only 2s, 5s, and 9s. Give examples using 47, 63, and 56. See Solutions Manual.

Wrap-Up

3. Leonhard Euler, the great Swiss mathematician, died in 1783 at the age of 76. Using only the numbers 1, 7, 8, and 3, rename 76. Sample answer: $8 \times 3 \times 3 + 3 + 1$.

SET-UP

Materials

- calculators

You may wish to use the Exploration worksheet provided on page 27 of the Lab Manual.

For Students Each student or group of students will need a calculator. If calculators are not available, pencil and paper can be used.

For the Overhead Projector If you choose to present this lesson on the overhead projector, an overhead projector calculator may be used to work several examples.

1-1 Order of Operations

Objective:
Evaluate expressions using the order of operations.

Key Terms:
order of operations
parentheses
brackets

If you play on any sports team, you know that there are certain rules that govern the play. These rules help avoid confusion and disagreements.

Rules are also important in algebra. Why? One reason is that numerical expressions often contain more than one operation. An expression like $9 + 2 \times 2$ might be computed in two ways.

$9 + 2 \times 2 = 9 + 4$ Multiply,
$9 + 2 \times 2 = 13 + 4$ then add.

$9 + 2 \times 2 = 11 \times 2$ Add, then
$9 + 2 \times 2 = 22 + 4$ multiply.

Just as in sports, we need a rule to avoid confusion and tell us which value is correct. This rule is called the **order of operations.**

First: Do all multiplications and divisions from left to right.
Second: Do all additions and subtractions from left to right.

The order of operations rule guarantees that each numerical expression has a *unique* value. Using this rule, the correct value of $9 + 2 \times 2$ is 13.

Examples

Find the value of each expression.

1 $\mathbf{5 \times 6 + 4}$

$5 \times 6 + 4 = 30 + 4$ Multiply 5 and 6.
$= 34$ Add 30 and 4.

2 $\mathbf{13 - 5 + 6 \times 2}$

$13 - 5 + 6 \times 2 = 13 - 5 + 12$ Multiply 6 and 2.
$= 8 + 12$ Subtract 5 from 13.
$= 20$ Add 8 and 12.

3 $\mathbf{9 \div 3 + 4 \times 7 - 20 \div 5}$

$9 \div 3 + 4 \times 7 - 20 \div 5 = 3 + 4 \times 7 - 20 \div 5$ Divide 9 by 3.
$= 3 + 28 - 20 \div 5$ Multiply 4 and 7.
$= 3 + 28 - 4$ Divide 20 by 5.
$= 31 - 4$ Add 3 and 28.
$= 27$ Subtract 4 from 31.

Calculator Hint

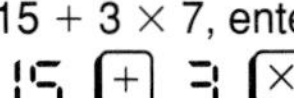

Calculators that follow the order of operations rule are called scientific calculators. To find the value of $15 + 3 \times 7$, enter 15 [+] 3 [×] 7. If your calculator displays 36, your calculator is a scientific calculator.

Bell Ringer

Play "I'm thinking of a number" with your students. Start with a number, add six, divide by three, etc. **Answers will vary.**

Lesson Notes 1-1

5-Minute Check

Find the value of each expression.
1. 28 × 7 **196**
2. 546 ÷ 6 **91**
3. 24 + 39 + 15 **78**
4. 9 × 7 × 5 **315**
5. 304 − 129 **175**

Transparency 1-1 contains the 5-Minute Check and a teaching aid for this lesson.

1 FOCUS

The purpose of the lesson is to help students understand that there are certain agreements used to evaluate expressions throughout mathematics to ensure that exactly one correct answer is found.

Motivating the Lesson

Put the following problem on the chalkboard: $2 \times 3 + 4 \div 2$. Then put the answers 5 and 8 on the chalkboard and ask which answer is correct. Discuss with students why they chose their answer.

2 TEACH

Using Calculators Have students use a calculator to find the answer to the problem above. Ask them to observe the display after each entry and explain what happens each time the display changes.

Chalkboard Examples

Find the value of each expression.

- *For Example 1*
  7 × 3 + 5 **26**
- *For Example 2*
  18 − 6 + 4 × 3 **24**
- *For Example 3*
  12 ÷ 4 + 5 × 2 − 24 ÷ 6 **9**

EE: 1E, 3A, 3B
TAAS: 2

Chalkboard Examples

Find the value of each expression.

- *For Example 4*
  $4(2 + 6) - 2 \cdot 3$ **26**
- *For Example 5*
  $3[(7 + 5) \div 4(2)]$ **18**
- *For Example 6*
  $\frac{19 + 2}{11 - 8}$ **7**

3 PRACTICE/APPLY

Checking the Concept

Write statements such as $5 \times 3 + 6$ and $5 \times (3 + 6)$ on the chalkboard or overhead. Have students discuss the difference between the two statements and the values they represent.

Error Analysis

Watch for students who try to do too many steps at one time.
Prevent by having students underline the first operation to be performed, then write the second line with only that operation completed. Repeat until the problem is completed.

Practice Masters Booklet, **p. 1**

Name ______________________ Date ______________

Practice Worksheet 1-1

Order of Operations

Find the value of each expression.

1. $8 + 9 - 3 + 5$ 19	2. $7 \cdot 5 + 2 \cdot 3$ 41
3. $18 - 5 \cdot 2$ 8	4. $(9 + 4)(8 - 7)$ 13
5. $(16 + 5) - (13 + 2)$ 6	6. $24 \div 6 + 2$ 6
7. $32 \cdot 4 \div 2$ 64	8. $18 - (9 + 3) + 2$ 8
9. $6 + 5 \cdot 2 + 3$ 19	10. $18 + 24 \div 12 + 3$ 23
11. $67 + 84 - 12 \cdot 4 \div 16$ 148	12. $75 \div 15 \cdot 6$ 30
13. $34 + 8 \div 2 + 4 \cdot 9$ 74	14. $6 \cdot 3 \div 9 \cdot 2 + 1$ 5
15. $(15 + 21) \div 3$ 12	16. $(45 + 21) \div 11$ 6
17. $5 \cdot 6 - 25 \div 5 - 2$ 23	18. $(84 \div 4) \div 3$ 7
19. $\frac{15 + 35}{21 + 4}$ 2	20. $6(38 - 12) + 4$ 160
21. $(13 \cdot 4) + (17 \cdot 4)$ 120	22. $\frac{18 + 66}{35 - 14}$ 4
23. $10[8(15 - 7) - (4 \cdot 3)]$ 520	24. $8[(26 + 10) - 4(3 + 2)]$ 128

True or false.

25. $16 + 24 \div 8 - 4 = 1$ false	26. $39 - 9 \cdot 3 + 6 = 18$ true
27. $5(35 - 18) + 1 = 102$ false	28. $60 \div 6 + 4 \cdot 3 = 2$ false
29. $25 \div 5 \cdot 4 = 20$ true	30. $17 - 4 + 8 \cdot 4 = 45$ true
31. $28 \div 7 \cdot 5 \div 5 = 4$ true	32. $2(3 + 4) - 2 \cdot 3 = 8$ true

The order of operations can be changed by using grouping symbols, such as **parentheses,** ( ), and **brackets,** [ ]. The value of the expression $(2 + 6) \times 3$ is found by performing the operation within the parentheses first.

$$(2 + 6) \times 3 = 8 \times 3 \quad \text{Compute } 2 + 6 \text{ first.}$$
$$= 24 \quad \text{Now multiply 8 and 3.}$$

The order for performing the operations in an expression is summarized as follows.

Order of Operations

1. Do all operations within grouping symbols first; start with the innermost grouping symbols.
2. Next, do all multiplications and divisions from left to right.
3. Then, do all additions and subtractions from left to right.

In algebra there are many ways to indicate multiplication and division. A raised dot or parentheses can be used to indicate multiplication.

Can you find these notations in the examples below?

$8 \cdot 7$ **means** 8×7

$3\,(4)$, $(3)\,4$, or $(3)\,(4)$ **means** 3×4

A fraction bar can be used to indicate division.

$\frac{26 - 2}{4 + 8}$ **means** $(26 - 2) \div (4 + 8)$

Examples

Find the value of each expression.

4 $2(3 + 5) - 3 \cdot 5 = 2(8) - 3 \cdot 5$ $3 \cdot 5$ means 3×5.
$= 16 - 15$
$= 1$

5 $4[(9 + 12) - 6(2)] = 4[(21) - 6(2)]$ Do the operations within the innermost grouping symbols.
$= 4[21 - 12]$
$= 4[9]$
$= 36$

6 $\frac{17 + 7}{19 - 13} = (17 + 7) \div (19 - 13)$ Rewrite the expression using parentheses.
$= (24) \div (6)$
$= 4$

Alternate Strategies: Reteaching the Lesson

Reteaching Activity

Using Lists Have students use three numbers, in the same order, to list as many expressions as possible; for example, $4 \times 2 + 1$ and $4 - 2 \times 1$. Evaluate each expression. Repeat using expressions involving parentheses, for example, $4 \times (2 + 1)$.

Reteaching Masters Booklet, **p. 1**

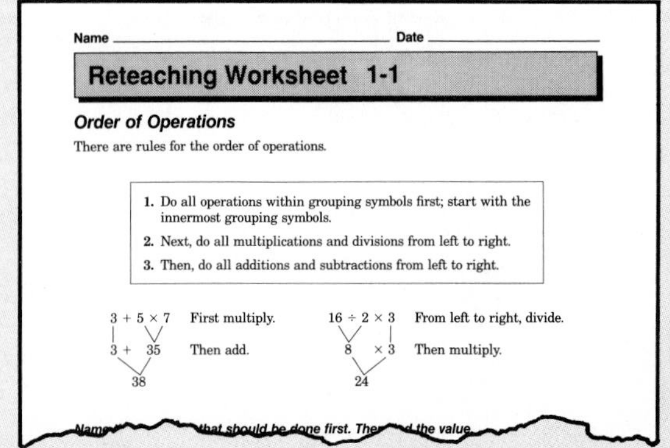

Name ______________________ Date ______________

Reteaching Worksheet 1-1

Order of Operations

There are rules for the order of operations.

1. Do all operations within grouping symbols first; start with the innermost grouping symbols.
2. Next, do all multiplications and divisions from left to right.
3. Then, do all additions and subtractions from left to right.

$3 + 5 \times 7$ First multiply.
$3 + 35$ Then add.
38

$16 \div 2 \times 3$ From left to right, divide.
8×3 Then multiply.
24

2. In first expression, multiply then add. In second expression, add then multiply.

Checking for Understanding

Communicating Algebra

1. If an expression contained only two operations, division and subtraction, which operation would you do first? **division**
2. Explain how $5 \cdot 3 + 5$ and $5(3 + 5)$ are different.
3. In the expression $2 \cdot 3 + 5 \cdot 3$, which multiplication would you do first? **$2 \cdot 3$**

Guided Practice

Name the operation that should be done first. Then find the value.

4. $5 + 3 \cdot 7$ **×; 26**
5. $54 - 42 \div 7$ **÷; 48**
6. $36 \div 9 \times 3$ **÷; 12**
7. $24 \div 6 - 9 \div 3$ **÷; 1**
8. $4 \cdot (5 + 7)$ **+; 48**
9. $3 \cdot (4 + 5) - 7$ **+; 20**
10. $71 - (17 + 4)$ **+; 50**
11. $(25 + 7) - (12 + 3)$ **+; 17**
12. $(8 - 5)(4 + 2)$ **−; 18**
13. $\frac{46 - 4}{6}$ **−; 7**
14. $\frac{20 - 8}{9 - 5}$ **−; 3**
15. $\frac{16 + 8}{15 - 7}$ **+; 3**

Exercises

Independent Practice

Find the value of each expression.

16. $12 \div 3 + 12 \div 4$ **7**
17. $21 \div 7 + 4 \cdot 11$ **47**
18. $6 \cdot 3 \div 9 - 1$ **1**
19. $12 \div 6 - 2$ **0**
20. $15 \div 5 \times 3$ **9**
21. $24 \div 6 \cdot 4$ **16**
22. $(25 \cdot 3) + (15 \cdot 3)$ **120**
23. $(40 \cdot 2) - (6 \cdot 11)$ **14**
24. $40 \cdot (6 - 2)$ **160**
25. $72 \div 9 \cdot 4 \div 2$ **16**
26. $96 \div 12(4) \div 2$ **16**
27. $144 \div 16 \cdot 9 \div 3$ **27**
28. $\frac{86 - 11}{9 + 6}$ **5**
29. $\frac{72 + 12}{35 + 7}$ **2**
30. $\frac{37 + 38}{30 - 5}$ **3**
31. $2[5(4 + 6) - 3]$ **94**
32. $3[6(12 - 3)] - 17$ **111**
33. $4[12(22 - 19) - 3 \cdot 6]$ **72**
34. $4[3(21 - 17) + 3]$ **60**
35. $3[(18 - 3) + 4(5 + 7)]$ **189**
36. $7[(12 + 5) - 3(19 - 14)]$ **14**

True or *false*.

37. $12 + 20 \div 4 - 5 = 3$ **false**
38. $36 - 6 \cdot 5 = 6$ **true**
39. $3(34 - 19) = 45$ **true**
40. $6 \div 2 + 5 \times 4 = 32$ **false**
41. $30 \div 6 \cdot 5 = 1$ **false**
42. $14 - 5 - 2 \times 2 = 6$ **false**

Calculator 

Copy each sentence below. Experiment with your calculator to find where to insert parentheses to make each sentence true. You may need to use the parentheses keys.

43. $(18 + 4) \times 3 = 66$
44. $18 \div (3 + 6) = 2$
45. $24 \div 2 - (4 + 8) = 0$
46. $15 \div (21 - 18) - 4 = 1$

Application

47. **Consumer Awareness** Write an expression that would help you find the total cost of fifty \$6 movie tickets and eight \$12 play tickets. Then find the total cost. **$50 \times 6 + 8 \times 12$; \$396**

Critical Thinking

48. Use six toothpicks to represent the number 17. **Sample answer: 17 × 1**

Wrap-Up

49. **Make Up a Problem** Write an expression involving addition and multiplication in which you should add first. **Sample answer: 3(1 + 2)**

Alternate Strategies: Extending the Lesson

Enrichment

Working in Pairs Have one student write an expression and solve it with pencil and paper. Have another student use a computer or calculator. Compare answers. If they don't match, have the students work together to write a computer program that will give the correct answer.

Cooperative Learning

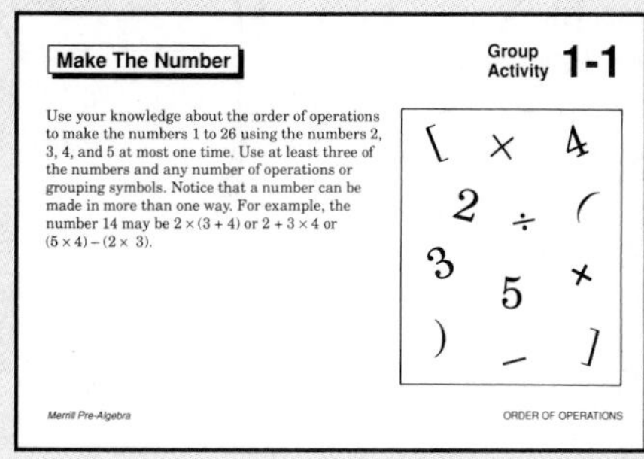

Make The Number

Group Activity 1-1

Use your knowledge about the order of operations to make the numbers 1 to 26 using the numbers 2, 3, 4, and 5 at most one time. Use at least three of the numbers and any number of operations or grouping symbols. Notice that a number can be made in more than one way. For example, the number 14 may be $2 \times (3 + 4)$ or $2 + 3 \times 4$ or $(5 \times 4) - (2 \times 3)$.

Merrill Pre-Algebra — ORDER OF OPERATIONS

Independent Practice

Homework Assignment	
Basic	17-41 odd, 45-49
Average	16-46 even, 47-49
Honors	22-42 even, 43-49

4 CLOSE

Assessment Option

Modeling Write numbers and mathematical symbols on 5 x 7 index cards. Attach a small magnet on the back of each or use tape to put some of the numbers on the chalkboard to form a numerical expression. Then give the students an answer for the expression and the mathematical symbols they will need to make the expression correct. Have the students then complete the expression. For example,

_ [8] _ [4] _ _ _ [3] _ [3] _ [=] [2]

needs to be completed with (, ÷ ,), × , (, ÷ ,), to make it correct.

Enrichment Masters Booklet, **p. 1**

Name ________ Date ________

Enrichment Worksheet 1-1

Operations Search

This is a fun activity that you can try, and then make up similar problems for your family or classmates.

In each exercise below, you are given some numbers. Insert operation symbols (+, −, ×, ÷) and parentheses so that a true mathematical sentence is formed.

1. You cannot change the order of the numbers and you must observe the order of operations.

a. 5 4 3 2 1 = 3 — $(5 \times 4) \div (3 + 2) - 1 = 3$

b. 5 4 3 2 1 = 0 — $(5 + 4) \div 3 - 2 - 1 = 0$

c. 5 4 3 2 1 = 1 — $(5 + 4) \div 3 - 2 \div 1 = 1$

d. 5 4 3 2 1 = 50 — $5 \times (4 + 3 + 2 + 1) = 50$

2. You cannot change the order of the numbers, but you may put two numbers together to form a two-digit number. You must observe the order of operations.

a. 1 2 3 4 5 6 7 8 = 90 — $1 + 23 + 45 + 6 + 7 + 8 = 90$

b. 8 7 6 5 4 3 2 1 = 25 — $(8 + 7 + 65) \div 4 + 3 + 2 \times 1 = 25$

3. You can change the order of the numbers and you may put numbers together to form a two- or three-digit number. You must observe the order of operations.

Use these four digits: 4 3 2 1

Make these totals:

a. 1312 — $41 \times 32 = 1312$

b. 2 — $(4 \times 2) \div (3 + 1) = 2$

c. 16 — $4 \times (3 + 2 - 1) = 16$

d. 1 — $(4 + 2) \div 3 - 1 = 1$

EXPLORATION
Algebraic Expressions

Objective Students will build on the concept of placeholder to develop a better understanding of variables and their role in algebraic expressions.

1 FOCUS

This exploration introduces the idea of using counters to represent amounts and a cup to represent variables.

2 TEACH

Model each example for the entire class. Help students write the corresponding expression.

Using Extensions

- Model both examples together as a third example.
- Use a second cup of a different size to represent a second variable and place a different number of counters in each cup.

3 PRACTICE/APPLY

Using Cooperative Groups

Divide the class into small groups. Circulate around the room as they model their problems.

4 CLOSE

Writing Connection

Use Exercise 6 to encourage students to articulate their understanding of the cup. Ask students the following questions.

- How much can the cup hold?
- Does the cup represent a specific value?

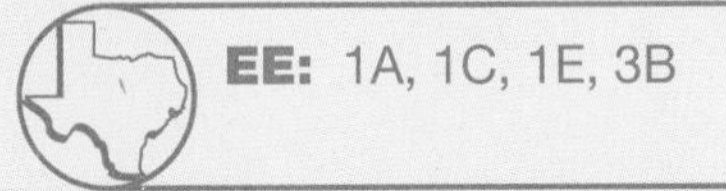
EE: 1A, 1C, 1E, 3B

Exploration

Algebraic Expressions

Materials: cups, counters

In this Exploration, you will model algebraic expressions.

Consider the phrase *the sum of 5 and some number.* This phrase contains a value that you know, 5, and a value that you do not know, some number. You use counters to represent 5 and an empty cup to represent the unknown value.

This cup can hold any number of counters. Suppose you place 3 counters in the cup. Instead of an unknown value, you know that the cup has a value of 3. When you empty the cup and count all the counters, the expression has a value of 8.

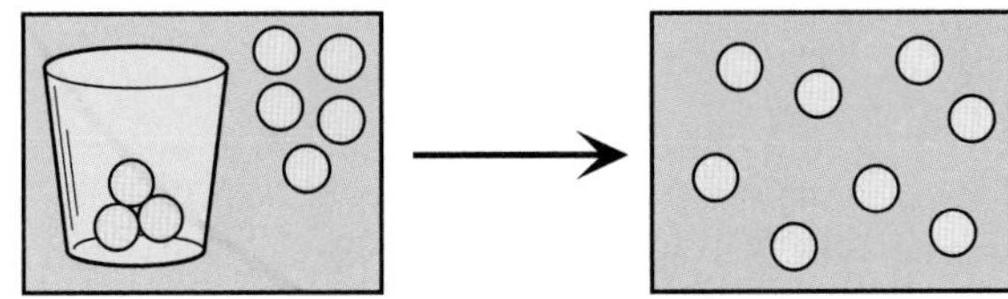

Consider the phrase *three times some number*. Because you do not know the value of the number, let an empty cup hold this value. In this case, you need three empty cups.

Your Turn: Model the phrase 5 *more than 3 times a number.* Place 4 counters in each cup. How many counters are there in all? 17

For the model above and diagrams to Exercises 1-5, see Solutions Manual.

Model each phrase.

1. 6 more than a number
2. four times a number
3. 4 more than 2 times a number
4. 3 times 5 more than a number
5. Model the phrase *2 more than 2 times a number.* Fill each cup with 3 counters. How many counters are there in all? 8

Analysis

6. Write a sentence that describes the meaning of the cup. The cup is a placeholder into which you can place any amount.

SET-UP

Materials

- Cups, Lab Manual, p. 6
- Counters, Lab Manual, p. 4

You may wish to use the Exploration worksheet provided on page 28 of the Lab Manual.

For Students Each student or group of students will need 10 counters and 2 cups. The counters can be pennies, buttons, jellybeans, or anything that is relatively uniform in size. Color is not a consideration at this time.

For the Overhead Projector If you choose to present this lesson on the overhead projector, a translucent cup will show up nicely on the screen.

1-2 Variables and Expressions

Objective:
Use variables.

Key Terms:
variable
algebraic expression

Did you know that you can estimate the temperature in degrees Fahrenheit by counting the number of times a cricket chirps in one minute? Just count the number of chirps, divide by 4 and then add 37.

Like any language, algebra is a language of symbols. You already know symbols for division and addition. So, one way to write the temperature relationship is: *chirps* ÷ 4 + 37.

Using arithmetic, you might write ■ ÷ 4 + 37, where ■ is the number of times the cricket chirped. The ■ acts as a placeholder.

In algebra, a placeholder is called a **variable** because the value can change or vary. Variables are usually letters. Probably the most popular letter is x, but in this case you choose c to stand for chirps or cricket. Now the temperature relationship is $c \div 4 + 37$.

This is called an **algebraic expression** because it is a combination of variables, numbers, and at least one operation.

An expression such as $c \div 4 + 37$ can be evaluated by replacing variables with numbers and then finding the value of the numerical expression. If you counted 80 chirps, you could estimate the temperature by evaluating the expression $80 \div 4 + 37$.

What is an estimate of the temperature if you count 110 chirps? **between 62° and 67° F**

$80 \div 4 + 37 = 20 + 37$ Divide first, then add.
$= 57$ The temperature is about 57° F.

When you replaced c with 80, you were using an important property of numbers.

Substitution Property of Equality: For all numbers a and b, if $a = b$, then a may be replaced with b.

Example

1 Evaluate $c + b - 23$ if $c = 25$ and $b = 16$.

$c + b - 23 = 25 + 16 - 23$ Replace c with 25 and b with 16.
$= (25 + 16) - 23$
$= 41 - 23$ $25 + 16 = 41$
$= 18$ $41 - 23 = 18$

Bell Ringer

Have the students evaluate each expression.
1. $8 \cdot 8$ 64
2. $\frac{2+4}{3}$ 2
3. $2[(4 + 11) \div (12 - 7)]$ 6

Lesson Notes 1-2

5-Minute Check
(over Lesson 1-1)

Find the value of each expression.
1. $35 \div 5 + 4 \cdot 2$ 15
2. $87 - (21 + 6)$ 60
3. $\frac{42+3}{17-8}$ 5
4. $2[3(14 - 2) - 20]$ 32

Transparency 1-2 contains the 5-Minute Check and a teaching aid for this lesson.

1 FOCUS

The purpose of this lesson is to introduce the concept of variable and the substitution property of equality.

Motivating the Lesson

Discuss with your students situations where substitutes are used; for example, in teaching, in sports, in cooking (perhaps butter for margarine). Emphasize the fact that equality is maintained with a substitute.

2 TEACH

Using Discussion Ask students to give some examples of non-math symbols and explain what they mean. For example, a Mr. Yuk symbol on a bottle means the contents may be harmful if swallowed.

Chalkboard Examples

Evaluate:
- *For Example 1*
  $r + s - 15$ if $r = 21$ and $s = 18$ 24
- *For Example 2*
  $2a + 7b$ if $a = 5$ and $b = 3$ 31
- *For Example 3*
  $\frac{xy}{4}$ if $x = 6$ and $y = 8$ 12
- *For Example 4*
  $2g + (4h - k) + 7$ if $g = 5$, $h = 3$, and $k = 8$ 21

3 PRACTICE/APPLY

Checking the Concept

Using Connections Review the need for a standardized order of operations by having students compare their answers to Exercises 12-15. If necessary, have them continue the comparisons for Exercises 16-30.

Error Analysis

Watch for students who evaluate an expression such as $2r$ as 2 tens and r ones.
Prevent by illustrating different ways of writing 2 times r: $2 \times r$, $2r$, $(2)(r)$. Emphasize that the r by itself is a number.

Practice Masters Booklet, **p. 2**

Name ______________________ Date ______________

Practice Worksheet 1-2

Variables and Expressions

Evaluate each expression if x = 7, y = 10, r = 15, t = 3, and c = 8.

1. $x + y - r$ 2
2. $c + c + y + y$ 36
3. $(r + t) + c$ 26
4. $x + t + c - r + y$ 13
5. $y + 15 - c + 12 - x$ 22
6. $85 - 17 + t - x + c$ 72
7. $72 - r + y - c$ 59
8. $t + t + t + t + t$ 15
9. $y + y + c - 10 + x$ 25
10. $125 + x - y + r - t$ 134

Evaluate each expression if x = 3, y = 4, and z = 5.

11. $6x - 3y$ 6
12. $6(x + y)$ 42
13. $\frac{y - x}{z - y}$ 1
14. $2x + 3z + y$ 25
15. $14x - (2y + z)$ 29
16. $2(x + z) - y$ 12
17. $4z - (2y + x)$ 9
18. $x(y + z + 4)$ 39
19. $\frac{10(z - x)}{z}$ 4
20. $\frac{21xy}{x + y}$ 36
21. $\frac{4z + 2y}{7}$ 4
22. $\frac{y(z + x + y)}{y}$ 12

Evaluate each expression if x = 15, y = 12, a = 5, b = 13, and c = 11.

23. $a + (c + x)$ 31
24. $b + a + 8$ 26
25. $x + c + y + a$ 43
26. $b - c + a$ 7
27. $(x + y) - c - x + (y - c)$ 2
28. $54 - 17 - c + 5 + b + 8$ 52
29. $2x + c + 2y + 9$ 74
30. $y - 5 + b + 9 + c$ 40
31. $c - a + x - y + 3$ 12
32. $x - (b - a) - (x - b) + a$ 10

Just as with numerical expressions, mathematicians agree on special notation for multiplication and division with variables.

$2a$ **means** $2 \times a$

mn **means** $m \times n$

$6bc$ **means** $6 \times b \times c$

$\frac{k}{5}$ **means** $k \div 5$

Examples

2 **Evaluate $3b + 4c$ if $b = 9$ and $c = 8$.**

$3b + 4c = 3(9) + 4(8)$ Replace b with 9 and c with 8.
$= 27 + 32$ Use the order of operations.
$= 59$

3 **Evaluate $\frac{xz}{3}$ if $x = 5$ and $z = 6$.**

$\frac{xz}{3} = (5)(6) \div 3$ $\frac{xz}{3} = xz \div 3$
$= 30 \div 3$ Multiply 5 and 6.
$= 10$ Divide 30 by 3.

4 **Evaluate $2x + (3y - z) + 7$ if $x = 5$, $y = 2$, and $z = 4$.**

$2x + (3y - z) + 7 = 2 \cdot 5 + (3 \cdot 2 - 4) + 7$
$= 2 \cdot 5 + (6 - 4) + 7$ Multiply inside parentheses first.
$= 10 + 2 + 7$
$= 19$

Checking for Understanding

Communicating Algebra

1. Write two different expressions that mean the same as $3y$. $3 \times y$, $3 \cdot y$ or $(3)(y)$
2. Write an expression that means the same as $\frac{a}{b}$. $a \div b$
3. Explain in your own words how variables are used. Sample answer: Variables are used as placeholders in expressions.

Guided Practice

Evaluate each expression if $a = 8$, $k = 7$, $m = 5$, $p = 6$, and $s = 11$.

4. $16 + k$ 23
5. $s - 8$ 3
6. $a - 3$ 5
7. $k + 18$ 25
8. $17 - m$ 12
9. $24 - a$ 16
10. $p + s$ 17
11. $a + k$ 15
12. $s - p + 37$ 42
13. $a + s - 9$ 10
14. $48 + m - k$ 46
15. $p + 104 - s - 26$ 73

Alternate Strategies: Reteaching the Lesson

Reteaching Activity

Using Models Model the examples using different sized or colored cups to represent the different variables in each expression. Use the substitution property to replace each cup with the number of counters each variable represents.

Reteaching Masters Booklet, **p. 2**

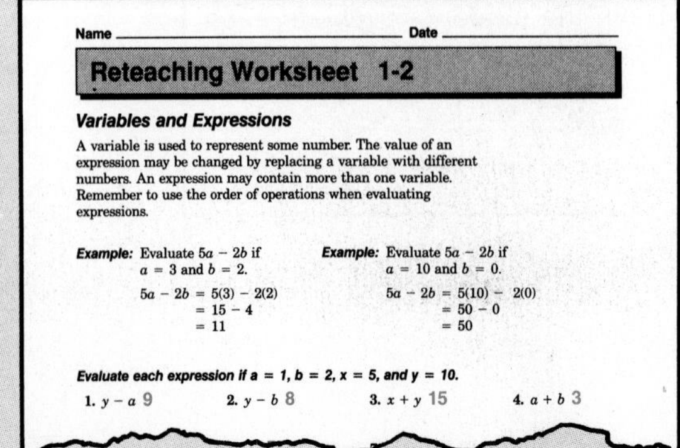
Name ______________________ Date ______________

Reteaching Worksheet 1-2

Variables and Expressions

A variable is used to represent some number. The value of an expression may be changed by replacing a variable with different numbers. An expression may contain more than one variable. Remember to use the order of operations when evaluating expressions.

Example: Evaluate $5a - 2b$ if $a = 3$ and $b = 2$.

$5a - 2b = 5(3) - 2(2)$
$= 15 - 4$
$= 11$

Example: Evaluate $5a - 2b$ if $a = 10$ and $b = 0$.

$5a - 2b = 5(10) - 2(0)$
$= 50 - 0$
$= 50$

Evaluate each expression if a = 1, b = 2, x = 5, and y = 10.

1. $y - a$ 9
2. $y - b$ 8
3. $x + y$ 15
4. $a + b$ 3

Exercises

Independent Practice

Evaluate each expression if $a = 4$, $b = 2$, and $c = 3$.

16. $a + b \cdot c$ 10
17. $6a - b \cdot c$ 18
18. $ab - bc$ 2
19. $4a + b \cdot b$ 20
20. $4a - (b + c)$ 11
21. $6a + 6b$ 36
22. $\frac{a}{b} + c$ 5
23. $\frac{6a}{c}$ 8
24. $\frac{ac}{b}$ 6
25. $7a - (2c + b)$ 20
26. $9a - (4b + 2c)$ 22
27. $2c + 3a + 6b$ 30
28. $\frac{3(4a - 3c)}{a - 3}$ 21
29. $\frac{6(a + b)}{3c}$ 4
30. $\frac{15ac}{3c + 6}$ 12

Computer

In the BASIC computer language, LET statements are used to assign values to the variables. Find the value assigned to A by each LET statement if X = 5 and Y = 15. Multiplication is shown by the symbol * and division by /.

31. `LET A = 2 * X + 9` 19
32. `LET A = 25 + X − 10` 20
33. `LET A = 40/X * 8` 64
34. `LET A = (19 + X)/12` 2
35. `LET A = 12/(31 − 2 * Y)` 12
36. `LET A = 3 * X * Y` 225

Mixed Review

37. If an expression contains only an addition and a division, which would you do first? (Lesson 1-1) division
38. Name the operation you would do first in the expression $(6 - 3)(5 + 1)$. (Lesson 1-1) subtraction
39. Evaluate the expression $2[3(11 - 7) + 1]$. (Lesson 1-1) 26
40. *True* or *false*: $9 \div 3 + 5 - 4 = 4$. (Lesson 1-1) true
41. Use different symbols to write the expression 8×7 in two other ways. (Lesson 1-1) $8 \cdot 7$, $(8)(7)$

Application

42. **Health** The expression $110 + \frac{A}{2}$ is used to estimate a person's normal blood pressure. In this expression, A stands for the person's age in years. Use this expression to estimate the blood pressure of a person who is 18 years old. 119

Critical Thinking

43. Juan and Maria have calculators. Juan starts at zero and adds 2. Maria starts at 100 and subtracts 3. If they push their keys at the same time, will their displays ever show the same number at the same time? If so, what number is it? yes, 40

Wrap-Up

44. Write a sentence that explains why the substitution property is important. Sample answer in the margin.

Biography

Al-Khowarizmi

One of the most influential giants of mathematics was an Arabian mathematician, Al-Khowarizmi. In A.D. 820, at the age of forty, Al-Khowarizmi wrote *Hisab al-jabr w'al-muqabala,* which freely translates into the "Science of Transposition and Cancellation." Note that our word *algebra* looks and sounds very much like *al-jabr.* Al-Khowarizmi did not originate algebra, but he brought organization to the mathematics we now call algebra.

Independent Practice

Homework Assignment	
Basic	16-32, 37-44
Average	19-34, 37-44
Honors	20-44

4 CLOSE

Assessment Option

Writing Have students write a mathematical expression using the letters k, m, or n and any numbers. Then have them exchange their expressions with another student and solve them if $k = 1$, $m = 2$, and $n = 0$.

Additional Answer

44. The substitution property allows you to replace variables with actual numbers so the mathematical expression can be solved.

Enrichment Masters Booklet, **p. 2**

Name ______________ Date ______________

Enrichment Worksheet 1-2

Sets

A **set** is a collection or group of objects. The members of a set are called **elements.** A set can be named by listing the elements within a pair of braces, { }. Here are two sets:

A = {0.5, 1.5, 2.5, 3.5} B = {0.01, 0.02, 0.03, 0.04}

The following symbols are frequently used with sets. Note that every element of a subset of a set must be an element of the set.

Symbol	Meaning	Example
$\in$	is an element of	$2.5 \in \{0.5, 1.5, 2.5, 3.5\}$
$\notin$	is not an element of	$0.2 \notin \{0.01, 0.02, 0.03, 0.04\}$
$\subseteq$	is a subset of	$\{2.5, 3.5\} \subseteq \{0.5, 1.5, 2.5, 3.5\}$
$\nsubseteq$	is not a subset of	$\{3, 4\} \nsubseteq \{0.5, 1.5, 2.5, 3.5\}$
Ø or { }	empty set (null set)	A set having no elements.

List the following sets. Use braces.

1. set C, decimals in tenths between 2.7 and 3.4 C = {2.8, 2.9, 3.0, 3.1, 3.2, 3.3}
2. set D, whole numbers between 8.3 and 13.7 D = {9, 10, 11, 12, 13}
3. set E, whole numbers between 2.1 and 2.5 E = { } or Ø
4. set F, decimals in hundredths between 4.56 and 4.62 F = {4.57, 4.58, 4.59, 4.60, 4.61}
5. set G, names of the first 3 place-values to the right of the decimal point G = {tenths, hundredths, thousandths}

Write true or false for each of the following.

6. $3.5 \in \{1.5, 2.5, 3.5, 4.5\}$ true
7. $0.1 \notin \{0.1, 0.01, 0.001\}$ false
8. $\{0.4, 0.6\} \subseteq \{0.2, 0.4, 0.6, 0.8\}$ true
9. $0.8 \in \{0.8, 0.9\}$ true
10. $5.1 \subseteq \{4.1, 5.1, 6.1, 7.1\}$ false
11. $0.5 \in \{0.2, 0.4, 0.6, 0.8\}$ false
12. $\{1.3\} \nsubseteq \{0.3, 1, 1.3, 2, 2.3\}$ false
13. $\{+, -, \times\} \subseteq \{+, -, \times, \div\}$ true
14. tenths $\notin$ {tenths, hundredths} false
15. $\{2, 3\} \nsubseteq \{1.5, 2.5, 3.5\}$ true

Alternate Strategies: Extending the Lesson

Enrichment

Using Resources Use an Algebra I textbook for additional problems. At first, use problems that include expressions similar to those in Lesson 1-2. When students are comfortable with these, expand to more complex problems.

Cooperative Learning

Guess My Expression Group Activity **1-2**

MATERIALS: 0-9 spinner • clock

SETUP: Each member of the group writes four algebraic expressions using the numbers 1-9 and a variable. For example, one such expression is $3n - 5$. The expression $\frac{3(n + 9)}{n + 4}$ is not acceptable since the variable "n" is used more than one time.

Players take turns spinning the spinner. They substitute the spinner result into their expression and announce the value to the other players. The other players must then guess the expression. If no one can guess the expression in one minute, the player spins again and announces another value. The first player to get the correct expression scores one point. If no player gets the expression after 4 spins, the writer of the expression scores one point and the spinner is passed to the next player. When all players have used all four of their expressions, the person with the greatest number of points wins.

Merrill Pre-Algebra VARIABLES AND EXPRESSIONS

Lesson Notes 1-3

5-Minute Check
(over Lesson 1-2)

Evaluate each expression if $a = 3$, $b = 5$, and $c = 4$.

1. $2a + 3b - 4c$ 5
2. $bc - ab$ 5
3. $6a - (5c - 2b)$ 8
4. $\frac{4(2b + c)}{2c}$ 7

Transparency 1-3 contains the 5-Minute Check and a teaching aid for this lesson.

1 FOCUS

The lesson introduces the properties for addition and multiplication and promotes their use through making arithmetic simpler.

Motivating the Lesson

Have students look up the words *commute, associate,* and *identity* in the dictionary and then relate their definitions to their mathematical meaning.

2 TEACH

Using Cooperative Groups Have each group decide if division and subtraction are associative. They should be prepared to give counterexamples to back-up their decision.

Chalkboard Examples

Compute mentally.

- *For Example 1*
  $45 + 37 + 65 + 53 = ?$ 200
- *For Example 2*
  $50 \cdot 8 \cdot 2 = ?$ 800

Rewrite each expression using the commutative property.

- *For Example 3*
  $6 + y$ $y + 6$
- *For Example 4*
  $a \cdot b$ $b \cdot a$

1-3 Properties

Objective:
Identify and use properties of addition and multiplication.

Key Terms:
commutative
associative
identity

When Thomas Jefferson wrote the Declaration of Independence, he stated certain rights that could be applied to all people. Among these are life, liberty, and the pursuit of happiness.

In mathematics, there are certain properties that are true for addition and multiplication of whole numbers. You may remember the commutative, associative, and identity properties from arithmetic. These properties are summarized in the chart below.

Commutative Properties of Addition and Multiplication	
The order in which numbers are added does not change the sum. $4 + 7 = 7 + 4$ For any numbers a and b, $a + b = b + a$.	The order in which numbers are multiplied does not change the product. $6 \cdot 4 = 4 \cdot 6$ For any numbers a and b, $a \cdot b = b \cdot a$.
Associative Properties of Addition and Multiplication	
The way in which addends are grouped does not change the sum. $(4 + 3) + 5 = 4 + (3 + 5)$ For any numbers a, b, and c, $(a + b) + c = a + (b + c)$.	The way in which factors are grouped does not change the product. $(4 \cdot 2) \cdot 3 = 4 \cdot (2 \cdot 3)$ For any numbers a, b, and c, $(a \cdot b) \cdot c = a \cdot (b \cdot c)$.
Identity Properties of Addition and Multiplication	
The sum of an addend and zero is the addend. $5 + 0 = 5$ For any number a, $a + 0 = a$.	The product of a factor and one is the factor. $7 \cdot 1 = 7$ For any number a, $a \cdot 1 = a$.
Multiplicative Property of Zero	
The product of a factor and zero is zero. $2 \cdot 0 = 0$ For any number a, $a \cdot 0 = 0$.	

You can use these properties to compute sums and products mentally. In the following examples, look for sums and products that are multiples of 10.

Bell Ringer

Substitute m for $o + u$, a for $n + b$, r for $x + y$, l for c, g for $j + q$, and e for $z + w$ into the expression $(n + b)(x + y)(o + u)$ and $c(z + w)(j + q)$. What do you get? An arm and a leg

Examples

Compute mentally.

1 $14 + 5 + 16 + 25 = ?$

$14 + 16 + 5 + 25 = ?$

$30 + 30 = 60$

2 $25 \cdot 9 \cdot 4 = ?$

$25 \cdot 4 \cdot 9 = ?$

$100 \cdot 9 = 900$

CONNECTION TO ALGEBRA

You can also use these properties to rewrite and simplify algebraic expressions.

Examples

Rewrite each expression using the commutative property.

Is subtraction commutative?
no

3 $x + 3$

$x + 3 = 3 + x$ Change the order.

4 $x \cdot y$

$x \cdot y = y \cdot x$

Rewrite each expression using the associative property. Then simplify.

Is subtraction associative?
no

5 $(y + 2) + 3$

$(y + 2) + 3 = y + (2 + 3)$ Change the grouping
$= y + 5$

6 $4(5m)$

$4(5m) = (4 \cdot 5)m$
$= 20m$

7 **Evaluate abc if $a = 6$, $b = 7$, and $c = 5$.**

$abc = 6 \cdot 7 \cdot 5$ Replace a with 6, b with 7, and c with 5.

$= 7 \cdot 6 \cdot 5$ Use the commutative property to change the order of 7 and 6.

$= 7 \cdot (6 \cdot 5)$ Group 6 and 5 to make the multiplication easier to do mentally.

$= 7 \cdot 30$

$= 210$

1. Commutative property: changes order of numbers, Associative property: changes grouping
2. Sample answer: $(2 \times 3) \times 4 = 2 \times (3 \times 4)$
3. The properties allow you to group together numbers that are added or multiplied more easily.

Checking for Understanding

Communicating Algebra

1. Explain the difference between the commutative and associative properties.
2. Using whole numbers, write a mathematical sentence that illustrates the associative property of multiplication.
3. Explain how the properties can help you add and multiply mentally.

Rewrite each expression using the associative property. Then simplify.

- *For Example 5*
  $(a + 9) + 3$ $a + (9 + 3) = a + 12$
- *For Example 6*
  $6(2x)$ $(6 \cdot 2)x = 12x$
- *For Example 7* 48
  Evaluate xyz if $x = 3, y = 8, z = 2$.

3 PRACTICE/APPLY

Checking the Concept

List the properties and ask the students for examples of each using whole numbers.

Error Analysis

Watch for students who always identify a property as commutative if there are two numbers and associative if there are three numbers.
Prevent by giving examples of the commutative property with three or more addends.

Practice Masters Booklet, **p. 3**

Name ____________ Date ____________

Practice Worksheet 1-3

Properties

Name the property shown by each statement.

1. $4 + (9 + 6) = (4 + 9) + 6$ Associative Property of Addition
2. $x + 12 = 12 + x$ Commutative Property of Addition
3. $(3 + y) + 0 = 3 + y$ Identity Property of Addition
4. $(x + y) + z = x + (y + z)$ Associative Property of Addition
5. $(15 + x) + 2 = 2 + (15 + x)$ Commutative Property of Addition
6. $x \cdot 1 = x$ Identity Property of Multiplication
7. $14xy = 14yx$ Commutative Property of Multiplication
8. $(3 + 5) + c = 3 + (5 + c)$ Associative Property of Addition
9. $(2 \cdot 5) \cdot 0 = 0$ Multiplicative Property of Zero
10. $6 \cdot (8 + c) = (8 + c) \cdot 6$ Commutative Property of Multiplication
11. $6 \cdot (4 \cdot 3) = (6 \cdot 4) \cdot 3$ Associative Property of Multiplication
12. $(3 \cdot 9) \cdot 1 = 3 \cdot 9$ Identity Property of Multiplication
13. $(a + b) + c = c + (a + b)$ Commutative Property of Addition
14. $(x + y) \cdot 5 = (y + x) \cdot 5$ Commutative Property of Addition
15. $ab + 0 = ab$ Identity Property of Addition
16. $a \cdot b = b \cdot a$ Commutative Property of Multiplication
17. $(x \cdot y) \cdot z = x \cdot (y \cdot z)$ Associative Property of Multiplication
18. $(7 \cdot 3) \cdot 5 = 7 \cdot (3 \cdot 5)$ Associative Property of Multiplication
19. $(2 + x) \cdot 0 = 0$ Multiplicative Property of Zero
20. $(8 + 5) + 3 = 3 + (8 + 5)$ Commutative Property of Addition
21. $(a + b) \cdot 1 = a + b$ Identity Property of Multiplication

Additional Answer

1. In the commutative property numbers change order in relation to the operation symbol. In the associative property numbers stay in the same position while the grouping changes.

Reteaching Masters Booklet, **p. 3**

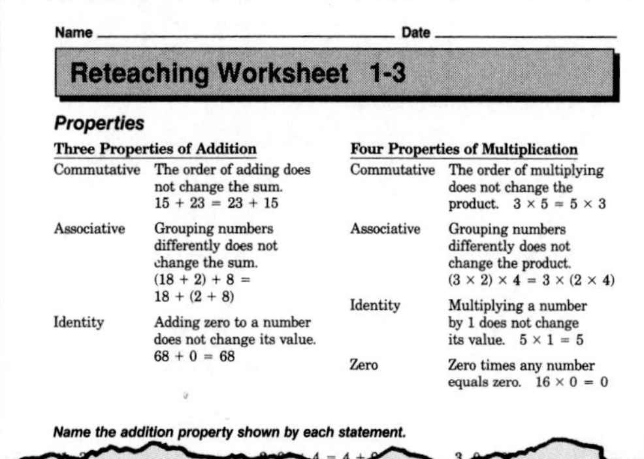

Name ____________ Date ____________

Reteaching Worksheet 1-3

Properties

Three Properties of Addition		Four Properties of Multiplication	
Commutative	The order of adding does not change the sum. $15 + 23 = 23 + 15$	Commutative	The order of multiplying does not change the product. $3 \times 5 = 5 \times 3$
Associative	Grouping numbers differently does not change the sum. $(18 + 2) + 8 = 18 + (2 + 8)$	Associative	Grouping numbers differently does not change the product. $(3 \times 2) \times 4 = 3 \times (2 \times 4)$
Identity	Adding zero to a number does not change its value. $68 + 0 = 68$	Identity	Multiplying a number by 1 does not change its value. $5 \times 1 = 5$
		Zero	Zero times any number equals zero. $16 \times 0 = 0$

Name the addition property shown by each statement.

Independent Practice

Homework Assignment	
Basic	17-41 odd, 43-50
Average	16-42 even, 43-50
Honors	18-42 even, 43-50

4 CLOSE

Assessment Option

Speaking Divide the class into small groups and give each group a series of expressions to evaluate. Have them discuss with each other which of the three properties is a justification for that statement. Then have each member of each group explain an expression to the class. For example, $(m + 4) + 5 = m + (4 + 5)$ is true because of the associative property.

Additional Answers

16. comm., +
17. assoc., ×
18. identity, ×
19. mult., zero
20. comm., ×
21. comm., +
48. Sample answer: putting on socks then putting on shoes.

Enrichment Masters Booklet, **p. 3**

Name ______________________ Date ______________

Enrichment Worksheet 1-3

Algebraic Proof

Axioms are statements assumed to be true without being proven. They are used in the proofs of theorems. The following properties are examples of algebraic axioms. Abbreviations for these properties are used in the examples below.

Commutative Property of Addition (CPA)
Associative Property of Addition (APA)
Subtraction Property of Equality (SPE)
Addition Property of Equality (APE)
Substitution Property of Equality (SPE)
Additive Identity Property (AIP)

Example: Prove: $a + (b + c) = c + (a + b)$

Statement	Reason
$a + (b + c) = (a + b) + c$	APA
$= c + (a + b)$	CPA

Example: Prove: $5 + (x + 2) = 7 + x$

Statement	Reason
$5 + (x + 2) = 5 + (2 + x)$	CPA
$= (5 + 2) + x$	APA
$= 7 + x$	SPE

Write the reason for each statement.

1. Prove: $(9 + 6) + (x + 3) = x + 18$

Statement	Reason
$(9 + 6) + (x + 3) = 15 + (x + 3)$	a. SPE
$= (15 + x) + 3$	b. APA
$= (x + 15) + 3$	c. CPA
$= x + (15 + 3)$	d. APA
$= x + 18$	e. SPE

Prove each of the following. Give a reason for each statement.

2. $9 + (x + 4) = 13 + x$
$9 + (x + 4) = 9 + (4 + x)$ CPA
$= (9 + 4) + x$ APA
$= 13 + x$ SPE

3. $5 + (x + 11) = x + (10 + 6)$
$5 + (x + 11) = (x + 11) + 5$ CPA
$= x + (11 + 5)$ APA
$= x + 16$ SPE
$= x + (10 + 6)$ SPE

Guided Practice

Name the property shown by each statement.

4. $(2 + 5) + 3 = 2 + (5 + 3)$ assoc, +
5. $7 + 4 = 4 + 7$ comm, +
6. $9 + 0 = 9$ identity, +
7. $3 \cdot 5 \cdot 0 = 0$ mult prop of zero
8. $7 \cdot 32 = 32 \cdot 7$ comm, ×
9. $(6 \cdot 15) \cdot 3 = 6 \cdot (15 \cdot 3)$ assoc, ×
10. $(9 + 7) + 4 = 4 + (9 + 7)$ comm, +
11. $8 \cdot 1 = 8$ identity, ×
12. $(6a)b = 6(ab)$ assoc, ×
13. $17m = m \cdot 17$ comm, ×
14. $(12 \cdot a) \cdot 5 = (a \cdot 12) \cdot 5$ comm, ×
15. $0 = a \times 0$ mult prop of zero

Exercises

Independent Practice

Name the property shown by each statement. For Exercises 16-24, see margin

16. $6 + a = a + 6$
17. $4(bc) = (4b)c$
18. $z \cdot 1 = z$
19. $0 \cdot 91 = 0$
20. $7ab = 7ba$
21. $0 + xy = xy + 0$
22. $21 + 0 = 21$
23. $9a + b = b + 9a$
24. $(4 + 7)0 = 0$

Mental Math

Compute mentally.

25. $18 + 13 + 2 + 7$ 40
26. $4 + 13 + 26 + 5$ 48
27. $5 \cdot 13 \cdot 2$ 130
28. $10 \cdot 11 \cdot 6$ 660
29. $23 + 37 + 82 + 58$ 200
30. $98 \cdot 24 \cdot 0$ 0

Rewrite each expression using a commutative property.

31. $9 + 12$ $12 + 9$
32. $3x + 5$ $5 + 3x$ or $x \cdot 3 + 5$
33. $7 + 2z$ $2z + 7$ or $7 + z \cdot 2$

Rewrite each expression using an associative property. Then simplify.

34. $(a + 3) + 4$
35. $12 + (15 + x)$
36. $5(3y)$
37. $(n \cdot 6)5$ $n(6 \cdot 5)$; $30n$
38. $(x + 25) + 18$
39. $3(2z)$ $(3 \cdot 2)z$; $6z$
40. $11 + (13 + m)$
41. $5(4x)$ $(5 \cdot 4)x$; $20x$
42. $(m \cdot 4)7$

34. $a + (3 + 4)$; $a + 7$
35. $(12 + 15) + x$; $27 + x$
36. $(5 \cdot 3)y$; $15y$
38. $x + (25 + 18)$; $x + 43$
40. $(11 + 13) + m$; $24 + m$
42. $m(4 \cdot 7)$; $28m$

43. Evaluate $a + b + c$ if $a = 25$, $b = 49$, and $c = 75$. 149

Mixed Review

44. Name the operation you would do first in the expression $\frac{18 - 3}{5}$. (Lesson 1-1) subtraction
45. Evaluate the expression $5 \cdot 6 \div 2 + 1$. (Lesson 1-1) 16
46. Write an expression that means the same as $\frac{ab}{2}$. (Lesson 1-2) $ab \div 2$
47. Evaluate the expression $b + 6$ if $b = 11$. (Lesson 1-2) 17
48. Evaluate the expression $2s - 3p$ if $p = 5$ and $s = 12$. (Lesson 1-2) 9

Application

49. **Chemistry** When chemists dilute acid, they always pour the acid into the water. Pouring water into acid could produce spattering and burns. These two actions are not commutative. Give another example from your life of actions that are not commutative. See margin.

Critical Thinking

50. Given the expression $(5a)(3b)(4c)(0)$, explain how you can find its value. $(5a \times 3b \times 4c) \times 0 = 0$; mult prop of zero

Wrap-Up

51. Find the value of ■ in the sentence $(50 + 18) + 20 = (■ + 50) + 20$. 18

Alternate Strategies: Extending the Lesson

Enrichment

Using Manipulatives Mark the faces of one number cube with 0, 1, 2, 3, 4, and 6; mark another cube with 1, 5, 7, 8, 9, and 10. Roll the cubes three times, noting the six numbers rolled. See who can devise the number sentence with the greatest value using all six numbers, parentheses, and × and + signs.

Cooperative Learning

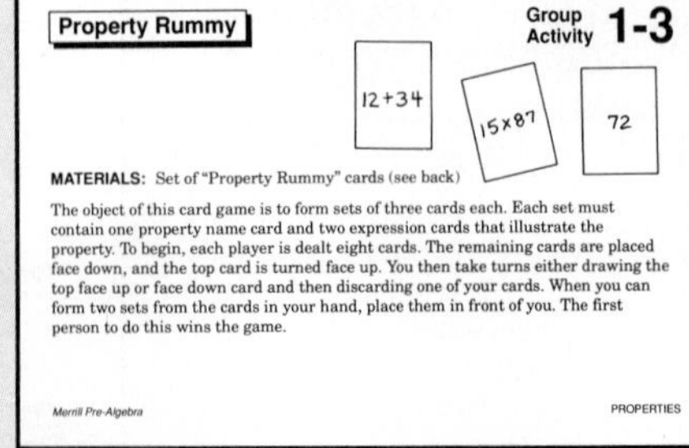
Property Rummy

Group Activity **1-3**

12+34
15×87
72

MATERIALS: Set of "Property Rummy" cards (see back)

The object of this card game is to form sets of three cards each. Each set must contain one property name card and two expression cards that illustrate the property. To begin, each player is dealt eight cards. The remaining cards are placed face down, and the top card is turned face up. You then take turns either drawing the top face up or face down card and then discarding one of your cards. When you can form two sets from the cards in your hand, place them in front of you. The first person to do this wins the game.

Merrill Pre-Algebra PROPERTIES

1-4 The Distributive Property

Objective:
Simplify algebraic expressions using the distributive property.

Key Terms:
distributive
terms
like terms
simplest form

In the previous lesson, you reviewed some of the properties of operations on whole numbers. There is another important property that ties addition and multiplication together. It is the **distributive property.** To see how this property works, study a situation that may occur in your own life.

Suppose you baby-sit for the Lopez family to earn spending money. You charge a fee of \$3 per hour. If you baby-sit 5 hours on Friday night and 7 hours on Saturday night, how much will you earn?

There are two ways to figure how much money you will earn.

fee per hour, total hours

$$3\,(5 + 7) = 3\,(12) = 36$$

money earned on Friday, money earned on Saturday

$$3 \cdot 5 + 3 \cdot 7 = 15 + 21 = 36$$

Is this a true statement: $4(8 - 2) = 4 \cdot 8 - 4 \cdot 2$? What might you conclude?
Yes; Multiplication is distributive over subtraction.

Each method shown above has the same result, 36.

$$3(5 + 7) = 3 \cdot 5 + 3 \cdot 7$$

Your fee is distributed over both days. The 3 is distributed as a multiplier over both 5 and 7. This is an example of the distributive property of multiplication over addition.

Distributive Property	For any numbers a, b, and c, $a(b + c) = ab + ac$ and $(b + c)a = ba + ca$.

Examples

1 Rewrite 8 • 6 + 8 • 7 using the distributive property.

$8 \cdot 6 + 8 \cdot 7$ 8 is a factor of both $8 \cdot 6$ and $8 \cdot 7$.
$8 \cdot 6 + 8 \cdot 7 = 8(6 + 7)$

2 Compute 15 • 12 mentally. Use the distributive property.

$15 \cdot 12 = 15(10 + 2)$ Use 10 + 2 for 12.
$= 15 \cdot 10 + 15 \cdot 2$ THINK: 150 + 30
$= 150 + 30$ or 180

Mental Math Hint
The Distributive Property allows you to break apart one of the factors into a sum. You can then add the two products mentally.

Bell Ringer
List the seven properties from Lesson 1-3 on the chalkboard. Have the class give an example of each property. **Answers will vary.**

Lesson Notes 1-4

5-Minute Check
(over Lesson 1-3)

Rewrite each expression using a commutative property.
1. $8x + 4$ — $4 + 8x$
2. $5 + 2y$ — $2y + 5$

Rewrite each expression using an associative property. Then simplify.
3. $(x + 6) + 9$ — $x + (6 + 9)$; $x + 15$
4. $2(4y)$ — $(2 \cdot 4)y$; $8y$
5. $(a \cdot 3)7$ — $a(3 \cdot 7)$; $21a$

Transparency 1-4 contains the 5-Minute Check and a teaching aid for this lesson.

1 FOCUS

The purpose of this lesson is to introduce the distributive property and then use it in evaluating expressions, combining like terms, and the initial phases of factoring.

Motivating the Lesson
Have the class look up the word "distributive" or "distribute" in the dictionary. Discuss some common things that are or need to be distributed, such as material that is shipped by truck, or test papers from school. Relate these to the mathematical application.

2 TEACH

Using Models Use a rectangular piece of graph paper as a geometric model to illustrate the distributive property.

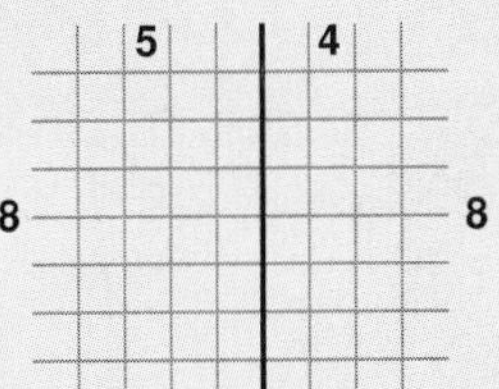

For example, the total number of squares shown above can be found in two ways, $8 \times (5 + 4)$ or $(8 \times 5) + (8 \times 4)$.

EE: 1E, 2D, 2E, 3A, 3B, 3H, 4E
TAAS: 2,11

Chalkboard Examples

- *For Example 1*
  Rewrite $4 \cdot 2 + 4 \cdot 3$ using the distributive property. $4(2 + 3)$
- *For Example 2*
  Compute $13 \cdot 14$ mentally. Use the distributive property.
  $13(10 + 4) = 182$

Simplify each expression.

- *For Example 3*
  $6a + 3a$ $(6 + 3)a$
- *For Example 4*
  $5x + x$ $x(5 + 1)$
- *For Example 5*
  $11b + 3 + 26b$ $37b + 3$
- *For Example 6*
  $m + 4(n + 8m)$ $33m + 4n$

CONNECTION TO ALGEBRA

Let's return to the baby-sitting situation. If you're like most baby-sitters, you vary your hourly rate depending on the number of children or the amount of responsibility you have. You can represent your hourly rate in dollars for a particular family with a variable like x.

If you baby-sit 5 hours on Friday night, you will earn $5x$ dollars.
If you baby-sit 7 hours on Saturday night at the same rate, you will earn $7x$ dollars.

Your total earnings can be represented by the expression $5x + 7x$.

The expression $5x + 7x$ has two **terms** with the same variable. These terms are called **like terms.** Some other pairs of like terms are $5a$ and $13a$, $2rs$ and $6rs$, and y and $7y$. You can use the distributive property to simplify expressions that have like terms. Example 3 shows how to simplify $5x + 7x$.

Examples

Simplify each expression.

3 $\mathbf{5x + 7x}$ — x is a factor of both $5x$ and $7x$.

$5x + 7x = (5 + 7)x$ — Distributive property

$= 12x$ — Substitution property

4 $\mathbf{m + 8m}$

$m + 8m = 1m + 8m$ — $m = 1 \cdot m$; Multiplicative identity

$= (1 + 8)m$ — Distributive property

$= 9m$ — Substitution property

FYI

In the United States, there are about 13.4 million 12- to 15-year-olds who earn an average of $24 per week. That adds up to about $16.7 billion per year.

One more time, let's return to the baby-sitting situation. Suppose that in addition to your hourly earnings, you receive a tip of $10. Your total earnings can now be represented by the expression $5x + 7x + 10$ or $12x + 10$. The expression $12x + 10$ is in **simplest form** because it has no like terms and no parentheses.

Alternate Strategies: Reteaching the Lesson

Reteaching Activity

Using Manipulatives Using concrete materials, such as colored cubes, show examples of the distributive property. For example, if a red cube represents a 69¢ cola, and green, a 79¢ cola, represent an order of six 69¢ colas and six 79¢ colas. Have students solve several problems using the manipulatives.

Reteaching Masters Booklet, p. 4

Name ________________ Date ________

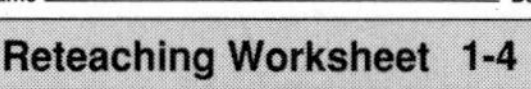

Reteaching Worksheet 1-4

The Distributive Property

The distributive property involves multiplication and addition. It states that the sum of two products with a common factor is equal to the sum of the other factors times the common factor.

$$(12 \times 5) + (4 \times 5) = (12 + 4) \times 5$$

Notice that the two products on the left have a common factor, 5.

The distributive property is used to combine like terms in algebraic expressions. Two or more terms with the same variables are combined by adding the coefficients.

$$12a + 4a = (12 + 4)a = 16a$$
$$b + 6b = (1 + 6)b = 6b$$

Use the distributive property to find the value of each of the following.

1. $(3 \times 8) + (3 \times 2)$ 30 **2.** $(2 \times 9) + (2 \times 11)$ 40

Examples

Simplify each expression.

5 $14a + 7 + 21a$

$14a + 7 + 21a = 14a + 21a + 7$ Commutative property of addition
$= (14 + 21)a + 7$ Distributive property
$= 35a + 7$ Simplest form

6 $r + 3(s + 7r)$

$r + 3(s + 7r) = r + 3s + 3 \cdot 7r$ Distributive property
$= r + 3s + 21r$ Substitution property of equality
$= r + 21r + 3s$ Commutative property of addition
$= 1r + 21r + 3s$ Multiplicative identity
$= (1 + 21)r + 3s$ Distributive property
$= 22r + 3s$ Simplest form

Checking for Understanding

Communicating Algebra

1. Name the like terms in $7s + 9y + y$. $9y, y$
2. Explain why $7a + 8z - 9x$ is in simplest form.
3. Explain why $4 + 2(x - 3)$ is not in simplest form. It has parentheses.

2. It has no like terms and no parentheses.

Guided Practice

Restate each expression using the distributive property. Do not compute.

4. $7(3 + 6)$ $7 \cdot 3 + 7 \cdot 6$
5. $8(5 + 9)$ $8 \cdot 5 + 8 \cdot 9$
6. $6(2 + 4)$ $6 \cdot 2 + 6 \cdot 4$
7. $5(11 + 12)$ $5 \cdot 11 + 5 \cdot 12$
8. $(c + d)3$ $3c + 3d$
9. $(x + y)5$ $5x + 5y$
10. $4 \cdot 6 + 4 \cdot 12$ $4(6 + 12)$
11. $8 \cdot 3 + 8 \cdot 6$ $8(3 + 6)$
12. $10r + 10s$ $10(r + s)$
13. $9x + 9y$ $9(x + y)$
14. $2a + 4b$ $2(a + 2b)$
15. $3x + 6y$ $3(x + 2y)$

Exercises

Independent Practice

Simplify each expression.

16. $4p + p$ $5p$
17. $x + 7x$ $8x$
18. $r + r$ $2r$
19. $k + 12k + 23$ $13k + 23$
20. $6d + d + 15$ $7d + 15$
21. $17x + 21x + 45$ $38x + 45$
22. $6m + 4m + 3$ $10m + 3$
23. $13a + 9a + 8$ $22a + 8$
24. $14bx + 31bx + 9bx$ $54bx$
25. $y + 9 + 14 + 2y$ $3y + 23$
26. $24a + a + 16$ $25a + 16$
27. $4f + 7q + 11f + 8g$ $15f + 8g + 7q$
28. $9(r + 7) + 12r$ $21r + 63$
29. $18y + 5(7 + 3y)$ $33y + 35$
30. $22c + 4(2 + 4c)$ $38c + 8$
31. $14(b + 3) + 8b$ $22b + 42$
32. $3(8 + a) + 7(6 + 4a)$ $31a + 66$
33. $6(x + y) + 4(2x + 3y)$ $14x + 18y$

3 PRACTICE/APPLY

Checking the Concept

Have students provide examples of expressions that have like terms and unlike terms. Have students name the like terms and the unlike terms. Then have them simplify the expressions with like terms. Ask them to discuss the properties that they are using to do so.

Error Analysis

Watch for students who do not complete the distribution. For example, $3(4 + 2) = 12 + 2$.
Prevent by having students check their answers by completing the operation in the parentheses and then multiplying.

Independent Practice

Homework Assignment	
Basic	17-45 odd, 46-54
Average	16-36 even, 42-54
Honors	27-37, 42-54

Practice Masters Booklet, **p. 4**

Name ______ Date ______

Practice Worksheet 1-4

The Distributive Property

Use the distributive property to compute each of the following.

1. $8(50 + 4)$ 432
2. $(20 + 9)5$ 145
3. $2 \cdot 60 + 2 \cdot 4$ 128
4. $7(40 - 2)$ 266
5. $4 \cdot 400 - 4 \cdot 2$ 1592
6. $67 \cdot 40$ 2680
7. $501 \cdot 11$ 5511
8. $210 \cdot 800$ 168,000
9. $89 \cdot 12$ 1068

Simplify each expression.

10. $5a + a$ $6a$
11. $k - k$ 0
12. $m + 3m + 8$ $4m + 8$
13. $10b - b + 1$ $9b + 1$
14. $9ab + 8ab - 7ab$ $10ab$
15. $6x + 3y + 6y - 2x$ $4x + 9y$
16. $3xy + 2xy - xy$ $4xy$
17. $18 + 7x - 12 + 5x$ $12x + 6$
18. $12a + 3 + 18 - 9a$ $3a + 21$
19. $5(x + 2y) + 6x$ $11x + 10y$
20. $5(r + 2) + 7r$ $12r + 10$
21. $x + 5x + 8(x + 2)$ $14x + 16$
22. $4(x + 2) + 3(x + 5)$ $7x + 23$
23. $8(r + 15) + 7(2r + 10)$ $22r + 190$
24. $2(r + 3) + 3(r + 7) - 10$ $5r + 17$
25. $12(c + 3d + 4e) + 2(2c + d + 6e)$ $16c + 38d + 60e$
26. $5 \cdot 4a + 6(5a + 2)$ $50a + 12$
27. $4 \cdot 8 + 9(3a + 5) + 8(2a + 1)$ $43a + 85$
28. $4 \cdot 3a + 2(a + 6b)$ $14a + 12b$
29. $10r + 100s + 50r$ $60r + 100s$
30. $9[5 + 3(x + 2)]$ $27x + 99$
31. $3[9(x + 4) + 2(x + 1)]$ $33x + 114$

4 CLOSE

Assessment Option

Speaking Write the following expressions on the chalkboard: $2(3 \cdot 6)$ and $2(3 + 6)$. Ask students to describe the difference between the two expressions. Have students rewrite each expression as $(2 \cdot 3 \cdot 6$ and $2 \cdot 3 + 2 \cdot 6)$. Ask students if the 2 is distributed in each case. Have them state how the distributive property applies to each of the four operations.

Additional Answer

54. Sample answer: Maria bought 3 notebooks for $2 each; then she decided to buy 2 more. The tax was fifty cents.

Enrichment Masters Booklet, **p. 4**

Name ____________________ Date ____________

Enrichment Worksheet 1-4

Finite and Infinite Sets

In many sets, all the elements cannot be listed (or cannot conveniently be listed). When this is the case, three dots inside the braces indicate that not all the elements are listed, but the pattern shown by those elements listed continues.

set of even numbers less than 100: E = {2, 4, 6, 8, . . . , 98}

set of whole numbers: W = {0, 1, 2, 3, . . .}

The set E is an example of a **finite** set. That is, all the elements could be listed. The set W is an example of an **infinite set.** That is, not all the elements can be listed without using the three dots.

The **cardinal number** of a set is the number obtained by counting the elements in the set. The cardinal number for set E is 49. Note that each element of a set is listed only once.

State whether the following sets are finite or infinite. For each finite set, give the cardinal number.

1. {3, 6, 9, 12} finite, 4
2. {0} finite, 1
3. {2, 4, 6, 8, . . .} infinite
4. {2, 4, 6, . . ., 30} finite, 15
5. the set of all counting numbers infinite
6. the set of all counting numbers less than 50 finite, 49
7. the set of digits used to make up telephone numbers finite, 10

Equal sets have the same elements. Equivalent sets have the same number of elements (same cardinal number). Each element is listed only once and order is not important.

Complete. Answers will vary. Sample answers are given.

8. List two sets equivalent to {+, −, ×}. {A, B, C}, {×, −, +}
9. List two infinite sets that are equivalent (the elements can be matched one-to-one), but not equal. {even numbers}, {odd numbers}

34. $8 \times 12 + 5 \times 12$

Language Skill **Write an expression to find the total for each situation.**

34. You buy eight $12-tickets on Monday. On Tuesday, you buy 5 more.
35. Joe bought 3 soft drinks for y cents each. Sally bought 5 soft drinks for y cents each. $3y + 5y$
36. You charge x dollars per hour to baby-sit. You baby-sit 8 hours on Saturday and 3 hours on Sunday. Then you receive a $5 tip. $8x + 3x + 5$
37. Sara bought 2 cassettes for $7 each, then she decided to buy 1 more. The tax was $1.25. $2 \times 7 + 1 \times 7 + 1.25$

47. $2 \times a \times b, 2 \cdot a \cdot b$ 49. $x + (5 + 1)$

Mental Math **Compute each product mentally. Use the distributive property.**

38. 3×27 81
39. 4×46 184
40. 4×93 372
41. 6×26 156
42. 7×42 294
43. 5×86 430
44. 12×14 168
45. 15×16 240

Mixed Review

46. Evaluate the expression $16 + 10 \div 2 + 3$. (Lesson 1-1) 24
47. Write two different expressions that mean the same as $2ab$. (Lesson 1-2)
48. Evaluate the expression $\frac{9(a + b)}{3c}$ if $a = 1$, $b = 3$, and $c = 2$. (Lesson 1-2) 6
49. Rewrite $(x + 5) + 1$ using the associative property. (Lesson 1-3)
50. What property says that any number multiplied by zero will equal zero? (Lesson 1-3) multiplicative property of zero
51. Simplify the expression $4(3z)$. (Lesson 1-3) $12z$

Connection

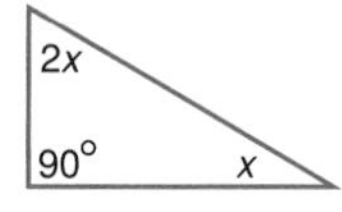

52. **Geometry** In the triangle shown at the right, one angle measures 90°, the second angle measures x, and the third measures $2x$. Write an expression for the sum of the measures of the angles. Simplify the expression. $90 + x + 2x; 90 + 3x$

Critical Thinking

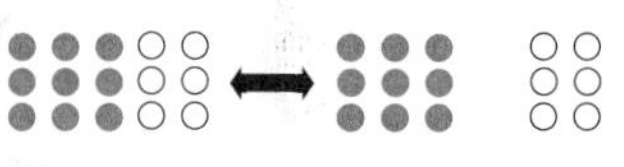

53. Use the distributive property to write two expressions for the figure at the right. $3(3 + 2); 3 \cdot 3 + 3 \cdot 2$

Wrap-Up

54. **Make Up a Problem** Write a problem that is similar to Exercise 37. See margin.

Team Problem Solving

Marcus, the Math Magician, likes to amaze his audiences with this mind-reading trick.

Think of a number.
Add 7 to the number.
Multiply the result by 2.
Subtract 4.
Divide by 2.
Subtract your original number.

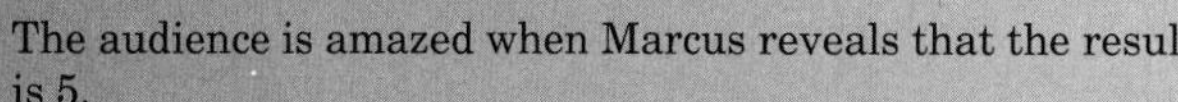

The audience is amazed when Marcus reveals that the result is 5.

Explain why this trick works. Then write one of your own.

Alternate Strategies: Extending the Lesson

Enrichment

Applying Principles Using menus from a local restaurant, give the class a choice of two main dishes, beverages, and so forth. If possible, choose at least two items with identical prices. Poll the class for a total order. Use the distributive property to write a number sentence for the total cost of the meal.

Cooperative Learning

Mental Manipulations Group Activity **1-4**

MATERIALS: 0-9 spinner

PROCEDURE: You and a partner take turns thinking of a two-digit number between 10 and 40. After you think of a number, you say it out loud. Your partner then decides how to break up the number to form a sum that can easily be used to do mental computations. He or she then spins the spinner to get another number and then mentally calculates the product of the sum and the number using the distributive property.

EXAMPLE: Suppose your number is 27. Your partner could break up the number into (20 + 7) or (25 + 2). If the spinner stops on 6, then your partner would mentally calculate either 120 + 42 = 162 or 150 + 12 = 162.

Merrill Pre-Algebra THE DISTRIBUTIVE PROPERTY

Distributive Property

Materials: tiles

In this Exploration, you will look at the distributive property from a geometric point of view.

▶ Let [1 × 1 tile] be a 1 × 1 square. That is, the length and width are each 1 unit. What is the area of this square? 1 square unit

▶ Let [1 × x tile] be a 1 × x rectangle. The width is 1 unit and the length is x units. What is the area of this rectangle? x square units

▶ Then [x and 1 tiles] is a rectangle that has a width of 1 unit and a length of $x + 1$ units. What is the area of this rectangle?
$x + 1$ square units

Your Turn: Using your tiles, make rectangles with areas of $x + 2$, $2x$, $2x + 1$, and $2x + 2$ square units. See Solutions Manual.

Explore: You can use a geometric idea to check the distributive property. Is it true that $2(x + 1) = 2x + 1$?

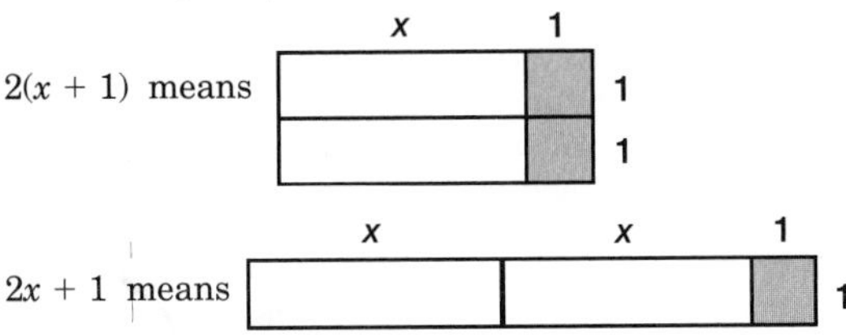

Therefore, $2(x + 1)$ is not the same as $2x + 1$. From the drawing above, $2(x + 1) = 2x + 2$.

Tell whether each statement is *true* or *false*. Justify your answer with tiles or a drawing.

1. $2x + 3 = 6x$ F
2. $2x = x + x$ T
3. $3x + 3 = 3(x + 1)$ T
4. $3x + 3 = 3(x + 3)$ F
5. $3x + 2x = 10x$ F
6. $3x + 2x = x(3 + 2)$ T

Analysis

7. A classmate decides that $3(x + 2) = 3x + 2$. How would you show your classmate that $3(x + 2) = 3x + 6$? Write your solution in paragraph form, complete with drawings. Sample answer in Solutions Manual.

SET-UP

Materials

- Algebra Tiles, Lab Manual, p. 1

You may wish to use the Exploration worksheet provided on page 29 of the Lab Manual.

For Students Students can use commercial or paper tiles. Each student or group of students will need a 1 by 1 and an x by 1 tile. Be sure that the width is always the same within each set.

For the Overhead Projector This exploration will work on the overhead with translucent or opaque tiles.

EXPLORATION

The Distributive Property

Objective Students will visualize the distributive property by modeling a geometric interpretation.

1 FOCUS

This exploration allows the student to understand the distributive property through modeling and seeing that both terms in the parentheses are distributed.

2 TEACH

Model each example for the entire class. You may need to remind students that the area of rectangles is found by multiplying the length by the width. Point out that if $2(x + 1)$ is modeled to create a rectangle with a width of 1, the area is $(x + 1) + (x + 1)$ square units. When modeled next to the model for $2x + 1$, students will see that $2(x + 1) \neq 2x + 1$.

3 PRACTICE/APPLY

Working With a Partner

One student can model a problem, while the other records it on paper. Then, switch roles.

4 CLOSE

Writing Connection

This activity provides a good opportunity for students to practice communicating mathematics. Encourage students to complete the last exercise.

5-Minute Check
(over Lesson 1-4)

Simplify each expression.
1. $9x + x$ **10x**
2. $11ab + 7ab + 5ab$ **23ab**
3. $7(m + 3) + 6m$ **13m + 21**
4. $2(8 + a) + 4(2 + 5a)$ **24 + 22a**
5. $5(m + 3n) + 3(2m + 6n)$ **11m + 33n**

Transparency 1-5 contains the 5-Minute Check and a teaching aid for this lesson.

1 FOCUS

The purpose of the lesson is to introduce equations and to have students solve them easily through inspection and the use of arithmetic facts.

2 TEACH

Chalkboard Examples

- *For Example 1*
  Which of the numbers 23, 31 or 41 is the solution of $94 + x = 125$? **31**

Practice Masters Booklet, **p. 5**

Name ______ Date ______

Practice Worksheet 1-5

Variables and Equations

Solve each equation mentally.

1. $8c = 24$ $c = 3$	2. $14 - 10 = y$ $y = 4$	3. $24 = 16 + b$ $b = 8$
4. $8 = \frac{x}{5}$ $x = 40$	5. $\frac{z}{15} = 2$ $z = 30$	6. $30 = 3w$ $w = 10$
7. $32 + p = 50$ $p = 18$	8. $\frac{r}{7} = 10$ $r = 70$	9. $21 - d = 5$ $d = 16$
10. $x + 13 = 22$ $x = 9$	11. $\frac{m}{5} = 20$ $m = 100$	12. $72 = 9k$ $k = 8$
13. $t - 25 = 25$ $t = 50$	14. $5m = 0$ $m = 0$	15. $12 + a = 29$ $a = 17$
16. $33 - h = 13$ $h = 20$	17. $44 = e - 1$ $e = 45$	18. $\frac{n}{8} = 0$ $n = 0$
19. $10 + q = 10$ $q = 0$	20. $66 - 33 = f$ $f = 33$	21. $\frac{l}{7} = 7$ $l = 49$
22. $\frac{u}{15} = 1$ $u = 15$	23. $36 - i = 0$ $i = 36$	24. $\frac{28}{x} = 4$ $x = 7$
25. $48 = t - 2$ $t = 50$	26. $17 = r + 7$ $r = 10$	27. $8 = \frac{32}{s}$ $s = 4$

1-5 Variables and Equations

Objective:
Identify and solve open sentences.

Key Terms:
equation
open sentence
solve
solution

Suppose you were asked to complete this sentence on your last history test.

___?___ was President of the United States during the Civil War.

This sentence is neither *true* nor *false* until you substitute a name for ?. If you choose *Abraham Lincoln,* the sentence is true. If you choose *George Washington,* the sentence is false.

In mathematics, a sentence that contains an equals sign, =, is called an **equation.** Some equations contain only numbers.

$25 - 15 = 10$ This equation is true.

$8 + 15 = 22$ This equation is false.

An equation that contains at least one variable is called an **open sentence.** For example, $x + 5 = 20$ is an open sentence. It is neither true nor false until x is replaced with some number. When you replace the variable so that the equation is true, you have **solved the equation.** Any number that makes the equation true is called a **solution.** For example, the solution of $x + 5 = 20$ is 15.

Name a number that is not a solution of $x + 5 = 20$. **13**

Example

Estimation Hint

Always estimate before you solve an equation. This allows you to check that your solution is reasonable.
THINK:
$110 + x = 140$

1 Which of the numbers 18, 26, or 28 is the solution of $112 + x = 140$?

$112 + 18 = 140$ Try $x = 18$.
$130 = 140$

This sentence is false.

$112 + 26 = 140$ Try $x = 26$.
$138 = 140$

This sentence is false.

$112 + 28 = 140$ Try $x = 28$.
$140 = 140$

This sentence is true. The solution is 28.

In this course, you will learn many ways to solve equations. Some equations can be solved mentally by using basic facts or arithmetic skills.

Bell Ringer

Write the equation $10y + 4y$ on the chalkboard or overhead. Ask students the following questions.
- Is it in its simplest form? **no**
- How can it be put into simplest form? **Use distributive property. $(10 + 4)y = 14y$**

EE: 1E, 3F, 4B, 4E
TAAS: 2, 4,11

Reteaching Masters Booklet, **p. 5**

Name ______ Date ______

Reteaching Worksheet 1-5

Variables and Equations

The solution of an equation is the number or numbers that make it true. When you have found the solution of an equation, you have solved it.

One way to solve an equation is to guess a number and then check to see if your guess is correct.

Example: Solve $m + 13 = 20$.

First guess: 33 $33 + 13 = 46$
So 33 is not the solution.

Next guess: 10 $10 + 13 = 23$
So 10 is not the solution.
But, 10 is closer than 33.

Next guess: 7 $7 + 13 = 20$
So 7 is the solution to the equation.

Examples

Solve each equation mentally.

2 $12 = y - 4$

$12 = 16 - 4$

$y = 16$

This solution is 16.

3 $2x = 24$

$2 \cdot 12 = 24$

$x = 12$

This solution is 12.

For Exercises 1-4, answers may vary. Sample answers given.

Checking for Understanding

Communicating Algebra

1. Write an equation that is always true. $5 + 2 = 7$
2. Write an equation that is always false. $5 + 2 = 8$
3. Write an open sentence and change it to one that is true.
4. Write an open sentence and change it to one that is false.

3. $n + 1 = 4; 3 + 1 = 4$; 4. $n - 2 = 6; 7 - 2 = 6$

Guided Practice

Name the number that is a solution of the given equation.

5. $5 - x = 2$; 3, 5, 7 **3**
6. $y + 27 = 58$; 29, 30, 31 **31**
7. $3x = 87$; 19, 29, 39 **29**
8. $110 = 145 - m$; 35, 40, 45 **35**
9. $7 = \frac{14}{a}$; 2, 21, 98 **2**
10. $11 = \frac{b}{3}$; 30, 31, 32 **none**
11. $2x + 1 = 7$; 3, 4, 5 **3**
12. $7 = 5b + 2$; 0, 1, 2 **1**

Exercises

Independent Practice

Solve each equation mentally.

13. $r + 11 = 17$ **6**
14. $y + 2 = 33$ **31**
15. $19 - q = 5$ **14**
16. $17 = k - 3$ **20**
17. $5x = 25$ **5**
18. $\frac{18}{a} = 9$ **2**
19. $\frac{y}{3} = 8$ **24**
20. $42 - y = 0$ **42**
21. $63 = 7q$ **9**

Mixed Review

22. What property is shown by the statement $(9 + 4) + 2 = 2 + (9 + 4)$? (Lesson 1-3) comm prop of add

Simplify each expression. (Lesson 1-4)

23. $3m + 7m + 1$ $10m + 1$
24. $5y + 3(7 + 2y)$ $11y + 21$

Connection

25. **Geometry** If you want to find the area of a rectangular garden, you use the formula $A = \ell w$, where ℓ is the length and w is the width. Solve the equation if $\ell = 15$ feet and $w = 12$ feet. $180\ \text{ft}^2$

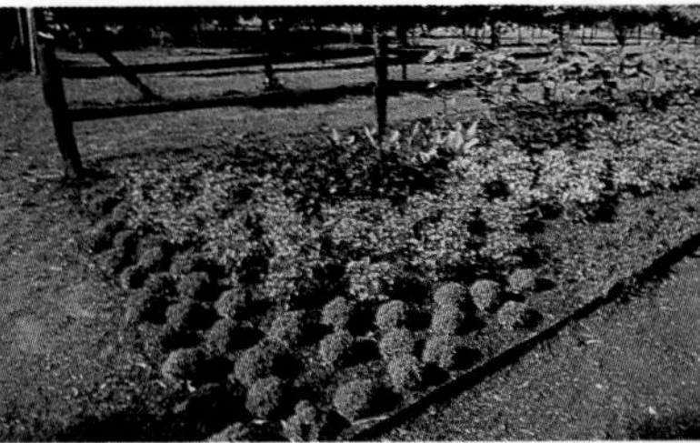

Critical Thinking

26. Write an open sentence that has no whole number solution. Sample answer:

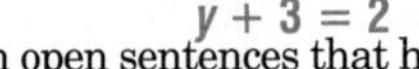

$y + 3 = 2$

Wrap-Up

27. Write an open sentences that has 5 as its solution. Sample answer: $y + 4 = 9$

Solve each equation.

- *For Example 2* $15 = x - 6$ **21**
- *For Example 3* $3m = 18$ **6**

3 PRACTICE/APPLY

Checking the Concept

Have students develop open, true, and false sentences. Then have them determine in which category each sentence belongs.

Independent Practice

Homework Assignment	
Basic	13-27
Average	13-27
Honors	13-27

4 CLOSE

Assessment Option

Modeling Give each student a card with a different number. Have each student create an equation with their number as the solution.

Enrichment Masters Booklet, **p. 5**

Name ________ Date ________

Enrichment Worksheet 1-5

Solution Sets

Consider the following open sentence.

It is a robot that starred in STAR WARS.

You know that a replacement for the word *It* must be found in order to determine if the sentence is true or false. If *It* is replaced by either *R2D2* or *C3PO,* the sentence is true.

The set {*R2D2, C3PO*} can be thought of as the *solution set* of the open sentence given above. This set includes all replacements for the word that make the sentence true.

Write the solution set of each open sentence.

1. It is the name of a state beginning with the letter A. {Alabama, Alaska, Arkansas, Arizona}
2. It is a primary color. {red, yellow, blue}
3. Its capital is Harrisburg. {Pennsylvania}
4. It is a New England state. {Connecticut, Maine, Massachusetts, New Hampshire, Rhode Island, Vermont}
5. In 1964 he was one of the Beatles. {John Lennon, George Harrison, Paul McCartney, Ringo Starr}
6. It is the name of a month that contains the letter q. ∅
7. During the 1970s, she was the wife of a U.S. President. {Patricia Nixon, Betty Ford, Rosalind Carter}
8. It is an even number between 1 and 13. {2, 4, 6, 8, 10, 12}
9. $x + 4 = 10$ {6}
10. $31 = 72 - k$ {41}
11. It is the square of 2, 3, or 4. {4, 9, 16}

Write a description of each set.

12. {A, E, I, O, U} The vowels
13. {1, 3, 5, 7, 9} The odd numbers between 0 and 10
14. {June, July, August} The months between May and September
15. {Atlantic, Pacific, Indian, Arctic} The oceans

Chapter 1, Quiz A (Lessons 1-1 through 1-5) is available in the Evaluation Masters Booklet, p. 7.

Cooperative Learning

Algebra Jumble Group Activity **1-5**

Some of the equations below have the number 5 as their solution. If 5 is a solution to an equation, write the variable used in that equation in one of the boxes below. When you have investigated each equation, rearrange the letters in the boxes to form the two-word message.

$\frac{80}{m} = 16$	$\frac{a + 11}{2} = 8$	$14s - 3 = 73$	$79 = 84 - t$
$l + 37 = 42$	$8h - 3 = 37$	$123 - a = 118$	$\frac{8d}{4} + 3 = 7$
$51 - i = 56$	$71 = 6 + 13n$	$3r + 4 = 19$	$\frac{6e}{3} = 10$

☐ ☐ ☐ ☐ ☐ ☐ ☐ ☐ ☐

YOUR MESSAGE:

__ __ __ __ __ __ __ __ __

Merrill Pre-Algebra VARIABLES AND EQUATIONS

Applying Algebra to the Real World

Objective This optional page shows how algebra is used in the real world and also provides a change of pace.

Using Discussion

Ask students if they have ever used a code of any kind. Some may have used Morse code or written a message where they substituted a number for a letter (for example, 1 = *a* and 2 = *b*). Have students write chalkboard examples of each type of code used.

Literature Connection

Have the class read a short story that involves the use of a cipher. Examples are *The Gold Bug* by Edgar Allen Poe, "The Dancing Man", a Sherlock Holmes story by A. Conan Doyle, and "The First Letter" from *Just So Stories* by Rudyard Kipling. An alternate approach is to work with a literature teacher to use literature and skills in cryptology in both classes.

Activity

Materials newspapers that contain cryptic puzzles

Using Cooperative Groups Provide groups of students with copies of newspapers that contain cryptic puzzles. Have students work as a group to solve the puzzles. Advise students that these puzzles are frequently difficult and the code does not follow a simple alphabet shift.

Algebra in Action–Cryptology

Codes and Ciphers

Can you read this message?

JBBQ JB XQ QEB IFYOXOV

The words appear to be nonsense; but if you have the key, you can decipher the message.

Cryptology, the science of writing and interpreting secret codes or ciphers, can be traced back to ancient Egypt. One of the easiest codes is the **substitution cipher,** in which each letter of the regular, or plaintext, alphabet is replaced by another letter. One such cipher was used by the Roman Emperor, Julius Caesar. In the Caesar cipher, the plaintext alphabet is shifted three letters to the right. The new alphabet is called the ciphertext.

Ciphertext	X	Y	Z	A	B	C	D	E	F	G	H	I	J	K	L	M	N	O	P	Q	R	S	T	U	V	W
Plaintext	A	B	C	D	E	F	G	H	I	J	K	L	M	N	O	P	Q	R	S	T	U	V	W	X	Y	Z

Using this key, DOG in Plaintext becomes ALD in ciphertext.

When you think of secret codes, you probably think of how they are used by secret agents or in military operations. Today, cryptology is a rapidly growing profession due to the increase in the need for computer security. It is important for businesses to protect the information they have stored in their computers. What better way is there than to design codes that only certain people in their businesses understand? That's what cryptology is all about.

1. The message above was written using the Caesar cipher. Decipher the message into plaintext. **MEET ME AT THE LIBRARY.**

2. If $c = p + 3$ means that the plaintext was shifted 3 places to the right, what does $c = p - 3$ mean? **It was shifted 3 places to the left.**

3. The following message was written using a substitution cipher. Can you decipher it? Hint: The plaintext alphabet was shifted either five, seven, nine, or ten letters to the right. **ALGEBRA IS EASY. Alphabet was shifted 7 letters to the right.**

   TEZXUKT BL XTLR.

4. **Make Up a Problem** Design your own substitution cipher. Ask a friend to decipher a message written in your ciphertext. **See students' work.**

1-6 Strategy: Guess and Check

Objective:
Solve problems using the guess-and-check strategy.

Key Term:
guess and check

The sports section of Anita's newspaper is torn and part of the article about the Franklin High School football game is missing. Anita can read that the team scored 34 points and made a total of 7 touchdowns and field goals. The team made just 1 extra point after the touchdowns. Anita wants to know how many touchdowns were made in the game. She can use a strategy called **guess and check.**

Explore Anita knows the number of points scored, the total number of touchdowns and field goals, and the number of extra points. She also knows that each touchdown is worth 6 points and each field goal is worth 3 points. She wants to know the number of touchdowns.

If Anita's guess results in a total score of 37, how should she change her guess? **Try fewer touchdowns.**

Plan Anita can guess the number of touchdowns. She can then calculate the total number of points. If her answer is 34, her guess is correct. If her answer is not 34, she must change her guess and try again.

Solve She guesses 3 touchdowns and 4 field goals.

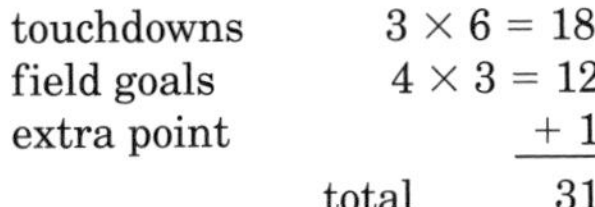

touchdowns		$3 \times 6 = 18$
field goals		$4 \times 3 = 12$
extra point		$+1$
	total	31

Since the total is too small, Anita knows she must try a greater number of touchdowns. She tries 4 touchdowns and 3 field goals.

touchdowns		$4 \times 6 = 24$
field goals		$3 \times 3 = 9$
extra point		$+1$
	total	34

There were 4 touchdowns.

How can you solve $y + 230 = 850$ using guess-and-check? **Try different numbers until you find the solution.**

Examine Try several other combinations to see if any have a total score of 34. For example, 5 touchdowns, 2 field goals and 1 extra point has a total score of 37, which is too great. Since no other combinations have a total of 34, Anita is sure that the team scored 4 touchdowns.

Lesson Notes 1-6

5-Minute Check
(over Lesson 1-5)

Solve each equation.
1. $m + 19 = 41$ 22
2. $68 - x = 27$ 41
3. $8a = 120$ 15
4. $\frac{x}{4} = 37$ 148
5. $30 - b = 12$ 18

Transparency 1-6 contains the 5-Minute Check and a teaching aid for this lesson.

1 FOCUS

The purpose of this lesson is to apply the strategy of guess and check. Many of the Critical Thinking problems throughout the text can be solved using this strategy so students should be given a formal experience with it.

Motivating the Lesson

Think of a number between 1 and 100. Have your students try to guess the number. Then tell them whether the number is higher or lower than the guess. Continue with another guess. Emphasize that some guesses are better than others. For example, starting with a guess of 50 is better than starting with a guess of 1.

2 TEACH

Chalkboard Examples

Fran reads in the sports column of the newspaper that the basketball team scored a total of 94 points. The team made 40 field goals and 11 foul shots. But the report did not give how many 2-point or 3-point field goals were made. Fran wants to find out how many of each field goals were made. **37 2-point field goals, 3 3-point field goals.**

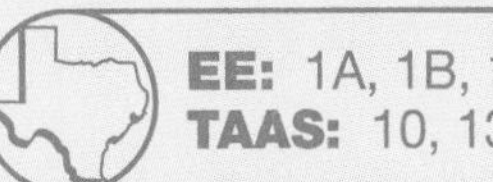

EE: 1A, 1B, 1C, 1D, 1E
TAAS: 10, 13

Bell Ringer

Have each student write an equation with a variable. What number will make the statement true? What number(s) will make it false?

Reteaching Activity

Working Backwards Give students problems that have only a few numbers filled in. Example:

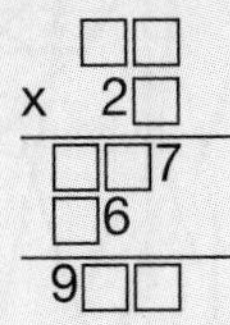

Using guess and check, have students complete the problems. For example, one place in this problem, □ × □ ends in a 7, so the numbers must be either 7 and 1, or 9 and 3.

```
  33
x 29
 297
 66
 957
```

3 PRACTICE/APPLY

Checking the Concept

Using Discussion Tell students that you are thinking of three numbers whose product is 30 and whose sum is 10. Ask for possible clues in the problem that will help find the missing numbers.

Independent Practice

Homework Assignment	
Basic	4-10
Average	4-10
Honors	4-10
All	Mid-Chapter Quiz 1-10

4 CLOSE

Assessment Option

Writing Have students write their solution to the example problem if the score of the game was 44, there were 9 touchdowns and field goals, and there were 2 extra points. 5 touchdowns, 4 field goals, and 2 extra points.

Practice Masters Booklet, **p. 6**

Name ______________________ Date ______________

Practice Worksheet 1-6

Problem Solving Strategy: Guess and Check

Solve using mental math skills, estimation, paper and pencil, or a calculator.

1. One number is 6 more than another. Their product is 520. Find the numbers. 20 and 26
2. One number is twice another. Their product is 128. Find the numbers. 8 and 16
3. Mr. Walsh is four times as old as his daughter. In 14 years, he will be twice as old as his daughter. Find the ages now. Mr. Walsh, 28 years; daughter, 7 years
4. The product of two consecutive odd numbers is 783. Find the numbers. 27 and 29
5. The product of two consecutive even numbers is 1088. Find the numbers. 32 and 34
6. The length of a rectangle is three times the width. The area is 243 square meters. Find the width. 9 meters
7. The length of a rectangle is 4 more than the width. The perimeter is 40 meters. Find the length. 12 meters
8. What is the only number you can multiply by itself and get a product of 4489? 67

Checking for Understanding

Communicating Algebra

1. Explain why it is important to use estimation with the guess-and-check strategy. Estimation may help you find the answer with fewer guesses.

Guided Practice

Solve using the guess-and-check strategy.

2. The sum of a number and 126 is 171. Find the number. 45
3. The product of two consecutive numbers is 930. Find the numbers. 30, 31

Exercises

Independent Practice

Solve using mental math skills, estimation, paper and pencil, or a calculator.

? ESTIMATION MENTAL MATH CALCULATOR PAPER/PENCIL

4. The product of a number and 15 is 105. Find the number. 7
5. The sum of a number and 89 is 122. Find the number. 33
6. The product of a number and itself is 196. Find the number. 14

7. Amos has a total of 10 nickels and quarters. If the value of the coins is $1.70, how many quarters does he have? 6 quarters
8. The Jackson Middle School choir buys 30 tickets to a musical play. The total cost of the tickets is $98.00. If student tickets cost $3.00 and adult tickets cost $5.00, how many adults are going with the choir? 4 adults
9. The Middletown Junior High School basketball team made 21 baskets to score 36 points. If two of the baskets were 3-point shots, how many baskets were worth 2 points and how many were worth 1 point? 11 2-point; 8 1-point

Wrap-Up

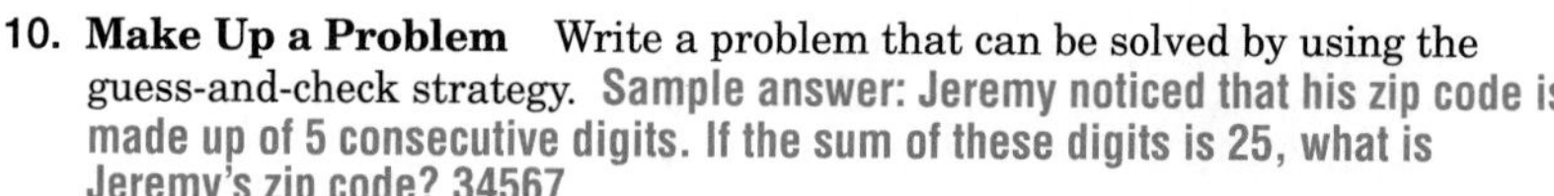

10. **Make Up a Problem** Write a problem that can be solved by using the guess-and-check strategy. Sample answer: Jeremy noticed that his zip code is made up of 5 consecutive digits. If the sum of these digits is 25, what is Jeremy's zip code? 34567

Mid-Chapter Quiz

Find the value of each expression. (Lesson 1-1)

1. $4(6) + 9$ 33
2. $20 - 6 \div 3 + 4 \cdot 8$ 50
3. $\frac{15 + 35}{21 + 4}$ 2

Evaluate each expression if $a = 36$ and $b = 12$. (Lesson 1-2)

4. $a \div b$ 3
5. $3(a + b)$ 144

Simplify each expression. (Lessons 1-3, 1-4)

6. $(x + 5) + 7$ $x + 12$
7. $5(3x)$ $15x$
8. $9x + 3x$ $12x$

Solve each equation mentally. (Lesson 1-5)

9. $24 = y - 5$ 29
10. $3a = 30$ 10

Alternate Strategies: Extending the Lesson

Enrichment

Working in Pairs Have each student create problems using coins. For example, if 2 quarters, 2 nickels, and 4 dimes are used, the problem might be: "I have 8 coins that total $1.00. The number of nickels equals the number of quarters. How many of each coin do I have?" Students can exchange and solve problems.

Cooperative Learning

Guess My Number Group Activity 1-6

In a group of two or more, one member of the group secretly chooses a number between 1 and 250 and writes it on a piece of paper without showing it to the other players. The other players then try to guess the number by asking questions that can be answered with a "yes" or "no." A player's turn consists of asking a question and making a guess as to the number. In groups of three or more, the players try to be the first player to guess the number. If only two people play the game, each player tries to guess the number in the least number of attempts.

Sample questions: Is the number greater than 100? Is the number a multiple of 5? Does the number end in 6?

Merrill Pre-Algebra PROBLEM-SOLVING STRATEGY: GUESS AND CHECK

1-7 Solving Equations Using Inverse Operations

Objective:
Solve equations using inverse operations.

Key Term:
Inverse operations

Here's a puzzle for you.

> I'm thinking of a number—
> If you multiply it by 15 and then subtract 17, you get 73.
> What's the number?

You could use the guess-and-check strategy to find the number. But that strategy might take too much time. Another way to solve this problem is to start with 73 and undo the operations.

$73 + 17 = 90$ Add 17.

$90 \div 15 = 6$ Divide by 15.

The number is 6. Check this solution.

What is the inverse of depositing $20 in a bank account? **Writing a $20 check**

You were able to undo the operations because addition and subtraction are **inverse operations.** This can be shown by these related sentences.

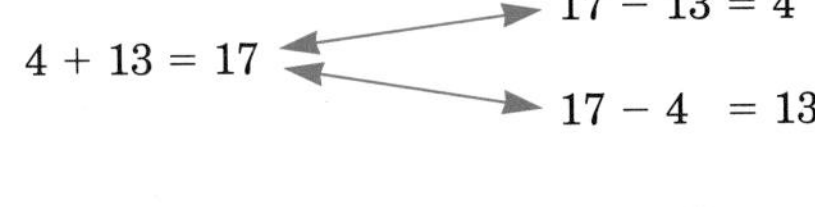

$4 + 13 = 17$ → $17 - 13 = 4$; $17 - 4 = 13$

Which sentence could help you find the value of t? **$48 - 15 = t$**

$15 + t = 48$ → $48 - 15 = t$; $48 - t = 15$

These sentences suggest the following definition.

Definition of Subtraction	For all numbers a, b, and c, $a - b = c$ and $a - c = b$ if $b + c = a$.

In a similar way, multiplication and division are inverse operations.

$6 \cdot 2 = 12$ → $12 \div 2 = 6$ or $\frac{12}{2} = 6$; $12 \div 6 = 2$ or $\frac{12}{6} = 2$

$15r = 60$ → $60 \div r = 15$ or $\frac{60}{r} = 15$; $60 \div 15 = r$ or $\frac{60}{15} = r$

Bell Ringer

Write the equations listed below on the chalkboard. Have students determine what the variables represent.

$60 = m$ in an h **minutes in an hour**
$36 = i$ in a y **inches in a yard**
$4 = c$ in a q **cups in a quart**
$3 = f$ in a y **feet in a yard**
$5280 = f$ in a m **feet in a mile**

EE: 1E, 3A, 3F, 4E, 5F
TAAS: 2, 11, 12

Lesson Notes 1-7

5-Minute Check
(over Lesson 1-6)

Solve using mental math skills, estimation, paper and pencil, or a calculator.

1. The sum of a number and 231 is 249. **18**
2. The product of a number and 42 is 378. **9**
3. Yuri has a total of 8 dimes and quarters. If the value of the coins is $1.55, how many quarters does he have? **5**

Transparency 1-7 contains the 5-Minute Check and a teaching aid for this lesson.

1 FOCUS

The purpose of this lesson is to use inverse operations to solve equations.

Motivating the Lesson

Draw the maze shown below on the overhead or chalkboard and work through it backwards. Show them why it was easier to work through backwards. **You can only go one way if you work through it backwards. You have three ways to go if you start at the beginning.**

2 TEACH

Using Models

On a two-pan balance scale, place a stack of nickels on one pan and an equal stack of pennies on each pan. Have students develop an equation that relates to the scale. Ask the students what you need to do to get the scale to balance and relate their solution to the equation.

Chalkboard Examples

Solve each equation by using inverse operations.

- *For Example 1*
  $x - 8 = 29$ 37
- *For Example 2*
  $m + 16.2 = 51.6$ 35.4
- *For Example 3*
  $\frac{a}{7} = 34$ 238
- *For Example 4*
  $2.4y = 48.0$ 20

These sentences suggest the following definition.

Definition of Division

For all numbers a, b, and c, with $b \neq 0$ and $c \neq 0$, $\frac{a}{b} = c$ and $\frac{a}{c} = b$ if $bc = a$.

CONNECTION TO ALGEBRA

You have already solved equations by using arithmetic skills and the guess-and-check strategy. You can also use inverse operations to solve equations.

Examples

Solve each equation by using inverse operations.

1 $m - 5 = 21$

$m = 21 + 5$ Write the related addition sentence.

$m = 26$

Estimation Hint

Always estimate before you solve the equation.
THINK: $a + 14 = 27$

The solution is about 13.

2 $a + 13.7 = 27.3$

$a = 27.3 - 13.7$ Write the related subtraction sentence.

27.3 [−] 13.7 [=] 13.6

$a = 13.6$

3 $\frac{r}{5} = 31$

$r = 31 \cdot 5$ Write the related multiplication sentence.

$r = 155$

4 $1.3b = 39.0$

$b = 39.0 \div 1.3$ Write the related division sentence.

39.0 [÷] 1.3 [=] 30

$b = 30$

Alternate Strategies: Reteaching the Lesson

Reteaching Activity

Working in Groups of Three Give students several problems to solve. To reinforce the importance of writing each step in the solution, have one student write the original problem, another student write the middle step, and the third student then write the solution.

Reteaching Masters Booklet, **p. 6**

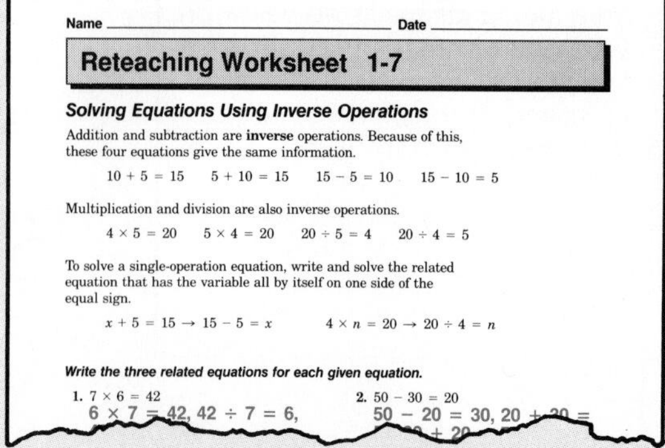

Name ______ Date ______

Reteaching Worksheet 1-7

Solving Equations Using Inverse Operations

Addition and subtraction are **inverse** operations. Because of this, these four equations give the same information.

$10 + 5 = 15$ $5 + 10 = 15$ $15 - 5 = 10$ $15 - 10 = 5$

Multiplication and division are also inverse operations.

$4 \times 5 = 20$ $5 \times 4 = 20$ $20 \div 5 = 4$ $20 \div 4 = 5$

To solve a single-operation equation, write and solve the related equation that has the variable all by itself on one side of the equal sign.

$x + 5 = 15 \rightarrow 15 - 5 = x$ $4 \times n = 20 \rightarrow 20 \div 4 = n$

Write the three related equations for each given equation.

1. $7 \times 6 = 42$
   $6 \times 7 = 42$, $42 \div 7 = 6$,
2. $50 - 30 = 20$
   $50 - 20 = 30$, $20 + 30 =$

For Exercises 1 and 2, sample answers given.

Checking for Understanding

Communicating Algebra

1. What is the inverse of gaining five yards in football? losing 5 yards

2. Write an addition sentence. Then write a related subtraction sentence. $4 + 5 = 9, 5 = 9 - 4$
3. Write an open sentence using multiplication. Then write a related division sentence. $3x = 12; x = 12 \div 3$

Guided Practice

For each sentence, write a related sentence using the inverse operation.

4. $4 + 7 = 11$ — $4 = 11 - 7$ or $7 = 11 - 4$
5. $21 + 15 = 36$ — $21 = 36 - 15$ or $15 = 36 - 21$
6. $23 = 17 + m$
7. $14 - 3 = 11$ — $14 = 11 + 3$
8. $21 - 17 = 4$ — $21 = 4 + 17$
9. $c - 18 = 6$ — $c = 6 + 18$
10. $8 \cdot 9 = 72$ — $8 = 72 \div 9$ or $9 = 72 \div 8$
11. $b = (6)(7)$ — $b \div 6 = 7$ or $b \div 7 = 6$
12. $4y = 16$
13. $28 \div 7 = 4$ — $28 = 4 \cdot 7$
14. $12 = \frac{x}{11}$ — $12 \cdot 11 = x$
15. $\frac{a}{19} = 7$ — $a = 7 \cdot 19$

6. $23 - 17 = m$ or $23 - m = 17$ 12. $y = 16 \div 4$ or $4 = 16 \div y$

Exercises

Independent Practice

Solve each equation by using the inverse operation. Use a calculator where necessary.

16. $5 + r = 12$ 7
17. $13 + z = 25$ 12
18. $a + 11 = 17$ 6
19. $x - 6 = 18$ 24
20. $16 = z - 25$ 41
21. $17 = t - 3$ 20
22. $34 = a \cdot 2$ 17
23. $16r = 48$ 3
24. $153 = 9x$ 17
25. $\frac{r}{9} = 15$ 135
26. $7 = \frac{g}{12}$ 84
27. $144 = x \cdot 12$ 12
28. $15b = 210$ 14
29. $45z = 315$ 7
30. $\frac{m}{15} = 8$ 120

Calculator

31. $n + 4.73 = 5.56$ 0.83
32. $4.37 = y - 9.32$ 13.69
33. $\frac{b}{5.4} = 3.7$ 19.98
34. $2.5r = 37.5$ 15
35. $19.75 = s + 15.98$ 3.77
36. $7.2 = 0.36y$ 20

Mixed Review

37. Evaluate the expression $10a - (7b + c)$ if $a = 2$, $b = 1$, and $c = 12$. (Lesson 1-2) 1
38. Restate $5x + 5y$ using the distributive property. (Lesson 1-4) $5(x + y)$

Simplify each expression. (Lessons 1-3, 1-4)

39. $5(6y)$ $30y$
40. $23c + 6(1 + 5c)$ $53c + 6$
41. Solve mentally: $7x = 63$. (Lesson 1-5) 9
42. Write an open sentence that has zero for a solution. (Lesson 1-5) $7 + x = 7$

Challenge

Solve for x by using the inverse operation.

43. $x + a = 3$ $x = 3 - a$
44. $x + 3 = m$ $x = m - 3$
45. $k = x - 21$ $x = k + 21$
46. $\frac{x}{a} = b$ $x = ab$
47. $12 = x + r$ $x = 12 - r$
48. $ax = q$ $x = \frac{q}{a}$

3 PRACTICE/APPLY

Checking the Concept

Use equations such as $x + y = z$ to check whether the students understand the concept. If they can solve $x + y = z$ for x, then they can probably do those with numbers. Remind them that variables are simply placeholders.

Error Analysis

Watch for students who use the operation in the problem instead of its inverse. For example, $x + 3 = 5$; $x + 3 + 3 = 5 + 3$

Prevent by estimating the solution before applying the property of equality or by checking the solution.

Independent Practice

Homework Assignment	
Basic	17-35 odd, 37-42, 49, 51, 53, 54
Average	20-34 even, 37-42, 43-51 odd, 53, 54
Honors	28-42, 44-48 even, 49-54

Practice Masters Booklet, **p. 7**

Name ________________ Date ________________

Practice Worksheet 1-7

Solving Equations Using Inverse Operations

Solve each equation by using the inverse operation. Use a calculator where necessary.

1. $9 + x = 16$ $x = 7$
2. $\frac{v}{16} = 1$ $v = 16$
3. $k - 13 = 18$ $k = 31$
4. $378 = 18$ $z = 21$
5. $55 = 5e$ $e = 11$
6. $32 = \frac{f}{8}$ $f = 256$
7. $z - 5 = 19$ $z = 24$
8. $m + 15 = 20$ $m = 5$
9. $6c = 54$ $c = 9$
10. $\frac{x}{6} = 19$ $x = 114$
11. $73 = b - 42$ $b = 115$
12. $155 = n + 137$ $n = 18$
13. $\frac{h}{10} = 100$ $h = 1000$
14. $27d = 945$ $d = 35$
15. $94 - p = 12$ $p = 82$
16. $98 = 38 + c$ $c = 60$
17. $201 = \frac{t}{10}$ $t = 2010$
18. $1479 = 17c$ $c = 87$
19. $145 = s - 121$ $s = 266$
20. $12 + r = 54$ $r = 42$
21. $\frac{b}{4.9} = 4.9$ $b = 24.01$
22. $64 = \frac{r}{91}$ $r = 5824$
23. $32 \cdot l = 288$ $l = 9$
24. $32 = 114 - h$ $h = 82$
25. $53 + y = 53$ $y = 0$
26. $18 = \frac{z}{27}$ $z = 486$
27. $7.2 = 0.18g$ $g = 40$
28. $l - 1492 = 3421$ $l = 4913$
29. $w + 3.74 = 6.55$ $w = 2.81$
30. $\frac{d}{2.3} = 6.7$ $d = 15.41$
31. $2.4j = 9.6$ $j = 4$
32. $5.73 - u = 3.73$ $u = 2$
33. $k + 453 = 846$ $k = 393$

4 CLOSE

Assessment Option

Writing Ask students to "undo" the following expression and find the original number.

1. Take a number, multiply it by 4, and then add 21 and you get 37. 4
2. Take a number, divide by 8, subtract 2, add 12 and you get 18. 64

Additional Answer

53. The multiplicative property of zero states that the product of a factor and zero equals zero. Therefore, $0 \cdot a$ cannot equal 4 and $\frac{4}{0}$ cannot be solved.

Enrichment Masters Booklet, **p. 6**

Name ______________________ Date ______________

Enrichment Worksheet 1-7

Mental Math: Compensation

To add or subtract in your head, work with multiples of 10 (20, 30, 40, . . .) or 100 (200, 300, 400, . . .) and then adjust your answer.

To add 52, first add 50, then add 2 more.

To subtract 74, first subtract 70, then subtract 4 more.

To subtract 38, first subtract 40, then add 2.

To add 296, first add 300, then subtract 4.

Write the second step you would use to do each of the following.

1. Add 83. 1) Add 80. 2) Add 3 more.	2. Add 304. 1) Add 300. 2) Add 4 more.	3. Subtract 62. 1) Subtract 60. 2) Subtract 2 more.
4. Add 27. 1) Add 30. 2) Subtract 3.	5. Subtract 79. 1) Subtract 80. 2) Add 1.	6. Subtract 103. 1) Subtract 100. 2) Subtract 3 more.
7. Add 499. 1) Add 294. 2) Subtract 1.	8. Add 294. 1) Add 300. 2) Subtract 6.	9. Subtract 590. 1) Subtract 600. 2) Add 10.

Use the method above to add 59 to each of the following.

10. 40 $40 + 60 - 1 = 99$ 11. 72 $72 + 60 - 1 = 131$ 12. 53 $53 + 60 - 1 = 112$ 13. 15 $15 + 60 - 1 = 74$

Use the method above to subtract 18 from each of the following.

14. 96 $96 - 20 + 2 = 78$ 15. 45 $45 - 20 + 2 = 27$ 16. 71 $71 - 20 + 2 = 53$ 17. 67 $67 - 20 + 2 = 49$

Connections

49. **Statistics** The average of three test scores is found by adding the scores and dividing the sum by 3. Suppose you score 86 and 88 on two tests. What must you score on the third test to have an average of 90? 96

50. **Geometry** The sum of the measures of two angles is 90°. One angle is 48°. Solve the equation $y + 48 = 90$ to find the measure of the second angle. 42°

Applications

51. **Sports** A skateboarder travels 40 meters in 16 seconds. Solve the equation $40 = r \cdot 16$ to find the speed in meters per second. 2.5 m/s

52. **Sports** The attendance at the Houston AstroDome was 35,892 on Friday. This was 3285 less than the attendance on Saturday. Solve the equation $35{,}892 = a - 3285$ to find Saturday's attendance. 39,177

53. See margin.

Critical Thinking

53. Consider the division sentence $\frac{4}{0} = a$ and its related multiplication sentence $4 = 0 \cdot a$. Use these statements to explain why division by zero is not possible.

Wrap-Up

54. **Make Up a Problem** Write a puzzle like the one presented at the beginning of the lesson. Ask a friend to solve it. Sample answer: If you divide a number by 3 and add 5, you get 9. What's the number? 12

Reading Algebra

Study the expressions below. How do the parentheses change the meaning of the expression?

Words	Symbols
three times x plus y	$3x + y$
three times the sum of x and y	$3(x + y)$

In the second expression, parentheses are used to show that the *sum,* $x + y$, is multiplied by three. In algebraic expressions, terms enclosed by parentheses are treated as one quantity. The expression $3(x + y)$ is sometimes read *three times the quantity x plus y.*

In verbal problems, look for key words that indicate that parentheses are to be used. Sometimes the words *sum, difference, quantity,* and *total* signal the use of parentheses. These key words should be helpful as you study the next lesson.

Alternate Strategies: Extending the Lesson

Enrichment

Using Reference Materials

Have students use other books to find simple mathematical formulas. Have students write problems using these formulas. Students can then exchange and solve the problems.

Cooperative Learning

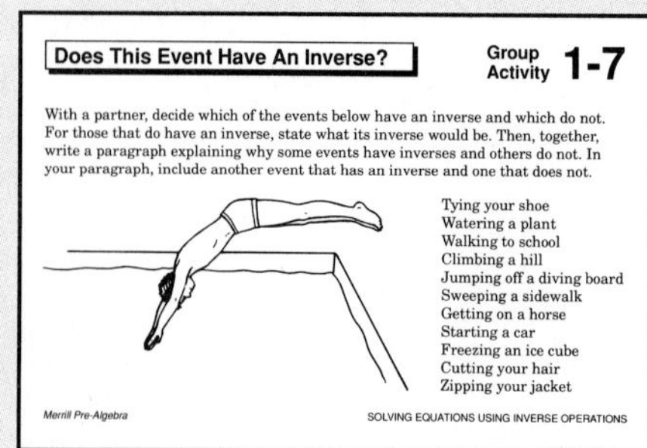

Does This Event Have An Inverse? Group Activity 1-7

With a partner, decide which of the events below have an inverse and which do not. For those that do have an inverse, state what its inverse would be. Then, together, write a paragraph explaining why some events have inverses and others do not. In your paragraph, include another event that has an inverse and one that does not.

Tying your shoe
Watering a plant
Walking to school
Climbing a hill
Jumping off a diving board
Sweeping a sidewalk
Getting on a horse
Starting a car
Freezing an ice cube
Cutting your hair
Zipping your jacket

Merrill Pre-Algebra — SOLVING EQUATIONS USING INVERSE OPERATIONS

1-8 Writing Expressions

Objective:
Translate verbal phrases into algebraic expressions.

Chemists use a system of symbols to write formulas for compounds. For example, H_20 is the chemical formula for water. It means that each water molecule is made up of two atoms of hydrogen (H) and one atom of oxygen (O). This shorthand method saves time and space and shows the pattern that exists between the hydrogen and oxygen molecules.

In the same way, mathematicians can use variables to show patterns in expressions. Suppose that in a certain rectangle, the length is 3 inches more than the width. The chart below shows several possibilities for the width and length.

Width	Length
2	2 + 3 or 5
4	4 + 3 or 7
5	5 + 3 or 8
10	10 + 3 or 13
w	$w + 3$

The algebraic expressions w and $w + 3$ summarize the pattern that exists between the length and the width.

There are many words and phrases that suggest addition and subtraction. The following phrases all suggest the algebraic expressions $n + 4$ or $4 + n$.

$n + 4$ or $4 + n$
a number plus 4 4 more than a number a number increased by 4 the sum of a number and 4

The following phrases all suggest subtraction. The phrases on the left suggest the algebraic expression $n - 3$. The phrases on the right suggest $3 - n$. Notice the difference in the phrases.

$n - 3$
a number decreased by 3 a number minus 3 subtract 3 from a number 3 less than a number

$3 - n$
3 decreased by a number 3 minus a number subtract a number from 3 3 less a number

Chemistry Connection

The formula for common table sugar is $C_{12}H_{22}O_{11}$, where C represents carbon atoms.

The formula for common table salt is NaCl, where Na represents sodium and Cl represents chlorine.

Bell Ringer

Ask students what operations they would use to undo subtraction and to undo multiplication.
addition, division

Lesson Notes 1-8

5-Minute Check
(over Lesson 1-7)

Solve each equation by using the inverse operation. Use a calculator where necessary.

1. $19 = x - 15$ 34
2. $a + 21 = 79$ 58
3. $104 = 8x$ 13
4. $\frac{m}{14} = 9$ 126
5. Evaluate the expression $20a - (5b + 2c)$ if $a = 9$, $b = 4$, and $c = 6$. 148

Transparency 1-8 contains the 5-Minute Check and a teaching aid for this lesson.

1 FOCUS

The purpose of this lesson is to help students translate words into mathematical symbols and vice-versa so that they can communicate with each other and with other people in mathematics.

Play "I'm thinking of a number . . .." again except this time use a letter to represent it and write out the statement. For example, a number plus one divided by eight can be written as x, then $x + 1$, then $(x + 1) \div 8$.

2 TEACH

Using Charts

To help students translate, use the charts on the student page to point out the key words that indicate certain operations. Emphasize that words such as "is" and "equals" indicate equations.

Using Cooperative Groups

Have small groups develop their own statements and expressions and exchange them with other groups to translate.

EE: 1E, 2F, 3A, 5E
TAAS: 12

Chalkboard Examples

Translate each phrase into an algebraic expression.

- *For Example 1*
  Seven more points than team B $b + 7$
- *For Example 2*
  Three less fouls than Chong has $f - 3$
- *For Example 3*
  The product of seven and x $7x$
- *For Example 4*
  The number of chairs divided by 4 $\frac{n}{4}$
- *For Example 5*
  Four times the sum of x and six $4(x + 6)$
- *For Example 6*
  Three times a number increased by five $3n + 5$

Examples

Translate each phrase into an algebraic expression.

1 six more baskets than team B

Let b represent the number of baskets made by team B.
The words *more than* suggest addition.
The algebraic expression is $b + 6$ or $6 + b$.

2 one less foul than Adita has

Let m represent the number of fouls Adita has.
The words *less than* suggest subtraction.
The algebraic expression is $m - 1$.

Likewise, there are many words and phrases that suggest multiplication and division. The following words and phrases all suggest the algebraic expressions $2x$ or $x \cdot 2$.

$2x$ or $x \cdot 2$
2 times a number
the product of 2 and a number
2 multiplied by a number
twice a number

The following phrases suggest division. The phrases on the left suggest the expression $n \div 3$. The phrases on the right suggest $3 \div n$.

$n \div 3$
a number divided by 3
the quotient of n and 3

$3 \div n$
3 divided by a number
the quotient of 3 and n

Examples

Translate each phrase into an algebraic expression.

3 the product of four and y

The words *product of* suggest multiplication.
The expression is $4y$ or $y \cdot 4$.

4 the number of batteries divided by two

Let b represent the number of batteries.
The words *divided by* suggest division.
The expression is $b \div 2$ or $\frac{b}{2}$.

Alternate Strategies: Reteaching the Lesson

Reteaching Activity

Using Cooperative Groups Have one student write a mathematical expression. Have another student write the expression in words. Have a third student then translate the words back to the expression. Compare initial and final expressions. If they differ, verbalize each step to determine what was done incorrectly.

Reteaching Masters Booklet, p. 7

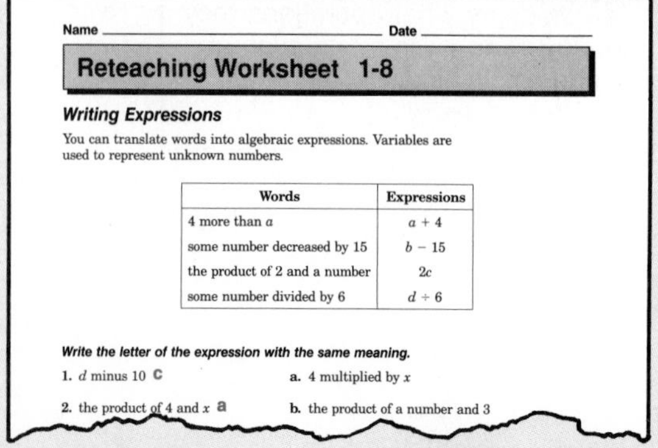

Name ____________ Date ____________

Reteaching Worksheet 1-8

Writing Expressions

You can translate words into algebraic expressions. Variables are used to represent unknown numbers.

Words	Expressions
4 more than a	$a + 4$
some number decreased by 15	$b - 15$
the product of 2 and a number	$2c$
some number divided by 6	$d \div 6$

Write the letter of the expression with the same meaning.

1. d minus 10 c
2. the product of 4 and x a

a. 4 multiplied by x
b. the product of a number and 3

Examples

5 twice the sum of x and nine

In this case, parentheses must be used for the word *sum*. The expression is $2(x + 9)$.

6 twice a number increased by eight

Let n represent the number.
No parentheses are needed.
The expression is $2n + 8$.

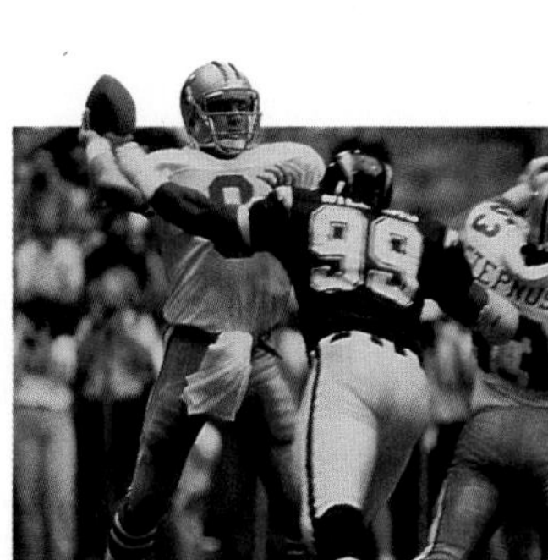

For Exercises 1 and 2, sample answers in margin.
3. the number of games the Cowboys won less 5

Checking for Understanding

Communicating Algebra

1. Write two verbal phrases for the algebraic expression $x + 4$.
2. Write two verbal phrases for the algebraic expression $5y$.
3. If m is the number of games the Cowboys won, what does the expression $m - 5$ represent?
4. Explain the difference between the expressions $x - 5$ and $5 - x$. a number minus 5; 5 minus a number

Guided Practice

Translate each phrase into an algebraic expression.

5. four more than w. $w + 4$
6. the sum of y and 3 $y + 3$
7. nine less than t $t - 9$
8. p decreased by 7 $p - 7$
9. eleven increased by x $11 + x$
10. five less than r $r - 5$
11. the sum of 6 and z $6 + z$
12. the difference of y and 9 $y - 9$
13. twenty minus r $20 - r$
14. twelve plus b $12 + b$
15. x more than eighty $80 + x$
16. twice a certain number $2n$
17. a number divided by seven $n \div 7$
18. fifteen less than m $m - 15$
19. product of z and six $z \cdot 6$
20. quotient of forty-six and y $46 \div y$

Exercises

Independent Practice

21. $j + 10$
23. $a + 300$
24. $2(n + 7)$

Translate each phrase into an algebraic expression.

21. ten more points than Jill scored
22. 3 years younger than Quint $q - 3$
23. Amy's salary plus a \$300 bonus
24. twice the sum of a number and 7
25. twice as many fouls as the Celtics had $2f$
26. three times as many dollars as Tom has $3d$
27. three times a number decreased by 8 $3n - 8$
28. Marty's age divided by four $m \div 4$

Using Connections

To help differentiate Examples 5 and 6 you may want to refer to the Reading Algebra feature on page 38.

3 PRACTICE/APPLY

Checking the Concept

Use the examples to make certain that the students are using key words to assist in their translations.

Error Analysis

Watch for students who are confused by varied syntax when words are used.
Prevent by having students list as many word expressions as possible for each of several different mathematical expressions.

Independent Practice

Homework Assignment	
Basic	21-33 odd, 35-41, 44-46
Average	22-34 even, 35-39, 42-46
Honors	24-34 even, 35-46

Practice Masters Booklet, **p. 8**

Additional Answers

1. the sum of a number and four; a number increased by four
2. five times a number; the product of five and a number

Name ______ Date ______

Practice Worksheet 1-8

Writing Expressions

Translate each phrase into an algebraic expression.

1. six minutes less than Bob's time $t - 6$
2. four points more than the Bearcubs scored $s + 4$ or $4 + s$
3. Joan's temperature increased by two degrees $t + 2$ or $2 + t$
4. the cost decreased by ten dollars $c - 10$
5. the sum of four feet and seven feet $4 + 7$ or $7 + 4$
6. the difference of 150 lb and 8 lb $150 - 8$
7. five more than x $x + 5$ or $5 + x$
8. fifteen less than c $c - 15$
9. three less than a number $n - 3$
10. a number increased by six $n + 6$ or $6 + n$
11. the product of a certain number and nine $n \cdot 9$ or $9n$
12. seven times a certain number $7n$ or $n \cdot 7$
13. twice a number decreased by four $2n - 4$
14. the quotient of ten and five $10 \div 5$ or $\frac{10}{5}$
15. eight decreased by y $8 - y$
16. twice the sum of two and y $2(2 + y)$ or $2(y + 2)$
17. the quotient of x and 2 $x \div 2$ or $\frac{x}{2}$
18. p more than twenty-nine $29 + p$ or $p + 29$
19. fifty minus k $50 - k$
20. sixteen less than m $m - 16$

4 CLOSE

Assessment Option

Writing Give students the width of a desk drawer but not the length. Ask them to write an expression for the perimeter and then write it in simplest form. For example, if the width is 12 in., the perimeter would be $12 + 12 + \ell + \ell$, or $24 + 2\ell$.

Additional Answers

29. a number plus three
30. fifteen minus a number
31. nine times a number
32. a number divided by five
33. two times the sum of a number and three
34. two times a number plus three

Enrichment Masters Booklet, **p. 7**

Name ______________________ Date ______________

Enrichment Worksheet 1-8

Mind Reading

Make four cards having the following numbers and letters.

Ask someone to think of a number from 1 to 15. Then ask the person which cards the number is on.

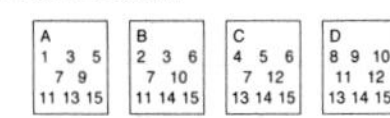

For example, suppose the number appears on cards A, B, and C. Add the least number on each card. This sum is 1 + 2 + 4, or 7. The person's number is 7. **2. C: Beginning with 4, there are four consecutive numbers, four missing numbers, four consecutive numbers; D: Beginning with 8, there are eight consecutive numbers.**

Answer these questions.

1. What is the pattern of the numbers on card A? **They are all odd numbers.**
2. The least number on card B is 2. Note that the next counting number, 3, is also on the card. The next two counting numbers, 4 and 5, are skipped. Then the next two counting numbers, 6 and 7, do appear on the card. This pattern is repeated up to 15. Can you explain the patterns on cards C and D? **See above.**
3. The least numbers on card A through card D are 1, 2, 4, 8. How are these numbers related to the base-two numeration system? **Since $1 = 2^0$, $2 = 2^1$, $4 = 2^2$, and $8 = 2^3$, then $1 = 1_2$, $2 = 10_2$, $4 = 100_2$, and $8 = 1000_2$.**

Tell the number chosen when it appears on the following cards.

4. C and D **12**
5. A, B, and D **11**
6. A, B, C, and D **15**

Each of the following numbers is chosen. Write the corresponding 4-digit base-two numeral. Arrange the cards in base-two place-value position from left to right, D (eights), C (fours), B (twos), A (ones). Interpret 1 as on the card and 0 as not on the card. Use the base-two numeral to tell on which cards each given number appears.

7. 6 **0110_2; DCBA; B and C**
8. 14 **1110_2; DCBA; B, C, and D**
9. 10 **1010_2; DCBA; A and C**

Suppose you want to do this trick with five cards, A through E. Which numbers should appear on each of the following cards?

10. card A
11. card B
12. card C
13. card D
14. card E

10. 1, 3, 5, 7, 9, 11, 13, 15, 17, 19, 21, 23, 25, 27, 29, 31
11. 2, 3, 6, 7, 10, 11, 14, 15, 18, 19, 22, 23, 26, 27, 30, 31
12. 4, 5, 6, 7, 12, 13, 14, 15, 20, 21, 22, 23, 28, 29, 30, 31
13. 8, 9, 10, 11, 12, 13, 14, 15, 24, 25, 26, 27, 28, 29, 30, 31
14. 16, 17, 18, 19, 20, 21, 22, 23, 24, 25, 26, 27, 28, 29, 30, 31

Language Skill **Write a verbal phrase for each algebraic expression.**

29. $x + 3$
30. $15 - y$
31. $9r$
32. $x \div 5$
33. $2(x + 3)$
34. $2x + 3$

For Exercises 29–34, sample answers in margin.

Mixed Review

35. Evaluate the expression $5a - (4b + 2c)$ if $a = 6$, $b = 7$, and $c = 1$. (Lesson 1-2) **35. 0**
36. Simplify the expression $3(4 + a) + 9(2 + 5a)$. (Lesson 1-4) **$48a + 30$**
37. Replace the variable to make the sentence $r + 3 = 7$ true. (Lesson 1-5) **4**
38. Use inverse operations to solve $7x = 182$. (Lesson 1-7) **26**
39. True or false: $14 + 3 = 17$ and $17 - 3 = 14$ are related sentences. (Lesson 1-7) **true**

Connections

40. **Geometry** In a certain rectangle, the length is 20 inches more than the width. Copy and complete the table below.

Width (in.)	5	11	■ **15**	16	w	■ **$z-20$**	$x + 1$
Length (in.)	■ **25**	■ **31**	35	■ **36**	■ **$w + 20$**	z	■ **$x + 21$**

Statistics **Use the information in the graph at the right to answer each question.**

41. If r represents the number of no-hitters that Nolan Ryan pitched, which pitcher can be represented by the expression $r - 2$? **41. Sandy Koufax**
42. If y represents the number of no-hitters Cy Young pitched, which other pitcher can be represented by the expression y? **Bob Feller**
43. If k represents the number of no-hitters Sandy Koufax pitched, write an expression that represents the number of no-hitters Nolan Ryan pitched. **$k + 2$**

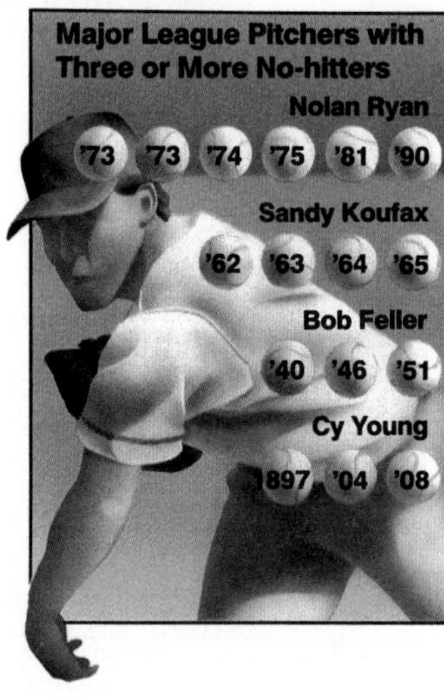

Application

44. **Space Exploration** Suppose you are an astronaut who travels to the moon to collect rock samples. When you get there, you find that you weighed 6 times as much on Earth as you weigh on the moon. Copy and complete the table below.

Weight on the moon (lb)	10	30	50	n	$2n$	**$y \div 6$**
Weight on Earth (lb)	**60**	180	**300**	**$6n$**	**$12n$**	y

Critical Thinking

45. If T represents Tom's age and J represents Jim's age, explain what the sentence $T = J + 5$ means. **Tom is 5 years older than Jim**

Wrap-Up

46. If a represents your present age in years, how old will you be in six years? **$a + 6$**

Alternate Strategies: Extending the Lesson

Enrichment

Using References Using statistics from the sports section in the newspaper, have students write phrases and their corresponding algebraic expressions. For example, if the Reds beat the Pirates by one run, and n is the number of Reds' runs, $n - 1$ is the number of runs for the Pirates.

Cooperative Learning

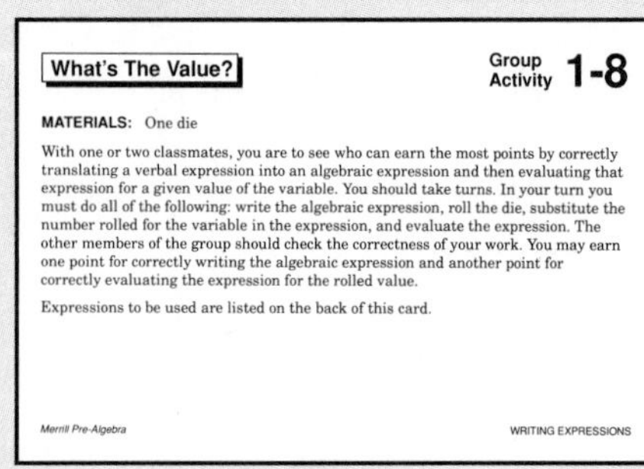
What's The Value? Group Activity **1-8**

MATERIALS: One die

With one or two classmates, you are to see who can earn the most points by correctly translating a verbal expression into an algebraic expression and then evaluating that expression for a given value of the variable. You should take turns. In your turn you must do all of the following: write the algebraic expression, roll the die, substitute the number rolled for the variable in the expression, and evaluate the expression. The other members of the group should check the correctness of your work. You may earn one point for correctly writing the algebraic expression and another point for correctly evaluating the expression for the rolled value.

Expressions to be used are listed on the back of this card.

Merrill Pre-Algebra WRITING EXPRESSIONS

Problem Solving

1-9 Use an Equation

Objective:
Solve problems by using an equation.

Key Term:
defining the variable

In a recent season, Michael Jordan was the leading scorer in the National Basketball Association with 2633 points. He scored 307 points more than the second leading scorer, Karl Malone. How many points did Karl Malone score?

Selecting and trying different strategies are an important part of problem solving in mathematics. You have already used the guess-and-check strategy in this chapter. Another method is to use an equation.

In the following example, the problem above is solved by using an equation.

Example

1 Find the number of points scored by Karl Malone.

Explore Skim the problem for the general idea. You need to find the number of points that Malone scored. Let p represent the number of points that Malone scored. This is called **defining the variable.**

Plan Translate the words into an equation using the variable. *307 more than* suggests addition. Write the equation.

Estimation Hint

Think:
$2600 - 300 = 2300$
The answer should be close to 2300 points.

Solve

points scored by Malone	plus	307	equals	points scored by Jordon
p	$+$	307	$=$	2633

$p + 307 = 2633$
$p = 2633 - 307$ Write the related subtraction sentence.
$p = 2326$

Karl Malone scored 2326 points.

Examine Check the answer against your estimate. Then check the answer in the words of the problem. 2633 points is 307 points more than 2326 points.

Bell Ringer
Make two columns. Put expressions on one side and their phrases on the other. Ask the students to match the expressions and phrases. Answers will vary.

Lesson Notes 1-9

5-Minute Check
(over Lesson 1-8)

Write a verbal phrase for each algebraic expression.

1. $3m$ three times a number
2. $7x + 2$ seven times a number plus two
3. $x \div 8$ a number divided by eight
4. $y - 1$ one less than y
5. $2(a + 5)$ twice the sum of a number and five

Transparency 1-9 contains the 5-Minute Check and a teaching aid for this lesson.

1 FOCUS

The purpose of the lesson is to develop a problem-solving technique that makes use of writing equations.

Motivating the Lesson

If Terry went shopping and spent \$5.99 on a tape, \$1.59 for a hamburger, and 89¢ for a drink, how much did he originally have if he has \$3.45 left? Ask the students which of the following equations is correct. Let x = original amount of money. 1 and 3

1. $3.45 + 5.99 + 1.59 + 0.89 = x$
2. $x + 5.99 + 1.59 + 0.89 = 3.45$
3. $x - 5.99 - 1.59 - 0.89 = 3.45$
4. $3.45 - 5.99 - 1.59 - 0.89 = x$

2 TEACH

Using Cooperative Learning

Have small groups of students collectively make up a word problem that can be solved by first translating the problem into an equation. Groups should exchange problems and solve them.

EE: 1D, 1E, 3A
TAAS: 10, 12, 13

Chalkboard Examples

- *For Example 1*
  Mrs. Baker bought a car for $16,495. Mrs. Snyder bought the same car for $1,500 less. How much did Mrs. Snyder pay for her car? $14,995
- *For Example 2*
  Twelve times some number is equal to 84. Find the number. 7

3 PRACTICE/APPLY

Checking the Concept

The Guided Practice could be done in cooperative groups with additional practice exercises produced by the groups.

Error Analysis

Watch for students who use incorrect operations in writing equations. **Prevent by** emphasizing the need to estimate a reasonable solution.

Example

How can you estimate the answer?
THINK: $20x = 100$, $x \approx 5$

2 Sixteen times some number is equal to 96. Find the number.

Explore You need to find a number. Let n represent the number. When you multiply the number by 16, you get 96.

Plan Translate the words into an equation using the variable.

Sixteen	times	number	equals	ninety-six
16	·	n	=	96

Solve

$16n = 96$

$n = 96 \div 16$ Write the related division sentence.

$n = 6$

The number is 6.

Examine Check your answer against your estimate. Then check the answer in the words of the problem. 16 times 6 is equal to 96.

1. Defining a variable is choosing a letter to represent the unknown quantity.

Checking for Understanding

Communicating Algebra

1. Explain what it means to *define a variable.*
2. Why should you check your answer in the words of the problem instead of in the equation? because your equation could be incorrect

Guided Practice

Translate each sentence into an equation.

3. Twice a certain number is 6. $2x = 6$
4. A number divided by 5 is 3. $x \div 5 = 3$
5. Four more than a number is 12. $x + 4 = 12$
6. Six less than a number is zero. $x - 6 = 0$
7. When a number is decreased by 5, the result is 7. $x - 5 = 7$
8. Twenty-seven more than a number is thirty-one. $x + 27 = 31$
9. Forty-two less than a number is sixty. $x - 42 = 60$
10. A number divided by three is 13. $x \div 3 = 13$

Practice Masters Booklet, **p. 9**

Name ____________ Date ____________

Practice Worksheet 1-9

Problem Solving: Use an Equation

Define a variable, write an equation, then solve.

1. During Saturday's game, the football team gained 87 yards rushing and 213 yards passing. How many more yards were gained passing than rushing? Let n = extra yards; $n + 87 = 213$; 126 yards
2. In a contest, 10,000 points are needed to win the grand prize. Kent has earned 7975 points so far. How many more points does he need in order to win the grand prize? Let p = points needed; $p + 7975 = 10{,}000$; 2025 points
3. The earth is about 93,000,000 miles from the sun. When Venus is on the opposite side of the sun from the earth, it is about 69,000,000 miles from the sun. What is the distance from the earth to Venus? Let d = distance from earth to Venus; $d = 93{,}000{,}000 + 69{,}000{,}000$; 162,000,000 miles
4. The distance by water from New York City to San Francisco by way of Cape Horn is about 13,200 miles. By going through the Panama Canal, the distance is only 5280 miles. How many miles does a ship save by going through the Panama Canal? Let m = miles saved; $m = 13{,}200 - 5280$; 7920 miles
5. Nicholas sold 86 newspapers on Monday, 79 on Tuesday, 68 on Wednesday, and 83 on Friday. How many newspapers did Nicholas sell on Thursday if he sold a total of 391 in the five days? Let n = newspapers sold on Thursday; $86 + 79 + 68 + 83 + n = 391$; 75 newspapers
6. Mrs. Walsh plans to drive from New York to Chicago, a distance of 850 miles. How long will it take her to make the trip if she averages 50 miles per hour? Let t = time; $850 = 50t$; 17 hours
7. A student earned 85 points on each of six weekly quizzes. For turning in his homework, he earned another 10 points each week. What is his total number of points for the six weeks? Let n = total points; $n = 6(85 + 10)$; 570 points
8. An automobile dealer sold 28 cars during April at an average price per car of $8689. What was the total selling price of all the cars? Let t = total selling price; $t \div 28 = 8689$; $243,292
9. The average daily attendance at the Lincoln School was 348 students during the month of March. If the month had 21 school days, what was the total attendance? Let a = total attendance; $a \div 21 = 348$; 7308 students
10. Mrs. Hill drove a school bus 8832 miles last year. School was in session 184 days. Find the average number of miles she drove each day. Let a = average number of miles; $a = 8832 \div 184$; 48 miles

Alternate Strategies: Reteaching the Lesson

Reteaching Activity

Solving a Simpler Problem Rewrite several problems from the lesson using student names and smaller numbers. For example, problem number 15 on page 45 could be rewritten as: Ann earned $50 last week. She worked 10 hours. How much did she earn per hour?

Reteaching Masters Booklet, **p. 8**

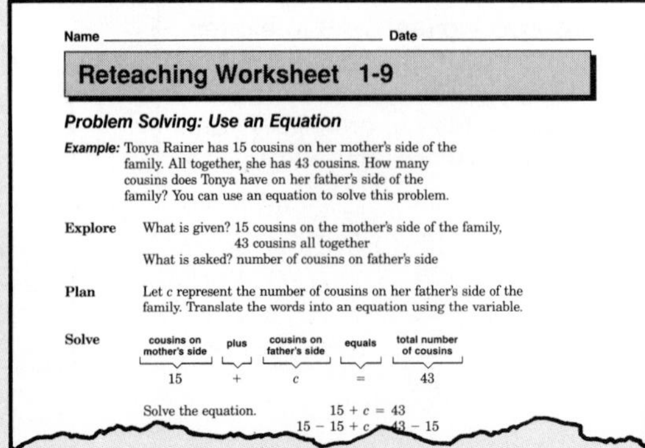

Name ____________ Date ____________

Reteaching Worksheet 1-9

Problem Solving: Use an Equation

Example: Tonya Rainer has 15 cousins on her mother's side of the family. All together, she has 43 cousins. How many cousins does Tonya have on her father's side of the family? You can use an equation to solve this problem.

Explore What is given? 15 cousins on the mother's side of the family, 43 cousins all together
What is asked? number of cousins on father's side

Plan Let c represent the number of cousins on her father's side of the family. Translate the words into an equation using the variable.

Solve

cousins on mother's side	plus	cousins on father's side	equals	total number of cousins
15	+	c	=	43

Solve the equation. $15 + c = 43$
$15 - 15 + c = 43 - 15$

Exercises

Independent Practice — **Define a variable, write an equation, then solve.**

11. Joe paid \$15 for a shirt on sale. It was reduced by \$9. What was the regular price? *(Answer: $x - 9 = 15$; \$24)*
12. Together two items cost \$16. One item costs \$7. What is the cost of the other item? *(Answer: $x + 7 = 16$; \$9)*
13. One season the Pittsburgh Pirates lost 72 games. They won 18 games more than they lost. How many games did they win? *(Answer: $x - 18 = 72$; 90 games)*
14. The 4-person relay team ran a race in 48 seconds. What was the average time for each person? $4x = 48$; 12 seconds
15. Clara Hardin earned \$175 last week. She worked 35 hours. How much did she earn per hour? $35x = 175$; \$5
16. In a recent year 4635 runners started the Fairfield Marathon. Only 2338 finished the race. How many runners did not finish? *(Answer: $x + 2338 = 4635$; 2297 runners)*
17. One season Roger Maris and Mickey Mantle hit a total of 117 home runs. Maris hit 61 that year. How many did Mantle hit? $x + 61 = 117$; 56 home runs

Mixed Review

18. Use inverse operations to solve $14 = z - 31$. (Lesson 1-7) 45
19. Write an algebraic expression for the phrase *twice a certain number.* (Lesson 1-8) $2n$
20. Write a verbal phrase for the algebraic expression $3(x + 2)$. (Lesson 1-8) three times the sum of a number and two

Decision Making — **Solve this problem using mental math skills, estimation, or paper and pencil. Explain your method.**

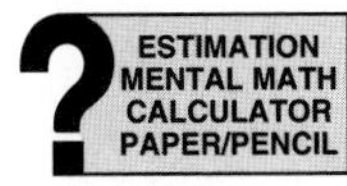

21. Felicia wants to buy 4 chrome wheels for her car. She can spend no more than \$74 per wheel. A local newspaper advertises 4 wheels on sale for \$320. They usually cost \$359. Can Felicia afford to buy the wheels? no

Critical Thinking

22. One-half of Celia's age increased by 12 is her sister's age. If her sister is 18 years old, how old is Celia? 12 years old

Wrap-Up

23. **Make Up a Problem** Write a problem based on this information: Let x = the number of students present in Mr. Wyatt's class. Use the equation $x + 5 = 33$. Sample answer in margin.

Independent Practice

Homework Assignment	
Basic	11-15, 18-23
Average	11-15, 18-23
Honors	13-23

4 CLOSE

Assessment Option

Speaking Have students verbalize the correct way to read the following equation. Then have them make up a problem for the equation. $9 - x = 5$

Nine minus x equals five. Sample answer: I made \$9.00 babysitting and had \$5 left after I bought some socks. How much were the socks?

Additional Answer

23. A total of 33 students are enrolled in Mr. Wyatt's class. Five students were out sick on Monday. How many students were in Mr. Wyatt's class on Monday?

Enrichment Masters Booklet, **p. 8**

Name ______________ Date ______________

Enrichment Worksheet 1-9

Four Fours

In mathematics, there are many ways to express numbers. For instance, the number five can be expressed as 5, V, 4 + 1, 10 ÷ 2, 2 + 3, 8 − 3, 20 ÷ 4, and so on.

Operations can be combined to produce a desired result. For example, the number one can be expressed using four fours as shown below.

$\frac{4+4}{4+4} = 1 \quad \frac{4 \times 4}{4 \times 4} = 1 \quad \frac{4}{4} \times \frac{4}{4} = 1 \quad \frac{44}{44} = 1$

Use four fours to express each result. Other answers are possible.

1. 2 $\frac{4}{4} + \frac{4}{4}$
2. 5 $\frac{4 \times 4 + 4}{4}$
3. 7 $4 + 4 - \frac{4}{4}$
4. 6 $\frac{4 + 4}{4} + 4$
5. 9 $4 + 4 + \frac{4}{4}$
6. 3 $\frac{4 + 4 + 4}{4}$
7. 8 $4 + 4 + 4 - 4$
8. 17 $4 \times 4 + \frac{4}{4}$
9. 16 $4 + 4 + 4 + 4$
10. 0 $4 - 4 + 4 - 4$
11. 4 $\frac{4 - 4}{4} + 4$
12. 15 $4 \times 4 - \frac{4}{4}$
13. 10 $\frac{44 - 4}{4}$
14. 12 $\frac{44 + 4}{4}$

Alternate Strategies: Extending the Lesson

Enrichment

Working in Pairs Have students create problems involving a collection of coins having the same denomination. A sample problem if 5 nickels are used might be: *I have some nickels. If I had 5¢ more I would have 30¢. How many nickels do I have?* Have the other student write an equation to represent the problem and solve the equation. Then switch roles.

Cooperative Learning

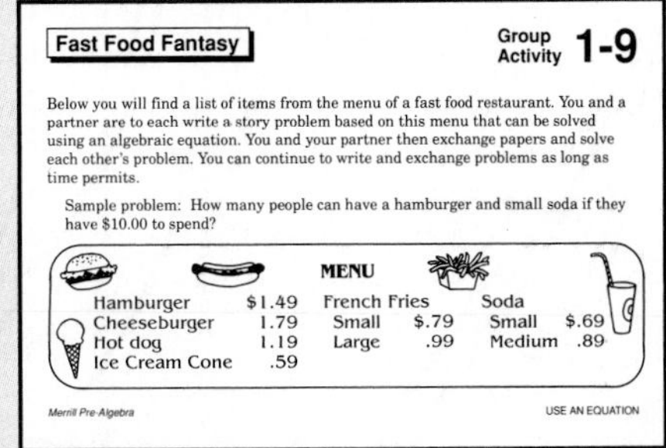

Fast Food Fantasy — Group Activity **1-9**

Below you will find a list of items from the menu of a fast food restaurant. You and a partner are to each write a story problem based on this menu that can be solved using an algebraic equation. You and your partner then exchange papers and solve each other's problem. You can continue to write and exchange problems as long as time permits.

Sample problem: How many people can have a hamburger and small soda if they have \$10.00 to spend?

MENU

Item	Price	French Fries	Price	Soda	Price
Hamburger	\$1.49	Small	\$.79	Small	\$.69
Cheeseburger	1.79	Large	.99	Medium	.89
Hot dog	1.19				
Ice Cream Cone	.59				

Merrill Pre-Algebra USE AN EQUATION

Lesson Notes 1-10

5-Minute Check
(over Lesson 1-9)

Define a variable, write an equation, then solve.

1. Olga paid $18 for a blouse on sale. It was reduced by $5. What was the regular price? $23

Transparency 1-10 contains the 5-Minute Check and a teaching aid for this lesson.

1 FOCUS

The purpose of the lesson is to introduce open sentence inequalities as a parallel to open sentences that are equations.

2 TEACH

Chalkboard Examples

For the given value, state whether each inequality is true or false.

- *For Example 1*
  $y - 7 \le 9, y = 15$ true
- *For Example 2*
  $23 \ge \frac{4x}{2} + 6, x = 8$ true

Practice Masters Booklet, **p. 10**

Name ____________ Date ____________

Practice Worksheet 1-10

Inequalities

State whether each inequality is true or false for the given value.

1. $b + 10 < 12, b = 4$ false
2. $3 < x - 8, x = 12$ true
3. $6m + 3 \le 8, m = 1$ false
4. $12 \le 2p - 6, p = 9$ true
5. $k - 12 < 18, k = 31$ false
6. $13 > 4 + c, c = 9$ false
7. $15 + n \ge 15, n = 6$ true
8. $2 \ge l - 3, l = 3$ true
9. $4t - 4 < 20, t = 7$ false
10. $29 < 24 + a, a = 6$ true
11. $10 \ge 2e + 4, e = 4$ false
12. $5v > 25, v = 4$ false
13. $21 < \frac{r}{3}, r = 66$ true
14. $\frac{s}{8} \ge 4, s = 32$ true
15. $5w + 8 \le 12, w = 0$ true
16. $2y - 7 < 41, y = 16$ true
17. $3z + z - 6 < 11, z = 4$ true
18. $5f - 2f + 3 \ge 9, f = 2$ true
19. $6h - 3 > 15, h = 2$ false
20. $81 + 3d \ge 90, d = 2$ false
21. $7g - 14 > 0, g = 3$ true
22. $9 \le 5j - 6, j = 3$ true

Evaluate each expression if a = 2, b = 4, and c = 6. Then write >, <, or = in the box to make a true sentence.

23. bc [>] ac
24. $c + 6$ [<] $3a + 2c$
25. $5b - 2a$ [=] $4b$
26. $3c$ [=] $2b + 4a + 2$
27. $4c - 5b$ [>] $b - a$
28. $5c - 3b - a + 16$ [>] 0

1-10 Inequalities

Objective:
Use inequalities.

Key Term:
inequality

Name a number that is a solution of $x < 4$. Then name a number that is not a solution. **1; 5**

Under normal conditions, water is in the form of a liquid at temperatures between 32° F and 212° F. When the temperature is less than 32° F, water is in the form of ice. At temperatures above 212° F, water is in the form of steam.

If we let the variable t represent the temperature, we can write mathematical sentences to describe the temperatures for ice or steam.

Say: *t is less than* 32
Write: $t < 32$ — Water is in the form of ice.

Say: *t is greater than* 212
Write: $t > 212$ — Water is in the form of steam.

Any mathematical sentence that contains < or > is called an **inequality.** Inequalities, just like equations, can be true, false, or open.

$15 > 12$	This sentence is true.
$8 < 3$	This sentence is false.
$x < 4$	This is an open sentence. It is neither true nor false until x is replaced with a number.

The symbols ≤ and ≥ can also be used in inequalities. They are combinations of the equal sign and the inequality symbol.

Say: *x is less than or equal to* 5
Write: $x \le 5$

Say: *y is greater than or equal to* 7
Write: $y \ge 7$

Examples

For the given value, state whether each inequality is *true* or *false*.

1 $y - 9 > 6, y = 12$

$12 - 9 > 6$

$3 > 6$

This sentence is false.

2 $12 \ge \frac{2k}{9} + 8, k = 18$

$12 \ge \frac{2 \cdot 18}{9} + 8$

$12 \ge 4 + 8$

$12 \ge 12$

This sentence is true.

FYI

Americans use more than 400 billion gallons of water daily.

Bell Ringer

Ask students the number of the month their birthday is in. Use an equation to see how many months older one student is than the other.

EE: 1E, 2F, 3A, 3F, 3H
TAAS: 2, 12

Reteaching Masters Booklet, **p. 9**

Name ____________ Date ____________

Reteaching Worksheet 1-10

Inequalities

An **inequality** is a number sentence which states that two expressions are *not* equal. Four symbols for inequality are >, <, ≥, and ≤. Notice that the point of the V-shaped symbol points toward the lesser expression.

$2 + 2 > 3$	Two plus two is greater than 3.
$2 + 2 \ge 3$	Two plus two is greater than or equal to 3.
$2 + 2 \ge 4$	Two plus two is greater than or equal to 4.
$2 + 2 < 5$	Two plus two is less than 5.
$2 + 2 \le 5$	Two plus two is less than or equal to 5.
$2 + 2 \le 4$	Two plus two is less than or equal to 4.

Translate each statement into an algebraic inequality.

1. x is less than 10.
   $x < 10$
2. 20 is greater than or equal to y.
   $20 \ge y$

Checking for Understanding

Communicating Algebra

1. Which symbol is read *is greater than or equal to*, $>$ or $\geq$? $\geq$
2. Name a value for x in which $2x > 1$ is false. 0
3. Write a sentence that explains the difference between an equation and an inequality. In an equation, both sides are equal; in an inequality, one side is greater than the other side.

Guided Practice

State whether each inequality is *true, false* or *open*.

4. $7 > 2$ True
5. $5 < 3$ False
6. $x + 2 > 7$ Open
7. $3 \geq 2$ True
8. $0 \leq 6$ True
9. $3x - 7 \geq 5$ Open
10. $x - 2 \leq 9$ Open
11. $5 > 6(2)$ False

State whether each inequality is *true* or *false* for the given value.

12. $r + 2 \geq 7, r = 6$ True
13. $14 \geq m + 6, m = 4$ True
14. $3t \geq 7, t = 0$ False
15. $2 < 2x - 5, x = 3$ False

Exercises

Independent Practice

State whether each inequality is *true* or *false* for the given value.

16. $5k + 10 < 20, k = 2$ False
17. $15 < 3m + 7, m = 4$ True
18. $0 < 3r - 5, r = 2$ True
19. $2r - 7 \leq 7, r = 7$ True
20. $3x + 2x - 9 \geq 17, x = 6$ True
21. $3x - 12 > 0, x = 4$ False

Evaluate each expression if $a = 3$, $b = 2$, and $c = 7$. Then replace each ■ with <, >, or = to make a true sentence.

22. ab ■ c <
23. $a + 2b$ ■ $c + 7$ <
24. $3a - 2b$ ■ $c + b$ <
25. $2c$ ■ $3a + 2b + 1$ =
26. $5a - 2c$ ■ $3b$ <
27. $4a + b - c$ ■ 0 >

Mixed Review

28. Use inverse operations to solve $17 = n + 8$. (Lesson 1-7) 9
29. Write an algebraic expression for the phrase *the quotient of 18 and y.* (Lesson 1-8) $18 \div y$
30. Write an equation for the sentence: *Six less than a number is 15.* (Lesson 1-9)
31. Write an equation and solve: Four swimmers swam a relay race in 56 seconds. What was the average time for each swimmer? (Lesson 1-9)

30. $x - 6 = 15$
31. $4t = 56$; 14 seconds

Applications

32. **Sports** The Mets are losing to the Astros by a score of 5 to 3. Write an inequality that would tell how many runs would give the Astros the lead.
33. **Recreation** During the last few years, in-line skating has become a popular pastime. Today there are about 400,000 people who participate in this sport. This is more than twice as many people as there were several years ago. Which inequality, $s > 200{,}000$ or $s < 200{,}000$, describes how many skaters there were several years ago? $s < 200{,}000$

32. $3 + x > 5$

Critical Thinking

34. If $x > 3$ and $x < 15$, explain what the open sentence $3 < x < 15$ means.

34. x is between 3 and 15.

Wrap-Up

35. Find at least two values for x that make $2x + 3 \geq 7$ true. Find two values for x that make it false. Sample answers: true: 2, 3; False: 0, 1

3 PRACTICE/APPLY

Checking the Concept

Ask students to compare inequalities to equations.

Error Analysis

Watch for students who reverse the greater than and less than signs.
Prevent by emphasizing that the smaller end of either sign points to the lesser number.

Independent Practice

Homework Assignment	
Basic	16-27 odd, 28-35
Average	19-24, 28-35
Honors	22-35

4 CLOSE

Assessment Option

Writing Use the *Guinness Book of World Records* to have students write inequality statements. For example, what would you have to do to be in the book for the long jump? (Jump more than □ feet, or $x >$ □).

Enrichment Masters Booklet, **p. 9**

Name ______ Date ______

Enrichment Worksheet 1-10

Make Up a Problem

You have seen that some problem situations can be solved using variables and open sentences. Usually in math, you are asked to solve problems. In this activity, you will be writing the problems.

Use the open sentence, story idea, and your imagination to write an interesting word problem. Answers will vary. Sample answers are given.

1. $x + 4 = 83$
   scores on a chapter test
   Betty outscored Sam by four points on the chapter test. She scored 83. What was Sam's score?
2. $15 - x \leq 10$
   money spent on clothes
   Jill has $15 to spend on a belt and earrings. She does not want to spend more than $10 on the belt. What is the most she can spend on the earrings?
3. $12 + v = 20$
   a team's won/loss record
   The Bulldogs have played 20 games this season. They have lost 12 games. How many have they won?
4. $9 > p - 10$
   people at a party
   A certain number of people were at a party. Then 10 people left. If there were less than 9 people left at the party, how many were there at the start?
5. $13 + y \geq 21$
   ages
   Bill will graduate from college when he is at least 21. If Bill is 13 now, in how many years will he finish college?
6. $36 + h = 47$
   temperatures
   When I got up this morning, the temperature was 36°F. It warmed up to 47°F by noon. How many degrees had the temperature risen by noon?

Alternate Strategies: Extending the Lesson

Enrichment

Using Logical Reasoning Give students the following information. *Mary runs faster than Joe, and Joe runs faster than Amy. Karin is the fastest. Joe ran 300 yards in 58 seconds and Mary ran 300 yards in 52 seconds.* Ask students to express Amy's time. Amy's time is more than 58 seconds.

Cooperative Learning

Is That True? Group Activity **1-10**

MATERIALS: Deck of "Inequality Cards" (see back) • 0-9 spinner

To begin this game for two players, shuffle the "Inequality Cards" and place them in a pile face down. Draw the top card and place it so both of you can see it. You then spin the spinner. The resulting number is substituted for the letter "a" in the inequality. Mentally determine if, using that number, the inequality is a true or false statement and state that fact.

Player two's task is to decide if you are correct. You score one point if you answered correctly. Player two then draws a card and play continues as before. After the 10 cards are used once, they are shuffled and used again.

The first player to score 10 points wins.

$5a \leq 25$

$\frac{a}{2} + 3 \leq 4a$

Merrill Pre-Algebra INEQUALITIES

Using the Chapter Review

The Chapter Review is a comprehensive review of the concepts presented in this chapter. This review may be used to prepare students for the Chapter Test.

Alternate Review Strategy

To provide a brief in-class review, you may wish to read the following questions to the class and require a verbal response.

1. Find the value of 51 divided by 3 plus 17. 34
2. Evaluate $2a - b \times 3$ if $a = 9$, and $b = 6$. 0
3. What property is involved when you add zero to a number? identity
4. Simplify $6x + 3y + 2x$. $8x + 3y$
5. Mentally solve $10 = c - 11$. 21
6. A number divided by 13 is 4. What is the number? Use the guess-and-check strategy. 52
7. Use the inverse operation to solve $34 = a \times 2$. $a = 17$
8. Translate *twice a number increased by 8* into a mathematical expression. $2n + 8$
9. Translate *thirty-six more than b is 47* into an equation. Solve the equation. $b + 36 = 47$; $b = 11$
10. Is $2 \leq 8x - 1$ true if x is 2? yes

Chapter 1, Quiz B (Lessons 1-6 through 1-10) is available in the Evaluation Masters Booklet, p. 7.

Review

Language and Concepts

Choose the correct term to complete each sentence.

1. When you replace a variable in an equation so that a true sentence results, you have (evaluated, <u>solved</u>) the equation.
2. Mathematical sentences like $x + 3 = 10$ and $2y = 14$ are examples of (<u>equations</u>, inequalities).
3. If an expression contains only the operations of multiplication and addition, you would (add, <u>multiply</u>) first.
4. If an expression contains an addition operation in parentheses and a multiplication operation not in parentheses, you would (<u>add</u>, multiply) first.
5. The inequality ($x \geq 2$, <u>$x \leq 2$</u>) means *x is less than or equal to 2.*

Skills

Find the value of each expression. (Lesson 1-1)

6. $47 - 7 \times 5$ 12
7. $72 \div 12 \times 3$ 18
8. $18 + 12 \div 3 - 6$ 16
9. $4 \cdot 3 + 8 \div 2 - 5$ 11
10. $(36 \div 6) \div (6 - 4)$ 3
11. $7[(29 + 11) - 3(16 - 9)]$ 133

Evaluate each expression if $a = 12$, $b = 11$, $k = 8$, and $s = 14$. (Lesson 1-2)

12. $29 + a - s$ 27
13. $2a - 9$ 15
14. $a - k$ 4
15. $b + (a - k)$ 15
16. $3a + 2b - k$ 50
17. $a / 3 + b$ 15

Name the property shown by each statement. (Lessons 1-3, 1-4)

18. $16 + 4 = 4 + 16$ comm of add
19. $317 + 0 = 317$ identity of add
20. $(7 + y) + 2 = 7 + (y + 2)$ assoc of add
21. $r \cdot 1 = r$ identity of mult
22. $8(6 \cdot 9) = (8 \cdot 6)9$ assoc of mult
23. $2(2 + 5) = 2 \cdot 2 + 2 \cdot 5$ distributive

Simplify each expression. (Lessons 1-3, 1-4)

24. $2(3y)$ $6y$
25. $3 + (4 + x)$ $7 + x$
26. $a + 9a$ $10a$
27. $2a + 3a + 10$ $5a + 10$
28. $8 + 36y - 14y$ $8 + 22y$
29. $4(a + 3) + 10a$ $14a + 12$

Solve each equation mentally. (Lesson 1-5)

30. $y + 3 = 15$ 12
31. $2x = 10$ 5
32. $16 = 25 - t$ 9
33. $\frac{m}{4} = 9$ 36
34. $a + 15 = 25$ 10
35. $4x = 20$ 5

Solve each equation by using the inverse operation. (Lesson 1-7)

36. $b + 48 = 55$ 7
37. $y - 57 = 72$ 129
38. $y + 12 = 33$ 21
39. $\frac{x}{2} = 18$ 36
40. $32m = 384$ 12
41. $672 = 21t$ 32

Translate each phrase into an algebraic expression. (Lesson 1-8)

42. *five more than x* $x + 5$
43. *the product of b and 5* $5b$
44. *ten less than y* $y - 10$
45. *a number divided by 6* $n \div 6$

State whether each inequality is true or false for the given value. (Lesson 1-10)

46. $3x > 15, x = 6$ true
47. $m + 9 < 15, m = 3$ true
48. $3x - 12 \geq 0, x = 4$ true
49. $2y + y > 21, y = 7$ false

Applications and Problem Solving

50. The sum of a number and itself is 92. Use the guess-and-check strategy to find the number. (Lesson 1-6) 46

Communicating Algebra

In your own words, explain why 12 is not a solution of the equation $2x + 5 = 30$.
If $x = 12$, then two times x plus 5 equals 29. Since 29 does not equal 30, 12 is not a solution of the equation.

Curriculum Connection

- **Science** Find an example of an equation in your science book. Explain how you use the Substitution property in science. Sample answer in margin.
- **Social Studies** In the chapter opener, you were asked to estimate how long it would take to pass a basketball across the country. Find the distance in miles across your state. Estimate how long it would take to pass the basketball across your state. See students' work.

Read More About It

Berry, Marilyn. *Help Is on the Way for Math Skills.*
Mango, Karin N. *Codes, Ciphers, and Other Secrets.*
Tobias, Sheila. *Succeed with Math.*

You may wish to use a Chapter Test (free-response format) as an additional chapter review. Two forms are provided in the Evaluation Masters Booklet as shown below.

Evaluation Masters Booklet, **p. 5**

Name ______ Date ______

Chapter 1 Test, Form 2A

Find the value of each expression.
1. $56 - 16 \div 8$ 2. $22 \cdot 2 + 3 \cdot 3$
3. $10 - 5 \cdot 2$ 4. $12 + 12 \div 3 \cdot 2$

Evaluate each expression if m = 3, r = 7, and t = 8.
5. $m + 13$ 6. $9 - r + t$
7. $m + r - t - 2$ 8. $rt - mt$
9. $r + t - m + t$ 10. $6r + 3m$

Name the property shown by each sentence.
11. $(8 + 12) + 15 = 8 + (12 + 15)$
12. $5 + x = x + 5$
13. $5(6 + 3) = 5 \cdot 6 + 5 \cdot 3$
14. $11 = 11 + 0$
15. $12 \cdot 0 = 0$
16. $3 \cdot (8 \cdot 4) = 3 \cdot (4 \cdot 8)$
17. $5 \cdot (2 \cdot 3) = (5 \cdot 2) \cdot 3$
18. $14 + x = 14$

Solve each equation. Check your solutions.
19. $28 = a + 15$ 20. $39 = t - 42$
21. $p + 47 = 71$ 22. $y - 16 = 5$

Solve each problem.
23. This week's game attracted 26 fewer fans than last week's game. If 342 fans came last week, how many fans attended this week?
24. John has 236 baseball cards. Juan has 36 more cards than John has. How many cards does Juan have?
25. Maria worked twice as many hours on Tuesday as she worked on Monday. She worked 4 hours Tuesday. How many hours did she work Monday?

BONUS Is $3 + x < 12$ true, false, or open?

1. 54
2. 53
3. 0
4. 20
5. 16
6. 10
7. 0
8. 32
9. 20
10. 51
11. Assoc., Add.
12. Comm., Add.
13. Distrib.
14. Add. Ident.
15. Mult. of Zero
16. Comm., Mult.
17. Assoc., Mult.
18. Add. Ident.
19. 13
20. 81
21. 24
22. 21
23. 316 fans
24. 272 cards
25. 2 hours
open

Evaluation Masters Booklet, **p.6**

Name ______ Date ______

Chapter 1 Test, Form 2B

Find the value of each expression.
1. $56 - 16 \div 4$ 2. $18 \cdot 2 + 5 \cdot 3$
3. $12 - 5 \cdot 2$ 4. $9 + 12 \div 3 \cdot 2$

Evaluate each expression if m = 5, r = 7, and t = 9.
5. $m + 15$ 6. $8 - r + t$
7. $m + r - t - 1$ 8. $rt - mt$
9. $r + t - m + t$ 10. $4r + 2m$

Name the property shown by each sentence.
11. $4 \cdot n = 4$
12. $14 + x = 14$
13. $2(m + 3) = 2 \cdot m + 2 \cdot 3$
14. $0 = 11 \cdot 0$
15. $12 + 0 = 12$
16. $3 + (8 + 4) = 3 + (4 + 8)$
17. $8 + m = m + 8$
18. $(6 + 8) + 10 = 6 + (8 + 10)$

Solve each equation. Check your solutions.
19. $26 = x - 15$ 20. $59 = t + 42$
21. $a + 15 = 73$ 22. $x - 12 = 6$

Solve each problem.
23. This week's game attracted 45 fewer fans than last week's game. If 826 fans came last week, how many fans attended this week?
24. Fred has 125 baseball cards. Mack has 18 more cards than Fred has. How many cards does Mack have?
25. Maria worked half as many hours on Tuesday as she worked on Monday. She worked 4 hours Tuesday. How many hours did she work Monday?

BONUS Is $3 + x < 12$ true, false, or open, if $x = 10$?

1. 52
2. 51
3. 2
4. 17
5. 20
6. 10
7. 2
8. 18
9. 20
10. 38
11. Mult. Ident.
12. Add. Ident.
13. Distrib.
14. Mult. of Zero
15. Add. Ident.
16. Comm., Add.
17. Comm., Add.
18. Assoc. Add.
19. 41
20. 17
21. 58
22. 18
23. 781 fans
24. 143 cards
25. 8 hours
false

Additional Answer

Science Connection Sample answer: Density = $\frac{mass}{volume}$; Use the substitution property to replace the variables *mass* and *volume* with actual values.

Using the Chapter Test
This page may be used as a test or as an additional review. Two forms of a Chapter Test (multiple-choice format) are provided in the Evaluation Masters Booklet.

Evaluation Masters Booklet, **pp. 1-2**

Name ______________________ Date ____________

Chapter 1 Test, Form 1A

1. What is the value of $3 + 2 \cdot 4$?
   A. 24 B. 20 C. 11 D. 9 — 1. C
2. What is the value of $6 + 8 - 2$?
   A. 10 B. 7 C. 11 D. 12 — 2. D
3. What is the value of $2 \cdot 5 - 3 \cdot 2$?
   A. 14 B. 4 C. 8 D. 6 — 3. B
4. What is the value of $a - b + 6$ if $a = 15$ and $b = 9$?
   A. 30 B. 18 C. 0 D. 12 — 4. D
5. What is the value of $j + p - 29$ if $j = 38$ and $p = 8$?
   A. 1 B. 13 C. 17 D. 7 — 5. C
6. What is the value of $a \cdot b + a \cdot c$ if $a = 3$, $b = 4$, and $c = 5$?
   A. 27 B. 15 C. 20 D. 22 — 6. A
7. What property of addition is shown by $8 + 4 = 4 + 8$?
   A. Associative B. Commutative C. Additive Identity D. Additive Inverse — 7. B
8. What property of addition is shown by $3 + 0 = 3$?
   A. Associative B. Commutative C. Additive Identity D. Additive Inverse — 8. C
9. What property of addition is shown by $8 + (s + t) = (8 + s) + t$?
   A. Associative B. Commutative C. Additive Identity D. Additive Inverse — 9. A
10. Rewrite $(2 + 3) + 4$ using the associative property.
    A. $3 \cdot (2 + 4)$ B. $2 + (3 + 4)$ C. $4 + (2 + 3)$ D. $(3 + 2) + 4$ — 10. B
11. What is the solution for $24 = x + 17$?
    A. 31 B. 41 C. 17 D. 7 — 11. D
12. What is the solution for $m - 28 = 57$?
    A. 85 B. 29 C. 75 D. 39 — 12. A
13. What is the solution for $86 = 39 + y$?
    A. 57 B. 53 C. 47 D. 125 — 13. C
14. What is the solution for $66 = w - 18$?
    A. 48 B. 84 C. 88 D. 46 — 14. B

Name ______________________ Date ____________

Chapter 1 Test, Form 1A (continued)

15. What is the solution for k if the sum of k and 19 is 26?
    A. 11 B. 45 C. 501 D. 7 — 15. D
16. What is the solution for r if the difference of r and 12 is 16?
    A. 28 B. 4 C. 192 D. 10 — 16. A
17. The expression *three miles more than Skip jogged* translates into what mathematical expression?
    A. $3 - j$ B. $3 \cdot j$ C. $j - 3$ D. $j + 3$ — 17. D
18. The expression *two more than six* translates into what mathematical expression?
    A. $6 + 2$ B. $6 \cdot 2$ C. $6 - 2$ D. $2 \div 6$ — 18. A
19. The expression *seven decreased by y* translates into what mathematical expression?
    A. $7 - y$ B. $7 \div y$ C. $7 + y$ D. $y \div 7$ — 19. A
20. The sentence *twice a number is 16* translates into what equation?
    A. $2x = 16$ B. $2 + x = 16$ C. $16 \cdot 2 = x$ D. $16 + 16 = x$ — 20. A
21. What word describes the inequality $4k + 4 < 20$ if $k = 5$?
    A. true B. false C. open D. addition — 21. B
22. What word describes the inequality $4x - 5 < 20$ if $x = 5$?
    A. true B. false C. open D. subtraction — 22. A
23. What word describes the inequality $9x + 3 < 21$?
    A. true B. false C. open D. addition — 23. C
24. Mary gave Ed 12 cents. Ed now has 48 cents. How many cents did Ed have before receiving Mary's gift?
    A. 60 B. 12 C. 36 D. 4 — 24. C
25. Jim caught 3 more fish than Tony caught. Tony caught t fish. How many fish did Jim catch?
    A. $3t$ B. $t + 3$ C. $t - 3$ D. $3 - t$ — 25. B

BONUS Which property says that $3(4 + 5)$ is equal to $3 \cdot 4 + 3 \cdot 5$?
A. Associative B. Additive Identity C. Commutative D. Distributive — D

Test

Find the value of each expression.

1. $9 \cdot 4 + 6 \cdot 7$ **78**
2. $6 + 3(9 + 11)$ **66**
3. $54 \div 9 - 3$ **3**
4. $36 \div 9 \times 4$ **16**
5. $4[6 \cdot (72 - 65) \div 3]$ **56**
6. $5[5 \times (41 - 36) - (8 + 14)]$ **15**

Evaluate each expression if $a = 7, b = 6,$ and $c = 5$.

7. $3ac - 2ab + 7$ **28**
8. $7b + 15 \div c$ **45**

Restate each expression using the distributive property.

9. $a(3 + b)$ **$a \cdot 3 + a \cdot b$**
10. $2 \cdot x + 2 \cdot y$ **$2(x + y)$**
11. $s \cdot 5 + 4 \cdot 5$ **$(s + 4)5$**

Simplify each expression.

12. $(x + 12) + 15$ **$x + 27$**
13. $2(5a)$ **$10a$**
14. $4(y \cdot 3)$ **$12y$**
15. $27r + 14r$ **$41r$**
16. $16xy - 9xy$ **$7xy$**
17. $7(m + 13) + 5(2m + 3)$ **$17m + 106$**

Solve each equation.

18. $y + 24 = 85$ **61**
19. $17 = x - 13$ **30**
20. $a + 5 = 5$ **0**
21. $7b = 784$ **112**
22. $\frac{k}{32} = 5$ **160**
23. $48 = 12z$ **4**

Solve.

24. Bill is reading a 216-page book. He needs to read twice as many pages as he has already read. Use the guess-and-check strategy to determine how many pages he has read. **72 pages**
25. **Traffic Engineering** In many cities, the number of cars on the road triples during rush hour. If the number of cars on the road during *non*rush hours is represented by c, then write an algebraic expression for how many cars there are *during* rush hour. **$3c$**

BONUS

Describe the solution of each equation.

a. $y = y$ b. $x + 4 = 2$ c. $x + 2 = x + 3$ d. $\frac{x}{x} = 1$

a. all numbers b. a negative number, −2 c. no solution d. all numbers except $x = 0$

Test Generator Software is provided in both Apple and IBM formats. You may use this software to create your own tests, based on the needs of your students.

Academic Skills Test

1. If $a = 5$ and $b = 20$, what is the value of $2a + b$?
   A 50
   B 45
   C 40
   (D) 30

2. $6 \times (10 + 5) =$
   A $(6 + 10) + 5$
   B $(6 + 10) \times 5$
   (C) $(6 \times 10) + (6 \times 5)$
   D $(6 + 10) \times (6 + 5)$

3. If $a + 15 = 24$, what is the value of a?
   (A) 9
   B 11
   C 24
   D 39

4. Which shows using inverse operations to solve $x + 14 = 35$?
   A $2 + x = 5$
   B $x = 35 + 14$
   C $14x = 35$
   (D) $x = 35 - 14$

5. Dan must earn 250 points to win a prize. He has 176 points. Which sentence could be used to find *p,* the number of points he still needs to earn?
   (A) $176 + p = 250$
   B $176 - p = 250$
   C $176 + 250 = p$
   D $p = 250 + 176$

6. Which expression is equivalent to $12a + 8b - 6a$?
   (A) $6a + 8b$
   B $14ab$
   C $8b - 6a$
   D $12a - 2b$

7. If $12y = 60$, what is the value of y?
   (A) 5
   B 12
   C 44
   D 192

8. The product of a number and 4 is 104. What is the number ?
   A 416
   B 108
   C 100
   (D) 26

9. If $8x = 112$, what is the value of x?
   (A) 14
   B 104
   C 120
   D 896

10. Jose worked 20 hours last week. He earned $4.00 per hour. Which equation can be used to find his total earnings?
    A $x = 20 \div 4$
    B $4x = 20$
    (C) $20 \times 4 = x$
    D $20x = 4.00$

Using the Academic Skills Test

This test familiarizes students with a standardized format while testing skills and concepts presented up to this point.

A Cumulative Review (free-response format) and a Cumulative Test (multiple-choice format) are also provided in the Evaluation Masters Booklet as shown at the right.

Test Item	1	2	3	4	5	6	7	8	9	10
Lesson Number	1-2	1-4	1-5	1-7	1-9	1-3	1-5	1-9	1-7	1-9
TAAS Objective	2	2	2	2	12	2	2	12	2	12

Evaluation Masters Booklet, **p. 8**

Name ______ Date ______

Cumulative Review, Chapter 1

Find the value of each expression. (Lesson 1–1)
1. $5 + 3 \cdot 4$ 2. $6 \cdot 3 - 2 \cdot 4$
3. $8 + 4 \div 4$ 4. $2 \cdot 3 + 5 - 2$
5. $21 \cdot 0 + 3 \cdot 2$ 6. $46 \cdot 1 \cdot 1 + 2$

Evaluate each expression if x = 10, y = 12, a = 8, b = 15, and c = 25. (Lesson 1–2)
7. $x + 21$ 8. $15 - b$
9. $y + a$ 10. $c - 10 + b$
11. $y + y + a$ 12. $24 - x + y$
13. $a + y - b$ 14. $50 - y + x - a$

Name the property shown by each sentence. (Lessons 1–3, 1–4)
15. $(8 + 3)r = 8r + 3r$ 16. $d + 0 = d$
17. $b + 18 = 18 + b$ 18. $n \cdot 1 = n$
19. $(a + 5) + 8 = a + (5 + 8)$ 20. $21 + (8 + 14) = 21 + (14 + 8)$

Solve each equation. Check your solution. (Lessons 1–5, 1–7)
21. $k + 29 = 48$ 22. $x - 31 = 15$
23. $35 = m - 12$ 24. $34 + a = 92$
25. $m - 62 = 15$ 26. $x - 21 = 8$
27. $3x = 15$ 28. $20 = 2y$

Solve. (Lesson 1–6)
29. The product of a number and 18 is 90. Find the number.

Translate the phrase into an algebraic expression. (Lesson 1–8)
30. w decreased by 12

Write an equation, then solve. (Lesson 1–9)
31. Marcia earned $234 last week. She is paid $6.50 per hour. How many hours did she work last week?

State whether each inequality is true, false, or open. (Lesson 1–10)
32. $3x + 2x > 15$
33. $6y + 4 < 20$, when $y = 3$

Answers: 1. 17 2. 10 3. 9 4. 9 5. 6 6. 48 7. 31 8. 0 9. 20 10. 30 11. 32 12. 26 13. 5 14. 40 15. Distrib. 16. Add. Ident. 17. Comm., Add. 18. Mult. Ident. 19. Assoc., Add. 20. Comm., Add. 21. 19 22. 46 23. 47 24. 58 25. 77 26. 29 27. 5 28. 10 29. 5 30. w − 12 31. 36 hours 32. open 33. false

Evaluation Masters Booklet, **p. 9**

Name ______ Date ______

Cumulative Test, Chapter 1

Find the value of each expression.

	A.	B.	C.	D.	Answer
1. $42 - 6 \cdot 5$	42	12	43	180	1. B
2. $3 + 4 \cdot 5$	12	35	2	23	2. D
3. $28 \div (2 \cdot 2)$	24	0	7	28	3. C
4. $2 + 3 \cdot 4 - 5$	15	5	9	45	4. C

Evaluate each expression if a = 4, b = 5, c = 6, and d = 0.

	A.	B.	C.	D.	Answer
5. $ad + b$	20	9	25	5	5. D
6. $a + c - b$	5	15	50	4	6. A
7. $cd + d$	0	6	7	8	7. A
8. $bc - ab$	2	10	130	600	8. B

Name the property shown by each statement.

9. $(4 + 3) + 2 = 4 + (3 + 2)$ A. Associative B. Commutative C. Distributive D. Identity — 9. A
10. $n + 8 = 8$ A. Associative B. Commutative C. Distributive D. Identity — 10. D
11. $x \cdot 1 = x$ A. Associative B. Commutative C. Distributive D. Identity — 11. D
12. $4 + (6 + 9) = 4 + (9 + 6)$ A. Associative B. Commutative C. Distributive D. Identity — 12. B
13. $3(n + 7) = 3 \cdot n + 3 \cdot 7$ A. Associative B. Commutative C. Distributive D. Identity — 13. C
14. $2 \cdot 3 = 3 \cdot 2$ A. Associative B. Commutative C. Distributive D. Identity — 14. B

Solve each equation.

	A.	B.	C.	D.	Answer
15. $x + 4 = 12$	8	16	3	48	15. A
16. $7y = 56$	8	49	63	392	16. A
17. $a - 8 = 10$	80	2	18	28	17. C
18. $n \div 4 = 6$	10	24	2	20	18. B
19. $5b = 20$	15	100	25	4	19. D
20. $16 + d = 32$	48	2	16	6	20. C
21. $c + 19 = 47$	53	18	63	28	21. D
22. $22d = 132$	154	110	6	8	22. C
23. $486 - a = 217$	269	279	169	179	23. A
24. $n \div 9 = 72$	63	648	8	81	24. B

Choose the word which best describes the inequality.

25. $15 + x < x + 15$ A. true B. false C. open D. identity — 25. B

Integers

Previewing the Chapter

This chapter explores the properties of integers. First, students are introduced to the set of integers and they find opposites, then the concept of absolute value is introduced as they compare and order integers. They use counters to model addition, subtraction, multiplication, and division of integers before they are given the rules for the computations. Students evaluate expressions and solve equations containing integers.

Logic Students are introduced to the formal definition of *statement*, the use of symbols to represent statements, and the negation of a statement.

Lesson (Pages)	Lesson Objectives	State/Local Objectives
2-1 (54-56)	2-1A: Graph integers on a number line. 2-1B: Find the absolute value of a number.	2D, 3A, 3C
2-2 (57-58)	2-2: Recognize the order of integers on the number line.	2D, 2F, 5E
2-3 (60-62)	2-3: Add integers using a number line.	2D, 2F, 3A, 3C, 3H
2-4 (63-64)	2-4: Use properties to add integers.	2D, 2E, 3A
2-5 (66-68)	2-5A: Subtract integers. 2-5B: Use the distributive property to combine like terms.	2D, 2E, 3A, 3H
2-6 (70-71)	2-6: Determine the truth value of a statement and its negation.	1A, 1E
2-7 (73-75)	2-7: Multiply integers.	2D, 3A, 3H
2-8 (76-78)	2-8: Divide integers.	2D, 3A, 3H, 5F
2-9 (79-81)	2-9: Solve problems involving integers.	1D, 1E, 3A

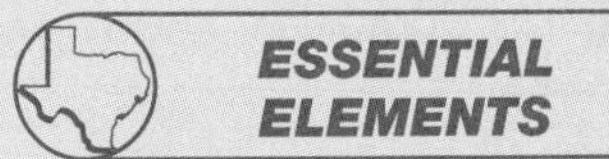

Organizing the Chapter

*You may want to refer to the **Course Planning Calendar** on Page T31.*

Planning Guide

Lesson (Pages)	Pacing Chart (in days)			Extra Practice (Student Edition)	Blackline Masters Booklets			Other Resources
	MINIMUM	STANDARD	ACCELERATED		Reteaching	Practice	Enrichment	
2-1 (54-56)	1	1	1	p. 592, Set 2A	p. 10	p. 11	p. 10	Transparency 2-1 Group Activity Card 2-1
2-2 (57-58)	1	1	0.5	p. 592, Set 2B		p. 12	p. 11	Transparency 2-2 Group Activity Card 2-2
2-3 (60-62)	1	1	1	p. 593, Set 2C	p. 12	p. 13	p. 12	Transparency 2-3 Group Activity Card 2-3
2-4 (63-64)	1	1	0.5	p. 593, Set 2C		p. 14	p. 13	Transparency 2-4 Group Activity Card 2-4
2-5 (66-68)	1	1	1	p. 593, Set 2C	p. 14	p. 15	p. 14	Transparency 2-5 Group Activity Card 2-5
2-6 (70-71)	1	1	0.5			p. 16		Transparency 2-6 Group Activity Card 2-6
2-7 (73-75)	1	1	1	p. 593, Set 2C	p. 15	p. 17	p. 15	Transparency 2-7 Group Activity Card 2-7
2-8 (76-78)	1	1	1	p. 593, Set 2C	p. 16	p. 18	p. 16	Transparency 2-8 Group Activity Card 2-8
2-9 (79-81)	1	1	1		p. 17	p. 19	p. 17	Transparency 2-9 Group Activity Card 2-9
Review (82-83)	1.5	1	1					Test Generator
Test (84)	1	1	1		Evaluation Masters, pp. 10-15			

Other Chapter Resources

Student Edition
Team Problem Solving, p. 56
Exploration, pp. 59, 65, 72
Algebra in Action, p. 69
Mid-Chapter Quiz, p. 75
History, p. 78
Academic Skills Test, p. 85

Teacher Resource Package
Interdisciplinary Activity, p. 2
Application Worksheet, p. 17
Cooperative Problem Solving, p. 32
Multicultural Activity, p. 47
Fun Activities, p. 62
Technology Worksheets, pp. 2, 17, 32
Lab Manual, pp. 30-32
Quizzes(2), p. 16
Class Review Game

Software
Test Generator

available for Apple and IBM

Enhancing the Chapter

Some of the blackline masters for enhancing this chapter are shown below.

Applications, p 17

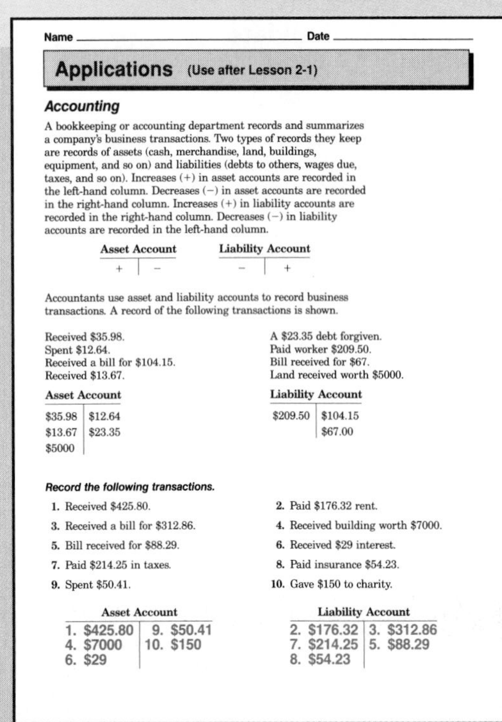

Name ______________________ Date ______________

Applications (Use after Lesson 2-1)

Accounting

A bookkeeping or accounting department records and summarizes a company's business transactions. Two types of records they keep are records of assets (cash, merchandise, land, buildings, equipment, and so on) and liabilities (debts to others, wages due, taxes, and so on). Increases (+) in asset accounts are recorded in the left-hand column. Decreases (−) in asset accounts are recorded in the right-hand column. Increases (+) in liability accounts are recorded in the right-hand column. Decreases (−) in liability accounts are recorded in the left-hand column.

Asset Account		Liability Account	
+	−	−	+

Accountants use asset and liability accounts to record business transactions. A record of the following transactions is shown.

Received \$35.98.
Spent \$12.64.
Received a bill for \$104.15.
Received \$13.67.

A \$23.35 debt forgiven.
Paid worker \$209.50.
Bill received for \$67.
Land received worth \$5000.

Asset Account

\$35.98	\$12.64
\$13.67	\$23.35
\$5000	

Liability Account

\$209.50	\$104.15
	\$67.00

Record the following transactions.

1. Received \$425.80.
2. Paid \$176.32 rent.
3. Received a bill for \$312.86.
4. Received building worth \$7000.
5. Bill received for \$88.29.
6. Received \$29 interest.
7. Paid \$214.25 in taxes.
8. Paid insurance \$54.23.
9. Spent \$50.41.
10. Gave \$150 to charity.

Asset Account

1. \$425.80	9. \$50.41
4. \$7000	10. \$150
6. \$29	

Liability Account

2. \$176.32	3. \$312.86
7. \$214.25	5. \$88.29
8. \$54.23	

The **Activity Masters Booklet** contains the page shown above.

Interdisciplinary Activity, p. 2

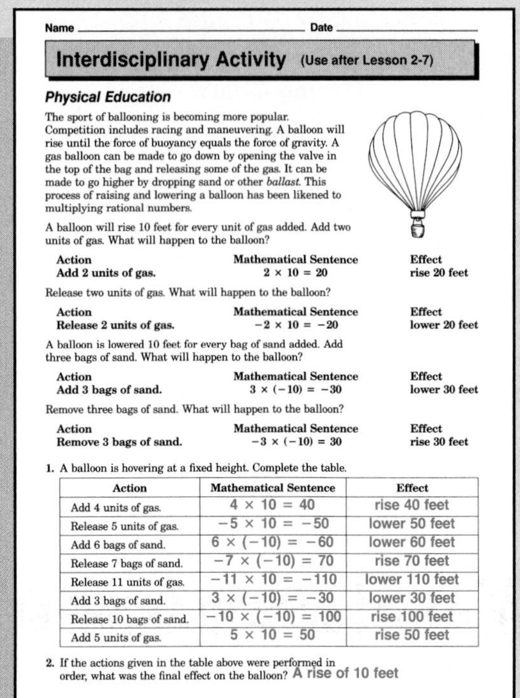

Name ______________________ Date ______________

Interdisciplinary Activity (Use after Lesson 2-7)

Physical Education

The sport of ballooning is becoming more popular. Competition includes racing and maneuvering. A balloon will rise until the force of buoyancy equals the force of gravity. A gas balloon can be made to go down by opening the valve in the top of the bag and releasing some of the gas. It can be made to go higher by dropping sand or other *ballast*. This process of raising and lowering a balloon has been likened to multiplying rational numbers.

A balloon will rise 10 feet for every unit of gas added. Add two units of gas. What will happen to the balloon?

Action	Mathematical Sentence	Effect
Add 2 units of gas.	$2 \times 10 = 20$	rise 20 feet

Release two units of gas. What will happen to the balloon?

Action	Mathematical Sentence	Effect
Release 2 units of gas.	$-2 \times 10 = -20$	lower 20 feet

A balloon is lowered 10 feet for every bag of sand added. Add three bags of sand. What will happen to the balloon?

Action	Mathematical Sentence	Effect
Add 3 bags of sand.	$3 \times (-10) = -30$	lower 30 feet

Remove three bags of sand. What will happen to the balloon?

Action	Mathematical Sentence	Effect
Remove 3 bags of sand.	$-3 \times (-10) = 30$	rise 30 feet

1. A balloon is hovering at a fixed height. Complete the table.

Action	Mathematical Sentence	Effect
Add 4 units of gas.	$4 \times 10 = 40$	rise 40 feet
Release 5 units of gas.	$-5 \times 10 = -50$	lower 50 feet
Add 6 bags of sand.	$6 \times (-10) = -60$	lower 60 feet
Release 7 bags of sand.	$-7 \times (-10) = 70$	rise 70 feet
Release 11 units of gas.	$-11 \times 10 = -110$	lower 110 feet
Add 3 bags of sand.	$3 \times (-10) = -30$	lower 30 feet
Release 10 bags of sand.	$-10 \times (-10) = 100$	rise 100 feet
Add 5 units of gas.	$5 \times 10 = 50$	rise 50 feet

2. If the actions given in the table above were performed in order, what was the final effect on the balloon? A rise of 10 feet

The **Activity Masters Booklet** contains the page shown above.

Models and Manipulatives

Students can practice adding and subtracting integers by telling a story using a model of a hot air balloon. Hot air blasts = positive integers, while sandbags = negative integers.

The illustration at the right represents six hot air blasts plus two sandbags or 6 + (-2) = 4. Have students solve similar examples.

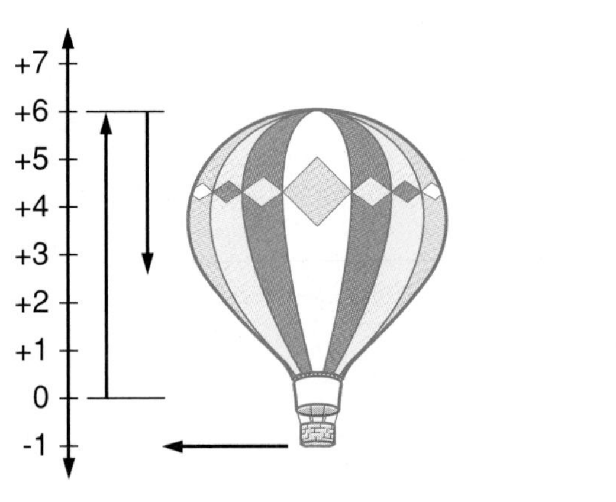

Multicultural Activity

Organize students in pairs and write an equation involving integers on the chalkboard. Ask each pair to write a short story of a situation that matches the equation. When they finish, write all the culturally diverse situations on the chalkboard and discuss different ways the same essential relationship was expressed.

Cooperative Learning

The following activity is provided in the **Activity Masters Booklet.**

Cooperative Problem Solving, p. 32

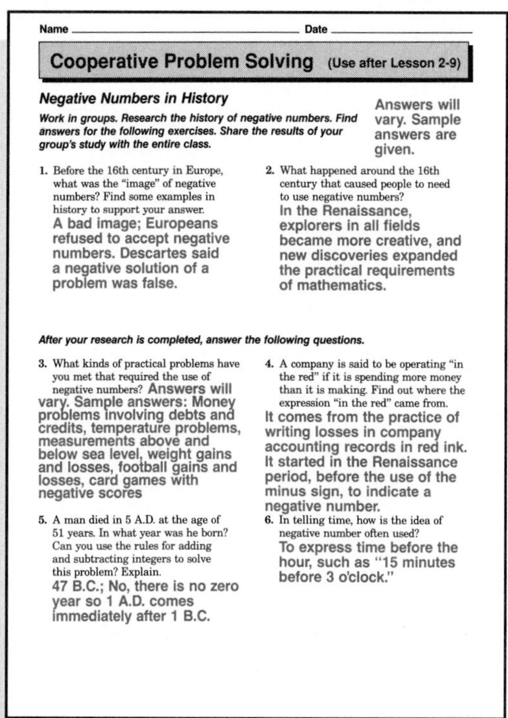

Name ______________________ Date ____________

Cooperative Problem Solving (Use after Lesson 2-9)

Negative Numbers in History

Work in groups. Research the history of negative numbers. Find answers for the following exercises. Share the results of your group's study with the entire class.

Answers will vary. Sample answers are given.

1. Before the 16th century in Europe, what was the "image" of negative numbers? Find some examples in history to support your answer.
   A bad image; Europeans refused to accept negative numbers. Descartes said a negative solution of a problem was false.

2. What happened around the 16th century that caused people to need to use negative numbers?
   In the Renaissance, explorers in all fields became more creative, and new discoveries expanded the practical requirements of mathematics.

After your research is completed, answer the following questions.

3. What kinds of practical problems have you met that required the use of negative numbers? Answers will vary. Sample answers: Money problems involving debts and credits, temperature problems, measurements above and below sea level, weight gains and losses, football gains and losses, card games with negative scores

4. A company is said to be operating "in the red" if it is spending more money than it is making. Find out where the expression "in the red" came from.
   It comes from the practice of writing losses in company accounting records in red ink. It started in the Renaissance period, before the use of the minus sign, to indicate a negative number.

5. A man died in 5 A.D. at the age of 51 years. In what year was he born? Can you use the rules for adding and subtracting integers to solve this problem? Explain.
   47 B.C.; No, there is no zero year so 1 A.D. comes immediately after 1 B.C.

6. In telling time, how is the idea of negative number often used?
   To express time before the hour, such as "15 minutes before 3 o'clock."

Cooperative Problem Solving

Using Discussion Discuss the fact that integers are an integral part of our lives. Have students relate various situations that require the use of integers. These situations should include, but not be limited to, measuring temperature, reading altitude with reference to sea level, yardage gained or lost by football teams, and keeping score in golf games (above or below par).

Interactive Bulletin Board

Social Studies Connection

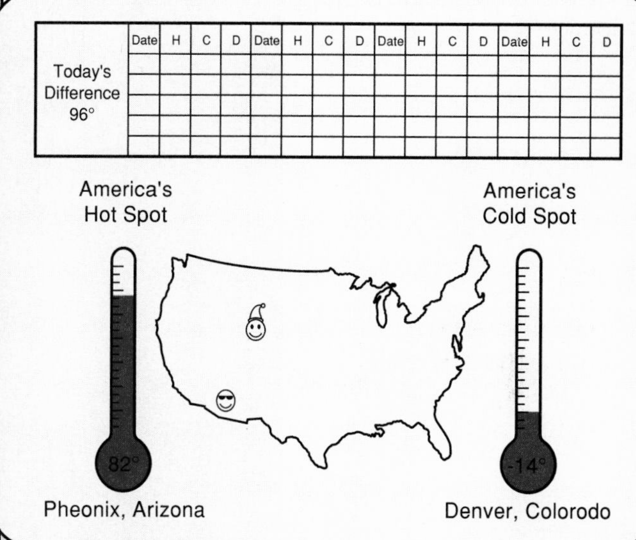

Purpose Provide practice in adding and subtracting integers.

How to Use It If possible, laminate all parts. All states can be outlined on the map or just the state where your school is located. Using the newspaper and/or other weather reports, find the locations that had the hottest and coldest temperatures for the previous day. Record the temperatures and their differences on the chart. Assign specific students the task of finding those cities representing the daily temperature extremes. Using a wipe-off marker, the assigned students write the names of the two cities on the map. They also adjust the mercury level on the thermometer.

Outside Resources

Books/Periodicals
Using the Math Challenger Calculator, A Sourcebook for Teachers, Chapter 4.

Films/Videotapes
Teaching Mathematics Effectively, ASCD

Software
Teasers by Tobbs with Integers, Sunburst

Technology

There are three pages in the ***Technology Masters Booklet*** that involve technology with concepts in this chapter. One page involves calculators and one page has a problem that can be solved using the BASIC program that is provided. Students should evaluate the information they obtain from running the program and solve a similar problem by extending the program.

Using the Chapter Opener

Transparency 2-0 is available in the Transparency Package. It provides a full-color visual and motivational activity that you can use to engage students in the mathematical content of the chapter.

Using Discussion

- Discuss severe weather watch and warning advisories with students and why they should be taken seriously.

CHAPTER OBJECTIVES

In this chapter you will learn to:

- ❑ graph integers on a number line
- ❑ compare and order integers
- ❑ compute with integers
- ❑ solve problems with integers
- ❑ use logic to find the negation of a statement

Integers

What rotates at 300 miles per hour, uproots large trees, overturns loaded railroad cars, and carries entire houses through the air? A tornado! This fiercest of storms can move forward at 30 to 40 miles per hour. That's so fast that a spotter on the ground can give people only about two minutes' warning. Luckily, Doppler radar can detect tornadoes 20 minutes before they touch down. Doppler radar can be a real lifesaver in tornado country.

Doppler radar shows a tornado's position, strength, wind speed, and direction. On the radar screen, bright green shows winds coming toward the radar, and red shows winds moving away. Where red and bright green appear close together, the winds are rotating—and that means a tornado.

Can you find the tornado on the radar screen shown here?

Science Connection

Class Project

Do research to find how many tornadoes touched down in each state for a recent year. Decide on a way to display the data on a class bulletin board. Discuss tornado safety procedures with your classmates.

Science Connection

If this information is not available in the library, you could involve the class in a cooperative activity by writing a letter to the American Meteorological Society, 45 Beacon St., Boston, MA, 02108.

Looking Ahead

You may want to have the following materials available to use in this chapter.

Explorations, pp. 59, 65, 72
- integer mat*
- counters**

Algebra in Action, p. 69
- globes or world maps
- overseas Official Airlines Guide

*You can use the Easy-to-Make Manipulative provided on page 2 of the Lab Manual.

**You can use the Easy-to-Make Manipulative provided on page 4 of the Lab Manual.

Lesson Notes 2-1

5-Minute Check
(over Lessons 1-1 to 1-10)

Find the value of each expression.
1. $6 \cdot 8 + 3 \cdot 4$ 60
2. $72 \div 9 \times 2$ 16
3. $4 + 2(6 + 3)$ 22

Simplify each expression.

4. $(x + 19) + 13$ $x + 32$
5. $4(m + 5) + 7(2m + 6)$ $18m + 62$

Transparency 2-1 contains the 5-Minute Check and a teaching aid for this lesson.

1 FOCUS

The purpose of the lesson is to locate and graph integers on the number line.

Note that the negative sign is centered rather than raised. The negative sign will be centered in this text because most calculators and computers use a centered sign.

Motivating the Lesson

Brainstorm applications of negative numbers. List them on the chalkboard or a flip chart and add to them as you work through the chapter.

2 TEACH

Using Questioning

Use a local or state map to locate the city or town where students live. Locate a city or town about 25 miles to the east of where students live. Locate another city or town about 25 miles to the west of where students live.

a. If someone asked you how far away the first town is, would you reply 25 miles? yes
b. If someone asked you how far away the second town is, would you reply 25 miles? yes
c. How do you distinguish between the location of the two towns? need a second locator such as east or west.

EE: 2D, 3A, 3C

2-1 Integers and Absolute Value

Objectives:
Graph integers on a number line.
Find absolute value.

Key Terms:
integers
absolute value
coordinate

Which integer is neither positive nor negative? zero

History Connection

In the 15th century, flour merchants used integers to tell whether flour barrels were overweight or underweight. For example, +5 means that the barrel was 5 pounds overweight; −5 meant that it was 5 pounds underweight.

Have you ever watched the launch of a space shuttle on TV? In the final seconds before liftoff, you might have heard "T minus 3, 2, 1, ignition, liftoff."

The number of seconds before the liftoff is indicated by negative numbers. In this case, the numbers are -3, -2, and -1. The number of seconds after liftoff is indicated by positive numbers like +1, +2, and +3. Ignition time is zero.

Negative and positive numbers are often used to show opposite situations. Zero is considered to be the starting point. These numbers are often shown on a number line.

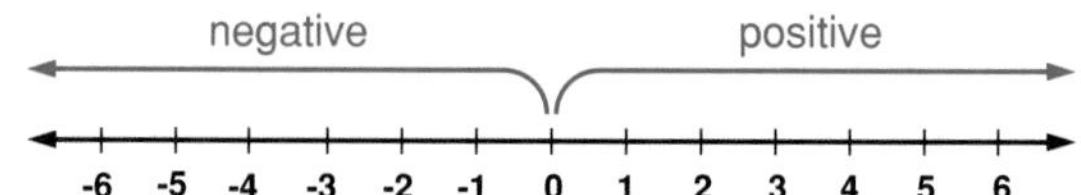

The numbers -1, -2, -3, . . . are called **negative integers.** The symbol for negative three is written -3.

The numbers 1, 2, 3, . . . are called **positive integers.** The symbol for positive four is written +4 or 4.

The set of all **integers** can be written {. . . -3, -2, -1, 0, 1, 2, 3 . . .} where . . . means *continues without end.*

To graph a particular set of integers, locate the integer points on a number line. The number that corresponds to a point on the number line is called the **coordinate** of the point.

Examples

1 **Name the coordinates of *A*, *C*, and *D*.**

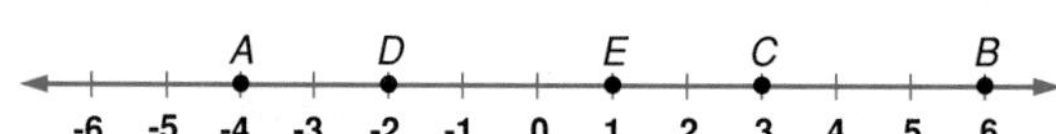

The coordinate of *A* is -4, *C* is 3, and *D* is -2.

2 **Graph {-1, 3, 5} on a number line.**

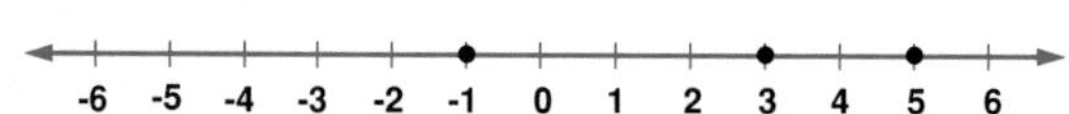

Bell Ringer

Replace each • with <, >, =, ≤, or ≥ to make a true sentence.
1. 5 • 3 > or ≥
2. 6 • 6 = or ≤ or ≥
3. 7 • 8 < or ≤

Looking at the number line shown below, you can see that 4 and -4 are different numbers. However, they are the same distance from the zero point. They both have the same **absolute value**.

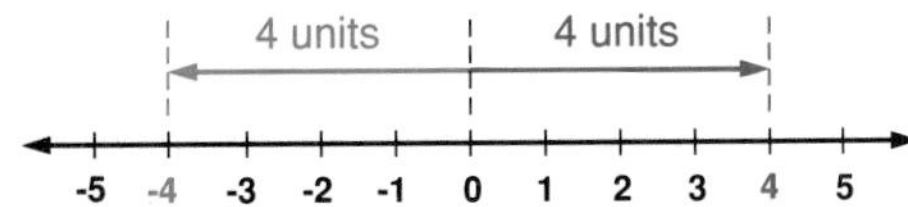

Absolute Value

The absolute value of a number is the distance the number is from the zero point on the number line.

What is the symbol for absolute value? | |

Say: *The absolute value of 4 is 4.*
Write: |4| = 4

Say: *The absolute value of -4 is 4.*
Write: |-4| = 4

Example

Simplify |-8| + |3|.

|-8| + |3| = 8 + 3   The absolute value of -8 is 8.
= 11   The absolute value of 3 is 3.

Checking for Understanding

Communicating Algebra

Replace each ■ with an integer that describes the situation.

1. 25° above zero, 25
   25° below zero, ■ -25
2. stock value down $3, -3
   stock value unchanged, ■ 0
3. 10 pound gain, 10
   8 pound loss, ■ -8
4. 40 m below sea level, -40
   15 m above sea level, ■ 15

True **or** ***false*****. Explain your answer.**

5. All whole numbers are integers. T
6. All integers are whole numbers. F

Guided Practice

Name the coordinates of the points that are graphed.

7. 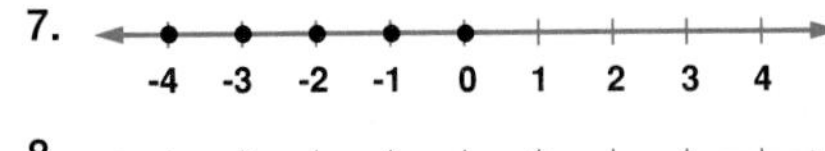 -4, -3, -2, -1, 0

8. (number line: -4 -3 -2 -1 0 1 2 3 4) -3, -1, 1, 3

Find each absolute value.

9. |-3| 3   10. |10| 10   11. |-16| 16   12. |25| 25

Chalkboard Examples

- *For Example 1*
  Name the coordinates of A, D, and E. **The coordinate of A is -2, D is 3, and E is 5.**

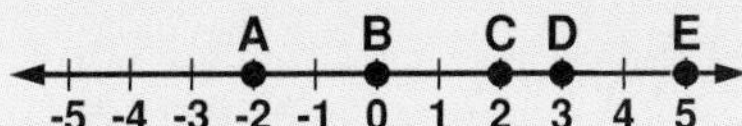

- *For Example 2*
  Graph {-2, 1, 3} on a number line.

- *For Example 3*
  Simplify |-9| + |4|. **13**

3 PRACTICE/APPLY

Checking the Concept

Check for understanding of absolute value using Exercises 9-12.

Error Analysis

Watch for students who write the absolute value as the opposite of the number.
Prevent by stressing the definitions of absolute value and opposites.

Practice Masters Booklet, **p. 11**

Name ______ Date ______

Practice Worksheet 2-1

Integers and Absolute Value

Graph each set of numbers on the number line provided.

1. {0, 1, 5}   2. {-1, 0, 3}
3. {-4, -2, 2}   4. {-3, 0, 4}

Find each absolute value.

5. |-3| 3	6. |-5| 5	7. |4| 4	8. |-7| 7
9. |6| 6	10. |-2| 2	11. |7| 7	12. |-9| 9
13. |8| 8	14. |9| 9	15. |-1| 1	16. |-4| 4
17. |1| 1	18. |-10| 10	19. |-8| 8	20. |5| 5

Name the absolute value of each integer.

21. -6 6	22. 12 12	23. 17 17	24. 0 0
25. 5 5	26. -9 9	27. -8 8	28. -16 16
29. 21 21	30. 4 4	31. -3 3	32. 10 10
33. -2 2	34. -11 11	35. 19 19	36. -1 1

Simplify.

37. |-10| 10	38. |4| + |-4| 8	39. |9| - |-5| 4
40. 0 + |-1| 1	41. |-6| + |-5| 11	42. |-8| - |-8| 0
43. |12| + |-3| 15	44. |-15| - |6| 9	45. |-13| + |-7| 20

Alternate Strategies: Reteaching the Lesson

Reteaching Activity

Using Small Groups Have students work in pairs. One student states an integer and requests the partner to state an integer that is greater or less than it. Then they switch roles and repeat the procedure.

Reteaching Masters Booklet, **p. 10**

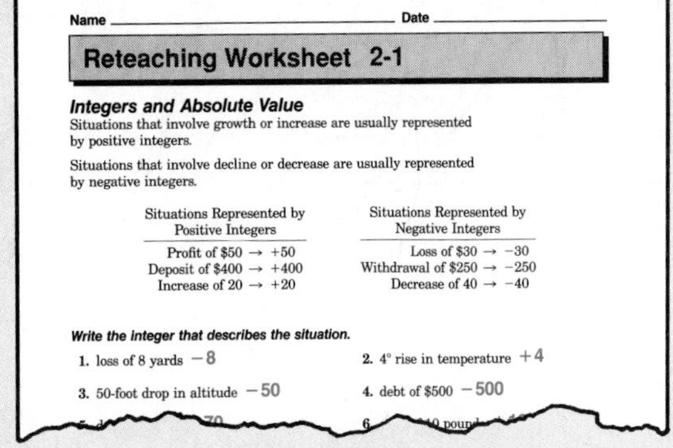

Name ______ Date ______

Reteaching Worksheet 2-1

Integers and Absolute Value

Situations that involve growth or increase are usually represented by positive integers.

Situations that involve decline or decrease are usually represented by negative integers.

Situations Represented by Positive Integers	Situations Represented by Negative Integers
Profit of $50 → +50	Loss of $30 → -30
Deposit of $400 → +400	Withdrawal of $250 → -250
Increase of 20 → +20	Decrease of 40 → -40

Write the integer that describes the situation.

1. loss of 8 yards -8   2. 4° rise in temperature +4
3. 50-foot drop in altitude -50   4. debt of $500 -500

Independent Practice

Homework Assignment	
Basic	13-31, 35-37
Average	13-27, 31-37
Honors	16-37

4 CLOSE

Assessment Option

Writing Have students write a sentence that describes the key sequence below.

7 [+] 8 [+/−] [=] −1

$7 + (-8) = -1$

Enrichment Masters Booklet, **p. 10**

Name ______________________ Date ______________

Enrichment Worksheet 2-1

Integers on the Number Line

We can graph integers on the number line, describe them in words, or describe them in mathematical sentences. Sometimes it is important to be able to think of them in several ways at the same time. The graphs can help us "check" if our problem solutions make sense. The mathematical sentences can let us express answers in a form of shorthand. The word description can help us use integers in a variety of problem situations.

In this activity, you will be completing the table below. Each row gives different ways of thinking about the same integers. You need to find ways to fill in the blanks. You can use the completed ones to help you figure out the ones that are missing.

	Integers	Open Sentence	Word Description	Number Line Graph
	−2, 2	$\lvert x\rvert = 2$	Integers 2 units from zero	-4 -3 -2 -1 0 1 2 3 4
1.	−3, −2	$-4 < x < -1$	Integers between −4 and −1	-4 -3 -2 -1 0 1 2 3 4
2.	−2, −1, 0, 1, 2	$\lvert x\rvert < 3$	Integers less than 3 units from zero	-4 -3 -2 -1 0 1 2 3 4
3.	−1, 1	$\lvert x\rvert = 1$	Integers 1 unit from zero	-4 -3 -2 -1 0 1 2 3 4
4.	1, 2, 3	$0 < x < 4$	Integers between 0 and 4	-4 -3 -2 -1 0 1 2 3 4
5.	−3, 3	$\lvert x\rvert = 3$	Integers 3 units from zero	-4 -3 -2 -1 0 1 2 3 4
6.	0, 1	$-1 < x < 2$	Integers between −1 and 2	-4 -3 -2 -1 0 1 2 3 4
7.	−1, 3	$\lvert x - 1\rvert = 2$	Integers 2 units from 1	-4 -3 -2 -1 0 1 2 3 4
8.	−2, 4	$\lvert x - 1\rvert = 3$	Integers 3 units from 1	-4 -3 -2 -1 0 1 2 3 4
9.	0, 4	$\lvert x - 2\rvert = 2$	Integers 2 units from 2	-4 -3 -2 -1 0 1 2 3 4

Exercises

For graphs to Exercises 13-15, see Solutions Manual.

Independent Practice

Graph each set of numbers on a number line.

13. {0, 2, 4}
14. {-2, -4, -6}
15. {-3, 0, 2}

Name the absolute value of each integer.

16. +6 6
17. -15 15
18. 13 13
19. 0 0

Simplify.

20. $|-8|$ 8
21. $|-3| + |2|$ 5
22. $|15| - |-3|$ 12
23. $|-20| + |-19|$ 39

Mixed Review

24. Evaluate the expression $5 \cdot 3 + 8 \div 2$. (Lesson 1-1) 19
25. Solve mentally: $k + 4 = 11$. (Lesson 1-5) 7
26. Using inverse operations, solve $16n = 48$. (Lesson 1-7) 3
27. Write an equation and solve: Alicia spent $41 on a new outfit. The pants cost $23. How much was the blouse? (Lesson 1-9) $x + 23 = 41$; $18

Logical Reasoning

28. does not exist
30. does not exist

If the number described below exists, name it.

28. the greatest positive integer
29. the least positive integer 1
30. the least negative integer
31. the greatest negative integer −1
32. an integer that is neither positive nor negative 0
33. a number that is not an integer fraction, decimal

Applications

34. **Geography** Death Valley, California, has the lowest altitude in the United States. Its elevation is 282 feet below sea level. What integer could be used to provide this information? −282
35. **Space Exploration** About six seconds before liftoff, the three main shuttle engines start. About 120 seconds after liftoff, the solid rocket boosters burn out. Use integers to describe these events. −6; 120

Critical Thinking

36. Find two values of x that make $|x| = 3$ a true statement. 3, −3

Wrap-Up

37. **Research** Find three examples of negative integers used in games. Sample answers: 500 Rummy, Hearts, Jeopardy, golf, football

Team Problem Solving

Luisa threw five darts at the dartboard, and all five hit the board. Which of the following numbers could have been her score?

5, 18, 28, 31, 37 5, 31

Alternate Strategies: Extending the Lesson

Enrichment

Using Lists Have students divide a sheet of paper into two columns. In one column, have students list sentences indicating integers, such as "Mary put $4 in the bank", and the corresponding integer 4. In the second column, have students write a sentence that is the opposite of the first and its corresponding integer.

Cooperative Learning

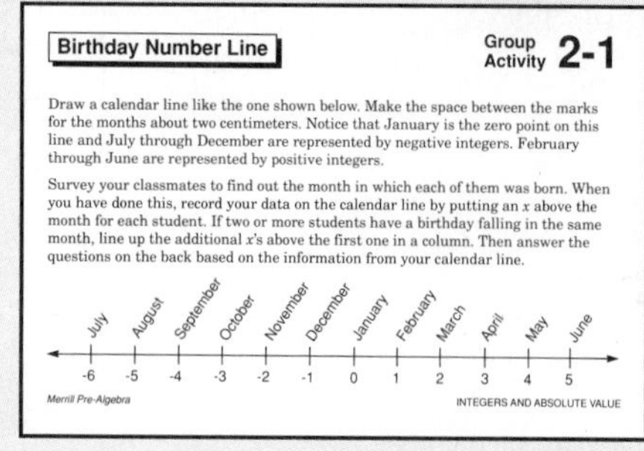

Birthday Number Line Group Activity **2-1**

Draw a calendar line like the one shown below. Make the space between the marks for the months about two centimeters. Notice that January is the zero point on this line and July through December are represented by negative integers. February through June are represented by positive integers.

Survey your classmates to find out the month in which each of them was born. When you have done this, record your data on the calendar line by putting an x above the month for each student. If two or more students have a birthday falling in the same month, line up the additional x's above the first one in a column. Then answer the questions on the back based on the information from your calendar line.

July	August	September	October	November	December	January	February	March	April	May	June
-6	-5	-4	-3	-2	-1	0	1	2	3	4	5

Merrill Pre-Algebra INTEGERS AND ABSOLUTE VALUE

2-2 Comparing and Ordering

Objective:
Compare and order integers.

Brush fires occur when the weather has been hot and dry for a period of time. Forest rangers use signs like the one at the right to inform people of the fire hazard. As the fire hazard increases, the indicator is moved to the right.

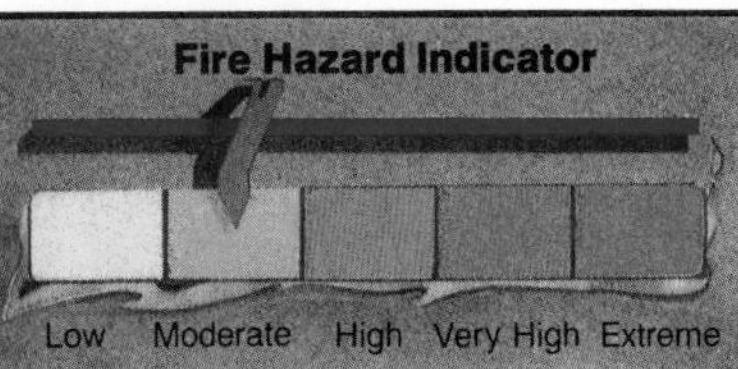

Similarly on a number line, values increase as you move to the right. This makes it easy to determine which of two numbers is greater. On the number line shown below, 5 is to the right of -3.

Say: *5 is greater than -3.*
Write: 5 > -3

You might also conclude that -3 is to the left of 5.

Say: *-3 is less than 5.*
Write: -3 < 5

Remember, the symbol points to the lesser number.

Remember that any mathematical sentence containing < or > is called an inequality. In inequalities, numbers are compared.

Example

1 **Use the integers graphed on the number line to write two inequalities.**

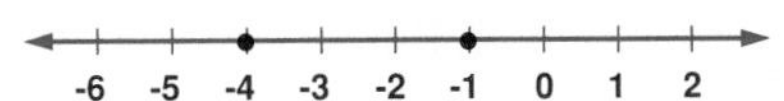

Since -4 is to the left of -1, write -4 < -1.
Since -1 is to the right of -4, write -1 > -4.

Checking for Understanding

Communicating Algebra

Use the numbers in each sentence to write an inequality. Use < or >.

1. -3 is less than 10. **-3 < 10**
2. 8 is greater than 7. **8 > 7**
3. -9°C is colder than -8°C. **-9 < -8**
4. 65 mph is faster than 55 mph. **4. 65 > 55**
5. $19.95 is more than $15. **19.95 > 15**
6. 6 ft is taller than 4 ft **6 > 4**

Guided Practice

Write an inequality for each of the following.

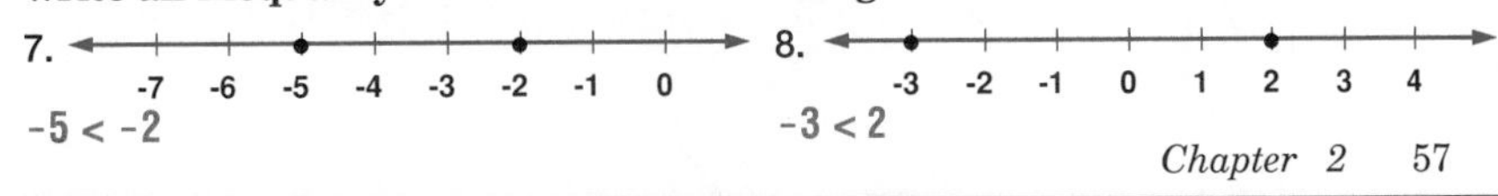

7. **-5 < -2**
8. **-3 < 2**

Lesson Notes 2-2

5-Minute Check
(over Lesson 2-1)

Graph each set of numbers on a number line.

1. {-3, 0, 2} -3 -2 -1 0 1 2
2. {-5, -1, 1} -5 -4 -3 -2 -1 0 1

Simplify.

3. |-5| - |2| **3**
4. |-31| + |-18| **49**

Transparency 2-2 contains the 5-Minute Check and a teaching aid for this lesson.

1 FOCUS

The purpose of the lesson is to determine which of two integers is greater and to order a set of integers.

2 TEACH

Chalkboard Examples

Use the integers graphed on the number line to write two inequalities. **-6 < -2, -2 > -6**

-7 -6 -5 -4 -3 -2 -1 0 1 2 3

Practice Masters Booklet, **p. 12**

Name ____________ Date ____________

Practice Worksheet 2-2

Comparing and Ordering

Write <, >, or = in each □.

1. 5 [>] −8	2. −3 [<] 2	3. −4 [>] −7	4. 4 [>] −6
5. 0 [>] −12	6. 35 [>] −21	7. −55 [<] 65	8. −16 [>] −40
9. 3 [>] 0	10. −5 [<] 5	11. −7 [<] 6	12. −10 [<] 12
13. −10 [<] 9	14. 6 [>] 4	15. −3 [<] 0	16. −1 [<] 1
17. |−4| [<] 5	18. |−1| [=] 1	19. −2 [<] |2|	20. 5 [>] |−3|

Order the numbers in each set from least to greatest.

21. {7, 0, 4} {0, 4, 7}
22. {9, −7, −3} {−7, −3, 9}
23. {11, 0, −2} {−2, 0, 11}
24. {−3, 1, −5, 2} {−5, −3, 1, 2}
25. {−4, −6, 0, −2} {−6, −4, −2, 0}
26. {−7, 5, −9, 4} {−9, −7, 4, 5}
27. {3, −6, 6, −3} {−6, −3, 3, 6}
28. {10, −7, 8, −9} {−9, −7, 8, 10}
29. {−4, 3, 0, −2} {−4, −2, 0, 3}

Write an inequality for each situation.

30. Yesterday's high wind speed was 25 mph. The low wind speed was 12 mph. 25 > 12, or 12 < 25
31. Rebecca made 7 foul shots in a game. In the same game, she missed 5 foul shots. 7 > −5, or −5 < 7
32. The team gained 15 yards. Then the team lost 6 yards. 15 > −6, or −6 < 15
33. Lucille spent $10. She had earned $9. −10 < 9, or 9 > −10

Bell Ringer

Brainstorm positive integer words and their opposites. Write them in two columns on the chalkboard. **Example: credit, debit**

Reteaching Activity

Using Logic A frog is trying to jump out of a hole 10 feet deep. After each 3-foot jump, he slides back one foot. Have students draw a number line, with -10 being his starting point and 0 being ground level. Have students plot each jump and slide and tell whether each new location is < or > the previous position.

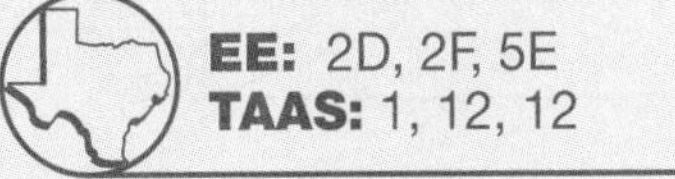

EE: 2D, 2F, 5E
TAAS: 1, 12, 12

3 PRACTICE/APPLY

Checking the Concept

The Guided Practice exercises will help you determine if students are able to correctly compare two integers. Encourage students to use a number line.

Error Analysis

Watch for students who say that, for example, -7 is greater than -5 or -7 is greater than 5 because 7 is greater than 5.
Prevent by locating both numbers on the number line.

Independent Practice

Homework Assignment	
Basic	9-20, 23-28
Average	11-28
Honors	12-28

4 CLOSE

Assessment Option

Speaking Tell about three examples where negative numbers are used to compare scientific data. For example, telling temperature in degrees below zero, or in chemistry with electrons and protons.

Enrichment Masters Booklet, **p. 11**

Name ______ Date ______

Enrichment Worksheet 2-2

Integers in Order

Connect the dots in each exercise in the order of the integers shown, from least to greatest. The least integer in each exercise is indicated by the arrow.

1. 2. 3. 4.

Exercises

Independent Practice

Replace each ● with <, >, or =.

9. 12 ● 14 <
10. -2 ● -3 >
11. 6 ● -6 >
12. 12 ● 0 >
13. 10 ● -3 >
14. -9 ● -15 >
15. -11 ● 5 <
16. |-4| ● 4 =

Order the numbers in each set from least to greatest.

17. {10, 0, -3} **{-3, 0, 10}**
18. {12, -9, -1} **{-9, -1, 12}**
19. {0, -4, -8, -3} **{-8, -4, -3, 0}**

Use the numbers to write an inequality. Use < or >.

20. Water boils at 212°F. It freezes at 32°F. **32 < 212 or 212 > 32**
21. Walking for 45 minutes burns 144 calories. Playing volleyball for the same amount of time burns 135 calories. **144 > 135 or 135 < 144**
22. Yesterday's high temperature was 65°F. The low temperature was 34°F. **65 > 34 or 34 < 65**

Mixed Review

23. Evaluate the expression $ac - ab$ if $a = 8$, $b = 3$, and $c = 5$. (Lesson 1-2) **16**
24. Graph the numbers {-1, 1, 4} on a number line. (Lesson 2-1) **See Solutions Manual**
25. Simplify the expression |-5| + |3|. (Lesson 2-1) **8**

Application

26. **Geology** Geologists often record important dates in Earth's history on a time line like the one shown below. The abbreviation M. Y. B. P. means *million years before present.*

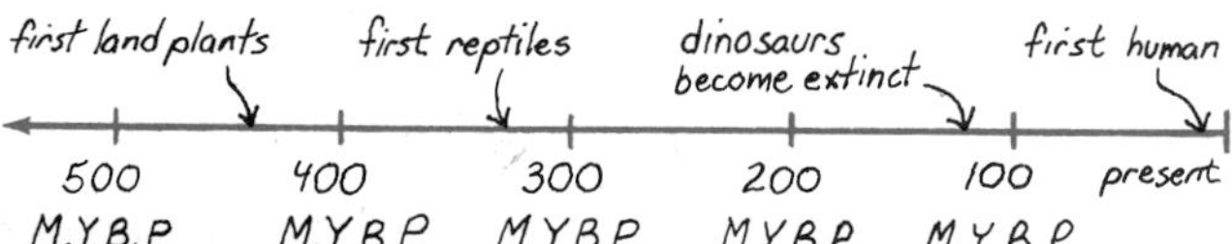

Copy the time line and record these events on it. **See students' work.**

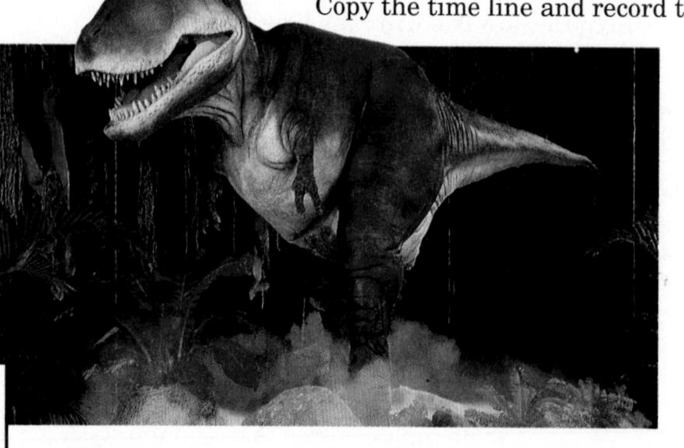

Event	M.Y.B.P.
Rocky Mountains rise	80
First dinosaurs	225
Beginning of ice age	1

Critical Thinking

27. Find all integer values for x that make $|x| < 3$ a true statement. Then graph the solution on a number line. **{-2, -1, 0, 1, 2} See Solutions Manual for graph**

Wrap-Up

28. Measure your height and a friend's height. Write an inequality that compares them. **See Students' work.**

Alternate Strategies: Extending the Lesson

Enrichment

Science Connection Two kilometers above ground, the temperature is 0 degrees Celsius. For each kilometer of altitude, the temperature drops 7 degrees. What is the temperature 13 kilometers above ground? **-77° Celsius**

Cooperative Learning

Don't Be The Joker Group Activity **2-2**

MATERIALS: 2–10 cards in diamonds and clubs from a deck of cards • one joker card • three 3x5 cards, with either ≤, ≥, or "has the same absolute value as" written on them

Shuffle the 19 cards and deal them. One player gets 9 cards and the other 10. Red cards represent negative integers. Black cards represent positive integers. The joker represents zero.

The player with 10 cards lays a card on the table, draws a card from the other player's hand, and lays that card beside the first card. Lastly, the player makes a true statement about those numbers using one of the 3x5 cards. If correct, the player discards the pair of cards. If incorrect, the player keeps the cards.

It is now the other player's turn. If a joker is drawn, the player must put the played card and the joker back into his or her hand, and it is the other player's turn. The person who runs out of cards wins, causing the other player to be the joker.

Merrill Pre-Algebra COMPARING AND ORDERING

Adding Integers

Materials: counters, mat

In this Exploration, you will use counters to model addition.

Remember that 2 + 3 means *combine a set of two items with a set of three items.* The integer addition +2 + (+3) means something similar. It tells you to combine a set of two positive items with a set of three positive items.

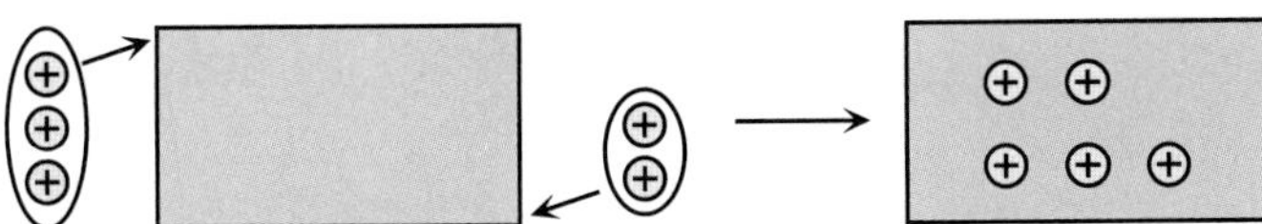

Therefore, +2 + (+3) = +5.

Consider -2 + (-3). This tells you to combine a set of two negative items with a set of three negative items.

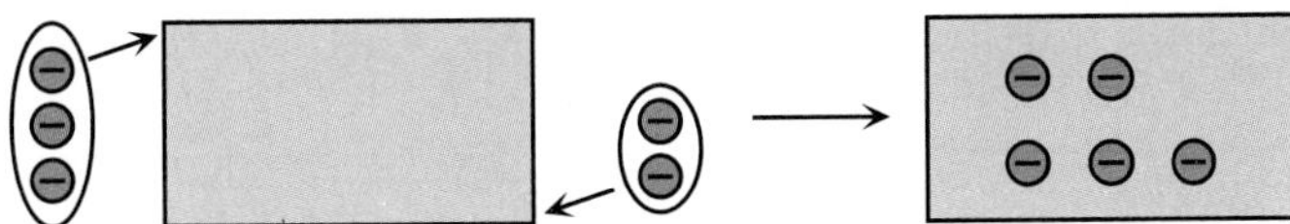

Therefore, -2 + (-3) = -5.

Finally, consider -2 + (+3). This tells you to combine a set of two negative items with a set of three positive items. In this case it is possible to pair a positive counter with a negative counter. This is called a *zero pair.* You can remove as many zero pairs as possible, because removing zero does not change the value of the set.

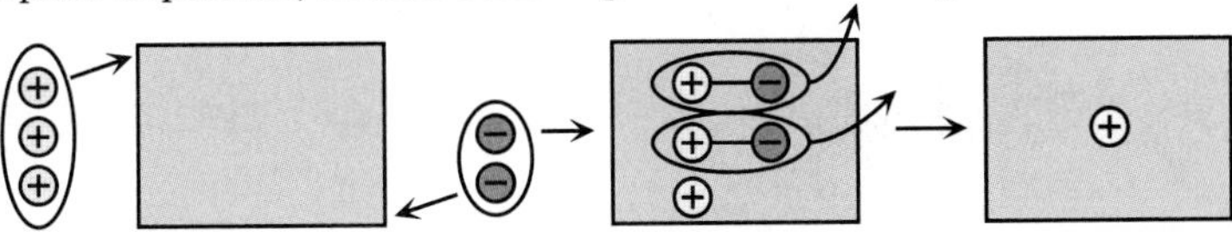

Therefore, -2 + (+3) = +1.

Your Turn: What does +2 + (-3) mean? Model this operation.
Combine a set of two positive items with a set of three negative items.

Model each problem. See Solutions Manual.

1. 5 + 2 **2.** 5 + (-2) **3.** -5 + 2 **4.** -5 + (-2)

Analysis

5. Suppose you add a positive integer and a negative integer. Explain how you use a zero pair to find the sum. Write your answer in paragraph form. See margin.

SET-UP

Materials

- Integer Mat, Lab Manual, p. 2
- Counters, Lab Manual, p. 4
- Exploration Worksheet, Lab Manual, p. 30

For Students Use two different colored counters or dry beans to represent the positive and negative integers. Each group of students will need a packet of 10 positive and 10 negative counters.

HINT: Assemble the counters in sandwich bags with a twist-tie for convenient management.

For the Overhead Projector If you choose to present this lesson on the overhead projector, cut small squares or circles out of transparency material. Color the shapes with permanent colored markers.

EXPLORATION

Adding Integers

Objective Students will become familiar with the property of opposites at an informal level. Students will be introduced to the formal rules for adding integers in Lesson 2-3. The property of opposites is introduced in Lesson 2-5.

1 FOCUS

Motivating the Exploration

Ask students if they have ever taken clothes out of a dryer and found a sock sticking to a shirt. The clothes stick together because one has a positive charge and the other has a negative charge. This is an example of static electricity. In this Exploration the idea of opposite charges is used as a model for adding integers.

2 TEACH

Model each example for the entire class. Help students write the corresponding addition sentence.

3 PRACTICE/APPLY

Using Cooperative Groups

Divide the class into small groups. Circulate around the room as they model their problems.

4 CLOSE

Writing Connection

Ask students to write a rule for adding integers.

5. Match all positive counters with negative counters to form zero pairs. These pairs can then be removed because zero does not change the value of the set. The counters remaining give you the sum.

EE: 1A, 1C, 1E, 2D

5-Minute Check
(over Lesson 2-2)

Replace each • with <, >, or =.
1. -3 • -4 > 2. | -7 | • 7 =
Order the numbers in each set from least to greatest.
3. {0, -4, 1} **{ -4, 0, 1}**
4. {2, 4, -1, -5} **{-5, -1, 2, 4}**

Transparency 2-3 contains the 5-Minute Check and a teaching aid for this lesson.

1 FOCUS

The purpose of the lesson is to use the number line to develop and apply the rules for adding integers.

Motivating the Lesson

Use your students to model or act out the following situation: One student has $5 but owes another student $3. How much is left once the debt is paid? Continue with similar situations. **$2**

2 TEACH

Using Models

The number line is used as a model for developing the rules for adding integers. Help students to discover these rules by modeling the Chalkboard Examples.

Chalkboard Examples

- *For Example 1*
  Find -2 + (-4). **-6**
- *For Example 2*
  Find -6 + 1. **-5**
- *For Example 3*
  Find 8 + (-5). **3**
- *For Example 4*
  Find 13 + (-7). **6**

EE: 2D, 2F, 3A, 3C, 3H
TAAS: 2, 6, 12

2-3 Adding Integers

Objective:
Add integers.

At night the average temperature on the surface of the planet Saturn is -150° Celsius. During the day the temperature rises 27°C. What is the average temperature on the planet's surface during the day?

Using counters to solve a problem like this would be inconvenient. Study the patterns in the following examples so that you can learn a rule for adding integers.

Example

If you know that -3 + (-4) = -7, what property allows you to say that -4 + (-3) = -7? **commutative property**

1 Find -3 + (-4).

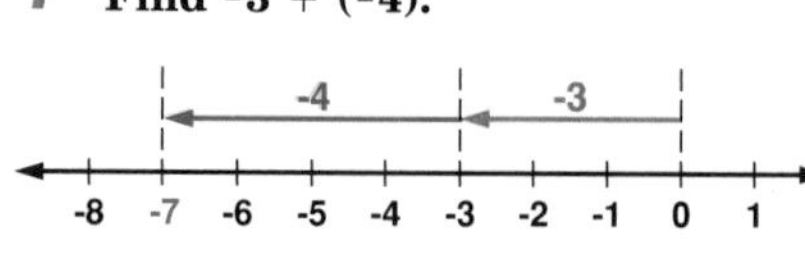

Start at zero. Move 3 units to the left. From there, move 4 more units to the left. The sum is -7.

-3 + (-4) = -7

This example suggests the following rule.

Adding Integers with the Same Signs

To add integers with the same sign, add their absolute values. Give the result the same sign as the integers.

Study the following examples to see if you can discover a rule for adding integers that have different signs.

Examples

FYI
The highest surface temperature on record in the United States is 57°C (134°F), measured in Death Valley, California. The lowest surface temperature on record in the United States is -62°C (-80°F), measured in Alaska.

2 Find -5 + 2.

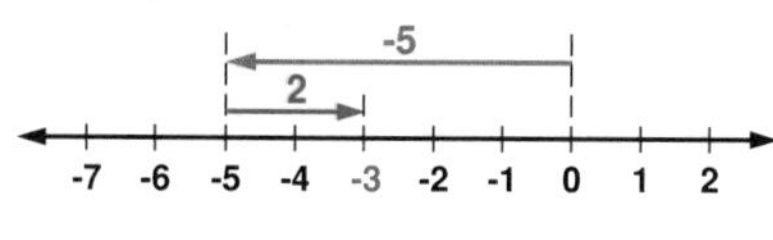

Start at zero. Move 5 units to the left. From there, move 2 units to the right. The sum is -3.

-5 + 2 = -3

3 Find 7 + (-3).

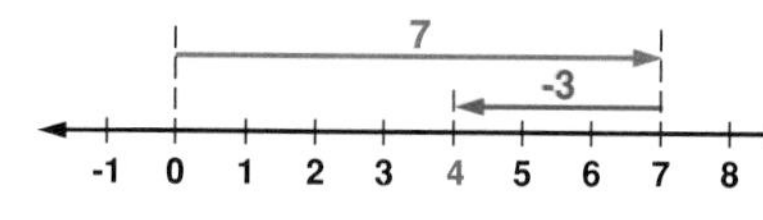

Start at zero. Move 7 units to the right. From there, move 3 units to the left. The sum is 4.

7 + (-3) = 4

Bell Ringer
Have students alternate giving greater and lesser negative integers.

Examples 2 and 3 suggest the following rule.

Adding Integers with Different Signs

To add integers with different signs, subtract their absolute values. Give the result the same sign as the integer with the greater absolute value.

Example

4 **Find 9 + (-2).**

$9 + (-2) = +(|9| - |-2|)$
$= +(9 - 2)$
$= +7$ or 7

Subtract absolute values. The result is positive because the integer with the greater absolute value, 9, is positive.

Checking for Understanding

Communicating Algebra **Write an addition sentence for each diagram.**

1. 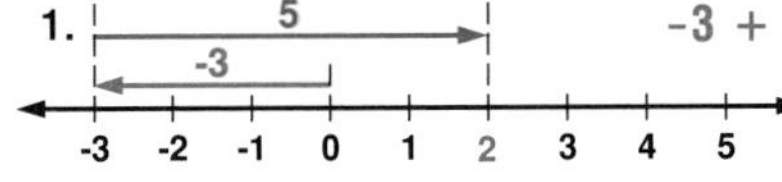

-3 + 5

2. 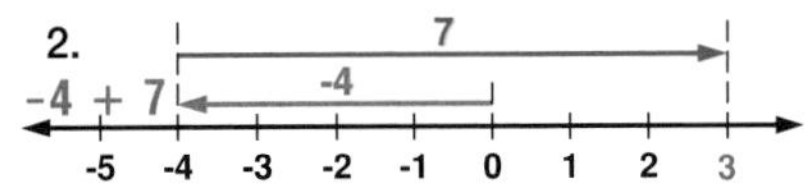

-4 + 7

3. 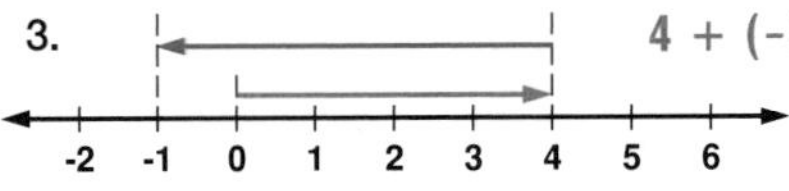

4 + (-5)

4. 6 + (-2) 

Guided Practice **State whether each sum is positive or negative.**

5. -5 + (-11) -
6. -14 + 13 -
7. -9 + 15 +
8. -5 + (-4) -

Find each sum or difference.

9. |-13| − |9| 4
10. |15| − |-3| 12
11. |-12| + |-3| 15
12. |-31| + |-12| 43

Exercises

Independent Practice **Add.**

13. +9 + (+7) 16
14. 18 + 21 39
15. -5 + (-13) -18
16. -18 + (-3) -21
17. -2 + (+17) 15
18. 15 + (-9) 6
19. 5 + 21 26
20. -10 + 3 -7
21. -11 + (-18) -29
22. -27 + (-43) -70
23. 88 + (-72) 16
24. 47 + (-63) -16
25. 33 + (-48) -15
26. -27 + 45 18
27. 67 + (-43) 24
28. -22 + 51 29

Evaluate each expression if a = -3, k = 5, and m = -6.

29. $8 + a$ 5
30. $13 + m$ 7
31. $-4 + k$ 1
32. $a + 12$ 9
33. $-31 + k$ -26
34. $-18 + a$ -21
35. $m + (-21)$ -27
36. $k + (-16)$ -11

3 PRACTICE/APPLY

Checking the Concept

Have students talk through Exercises 5-8 with a partner. Review rules before students begin to work independently.

Error Analysis

Watch for students who always use the sign of the first addend for the sign of the sum and for students who confuse the two rules.
Prevent by emphasizing the use of the number line.

Independent Practice

Homework Assignment	
Basic	13-43 odd, 45-49, 51-53
Average	14-44 even, 45-53
Honors	18-40 even, 42-53

Practice Masters Booklet, **p. 13**

Name ______________ Date ______________

Practice Worksheet 2-3

Adding Integers

Add.

1. −7 + (−5) −12
2. 10 + 9 19
3. −13 + (−3) −16
4. −12 + (−5) −17
5. −5 + 0 −5
6. −11 + (−6) −17
7. 8 + 9 17
8. −3 + (−17) −20

Find each sum or difference.

9. |−41| − |29| 12
10. |35| − |−19| 16
11. |−17| + |−9| 26
12. |−33| + |18| 51

State whether each sum is positive or negative.

13. 2 + (−4) negative
14. 8 + (−6) positive
15. −5 + 9 positive
16. 9 + (−1) positive
17. 8 + (−5) positive
18. 9 + (−7) positive
19. −73 + 17 negative
20. 57 + (−13) positive

Add.

21. −7 + (−4) −11
22. −52 + 52 0
23. −5 + 10 5
24. −10 + 12 2
25. 100 + (−300) −200
26. −7 + 8 1
27. 62 + (−65) −3
28. 500 + (−500) 0
29. 72 + 10 82
30. 72 + (−10) 62
31. −63 + (−18) −81
32. −100 + 12 −88
33. 164 + (−164) 0
34. 0 + (−21) −21
35. −287 + 300 13
36. 33 + (−37) −4
37. −101 + 111 10
38. −85 + 85 0
39. −37 + 0 −37
40. −13 + (−11) −24

Evaluate each expression if x = −12, y = 8, and z = −6.

41. −5 + x −17
42. y + (−13) −5
43. z + 15 9
44. x + (−10) −22
45. −8 + y 0
46. 20 + z 14
47. 31 + x 19
48. −27 + z −33

Alternate Strategies: Reteaching the Lesson

Reteaching Activity

Using Models Have students sketch a model of twenty yards of a football field. Using a coin or counter to represent a football, have them place the "ball" on the middle of the twenty-yard field. Describe two plays at a time and ask where the ball is in relation to the starting point.

Reteaching Masters Booklet, **p. 12**

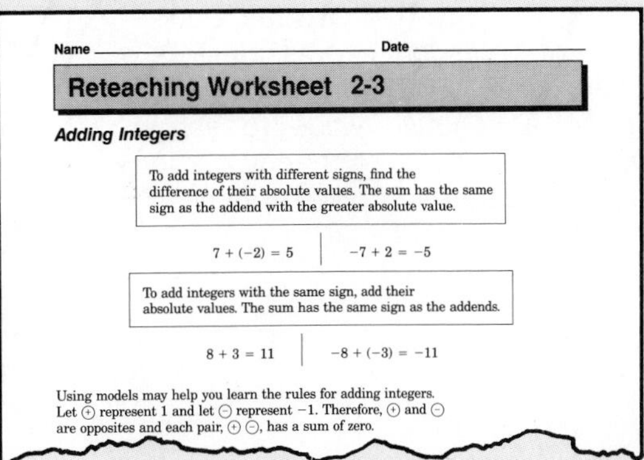

Name ______________ Date ______________

Reteaching Worksheet 2-3

Adding Integers

To add integers with different signs, find the difference of their absolute values. The sum has the same sign as the addend with the greater absolute value.

7 + (−2) = 5 | −7 + 2 = −5

To add integers with the same sign, add their absolute values. The sum has the same sign as the addends.

8 + 3 = 11 | −8 + (−3) = −11

Using models may help you learn the rules for adding integers. Let ⊕ represent 1 and let ⊖ represent −1. Therefore, ⊕ and ⊖ are opposites and each pair, ⊕ ⊖, has a sum of zero.

4 CLOSE

Assessment Option

Writing Have students write a descriptive phrase for what -6 + 8 could represent.

52. Sample answer: On a day in December, the low temperature in Anchorage, Alaska was 15°F below zero. The temperature rose 25°F that day. What was the high temperature?

Enrichment Masters Booklet, **p. 12**

Name ______________________ Date ______________

Enrichment Worksheet 2-3

Modular Arithmetic

In modular arithmetic, there is a finite set of numbers. An example of a finite set would be the numbers on the face of a clock. No matter how many numbers are added together, the answer will still be one of the twelve numbers found on the face of the clock.

Example: In mod 12, 5 + 8 + 2 = 3.

To find the sum, start at 0. Count 5 units in a clockwise direction, then 8 units, and then 2 units. You should end at the number 3.

Find each sum in mod 12.

1. 6 + 8 + 4 6
2. 7 + 9 + 11 + 5 8
3. 6 + 4 + 11 + 12 + 5 2
4. 1 + 4 + 9 + 11 + 6 7
5. 7 + 10 + 9 + 12 + 10 0
6. 6 + 12 + 5 + 12 + 8 + 12 7
7. 12 + 12 + 12 + 12 + 6 6
8. 4 + 9 + 3 + 7 + 8 + 11 + 5 11
9. 6 + 10 + 7 + 8 + 4 + 3 + 9 11
10. 9 + 2 + 4 + 3 + 10 + 12 + 4 + 11 7

Example: In mod 7, 3 + 5 + 2 = 3.

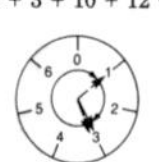

To find the sum, start at 0. Count 3 units in a clockwise direction, then 5 units, and then 2 units. You should end at the number 3.

Find each sum in mod 7.

11. 2 + 4 + 3 2
12. 5 + 1 + 6 + 3 1
13. 2 + 2 + 4 + 6 + 7 0
14. 5 + 3 + 4 + 6 + 1 5
15. 7 + 7 + 7 + 7 + 5 5
16. 6 + 5 + 1 + 2 + 4 4
17. 4 + 3 + 1 + 5 + 6 + 2 0
18. 4 + 2 + 1 + 6 + 7 + 5 + 4 + 3 4
19. 6 + 5 + 4 + 3 + 2 + 1 + 7 + 6 6
20. 5 + 7 + 4 + 4 + 2 + 6 + 1 + 2 3
21. Can you find a pattern to these exercises? Explain.
Yes; the sum in mod x is the remainder when the sum is divided by x.

Language Skill

Write an addition sentence for each situation. Then find the sum.

37. You withdraw \$40 from your savings account. Then you withdraw \$23.95 more. -40 + (-23.95); -63.95
38. In Saturday's football game, the Jackson Terriors lost 3 yards on one play. They gained 5 yards on the next.
39. The temperature was 16°F. The wind chill made it seem 25° colder. 16 + (-25); -9
40. Your paycheck is \$124.95. You spend \$15.50.
41. You jog 150 meters east. Then you turn around and jog 275 meters west. 150 + (-275); -125

38. -3 + 5; 2

40. 124.95 + (-15.50); 109.45

Logical Reasoning

Replace each ● with *always, sometimes,* or *never.*

42. The sum of two negative integers is ● negative. always
43. The sum of two positive integers is ● negative. never
44. The sum of a positive and a negative integer is ● positive. sometimes

Mixed Review

45. Simplify the expression $14y + 5(6 + 2y)$. (Lesson 1-4) $24y + 30$
46. Write a sentence that explains the meaning of |-3|. (Lesson 2-1)
47. Write the inequality for *3 feet is shorter than 8 feet.* (Lesson 2-2) 3 < 8
48. Write an inequality that compares the number of days in November to the number of days in January. (Lesson 2-2) 30 < 31
49. Write the algebraic expression for the phrase *the number of pencils divided by three.* (Lesson 1-8) $n \div 3$

46. |-3| means that -3 is 3 units from zero on the number line.

Applications

50. **Oceanography** A submarine at 1300 m below sea level descends an additional 1150 m. How far below sea level is the submarine now? -2450 m
51. **Astronomy** Using the information at the top of page 60, find the average surface temperature on Saturn's surface during the day. -123°C

Critical Thinking

52. **Make Up a Problem** Write a problem that can be solved using the addition sentence -15 + 25 = *c*. See margin for sample answer.

Wrap-Up

53. Draw a number line to show the addition sentence -3 + (-2) = -5. See Solutions Manual for graph.

Alternate Strategies: Extending the Lesson

Enrichment

Using Cooperative Groups Each student writes four expressions like Exercises 29-36 on an index card, giving a negative value to each variable. Students exchange cards and evaluate each other's expressions.

Cooperative Learning

Make That Sum Group Activity **2-3**

MATERIALS: 0–9 spinner • coin

The object of this game is for each of 2 to 4 players to be the first to start at zero and make a sum that fits a description given on the back of this card. Each description is a new game.

In order, spin the spinner to get a number and flip the coin to determine the sign of that number. A head makes the number positive and a tail makes it negative.

For each turn, determine the sum of the integer you just made and your previous total. Then record this on a piece of paper in front of you. The first player to reach a sum which fits the description wins the game.

Merrill Pre-Algebra ADDING INTEGERS

2-4 More on Adding Integers

Objective:
Add more than two integers using properties.

A weather balloon rises 200 feet from the ground, drops 150 feet, and then rises 300 feet. What is the new height of the balloon? One way to solve this problem is by adding the integers 200, -150, and 300.

rise of 200 feet	+	drop of 150 feet	+	rise of 300 feet	=	final height above the ground

$$200 + (-150) + 300 = h$$

$$[200 + (-150)] + 300 = h \quad \text{Associative property, addition}$$

$$50 + 300 = h$$

$$350 = h$$

The final height of the balloon is 350 feet above the ground.

Sometimes you can add integers mentally. Study the following example to see how the associative and commutative properties are used to find the sum.

How can you check your addition?
Add in a different order.

Example

1 Solve $x = 10 + 22 + (-7) + (-31)$.

$x = 10 + 22 + (-7) + (-31)$

$= 10 + (-7) + 22 + (-31)$ Think: $10 + (-7) = 3$, $22 + (-31) = -9$

$= 3 + (-9)$

$= -6$

CONNECTION TO ALGEBRA

You can use the distributive property and the rules for adding integers to combine like terms. Notice that the distributive property can be applied to more than two terms.

Example

2 Simplify $5y + (-12y) + 6y$.

$5y + (-12y) + 6y = [5 + (-12) + 6]y$ Distributive property

$= -1y$ Add 5, -12, and 6.

$= -y$ $-1y$ can be written as $-y$.

5-Minute Check
(over Lesson 2-3)

Add.
1. $-8 + (-15)$ **-23** 2. $-29 + 52$ **23**

Evaluate each expression if $a = -5$, $m = 3$, and $n = -7$.
3. $a + 8$ **3** 4. $n + (-18)$ **-25**

Transparency 2-4 contains the 5-Minute Check and a teaching aid for this lesson.

1 FOCUS

The emphasis of the lesson is on the convenience of using the associative and commutative properties when adding more than two integers. The distributive property is used to add like terms.

2 TEACH

Chalkboard Examples

- *For Example 1*
  Solve $x = 26 + (-5) + (-11)$. **10**
- *For Example 2*
  Simplify $3m + 14m + (-9m)$. **8m**

Practice Masters Booklet, **p. 14**

Name ________________ Date ________________

Practice Worksheet 2-4

More on Adding Integers

Solve each equation.

1. $6 + 5 + (-4) = t$ $t = 7$
2. $-4 + (-5) + 6 = m$ $m = -3$
3. $k = -3 + 8 + (-9)$ $k = -4$
4. $a = -6 + (-2) + (-1)$ $a = -9$
5. $10 + (-5) + 6 = n$ $n = 11$
6. $c = -8 + 8 + (-10)$ $c = -10$
7. $r = 3 + (-9) + (-4) + 7$ $r = -3$
8. $-5 + 8 + (-3) + 10 = s$ $s = 10$
9. $-15 + (-2) + 20 + 7 = l$ $l = 10$
10. $w = -21 + 17 + (-9) + 6$ $w = -7$
11. $36 + (-28) + (-16) + 24 = y$ $y = 16$
12. $x = -31 + 19 + (-15) + (-6)$ $x = -33$

Simplify each expression.

13. $6y + (-13y)$ $-7y$
14. $-12z + (-9z)$ $-21z$
15. $-8x + 9x + (-3x)$ $-2x$
16. $18e + (-7e) + (-14e)$ $-3e$
17. $5m + 29m + (-15m)$ $19m$
18. $-3d + (-8d) + (-17d)$ $-28d$
19. $12n + (-25n) + 20n$ $7n$
20. $-9t + (-9t) + 17t$ $-t$
21. $8f + 5f + 19f$ $32f$
22. $-16k + (-8k) + (-19k)$ $-43k$

Bell Ringer

Write ten addition sentences whose sum is -3. **Answers may vary. A typical answer is 5 + (-8) = -3.**

Reteaching Activity

Business Connection Supply students with a checking account balance sheet and a starting balance. Have them list checks and amounts they might write, and deposits they might make. Have each student determine a final balance. (Emphasize that negative balances are unacceptable.)

EE: 2D, 2E, 3A
TAAS: 2, 6, 12

3 PRACTICE/APPLY

Checking the Concept

In the **Guided Practice** exercises, ask students to identify the property they would first use before determining the sign of the sum.

Error Analysis
Watch for students who always add numbers in the order they appear. **Prevent by** encouraging students to look at the whole problem for parts that they can apply properties to.

Independent Practice

Homework Assignment	
Basic	9-31 odd, 33-39
Average	10-32 even, 33-39
Honors	12-26 even, 27-39

4 CLOSE

Assessment Option

Using Models Have students use counters to model the convenience of using the commutative, associative, and distributive properties by applying the *zero pair* principle that was used in the Exploration on page 59.

Enrichment Masters Booklet, **p. 13**

Name ______________ Date ______________

Enrichment Worksheet 2-4

Sums of Even and Odd Numbers

How do you find the sums of even and odd numbers?

The formula $k(k + 1)$ can be used to find the sum of the first k even numbers. | The sum of the first k odd numbers can be found by using the formula k^2.

Example: Find the sum of the first 9 even numbers.

List the first nine even numbers. Then add them together.
$2 + 4 + 6 + 8 + 10 + 12 + 14 + 16 + 18 = 90$

Now use the formula $k(k + 1)$ if $k = 9$.
$k(k + 1) = 9(9 + 1)$
$= 9(10)$ or 90 The sum is the same!

Example: Find the sum of the first 8 odd numbers.

Use the formula $k \cdot k$ if $k = 8$ to find the sum.
$k \cdot k = 8 \cdot 8$
$= 64$

List the first eight odd numbers. Then add them together.
$1 + 3 + 5 + 7 + 9 + 11 + 13 + 15 = 64$ The sum checks.

Example: Find the sum of the first 10 even numbers plus the first 10 odd numbers.

$k(k + 1) + k^2 = 10(11) + 10^2$
$= 110 + 100$
$= 210$

Solve. Use the correct formula to find the sum of each.

1. the first 10 even numbers 100
2. the first 16 even numbers 272
3. the first 100 even numbers 10,100
4. the first 50 even numbers 2550
5. the first 5 odd numbers 25
6. the first 10 odd numbers 100
7. the first 100 odd numbers 10,000
8. the first 300 odd numbers 90,000
9. the first 60 numbers $30(31) + 30^2 = 1830$
10. the first 75 numbers $75(76) + 75^2 = 11{,}325$
11. the first 50 odd numbers plus the first 50 even numbers $50^2 + 50(51) = 5050$
12. the first 20 even numbers minus the first 20 odd numbers $20(21) - 20^2 = 20$
13. the first 20 even numbers plus the first 10 odd numbers $20(21) + 10^2 = 520$

Checking for Understanding

Communicating Algebra

1. What property allows you to add in any order? **Commutative**
2. Tell two different ways to solve $x = 8 + 24 + (-5) + (-25)$. **See margin.**

Guided Practice

State whether each sum is positive or negative.

3. $-3 + 4 + 7$ +
4. $-10 + 9 + 8$ +
5. $-8 + 7 + (-3)$ -
6. $-5 + (-6) + (-9)$ -
7. $-11 + 13 + 2$ +
8. $-15 + 9 + (-10)$ -

Exercises

Independent Practice

Solve each equation.

9. $x = 4 + (-12) + (-18)$ **-26**
10. $y = 7 + (-11) + 32$ **28**
11. $h = 8 + (-15) + 13$ **6**
12. $5 + (-7) + 20 = a$ **18**
13. $-18 + (-23) + 10 = c$ **-31**
14. $-12 + 14 + 8 = d$ **10**
15. $f = -17 + 36 + (-45)$ **-26**
16. $g = -31 + (-9) + 62$ **22**
17. $r = 47 + 32 + (-16)$ **63**
18. $83 + (-19) + 16 = m$ **80**

Simplify each expression.

19. $5x + (-21x)$ **-16x**
20. $-3z + (-17z)$ **-20z**
21. $-12y + 5y$ **-7y**
22. $-3a + 12a + (-14a)$ **-5a**
23. $16d + (-9d) + (-27d)$ **-20d**
24. $9m + 43m + (-16m)$ **36m**
25. $-4f + (-6f) + (-19f)$ **-29f**
26. $14b + (-21b) + 37b$ **30b**

Mental Math

Solve each equation mentally.

27. $x = -11 + 10 + (-7) + 9$ **1**
28. $-14 + (-15) + 26 + 7 = y$ **4**
29. $-35 + 15 + 25 + (-10) = a$ **-5**
30. $c = 98 + (-102) + 102 + (-98)$ **0**
31. $m = 28 + (-56) + 32 + (-75)$ **-71**
32. $-69 + 33 + (-8) + (-15) = y$ **-59**

Mixed Review

33. *True* or *false:* $30 - 18 \div 9 + 3 = 1$. (Lesson 1-1) **F**
34. Find two values for m that make $3m - 7 \leq 0$ true. (Lesson 1-10)
35. Simplify $|19| - |-4|$. (Lesson 2-1) **15**
36. State whether the sum of -5 and -8 is positive or negative. (Lesson 2-3) -

34. Sample answers: 0, 2

Application

37. **Consumer Awareness** Karen opened a checking account at a local bank on May 7. A record of her checks and deposits is shown below. What is the balance in her account on May 22?
100 + (-15.95) + 18 + (-52.87); $49.18

DATE	DESCRIPTION	CHECK	DEPOSIT
5/7	Opening Deposit		$100.00
5/9	Jim's Record Mart	$15.95	
5/14	Babysitting		$18.00
5/22	Diller's Department Store	$52.87	

Critical Thinking

38. Roderico bought two shirts for $38. He paid $4 more for one shirt than for the other. How much did he pay for each shirt? **$17; $21**

Wrap-Up

39. Give a real-world example that involves finding sums of many integers. **Sample answer: grocery shopping with coupons.**

2. Sample answers:

- **Add the numbers from left to right.**
- **Add mentally:**

$x = (8 + (-5)) + (25 + (-24))$
$= 3 + 1$
$= 4$

Cooperative Learning

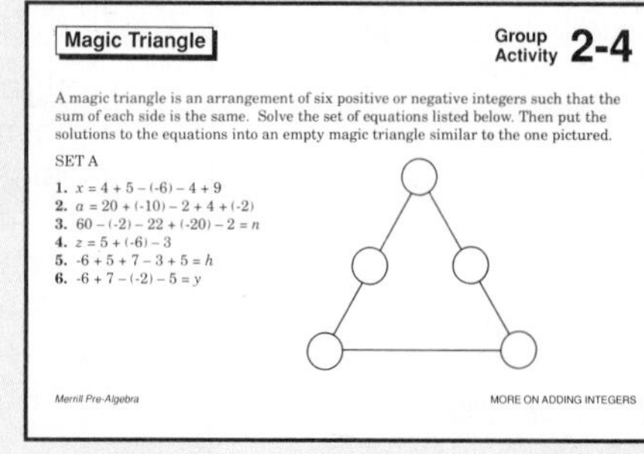

Magic Triangle Group Activity **2-4**

A magic triangle is an arrangement of six positive or negative integers such that the sum of each side is the same. Solve the set of equations listed below. Then put the solutions to the equations into an empty magic triangle similar to the one pictured.

SET A

1. $x = 4 + 5 - (-6) - 4 + 9$
2. $a = 20 + (-10) - 2 + 4 + (-2)$
3. $60 - (-2) - 22 + (-20) - 2 = n$
4. $z = 5 + (-6) - 3$
5. $-6 + 5 + 7 - 3 + 5 = h$
6. $-6 + 7 - (-2) - 5 = y$

Merrill Pre-Algebra MORE ON ADDING INTEGERS

Exploration

Subtracting Integers

Materials: counters, mat

In this Exploration, you will use counters to model subtraction.

▶ Consider +8 − (+3). To model this operation, start with a set of eight positive counters and remove three.

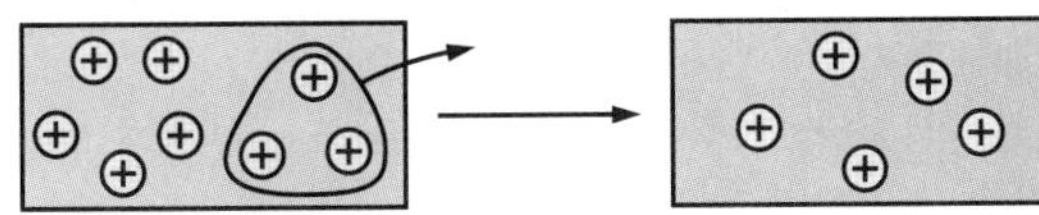

Therefore +8 − (+3) = +5.

▶ Consider -8 − (-3). Start with a set of eight negative counters and remove three.

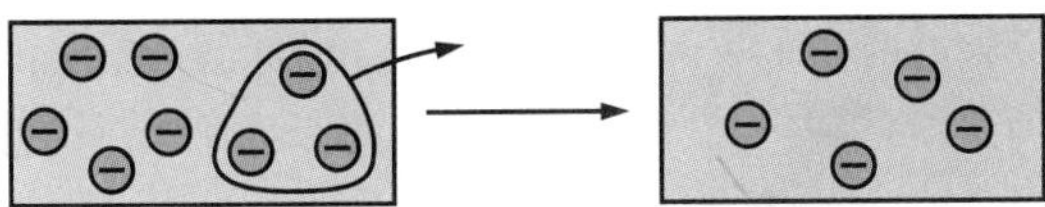

Therefore -8 − (-3) = -5.

▶ Now consider +8 − (-3). This means start with a set of eight *positive* counters and remove three *negative* counters. If you add three zero pairs to the set, the value of the set does not change. Now you can remove three negative counters.

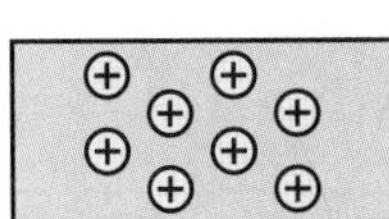 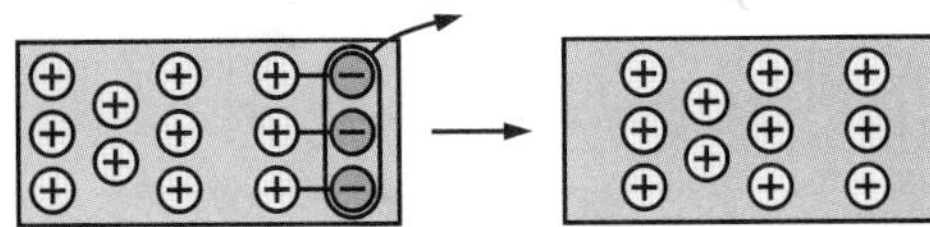

Therefore +8 − (-3) = 11.

Your turn: What does -8 − (+3) mean? Model this operation. Explain how zero pairs are used in this subtraction.

Model each problem. For diagrams to Exercises 1-8, see Solutions Manual.

1. 5 − 2
2. -5 − (-2)
3. 5 − (-2)
4. -5 − 2
5. 3 − 7
6. 3 − (-7)
7. -3 − 7
8. -3 − (-7)

Analysis

9. Notice the relationship between 5 − 2 and 5 + (-2). How are these two the same? How are they different? Model both operations. See Solutions Manual.

SET-UP

Materials

- Integer Mat, Lab Manual, p. 2
- Counters, Lab Manual, p. 4
- Exploration Worksheet, Lab Manual, p. 31

For Students Use two different colored counters or dry beans to represent the positive and negative integers. Each group of students will need a packet of 10 positive and 10 negative counters.

HINT: Assemble the counters in sandwich bags with a twist-tie for convenient management.

For the Overhead Projector Two different colored counters were used in the integer addition exploration. Another option is to use transparent bingo chips. They are inexpensive, easy to handle, and show up clearly on the overhead screen.

EXPLORATION
Subtracting Integers

Objective Students will be able to model integer subtraction, and will begin to understand the connection between addition and subtraction.

1 FOCUS

Problem Solving

Pose the following problem to students: A debtor owes you $12, but he only has $10. So you want to take 12 from his 10. That is, you want to perform 10 − 12. How is this possible? **He still owes you $2.**

2 TEACH

Using Discussion

When modeling the operations for students, encourage students to discuss what occurs during each operation. Let students hypothesize and justify what they expect is going to happen before you reveal the solution.

3 PRACTICE/APPLY

Using Manipulatives

Encourage students to model each of the operations and make notes about what occurs in each operation.

4 CLOSE

Using Connections

Use Exercises 9 and 10 to build patterns regarding the relationship between addition and subtraction.

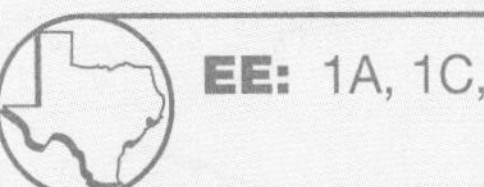

Lesson Notes 2-5

5-Minute Check
(over Lesson 2-4)

Solve each equation.
1. $y = -2 + (-17) + 6$ **-13**
2. $x = 9 + (-41) + 22$ **-10**

Simplify each expression.

3. $21y + (-30y) + 15y$ **6y**
4. $67m + (-52m) + (-34m)$ **-19m**
5. $-4x + (-8x) + (-41x)$ **-53x**

Transparency 2-5 contains the 5-Minute Check and a teaching aid for this lesson.

1 FOCUS

The purpose of the lesson is to develop the concept of additive inverse and apply this concept to the rules for subtracting integers.

Motivating the Lesson

Tell students that you borrowed $5 from a friend and later borrowed another $3. Ask students:

- How much do I owe my friend? **$8**
- How can this example be written as an addition problem? **-5 + (-3) = -8**
- How can this example be written as a subtraction problem? **-5 − 3 = -8**

2 TEACH

Chalkboard Examples

Solve each equation.

- *For Example 1*
  $x = 5 - 14$ **-9**
- *For Example 2*
  $7 - (-9) = y$ **16**
- *For Example 3*
  $m = -6 - (-15)$ **9**
- *For Example 4*
  $-3 - 18 = f$ **-21**

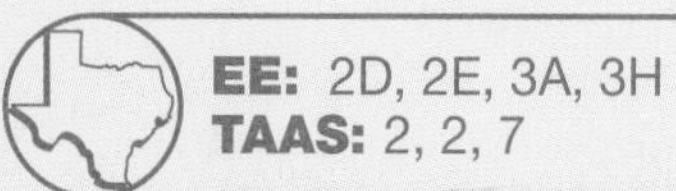

EE: 2D, 2E, 3A, 3H
TAAS: 2, 2, 7

2-5 Subtracting Integers

Objective:
Subtract integers.

Key Terms:
opposite
additive inverse

Lightning occurs when there are an unequal number of positive and negative electrical charges in the atmosphere. Positive charges and negative charges are opposites of each other.

Similarly, every positive integer can be paired with a negative integer. These pairs are called **opposites.** For example, the opposite of +3 is -3.

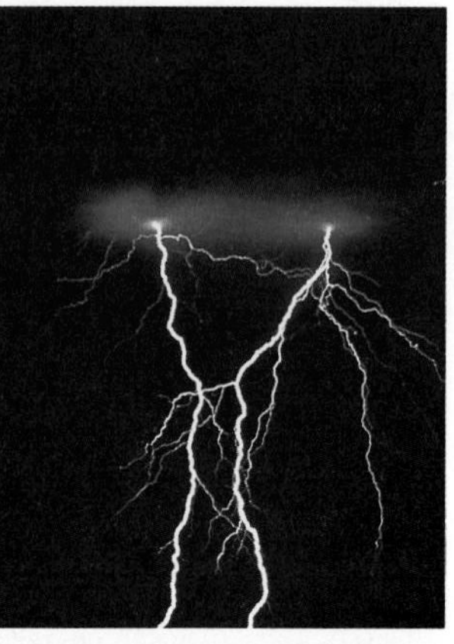

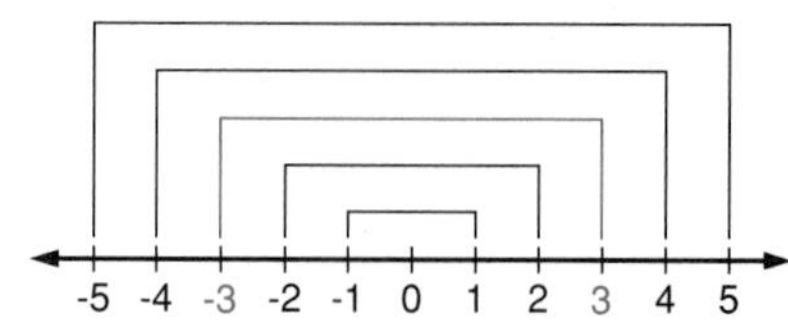

Notice that +3 and -3 are on opposite sides of 0. Both +3 and -3 are 3 units away from 0.

A number and its opposite are called **additive inverses** of each other. What do you notice about the sum of a number and its additive inverse?

$3 + (-3) = 0$ $\quad -41 + 41 = 0$ $\quad 236 + (-236) = 0$

Additive Inverse Property

In words: The sum of any number and its additive inverse is zero, the additive identity.
In symbols: For any number a, $a + (-a) = 0$.

Additive inverses can be used to define subtraction for integers. Compare the following addition and subtraction sentences.

Subtraction	**Addition**
$8 - 3 = 5$	$8 + (-3) = 5$

additive inverses (3 and -3)
same result (5 and 5)

Subtracting Integers

In words: To subtract an integer, add its additive inverse.
In symbols: For any integers a and b, $a - b = a + (-b)$.

Bell Ringer

Write ten integer expressions using addition, each with at least three numbers, whose value is -1. **Answers may vary. A typical answer is -2 + 4 + (-3).**

The subtraction rule allows you to rewrite any subtraction expression as an addition expression. This is useful because you already know how to add integers.

Examples

Solve each equation.

1
$a = 6 - 11$
$a = 6 + (-11)$
$a = -5$

2
$5 - (-8) = x$
$5 + 8 = x$
$13 = x$

3
$c = -4 - (-7)$
$c = -4 + 7$
$c = 3$

4
$-8 - 19 = d$
$-8 + (-19) = d$
$-27 = d$

CONNECTION TO ALGEBRA

The rule for subtraction of integers and the distributive property can be used to combine like terms.

Example

5 **Simplify $3y - 5y$.**

Why is -5y the additive inverse of 5y?
$5y + (-5y) = 0$

$3y - 5y = 3y + (-5y)$ — Subtract 5y by adding its additive inverse, -5y.

$= [3 + (-5)]y$ — Use the distributive property.

$= -2y$

Checking for Understanding

Communicating Algebra

Replace each ■ with a word or phrase to make a true sentence.

1. The opposite of a positive integer is ■. a negative integer
2. The opposite of a negative integer is ■. a positive integer
3. The opposite of the opposite of a positive integer is ■. a positive integer
4. If $n = 3$, then $-n =$ ■. -3

Guided Practice

State the additive inverse of each number.

5. +6 -6
6. -6 6
7. -13 13
8. 0 0
9. b $-b$
10. -b b
11. cd $-cd$
12. $-ef$ ef
13. $-5x$ $5x$
14. $9cd$ $-9cd$

15. $7 + (-13) = x$ 16. $-8 + (-5) = a$ 17. $-17 + (-9) = b$ 20. $-24 + 23 = x$

Restate each subtraction sentence as an addition sentence.

15. $7 - 13 = x$
16. $-8 - 5 = a$
17. $-17 - 9 = b$
18. $9 - (-2) = c$
$9 + 2 = c$
19. $-18 - (-16) = y$
$-18 + 16 = y$
20. $-24 - (-23) = x$

3 PRACTICE/APPLY

Checking the Concept

Exercises 15-20 require students to rewrite the subtraction problem as an addition problem. Monitor work carefully. If necessary, have students rewrite Exercises 21-35 as addition problems before they begin working independently.

Error Analysis

Watch for students who get so involved in the process that they forget to assign a sign to the solution. **Prevent by** having students check the reasonableness of the solution. For many problems, students should be able to look at the problem and tell the sign of the solution.

Practice Masters Booklet, **p. 15**

Name ______ Date ______

Practice Worksheet 2-5

Subtracting Integers

Restate each subtraction sentence as an addition sentence.

1. $39 - 18 = x$ $39 + (-18) = x$
2. $65 - 72 = y$ $65 + (-72) = y$
3. $-85 - (-42) = z$ $-85 + 42 = z$
4. $-15 - (-86) = a$ $-15 + 86 = a$
5. $-21 - 24 = b$ $-21 + (-24) = b$
6. $-16 - (-57) = c$ $-16 + 57 = c$
7. $84 - 92 = t$ $84 + (-92) = t$
8. $-32 - 74 = w$ $-32 + (-74) = w$
9. $-74 - (-21) = d$ $-74 + 21 = d$

Simplify each expression.

10. $-124k - (-65k)$ $-59k$
11. $15x - 21x$ $-6x$
12. $-32y - (-15y)$ $-17y$
13. $65x - (-12x)$ $77x$
14. $-74a - 56a$ $-130a$
15. $-21xy - 32xy$ $-53xy$
16. $-95ab - (-16ab)$ $-79ab$
17. $84ac - 15ac$ $69ac$
18. $124ad - (-203ad)$ $327ad$
19. $56xy - 83xy$ $-27xy$
20. $-453ab - (-675ab)$ $222ab$
21. $2045m - (-3056m)$ $5101m$

Solve each equation.

22. $-4 - 1 = f$ $f = -5$
23. $h = -5 - (-7)$ $h = 2$
24. $z = 9 - 12$ $z = -3$
25. $a = -765 - (-34)$ $a = -731$
26. $652 - (-57) = b$ $b = 709$
27. $c = 346 - 865$ $c = -519$
28. $d = -136 - (-158)$ $d = 22$
29. $x = 342 - (-456)$ $x = 798$
30. $y = -684 - (-379)$ $y = -305$
31. $b = -658 - 867$ $b = -1525$
32. $657 - 899 = t$ $t = -242$
33. $3004 - (-1007) = r$ $r = 4011$
34. $n = -1004 - (-6125)$ $n = 5121$
35. $p = -8734 - 5276$ $p = -14{,}010$
36. $q = 9647 - (-4253)$ $q = 13{,}900$

Alternate Strategies: Reteaching the Lesson

Reteaching Activity

Using Models Have each student write two integer absolute values on cards. Have each student write all the subtraction problems that would use the integers or the absolute values. For example, if cards show 2 and 3, write the problems 2 − 3, 2 − (-3), -2 − 3, and -2 − (-3). Solve. To check the solutions, model the four problems in the same manner as in the Exploration on page 65.

Reteaching Masters Booklet, **p. 14**

Name ______ Date ______

Reteaching Worksheet 2-5

Subtracting Integers

To subtract an integer, add its opposite.

$15 - 20 = 15 + (-20) = -5$ — To subtract 20, add −20.

$5 - (-9) = 5 + 9 = 14$ — To subtract −9, add 9.

Write an addition expression for each of the following.

1. $9 - 16$ $9 + (-16)$
2. $12 - (-8)$ $12 + 8$
3. $-7 - (-7)$ $-7 + 7$
4. $-3 - 18$ $-3 + (-18)$
5. $\frac{4}{9} - \frac{4}{9}$ $\frac{4}{9} + \left(-\frac{4}{9}\right)$
6. $-3.5 - (-4.7)$ $-3.5 + 4.7$

Simplify each expression.

7. $-5x - 5x$ $-10x$
8. $7y - (-12y)$ $19y$
9. $4z - 15z$ $-11z$
10. [illegible] $5ab$
11. $-21rs - 14rs$
12. 17[illegible]

Independent Practice

Homework Assignment	
Basic	21-51 odd, 53-60, 64-66
Average	22-52 even, 53-60, 63-66
Honors	26-52 even, 53-66

Chapter 2, Quiz A (Lessons 2-1 through 2-5) is available in the Evaluation Masters Booklet, p. 16.

4 CLOSE

Assessment Option

Modeling Have the students model the following problem situation using play money: A business did $5000 worth of business in one week. They spent $2750 on supplies and made a profit of $2250.

Enrichment Masters Booklet, **p. 14**

Name ______________________ Date ______________

Enrichment Worksheet 2-5

Subtracting in a Finite Number System

To subtract in a finite number system, add a number's additive inverse. The additive inverse of a number in a finite number system is that number which when added to the first number results in a sum that is the mod or identity.

Example: What is the additive inverse of 4 in mod 7?

$-(4) = 3$ **What is added to 4 to equal 7? The answer is 3. The additive inverse of 4 in mod 7 is 3.**

The additive inverses for 1, 2, 3, 5, and 6 are 6, 5, 4, 2, and 1, respectively.

In mod 7, subtraction is the same as adding the additive inverse.

Example: $3 - 4 = 3 + (-4) = 3 + 3 = 6$ **Subtract 4 by adding its additive inverse, 3.**
$1 - 6 = 1 + (-6) = 1 + 1 = 2$ **Subtract 6 by adding its additive inverse, 1.**

Solve each equation in mod 7.

1. $x = 1 - 3$ $x = 1 + 4 = 5$
2. $5 - 6 = y$ $y = 5 + 1 = 6$
3. $2 - 5 = z$ $z = 2 + 2 = 4$
4. $q = 6 - 4$ $q = 6 + 3 = 2$
5. $b = 2 - 6$ $b = 2 + 1 = 3$
6. $3 - 4 = z$ $z = 3 + 3 = 6$
7. $y = 0 - 4$ $y = 0 + 3 = 3$
8. $3 - 6 = x$ $x = 3 + 1 = 4$
9. $4 - 5 = p$ $p = 4 + 2 = 6$

Solve each equation in mod 12.

10. $y = 2 - 9$ $y = 2 + 3 = 5$
11. $x = 1 - 8$ $x = 1 + 4 = 5$
12. $3 - 5 = r$ $r = 3 + 7 = 10$
13. $z = 0 - 4$ $z = 0 + 8 = 8$
14. $q = 4 - 10$ $q = 4 + 2 = 6$
15. $6 - 11 = p$ $p = 6 + 1 = 7$
16. $5 - 3 = k$ $k = 5 + 9 = 2$
17. $7 - 11 = z$ $z = 7 + 1 = 8$
18. $2 - 3 = b$ $b = 2 + 9 = 11$
19. $8 - 10 = r$ $r = 8 + 2 = 10$
20. $9 - 7 = f$ $f = 9 + 5 = 2$
21. $4 - 7 = w$ $w = 4 + 5 = 9$
22. $m = 1 - 11$ $m = 1 + 1 = 2$
23. $z = 3 - 8$ $z = 3 + 4 = 7$
24. $g = 5 - 9$ $g = 5 + 3 = 8$

Exercises

Independent Practice

Solve each equation.

21. $x = -5 - 3$ **-8**
22. $y = -6 - (-8)$ **2**
23. $a = 7 - 13$ **-6**
24. $-11 - 9 = c$ **-20**
25. $-13 - (-18) = d$ **5**
26. $-24 - 19 = h$ **-43**
27. $7 - 25 = f$ **-18**
28. $-17 - (-2) = g$ **-15**
29. $j = -15 - 23$ **-38**
30. $29 - 32 = a$ **-3**
31. $b = -34 - (-19)$ **-15**
32. $c = 51 - (-11)$ **62**
33. $-42 - 38 = q$ **-80**
34. $n = -29 - 36$ **-65**
35. $-18 - (-18) = m$ **0**

Evaluate each expression.

36. $y - 5$, if $y = -8$ **-13**
37. $a - (-7)$, if $a = 19$ **26**
38. $b - (-5)$, if $b = -13$ **-8**
39. $h - (-13)$, if $h = -18$ **-5**
40. $k - (-12)$, if $k = 27$ **39**
41. $w - 37$, if $w = -18$ **-55**
42. $9 - n$, if $n = -7$ **16**
43. $11 - m$, if $m = 5$ **6**

Simplify each expression.

44. $3x - 18x$ **$-15x$**
45. $11a - 21a$ **$-10a$**
46. $-2b - (-3b)$ **b**
47. $-16ab - 13ab$ **$-29ab$**
48. $24cd - (-24cd)$ **$48cd$**
49. $-28d - 17d$ **$-45d$**
50. $41x - (-29x)$ **$70x$**
51. $30y - (-11y)$ **$41y$**
52. $-39ad - 15ad$ **$-54ad$**

Mixed Review

53. Which number, 4, 16, or 32, is a solution of the equation $8 = \frac{x}{4}$? (Lesson 1-5) **32**
54. Name the absolute value of -21. (Lesson 2-1) **21**
55. Find the sum of 84 and -56. (Lesson 2-3) **28**
56. State whether the sum of -6, -3, and 10 is positive or negative. (Lesson 2-4) **positive**
57. Solve the equation $h = 1 + (-14) + 19$. (Lesson 2-4) **6**
58. Simplify the expression $-4x + 6x + (-13x)$. (Lesson 2-4) **$-11x$**

Calculator

The [+/−] key on a calculator is called the change-sign key. When it is pressed, the calculator changes the sign of the number in the display. For each of the following, tell what number is in the display.

59. Enter 8, press [+/−] once. **-8**
60. Enter 10, press [+/−] twice. **10**
61. Enter 3, press [+/−] 25 times. **-3**
62. Enter 5, press [+/−] 100 times. **5**

Applications

63. -$1475

63. **Business** The formula $P = I - E$ is used to find the profit (P) when income (I) and expenses (E) are known. Find P if $I = \$15,525$ and $E = \$17,000$.
64. **Meteorology** The temperature outside was 20°F. The wind chill made it feel like -15°F. Find the difference between the real temperature and the apparent temperature. **-35°F**

Critical Thinking

65. *True* or *false:* $-n$ names a negative number. **false**

Wrap-Up

66. **Make Up a Problem** Write a subtraction problem in which the difference is a negative integer. **Sample answer: 5 − 8 = −3**

Alternate Strategies: Extending the Lesson

Enrichment

Using Models Have students write a number on each of three cards. Write as many addition, subtraction, and combination problems as possible. Solve. For example, if 3, 4, and 5 are drawn, the following problems are some that can be written: 3 + (-4) − (-5) and -3 − 4 + (-5).

Cooperative Learning

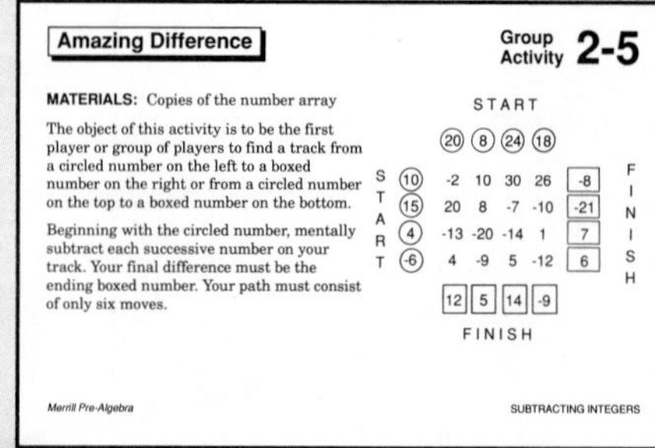

Amazing Difference Group Activity **2-5**

MATERIALS: Copies of the number array

The object of this activity is to be the first player or group of players to find a track from a circled number on the left to a boxed number on the right or from a circled number on the top to a boxed number on the bottom.

Beginning with the circled number, mentally subtract each successive number on your track. Your final difference must be the ending boxed number. Your path must consist of only six moves.

START

	(20)	(8)	(24)	(18)	
(10)	-2	10	30	26	[-8]
(15)	20	8	-7	-10	[-21]
(4)	-13	-20	-14	1	[7]
(-6)	4	-9	5	-12	[6]
	[12]	[5]	[14]	[-9]	

FINISH

Merrill Pre-Algebra SUBTRACTING INTEGERS

Algebra in Action-Geography

Time Zones

The prime meridian is a semicircle passing through Greenwich, England. Lines of longitude indicate degrees west or east of the prime meridian. The prime meridian is at 0°.

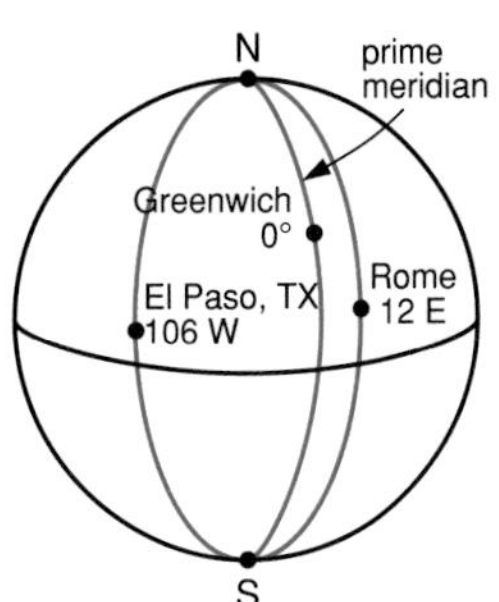

A city's longitude determines its time zone. The zone labeled zero is centered about the prime meridian. The time zones to the east of the prime meridian are named by negative numbers. The time zones to the west are named by positive numbers.

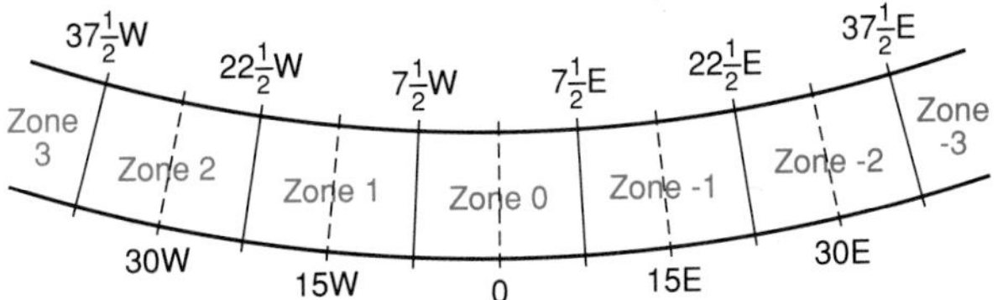

How does this differ from the integer number line?
Positive and negatives are reversed.

Various cities and their time zones are given below.

City	Time Zone	City	Time Zone
Athens, Greece	-2	Los Angeles, USA	8
Bombay, India	-5	Moscow, USSR	-3
Chicago, USA	6	New York, USA	5
El Paso, USA	7	Paris, France	0
Honolulu, USA	11	Rome, Italy	-1

To find the time in another city, subtract the time zone of the other city from the time zone of your own location. For example, if you are in El Paso and wish to know the time in Athens, subtract.

$$\text{El Paso time zone} - \text{Athens time zone} = 7 - (-2) = 9$$

Since 9 is positive, the time in Athens is 9 hours *ahead* of El Paso. Thus, if it is 1:00 P.M. in El Paso, it is 10:00 P.M. in Athens.

1. If the time in Chicago is 4:00 P.M., find the time in Rome. **11:00 P.M.**
2. If the time in El Paso is 11:00 A.M., find the time in Honolulu. **7:00 A.M.**
3. If the time in Honolulu is 5:00 P.M., find the time in New York. **11:00 P.M.**
4. The person you wish to reach by phone lives in Paris and is available from 9:00 A.M. to 5:00 P.M., Paris time. During what hours should you call if you live in Chicago? **between 3:00 A.M. and 11: 00 A.M., Chicago time.**

Applying Algebra to the Real World

Objective This optional page shows how algebra is used in the real world and also provides a change of pace.

Using Discussion

Ask students if they have relatives who live in a different time zone or if they have ever been awakened in the middle of the night by someone phoning from a time zone that is located to the west. Discuss the reasons why the students think the different time zones exist.

Using Models

Borrow some globes and world maps from the geography teachers to show students the exact location of the cities used in the example and exercises. A globe can be used to explain why time zones exist (so the position of the sun is relatively the same at the same time of day). A world map may have the time zones marked on it.

Activity

Cooperative Learning (Materials: old overseas Official Airlines Guides) Have students work in small groups to study the schedules and take turns asking questions about arrival and departure times.

Lesson Notes 2-6

5-Minute Check
(over Lesson 2-5)

Evaluate each expression.
1. $a - 6$, if $a = -9$ **-15**
2. $k - (-42)$, if $k = 51$ **93**
3. $5 - m$, if $m = -12$ **17**
4. $13 - x$, if $x = 8$ **5**
5. $n - 27$, if $n = -30$ **-57**

Transparency 2-6 contains the 5-Minute Check and a teaching aid for this lesson.

1 FOCUS

The purpose of this lesson is to introduce students to a logic statement, the negation of a statement, and how to determine the truth value of a statement.

Motivating the Lesson

Go around the room and have each student make a statement about themselves or their surroundings and then give the negation of that statement.

2 TEACH

Using Discussion

Point out that a variable such as p or q may represent a statement instead of a number.

Emphasize that a negation must always negate the statement. Give several examples.

Chalkboard Examples

Let p represent the statement *a dog does not have four legs*. State whether the statement is true or false. Then state whether its negation is true or false. **p, false; negation, true**

EE: 1A, 1E

2-6 Statements and Negations

Objective:
Determine if a statement and its negation are true or false.

Key Terms:
statement
logic
negation

Which of the following sentences are true? Which are false?

Mammals are warm-blooded. **true**
The word *pizza* is a verb. **false**
Indianapolis is the capital of Indiana. **true**
$1 + 2 \times 5 = 15$ **false**

Note that each of the previous sentences is either true or false. A **statement** is any sentence that is either true or false, but not both. **Logic,** the study of formal reasoning, is based on statements.

You can refer to a specific statement by representing it with a letter such as p or q. For example, let p represent the statement *Dublin is a city in Ireland.* This statement is true. To find the **negation** of statement p, write $\sim p$, which is read "not p." This represents the statement *Dublin is not a city in Ireland.* This statement is false.

The example above illustrates the principle that the negation of a true statement is false and the negation of a false statement is true.

Example

1 Let p represent the statement $9 + 3 = 11$. Let q represent the statement *A spider does not have six legs.* State whether each statement is true or false. Then state whether its negation is true or false.

a. p $\quad 9 + 3 = 11$ This statement is false.
$\sim p$ $\quad 9 + 3 \neq 11$ This statement is true.

b. q A spider does not have six legs. This statement is true.
$\sim q$ A spider has six legs. This statement is false.

What is the negation of the statement *No roses are yellow?* You might think it is *All roses are yellow.* But then the original statement and its negation are both false. It is true, though, that some roses are yellow. So the negation is *Some roses are yellow.*

Bell Ringer

Write five subtraction problems whose difference is -2 and five subtraction problems whose difference is 2. **Answers may vary. Typical answers are $3 - 5 = -2$ and $5 - 3 = 2$.**

Reteaching Activity

Using Discussion Remind students that the negation must *always* be false if the statement is true. Divide the class into groups. In each group, one student makes a statement. Other students write its negation. Repeat until all have made a statement. Have students read negations for each statement and discuss whether they are valid.

Checking for Understanding

Communicating Algebra

Complete each sentence.

1. A ___?___ is a sentence that is either true or false. statement
2. $\sim p$ refers to the ___?___ of statement p. negation
3. Choose the statement that is the negation of the statement *All integers are even.* c.
   a. All integers are odd. b. No integers are even.
   c. Some integers are even. d. Some integers are odd.

Guided Practice

State whether each statement is *true* or *false*.

4. Water freezes at 0°C. T
5. $9 \leq 9$ T

State the negation of each statement. Then state whether the statement and its negation are *true* or *false*. See Solutions Manual.

6. Corn is a vegetable.
7. $3(11 - 5) \neq 18$

Exercises

Independent Practice

State whether each statement is *true* or *false*.

8. Missouri is west of the Mississippi River. T
9. Clarinets are not members of the woodwind family. F
10. $2x = 6$ is an equation. T
11. $2n = 4$ when $n = 1$ F
12. $\frac{1}{2} + \frac{3}{4} = \frac{3}{2} + \frac{1}{4}$ F
13. $0.1 + 0.11 = 0.21$ T

Write the negation of each statement. Then state whether the statement and its negation are true or false. See margin.

14. All years have 365 days.
15. Mozart was not a poet.
16. The solution to $5x = 5$ is 1.
17. $3y - 2y = 1$
18. Some cars have four doors.
19. $45 > 2(16 - 9)$

Using Logic

20. Ben hollered from his room, "Mom, I don't have no clean socks." His mom replied, "Please don't use double negatives, Ben!" What did she mean? Could Ben's statement be interpreted as "I have clean socks?" Why or why not? See margin.

Mixed Review

21. Solve the equation $-34 + 9 = h$. (Lesson 2-3) −25
22. If $x = 4$, then $-x =$ ■. (Lesson 2-5) −4

Challenge

23. If p represents a true statement, is $\sim p$ true or false? $\sim(\sim p)$? $\sim(\sim(\sim p))$? false, true, false

Critical Thinking

24. The gasoline tank of Mr. Steiner's car is one-third full. After he adds 2.5 gallons to it, the tank is one-half full. What is the capacity of his car's tank? 15 gallons

Wrap-Up

25. Write an example of a statement. State whether it is true or false. Then write its negation and state whether it is true or false. See margin.

3 PRACTICE/APPLY

Checking the Concept

Have students verbalize negations for Exercises 4 and 5.

Error Analysis

Watch for students who give negations that are not always true for a false statement or not always false for a true statement.

Prevent by encouraging students to closely examine negations to see if there are instances where they are not valid.

Independent Practice

Homework Assignment	
Basic	8-19, 21, 22, 24, 25
Average	8-22, 24, 25
Honors	10-25

4 CLOSE

Assessment Option

Speaking Ask students to give the negation of each statement.

1. My hair is brown. My hair is not brown.
2. The time is 8:00 A.M. The time is not 8:00 A.M.

Practice Masters Booklet, **p. 16**

Name ________________ Date ________________

Practice Worksheet 2-6

Logic: Statements and Negations

State whether each statement is true or false.

1. All whole numbers are odd. false
2. The Atlantic Ocean is a lake. false
3. Water boils at 212°F. true
4. All months have less than 31 days. false
5. $3x - 1 > 5$ is an inequality. true
6. $\frac{1}{2} + \frac{3}{4} = \frac{2}{3}$ false
7. $18 + (-18) = -16 + 16$ true
8. $(a + b) + c = a + (b + c)$ true
9. The United States is part of North America. true
10. Some trucks have more than four wheels. true
11. Two cups of milk is the same as one quart of milk. false
12. A football is not used in field hockey games. true
13. The Identity Property of Multiplication may be shown by $a + 0 = a$. false
14. October, November, and December have the same number of days. false

Write the negation of each statement. Then state whether the statement and its negation are true or false.

15. Robert Frost is a poet. Robert Frost is not a poet; true; false
16. The solution to $x + 6 = 15$ is not 8. The solution to $x + 6 = 15$ is 8; true; false
17. $5x - 3x = 2$ $5x - 3x \neq 2$; false; true
18. $2 \cdot 8 \div 4 \neq 2 + 3$ $2 \cdot 8 \div 4 = 2 + 3$; true; false
19. $65 \geq 65$ $65 \ngeq 65$; true; false
20. The solution to $3x < 10$ is $x < 3$. The solution to $3x < 10$ is not $x < 3$; false; true
21. Some apples are green. Some apples are not green; true; true
22. $a \cdot b = b \cdot a$ $a \cdot b \neq b \cdot a$; true; false

Alternate Strategies: Extending the Lesson

Enrichment

Using Groups of Two Introduce students to a new form of statement called a **conditional**. Explain that conditionals are formed by connecting two statements with the words *if . . . then.* "If Charlie is a horse, then Charlie has four legs" is a conditional. Have one student create a conditional and the other try to determine its truth value.

Cooperative Learning

Negative Messages Group Activity **2-6**

Listed on the back are 12 sentences that contain a secret message. To learn the message, do the following:

1. Write the negation of each sentence.
2. Determine if the negation is true or false.
3. If the negation is true, copy the first letter of the sentence onto the line.
4. If the negation is false, copy the last letter of the sentence onto the line.
5. Decide how to break the letters into words to make a secret message.
6. Write the negation of the message to get the correct secret message.

Merrill Pre-Algebra STATEMENTS AND NEGATIONS

EXPLORATION
Multiplying Integers

Objective Students will be able to model integer multiplication.

1 FOCUS

Integer multiplication is characterized by obscure rules with little apparent meaning. This exploration provides an opportunity to model integer multiplication and demonstrate how the multiplication rules really do make sense.

2 TEACH

Using Patterns

Use the examples, as well as the practice exercises, to build the patterns in multiplication and to justify the rules for integer multiplication.

3 PRACTICE/APPLY

Using Critical Thinking

Although the students can model and solve the problems, encourage students to look for patterns and discern the multiplication rules themselves. Have them write their explanations and observations.

4 CLOSE

Using Connections

Use Exercise 9 to stress and to connect to the commutative property of multiplication. Make note of an important concept: Although the product is the same, the two operations have different meanings.

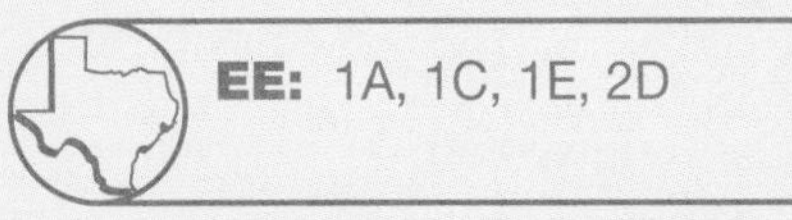

Exploration

Multiplying Integers

Materials: counters, mat

In this Exploration, you will use counters to model multiplication.

▶ Remember that the whole number multiplication 2 × 3 means *two sets of three items.* The integer multiplication, +2 × (+3), means something similar. *It tells you to* ***put in*** *two sets of three* ***positive*** *items.*

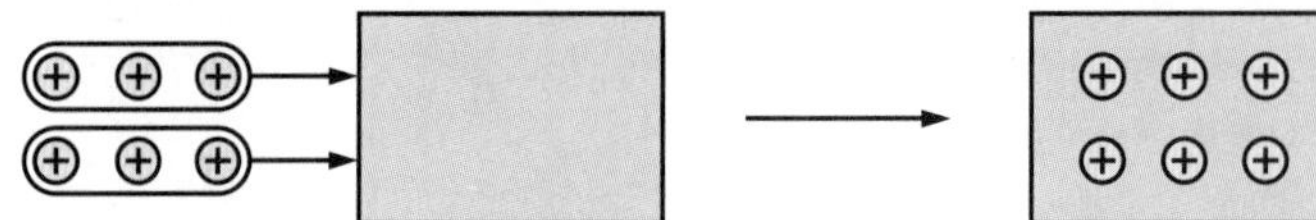

Therefore, +2 × (+3) = +6.

▶ Consider +2 × (-3). This tells you to ***put in*** *two sets of three* ***negative*** *items.*

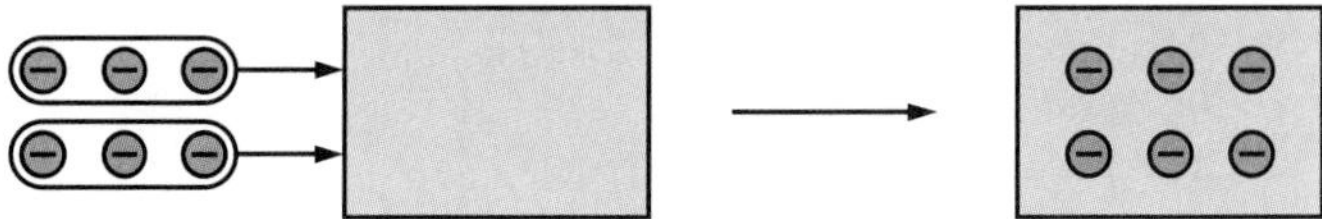

Therefore, +2 × (-3) = -6.

▶ Finally, consider -2 × (+3). Since one meaning of the negative sign is *the opposite of,* -2 × (+3) means to ***take out*** *two sets of three* ***positive*** *items.* How can you take out two sets? First, put in as many zero pairs as you need. Then take out two sets of three positive items.

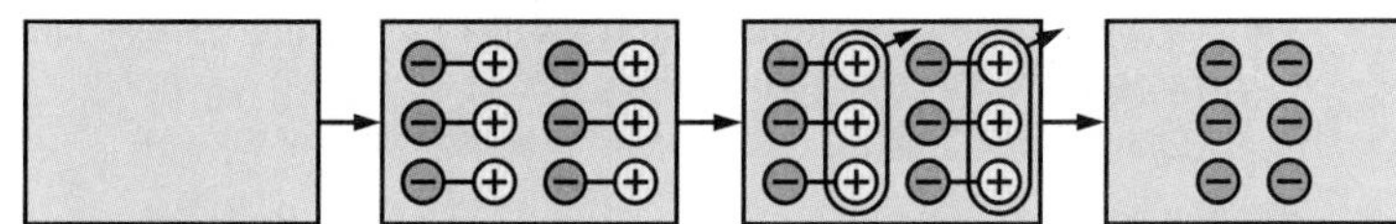

Therefore, -2 × (+3) = -6.

Your Turn: What does -2 × (-3) mean? Model this operation. Write your explanation in paragraph form.

Model each problem. For diagrams to Exercises 1-8, see Solutions Manual.

1. 3 × 4	**2.** 3 × (-4)	**3.** -3 × 4	**4.** -3 × (-4)
5. 4 × 3	**6.** 4 × (-3)	**7.** -4 × 3	**8.** -4 × (-3)

Analysis

9. How are the operations -3 × 4 and 4 × (-3) the same? How do they differ? The product is the same. The order of multiplication is different.

72 *Integers*

SET-UP

Materials

- Integer Mat, Lab Manual, p. 2
- Counters, Lab Manual, p. 4
- Exploration Worksheet, Lab Manual, p. 32

For Students Use two different colored counters or dry beans to represent the positive and negative integers. Each group of students will need a packet of 12 positive and 12 negative counters.

HINT: Assemble the counters in sandwich bags with a twist-tie for convenient management.

For the Overhead Projector You may wish to create a blank "mat" to use on the overhead as your place of operation.

2-7 Multiplying Integers

Objective:
Multiply integers.

Most weather activity occurs in the airspace between the ground and 11 kilometers above the ground. The temperature in this airspace drops about 7° Celsius for each kilometer of increase in altitude. Suppose the ground temperature is 0°C. What is the temperature 3 kilometers above the ground?

Since the temperature drops 7°C for each kilometer, the temperature change can be expressed by the following sentences.

$-7 + (-7) + (-7) = -21$ The temperature drops 7°C per km.

or

$3 \times (-7) = -21$ The repeated addition sentence can be changed to a multiplication sentence.

The temperature 3 kilometers above the ground would be -21°C.

What property allows you to say this? **Commutative property**

Now you know that $3 \times (-7) = -21$, then $-7 \times 3 = -21$. Notice that one factor is positive and one is negative. That is, the signs are different. Notice also that the product is negative. These and other similar examples suggest the following rule.

Multiplying Integers with Different Signs

The product of two integers with different signs is negative.

Example

1 Solve $x = -3(29)$.

$x = -3(29)$ The signs are different.

$x = -87$ The product is negative.

You already know that the product of two positive integers is positive.

Both factors are positive. $3 \times 4 = 12$ The product is positive.

Bell Ringer

Ask students whether the negation of the following statement is true or false: I had math homework last night. **Answers may vary depending upon individual situations.**

5-Minute Check
(over Lesson 2-6)

State whether each statement is true or false.

1. Florida is west of California. **false**
2. Cats are not mammals. **false**
3. $9x = 27$ when $x = 3$ **true**
4. $0.4 + 0.35 = 0.39$ **false**
5. $\frac{3}{5} + \frac{1}{4} = \frac{1}{4} + \frac{3}{5}$ **true**

Transparency 2-7 contains the 5-Minute Check and a teaching aid for this lesson.

1 FOCUS

The purpose of the lesson is to have students develop and apply the rules for multiplying integers.

Motivating the Lesson

In a golf match, what is par? How is three above par represented? Three below par? Make up a player's score for each of six holes and ask students what the player's total score is. **Par is matching the assigned score for the hole; + 3; - 3**

2 TEACH

Using Modeling

Students should recall from earlier grades that multiplication is repeated addition. Use this concept to develop the first rule by modeling

Chalkboard Examples

- *For Example 1*
  Solve $x = -6(23)$. **-138**
- *For Example 2*
  Solve $x = (-2)(-51)$. **102**
- *For Example 3*
  Find $-4 \cdot (-7) \cdot (-2)$. **-56**
- *For Example 4*
  Find the product of -8 and $5x$. **$-40x$**

EE: 2D, 3A, 3H
TAAS: 2, 8

3 PRACTICE/APPLY

Checking the Concept

Write examples of two positive integers, one positive and one negative, one negative and one positive, and two negative integers on the chalkboard. Have students state the rule for multiplying each. Then have students alternate, repeating the appropriate rule to a partner while working Exercises 2-13.

Error Analysis

Watch for students who interchange the rules for adding integers with the rules for multiplying integers.
Prevent by having students write the rules at the top of the paper with examples. Refer to the rules as the problems are being worked.

What is the sign of the product of two negative numbers? Think about the problem at the beginning of the lesson. Suppose the temperature at 2 kilometers is 0°C. What would the ground temperature be?

$-2 \times (-7) = ?$ -2 represents 2 km lower
-7 represents a drop of 7°C
$-2 \times (-7) = 14$ 2 km lower, it is 14° warmer.

These and other similar examples suggest the following rule.

Multiplying Integers with the Same Sign — The product of two integers with the same sign is positive.

Examples

Mental Math Hint
To multiply 6 and 25 mentally, use the distributive property:
6×25
$= 6 \times (20 + 5)$
$= 6 \times 20 + 6 \times 5$
$= 120 + 30$ or 150

2 **Solve $x = (-6)(-25)$.**
$x = (-6)(-25)$ The signs are the same.
$x = 150$ The product is positive.

3 **Find $-8 \cdot (-9) \cdot (-3)$.**
$-8 \cdot (-9) \cdot (-3) = [-8 \cdot (-9)] \cdot (-3)$ Associative property, multiplication
$= (72) \cdot (-3)$ The product of -8 and -9 is positive.
$= -216$ The product of 72 and -3 is negative.

CONNECTION TO ALGEBRA

4 **Find the product of -2 and $3x$.**
$-2 \cdot (3x) = (-2 \cdot 3)x$ Associative property, multiplication
$= -6x$
The product is $-6x$.

Checking for Understanding

Communicating Algebra

1. The temperature has been changing at a rate of -2°F per hour and is predicted to continue at this rate. The temperature is now 0°. Write a multiplication sentence using integers to represent the following questions. Answer each question.
   a. What was the temperature 3 hours ago? **$-3 \times (-2)$; 6°F**
   b. What temperature is predicted for 5 hours from now? **5×-2; -10°F**

Guided Practice

State whether each product is positive or negative.

2. $-9 \cdot 5$ −
3. $4 \cdot (-8)$ −
4. $-3 \cdot (-7)$ +
5. $-12 \cdot (-18)$ +
6. $5 \cdot 27$ +
7. $-3 \cdot 31$ −
8. $-45 \cdot (-47)$ +
9. $-361 \cdot 42$ −
10. $-3 \cdot 2 \cdot 7$ −
11. $-3 \cdot 4 \cdot 7$ −
12. $-7 \cdot (-8) \cdot 5$ +
13. $-2 \cdot (-4) \cdot (-5)$ −

***Practice Masters Booklet,* p. 17**

Name ______________ Date ______________

Practice Worksheet 2-7

Multiplying Integers

Multiply.

1. $-2 \cdot 3x$ $-6x$
2. $-4 \cdot 5y$ $-20y$
3. $9 \cdot (-2z)$ $-18z$
4. $-5 \cdot (-6a)$ $30a$
5. $8t \cdot (-3)$ $-24t$
6. $2n \cdot (-1)$ $-2n$
7. $-5 \cdot 2w$ $-10w$
8. $8c \cdot (-2)$ $-16c$
9. $-3c \cdot (-5d)$ $15cd$
10. $4r \cdot 7s$ $28rs$
11. $-3x \cdot (-z)$ $3xz$
12. $-4ab \cdot (-6)$ $24ab$
13. $(-3)(4)(-x)$
14. $-3(5)(-y)$ $15y$
15. $(-6)(-2)(8r)$ $96r$
16. $-5(0)(-xy)$ 0
17. $5(-7)(4w)$ $-140w$
18. $(-8)(-4)(m)$ $32m$
19. $(-3)(6n)(-2p)$ $36np$
20. $(3)(9)(-d)$ $-27d$
21. $(0)(6m)(-10f)$ 0
22. $7k(-3)(-5t)$ $105kt$
23. $(7)(-x)(-y)$ $7xy$
24. $(-5)(-8g)(-h)$ $-40gh$

Solve each equation.

25. $x = -6 \cdot -8$ $x = 48$
26. $y = -12 \cdot 4$ $y = -48$
27. $x = -9 \cdot (-11)$ $x = 99$
28. $y = (-7)(17)$ $y = -119$
29. $-14(-4) = h$ $h = 56$
30. $-15(10) = k$ $k = -150$
31. $-22(-3) = c$ $c = 66$
32. $7(-24) = d$ $d = -168$
33. $p = -21(13)$ $p = -273$
34. $(-5)(-6)(-4) = m$ $m = -120$
35. $(10)(-8)(-2) = r$ $r = 160$
36. $(-3)(3)(-10) = t$ $t = 90$
37. $w = (-12)(-1)(6)$ $w = 72$
38. $y = (20)(-5)(-5)$ $y = 500$
39. $x = (4)(-16)(-6)$ $x = 384$
40. $n = (16)(9)(-2)$ $n = -288$
41. $z = (-11)(-4)(-7)$ $z = -308$
42. $f = (21)(-7)(-2)$ $f = 294$

Evaluate each expression if $x = -5$ and $y = -6$.

43. $3y$ -18
44. $-8x$ 40
45. $-4y$ 24
46. $12x$ -60
47. $-15x$ 75
48. $-19y$ 114
49. $-6xy$ -180
50. $4xy$ 120

Alternate Strategies: Reteaching the Lesson

Reteaching Activity

Using Models Students can practice multiplying integers by telling a story using a vertical number line and a model of a hot air balloon. Hot air blasts = positive integers, while sandbags = negative integers. See page 52C for a sample illustration.

***Reteaching Masters Booklet,* p. 15**

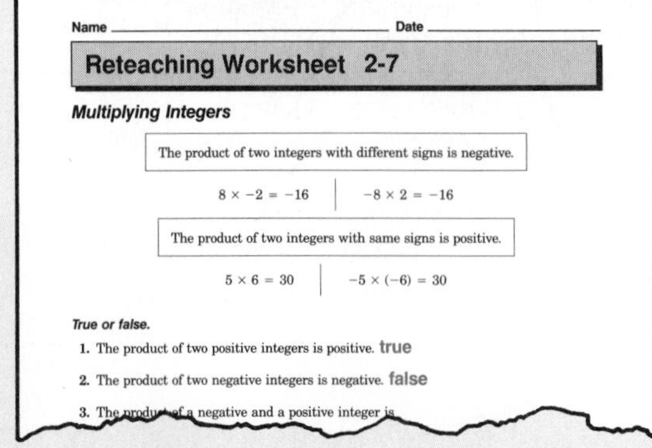

Name ______________ Date ______________

Reteaching Worksheet 2-7

Multiplying Integers

The product of two integers with different signs is negative.

$8 \times -2 = -16$ | $-8 \times 2 = -16$

The product of two integers with same signs is positive.

$5 \times 6 = 30$ | $-5 \times (-6) = 30$

True or false.

1. The product of two positive integers is positive. true
2. The product of two negative integers is negative. false
3. The product of a negative and a positive integer is

Exercises

Independent Practice

Solve each equation.

14. $x = -3 \cdot (-7)$ 21
15. $y = -11(-6)$ 66
16. $x = -7(28)$ -196
17. $y = (-9)(18)$ -162
18. $-16(-2) = h$ 32
19. $-17 \cdot (-4) = a$ 68
20. $(-7)(-6)(3) = c$ 126
21. $(10)(-17)(5) = d$ -850
22. $(5)(-7)(-4) = f$ 140
23. $a = (-3)(9)(10)$ -270
24. $(-8)(-8)(2) = x$ 128
25. $(21)(-3)(2) = w$ -126

Evaluate each expression.

26. $5a$, if $a = -2$ -10
27. $-6b$, if $b = 8$ -48
28. $-15c$, if $c = -1$ 15
29. $2ab$, if $a = -3$, $b = -2$ 12
30. $5cd$, if $c = 2$, $d = -4$ -40

Multiply. 34. $-54a$ 38. $-24ab$ 42. $-12y$

31. $-4 \cdot b$ $-4b$
32. $8 \cdot (-x)$ $-8x$
33. $-5 \cdot (3x)$ $-15x$
34. $6 \cdot (-9a)$
35. $(-5y)(-6)$ $30y$
36. $(-9h)(-9)$ $81h$
37. $(7y)(5z)$ $35yz$
38. $2ab \cdot 6 \cdot (-2)$
39. $-3(-a)(-b)$ $-3ab$
40. $7(-m)(k)$ $-7mk$
41. $5x \cdot (-4)(-2)$ $40x$
42. $(-3)(-4)(-y)$

Mixed Review

44. {-6, -2, 3}

43. Using inverse operations, solve the equation $17 + z = 23$. (Lesson 1-7) 6
44. Order the numbers {3, -2, -6} from least to greatest. (Lesson 2-2)
45. Simplify the expression $14y + 13y + (-5y)$. (Lesson 2-4) $22y$
46. Solve the equation $n = -24 - 16$. (Lesson 2-5) -40
47. Write the negation of the statement *All horses are brown.* (Lesson 2-6) Some horses are not brown.

Application

48. **Geology** A certain glacier melts at a rate of 9 centimeters per day. Let the integer -9 represent melting 9 centimeters per day. What will the glacier's position be after four days? -36 cm

Critical Thinking

49. Suppose you are multiplying more than two integers. Write a rule that will help you determine the sign of the product. See margin.

Wrap-Up

50. In your own words, explain why the product of a positive integer and a negative integer is always negative. See margin for sample answer.

Mid-Chapter Quiz

Simplify. (Lesson 2-1)

1. $|-2|$ 2
2. $|-3| + |-4|$ 7
3. $|8| - |-3|$ 5

Replace each ● with <, >, or =. (Lesson 2-2)

4. -5 ● -6 >
5. $|-3|$ ● -3 >
6. 5 ● -2 >

Solve each equation. (Lessons 2-3, 2-4, 2-5, 2-6)

7. $y = -3 + (-8)$ -11
8. $-21 + 10 + (-3) = y$ -14
9. $a = 4 - (-2)$ 6
10. $m = -3 - 5$ -8
11. $x = -3(15)$ -45
12. $-5 \cdot (-3) = y$ 15

Independent Practice

Homework Assignment	
Basic	15-41 odd, 43-50
Average	14-42 even, 43-50
Honors	14-42 even, 43-50
All	Mid-Chapter Quiz 1-12

4 CLOSE

Assessment Option

Writing Have students write a descriptive phrase for what the expression -2×9 could mean.

49. If there is an even number of negative integers being multiplied, the product will be positive. If there is an odd number of negative integers being multiplied, the product will be negative.

50. Sample answer: Multiplying a positive integer, x, and a negative integer, y, is the same as adding the negative integer x times. The result will always be a negative integer.

Alternate Strategies: Extending the Lesson

Enrichment

Using Cooperative Groups Give each group a bag with five red and five blue number cubes in it. Red cubes are positive, and blue cubes are negative. Draw four cubes. Find the product and record the results. Play five rounds. Have each group find the sum of the absolute values of all results. The group with the highest total wins.

Cooperative Learning

Powerful Integer Products Group Activity **2-7**

MATERIALS: One calculator • a die • a coin • paper • pencils

Three students should do this activity with one of them being the leader. Another player uses the calculator to compute products, and the other player is to use mental computation or paper and pencil. The object is to be first in computing the product of given integers.

To begin, the leader writes the first expression given on the back of this card without showing it to the two players. The leader also states which side of the coin indicates positive or negative, rolls the die, and flips the coin. This integer will replace the variable in the expression the leader has written on the paper. The leader next shows the players the expression. They are to compute the product as quickly as possible and show it to the leader. The leader decides who gave the first correct answer, and the winner earns one point. The first player to earn five points wins the game. The leader should watch the player with the calculator to make sure that all the necessary strokes and not just the final answer are input.

Merrill Pre-Algebra MULTIPLYING INTEGERS

Enrichment Masters Booklet, p. 15

Name ______________________ Date ____________

Enrichment Worksheet 2-7

Carpeting

Suppose you want to figure the cost of carpeting a room. Room sizes are usually given in square feet. Carpet prices are usually given in square yards. You need to apply three formulas.

The formula $a = lw$ is used to compute area, a, of a rectangle in square feet.

a (area in square feet) $= l$ (length in feet) $\cdot$ w (width in feet)

The formula for the area in square yards is given below.

A (area in square yards) $= \frac{a \text{ (area in square feet)}}{9}$

The following formula can be used to compute the cost of carpeting.

c (cost) $= A$ (number of square yards) $\cdot$ p (price per square yard)

Example: Find the cost of carpeting a room 21 feet long and 15 feet wide if the carpeting costs $7.70 per square yard.

$a = l \cdot w$
$= 21 \cdot 15$
$= 315$ square feet

$A = \frac{a}{9}$
$= \frac{315}{9}$
$= 35$ square yards

$c = A \cdot p$
$= 35 \cdot \$7.70$
$= \$269.50$

The cost of carpeting the room is $269.50.

Find the cost of carpeting each room listed in the chart below.

	Room	Length	Width	Price Per Sq. Yd	Cost Per Room
1.	Living Room	18	24	$17.00	$816
2.	Dining Room	15	15	$22.50	$562.50
3.	Den	12	9	$15.00	$180
4.	Bedroom A	12	18	$18.50	$444
5.	Bedroom B	9	15	$21.00	$315
6.	Bathroom	6	6	$ 8.95	$35.80

7. Find the total carpeting bill. $2353.30

Lesson Notes 2-8

5-Minute Check
(over Lesson 2-7)

Solve each equation.
1. (-5)(-3)(4) = y **60**
2. (20)(-6)(2) = k **-240**

Multiply.
3. (-8x)(-9) **72x**
4. (3xy)(7)(-3) **-63xy**
5. 9(-m)(-n) **9mn**

Transparency 2-8 contains the 5-Minute Check and a teaching aid for this lesson.

1 FOCUS

The purpose of the lesson is to relate division to multiplication and develop and apply the rules for division of integers based on the rules for multiplication.

Motivating the Lesson

Have students use a drawing of a football field to represent the following problem. A football team was penalized a total of 35 yards in one game. If each penalty was 5 yards, how many penalties did they receive? **-35 ÷ (-5) = 7**

2 TEACH

Using Discussion

Ask students to rewrite the following multiplication sentences as division sentences in more than one way.

a. 4 · 9 = 36 **36 ÷ 4 = 9**
36 ÷ 9 = 4

b. -6 · 5 = -30 **-30 ÷ -6 = 5**
-30 ÷ 5 = -6

EE: 2D, 3A, 3H, 5F
TAAS: 2, 5, 9, 11

2-8 Dividing Integers

Objective:
Divide integers.

The Bears football team was penalized the same amount on 3 consecutive plays. The total of the 3 penalties was 45 yards. The number of yards of each penalty can be expressed by the following sentence.

-45 ÷ 3 = ■ — -45 represents a loss of 45 yards. 3 represents the number of plays.

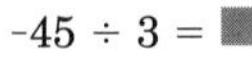

To divide, think of a related multiplication sentence.

■ × 3 = -45
-15 × 3 = -45 So, -45 ÷ 3 = -15.

In the example above, the dividend is negative. Let's try a case where the divisor is negative.

Why is the missing factor negative? **The product is negative. The factors must have different signs.**

27 ÷ (-3) = ■ ⟶ ■ × (-3) = 27
-9 × (-3) = 27 So, 27 ÷ (-3) = -9.

These and other similar examples suggest the following rule.

Dividing Integers with Different Signs: The quotient of two integers with different signs is negative.

Examples

1 Find -38 ÷ 2.

-38 ÷ 2 = -19

2 Solve $y = \frac{54}{-9}$.

$y = \frac{54}{-9}$

$y = -6$

You know the quotient of two positive numbers is positive.

Both the dividend and divisor are positive. 48 ÷ 8 = 6 The quotient is positive.

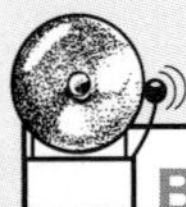

Bell Ringer

Write ten multiplication sentences, each with a product of -36. **Answers may vary. A typical answer is 9 × (-4) = -36.**

What do you think will be true about the quotient of two negative numbers? Check your prediction.

$-32 \div (-4) = ■ \longrightarrow ■ \times (-4) = -32$

For the product to be negative, one factor must be positive and the other negative. So, the missing factor is positive 8.

$-32 \div (-4) = 8$

These and other similar examples suggest the following rule.

Dividing Integers with the Same Sign

The quotient of two integers with the same sign is positive.

Examples

3 **Find -90 ÷ (-15).**

$-90 \div (-15) = 6$

4 **Solve $\frac{72}{9} = x$.**

$\frac{72}{9} = x$

$8 = x$

Checking for Understanding

Communicating Algebra

1. An elevator is moving up at a rate of 3 feet each second. The elevator is now at the street level. Write a division sentence using integers to represent the following questions. Answer each question.
   a. When was the elevator 15 feet below street level?
   b. When will the elevator be 30 feet above street level?

   1a. -15 ÷ 3; -5 sec 1b. 30 ÷ 3; 10 sec

Guided Practice

State whether each quotient is positive or negative.

2. -63 ÷ 7 -
3. -54 ÷ 9 -
4. 16 ÷ 2 +
5. -36 ÷ (-6) +
6. -48 ÷ (-16) +
7. 64 ÷ (-4) -
8. 42 ÷ (-7) -
9. 63 ÷ 21 +
10. $\frac{-570}{19}$ -
11. $\frac{-804}{67}$ -
12. $\frac{68}{-17}$ -
13. $\frac{-48}{32}$ -

Exercises

Independent Practice

Divide.

14. 48 ÷ (-3) **-16**
15. -56 ÷ (-8) **7**
16. -72 ÷ 9 **-8**
17. 84 ÷ (-7) **-12**
18. -52 ÷ (-4) **13**
19. -72 ÷ (-12) **19. 6**
20. -91 ÷ 13 **-7**
21. -51 ÷ (-17) **3**
22. 64 ÷ (-16) **22. -4**
23. 98 ÷ (-14) **-7**
24. 80 ÷ (-16) **-5**
25. -343 ÷ (-7) **49**

Solve each equation.

26. $d = \frac{-240}{-6}$ **40**
27. $\frac{-96}{24} = k$ **-4**
28. $\frac{-105}{-15} = m$ **7**
29. $\frac{-450}{-45} = y$ **10**
30. $x = \frac{-120}{-15}$ **8**
31. $a = \frac{-144}{-36}$ **4**
32. $b = \frac{-175}{-25}$ **7**
33. $\frac{-288}{24} = k$ **-12**

Chalkboard Examples

- *For Example 1*
  Find -45 ÷ 5. **-9**
- *For Example 2*
  Solve $x = \frac{72}{-9}$ **-8**
- *For Example 3*
  Find -32 ÷ 8. **-4**
- *For Example 4*
  Solve $\frac{56}{8} = m$. **7**

3 PRACTICE/APPLY

Checking the Concept

In Exercises 2-13 students are to state the sign of the quotient. If students are still having difficulty with the signs, continue to practice identifying the sign of the quotient using the Independent Practice exercises.

***Practice Masters Booklet,* p. 18**

Name ______________ Date ______________

Practice Worksheet 2-8

Dividing Integers

Divide.

1. 16 ÷ 4 **4**
2. −27 ÷ 3 **−9**
3. 25 ÷ (−5) **−5**
4. 63 ÷ (−9) **−7**
5. −15 ÷ (−3) **5**
6. 14 ÷ (−7) **−2**
7. −124 ÷ 4 **−31**
8. 60 ÷ 15 **4**
9. 28 ÷ (−4) **−7**
10. −56 ÷ (−8) **7**
11. 72 ÷ 8 **9**
12. −21 ÷ (−7) **3**
13. −32 ÷ 4 **−8**
14. 45 ÷ 9 **5**
15. −45 ÷ 3 **−15**
16. −25 ÷ (−5) **5**
17. 35 ÷ (−7) **−5**
18. −63 ÷ (−7) **9**
19. −144 ÷ 12 **−12**
20. 48 ÷ (−6) **−8**
21. −72 ÷ 9 **−8**
22. 24 ÷ (−6) **−4**
23. −30 ÷ (−5) **6**
24. −42 ÷ 7 **−6**

Evaluate each expression if x = −8 and y = −12.

25. $x \div 2$ **−4**
26. $x \div (-4)$ **2**
27. $36 \div y$ **−3**
28. $0 \div y$ **0**
29. $\frac{y}{-6}$ **2**
30. $\frac{x}{4}$ **−2**
31. $\frac{-144}{y}$ **12**
32. $\frac{-136}{x}$ **17**

Solve each equation.

33. $x = \frac{-150}{-25}$ **x = 6**
34. $k = \frac{-98}{14}$ **k = −7**
35. $m = \frac{-144}{-16}$ **m = 9**
36. $y = \frac{243}{-81}$ **y = −3**
37. $\frac{-208}{-26} = t$ **t = 8**
38. $\frac{-180}{15} = n$ **n = −12**
39. $\frac{-189}{-21} = p$ **p = 9**
40. $\frac{288}{-18} = d$ **d = −16**
41. $z = \frac{930}{-30}$ **z = −31**
42. $w = \frac{-312}{24}$ **w = −13**
43. $b = \frac{-396}{-36}$ **b = 11**
44. $c = \frac{-336}{12}$ **c = −28**

Alternate Strategies: Reteaching the Lesson

Reteaching Activity

Have students represent the quotient with a box and rewrite the division problem as a multiplication problem.

-56 ÷ 7 = ■ → ■ × 7 = -56

***Reteaching Masters Booklet,* p. 16**

Name ______________ Date ______________

Reteaching Worksheet 2-8

Dividing Integers

35 ÷ 7 = 5

−35 ÷ 7 = −5 (The opposite of 35. / The opposite of 5.)

−35 ÷ (−7) = 5 (The opposite of 7. / The opposite of −5.)

35 ÷ 7 = 5
−35 ÷ 7 = −5 ← Take the opposite of 5.
−35 ÷ (−7) = 5 ← Take the opposite of 5 again.

Check by multiplying the quotient by the divisor.

35 ÷ 7 = 5	−35 ÷ 7 = −5	35 ÷ (−7) = −5	−35 ÷ (−7) = 5
7 × 5 = 35	7 × (−5) = −35	−7 × (−5) = 35	−7 × 5 = −35

State whether each quotient is positive or negative.

1. 132 ÷ 11 **positive**
2. −108 ÷ 12 **negative**
3. −80 ÷ (−16) **positive**
4. 98 ÷ (−14) **negative**
5. 30 ÷ (−3) **negative**
6. −88 ÷ 8 **negative**

Independent Practice

Homework Assignment	
Basic	15-39 odd, 40-48
Average	14-38 even, 40-48
Honors	20-32 even, 34-48

4 CLOSE

Assessment Option

Writing Have the students write a problem that can be solved by using the equation -36 ÷ (-6) = 6.

48. Write a related multiplication equation. For example: 12 ÷ -3 = ■ → -3 × ■ = 12. Think: What would have to be the sign of ■ for the product of -3 and ■ to be positive?

Enrichment Masters Booklet, **p. 16**

Name ______________________ Date ______________

Enrichment Worksheet 2-8

Cross-Number Puzzle

Use the clues below to complete the following cross-number puzzle. Any negative signs should be placed in the same box as the first digit of the integer.

			[1] −1	[2] 2	[3] 4	[4] 2			
[5] −7	[6] 1		[7] 3	0	3	3		[8] −3	[9] 6
[10] 4	0		[11] 4	4	5	6		[12] 8	0
8									8
		[13] −7	[14] 2	1		[15] −2	[16] 4		
[17] −7		[18] 5	3		[19] −9	0	5		[20] 8
[21] 1	[22] 9		[23] 2	[24] 4	7	0		[25] −5	8
[26] 1	8		[27] 9	6	4	0		[28] 1	6
			[29] 6	0	5	0			

Across

1. 23 × (−54)
5. −56 − 15
7. −4283 + 7316
8. 46.8 ÷ (−1.3)
10. −3840 ÷ (−96)
11. −1.6 × (−2785)
12. 91.5 + (−11.5)
13. −42 − 679
15. 50 × (−0.48)
18. −53,000 × (−0.001)
19. −181 × 5
21. −42 + 61
23. 10 × (−13) × (−19)
25. 26.1 ÷ (−0.45)
26. −750 × (−0.024)
27. −38.56 ÷ (−0.004)
28. −38 − (−54)
29. 11,260 + (−5210)

Down

1. −718 + 584
2. −0.8 × (−255)
3. 198 − (−237)
4. −118 ÷ (−0.5)
5. −2 × (−22) × (−17)
6. −1000 ÷ (−100)
8. −6.46 ÷ 0.17
9. 1547 + (−939)
13. −5000 × 0.015
14. −832 × (−28)
15. −40 × (−20) × (−25)
16. −9 × (−5)
17. −79 × 3 × 3
19. −13,406 + 3661
20. −649 + 1535
22. 46 − (−52)
24. −10 × (−46)
25. −0.663 ÷ 0.013

Evaluate each expression.

34. $\frac{y}{5}$, if $y = -50$ **-10**
35. $\frac{32}{m}$, if $m = -8$ **-4**
36. $\frac{b}{-7}$, if $b = -98$ **14**
37. $\frac{42}{z}$, if $z = -14$ **-3**
38. $\frac{x}{-5}$, if $x = -65$ **13**
39. $\frac{-66}{w}$, if $w = -33$ **2**

Mixed Review

40. 166 pages

40. Write an equation and solve: Glen is reading a book that has 342 pages. If he is on page 176, how many pages does he have left to read? (Lesson 1-9)
41. Name the absolute value of zero. (Lesson 2-1) **0**
42. *True* or *false:* The sum of two negative integers is always negative. (Lesson 2-3) **true**
43. State whether the product of -9 and 18 is positive or negative. (Lesson 2-7) **negative**
44. Multiply: $2x(-6)(3)$. (Lesson 2-7) **$-36x$**

Connection

45. **Statistics** Five years ago, East Street High School had 250 more students than it does now. What was the average change in school population each year? **-50 students**

Application

46. **Business** Stock in ABC Company has a change of -2 dollars each day for 4 days. What is the overall change? **-8 dollars**

Critical Thinking

47. Find two integers a and b so that $a + b = -5$ and $ab = 6$. **$a = -2$; $b = -3$**

Wrap-Up

48. If you forget the rules for dividing integers, explain how you can use the rules for multiplying integers to decide whether the quotient is positive or negative. **See margin.**

History

The Egyptian Number System

About 5000 years ago, ancient Egyptians began to keep records by carving pictures into stone. These *hieroglyphics* contain a well organized number system based on groups of ten. In this system, a vertical stroke represents one unit. Other symbols are shown below.

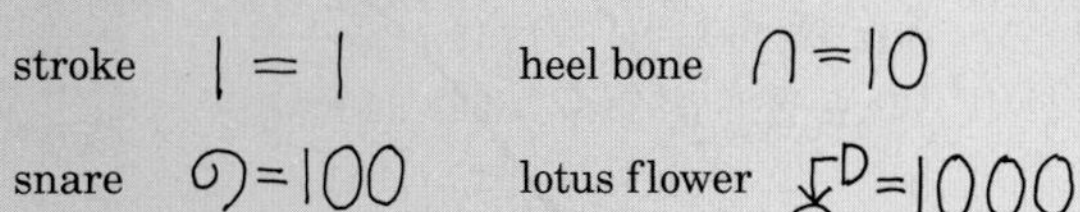

Using these hieroglyphics, the number 436 would be written.

By studying carvings like the one pictured here, scholars have concluded that the ancient Egyptians were very accurate in counting and measuring.

78 *Integers*

Alternate Strategies: Extending the Lesson

Enrichment

Evaluate each expression if $a = -4$.

1. $\frac{1092}{7a}$ -39
2. $\frac{-225}{(a+1)}$ 75
3. $\frac{144}{a}$ -36
4. $\frac{-544}{8a}$ 17

Cooperative Learning

Division Rummy Group Activity **2-8**

MATERIALS: Deck of "Integer Division" cards, with expressions given on back

This is a game for two or three players. To begin, the deck of "Integer Division" cards is shuffled and five cards are dealt to each player, with the remaining cards placed face down in a pile in the middle of the table. The top card is removed, turned over, and becomes the discard pile. The rules and procedures for rummy are used for this game.

Players try to make a "book" of three cards, all of which have the same quotient represented by the division problem on them.

Players take turns drawing a card from the face-down pile or the discard pile. After drawing a card, a player may lay down a book or play a card on a book already on the table before discarding a card from his or her hand. The first player to run out of cards wins.

Merrill Pre-Algebra DIVIDING INTEGERS

Problem Solving

2-9 Using Integers

Objective:
Solve problems using integers.

Suppose you started for school at 7:30 A.M. and found that the outside temperature was -4°F. You realized you had forgotten your homework and went back inside. When you stepped back outside at 7:32 A.M., the temperature was 45°F! This dramatic temperature change was recorded on January 22, 1943 in Spearfish, South Dakota. How much did the temperature rise in 2 minutes?

Explore Read the problem carefully. Select the important data.

- The beginning temperature was -4°F.
- The final temperature was 45°F.

Estimate: Was the change greater than 45° or less than 45°? **greater than 45°**

What is asked?

- You need to find the temperature change.
- Let c = the temperature change.

Plan You can compare the temperatures by using subtraction. Write an equation.

The temperature rose during the time period. Will the amount of change be represented by a positive or a negative number? **positive**

$$\underbrace{\text{change in temperature}}_{c} = \underbrace{\text{final temperature}}_{45} - \underbrace{\text{beginning temperature}}_{(-4)}$$

Solve $c = 45 + 4$ Subtract -4 by adding its inverse, 4.

$c = 49$

In two minutes, the temperature rose 49°F!

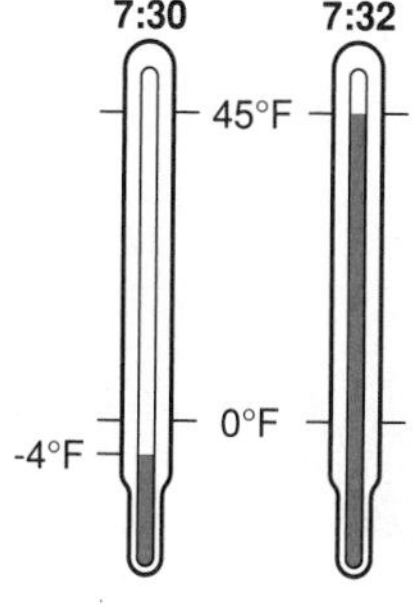

Examine Is your answer reasonable? Think about the scale on a thermometer. The temperature started at 4° *below* zero and ended at 45° *above* zero. The temperatures are 49° apart.

Compare your answer to the estimate. The answer is reasonable.

FYI

A chinook wind is a warm dry wind that descends the eastern slopes of the Rocky Mountains. Such winds occasionally cause the temperature to rise 40° to 50°F in a few minutes.

Bell Ringer

Solve mentally.

1. Find -2 × (-3) + 4. **10**
2. Find -5 × 3 − 2. **-17**
3. Find $\frac{4 \times (-4)}{-2}$. **8**
4. Find $\frac{2 \times (-3)}{-2 + 5}$. **-2**

Lesson Notes 2-9

5-Minute Check
(over Lesson 2-8)

Solve each equation.

1. $k = \frac{125}{-25}$ **-5**
2. $x = \frac{-204}{34}$ **-6**
3. $\frac{252}{-7} = b$ **-36**
4. $m = \frac{-154}{-14}$ **11**

Transparency 2-9 contains the 5-Minute Check and a teaching aid for this lesson.

1 FOCUS

The purpose of the lesson is to help students develop a positive attitude toward solving verbal problems. It focuses on exploring facts about each problem and applying the rules for adding, subtracting, multiplying, and dividing integers.

Motivating the Lesson

In a series of 3 plays, a football team had 3 penalties totaling 45 yards. The yards stepped off for each penalty were the same. Use an integer to describe the distance of each penalty. **-15**

2 TEACH

Using Models

Use a demonstration thermometer to illustrate the example problem. Encourage students to draw diagrams to help them visualize any problem situation or to help them check their solution.

Chalkboard Examples

The highest temperature ever recorded in the United States was 134°F in Death Valley, CA on July 10, 1913. The lowest temperature ever recorded in the United States was -80°F in Prospect Creek, AK on January 23, 1971. What is the difference between these two extremes? **214° F**

EE: 1D, 1E, 3A
TAAS: 6, 7, 8, 9, 10, 13

3 PRACTICE/APPLY

Checking the Concept

Be sure students understand how to state expressions needed to solve Exercises 1 and 2 before assigning the remainder of the exercises.

Error Analysis

Watch for students who use incorrect operations in writing expressions.
Prevent by emphasizing the need to estimate a reasonable solution and pick out key words in the problem.

Practice Masters Booklet, **p. 19**

Name ______________________ Date ____________

Practice Worksheet 2-9

Problem Solving: Using Integers

Solve.

1. If the high temperature for the day was 19°F and the low temperature was −5°F, what was the change in temperature? **24°F**
2. Anna jogged 14 blocks in one direction and then 27 blocks in the opposite direction. How far was Anna from her starting point? **13 blocks**
3. An elevator at the 25th floor went down 16 floors and then up 11 floors. How far from the 25th floor was it? **5 floors below**
4. On a winter day the temperature was −9°F. The temperature dropped 14°F. What was the temperature after the drop? **−23°F**
5. Find the final balance for Ms. Switch's checking account if she started with a balance of $585, wrote a check for $70, deposited $49, wrote another check for $225, and deposited a check for $347. **$686**
6. The 6 A.M. Fahrenheit temperature readings were taken each morning during a certain week. The temperatures were 15°, 3°, −2°, −5°, −7°, −3°, and 6°. Find the average 6 A.M. temperature for that week. **1°F**
7. To raise $300, the ninth grade presented a play for which they paid a royalty of $25. Scenery and costumes cost $45, and the programs and other expenses amounted to $28. The sale of the tickets totaled $295. Program advertisements brought $87. By how much did the ninth grade exceed or fall short of its goal? **$16 short**
8. In figuring his net income, Mr. Halkides listed his salary income of $15,000, $258 from dividends, and $2562 from the sale of property. His deductions included $1346 in taxes, $1598 in business expenses, and $48 in interest payments. What was his net income? **$14,828**
9. Some number divided by −45 is 23. What is the number? **−1035**
10. A number multiplied by −11 is 187. What is the number? **−17**

Example

In Fairfield, Montana, on December 24, 1924, the temperature fell from 63°F at noon to -21°F 12 hours later. What was the average temperature change each hour?

The temperature fell during the time period. Will the change be represented by a positive or a negative number? ***negative***

Explore You need to find the average temperature change. You know the temperature at noon and 12 hours later.

Plan Find the total temperature change. Then divide the total by the number of hours.

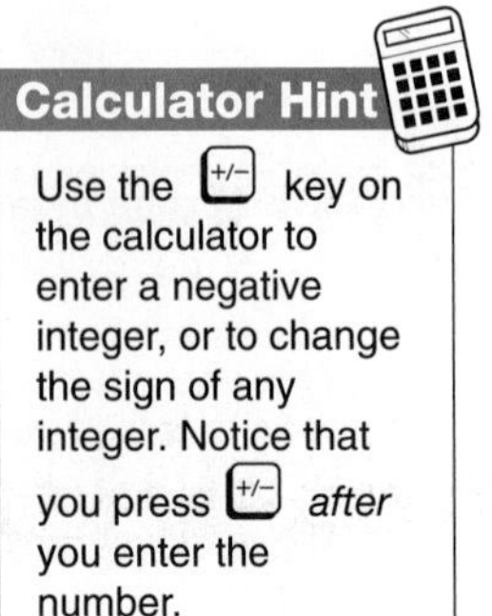

Calculator Hint

Use the [+/−] key on the calculator to enter a negative integer, or to change the sign of any integer. Notice that you press [+/−] *after* you enter the number.

Solve

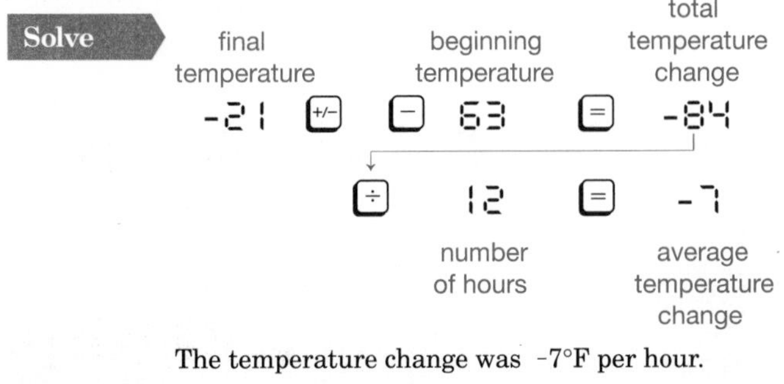

The temperature change was -7°F per hour.

Examine You can check the solution as follows:

7 [+/−] [×] 12 [=] -84 change in 12 hours

63 [+] 84 [+/−] [=] -21 final temperature

The solution checks.

Checking for Understanding

For each problem, answer the related questions.

1. A traffic helicopter descended 160 meters to observe road conditions. It leveled off at 225 meters. What was its original altitude?
   a. What is asked? **the original altitude**
   b. What was the final altitude of the helicopter? **225 meters**
   c. How far did the helicopter descend? **160 meters**
   d. Make a drawing to represent the problem. **See margin.**
   e. Write an expression that represents the original altitude. $a = 225 + 160$
2. The product of two integers is -36. One of the integers is 9. What is the other integer?
   a. What is asked? **the other integer**
   b. What is the product of the integers? **-36**
   c. What is one of the integers? **9**
   d. How can you find the second integer? **divide**
   e. Write an expression that represents the second integer. $a = -36 \div 9$

Alternate Strategies: Reteaching the Lesson

Reteaching Activity

Using Cooperative Groups Have students draw three cards from a deck that has had the face cards removed. Red cards are negative; black cards are positive. Allow students five minutes to write a list of expressions using the three card numbers. Have students make up a problem for each expression.

Reteaching Masters Booklet, **p. 17**

Name ______________________ Date ____________

Reteaching Worksheet 2-9

Problem Solving: Using Integers

Sandra Jean was watching the thermometer carefully. If the temperature dropped too low, she would need to protect some of her plants from frost. Starting about 5 P.M., the temperature dropped 2 degrees each hour for the next 3 hours. How much did the temperature change during those 3 hours? You can use an equation with integers to solve this problem.

Explore The problem suggests multiplication because the same event—a temperature drop of 2 degrees—is repeated 3 times.

Plan Let t stand for the total change in temperature. This is the quantity asked for in the problem.

total change	equals	change per hour	times	number of hours
t	=	−2	×	3

Solve $t = -2 \times 3 = -6$

The total change in temperature was −6 in 3 hours.

Exercises

Independent Practice

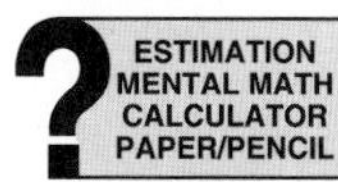

3. The record high temperature in Florida is 109°F. The record low temperature is -2°F. What is the difference in temperature between the record high and the record low? **111°F**
4. A scuba diver descended to a depth of 75 meters below sea level. He then rose 30 meters to an underwater living quarters. How far beneath the surface were the living quarters? **-45 m**

5. Three subtracted from some number is equal to -7. What is the number? **-4**
6. Ray's score at the end of a game was 80. Halfway through the game his score was -35. How many points did he score during the last half of the game? **115 points**
7. From the top of Mt. McKinley to the floor of Death Valley is 6280 meters. If Death Valley is 86 meters below sea level, what is the height of Mt. McKinley? **6194 m**
8. The temperature in Upper Scioto rose 2°F every minute for 7 minutes. The low temperature was -4°F. What was the temperature after 7 minutes? **10°F**
9. The World Trade Center is 1350 feet tall. Each floor is about 12 feet high. Wei-Min rides the elevator 60 floors down from the top. About how far is she above the ground floor? **630 ft**
10. The quotient of two integers is -32. The divisor is -8. What is the other integer? **256**
11. An elevator at the first floor takes one passenger up 10 floors and a second passenger up 12 more floors. If a third passenger goes down 14 floors, on what floor is the elevator? **8th floor**

Decision Making

12. Suppose your class is presenting a play to raise money. You pay a royalty of $45, scenery and costumes cost $77, and the programs and other expenses amount to $36. You make $128 selling advertisements. If you can sell 150 tickets, how much should you charge per ticket to make $300? **$2.20**

Mixed Review

13. State whether the quotient 72 ÷ 8 is positive or negative. (Lesson 2-8) **positive**
14. Solve the equation $x = -\frac{152}{4}$. (Lesson 2-8) **-38**

Critical Thinking

15. Here is a famous problem. A snail at the bottom of a 10-foot hole crawls up 3 feet each day, but slips back 2 feet each night. How many days will it take the snail to reach the top of the hole and escape? **8 days**

Wrap-Up

16. Choose one problem from among Exercises 3-12. Write the steps you used to solve the problem. **See margin for sample answer.**

Independent Practice

Homework Assignment	
Basic	3-9 odd, 12-16
Average	4-10 even,12-16
Honors	7-16

Chapter 2, Quiz B (Lessons 2-6 through 2-9) is available in the Evaluation Masters Booklet, p. 16.

4 CLOSE

Assessment Option

Speaking Have students tell a problem that can be solved using the expression 10° − 10°*x*.

16. Sample answer, using Exercise 3:
Let *t* = temperature difference.
Write an equation: *t* = 109 − (-2).
Find the difference: *t* = 111.
The temperature difference, then, is 111°F.

Enrichment Masters Booklet, **p. 17**

Name ________________ Date ________________

Enrichment Worksheet 2-9

Operations with Units of Measurement

Units of measurement can be added, subtracted, multiplied, or divided. Before performing any operation, remember to regroup whenever necessary. See the examples below for the regrouping steps.

Example:

```
   2    1
 4 yd 1 ft  7 in.
 1 yd 2 ft  3 in.
+3 yd 2 ft  9 in.
      6 ft 19 in.
10 yd 0 ft  7 in.
```

Add the inches column. Regroup the sum, 19 in. = 1 ft 7 in. Record 7 in. Add 1 ft to the next column on the left. Find the sum of the numerals in the feet column. Regroup the sum, 6 ft = 2 yd. Add 2 yd to the next column on the left. Find the sum of the numerals in the yards column.

Example:

```
      3
  2   0   17
  3 yd 1 ft 5 in.
 -1 yd 2 ft 8 in.
  1 yd 1 ft 9 in.
```

Begin subtraction with the inches column. In order to subtract, regroup 1 ft as 12 in. Add 12 in. and 5 in. Then subtract 17 in. − 8 in. = 9 in. To subtract in the feet column, regroup 1 yd as 3 ft. Add 0 ft + 3 ft = 3 ft. Then subtract 3 ft − 2 ft = 1 ft. Subtract in the yards column.

Example:

```
  2 ft  8 in.
×       4
  8 ft 32 in.
 10 ft  8 in.
```

Begin multiplication by multiplying 4 · 8 in. = 32 in. Regroup 32 in. as 2 ft 8 in. Record 8 in. Then multiply 4 · 2 ft = 8 ft. Add 2 ft from regrouping inches, 8 ft + 2 ft = 10 ft.

Perform the indicated operations.

1. 2 yd 1 ft 11 in. + 5 yd 2 ft 9 in. **8 yd 1 ft 8 in.**
2. 7 lb 5 oz + 4 lb 14 oz **12 lb 3 oz**
3. 3 yd 25 in. − 1 yd 30 in. **1 yd 31 in.**
4. 6 d 4 h − 21 h **5 d 7 h**
5. 5 gal − 2 gal 3 qt **2 gal 1 qt**
6. 4 mi 600 yd × 5 **21 mi 1240 yd**
7. 8 T 400 lb × 6 **49 T 400 lb**
8. 4 yd 2 ft 10 in. × 4 **19 yd 2 ft 4 in.**
9. 4 h 15 min 16 s × 10 **42 h 32 min 40 s**

Alternate Strategies: Extending the Lesson

Enrichment

Using Communication Play "Guess My Number". Have students work in pairs asking questions such as, "I am thinking of two integers. The difference of the integers is 26. The lesser integer is -11. What is the other integer?" Only one operation may be used. Have students explain why their solution is correct.

Cooperative Learning

Integer Interactions — Group Activity **2-9**

MATERIALS: 0-9 spinner • coin • paper • pencil

In a group of two to four students, create problems for each other that use integers in their solutions.

To begin, one member of the group mentally chooses a two-digit number and flips a coin to determine whether that number will be positive or negative. (Heads is positive; tails is negative.) Announce that integer and write it on a piece of paper for the others to see. Next, spin the spinner and flip the coin again.

After recording the resulting integer, create a short story problem that uses these two integers and either addition, subtraction, multiplication or division for its solution.

Group members should take turns in writing problems for the others in the group. All four operations should be used sometime during this activity.

Merrill Pre-Algebra USING INTEGERS

Using the Chapter Review

The Chapter Review is a comprehensive review of the concepts presented in this chapter. This review may be used to prepare students for the Chapter Test.

Alternate Review Strategy

To provide a brief in-class review, you may wish to read the following questions to the class and require a verbal response.

1. Find the absolute value of one million. 1,000,000
2. Which is greater, -2 or -3? -2
3. What is the sum of 8 and -18? -10
4. What is -2 plus -8 minus 5? -15
5. Solve $x = 10 - (-4)$. 14
6. What is the negation of the statement *Everything that swims in the ocean has gills.* Some things that swim in the ocean do not have gills.
7. Find the product of 3 and -4. -12
8. What is -14 divided by 7? -2
9. Four subtracted from some number is -8. What is the number? -4
10. The quotient of two integers is 8. The divisor is -7. What is the other integer? -56

Review

Language and Concepts

Choose the letter of the correct word to complete each sentence.

1. __?__ is neither positive nor negative. g
2. When comparing integers, the greater integer is found to the __?__ of the lesser integer on a number line. e
3. If two addends are negative, their sum is __?__ negative. a
4. To subtract an integer, add its __?__. f
5. The product of two positive integers is __?__ negative. b
6. The quotient of two integers with the same sign is __?__ positive. a

a. always
b. never
c. sometimes
d. left
e. right
f. opposite
g. zero

Skills

Replace each ■ with an integer that describes the situation. (Lesson 2-1)

7. a golf score of 3 under par, -3
   a golf score of 2 over par, ■ 2
8. 780 feet above sea level, +780
   5 feet below sea level, ■ -5

Write the absolute value of each integer. (Lesson 2-1)

9. -3 3
10. -5 5
11. 59 59
12. 8 8

Replace each ● with >, <, or = to make a true sentence. (Lesson 2-2)

13. 8 ● 5 >
14. -4 ● -2 <
15. -5 ● 5 <
16. 3 ● |-6| <

Add. (Lessons 2-3, 2-4)

17. $-2 + (-6)$ -8
18. $-7 + 5$ -2
19. $-8 + 0$ -8
20. $51 + (-33)$ 18
21. $-3 + (-7) + 5$ -5
22. $-15 + 25 + 20 + (-10)$ 20

Solve each equation. (Lesson 2-5)

23. $a = 5 - (-2)$ 7
24. $-10 - 4 = x$ -14
25. $y = 15 - 20$ -5
26. $-9 - 2 = b$ -11
27. $x = 14 - 21$ -7
28. $-10 - (-2) = z$ -8

Simplify each expression. (Lessons 2-4, 2-5)

29. $-3a + 4a + (-5a)$ $-4a$
30. $7x - 9x$ $-2x$
31. $-13c + (-11c) + 8c$ $-16c$

Solve each equation. (Lessons 2-7, 2-8)

32. $s = -13(10)$ -130
33. $-17(-8) = y$ 136
34. $-5(-8)(3) = r$ 120
35. $a = \frac{-15}{3}$ -5
36. $\frac{-12}{-6} = b$ 2
37. $c = \frac{18}{-3}$ -6

Evaluate each expression. (Lessons 2-3, 2-4, 2-5, 2-7, 2-8)

38. $5x$, if $x = -3$ **-15**

39. $z + (-6)$, if $z = 8$ **2**

40. $b - (-23)$, if $b = 20$ **43**

41. $a + b + (-4)$, if $a = -2$, $b = 7$ **1**

42. $\frac{-16}{m + n}$, if $m = -2$, $n = 6$ **-4**

43. $8bn$ if $b = -3$, $n = -2$ **48**

Applications and Logic

Write the negation of each statement. (Lesson 2-6)

44. $4 + 3 \cdot 5 = 35$ **$4 + 3 \cdot 5 \neq 35$**

45. Violins are members of the string family. **Violins are not members of the string family.**

Solve. (Lesson 2-9)

46. Personal Finance Sarah Bly's account at the bank is overdrawn by \$25. How much does she need to deposit to have a balance of \$100? **\$125**

47. Meteorology The temperature at 8:00 A.M. is 19°F. It rises 5° and then drops 7° by nightfall. What is temperature at nightfall? **17°F**

Communicating Algebra

The addition of integers is both commutative and associative. Explain in your own words what this means. **Sample answer: you can change the order and grouping of the addends.**

Curriculum Connection

- **Science** Investigate what is meant by *windchill.* How are integers used in determining windchill? **See margin.**
- **Social Studies** Research the effect weather has on economic issues. **See margin.**
- **Language Arts** Write a paragraph about a personal experience you have had during some type of severe weather. **See students' work.**

Read More About It

Adler, Irving. *Integers: Positive and Negative*

Asimov, Isaac. *Realm of Algebra*

Stwertka, Albert. *Recent Revolutions in Mathematics*

Thomas, David A. *Math Projects For Young Scientists*

Science:
Wind chill refers to the effect of wind speed and temperature on living things. That is, if the wind is blowing on a person's body, the person will feel as if the temperature is lower because he/she is losing body heat. For example, if the temperature is 10°F and the wind is blowing at 10 mph, the person will feel as cold as they do when it is -9°F and the wind is calm. The wind chill, then, is -9°F. Positive and negative integers are used in determining wind chill.

Social Studies:
The weather has an effect on certain industries (e.g. farming, construction, and tourism), and thereby has an effect on economic issues.

You may wish to use a Chapter Test (free-response format) as an additional chapter review. Two forms are provided in the Evaluation Masters Booklet as shown below.

Evaluation Masters Booklet, **p. 14**

Name ______________________ Date ____________

Chapter 2 Test, Form 2A

Simplify.

1. $|-3|$ 2. $46 + 21$ 3. $32 - 18$
4. $16 \cdot 8$ 5. $564 \div 4$ 6. $|-12| + |16|$
7. $-16 - (-12)$ 8. $-32 + (-17)$ 9. $-41 \cdot (-5)$
10. $-93 \div (-3)$ 11. $|20| - |-5|$ 12. $-51 + 13$
13. $-14 - 12$ 14. $-6 \cdot 18$ 15. $-105 \div 7$

Replace the ● with <, >, or = to make a true sentence.

16. -6 ● 2
17. 8 ● -7
18. $6 \cdot (-3)$ ● $-2 \cdot (-9)$
19. $3 \cdot 8$ ● $-4 \cdot (-6)$
20. $x + 14$ ● 8, if $x = -7$

Evaluate each expression if $r = 2$, $s = -3$, and $t = 5$.

21. $2r + 3t$ 22. $5s - t$
23. $4s - 3r$ 24. st
25. $12r \div 2s$ 26. $6t - 2s$
27. $s - 4s$ 28. $rst + st$

Write the negation of each statement.

29. Today is not Tuesday.
30. $2 + 3 \neq 6$
31. $5 + 4 = 9$

Solve each problem.

32. Edward's game scores are 7, −2, 5, and −3. Find his total score.
33. An airplane flying at an altitude of 18,500 feet passes over a submarine at a depth of 78 feet. How many feet separate the vehicles?

BONUS The product of two integers is −64. One integer is between 10 and 20. Find the two integers.

Answers: 1. **3** 2. **67** 3. **14** 4. **128** 5. **141** 6. **28** 7. **−4** 8. **−49** 9. **205** 10. **31** 11. **15** 12. **−38** 13. **−26** 14. **−108** 15. **−15** 16. **<** 17. **>** 18. **<** 19. **=** 20. **<** 21. **19** 22. **−20** 23. **−18** 24. **−15** 25. **−4** 26. **36** 27. **9** 28. **−45** 29. **Today is Tuesday.** 30. **$2 + 3 = 6$** 31. **$5 + 4 \neq 9$** 32. **7** 33. **18,578 ft** BONUS **16, −4**

Evaluation Masters Booklet, **p. 15**

Name ______________________ Date ____________

Chapter 2 Test, Form 2B

Simplify.

1. $|-7|$ 2. $46 - 21$ 3. $32 + 18$
4. $14 \cdot 9$ 5. $864 \div 8$ 6. $|-10| + |13|$
7. $-18 - (-17)$ 8. $-45 + (-19)$ 9. $-63 \cdot (-6)$
10. $-91 \div (-7)$ 11. $|30| - |-2|$ 12. $-47 + 28$
13. $-25 - 41$ 14. $-4 \cdot 14$ 15. $-136 \div 4$

Replace the ● with <, >, or = to make a true sentence.

16. 16 ● -20
17. -8 ● -7
18. $6 \cdot 10$ ● $-8 \cdot (-7)$
19. $3 \cdot 9$ ● $-4 \cdot (-6)$
20. $x + 14$ ● 9, if $x = -5$

Evaluate each expression if $r = -2$, $s = 3$, and $t = 4$.

21. $2s + 3t$ 22. $2s - 5t$
23. $4r - 3r$ 24. rt
25. $12r \div 2s$ 26. $6t - 5r$
27. $r - 3r$ 28. $rst - st$

Write the negation of each statement.

29. $4 + 7 = y$
30. $5 \neq 3 + 6$
31. Yesterday was a holiday.

Solve each problem.

32. On Monday, the high temperature was 63°F. On successive days, the high temperature rose 8°, fell 4°, fell 7°, rose 4°, and rose 7°. What was the high temperature Saturday?
33. Suzette's game scores were 5, −2, −8, and 5. Find her total score.

BONUS The product of two integers is 45. One integer is between −10 and −20. Find the two integers.

Answers: 1. **7** 2. **25** 3. **50** 4. **126** 5. **108** 6. **23** 7. **−1** 8. **−64** 9. **378** 10. **13** 11. **28** 12. **−19** 13. **−66** 14. **−56** 15. **−34** 16. **>** 17. **<** 18. **>** 19. **>** 20. **=** 21. **18** 22. **−14** 23. **−2** 24. **−8** 25. **−4** 26. **34** 27. **4** 28. **−36** 29. **$4 + 7 \neq y$** 30. **$5 = 3 + 6$** 31. **Yesterday was not a holiday.** 32. **71°F** 33. **0** BONUS **−3, −15**

Using the Chapter Test

This page may be used as a test or as an additional review. Two forms of a Chapter Test (multiple-choice format) are provided in the Evaluation Masters Booklet.

Evaluation Masters Booklet, **pp. 10-11**

Name ______________________ Date ____________

Chapter 2 Test, Form 1A

Simplify.

1. |−12|
   A. −12 B. 12 C. −120 D. 0 1. B
2. |−8| + |8|
   A. 16 B. −16 C. 0 D. 64 2. A
3. |18| − |−3|
   A. 21 B. 15 C. −21 D. −15 3. B

Choose the correct symbol to replace ● to make a true sentence.

4. −4 ● −8
   A. < B. = C. > D. + 4. C
5. 1 ● −12
   A. < B. = C. > D. + 5. C
6. −6 ● 4
   A. < B. = C. > D. + 6. A

Simplify.

7. 19 + 21
   A. −40 B. −2 C. 2 D. 40 7. D
8. −3 + 8
   A. 11 B. −5 C. 5 D. −11 8. C
9. −17 + (−12)
   A. 29 B. −5 C. 5 D. −29 9. D
10. 18 − 22
   A. 40 B. −4 C. 4 D. −40 10. B
11. −16 − 15
   A. −31 B. 31 C. −1 D. 1 11. A
12. −6 − (−18)
   A. −24 B. 24 C. 12 D. −12 12. C
13. −6 · 3
   A. 9 B. −18 C. 18 D. −9 13. B
14. − 7 · (−4)
   A. −11 B. −28 C. 28 D. −3 14. C
15. 12 · (−8)
   A. −96 B. 4 C. −20 D. 96 15. A

Name ______________________ Date ____________

Chapter 2 Test, Form 1A (continued)

Simplify.

16. −6 ÷ (−3)
   A. −2 B. 2 C. −3 D. −9 16. B
17. 12 ÷ (−2)
   A. −6 B. 6 C. −10 D. 14 17. A
18. −24 ÷ 8
   A. −32 B. −16 C. 3 D. −3 18. D

Evaluate each expression if a = −3, b = 4, and c = −6.

19. $a + c$
   A. −9 B. −3 C. 3 D. 9 19. A
20. $b \cdot c - a$
   A. −21 B. −27 C. 6 D. 72 20. A
21. $(b \cdot c) \div a$
   A. −21 B. −8 C. 27 D. 8 21. D
22. $a \cdot c$
   A. −18 B. −9 C. 18 D. 3 22. C

Choose the negation of each statement.

23. 1 + 2 = 4
   A. 4 = 1 + 2 B. 2 + 1 = 4
   C. 1 + 2 ≠ 4 D. 1 + 2 < 4 23. C
24. 3 + 3 ≠ 7
   A. 3 + 3 = 7 B. 7 ≠ 3 + 3
   C. 3 + 3 < 7 D. 7 > 3 + 3 24. A

Solve.

25. An elevator was at floor 24. It went down 6 floors, up 10 floors, and then down 8 floors. At what floor did it stop?
   A. 28 B. 26 C. 20 D. 40 25. C

BONUS An airplane ascended 30,000 feet. It descended 7500 feet, and then ascended 4700 feet. At what altitude was the plane then?
   A. 32,800 B. 27,200 C. 17,800 D. 42,200 B

Test

Replace each ■ with an integer that describes the situation.

1. gain 4 kg, + 4
   lose 6 kg, ■ **-6**
2. 8 inches below ground level, -8
   5 inches above ground level, ■ **5**

Replace each ● with >, <, or = to make a true sentence.

3. 0 ● 4 <
4. -3 ● 8 <
5. -6 ● |-9| <
6. |-3| ● 3 =

Solve each equation.

7. $-4 + (-5) = a$ **-9**
8. $-3 + 5 = b$ **2**
9. $y = 35 + (-19)$ **16**
10. $-9 + (-15) + 4 = q$ **-20**
11. $-12 + 15 + (-3) = x$ **0**
12. $-8 - 3 = a$ **-11**
13. $r = -15 - (-13)$ **-2**
14. $12 - 25 = d$ **-13**
15. $c = -33(3)$ **-99**
16. $-14 \cdot (-7) = d$ **98**
17. $-15[7 \cdot (-2)] = y$ **210**
18. $-143 \div 11 = g$ **-13**
19. $\frac{-270}{-90} = x$ **3**
20. $268 \div (-67) = b$ **-4**
21. $c = \frac{-650}{-5}$ **130**

Simplify each expression.

22. $-21x + (-15x)$ **-36x**
23. $8x + (-9x) + 6x + 7x$ **12x**
24. $-15y - (-10y)$ **-5y**

Evaluate each expression.

25. $-150 \div x$, if $x = -3$ **50**
26. $-16 + b$, if $b = -9$ **-25**
27. $-6cd$, if $c = -5, d = -3$ **-90**
28. $a \div b$, if $a = -12, b = -2$ **6**
29. $-25 - c$, if $c = -4$ **-21**
30. $d + x$, if $d = -7, x = -15$ **-22**

Solve.

31. Write the negation of the statement
    All dogs are dalmatians.
    All dogs are not dalmatians.
32. Maria's game scores were 40, -20, and 10. What was her total score? **30**
33. Denver, Colorado, has an altitude of 5280 feet above sea level. New Orleans, Louisiana, has an altitude of 5 feet below sea level. Find the difference in their altitudes. **5285 feet**

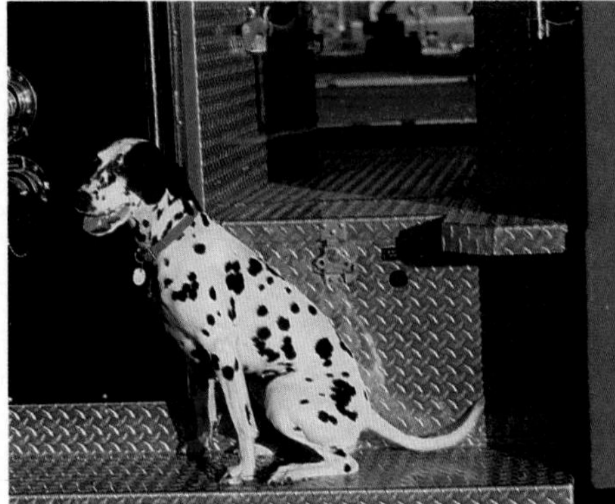

BONUS

In your own words, explain why the product of seven negative integers is negative. **See margin.**

Test Generator Software is provided in both Apple and IBM formats. You may use this software to create your own tests, based on the needs of your students.

Academic Skills Test

Cumulative, Chapters 1–2

1. Which is equivalent to $3 \times 8 - 6 \div 2$?
   - A 3
   - B 9
   - C 13
   - **D 21**

2. The perimeter of a rectangle is $2(\ell + w)$ where ℓ is the length and w is the width. What is the perimeter of a rectangle with length 15 cm and width 5 cm?
   - **A 40 cm**
   - B 35 cm
   - C 30 cm
   - D 20 cm

3. If $36 - b = 20$, what is the value of b?
   - A 56
   - B 26
   - **C 16**
   - D 6

4. Ken has two more brothers than sisters. If Ken has n brothers, which sentence could be used to find s, the number of sisters he has?
   - A $n = s - 2$
   - **B $n - 2 = s$**
   - C $s = n + 2$
   - D $s = 2n$

5. Which set of numbers is in order from greatest to least?
   - A {15, -8, -1}
   - **B {10, 0, -5}**
   - C {-5, -3, 1, 14}
   - D {-1, -6, 8, 11}

6. You are riding in a hot air balloon. The balloon rises 100 m, drops 55 m, and then rises 50 m. How far from the ground are you now?
   - A 5 m
   - B 50 m
   - **C 95 m**
   - D 195 m

7. At 2:00 P.M. the temperature was 43°F. By 7:00 P.M. the temperature had fallen 19°F. What was the temperature at 7:00 P.M.?
   - A 19°F
   - B 22°F
   - **C 24°F**
   - D 62°F

8. If a diver descends at a rate of 5 m per minute, at what depth will she be after 12 minutes?
   - A +60 m
   - B -17 m
   - C -50 m
   - **D -60 m**

9. Tom bought 80 shares of stock and later sold them for a loss of $240. Which integer represents the loss per share of stock?
   - A 30
   - B 3
   - **C -3**
   - D -30

10. What is the value of $-3k$ if $k = -33$?
    - A -99
    - B -11
    - C 11
    - **D 99**

A Cumulative Review (free-response format) and a Cumulative Test (multiple-choice format) are also provided in the Evaluation Masters Booklet as shown at the right.

Test Item	1	2	3	4	5	6	7	8	9	10
Lesson Number	1-1	1-2	1-7	1-8	2-2	2-4	2-5	2-6	2-7	2-8
TAAS Objective	2	2	2	12	1	6	7	8	9	9

Using the Academic Skills Test

This test familiarizes students with a standardized format while testing skills and concepts presented up to this point.

Evaluation Masters Booklet, **p. 17**

Name ______________ Date ______________

Cumulative Review, Chapters 1-2

Find the value of each expression. (Lessons 1–1, 1–2)

1. $12 + 12 \div 3$
2. $x - y + 7$, if $x = 20$ and $y = 9$
3. $m \cdot p + 5 \cdot m$, if $m = 6$ and $p = 7$

Write the property shown. (Lesson 1–3)

4. $3(6 + 4) = 3 \cdot 6 + 3 \cdot 4$

Find the solution for each variable. (Lesson 1–5, 1–6, 1–7)

5. $y + 9 = 36$
6. $16 = m - 4$
7. x, if 24 less than x is 8.

Translate each phrase into an algebraic expression. (Lesson 1–8)

8. twice as many as John has
9. eighteen increased by x

Describe the inequality as true, false, or open. (Lesson 1–10)

10. $5x + 2 < 12$, when $x = 5$
11. $3y - 5 > 7$, when $y = 4$

Simplify. (Lesson 2–1)

12. $|-18| - |-3|$
13. $|-36| + |-5|$

Replace each ● with > or <. (Lesson 2–2)

14. $-2 + (-3)$ ● -8
15. $16 - k$ ● -18, if $k = -4$

Simplify. (Lessons 2–3, 2–5)

16. $12 - 18$
17. $-9 + (-15)$
18. $36 + (-53)$
19. $-4 - (-16)$

Simplify. (Lessons 2–7, 2–8)

20. $-18 \cdot 3$
21. $(-15)(-23)$
22. $24 \div (-8)$
23. $-522 \div (-18)$

Solve. (Lesson 2–9)

24. At midnight, the temperature was −15°F. By the next morning, the temperature had gone up 20 degrees. What was the temperature then?
25. From 8 A.M. to noon, the temperature change was −16°F. Find the average change per hour.

Answers: 1. 16 2. 18 3. 72 4. Distrib. 5. 27 6. 20 7. 32 8. 2j 9. 18 + x 10. false 11. false 12. 15 13. 41 14. > 15. > 16. −6 17. −24 18. −17 19. 12 20. −54 21. 345 22. −3 23. 29 24. 5°F 25. −4°F

Evaluation Masters Booklet, **p. 18**

Name ______________ Date ______________

Cumulative Test, Chapters 1-2

1. What is the value of $8 + 6 \cdot 3$?
   A. 6 B. 17 C. 26 D. 42 — 1. C
2. What is the value of $a + b - 6$, if $a = 12$ and $b = 7$?
   A. 11 B. 13 C. 25 D. 1 — 2. B
3. What is the value of $ab + bc$, if $a = 4$, $b = 5$, and $c = 2$?
   A. 80 B. 50 C. 60 D. 30 — 3. D
4. What property of addition is shown by $(6 + 3) + 5 = 6 + (3 + 5)$?
   A. Associative B. Commutative C. Additive Identity D. Additive Inverse — 4. A
5. What is the solution for $37 = x + 12$?
   A. 25 B. 49 C. 35 D. 39 — 5. A
6. What is the solution for $54 = y - 12$?
   A. 76 B. 66 C. 42 D. 32 — 6. B
7. What is the solution for m, if the sum of m and 16 is 42?
   A. 68 B. 36 C. 58 D. 26 — 7. D
8. The expression *5 increased by 7* translates into what expression?
   A. $7 - 5$ B. $5 - 7$ C. $5 + 7$ C. $5(7)$ — 8. C
9. The expression *9 decreased by w* translates into what expression?
   A. $9w$ B. $w - 9$ C. $9 + w$ D. $9 - w$ — 9. D
10. Which word describes the inequality $6x + 3 > 15$?
    A. true B. false C. open D. addition — 10. C
11. Simplify $|-12| + |12|$.
    A. 24 B. −24 C. 0 D. 144 — 11. A
12. Which symbol replaces ● to make −5 ● −3 a true sentence?
    A. > B. = C. < D. − — 12. C
13. If $k = 3$, which symbol replaces ● to make $8k$ ● −24 true?
    A. > B. = C. < D. − — 13. A

Simplify.

14. $18 - 22$ A. 4 B. −4 C. 40 D. −40 — 14. B
15. $-6 + (-16)$ A. 10 B. −10 C. −22 D. 22 — 15. C
16. $-9 - (-16)$ A. −25 B. 25 C. 7 D. −7 — 16. C
17. $12 \cdot (-6)$ A. 6 B. −72 C. 72 D. −18 — 17. B
18. $18 \div (-3)$ A. 15 B. −21 C. 6 D. −6 — 18. D
19. Evaluate $ab - c$, if $a = 3$, $b = -4$, and $c = -6$.
    A. 6 B. −18 C. −30 D. −6 — 19. D
20. Evaluate $bc \div a$, if $a = 3$, $b = -4$, and $c = -6$.
    A. 27 B. −21 C. −8 D. 8 — 20. D

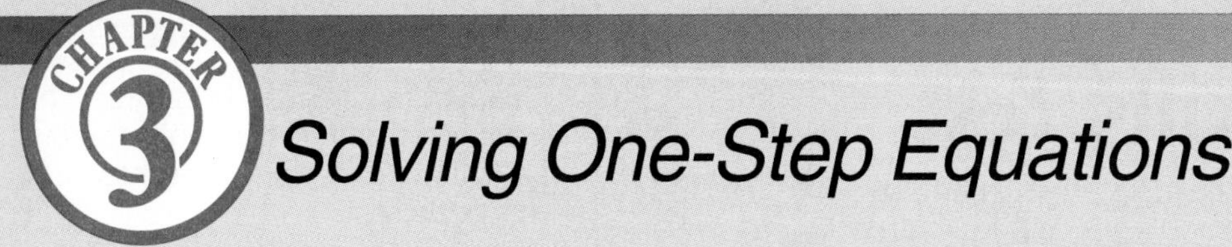

Solving One-Step Equations

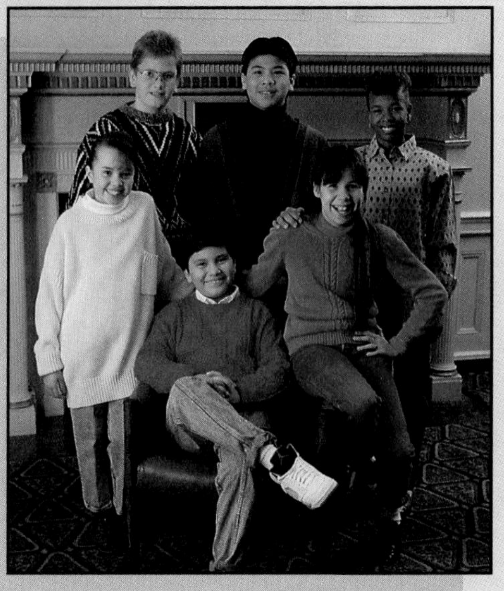

Previewing the Chapter

This chapter begins with the algebraic solution of one-step equations, using the properties of equality. The application of problem-solving techniques and the concept of a variable are further developed with problems involving formulas. Students apply these techniques in finding the perimeter and area of rectangles. The techniques used in solving one-step equations are extended to solving inequalities and problems involving inequalities.

Logic The compound statements *conjunction* and *disjunction* are introduced. Students find their truth values and write pairs of inequalities as compound inequalities.

Lesson (Pages)	Lesson Objectives	State/Local Objectives
3-1 (89-91)	3-1: Use the subtraction property of equality to solve one-step equations.	1E, 2F, 3A, 3F
3-2 (92-94)	3-2: Use the addition property of equality to solve one-step equations.	1E, 2F, 3A, 3F
3-3 (95-97)	3-3: Use the division property of equality to solve one-step equations.	1E, 2F, 3A, 3F, 4B, 5F
3-4 (98-100)	3-4: Use the multiplication property of equality to solve one-step equations.	1E, 3A, 3F
3-5 (101-103)	3-5: Apply the properties of equality to solve problems involving formulas.	1E, 3A, 3F, 3H
3-6 (105-108)	3-6: Find the perimeter and area of squares and rectangles.	1E, 3A, 3F, 3H, 4B, 4E
3-7 (110-112)	3-7: Use the addition and subtraction properties of equality to solve inequalities.	1E, 2F, 3A, 3F, 5E
3-8 (113-115)	3-8: Use the multiplication and division properties of equality to solve inequalities.	1E, 2F, 3A, 3F
3-9 (116-118)	3-9: Determine the truth value of compound statements.	1A, 1E
3-10 (119-121)	3-10: Solve verbal problems by translating them into equations and inequalities.	1D, 1E, 3A, 3F

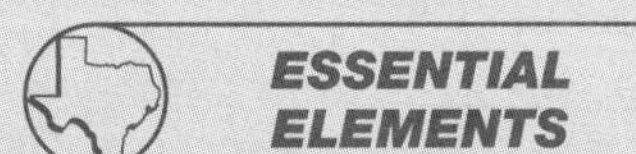

Organizing the Chapter

*You may want to refer to the **Course Planning Calendar** on Page T31.*

Planning Guide

Lesson (Pages)	Pacing Chart (in days)			Extra Practice (Student Edition)	Blackline Masters Booklets			Other Resources
	MINIMUM	STANDARD	ACCELERATED		Reteaching	Practice	Enrichment	
3-1 (89-91)	1	1	1	p. 593, Set 3A	p. 18	p. 20	p. 18	Transparency 3-1 Group Activity Card 3-1
3-2 (92-94)	1	1	1	p. 593, Set 3A	p. 19	p. 21	p. 19	Transparency 3-2 Group Activity Card 3-2
3-3 (95-97)	1	1	1	p. 593, Set 3A	p. 20	p. 22	p. 20	Transparency 3-3 Group Activity Card 3-3
3-4 (98-100)	1	1	1	p. 593, Set 3A	p. 21	p. 23	p. 21	Transparency 3-4 Group Activity Card 3-4
3-5 (101-103)	1	1	1	p. 594, Set 3B	p. 22	p. 24	p. 22	Transparency 3-5 Group Activity Card 3-5
3-6 (105-108)	1.5	1	1	p. 594, Set 3B	p. 23	p. 25	p. 23	Transparency 3-6 Group Activity Card 3-6
3-7 (110-112)	1	1	1	p. 594, Set 3C	p. 24	p. 26	p. 24	Transparency 3-7 Group Activity Card 3-7
3-8 (113-115)	1	1	1	p. 594, Set 3C	p. 25	p. 27	p. 25	Transparency 3-8 Group Activity Card 3-8
3-9 (116-118)	1	1	1			p. 28		Transparency 3-9 Group Activity Card 3-9
3-10 (119-121)	1	1	1			p. 29		Transparency 3-10 Group Activity Card 3-10
Review (122-123)	1.5	1	1					Test Generator
Test (124)	1	1	1		Evaluation Masters, pp. 19-24			

Other Chapter Resources

Student Edition
Exploration, pp. 88, 109
Team Problem Solving, p. 91
Career, p. 97
Mid-Chapter Quiz, p. 103
Algebra in Action, p. 104
Academic Skills Test, p. 125

Teacher Resource Package
Interdisciplinary Activity, p. 3
Application Worksheet, p. 18
Cooperative Problem Solving, p. 33
Multicultural Activity, p. 48
Fun Activities, p. 63
Technology Worksheets, pp. 3, 18, 33
Lab Manual, pp. 33-35
Quizzes(2), p. 25
Class Review Game

Software
Test Generator

available for Apple and IBM

Enhancing the Chapter

Some of the blackline masters for enhancing this chapter are shown below.

Applications, p. 18

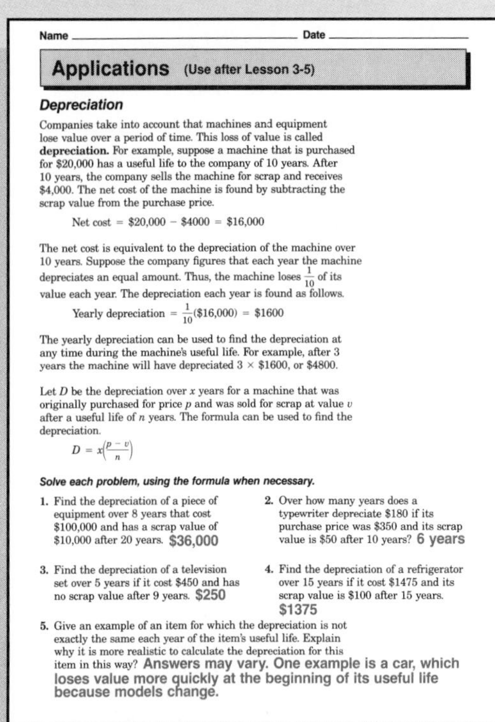

Name ______________________ Date ______________

Applications (Use after Lesson 3-5)

Depreciation

Companies take into account that machines and equipment lose value over a period of time. This loss of value is called **depreciation.** For example, suppose a machine that is purchased for $20,000 has a useful life to the company of 10 years. After 10 years, the company sells the machine for scrap and receives $4,000. The net cost of the machine is found by subtracting the scrap value from the purchase price.

Net cost = $20,000 − $4000 = $16,000

The net cost is equivalent to the depreciation of the machine over 10 years. Suppose the company figures that each year the machine depreciates an equal amount. Thus, the machine loses $\frac{1}{10}$ of its value each year. The depreciation each year is found as follows.

Yearly depreciation = $\frac{1}{10}$($16,000) = $1600

The yearly depreciation can be used to find the depreciation at any time during the machine's useful life. For example, after 3 years the machine will have depreciated 3 × $1600, or $4800.

Let D be the depreciation over x years for a machine that was originally purchased for price p and was sold for scrap at value v after a useful life of n years. The formula can be used to find the depreciation.

$$D = x\left(\frac{p - v}{n}\right)$$

Solve each problem, using the formula when necessary.

1. Find the depreciation of a piece of equipment over 8 years that cost $100,000 and has a scrap value of $10,000 after 20 years. **$36,000**
2. Over how many years does a typewriter depreciate $180 if its purchase price was $350 and its scrap value is $50 after 10 years? **6 years**
3. Find the depreciation of a television set over 5 years if it cost $450 and has no scrap value after 9 years. **$250**
4. Find the depreciation of a refrigerator over 15 years if it cost $1475 and its scrap value is $100 after 15 years. **$1375**
5. Give an example of an item for which the depreciation is not exactly the same each year of the item's useful life. Explain why it is more realistic to calculate the depreciation for this item in this way? **Answers may vary. One example is a car, which loses value more quickly at the beginning of its useful life because models change.**

The **Activity Masters Booklet** contains the page shown above.

Interdisciplinary Activity, p. 3

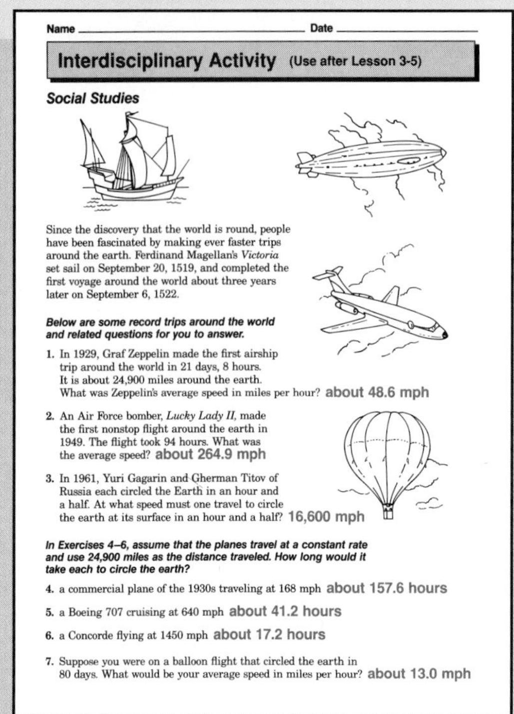

Name ______________________ Date ______________

Interdisciplinary Activity (Use after Lesson 3-5)

Social Studies

Since the discovery that the world is round, people have been fascinated by making ever faster trips around the earth. Ferdinand Magellan's *Victoria* set sail on September 20, 1519, and completed the first voyage around the world about three years later on September 6, 1522.

Below are some record trips around the world and related questions for you to answer.

1. In 1929, Graf Zeppelin made the first airship trip around the world in 21 days, 8 hours. It is about 24,900 miles around the earth. What was Zeppelin's average speed in miles per hour? **about 48.6 mph**
2. An Air Force bomber, *Lucky Lady II,* made the first nonstop flight around the earth in 1949. The flight took 94 hours. What was the average speed? **about 264.9 mph**
3. In 1961, Yuri Gagarin and Gherman Titov of Russia each circled the Earth in an hour and a half. At what speed must one travel to circle the earth at its surface in an hour and a half? **16,600 mph**

In Exercises 4–6, assume that the planes travel at a constant rate and use 24,900 miles as the distance traveled. How long would it take each to circle the earth?

4. a commercial plane of the 1930s traveling at 168 mph **about 157.6 hours**
5. a Boeing 707 cruising at 640 mph **about 41.2 hours**
6. a Concorde flying at 1450 mph **about 17.2 hours**
7. Suppose you were on a balloon flight that circled the earth in 80 days. What would be your average speed in miles per hour? **about 13.0 mph**

The **Activity Masters Booklet** contains the page shown above.

Models and Manipulatives

Borrow at least one balance scale from the science department and several objects of different known weights. Place different objects on each side of the scale, making sure that it is balanced. Ask students to add or to remove weights. Have a class discussion on the observations of the students and relate the scale to the concept of an equation. What (operations) can be done to keep the scales balanced?

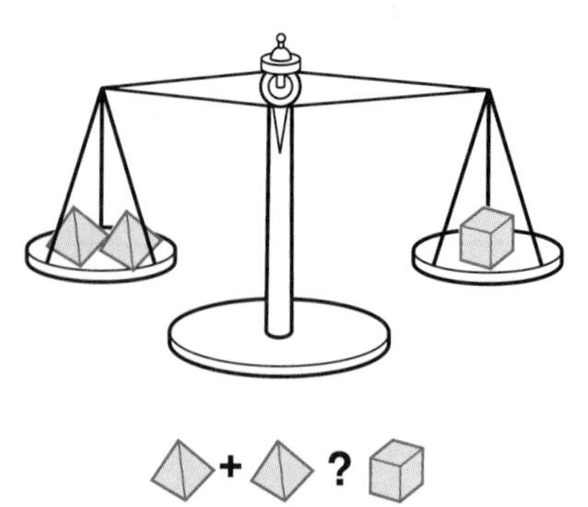

Multicultural Activity

Students in most of the other countries of the world use metric measurements. When discussing the idea of an equation and its relationship to a balance scale, ask students to see how metric weights affect the scale. Ask pairs of students to write a short story of a situation where metric weights are involved. When they finish, write all the culturally diverse situations on the chalkboard and discuss the effects not using metric measurements has on the United States.

Cooperative Learning

The following activity is provided in the **Activity Masters Booklet.**

Cooperative Problem Solving, p. 33

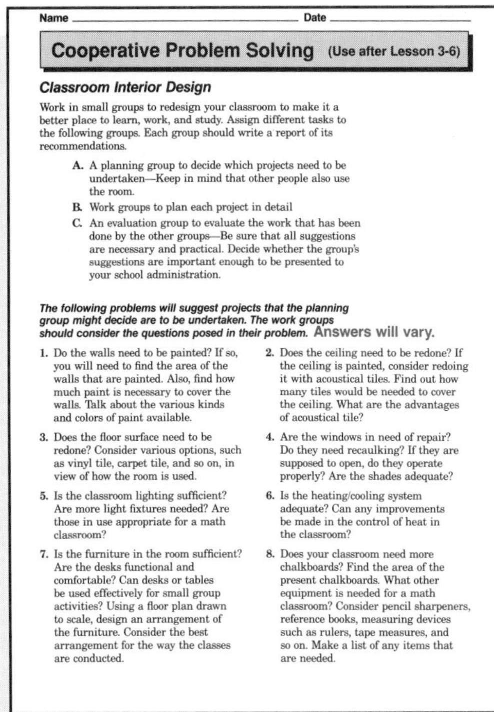

Name ______________________ Date ______________

Cooperative Problem Solving (Use after Lesson 3-6)

Classroom Interior Design

Work in small groups to redesign your classroom to make it a better place to learn, work, and study. Assign different tasks to the following groups. Each group should write a report of its recommendations.

A. A planning group to decide which projects need to be undertaken—Keep in mind that other people also use the room.

B. Work groups to plan each project in detail

C. An evaluation group to evaluate the work that has been done by the other groups—Be sure that all suggestions are necessary and practical. Decide whether the group's suggestions are important enough to be presented to your school administration.

The following problems will suggest projects that the planning group might decide are to be undertaken. The work groups should consider the questions posed in their problem. Answers will vary.

1. Do the walls need to be painted? If so, you will need to find the area of the walls that are painted. Also, find how much paint is necessary to cover the walls. Talk about the various kinds and colors of paint available.
2. Does the ceiling need to be redone? If the ceiling is painted, consider redoing it with acoustical tiles. Find out how many tiles would be needed to cover the ceiling. What are the advantages of acoustical tile?
3. Does the floor surface need to be redone? Consider various options, such as vinyl tile, carpet tile, and so on, in view of how the room is used.
4. Are the windows in need of repair? Do they need recaulking? If they are supposed to open, do they operate properly? Are the shades adequate?
5. Is the classroom lighting sufficient? Are more light fixtures needed? Are those in use appropriate for a math classroom?
6. Is the heating/cooling system adequate? Can any improvements be made in the control of heat in the classroom?
7. Is the furniture in the room sufficient? Are the desks functional and comfortable? Can desks or tables be used effectively for small group activities? Using a floor plan drawn to scale, design an arrangement of the furniture. Consider the best arrangement for the way the classes are conducted.
8. Does your classroom need more chalkboards? Find the area of the present chalkboards. What other equipment is needed for a math classroom? Consider pencil sharpeners, reference books, measuring devices such as rulers, tape measures, and so on. Make a list of any items that are needed.

Cooperative Problem Solving

Using Tables Using graph paper or square tiles, find as many different whole number rectangles as possible that have the area of 36 square units. Then find the area and the perimeter of each rectangle. List your findings in a table and make at least three general observations. Look for: (1) when the perimeter changes, but the area stays the same; (2) a square has the smallest perimeter; (3) the sides of the rectangles are factors of 36; (4) the perimeter increases as the difference in the factors increases.

Interactive Bulletin Board

Science Connection

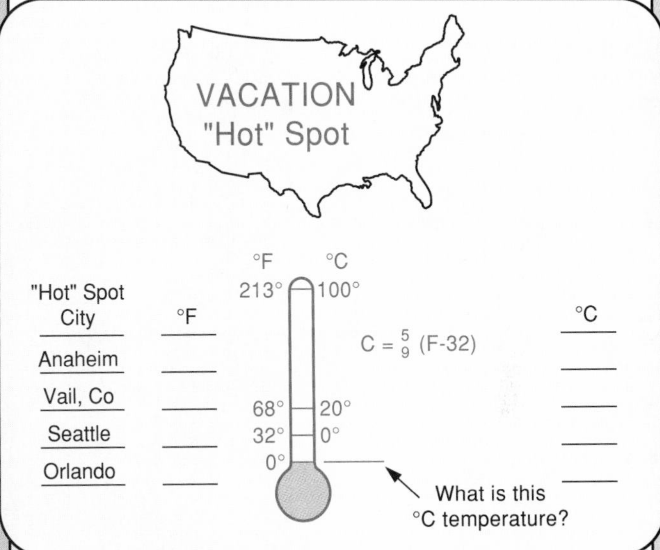

Purpose Help students understand the concepts and provide practice in using formulas.

How to Use It Laminate the columns for degrees Fahrenheit and degrees Celsius and use a wipe-off marker so the temperature readings can be changed daily. Divide students into four major groups with each student working independently. Assign each group a city. Have students use the newspaper to find the temperature of the assigned cities. Record the temperatures in degrees Fahrenheit and determine the equivalent degrees Celsius. Use the formula for changing Fahrenheit temperature to Celsius temperature.

Outside Resources

Books/Periodicals

666 Jellybeans! All That? An Introduction to Algebra, Crowell.

Films/Videotapes

Equations in Algebra, International Film Bureau, Inc.

Software

Keep Your Balance!, Sunburst.

Technology

There are three pages in the ***Technology Masters Booklet*** that involve technology with concepts in this chapter. One page involves calculators and one page has a problem that can be solved using the BASIC program that is provided. Students should evaluate the information they obtain from running the program and solve a similar problem by extending the program.

Using the Chapter Opener

Transparency 3-0 is available in the Transparency Package. It provides a full-color visual and motivating activity that you can use to engage students in the mathematical content of the chapter.

Using Diagrams

Have students brainstorm a list of aspects of health, such as eating correctly or getting along well with others. Have students make a large Venn Diagram, consisting of three overlapping circles. Label the circles "Mental Health", "Physical Health", and "Social Health". Using the list of health aspects, have students place items in the correct area of the diagram. Discuss how some items are in an overlap area and may be common to two or three health areas. Have each student look at his or her own diagram and answer to himself or herself how healthy he or she is in each area and what might be done to improve his or her health.

CHAPTER OBJECTIVES

In this chapter you will learn to:

- solve equations using the properties of equality
- apply equation-solving techniques to solve problems involving formulas
- solve inequalities
- solve problems involving equations and inequalities
- use logic to determine the truth value of compound statements

Solving One-Step Equations

How healthy are you?

Your answer may be "I'm almost never sick, so I'm very healthy." Or you might say, "I have a cold today, so I'm not feeling very healthy." But, did you know that there is much more to being healthy than how you feel physically?

Besides physical health, you need to consider your mental health and social health. These three parts of your health are connected, like the three sides of a triangle or the two sides of an equation. Each side affects the other one or two. To be considered really healthy, you need to have a *balanced* health triangle. You can accomplish this by working to keep each side of your health triangle healthy.

Now answer the question, "How healthy are you?"

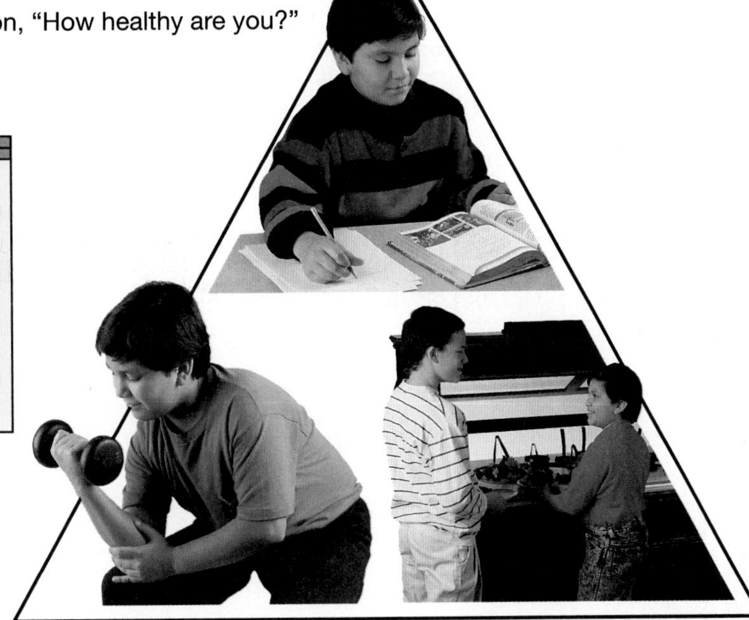

Health Connection

Class Project

Research what it means to have a *balanced diet.* Keep a record of everything you eat for three days. Then compare your diet to a balanced diet.

List three ways in which you can improve your diet.

Health Connection Health and life science books may be used to review the four basic food groups and the number of daily servings of each necessary to have a balanced diet. Have students make three charts, labeling five columns with each of the food groups and a "none of the groups" category. Label four rows with breakfast, lunch, dinner, and snacks. Students should list all food eaten for the three days in the correct column on a chart. After three days, have students discuss how to improve their lists.

Looking Ahead

You may want to have the following materials available to use in this chapter.

Exploration, p. 88
cups*, counters**, mats***

Algebra in Action, p. 104
stopwatches, objects to drop

Exploration, p. 109
small tiles#or grid paper##

*You can use the Easy-to-Make Manipulative provided on page 6 of the Lab Manual.

**You can use the Easy-to-Make Manipulative provided on page 4 of the Lab Manual.

***You can use the Easy-to-Make Manipulative provided on page 3 of the Lab Manual.

#You can use the Easy-to-Make Manipulative provided on page 1 of the Lab Manual.

##You can use the Easy-to-Make Manipulative provided on page 7 of the Lab Manual.

EXPLORATION:
Algebraic Expressions

Objective Students will build on the concept of expression by modeling one-step equations and develop an understanding of the subtraction property of equality.

1 *FOCUS*

This exploration introduces the idea of using integer mats to represent pans of a two-pan balance scale.

2 *TEACH*

Model each example for the entire class. Help students write the corresponding equations.

3 *PRACTICE/APPLY*

Using Cooperative Groups

Divide the class into small groups. Circulate around the room as they model their problems.

Additional Answers

Your turn.

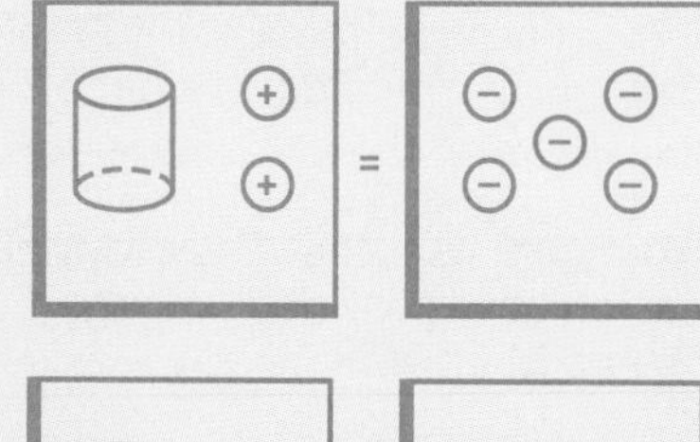

5.

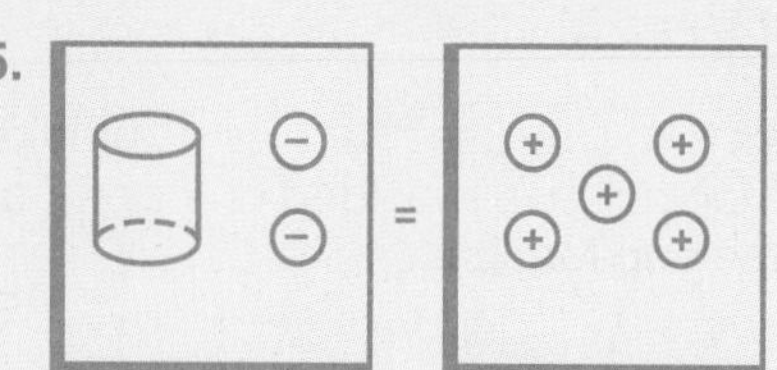

The model for this equation is the same as the model for $x + (-2) = 5$. Add enough zero pairs on the right to match up the negative counters on the left.

4 *CLOSE*

Writing Connection

Ask students to write a general rule for solving equations involving addition.

Exploration

Solving Equations

Materials: cups, counters, mats

In this Exploration, you will use cups and counters as models for building and solving equations.

▶ Recall from Chapter 1 that cups and counters are models for building an expression. For example, the expression $x + 2$ is shown below at the left. In the expression $x + 2$, x could be any value. But if there is a restriction on the expression, like $x + 2$ must have the same value as 5, you have an equation, $x + 2 = 5$.

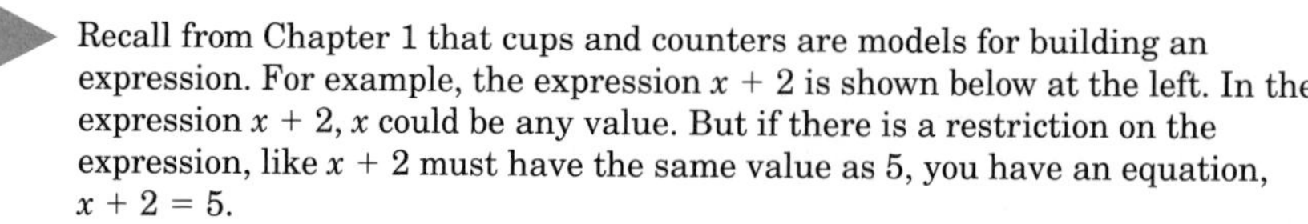

What are the possible values of x so that $x + 2 = 5$ is a true equation? In other words, how many counters are in the cup? If you pair each counter on the left side with one on the right side, then you can see how many remain to fill the cup. In this case, the cup must contain 3 positive counters. So, $x = 3$.

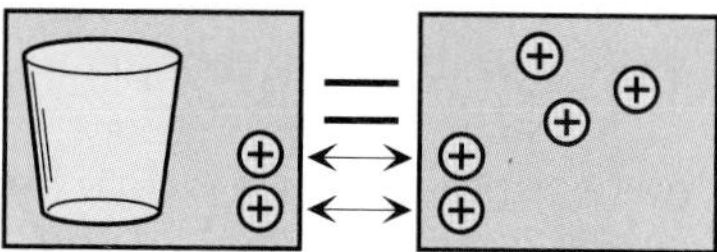

▶ Now consider $x + (-2) = 5$. In this example, there are no negative counters on the right side. Therefore, add enough zero pairs to match up the negative counters.

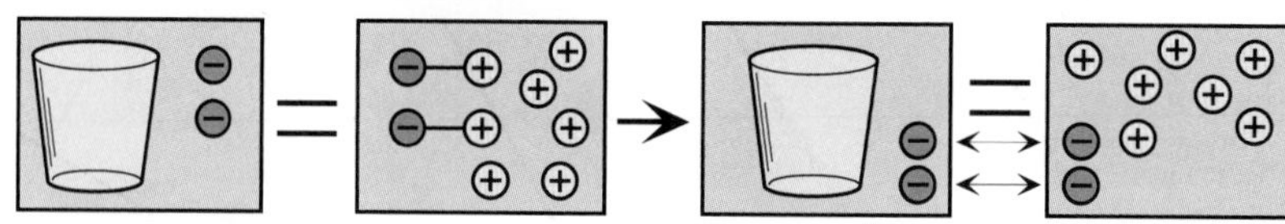

The cup contains 7 positive counters. So, $x = 7$.

Your Turn: Model $x + 2 = -5$. **See margin.**

Model each equation and solve. **For diagrams, see Solutions Manual.**

1. $s + 4 = 5$
2. $z + (-3) = -1$
3. $y + 7 = -4$
4. $t + (-6) = 7$

Analysis

5. Consider the equation $x - 2 = 5$. Model this equation. Describe the model and the procedure for solving this equation. **See margin.**

SET-UP

Materials

- Cups, Lab Manual, p. 6
- Counters, Lab Manual, p. 4
- Integer Mats, Lab Manual, p. 2

You may wish to use the Exploration worksheet provided on page 33 of the Lab Manual.

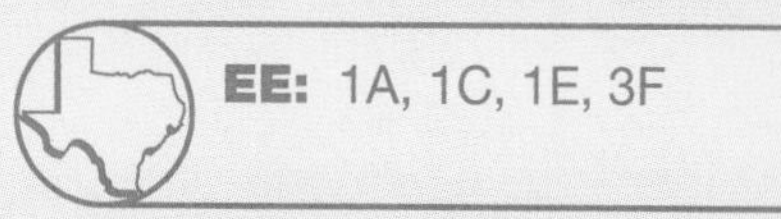

For Students Each student or group of students will need a packet of 10 positive and 10 negative counters.

For the Overhead Projector Use two mats separated by an equal sign. This will allow students to see each side of the equation as being distinct and the emphasis can be on making sure the contents of each mat are the same.

3-1 Solving Equations: $x + a = b$

Objective:
Solve equations by using the subtraction property of equality.

Key Term:
equivalent equation

Science Connection

The observations about action-reaction pairs are summarized in Newton's third law of motion. Isaac Newton also made important discoveries about gravitation and the spectrum of light.

Have you ever heard the expression *for every action there is an equal and opposite reaction?* In physical science, this means that forces always occur in pairs. The photo shows two teams having a tug-of-war. If the force of the red team equals the force of the blue team, the rope does not move. The teams are *balanced.* You can use this tug-of-war as a model of an equation.

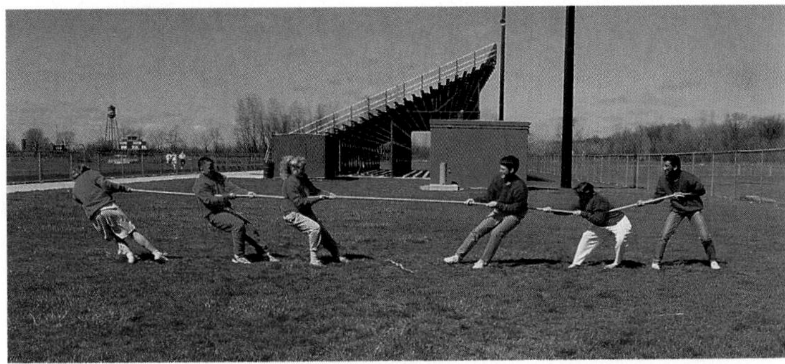

Consider the equation $x + 8 = 3$. If you subtract 8 from the left side of the equation, you must also subtract 8 from the right side of the equation. This keeps the equation *balanced.*

Why was 8 subtracted from the left side?
to undo the addition of 8

$x + 8 = 3$

$x + 8 - 8 = 3 - 8$ Subtract 8 from each side.

$x + 0 = -5$ $8 - 8 = 0, 3 - 8 = -5$

$x = -5$ $x + 0 = x$

All of the equations shown above are **equivalent equations** because they have the same solution, -5.

The property that you used to subtract 8 from each side of the equation is called the subtraction property of equality.

Subtraction Property of Equality

In words: If you subtract the same number from each side of an equation, the two sides remain equal.
In symbols: For any numbers a, b, and c, if $a = b$ then $a - c = b - c$.

Bell Ringer

Using at least three addends, write ten addition sentences whose sum is -1.

Lesson Notes 3-1

5-Minute Check
(over Chapter 2)

Solve each equation.
1. $m = -4 - 8$ -12
2. $12 - 14 = x$ -2
3. $-2(3)(-5) = y$ 30

Simplify each expression.
4. $-6x + 2x - 3x$ $-7x$
5. $4y + (-11y) + 9y$ $2y$

Transparency 3-1 contains the 5-Minute Check and a teaching aid for this lesson.

1 FOCUS

The purpose of the lesson is to solve equations of the form $x + a = b$ by using one of the following two methods: (1) the subtraction property of equality and (2) the additive inverse property.

Motivating the Lesson

Place an equal amount of pennies on each pan of a two-pan balance. Remove some of the pennies from one pan. Ask students what can be done to get the scale to balance.

2 TEACH

Using Questioning

Ask students to solve these equations intuitively.
$x + 3 = 7$ 4
$y + 5 = 10$ 5
Then formalize the method, using the examples in the lesson.

Chalkboard Examples

Solve each equation. Check your solution.

- *For Example 1*
  $m + 13 = -4$ $m = -17$
- *For Example 2*
  $y + 15 = -8$ $y = -23$
- *For Example 3*
  $-43 = x + (-9)$ $x = -34$

EE: 1E, 2F, 3A, 3F
TAAS: 2, 7, 12

3 PRACTICE/APPLY

Checking the Concepts

Using Discussion Ask students to relate the following to the lesson. Middle School A and Middle School B are having a spelling bee. Each school has a team of 25 students. However, on the day of the bee, two students are absent from team B. In the sense of fairness, what can be done to make the teams even? How does this relate to this lesson?

Error Analysis

Watch for students who have trouble working problems when the variable is on the right side of the equation.

Prevent by writing an equation with the variable on the left, and the same equation with the variable on the right. For example, $x + 3 = 7$ and $7 = x + 3$. Solve both equations, showing that they are identical.

Practice Masters Booklet, **p. 20**

Name ______________________ Date ______________

Practice Worksheet 3-1

Solving Equations: x + a = b

Solve each equation. Check your solution.

1. $m + 7 = 12$ 5
2. $h + 3 = -5$ −8
3. $y + 19 = 15$ −4
4. $x + (-12) = 4$ 16
5. $12 = t + 3$ 9
6. $z + (-7) = -8$ −1
7. $13 = z + 18$ −5
8. $-13 = 6 + m$ −19
9. $y + (-7) = -5$ 2
10. $m + 18 = -9$ −27
11. $c + (-11) = 0$ 11
12. $n + 25 = 26$ 1
13. $p + (-9) = -7$ 2
14. $17 + k = 11$ −6
15. $-8 + t = -12$ −4
16. $y + (-39) = 17$ 56
17. $u + 38 = 34$ −4
18. $47 = -19 + p$ 66
19. $35 = w + 35$ 0
20. $0 = -16 + l$ 16
21. $e + (-15) = 15$ 30
22. $19 = g + (-8)$ 27
23. $-15 = 15 + f$ −30
24. $-9 = -4 + s$ −5
25. $3 + r = -14$ −17
26. $-204 + n = 215$ 419

Example

1 Solve $m + 37 = -4$. Check your solution.

$m + 37 = -4$

$m + 37 - 37 = -4 - 37$ Subtract 37 from each side.

$m = -41$

Check: $m + 37 = -4$

$-41 + 37 \stackrel{?}{=} -4$ Replace m with -41.

$-4 = -4$ ✓ The solution is -41.

Subtracting a number is the same as adding its additive inverse. Therefore, another way to solve this type of equation is to use the additive inverse property, $a + (-a) = 0$.

Examples

Solve each equation. Check your solution.

2 $y + 21 = -7$

$y + 21 = -7$ Add -21 to each side

$y + 21 + (-21) = -7 + (-21)$ because $21 + (-21) = 0$.

$y + 0 = -28$ -21 is the additive inverse of 21.

$y = -28$

Check: $y + 21 = -7$

$-28 + 21 \stackrel{?}{=} -7$ Replace y with -28.

$-7 = -7$ ✓ The solution is -28.

3 $-23 = k + (-5)$

$-23 = k + (-5)$

$-23 + 5 = k + (-5) + 5$ The additive inverse of -5 is 5.

$-18 = k + 0$

$-18 = k$ The solution is -18.

Checking for Understanding

Communicating Algebra

1. What is the name of the property that enables you to subtract the same number from each side of an equation? **Subtraction property of equality**
2. Are $x + 4 = 10$ and $x = 5$ equivalent equations? Explain why or why not. **2. no; see margin.**
3. Explain how to solve $y + 12 = -7$. **Subtract 12 from each side.**
4. Explain how to solve $z + (-13) = 12$. **Add 13 to each side.**

Guided Practice

Solve each equation. Check your solution.

5. $k + 17 = 9$ **-8**
6. $4 + b = -13$ **-17**
7. $-11 = y + 27$ **-38**
8. $-33 = x + 16$ **-49**
9. $m + 10 = 7$ **-3**
10. $9 = x + 13$ **-4**

Alternate Strategies: Reteaching the Lesson

Reteaching Activity

Using Models Divide students into small groups to play "I Am Thinking of a Number". Have one student state an addition equality. For example, "When I add -5 to my number, I get 13. What is my number?" Other students can model the equation and use the model to solve the equation.

Reteaching Masters Booklet, ***p. 18***

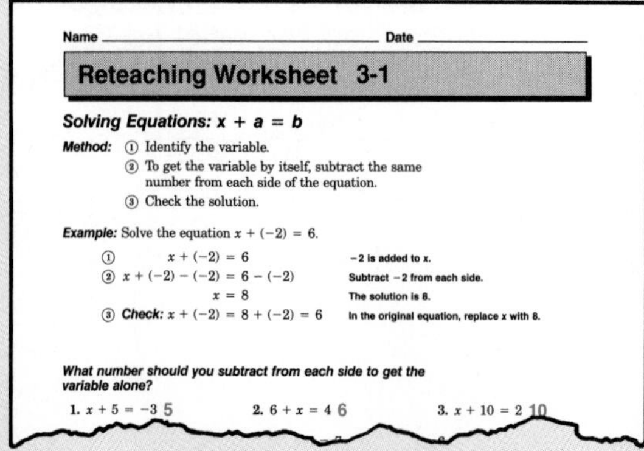

Name ______________________ Date ______________

Reteaching Worksheet 3-1

Solving Equations: x + a = b

Method: ① Identify the variable.
② To get the variable by itself, subtract the same number from each side of the equation.
③ Check the solution.

Example: Solve the equation $x + (-2) = 6$.

① $x + (-2) = 6$ **−2 is added to x.**
② $x + (-2) - (-2) = 6 - (-2)$ **Subtract −2 from each side.**
$x = 8$ **The solution is 8.**
③ ***Check:*** $x + (-2) = 8 + (-2) = 6$ **In the original equation, replace x with 8.**

What number should you subtract from each side to get the variable alone?

1. $x + 5 = -3$ 5
2. $6 + x = 4$ 6
3. $x + 10 = 2$ 10

Exercises

Independent Practice

Solve each equation. Check your solution.

11. $18 + m = -57$ **-75**
12. $11 + c = -5$ **-16**
13. $w + 42 = -51$ **-93**
14. $y + 23 = 15$ **-8**
15. $44 = b + 63$ **-19**
16. $67 = h + 38$ **29**
17. $-22 = z + 13$ **-35**
18. $a + (-7) = 8$ **15**
19. $g + (-19) = 24$ **43**
20. $-13 + b = 14$ **27**
21. $-17 + z = 5$ **22**
22. $43 = r + (-15)$ **58**
23. $-12 + k = -37$ **-25**
24. $k + (-11) = -21$ **-10**
25. $p + (-8) = -21$ **-13**
26. $15 = x + 42$ **-27**
27. $x + (-21) = -59$ **-38**
28. $24 = m + 37$ **-13**
29. $q + (-3) = 17$ **20**
30. $b + 68 = 59$ **-9**
31. $m + 37 = 14$ **-23**

Language Skills

Write an equation for each situation. Then solve the equation.

32. Lone Star Supply Company bought a computer system with a color monitor for \$1598. If the color monitor cost \$699, how much did the rest of the system cost? **$x + 699 = 1598$; \$899**
33. The best price Dawn found on a new compact car with a sports option package was \$10,935. If the option package cost \$850, what was the price of the car? **$x + 850 = 10{,}935$; \$10,085**

Mixed Review

34. Evaluate the expression $35 - c - b$ if $b = 13$ and $c = 7$. (Lesson 1-2) **15**
35. Simplify the expression $21k + 3(k + 1)$. (Lesson 1-4) **$24k + 3$**
36. Order the numbers -2, -7, 9 from least to greatest. (Lesson 2-2) **-7, -2, 9**
37. Solve the equation $x = -15 + 4 + (-9)$. (Lesson 2-4) **-20**
38. State whether the quotient of -42 and -7 is positive or negative. (Lesson 2-8) **positive**

Application

39. **Meteorology** A maximum and minimum thermometer records both the high and low temperatures of the day. If the difference between one day's high and low was 49 degrees and the high temperature was 67 degrees, what was the low temperature? **18 degrees**

Critical Thinking

40. Write two equations that are equivalent. Then write two equations that are not equivalent. **Sample answer: $2x = 10$, $x = 5$; $3x = 21$, $x + 4 = 10$**

Wrap-Up

41. In this lesson you solved an equation by removing the same quantity from each side of the equation. Give an example of an everyday experience where both sides are treated equally. **Sample answer: Parents try to treat their children equally.**

Team Problem Solving

Suppose that one pyramid balances two cubes and one cylinder balances three cubes. Determine whether each statement below is *true* or *false*.

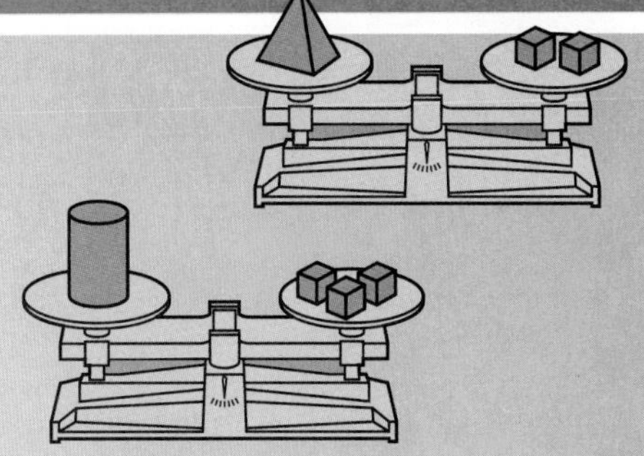

a. One pyramid and one cube balance one cylinder. **T**

b. One cylinder and one pyramid balance four cubes. **F**

c. One pyramid and one cube balance three cubes. **T**

d. One pyramid and two cubes balance one cylinder. **F**

Independent Practice

Homework Assignment	
Basic	11-33 odd, 34-41
Average	14-30 even, 32-41
Honors	22-41

4 CLOSE

Assessment Option

Writing Ask students to give a written summary of what they learned from this lesson.

Alternate Strategies: Extending the Lesson

Enrichment

Consumer Awareness Have students find newspaper ads for purchasing items that can be paid in installments. Using the cash price of the item and the total amount paid if the item is bought using installments, have students determine the finance charge.

Cooperative Learning

Equation Creation Group Activity **3-1**

MATERIALS: 0-9 spinner • coin • paper • pencils

Two to four players create equations for others in the group to solve. To begin, someone in the group spins the spinner four times and flips the coin two times. The four digits and the two operations (+ or −) are recorded on a piece of paper for each player to see. Everyone in the group now writes an equation of the form $x + a = b$ or $b = a + x$ using all four digits and the two operations. The digits may be used to form 1-, 2-, or 3-digit numbers in the equation.

Everyone then exchanges their equation with someone in the group and solves the given equation. The player who wrote the equation checks to be sure the equation is solved correctly.

Each player who solved an equation correctly earns a point. The winners are the players who score the most points after five rounds.

Merrill Pre-Algebra SOLVING EQUATIONS: $x + a = b$

Enrichment Masters Booklet, **p. 18**

Name ______________ Date ______________

Enrichment Worksheet 3-1

Intersection and Union of Sets

The set of all factors of 8 and 12 can be listed in set notation as follows.

factors of 8 A = {1, 2, 4, 8}
factors of 12 B = {1, 2, 3, 4, 6, 12}

The **intersection** of sets A and B is the set of elements that are in both A and B. The diagram shows the intersection of A and B.

A intersection B = the set containing 1, 2, and 4

$A \cap B = \{1, 2, 4\}$

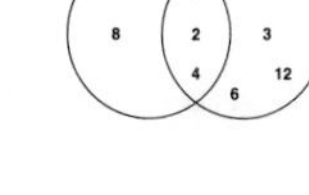

The **union** of sets A and B is the set of elements that are in A or in B or in both.

A union B = the set containing 1, 2, 3, 4, 6, 8, and 12

$A \cup B = \{1, 2, 3, 4, 6, 8, 12\}$

Give the intersection and union for each of the following.

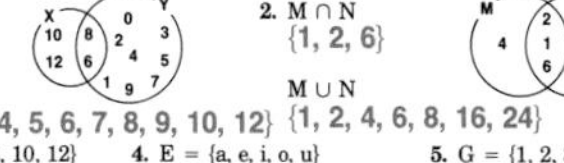

1. $X \cap Y$ **{6, 8}**
   $X \cup Y$ **{0, 1, 2, 3, 4, 5, 6, 7, 8, 9, 10, 12}**
2. $M \cap N$ **{1, 2, 6}**
   $M \cup N$ **{1, 2, 4, 6, 8, 16, 24}**
3. C = {2, 4, 6, 8, 10, 12}
   D = {0, 3, 6, 9, 12, 15, 18}
   $C \cap D$ = {6, 12}
   $C \cup D$ {0, 2, 3, 4, 6, 8, 9, 10, 12, 15, 18}
4. E = {a, e, i, o, u}
   F = {c, a, k, e}
   $E \cap F$ = {a, e}
   $E \cup F$ = {a, c, e, i, k, o, u}
5. G = {1, 2, 3, 4, 5}
   H = {2, 3, 5, 7, 11}
   $G \cap H$ = {2, 3, 5}
   $G \cup H$ = {1, 2, 3, 4, 5, 7, 11}
6. Let J = {3, 12, 21, 30} and R = {2, 11, 20}. What is $J \cap R$?
   Hint: The empty set has no elements. The empty set is written ø. **Ø**

Let K be the set of all counting numbers less than 60. Let L be the set of all counting numbers greater than 50.

7. Find $K \cap L$. **{51, 52, 53, ..., 59}**
8. Find $K \cup L$. **{1, 2, 3, ...}**
9. Describe $K \cap L$ using the words greater than and less than.
   The set of counting numbers greater than 50 and less than 60

Lesson Notes 3-2

5-Minute Check
(over Lesson 3-1)

Solve each equation. Check your solution.

1. $h + 9 = -16$ **-25**
2. $-7 + x = 5$ **12**
3. $y + 14 = -22$ **-36**
4. $m + (-21) = 35$ **56**
5. $-12 + x = -43$ **-31**

Transparency 3-2 contains the 5-Minute Check and a teaching aid for this lesson.

1 FOCUS

The purpose of the lesson is to solve equations in the form $x - b = c$ by using the addition property of equality.

Motivating the Lesson

Place an equal amount of pennies on each pan of a two-pan balance. Add some pennies to one pan. Ask students what can be done to get the scale to balance.

2 TEACH

Using Questioning

Write these equations on the chalkboard.

$x - (-9) = 12$ $x + 9 = 12$

Ask students why 3 is the solution to both equations. Then ask what the relationship is between the two equations.

Chalkboard Examples

Solve each equation. Check your solution.

- *For Example 1*
  $y - 3 = 6$ **9**
- *For Example 2*
  $-28 = y - (-6)$ **-34**
- *For Example 3*
  $y + (-28) = 12$ **40**

EE: 1E, 2F, 3A, 3F
TAAS: 2, 6, 10, 12

3-2 Solving Equations: $x - b = c$

Objective:
Solve equations by using the addition property of equality.

Mrs. Neish is a pharmacist at North Penn Hospital. She weighs various medicines using a scale like the one shown at the right. Suppose the scale is balanced. Next, she places a weight on one side of the scale. Then she must add an equal amount of the medicine to the other side to keep the scale balanced.

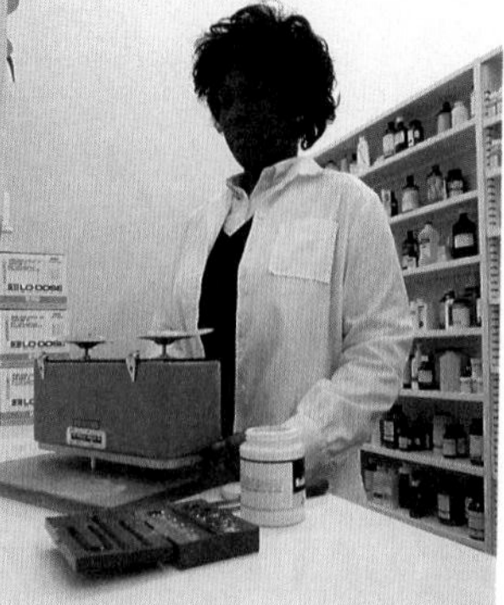

If a 12-gram weight were placed on the right side of the scale, then 12 grams of the medicine must be added to the left side to balance the scale.

In mathematics, some equations can be solved by adding the same number to each side of the equation. The equation $t - 12 = 42$ can be solved by adding 12 to each side.

Example

1 **Solve $t - 12 = 42$. Check your solution.**

$t - 12 = 42$

$t - 12 + 12 = 42 + 12$ Add 12 to each side to undo subtraction of 12.

$t = 54$

Check: $t - 12 = 42$

$54 - 12 \stackrel{?}{=} 42$ Replace t with 54.

$42 = 42$ ✓

Addition Property of Equality

In words: If you add the same number to each side of an equation, the two sides remain equal.

In symbols: For any numbers a, b, and c, if $a = b$, then $a + c = b + c$.

Both allow you to perform an operation to each side of an equation.

Recall from Chapter 2 that to subtract an integer, you add its inverse.

subtraction — additive inverse — addition

$7 - (-2) = 9$ $\quad$ $7 + 2 = 9$

same result

When solving equations, it is usually helpful to eliminate double signs first.

Bell Ringer

Write ten equations in the form $x + b = c$ whose solution is -3.

Examples

2 **Solve $-17 = y - (-9)$. Check your solution.**

$-17 = y - (-9)$

$-17 = y + 9$ Rewrite as an addition sentence.

$-17 - 9 = y + 9 - 9$ Subtract 9 from each side.

$-26 = y$

Check: $-17 = y - (-9)$

$-17 \stackrel{?}{=} -26 - (-9)$ Replace y with -26.

$-17 = -17$ ✓

The solution is -26.

Estimation Hint

THINK: $y - 20 = 30$ The solution should be about 50.

Always check your solution against your estimate to see if it is reasonable.

3 **Solve $y + (-17) = 32$.**

$y + (-17) = 32$

$y - 17 = 32$ Rewrite as a subtraction sentence.

$y - 17 + 17 = 32 + 17$ Add 17 to each side.

$y = 49$ Check this solution.

The solution is 49.

Checking for Understanding

Communicating Algebra

1. What is the name of the property that enables you to add the same number to each side of an equation? **addition property of equality**
2. Explain how to solve $b - 7 = 3$. **Add 7 to each side.**
3. Explain how to solve $y - (-8) = 4$. **Eliminate double signs then subtract 8.**
4. Write an equation in the form $x - b = c$ where the solution is -12. **Sample answer: $x - 3 = -15$**

Guided Practice

Rewrite each sentence as a corresponding addition or subtraction sentence. Then solve.

5. $x + (-9) = 15$
6. $y - (-16) = 24$
7. $p - (-7) = -18$
8. $-5 = r + (-12)$
9. $18 = t + (-4)$
10. $k - (-36) = 30$
11. $p - (-17) = 2$
12. $-23 = n + (-5)$
13. $m + (-8) = -15$

5. $x - 9 = 15$; 24 6. $y + 16 = 24$; 8 7. $p + 7 = -18$; -25 8. $-5 = r - 12$; 7 9. $18 = t - 4$; 22 10. $k + 36 = 30$; -6; 11. $p + 17 = 2$; -15 12. $-23 = n - 5$; -18 13. $m - 8 = -15$; -7

Exercises

Independent Practice

Solve each equation. Check your solution.

14. $a - 16 = 33$ **49**
15. $k - 36 = -37$ **-1**
16. $y - 8 = -22$ **-14**
17. $r - 21 = 58$ **79**
18. $y + (-7) = 19$ **26**
19. $y + (-8) = -31$ **-23**
20. $b + (-14) = 6$ **20**
21. $k + (-13) = 21$ **34**
22. $z - (-7) = -19$ **-26**
23. $x - (-18) = 14$ **-4**
24. $t - (-34) = 66$ **32**
25. $s - (-47) = -27$ **-74**

26. $42 = y - (-47)$ **-5**
27. $59 = r - (-95)$ **-36**
28. $-23 = q - 81$ **58**
29. $-17 = p - 93$ **76**
30. $x - (-33) = 14$ **-19**
31. $d - 27 = -63$ **-36**

Independent Practice

Homework Assignment	
Basic	15-33 odd, 34-40, 45-47
Average	22-32 even, 34-47
Honors	27-47

3 PRACTICE/APPLY

Checking the Concept

Write several equations in the form $x - b = c$ on the chalkboard or overhead using three and four digit numbers for b and c. Ask students to estimate the value of x.

Error Analysis

Watch for students who add if the equation contains a + sign and subtract if the equation contains a - sign.

Prevent by reviewing rules for equation solving, and have students check solutions to equations.

Practice Masters Booklet, **p. 21**

Name ______ Date ______

Practice Worksheet 3-2

Solving Equations: x − b = c

Solve each equation. Check your solution.

1. $x - 12 = 10$ 22
2. $x - 15 = -6$ 9
3. $y - (-13) = 14$ 1
4. $z - (-12) = -28$ −40
5. $n - 7 = 11$ 18
6. $f + (-8) = 14$ 22
7. $z + (-6) = -7$ −1
8. $r + (-12) = 17$ 29
9. $m - (-14) = -17$ −31
10. $h - (-6) = 6$ 0
11. $12 = m - 4$ 16
12. $-14 = z - (-6)$ −20
13. $-13 = t - (-8)$ −21
14. $15 = c - 40$ 55
15. $k - 17 = -8$ 9
16. $-54 = c - 38$ −16
17. $u - (-35) = 12$ −23
18. $f - (-19) = -15$ −34
19. $e - 39 = 19$ 58
20. $i - 7 = -16$ −9
21. $0 = j - 100$ 100
22. $w - 12 = -12$ 0
23. $t - (-47) = 61$ 14
24. $-80 = b - 91$ 11
25. $l - 13 = -19$ −6
26. $j - (-8) = -13$ −21

Alternate Strategies: Reteaching the Lesson

Reteaching Activity

Solve the Chalkboard Examples using a vertical format. For Example 1:

$y - 3 = 6$

$\underline{\;+3 = +3\;}$

$x + 0 = 9$ or $x = 9$

Reteaching Masters Booklet, **p. 19**

Name ______ Date ______

Reteaching Worksheet 3-2

Solving Equations: x − b = c

Method: ① Identify the variable.
② To get the variable by itself, add the same number to each side of the equation.
③ Check the solution.

Example: Solve the equation $x - 9 = -13$.

① $x - 9 = -13$ **9 is subtracted from x.**
② $x - 9 + 9 = -13 + 9$ **Add 9 to each side.**
$x = -4$ **The solution is −4.**
③ *Check:* $x - 9 = -4 - 9 = -13$ **In the original equation, replace x with −4.**

Solve each equation by adding the same number to each side.

1. $x - 7 = 3$ 10
2. $14 = x - 5$ 19
3. $x - (-3) = 10$ 7

4 CLOSE

Assessment Option

Writing Have students write a general rule for solving addition and subtraction equations that contain double negative signs; for example, $d - (-16) = 9$.

Additional Answer

47. $5; yes; Sample answer: If you buy a coat for $30 off the regular price and then pay a $10 layaway charge, the amount you save is -30 - (-10), or -30 + 10 dollars.

Language Skill **Write an equation for each situation. Then solve the equation.**

32. Murielle had $175 when she started shopping for clothes. After buying a skirt, a pair of shoes, and a hat in three different stores, she had $41 left. How much did she spend? $175 - x = 41$; $134
33. Jennifer made a deposit of $150 for soccer camp. Her unpaid balance was $300. What was the fee for soccer camp? $x - 150 = 300$; $450

Mixed Review

34. Write the algebraic expression $3x + 12$ using words. (Lesson 1-8) 34. 12 more than 3 times x
35. Name the absolute value of 131. (Lesson 2-1) 131
36. Add the integers -27 and 5. (Lesson 2-3) -22
37. Is -16 a solution of $-28 = z + 12$? (Lesson 3-1) no
38. Solve the equation $g + (-3) = 16$. (Lesson 3-1) $g = 19$
39. Write an equation and solve: The temperature rose 34°F in one day. The high temperature was 21°. What was the low temperature? (Lesson 3-1) $x + 34 = 21$; -13°

Challenge **Solve each equation. Check each solution.**

40. $[b + (-3)] + 2 = 4$ 5
41. $(d + 5) + (-2) = 6$ 3
42. $-10 = [n + (-4)] + 2$ -8
43. $14 = [g - (-3)] + (-12)$ 23

Applications

44. **Personal Finance** After writing a check for $65 to pay her electric bill, Darlene has $139 left in her checking account. What was the original amount in her account? $204
45. **Recreation** Phil is playing Jeopardy. After answering a 200-point question correctly, his score is -500. What was his score before he answered the question? -700

Critical Thinking

46. Place the digits 1, 2, 3, 5, and 8 in the boxes to make a true sentence. Use each digit exactly once. ■■ + -■ = ■■ (2 3 + -8 = 1 5)

Wrap-Up

47. John owes Bill $7, that is, John has -$7. Suppose Bill forgives $2 of that debt. In other words, he takes away -$2 of John's debt. How much does John still owe? Is this similar to saying that subtracting a negative integer is the same thing as adding a positive integer? Give another example in everyday life that also illustrates this principle. $5; yes; See margin for sample.

Writing Connection

The problem below is missing information. Write a sentence that would provide the necessary information to solve the problem.

(You do not have to solve the problem.)
In the first 4 days of a 5-day cold spell, the lowest temperature was -8°C. What was the highest temperature during the 4 days?
The temperature span was 12°C.

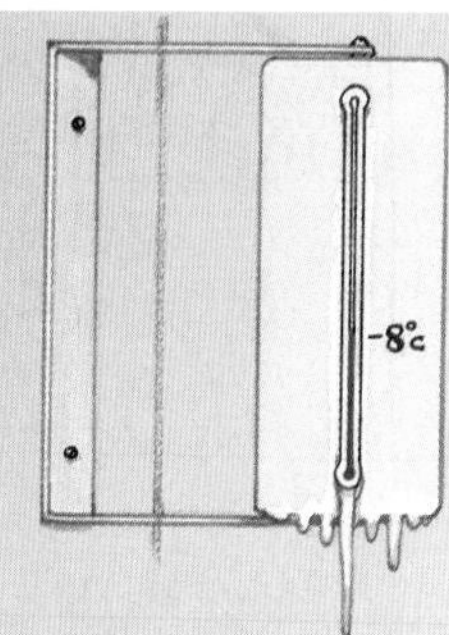

Alternate Strategies: Extending the Lesson

Enrichment

Consumer Awareness Provide students with a check register with the final balance and all checks and deposits filled in. Have students work backwards, writing an equation for each step, to determine the initial balance.

Cooperative Learning

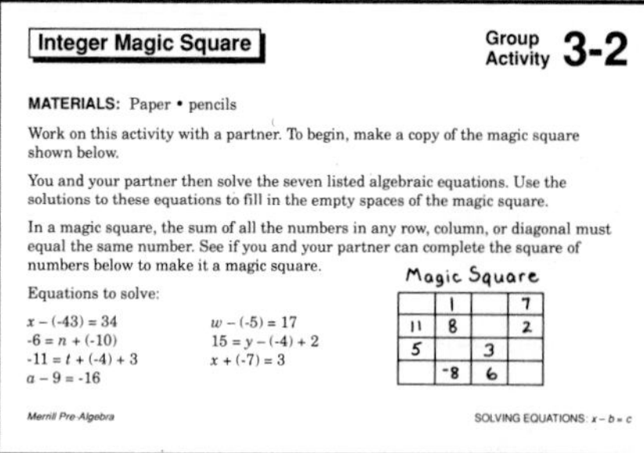

Integer Magic Square Group Activity **3-2**

MATERIALS: Paper • pencils

Work on this activity with a partner. To begin, make a copy of the magic square shown below.

You and your partner then solve the seven listed algebraic equations. Use the solutions to these equations to fill in the empty spaces of the magic square.

In a magic square, the sum of all the numbers in any row, column, or diagonal must equal the same number. See if you and your partner can complete the square of numbers below to make it a magic square.

Equations to solve:

$x - (-43) = 34$
$-6 = n + (-10)$
$-11 = t + (-4) + 3$
$a - 9 = -16$
$w - (-5) = 17$
$15 = y - (-4) + 2$
$x + (-7) = 3$

Magic Square

	1		7
11	8		2
5		3	
	-8	6	

Merrill Pre-Algebra SOLVING EQUATIONS: $x - b = c$

Enrichment Masters Booklet, **p. 19**

Name ________ Date ________

Enrichment Worksheet 3-2

Solving Equations Using Addition and Subtraction

Write an equation and then solve.

1. The sum of a number and 8 is 15. Find the number. $x + 8 = 15$; 7
2. The difference of a number and 12 is 15. Find the number. $x - 12 = 15$; 27
3. If 17 less than a number is 25, find the number. $x - 17 = 25$; 42
4. 29 is twelve more than a number. What is the number? $29 = 12 + x$; 17
5. The sum of a number and $6\frac{1}{2}$ is $12\frac{3}{4}$. Find the number. $x + 6\frac{1}{2} = 12\frac{3}{4}$; $6\frac{1}{4}$
6. A number decreased by 6.2 is equal to 10.9. Find the number. $x - 6.2 = 10.9$; 17.1
7. The difference of some number and 36 is $12\frac{1}{2}$. What is the number? $x - 36 = 12\frac{1}{2}$; $48\frac{1}{2}$
8. If $2\frac{2}{3}$ more than a number is $6\frac{1}{2}$, find the number. $2\frac{2}{3} + x = 6\frac{1}{2}$; $3\frac{5}{6}$
9. 14.32 is 15 less than x. Find x. $14.32 = x - 15$; 29.32
10. $3\frac{1}{2}$ increased by m is $12\frac{3}{4}$. Find m. $3\frac{1}{2} + m = 12\frac{3}{4}$; $9\frac{1}{4}$
11. The sum of y and 25.8 is 36.5. Find y. $y + 25.8 = 36.5$; 10.7
12. The difference of 35.9 and p is 12.7. Find p. $35.9 - p = 12.7$; 23.2

3-3 Solving Equations: $ax = c$

Objective:
Solve equations using the division property of equality.

As a forest ranger, Michael Volrath must check the size of trees in his forest district to see if they are growing at the expected rate. He records the distance around standing trees. He knows that the distance around a tree is about three times the thickness of the tree. Michael translates this into the equation $d = 3 \cdot t$, or $d = 3t$.

If Michael measures a tree that is 51 inches around, he must solve the equation $51 = 3t$ to estimate the thickness of the tree.

In mathematics, some equations can be solved by dividing each side of the equation by the same number. The equation $51 = 3t$ can be solved by dividing each side by 3.

How can you estimate the solution?
THINK: $60 = 3t$
The solution is less than 20.

Example

1 Solve $51 = 3t$. Check your solution.

$51 = 3t$

$\frac{51}{3} = \frac{3t}{3}$ Divide each side by 3 to undo the multiplication $3 \cdot t$.

$17 = t$

Check: $51 = 3t$

$51 \stackrel{?}{=} 3(17)$ Replace t with 17.

$51 = 51$ ✓

The solution is 17. The tree is about 17 inches thick.

Division Property of Equality	
In words:	If you divide each side of an equation by the same nonzero number, the two sides remain equal.
In symbols:	For numbers a, b, and c, where $c \neq 0$, if $a = b$, then $\frac{a}{c} = \frac{b}{c}$.

FYI
One way to estimate the age, in years, of a sugar maple is to multiply the diameter, in inches, of the tree by 6.

2 Solve $9y = -36$.

$9y = -36$

$\frac{9y}{9} = \frac{-36}{9}$ Divide each side by 9.

$y = -4$ Check this solution. The solution is -4.

Lesson Notes 3-3

5-Minute Check
(over Lesson 3-2)

Solve each equation. Check your solution.

1. $m - (-8) = 20$ **12**
2. $x + 7 = -12$ **-19**
3. $k - 43 = -12$ **31**
4. $61 = y + 41$ **20**
5. $18 = r + 39$ **-21**

Transparency 3-3 contains the 5-Minute Check and a teaching aid for this lesson.

1 FOCUS

The purpose of the lesson is to solve equations in the form $ax = c$ by using the division property of equality.

Motivating the Lesson

Bring in a recipe that is meant to serve 8 people. Ask students what they would do if they only wanted to make enough for 4 people.

2 TEACH

Using Models

On a two-pan balance, place an even number of pennies or other similar objects on each pan. Remove half of the contents of one pan. Ask students what must be done to balance the scale.

Chalkboard Examples

Solve each equation. Check your solution.

- *For Example 1*
  $65 = 5x$ **13**
- *For Example 2*
  $6y = -72$ **-12**
- *For Example 3*
  $-330 = -15x$ **22**

Bell Ringer

Greg said to Yoki, "Give me 7 of your marbles and I will have twice as many as you have." Yoki said, "No, give me 7 of your marbles, and I will have just as many as you have." How many marbles does Greg have? **49**

EE: 1E, 2F, 3A, 3F, 4B, 5F
TAAS: 2, 4, 5, 9, 12

3 PRACTICE/APPLY

Checking the Concept

Using Questioning Ask students the question below.

- Would you solve $14n = 56$ and $56 = 14n$ the same way? Why?

Error Analysis
Watch for students who have trouble working with fractions in the problem or as a solution. **Prevent by** reviewing fraction multiplication and division rules.

Independent Practice

Homework Assignment	
Basic	13-31 odd, 33-39, 41-43
Average	14-32 even, 33-43
Honors	23-43

Practice Masters Booklet, **p. 22**

Name ____________________ Date ____________

Practice Worksheet 3-3

Solving Equations: ax = b

Solve each equation. Check your solution.

1. $-4 = 4t$ −1	2. $2g = -24$ −12	3. $-16y = -16$ 1
4. $7x = 63$ 9	5. $-5z = 50$ −10	6. $24 = -3m$ −8
7. $0 = -9r$ 0	8. $6p = -42$ −7	9. $9x = 81$ 9
10. $-7n = 49$ −7	11. $4a = 36$ 9	12. $-72 = 8k$ −9
13. $-22 = -2e$ 11	14. $28 = -7f$ −4	15. $108 = 9l$ 12
16. $-64 = -8t$ 8	17. $10i = 110$ 11	18. $-7z = 91$ −13
19. $-8h = -112$ 14	20. $12b = -84$ −7	21. $9r = 522$ 58
22. $-244 = 4q$ −61	23. $-11s = -231$ 21	24. $540 = 3f$ 180
25. $-7x = 175$ −25	26. $-96 = -8w$ 12	27. $12y = 132$ 11
28. $12u = -96$ −8	29. $-14h = -182$ 13	30. $225 = -15x$ −15
31. $-12x = 156$ −13	32. $-15q = -165$ 11	33. $24e = 312$ 13
34. $-36 = 36m$ −1	35. $-12y = 288$ −24	36. $17y = 136$ 8
37. $-68a = -476$ 7	38. $-17d = 323$ −19	39. $-108 = -4t$ 27

Example

3 Solve -1675 = -25*c*. Check your solution.

$-1675 = -25c$

$\frac{-1675}{-25} = \frac{-25c}{-25}$ Divide each side by -25.

-1675 [+/-] [÷] 25 [+/-] [=] 67

$67 = c$

Check: $-1675 = -25c$

$-1675 \stackrel{?}{=} -25 \cdot 67$ Replace *c* with 67.

$-1675 = -1675$ ✓

The solution is 67.

Checking for Understanding

Communicating Algebra

1. Explain how to check your solution to an equation. Replace the variable with the solution and check.
2. What is the name of the property that enables you to divide each side of an equation by the same number? division property of equality
3. Explain how to solve $7x = 91$. Divide each side by 7.
4. Write an equation in the form $ax = c$ where the solution is -5 Sample answer: $-2x = 10$

Guided Practice

Solve each equation. Check your solution.

5. $\frac{20}{-5} = y$ -4
6. $\frac{-38}{2} = q$ -19
7. $r = \frac{-56}{-7}$ 8
8. $t = \frac{-84}{-4}$ 21
9. $k = \frac{27}{-3}$ -9
10. $\frac{-48}{16} = m$ -3
11. $\frac{-24}{-6} = k$ 4
12. $s = \frac{63}{9}$ 7

Exercises

Independent Practice

Solve each equation. Check your solution.

13. $-7x = 56$ -8
14. $4y = -52$ -13
15. $6k = -78$ -13
16. $-9m = 99$ -11
17. $-104 = 8r$ -13
18. $42 = -3y$ -14
19. $-2p = -38$ 19
20. $-13a = -39$ 3
21. $-68 = 17c$ -4
22. $165 = -11d$ -15
23. $-13a = 52$ -4
24. $-60 = -15h$ 4
25. $-27q = 81$ -3
26. $-13z = -65$ 5
27. $-85 = 17r$ -5
28. $-14x = -98$ 7
29. $-180 = 12f$ -15
30. $-14g = 406$ -29

Language Skills

Write an equation for each situation. Then solve the equation.

31. Ben and his brother Jason are having their annual medical checkups. The nurse records their heights and weights. She tells Ben that he is 5 feet 7 inches tall and weighs 3 times as much as Jason. If Ben weighs 144 pounds, how much does Jason weigh? $3j = 144$; 48 pounds
32. Fax machines transmit printed copy by telephone lines but at different speeds. Model F transmits at twice the rate of Model G. If Model F transmits 9600 bits per second, how many bits per second does Model G transmit? $2G = 9600$; 4800 bits per second

Alternate Strategies: Reteaching the Lesson

Reteaching Activity

Working Backwards Have each student count the number of letters in his or her first name and write five multiplication equations that have that number as the solution.

Reteaching Masters Booklet, **p. 20**

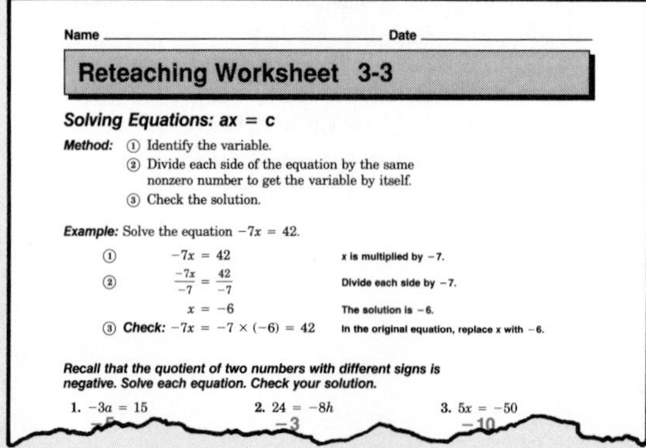
Name ____________________ Date ____________

Reteaching Worksheet 3-3

Solving Equations: ax = c

Method: ① Identify the variable.
② Divide each side of the equation by the same nonzero number to get the variable by itself.
③ Check the solution.

Example: Solve the equation $-7x = 42$.

① $-7x = 42$ — x is multiplied by −7.

② $\frac{-7x}{-7} = \frac{42}{-7}$ — Divide each side by −7.

$x = -6$ — The solution is −6.

③ ***Check:*** $-7x = -7 \times (-6) = 42$ — In the original equation, replace x with −6.

Recall that the quotient of two numbers with different signs is negative. Solve each equation. Check your solution.

1. $-3a = 15$ −5
2. $24 = -8h$ −3
3. $5x = -50$ −10

Mixed Review

33. State whether the inequality $0 < 4k - 5$ is true for $k = 1$. (Lesson 1-10) F
34. If $y = -9$, then $-y = \underline{?}$. (Lesson 2-5) 9
35. Solve the equation $x = -4(13)$. (Lesson 2-7) -52
36. Solve the equation $b + (-17) = -4$. (Lesson 3-1) 13
37. Rewrite the addition sentence $y + (-19) = 14$ as a subtraction sentence. (Lesson 3-2) $y - 19 = 14$
38. Solve the equation $d - (-14) = 5$. (Lesson 3-2) -9

Connections

39. **Geometry** The perimeter of any square is 4 times the length of one of its sides. If the perimeter of a square is 56 inches, what is the length of each side of the square? 14 in.

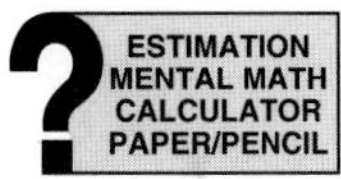

40. **Statistics** For many years, immigrants to the United States arrived at Ellis Island in New York. The flow of immigrants peaked in 1907 with more than 1 million. During that year, 37,807 people arrived from Germany. Estimate the average number of Germans who arrived daily at Ellis Island in 1907. about 100 people

Application

41. **Sports** Millicent is a hot air balloonist. The distance she can travel depends on the wind velocity. If the wind is blowing at a steady rate of 8 miles per hour, how long will it take her to fly 24 miles in her hot air balloon? 3 hours

Critical Thinking

42. If a number is multiplied by itself and the answer is doubled, the result is 32. What is the number? 4

Wrap-Up

43. Twenty-three people shared the cost of lottery tickets. They split the \$11,500,000 prize money. Write an equation that represents how to find each person's share of the prize money. How much was each person's share of the prize money? $23x = 11{,}500{,}000$; \$500,000

Career

Medical Laboratory Technician

A medical laboratory technician is an important part of the health profession. Using a microscope and an automatic analyzer, a laboratory technician can measure the amount of different substances in your blood to determine if they are within normal ranges.

For example, a laboratory technician can measure the amount of cholesterol in a sample of a person's blood. The normal range is less than 200 milligrams/deciliter (mg/dL). If a blood test reveals a cholesterol level that is higher than 200 mg/dL, a doctor will prescribe a course of action to lower this level.

4 CLOSE

Assessment Option

Writing Have the students write four equations that require using the division property of equality to be solved. Then have them exchange the equations with another student and solve them.

Enrichment Masters Booklet, **p. 20**

Name ________________ Date __________

Enrichment Worksheet 3-3

The Distance Formula

The equation $ax = c$ can be used to solve many types of problems encountered in daily life. The **distance formula,** $d = rt$ where d = distance, r = rate (speed), and t = time, is of this type.

If the distance and either the rate or time are known, the formula can be used to find the unknown quantity.

Example: How long will it take a car to travel 300 miles if its speed is 50 miles per hour?

Use $d = rt$ with $d = 300$ miles and $r = 50$ mph.

$300 = 50t$

$\frac{300}{50} = \frac{50t}{50}$

$6 = t$ It will take 6 hours for the car to travel 300 miles at 50 mph.

Write and solve an equation for these distance problems. (More than one equation is needed for Exercise 5.)

1. How long will it take a bus to travel 360 miles at 45 miles per hour?
 $360 = 45t$; 8 hours
2. It is about 93 million miles from the earth to the sun. If the speed of light is approximately 183,000 miles per second, how long does it take light from the sun to reach the earth?
 $93{,}000{,}000 = 183{,}000t$; about 508 seconds or 8.5 minutes
3. The Indianapolis 500 is an automobile race in which the first car to travel 500 miles wins the race. If the winning time one year was 3 hours, what was the car's speed?
 $500 = 3r$; $166\frac{2}{3}$ mph
4. If you see lightning far away, you must wait a few seconds until you hear the thunder. If you see lightning strike a water tower two miles from your home, and it takes 9.7 seconds to hear the thunder, what was the speed of the sound in miles per hour? (Recall that there are 3600 seconds in 1 hour.)
 $2 = 9.7r$; about 0.206 miles per second or 742 mph
5. How much longer will it take to drive 400 miles at 60 miles per hour than to travel 500 miles at 80 miles per hour?
 $400 = 60t_1$; $500 = 80t_2$; $t = t_1 - t_2$; $\frac{5}{12}$ hour or 25 minutes

Alternate Strategies: Extending the Lesson

Enrichment

Consumer Awareness Using a recent bill from the electric company, have students use the total cost and the charge per kilowatt to determine the number of kilowatts used. Have students compare this figure to the number of kilowatts on the bill.

Cooperative Learning

From Solution to Equation Group Activity **3-3**

8

MATERIALS: Paper • pencils

This activity is to be done in a group of two to four members.

A designated leader thinks of a 1- or 2-digit positive or negative integer. This member announces the number to the rest of the group. All of the group members then write an equation of the form $ax = c$ for which the given integer is the *solution.*

For example, if the announced integer were -14, then $3x = -42$ would be a correct equation.

Group members then exchange equations and check to be sure that the equation they get is a correct one. Group members should take turns thinking of the integer to be used.

Merrill Pre-Algebra SOLVING EQUATIONS: $ax = c$

Lesson Notes 3-4

5-Minute Check
(over Lesson 3-3)

Solve each equation. Check your solution.

1. $-4x = 52$ -13
2. $-7m = -105$ 15
3. $-126 = 21r$ -6
4. $56 = 14k$ 4
5. $-9y = -288$ 32

Transparency 3-4 contains the 5-Minute Check and a teaching aid for this lesson.

1 FOCUS

The purpose of the lesson is to solve equations in the form $\frac{x}{a} = b$, where $a \neq 0$ by using the multiplication property of equality.

Motivating the Lesson

Measure the hallway outside your classroom and have students find how many "hallways" are in a mile. Then time a student while he or she walks the hallway and have students find how long it would take him or her to walk a mile.

2 TEACH

Sports Connection

How many players are on 16 basketball teams? 80 6 football teams? 66 3 baseball teams? 27 Have students intuitively solve, then formalize using division equations.

Chalkboard Examples

Solve each equation. Check your solution.

- *For Example 1*

  $\frac{r}{2} = 52$ 104
- *For Example 2*

  $-21 = \frac{s}{3}$ -63

EE: 1E, 3A, 3F
TAAS: 2, 8

3-4 Solving Equations $\frac{x}{a} = b$

Objective:
Solve equations by using the multiplication property of equality.

Craig is training for the local Special Olympics. He practices by running around a $\frac{1}{4}$-mile track. Suppose he can run 1 lap in 2 minutes. At this rate, how many minutes does it take him to run 1 mile? Let t represent the number of minutes.

How do you know he runs 4 laps?
There are four $\frac{1}{4}$-miles in 1 mile.

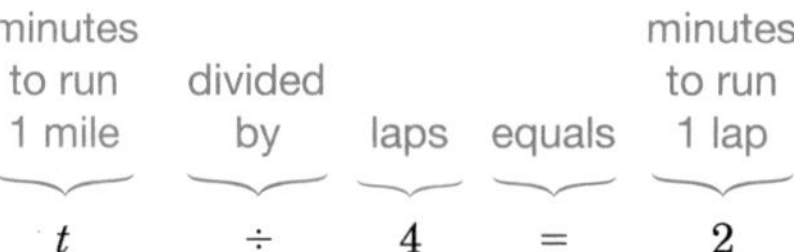

minutes to run 1 mile	divided by	laps	equals	minutes to run 1 lap
t	$\div$	4	=	2

In mathematics, some equations can be solved by multiplying each side of the equation by the same number. The equation $\frac{t}{4} = 2$ can be solved by multiplying each side by 4.

FYI

The Special Olympics includes over 1 million participants from 36 countries. Local games take place in more than 10,000 communities worldwide.

Example

1 Solve $\frac{t}{4} = 2$. Check your solution.

$\frac{t}{4} = 2$

$\frac{t}{4} \cdot 4 = 2 \cdot 4$ Multiply each side by 4 to undo the division in $\frac{t}{4}$.

$t = 8$

Check: $\frac{t}{4} = 2$

$\frac{8}{4} \stackrel{?}{=} 2$ Replace t with 8.

$2 = 2$ ✓ The solution is 8.

Craig can run 1 mile in 8 minutes.

Multiplication Property of Equality

In words: If you multiply each side of an equation by the same number, the two sides remain equal.
In symbols: For numbers a, b, and c, if $a = b$, then $ac = bc$.

Bell Ringer

Write ten equations in the form $ax = c$ whose solution is 8.

Example

2 Solve $-13 = \frac{k}{-5}$. Check the solution.

$$-13 = \frac{k}{-5}$$

$$-13(-5) = \frac{k}{-5}(-5) \quad \text{Multiply each side by -5.}$$

$$65 = k$$

Check: $-13 = \frac{k}{-5}$

$$-13 \stackrel{?}{=} \frac{65}{-5} \quad \text{Replace } k \text{ with 65.}$$

$$-13 = -13 \checkmark \quad \text{The solution is 65.}$$

Checking for Understanding

Communicating Algebra

1. What is the name of the property that enables you to multiply each side of an equation by the same number?
2. Explain how to solve $3 = \frac{z}{12}$. Multiply each side by 12.
3. Explain how to solve $\frac{p}{-7} = 23$. Multiply each side by -7.
4. Write an equation in the form $\frac{x}{a} = b$ where the solution is -14. Sample answer: $\frac{x}{2} = -7$
5. In an equation of the form $\frac{x}{a} = b$, explain why a cannot be 0. Division by 0 is undefined.
6. Is 88 a solution of $8 = \frac{f}{-11}$? Explain why or why not. No; $8 \neq \frac{88}{-11}$

1. multiplication property of equality

Guided Practice

Name the number to multiply each side by to solve each equation. Then solve. 8. 13; -117 9. -16; -64 10. -7; 91 11. -7; -161 14. -5; 70

7. $3 = \frac{z}{12}$ 12; 36
8. $\frac{m}{13} = -9$
9. $4 = \frac{r}{-16}$
10. $-13 = \frac{m}{-7}$
11. $\frac{p}{-7} = 23$
12. $\frac{x}{9} = 40$ 9; 360
13. $-16 = \frac{q}{13}$ 13; -208
14. $\frac{h}{-5} = -14$

Exercises

Independent Practice

Solve each equation. Check your solution.

15. $14 = \frac{a}{-7}$ -98
16. $\frac{b}{8} = -24$ -192
17. $\frac{k}{-12} = 13$ -156
18. $-10 = \frac{m}{11}$ -110
19. $\frac{r}{-21} = -6$ 126
20. $\frac{v}{-17} = -9$ 153
21. $21 = \frac{x}{7}$ 147
22. $18 = \frac{f}{-6}$ -108
23. $-15 = \frac{f}{14}$ -210
24. $\frac{h}{16} = 28$ 448
25. $-32 = \frac{c}{22}$ -704
26. $-26 = \frac{d}{47}$ -1222
27. $\frac{x}{-3} = 136$ -408
28. $\frac{y}{8} = -117$ -936
29. $-321 = \frac{t}{9}$ -2889
30. $5 = \frac{s}{-264}$ -1320
31. $\frac{a}{39} = -65$ -2535
32. $\frac{b}{-46} = 216$ -9936
33. $-71 = \frac{x}{24}$ -1704
34. $-42 = \frac{y}{33}$ -1386
35. $-171 = \frac{x}{-124}$ 21,204
36. $273 = \frac{p}{-784}$ -214,032
37. $\frac{m}{319} = -467$ -148,973
38. $\frac{z}{-639} = -408$ 260,712

Alternate Strategies: Reteaching the Lesson

Reteaching Activity

Using Lists Give students an answer, for example, 12. Have students create a list of ten division equations with a solution of 12.

Reteaching Masters Booklet, **p. 21**

Name ______ Date ______

Reteaching Worksheet 3-4

Solving Equations: $\frac{x}{a} = b$

Method: ① Identify the variable.
② Multiply each side of the equation by the same nonzero number to get the variable by itself.
③ Check the solution.

Example: Solve the equation $\frac{y}{-3} = -29$.

① $\frac{y}{-3} = -29$ — y is divided by -3.
② $\frac{y}{-3} \times (-3) = -29 \times (-3)$ — Multiply each side by -3.
$y = 87$ — The solution is 87.
③ *Check:* $\frac{y}{-3} = \frac{87}{-3} = -29$ — In the original equation, replace the variable with 87.

Name the number to multiply each side by to solve each equation.

1. ... 2. ... 10 3. ...

3 PRACTICE/APPLY

Checking the Concept

Have students state the sign of the solution to Exercises 7-14 before they solve the equation.

Error Analysis

Watch for students who multiply instead of divide, and divide instead of multiply.
Prevent by use of models and having students check each solution.

Independent Practice

Homework Assignment	
Basic	15-37 odd, 39-45, 48,49
Average	16-38 even, 39-44, 46-49
Honors	28-49

Practice Masters Booklet, **p. 23**

Name ______ Date ______

Practice Worksheet 3-4

Solving Equations: $\frac{x}{a} = b$

Solve each equation. Check your solution.

1. $\frac{c}{-6} = 14$ −84
2. $\frac{y}{7} = 3$ 21
3. $\frac{v}{-5} = 20$ −100
4. $\frac{x}{-2} = -24$ 48
5. $12 = \frac{s}{7}$ 84
6. $13 = \frac{m}{-3}$ −39
7. $\frac{w}{4} = -8$ −32
8. $\frac{e}{-9} = -9$ 81
9. $-1 = \frac{f}{20}$ −20
10. $\frac{k}{5} = -14$ −70
11. $-6 = \frac{z}{-7}$ 42
12. $-8 = \frac{d}{-16}$ 128
13. $9 = \frac{l}{-5}$ −45
14. $-4 = \frac{n}{-5}$ 20
15. $5 = \frac{r}{18}$ 90
16. $\frac{w}{13} = -15$ −195
17. $\frac{u}{-4} = 0$ 0
18. $\frac{a}{-3} = -9$ 27
19. $\frac{c}{4} = -11$ −44
20. $12 = \frac{z}{6}$ 72
21. $15 = \frac{k}{-5}$ −75
22. $7 = \frac{h}{61}$ 427
23. $\frac{i}{-6} = -51$ 306
24. $-24 = \frac{l}{33}$ −792
25. $\frac{s}{-65} = -14$ 910
26. $\frac{k}{19} = 19$ 361
27. $\frac{m}{-31} = 13$ −403
28. $\frac{n}{-39} = -101$ 3939
29. $247 = \frac{x}{-48}$ −11,856
30. $\frac{r}{98} = -249$ −24,402

4 CLOSE

Assessment Option

Writing Have students write four equations that require using the multiplication property of equality to be solved. Then have them exchange the equations with another student and solve them.

Enrichment Masters Booklet, **p. 21**

Name ______________________ Date ____________

Enrichment Worksheet 3-4

Puzzle

Solve each equation. The first one is completed.

1. $\frac{m}{12} = 13$	1. 156	U
2. $17v = -578$	2. −34	E
3. $\frac{c}{75} = 18$	3. 1350	R
4. $-252d = -5796$	4. 23	H
5. $64 \cdot w = 5568$	5. 87	O
6. $g \div 29 = 61$	6. 1769	B
7. $p(85) = -7225$	7. −85	T
8. $39x = 663$	8. 17	I
9. $\frac{k}{18} = 30$	9. 540	A
10. $\frac{z}{-94} = -32$	10. 3008	N
11. $-112q = 1456$	11. −13	F
12. $201y = -1608$	12. −8	S

Put the letter that is next to each solution in the box below the corresponding solution shown above.

What is a RINGLEADER?

-85	23	-34		-13	17	1350	-8	-85		87	3008	-34
T	H	E		F	I	R	S	T		O	N	E

17	3008		-85	23	-34		1769	540	-85	23	-85	156	1769
I	N		T	H	E		B	A	T	H	T	U	B

Mixed Review

39. Name the operation you would do first in the expression $2 \cdot (3 + 4) - 9$. (Lesson 2-2) Add 3 and 4.
40. Write an inequality for the phrase *45 mph is slower than 55 mph.* (Lesson 2-2) $45 < 55$
41. Write an equation and solve: A skydiver jumps out of a plane at a height of 5140 feet. He descends 2900 feet before opening his parachute. What height is he at when he opens the parachute? (Lesson 2-9)

    41. $x + 2900 = 5140$; 2240 feet
42. Solve the equation $r - 8 = -5$. (Lesson 3-2) 3
43. Name the number to divide each side by in the equation $84 = -7n$. (Lesson 3-3) −7
44. Solve the equation $15g = -75$. (Lesson 3-3) −5

Applications

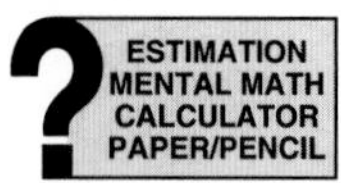

45. **Ecology** On June 8, 1990 the tanker *Mega Borg* released millions of gallons of oil into the waters of the Gulf of Mexico. It is estimated that the spilled oil would fill 4222 tanker trucks, each capable of holding 9000 gallons. Estimate the total amount of oil spilled in gallons. If a barrel holds 42 gallons, about how many barrels were spilled? about 36 million gallons; about 900,000 barrels

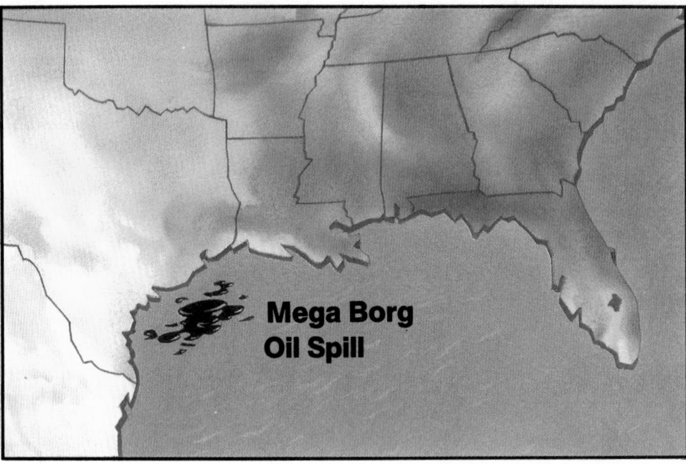

46. **Consumer Awareness** Judy keeps a record of the gasoline she uses in her car. Last month she used 115 gallons. If her car averages 22 miles per gallon, how far did she drive last month? 2530 miles
47. **Sports** Randy is training for a triathalon. He runs an average of 27 miles per week. Since he began training, he has run 91 miles. How many weeks has he been training? 3 weeks

Critical Thinking

48. Alan took a weekend ski trip to the mountains. He drove his car an average of 60 miles per hour for the first two hours and, because of snow-covered roads, had to slow down to 40 miles per hour for the last three hours. What was his overall average speed for the trip? 48 mph

Wrap-Up

49. **Make Up a Problem** Write a problem that can be solved using the division sentence $\frac{x}{3} = -2$. Sample answer: For 3 consecutive hours, the temperature fell 2°F each hour. What was the total temperature change?

Alternate Strategies: Extending the Lesson

Enrichment

Using Groups of Two Have students choose a pair of related measurement units. Have one student give a number of the larger unit chosen and the other student write an equation and determine the number of smaller units. For example, 15 feet is given. Use $\frac{x}{12} = 15$ to find the number of inches, 180 inches.

Cooperative Learning

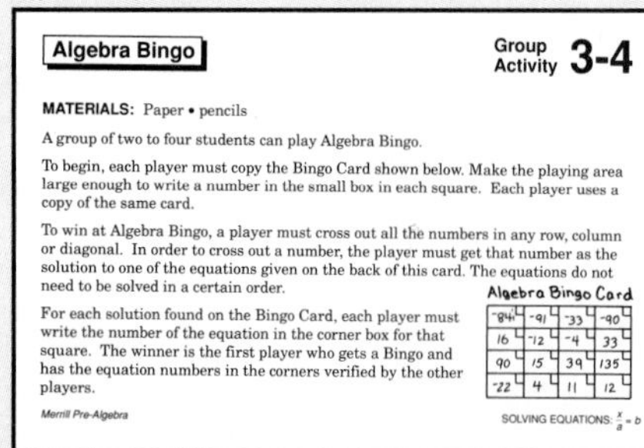

Algebra Bingo Group Activity **3-4**

MATERIALS: Paper • pencils

A group of two to four students can play Algebra Bingo.

To begin, each player must copy the Bingo Card shown below. Make the playing area large enough to write a number in the small box in each square. Each player uses a copy of the same card.

To win at Algebra Bingo, a player must cross out all the numbers in any row, column or diagonal. In order to cross out a number, the player must get that number as the solution to one of the equations given on the back of this card. The equations do not need to be solved in a certain order.

For each solution found on the Bingo Card, each player must write the number of the equation in the corner box for that square. The winner is the first player who gets a Bingo and has the equation numbers in the corners verified by the other players.

Algebra Bingo Card

-84	-91	-33	-90
16	-12	-4	33
90	15	39	135
-22	4	11	12

Merrill Pre-Algebra SOLVING EQUATIONS: $\frac{x}{a} = b$

Application

3-5 Formulas

Objective:
Solve problems by applying formulas.

Key Term:
formula

In league bowling, the team that knocks down the most pins does not always win. Some teams have more skillful bowlers than others. To make sure that each team has an equal chance of winning, a handicap is given to each team based on the averages of the individual members. The final score is determined by adding the handicap to the actual score.

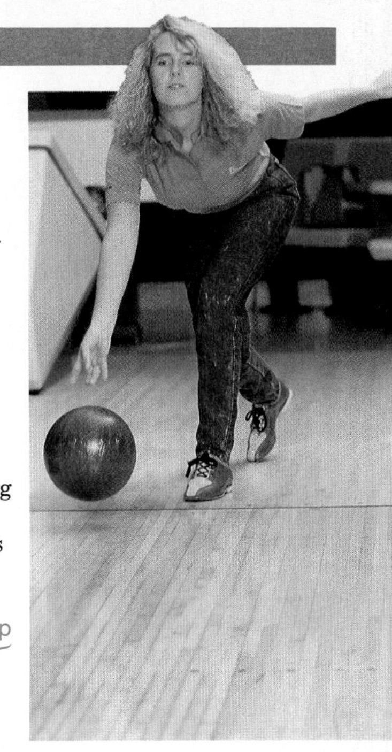

A **formula** shows the relationship among certain quantities. The formula below can be used to compute a league bowler's final handicap score.

$$\underbrace{\text{handicap score}}_{s} = \underbrace{\text{game score}}_{g} + \underbrace{\text{handicap}}_{h}$$

Example

1 Susan had a handicap bowling score of 186. Her handicap was 14. What was her game score?

$s = g + h$	
$186 = g + 14$	Replace *s* with 186 and *h* with 14.
$186 - 14 = g + 14 - 14$	Subtract 14 from each side of the equation.
$172 = g$	Susan's game score was 172.

What could be done instead of subtracting 14 from each side?
adding -14

Formulas are often used in science. For example, the formula for the relationship among the current (I), voltage (V), and resistance (R) in an electrical circuit is $I = \frac{V}{R}$. This formula is known as Ohm's law.

Science Connection

Ohm's law is named after George Ohm (1789–1854). Ohm worked on electrical conduction, but when the Berlin Academy of Science refused to publish his work, he retired from scientific life in discouragement.

Example

2 Suppose I is 24 amperes and R is 5 ohms. Find the voltage (V).

$I = \frac{V}{R}$	Write the formula.
$24 = \frac{V}{5}$	Replace *I* with 24 and *R* with 5.
$24 \times 5 = \frac{V}{5} \times 5$	Multiply each side by 5.
$120 = V$	The voltage is 120 volts.

Bell Ringer

A rock rolls down a hill 10 cm the first second, 20 cm the second second, 40 cm the third second, and so on. How many centimeters does the rock roll in 5 seconds?
310 cm

Lesson Notes 3-5

5-Minute Check
(over Lesson 3-4)

Solve each equation. Check your solution.

1. $13 = \frac{a}{-8}$ **-104**
2. $\frac{x}{-9} = -26$ **234**
3. $\frac{b}{21} = -8$ **-168**
4. $34 = \frac{x}{-26}$ **-884**
5. $-51 = \frac{k}{-13}$ **663**

Transparency 3-5 contains the 5-Minute Check and a teaching aid for this lesson.

1 FOCUS

This lesson applies the skills in solving one-step equations to formulas and word problems.

Motivating the Lesson

Help students develop formulas for the following situations:

1. circumference of a circle equals pi times the diameter ($C = \pi d$)
2. earned runs divided by innings pitched equals the earned run average ($\frac{e}{i} = a$)

2 TEACH

Using Discussion

Write the distance formula ($d = rt$) on the chalkboard and relate the following situation to the class.
A radio controlled model car travelled around a 400 meter track in 50 seconds. On average how fast was the car travelling?
Ask students what steps they would take to answer the question.

Chalkboard Examples

- *For Example 1*
  Kevin had a handicap bowling score of 192. His handicap was 17. What was his game score?
  175

EE: 1E, 3A, 3F, 3H
TAAS: 2, 6, 7, 8, 9

Chalkboard Examples

- *For Example 2*
  Suppose I is 32 amperes and R is 4 ohms. Find the voltage (V). **128 volts**
- *For Example 3*
  The Jonson family will drive 750 miles this summer to attend a family wedding. If the average rate of speed is 50 miles per hour, what will their driving time be? $d = rt$ **15 hours**

3 PRACTICE/APPLY

Checking the Concept

After solving and checking Exercises 4-7, change one or both numbers in the problem and have students determine the new answers.

Error Analysis

Watch for students who try to do too many steps at once.
Prevent by having the students work in pairs and take turns writing the steps that are used in solving the equation.

Practice Masters Booklet, **p. 24**

Name ______________ Date ______________

Practice Worksheet 3-5

Application: Formulas

Solve. Use the correct formula.

1. A salesclerk must put a $4 markup on a shirt that costs $12.00 wholesale. What should the retail price be? **$16**

The formula for the retail price is given below.

Retail Price	=	Wholesale Price	+	Markup
p	=	w	+	m

2. A pair of boots has a retail price of $75. The store's markup is $12. What is the wholesale price? **$63**

3. A record that regularly sells for $8.99 has a discount of $2.50. What is the sale price? **$6.49**

The following is the formula for the sale price.

Sale Price	=	Regular Price	−	Discount (markdown)
s	=	p	−	d

4. A book which regularly sells for $14.50 was marked $11.95. How much of a discount was there? **$2.55**

5. An account opened three years ago with a principal of $250 now has $300.50. Find the amount of interest. **$50.50**

The formula for adding principal and interest is given below.

Amount	=	Principal	+	Interest
a	=	p	+	i

6. After 4 years an account has $884. The interest is $234. Find the principal. **$650**

Another important formula relates distance, rate, and time.

$$\underbrace{\text{distance}}_{d} = \underbrace{\text{rate}}_{r} \cdot \underbrace{\text{time}}_{t} \quad \text{or } d = rt$$

Example

3 **The Sanderson family plans to drive about 960 miles to visit relatives in Indianapolis. If the average rate of speed is 45 miles per hour, what will their driving time be?**

Estimation Hint

THINK:
$1000 = 50t$
The solution should be about 20.

$d = rt$ Write the formula.

$960 = 45t$

$\frac{960}{45} = \frac{45t}{45}$ Divide each side by 45.

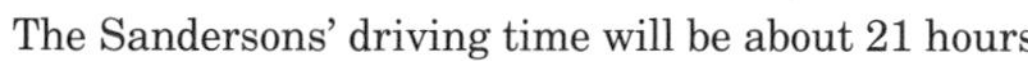

960 ÷ 45 = 21.333333

The Sandersons' driving time will be about 21 hours.

Checking for Understanding

Communicating Algebra

1. Write a formula with which you are familiar. **Sample answer: $A = lw$**

Translate each sentence into a formula.

2. The sale price (s) of an item is equal to the list price (l) less the discount (d). **2. $s = l - d$**
3. The diameter (d) of a circle is twice the length of the radius (r). **$d = 2r$**

Guided Practice

Solve. Use the correct formula.

4. Find the game score if the handicap score is 175 and the handicap is 12. **163**
5. Find the distance you travel if your train goes 60 miles per hour for 4 hours. **5. 240 miles**
6. Find the average number of amperes if $V = 60$ and $R = 5$ ohms. **12 amperes**
7. Find the speed if your plane flies 2000 miles to Hawaii in 5 hours. **400 mph**

Exercises

Independent Practice

Solve mentally by substituting the variables with the given values. **9. 221**

8. $f = t - h$, if $t = 125$ and $h = 25$ **100**
9. $s = g + c$, if $g = 200$ and $c = 21$
10. $P = s + s + s$, if $s = 12$ **36**
11. $s = l - d$, if $l = \$50$ and $d = \$1$ **49**
12. $d = rt$, if $r = 50$ and $t = 6$ **300**
13. $d = rt$, if $r = 40$, and $t = 4$ **160**
14. $I = \frac{V}{R}$, if $V = 110$ and $R = 10$ **11**
15. $I = \frac{V}{R}$, if $V = 60$ and $R = 2$ **30**

Alternate Strategies: Reteaching the Lesson

Reteaching Activity

Making and Using Tables Use a simple formula, such as $A = \ell \times w$, to solve several problems. Record the results in a table.

Reteaching Masters Booklet, **p. 22**

Name ______________ Date ______________

Reteaching Worksheet 3-5

Application: Formulas

A **formula** shows the relationship between certain quantities. The formula for the distance traveled by a moving object is $d = rt$. In the formula, d represents distance in kilometers (km), r represents the rate in kilometers per hour (km/h), and t represents the time in hours (h).

Example: Suppose r is 40 kilometers per hour and t is 3 hours. Find the distance traveled (d).

$d = rt$
$d = 40 \times 3$ Replace r with 40 and t with 3.
$d = 120$ The distance traveled is 120 kilometers.

Use the formula $d = rt$ to find the distance traveled for each of the following.

1. r: 60 km/h; t: 4 h
2. r: 50 km/h; t: 2 h

Mixed Review

16. Solve the equation $-13a = -78$. (Lesson 3-3) **6**

17. Name the number to multiply each side by in the equation $\frac{r}{-6} = 53$. (Lesson 3-4) **-6**

18. Solve the equation $-5 = \frac{x}{-14}$. (Lesson 3-4) **70**

Applications

Solve. Use the correct formula.

19. **Travel** The formula for finding gas mileage is $m = d \div g$ where m is miles per gallon, d is the distance traveled, and g is the number of gallons of gasoline used. Glen's car gets 34 miles per gallon. How many gallons of gasoline does he need to travel 289 miles? **8.5 gallons**

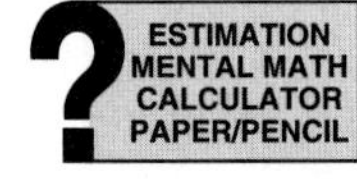

20. **Sports** Angela's final handicap score in bowling was 186. Her handicap was 17. What was her game score? **169**

21. **Travel** Mai Li travels 371 miles in 7 hours on a bus trip to her aunt's house. What rate of speed does she travel? **53 mph**

22. **Electronics** Automobiles have 12-volt systems. What is the current in a 12-volt circuit that has a resistance of 3 ohms? **4 amperes**

23. **Meteorology** How far away is the lightning if you hear the sound of the thunder 4 seconds after you see the flash of lightning? Use 344 meters per second as the speed of sound. **1376 meters or about 1.4 kilometers**

Critical Thinking

24. The area (A) of a triangle is equal to the product of the base (b) and the height (h) divided by two. What are some strategies you could use to find the height of a triangle that has an area of 24 square inches and a base of 8 inches?
Sample answer: Double the area, divide by the base; $h = 6$ in.

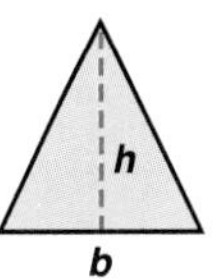

Wrap-Up

25. **Research** Find an example of a formula that is used in geometry.
Sample answers: $A = lw$, $P = 2(l + w)$, $C = \pi d$

Mid-Chapter Quiz

Solve each equation. (Lessons 3-1, 3-2, 3-3, 3-4)

1. $m + 59 = -123$ **-182**
2. $27 = n + 64$ **-37**
3. $278 = x + (-365)$ **643**
4. $w - 9 = -24$ **-15**
5. $73 = y - (-81)$ **-8**
6. $-19 = b - 76$ **57**
7. $-64 = -16r$ **4**
8. $-52 = 4m$ **-13**
9. $-17x = 595$ **-35**
10. $\frac{y}{11} = 13$ **143**
11. $-27 = \frac{x}{15}$ **-405**
12. $\frac{a}{-7} = -35$ **245**

Which equation would you use to solve the problem below? (Lessons 3-1, 3-2)

13. Vickie removes 33.5 gallons of water from her baby sister's wading pool so she can add hot water to raise the temperature. The pool now contains 45 gallons of water. How many gallons did it contain before?

a. $33.5 - x = 45$ b. $45 - 33.5 = x$ (c.) $x - 33.5 = 45$ d. $45 + x = 33.5$

Independent Practice

Homework Assignment	
Basic	8-19, 24, 25
Average	10-21, 24, 25
Honors	13-25
All	Mid-Chapter Quiz 1-13

4 CLOSE

Assessment Option

Speaking Write the formulas developed in this lesson on the chalkboard and ask students to state the formulas in their own words.

Chapter 3, Quiz A (Lessons 3-1 through 3-5) is available in the Evaluation Masters Booklet, p. 25.

Alternate Strategies: Extending the Lesson

Enrichment

Using Reference Material Have students do research to find several useful formulas. Have students use these formulas to write several word problems. Trade problems and solve.

Cooperative Learning

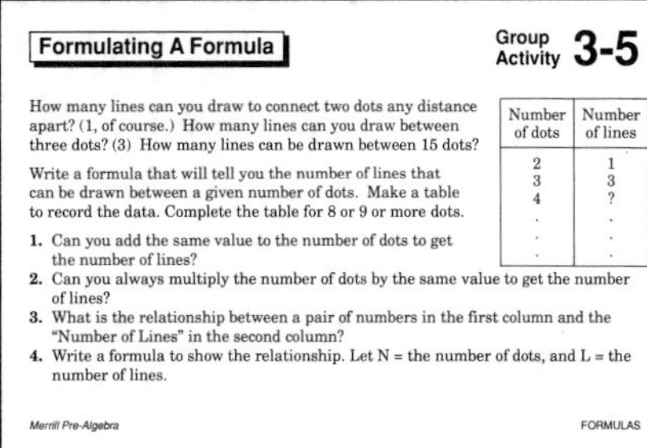

Formulating A Formula Group Activity **3-5**

How many lines can you draw to connect two dots any distance apart? (1, of course.) How many lines can you draw between three dots? (3) How many lines can be drawn between 15 dots?

Write a formula that will tell you the number of lines that can be drawn between a given number of dots. Make a table to record the data. Complete the table for 8 or 9 or more dots.

Number of dots	Number of lines
2	1
3	3
4	?
.	.
.	.
.	.

1. Can you add the same value to the number of dots to get the number of lines?
2. Can you always multiply the number of dots by the same value to get the number of lines?
3. What is the relationship between a pair of numbers in the first column and the "Number of Lines" in the second column?
4. Write a formula to show the relationship. Let N = the number of dots, and L = the number of lines.

Merrill Pre-Algebra FORMULAS

Enrichment Masters Booklet, **p. 22**

Name ____________ Date ____________

Enrichment Worksheet 3-5

Formulas

The following formula can be used to determine the specific day of the week on which a date occurred.

$s = d + 2m + [(3m + 3) \div 5] + y + \left[\frac{y}{4}\right] - \left[\frac{y}{100}\right] + \left[\frac{y}{400}\right] + 2$

s = sum
d = day of the month, using numbers from 1–31
m = month, beginning with March is 3, April is 4, and so on, up to December is 12, January is 13, and February is 14
y = year except for dates in January or February when the previous year is used

For example, for February 13, 1985, $d = 13$, $m = 14$, and $y = 1984$; and for July 4, 1776, $d = 4$, $m = 7$, and $y = 1776$

The brackets, [ ], mean you are to do the division inside them, discard the remainder, and use only the whole number part of the quotient. The next step is to divide s by 7 and note the remainder. The remainder 0 is Saturday, 1 is Sunday, 2 is Monday, and so on, up to 6 is Friday.

Example: What day of the week was October 3, 1854?

For October 3, 1854, $d = 3$, $m = 10$, and $y = 1854$.

$s = 3 + \underbrace{2(10)}_{20} + \underbrace{[(3 \times 10 + 3) \div 5]}_{6} + 1854 + \left[\frac{1854}{4}\right] - \left[\frac{1854}{100}\right] + \left[\frac{1854}{400}\right] + 2$
$= 3 + 20 + 6 + 1854 + 463 - 18 + 4 + 2$
$= 2334$

$s \div 7 = 2334 \div 7 = 333$ R3
Since the remainder is 3, the day of the week was Tuesday.

Solve.

1. See if the formula works for today's date.
Answers will vary.
2. On what day of the week were you born?
Answers will vary.
3. What will be the day of the week on April 13, 1996?
$s = 13 + 2(4) + [(3 \times 4 + 3) \div 5] + 1996 + \left[\frac{1996}{4}\right] - \left[\frac{1996}{100}\right] + \left[\frac{1996}{400}\right] + 2$
$= 13 + 8 + 3 + 1996 + 499 - 19 + 4 + 2 = 2506$; $2506 \div 7 = 358$ R0 → Saturday
4. On what day of the week was July 4, 1776?
$s = 4 + 2(7) + [(3 \times 7 + 3) \div 5] + 1776 + \left[\frac{1776}{4}\right] - \left[\frac{1776}{100}\right] + \left[\frac{1776}{400}\right] + 2$
$= 4 + 14 + 4 + 1776 + 444 - 17 + 4 + 2 = 2231$; $2231 \div 7 = 318$ R5 → Thursday

Applying Algebra to the Real World

Objective This optional page shows how algebra is used in the real world and also provides a change of pace.

Using Discussion

Discuss with students differences in acceleration and velocity (speed). Ask students what changes they can feel when they are passengers in a car that is accelerating (pressed against the seat during positive acceleration, leaning forward during negative acceleration). Emphasize that the speed is changing in both instances.

Using Questioning

Ask students to list instances when knowing an object's acceleration is important. The list might include determining the length of an airport runway, pitching or hitting a baseball, designing automobile and roadway safety devices, or launching a rocket.

Activity

Materials: stopwatches, objects to drop, such as a paper clip, a pencil, or a hairbrush

Using Cooperative Groups Have students drop objects from the same heights and time the drops. Tell students that the starting speed of the object is zero meters per second and that all objects fall to Earth at a constant acceleration of -9.8 meters per second each second. Have students determine the final speed of an object by substituting these values and their times into the formula. Compare this value for the different objects dropped from the same height. Discuss factors, such as friction from the air or human error in timing, that could cause differences in these values.

Algebra in Action–Physics

Acceleration

When a skateboard accelerates, it changes speed. **Acceleration** is the rate at which speed is changing with respect to time.

To find the acceleration, first find the change in speed by subtracting the starting speed (s) from the final speed (f). Then divide by the time it took to make the change. The formula is shown below.

$$a = \frac{f-s}{t}$$

A race car goes from 44 meters per second (m/s) to 77 m/s in 11 seconds. Find the acceleration.

$a = \frac{f-s}{t}$

$a = \frac{77-44}{11}$ Replace f with 77, s with 44, and t with 11.

$a = \frac{33}{11}$ or 3

The car accelerates 3 meters per second each second.

Suppose a race car *decreases* its speed from 80 m/s to 20 m/s in 15 seconds. The same equation can be used. Subtracting the starting speed from the final speed gives a negative value. This means that the acceleration is negative. Negative acceleration is called *deceleration.*

$a = \frac{f-s}{t}$

$a = \frac{20-80}{15}$ Replace f with 20, s with 80, and t with 15.

$a = \frac{-60}{15}$ or -4 The acceleration is -4 meters per second each second.

Find the acceleration.

1. A motorcycle goes from 2 m/s to 14 m/s in 6 seconds. **2 m/s each second**
2. A skateboard goes from 6 m/s to 0 m/s in 3 seconds. **-2 m/s each second**
3. A car starts from a standstill. It accelerates to 40 mph in 10 seconds. **4 mph each second**
4. A jet plane decreased its speed from 500 km/h to 350 km/h in 30 seconds. **-5 km/h each second**
5. A skateboard goes from 0 feet per second to 22 feet per second in 2 seconds. **11ft/s each second**
6. A 110-car coal train goes from 1.2 mph to 6.8 mph in 4 minutes. **1.4 mph each minute**

3-6 Perimeter and Area

Objective:
Find the perimeter and area of rectangles and squares.

Key Terms:
perimeter
area

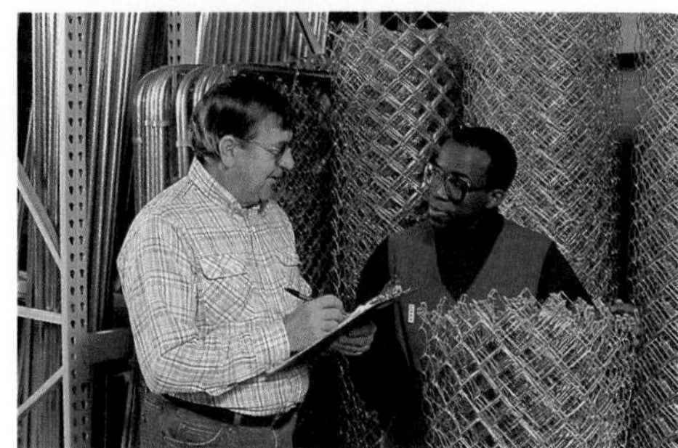

Mr. O'Neill is the groundskeeper at Kennedy Jr. High. He wants to put a fence around the practice football field to keep people off the new grass he planted. How much fencing does he need?

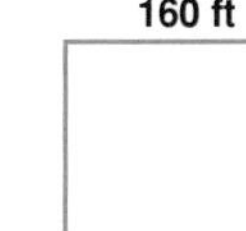

The distance around a geometric figure is called the **perimeter.** To find the perimeter of the field, Mr. O'Neill adds the measure of the sides.

$$160 + 360 + 160 + 360 = 160 + 160 + 360 + 360$$
$$= 320 + 720$$
$$= 1040$$

The perimeter of the football field is 1040 feet. So, Mr. O'Neill needs 1040 feet of fencing.

Suppose P represents the measure of the perimeter of a rectangle. Let ℓ be the measure of the length. Let w be the measure of the width.

$P = \ell + w + \ell + w$	Definition of perimeter
$P = \ell + \ell + w + w$	Commutative property of addition
$P = 2\ell + 2w$	
$P = 2(\ell + w)$	Distributive property

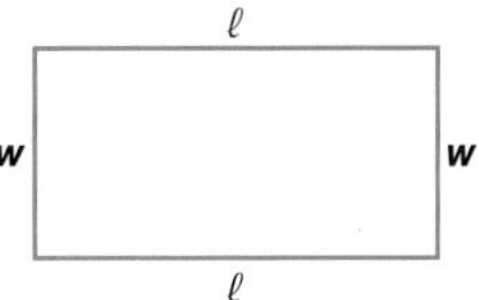

Perimeter of a Rectangle

In words: If a rectangle has a length of ℓ units and a width of w units, then the perimeter is twice the sum of the length and width.
In symbols: $P = 2(\ell + w)$.

Bell Ringer

A package contains 4 pounds 5 ounces of ground beef. Write a formula to find the number of hamburgers that can be made if 3 ounces of meat are used to make each hamburger. $\frac{69}{h} = 3$ or $69 = 3h$

Lesson Notes 3-6

5-Minute Check
(over Lesson 3-5)

Solve by substituting the variables with the given values.

1. $I = \frac{V}{R}$, if $I = 44$ and $R = 5$ $V = 220$
2. $d = rt$, if $r = 40$ and $t = 7$ $d = 280$
3. $s = \ell - d$, if $\ell = \$49$ and $d = \$12$ $s = \$37$
4. $P = s + s + s$, if $s = 18$ $P = 54$
5. $s = g + c$, if $g = 163$ and $c = 24$ $s = 187$

Transparency 3-6 contains the 5-Minute Check and a teaching aid for this lesson.

1 FOCUS

The purpose of this lesson is to refresh students' knowledge of perimeter and area and to apply the division property of equality to the formula for area of rectangles.

Motivating the Lesson

Draw a rectangle on graph paper or construct a rectangle on a geoboard. Ask students what characteristics of the figure can be measured.

2 TEACH

Using Manipulatives

Remind students that perimeter is the distance around a figure. Then have students find the perimeter of their desk while writing down the steps they take to find it. List the different ways students found the perimeter on the chalkboard. Ask students to use a different method to see if they get the same result.

EE: 1E, 3A, 3F, 3H, 4B, 4E
TAAS: 2, 4, 11

Chalkboard Examples

Find the perimeter of each rectangle given its length and width.

- *For Example 1*
  $\ell = 14$ ft, $w = 7$ ft **42 ft**
- *For Example 2*
  $\ell = 9$ cm, $w = 9$ cm **36 cm**
- *For Example 3*
  Find the area of a rectangle with length 16 m and width 7 m.
  112 m²

3 PRACTICE/APPLY

Checking the Concept

Using Questioning Ask students to explain why the labels to their answers in Exercises 5-10 differ.

Error Analysis

Watch for students who interchange the terms *area* and *perimeter*.
Prevent by emphasizing the definitions of the terms and consistently using the variables *A* and *P* to represent area and perimeter.

Examples

Find the perimeter of each rectangle.

1

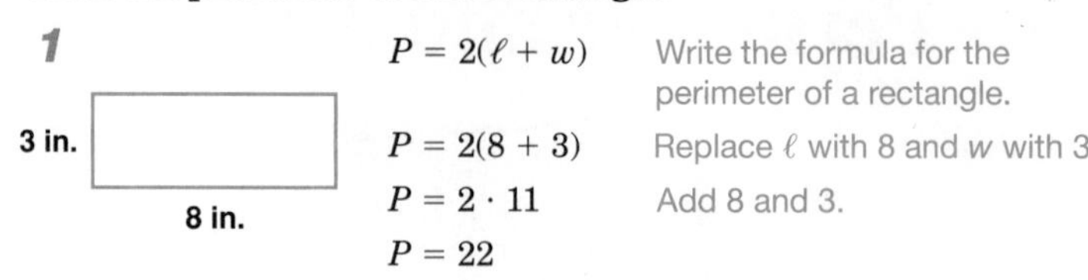

$P = 2(\ell + w)$ Write the formula for the perimeter of a rectangle.

$P = 2(8 + 3)$ Replace ℓ with 8 and w with 3.

$P = 2 \cdot 11$ Add 8 and 3.

$P = 22$

The perimeter is 22 inches.

Are all squares rectangles? Explain.
Yes; Squares have 4 right angles and opposite sides parallel.

2

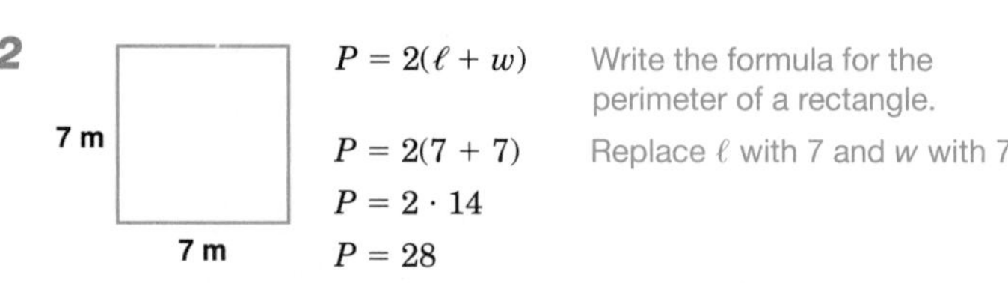

$P = 2(\ell + w)$ Write the formula for the perimeter of a rectangle.

$P = 2(7 + 7)$ Replace ℓ with 7 and w with 7.

$P = 2 \cdot 14$

$P = 28$

The perimeter is 28 meters.

The previous examples all deal with the distance *around* a geometric figure. Another measurement to consider is the surface *enclosed by* a geometric figure.

The measure of the surface enclosed by a geometric figure is called the **area.** By counting the number of 1 yard by 1 yard squares, you can find that the area of the rectangle shown at the right is 20 square yards. This area can also be found by multiplying the measures of the length and the width. So, the area is $4 \cdot 5$ or 20 square yards.

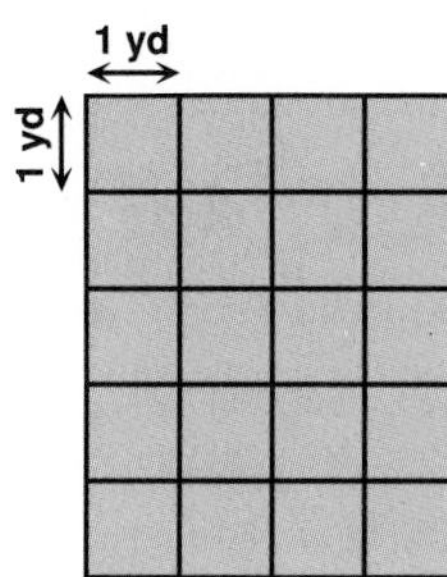

Area of a Rectangle

In words: If a rectangle has a length of ℓ units and a width of w units, then the area is $\ell \cdot w$ square units.
In symbols: $A = \ell w$

Examples

3 **Find the area of a rectangle with length 15 m and width 4 m.**

$A = \ell w$ Write the formula for the area of a rectangle.

$A = 15 \cdot 4$ Replace ℓ with 15 and w with 4.

$A = 60$ The area is 60 square meters.

The unit of measure of the sides is meter, so the area is stated in square meters.

Alternate Strategies: Reteaching the Lesson

Reteaching Activity

Using Models On graph paper, have students design a small, one-level house with rectangular rooms. Use a scale where one grid unit represents one foot. Ignoring doorways, determine the amount of molding needed for baseboards and the area of carpet needed for flooring.

Reteaching Masters Booklet, p. 23

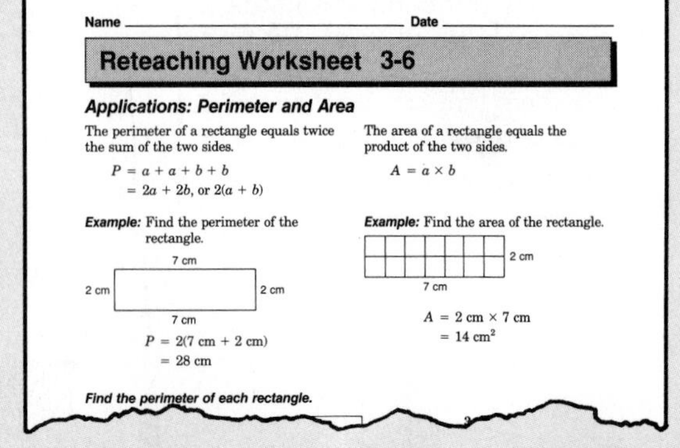

Name ____ Date ____

Reteaching Worksheet 3-6

Applications: Perimeter and Area

The perimeter of a rectangle equals twice the sum of the two sides.

$P = a + a + b + b$
$= 2a + 2b$, or $2(a + b)$

The area of a rectangle equals the product of the two sides.

$A = a \times b$

Example: Find the perimeter of the rectangle.

7 cm, 2 cm, 2 cm, 7 cm

$P = 2(7\text{ cm} + 2\text{ cm})$
$= 28$ cm

Example: Find the area of the rectangle.

2 cm, 7 cm

$A = 2\text{ cm} \times 7\text{ cm}$
$= 14\text{ cm}^2$

Find the perimeter of each rectangle.

4 **Find the width of a rectangle with area 540 square feet and length 30 ft.**

$A = \ell w$ Write the formula for the area of a rectangle.

$540 = 30 \cdot w$ Replace A with 540 and ℓ with 30.

$\frac{540}{30} = \frac{30w}{30}$ Divide each side by 30.

540 ÷ 30 = 18

$18 = w$

Check: $540 = 30w$

$540 \stackrel{?}{=} 30 \cdot 18$ Replace w with 18.

$540 = 540$ ✓

The width is 18 feet.

Checking for Understanding

1. See margin. 3. Perimeter is the distance around a figure.

Communicating Algebra

1. Draw and label a rectangle that has a length of 2 inches and a width of 1 inch.
2. Explain how to find the perimeter and area of a rectangle that is 9 cm long and 5 cm wide. **Perimeter: Add 9 and 5, multiply by 2; Area: multiply 9 and 5.**
3. In your own words, write a definition of perimeter.
4. Explain how perimeter and area are different. **Perimeter is the measure of the outside of a figure; area is the measure of the surface enclosed by the figure.**

Guided Practice

Find the perimeter and area of each rectangle.

5. 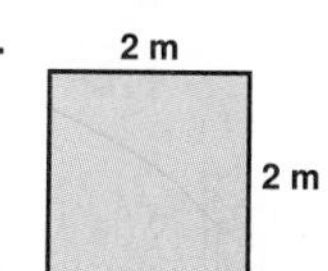

P = 8 m; A = 4 m^2

6. 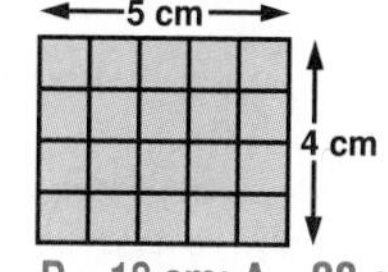

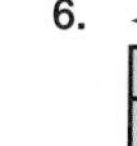

P = 18 cm; A = 20 cm^2

7. 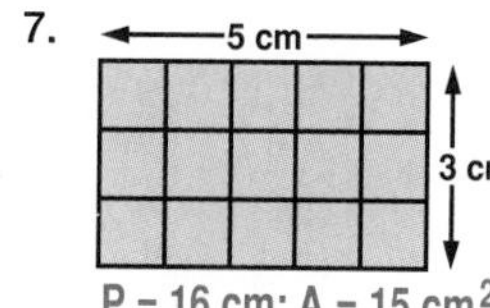

P = 16 cm; A = 15 cm^2

8. 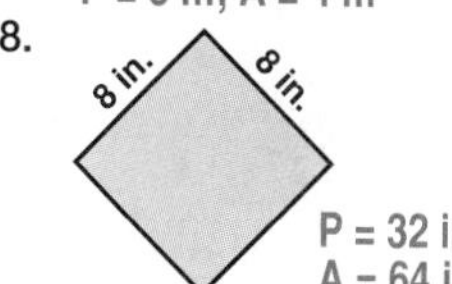

P = 32 in. A = 64 in.^{2}

9. 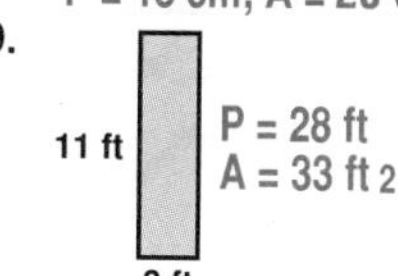

P = 28 ft A = 33 ft 2

10. 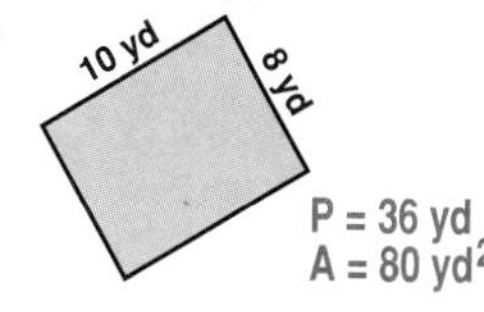

P = 36 yd A = 80 yd^2

Exercises

Independent Practice

Find the perimeter and area of each rectangle.

	Length	Width	
11.	9 m	4 m	26 m; 36 m^2
12.	31 km	9 km	80 km; 279 km^2
13.	129 yd	32 yd	322 yd; 4128 yd^2

Given each area, find the missing length or width of each rectangle.

	Area	Length	Width	
14.	168 ft^2	24 ft	?	7 ft
15.	195 cm^2	?	13 cm	15 cm
16.	144 yd^2	16 yd	?	9 yd

Alternate Strategies: Extending the Lesson

Enrichment

Using Diagrams Have students draw as many rectangles as possible that have an area of 24 square units. Have students order these rectangles according to the perimeters of the rectangles, smallest to largest.

Cooperative Learning

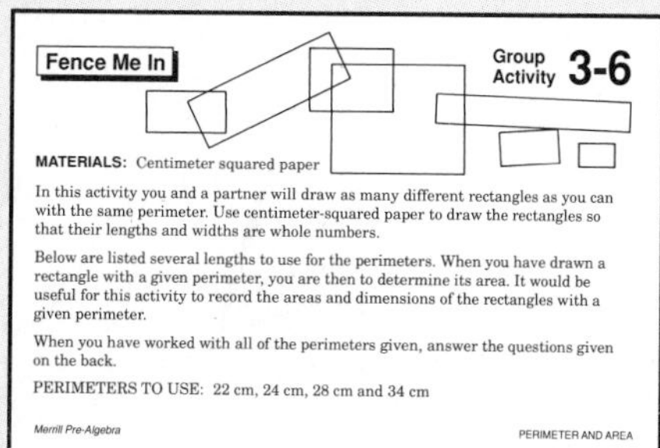

Fence Me In — Group Activity 3-6

MATERIALS: Centimeter squared paper

In this activity you and a partner will draw as many different rectangles as you can with the same perimeter. Use centimeter-squared paper to draw the rectangles so that their lengths and widths are whole numbers.

Below are listed several lengths to use for the perimeters. When you have drawn a rectangle with a given perimeter, you are then to determine its area. It would be useful for this activity to record the areas and dimensions of the rectangles with a given perimeter.

When you have worked with all of the perimeters given, answer the questions given on the back.

PERIMETERS TO USE: 22 cm, 24 cm, 28 cm and 34 cm

Merrill Pre-Algebra PERIMETER AND AREA

Independent Practice

Homework Assignment	
Basic	11-20, 25-28
Average	13-21, 24-28
Honors	14-28

Additional Answer

1.

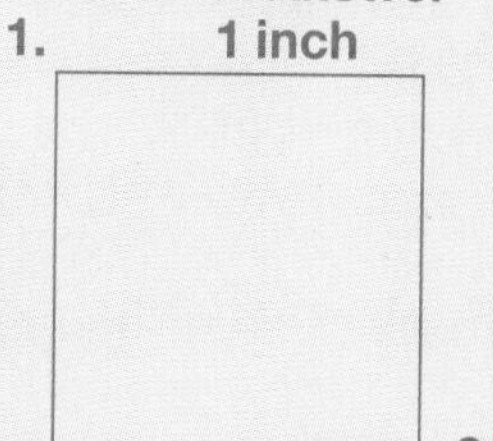

Practice Masters Booklet, **p. 25**

Name ______ Date ______

Practice Worksheet 3-6

Applications: Perimeter and Area

Find the perimeter and area of each rectangle.

1. 16 m by 7 m — 46 m; 112 m^2
2. 8 m by 8 m — 32 m; 64 m^2
3. 21 cm by 4 cm — 50 cm; 84 cm^2
4. 10 mm by 9 mm — 38 mm; 90 mm^2
5. 17 cm by 7 cm — 48 cm; 119 cm^2
6. 4 m by 11 m — 30 m; 44 m^2
7. a square with each side 15 meters long 60 m; 225 m^2
8. a rectangle with a length of 27 meters and a width of 8 meters 70 m; 216 m^2
9. a square with each side 21 centimeters long 84 cm; 441 cm^2
10. a rectangle, 13 m by 11 m 48 m; 143 m^2
11. a square with each side 2 miles long 8 mi; 4 mi^2

Given each area, find the missing length or width of each rectangle described below.

12. A = 255 m^2, l = 17 m, w = ? 15 m
13. A = 216 cm^2, l = ?, w = 12 cm 18 cm
14. A = 250 km^2, l = 25 km, w = ? 10 km
15. A = 45 yd^2, l = ?, w = 3 yd 15 yd
16. A = 105 mm^2, l = 15 mm, w = ? 7 mm
17. A = 3055 m^2, l = 65 m, w = ? 47 m

4 CLOSE

Assessment Option

Modeling Cut rectangles of various sizes and shapes and give one to each student. Then have each student find the perimeter and area of their rectangle by measuring the sides with a ruler and applying the perimeter and area formulas. Have students find the perimeter and area in both centimeters and inches.

Enrichment Masters Booklet, **p. 23**

Name ______________________ Date ______________

Enrichment Worksheet 3-6

Area and Perimeter

There are countless rectangles with a perimeter of 16 feet. Here are three of them, and their areas.

5 by 3: Area = 5 × 3 = 15 ft²
6.5 by 1.5: Area = 6.5 × 1.5 = 9.75 ft²
4 by 4: Area = 4 × 4 = 16 ft²

In Exercises 1–4, can you find a rectangle that has a perimeter of 16 feet and the given area? HINT: ***One rectangle is not possible.***

1. Area: 12 ft² 6 ft × 2 ft
2. Area: 7 ft² 7 ft × 1 ft
3. Area: less than 7 ft² length: $7 < l < 8$ width: $0 < w < 1$ example: 7.5 ft × 0.5 ft
4. Area: greater than 16 ft² not possible
5. What is the largest possible area for a rectangle with a perimeter of 20 feet? 5 ft × 5 ft = 25 ft²

Find the area and perimeter of each figure. All angles are right angles.

6. area: 28 ft² perimeter: 26 ft
7. area: 48 ft² perimeter: 34 ft
8. area: 42 ft² perimeter: 30 ft
9. area: 60 ft² perimeter: 48 ft

Mixed Review

17. Simplify the expression $13rs + (-8rs) + 5rs$. (Lesson 2-4) $10rs$
18. Solve the equation $\frac{m}{-38} = 14$. (Lesson 3-4) -532
19. Write a formula for the sentence *The radius (r) of a circle is equal to the diameter (d) divided by two.* (Lesson 3-5) $r = d \div 2$
20. Alice travels 330 miles at a rate of 55 mph. How many hours was she driving? (Lesson 3-5) 6 hours

Challenge

Find the area of the red part of each rectangle.

21.

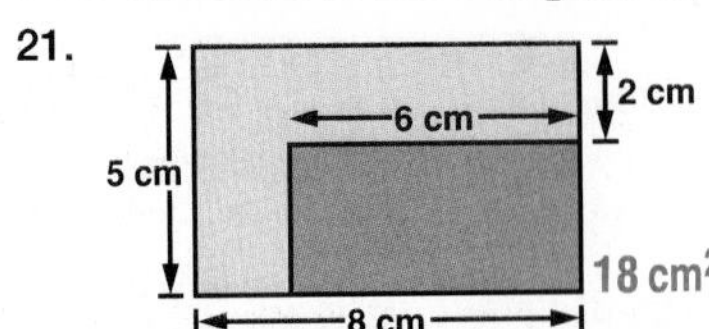

18 cm²

22.

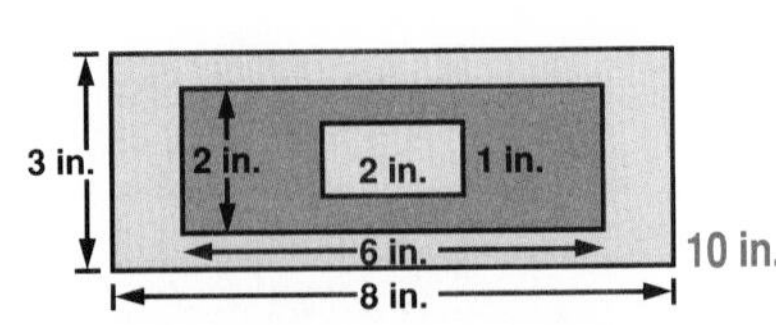

10 in.²

Applications

23. **Construction** Dan Block added a square deck to the back of his house. Draw and label a diagram of his deck if the perimeter of the deck is 84 feet. See margin.

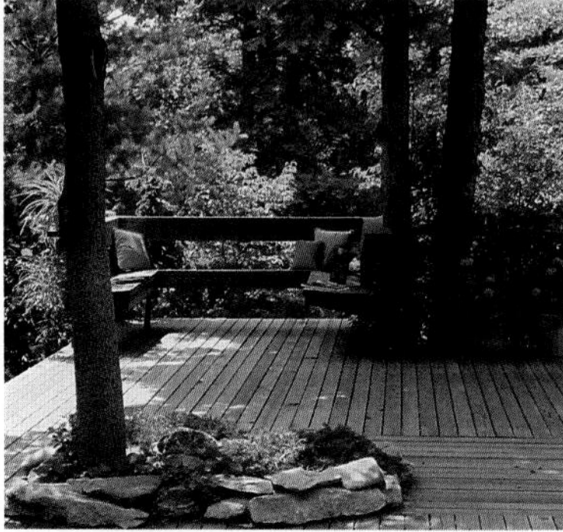

24. **Home Economics** Barb cut some material to make a skirt. She cut a rectangular-shaped piece that is 28 in. wide and 36 in. long. Find the area of the cut material. 1008 sq. in.
25. **Landscaping** Steve Kocher used old railroad ties to enclose a rectangular-shaped garden that was 30 ft long and 12 ft wide. What was the perimeter of the garden? 84 ft

Connection

26. **Geometry** The outer triangle has an area of 56 square inches. This is 4 times as great as each inner triangle. Find the area of each inner triangle. 14 sq. in.

Critical Thinking

27. A square is a rectangle in which the length is equal to the width. Write a formula that can be used to find the area of a square. $A = s \cdot s$ or $A = s^2$

Wrap-Up

28. **Research** Find the dimensions of the courts or playing fields of five different sports. Rank them from greatest to least with respect to area and then with respect to perimeter. See margin.

Additional Answers

23.

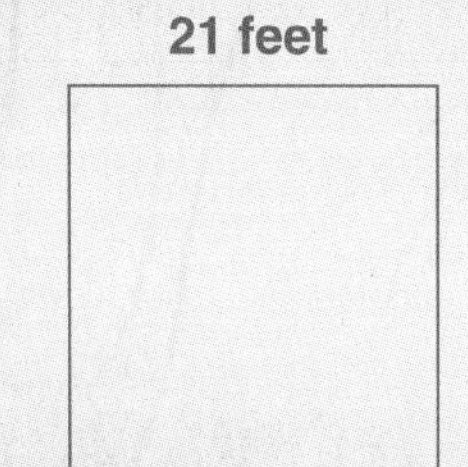

28. basketball: 84 ft by 50 ft (H.S.)
football: 160 ft by 360 ft
hockey: 85 ft by 200 ft
tennis: 27 ft by 78 ft (singles)
volleyball: 30 ft by 60 ft

Area:	Perimeter:
football	football
hockey	hockey
basketball	basketball
tennis	tennis
volleyball	volleyball

Area and Perimeter

Materials: small tiles or grid paper

In this Exploration, you will investigate the relationship between perimeter and area by building regions of given areas.

▶ The figures below show several figures with an area of 4 square units.

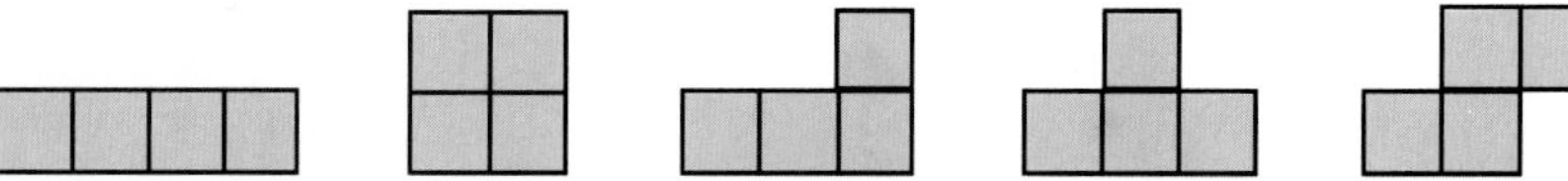

▶ Find the perimeter of each figure shown above by counting the units on the outside of the figure.

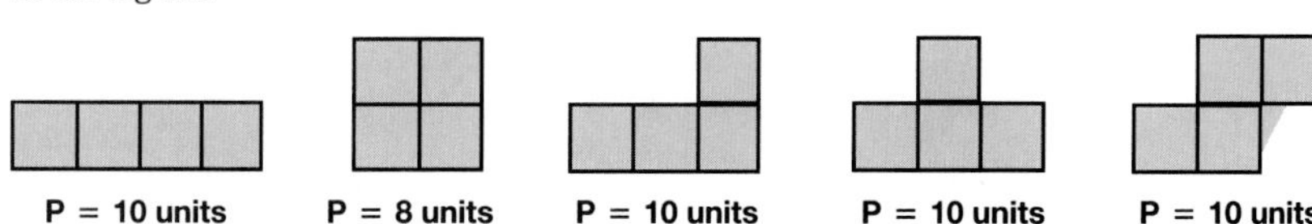

▶ It appears that, for an area of 4 square units, the greatest possible perimeter is 10 units.

Your Turn: Repeat the activities described above for areas of 1, 2, 3, 5, and 6 square units. Find the greatest possible perimeter for each area. Record your results in a table. See margin.

See Solutions Manual for Exercises 1-3.

For each given area, find the greatest possible perimeter. Draw a figure to show the greatest possible perimeter.

1. 8 square units 18 units
2. 10 square units 22 units
3. 15 square units 32 units

Analysis

4. A figure has an area of 50 square units. Predict the greatest possible perimeter. 102 units
5. Explain why the two figures shown at the right have the same perimeter. Draw another figure with the same perimeter. See margin.
6. Suppose a figure has an area of x square units. Write an expression for the greatest possible perimeter. $2x + 2$

EXPLORATION:
Area and Perimeter

Objective Students will discover that the relationship between perimeter and area does not remain constant when the area is constant.

1 FOCUS

This exploration allows students to understand that sometimes figures with the same area do not have the same perimeter by modeling and seeing the different shapes and then finding the perimeter.

2 TEACH

Model the example for the entire class. Encourage students to draw a diagram of each shape they create in case they do not have enough tiles to model all the possible shapes at one time.

3 PRACTICE/APPLY

Using Cooperative Groups

Have each group make a table with two columns. Tell them to label the first column "square units" and the second column "greatest possible perimeter." Then have each group complete the table with data from *Your turn* and Exercises 1-3.

4 CLOSE

Writing Connection

This activity provides a good opportunity for students to practice communicating mathematics. Encourage the cooperative groups to complete the last exercise.

Additional Answer

5. The two figures have the same perimeter because only one square unit changed its position.

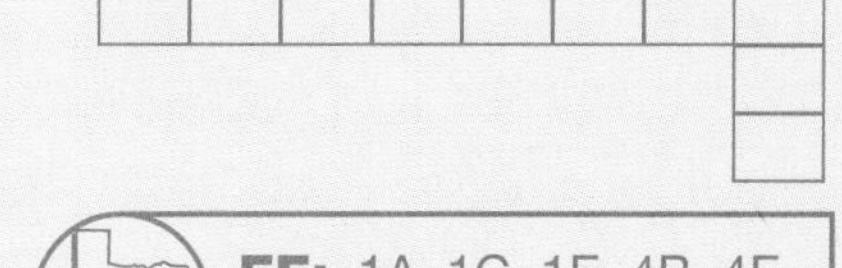

SET-UP

Materials

- Algebra Tiles, Lab Manual, p. 1

You may wish to use the Exploration worksheet provided on page 34 of the Lab Manual.

For Students Students can use commercial or paper tiles. If tiles are not available, students may draw the different shapes on graph paper.

For the Overhead Projector This exploration will work on the overhead with translucent or opaque tiles.

Additional Answer

Your turn.

square units	greatest perimeter
1	4
2	6
3	8
5	12
6	14

Lesson Notes 3-7

5-Minute Check
(over Lesson 3-6)

Find the perimeter and area of each rectangle described below.

	length	width	
1.	17 m	3 m	$P = 40$ m $A = 51$ sq m
2.	52 km	20 km	$P = 144$ km $A = 1040$ sq km
3.	125 yd	32 yd	$P = 314$ yd $A = 4,000$ sq yd

Transparency 3-7 contains the 5-Minute Check and a teaching aid for this lesson.

1 FOCUS

The purpose of this lesson is to apply the addition and subtraction properties of equality to solving one-step inequalities.

Motivating the Lesson

Set up a balance so that one side is slightly heavier than the other. Be sure some equal weights are used on both sides. Remove an equal amount of weight from both sides and point out that the sides are still unequal, the heavier side still being heavier.

2 TEACH

Using Models

Draw the graphs for $y \leq 8$ and $y > 8$ on the chalkboard or overhead. Ask students how each graph should be labeled. Ask students how many solutions there are for each inequality. Ask students which graph has 8 as a solution.

Chalkboard Examples

Solve each inequality. Check your solution.

- *For Example 1*
  $y + 4 > -3$ **$y > -7$**
- *For Example 2*
  $-5 \geq m - 3$ **$-2 \geq m$**

EE: 1E, 2F, 3A, 3F, 5E
TAAS: 12

3-7 Solving Inequalities: Adding or Subtracting

Objective:
Solve inequalities by using the addition and subtraction properties.

Beth had \$99 in her savings account and Jim had \$82 in his account. They each received \$25 for mowing lawns and deposited the money in their accounts. Whose account has more money?

Beth		Jim	
99	>	82	
99 + 25	>	82 + 25	Add 25 to each side.
124	>	107	

Beth had more money in her account at the beginning, and she had more money in her account at the end.

Recall from Chapter 1 that an inequality is a mathematical sentence with < or >. The sentences 99 > 82 and 124 > 107 are inequalities. Adding the same number to each side of the inequality 99 > 82 did not change the truth of the inequality.

Suppose Jim and Beth each withdrew, or subtracted, \$10 from their accounts.

Beth		Jim	
124	>	107	
124 − 10	>	107 − 10	Subtract 10 from each side.
114	>	97	

Beth still has more money than Jim. Subtracting the same number from each side of an inequality did not change the truth of the inequality.

These and other examples suggest the following properties.

Addition and Subtraction Properties of Inequalities

In words: Adding or subtracting the same number from each side of an inequality does not change the truth of the inequality.

In symbols: For all numbers a, b, and c:

1. If $a > b$, then $a + c > b + c$ and $a - c > b - c$.
2. If $a < b$, then $a + c < b + c$ and $a - c < b - c$.

Bell Ringer

Nathan looks in a drawer for a marker. All the markers are blue except two, all are red except two, and all are green except two. How many markers are in the drawer? **3: 1 red, 1 blue, and 1 green.**

Examples

1 **Solve $m + 8 > 3$. Check your solution.**

$m + 8 > 3$

$m + 8 - 8 > 3 - 8$ Subtract 8 from each side.

$m > -5$

Check: Try -4, a number greater than -5.

$-4 + 8 \overset{?}{>} 3$

$4 > 3$ ✓

The solution is $m > -5$, all numbers greater than -5.

2 **Solve $-26 \le r - 16$. Check your solution.**

$-26 \le r - 16$

$-26 + 16 \le r - 16 + 16$ Add 16 to each side.

$-10 \le r$

How can $-10 \le r$ also be written using the $\ge$ symbol? **$r \ge -10$**

Check: Try -10 and 0, a number greater than -10.

$-26 \overset{?}{\le} -10 - 16$ $-26 \overset{?}{\le} 0 - 16$

$-26 \le -26$ ✓ $-26 \le -16$ ✓

The solution is $r \ge -10$, all numbers greater than or equal to -10.

Checking for Understanding

Communicating Algebra

1. What is the name of the property that enables you to add the same number to each side of an inequality? **addition property for inequalities**
2. Explain how to solve $y - 9 > 3$. **Add 9 to each side.**
3. Explain how to solve $-11 < b + 6$. **Subtract 6 from each side.**
4. Write an inequality involving addition where the solution is $k \le 18$. **Sample answer: $k + 5 \le 23$**

Guided Practice

Solve each inequality. Check your solution.

5. $m + 6 > 5$ **$m > -1$**
6. $r - 12 < -6$ **$r < 6$**
7. $7 < t - 9$ **$16 < t$**
8. $-8 > p - 1$ **$-7 > p$**
9. $k + 10 \ge -5$ **$k \ge -15$**
10. $16 + s \le -1$ **$s \le -17$**

Exercises

Independent Practice

Solve each inequality. Check your solution.

11. $y - 7 < 10$ **$y < 17$**
12. $x - 2 < -14$ **$x < -12$**
13. $m + 13 > 8$ **$m > -5$**
14. $k + 17 > 36$ **$k > 19$**
15. $5 + z > 27$ **$z > 22$**
16. $12 + a > -9$ **$a > -21$**
17. $-7 + b < -5$ **$b < 2$**
18. $-9 + d < 10$ **$d < 19$**
19. $w + (-3) < -7$ **$w < -4$**
20. $-42 + k > 18$ **$k > 60$**
21. $4 < y - 23$ **$y > 27$**
22. $f + (-8) > -12$ **$f > -4$**
23. $20 > z + (-19)$ **$z < 39$**
24. $-31 < p - 7$ **$p > -24$**
25. $t - (-5) > -6$ **$t > -11$**
26. $10 < s - (-3)$ **$s > 7$**
27. $-41 > r - (-8)$ **$r < -49$**
28. $24 + m > 10$ **$m > -14$**
29. $72 + k < 56$ **$k < -16$**
30. $22 < m - (-16)$ **$m > 6$**
31. $-30 \le x + (-5)$
32. $-15 + t \le 12$ **$t \le 27$**
33. $-67 + p \ge -48$ **$p \ge 19$**
34. $11 + c \ge -29$

31. $x \ge -25$ 34. $c \ge -40$

3 PRACTICE/APPLY

Checking the Concept

Have students graph their solutions to Exercises 5-10. Ask students if the number they picked to check each inequality is in the shaded part of each graph.

Error Analysis

Watch for students who have trouble distinguishing between $>$ and $\ge$, and $<$ and $\le$.

Prevent by solving two similar inequalities. Graph the results, and read other graphs where the only difference is the "or equal to" part.

Independent Practice

Homework Assignment	
Basic	11-31 odd, 38-45, 47, 48
Average	18-38 even, 39-48
Honors	28-48

Practice Masters Booklet, **p. 26**

Name ______________ Date ______

Practice Worksheet 3-7

Solving Inequalities: Adding and Subtracting

Solve each inequality. Check your solution.

1. $y - 7 \le 10$ $y \le 17$
2. $14 \ge b - 3$ $b \le 17$
3. $4 + x > -1$ $x > -5$
4. $-3 < k + 4$ $k > -7$
5. $k - 3 > -4$ $k > -1$
6. $1 > l - 3$ $l < 4$
7. $m + 7 \le -9$ $m \le -16$
8. $-12 \le y + 1$ $y \ge -13$
9. $-7 + f \ge 4$ $f \ge 11$
10. $5 < z - 4$ $z > 9$
11. $s - 12 \ge 17$ $s \ge 29$
12. $-7 < 3 + e$ $e > -10$
13. $t - 86 > -106$ $t > -20$
14. $2 \ge 4 + r$ $r \le -2$
15. $p - 12 \le 18$ $p \le 30$
16. $-12 > -4 + a$ $a < -8$
17. $-15 + n \ge -5$ $n \ge 10$
18. $y - (-15) < -12$ $y < -27$
19. $85 + c \ge -18$ $c \ge -103$
20. $36 + v > 11$ $v > -25$
21. $-40 > p - 8$ $p < -32$
22. $f + (-9) > -13$ $f > -4$
23. $34 < u - (-19)$ $u > 15$
24. $-90 + y \ge -53$ $y \ge 37$
25. $12 + e \ge -30$ $e \ge -42$
26. $62 + y < 49$ $y < -13$

Alternate Strategies: Reteaching the Lesson

Reteaching Activity

Using Models Draw this graph on the chalkboard or overhead. Write $x < -2$, $x + 3 < 1$, and $x - 4 < -6$ underneath the graph.

-3 -2 -1 0 1 2

Ask students which inequality is graphed. **They all are.** Then write $x > 5$ on the chalkboard and ask for other inequalities that would have the same graph. **Sample Answers: $x + 1 > 6$, $x - 2 > 3$**

Reteaching Masters Booklet, **p. 24**

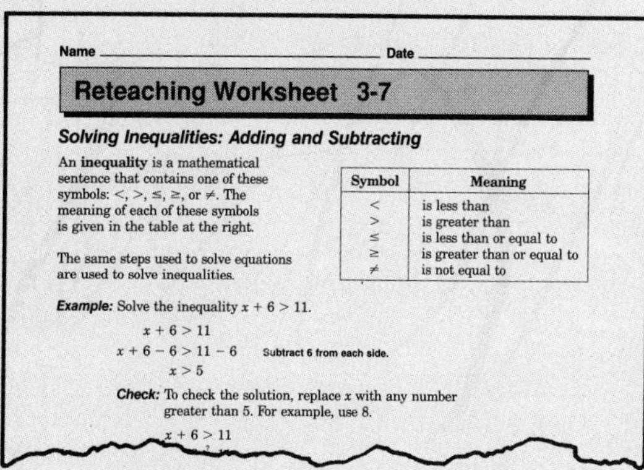

Name ______________ Date ______

Reteaching Worksheet 3-7

Solving Inequalities: Adding and Subtracting

An **inequality** is a mathematical sentence that contains one of these symbols: <, >, ≤, ≥, or ≠. The meaning of each of these symbols is given in the table at the right.

Symbol	Meaning
<	is less than
>	is greater than
≤	is less than or equal to
≥	is greater than or equal to
≠	is not equal to

The same steps used to solve equations are used to solve inequalities.

Example: Solve the inequality $x + 6 > 11$.

$x + 6 > 11$

$x + 6 - 6 > 11 - 6$ **Subtract 6 from each side.**

$x > 5$

Check: To check the solution, replace x with any number greater than 5. For example, use 8.

$x + 6 > 11$

4 CLOSE

Assessment Option

Speaking Have the students tell what number needs to be added to or subtracted from each side of the following inequalities to solve them:

1. $y - 8 < 12$ add 8
2. $x + 6 < 4$ subtract 6
3. $x - 12 > 8$ add 12
4. $m + (-11) > 11$ subtract -11 or add 11

Additional Answer

47. one quart: measure out two 4-quart containers and take away one 7-quart container
two quarts: measure out two 7-quart containers and take away three 4-quart containers
three quarts: measure out one 7-quart container and take away one 4-quart container
five quarts: measure out three 4-quart containers and take away one 7-quart container

Enrichment Masters Booklet, **p. 24**

Name ______________________ Date ____________

Enrichment Worksheet 3-7

Solving Inequalities Using Addition and Subtraction

Inequalities can be written many different ways in English.

English Phrase	Mathematical Phrase
at most x	$\leq x$
at least x	$\geq x$
5 less than x	$x - 5$
5 more than x	$x + 5$
5 is less than x	$5 < x$
x is between 4 and 6	$4 < x < 6$
x is between 4 and 6	$x > 4$ and $x < 6$

1. Write a mathematical phrase for each of the following English phrases.
   a. 8 is no more than x. $8 \leq x$
   b. x is no less than 3. $x \geq 3$
   c. x is not between 6 and 12. $x \leq 6$ or $x \geq 12$
   d. x cannot exceed -5. $x \leq -5$
2. For what values of x, if any, is the mathematical phrase $5 > x > 7$ true? none

To solve compound inequalities, you must perform the same operation on each of the three parts of the inequality.

Example: Solve the compound inequality $3 < x - 2 < 5$.

$3 < x - 2 < 5$
$3 + 2 < x - 2 + 2 < 5 + 2$ To get x by itself, add 2 to each part.
$5 < x < 7$

Thus, x is all numbers between 5 and 7.

Solve each compound inequality.

3. $-2 < x + 1 < 4$
   $-3 < x < 3$
4. $-4 \leq x - 1 \leq 0$
   $-3 \leq x \leq 1$
5. $3 < 15 + x < 10$
   $-12 < x < -5$
6. $-12 < x - 3 \leq 1$
   $-9 < x \leq 4$

Language Skill

Write an inequality for each sentence.

35. Ellen spent more than \$15 at the amusement park. $x > 15$
36. The temperature is less than or equal to negative seven degrees. $t \leq -7$
37. The number of players on the soccer team was greater than or equal to 13. $x \geq 13$
38. George plans to spend no more than \$48 for clothes. $x \leq 48$

Mixed Review

39. identity for multiplication 40. Some integers are not even.

39. State the property shown by the statement $7 \cdot 1 = 7$. (Lesson 1-3)
40. Write the negation of the statement *All integers are even.* (Lesson 2-6)
41. Evaluate the expression $\frac{c}{-4}$ if $c = 28$. (Lesson 2-8) -7
42. Use the formula $f = t - h$ to find the actual time (t) if the actual boat race score (f) is 93 hours and the handicap (h) is 12. (Lesson 3-5) 105 hours

43. 16 miles

43. Find the perimeter of the rectangle shown at the right. (Lesson 3-6)

6 mi
2 mi

44. Find the area of a rectangle whose length is 18 ft and whose width is 4 ft. (Lesson 3-6) 72 square feet

Applications

Write an inequality for each situation. Then solve the inequality.

45. **Sports** The graph at the right shows the states with the most little league teams in 1990. How many teams could Florida add and still have fewer than Pennsylvania? $6909 + x < 7687$; 778 teams

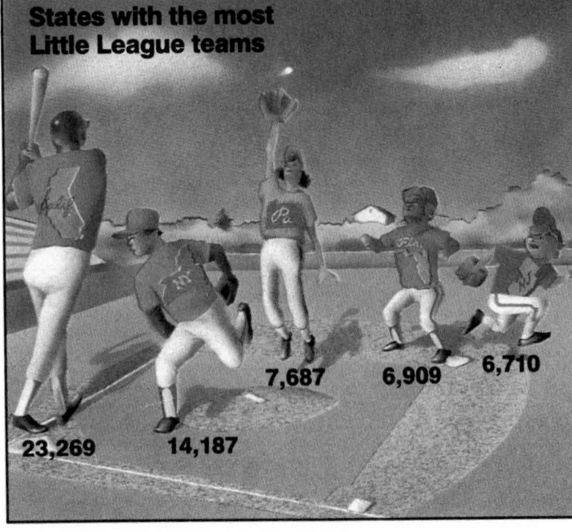

46. **Hobbies** Emilio wants to spend at most \$25 to buy new stamps for his collection. He has selected a new stamp that costs \$4. What is the most he can spend on other stamps? $4 + x \leq 25$; \$21

Critical Thinking

47. How can you use unmarked 7-quart and 4-quart containers to measure out exactly one quart? two quarts? three quarts? five quarts? See margin.

Wrap-Up

48. Measure your height and a friend's height. Write an inequality that compares your heights. Suppose that each of you were to grow 3 more inches. Now write an inequality that compares your new heights. Sample answer: $65 > 63$; $68 > 66$

Alternate Strategies: Extending the Lesson

Enrichment

Have students graph the solution to $|x| \geq 2$ on a number line.

Cooperative Learning

Inequality Detective Group Activity **3-7**

MATERIALS: 0-9 spinner • three dice • coin

Write inequalities for others in your group to solve. The inequalities you write should use only the operations of addition and subtraction and the symbols >, <, ≥, ≤.

To begin, group members roll three dice and flip the coin. From these, each person writes a 1-digit and a 2-digit number. If the coin is heads, both numbers are positive. If the coin is tails, one number is positive and the other number is negative. Next, spin the spinner and flip the coin to obtain the integer value that will be substituted for the variable in your inequalities. Using these values, write one correct inequality and one incorrect inequality. As a group, determine which are correct.

For example, if a 3, 5, and 6 are obtained on the dice and the coin gives a negative, you make an inequality from these numbers. If a 9 is the number from the spinner and the second flip of the coin is heads (positive), then +9 is the value to be substituted for the variable in the inequality. Hence, a correct inequality you could write is $x + (-35) < 6$, and an incorrect inequality could be $x + 6 < -35$.

Merrill Pre-Algebra SOLVING INEQUALITIES: ADDING OR SUBTRACTING

3-8 Solving Inequalities: Multiplying or Dividing

Objective:
Solve inequalities by using the multiplication and division properties.

When a pilot prepares for take-off, the engine power is increased, or multiplied, until there is enough thrust to push the airplane forward and get it airborne.

Upon landing, the airplane is slowed by again *multiplying* the power. This increase in power is made negative by using a thrust-reverser brake, which changes the direction of the thrust.

Similar characteristics exist when working with inequalities.

Consider multiplying or dividing each side of the inequality $4 < 6$ by a *positive* integer.

$4 < 6$		$4 < 6$	
$4 \cdot 2 < 6 \cdot 2$	Multiply each side by 2.	$4 \div 2 < 6 \div 2$	Divide each side by 2.
$8 < 12$		$2 < 3$	

The inequalities $8 < 12$ and $2 < 3$ are true. These and other examples suggest the following property.

Multiplication and Division Properties of Inequalities

In words: When you multiply or divide each side of a true inequality by a *positive* integer, the result remains true.
In symbols: For all integers a, b, and c, where $c > 0$, if $a > b$, then $a \cdot c > b \cdot c$ and $\frac{a}{c} > \frac{b}{c}$.

The rule is similar for $a < b$, $a \geq b$, and $a \leq b$.

Consider multiplying or dividing each side of $2 < 4$ by a *negative* integer.

$2 < 4$	Multiply each side by -1.	$2 < 4$	Divide each side by -2.
$2(-1) < 4(-1)$		$2 \div (-2) < 4 \div (-2)$	
$-2 < -4$	False	$-1 < -2$	False

The inequalities $-2 < -4$ and $-1 < -2$ are both false. However, notice that both inequalities would be true if you reverse the order symbol. That is, change $<$ to $>$.

$-2 > -4$ and $-1 > -2$ are both true.

Bell Ringer

Jim has \$24. Sue has \$14. They each receive \$5 from their Uncle Ted. Who has more money? **Jim**

Lesson Notes 3-8

5-Minute Check
(over Lesson 3-7)

Solve each inequality. Check your solution.
1. $x - 8 < 14$ $x < 22$
2. $m + (-7) > 9$ $m > 16$
3. $-16 + t \leq 11$ $t \leq 27$
4. $-29 > r - (-5)$ $-34 > r$
5. $17 + c \geq -25$ $c \geq -42$

Transparency 3-8 contains the 5-Minute Check and a teaching aid for this lesson.

1 FOCUS

The purpose of the lesson is to apply the multiplication and division properties of equality to solving one-step inequalities.

Motivating the Lesson

Name some situations that illustrate inequalities. For example, you have more money than I do, I am taller than you, you live farther from school than I do. Have students give examples of their own.

2 TEACH

Using Models

Model the jet engine's thrust-reverser brake using a hair dryer. One with two speed settings would be better at showing the concept of multiplying. To reverse the air flow, use an insulated cup or bowl to act as the "reverser."

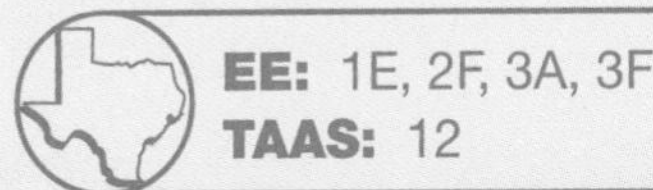

EE: 1E, 2F, 3A, 3F
TAAS: 12

Chalkboard Examples

Solve each inequality. Check your solution.

- *For Example 1*
  $\frac{x}{-8} > 2$ $x < -16$
- *For Example 2*
  $9x < -27$ $x < -3$
- *For Example 3*
  $-7m \le -42$ $m \ge 6$

3 PRACTICE/APPLY

Checking the Concept

Using Cooperative Groups Have student work in groups of three to do the Guided Practice exercises. Have each student do a different part of the instructions. Students should rotate roles for each exercise and check each other's work.

Error Analysis

Watch for students who don't change the inequality sign when multiplying or dividing by a negative number.
Prevent by emphasizing the rule and using a number line to check solutions.

Practice Masters Booklet, **p. 27**

Name ______________________ Date ____________

Practice Worksheet 3-8

Solving Inequalities: Multiplying and Dividing

Solve each inequality. Check your solution.

1. $-5x < -25$ $x > 5$
2. $\frac{m}{-15} \le -19$ $m \ge 285$
3. $6z > -72$ $z > -12$
4. $21 < \frac{p}{-14}$ $p < -294$
5. $225 \ge -15k$ $k \ge -15$
6. $\frac{b}{-16} > 1$ $b < -16$
7. $11e \ge -319$ $e \ge -29$
8. $\frac{r}{-8} \le -39$ $r \ge 312$
9. $-13q < -234$ $q > 18$
10. $-17 \ge \frac{n}{-8}$ $n \ge 136$
11. $2f > -120$ $f > -60$
12. $\frac{w}{18} \le -5$ $w \le -90$
13. $-62 \ge 2s$ $s \le -31$
14. $-220 < \frac{t}{-22}$ $t < 4840$
15. $3h \le 15$ $h \le 5$
16. $\frac{i}{-101} \ge 32$ $i \le -3232$
17. $-28 > -7y$ $y > 4$
18. $\frac{c}{-100} > 400$ $c < -40{,}000$
19. $7d < -35$ $d < -5$
20. $\frac{c}{-4} \ge 12$ $c \le -48$
21. $-144 < 6v$ $v > -24$
22. $\frac{x}{7} > -21$ $x > -147$
23. $-12b \ge 144$ $b \le -12$
24. $\frac{z}{2} < 25$ $z < 50$
25. $-64 \le -4a$ $a \le 16$
26. $\frac{h}{-3} < -16$ $h > 48$
27. $6g \ge 162$ $g \ge 27$
28. $\frac{c}{-5} \ge -25$ $c \le 125$
29. $-176 > 11u$ $u < -16$
30. $\frac{a}{12} \ge -3$ $a \ge -36$
31. $17t < 0$ $t < 0$
32. $-4 \le \frac{n}{7}$ $n \ge -28$
33. $425 > -5j$ $j > -85$
34. $\frac{x}{-2} < 0$ $x > 0$
35. $-17r > 102$ $r < -6$
36. $-15 < \frac{e}{12}$ $e > -180$
37. $-256 > 16k$ $k < -16$
38. $\frac{v}{11} < 19$ $v < 209$
39. $-437 \ge 19y$ $y \le -23$

The previous examples suggest the following property.

Multiplication and Division Properties of Inequalities

In words: When you multiply or divide each side of an inequality by a *negative* integer, you must *reverse the order symbol.*
In symbols: For all integers a, b, and c, where $c < 0$, if $a > b$, then $a \cdot c < b \cdot c$ and $\frac{a}{c} < \frac{b}{c}$.

The rule is similar for $a < b$, $a \le b$, and $a \ge b$.

Examples

1 **Solve $\frac{x}{-5} > 2$. Check your solution.**

$\frac{x}{-5} > 2$

$\frac{x}{-5} \cdot (-5) < 2 \cdot (-5)$ Multiply each side by -5. Reverse the order symbol.

$x < -10$

Check: Try -15, a number less than -10.

$\frac{-15}{-5} \overset{?}{>} 2$

$3 > 2$ ✓

The solution is $x < (-10)$, all numbers less than -10.

2 **Solve $6x < -18$.**

$6x < -18$

$\frac{6x}{6} < \frac{-18}{6}$ Divide each side by 6.

$x < -3$

The solution is $x < -3$, all numbers less than -3.

Why was the order symbol not reversed? **Each side was divided by positive 6.**

3 **Solve $-4k \le -20$.**

$-4k \le -20$

$\frac{-4k}{-4} \ge \frac{-20}{-4}$ Divide each side by -4. Reverse the order symbol.

$k \ge 5$

The solution is $k \ge 5$, all numbers greater than or equal to 5.

Why was the order symbol reversed? **Each side was divided by negative 4.**

Checking for Understanding

Communicating Algebra

1. Write an inequality that is always true. **Sample answer: 5 > 4**
2. Write an inequality that is always false. **Sample answer -1 < -5**
3. Explain how to solve $-7m \ge -49$. **Divide each side by -7; reverse the order symbol.**
4. Write an inequality involving division where the solution is $x < 9$. **Sample answer: -5x > -45**

Guided Practice

State the number to multiply or divide each side by to solve each inequality. Then tell whether the order symbol should be reversed.

5. $-24 < 6a$ **6; no**
6. $3y < 21$ **3; no**
7. $-4x \ge 8$ **-4; yes**
8. $-6z \le 18$ **-6; yes**
9. $\frac{d}{9} \le 12$ **9; no**
10. $\frac{r}{3} \ge -4$ **3; no**
11. $\frac{s}{-6} > -11$ **-6; yes**
12. $-35 \le \frac{g}{-7}$ **-7; yes**

Alternate Strategies: Reteaching the Lesson

Reteaching Activity

Making and Using Graphs Solve an inequality that uses only multiplication or division. Graph the results. Have students pick several possible values of the variable from the graph, and use these values to test the validity of the solution.

Reteaching Masters Booklet, p. 25

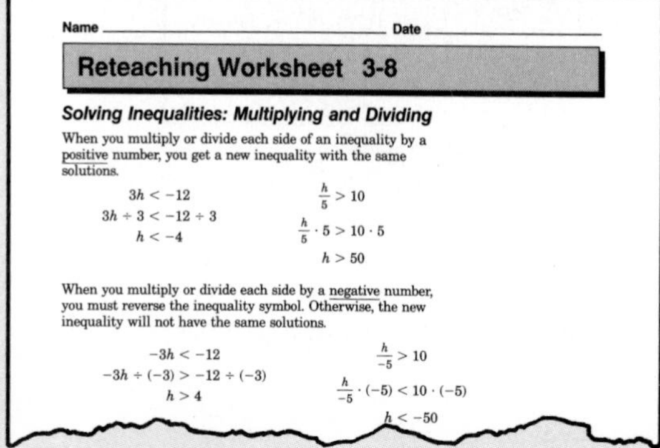

Name ______________________ Date ____________

Reteaching Worksheet 3-8

Solving Inequalities: Multiplying and Dividing

When you multiply or divide each side of an inequality by a positive number, you get a new inequality with the same solutions.

$3h < -12$
$3h \div 3 < -12 \div 3$
$h < -4$

$\frac{h}{5} > 10$
$\frac{h}{5} \cdot 5 > 10 \cdot 5$
$h > 50$

When you multiply or divide each side by a negative number, you must reverse the inequality symbol. Otherwise, the new inequality will not have the same solutions.

$-3h < -12$
$-3h \div (-3) > -12 \div (-3)$
$h > 4$

$\frac{h}{-5} > 10$
$\frac{h}{-5} \cdot (-5) < 10 \cdot (-5)$
$h < -50$

Exercises

Independent Practice

Solve each inequality. Check your solution. 16. $a \geq -12$ 18. $p > 9$ 20. $y > 8$

25. $p \geq -168$ 26. $n < 390$ 27. $h < 360$ 28. $f \leq -255$ 30. $x > 17$ 32. $13 > y$

13. $-3y < -39$ $y > 13$
14. $4x \geq -16$ $x \geq -4$
15. $-5z > -65$ $z < 13$
16. $-9a \leq 108$
17. $4r \geq -72$ $r \geq -18$
18. $-12p < -108$
19. $8 \leq 2x$ $x \geq 4$
20. $-48 > -6y$
21. $\frac{w}{-2} \leq 73$ $w \geq -146$
22. $\frac{s}{-9} \geq 13$ $s \leq -117$
23. $\frac{m}{8} > 21$ $m > 168$
24. $\frac{k}{6} \leq -8$ $k \leq -48$
25. $\frac{p}{-14} \leq 12$
26. $\frac{n}{-15} > -26$
27. $-20 < \frac{h}{-18}$
28. $-17 \geq \frac{f}{15}$
29. $21r \leq -378$ $r \leq -18$
30. $-27x < -459$
31. $-3n \leq 51$ $n \geq -17$
32. $-143 < -11y$
33. $-25 \leq \frac{a}{-16}$ $400 \geq a$
34. $50 \leq \frac{k}{-32}$ $-1600 \geq k$
35. $\frac{x}{34} \leq -3$ $x \leq -102$
36. $\frac{g}{-21} \geq 33$ $g \leq -693$

Language Skill

Write an inequality for each situation. Then solve the inequality.

37. Seven times an integer is greater than -56. $7x > -56$; $x > -8$
38. The product of negative three and an integer is less than 21. $-3x < 21$; $x > -7$

Mixed Review

39. Simplify the expression $|-12| - |9|$. (Lesson 2-1) 3
40. Solve the equation $15x = 150$. (Lesson 3-3) 10
41. Find the area of a rectangle whose length is 15 yards and whose width is 9 yards. (Lesson 3-6) 135 square yards
42. Solve the inequality $-23 < p - 17$. (Lesson 3-7) $-6 < p$
43. Write the inequality for the sentence *Mr. Luez will spend no more than $19 for a shovel.* (Lesson 3-7) $s \leq 19$

Applications

44. **Economics** The *Norfolk Ledger* pays 8 cents per paper to the delivery person. How many papers must Kristen deliver to earn $4 or more per day? 50 papers

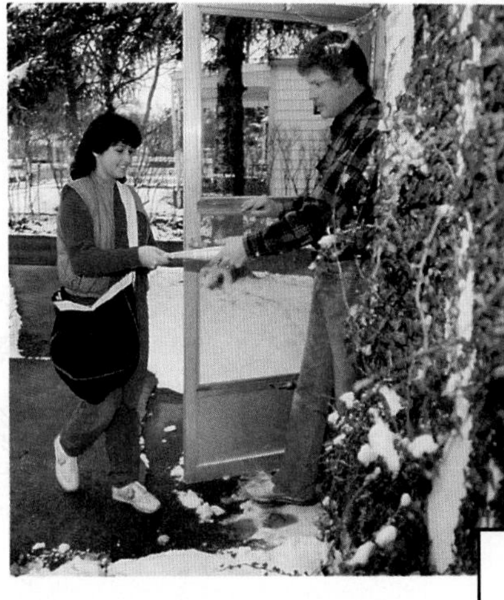

45. **Automobile Repair** Felix Virtullo is a repair service estimator. The owner of a vehicle describes the problem and Felix makes an estimate of the cost of repair. When Mr. Virtullo gives a customer an estimate, he guarantees that the cost of the repair will be no more than $30 over the estimate. Suppose Mr. Virtullo thinks that the work is going to cost $300. Write an inequality to represent his estimate. Sample answer: $c \leq 300 + 30$

Critical Thinking

46. The product of an integer and negative four is greater than -24. Find the greatest integer that meets this condition. 5

Wrap-Up

47. In your own words, explain why when you multiply or divide an inequality by a negative integer you must change the order of the inequality. Sample answer Multiplying and dividing any integer by a negative integer results in a different sign for the product or quotient. The order symbol then needs to be changed.

Alternate Strategies: Extending the Lesson

Enrichment

Using Cooperative Groups After each group determines a group name, they code the name using the solutions to inequalities involving multiplication and division. For example if the solutions are, $x < 4$: B, $y > 9$: E, $a > -2$: A, $c \leq -8$: R, and $g < 15$: S, the group's name is the Bears. Have groups exchange inequalities and decode each others' names.

Cooperative Learning

Hit That Range — Group Activity 3-8

MATERIALS: Three dice • a coin

To begin the activity roll the three dice and flip the coin (to get a positive or negative sign). Using the numbers and sign obtained, each group member writes an inequality involving multiplication or division and one of the inequality symbols (>, <, ≥, ≤.). The three digits are to be used to make a 1-digit and a 2-digit number in the expression. If the flip of the coin indicates a negative, then one of the numbers must be negative; otherwise they are both positive.

Everyone must write an inequality that satisfies either of the following conditions: the solution set for the inequality begins at a number between -5 and 5, or the solution set for the inequality begins at a number whose absolute value is greater than 100.

After writing your inequality, exchange it for someone else to solve. That person must check to see if the solution to the inequality satisfies the conditions given above.

Merrill Pre-Algebra SOLVING EQUATIONS: MULTIPLYING OR DIVIDING

Independent Practice

Homework Assignment	
Basic	13-37 odd, 39-44, 46, 47
Average	16-36 even, 37-47
Honors	26-47

4 CLOSE

Assessment Option

Modeling Have students model inequalities on a two-pan balance scale by placing unequal but even numbers of counters on each pan and demonstrate how the multiplication and division properties of equality are true for inequalities by doubling and halving the counters on each pan.

Enrichment Masters Booklet, **p. 25**

Name ______ Date ______

Enrichment Worksheet 3-8

Hidden Word

In each group of five inequalities, only two have the same solution set. For each group, write the solution of each inequality and then circle the letters of the two inequalities having the same solution set. After completing all four groups, use the circled letters to form a one-word answer to the question at the bottom of the page.

GROUP 1

(P.) $3x < 30$ $x < 10$ B. $-3x < -30$ $x > 10$ F. $-30 > 3x$ $-10 > x$ (O.) $-30 < -3x$ $10 > x$ D. $-3x < 30$ $x > -10$

GROUP 2

M. $\frac{x}{5} \leq -2$ $x \leq -10$ N. $\frac{-x}{5} \leq 2$ $x \geq -10$ (I.) $\frac{x}{-5} \leq -2$ $x \geq 10$ (H.) $\frac{-x}{2} \leq -5$ $x \geq 10$ R. $\frac{-x}{5} < -2$ $x > 10$

GROUP 3

Q. $\frac{3x}{2} < 0$ $x < 0$ K. $0 \leq -12x$ $0 \geq x$ L. $\frac{-1}{x} \leq 0$ $x > 0$ (C.) $0.73x \geq 0$ $x \geq 0$ (N.) $0 \geq -912x$ $0 \leq x$

GROUP 4

L. $200 > 0.05x$ $4000 > x$ (A.) $0.05x < 20$ $x < 400$ D. $\frac{1}{5}x > 20$ $x > 100$ E. $200 > 5x$ $40 > x$ (M.) $\frac{x}{0.1} < 4000$ $x < 400$

QUESTION: What was the name of Gene Autry's horse on the "The Gene Autry Show?" Champion

5-Minute Check
(over Lesson 3-8)

Solve each inequality. Check your solution.
1. $-2x < -52$ $x > 26$
2. $\frac{w}{-5} \leq 65$ $w \geq -325$
3. $-16y < -336$ $y > 21$
4. $28 \geq \frac{k}{-12}$ $-336 \leq k$
5. $\frac{m}{-11} \geq 48$ $m \leq -528$

Transparency 3-9 contains the 5-Minute Check and a teaching aid for this lesson.

1 FOCUS

The purpose of the lesson is to extend the use of logical reasoning for determining the truth value of a statement to determining the truth value of *compound* statements.

Motivating the Lesson

Start the lesson with comments about the students that are true or false. For example, Joe is older than Amy; Frank is taller than Steve. Then combine the statements using "and" and "or" and ask if they are still true, still false, or if they have changed.

2 TEACH

Using Models

On an overhead transparency, graph the solution to $x > -5$ using a red marker. Using the same scale, graph the solution to $x < 1$ on another transparency but use a blue marker. Place one graph on top of the other. Repeat the procedure graphing $y < -3$ in red and $y > 2$ in blue. Refer to the graphs to determine the truth values of the conjunction and disjunction of each pair of statements used in creating the graphs.

EE: 1A, 1E

3-9 Compound Statements

Objective:
Determine the truth value of compound statements.

Key Terms:
compound statement
conjunction
disjunction
counterexample

For their summer vacation, the Elliott family drove to Yellowstone National Park. On the way there, they noticed on several of the interstate highways that the minimum speed was 45 mph and the maximum speed was 65 mph.

For the Elliotts to be driving at a legal speed, they had to drive:

at least 45 mph

and

no faster than 65 mph.

The word *and* is used to connect the statements.

Two statements connected by the word *and* form a **compound statement.** Such a statement is called a **conjunction.** For a conjunction to be true, *both* statements must be true. For example, suppose the Elliotts drove at 68 mph. Then the first statement would be true, but the second statement would be false. So they would not be driving at a legal speed.

You can use inequalities to describe the speed at which the Elliotts should drive. Let s represent their speed.

They should drive at least 45 mph. $s \geq 45$

They should drive no faster than 65 mph. $s \leq 65$

These inequalities can then be combined in a compound inequality.

$$45 \leq s \leq 65$$

This is read: "45 is less than or equal to s is less than or equal to 65."

FYI

There are 42,500 miles of interstate highways in the U.S. If they were connected end to end, they would go around the equator almost two times.

Examples

1 **Determine whether the following conjunction is *true* or *false*. A triangle has three sides, and a pentagon has four sides.**

For a conjunction to be true, both parts of it must be true. Since triangles have three sides, the first part is true. However, pentagons have five sides, not four, so the conjunction is false.

2 **Write the inequalities $x > -2$ and $x < 4$ as a compound inequality.**

$x > (-2)$ is the same as $-2 < x$.
So, $x > (-2)$ and $x < 4$ can be written as $-2 < x < 4$.

Bell Ringer

Tell whether you will need to reverse the order symbol to solve each problem.
1. $6x < -12$ No 2. $-4y > -8$ Yes

Every year, Steve Herr and his sister Suzi plan an outing to King's Point Amusement Park with their 12 cousins, parents, and grandparents. Admission is free if you are under 2 years of age or if you are a senior citizen (65 or older).

So, for anyone to get in free, he or she must be:

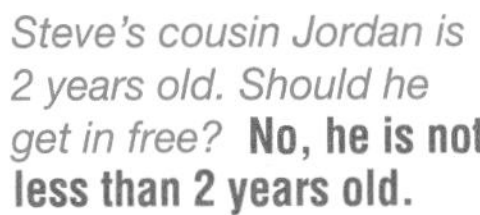

Steve's cousin Jordan is 2 years old. Should he get in free? **No, he is not less than 2 years old.**

less than 2 years old

or

65 years or older.

The word *or* is used to connect the statements.

Two statements connected by the word *or* form another type of compound statement called a **disjunction.** For a disjunction to be true, *only one* of the statements must be true. For example, suppose Steve's cousin Kelsey is 10 months old. Then she gets into the park free because she is less than 2 years old.

Obviously, it is not possible for anyone to be less than 2 years old and also 65 years or older. However, in logic it is possible for both statements of a disjunction to be true. For example, if we say that it may rain Friday or it may rain Saturday, we mean that it could rain one or both days. So, a disjunction is true if at least one of its statements is true. It is false only if both of its statements are false.

Example

3 Determine whether the following disjunction is *true* or *false*. The solution to the equation $x - 14 = 76$ is 62, or the sum of two odd numbers is always an odd number.

Solve $x - 14 = 76$ to see whether the first statement is true or false.

$$x - 14 = 76$$
$$x - 14 + 14 = 76 + 14$$
$$x = 90$$

The first statement is false.

Check the sums of several pairs of odd numbers to see if the second statement is true or false. You only need one example to show that it is false. The example is called a **counterexample.**

$9 + 7 = 16$ even The statement is false.

Since both statements are false, the disjunction is false.

Chalkboard Examples

- *For Example 1*
  Determine whether the following conjunction is true or false.
  A square has four vertices and a rectangle has four vertices. **true**
- *For Example 2*
  Write the inequalities $x > -6$ and $x < 2$ as a compound inequality.
  $-6 < x < 2$
- *For Example 3*
  Determine whether the following disjunction is true or false.
  The solution to the equation $x - 19 = 42$ is 73 or the product of any number and zero is zero.
  true

3 PRACTICE/APPLY

Checking the Concept

Have students explain how they determined the truth value of the compound statements in Exercises 3-6.

Error Analysis

Watch for students who confuse the *and* and the *or* statements.
Prevent by modeling an example, using an *or*, and then an *and*. Show the model on the chalkboard for reference.

Alternate Strategies: Reteaching the Lesson

Reteaching Activity

Using Tables Have students complete two truth tables to help them decide the truth value of compound statements.

First Statement	Second Statement	And/Or Statement
T	T	T/T
T	F	F/T
F	T	F/T
F	F	F/F

Independent Practice

Homework Assignment	
Basic	9-19 odd, 20-25
Average	11-17, 20-25
Honors	13-25

4 CLOSE

Assessment Option

Writing Have students write two true conjunctions and two false conjunctions. Then have them write two true disjunctions and two false disjunctions.

Additional Answer

1. conjunction, disjunction; They both contain two state-ments. The statements in a conjunction are connected by the word *and.* The statements in a disjunction are connected by the word *or.* Both statements of a conjunction must be true for it to be true. Only one statement of a disjunction must be true for it to be true.

Practice Masters Booklet, **p. 28**

Name ____________ Date ____________

Practice Worksheet 3-9

Logic: Compound Statements

Determine whether each compound statement is true or false.

1. Canada is part of North America, and Brazil is part of South America. true
2. A rectangle has four sides, and a circle has one diameter. false
3. The temperature is below freezing, or the temperature is above freezing. true
4. $3 + 4 = 7$ or $9 - 6 = 2$ true
5. $3 + 4 = 7$ and $9 - 6 = 2$ false
6. $15 > 10$ and $15 > 14$ true
7. $3 < -2$ or $-3 < -4$ false
8. $6 > 5$ and $-6 > 5$ false
9. $11 < 0$ or $0 > -11$ true
10. $-9 > -8$ or $-8 < -7$ true
11. $10 > -10$ and $-13 < -12$ true
12. $0 \le 0$ or $5 \ge 4$ true
13. $1 \ge 1$ and $-3 \ge -4$ true
14. The product of two even numbers is even, or the product of two odd numbers is odd. true

Write each pair of inequalities as a compound inequality.

15. $0 \le x$ and $x \le 2$ $0 \le x \le 2$
16. $y > -2$ and $y < 2$ $-2 < y < 2$
17. $-3 \le t$ and $t < -1$ $-3 \le t < -1$
18. $z > 0$ and $z \le 10$ $0 < z \le 10$
19. $j \le 5$ and $j \ge -1$ $-1 \le j \le 5$
20. $k \ge -6$ and $k < 0$ $-6 \le k < 0$

Checking for Understanding

Communicating Algebra

1. Name the two types of compound sentences. State how they are alike and how they are different. See margin.
2. The compound statement *Alan may go to the football game, or Mieko might go to the mall* is an example of a __?__. disjunction

Guided Practice

Determine whether each compound statement is *true* or *false*.

3. A hexagon has six sides, and an octagon has nine sides. F
4. The product of two odd numbers is even, or $-17 + 4 = -13$. T
5. $3 > 4$ or $7 < 6$ F
6. $7 \ge 6$ and $7 > 4$ T

Write each pair of inequalities as a compound inequality.

7. $0 \le n$ and $n \le 10$ $0 \le n \le 10$
8. $r > -3$ and $r < 8$ $-3 < r < 8$

Exercises

Independent Practice

Determine whether each compound statement is *true* or *false*.

9. Austin is the capital of Texas, and Cincinnati is the capital of Ohio. F
10. Abraham Lincoln was a U.S. president, or Dolly Madison was the wife of President Madison. T
11. The sum of $4n$ and $2n$ is $6n$, and 5 is a solution to the equation $3 + c = 8$. T
12. $13 > 9$ and $13 > 12$ T
13. $9 > 0$ and $12 < 17$ T
14. $5 > -3$ and $-5 > -1$ F
15. $13 > 6$ or $0 < -2$ T

Write each pair of inequalities as a compound inequality.

16. $0 < y$ and $y \le 12$ $0 < y \le 12$
17. $p > 3$ and $p \le 11$ $3 < p \le 11$
18. $z > -4$ and $z < 0$ $-4 < z < 0$
19. $m > -13$ and $m < -6$ $-13 < m < -6$

Mixed Review

20. *True* or *false:* All open sentences are equations. (Lesson 1-5) F
21. Simplify the expression $-17ab - (-5ab)$. (Lesson 2-5) $-12ab$
22. State whether the order symbol should be reversed to solve the inequality $\frac{r}{4} > -12$. (Lesson 3-8) no

Application

23. **Consumer Awareness** The label on a can of paint reads *For proper results, do not apply if the temperature is below 30°F or above 85°F.* Write a compound inequality that describes the range of acceptable temperatures for applying the paint. $30 \le t \le 85$

Critical Thinking

24. Suppose you are to determine if a conjunction is true. You determine that the first statement of the conjunction is false. Is it necessary to determine if the second statement is true or false? Why or why not? No. Both parts must be true.

Wrap-Up

25. Describe a situation relating to water where the inequality $32 < t < 212$ might be used. Water is a liquid between 32°F and 212°F.

Alternate Strategies: Extending the Lesson

Enrichment

Using Manipulatives Place several figures having different shapes in a bag. Have students draw out two figures each and make a compound statement about them. Have other students determine the truth value of the compound statements. Encourage the use of disjunctions as well as conjunction.

Cooperative Learning

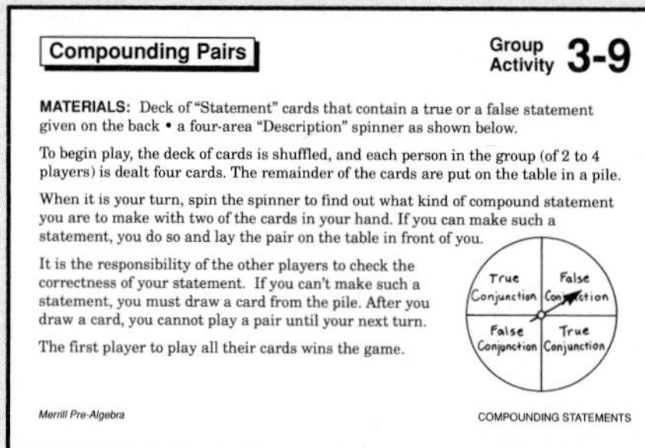

Compounding Pairs Group Activity **3-9**

MATERIALS: Deck of "Statement" cards that contain a true or a false statement given on the back • a four-area "Description" spinner as shown below.

To begin play, the deck of cards is shuffled, and each person in the group (of 2 to 4 players) is dealt four cards. The remainder of the cards are put on the table in a pile.

When it is your turn, spin the spinner to find out what kind of compound statement you are to make with two of the cards in your hand. If you can make such a statement, you do so and lay the pair on the table in front of you.

It is the responsibility of the other players to check the correctness of your statement. If you can't make such a statement, you must draw a card from the pile. After you draw a card, you cannot play a pair until your next turn.

The first player to play all their cards wins the game.

Merrill Pre-Algebra COMPOUNDING STATEMENTS

3-10 Using Equations and Inequalities

Objective:
Solve verbal problems by translating them into equations and inequalities.

Pedro rides his 10-speed bike for exercise. The last time he rode his bike he had trouble changing gears. Pedro took his bike to the Lewis Bike Shop to have it repaired. At the shop Pedro was told the total bill for labor and parts would be at least \$48. The cost of the parts was \$33. How much could Pedro expect to pay for labor?

In the first example below, the problem is solved using an inequality.

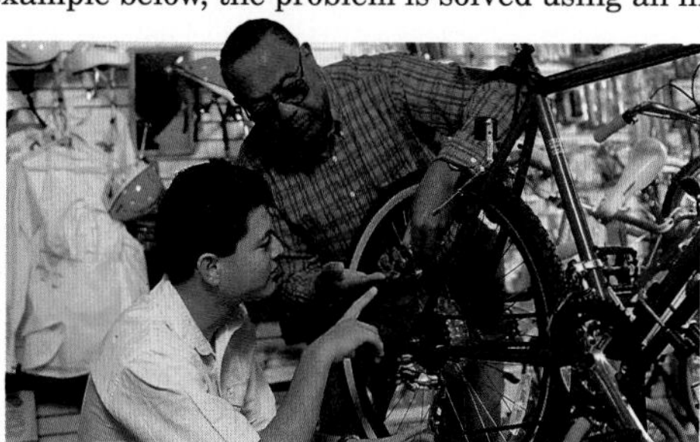

Example

1 Find the amount Pedro could expect to pay for labor.

Explore Skim the problem for the general idea. You need to find the expected cost of labor. Let c = cost of labor.

Select the important data.
- The total bill will be at least \$48.
- The cost for parts was \$33.

Since c is the cost of labor, the total cost of parts and labor is $33 + c$.

Plan *At least* \$48 means \$48 or more. That is, the total cost will be more than or equal to \$48.

Solve

Total cost	is greater than or equal to	\$48.
$33 + c$	$\geq$	48

$$33 - 33 + c \geq 48 - 33$$
$$c \geq 15$$

Pedro will pay \$15 or more for labor.

Examine Check the answer against your estimate. Then, check the answer in the words of the problem. \$33 plus \$15 is at least \$48.

Estimation Hint
THINK:
$50 - 30 = 20$
The answer should be close to \$20.

Bell Ringer
The compound statement below is false. State two ways to make it true.
Four is not a number and $11 \leq 11$.
Four is a number; change "and" to "or".

Lesson Notes 3-10

5-Minute Check
(over Lesson 3-9)

Determine whether each compound statement is true or false.
1. $5x + 2x = 9x$ and $-4 < 3$ **false**
2. $0 > 5$ and $-2 > 0$ **false**
3. $7 + (-3) > 6 + 5$ and $12 < 4 + 9$ **false**

Write each pair of inequalities as a compound inequality.

4. $m > 2$ and $m < 10$ **$2 < m < 10$**
5. $x > -3$ and $x \leq 5$ **$-3 < x \leq 5$**

Transparency 3-10 contains the 5-Minute Check and a teaching aid for this lesson.

1 FOCUS

The purpose of this lesson is to incorporate previously introduced problem-solving strategies into the solving of verbal problems that can be translated into equations or inequalities.

2 TEACH

Using Discussion

While working through the examples, emphasize key words in the problems that indicate correct operations and order symbols. You may want to have students make a list of the words and their corresponding signs or symbols.

Chalkboard Examples

- *For Example 1*
  Marta is graduating from college. Her parents reserved a dining room for 25 people for a reception after the ceremonies. The cost for the room is \$20. Each meal will cost at least \$8. What is the cost of the dinner going to be? **cost $\geq$ \$220**

EE: 1D, 1E, 3A, 3F
TAAS: 10, 12, 13

Chalkboard Examples

- *For Example 2*
  The largest fish caught at a local fishing contest was a 78-pound striped bass. This was 6 times the size of the smallest bass brought in that day. What was the size of the smallest bass? **13 pounds**

3 PRACTICE/APPLY

Checking the Concept

After students complete the Guided Practice exercises, have them compare and discuss their solutions with a partner. Circulate around the room listening to the explanations.

Error Analysis

Watch for students who have difficulty translating between word sentences and mathematical sentences.
Prevent by writing the word sentence on one line and the mathematical sentence directly under it.

Independent Practice

Homework Assignment	
Basic	9-17 odd, 18-22
Average	10-16 even, 18-22
Honors	13-22

Example

2 **The last-place runner in a 10-kilometer race took 88 minutes to finish the race. This was twice the winner's time. What was the first-place time?**

Explore You need to find the time of the first-place runner. You know the last runner took 88 minutes, twice the winner's time. Let t be the winner's time.

Plan Translate the words into an equation using the variable. *Twice* suggests multiplication.

How can you estimate the answer?
THINK: $80 = 2t$
The solution is greater than 40.

Solve

$$\underbrace{\text{Last-place time}}_{88}\ \underbrace{\text{is}}_{=}\ \underbrace{\text{twice the winning time.}}_{2t}$$

$$\frac{88}{2} = \frac{2t}{2}$$

$$44 = t$$

The first-place time was 44 minutes.

Examine Check the answer against your estimate and in the words of the problem. 88 is two times 44.

Checking for Understanding

Communicating Algebra **For each problem, answer the related questions.**

1. Jimmy wants to spend at most $25 for new baseball cards for his collection. He has selected a new card that costs $9. How much can he spend on other cards?
   a. What is asked? **the amount he can spend on other cards**
   b. What does the phrase *at most $25* mean? $x \le 25$
   c. Write an equation or inequality that describes the problem. **c. $9 + x \le 25$**
   d. Would you reverse the inequality symbol to solve this problem? **no**

2. A florist shop makes a profit of $5 on each special flower arrangement sold. How many of these arrangements must be sold in order to make a profit of at least $150?
   a. What is asked? **the number of arrangements that must be sold**
   b. What is the profit on one arrangement? **$5**
   c. What does the phrase *at least $150* mean? $x \ge 150$
   d. Write an equation or an inequality that describes the problem. $5x \ge 150$

Answers: 3. $x + 4 = 16$ 4. $5x = -85$ 5. $\frac{x}{7} = 49$ 6. $x - 7 = 12$ 7. $21x \le -84$ 8. $\frac{x}{-7} < 112$

Guided Practice **Define a variable and translate each situation into an equation or an inequality.**

3. A number increased by 4 is 16.
4. Five times some number equals -85.
5. The result of dividing a number by 7 is 49.
6. Seven dollars less than the cost of the compact disc is $12.
7. The product of 21 and a number is at most -84.
8. The quotient when dividing a number by -7 is less than 112.

Alternate Strategies: Reteaching the Lesson

Reteaching Activity

Using Lists List the symbols +, −, ×, ÷, <, >, and = on the chalkboard. Read through several word problems and pick out words or terms that have the same meaning as each listed symbol. List these words or terms under the symbol. Add other words or terms. Write problems using these terms.

Exercises

Independent Practice

Define a variable, write an equation or an inequality, and then solve.

9. Four times a number is greater than 76. What is the number? $4x > 76$; $x > 19$

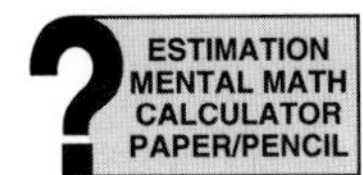

10. Janice has averaged 17 points per game as a forward for the Northern Potter High School girls varsity basketball team. She has scored 221 points this season. In how many games has she played? $17x = 221$; 13 games

11. The quotient of a number and 8 is greater than 72. Find the number. $\frac{x}{8} > 72$; $x > 576$

12. Room 308 at Darien High School sold more class play tickets than any other room, more than $1350 worth. If the tickets cost $3 each, how many tickets did Room 308 sell? $3x > 1350$; more than 450 tickets

13. Maria bought 3 pairs of jeans for $75. If each pair cost the same amount, how much did each pair cost? $3x = 75$; $25

14. Tracy works for a hotel taking reservations over the phone. She earns $6 per hour. Last week she made $72. How many hours did she work? $6x = 72$; 12 hours

15. Three friends went to dinner together to celebrate one of them getting a job promotion. The total of the check was less than $36. If the cost was shared evenly, how much did each person pay for dinner? $3x < 36$; $x < 12$

16. Marty saves $8 each week from money he earns from his paper route. How many weeks will he have to save before he can buy a camera that sells for $192? $8x = 192$; 24 weeks

17. Girl Scouts who sell at least 75 boxes of cookies earn a sweatshirt. Matilda needs to sell 17 more boxes to qualify for the sweatshirt. Each box costs $2. How many boxes has she sold so far? $x + 17 = 75$; 58 boxes

Mixed Review

18. Solve the inequality $\frac{f}{3} \geq -9$. (Lesson 3-8) $f \geq -27$

19. Write the inequalities $s > -4$ and $s < -2$ as a compound inequality. (Lesson 3-9) $-4 < s < -2$

Decision Making

20. Carlos needs to buy at least seven pairs of socks to use the week he goes to basketball camp. The socks he wants are sold separately for $2 a pair or in packages of three pair for $5. List all of the different combinations of packages that Carlos could buy. In what combination should Carlos buy the socks? Explain your answer. See margin.

Critical Thinking

21. In the figures at the right, the area of rectangle C is 6 times the area of rectangle A. If the difference between the areas of rectangle B and rectangle A is 12 square units, what is the area of rectangle C? 216 square inches

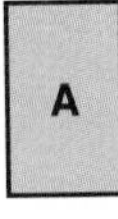

B
48 square inches

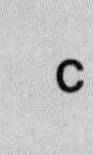

Wrap-Up

22. **Make Up a Problem** Write a problem using the following information: Let w = Noel's weight in pounds. Use the equation $w - 4 = 139$.
Sample answer: Noel recently lost 4 pounds. His weight now is 139 pounds. What was his weight before?

4 CLOSE

Assessment Option

Speaking Have students read each equation or inequality and then state the first step in solving it.

1. $10x \leq 100$ divide each side by 10
2. $-m > 12$ multiply each side by -1
3. $-k + 21 = 36$ add -21 to each side
4. $12 = 10 + n$ subtract 10 from each side

Chapter 3, Quiz B (Lessons 3-6 through 3-10) is available in the Evaluation Masters Booklet, p. 25.

Additional Answer

20. seven single pairs; one package and four single pairs; two packages and one single pair; three packages; If Carlos buys two packages and one single pair it would satisfy his needs for the least amount of money ($12).

Practice Masters Booklet, **p. 29**

Name ______________ Date ______________

Practice Worksheet 3-10

Problem Solving: Using Equations and Inequalities

Define a variable, write an equation or inequality, and then solve.

1. The sum of 39 and some number is 103. What is the number? Let n be the number. $39 + n = 103$; $n = 64$ The number is 64.
2. An unknown number less 7 is 19. What is the number? Let n be the number. $n - 7 = 19$; $n = 26$ The number is 26.
3. Six times a number is −84. What is the number? Let n be the number. $6n = -84$; $n = -14$ The number is −14.
4. Some number divided by −8 is equal to −15. What is the number? Let n be the number. $\frac{n}{-8} = -15$; $n = 120$ The number is 120.
5. The product of a number and 6 is less than 36. Find the number. Let n be the number. $6n < 36$; $n < 6$ Any number less than 6.
6. A store makes a profit of $25 on each moon watch it sells. How many of these must it sell to make a profit of at least $275? Let w be the number of watches. $25w \geq 275$; $w \geq 11$ They must sell at least 11 moon watches.
7. Kim bought a new fishing pole. It was on sale for $35. She saved $8. What was the original price? Let p be the original price. $p - 8 = 35$; $p = 43$ The original price was $43.
8. Leif's score on his second test was 87. This was 14 points more than his score on the first test. What was his score on the first test? Let s be Leif's score on the first test. $s + 14 = 87$; $s = 73$ Leif's score on the first test was 73.
9. Carol sold 20 shares of stock for a total of $2980. What was the value of one share? Let v be the value of one share. $20v = 2980$; $v = 149$ The value of one share was $149.
10. Jake worked a total of 38 hours last week. His earnings for the week were more than $228. What is his hourly rate of pay? Let r be his hourly rate. $38r > 228$; $r > 6$ His hourly rate of pay is more than $6.
11. The sum of two integers is at most −57. One integer is 33. What is the other integer? Let z be the other integer. $z + 33 \leq -57$; $z \leq -90$ Any integer less than or equal to −90.
12. The difference between two integers is at least 12. The smaller integer is 2. What is the larger integer? Let z be the larger integer. $z - 2 \geq 12$; $z \geq 14$ Any integer greater than or equal to 14.

Alternate Strategies: Extending the Lesson

Enrichment

Using Writing Have students write problems of their own involving equations and inequalities. Encourage students to use the names and interests of the students in the class. Trade problems and solve.

Cooperative Learning

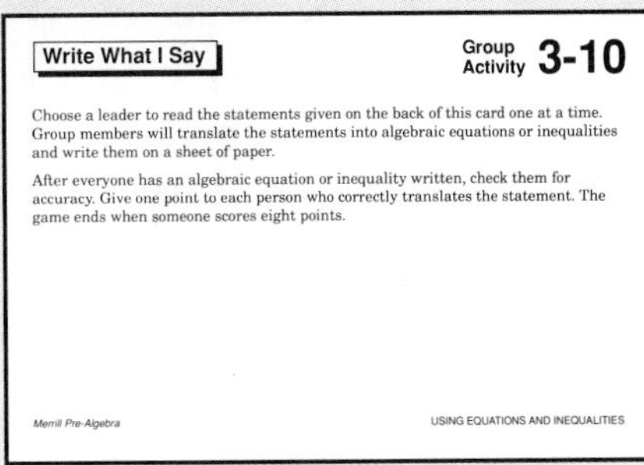

Write What I Say Group Activity **3-10**

Choose a leader to read the statements given on the back of this card one at a time. Group members will translate the statements into algebraic equations or inequalities and write them on a sheet of paper.

After everyone has an algebraic equation or inequality written, check them for accuracy. Give one point to each person who correctly translates the statement. The game ends when someone scores eight points.

Merrill Pre-Algebra USING EQUATIONS AND INEQUALITIES

Using the Chapter Review

The Chapter Review is a comprehensive review of the concepts presented in this chapter. This review may be used to prepare students for the Chapter Test.

Alternate Review Strategy

To provide a brief in-class review, you may wish to read the following questions to the class and require a verbal response.

1. Explain how to solve $x + 9 = 30$. **subtract 9 from each side**
2. Explain how to solve $m - 5 = 15$. **add 5 to each side**
3. Explain how to solve $42 = 6x$. **divide each side by 6**
4. Explain how to solve $\frac{r}{8} = 9$. **multiply each side by 8**
5. What formula could you use to solve this situation? *The eighth grade class is going on a field trip to Washington, D.C. They will travel 330 miles. If the bus travels at an average rate of 55 miles per hour, what will the driving time be?* **$d = rt$**
6. Find the perimeter and area of a rectangle that is 6 meters long and 5 meters wide. **22 m, 30 m^2**
7. Explain how to solve $t - 7 > 9$. **add 7 to each side**
8. When is the order symbol in an inequality reversed? **when you multiply or divide each side of the inequality by a negative integer**
9. When is a conjunction true? When is a disjunction true? **conjunction: when both statements are true; disjunction: when at least one statement is true**
10. Translate the following sentence into an inequality and solve. *Twice a number is at least 16.* **$2n \geq 16$, $n \geq 8$**

Review

Language and Concepts

Choose the letter that best matches each phrase.

1. a mathematical sentence that shows the relationship between certain quantities **h**
2. *x is less than or equal to 2* written as a mathematical sentence **g**
3. an example of an equation **d**
4. a measure of the space enclosed by a rectangle **k**
5. the number added to each side of the equation $n - 42 = 9$ to solve it **b**
6. the number you would multiply each side of the equation $\frac{y}{-42} = 9$ by to solve it **c**
7. the distance around a rectangle **j**

a. 9
b. 42
c. -42
d. x + 3 = 10
e. x + 3
f. x ≥ 2
g. x ≤ 2
h. formula
i. variable
j. perimeter
k. area

Skills

Solve each equation. Check your solution. (Lessons 3-1, 3-2, 3-3, 3-4)

8. $x + 28 = 42$ **14**
9. $-7 = -12 + g$ **5**
10. $72 = p + (-56)$ **128**
11. $k - 2 = -6$ **-4**
12. $a - 5 = 4$ **9**
13. $r - (-7) = -19$ **-26**
14. $-156 = -12f$ **13**
15. $180 = -15y$ **-12**
16. $9k = -117$ **-13**
17. $\frac{x}{11} = 10$ **110**
18. $\frac{m}{25} = -4$ **-100**
19. $-18 = \frac{r}{-16}$ **288**

Solve. Use the formula $d = rt$. (Lesson 3-5)

20. Find d if $r = 40$ mph and $t = 9$ h. **360 miles**
21. Find r if $d = 15$ miles and $t = 5$ h. **3 mph**
22. Find t if $d = 144$ miles and $r = 48$ mph. **3 h**

Find the perimeter of each rectangle. (Lesson 3-6)

23.
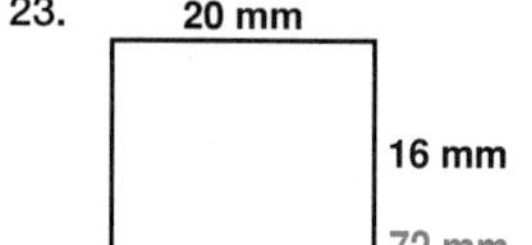

24.
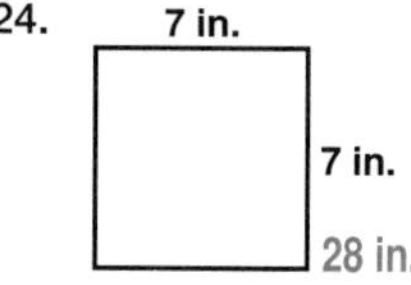

25.
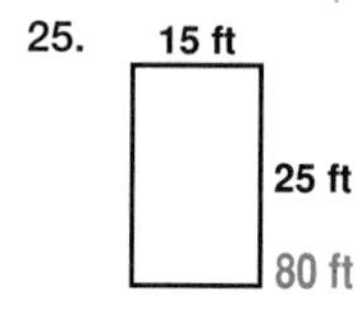

Find the area of each rectangle. (Lesson 3-6)

26.
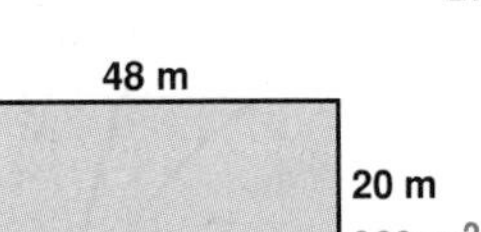

27.
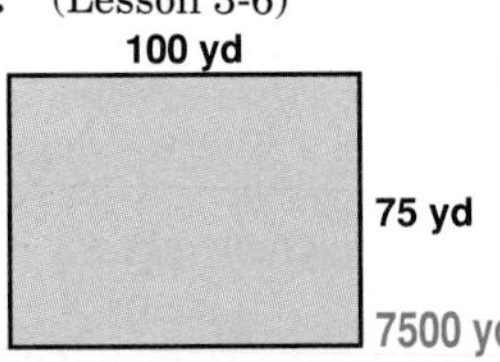

28.
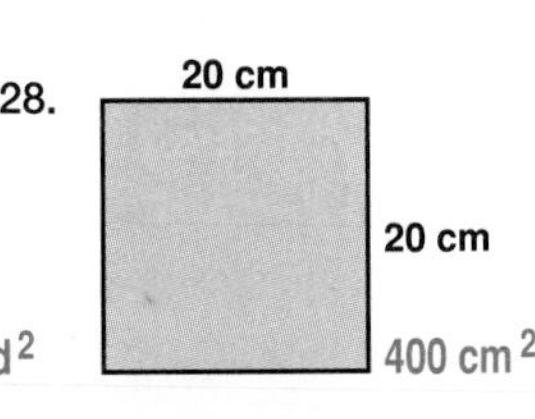

Solve each inequality. (Lessons 3-7, 3-8)

29. $a - 4 > -2$ $a > 2$
30. $-18 \leq x - 10$ $x \geq -8$
31. $56 > m + 16$ $m < 40$
32. $b + 33 < -2$ $b < -35$
33. $-5c > 30$ $c < -6$
34. $\frac{x}{-11} \geq 8$ $x \leq -88$
35. $-14 < \frac{d}{-6}$ $d < 84$
36. $3y \leq -123$ $y \leq -41$
37. $\frac{-k}{4} \leq -21$ $k \geq 84$

Applications and Logic

Determine whether each compound statement is *true* or *false*. (Lesson 3-9)

38. A heptagon has 6 sides or $2 + 3 = 5$. T
39. A square has four equal sides and $10 - 4 > 6$. F
40. $7 > 7$ and $6 > 4$ F
41. $0 > -4$ or $2 \leq -2$ T

Define a variable, write an equation or an inequality, and then solve. (Lesson 3-10)

42. Alberto buys 2 dozen eggs. After making omelets he has 9 eggs left. How many eggs did he use in the omelets? $x + 9 = 24$; 15 eggs
43. Sally earns $5 for mowing the lawn and $4 for weeding the garden. How many times must she mow the lawn to earn $60? $5x = 60$; 12 times
44. A number increased by 13 is at least -39. What is the number? $x + 13 \geq -39$; $x \geq -52$
45. Five friends share the cost of a lunch equally. Each person pays $4. What is the total of the lunch? $\frac{x}{5} = 4$; $20

Communicating Algebra

Write a sentence that explains the difference between an equation and an inequality. In an equation the two sides are equal; in an inequality, one side is greater than the other.

Curriculum Connection

- **Health** Research the chemical formulas for vitamins. Include a description of how the body uses each vitamin and natural sources of each vitamin. See students' work.
- **Science** Write a brief paragraph about Isaac Newton's contributions to science. See students' work.

Read More About It

Bitter, Gary G. *Exploring with Pocket Calculators.*

Burns, Marilyn. *Math for Smarty Pants.*

Ross, Frank X. *The Metric System — Measures for all Mankind.*

You may wish to use a Chapter Test (free-response format) as an additional chapter review. Two forms are provided in the Evaluation Masters Booklet as shown below.

Evaluation Masters Booklet, **p. 23**

Name ________ Date ________

Chapter 3 Test, Form 2A

Solve each equation.

1. $a + (-18) = -42$
2. $b + 6 = -24$
3. $c - 12 = 31$
4. $d - (-18) = -27$
5. $e - 18 = -16$
6. $5f = -35$
7. $-7g = -56$
8. $-11h = 66$
9. $\frac{k}{4} = -16$
10. $\frac{m}{-82} = -24$

Use each formula to find the value of M.

11. $M = a - b$, if $a = 245$ and $b = 71$
12. $M = cd$, if $c = 14$ and $d = 12$
13. $M = ef - g$, if $e = 3, f = 9$, and $g = 38$

Solve each problem.

14. Find the perimeter of a square with sides 12 inches long.
15. Find the area of a rectangle with a length of 14 cm and a width of 20 cm.

Solve each inequality.

16. $x + 8 < 16$
17. $y - 12 \geq 15$
18. $-12y < -108$
19. $-5z \geq 50$

Solve each problem.

20. Is $-7 \leq y \leq 7$ true or false if $y = 7$?
21. Is the disjunction $4 < 1$ or $8 > 3$ true or false?
22. Is the conjunction $6 \leq 4 + 2$ and $9 > 7$ true or false?
23. Ron and Ed spent at least $75 buying music. Ron spent $28. Find the smallest amount Ed must have spent.
24. Fred needs at least 86 points to tie Ellen's score. Ellen has 631 points. How many points does Fred have?
25. Dave has at least 38 oranges. How many bags can he completely fill if a full bag contains 6 oranges?

BONUS If $(2 \leq 8 - 6)$ and $(6 > 3$ or $4 < 7)$, then fish can whistle. Based upon this example, can fish whistle?

1. −24
2. −30
3. 43
4. −45
5. 2
6. −7
7. 8
8. −6
9. −64
10. 1968
11. 174
12. 168
13. −11
14. 48 in.
15. 280 cm^2
16. $x < 8$
17. $y \geq 27$
18. $y > 9$
19. $z \leq -10$
20. true
21. true
22. true
23. $47
24. 545
25. 6

yes

Evaluation Masters Booklet, **p. 24**

Name ________ Date ________

Chapter 3 Test, Form 2B

Solve each equation.

1. $a + (-12) = -45$
2. $b + 8 = -31$
3. $c - 15 = 42$
4. $d - (-16) = -37$
5. $e - 14 = -12$
6. $6f = -36$
7. $-7g = -63$
8. $-13h = 78$
9. $\frac{k}{5} = -16$
10. $\frac{m}{-62} = -35$

Use each formula to find the value of M.

11. $M = a - b$, if $a = 245$ and $b = 93$
12. $M = cd$, if $c = 14$ and $d = 16$
13. $M = ef - g$, if $e = 5, f = 8$, and $g = 38$

Solve each problem.

14. Find the perimeter of a square with sides 16 inches long.
15. Find the area of a rectangle with a length of 12 cm and a width of 30 cm.

Solve each inequality.

16. $x + 4 \leq 16$
17. $y - 12 > 28$
18. $-14y \leq -210$
19. $-4z > 36$

Solve each problem.

20. Is $-3 \leq y \leq 3$ true or false if $y = -3$?
21. Is the disjunction $2 < 1$ or $9 > 5$ true or false?
22. Is the conjunction $6 > 4 + 2$ and $8 > 7$ true or false?
23. Don and Brian spent at least $95 buying music. Don spent $18. Find the smallest amount Brian must have spent.
24. Marc needs at least 36 points to tie Roger's score. Roger has 520 points. How many points does Marc have?
25. Dave has at least 68 apples. How many bags can he completely fill if a full bag contains 9 apples?

BONUS If $(3 \leq 9 - 6)$ and $(6 > 8$ or $4 < 3)$, then pigs can fly. Based upon this example, can pigs fly?

1. −33
2. −39
3. 57
4. −53
5. 2
6. −6
7. 9
8. −6
9. −80
10. 2170
11. 152
12. 224
13. 2
14. 64 in.
15. 360 cm^2
16. $x \leq 12$
17. $y > 40$
18. $y \geq 15$
19. $z < -9$
20. true
21. true
22. false
23. $77
24. 484
25. 7

no

Using the Chapter Test

This page may be used as a test or as an additional review. Two forms of a Chapter Test (multiple-choice format) are provided in the Evaluation Masters Booklet.

Evaluation Masters Booklet, **pp. 19-20**

Name ______________________ Date ______________

Chapter 3 Test, Form 1A

Solve each equation.

1. $p + (-12) = -14$ A. 26 B. 2 C. −2 D. −26 — 1. C
2. $x + 7 = -15$ A. −22 B. 22 C. −8 D. 8 — 2. A
3. $k - 15 = 26$ A. 11 B. −11 C. −41 D. 41 — 3. D
4. $w - (-15) = -12$ A. 3 B. −3 C. −27 D. 27 — 4. C
5. $x - 26 = -32$ A. 6 B. −6 C. −58 D. 58 — 5. B
6. $4y = -12$ A. −3 B. 3 C. −16 D. −8 — 6. A
7. $-8m = -24$ A. −16 B. −3 C. 3 D. −32 — 7. C
8. $-12x = 36$ A. −48 B. −3 C. 3 D. −24 — 8. B
9. $\frac{m}{-3} = 24$ A. 8 B. −8 C. 72 D. −72 — 9. D
10. $\frac{a}{-6} = -12$ A. 18 B. −18 C. 72 D. −72 — 10. C

Use each formula to find the value of B.

11. $B = t - n$, if $t = 378$ and $n = 63$ A. 305 B. 315 C. 441 D. 6 — 11. B
12. $B = ac$, if $a = 8$ and $c = 16$ A. 2 B. 24 C. 128 D. 8 — 12. C
13. $B = de - f$, if $d = 10$, $e = 8$, and $f = 6$ A. 74 B. 20 C. 12 D. 102 — 13. A

Solve.

14. Find the perimeter of a square whose side measures 12 m. A. 16 m B. 12 m C. 144 m D. 48 m — 14. D

Name ______________________ Date ______________

Chapter 3 Test, Form 1A (continued)

15. Find the area of a rectangle if the length is 14 cm and the width is 12 cm. A. 52 cm^2 B. 168 cm^2 C. 26 cm^2 D. 158 cm^2 — 15. B

Solve each inequality.

16. $x + 4 < 12$ A. $x < 8$ B. $x < 16$ C. $x > 8$ D. $x > 16$ — 16. A
17. $y - 3 > -16$ A. $y < -13$ B. $y > -19$ C. $y < -19$ D. $y > -13$ — 17. D
18. $6x > -12$ A. $x > -2$ B. $x > 2$ C. $x > -6$ D. $x > -18$ — 18. A
19. $-5y < -105$ A. $y < 21$ B. $y > 21$ C. $y > -21$ D. $y > -21$ — 19. B

Choose the word which best describes the compound statement.

20. $-12 < x < -8$, if $x = -9$ A. true B. false C. open D. disjunction — 20. A
21. $8 < 3$ or $9 > 3$ A. true B. false C. open D. conjunction — 21. A

Solve.

22. Mary and Sue spent more than $230 while shopping. Mary spent $138. What amount did Sue spend? A. $s > 108$ B. $s < 92$ C. $s = 92$ D. $s > 92$ — 22. D
23. Don has more than 5 times as many baseball cards as Frank has. Frank has 36 cards. How many cards does Don have? A. $d < 180$ B. $d = 180$ C. $d > 180$ D. $d < 181$ — 23. C
24. Carlo plans to put a fence around his garden which measures 40 feet long and 18 feet wide. How many feet of fencing does he need? A. 98 B. 116 C. 720 D. 58 — 24. B
25. Suzette buys a square piece of stained glass measuring 30 inches on a side. Find the area of the glass. A. 90 in^2 B. 60 in^2 C. 900 in^2 D. 120 in^2 — 25. C

BONUS Which is a solution of $45 \le x < 47$? A. 42 B. 45 C. 47 D. 48 — B

Test

Solve each equation. Check your solution.

1. $11 + m = 19$ **8**
2. $-15 + z = 3$ **18**
3. $8 = 15 + b$ **-7**
4. $x + 32 = 58$ **26**
5. $-9 = -12 + h$ **3**
6. $95 = p + (-38)$ **133**
7. $k - 5 = -8$ **-3**
8. $a - 6 = 5$ **11**
9. $r - (-4) = -19$ **-23**
10. $34 = w - 55$ **89**
11. $-13 = z - 21$ **8**
12. $94 = t - (-76)$ **18**
13. $-8y = 72$ **-9**
14. $84x = 252$ **3**
15. $-12y = -84$ **7**
16. $-180 = -12d$ **15**
17. $165 = -15a$ **-11**
18. $9r = -144$ **-16**
19. $\frac{w}{15} = 10$ **150**
20. $\frac{n}{30} = -6$ **-180**
21. $-14 = \frac{r}{-18}$ **252**

Solve. Use the formula $d = rt$.

22. Find r if $t = 3$ hours and $d = 114$ miles. **38 mph**
23. Find t if $d = 177$ kilometers and $r = 59$ kilometers/hour. **3 hours**

Find the area and perimeter of each rectangle described below.

24. length, 8 ft; width, 9 ft **72 square feet; 34 feet**
25. length, 30 in.; width, 17 in. **510 square inches; 94 inches**

Solve each inequality. Check your solution.

26. $11 \le r + 28$ **$-17 \le r$**
27. $z - 25 > -30$ **$z > -5$**
28. $-7s \le 63$ **$s \ge -9$**
29. $7 > \frac{x}{-8}$ **$-56 < x$**

Determine whether each compound statement is *true* or *false*.

30. $6 > 0$ and $-6 < 0$ **T**
31. $2 = 0$ or $-2 > 3$ **F**

Define a variable, write an equation or an inequality, then solve.

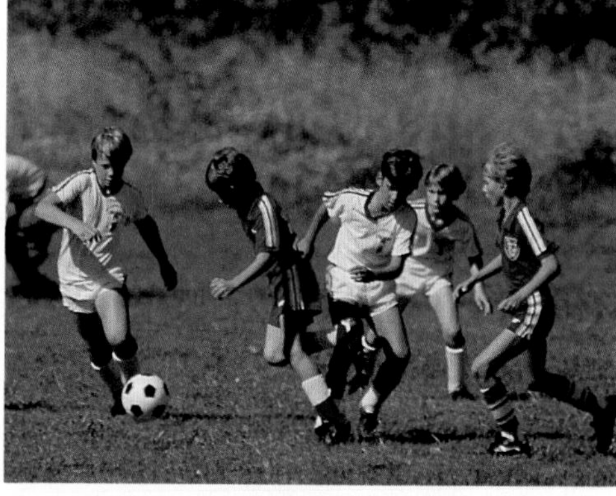

32. The YMCA had registration for a summer soccer league. The number of players was divided by 12 to form 11 teams. How many players signed up? **$\frac{x}{12} = 11$; 132 players**
33. Allie and her father spent at least $110 while shopping. Allie spent $47. How much did her father spend? **$x + 47 \ge 110$; $x \ge 63$**

BONUS

The length of a rectangular picture frame is 3 inches longer than twice its width. The perimeter is 78 inches. Make a labeled drawing of the picture frame and find its dimensions. **See margin.**

Additional Answer

Bonus

length: 25 in.
width: 11 in.

Test Generator Software is provided in both Apple and IBM formats. You may use this software to create your own tests, based on the needs of your students.

Cooperative Learning

The following activity is provided in the **Activity Masters Booklet.**

Cooperative Problem Solving, p. 34

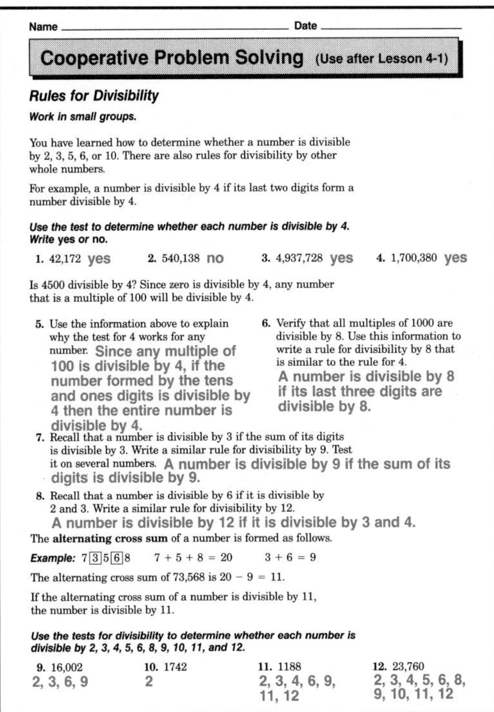

Name ______________________ Date ______________

Cooperative Problem Solving (Use after Lesson 4-1)

Rules for Divisibility

Work in small groups.

You have learned how to determine whether a number is divisible by 2, 3, 5, 6, or 10. There are also rules for divisibility by other whole numbers.

For example, a number is divisible by 4 if its last two digits form a number divisible by 4.

Use the test to determine whether each number is divisible by 4. Write yes or no.

1. 42,172 yes 2. 540,138 no 3. 4,937,728 yes 4. 1,700,380 yes

Is 4500 divisible by 4? Since zero is divisible by 4, any number that is a multiple of 100 will be divisible by 4.

5. Use the information above to explain why the test for 4 works for any number. Since any multiple of 100 is divisible by 4, if the number formed by the tens and ones digits is divisible by 4 then the entire number is divisible by 4.
6. Verify that all multiples of 1000 are divisible by 8. Use this information to write a rule for divisibility by 8 that is similar to the rule for 4. A number is divisible by 8 if its last three digits are divisible by 8.
7. Recall that a number is divisible by 3 if the sum of its digits is divisible by 3. Write a similar rule for divisibility by 9. Test it on several numbers. A number is divisible by 9 if the sum of its digits is divisible by 9.
8. Recall that a number is divisible by 6 if it is divisible by 2 and 3. Write a similar rule for divisibility by 12. A number is divisible by 12 if it is divisible by 3 and 4.

The **alternating cross sum** of a number is formed as follows.

Example: 7[3]5[6]8 7 + 5 + 8 = 20 3 + 6 = 9

The alternating cross sum of 73,568 is 20 − 9 = 11.

If the alternating cross sum of a number is divisible by 11, the number is divisible by 11.

Use the tests for divisibility to determine whether each number is divisible by 2, 3, 4, 5, 6, 8, 9, 10, 11, and 12.

9. 16,002 — 2, 3, 6, 9
10. 1742 — 2
11. 1188 — 2, 3, 4, 6, 9, 11, 12
12. 23,760 — 2, 3, 4, 5, 6, 8, 9, 10, 11, 12

Cooperative Problem Solving

Have students work in groups of two to solve the following problem: In a large apartment building, Joe lives 8 floors above Jane, Shawndra lives 12 floors above Sean, and Jane lives 6 floors above Sean. What is the minimum number of floors in this building? (Answer: 15 floors)

Each group will be responsible for the solution, written explanation of their solution, and diagram to show the solution. Note: This is a simple problem if students draw a diagram.

Interactive Bulletin Board

Physics Connection

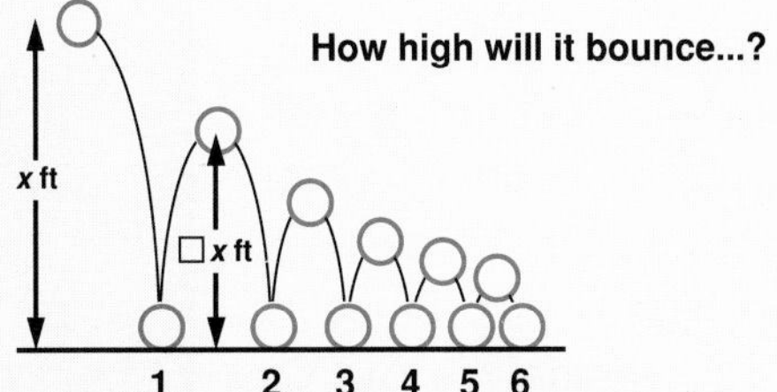

A Ball is dropped from △ feet above the ground. After it hits the ground, it bounces to □ of its original height. If each subsequent bounce is □ of the height of the last bounce, how far has the ball travelled when it hits the ground the ⓝ time.

Distance travelled $= x + 2\square x + 2\square(\square x)$ (1st bounce, 2nd bounce)

$+ 2\square(\square(\square x)) + \text{etc.}$ (3rd bounce)

$= x + 2\square x + 2\square^2 x + 2\square^3 x + m$

Purpose Provide practice in using a diagram to solve the problem.

How to Use It Use laminated paper and wipe-off markers. Use one basic problem and change the number associated with the problem on a daily basis or have the students create their own problem. Show the pattern involved in solving the problem. Have students work in groups of two or three. Sample problem: A ball is dropped from ____ feet above the ground. After it hits the ground, it bounces to ____ of its original height. If each subsequent bounce is ____ of the height of the last bounce, how far has the ball travelled when it hits the ground the ____ time?

Outside Resources

Books/Periodicals
Getting Started in Problem Solving and Math Contests, Franklin Watts

Films/Videotapes
The Weird Number, Xerox Films

Software
Fraction Practice Unlimited, MECC

Technology

There are three pages in the ***Technology Masters Booklet*** that involve technology with concepts in this chapter. One page involves calculators and one page has a problem that can be solved using the BASIC program that is provided. Students should evaluate the information they obtain from running the program and solve a similar problem by extending the program.

Using the Chapter Opener

Transparency 4-0 is available in the Transparency Package. It provides a full-color visual and motivational activity that you can use to engage students in the mathematical content of the chapter.

Using Models

If an electronic keyboard is available, have students experiment to find note combinations that are harmonious. You may suggest using combinations of notes with small, whole-number ratios such as C and A ($\frac{3}{5}$ for middle C, $\frac{5}{6}$ for high C), D and G ($\frac{3}{4}$), E and A ($\frac{3}{4}$), and E and high C ($\frac{5}{8}$). Students may also discover that the two Cs have a ratio of $\frac{1}{2}$. Students may mention that there are several harmonious combinations, such as C and F, that do not have small-number ratios. Emphasize that harmonious combinations may or may not have such ratios, but combinations that do not blend definitely do not have small-number ratios.

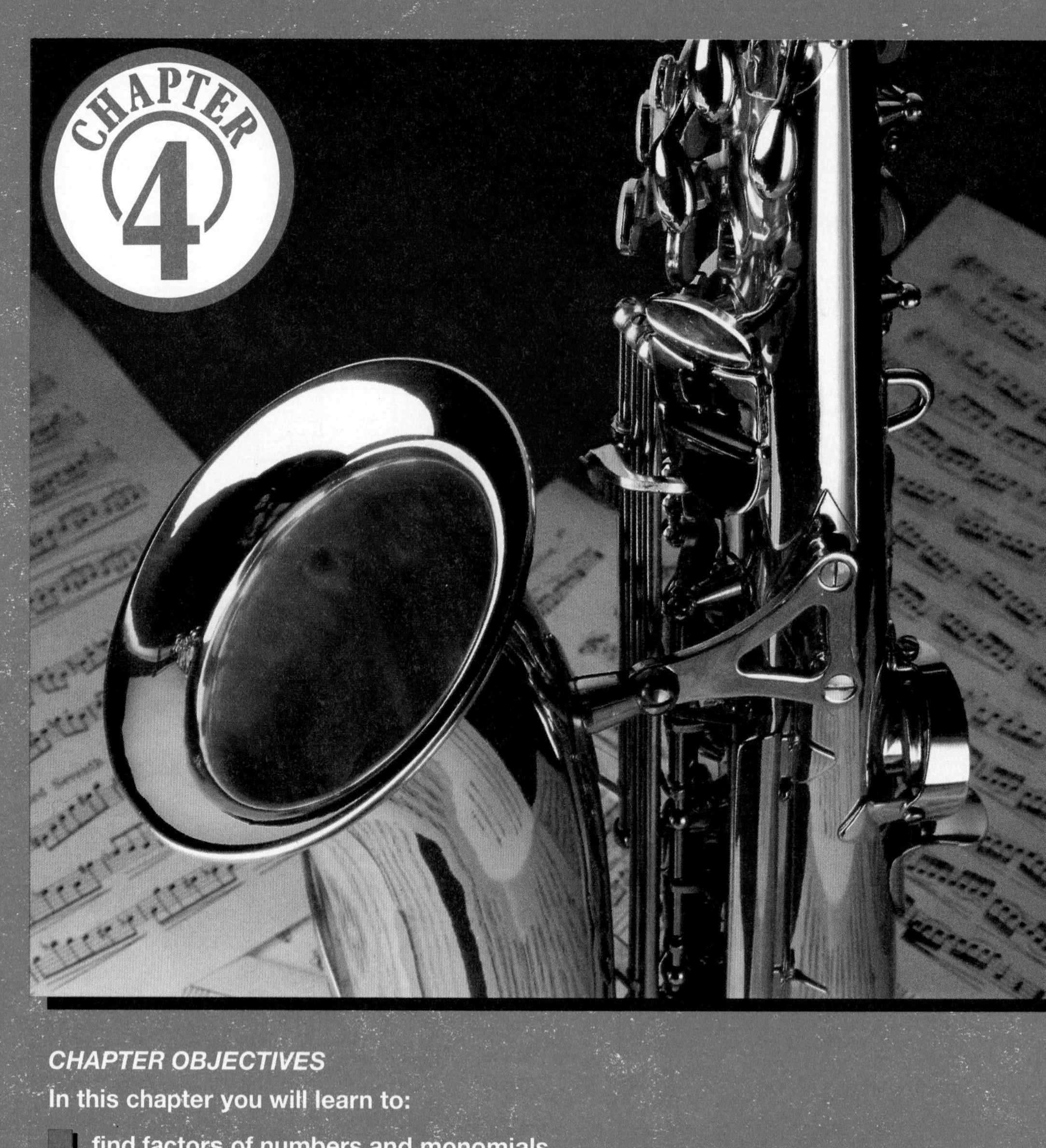

CHAPTER OBJECTIVES

In this chapter you will learn to:

- find factors of numbers and monomials
- use prime factorization to find the GCF and LCM
- use the LCM to write equivalent fractions
- multiply and divide powers
- solve problems by drawing a diagram

Factors and Fractions

You probably think of music as being sounds or notes. But did you know that music can also be represented mathematically?

Take two notes commonly played together: C and E. We find these two notes harmonious. That's because each note vibrates at a frequency that harmonizes with the other. Even if you can't tell harmony from noise, you can figure whether the frequencies can be expressed as a simple fraction made up of small whole numbers or not. If the fraction can be simplified into something like $\frac{8}{5}$ or $\frac{2}{3}$, you have harmony. If you end up with a fraction like $\frac{247}{264}$, then you have noise.

From the chart below you can see that C is to E as 264 is to 330. In simplest form $\frac{264}{330}$ is equal to $\frac{4}{5}$.

Can you find other harmonious combinations of notes?

Music Connection

Class Project

A famous sequence of numbers is the Fibonacci sequence, 1, 1, 2, 3, 5, 8, ... The sequence begins with 1 and each number that follows is the sum of the previous two numbers. Find examples of Fibonacci numbers in music.

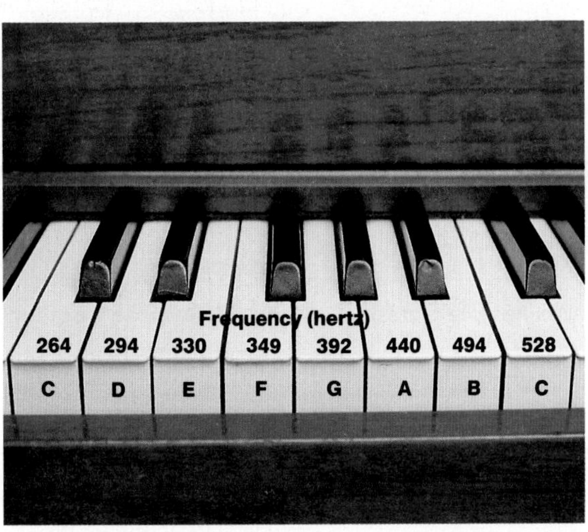

Music Connection

Have students continue the Fibonacci sequence to find several more numbers and use these for future reference. Then have students list examples of these numbers found in music. Examples from the octave of piano keys pictured might include 5 black keys in sets of 2 and 3 keys, 13 total keys, and 8 white keys. Fibonacci numbers are also used in some of the small-number ratios of harmonious note combinations.

Looking Ahead

You may want to have the following materials available to use in this chapter.

Exploration, p. 139
computers

5-Minute Check
(over Chapter 3)

Solve each inequality. Check your solution.

1. $x + (-6) > 4$ $x > 10$
2. $-21 < m - (-3)$ $-24 < m$
3. $\frac{r}{-4} > 15$ $r < -60$
4. $-8y \leq -32$ $y \geq 4$
5. $\frac{c}{6} \leq -2$ $c \leq -12$

Transparency 4-1 contains the 5-Minute Check and a teaching aid for this lesson.

1 FOCUS

The purpose of this lesson is to identify factors using division.

Motivating the Lesson

Place 30 counters on the overhead. Ask students if it is possible to distribute them to 3 students without having any left over. **yes** Then ask for other numbers of students that you can distribute an equal amount and not have any left over. **1, 2, 5, 6, 10, 15, 30**

2 TEACH

Chalkboard Examples

- *For Example 1*
  Determine whether 7 is a factor of 112. **112 ÷ 7 = 16, yes**
- *For Example 2*
  Determine whether 225 is divisible by 2, 3, 5, 6, or 10. **3, 5**

Determine whether each expression is a monomial.

- *For Example 3* $3x + 5$ **no**
- *For Example 4* $6xy$ **yes**

EE: 1E, 2B, 3A

4-1 Factors and Monomials

Objective:
Determine whether one number is a factor of another.

Key Terms:
factor
monomial
divisible

The Beechcroft Junior High School Marching Band has 78 members. Can they be arranged in six equal rows to march in the Holiday Parade?

This is another way of asking if 6 is a **factor** of 78. You can divide to find factors. The factors of a whole number divide that number with a remainder of 0.

Example

What are the other factors of 78?
1, 2, 3, 13, 26, 39, 78

1 Determine whether 6 is a factor of 78.

78 [÷] 6 [=] 13

Since the quotient is a whole number, 6 is a factor of 78. You can also say that 78 is **divisible** by 6. Therefore, the band can march in 6 equal rows.

Sometimes you can test for divisibility mentally. The following rules will help you determine whether a number is divisible by 2, 3, 5, 6, or 10.

A number is divisible by:
- 2 if the ones digit is divisible by 2.
- 3 if the sum of its digits is divisible by 3.
- 5 if the ones digit is 0 or 5.
- 6 if the number is divisible by 2 *and* 3.
- 10 if the ones digit is 0.

Example

What are the factors of 135?
1, 3, 5, 9, 15, 27, 45, 135

2 Determine whether 135 is divisible by 2, 3, 5, 6, or 10.

- The ones digit is *not* divisible by 2, so 135 is *not* divisible by 2.
- The sum of the digits, $1 + 3 + 5 = 9$, is divisible by 3, so 135 is divisible by 3.
- The ones digit is 5, so 135 is divisible by 5.
- The number is divisible by 3 but *not* by 2, so 135 is *not* divisible by 6.
- The ones digit is *not* 0, so 135 is *not* divisible by 10.

Therefore, 135 is divisible by 3 and 5, but not 2, 6, or 10.

Bell Ringer

Have students play a game like "Hangman" using terms from the previous chapter

CONNECTION TO ALGEBRA

You know that 6 and 13 are factors of 78 because $6 \cdot 13 = 78$. Consider the algebraic expression $3x$. Since this notation means $3 \cdot x$, it follows that 3 and x are factors of $3x$.

What makes $2x + 3$ and $m - 6$ different from the monomials listed? **They have 2 terms.**

An expression such as $3x$ is called a **monomial.** A monomial is an integer, a variable, or a product of integers or variables. Other examples of monomials are y, 15, ab, and $4mk$. Expressions like $2x + 3$ and $m - 6$ are not monomials.

Examples

Determine whether each expression is a monomial.

3 $2(\ell + w)$

This expression is not a monomial because it involves addition.

4 $-12abc$

This expression is a monomial because it is the product of integers and variables.

Checking for Understanding

Communicating Algebra

1. In your own words, explain why 7 is a factor of 63. **7 divides 63 evenly.**
2. Is 8 a factor of 68? Explain why or why not. **No; 8 does not divide 68 evenly.**
3. Discuss why 1 is a factor of every number. **because $1 \cdot n = n$**
4. Can 0 be a factor of any number? **No; $0 \cdot n \neq n$.**

Guided Practice

Determine whether each expression is a monomial. Explain why or why not.

5. $5m$ **yes**
6. $2x + 1$ **no; has an addition**
7. $-6xy$ **yes**
8. -175 **yes**

Using divisibility rules, state whether each number is divisible by 2, 3, 5, 6, or 10.

9. 38 **2**
10. 117 **3**
11. 576 **2, 3, 6**
12. 1630 **2, 5, 10**

Exercises

Independent Practice

Use divisibility rules to determine if the first number is divisible by the second number.

13. 1075; 5 **yes**
14. 999; 3 **yes**
15. 285; 6 **no**
16. 705; 10 **no**
17. 117; 3 **yes**
18. 11,112; 2 **yes**
19. 3241; 3 **no**
20. 1002; 6 **yes**

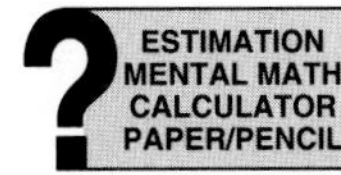

Use mental math skills, paper and pencil, or a calculator to find a number that satisfies the given conditions. **Sample answers given.**

21. a four-digit number divisible by 3 **3891**
22. a five-digit number divisible by both 2 and 5 **87,240**
23. a three-digit number *not* divisible by 6 **183**
24. a three-digit number divisible by 2 but *not* 4 **410**
25. a three-digit number divisible by 2, 3, and 5. **120**
26. a three-digit number *not* divisible by 2, 3, or 5 **821**

3 PRACTICE/APPLY

Checking the Concept

After solving Exercises 9-12 in the Guided Practice, have each student write down his or her house number or the last four digits of his or her phone number and determine if the number is divisible by 2, 3, 5, 6, or 10.

Error Analysis

Watch for students who think a number is divisible by 3 if the last digit is divisible by 3.
Prevent by giving small number examples, such as 13, 16, 19, 23, 26, and 29, which are not divisible by 3.

Independent Practice

Homework Assignment	
Basic	13-29 odd, 30-37, 39, 40
Average	14-28 even, 30-40
Honors	19-27, 30-40

Practice Masters Booklet, **p. 30**

Name ______________ Date ______________

Practice Worksheet 4-1

Factors and Monomials

Use divisibility rules to determine if the first number is divisible by the second number. Write yes or no.

1. 39; 3 Yes
2. 82; 5 No
3. 157; 10 No
4. 56; 2 Yes
5. 315; 5 Yes
6. 30; 6 Yes
7. 81; 3 Yes
8. 105; 2 No
9. 136; 6 No
10. 195; 3 Yes
11. 75; 5 Yes
12. 29; 3 No
13. 350; 10 Yes
14. 42; 3 Yes
15. 50; 2 Yes
16. 86; 5 No
17. 72; 2 Yes
18. 88; 6 No
19. 90; 5 Yes
20. 27; 2 No
21. 70; 5 Yes
22. 45; 3 Yes
23. 96; 6 Yes
24. 100; 5 Yes
25. 69; 3 Yes
26. 86; 2 Yes
27. 85; 10 No
28. 78; 3 Yes
29. 1025; 5 Yes
30. 969; 6 No
31. 805; 10 No
32. 888; 3 Yes
33. 177; 3 Yes
34. 1046; 2 Yes
35. 282; 6 Yes
36. 1010; 10 Yes
37. 6237; 2 No
38. 6237; 3 Yes
39. 6237; 5 No
40. 6237; 6 No

Determine whether each expression is a monomial. Explain why or why not.

41. $21abc$ Yes; it is the product of an integer and variables.
42. $-3(x + y)$ No; it involves addition.
43. $4n - 7$ No; it involves subtraction.
44. -512 Yes; it is just an integer.
45. z Yes; it is just a variable.
46. $-16p$ Yes; it is the product of an integer and a
47. $r - st$ No; it involves subtraction.
48. $35df$ Yes; it is the product of an integer and

Alternate Strategies: Reteaching the Lesson

Reteaching Activity

Using Tables Display a chart of the first twenty multiples of 2, 3, 5, 6, and 10 on the chalkboard or overhead. Have students describe the similarities and patterns in each sequence.

Reteaching Masters Booklet, **p. 27**

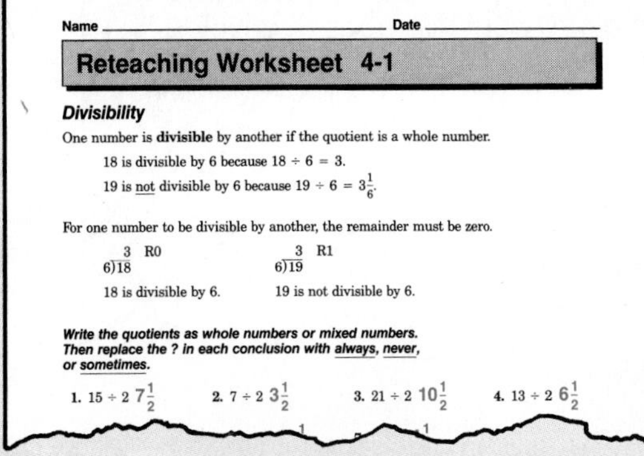

Name ______________ Date ______________

Reteaching Worksheet 4-1

Divisibility

One number is **divisible** by another if the quotient is a whole number.

18 is divisible by 6 because $18 \div 6 = 3$.

19 is not divisible by 6 because $19 \div 6 = 3\frac{1}{6}$.

For one number to be divisible by another, the remainder must be zero.

$6\overline{)18}$ = 3 R0 — 18 is divisible by 6.

$6\overline{)19}$ = 3 R1 — 19 is not divisible by 6.

Write the quotients as whole numbers or mixed numbers. Then replace the ? in each conclusion with always, never, or sometimes.

1. $15 \div 2$ $7\frac{1}{2}$
2. $7 \div 2$ $3\frac{1}{2}$
3. $21 \div 2$ $10\frac{1}{2}$
4. $13 \div 2$ $6\frac{1}{2}$

4 CLOSE

Assessment Option

Speaking Have the students state the divisibility rules in their own words.

Logical Thinking

27. What number is a factor of every nonzero number? **1**
28. Is every nonzero number a factor of itself? **yes**
29. Name two factors for every nonzero number. **1 and the number**

Mixed Review

30. Evaluate the expression $k + 14$ if $k = 8$. (Lesson 1-2) **22**
31. If $n = -5$, then $-n = \blacksquare$. (Lesson 2-5) **5**
32. Solve the equation $x = (6)(-4)(-3)$. (Lesson 2-7) **72**
33. *True* or *false:* If $y + c = d$, then $y = d - c$. (Lesson 3-1) **true**
34. Solve the equation $63 = -9y$. (Lesson 3-3) **-7**
35. **Physics** Lorena rides her bike 21 miles in 3 hours. At what rate of speed does she travel? (Lesson 3-5) **7 mph**
36. Write an inequality for the sentence: *The temperature is greater than sixty degrees.* (Lesson 3-7) **$t > 60$**

Applications

37. **Measurement** A leap year occurs when the year is divisible by 4. A century year is a leap year if it is divisible by 400. Name the last and the next century leap years. **1600, 2000**
38. **Arts and Crafts** A rectangular quilt has 24 squares. Draw all the shapes in which the quilt can be arranged. **See Solutions Manual.**

Critical Thinking

39. What is the greatest 3-digit number that is *not* divisible by 2, 3, or 5? **997**

Wrap-Up

40. If a number is divisible by 2 and 10, is it always divisible by 20? If not, give a counterexample. **No; 30 is divisible by 2 and 10, but not 20.**

Enrichment

Perfect Numbers

A **perfect number** is equal to the sum of its factors, except itself. There are two perfect numbers less than 30. The third perfect number is 496.

$$496 = 1 + 2 + 4 + 8 + 16 + 31 + 62 + 124 + 248$$

1. Find a perfect number between 1 and 10. **6**
2. Find a perfect number between 20 and 30. **28**
3. **Research** Find other perfect numbers. **The next two are 8128 and 33,550,336.**

Alternate Strategies: Extending the Lesson

Enrichment

Using Cooperative Groups Have students work in groups to develop divisibility rules for 15 and 25.

Cooperative Learning

Factor To Win — Group Activity 4-1

MATERIALS: Pencil • paper

In this game you try to get more points than your opponent by choosing the best numbers from those that are less than the starting number. You get as many points as the number you choose, but your opponent gets the total from the factors of the number you chose. Make your best choice, but remember each number may be used only once.

The winner is the person who has the highest score after all numbers are used.

Example: If the given number is 25 and you start out by choosing number 24, you will score 24 points; however, your opponent will score the sum of 1, 2, 4, 6, 8, and 12 since these are all factors of 24. He or she will be ahead of you, and all the numbers listed may not be counted again this game. On your opponent's turn if the number 16 is picked, you will score 0 points since all the factors of 16 have been used.

Starting Numbers: 39, 42, 56, 122, 339, 57, 79, 81, 184, 49, 67, 228

Merrill Pre-Algebra FACTORS AND MONOMIALS

Enrichment Masters Booklet, **p. 27**

Name ________________ Date ________________

Enrichment Worksheet 4-1

Divisibility

Divisibility rule for 7

Determine the divisibility by 7 for 4032.

- 4032 (2 crossed out) — Cross out the ones digit.
  −4 — Subtract twice the value of the ones digit from the rest of the number.
  399 (9 crossed out) — If the difference is a number that you know is divisible by 7, stop. If not, repeat.
  −18
  21 — Since 21 is divisible by 7, 4032 is divisible by 7.

Divisibility rules for 11

Determine the divisibility by 11 for 5159.

- 5159 (9 crossed out) — Cross out the ones digit.
  −9 — Subtract the value of the ones digit from the rest of the number.
  506 (6 crossed out) — If the difference is a number that you know is divisible by 11, stop. If not, repeat.
  −6
  44 — Since 44 is divisible by 11, 5159 is divisible by 11.

- 5159 — Note: The 1st digit is 5, 2nd digit is 1, 3rd digit is 5, 4th digit is 9.
  $5 + 5 = 10$ — Find the sum of the values of the odd-numbered digits.
  $1 + 9 = 10$ — Find the sum of the values of the even-numbered digits.
  0 — Subtract the sums. If the difference is divisible by 11, the number is divisible by 11.
  Since 0 is divisible by 11, 5159 is divisible by 11.

Determine the divisibility by 11 for 6238.

- 6238
  $2 + 8 = 10$
  $6 + 3 = 9$
  1 — Since 1 is not divisible by 11, 6238 is not divisible by 11.

Determine the divisibility by 7 and 11 for each of the following.

1. 266 **Divisible by 7, Not divisible by 11**
2. 4312 **Divisible by 7 and 11**
3. 8976 **Not divisible by 7, Divisible by 11**
4. 936 **Not divisible by 7 or 11**
5. 13,293 **Divisible by 7, Not divisible by 11**
6. 7085 **Not divisible by 7 or 11**
7. 2957 **Not divisible by 7 or 11**
8. 3124 **Not divisible by 7, Divisible by 11**
9. 6545 **Divisible by 7 and 11**

4-2 Powers and Exponents

Objective:
Use powers and exponents in expressions and equations.

Key Terms:
standard form
base
exponent
power

There are over 10,000 private airports in the United States. The number 10,000 is in **standard form.** You can also express 10,000 as the product $10 \cdot 10 \cdot 10 \cdot 10$.

A shorter way to express $10 \cdot 10 \cdot 10 \cdot 10$ is by using exponents. An **exponent** tells how many times a number, called the **base,** is used as a factor.

The expression $10 \cdot 10 \cdot 10 \cdot 10$ can be written 10^4.

base → $\mathbf{10^4}$ ← *exponent*

The number 10 is the **base.**
The number 4 is the **exponent.**

Numbers that are expressed using exponents are called **powers.** The *powers* 5^2, 9^3, and 8^4 are read as follows.

5^2 five to the *second* power or five *squared*

9^3 nine to the *third* power or nine *cubed*

8^4 eight to the *fourth* power

Using exponents, how would you write x to the fifth power? x^5

Examples

Write each power as a product of the same factor.

1 2^4

The base is 2. The exponent 4 means 2 is a factor 4 times.

$2^4 = 2 \cdot 2 \cdot 2 \cdot 2$

2 b^3

The base is b. The exponent 3 means b is a factor 3 times.

$b^3 = b \cdot b \cdot b$

Write each product using exponents.

3 $6 \cdot 6$

The base is 6. Because 6 is a factor 2 times, the exponent is 2.

$6 \cdot 6 = 6^2$

4 $x \cdot x \cdot x \cdot x \cdot x$

The base is x. Because x is a factor 5 times, the exponent is 5.

$x \cdot x \cdot x \cdot x \cdot x = x^5$

Calculator Hint

Many calculators have a key labeled y^x. This key allows you to compute exponents very quickly. Suppose you want to find 16^5.

16 [y^x] 5 [=]
1048576

The result appears immediately.

Bell Ringer

Play a game like "20 Questions" in which students try to guess your number by asking questions such as "Does the number have a factor of 3?" or "Is the number divisible by 7?"

Lesson Notes 4-2

5-Minute Check
(over Lesson 4-1)

Use divisibility rules to determine if the first number is divisible by the second number.

1. 91; 9 **no**
2. 70; 5 **yes**
3. 76; 4 **yes**
4. 96; 12 **yes**

Transparency 4-2 contains the 5-Minute Check and a teaching aid for this lesson.

1 FOCUS

The purpose of this lesson is to introduce the use of powers and exponents in expressions and include powers in the order of operations.

Motivating the Lesson

Have students find the sum of 4 + 4 + 4 + 4 + 4 + 4. Determine by a show of hands how many students used multiplication instead of addition. Ask students to rewrite the addition problem as a multiplication problem.

2 TEACH

Using Calculators

Give pairs of students key sequences similar to the following pair.
6 [×] 6 [×] 6 [=] and 6 [y^x] 3 [=]
Have students compare results. Tell students that the first number of the second sequence is the base and the second number is the number of times it was used as a factor.

Chalkboard Examples

Write each power as a product of the same factor.

- *For Example 1* $(-4)^3$ **$(-4)(-4)(-4)$**
- *For Example 2* n^2 **$n \cdot n$**

EE: 1E, 2F, 3A, 3B, 3D, 3H, 4B
TAAS: 1, 2, 12

Chalkboard Examples

Write each product using exponents.

- *For Example 3*
  $7 \cdot 7 \cdot 7 \cdot 7$ 7^4
- *For Example 4*
  $m \cdot m \cdot m \cdot m \cdot m \cdot m$ m^6

Evaluate each expression.

- *For Example 5* y^3 if $y = 4$ 64
- *For Example 6* $7k^2$ if $k = 4$ 112

3 PRACTICE/APPLY

Checking the Concept

After completing the exercises in the Guided Practice, have students evaluate Exercises 11-15. Then have students check their answers by using the y^x key on their calculators.

Error Analysis

Watch for students who write exponents carelessly and then mistake them for digits in the whole numbers.
Prevent by mentioning the possible mistake and checking students' work.

Practice Masters Booklet, **p. 31**

Name ____________ Date ____________

Practice Worksheet 4-2

Powers and Exponents

Write each product using exponents.

1. $2 \cdot 2 \cdot 2 \cdot 3 \cdot 3 \cdot 7$ $2^3 \cdot 3^2 \cdot 7$
2. $2 \cdot 3 \cdot 3 \cdot 7 \cdot 7 \cdot 7 \cdot 11$ $2 \cdot 3^2 \cdot 7^3 \cdot 11$
3. $3 \cdot 3 \cdot 5 \cdot 7 \cdot x \cdot x \cdot x$ $3^2 \cdot 5 \cdot 7 \cdot x^3$
4. $5 \cdot 7 \cdot 7 \cdot r \cdot r \cdot t \cdot t \cdot t$ $5 \cdot 7^2 \cdot r^2 \cdot t^3$
5. $a \cdot a \cdot b \cdot b \cdot c \cdot c \cdot c$ $a^2 \cdot b^2 \cdot c^3$
6. $2 \cdot n \cdot p \cdot p \cdot s \cdot s \cdot s \cdot s$ $2 \cdot n \cdot p^2 \cdot s^4$
7. $2 \cdot 2 \cdot n \cdot n$ $2^2 \cdot n^2$
8. $5 \cdot 5 \cdot 5 \cdot x \cdot x \cdot y \cdot y \cdot y$ $5^3 \cdot x^2 \cdot y^3$
9. $7 \cdot x \cdot x \cdot x \cdot x$ $7x^4$
10. $t \cdot t \cdot t \cdot t \cdot t$ t^5
11. 8 to the fourth power 8^4
12. m to the third power m^3
13. n to the seventh power n^7
14. h cubed h^3

Evaluate each expression if $p = 1$, $m = 6$, $r = 2$, $y = 3$, and $z = 5$.

15. $3ry$ 18
16. p^2m^2 36
17. $(rm)^2$ 144
18. $4my$ 72
19. $3z$ 15
20. p^6z^2 25
21. $p^2(ry)$ 6
22. $2zy^2$ 90
23. $y^3r^3p^3$ 216
24. $5p^8$ 5
25. $p^{10}y^4$ 81
26. $r^2y^2z^2$ 900
27. $3r^4$ 48
28. $6z^2$ 150
29. $5p^2r^5$ 160
30. m^2y^3 972
31. $3m^2z$ 540
32. $8r^3y$ 192

Since powers are a short form of repeated multiplication, they need to be included in the rules for order of operations.

Order of Operations

1. Do all operations within grouping symbols first; start with the innermost grouping symbols.
2. *Evaluate all powers from left to right.*
3. Next do all multiplications and divisions from left to right.
4. Then do all additions and subtractions from left to right.

Examples

Evaluate each expression.

5 n^2 **if** $n = 5$

$n^2 = 5^2$ Replace n with 5.
$= 5 \cdot 5$
$= 25$

6 $8r^3$ **if** $r = 3$

$8r^3 = 8 \cdot 3^3$ Replace r with 3.
$= 8 \cdot 27$ Find the power first.
$= 216$

Checking for Understanding

Communicating Algebra

1. To evaluate the expression five to the seventh power, __?__ would be used as a factor __?__ times. 5, 7
2. In the power 3^5, the base is __?__ and the exponent is __?__ . 3, 5
3. What is another way to say *four to the second power?* four squared
4. What is another way to say *x to the third power?* x cubed
5. Explain how you can find 1^{405} very quickly. 1 to any power is 1.

Guided Practice

Write each power as the product of the same factor.

6. 2^4 $2 \cdot 2 \cdot 2 \cdot 2$
7. m^2 $m \cdot m$
8. 5^3 $5 \cdot 5 \cdot 5$
9. a^5 $a \cdot a \cdot a \cdot a \cdot a$
10. 6^4 $6 \cdot 6 \cdot 6 \cdot 6$

Write each product using exponents.

11. $2 \cdot 2 \cdot 2$ 2^3
12. $8 \cdot 8$ 8^2
13. $1 \cdot 1 \cdot 1 \cdot 1$ 1^4
14. $9 \cdot 9$ 9^2
15. $6 \cdot 6 \cdot 6$ 6^3

Exercises

Independent Practice

Write each product using exponents.

16. $4 \cdot 4 \cdot 4 \cdot 4$ 4^4
17. $t \cdot t \cdot t \cdot t \cdot t$ t^5
18. $(p \cdot p)(p \cdot p)$ p^4
19. $a(a \cdot a)$ a^3

Use a calculator to determine whether each sentence is *true* or *false*.

20. $2^{10} > 10^2$ T
21. $9^8 > 8^9$ F
22. $2^4 = 4^2$ T
23. $2^3 \neq 3^2$ T

Evaluate each expression.

24. x^3 if $x = 1$ 1
25. m^2 if $m = 9$ 81
26. r^4 if $r = 3$ 81
27. $3y^4$ if $y = 2$ 48
28. $4r^3$ if $r = 3$ 108
29. $2m^3$ if $m = 5$ 250

Language Skills

Evaluate.

30. nineteen cubed 6859
31. eight squared 64
32. three to the sixth power 729
33. eleven squared 121
34. sixteen cubed 4096
35. five to the seventh power 78,125
36. the sum of four squared and six cubed 232
37. seven cubed divided by seven squared 7

Alternate Strategies: Reteaching the Lesson

Reteaching Activity

Using Models Have students construct different-sized squares on graph paper. Then have them express the number of enclosed smaller squares using exponents. For example, a 3 by 3 square encloses 9 or 3^2 smaller squares.

Reteaching Masters Booklet, **p. 28**

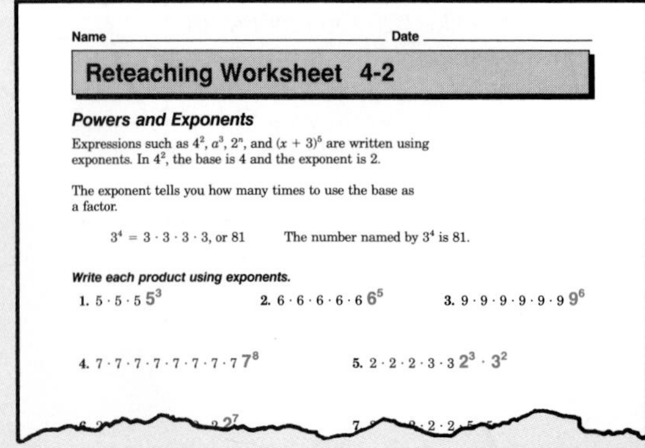

Name ____________ Date ____________

Reteaching Worksheet 4-2

Powers and Exponents

Expressions such as 4^2, a^3, 2^n, and $(x + 3)^5$ are written using exponents. In 4^2, the base is 4 and the exponent is 2.

The exponent tells you how many times to use the base as a factor.

$3^4 = 3 \cdot 3 \cdot 3 \cdot 3$, or 81 The number named by 3^4 is 81.

Write each product using exponents.

1. $5 \cdot 5 \cdot 5$ 5^3
2. $6 \cdot 6 \cdot 6 \cdot 6 \cdot 6$ 6^5
3. $9 \cdot 9 \cdot 9 \cdot 9 \cdot 9 \cdot 9$ 9^6
4. $7 \cdot 7 \cdot 7 \cdot 7 \cdot 7 \cdot 7 \cdot 7 \cdot 7$ 7^8
5. $2 \cdot 2 \cdot 2 \cdot 3 \cdot 3$ $2^3 \cdot 3^2$

Mixed Review

38. Solve the equation $4 - r = -15$. (Lesson 3-2) **19**
39. Write the inequalities $b < 1.6$ and $b \geq 0.3$ as a compound inequality. (Lesson 3-9) **$0.3 \leq b < 1.6$**
40. *True* or *false:* Every number is a factor of itself. (Lesson 4-1) **true**
41. Is the expression $-17cd$ a monomial? (Lesson 4-1) **yes**
42. Use divisibility rules to determine if 3 is a factor of 2345. (Lesson 4-1) **$2 + 3 + 4 + 5 = 14$, so 3 is not a factor.**

Challenge

Evaluate.

43. $a^2 - b^2$ if $a = 3$ and $b = 2$ **5**
44. $(a + b)^2 - 2b$ if $a = 3$ and $b = 2$ **21**
45. $a^2 - b^2$ if $a = 2$ and $b = 4$ **-12**
46. $(a^2 - b)^2$ if $a = 2$ and $b = 4$ **0**

Connection

47. **Geometry** To find the measure of the volume of a cube, you find the product of its length, width, and height. Use exponents to write an expression that represents the volume of a cube that measures s units on each side. **s^3**

Application

48. **Computer Science** Computers use the binary, or base two, number system. Each place-value position is a power of two. For example, $101011_2 = (1 \times 2^5) + (0 \times 2^4) + (1 \times 2^3) + (0 \times 2^2) + (1 \times 2^1) + (1 \times 2^0) = 43$. Find the value of 11010_2. **26**

Critical Thinking

49. Each whole number from 1 to 15 can be expressed using the numerals 1, 2, 3, and 4 exactly once and any of the operation signs. For example, $1 = (1 + 4) \div (2 + 3)$. Write an expression for each of the others. **See margin.**

Wrap-Up

50. Explain why $2^3 \neq 3^2$. **$2^3 = 2 \cdot 2 \cdot 2$ or 8; $3^2 = 3 \cdot 3$ or 9.**

Reading Algebra

Powers

Remember that in a power the exponent indicates the number of times the base is used as a factor. Suppose you are to write each of the following in symbols.

Words	Symbols
three times x squared	$3x^2$
three times x, the quantity squared	$(3x)^2$

Suppose $x = 2$. Then $3x^2 = 3 \cdot 2^2$ or 12, and $(3x)^2 = (3 \cdot 2)^2$ or 36. The values are not the same.

In the second expression, the parentheses are used to show that the expression $3x$ is used as a factor twice.

$$(3x)^2 = (3x)(3x)$$

The phrase *the quantity* is used to indicate parentheses when reading expressions.

State how to read each expression. **See margin.**

1. 3^3
2. $(12r)^5$
3. $(x + 2y)^2$
4. $4m^2n^4$
5. $a - b^3$
6. $(2a)^4 + b$

Decide if the expressions are equivalent. Write *yes* or *no*.

7. $12 \cdot x^3$ and $12 \cdot x \cdot x \cdot x$ **yes**
8. $3xy^5$ and $3(xy)^5$ **no**
9. $(2a)^3$ and $8a^3$ **yes**
10. $(ab)^2$ and $a^2 \cdot b^2$ **yes**
11. xy^3 and x^3y^3 **no**
12. $4(x^3)^2$ and $4x^6$ **yes**

Independent Practice

Homework Assignment	
Basic	17-37 odd, 38-42, 48-50
Average	18-36 even, 38-42, 46-50
Honors	24-36 even, 38-50

4 CLOSE

Assessment Option

Writing Ask students to write the following expressions symbolically.

1. m squared m^2
2. fourteen times x cubed $14x^3$
3. eleven times the sum of a and b squared $11(a + b^2)$

Additional Answers

49. Sample answers:
$2 = (3 + 1) - (4 \div 2)$
$3 = (4 - 1) \div (3 - 2)$
$4 = (4 - 2) + (3 - 1)$
$5 = (4 + 1) \div (3 - 2)$
$6 = (4 + 3) - (2 - 1)$
$7 = (4 + 3) \div (2 - 1)$
$8 = (3 - 1) + (4 + 2)$
$9 = (4 - 1) + (2 \cdot 3)$
$10 = (1 \cdot 4) + (2 \cdot 3)$
$11 = (2 \cdot 3) + (4 + 1)$
$12 = (4 \cdot 2) + (3 + 1)$
$13 = (2 - 1) + (4 \cdot 3)$
$14 = (3 + 4) \cdot (2 \cdot 1)$
$15 = (4 \cdot 3) + (2 + 1)$

Enrichment Masters Booklet, **p. 28**

Name ______________ Date ______________

Enrichment Worksheet 4-2

Exponents

Numbers can be expressed in several ways. Some numbers are expressed as sums. Some numbers are expressed as products of factors, while other numbers are expressed as powers.

Two ways to express 27 are $3 \cdot 3 \cdot 3$ and 3^3.

The number 1 million can be expressed in the following ways.

1,000,000	$1000 \cdot 1000$	$100 \cdot 100 \cdot 100$	$10^2 \cdot 10^2 \cdot 10^2$
$1{,}000{,}000^1$	1000^2	100^3	10^6

Write names for each number below using the given exponents.

1. 16, exponents: 2 and 4 $4^2, 2^4$
2. 81, exponents: 2 and 4 $9^2, 3^4$
3. 64, exponents: 2 and 6 $8^2, 2^6$
4. 256, exponents: 2 and 8 $16^2, 2^8$
5. 625, exponents: 2 and 4 $25^2, 5^4$
6. 729, exponents: 2 and 6 $27^2, 3^6$
7. 2401, exponents: 2 and 4 $49^2, 7^4$
8. 4096, exponents: 2 and 12 $64^2, 2^{12}$
9. 6561, exponents: 2 and 8 $81^2, 3^8$
10. 390,625, exponents: 2 and 8 $625^2, 5^8$

Numbers that can be named as powers with like bases can be multiplied by adding the exponents.

$$8 \cdot 8 = 2^3 \cdot 2^3 = 2^{3+3} = 2^6$$

Write the product of each pair of factors in exponential form.

11. $9 \cdot 9$ $3^2 \cdot 3^2 = 3^4$
12. $4 \cdot 4$ $2^2 \cdot 2^2 = 2^4$
13. $16 \cdot 8$ $2^4 \cdot 2^3 = 2^7$
14. $125 \cdot 25$ $5^3 \cdot 5^2 = 5^5$
15. $27 \cdot 9$ $3^3 \cdot 3^2 = 3^5$
16. $81 \cdot 27$ $3^4 \cdot 3^3 = 3^7$
17. $49 \cdot 49$ $7^2 \cdot 7^2 = 7^4$
18. $121 \cdot 121$ $11^2 \cdot 11^2 = 11^4$

Reading Algebra Additional Answers

1. three cubed or three to the third power
2. twelve times r, the quantity to the fifth power
3. x plus two times y, the quantity squared
4. four times m squared times n to the fourth power
5. a minus b cubed
6. two times a, the quantity to the fourth power, plus b

Cooperative Learning

Make An Exponential Score Group Activity **4-2**

MATERIALS: Deck of "Exponential Expressions" cards using expressions given on back • 0-9 spinner • paper • pencil

Before play begins, shuffle the "Exponential Expression" cards and deal four cards to 2-4 players.

Spin the spinner and use that number to evaluate the exponential expression on one of your cards, which you then lay down in front of you. If evaluated correctly, you then record that value on your piece of paper. If evaluated incorrectly, you get no points.

Play continues around the table, with players adding the score they get on each round to their previous total. Each player spins the spinner once on each of four turns. After players have played all of their cards, the person with the highest final total wins the game.

Play the game several times to see if you can develop a strategy to help you get a high score.

Merrill Pre-Algebra POWERS AND EXPONENTS

Lesson Notes 4-3

5-Minute Check
(over Lesson 4-2)

Evaluate each expression.
1. n^3 if $n = 3$ 27
2. $2x^3$ if $x = 5$ 250
3. $6m^2$ if $m = 4$ 96
4. r^5 if $r = 2$ 32
5. $5y^2$ if $y = 7$ 245

Transparency 4-3 contains the 5-Minute Check and a teaching aid for this lesson.

1 FOCUS

The purpose of this lesson is to draw appropriate diagrams and use them to solve problems.

Motivating the Lesson

Bring in a program from an athletic event, a musical, or a play that has a diagram of the arena or the hall. Ask students why these diagrams are included in the program. **It helps people find their seats, and where other places are located such as restrooms and exits.**

2 TEACH

Using Models

Have students use toothpicks to model the following situation. Let one toothpick = one block.
In order to get home from the store, Cindy needs to go straight one block, turn right, go straight two blocks, turn left, turn right at the next block, left at the block after that, and go straight for two more blocks.

Chalkboard Examples

A tennis class of 16 students will participate in a single elimination tournament; that is, only the winners continue to play. How many games will be played during the tournament? **15 games**

EE: 1A, 1B, 1C, 1D, 1E
TAAS: 10, 13

Problem Solving

4-3 Strategy: Draw a Diagram

Objective:
Solve problems by drawing diagrams.

Seth is planning a chess tournament for his class. Eight students will participate in a single elimination format; that is, only the winners continue to play. Seth needs to know how many games will be played so he can contact the teachers that are to be at each game. How many games will be played during this tournament?

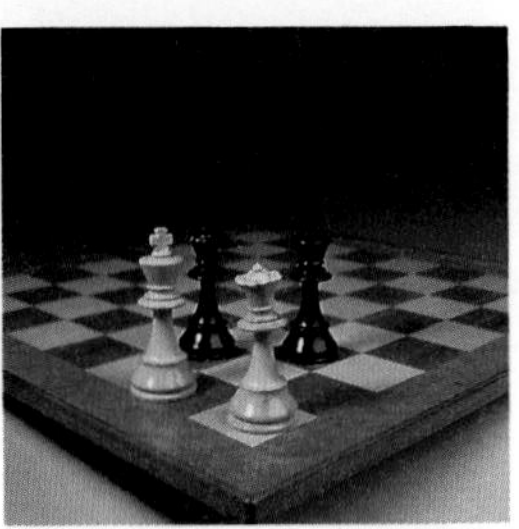

Explore There are 8 students in a single elimination tournament. The problem asks how many games will be played.

Plan In planning the tournament, Seth makes a diagram to show how the winners advance through the tournament. Such a diagram will help to count the number of games.

Solve

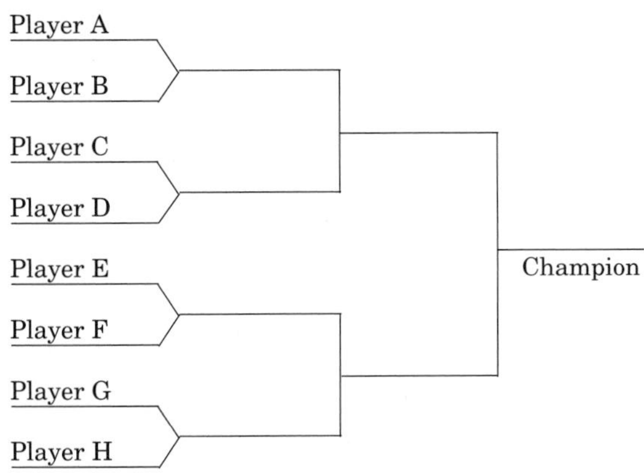

Notice that 4 games are played in the first round, 2 games are played in the second round, and 1 final game is played for the championship.

$$4 + 2 + 1 = 7$$

There will be 7 games played in the tournament.

Examine Every player loses exactly once except the champion. Therefore, 8 − 1 or 7 games are played. The answer is correct.

Diagrams are useful tools in solving some problems. These diagrams do not need to be elaborate, but can be very simple illustrations.

Bell Ringer

What will the exponent be if you multiply the number 2 four times? **4** if you multiply it six times? **6**

Reteaching Activity

Using Questioning Use a diagram to solve.
A ferry carrying 37 cars, each with two people in it, is crossing the river. Each person has three suitcases. The captain and his assistant each have two suitcases. Each of the rest of the crew of 15 has one suitcase. How many suitcases are there on the ferry? **241 suitcases**

Checking for Understanding

Communicating Algebra

1. Why is drawing a diagram a good strategy for solving problems? See margin.
2. Is drawing a diagram a good strategy for solving all problems? Why or why not?
   No. Sometimes there may be another strategy that is more useful.

Guided Practice

3. Draw a diagram to determine how many games have to be played to determine a champion from 32 teams in a single elimination softball tournament? See Solutions Manual.
4. Look at the staircase at the right. How many cubes would be needed for a staircase with seven steps? 28 cubes

Exercises

Independent Practice

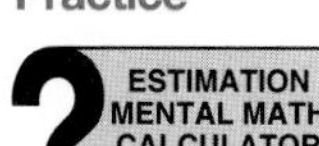

Solve. Use any strategy.

5. Sam made a list of his mother's parents, grandparents, great grandparents, and great-great grandparents. If Sam did not list any stepgrandparents, how many people are listed? 30 people
6. Sybil's score on her math test is 89. Some of the questions are worth 5 points and the rest of the questions are worth 2 points. The teacher gave no partial credit for any question. If 37 problems are correct, how many 5-point questions did Sybil answer correctly? five 5-point questions
7. A volleyball team has 6 members. Suppose each member shakes hands with every other member. How many handshakes take place? 15 handshakes
8. During the first minute of a game of tug-of-war, team A pulled team B forward 2 feet. During the second minute, team B pulled team A forward 1 foot. Then, during the third minute, team A pulled team B forward 2 feet. If this pattern continues, how long will it take team A to pull team B forward a total of 10 feet to win the game? 17 minutes
9. Replace each ● with an operation symbol to make the equation true. Add parentheses if necessary.
   4 ● 3 ● 6 ● 3 = 45 $(4 + 3) \times 6 + 3 = 45$
10. A ball is dropped from 10 meters above the ground. It hits the ground and bounces up $\frac{1}{2}$ as high as it fell. If each bounce is $\frac{1}{2}$ the height of the last bounce, how far has the ball traveled down when it hits the ground the fifth time? $\frac{5}{8}$ m

Critical Thinking

11. Willis is cutting a round pizza. What is the greatest number of pieces he can get from 1 pizza with 4 straight cuts? 11 pieces

Wrap-Up

12. **Make Up a Problem** Write a problem where a diagram would be helpful in solving the problem. See margin.

Additional Answers

1. Drawing a diagram allows you to gain a quick overview of the problem at a glance. This may also give you a perspective and a way to solve the problem that had not been thought of before.
12. Sample answer: Seven teams are to play each other in a tournament. How many games are needed?

Cooperative Learning

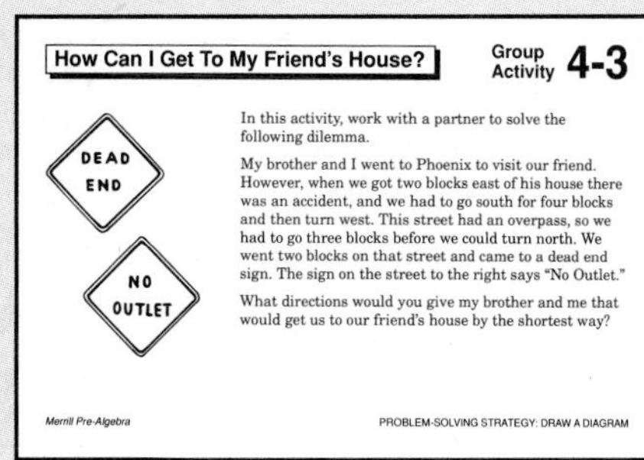

How Can I Get To My Friend's House? Group Activity **4-3**

DEAD END

NO OUTLET

In this activity, work with a partner to solve the following dilemma.

My brother and I went to Phoenix to visit our friend. However, when we got two blocks east of his house there was an accident, and we had to go south for four blocks and then turn west. This street had an overpass, so we had to go three blocks before we could turn north. We went two blocks on that street and came to a dead end sign. The sign on the street to the right says "No Outlet."

What directions would you give my brother and me that would get us to our friend's house by the shortest way?

Merrill Pre-Algebra PROBLEM-SOLVING STRATEGY: DRAW A DIAGRAM

3 PRACTICE/APPLY

Checking the Concept

Have students try to solve Exercise 3 without drawing a diagram. Then have them solve using a diagram and compare the ease of solution.

Error Analysis
Watch for students who draw diagrams inaccurately. **Prevent by** encouraging students to draw pertinent information as it is read in the problem and be careful to make all parts neat and legible.

Independent Practice

Homework Assignment	
Basic	5-12
Average	5-12
Honors	5-12

4 CLOSE

Assessment Option

Speaking Ask students to describe personal situations where they used a diagram to solve a problem. Sample answers could include travel, geometry, or finding patterns.

Practice Masters Booklet, p. 32

Name ______ Date ______

Practice Worksheet 4-3

Problem Solving Strategy: Draw a Diagram

Solve. Use any strategy.

1. A sandwich shop has 7 kinds of sandwiches and 4 kinds of drinks. How many different orders of one sandwich and one drink could you order? 28
2. There are 16 golfers in a single-elimination tournament. How many golf matches will be played during the tournament? 15
3. Ethel, Mike, Pete, and Gail wanted to go to the movies. In how many different ways could they stand in line to buy their tickets? 24
4. If you have 4 pairs of jeans, 3 shirts, and 2 pairs of running shoes, how many different outfits can you make? Each outfit contains one pair of jeans, one shirt, and one pair of running shoes. 24
5. There are 5 members in the Washington family. Suppose each member hugs every other member. How many hugs take place? 10
6. Show how you can cut this cake into sixteenths with exactly 5 cuts.

Lesson Notes 4-4

5-Minute Check
(over Lesson 4-3)

The Smiths planted 24 evergreen seedlings in each row. The trees need to be thinned out so Mr. Smith is cutting down every third tree. How many trees will be left in each row? **16 trees**

Transparency 4-4 contains the 5-Minute Check and a teaching aid for this lesson.

1 FOCUS

The purpose of this lesson is to differentiate between prime and composite numbers and to apply the *fundamental theorem of arithmetic* which states that every integer greater than one can be expressed as a product of prime factors in only one way, except for the order of the factors.

Motivating the Lesson

Have students state pairs of numbers that have a product of 48.

2 TEACH

Using Models

Have students construct the Sieve of Eratosthenes by listing the numbers 1-100 in rows in a 10 by 10 array like the one shown below.

1	2	3	4	5	6	7	8	9	10
11	12	13	14	15	16	17	18	19	20
21	22	23	24	25	26	27	28	29	30
31	32	33	34	35	36	37	38	39	40
41	42	43	44	45	46	47	48	49	50
51	52	53	54	55	56	57	58	59	60
61	62	63	64	65	66	67	68	69	70
71	72	73	74	75	76	77	78	79	80
81	82	83	84	85	86	87	88	89	90
91	92	93	94	95	96	97	98	99	100

Tell students to cross out 1, then circle 2 and cross out all its multiples. Proceed to the next number that is not circled or crossed out (3) and repeat the process. Continue until all number are circled (prime) or crossed out (composite).

EE: 1E, 2B, 3A, 4B
TAAS: 1, 2, 4

4-4 Prime Factorization

Objectives:
Identify prime and composite numbers.
Write the prime factorization of a composite number.

Key Terms:
prime
composite
factor tree

The Food Basket has 30 boxes of a new flavored pretzel to put on display. The display is being set up by two stock clerks.

$30 = 2 \cdot 15$ — Each of the 2 clerks sets up 15 boxes. $30 \div 2 = 15$

$30 = 2 \cdot (3 \cdot 5)$ — Suppose each clerk is responsible for setting up 3 rows with 5 boxes per row. $15 \div 3 = 5$

The work cannot be divided into any smaller whole number parts.

Notice that the only factors of 2 are 1 and 2. Also notice that the only factors of 3 and 5 are 1 and the original number. A whole number *greater than one* that has *exactly* two factors, 1 and itself, is called a **prime number.**

Any whole number, besides 0, that is not prime can be written as a product of prime numbers. A whole number *greater than one* that has more than two factors is called a **composite number.**

The numbers 1 and 0 are *neither* prime *nor* composite. Zero has an endless number of factors. The number 1 has only one factor, itself. However, every number greater than one is either prime or composite.

How are divisibility rules helpful in finding prime factors?
You can easily determine if 2, 3, or 5 are factors.

Sometimes a number can be factored in several ways. The diagrams below show how three different students found all the prime factors of 36. These diagrams are called **factor trees.**

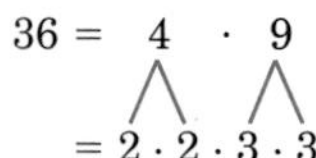

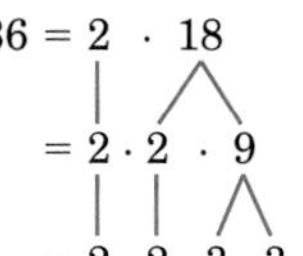

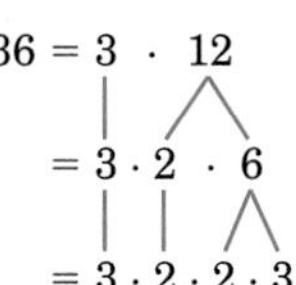

Although the factors are in different order, the result is the same. The order in which you factor does not matter. The factoring process stops when all factors are prime. When a number is expressed as a product of factors that are all prime, the expression is called the **prime factorization** of the number.

Bell Ringer

A large sheet of paper is placed on the floor. The paper is not torn or folded. Two people stand face to face on the sheet of paper. Neither person can touch the other and their hands are not tied. How can this be? **The paper is centered under a glass door. One person is on each side of the door.**

Calculator Hint

When you use a calculator to find prime factors, it is helpful to record them on paper as you find each one.

A calculator can also be used to find the prime factorization of a number.

Example

1 Find the prime factorization of 180. Divide by prime factors until the quotient is prime.

180 [÷] 2 [=] 90 [÷] 2 [=] 45 [÷] 3 [=] 15 [÷] 3 [=] 5

(2, 2, 3, 3, 5: prime factors)

$180 = 2 \cdot 2 \cdot 3 \cdot 3 \cdot 5$

Sometimes you may need to factor a negative integer. Any negative integer may be written as the product of -1 and a whole number.

Example

2 Factor -273 completely.

$-273 = -1 \cdot 273$	Now find the prime factorization of 273.
$= -1 \cdot 3 \cdot 91$	Will 2 divide 273 evenly? No, try 3.
	91 is not divisible by 2, 3, or 5.
$= -1 \cdot 3 \cdot 7 \cdot 13$	Try 7, the next greater prime.
$-273 = -1 \cdot 3 \cdot 7 \cdot 13$	13 is a prime number.

CONNECTION TO ALGEBRA

A monomial can also be written in factored form as a product of prime numbers, -1, and variables with no exponent greater than 1.

Example

3 Factor $18xy^2$.

$18xy^2 = 2 \cdot 9 \cdot x \cdot y^2$

$= 2 \cdot 3 \cdot 3 \cdot x \cdot y \cdot y$

1. A prime number has exactly 2 factors; a composite number has more than 2.

Checking for Understanding

Communicating Algebra

1. In your own words, explain the difference between prime and composite numbers.
2. Draw a factor tree to find the prime factorization of 144. See margin.

Guided Practice

Determine whether each number is *prime* or *composite*.

3. 33 composite
4. 57 composite
5. 13 prime
6. 19 prime

Find the least prime number that is a factor of each number.

7. 36 2
8. 55 5
9. 77 7
10. 88 2

Find the prime factorization of each number.

11. 63 $3 \cdot 3 \cdot 7$
12. 51 $3 \cdot 17$
13. 98 $2 \cdot 7 \cdot 7$
14. 110 $2 \cdot 5 \cdot 11$

Chalkboard Examples

- *For Example 1*
  Find the prime factorization of 50. $50 = 2 \cdot 5 \cdot 5$
- *For Example 2*
  Factor -140 completely. $-140 = -1 \cdot 2 \cdot 2 \cdot 5 \cdot 7$
- *For Example 3*
  Factor $56m^2x^3$.
  $7 \cdot 2 \cdot 2 \cdot 2 \cdot m \cdot m \cdot x \cdot x \cdot x$

3 PRACTICE/APPLY

Checking the Concept

Have students complete the Guided Practice exercises without using the Sieve of Eratosthenes. Then allow students to use it to check their answers.

Additional Answer

2. $144 = 12 \cdot 12$

$= 3 \cdot 4 \cdot 3 \cdot 4$

$= 3 \cdot 2 \cdot 2 \cdot 3 \cdot 2 \cdot 2$

***Practice Masters Booklet,* p. 33**

Name ____________ Date ____________

Practice Worksheet 4-4

Prime Factorization

Factor each number or monomial completely.

1. 16 $2 \cdot 2 \cdot 2 \cdot 2$
2. 72 $2 \cdot 2 \cdot 2 \cdot 3 \cdot 3$
3. 75 $3 \cdot 5 \cdot 5$
4. −80 $-1 \cdot 2 \cdot 2 \cdot 2 \cdot 2 \cdot 5$
5. −55 $-1 \cdot 5 \cdot 11$
6. 44 $2 \cdot 2 \cdot 11$
7. −60 $-1 \cdot 2 \cdot 2 \cdot 3 \cdot 5$
8. 54 $2 \cdot 3 \cdot 3 \cdot 3$
9. 96 $2 \cdot 2 \cdot 2 \cdot 2 \cdot 2 \cdot 3$
10. −98 $-1 \cdot 2 \cdot 7 \cdot 7$
11. 105 $3 \cdot 5 \cdot 7$
12. 125 $5 \cdot 5 \cdot 5$
13. 144 $2 \cdot 2 \cdot 2 \cdot 2 \cdot 3 \cdot 3$
14. −110 $-1 \cdot 2 \cdot 5 \cdot 11$
15. −123 $-1 \cdot 3 \cdot 41$
16. −200 $-1 \cdot 2 \cdot 2 \cdot 2 \cdot 5 \cdot 5$
17. 275 $5 \cdot 5 \cdot 11$
18. −280 $-1 \cdot 2 \cdot 2 \cdot 2 \cdot 5 \cdot 7$
19. 297 $3 \cdot 3 \cdot 3 \cdot 11$
20. −900 $-1 \cdot 2 \cdot 2 \cdot 3 \cdot 3 \cdot 5 \cdot 5$
21. 108 $2 \cdot 2 \cdot 3 \cdot 3 \cdot 3$
22. −1500 $-1 \cdot 2 \cdot 2 \cdot 3 \cdot 5 \cdot 5 \cdot 5$
23. 1521 $3 \cdot 3 \cdot 13 \cdot 13$
24. −1600 $-1 \cdot 2 \cdot 2 \cdot 2 \cdot 2 \cdot 2 \cdot 2 \cdot 5 \cdot 5$
25. $35xy^2$ $5 \cdot 7 \cdot x \cdot y \cdot y$
26. $-12x^2z^2$ $-1 \cdot 2 \cdot 2 \cdot 3 \cdot x \cdot x \cdot z \cdot z$
27. $32pq$ $2 \cdot 2 \cdot 2 \cdot 2 \cdot 2 \cdot p \cdot q$
28. $-42mn^3$ $-1 \cdot 2 \cdot 3 \cdot 7 \cdot m \cdot n \cdot n \cdot n$
29. $51e^2f$ $3 \cdot 17 \cdot e \cdot e \cdot f$
30. $-64jk$ $-1 \cdot 2 \cdot 2 \cdot 2 \cdot 2 \cdot 2 \cdot 2 \cdot j \cdot k$
31. $98r^2t^3$ $2 \cdot 7 \cdot 7 \cdot r \cdot r \cdot t \cdot t \cdot t$
32. $-27v^3w$ $-1 \cdot 3 \cdot 3 \cdot 3 \cdot v \cdot v \cdot v \cdot w$
33. $90l^3m^2$ $2 \cdot 3 \cdot 3 \cdot 5 \cdot l \cdot l \cdot l \cdot m \cdot m$
34. $105ab^2$ $3 \cdot 5 \cdot 7 \cdot a \cdot b \cdot b$
35. $143m^2p$ $11 \cdot 13 \cdot m \cdot m \cdot p$
36. $525ac^2$ $3 \cdot 5 \cdot 5 \cdot 7 \cdot a \cdot c \cdot c$
37. $-150c^2d^3$ $-1 \cdot 2 \cdot 3 \cdot 5 \cdot 5 \cdot c \cdot c \cdot d \cdot d \cdot d$
38. $600xy$ $2 \cdot 2 \cdot 2 \cdot 3 \cdot 5 \cdot 5 \cdot x \cdot y$
39. $-450s^2t^3$ $-1 \cdot 2 \cdot 3 \cdot 3 \cdot 5 \cdot 5 \cdot s \cdot s \cdot t \cdot t \cdot t$
40. $100kl^3$ $2 \cdot 2 \cdot 5 \cdot 5 \cdot k \cdot l \cdot l \cdot l$
41. $500hj^2$ $2 \cdot 2 \cdot 5 \cdot 5 \cdot 5 \cdot h \cdot j \cdot j$
42. $-625b^3c$ $-1 \cdot 5 \cdot 5 \cdot 5 \cdot 5 \cdot b \cdot b \cdot b \cdot c$

Alternate Strategies: Reteaching the Lesson

Reteaching Activity

Using Discussion Discuss the use of factor trees and division and see which method is more easily understood by the students. Concentrate on that method, giving the students simple problems to solve. Work up to more complex problems.

***Reteaching Masters Booklet,* p. 29**

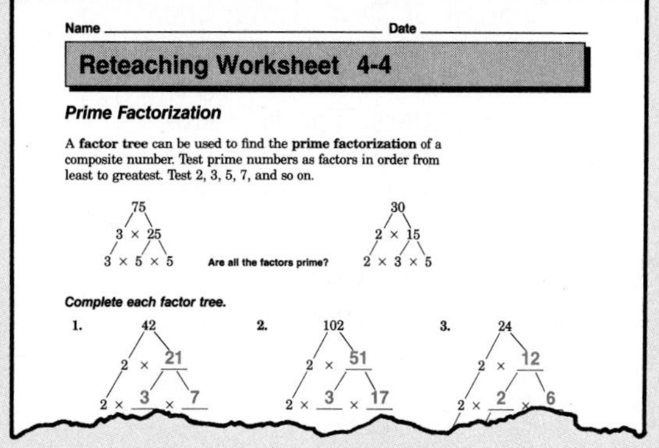

Name ____________ Date ____________

Reteaching Worksheet 4-4

Prime Factorization

A **factor tree** can be used to find the **prime factorization** of a composite number. Test prime numbers as factors in order from least to greatest. Test 2, 3, 5, 7, and so on.

75 → 3 × 25 → 3 × 5 × 5 **Are all the factors prime?** 30 → 2 × 15 → 2 × 3 × 5

Complete each factor tree.

1. 42 → 2 × 21 → 2 × 3 × 7
2. 102 → 2 × 51 → 2 × 3 × 17
3. 24 → 2 × 12 → 2 × 2 × 6

Error Analysis

Watch for students who do not factor completely.
Prevent by having students list common primes at the top of the paper. If a number in the final factorization is not one of these numbers, check the problem to be sure factorization is complete.

Independent Practice

Homework Assignment	
Basic	15-33 odd, 35-38, 41, 42
Average	20-34 even, 35-42
Honors	27-42

4 CLOSE

Assessment Option

Modeling Have the students use a calculator to make factor trees for the following numbers:

1. 2261 7 · 17 · 19
2. 3080 2 · 2 · 2 · 5 · 7 · 11
3. 14,490 2 · 3 · 3 · 5 · 7 · 23
4. 37,856 2 · 2 · 2 · 2 · 2 · 7 · 13 · 13

Additional Answer

39. 5 and 7, 11 and 13, 17 and 19, 29 and 31, 41 and 43, 59 and 61, 71 and 73; They are all even and all multiples of 6.

Enrichment Masters Booklet, **p. 29**

Name __________ Date __________

Enrichment Worksheet 4-4

Prime Pyramid

A **prime number** is a whole number that has exactly two factors—itself and 1. A pyramid composed of prime numbers is called a *prime pyramid.* Each row of the prime pyramid below begins with 1 and ends with the number of that row. In each row, the numbers from 1 to the row number are arranged such that the sum of any two adjacent numbers is a prime.

For example, look at row 4:

It must contain the numbers 1, 2, 3, and 4.
It must begin with 1 and end with 4.
The sum of adjacent pairs must be a prime number:
1 + 2 = 3, 2 + 3 = 5, 3 + 4 = 7

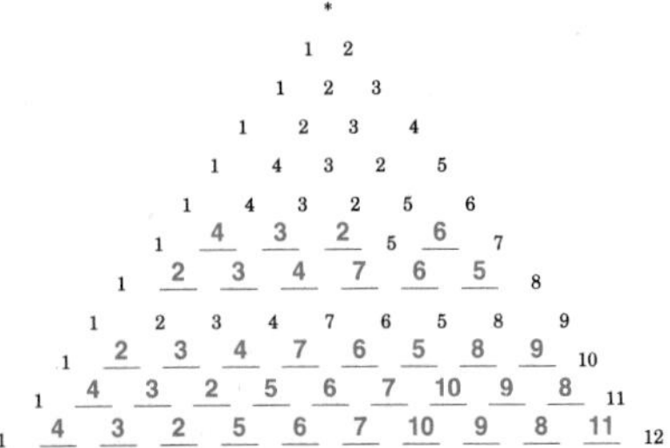

1. Complete the pyramid by filling in the missing numbers.
2. Extend the pyramid to row 13.
   1, 4, 3, 2, 5, 6, 7, 12, 11, 8, 9, 10, 13
3. Explain the patterns you see in the completed pyramid.
   Answers will vary. Each row alternates odd and even numbers.

Exercises

Factors are shown with exponents for your convenience.

Independent Practice

ESTIMATION
MENTAL MATH
CALCULATOR
PAPER/PENCIL

Factor each number or monomial completely.

15. 30 $2 \cdot 3 \cdot 5$
16. 45 $3^2 \cdot 5$
17. 49 7^2
18. 81 3^4
19. 68 $2^2 \cdot 17$
20. 48 $2^4 \cdot 3$
21. -26 $-1 \cdot 2 \cdot 13$
22. -63 $-1 \cdot 7 \cdot 3^2$
23. 80 $2^4 \cdot 5$
24. 128 2^7
25. -112 $-1 \cdot 2^4 \cdot 7$
26. -95 $-1 \cdot 5 \cdot 19$
27. $28x^2y$
28. $400a^2b^3$
29. $-72ab^3$
30. $560x^4y^2$
31. $42xy^2$ $2 \cdot 3 \cdot 7 \cdot x \cdot y^2$
32. $75m^2k$ $3 \cdot 5^2 \cdot m^2 \cdot k$
33. $210ab^3$ $2 \cdot 3 \cdot 5 \cdot 7 \cdot a \cdot b^3$
34. $-65r^2s$ $-1 \cdot 5 \cdot 13 \cdot r^2 \cdot s$

Mixed Review

35. Order the numbers in the set {3, -6, 0, -2} from least to greatest. (Lesson 2-2) {-6, -2, 0, 3}
36. Solve the equation $\frac{b}{-11} = -6$. (Lesson 3-4) 66
37. Write the expression *eight cubed* using exponents. (Lesson 4-2) 8^3
38. Evaluate the expression $(x - y^2)^2$ if $x = 11$ and $y = 3$. (Lesson 4-2) 4

Challenge

39. Primes that differ by 2 are called *twin primes.* One such pair is 3 and 5. Find all pairs of twin primes less than 100. What can you say about the numbers between twin primes? See margin.

Connection

40. **Geometry** Mr. Rathburn's back yard measures 10 yards wide by 10 yards long. He wants to construct a rectangular garden that has an area of 90 square feet. What are the whole number dimensions that are possible for the garden? 3' × 30', 6' × 15', 9' × 10'

Critical Thinking

41. A number is divisible by 2 if its last digit is divisible by 2, and a number is divisible by 4 if the number formed by its last two digits is divisible by 4. Continue the pattern and determine the rule for divisibility by 8. A number is divisible by 8 if its last 3 digits are divisible by 8.

Wrap-Up

42. In your own words, write an explanation of how to use a calculator to find the prime factorization of a number.
Keep dividing by primes until the number in the display is prime.

27. $2^2 \cdot 7 \cdot x^2 \cdot y$ 28. $2^4 \cdot 5^2 \cdot a^2 \cdot b^3$ 29. $-1 \cdot 2^3 \cdot 3^2 \cdot a \cdot b^3$ 30. $2^4 \cdot 5 \cdot 7 \cdot x^4 \cdot y^2$

History

The Mayan Number System

The Mayan civilization of Central America was highly advanced in astronomy, the calendar, architecture, and commerce. It was at its height from A.D. 300 to A.D. 900, and mathematics was an important part of its civilization.

One notable accomplishment was the development of a base-twenty number system with a special symbol for zero. The symbol for zero, ⊖, resembles a shell, but more probably it is a front view of a closed fist.

The Mayans also developed an amazingly accurate calendar. The Mayan calendar consisted of eighteen months of 20 days each, plus an additional "month" of 5 days, for a total of 365 days. In fact, the Mayans modified their base-twenty system to correspond to their calendar. Instead of the third position being 20^2, or 400, it was 18 × 20 or 360.

Alternate Strategies: Extending the Lesson

Enrichment

Using Groups of Two Have one student draw a tic-tac-toe board. Have students take turns writing in composite numbers. The first student to complete a row where all numbers are divisible by the same prime number wins.

Cooperative Learning

Mind Those Prime Factors Group Activity **4-4**

MATERIALS: 0-9 spinner

In this activity each group member tries to create the three-digit number with the greatest number of *prime* factors and the greatest prime factor.

To begin each round of the activity, the spinner is spun four times to determine the four digits each person can use to make a number. Each member is to use any three of the four digits to make any three-digit number, but it should have 1) as many prime factors as possible and 2) the largest prime factor possible.

For example, suppose the digits 0, 2, 7, 8 are spun. You could make the number 208 which factors into (24) (13) or 782 which factors into (2) (391). If these two were the only two numbers made, 208 would have the most prime factors (5), while 782 would have the greater prime factor (391). Thus, each player would "win" a part of that round.

A calculator could be used to check the factorization given by each member.

Merrill Pre-Algebra PRIME FACTORIZATION

Factor Patterns

Materials: computer

You already know that prime numbers have exactly two factors. What numbers have exactly three factors? or four factors? In this Exploration, you will investigate factor patterns.

The numbers 2 through 18 and their factors have been placed in the chart according to the number of factors.

Exactly 2 Factors	Exactly 3 Factors	Exactly 4 Factors	Exactly 5 Factors	Exactly 6 Factors
2: 1, 2 3: 1, 3 5: 1, 5 7: 1, 7 11: 1, 11 13: 1, 13 17: 1, 17 19, 23, 29, 31, 37, 41, 43, 47	4: 1, 2, 4 9: 1, 3, 9 25, 49	6: 1, 2, 3, 6 8: 1, 2, 4, 8 10: 1, 2, 5, 10 14: 1, 2, 7, 14 15: 1, 3, 5, 15 21, 22, 26, 27, 33, 34, 35, 38, 39, 46	16: 1, 2, 4, 8, 16	12: 1, 2, 3, 4, 6, 12 18: 1, 2, 3, 6, 9, 18 20, 28, 32, 44 45, 50 More than 6 factors: 24, 30, 36, 40, 42, 48

Your Turn: Copy and complete the chart for the numbers 19 through 30.

Work at a computer.

1. The BASIC program at the right will print the factors of a given number. Using the program, find the factors of the numbers 31 through 50. Then place these numbers in the correct column of the chart. See table above.

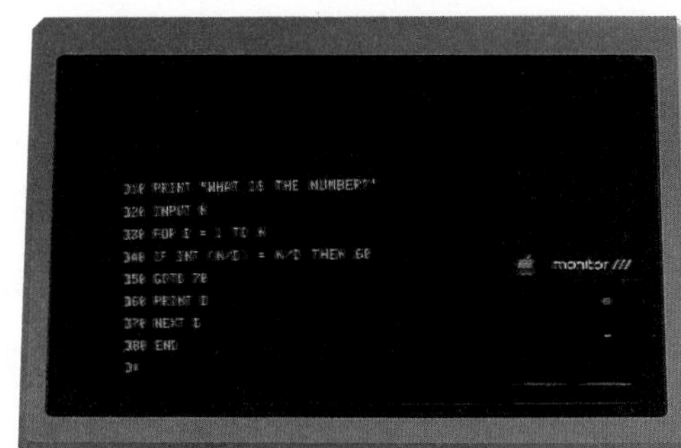

Analysis Sample answer: 67, 121, 55, 81, 63, 66

2. Predict a number from 50 through 150 that can be placed in each column. Check your prediction with the computer.
3. Write a paragraph that describes the pattern in each column. See Solutions Manual.

SET-UP

Materials

- computers or calculators

You may wish to use the Exploration worksheet provided on page 36 of the Lab Manual.

For Students Each student or pair of students should be stationed at a computer or calculator. If technology is not available, paper and pencil can be used to create factor trees.

For the Overhead Projector You can connect a computer to an overhead projection panel and complete the activity along with your students. Overhead projector calculators can also be programmed for this purpose.

EXPLORATION: *Factor Patterns*

Objective Students will apply the divisibility rules and use technology to investigate the number of factors a number has and the resulting patterns.

1 FOCUS

The purpose of this exploration is to allow students to discover patterns and develop a generalization for each pattern.

2 TEACH

Using Calculators

Remind students how to find factors using a calculator. You may want to refer them to page 137, Example 2. When students realize there are numbers with more than six factors (24 and 30 each have 8 factors) tell them they can create another column but it does not need to be included when completing Exercise 3.

3 PRACTICE/APPLY

Using Cooperative Groups

Have the students complete the application in pairs. Circulate around the room as they run the program to complete Exercise 1.

4 CLOSE

Writing Connection

Ask students to write a definition of prime numbers and square numbers based on the number of factors they have.

EE: 1A, 1C, 1E, 2B

Lesson Notes 4-5

5-Minute Check
(over Lesson 4-4)

Factor each number or monomial completely.

1. 108 $2 \cdot 2 \cdot 3 \cdot 3 \cdot 3$
2. 117 $3 \cdot 3 \cdot 13$
3. -88 $-1 \cdot 2 \cdot 2 \cdot 2 \cdot 11$
4. $72x^2y^2$ $2 \cdot 2 \cdot 2 \cdot 3 \cdot 3 \cdot x \cdot x \cdot y \cdot y$
5. $-175rs^3$ $-1 \cdot 5 \cdot 5 \cdot 7 \cdot r \cdot s \cdot s \cdot s$

Transparency 4-5 contains the 5-Minute Check and a teaching aid for this lesson.

1 FOCUS

The purpose of this lesson is to provide systematic methods to find the greatest common factor for two or more integers or monomials.

Motivating the Lesson

Choose two students and have the other students list things they have in common. Then list things they do not have in common. Transfer the concept to numbers.

2 TEACH

Using Connections

Emphasize the use of divisibility rules in finding the prime factorization of the numbers in the examples.

Chalkboard Examples

- *For Example 1*
  Use prime factorization to find the GCF of 32 and 28. 4
- *For Example 2*
  Use prime factorization to find the GCF of 14, 42, and 56. 14
- *For Example 3*
  Find the GCF of $18k^2$ and $24km$. $6k$
- *For Example 4*
  Find the GCF of $8a^2$, $10a^2b$, and $12ab^2$. $2a$

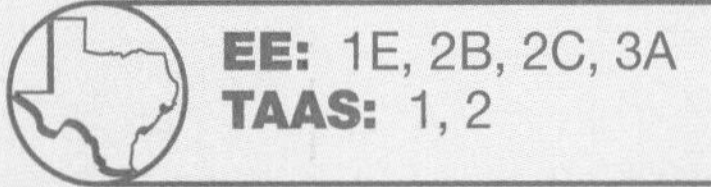

EE: 1E, 2B, 2C, 3A
TAAS: 1, 2

4-5 Greatest Common Factor (GCF)

Objective:
Find the greatest common factor for two or more integers or monomials.

Key Terms:
greatest common factor
GCF

For his project in home economics, Adita wants to create a giant American flag. The widest white material he could find was 78 inches wide, while the widest red material he could find was 91 inches wide. The stripes are to be the same width. If he does not want to waste any material, what is the widest the stripes on his flag can be?

factors of 78: 1, 2, 3, 6, 13, 26, 39, 78

factors of 91: 1, 7, 13, 91

How are divisibility rules helpful in finding the GCF?
You can determine factors without a calculator or paper/pencil.

The *common factors* of 78 and 91, shown in blue, are 1 and 13. The greatest of the factors common to two or more numbers is called the **greatest common factor (GCF)** of each number. The greatest common factor of 78 and 91 is 13.

Each stripe should be 13 inches wide. Adita cuts the 78-inch material into 6 pieces of 13 inches each, and he cuts the 91-inch material into 7 pieces of 13 inches each.

Prime factorization can be used to find the GCF of numbers as follows. Find the prime factorization of each number. Then find the product of their common factors.

Examples

1 **Use prime factorization to find the GCF of 56 and 84.**

First, find the prime factorization of each number.

$$56 = 2 \cdot 28 = 2 \cdot 2 \cdot 14 = 2 \cdot 2 \cdot 2 \cdot 7$$

$$84 = 2 \cdot 42 = 2 \cdot 2 \cdot 21 = 2 \cdot 2 \cdot 3 \cdot 7$$

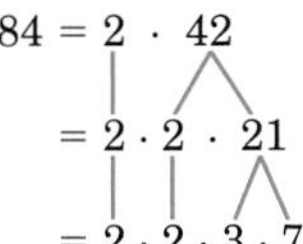

Then find the common factors.

$56 = (2) \cdot (2) \cdot 2 \cdot (7)$
$84 = (2) \cdot (2) \cdot 3 \cdot (7)$

The loops indicate each common factor. They are 2, 2, and 7.

The greatest common factor of 56 and 84 is $2 \cdot 2 \cdot 7$ or 28.

FYI
The largest American flag ever made was first displayed in Evansville, Indiana, on March 22, 1980. It weighs 7.7 tons and is 411 feet long by 210 feet wide.

Bell Ringer

List the first ten prime numbers. 2, 3, 5, 7, 11, 13, 19, 23, 29, 31

2 **Use prime factorization to find the GCF of 60, 20, and 180.**

Write each number as a product of prime factors.

$60 = 2 \cdot 2 \cdot 3 \cdot 5$

$20 = 2 \cdot 2 \cdot 5$

$180 = 2 \cdot 2 \cdot 3 \cdot 3 \cdot 5$

The common factors are 2, 2, and 5.

Thus, the GCF is $2 \cdot 2 \cdot 5$ or 20.

CONNECTION TO ALGEBRA

The GCF of two or more monomials is also the product of their common factors.

Examples

3 **Find the GCF of $24x^2$ and $18x$.**

$24x^2 = 2 \cdot 2 \cdot 2 \cdot 3 \cdot x \cdot x$

$18x = 2 \cdot 3 \cdot 3 \cdot x$

The common factors are 2, 3, and x.

The GCF of $24x^2$ and $18x$ is $2 \cdot 3 \cdot x$ or $6x$.

4 **Find the GCF of $20m^2k$, $30mk^2$, and $45mk$.**

How do you know just by looking that a number will have 5 as a factor? **It ends in 5 or 0.**

$20m^2k = 2 \cdot 2 \cdot 5 \cdot m \cdot m \cdot k$

$30mk^2 = 2 \cdot 3 \cdot 5 \cdot m \cdot k \cdot k$

$45mk = 3 \cdot 3 \cdot 5 \cdot m \cdot k$

The common factors are 5, m, and k.

The GCF of $20m^2k$, $30mk^2$, and $45mk$ is $5mk$.

Checking for Understanding

Communicating Algebra

1. In your own words, explain how to find the GCF of two or more numbers. **1. Find the common prime factors and multiply them.**
2. Use factor trees to find the prime factorization of 135 and 315. Then circle the common factors. **See margin.**
3. Name two numbers whose GCF is 12. **Sample answer: 24, 36**

Guided Practice

Find the GCF of each pair of numbers or monomials.

4. $6 = 2 \cdot 3$, $8 = 2 \cdot 2 \cdot 2$ **2**
5. $20 = 2 \cdot 2 \cdot 5$, $12 = 2 \cdot 2 \cdot 3$ **4**
6. $135 = 3 \cdot 3 \cdot 3 \cdot 5$, $315 = 3 \cdot 3 \cdot 5 \cdot 7$ **45**
7. $20 = 2 \cdot 2 \cdot 5$, $30 = 2 \cdot 3 \cdot 5$ **10**
8. $15r^2s = 3 \cdot 5 \cdot r \cdot r \cdot s$, $27rs^2 = 3 \cdot 3 \cdot 3 \cdot r \cdot s \cdot s$ **3rs**
9. $24a^2b = 2 \cdot 2 \cdot 2 \cdot 3 \cdot a \cdot a \cdot b$, $36ab^2 = 2 \cdot 2 \cdot 3 \cdot 3 \cdot a \cdot b \cdot b$ **12ab**
10. 3, 12 **3**
11. $18ab$, $27a$ **9a**
12. $12x$, $40x^2$ **4x**
13. −5, −7 **−1**

3 PRACTICE/APPLY

Checking the Concept

Have students copy the prime factorization of the numbers and expressions in Exercises 4-9. Observe students while they circle the factors that are common to the two numbers or expressions and check that they do not circle factors common to only one number or expression.

Additional Answer

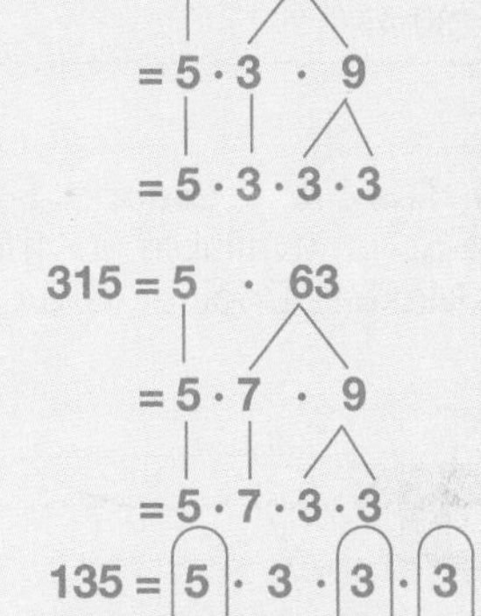

Practice Masters Booklet, **p. 34**

Name ______ Date ______

Practice Worksheet 4-5

Greatest Common Factor (GCF)

Find the GCF for each set of numbers or expressions.

1. 14, 21 **7**	2. 15, 18 **3**	3. −14, 28 **14**
4. 36, 45 **9**	5. −28, 32 **4**	6. 48, 56 **8**
7. 25, −30 **5**	8. 25, 27 **1**	9. −60, 24 **12**
10. 32, 48, 96 **16**	11. 20, 28, 36 **4**	12. −72, 84, 132 **12**
13. 10, 25, 30 **5**	14. −14, 28, 42 **14**	15. 40, 60, 180 **20**
16. −42, 105, 126 **21**	17. 33, 198, 330 **33**	18. −126, 168, 210 **42**
19. $15ab$, $10ac$ **5a**	20. $14xy$, 28 **14**	21. $17xy$, $15x^2z$ **x**
22. $12am^2$, $18a^3m$ **6am**	23. $-120x^2$, $150xy$ **30x**	24. $105x^3y^2$, $165x^2y^4$ **$15x^2y^2$**
25. $9r^2t^2$, $12r^2$ **$3r^2$**	26. $-160zw$, $240w^2$ **80w**	27. $280ac^3$, $320a^3c$ **40ac**
28. $14m$, $21ny$, 28 **7**	29. $21pt$, $49p^2t$, $42pt^2$ **7pt**	30. $-5m^2$, $10m$, $15m^3$ **5m**
31. $5a^2$, $25b^2$, $50ab$ **5**	32. $9x$, $30xy$, $42y$ **3**	33. $15np$, $6n^2$, $39n^2p$ **3n**

Alternate Strategies: Reteaching the Lesson

Reteaching Activity

Using Calculators Have students use calculators and the short division method shown below to write the prime factorization of the number in the examples.

3⟌819	819 ÷ 3 = 273
3⟌273	273 ÷ 3 = 91
7⟌91	91 ÷ 7 = 13
13	

$819 = 3 \cdot 3 \cdot 7 \cdot 13$

Reteaching Masters Booklet, **p. 30**

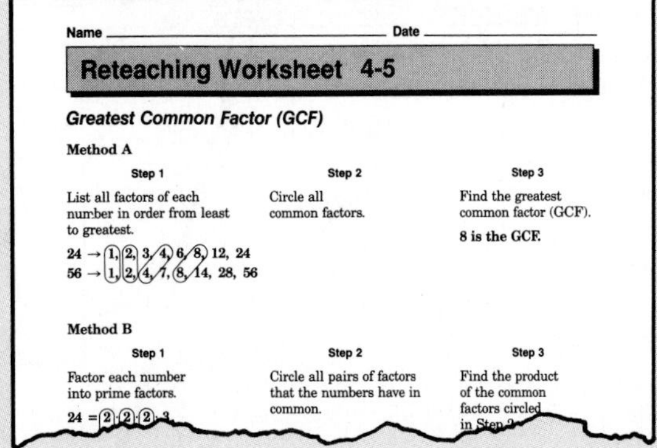
Name ______ Date ______

Reteaching Worksheet 4-5

Greatest Common Factor (GCF)

Method A

Step 1	Step 2	Step 3
List all factors of each number in order from least to greatest.	Circle all common factors.	Find the greatest common factor (GCF). 8 is the GCF.

24 → 1, 2, 3, 4, 6, 8, 12, 24
56 → 1, 2, 4, 7, 8, 14, 28, 56

Method B

Step 1	Step 2	Step 3
Factor each number into prime factors.	Circle all pairs of factors that the numbers have in common.	Find the product of the common factors circled in Step 2.

24 = 2 · 2 · 2 · 3

Error Analysis

Watch for students who cannot differentiate between a list of factors and prime factorization.
Prevent by emphasizing that the student may use only one method if he or she is confused by using both.

Independent Practice

Homework Assignment	
Basic	15-35 odd, 38-43, 46, 47
Average	20-34 even, 38-47
Honors	30-47

Chapter 4, Quiz A, (Lessons 4-1 through 4-5) is available in the Evaluation Masters Booklet, p. 34.

4 CLOSE

Assessment Option

Writing Find the greatest common factor of the following numbers.

1. 14 and 15 1
2. $12p$ and $4p^2$ $4p$
3. $18x^3y^4$ and $9x^2y^6$ $9x^2y^4$

Enrichment Masters Booklet, **p. 30**

Name ______________ Date ______________

Enrichment Worksheet 4-5

Perfect and Imperfect Numbers

In addition to being classified as composite or prime, numbers can be classified as perfect or imperfect.

A **perfect number** is one that is equal to the sum of all of its factors, except itself. There are two perfect numbers less than 30. The third perfect number is 496.

$$496 = 1 + 2 + 4 + 8 + 16 + 31 + 62 + 124 + 248$$

An **imperfect number** is one that is not equal to the sum of its factors, except itself. When the sum of its factors is greater than the number, it is called an **abundant number.** When the sum of its factors is less than the number, it is called a **deficient number.**

Solve.

1. Find a perfect number between 1 and 10. $6 = 1 + 2 + 3$
2. Find a perfect number between 20 and 30. $28 = 1 + 2 + 4 + 7 + 14$
3. The formula $N = (2^{n+1} - 1) \cdot 2^n$ can be used to find perfect numbers. N is a perfect number *if* $(2^{n+1} - 1)$ is a prime number. Find N when $n = 1$. 6
4. Find N when $n = 2$. Is N a perfect number? 28; yes
5. Find N when $n = 3$. Is N a perfect number? 120; no
6. Find the value of n that produces a value of 496 for N. 4
7. Find the fourth perfect number. when $n = 6$, $N = 8128$
8. Find an abundant number between 20 and 30. 24
9. Find a deficient number between 15 and 20. 16, 17, or 19

Exercises

Independent Practice

ESTIMATION
MENTAL MATH
CALCULATOR
PAPER/PENCIL

Find the GCF for each set of numbers or monomials.

14. 40, 24 8 **15.** 24, 36 12 **16.** 93, 69 3 **17.** 42, 56 14
18. 56, 16 8 **19.** 48, 84 12 **20.** 6, 8, 12 2 **21.** 10, 15, 25 5
22. 108, 144 36 **23.** 72, 216 72 **24.** 12, 18, 30 6 **25.** 9, 15, 24 3
26. $7m^2$, $35m$ $7m$ **27.** $14k$, $42k^2$ $14k$ **28.** $33y^2$, $44y$ $11y$
29. $-26m^2$, $52m^3$ $13m^2$ **30.** $-25ab$, $35b$ $5b$ **31.** -18, $45xy$ 9
32. $24x^2$, $-60x$ $12x$ **33.** $16y$, $40y^2$ $8y$ **34.** $14m$, $-56m^3$ $14m$
35. $18a$, $30ab$, $42b$ 6 **36.** $15x^2$, $35y^2$, $70xy$ 5 **37.** $18mk$, $6m^2$, $42m^2k$ $6m$

Mixed Review

38. Simplify the expression $-18xy + 12xy + (-13xy)$. (Lesson 2-4) $-19xy$
39. Find the perimeter of a rectangle whose sides are 12 cm and 3 cm. (Lesson 3-6) 30 cm
40. Solve the inequality $-26 < \frac{m}{-3}$. (Lesson 3-8) $78 > m$
41. Use divisibility rules to determine if 231 is divisible by 6. (Lesson 4-1) no
42. Evaluate the expression $4k^3$ if $k = 3$. (Lesson 4-2) 108

Applications

43. Engineering A bicycle path being planned along State Route 80 will run 42 miles between the first two cities. The path will continue on to a third city 70 miles farther away. The planners wish to make rest-stops at each city and at equal distances along the entire course. If the distances between stops is as great as possible, how far apart should the rest-stops be? 14 miles

44. Carpentry The industrial technology class is building a storage shelf. The class wants to make the best use of a piece of plywood that measures 48 in. by 72 in. How many shelves measuring 12 in. by 16 in. could be cut from the plywood with no waste? 18 shelves

Connection

45. Algebra Alberto is 14 years old. The GCF of his age and his younger sister's age is 7. How old is his sister? 7 years old

Critical Thinking

46. Numbers that have a GCF of 1 are said to be **relatively prime.** Find the least two composite numbers that are relatively prime. 4, 9

Wrap-Up

47. Write three numbers that have a GCF of 8. Sample answer: 24, 40, 72

Alternate Strategies: Extending the Lesson

Enrichment

Using Models Use counters to model Euclid's method for finding the GCF. Find the GCF of 20 and 56.

1. Divide the greater number by the lesser number.
2. Divide the lesser number by the remainder.
3. Continue until there is a remainder of zero. The last nonzero remainder is the GCF.

The GCF of 20 and 56 is 4.

Cooperative Learning

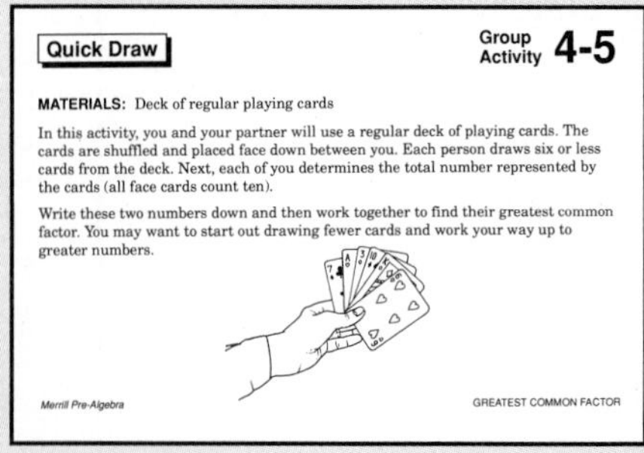
Quick Draw

Group Activity **4-5**

MATERIALS: Deck of regular playing cards

In this activity, you and your partner will use a regular deck of playing cards. The cards are shuffled and placed face down between you. Each person draws six or less cards from the deck. Next, each of you determines the total number represented by the cards (all face cards count ten).

Write these two numbers down and then work together to find their greatest common factor. You may want to start out drawing fewer cards and work your way up to greater numbers.

Merrill Pre-Algebra GREATEST COMMON FACTOR

4-6 Simplifying Fractions

Objective:
Simplify fractions by using the GCF.

Key Terms:
ratio
simplest form
algebraic fraction

A pizza was cut into 4 equal pieces. There are three pieces left. The ratio of pieces left to total pieces is 3 to 4.

A **ratio** is a comparison of two numbers by division. The ratio above can be expressed in the following ways.

3 to 4   3:4 $\frac{3}{4}$ $3 \div 4$

A ratio is most commonly expressed as a fraction in **simplest form.** A fraction is in simplest form when the GCF of the numerator and denominator is 1.

Example

1 Write $\frac{24}{40}$ in simplest form.

$24 = (2) \cdot (2) \cdot (2) \cdot 3$

$40 = (2) \cdot (2) \cdot (2) \cdot 5$

The GCF of 24 and 40 is $2 \cdot 2 \cdot 2$ or 8.

$\frac{24}{40} \overset{\div 8}{=} \frac{3}{5}$ ($\div 8$)

Since the GCF of 3 and 5 is 1, the fraction $\frac{3}{5}$ is in simplest form.

The division in the example above can be represented in another way.

$\frac{24}{40} = \frac{\not{2} \cdot \not{2} \cdot \not{2} \cdot 3}{\not{2} \cdot \not{2} \cdot \not{2} \cdot 5} = \frac{3}{5}$ The slashes indicate that the numerator and denominator are divided by $2 \cdot 2 \cdot 2$, the GCF.

Example

2 Write $\frac{20}{36}$ in simplest form.

$\frac{20}{36} = \frac{5 \cdot \not{2} \cdot \not{2}}{3 \cdot 3 \cdot \not{2} \cdot \not{2}}$ Divide both the numerator and the denominator by $2 \cdot 2$, the GCF.

$= \frac{5}{9}$

History Connection

Fractions occur in the oldest mathematical records. As early as 2000 B.C., the Babylonians used fractions based on powers of 60. Our numeral $1\frac{1}{2}$ would have been written 1 30 (meaning $1\frac{30}{60}$). Using Babylonian numerals, 1 30 would have been written

Bell Ringer

Play "20 Questions" with two numbers. Give students their GCF as a hint to begin.

Lesson Notes 4-6

5-Minute Check
(over Lesson 4-5)

Find the GCF for each set of numbers or expressions.
1. 14, –35 **7**
2. 27, 39 **3**
3. 15, 24, 36 **3**
4. $12s^2t$, $30st^2$ **$6st$**
5. $36m^3k$, $45m^2$, $63mk$ **$9m$**

Transparency 4-6 contains the 5-Minute Check and a teaching aid for this lesson.

1 FOCUS

The purpose of this lesson is to demonstrate how the GCF can be applied to simplifying fractions.

Motivating the Lesson

Have one student pour two half cups of water into a clear jar. Have another student pour four quarter cups of water into an identical container. Point out that the same amount of water was poured into each container. Relate this to simplifying fractions.

2 TEACH

Using Manipulatives

Have students write the number 2 on several slips of paper. Repeat with other prime numbers through 11. Draw two groups of five slips of paper each, each group representing factors of the numerator and the denominator. Remove common factors and name the fraction in simplest form.

Chalkboard Examples

- *For Example 1*
  Write $\frac{45}{63}$ in simplest form. $\frac{5}{7}$
- *For Example 2*
  Write $\frac{30}{48}$ in simplest form. $\frac{5}{8}$
- *For Example 3*
  Simplify $\frac{21a^2b}{24ab}$. $\frac{7a}{8}$

EE: 1E, 2C, 3A
TAAS: 1, 2, 11

3 PRACTICE/APPLY

Checking the Concept

For each fraction in Exercises 7-16 that is not in simplest form, have students list prime factors for the numerator and denominator before dividing. If their answer is not in simplest form, check to see if students eliminated all the common factors.

Error Analysis

Watch for students who forget to divide both numbers by the GCF. **Prevent by** having students check their problem by multiplying both the numerator and the denominator of the simplified fraction by the GCF to get the original fraction.

Practice Masters Booklet, **p. 35**

Name ________________ Date ________________

Practice Worksheet 4-6

Simplifying Fractions

Write each fraction in simplest form.

1. $\frac{3}{9}$ $\frac{1}{3}$	2. $\frac{6}{10}$ $\frac{3}{5}$	3. $\frac{12}{18}$ $\frac{2}{3}$	4. $\frac{5}{20}$ $\frac{1}{4}$
5. $\frac{9}{12}$ $\frac{3}{4}$	6. $\frac{15}{20}$ $\frac{3}{4}$	7. $\frac{9}{21}$ $\frac{3}{7}$	8. $\frac{28}{32}$ $\frac{7}{8}$
9. $\frac{10}{35}$ $\frac{2}{7}$	10. $\frac{24}{30}$ $\frac{4}{5}$	11. $\frac{49}{98}$ $\frac{1}{2}$	12. $\frac{28}{48}$ $\frac{7}{12}$
13. $\frac{14}{26}$ $\frac{7}{13}$	14. $\frac{11}{88}$ $\frac{1}{8}$	15. $\frac{45}{81}$ $\frac{5}{9}$	16. $\frac{27}{45}$ $\frac{3}{5}$
17. $\frac{16}{48}$ $\frac{1}{3}$	18. $\frac{45}{99}$ $\frac{5}{11}$	19. $\frac{13}{91}$ $\frac{1}{7}$	20. $\frac{30}{42}$ $\frac{5}{7}$
21. $\frac{84}{140}$ $\frac{3}{5}$	22. $\frac{96}{112}$ $\frac{6}{7}$	23. $\frac{52}{78}$ $\frac{2}{3}$	24. $\frac{62}{66}$ $\frac{31}{33}$
25. $\frac{15}{90}$ $\frac{1}{6}$	26. $\frac{56}{84}$ $\frac{2}{3}$	27. $\frac{105}{175}$ $\frac{3}{5}$	28. $\frac{258}{387}$ $\frac{2}{3}$
29. $\frac{300}{375}$ $\frac{4}{5}$	30. $\frac{240}{255}$ $\frac{16}{17}$	31. $\frac{64}{776}$ $\frac{8}{97}$	32. $\frac{1320}{1650}$ $\frac{4}{5}$
33. $\frac{5x^2y}{30xy}$ $\frac{x}{6}$	34. $\frac{24c^3d}{36c^2d}$ $\frac{2c}{3}$	35. $\frac{15ef^2}{35ef}$ $\frac{3f}{7}$	36. $\frac{3r^2s^2}{27rs}$ $\frac{rs}{9}$
37. $\frac{15wx}{45w}$ $\frac{x}{3}$	38. $\frac{36l^2m}{81lm^2}$ $\frac{4l}{9m}$	39. $\frac{27m^2n^2}{45mn}$ $\frac{3mn}{5}$	40. $\frac{24xz}{64x^2z}$ $\frac{3}{8x}$
41. $\frac{18h^2d}{54d}$ $\frac{h^2}{3}$	42. $\frac{36st^2}{72t^2}$ $\frac{s}{2}$	43. $\frac{19x^2y^2}{38xy}$ $\frac{xy}{2}$	44. $\frac{48a^2b^2}{64a^2b}$ $\frac{3b}{4}$

CONNECTION TO ALGEBRA

Fractions with variables in the numerator or denominator are called **algebraic fractions.** Algebraic fractions can also be written in simplest form.

Example

3 **Simplify $\frac{8a^2b}{12ab}$.** Both *a* and *b* must not be zero.

What is the GCF of $8a^2b$ and $12ab$? **4ab**

$$\frac{8a^2b}{12ab} = \frac{\cancel{2} \cdot \cancel{2} \cdot 2 \cdot \cancel{a} \cdot a \cdot \cancel{b}}{\cancel{2} \cdot \cancel{2} \cdot 3 \cdot \cancel{a} \cdot \cancel{b}}$$ Divide both the numerator and the denominator by $2 \cdot 2 \cdot a \cdot b$.

$$= \frac{2a}{3}$$

Checking for Understanding

Communicating Algebra

1. Explain how you would write $\frac{24}{26}$ in simplest form. **1. Divide numerator and denominator by 2.**
2. Explain how you know whether a fraction is in simplest form. **If the GCF of the numerator and denominator is 1.**

Guided Practice

Express each ratio as a fraction.

3. $7 \div 8$ $\frac{7}{8}$
4. 5 to 8 $\frac{5}{8}$
5. 9:10 $\frac{9}{10}$
6. three to six $\frac{3}{6}$ or $\frac{1}{2}$

State whether each fraction is in simplest form. If it is not in simplest form, write it in simplest form.

7. $\frac{3}{5}$ yes
8. $\frac{3}{6}$ no, $\frac{1}{2}$
9. $\frac{15}{21}$ no, $\frac{5}{7}$
10. $\frac{30}{37}$ yes
11. $\frac{51}{60}$ no, $\frac{17}{20}$
12. $\frac{8ab}{15cd}$ yes
13. $\frac{7x}{14xy}$ no, $\frac{1}{2y}$
14. $\frac{11m}{13t}$ yes
15. $\frac{8z^2}{16z}$ no, $\frac{z}{2}$
16. $\frac{12cd}{20}$ no, $\frac{3cd}{5}$

Exercises

Independent Practice

ESTIMATION / MENTAL MATH / CALCULATOR / PAPER/PENCIL

Write each fraction in simplest form.

17. $\frac{2}{10}$ $\frac{1}{5}$	18. $\frac{8}{12}$ $\frac{2}{3}$	19. $\frac{12}{16}$ $\frac{3}{4}$	20. $\frac{2}{14}$ $\frac{1}{7}$	21. $\frac{9}{15}$ $\frac{3}{5}$
22. $\frac{4}{18}$ $\frac{2}{9}$	23. $\frac{7}{21}$ $\frac{1}{3}$	24. $\frac{15}{30}$ $\frac{1}{2}$	25. $\frac{16}{24}$ $\frac{2}{3}$	26. $\frac{10}{22}$ $\frac{5}{11}$
27. $\frac{20}{28}$ $\frac{5}{7}$	28. $\frac{24}{32}$ $\frac{3}{4}$	29. $\frac{18}{36}$ $\frac{1}{2}$	30. $\frac{27}{33}$ $\frac{9}{11}$	31. $\frac{30}{35}$ $\frac{6}{7}$
32. $\frac{12}{40}$ $\frac{3}{10}$	33. $\frac{25}{40}$ $\frac{5}{8}$	34. $\frac{40}{42}$ $\frac{20}{21}$	35. $\frac{18}{44}$ $\frac{9}{22}$	36. $\frac{21}{45}$ $\frac{7}{15}$

37. $\frac{12m^2k}{15mk}$ $\frac{4m}{5}$	38. $\frac{36a^3b}{48a^2b}$ $\frac{3a}{4}$	39. $\frac{15rs^2}{50rs}$ $\frac{3s}{10}$	40. $\frac{3x^2y^2}{51xy}$ $\frac{xy}{17}$
41. $\frac{28rsy}{52rsy}$ $\frac{7}{13}$	42. $\frac{40p^2q}{52pq^2}$ $\frac{10p}{13q}$	43. $\frac{17k^2z}{51z}$ $\frac{k^2}{3}$	44. $\frac{48m^2r^2}{56m^2r}$ $\frac{6r}{7}$

Alternate Strategies: Reteaching the Lesson

Reteaching Activity

Using a Diagram On the chalkboard or overhead draw a picture of a pizza, cut into six pieces. For one piece, write the fraction representing the part of the pizza included. Simplify the fraction, if possible. Repeat for two through six pieces.

Reteaching Masters Booklet, **p. 31**

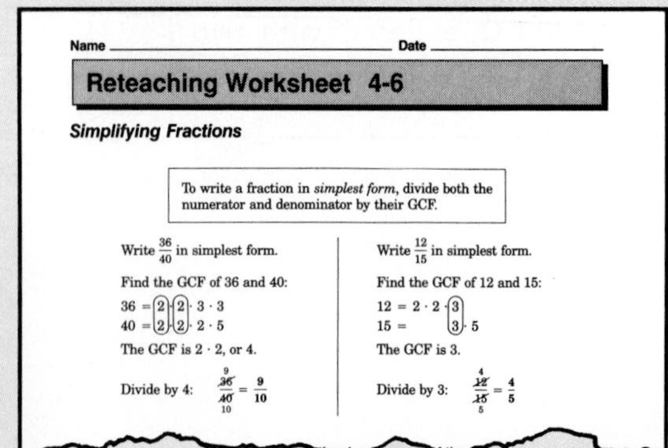

Name ________________ Date ________________

Reteaching Worksheet 4-6

Simplifying Fractions

To write a fraction in *simplest form*, divide both the numerator and denominator by their GCF.

Write $\frac{36}{40}$ in simplest form.

Find the GCF of 36 and 40:

$36 = 2 \cdot 2 \cdot 3 \cdot 3$

$40 = 2 \cdot 2 \cdot 2 \cdot 5$

The GCF is $2 \cdot 2$, or 4.

Divide by 4: $\frac{36}{40} = \frac{9}{10}$

Write $\frac{12}{15}$ in simplest form.

Find the GCF of 12 and 15:

$12 = 2 \cdot 2 \cdot 3$

$15 = 3 \cdot 5$

The GCF is 3.

Divide by 3: $\frac{12}{15} = \frac{4}{5}$

Mixed Review

45. Write the negation of the statement *The greatest common factor of 10 and 15 is 5.* (Lesson 2-6) **The GCF of 10 and 15 is not 5.**

46. Solve the equation $a + 9 = -13$. (Lesson 3-1) **-22**

47. **Sports** The Brandon Bobcats need at least 10 more points to win the football game. If the opponent's score is 26, what is the Bobcats' score? (Lesson 3-10) **17**

48. Is the number 51 a *prime* or *composite?* (Lesson 4-4) **composite**

49. State the least prime number that is a factor of the number 48. (Lesson 4-4) **2**

Applications

50. **Conservation** The fish commission is stocking fish in Beechwood Lake. Suppose 2800 brown trout and 2100 rainbow trout are put in the lake. Express the ratio of rainbow trout to the total fish stocked as a fraction in simplest form. $\frac{3}{7}$

51. **Sports** Karen made 8 of 14 free throws in her last basketball game. How would you describe her success as a fraction in simplest form? $\frac{4}{7}$

Connection

52. **Statistics** In a school district census, 2800 students are female and 2400 students are male. Express the ratio of males to females as a fraction in simplest form. $\frac{6}{7}$

Critical Thinking

53. Any odd number that is greater than 5 can be written as the sum of three prime numbers, $(7 = 3 + 2 + 2)$. Show that this statement is true for odd numbers between 50 and 60. **$51 = 17 + 17 + 17$; $53 = 17 + 17 + 19$; $55 = 17 + 19 + 19$; $57 = 19 + 19 + 19$; $59 = 17 + 19 + 23$**

Wrap-Up

54. Describe a situation where a fraction in simplest form would be more easily understood than the original equivalent fraction. **Sample answer: See Exercise 50.**

Mid-Chapter Quiz

Use divisibility rules to determine whether the first number is a factor of the second number. Write *yes* or *no*. (Lesson 4-1)

1. 6; 236 **no**
2. 3; 342 **yes**
3. 2; 838 **yes**
4. 5; 1024 **no**

Evaluate each expression. (Lesson 4-2)

5. $42 - 3 \cdot 9$ **15**
6. $\frac{4^2 - 2}{5 + 3^2}$ **1**
7. $\frac{2^2 \cdot 3^2 + 5}{2^2(3^2 + 5)}$ $\frac{41}{56}$
8. $\frac{4 \cdot 9 - 2^2}{4 - 3 \cdot 4}$ **-4**

Solve. (Lesson 4-3)

9. Eight softball teams are to play in a round-robin tournament; that is, they play each other once. For how many games will umpires be needed? **28**

Factor each number or monomial completely. (Lesson 4-4)

10. 40 $2^3 \cdot 5$
11. 75 $3 \cdot 5^2$
12. -180 $-1 \cdot 2^2 \cdot 3^2 \cdot 5$
13. $154a^2bc^2$ $2 \cdot 7 \cdot 11 \cdot a^2 \cdot b \cdot c^2$

Find the GCF. (Lesson 4-5)

14. 54, 72 **18**
15. $25x^2$, $30xy$ $5x$
16. 36, 120 **12**
17. $24xy^2$, $36x^2y$, $48xy$ $12xy$

Alternate Strategies: Extending the Lesson

Enrichment

Using Cooperative Groups Have each group use sports to generate problems that result in fractions that can be simplified. For example, during a basketball game, what fraction of players are home players? Trade and solve.

Cooperative Learning

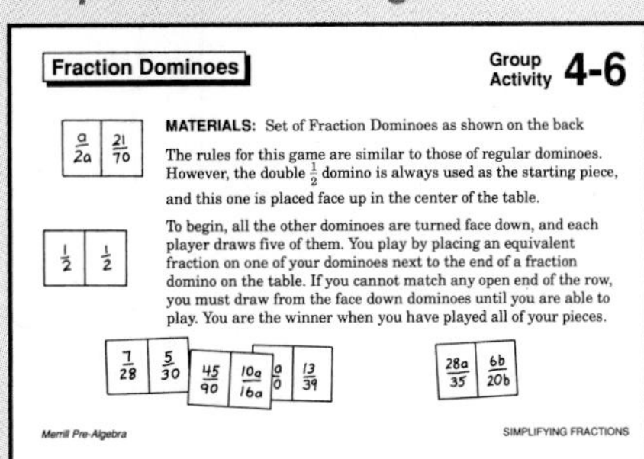

Fraction Dominoes Group Activity **4-6**

MATERIALS: Set of Fraction Dominoes as shown on the back

The rules for this game are similar to those of regular dominoes. However, the double $\frac{1}{2}$ domino is always used as the starting piece, and this one is placed face up in the center of the table.

To begin, all the other dominoes are turned face down, and each player draws five of them. You play by placing an equivalent fraction on one of your dominoes next to the end of a fraction domino on the table. If you cannot match any open end of the row, you must draw from the face down dominoes until you are able to play. You are the winner when you have played all of your pieces.

Merrill Pre-Algebra SIMPLIFYING FRACTIONS

Independent Practice

Homework Assignment	
Basic	17-43 odd, 45-50, 53, 54
Average	22-44 even, 45-54
Honors	33-54
All	Mid-Chapter Quiz 1-17

4 CLOSE

Assessment Option

Speaking Have students explain how to simplify the fractions below.

1. $\frac{15}{20}$ **divide numerator and denominator by 5**
2. $\frac{3}{6}$ **divide numerator and denominator by 3**
3. $\frac{11}{22}$ **divide numerator and denominator by 11**

Enrichment Masters Booklet, **p. 31**

Name ______________________ Date ____________

Enrichment Worksheet 4-6

Matching Equivalent Fractions

Cut out the pieces below and match the edges so that equivalent fractions meet. The pieces form a rectangle. The outer edges of the rectangle formed will have no fractions on them.

Piece	Top	Left	Right	Bottom
15	9/10	15/35	5/9	3/24
18	1/7	12/42	3/8	2/10
11	11/12	16/28	5/8	45/50
10	12/13	8/20	4/7	40/45
14	8/9	5/15	3/7	3/21
8	9/11	15/21		40/44
5	3/10		1/2	52/56
23	1/6	35/77	7/13	
19	1/8	18/48	4/9	2/18
4		8/10		27/33
20	1/12	24/54		2/20
24	1/10	49/91		
3		6/8	4/5	21/33
13	7/8		1/3	3/18
7	7/11	9/15	5/7	44/48
2		4/6	3/4	9/33
22	1/5	14/56	5/11	
21	1/4		2/8	
17	1/6		2/7	2/8
9	13/14		2/5	35/40
1			2/3	6/20
16	6/7	25/45		3/36
6	3/11	3/6	3/5	48/52
12	10/11	20/32		30/35

1	2	3	4
5	6	7	8
9	10	11	12
13	14	15	16
17	18	19	20
21	22	23	24

Lesson Notes 4-7

5-Minute Check
(over Lesson 4-6)

Write each fraction in simplest form.

1. $\frac{8}{24}$ $\frac{1}{3}$ 2. $\frac{15}{25}$ $\frac{3}{5}$ 3. $\frac{15x^2}{18xy}$ $\frac{5x}{6y}$
4. $\frac{17y^3z}{34y^2z^2}$ $\frac{y}{2z}$ 5. $\frac{36m^2x^3}{42m^2x}$ $\frac{6x^2}{7}$

Transparency 4-7 contains the 5-Minute Check and a teaching aid for this lesson.

1 FOCUS

The purpose of this lesson is to provide systematic methods to find the least common multiple of two or more integers or monomials.

2 TEACH

Using Discussion

Write the following lists on the chalkboard or overhead.

1, 2, 3, 4, 6, 12
12, 24, 36, 48, 60, 72

Ask students how they would classify each list. **The first list shows the factors of 12 and the second list shows the first 6 multiples of 12.**

Chalkboard Examples

- *For Example 1*
  List the first five multiples of 3. **0, 3, 6, 9, 12**
- *For Example 2*
  List the first five multiples of x. **0, x, $2x$, $3x$, $4x$**

Find the LCM for each pair of numbers.

- *For Example 3* 5, 7 **35**
- *For Example 4* 6, 8 **24**

EE: 1E, 2C, 3A
TAAS: 1, 2

4-7 Least Common Multiple (LCM)

Objective:
You will learn how to find the least common multiple of two or more numbers.

Key Terms:
multiple
least common multiple
LCM

Joe and Rosa are training for the Boston Marathon. Joe can go around the park in his wheelchair in 3 minutes; Rosa can go the same distance in 4 minutes. If they start at the same time, when will they be side-by-side again?

Multiples can be used to answer this question. A **multiple** of a number is the product of that number and any whole number.

Recall that whole numbers are 0, 1, 2, 3, . . .

multiples of 3: 0, 3, 6, 9, 12, 15, 18, 21, 24, . . .

multiples of 4: 0, 4, 8, 12, 16, 20, 24, 28, 32, . . .

Common multiples of 3 and 4 are 0, 12, 24, 36, ... The least of the nonzero common multiples of two or more numbers is called the **least common multiple (LCM)** of the numbers. The least common multiple of 3 and 4 is 12. So, Joe and Rosa will be side-by-side again in 12 minutes.

Examples

1 List the first five multiples of 4.

	$0 \cdot 4$	$1 \cdot 4$	$2 \cdot 4$	$3 \cdot 4$	$4 \cdot 4$
multiples of 4	0,	4,	8,	12,	16

What can you say about the first multiple of any number? **It is 0.**

2 List the first five multiples of n.

	$0 \cdot n$	$1 \cdot n$	$2 \cdot n$	$3 \cdot n$	$4 \cdot n$
multiples of n	0,	n,	$2n$,	$3n$,	$4n$

Calculator Hint

You can use a calculator to find the LCM. Divide multiples of the greater number by the lesser number until you get a whole number quotient.

Find the LCM for each pair of numbers.

3 3, 5

multiples of 3:
0, 3, 6, 9, 12, 15, . . .
multiples of 5:
0, 5, 10, 15, 20, . . .

The LCM is 15.

4 4, 6

multiples of 4:
0, 4, 8, 12, 16, . . .
multiples of 6:
0, 6, 12, 18, . . .

The LCM is 12.

Bell Ringer

Which of the following fractions is in simplest form?
$\frac{7}{21}$, $\frac{3}{33}$, $\frac{8}{23}$ $\frac{8}{23}$

Prime factorization can be used to find the LCM of a set of numbers. A common multiple contains *all* of the prime factors of each number. The LCM contains *each* factor the greatest number of times it appears for any of the numbers.

Examples

Use prime factorization to find the LCM for each set of numbers.

5 **12, 16**

$12 = 2 \cdot 2 \cdot 3$ or $2^2 \cdot 3$

$16 = 2 \cdot 2 \cdot 2 \cdot 2$ or 2^4

Find the common factors. Multiply all the factors, using the common factors only once.

So, the LCM of 12 and 8 is $2 \cdot 2 \cdot 2 \cdot 2 \cdot 3$ or 48.

6 **15, 18, 12**

$15 = 3 \cdot 5$

$18 = 2 \cdot 3 \cdot 3$ or $2 \cdot 3^2$

$12 = 2 \cdot 2 \cdot 3$ or $2^2 \cdot 3$

The greatest power of 2 is 2^2.
The greatest power of 3 is 3^2.
The greatest power of 5 is 5^1.

The LCM is $2^2 \cdot 3^2 \cdot 5$ or 180.

CONNECTION TO ALGEBRA

The LCM of two or more monomials is also the product of the greatest power of each factor.

Example

7 **Find the LCM of $5x$ and $10x^2$.**

$5x = 5 \cdot x$

$10x^2 = 2 \cdot 5 \cdot x \cdot x$

The greatest power of 2 is 2^1.
The greatest power of 5 is 5^1.
The greatest power of x is x^2.

The LCM is $2 \cdot 5 \cdot x^2$ or $10x^2$.

Checking for Understanding

Communicating Algebra

1. Explain how to find the first five multiples of 6. **6 • 0, 6 • 1, 6 • 2, 6 • 3, 6 • 4**
2. In your own words, describe how to find the LCM of a set of numbers if you have the prime factorization of each number. **Multiply the greatest power of each number.**

Guided Practice

List the first four multiples of each number.

3. 12 **0, 12, 24, 36**
4. 7 **0, 7, 14, 21**
5. 30 **0, 30, 60, 90**
6. k **0, k, $2k$, $3k$**

Find the LCM.

7. multiples of 2: 0, 2, 4, 6, 8, 10, 12, . . .
   multiples of 5: 0, 5, 10, 15, 20, 25, . . . **10**
8. multiples of 6: 0, 6, 12, 18, 24, . . .
   multiples of 9: 0, 9, 18, 27, 36, . . . **18**

Use prime factorization to find the LCM for each set of numbers.

9. 8, 9 **72**
10. 10, 14 **70**
11. 20, 12 **60**
12. 45, 30, 35 **630**

Chalkboard Examples

Use prime factorization to find the LCM for each set of numbers.

- *For Example 5*
  16, 20 **80**
- *For Example 6*
  10, 25, 60 **300**
- *For Example 7*
  $4m$ and $6m^3$ **$12m^3$**

3 PRACTICE/APPLY

Checking the Concept

After students have completed the Guided Practice exercises, ask students if the way they determined the answer to Exercise 12 was different from the way they determined the answers to Exercises 9-11.

Error Analysis

Watch for students who multiply common factors more than one time when determining the LCM. **Prevent by** having students circle factors as they multiply them.

Practice Masters Booklet, **p. 36**

Name ________ Date ________

Practice Worksheet 4-7

Least Common Multiple (LCM)

Determine whether the first number is a multiple of the second number.

1. 75; 15 Yes	2. 63; 18 No	3. 50; 5 Yes	4. 60; 12 Yes
5. 48; 9 No	6. 28; 7 Yes	7. 56; 7 Yes	8. 98; 16 No
9. 42; 8 No	10. 54; 6 Yes	11. 144; 12 Yes	12. 220; 15 No
13. 300; 10 Yes	14. 207; 23 Yes	15. 625; 25 Yes	16. 650; 26 Yes

List the first four multiples of each number.

17. 18 0, 18, 36, 54	18. 1 0, 1, 2, 3	19. 13 0, 13, 26, 39	20. 8 0, 8, 16, 24
21. 11 0, 11, 22, 33	22. 25 0, 25, 50, 75	23. 50 0, 50, 100, 150	24. 81 0, 81, 162, 243

Find the LCM for each set of numbers or monomials.

25. 24, 36 72	26. 54, 63 378	27. 18, 72 72	28. 27, 36 108
29. 4, 5 20	30. 10, 15 30	31. 5, 8 40	32. 8, 20 40
33. 8, 12 24	34. 32, 64 64	35. 12, 18 36	36. 10, 25 50
37. $5x$, $12x$ $60x$	38. $15x$, $45y$ $45xy$	39. $15k$, $35k^2$ $105k^2$	40. $12h^2$, 28 $84h^2$
41. $6p$, $8p$, $12p$ $24p$	42. $3x$, $15x^2$, 30 $30x^2$	43. $8l$, $20l$, $24l^2$ $120l^2$	44. $3e$, $5e^2$, $7e$ $105e^2$

Alternate Strategies: Reteaching the Lesson

Reteaching Activity

Using Lists Concentrate on one method for determining LCM. For most students, listing the multiples is easier. Provide students with a worksheet where the multiples must be listed, common multiples circled, and LCM identified.

Reteaching Masters Booklet, **p. 32**

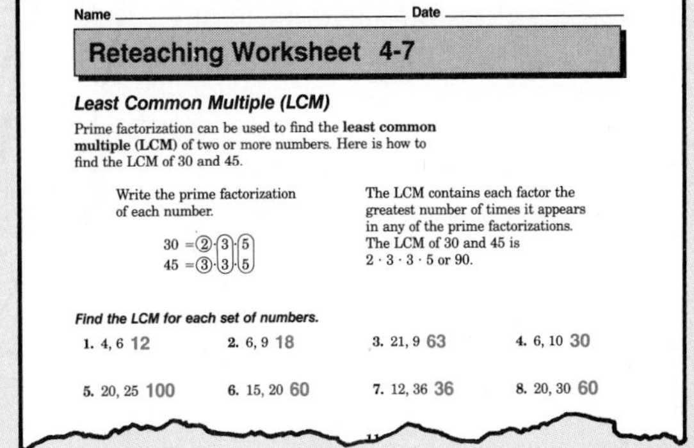

Name ________ Date ________

Reteaching Worksheet 4-7

Least Common Multiple (LCM)

Prime factorization can be used to find the **least common multiple (LCM)** of two or more numbers. Here is how to find the LCM of 30 and 45.

Write the prime factorization of each number.

$30 = 2 \cdot 3 \cdot 5$
$45 = 3 \cdot 3 \cdot 5$

The LCM contains each factor the greatest number of times it appears in any of the prime factorizations. The LCM of 30 and 45 is $2 \cdot 3 \cdot 3 \cdot 5$ or 90.

Find the LCM for each set of numbers.

1. 4, 6 12	2. 6, 9 18	3. 21, 9 63	4. 6, 10 30
5. 20, 25 100	6. 15, 20 60	7. 12, 36 36	8. 20, 30 60

Independent Practice

Homework Assignment	
Basic	13-39 odd, 45-50, 52, 53
Average	20-44 even, 45-53
Honors	20-30 even, 38-53

4 CLOSE

Assessment Options

Writing Find the LCM of each set of numbers.
1. 5 and 13 65
2. 3 and 11 33
3. 17 and 2 34

Speaking What characteristic do all the numbers above have in common? They are all prime numbers.
Explain how to find the LCM of two prime numbers. Find the product of the two numbers.

Enrichment Masters Booklet, **p. 32**

Name ______________________ Date ______________

Enrichment Worksheet 4-7

GCF, LCM, and Ladders

When two or more numbers have common factors, the greatest of these is termed the **greatest common factor (GCF).** When two or more numbers have nonzero common multiples, the least of these is called the **least common multiple (LCM)** of the numbers. A method of determining the GCF and LCM for two or more numbers is the *ladder.*

Example: Find the GCF and LCM of 24 and 36.

6 | 24 36 — Find any number that will divide into both numbers.
2 | 4 6 — Both 24 and 36 can be divided evenly by 6.
1 | 2 3 — Continue to choose divisors until the only remaining divisor is 1.
2 3

To find the GCF, multiply all the divisors.
$6 \cdot 2 \cdot 1 = 12$ The GCF is 12.

To find the LCM, multiply the GCF and the numbers left on the bottom of the ladder.
$12 \cdot 2 \cdot 3 = 72$ The LCM is 72.

The numbers used as divisors in the ladder may vary.
Find the GCF and LCM for each pair of numbers by using a ladder.

1. 18, 27 GCF: 9 LCM: 54
2. 24, 42 GCF: 6 LCM: 168
3. 44, 66 GCF: 22 LCM: 132
4. 36, 81 GCF: 9 LCM: 324
5. 42, 48 GCF: 6 LCM: 336
6. 100, 125 GCF: 25 LCM: 500
7. 64, 72 GCF: 8 LCM: 576
8. 90, 150 GCF: 30 LCM: 450
9. 250, 300 GCF: 50 LCM: 1500

Exercises

Independent Practice

Determine whether the first number is a multiple of the second number.

13. 28; 7 yes
14. 32; 5 no
15. 24; 3 yes
16. 42; 6 yes
17. 52; 13 yes
18. 144; 9 yes
19. 108; 8 no
20. 116; 7 no
21. 156; 12 yes
22. 162; 18 yes
23. 4500; 18 yes
24. 8664; 36 no

Find the LCM for each set of numbers or monomials.

25. 6, 10 30
26. 4, 10 20
27. 8, 12 24
28. 2, 9 18
29. 15, 18 90
30. 6, 15 30
31. 5, 7 35
32. 8, 14 56
33. 21, 28 84
34. 14, 21 42
35. 18, 32 288
36. 15, 75 75
37. $7y$, $12y$ $84y$
38. $20cd$, $50d$ (38. $100cd$)
39. $16x$, $24y$ $48xy$
40. $12x$, $35x^2$ (40. $420x^2$)
41. $4k$, $8k$, $12k$ $24k$
42. 9, 12, 15 180
43. 7, 21, 84 84
44. $3c$, $5c^2$, 7 $105c^2$

Mixed Review

45. Solve the equation $d = \frac{225}{-5}$. (Lesson 2-8) -45
46. *True* or *false:* To solve the equation $-4m = 56$, divide each side of the equation by 56. (Lesson 3-3) false
47. Using the formula $I = \frac{V}{R}$, find the amperes if the voltage is 88 volts and the resistance is 8 ohms. (Lesson 3-5) 11 amps
48. Factor the monomial $45a^2b^3$. (Lesson 4-4) $3 \cdot 3 \cdot 5 \cdot a \cdot a \cdot b \cdot b \cdot b$
49. Find the GCF of 39 and 65. (Lesson 4-5) 13

Applications

50. **Biology** Cicadas are sometimes called 17-year locusts because they emerge from the ground every 17 years. The number of one type of caterpillar peaks every 5 years. If the peak cycles of the caterpillars and cicadas coincided in 1990, what will be the next year in which they coincide? 2075

51. **Interior Decorating** In a pattern of floor tiles laid in rows, one row has tiles 4 inches long, another has tiles 5 inches long, and a third row has tiles 6 inches long. In how many inches will the ends of all three rows be even and the pattern start to repeat? 60 in.

Critical Thinking

52. The LCM of two numbers is $2^2 \cdot 3 \cdot 5^2$. The GCF of the same numbers is $2 \cdot 5$. If one of the numbers is $2 \cdot 3 \cdot 5$, what is the other numbers? $2^2 \cdot 5^2$ or 100

Wrap-Up

53. Name a pair of numbers that have 24 as their LCM. Sample answer: 8, 12

Alternate Strategies: Extending the Lesson

Enrichment

Using Questioning Have students examine a list of pairs of numbers. Find the LCM and GCF for each. Is the product of the pair of numbers always the same as the product of the LCM and GCF? If so, can this be used as a check for the problem? Does this rule apply to sets of three numbers? Why does it hold true?

Cooperative Learning

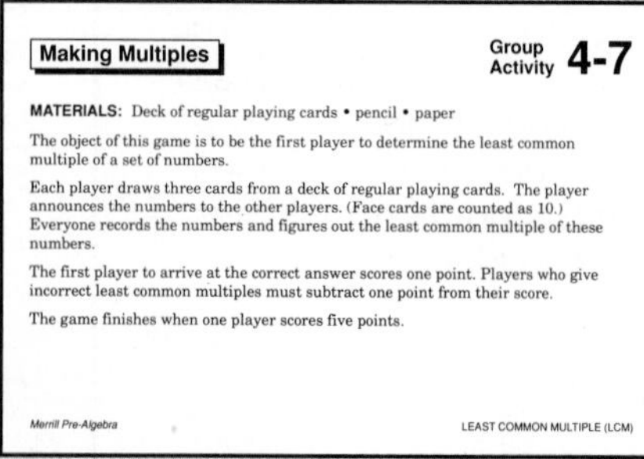

Making Multiples — Group Activity **4-7**

MATERIALS: Deck of regular playing cards • pencil • paper

The object of this game is to be the first player to determine the least common multiple of a set of numbers.

Each player draws three cards from a deck of regular playing cards. The player announces the numbers to the other players. (Face cards are counted as 10.) Everyone records the numbers and figures out the least common multiple of these numbers.

The first player to arrive at the correct answer scores one point. Players who give incorrect least common multiples must subtract one point from their score.

The game finishes when one player scores five points.

Merrill Pre-Algebra — LEAST COMMON MULTIPLE (LCM)

4-8 Comparing Fractions

Objective:
Compare fractions with different denominators and find the least common denominator for algebraic fractions.

Key Terms:
least common denominator
LCD

Jenny and her friends went to the Pizza Parlor. The pepperoni pizza was cut into 8 equal pieces while the Hawaiian pizza was cut into 7 equal pieces. After eating 3 pieces from each pizza, $\frac{5}{8}$ remained of the pepperoni pizza and $\frac{4}{7}$ remained of the Hawaiian pizza. Which pizza has more remaining?

One way to compare $\frac{5}{8}$ and $\frac{4}{7}$, is to write them as equivalent fractions with the *same* denominator. Any common denominator could be used. However, the computation may be easier if the least common denominator is used.

The **least common denominator (LCD)** is the least common multiple of the denominators. The LCM of 8 and 7 is 56.

Multiplying the numerator and denominator of a fraction by the same number is like multiplying the fraction by what number? 1

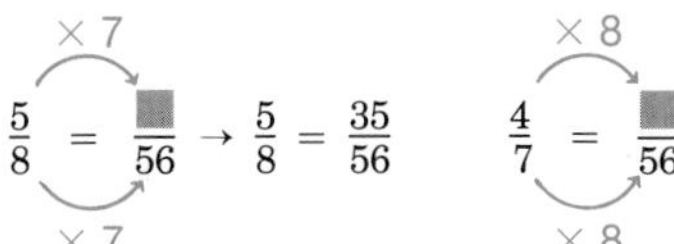

$\frac{5}{8} = \frac{\blacksquare}{56} \rightarrow \frac{5}{8} = \frac{35}{56}$ (× 7) $\frac{4}{7} = \frac{\blacksquare}{56} \rightarrow \frac{4}{7} = \frac{32}{56}$ (× 8)

Comparing $\frac{35}{56}$ to $\frac{32}{56}$, the greater fraction has the greater numerator.

Thus, $\frac{5}{8} > \frac{4}{7}$. So, there is more pepperoni pizza remaining.

Pizza is often thought of as junk food. However, the vitamins thiamin and niacin are in the flour used to make the crust. Tomato sauce is high in vitamins A and C, while cheese contains calcium and riboflavin. Toppings such as peppers and mushrooms also contain several vitamins and minerals.

Example

1 Which is greater, $\frac{3}{8}$ or $\frac{5}{12}$?

Write $\frac{3}{8}$ and $\frac{5}{12}$ as equivalent fractions with the same denominators.
The LCM of 8 and 12 is 24.

Find equivalent fractions with the LCM as the denominator.

$\frac{3}{8} = \frac{\blacksquare}{24} \rightarrow \frac{3}{8} = \frac{9}{24}$ (× 3) $\frac{5}{12} = \frac{\blacksquare}{24} \rightarrow \frac{5}{12} = \frac{10}{24}$ (× 2)

Since $\frac{10}{24} > \frac{9}{24}$, $\frac{5}{12} > \frac{3}{8}$.

Bell Ringer

Play "20 Questions" with two numbers. Give students the LCM as a hint.

Lesson Notes 4-8

5-Minute Check
(over Lesson 4-7)

Find the LCM for each set of numbers or expressions.
1. 15, 18 90
2. 12, 30 60
3. 12, 18, 75 900
4. 8, 15, 24 120
5. $5y^2$, $6y$ $30y^2$

Transparency 4-8 contains the 5-Minute Check and a teaching aid for this lesson.

1 FOCUS

The purpose of this lesson is to demonstrate how the LCM can be used to compare fractions.

Motivating the Lesson

Ask students which situation below is a better buy.
Farmer's Market sells 3 apples for 78¢. Market Basket sells 4 apples for $1.00.
Then ask students to explain how they determined their answer.

2 TEACH

Using Models

On quarter-inch grid paper, have students model the fractions below.

$\frac{3}{4}, \frac{4}{9}, \frac{7}{16}, \frac{13}{25}$

For example, to show $\frac{4}{9}$ they can shade 4 boxes of a 3 by 3 square. Using the models, have students order the fractions from least to greatest.

Chalkboard Examples

- *For Example 1*
  Which is greater $\frac{3}{7}$ or $\frac{4}{9}$? $\frac{4}{9}$
- *For Example 2*
  Find the LCD for $\frac{2}{5a}$ and $\frac{3}{20a^2}$. $20a^2$

EE: 1E, 2B, 2C, 3A, 5E
TAAS: 1, 2, 12

3 PRACTICE/APPLY

Checking the Concept

Ask students to state in their own words the steps they should take to answer Exercises 11-14. Also ask how they know they have chosen the correct symbol.

Additional Answer

31.
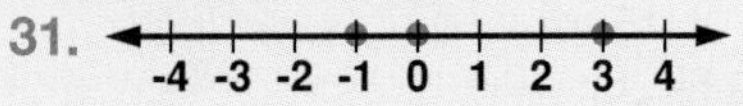

Error Analysis

Watch for students who write the multiplier as the new numerator or denominator. For example, students may write $\frac{2}{5} = \frac{6}{15}$.

Prevent by having students indicate the multiplication on the working side of the problem. For example, write $\frac{2 \cdot 3}{5 \cdot 3} = \frac{6}{15}$.

Practice Masters Booklet, **p. 37**

Name ______ Date ______

Practice Worksheet 4-8

Comparing Fractions

Find the LCD for each pair of fractions.

1. $\frac{1}{2}, \frac{1}{3}$ 6
2. $\frac{1}{4}, \frac{3}{8}$ 8
3. $\frac{3}{4}, \frac{7}{9}$ 36
4. $\frac{5}{8}, \frac{1}{6}$ 24
5. $\frac{4}{5}, \frac{2}{7}$ 35
6. $\frac{3}{4}, \frac{7}{10}$ 20
7. $\frac{3}{5}, \frac{5}{9}$ 45
8. $\frac{2}{5}, \frac{3}{8}$ 40
9. $\frac{1}{10}, \frac{4}{15}$ 30
10. $\frac{1}{3}, \frac{2}{9}$ 9
11. $\frac{2}{3}, \frac{5}{12}$ 12
12. $\frac{8}{3}, \frac{9}{5}$ 15
13. $\frac{1}{4}, \frac{5}{7}$ 28
14. $\frac{1}{8}, \frac{1}{7}$ 56
15. $\frac{3}{5}, \frac{3}{10}$ 10
16. $\frac{5}{12}, \frac{1}{5}$ 60
17. $\frac{5}{4a}, \frac{7}{5a^2}$ $20a^2$
18. $\frac{1}{7x}, \frac{1}{9x}$ $63x$
19. $\frac{3}{8m}, \frac{7}{9k}$ $72mk$
20. $\frac{3}{10x}, \frac{7}{20x^2}$ $20x^2$
21. $\frac{7}{8e}, \frac{2}{7}$ $56e$
22. $\frac{1}{6c}, \frac{3}{8cd}$ $24cd$
23. $\frac{5}{9f^2}, \frac{1}{6f^2}$ $18f^2$
24. $\frac{9}{10a^2}, \frac{10}{11a}$ $110a^2$

Write > or < in the ☐ to make a true statement.

25. $\frac{2}{3}$ [>] $\frac{5}{9}$
26. $\frac{1}{3}$ [<] $\frac{5}{6}$
27. $\frac{2}{3}$ [>] $\frac{3}{5}$
28. $\frac{2}{7}$ [<] $\frac{1}{3}$
29. $\frac{3}{5}$ [<] $\frac{2}{3}$
30. $\frac{1}{5}$ [<] $\frac{3}{7}$
31. $\frac{7}{9}$ [<] $\frac{5}{6}$
32. $\frac{3}{4}$ [<] $\frac{9}{10}$
33. $\frac{5}{9}$ [<] $\frac{7}{12}$
34. $\frac{1}{15}$ [<] $\frac{1}{12}$
35. $\frac{1}{25}$ [>] $\frac{1}{50}$
36. $\frac{11}{12}$ [>] $\frac{8}{9}$

CONNECTION TO ALGEBRA

Prime factorization can be used to find the LCD for algebraic fractions that have different denominators.

Example

2 **Find the LCD for $\frac{5}{3b^2}$ and $\frac{4}{2b}$.**

$3b^2 = 3 \cdot b \cdot b$ First, find the LCM of $3b^2$ and $2b$.

$2b = 2 \cdot b$

The LCM of $3b^2$ and $2b$ is $3 \cdot 2 \cdot b \cdot b$ or $6b^2$.

The LCD of $\frac{5}{3b^2}$ and $\frac{4}{2b}$ is $6b^2$.

Checking for Understanding

Communicating Algebra

1. Write the steps you would take to compare $\frac{3}{8}$ and $\frac{1}{3}$. **1. Find the LCD, make equivalent fractions, and compare numerators.**
2. Explain how the LCM and LCD are alike and how they are different. **The LCD is the LCM of two or more denominators.**

Guided Practice

Find the LCD for each pair of fractions.

3. $\frac{1}{2}, \frac{3}{5}$ 10
4. $\frac{7}{9}, \frac{1}{4}$ 36
5. $\frac{1}{4}, \frac{3}{8}$ 8
6. $\frac{2}{9}, \frac{5}{12}$ 36
7. $\frac{7}{a}, \frac{8}{a^2}$ a^2
8. $\frac{1}{2m}, \frac{3}{5m^2}$ $10m^2$
9. $\frac{4}{5a}, \frac{7}{25a^2}$ $25a^2$
10. $\frac{5}{6am}, \frac{7}{9a^2m}$ $18a^2m$

Replace each ● with < or > to make a true statement.

11. $\frac{2}{3}$ ● $\frac{3}{4}$ <
12. $\frac{7}{8}$ ● $\frac{5}{6}$ >
13. $\frac{9}{10}$ ● $\frac{10}{11}$ <
14. $\frac{6}{5}$ ● $\frac{7}{6}$ >

Exercises

Independent Practice

Find the LCD for each pair of fractions.

15. $\frac{1}{2}, \frac{1}{4}$ 8
16. $\frac{1}{3}, \frac{1}{8}$ 24
17. $\frac{1}{5}, \frac{2}{7}$ 35
18. $\frac{5}{6}, \frac{6}{9}$ 18
19. $\frac{7}{8a}, \frac{2}{15a}$ $120a$
20. $\frac{2}{9m}, \frac{3}{25m^2}$ $225m^2$
21. $\frac{5}{6k^2}, \frac{4}{8km}$ $24k^2m$
22. $\frac{7}{9x^2}, \frac{5}{8x}$ $72x^2$

Replace each ● with < or > to make a true statement.

23. $\frac{1}{3}$ ● $\frac{3}{12}$ >
24. $\frac{3}{8}$ ● $\frac{5}{16}$ >
25. $\frac{11}{12}$ ● $\frac{50}{60}$ >
26. $\frac{3}{4}$ ● $\frac{4}{5}$ <
27. $\frac{10}{12}$ ● $\frac{9}{11}$ >
28. $\frac{5}{7}$ ● $\frac{7}{9}$ <
29. $\frac{7}{11}$ ● $\frac{8}{13}$ >
30. $\frac{7}{9}$ ● $\frac{8}{10}$ <

Mixed Review

31. Graph the set of numbers {0, -1, 3} on a number line. (Lesson 2-1) **See margin.**
32. Solve the inequality $-10 < x + 23$. (Lesson 3-7) $-33 < x$
33. *True* or *false:* All squares are rectangles and all rectangles are squares. (Lesson 3-9) **false**

Alternate Strategies: Reteaching the Lesson

Reteaching Activity

Using Manipulatives Have students identify a pair of equivalent fractions. Write the division or multiplication used in changing the fraction. For example, if $\frac{2}{3}$ and $\frac{4}{6}$ have been identified, write $\frac{2 \times 2}{3 \times 2} = \frac{4}{6}$ and $\frac{4 \div 2}{6 \div 2} = \frac{2}{3}$

Reteaching Masters Booklet, **p. 33**

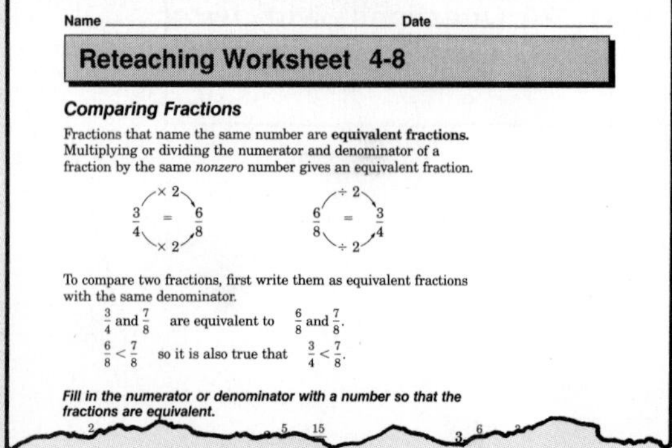

Name ______ Date ______

Reteaching Worksheet 4-8

Comparing Fractions

Fractions that name the same number are **equivalent fractions.** Multiplying or dividing the numerator and denominator of a fraction by the same *nonzero* number gives an equivalent fraction.

$\frac{3}{4} \overset{\times 2}{=} \frac{6}{8}$ $\frac{6}{8} \overset{\div 2}{=} \frac{3}{4}$

To compare two fractions, first write them as equivalent fractions with the same denominator.

$\frac{3}{4}$ and $\frac{7}{8}$ are equivalent to $\frac{6}{8}$ and $\frac{7}{8}$.

$\frac{6}{8} < \frac{7}{8}$ so it is also true that $\frac{3}{4} < \frac{7}{8}$.

Fill in the numerator or denominator with a number so that the fractions are equivalent.

34. Find the GCF for 9, −63, 108. (Lesson 4-5) 9

35. Is the fraction $\frac{9}{28}$ in simplest form? (Lesson 4-6) yes

36. Write the fraction $\frac{14r^2}{2rs^2}$ in simplest form. (Lesson 4-6) $\frac{7r}{s^2}$

Applications

37. **Ecology** The graph at the right gives statistics for the amount of ticker tape produced in parades in New York City. Use equivalent fractions to *estimate* a simple fraction that compares the amount of paper in the Mets' victory parade of 1969 to the parade for the return of the U.S. hostages in 1981. $\frac{1}{2}$

38. **Auto Mechanics** Phil is tuning up a foreign car and left his metric wrenches at home. He needs to remove a 12 mm bolt. He measures the bolt with a tape measure and finds 12 mm to be about $\frac{15}{32}$ in. Will his $\frac{9}{16}$ in. wrench or $\frac{1}{2}$ in. wrench be a closer fit? $\frac{1}{2}$ in.

Critical Thinking

39. I am a fraction less than one and in simplest form. My numerator and denominator are both prime numbers between 25 and 36. Who am I? $\frac{29}{31}$

Wrap-Up

40. **Make Up a Problem** Write a problem that involves comparing fractions. See margin.

Team Problem Solving

Work in small groups.
In the diagram at the right, find the total number of squares. Then tell how many of them contain a number of dots that is a multiple of 3. (Hint: There are more than 10 squares.)
14 squares, 5 have multiples of 3

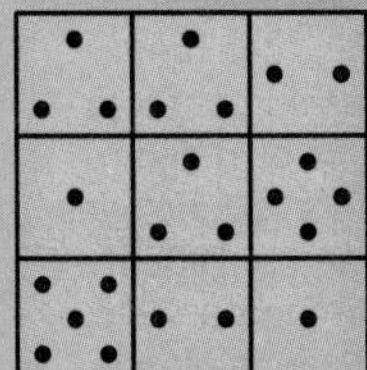

Alternate Strategies: Extending the Lesson

Enrichment

Using Models Use a set of dominoes to generate problems. Have a student draw two dominoes and write fractions to represent the dominoes. Compare the fractions.

Cooperative Learning

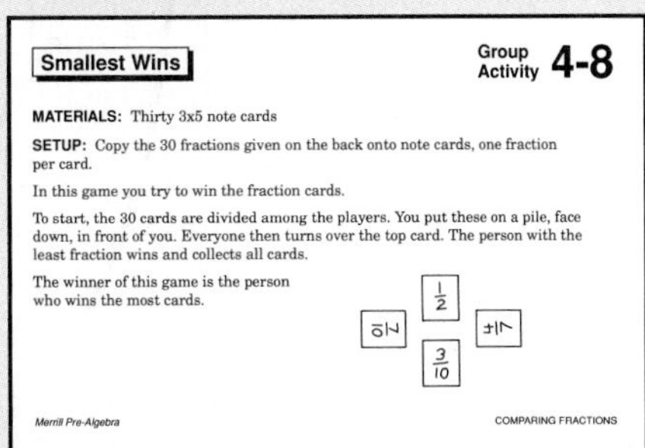

Smallest Wins Group Activity **4-8**

MATERIALS: Thirty 3x5 note cards

SETUP: Copy the 30 fractions given on the back onto note cards, one fraction per card.

In this game you try to win the fraction cards.

To start, the 30 cards are divided among the players. You put these on a pile, face down, in front of you. Everyone then turns over the top card. The person with the least fraction wins and collects all cards.

The winner of this game is the person who wins the most cards.

Merrill Pre-Algebra COMPARING FRACTIONS

Independent Practice

Homework Assignment	
Basic	15-29 odd, 31-37, 39, 40
Average	16-30 even, 31-40
Honors	18-22 even, 26-40

Additional Answer

40. Sample answer: About $\frac{2}{25}$ of the world's population lives in North America. About $\frac{1}{10}$ lives in Africa. Which continent has the greater number of people?

4 CLOSE

Assessment Option

Speaking State the LCD of the following pairs of fractions. Then tell which is greater.

1. $\frac{1}{3}$ and $\frac{2}{6}$ 6, they are equal
2. $\frac{1}{2}$ and $\frac{4}{7}$ 14, $\frac{4}{7}$
3. $\frac{2}{5}$ and $\frac{7}{15}$ 15, $\frac{7}{15}$

Enrichment Masters Booklet, **p. 33**

Name ______________ Date ______________

Enrichment Worksheet 4-8

Comparing Fractions

If $\frac{A}{B}$ and $\frac{C}{D}$ are positive fractions, then it can be shown by algebra that if $AD < BC$, then $\frac{A}{B} < \frac{C}{D}$.
For example, $\frac{2}{3} < \frac{3}{4}$ since $2 \cdot 4 < 3 \cdot 3$.

Use this multiplication method to insert the correct inequality sign, < or >, between each pair of fractions.

1. $\frac{1}{2} < \frac{3}{5}$
2. $\frac{7}{9} < \frac{8}{10}$
3. $\frac{4}{3} > \frac{6}{5}$
4. $\frac{3}{20} > \frac{2}{19}$
5. $\frac{9}{5} > \frac{5}{9}$
6. $\frac{18}{54} > \frac{33}{100}$
7. $\frac{101}{1000} > \frac{1}{10}$
8. $\frac{62}{112} > \frac{58}{105}$

9. Coach Runge had each student in his gym class run for five minutes and then tell him how far he or she had gone. Each runner told him what fraction of a mile they had run. Rank the students from fastest to slowest if the distances were as follows.

Bob: $\frac{3}{4}$ mile Ray: $\frac{5}{7}$ mile Julie: $\frac{6}{7}$ mile
Ida: $\frac{4}{7}$ mile Flo: $\frac{8}{11}$ mile Zina: $\frac{5}{8}$ mile
Dale: $\frac{6}{10}$ mile Doug: $\frac{7}{12}$ mile Tina: $\frac{11}{16}$ mile

Julie, Bob, Flo, Ray, Tina, Zina, Dale, Doug, Ida

A baseball player's "batting average" is found by dividing the number of hits by the number of times at bat.

For example, if Susan had 3 hits in 10 times at bat, her batting average would be $\frac{3}{10}$ or $\frac{300}{1000}$.

10. Susan's brother Phil had 21 hits in 72 times at bat. Her other brother Bill had 10 hits in 41 times at bat. How many hits in a row would Bill need in order to have a higher batting average than his brother?
3 hits, $\frac{13}{44} > \frac{21}{72}$

11. At the end of the first month of the baseball season, Ramon had been to bat 60 times and had 17 hits. For each of the next twelve days he was at bat three times and had one hit. Was this hitting streak enough for him to now be batting over "three hundred"? Show how you got your answer by comparing his new batting average to $\frac{300}{1000}$.
yes; $\frac{17 + 12}{60 + (3 \cdot 12)} = \frac{29}{96} > \frac{300}{1000}$

5-Minute Check
(over Lesson 4-8)

Find the LCM for each pair of expressions.
1. $7m, 14m^2$ $14m^2$
2. $4a^2, 18a$ $36a^2$
3. $6y^3k, 21y^2k^2$ $84y^3k^2$

Find the LCD for each pair of fractions.
4. $\frac{7}{3m^2}, \frac{4}{5m}$ $15m^2$
5. $\frac{7}{12ab}, \frac{5}{3ab^2}$ $12ab^2$

Transparency 4-9 contains the 5-Minute Check and a teaching aid for this lesson.

1 FOCUS

The purpose of this lesson is for students to understand the rule for finding the product of powers.

Motivating the Lesson

Under ideal conditions, one pair of fleas can produce 10^5 fleas in just 30 days. Ask students to use a power to express the number of fleas there would be in 30 days if you started with 10^3 parent fleas. 10^8 fleas

2 TEACH

Using Tables

Have students use the y^x key on their calculator to create a table for powers of 3 similar to the table on page 152. Have students use calculators and their table to find $3 \cdot 9$, $27 \cdot 9$, and $81 \cdot 243$. Then ask students to find $243 \cdot 81$ without using a calculator. 27; 243; 19,683

EE: 1E, 2F, 3A, 3D
TAAS: 1, 2, 12

4-9 Multiplying Powers

Objective:
Multiply monomials.

Key Term:
product of powers

One hundred eighth-graders at Colestock Junior High School participated in a relay marathon over the Labor Day weekend to raise money for Muscular Dystrophy research. At the end of each lap of the 1000-meter course the runner relayed the baton to the next runner. If each student completed 10 laps, how many meters were run?

Each number above can be expressed as a power of 10.

8th graders	laps per student	meters per lap
$100 = 10^2$	$10 = 10^1$	$1000 = 10^3$

To answer the question, you need to find the product of 10^2, 10^1, and 10^3.

Example

1 **Find $10^2 \cdot 10^1 \cdot 10^3$.**

Do you see a pattern with the exponents? $2 + 1 + 3 = 6$

$$10^2 \cdot 10^1 \cdot 10^3 = (10 \cdot 10) \cdot 10 \cdot (10 \cdot 10 \cdot 10)$$
$$= 10^6 \quad \text{10 is used as a factor 6 times.}$$

10  6 = 1000000

One million meters were run in the relay marathon.

FYI
A googol is defined as 10^{100}. It is the largest number to have its own name. The term googol was invented in 1938 by Milton Sirotta. He was 9 years old at the time!

Study the pattern of products shown below. Each factor and each product has been replaced with a power of 2.

$2 \cdot 4 = 8$	$8 \cdot 4 = 32$	$16 \cdot 32 = 512$
↓ ↓ ↓	↓ ↓ ↓	↓ ↓ ↓
$2^1 \cdot 2^2 = 2^3$	$2^3 \cdot 2^2 = 2^5$	$2^4 \cdot 2^5 = 2^9$

$2^1 = 2$
$2^2 = 4$
$2^3 = 8$
$2^4 = 16$
$2^5 = 32$
$2^6 = 64$
$2^7 = 128$
$2^8 = 256$
$2^9 = 512$

Look at the powers only. Do you see a pattern with the exponents? In Example 2 you will see if your pattern is true for $32 \cdot 8 = 256$.

Bell Ringer

Is the fraction $\frac{3}{24}$ greater than, less than, or equal to $\frac{1}{8}$?

Example

2 **Find 32 • 8 or $2^5 \cdot 2^3$.**

$$2^5 \cdot 2^3 = (2 \cdot 2 \cdot 2 \cdot 2 \cdot 2) \cdot (2 \cdot 2 \cdot 2)$$
$$= 2 \cdot 2 \cdot 2 \cdot 2 \cdot 2 \cdot 2 \cdot 2 \cdot 2$$
$$= 2^8$$
$$2^5 \cdot 2^3 = 2^{5+3} \text{ or } 2^8$$

2 [y^x] 8 [=] 256

CONNECTION TO ALGEBRA

Monomials such as m^4 and m^3 can also be multiplied using the pattern shown in Example 2.

Example

3 **Find $m^4 \cdot m^3$.**

$m^4 \cdot m^3 = (m \cdot m \cdot m \cdot m) \cdot (m \cdot m \cdot m)$ 4 factors • 3 factors

$= m \cdot m \cdot m \cdot m \cdot m \cdot m \cdot m$ 7 factors

$= m^7$

$m^4 \cdot m^3 = m^{4+3} \text{ or } m^7$

These and other examples suggest the following rule.

Product of Powers

In words: You can multiply powers *that have the same base* by adding their exponents.
In symbols: For any number a and positive integers m and n, $a^m \cdot a^n = a^{m+n}$.

Example

4 **Find $(-7y^2)(3y^3)$.**

$(-7y^2)(3y^3) = (-7 \cdot 3)(y^2 \cdot y^3)$ Commutative and associative properties

$= -21 \cdot y^{2+3}$ Product of powers

$= -21y^5$

Checking for Understanding

Communicating Algebra

1. Explain how you would find the product of $3^5 \cdot 3^2$? Add 5 and 2; 3^7
2. How would you show that $7^2 \cdot 7 = 7^{2+1}$? $7 = 7^1$; so, $7^2 \cdot 7 = 7^2 \cdot 7^1$ or 7^3
3. Make up a product of powers problem that has a solution of a^6. Sample answer: $a^2 \cdot a^4$

Guided Practice

Verify each product by multiplication. 6. $16 \cdot 16 = 256$ 9. $9 \cdot 81 = 729$

4. $3^1 \cdot 3^2 = 3^3$ $3 \cdot 9 = 27$
5. $2^3 \cdot 2^2 = 2^5$ $8 \cdot 4 = 32$
6. $4^2 \cdot 4^2 = 4^4$
7. $2^5 \cdot 2^2 = 2^7$ $32 \cdot 4 = 128$ 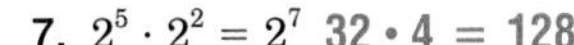
8. $5^2 \cdot 5 = 5^3$ $25 \cdot 5 = 125$
9. $3 \cdot 3^4 = 3^6$

Find each product.

10. $x^3 \cdot x^5$ x^8
11. $y^7 \cdot y^2$ y^9
12. $a^4 \cdot a^4$ a^8

Chalkboard Examples

- *For Example 1*
  Find $10^4 \cdot 10^5 \cdot 10^3 \cdot 10^1$. 10,000,000,000,000
- *For Example 2*
  Find $9 \cdot 81$ or $3^2 \cdot 3^4$. 3^{2+4} or 3^6
- *For Example 3*
  Find $x^3 \cdot x^2$. x^{3+2} or x^5
- *For Example 4*
  Find $(-5r^3)(6r^5)$. $-30r^8$

3 PRACTICE/APPLY

Checking the Concept

Remind students that there are 1000 or 10^3 millimeters in a meter. Ask students to find the number of millimeters in a kilometer (1000 meters). 1,000,000 or 10^6 mm

Error Analysis

Watch for students who multiply instead of adding exponents in a multiplication problem.
Prevent by reviewing rules for multiplication using exponents.

Practice Masters Booklet, **p. 38**

Name ________________ Date ________________

Practice Worksheet 4-9

Multiplying Powers

Find each product.

1. $2^4 \cdot 2^5$ 512
2. $10^3 \cdot 10^3$ 1,000,000
3. $6^2 \cdot 6^4 \cdot 6$ 279,936
4. $x^4 \cdot x^2 \cdot x^5$ x^{11}
5. $k \cdot k^6 \cdot k^3$ k^{10}
6. $e \cdot e^5 \cdot e^7$ e^{13}
7. $(3x^2)(-2xy)$ $-6x^3y$
8. $x \cdot y \cdot z \cdot x \cdot y \cdot x \cdot z$ $x^3y^2z^2$
9. $(-2)(5kp^2)(k^2p)$ $-10k^3p^3$
10. $(4xyz)(-10x^3y^2)$ $-40x^4y^3z$
11. $(x^2y)(-4x^6y^3)$ $-4x^8y^4$
12. $(-5a^2m^7)(-3a^5m)$ $15a^7m^8$
13. $(-x^2z)(-xyz)$ x^3yz^2
14. $(-2n^2)(y^4)(-3n)$ $6n^3y^4$
15. $4a \cdot 3b \cdot 7c^2$ $84abc^2$
16. $(9a^3)(-4ab^3)$ $-36a^4b^3$
17. $\left(\frac{1}{2}a^4\right)(6a^3)$ $3a^7$
18. $\left(\frac{2}{3}b^3\right)(9b^2)$ $6b^5$
19. $x^3(x^4y^2)$ x^7y^2
20. $(-5r^2s)(-3rs^4)$ $15r^3s^5$
21. $(a^2b^2)(a^3b)$ a^5b^3
22. $(2n^3)(-6n^4)$ $-12n^7$
23. $5wz^2 \cdot 8w^4z^3$ $40w^5z^5$
24. $(c^2d)(-10c^3d)$ $-10c^5d^2$
25. $(3h^2)(-2h^3)(-h)$ $6h^6$
26. $(14rt)(5r)(t^2)$ $70r^2t^3$
27. $(m^3p^2)(-2mp^2)(mp)$ $-2m^5p^5$
28. $(-w^2z)(-wz)(5z^3)$ $5w^3z^5$

Alternate Strategies: Reteaching the Lesson

Reteaching Activity

Using Discussion Give students a list of several products of powers with ten as the base. Have students rewrite each power as a product of ten. Then have students count the number of factors on each side of the equal sign. Discuss the pattern that results. Have students use calculators to determine if the pattern holds for other bases.

Reteaching Masters Booklet, **p. 34**

Name ________________ Date ________________

Reteaching Worksheet 4-9

Multiplying Powers

To multiply expressions with exponents and the same base, add the exponents.

$100 \cdot 10 = 1000$ $\quad$ $100 \cdot 1000 = 100{,}000$

$10^2 \cdot 10^1 = 10^3$ $\quad$ $10^2 \cdot 10^3 = 10^5$

For each exercise, write the first product in standard form. Write the second product with an exponent.

1. a. $1000 \cdot 10$ 10,000
   b. $10^3 \cdot 10^1$ 10^4
2. a. $10{,}000 \cdot 10$ 100,000
   b. $10^4 \cdot 10^1$ 10^5
3. a. $1000 \cdot 1000$ 1,000,000
   b. $10^3 \cdot 10^3$ 10^6
4. a. $9 \cdot 3$ 27
5. a. $4 \cdot 8$ 32
6. a. $5 \cdot 125$ 625

Independent Practice

Homework Assignment	
Basic	13-29 odd, 31-38
Average	14-30 even, 31-38
Honors	22-38

4 CLOSE

Assessment Option

Writing Write ten equations using powers such as $3^3 \times 3^2 = 3^5$ or $b^4 \times b^4 = b^8$. Use a calculator if possible to solve them.

Enrichment Masters Booklet, **p. 34**

Name ______________________ Date ____________

Enrichment Worksheet 4-9

Truth Tables

A **conditional statement** is a statement formed by two statements (p and q) connected by *if . . . , then.*

Statement: ABC is a triangle.
Statement: ABC has 3 sides.
Conditional: If ABC is a triangle, then ABC has 3 sides.

The logic symbol for a conditional is $p \rightarrow q$, read "if p, then q."

Three other statements can be formed by changing the order of p and q, or by *negating* p and q.

$q \rightarrow p$ **Converse:** If ABC has 3 sides, then ABC is a triangle.
$\sim p \rightarrow \sim q$ **Inverse:** If ABC is not a triangle, then ABC does not have 3 sides. The symbol ~ is used for *not.*
$\sim q \rightarrow \sim p$ **Contrapositive:** If ABC does not have 3 sides, then ABC is not a triangle.

Write the converse, inverse, and contrapositive of each conditional. Then complete the truth table.

1. $p \rightarrow q$ If $x + 3 = 8$, then $x = 5$.
   $q \rightarrow p$ If x = 5, then x + 3 = 8.
   $\sim p \rightarrow \sim q$ If x + 3 ≠ 8, then x ≠ 5.
   $\sim q \rightarrow \sim p$ If x ≠ 5, then x + 3 ≠ 8.

$p \rightarrow q$	$q \rightarrow p$	$\sim p \rightarrow \sim q$	$\sim q \rightarrow \sim p$
True	T	T	T

2. $p \rightarrow q$ If $ABCD$ is a square, then $ABCD$ has 4 sides.
   $q \rightarrow p$ If *ABCD* has 4 sides, then *ABCD* is a square.
   $\sim p \rightarrow \sim q$ If *ABCD* is not a square, then *ABCD* does not have 4 sides.
   $\sim q \rightarrow \sim p$ If *ABCD* does not have 4 sides, then *ABCD* is not a square.

$p \rightarrow q$	$q \rightarrow p$	$\sim p \rightarrow \sim q$	$\sim q \rightarrow \sim p$
True	F	F	T

3. $p \rightarrow q$ If it is 9 A.M., it is morning.
   $q \rightarrow p$ If it is morning, then it is 9 A.M.
   $\sim p \rightarrow \sim q$ If it is not 9 A.M., then it is not morning.
   $\sim q \rightarrow \sim p$ If it is not morning, then it is not 9 A.M.

$p \rightarrow q$	$q \rightarrow p$	$\sim p \rightarrow \sim q$	$\sim q \rightarrow \sim p$
True	F	F	T

Exercises

Independent Practice

Find each product.

13. $3^4 \cdot 3^6$ 3^{10}
14. $10^5 \cdot 10^5$ 10^{10}
15. $8^2 \cdot 8^3 \cdot 8$ 8^6
16. $b^5 \cdot b^2$ b^7
17. $m \cdot m^3$ m^4
18. $d \cdot d^6$ d^7
19. $(3a^2)(4a^3)$ $12a^5$
20. $(5x^3)(4x^4)$ $20x^7$
21. $(3x^4)(-5x^2)$ $-15x^6$
22. $(5n^3)(-6n^2)$ $-30n^5$
23. $(-10x^3y)(2x^2)$ $-20x^5y$
24. $(-3y^3z)(7y^4)$ $-21y^7z$
25. $(a^2b)(ab^3)$ a^3b^4
26. $(y^3z^4)(yz^5)$ y^4z^9
27. $m^4(m^3b^2)$ m^7b^2

Language Skill

Write a mathematical expression for each phrase.

28. the sum of three to the eighth power and six $3^8 + 6$
29. seven to the fourth power times four to the fifth power $7^4 \cdot 4^5$
30. four times three to the second power plus four times five squared $4 \cdot 3^2 + 4 \cdot 5^2$

Mixed Review

31. Solve the equation $17 = a - (-4)$. (Lesson 3-2) 13
32. By which number should you multiply to solve the equation $-9 = \frac{m}{11}$? (Lesson 3-4) 11
33. Write the fraction $\frac{16a^3b^2}{2a^2b^2}$ in simplest form. (Lesson 4-6) $8a$
34. *True* or *false*: 3 is the LCM of 18. (Lesson 4-7) false
35. Find the LCM of 9 and 21. (Lesson 4-7) 63

Application

36. **Meteorology** The intensity of an earthquake is measured on the Richter scale. Each increase of one on the Richter scale means a ten-times increase in intensity. In 1906 an earthquake in San Francisco measured 8.3 on the Richter scale. Another earthquake that measured 7.1 shook the same area in October of 1989. Estimate how many times more intense the 1906 earthquake was. a little more than 10 times

Critical Thinking

37. Complete this problem using only two different digits.

■,■■■ × ■■■ = ■■■,■■■
1 0 0 0   1 0 0   1 0 0 0 0 0

Wrap-Up

38. In your own words, describe or write the rule for multiplying powers. Sample answer: If the bases are the same, add the exponents.

Alternate Strategies: Extending the Lesson

Enrichment

Using Calculators Have students use the y^x key on their calculators to determine the difference between the product of powers and the power of a power. For example, have students key in the following sequences.

2 [y^x] 3 [×] 2 [y^x] 2 [=] $(2^3 \cdot 2^2) = 32$
2 [y^x] 3 [y^x] 2 [=] $((2^3)^2) = 64$

Cooperative Learning

More Power To You — Group Activity **4-9**

For this activity students work in groups.

To begin, each student writes down two simplified monomials that include constants, variables, and exponents. Then they exchange papers with any other student, and that student must rewrite each expression as the product of two or three other monomials in two different ways, one set correct and the other incorrect.

Lastly, they give the papers to someone else, and that person checks to see which expression is correct.

The first one to determine the correct expressions scores one point. The winner is the first person to score five points.

Merrill Pre-Algebra MULTIPLYING POWERS

4-10 Dividing Powers

Objective:
Divide monomials and simplify expressions containing negative exponents.

Key Term:
quotient of powers

The population of the People's Republic of China exceeds one billion people. The land area of this country is about ten million square kilometers. What is the average number of people per square kilometer?

Each number above can be expressed as a power of ten.

one billion (1,000,000,000) = 10^9

ten million (10,000,000) = 10^7

To answer the question, you need to find the quotient of one billion and ten million.

Example

Do you see a pattern with the exponents? $9 - 7 = 2$

1 Find $\frac{10^9}{10^7}$.

Use a calculator.

10 [y^x] 9 [÷] 10 [y^x] 7 [=] 100 or 10^2

There are about 100 people per square kilometer.

Social Studies Connection

Sociology is the study of human society. A sociologist who specializes in **demography** studies the size, composition, and distribution of human populations within a specific geographical area. This could involve the use of very large numbers as seen at the beginning of this lesson.

Study the pattern of products below. Each dividend, divisor, and quotient has been replaced with a power of 2.

$8 \div 2 = 4$	$32 \div 8 = 4$	$512 \div 16 = 32$
$\downarrow \quad \downarrow \quad \downarrow$	$\downarrow \quad \downarrow \quad \downarrow$	$\downarrow \quad \downarrow \quad \downarrow$
$2^3 \div 2^1 = 2^2$	$2^5 \div 2^3 = 2^2$	$2^9 \div 2^4 = 2^5$

$2^1 = 2$
$2^2 = 4$
$2^3 = 8$
$2^4 = 16$
$2^5 = 32$
$2^6 = 64$
$2^7 = 128$
$2^8 = 256$
$2^9 = 512$

Look at the powers only. Do you see a pattern with the exponents? In Example 2 you will see if your pattern is true for $256 \div 8 = 32$.

Lesson Notes 4-10

5-Minute Check
(over Lesson 4-9)

Find each product.
1. $r^4 \cdot r^6$ r^{10}
2. $8^2 \cdot 8^3$ $8^5 = 32{,}768$
3. $(3x^4)(-2x^3)$ $-6x^7$
4. $(b^3m^3)(a^2m^2)$ $a^2b^3m^5$
5. $(4b^2c^3)(5c^3k^2)$ $20b^2c^6k^2$

Transparency 4-10 contains the 5-Minute Check and a teaching aid for this lesson.

1 FOCUS

The purpose of this lesson is for students to understand the rule for finding the quotient of powers.

Motivating the Lesson

To get rid of all the fleas produced in the Motivating the Lesson for Lesson 4-9, the Friendly Flea Company sells 10^2 cans of flea spray. Ask students to find out how many fleas each can will get rid of. 10^6 fleas

2 TEACH

Using Discussion

The lesson opener introduces the concept of *population density.* Discuss with students that the answer to Example 1 is an average. Some areas of China will be more densely populated while other areas will be less densely populated.

Bell Ringer

A box contains more than 30 marbles but fewer than 65. If the number of marbles is divided by 8, the remainder is 3. If the number of marbles is divided by 7, the remainder is 2. How many marbles are in the box? 51 marbles

EE: 1E, 2C, 3A, 3D
TAAS: 1, 2

Chalkboard Examples

- *For Example 1*
  Find $\frac{10^8}{10^5}$. 10^3
- *For Example 2*
  Find $243 \div 9$ or $\frac{3^5}{3^2}$. 3^3
- *For Example 3*
  Find $\frac{y^{12}}{y^8}$. y^4
- *For Example 4*
  Simplify $\frac{9^{13}}{9^6}$. 9^7
- *For Example 5*
  Simplify $\frac{m^{12}}{m^3}$. m^9
- *For Example 6*
  Express 4^{-2} with positive exponents. $\frac{1}{4^2}$

Example

2 **Find $256 \div 8$ or $\frac{2^8}{2^3}$.**

$$\frac{2^8}{2^3} = \frac{\not{2} \cdot \not{2} \cdot \not{2} \cdot 2 \cdot 2 \cdot 2 \cdot 2 \cdot 2}{\not{2} \cdot \not{2} \cdot \not{2}}$$

Divide the numerator and denominator by $2 \cdot 2 \cdot 2$.

$$= 2 \cdot 2 \cdot 2 \cdot 2 \cdot 2$$
$$= 2^5$$

2 [y^x] 5 [=] 32

$$2^8 \div 2^3 = 2^{8-3} \text{ or } 2^5$$

CONNECTION TO ALGEBRA

Monomials such as a^6 and a^2 can also be divided using the pattern shown in Example 2.

Example

3 **Find $\frac{a^6}{a^2}$.**

What value of **a** *is not allowed? Why?*
Zero. Division by zero is undefined.

$$\frac{a^6}{a^2} = \frac{\not{a} \cdot \not{a} \cdot a \cdot a \cdot a \cdot a}{\not{a} \cdot \not{a}}$$

← 6 factors
← 2 factors

Notice that $\frac{a \cdot a}{a \cdot a} = 1$.

$$= a \cdot a \cdot a \cdot a$$

The quotient has 4 factors.

$$= a^4$$

$$\frac{a^6}{a^2} = a^{6-2} \text{ or } a^4$$

Quotient of Powers

In words: You can divide powers *that have the same base* by subtracting their exponents.

In symbols: For any whole numbers m and n, and nonzero number a, $\frac{a^m}{a^n} = a^{m-n}$.

Examples

4 **Simplify $\frac{7^4}{7^2}$.**

$\frac{7^4}{7^2} = 7^{4-2}$ The bases are the same.

$= 7^2$ Subtract the exponents.

5 **Simplify $\frac{x^7}{x^3}$.**

$\frac{x^7}{x^3} = x^{7-3}$

$= x^4$

What happens if $m = n$ in the rule above? Try $\frac{a^2}{a^2}$.

$\frac{a^2}{a^2} = \frac{\not{a} \cdot \not{a}}{\not{a} \cdot \not{a}}$ or $\frac{a^2}{a^2} = a^{2-2}$ Use the rule for dividing powers.

$= 1$ $= a^0$

Since $\frac{a^2}{a^2}$ cannot have two different values, you can conclude that $a^0 = 1$.

Alternate Strategies: Reteaching the Lesson

Reteaching Activity

Using Discussion Give students a list of several quotients of powers with ten as the base. Have students rewrite each power as a product of ten. Then have students count the number of factors in the numerator, denominator, and the quotient. Discuss the pattern that results. Have students use calculators to determine if the pattern holds for other bases.

Reteaching Masters Booklet, **p. 35**

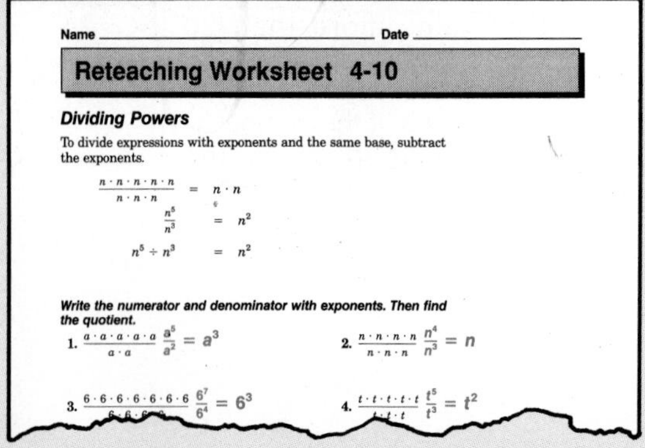

Name ______ Date ______

Reteaching Worksheet 4-10

Dividing Powers

To divide expressions with exponents and the same base, subtract the exponents.

$\frac{n \cdot n \cdot n \cdot n \cdot n}{n \cdot n \cdot n} = n \cdot n$

$\frac{n^5}{n^3} = n^2$

$n^5 \div n^3 = n^2$

Write the numerator and denominator with exponents. Then find the quotient.

1. $\frac{a \cdot a \cdot a \cdot a \cdot a}{a \cdot a}$ $\frac{a^5}{a^2} = a^3$
2. $\frac{n \cdot n \cdot n \cdot n}{n \cdot n \cdot n}$ $\frac{n^4}{n^3} = n$
3. $6 \cdot 6 \cdot 6 \cdot 6 \cdot 6 \cdot 6 \cdot 6$ $\frac{6^7}{6^4} = 6^3$
4. $t \cdot t \cdot t \cdot t \cdot t$ $\frac{t^5}{t^3} = t^2$

You can use the quotient of powers rule to simplify $\frac{a^2}{a^6}$.

$$\frac{a^2}{a^6} = a^{2-6} \quad \text{Use the rule for dividing powers.} \qquad \text{or} \qquad \frac{a^2}{a^6} = \frac{\cancel{a} \cdot \cancel{a}}{\cancel{a} \cdot \cancel{a} \cdot a \cdot a \cdot a \cdot a}$$

$$= a^{-4} \quad 2 - 6 = -4 \qquad\qquad = \frac{1}{a \cdot a \cdot a \cdot a}$$

$$= \frac{1}{a^4}$$

Since $\frac{a^2}{a^6}$ cannot have two different values, you can conclude that a^{-4} is equal to $\frac{1}{a^4}$. In general, any power such as a^{-n} can be written $\frac{1}{a^n}$.

Example

6 Express 5^{-3} with positive exponents.

$$5^{-3} = \frac{1}{5^3}$$

Checking for Understanding

Communicating Algebra

1. In your own words, explain the quotient of powers rule. *1. If the bases are the same, subtract the exponents.*
2. How would you show that $\frac{7^2}{7} = 7^{2-1}$ or 7? $\frac{7 \cdot \cancel{7}}{\cancel{7}} = 7$
3. Explain how to express a^{-2} with a positive exponent. $a^{-2} = \frac{1}{a^2}$

Guided Practice

Verify each quotient by replacing the powers with their values.

4. $\frac{3^5}{3^2} = 3^3$ $243 \div 9 = 27$
5. $\frac{4^3}{4} = 4^2$ $64 \div 4 = 16$
6. $\frac{2^4}{2^6} = 2^{-2}$ $\frac{16}{64} = \frac{1}{4}$
7. $\frac{5^4}{5^4} = 5^0$ $625 \div 625 = 1$

Find each quotient.

8. $\frac{x^9}{x^4}$ x^5
9. $\frac{y^8}{y^6}$ y^2
10. $\frac{a^4}{a^4}$ a^0 or 1
11. $\frac{x^2}{x^3}$ x^{-1} or $\frac{1}{x}$

Exercises

Independent Practice

Find each quotient.

12. $\frac{8^4}{8^3}$ 8^1 or 8
13. $\frac{(-2)^6}{(-2)^5}$ $(-2)^1$ or -2
14. $\frac{10^{10}}{10^3}$ 10^7
15. $\frac{(-7)^3}{(-7)}$ $(-7)^2$
16. $\frac{y^5}{y^2}$ y^3
17. $\frac{a^{10}}{a^6}$ a^4
18. $\frac{(-x)^4}{(-x)^3}$ $(-x)^1$ or $-x$
19. $\frac{c^8}{c^8}$ c^0 or 1
20. $\frac{z^3}{z}$ z^2
21. $\frac{m^{15}}{m^{11}}$ m^4
22. $\frac{f^{20}}{f^8}$ f^{12}
23. $\frac{y^{100}}{y^{100}}$ y^0 or 1

3 PRACTICE/APPLY

Checking the Concept

As students work Exercises 4-7 in the Guided Practice, encourage the use of the simplifying fractions skills from Lesson 4-6.

Error Analysis

Watch for students who divide instead of subtracting exponents in a division problem.
Prevent by reviewing rules for division using exponents.

Independent Practice

Homework Assignment	
Basic	13-31 odd, 32-39, 44-47
Average	14-30 even, 32-40, 44-47
Honors	18-30 even, 32-47

Chapter 4, Quiz B, (Lessons 4-6 through 4-10) is available in the Evaluation Masters Booklet, p. 34.

Practice Masters Booklet, **p. 39**

Name ______________________ Date ______________

Practice Worksheet 4-10

Dividing Powers

Find each quotient.

1. $\frac{12a^2b^3}{6a^2b}$ $2b^2$
2. $\frac{-14ab^2c}{21a^2bc^2}$ $-\frac{2b}{3ac}$
3. $\frac{x^4y^3}{x^2y^2}$ x^2y
4. $\frac{m^3n^4}{m^5n^3}$ $\frac{n}{m^2}$
5. $\frac{c^3d^2}{c^8d^4}$ $\frac{1}{c^5d^2}$
6. $\frac{15a^2c^3}{-3ac^4}$ $-\frac{5a}{c}$
7. $\frac{3x^3}{12x^4}$ $\frac{1}{4x}$
8. $\frac{6x^2}{16y^3}$ $\frac{3x^2}{8y^3}$
9. $\frac{4p^2q^3}{12pq}$ $\frac{pq^2}{3}$
10. $\frac{3ab}{15a^2b^3}$ $\frac{1}{5ab^2}$
11. $\frac{-3r^2s^5}{-12r^3s^6}$ $\frac{1}{4rs}$
12. $\frac{7m^3n^{12}}{15mn^8}$ $\frac{7m^2n^4}{15}$
13. $\frac{-13p^4q^3}{26p^5q^7}$ $-\frac{1}{2pq^4}$
14. $\frac{12a^4m^3}{16a^3m^8}$ $\frac{3a}{4m^5}$
15. $\frac{6q^3v^3}{18q^2v^4}$ $\frac{q}{3v}$
16. $\frac{-5v^4z^3}{-12v^2z^5}$ $\frac{5v^2}{12z^2}$
17. $\frac{-11a^2p^3}{22a^8p}$ $-\frac{p^2}{2a^6}$
18. $\frac{80p^2t^2}{4p^2t^4}$ $\frac{20}{t^2}$
19. $\frac{9u^2z^3}{-12u^3z^2}$ $-\frac{3z}{4u}$
20. $\frac{5a^2}{10ab^2}$ $\frac{a}{2b^2}$
21. $\frac{5a^4c^2}{15a^3c^6}$ $\frac{a}{3c^4}$
22. $\frac{f^5g^2}{f^3g^5}$ $\frac{f^2}{g^3}$
23. $\frac{12x^3y^2}{18x^4y^3}$ $\frac{2}{3xy}$
24. $\frac{-80a^3b^2}{12ab^2}$ $-\frac{20a^2}{3}$
25. $\frac{10m^2n^2}{15m^4n}$ $\frac{2n}{3m^2}$
26. $\frac{3n^3z^2}{4n^3z^3}$ $\frac{3}{4z}$
27. $\frac{5p^3q^2}{-15p^2q^3}$ $-\frac{p}{3q}$
28. $\frac{x^4y^7}{x^3y^3}$ xy^4
29. $\frac{12abc}{15a^2bc^3}$ $\frac{4}{5ac^2}$
30. $\frac{9a^2b^4}{18a^3b^5}$ $\frac{1}{2ab}$

4 CLOSE

Assessment Option

Writing Write ten equations using powers, such as $\frac{a^2}{a^4} = a^{-2}$ or $\frac{5^5}{5^0} = 5^5$. Verify their equality using a calculator, if possible.

Simplify. Express each result with positive exponents. Assume no denominator is equal to zero.

24. 5^0 1
25. $(-3)^0$ 1
26. 4^{-1} $\frac{1}{4}$
27. 10^{-2} $\frac{1}{a^2}$
28. 3^{-2} $\frac{1}{3^2}$
29. x^{-1} $\frac{1}{x}$
30. n^{-3} $\frac{1}{n^3}$
31. $s^{-2}t^3$ $\frac{t^3}{s^2}$

Mixed Review

32. *True* or *false:* The sum of a positive number and a negative number is always negative. (Lesson 2-3) false
33. Find the area of a rectangle whose sides are 8 ft and 6 ft. (Lesson 3-6) 48 ft^2
34. Write an inequality for the sentence: *The quotient of an integer and four is greater than or equal to nine.* (Lesson 3-8) $\frac{x}{4} \geq 9$
35. Write the fraction $\frac{18}{126}$ in simplest form. (Lesson 4-6) $\frac{1}{7}$
36. Find the LCM of 4, 6, and 18. (Lesson 4-7) 36
37. Which is greater, $\frac{1}{4}$ or $\frac{3}{11}$? (Lesson 4-8) $\frac{3}{11}$
38. Find the LCD of $\frac{1}{9r}$ and $\frac{3}{4r^2}$. (Lesson 4-8) $36r^2$

Logical Thinking

Determine which column contains the expression that does not belong. Be prepared to give the reason for your answer.

		A	B	C	D
$\frac{21}{82} \neq \frac{1}{4}$	39.	$\frac{21}{82}$ (circled)	$\frac{5}{20}$	$\frac{10}{40}$	$\frac{15}{60}$
$\frac{36}{49}$ is in lowest terms.	40.	$\frac{9}{12}$	$\frac{36}{49}$ (circled)	$\frac{12}{14}$	$\frac{26}{52}$
10^{-2} has a negative exponent.	41.	10^3	10^{-2} (circled)	10^8	10^5
21 is composite.	42.	31	21 (circled)	11	37

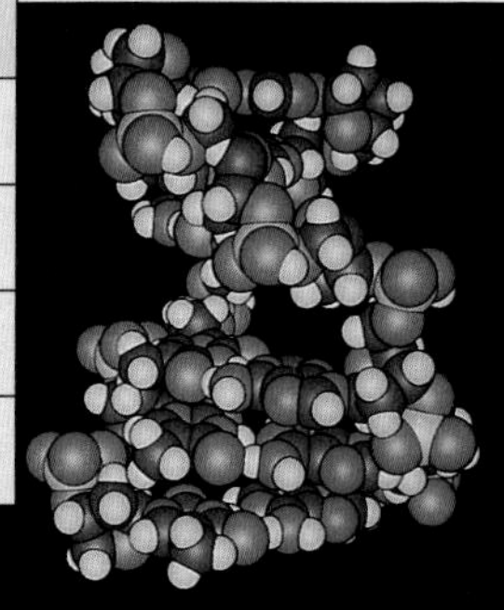

Applications

43. **Microbiology** A human blood cell is about 2^{-17} meters in diameter. The length of a DNA strand is about 2^{-18} meters long. How many DNA strands could be laid end to end across the diameter of a human blood cell? 2

44. **Computer Science** Large computers can perform operations in nanoseconds. A nanosecond is one billionth of a second or 10^{-9} seconds. If a computer takes 10 seconds to compute a problem, how many nanoseconds of time elapsed? 10^{10}

Connection

45. **Measurement** A millimeter is $\frac{1}{1000}$ of a meter or 10^{-3} meters. A kilometer is 1000 meters. How many millimeters are in a kilometer? 10^6 or 1 million

Critical Thinking

46. Simplify $x^4 \cdot x^{-2} \cdot x^8 \cdot x^{-10}$. 1

Wrap-Up

47. Write in your own words the relationship between the rules for multiplying powers and dividing powers. In both rules, the bases are the same. To multiply powers, add the exponents; to divide powers, subtract exponents.

Enrichment Masters Booklet, **p. 35**

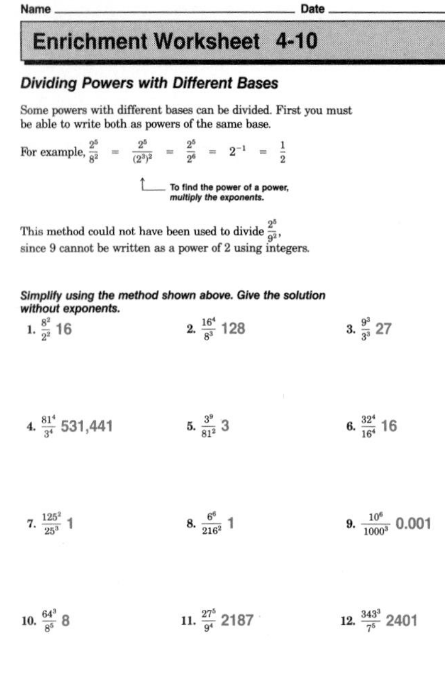

Name ______________ Date ______________

Enrichment Worksheet 4-10

Dividing Powers with Different Bases

Some powers with different bases can be divided. First you must be able to write both as powers of the same base.

For example, $\frac{2^5}{8^2} = \frac{2^5}{(2^3)^2} = \frac{2^5}{2^6} = 2^{-1} = \frac{1}{2}$

↑ To find the power of a power, *multiply the exponents.*

This method could not have been used to divide $\frac{2^5}{9^2}$, since 9 cannot be written as a power of 2 using integers.

Simplify using the method shown above. Give the solution without exponents.

1. $\frac{8^2}{2^2}$ 16
2. $\frac{16^4}{8^3}$ 128
3. $\frac{9^3}{3^3}$ 27
4. $\frac{81^4}{3^4}$ 531,441
5. $\frac{3^9}{81^2}$ 3
6. $\frac{32^4}{16^4}$ 16
7. $\frac{125^2}{25^3}$ 1
8. $\frac{6^6}{216^2}$ 1
9. $\frac{10^6}{1000^3}$ 0.001
10. $\frac{64^3}{8^5}$ 8
11. $\frac{27^5}{9^4}$ 2187
12. $\frac{343^3}{7^5}$ 2401

Alternate Strategies: Extending the Lesson

Enrichment

Using Research Have students research situations using powers and write problems involving division using exponents. Example: The Milky Way has about 10^{11} stars. If one in every 10^6 stars is the sun of a planet with intelligent life, how many planets with intelligent life are there in the Milky Way?

Cooperative Learning

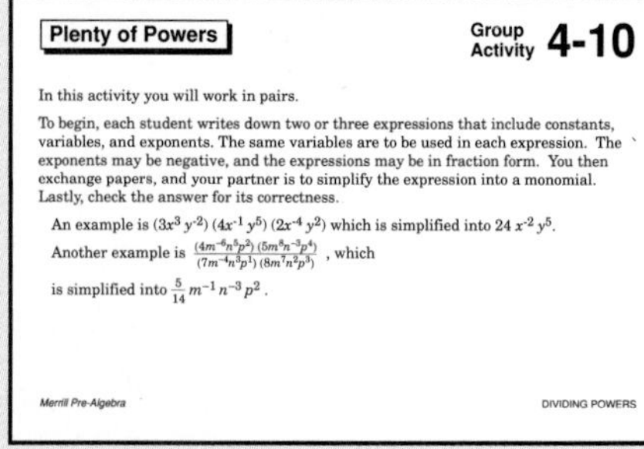

Plenty of Powers Group Activity **4-10**

In this activity you will work in pairs.

To begin, each student writes down two or three expressions that include constants, variables, and exponents. The same variables are to be used in each expression. The exponents may be negative, and the expressions may be in fraction form. You then exchange papers, and your partner is to simplify the expression into a monomial. Lastly, check the answer for its correctness.

An example is $(3x^3y^{-2})(4x^{-1}y^5)(2x^{-4}y^2)$ which is simplified into $24x^{-2}y^5$.

Another example is $\frac{(4m^{-6}n^5p^2)(5m^8n^{-3}p^4)}{(7m^{-4}n^3p^1)(8m^7n^2p^3)}$, which is simplified into $\frac{5}{14}m^{-1}n^{-3}p^2$.

Merrill Pre-Algebra DIVIDING POWERS

Algebra in Action-Physics

Measuring Sound

Scientists use a unit called the decibel to measure the intensity level of sound. A decibel equals one-tenth of a *bel,* a unit named after the Scottish-born inventor and scientist Alexander Graham Bell. Decibel measurements use numbers in a different way. For instance, 20 decibels does not mean the sound is 20 times the intensity of one decibel. A measurement of 20 decibels means ten used as a factor two times ($10 \cdot 10 = 10^2$) or 100 times the intensity of one decibel.

The chart lists the intensity of various sounds and the algebraic expression for each measurement.

Sound	Decibels	Expression
barely heard	0	10^0
breathing	10	10^1
whispering	30	10^3
normal conversation	50	10^5
noisy office	60	10^6
telephone bell	70	10^7
vacuum cleaner	80	10^8
subway train	100	10^{10}
motorcycle	110	10^{11}
rock concert	130	10^{13}
jet airplane	150	10^{15}

Sounds of 140 decibels or more produce pain in the ear and could damage the tissues of the inner ear.

How many times more intense is the sound of a motorcycle than the sound of a telephone bell?

motorcycle → 110 decibels → 10^{11} or ten used as a factor 11 times
bell → 70 decibels → 10^7 or ten used as a factor 7 times

Notice that $11 - 7 = 4$. This means that the sound of the motorcycle is 10^4 or 10,000 times more intense than the sound of a telephone bell.

1. Is it safer for your ears if you run a vacuum cleaner or attend a rock concert? vacuum
2. What is the expression for the decibel level that results in pain? 10^{14}
3. How many more times intense is the sound of a subway than someone whispering? 10^7 times
4. **Research** Find the decibel levels of other common activities such as using a power mower. See margin.

Applying Algebra to the Real World

Objective This optional page shows how algebra is used in the real world and also provides a change of pace.

Using Discussion

Discuss the meaning of the term *noise pollution.* Ask students what in their environment contributes to noise pollution. Ask students for situations where they think noise levels need to be reduced. List one or more ways the noise pollution could be reduced.

Science Connection

Explain to students that the decibel scale is not the only time numbers relate powers of 10. The Richter scale, used to measure the intensity of earthquakes, uses an exponential scale also. An earthquake with a magnitude of 5 on the Richter scale is 10 times more powerful than an earthquake with a magnitude of 4.

Activity

Using Charts Using the values from the decibel chart, estimate the noise level in decibels in the hall during a class change. If possible, borrow a decibel meter to check the estimation. Make suggestions as to how the noise level could be improved.

Additional Answer

4. Some other common activities and their decibel levels are:
rustling leaves: 20
purring cat: 25
noisy restaurant: 80
power mower: 100
chain saw: 115

Using the Chapter Review

The Chapter Review is a comprehensive review of the concepts presented in this chapter. This review may be used to prepare students for the Chapter Test.

Alternate Review Strategy

To provide a brief in-class review, you may wish to read the following questions to the class.

1. Is 9 a factor of 72? Explain why or why not. yes, because 72 ÷ 9 is a whole number
2. Name the exponent and base in 4^5. exponent is 5; base is 4
3. Draw a diagram to illustrate this situation. There was a row of 24 chairs. Every fifth chair was removed to create aisles.
   XXXX⊗XXXX⊗XXXX⊗XXXX⊗XXXX
4. Explain whether 21 is a prime or composite number. composite, because it has more than 2 factors
5. Describe the GCF of two or more monomials? the product of their common factors
6. Explain how you would write $\frac{32}{54}$ in simplest form. write the prime factorization of the numerator and the denominator; divide both numerator and denominator by the GCF
7. Explain how to find the first five multiples of 3. multiply 3 by 0, 3 by 1, 3 by 2, 3 by 3, and 3 by 4
8. How would you compare $\frac{3}{10}$ and $\frac{5}{14}$? write fractions as equivalent fractions with same denominator
9. What is the product of $y^5 \cdot y^3$? y^8
10. What is the quotient of $\frac{x^6}{x^2}$? x^4

Review

Language and Concepts

State whether each sentence is *true* or *false*. If false, replace the underlined word or number to make a true sentence.

1. The least common multiple of 10 and 15 is <u>30</u>. true
2. The number 27 is an example of a <u>prime</u> number. false, composite
3. $\frac{8}{12}$ is the simplest form of $\frac{16}{24}$. false, $\frac{2}{3}$
4. The fraction $\frac{3}{4}$ is equivalent to the fraction $\frac{12}{16}$. true
5. 14 is the <u>GCF</u> of 28 and 42. true
6. <u>$5m$</u> is a factor of $675mn$. true
7. Numbers such as 2, 3, 5, and 7 are examples of <u>odd</u> numbers. false, prime
8. In the expression 10^5, the <u>base</u> is 5. false, exponent
9. The expression 10^{-3} is equivalent to $\frac{1}{10^3}$. true
10. $3^4 \cdot 3^5 = \underline{9^{20}}$. false 3^9

Skills

Determine whether each expression is a monomial. (Lesson 4-1)

11. $2x$ yes
12. $\frac{m}{3}$ no
13. amq yes
14. $p - 3$ no

Determine whether each number is divisible by 2, 3, 5, 6, or 10. (Lesson 4-1)

15. 84 2, 3, 6
16. 45 3, 5
17. 420 2, 3, 5, 6, 10
18. 51 3

Write each product using exponents. (Lesson 4-2)

19. $4 \cdot 4$ 4^2
20. $7 \cdot 7$ 7^2
21. $3 \cdot 3 \cdot 3$ 3^3
22. $y \cdot y \cdot y \cdot y$ y^4

Evaluate each expression. (Lesson 4-2)

23. $3t^4$ if $t = 2$ 48
24. a^2 if $a = 12$ 144
25. $2y^3$ if $y = 5$ 250

Factor each number or monomial completely. (Lesson 4-4)

26. 28 $2^2 \cdot 7$
27. -50 $-1 \cdot 2 \cdot 5^2$
28. 124 $2^2 \cdot 31$
29. $200a^2b$ $2^3 \cdot 5^2 \cdot a \cdot a \cdot b$

Find the GCF for each set of numbers or monomials. (Lesson 4-5)

30. 24, 120 24
31. 64, 48 16
32. $-16a^2$, $30a^3$ $2a^2$
33. $24xy^3$, $36z^2$ 12
34. $12xy^3$, $72x^2y$, $24x^3y$ $12xy$
35. $60a^3b$, $150a^2b^2$, $36a^2b$ $6a^2b$

Write each fraction in simplest form. (Lesson 4-6)

36. $\frac{10}{30}$ $\frac{1}{3}$
37. $\frac{13a^2}{52a}$ $\frac{a}{4}$
38. $\frac{12}{60}$ $\frac{1}{5}$
39. $\frac{27x^2y^2}{15xy^3}$ $\frac{9x}{5y}$

Organizing the Chapter

You may want to refer to the ***Course Planning Calendar*** *on Page T31.*

Planning Guide

Lesson (Pages)	Pacing Chart (in days)			Extra Practice (Student Edition)	Blackline Masters Booklets			Other Resources
	MINIMUM	STANDARD	ACCELERATED		Reteaching	Practice	Enrichment	
5-1 (166-168)	1	1	1	p. 597, Set 5A	p. 36	p. 40	p. 36	Transparency 5-1 Group Activity Card 5-1
5-2 (169-171)	1	1	1	p. 597, Set 5A	p. 37	p. 41	p. 37	Transparency 5-2 Group Activity Card 5-2
5-3 (172-173)	1	1	0.5	p. 597, Set 5A	p. 38	p. 42	p. 38	Transparency 5-3 Group Activity Card 5-3
5-4 (174-176)	1	1	1	p. 597, Set 5A	p. 39	p. 43	p. 39	Transparency 5-4 Group Activity Card 5-4
5-5 (177-179)	1	1	1	p. 597, Set 5A	p. 40	p. 44	p. 40	Transparency 5-5 Group Activity Card 5-5
5-6 (180-182)	1	1	1	p. 597, Set 5A	p. 41	p. 45	p. 41	Transparency 5-6 Group Activity Card 5-6
5-7 (184-187)	1.5	1	1	p. 597, Set 5B	p. 42	p. 46	p. 42	Transparency 5-7 Group Activity Card 5-7
5-8 (188-189)	1	1	0.5			p. 47		Transparency 5-8 Group Activity Card 5-8
5-9 (190-193)	1.5	1	1	p. 598, Set 5C	p. 43	p. 48	p. 43	Transparency 5-9 Group Activity Card 5-9
5-10 (195-197)	1	1	1	p. 598, Set 5D	p. 44	p. 49	p. 44	Transparency 5-10 Group Activity Card 5-10
Review (198-199)	1.5	1	1					Test Generator
Test (200)	1	1	1		Evaluation Masters, pp. 37-42			

Other Chapter Resources

Student Edition
History, p. 169
Mid-Chapter Quiz, p. 179
Algebra in Action, p. 183
Writing Connection, p. 187
Biography, p. 193
Exploration, p. 194
Team Problem Solving, p. 197
Academic Skills Test, p. 201

Teacher Resource Package
Interdisciplinary Activity, p. 5
Application Worksheet, p. 20
Cooperative Problem Solving, p. 35
Multicultural Activity, p. 50
Fun Activities, pp. 66, 67
Technology Worksheets, pp. 5, 20, 35
Lab Manual, pp. 39-41
Quizzes(2), p. 43
Class Review Game

Software
Test Generator

available for Apple and IBM

Enhancing the Chapter

Some of the blackline masters for enhancing this chapter are shown below.

Applications, p. 20

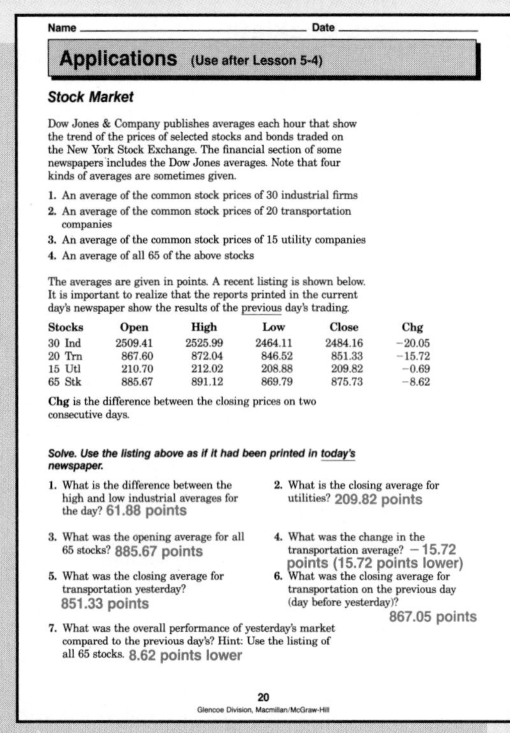

Name ________________ Date ________________

Applications (Use after Lesson 5-4)

Stock Market

Dow Jones & Company publishes averages each hour that show the trend of the prices of selected stocks and bonds traded on the New York Stock Exchange. The financial section of some newspapers includes the Dow Jones averages. Note that four kinds of averages are sometimes given.

1. An average of the common stock prices of 30 industrial firms
2. An average of the common stock prices of 20 transportation companies
3. An average of the common stock prices of 15 utility companies
4. An average of all 65 of the above stocks

The averages are given in points. A recent listing is shown below. It is important to realize that the reports printed in the current day's newspaper show the results of the previous day's trading.

Stocks	Open	High	Low	Close	Chg
30 Ind	2509.41	2525.99	2464.11	2484.16	−20.05
20 Trn	867.60	872.04	846.52	851.33	−15.72
15 Utl	210.70	212.02	208.88	209.82	−0.69
65 Stk	885.67	891.12	869.79	875.73	−8.62

Chg is the difference between the closing prices on two consecutive days.

Solve. Use the listing above as if it had been printed in today's newspaper.

1. What is the difference between the high and low industrial averages for the day? 61.88 points
2. What is the closing average for utilities? 209.82 points
3. What was the opening average for all 65 stocks? 885.67 points
4. What was the change in the transportation average? −15.72 points (15.72 points lower)
5. What was the closing average for transportation yesterday? 851.33 points
6. What was the closing average for transportation on the previous day (day before yesterday)? 867.05 points
7. What was the overall performance of yesterday's market compared to the previous day's? Hint: Use the listing of all 65 stocks. 8.62 points lower

20

Glencoe Division, Macmillan/McGraw-Hill

The **Activity Masters Booklet** contains the page shown above.

Interdisciplinary Activity, p. 5

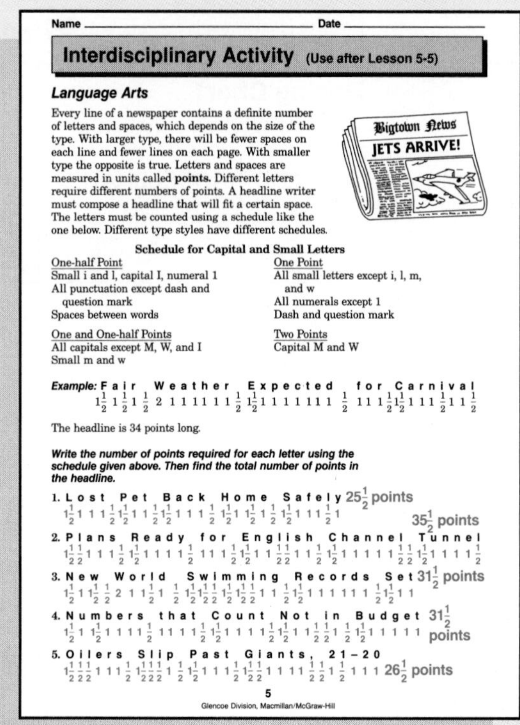

Name ________________ Date ________________

Interdisciplinary Activity (Use after Lesson 5-5)

Language Arts

Every line of a newspaper contains a definite number of letters and spaces, which depends on the size of the type. With larger type, there will be fewer spaces on each line and fewer lines on each page. With smaller type the opposite is true. Letters and spaces are measured in units called **points.** Different letters require different numbers of points. A headline writer must compose a headline that will fit a certain space. The letters must be counted using a schedule like the one below. Different type styles have different schedules.

Schedule for Capital and Small Letters

One-half Point	One Point
Small i and l, capital I, numeral 1	All small letters except i, l, m, and w
All punctuation except dash and question mark	All numerals except 1
Spaces between words	Dash and question mark

One and One-half Points	Two Points
All capitals except M, W, and I	Capital M and W
Small m and w	

Example: F a i r W e a t h e r E x p e c t e d f o r C a r n i v a l

$1\frac{1}{2}\ 1\ \frac{1}{2}\ 1\ \frac{1}{2}\ 2\ 1\ 1\ 1\ 1\ 1\ 1\ \frac{1}{2}\ 1\frac{1}{2}\ 1\ 1\ 1\ 1\ 1\ 1\ 1\ \frac{1}{2}\ 1\ 1\ 1\ \frac{1}{2}\ 1\frac{1}{2}\ 1\ 1\ 1\ \frac{1}{2}\ 1\ 1\ \frac{1}{2}$

The headline is 34 points long.

Write the number of points required for each letter using the schedule given above. Then find the total number of points in the headline.

1. L o s t P e t B a c k H o m e S a f e l y $25\frac{1}{2}$ points
   $1\frac{1}{2}\ 1\ 1\ 1\ \frac{1}{2}\ 1\frac{1}{2}\ 1\ 1\ \frac{1}{2}\ 1\frac{1}{2}\ 1\ 1\ 1\ \frac{1}{2}\ 1\frac{1}{2}\ 1\ 1\frac{1}{2}\ 1\ \frac{1}{2}\ 1\frac{1}{2}\ 1\ 1\ 1\ \frac{1}{2}\ 1$
2. P l a n s R e a d y f o r E n g l i s h C h a n n e l T u n n e l $35\frac{1}{2}$ points
   $1\frac{1}{2}\ \frac{1}{2}\ 1\ 1\ 1\ \frac{1}{2}\ 1\frac{1}{2}\ 1\ 1\ 1\ 1\ \frac{1}{2}\ 1\ 1\ 1\ \frac{1}{2}\ 1\frac{1}{2}\ 1\ 1\ \frac{1}{2}\ \frac{1}{2}\ 1\ 1\ \frac{1}{2}\ 1\frac{1}{2}\ 1\ 1\ 1\ 1\ 1\ \frac{1}{2}\ \frac{1}{2}\ 1\frac{1}{2}\ 1\ 1\ 1\ 1\ \frac{1}{2}$
3. N e w W o r l d S w i m m i n g R e c o r d s S e t $31\frac{1}{2}$ points
   $1\frac{1}{2}\ 1\ 1\frac{1}{2}\ \frac{1}{2}\ 2\ 1\ 1\ \frac{1}{2}\ 1\ \frac{1}{2}\ 1\frac{1}{2}\ 1\frac{1}{2}\ \frac{1}{2}\ 1\frac{1}{2}\ 1\frac{1}{2}\ \frac{1}{2}\ 1\ 1\ \frac{1}{2}\ 1\frac{1}{2}\ 1\ 1\ 1\ 1\ 1\ 1\ \frac{1}{2}\ 1\frac{1}{2}\ 1\ 1$
4. N u m b e r s t h a t C o u n t N o t i n B u d g e t $31\frac{1}{2}$ points
   $1\frac{1}{2}\ 1\ 1\frac{1}{2}\ 1\ 1\ 1\ 1\ \frac{1}{2}\ 1\ 1\ 1\ 1\ \frac{1}{2}\ 1\frac{1}{2}\ 1\ 1\ 1\ 1\ \frac{1}{2}\ 1\frac{1}{2}\ 1\ 1\ \frac{1}{2}\ \frac{1}{2}\ 1\ \frac{1}{2}\ 1\frac{1}{2}\ 1\ 1\ 1\ 1\ 1$
5. O i l e r s S l i p P a s t G i a n t s , 2 1 – 2 0 $26\frac{1}{2}$ points
   $1\frac{1}{2}\ \frac{1}{2}\ \frac{1}{2}\ 1\ 1\ 1\ \frac{1}{2}\ 1\frac{1}{2}\ \frac{1}{2}\ \frac{1}{2}\ 1\ \frac{1}{2}\ 1\frac{1}{2}\ 1\ 1\ 1\ \frac{1}{2}\ 1\frac{1}{2}\ \frac{1}{2}\ 1\ 1\ 1\ 1\ \frac{1}{2}\ \frac{1}{2}\ 1\ \frac{1}{2}\ 1\ 1\ 1$

5

Glencoe Division, Macmillan/McGraw-Hill

The **Activity Masters Booklet** contains the page shown above.

Models and Manipulatives

Students will be asked to make a picture representation of a fraction, such as $\frac{3}{4}$. Brainstorm different ways of representing this number. Be as creative as possible. Ask students to look for similarities and differences in the representations. Have students solve other similar examples.

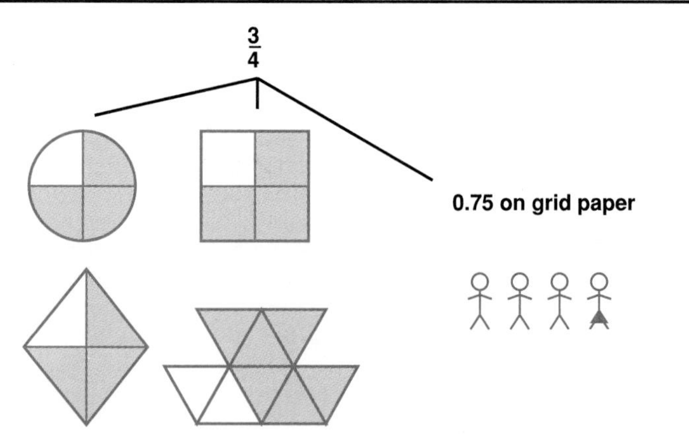

Limited English Proficiency (LEP) Activity

Egyptians used the following method to multiply. Halve the number on the left, without regard to any remainders, double the number on the right. Then cross out any even numbers on the left as well as its double and add the numbers that remain on the right. Why does this work? Note the pattern used to determine the answer. If a student is able to see the pattern, but has difficulty expressing it, help him or her write out the pattern.

Example:

~~26~~	×	~~15~~
13		30
~~6~~		~~60~~
3		120
1		240
		390

Cooperative Learning

The following activity is provided in the **Activity Masters Booklet.**

Cooperative Problem Solving, p. 35

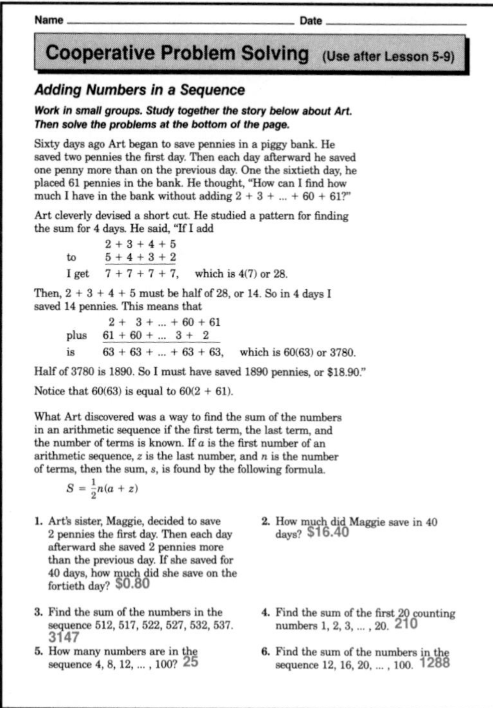

Name ____________ Date ____________

Cooperative Problem Solving (Use after Lesson 5-9)

Adding Numbers in a Sequence

Work in small groups. Study together the story below about Art. Then solve the problems at the bottom of the page.

Sixty days ago Art began to save pennies in a piggy bank. He saved two pennies the first day. Then each day afterward he saved one penny more than on the previous day. One the sixtieth day, he placed 61 pennies in the bank. He thought, "How can I find how much I have in the bank without adding 2 + 3 + ... + 60 + 61?"

Art cleverly devised a short cut. He studied a pattern for finding the sum for 4 days. He said, "If I add

2 + 3 + 4 + 5
to 5 + 4 + 3 + 2
I get 7 + 7 + 7 + 7, which is 4(7) or 28.

Then, 2 + 3 + 4 + 5 must be half of 28, or 14. So in 4 days I saved 14 pennies. This means that

2 + 3 + ... + 60 + 61
plus 61 + 60 + ... 3 + 2
is 63 + 63 + ... + 63 + 63, which is 60(63) or 3780.

Half of 3780 is 1890. So I must have saved 1890 pennies, or $18.90."

Notice that 60(63) is equal to 60(2 + 61).

What Art discovered was a way to find the sum of the numbers in an arithmetic sequence if the first term, the last term, and the number of terms is known. If a is the first number of an arithmetic sequence, z is the last number, and n is the number of terms, then the sum, s, is found by the following formula.

$$S = \frac{1}{2}n(a + z)$$

1. Art's sister, Maggie, decided to save 2 pennies the first day. Then each day afterward she saved 2 pennies more than the previous day. If she saved for 40 days, how much did she save on the fortieth day? $0.80
2. How much did Maggie save in 40 days? $16.40
3. Find the sum of the numbers in the sequence 512, 517, 522, 527, 532, 537. 3147
4. Find the sum of the first 20 counting numbers 1, 2, 3, ... , 20. 210
5. How many numbers are in the sequence 4, 8, 12, ... , 100? 25
6. Find the sum of the numbers in the sequence 12, 16, 20, ... , 100. 1288

Cooperative Problem Solving

Have students work in groups of two or three to find out how many squares are in the 12th term of this sequence. They should then use this pattern to figure out how many squares are in the 100th term. Ask them to describe in words how they determined the answer.
(Answer: 12th term—45 squares; 100th term—397 squares)

Interactive Bulletin Board

Business Connection

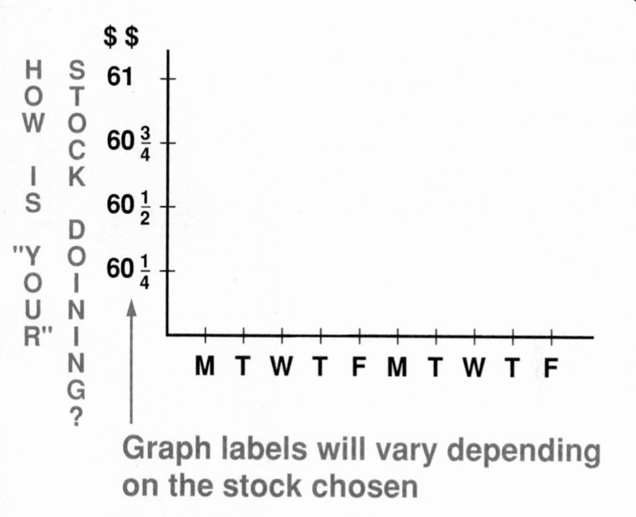

Purpose Provide practice in adding and subtracting fractions.

How to Use It Divide students into about six groups. Have each group pick a stock and each day graph its value at closing. Most stocks do not fluctuate more than a fractional point up or down in a day. It is interesting to note that the stocks are listed in eighths because the monetary exchange at one time was in pieces of eight, dating back to the days of pirates.

Outside Resources

Books/Periodicals
Adventures in Pre-Algebra, Davis

Films/Videotapes
Between Rational Numbers, Silver Burdett

Software
Conquering Fractions (+, –), MECC

Technology

There are three pages in the ***Technology Masters Booklet*** that involve technology with concepts in this chapter. One page involves calculators and one page has a problem that can be solved using the BASIC program that is provided. Students should evaluate the information they obtain from running the program and solve a similar problem by extending the program.

Using the Chapter Opener

Transparency 5-0 is available in the Transparency Package. It provides a full-color visual and motivational activity that you can use to engage students in the mathematical content of the chapter.

Using Lists

Have each student divide a piece of paper into two columns. In the first column, brainstorm a list of those sports and games that are scored according to arithmetic sequences. In the second column, list those that are not. Additional examples of arithmetic sequences might be postage rates, yardage down the field for lines on a football field, or consecutive odd integers.

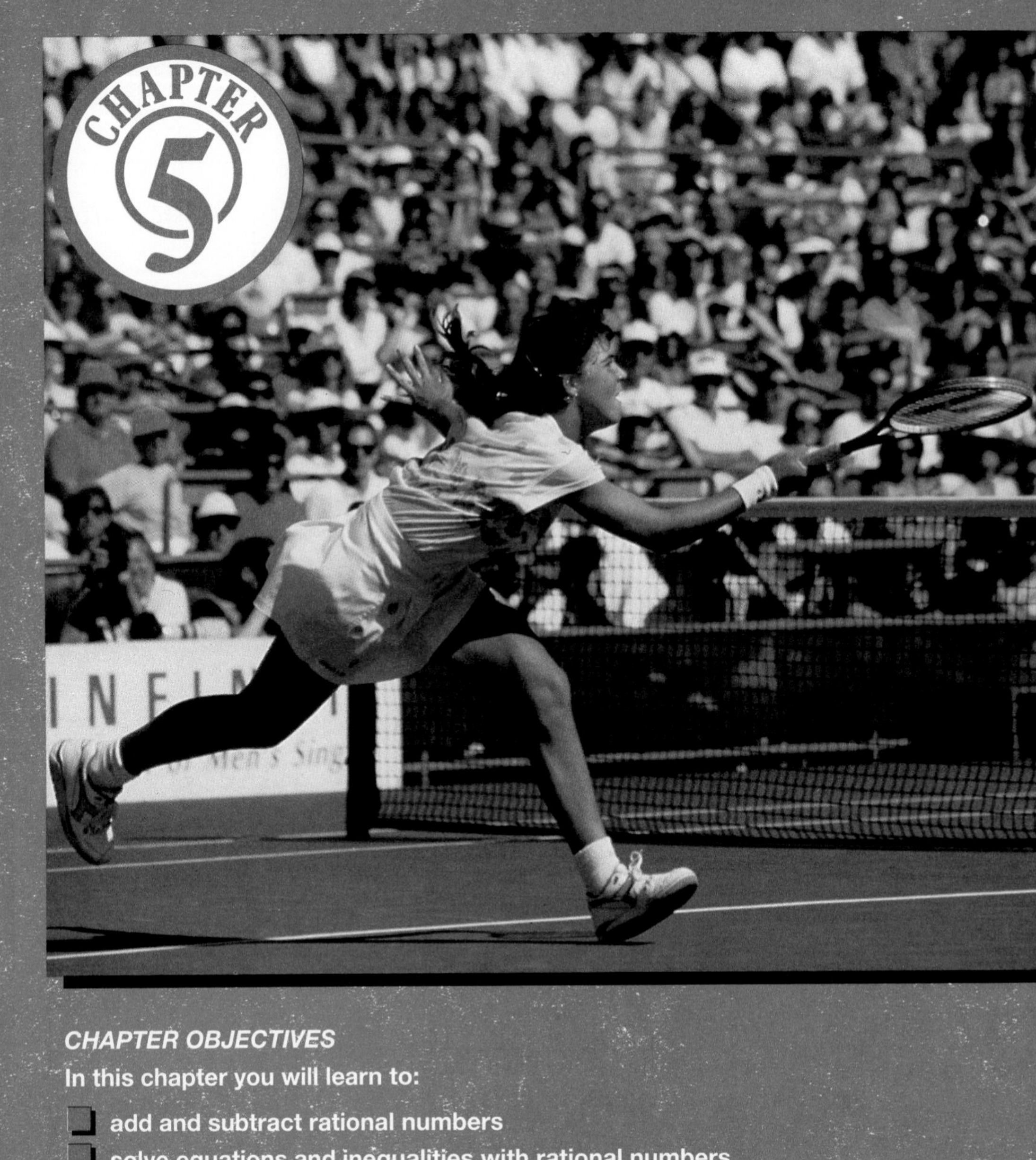

CHAPTER OBJECTIVES

In this chapter you will learn to:

- add and subtract rational numbers
- solve equations and inequalities with rational numbers
- find terms of an arithmetic sequence
- convert within the customary system
- solve problems by looking for a pattern

Rationals: Adding and Subtracting Patterns

What do volleyball, hockey, and tennis have in common? Yes, they all are team sports, but that's not the answer. Here's another hint. This particular characteristic is not shared by football, basketball, and tennis.

Give up? In volleyball, every time your team wins a point, the score increases by one. The same is true when you score a goal in hockey or win a set in tennis. What about basketball? Some baskets are worth one, two, or three points. The scoring does not increase in a regular pattern.

The scoring in volleyball, hockey, and tennis is an example of an arithmetic sequence. Can you think of another example of an arithmetic sequence?

Chapter Project

Different sports offer different fitness benefits. Some are better for increasing flexibility, while others build muscle strength or endurance.

Do research to find out about the fitness benefits of an exercise or sport you like.

Health Connection

Health books and books on individual sports and exercises offer resources on fitness benefits. Encourage students to use their own experiences to add to the benefit lists. Information from the Chapter 3 opener can be used to discuss the beneficial effects of a combination of proper diet and exercise. Discuss how an improper diet can reduce the benefits of exercise.

Looking Ahead

You may want to have the following materials available to use in this chapter.

Algebra in Action, p. 183
business section of a newspaper

Exploration, p. 194
calculators

Lesson Notes 5-1

5-Minute Check
(over Chapter 4)

Find the GCF for each set of numbers or monomials.

1. 14, 42 **14**
2. $10x^2y^3$, $12x^3y^2$, $8x^3y$ **$2x^2y$**

Write each fraction in simplest form.

3. $\frac{15}{45}$ **$\frac{1}{3}$**
4. $\frac{16a^3b^2}{40a^2b^2}$ **$\frac{2a}{5}$**

Transparency 5-1 contains the 5-Minute Check and a teaching aid for this lesson.

1 FOCUS

The purpose of this lesson is to introduce the set of rational numbers and compare rational numbers by graphing them on a number line.

Motivating the Lesson

Have students replace each ● with <, >, or = to make a true sentence.

1. -1 ● -3 **>**
2. -2 ● 2 **<**
3. -4 ● 5 **<**
4. 0 ● -8 **>**

2 TEACH

Using Discussion

Write the following rational numbers on the chalkboard: -8, $-3\frac{1}{3}$, -3, $-\frac{3}{5}$, 0, 0.3, $\frac{1}{2}$, $2\frac{2}{3}$, 8. Ask students if these numbers can be organized into two different types of numbers. **Possible answer: integers and nonintegers** Ask students if each of the two types of numbers can be organized in any way. **Possible answer: order from least to greatest**

Chalkboard Examples

Name the set of numbers to which each number belongs.

- *For Example 1* 24 **W, I, R**
- *For Example 2* -12 **I, R**
- *For Example 3* $-3\frac{2}{5}$ **R**

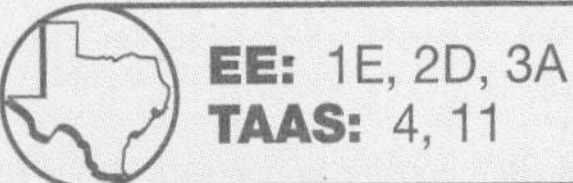

EE: 1E, 2D, 3A
TAAS: 4, 11

5-1 Rational Numbers

Objective:
Identify and compare rational numbers.

Key Term:
rational number

One skill that you will need to use throughout your life is the ability to organize. The loose-leaf binder that you carry to school is probably organized by subject. You may have noticed that numbers can be organized into sets. One set of numbers is *whole numbers.*

Whole Numbers
This set includes 0, 1, 2, 3, ... It also includes any number, such as $\frac{4}{4}$, that can be written as a whole number.

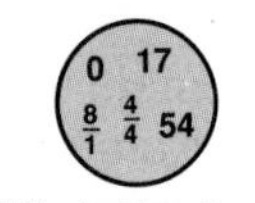

Whole Numbers

Another set of numbers is *integers.*

Name an integer that is not a whole number. **-2**

Integers
This set includes . . . -2, -1, 0, 1, 2, ... Notice that all whole numbers are included in the set of integers. Integers also include any number, such as $\frac{-3}{1}$, that can be written as an integer.

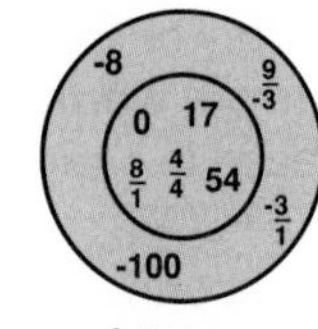

Integers

Of course, you have used numbers that are not whole numbers or integers. Consider this situation.

Suppose you and your friend form a small lawn-care company. You agree to share the profit or loss equally. During the first month the company loses \$15. If a represents the amount due each person, then the equation $2a = -15$ can be used to find each person's loss. To solve the equation, divide each side by 2.

$$2a = -15$$

$$a = \frac{-15}{2} \text{ or } -7\frac{1}{2} \text{ or } -7.5 \qquad \text{Each person loses \$7.50.}$$

Both 2 and -15 are integers, but $\frac{-15}{2}$ is not an integer. The number system must be extended to include numbers like $\frac{-15}{2}$. The number $\frac{-15}{2}$ is called a **rational number.**

Definition of a Rational Number

Any number that can be expressed in the form $\frac{a}{b}$, where a and b are integers and $b \neq 0$, is called a rational number.

Bell Ringer

State in your own words the rule for dividing powers. **When dividing powers with the same base, subtract their exponents.**

Rational Numbers

This includes common fractions, such as $\frac{1}{2}$. It also includes mixed numbers and decimals. All integers are included because any integer, such as -5, can be written in the form $\frac{-5}{1}$.

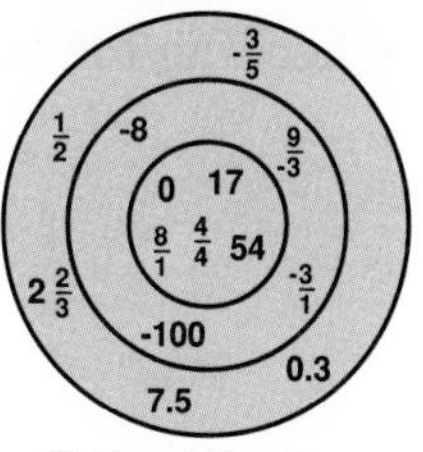

Rational Numbers

Examples

Name the set of numbers to which each number belongs.

1 15 — 15 is a whole number and an integer. Since it can be written as $\frac{15}{1}$, it is also a rational number.

2 -9 — -9 is an integer and a rational number.

3 $-2\frac{1}{2}$ — Since $-2\frac{1}{2}$ can be written as $\frac{-5}{2}$, it is a rational number.

Recall from Chapter 2 that $\frac{-4}{2} = \frac{4}{-2} = -2$. Similarly, any rational number such as $\frac{-2}{5}$ can also be written as $\frac{2}{-5}$ or $-\frac{2}{5}$. This will be useful when you graph rational numbers on a number line. You can also use a number line to compare rational numbers.

Examples

4 **Graph $\frac{-2}{3}$ on a number line. Then give two other names for $\frac{-2}{3}$.**

$\frac{-2}{3}$ can be written as $-\frac{2}{3}$ or $\frac{2}{-3}$.

5 **Use the number line to determine which is greater, $-\frac{3}{4}$ or $-\frac{1}{2}$.**

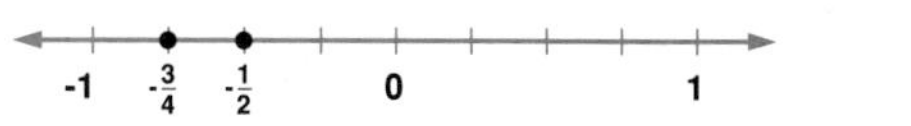

$-\frac{1}{2} = -\frac{2}{4}$

On the number line shown above, $-\frac{1}{2}$ is graphed to the right of $-\frac{3}{4}$. Therefore, $-\frac{1}{2} > -\frac{3}{4}$.

Chalkboard Examples

- *For Example 4*
  Graph $-\frac{1}{4}$ on a number line. Then give two other names for $-\frac{1}{4}$.
  -1 0 1
  $\frac{-1}{4}, \frac{1}{-4}$
- *For Example 5*
  Use a number line to determine which is greater, $-\frac{2}{3}$ or $-\frac{3}{4}$.

3 PRACTICE/APPLY

Checking the Concept

If students are using a number line to complete Exercises 8-10 in the Guided Practice, point out that numbers to the right are greater.

Error Analysis

Watch for students who will identify -7 as greater than -5 because 7 is larger than 5, or identify -7 as greater than 5 for the same reason.

Prevent by locating both numbers on the number line.

Practice Masters Booklet, **p. 40**

Name ______________ Date ______________

Practice Worksheet 5-1

Rational Numbers

Name the set of numbers to which each number belongs.

1. 0 W, I, R
2. 5 W, I, R
3. −5 I, R
4. −10.0 I, R
5. $\frac{1}{4}$ R
6. $1\frac{1}{2}$ R
7. 0.3 R
8. $-1\frac{1}{3}$ R
9. −625 I, R
10. 100 W, I, R
11. $-\frac{2}{3}$ R
12. $\frac{-3}{5}$ R

Graph each number on a number line. Then give two other names for each number. Answers will vary. Sample answers given.

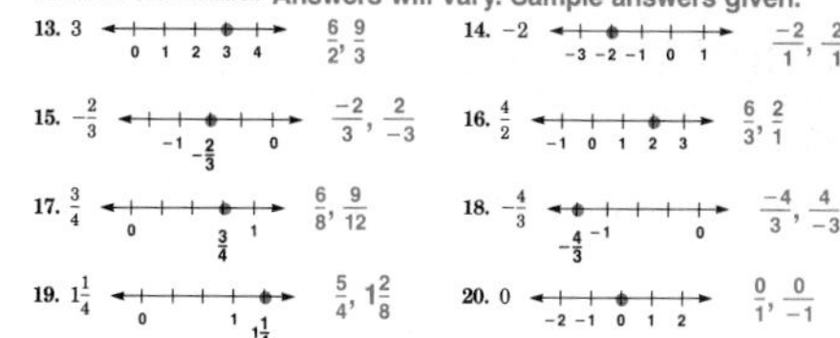

13. 3 — $\frac{6}{2}, \frac{9}{3}$
14. −2 — $\frac{-2}{1}, \frac{2}{-1}$
15. $-\frac{2}{3}$ — $\frac{-2}{3}, \frac{2}{-3}$
16. $\frac{4}{2}$ — $\frac{6}{3}, \frac{2}{1}$
17. $\frac{3}{4}$ — $\frac{6}{8}, \frac{9}{12}$
18. $-\frac{4}{3}$ — $\frac{-4}{3}, \frac{4}{-3}$
19. $1\frac{1}{4}$ — $\frac{5}{4}, 1\frac{2}{8}$
20. 0 — $\frac{0}{1}, \frac{0}{-1}$

Write <, >, or = in each box to make a true sentence.

21. $\frac{1}{3}$ [>] $-\frac{1}{3}$
22. $-\frac{5}{4}$ [=] $-1\frac{1}{4}$
23. $-\frac{2}{3}$ [<] $-\frac{3}{5}$
24. $1\frac{1}{3}$ [>] $-\frac{6}{3}$
25. $-\frac{1}{10}$ [>] $-\frac{1}{9}$
26. $\frac{3}{10}$ [>] $\frac{1}{8}$
27. $\frac{8}{5}$ [=] $1\frac{3}{5}$
28. $-\frac{5}{9}$ [<] $-\frac{4}{9}$
29. $\frac{10}{16}$ [=] $\frac{5}{8}$
30. $\frac{1}{2}$ [>] $-\frac{1}{3}$
31. $\frac{-8}{2}$ [=] −4
32. $-\frac{6}{5}$ [<] $-\frac{5}{6}$

Alternate Strategies: Reteaching the Lesson

Reteaching Activity

Using Calculators Have students list multiples to determine the LCD of pairs of fractions. Since many of the same numbers are used in different pairs of fractions, a master list of commonly used numbers and their multiples will help students compare fractions more quickly.

Reteaching Master Booklet, **p. 36**

Name ______________ Date ______________

Reteaching Worksheet 5-1

Rational Numbers

Any number that can be written as a ratio is called a **rational number.**

$3 = \frac{3}{1}$ $-5 = \frac{-5}{1}$ $1\frac{2}{3} = \frac{5}{3}$ $-0.25 = \frac{-1}{4}$ $1.05 = \frac{105}{100}$

All whole numbers, integers, fractions, and decimals are members of the set of rational numbers.

Circle the positive rational numbers in each set.

1. −5, 0, $\frac{3}{-4}$, ($1\frac{1}{5}$), −2.58, (0.006), (34), −0.9
2. −0.5, −0.25, −0.125, 0, (0.125), (0.25), (0.5)

Circle the negative rational numbers in each set.

3. $\frac{2}{5}$, ...

Independent Practice

Homework Assignment	
Basic	11-23 odd, 25-29, 31, 32
Average	12-24 even, 25-32
Honors	13-16, 22-32

4 CLOSE

Assessment Option

Writing Have students write six rational numbers. Tell students to use an equal number of positive and negative numbers and to include at least one common fraction, one mixed number, and one decimal. Then have them write their numbers in order from least to greatest.

Additional Answers

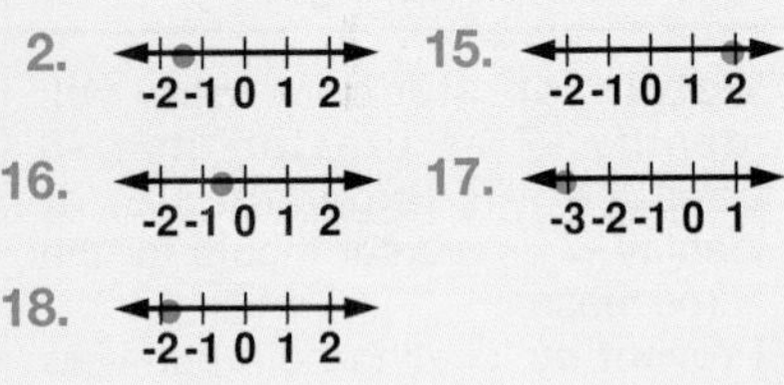

Enrichment Masters Booklet, **p. 36**

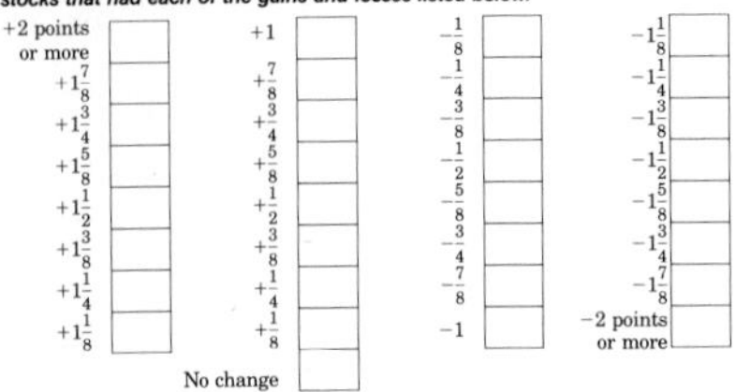

Name ______ Date ______

Enrichment Worksheet 5-1

Problem Solving: Gathering Data

When investors decide to buy or sell stock, they usually base their decisions on data. They read stock market reports, investigate companies they are interested in, and look at economic trends. This activity focuses on reading stock market reports.

To read a stock market report, you need to become familiar with the terms that are used, the facts and figures that are published in the newspaper, and the methods used to keep track of the stocks.

Many newspapers print stock reports such as the New York Stock Exchange (NYSE) report. The final entry for each stock is a fraction or mixed number which is positive (indicating a gain in value) or negative (indicating a loss).

Get the business section of your local Sunday newspaper and find the New York Stock Exchange (NYSE) report. Using just those stocks that begin with A, B, or C, tally the number of stocks that had each of the gains and losses listed below.

+2 points or more		+1		$-\frac{1}{8}$		$-1\frac{1}{8}$	
$+1\frac{7}{8}$		$+\frac{7}{8}$		$-\frac{1}{4}$		$-1\frac{1}{4}$	
$+1\frac{3}{4}$		$+\frac{3}{4}$		$-\frac{3}{8}$		$-1\frac{3}{8}$	
$+1\frac{5}{8}$		$+\frac{5}{8}$		$-\frac{1}{2}$		$-1\frac{1}{2}$	
$+1\frac{1}{2}$		$+\frac{1}{2}$		$-\frac{5}{8}$		$-1\frac{5}{8}$	
$+1\frac{3}{8}$		$+\frac{3}{8}$		$-\frac{3}{4}$		$-1\frac{3}{4}$	
$+1\frac{1}{4}$		$+\frac{1}{4}$		$-\frac{7}{8}$		$-1\frac{7}{8}$	
$+1\frac{1}{8}$		$+\frac{1}{8}$		-1		-2 points or more	
		No change					

1. Did more stocks gain or lose? Answers will vary.
2. How did the market do as a whole? Answers will vary.
3. How did the newspaper describe the trading this week? Answers will vary.

Project

4. Watch two specific stocks each weekday for a month, and graph their daily closing price.

Checking for Understanding

Communicating Algebra

1. In your own words, what is a rational number? Sample answer: a number that can be written as a fraction.
2. Graph $-1\frac{2}{5}$ on a number line. See margin.
3. Give an example of a rational number that is not an integer. Sample answer: $\frac{2}{3}$

Guided Practice

Name the set of numbers to which each number belongs.

4. -6 I, R
5. $-7\frac{2}{3}$ R
6. 0 W, I, R
7. $\frac{20}{7}$ R

Replace each ● with <, >, or = to make a true sentence. Use a number line if necessary.

8. $\frac{2}{3}$ ● $-\frac{2}{3}$ >
9. -5 ● $\frac{-10}{2}$ =
10. $\frac{-4}{3}$ ● 0 <

Exercises

Independent Practice

Name the set of numbers to which each number belongs.

11. -1 I, R
12. -379 I, R
13. 9.0 W, I, R
14. $\frac{1}{100}$ R

Graph each number on a number line. Then give two other names for each number. See margin.

15. 2 $\frac{2}{1}$, $\frac{4}{2}$
16. $-\frac{1}{2}$ $\frac{-1}{2}$, $\frac{1}{-2}$
17. $\frac{6}{-2}$ -3, $-\frac{6}{2}$
18. $-1\frac{3}{4}$ $\frac{-7}{4}$, $-\frac{7}{4}$

Replace each ● with <, >, or = to make a true sentence.

19. $\frac{3}{4}$ ● $-\frac{3}{4}$ >
20. $-5\frac{1}{2}$ ● $\frac{-11}{2}$ =
21. $\frac{2}{5}$ ● $-\frac{2}{3}$ >
22. $3\frac{1}{3}$ ● $\frac{10}{3}$ =
23. $-\frac{3}{8}$ ● $-\frac{1}{8}$ <
24. $\frac{10}{12}$ ● $\frac{5}{6}$ =

Mixed Review

25. Solve $y + 18 = -5$. (Lesson 3-1) -23
26. **Personal Finance** In order to open a special savings account, Jan needs a minimum of \$100. She currently has \$82. How many hours would she have to baby-sit at a rate of \$3 per hour to have enough money to open the account? (Lesson 3-10) 6 or more hours
27. State whether 37 is prime or composite. (Lesson 4-4) prime
28. Simplify $(3m^3)(-7m^2)$. (Lesson 4-9) $-21m^5$

Applications

29. **Measurement** Tina has a complete set of wrenches measured in 16th inches, 8ths, and 4ths. Her $\frac{5}{8}$-inch wrench is too small for a job. What is the next size larger that Tina has? $\frac{11}{16}$-inch
30. **Personal Finance** On Monday Mr. Brown received a check for \$47.58 and paid a bill for \$59.23. At the end of the day, does he have more or less money than he had in the morning? How do you know? less; bill is for more than check

Critical Thinking

31. Does $\frac{6}{2.4}$ name a rational number? If so, what one? If not, why not? yes; $\frac{5}{2}$

Wrap-Up

32. Write a sentence explaining why rational numbers are needed. Sample answer: Some situations cannot be described using whole numbers or integers.

Alternate Strategies: Extending the Lesson

Enrichment

Using Groups of Two Have students play "War" with a set of dominoes from which the doubles have been removed. Have each student draw a domino and form a proper fraction from the numbers on the domino. Have students compare fractions. The student with the greater fraction keeps both dominoes.

Cooperative Learning

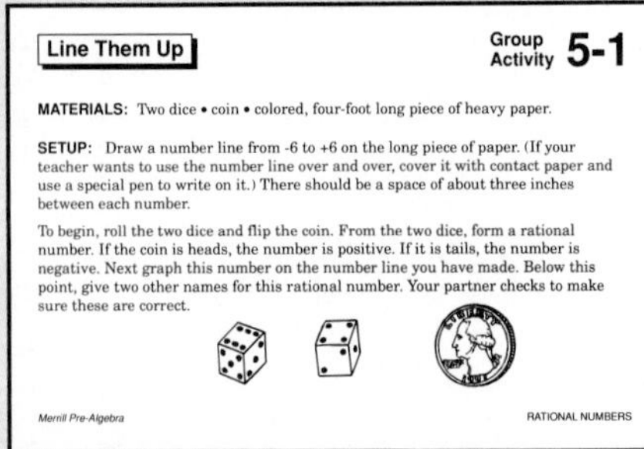

Line Them Up Group Activity **5-1**

MATERIALS: Two dice • coin • colored, four-foot long piece of heavy paper.

SETUP: Draw a number line from -6 to +6 on the long piece of paper. (If your teacher wants to use the number line over and over, cover it with contact paper and use a special pen to write on it.) There should be a space of about three inches between each number.

To begin, roll the two dice and flip the coin. From the two dice, form a rational number. If the coin is heads, the number is positive. If it is tails, the number is negative. Next graph this number on the number line you have made. Below this point, give two other names for this rational number. Your partner checks to make sure these are correct.

Merrill Pre-Algebra RATIONAL NUMBERS

5-2 Writing Decimals as Fractions

Objective:
Rename decimals as fractions.

Key Terms:
terminating
repeating
bar notation

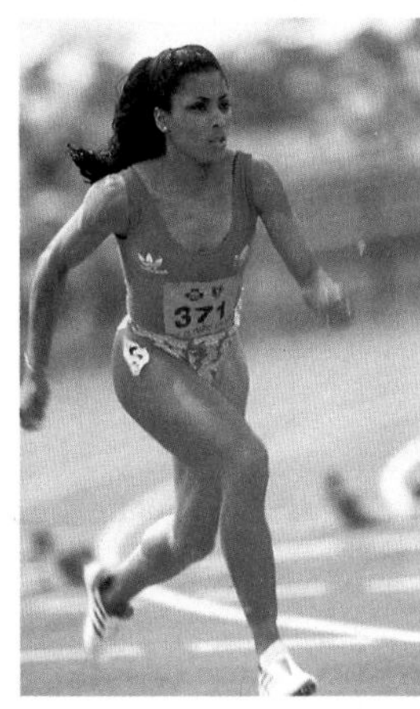

Florence Griffith-Joyner set a world record by running 100 meters in just 10.49 seconds. While you might often hear this read as 10 *point* 49 seconds, 10.49 means 10 and $\frac{49}{100}$. The decimal 10.49 is an example of a *terminating* decimal. The chart below shows examples of other terminating decimals.

Decimal	Words	Fraction
9.3	nine and three tenths	$9\frac{3}{10}$
-0.7	negative seven tenths	$-\frac{7}{10}$
65.12	sixty-five and twelve hundredths	$65\frac{12}{100}$
0.13	thirteen hundredths	$\frac{13}{100}$
0.004	four thousandths	$\frac{4}{1000}$

Every **terminating decimal** can be written as a fraction with a denominator of 10, 100, 1000, and so on.

Examples

Express each decimal as a fraction or mixed number in simplest form.

1 0.08 ➡ $0.08 = \frac{8}{100}$

$= \frac{2}{25}$ Simplify. The GCF of 8 and 100 is 4.

2 2.25 ➡ $2.25 = 2\frac{25}{100}$

$= 2\frac{1}{4}$ Simplify.

History Connection

The decimal system was named for the Latin word for tenth, *decimus*. Decimeter means one tenth of a meter. In the old Roman calendar, December was the tenth month.

Decimals either terminate or they go on forever. Decimals like 0.3333333 . . . are called **repeating decimals.** Because it is inconvenient to write all of these digits, you can use the **bar notation** $0.\overline{3}$ to indicate that the 3 repeats. Other examples follow.

$5.19191919\ldots = 5.\overline{19}$ The digits 19 repeat.
$2.4123123123\ldots = 2.4\overline{123}$ The digits 123 repeat.

Bell Ringer
Write ten rational numbers that are not whole numbers or integers.

Lesson Notes 5-2

5-Minute Check
(over Lesson 5-1)

Name the set of numbers to which each number belongs.
1. -231 I, R
2. 78 W, I, R
3. $8\frac{9}{10}$ R

Replace each ● with <, >, or = to make a true sentence.
4. $2\frac{1}{5}$ ● $\frac{13}{5}$ <
5. $-4\frac{1}{2}$ ● $-\frac{7}{2}$ <

Transparency 5-2 contains the 5-Minute Check and a teaching aid for this lesson.

1 FOCUS

The purpose of this lesson is to provide students with the techniques to write terminating and repeating decimals as fractions.

Motivating the Lesson

Use a stopwatch to time how long it takes each student to write his or her address. Then make a table like the one in the text and record the times as decimals, fractions, and in words.

2 TEACH

Reading Connection

Have students read decimal numbers aloud, emphasizing the use of *and* for the decimal point and correct place value names. From what is read, write the fraction. Simplify, if necessary.

Chalkboard Examples

Rename each decimal as a fraction or mixed number in simplest form.

- *For Example 1* 0.05 $\frac{1}{20}$
- *For Example 2* 0.425 $\frac{17}{40}$
- *For Example 3* 3.55 $3\frac{11}{20}$

EE: 1E, 2D, 3A
TAAS: 1, 4, 11

Chalkboard Examples

- *For Example 4*
  Rename $0.\overline{7}$ as a fraction. $\frac{7}{9}$
- *For Example 5*
  Rename 4.454545... as a fraction. $4\frac{5}{11}$

3 PRACTICE/APPLY

Checking the Concept

Ask students how they would use a calculator to check their answers to Exercises 10-15. Divide the numerator by the denominator and see if the display matches the exercise. Ask students how they would use a bar to rewrite Exercises 16 and 17.

Error Analysis

Watch for students who do not multiply by the correct power of ten to change a repeating decimal to a fraction.
Prevent by having students carefully count the number of places to the right of the decimal that are involved in a repeating pattern.

Practice Masters Booklet, **p. 41**

Name ______________________ Date ______________

Practice Worksheet 5-2

Writing Decimals as Fractions

Express each decimal as a fraction or mixed number in simplest form.

1. 0.4 $\frac{2}{5}$	2. −0.9 $-\frac{9}{10}$	3. 0.6 $\frac{3}{5}$
4. −0.25 $-\frac{1}{4}$	5. 0.15 $\frac{3}{20}$	6. −0.48 $-\frac{12}{25}$
7. 0.79 $\frac{79}{100}$	8. 0.04 $\frac{2}{50}$	9. −0.05 $-\frac{1}{20}$
10. 0.64 $\frac{16}{25}$	11. −0.95 $-\frac{19}{20}$	12. 0.99 $\frac{99}{100}$
13. −1.5 $-1\frac{1}{2}$	14. 2.375 $2\frac{3}{8}$	15. −3.75 $-3\frac{3}{4}$
16. −0.125 $-\frac{1}{8}$	17. 8.625 $8\frac{5}{8}$	18. −2.875 $-2\frac{7}{8}$
19. 1.025 $1\frac{1}{40}$	20. −0.755 $-\frac{151}{200}$	21. 0.432 $\frac{54}{125}$
22. −2.425 $-2\frac{17}{40}$	23. 0.1875 $\frac{3}{16}$	24. 0.364 $\frac{91}{250}$
25. −0.202 $-\frac{101}{500}$	26. −6.175 $-6\frac{7}{40}$	27. 9.08 $9\frac{2}{25}$
28. 5.25 $5\frac{1}{4}$	29. −0.57 $-\frac{57}{100}$	30. −1.0625 $-1\frac{1}{16}$
31. $0.\overline{7}$ $\frac{7}{9}$	32. $-0.\overline{91}$ $-\frac{91}{99}$	33. $0.\overline{1}$ $\frac{1}{9}$
34. $-0.\overline{12}$ $-\frac{4}{33}$	35. $0.\overline{45}$ $\frac{5}{11}$	36. $0.\overline{81}$ $\frac{9}{11}$
37. $-0.\overline{98}$ $-\frac{98}{99}$	38. $-0.\overline{072}$ $-\frac{8}{111}$	39. $0.\overline{253}$ $\frac{253}{999}$
40. $-1.\overline{09}$ $-1\frac{1}{11}$	41. $2.\overline{019}$ $2\frac{19}{999}$	42. $-0.\overline{1234}$ $-\frac{1234}{9999}$

Mental Math Hint

Here are some commonly used decimal-fraction equivalences. It is helpful to know them by memory.

$0.5 = \frac{1}{2}$

$0.\overline{3} = \frac{1}{3}$

$0.25 = \frac{1}{4}$

$0.2 = \frac{1}{5}$

$0.125 = \frac{1}{8}$

Examples 3 and 4 explain how to rename repeating decimals as fractions.

Examples

3 Express $0.\overline{6}$ as a fraction.

Let $N = 0.666 \ldots$. Then $10N = 6.666 \ldots$. — Multiply N by 10, because 1 digit repeats. Recall that $10N - 1N = 9N$.

Subtract $N = 0.666$ to eliminate the repeating part, $0.666 \ldots$.

$$\begin{aligned} 10N &= 6.666 \ldots \\ -\ N &= 0.666 \ldots \\ \hline 9N &= 6 \\ N &= \frac{6}{9} \text{ or } \frac{2}{3} \end{aligned}$$

So, $0.\overline{6} = \frac{2}{3}$.

4 Express 2.272727 . . . as a fraction.

Which multiplier should you choose to express $0.\overline{817}$ as a fraction? **1000**

Let $N = 2.272727 \ldots$. Then $100N = 227.2727 \ldots$. — Multiply N by 100, because 2 digits repeat.

$$\begin{aligned} 100N &= 227.2727 \ldots \\ -\ N &= 2.2727 \ldots \\ \hline 99N &= 225 \\ N &= \frac{225}{99} \text{ or } 2\frac{3}{11} \end{aligned}$$

Subtracting eliminates the repeating part, $0.2727 \ldots$.

So, $2.272727 \ldots = \frac{225}{99}$ or $2\frac{3}{11}$.

These and other examples suggest that you can rename any repeating decimal as a fraction. Therefore, repeating decimals are included in the set of rational numbers.

Checking for Understanding

1. Sample answer: 0.125 is equal to $\frac{1}{8}$.

Communicating Algebra

1. In your own words, explain why 0.125 is a rational number.
2. Explain how you would choose a multiplier to express $6.\overline{12}$ as a fraction. **Multiply by 100 since 2 digits repeat.**

Write each expression as a decimal and then as a fraction.

3. five hundredths **0.05, $\frac{5}{100}$**
4. seven tenths **0.7, $\frac{7}{10}$**
5. six thousandths **0.006, $\frac{6}{1000}$**
6. ninety-two hundredths **0.92, $\frac{92}{100}$**
7. two and six tenths **2.6, $2\frac{6}{10}$**
8. one and three thousandths **1.003, $1\frac{3}{1000}$**
9. sixteen and twenty-two hundredths **16.22, $16\frac{22}{100}$**

Alternate Strategies: Reteaching the Lesson

Reteaching Activity

Using Manipulatives Have students work in pairs with a set of dominoes and a calculator. One student creates a decimal by dividing the two numbers of a domino. The other student identifies the decimal as terminating or repeating and writes repeating decimals using bar notation.

Reteaching Masters Booklet, **p. 37**

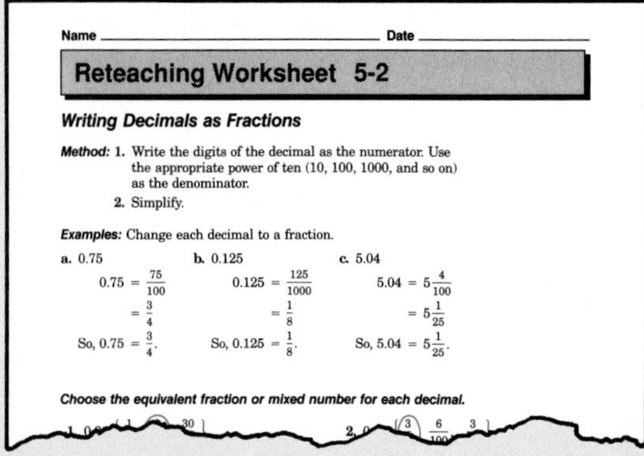
Name ______________________ Date ______________

Reteaching Worksheet 5-2

Writing Decimals as Fractions

Method: 1. Write the digits of the decimal as the numerator. Use the appropriate power of ten (10, 100, 1000, and so on) as the denominator.
2. Simplify.

Examples: Change each decimal to a fraction.

a. 0.75
$0.75 = \frac{75}{100} = \frac{3}{4}$
So, $0.75 = \frac{3}{4}$.

b. 0.125
$0.125 = \frac{125}{1000} = \frac{1}{8}$
So, $0.125 = \frac{1}{8}$.

c. 5.04
$5.04 = 5\frac{4}{100} = 5\frac{1}{25}$
So, $5.04 = 5\frac{1}{25}$.

Choose the equivalent fraction or mixed number for each decimal.

Guided Practice

Complete.

10. $0.9 = \frac{■}{10}$ 9
11. $0.7 = \frac{■}{10}$ 7
12. $0.25 = \frac{■}{100} = \frac{■}{4}$ 25, 1
13. $2.53 = 2\frac{■}{100}$ 53
14. $3.05 = 3\frac{■}{100} = 3\frac{■}{20}$ 5, 1
15. $0.408 = \frac{■}{1000} = \frac{■}{125}$ 408, 51

What multiplier, 10 or 100, would you use to express each decimal as a fraction?

16. 9.222 . . . 10
17. 0.181818 . . . 100
18. $5.\overline{29}$ 100

Exercises

Independent Practice

Express each decimal as a fraction or mixed number in simplest form.

19. 0.5 $\frac{1}{2}$
20. 0.8 $\frac{4}{5}$
21. 0.32 $\frac{8}{25}$
22. 0.75 $\frac{3}{4}$
23. 0.84 $\frac{21}{25}$
24. 0.05 $\frac{1}{20}$
25. 0.98 $\frac{49}{50}$
26. 0.52 $\frac{13}{25}$
27. -0.66 $-\frac{33}{50}$
28. 0.57 $\frac{57}{100}$
29. -2.26 $-2\frac{13}{50}$
30. 3.54 $3\frac{27}{50}$
31. -9.64 $-9\frac{16}{25}$
32. -1.38 $-1\frac{19}{50}$
33. 5.31 $5\frac{31}{100}$
34. 0.125 $\frac{1}{8}$
35. -0.744 $-\frac{93}{125}$
36. 2.75 $2\frac{3}{4}$
37. 1.51 $1\frac{51}{100}$
38. 0.101 $\frac{101}{1000}$
39. -0.562 $-\frac{281}{500}$
40. 0.303 $\frac{303}{1000}$
41. 0.486 $\frac{243}{500}$
42. 4.309
43. 9.626
44. $0.\overline{2}$ $\frac{2}{9}$
45. $0.\overline{3}$ $\frac{1}{3}$
46. $-0.\overline{5}$ $-\frac{5}{9}$
47. $1.\overline{4}$ $1\frac{4}{9}$
48. $0.\overline{8}$ $\frac{8}{9}$
49. $0.\overline{12}$ $\frac{4}{33}$
50. $1.\overline{13}$ $1\frac{13}{99}$
51. $0.\overline{15}$ $\frac{5}{33}$
52. $-0.\overline{81}$ $-\frac{9}{11}$
53. $2.\overline{45}$ $2\frac{5}{11}$

42. $4\frac{309}{1000}$ 43. $9\frac{313}{500}$

Challenge

54. Express $0.\overline{9}$ as a fraction. 1
55. Express $0.1\overline{6}$ as a fraction. $\frac{3}{18}$

Mixed Review

56. Translate this phrase into an expression: *the sum of 8 and x.* (Lesson 1-8) $8 + x$
57. Translate this sentence into a formula: *The unit price (u) of an item equals the total price (t) divided by the weight (w).* (Lesson 3-5) $u = \frac{t}{w}$
58. Find the LCD for the fractions $\frac{2}{7}$ and $\frac{3}{4}$. (Lesson 4-8) 28
59. Rename $\frac{-4}{5}$ as a fraction in two different ways. (Lesson 5-1) $\frac{4}{-5}$, $-\frac{4}{5}$
60. *True* or *false:* $-2\frac{1}{2} < -3$. (Lesson 5-1) F

Applications

61. **Measurement** A gauge measured the thickness of a piece of metal as 0.023 inches. What fraction of an inch is this? $\frac{23}{1000}$-inch
62. **Measurement** A trash bag has a thickness of 1.75 mils. This is 0.00175 inches. What fraction of an inch is this? $\frac{7}{4000}$-inch

Critical Thinking

63. A machinist made a stainless steel peg 2.37 inches in diameter for a $2\frac{3}{8}$-inch diameter hole. Will the peg fit? How do you know? Yes; $2.37 < 2\frac{3}{8}$

Wrap-Up

64. Write a sentence explaining why terminating and repeating decimals are rational numbers. Sample answer: Terminating and repeating decimals can be written as fractions.

Independent Practice

Homework Assignment	
Basic	19-49 odd, 56-60, 62-64
Average	28-54 even, 56-64
Honors	42-64

4 CLOSE

Assessment Option

Writing Write the following decimals as fractions.

1. $0.\overline{5}$ $\frac{5}{9}$
2. $0.\overline{2}$ $\frac{2}{9}$
3. $0.\overline{63}$ $\frac{7}{11}$
4. 4.25 $4\frac{1}{4}$

Enrichment Masters Booklet, **p. 37**

Name ______________________ Date ______________

Enrichment Worksheet 5-2

Irrational Numbers

Decimals in which a digit or group of digits repeats are called **repeating decimals.**

Example: $0.333... = 0.\overline{3}$ The bar indicates the repeating digit or digits.
$1.454545... = 1.\overline{45}$

Decimals in which only a 0 repeats are called **terminating decimals.**

Example: $0.5000... = 0.5$
$42.19500... = 42.195$

Consider the decimal 0.757757775.... It does not terminate in zero nor does it have a group of digits that repeat. Numbers that are represented by nonterminating, nonrepeating decimals are **irrational numbers.**

Example: $\pi = 3.14159...$
$\sqrt{5} = 2.236068...$

Write whether the given decimal is repeating or nonrepeating.

1. 0.373373337... nonrepeating
2. 24.15971597... repeating
3. 5.71571571... repeating
4. 0.5795579555... nonrepeating
5. 8.3121121112... nonrepeating

Name the next three digits in the following irrational numbers.

6. 0.13141516... 171
7. 0.96796679666... 796

Name an irrational number between the given numbers. Answers will vary. Sample answers given.

8. 6.7 and 6.8 6.7121221222...
9. 17.3 and 17.4 $10\sqrt{3}$
10. 0.1231233... and 0.1231134111... 0.1231152552555...
11. 2.333... and 2.444... 2.43344333444...

Find each sum.

12. 0.232232223... + 0.323323332... 0.555555555... or $0.\overline{5}$
13. 0.131131113... + 0.868868886... 0.999999999... or $0.\overline{9}$

Alternate Strategies: Extending the Lesson

Enrichment

Using Calculators Have students work in pairs. One student displays a decimal on the calculator by dividing two numbers less than 50. The other student gets three chances to recreate the decimal. Have students reverse roles and continue.

Cooperative Learning

Question Me Group Activity **5-2**

MATERIALS: Calculator • paper • pencil

In this game you attempt to guess a fraction by asking questions about its decimal form. The fraction may have either a terminating or repeating decimal representation.

The leader first thinks of a fraction whose numerator and denominator are 12 or less, using the calculator to change the fraction to its decimal equivalent.

The rest of the players ask questions about the number displayed and try to guess the original fraction. Questions have to be of a form that can be answered with "yes" or "no."

Each player may make only four guesses. The one to get the correct fraction scores one point and the calculator is passed to the next person.

Merril Pre-Algebra WRITING DECIMALS AS FRACTIONS

5-Minute Check
(over Lesson 5-2)

Rename each decimal as a fraction or mixed number in simplest form.

1. 0.26 $\frac{13}{50}$ 2. -8.75 $-8\frac{3}{4}$
3. 4.108 $4\frac{27}{250}$ 4. $0.\overline{24}$ $\frac{8}{33}$

Transparency 5-3 contains the 5-Minute Check and a teaching aid for this lesson.

1 FOCUS

The purpose of this lesson is to provide students with a technique for checking to see if an answer is reasonable.

2 TEACH

Chalkboard Examples

- *For Example 1*
  Round 3.7 to the nearest whole number. 4
- *For Example 2*
  Round 7.136 to the nearest tenth. 7.1

Practice Masters Booklet, p. 42

Name ______ Date ______

Practice Worksheet 5-3

Estimating Sums and Differences

Round to the nearest whole number or dollar.

1. 615.813 616	2. 213.904 214	3. 86.399 86
4. 6157.501 6158	5. 753.18 753	6. 32,156.909 32,157
7. $67.31 $67	8. $86.70 $87	9. $853.76 $854
10. $32.87 $33	11. $91.99 $92	12. $54.87 $55

Round to the nearest tenth.

13. 54.317 54.3	14. 6.1958 6.2	15. 113.6572 113.7
16. 12.9119 12.9	17. 81.95 82.0	18. 64.0975 64.1
19. 235.8587 235.9	20. 810.88 810.9	21. 971.09 971.1
22. 2.199 2.2	23. 7089.345 7089.3	24. 0.749 0.7

Estimate.

25. 0.58 + 0.72 = 1.3	26. 8.53 + 3.95 = 13	27. 746.3 + 13.89 = 760
28. 36.91 − 1.26 = 36	29. 15.62 − 1.79 = 15	30. 15.63 − 1.987 = 14
31. 17.46 − 8.32 = 9	32. 24.02 + 7.83 = 32	33. 28.3 − 3.729 = 24
34. 10.13 − 8.29 = 2	35. 0.752 + 0.8 + 0.31 = 1.9	36. 21.62 − 5.827 = 16

5-3 Estimating Sums and Differences

Objectives:
Round decimals.
Estimate sums and differences of decimals.

The freshman class needs to earn $250 for their annual trip to a waterpark. They made $49.50 at a car wash, $37.83 at a bake sale, $121.93 at a concert, and $52.65 at a game booth. The class treasurer made the following estimate.

$ 49.50	→	$ 50
37.83		40
121.93		120
+ 52.65		+ 50
		$260

Round to the nearest ten.

The class has earned *about* $260 and should have enough for the trip.

One way to estimate is to use rounding. A review of the rules for rounding is given in Examples 1 and 2.

Examples

1 Round 2.6 to the nearest whole number.

Look at the digit to the right of the ones place. Since $6 > 5$, round the digit in the ones place up.

To the nearest whole number, 2.6 is 3.

2 Round 9.328 to the nearest tenth.

Look at the digit to the right of the tenths place. Since $2 < 5$, the digit in the tenths place remains the same.

To the nearest tenth, 9.328 is 9.3.

Estimation is often used to provide a quick and easy answer when an exact answer is not necessary. It is also an excellent way to check the reasonableness of answers.

Calculator Hint

Always estimate before using a calculator to solve problems. It is a good way to check that you have entered the numbers correctly.

Example

3 Suppose you choose three items at the grocery store that cost $1.83, $0.95, and $2.10. The cashier tells you that the total is $6.88. Is this reasonable?

Round each item to the nearest dollar amount.

$1.83 rounds to $2. $0.95 rounds to $1. $2.10 rounds to $2.

The total should be about $2 + $1 + $2 or $5. Therefore, a total of $6.88 is *not* reasonable.

Bell Ringer

Write the following decimals as fractions and simplify.

1. 0.7 $\frac{7}{10}$ 2. 0.72 $\frac{18}{25}$ 3. 0.724 $\frac{181}{250}$

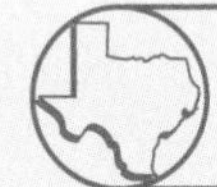

EE: 1B, 1C, 3A
TAAS: 1, 10, 13

Reteaching Masters Booklet, p. 38

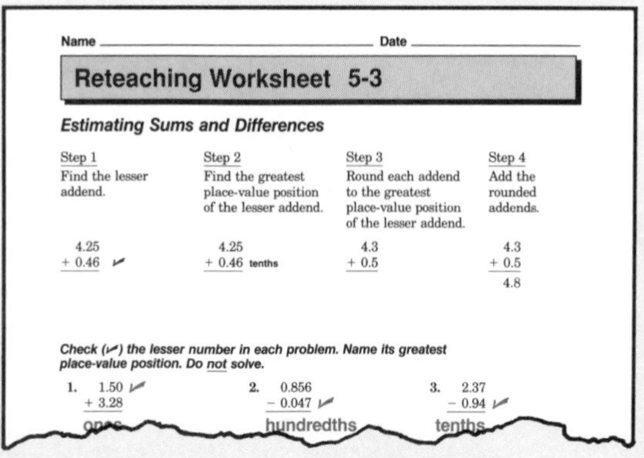

Name ______ Date ______

Reteaching Worksheet 5-3

Estimating Sums and Differences

Step 1	Step 2	Step 3	Step 4
Find the lesser addend.	Find the greatest place-value position of the lesser addend.	Round each addend to the greatest place-value position of the lesser addend.	Add the rounded addends.
4.25 + 0.46 ✓	4.25 + 0.46 tenths	4.3 + 0.5	4.3 + 0.5 = 4.8

Check (✓) the lesser number in each problem. Name its greatest place-value position. Do not solve.

1. 1.50 ✓ + 3.28 ones
2. 0.856 − 0.047 ✓ hundredths
3. 2.37 − 0.94 ✓ tenths

Checking for Understanding

1. an exact answer is not needed; to check reasonableness

Communicating Algebra

1. State two reasons for using estimation.
2. Give two examples of numbers that round to the nearest whole number. One example should round up; the other should not. Sample answer: 1.95 → 2; 3.25 → 3

Guided Practice

Round to the nearest whole number or dollar.

3. 7.058 7	4. 6.92 7	5. 12.461 12	6. 902.496 902
7. 40.47 40	8. \$5.69 \$6	9. \$45.04 \$45	10. \$0.88 \$1

Estimate. Then state whether the answer shown in color is reasonable.

11. 7.6 + 12.4 + 13.2 43.2 33, no
12. 24.62 + 15.31 + 12.76 52.69 50, yes
13. 195.7 − 156.8 38.9 40, yes
14. 7810 − 5670 1140 2000, no

Exercises

Independent Practice

Round to the nearest tenth.

15. 6.028 6.0	16. 1.84 1.8	17. 24.692 24.7	18. 35.95 36.0
19. 95.499 95.5	20. 35.506 35.5	21. 49.573 49.6	22. 24.692 24.7

Sample answers given.

Estimate. Use the data at the right. Be prepared to explain your answers.

23. cost of small popcorn and large drink \$3
24. cost of nachos with cheese and medium drink \$3
25. change from \$10 for 2 orders of nachos \$6
26. cost of a T-shirt and poster \$9
27. Is \$3.50 enough to buy a large popcorn, apple, and medium drink? no
28. Is \$16.23 the right change from \$20 for a large ice cream and medium drink? no
29. What items would you buy if you had \$10 to spend? See students' work.

Item	Size	Price
Popcorn	sm.	\$1.38
	lg.	\$2.29
Nachos w/cheese		\$1.88
Soft drinks	sm.	\$0.85
	med.	\$1.05
	lg.	\$1.75
Apples		\$0.65
Ice cream	sm.	\$1.29
	lg.	\$1.72

T-shirts	\$5.25
Posters	\$3.75

Mixed Review

30. Write an expression for the phrase *the product of nine to the third power and two.* (Lesson 4-2) $9^3 \times 2$
31. Graph $\frac{-8}{4}$ on a number line. (Lesson 5-1) See margin.
32. Express -0.34 as a fraction in simplest form. (Lesson 5-2) $-\frac{17}{50}$

Application

33. **Personal Finance** Martin had \$10 when he went to the store. He bought toothpaste, \$1.89, suntan lotion, \$4.39, paper, \$1.27, and soap, \$2.04. He estimated his total to see whether he had enough money. What is *your* estimate? Did he have enough money? 2 + 4 + 1 + 2 = 9; yes

Critical Thinking

34. The sum of 11, 29, and 61 is 101. Find three 3-digit numbers that have a sum of 1001. Use the digits 1, 1, 2, 9, 6, 1, and any three other digits. Sample answer: 121, 239, 641

Wrap-Up

35. Tell about a real-life situation that does not require an exact answer, only an estimate. Sample answer: Do you have enough money to buy certain items?

Additional Answer

31. [Number line from -3 to 3 with a point at -2]

-3 -2 -1 0 1 2 3

Cooperative Learning

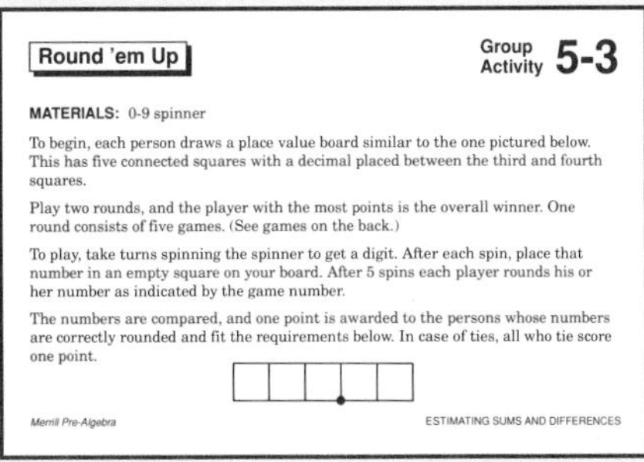

Round 'em Up Group Activity **5-3**

MATERIALS: 0-9 spinner

To begin, each person draws a place value board similar to the one pictured below. This has five connected squares with a decimal placed between the third and fourth squares.

Play two rounds, and the player with the most points is the overall winner. One round consists of five games. (See games on the back.)

To play, take turns spinning the spinner to get a digit. After each spin, place that number in an empty square on your board. After 5 spins each player rounds his or her number as indicated by the game number.

The numbers are compared, and one point is awarded to the persons whose numbers are correctly rounded and fit the requirements below. In case of ties, all who tie score one point.

Merrill Pre-Algebra ESTIMATING SUMS AND DIFFERENCES

3 PRACTICE/APPLY

Checking the Concept

After students have completed and checked Exercises 3-10, have them round each exercise to the nearest tenth and hundredth.

Error Analysis

Watch for students who round numbers incorrectly when the digit in the place to be rounded to is a 9. **Prevent by** reminding students that a 9 is just like any other digit; if it is not rounded up, it remains a 9, and if it is, it must increase by one.

Independent Practice

Homework Assignment	
Basic	15-29 odd, 30-35
Average	16-28, 30-35
Honors	22-35

4 CLOSE

Assessment Option

Speaking Ask students in what situations they use estimation. Sample answer: how much time it takes to complete homework

Enrichment Masters Booklet, **p. 38**

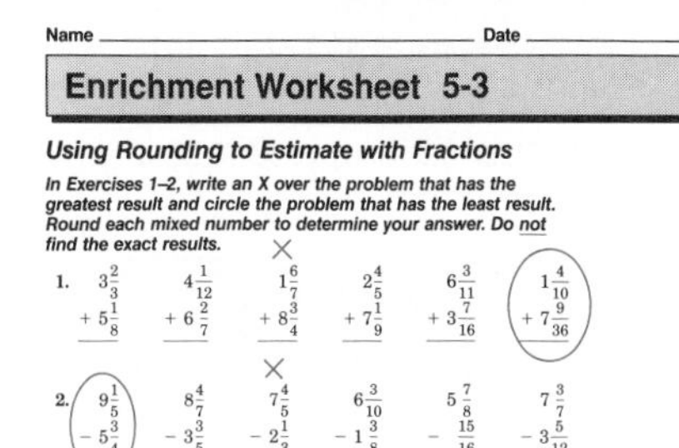

Name ________ Date ________

Enrichment Worksheet 5-3

Using Rounding to Estimate with Fractions

In Exercises 1–2, write an X over the problem that has the greatest result and circle the problem that has the least result. Round each mixed number to determine your answer. Do not find the exact results.

1. $3\frac{2}{3} + 5\frac{1}{8}$ $4\frac{1}{12} + 6\frac{2}{7}$ $1\frac{6}{7} + 8\frac{3}{4}$ (X) $2\frac{4}{5} + 7\frac{1}{9}$ $6\frac{3}{11} + 3\frac{7}{16}$ $1\frac{4}{10} + 7\frac{9}{36}$ (circled)

2. $9\frac{1}{5} - 5\frac{3}{4}$ (circled) $8\frac{4}{7} - 3\frac{3}{5}$ $7\frac{4}{5} - 2\frac{1}{3}$ (X) $6\frac{3}{10} - 1\frac{3}{8}$ $5\frac{7}{8} - \frac{15}{16}$ $7\frac{3}{7} - 3\frac{5}{12}$

For each problem, use rounding to estimate the result. Then decide if the exact result is greater than or less than your estimate. If the actual result will be greater than your estimate, write "up" below your estimate. If the actual result will be less than your estimate, write "down."

3. $4\frac{1}{3} + 7\frac{2}{8}$ 11 up
4. $2\frac{2}{3} - 1\frac{1}{5}$ 2 down
5. $6\frac{4}{7} + 3\frac{5}{6}$ 11 down
6. $8\frac{1}{10} - 5\frac{3}{4}$ 2 up
7. $9\frac{3}{7} - \frac{5}{8}$ 8 up
8. $2\frac{6}{7} + 5\frac{9}{10}$ 9 down
9. $3\frac{5}{7} + 7\frac{3}{5}$ 12 down
10. $8\frac{7}{10} - 4\frac{1}{3}$ 5 down
11. $6\frac{2}{9} - 2\frac{7}{8}$ 3 up

Lesson Notes 5-4

5-Minute Check
(over Lesson 5-3)

Round to the nearest tenth.
1. 5.182 **5.2** 2. 1.93 **1.9**
3. 34.694 **34.7** 4. 62.96 **63.0**

Transparency 5-4 contains the 5-Minute Check and a teaching aid for this lesson.

1 FOCUS

The purpose of this lesson is to apply the addition properties of integers to adding and subtracting decimals.

Motivating the Lesson

Using catalog pages, have your students find the exact cost of a combination of items. Then have them determine exact differences if they had $100 to spend.

2 TEACH

Using Connections

Point out the use of estimation in each of the examples. Have students estimate the answers to the Chalkboard Examples before solving them.

Checking Prerequisite Skills You may wish to review aligning decimal points and place values when adding and subtracting decimals. Solve each equation.

Chalkboard Examples

- *For Example 1*
  $x = 15.6 + 11.2$ $x = 26.8$
- *For Example 2*
  $y = 238 - 112.9$ $y = 125.1$
- *For Example 3*
  $r = 6.5 - 8.4$ $r = -1.9$
- *For Example 4*
  Simplify $1.3x + 6.8x - 10.2x$.
  $-2.1x$

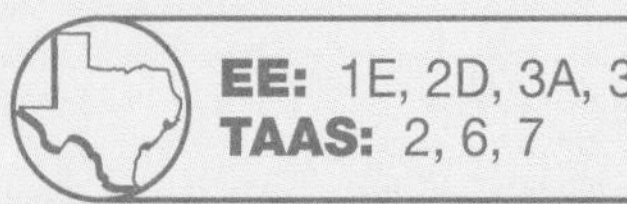

EE: 1E, 2D, 3A, 3H
TAAS: 2, 6, 7

5-4 Rationals: Adding and Subtracting Decimals

Objective:
Add and subtract decimals.

Key Terms:
closure
commutative
associative
identity
inverse

The Mustang Band Boosters ledger shows these entries for the week.

Item	Credit	Debit
Beginning Balance	$148.50	
Rummage Sale	129.38	
Bus Trip		$258.30
Dues Collected	155.00	
Refund on Sales Tax	43.28	
Postage and Mailing		74.80

Credits represent positive rational numbers and debits represent negative rational numbers. In order to find the amount of money that the band boosters have at the end of the week, you will need to add rational numbers. All the properties of addition of whole numbers and integers also apply to rational numbers.

Is subtraction of whole numbers closed? If not, give a counterexample.
No; 2 − 3 = -1, -1 is not a whole number.

Properties of Addition	Examples
Closure Property For any rational numbers *a* and *b*, $a + b$ is a rational number.	$3 + 4 = 7$ $1 + (-5) = -4$ $3.7 + 4.2 = 7.9$
Commutative Property For any rational numbers *a* and *b*, $a + b = b + a$.	$-3 + 4 = 4 + (-3)$ $-5.9 + 6.3 = 6.3 + (-5.9)$
Associative Property For any rational numbers *a*, *b*, and *c*, $(a + b) + c = a + (b + c)$.	$(-8.2 + 3.7) + 6.5 =$ $-8.2 + (3.7 + 6.5)$
Identity Property For every rational number *a*, $a + 0 = a$ and $0 + a = a$.	$-2 + 0 = -2$ $-9.3 + 0 = -9.3$
Inverse Property For every rational number *a*, $a + (-a) = 0$.	$5 + (-5) = 0$ $17.5 + (-17.5) = 0$

Bell Ringer

Estimate the total cost of the following items.
$1.99, $5.23, $3.72 **$11.00**

Estimation Hint

One way to estimate with fractions and mixed numbers is to use rounding. If the fraction is $\frac{1}{2}$ or greater, round up to the next whole number. If the fraction is less than $\frac{1}{2}$, the whole number remains the same.

2 **Solve $\frac{1}{3} - \frac{3}{4} = c$.**

$\frac{1}{3} - \frac{3}{4} = c$

$\frac{4}{12} - \frac{9}{12} = c$ The LCD of 3 and 4 is 12.

$\frac{4}{12} + \left(-\frac{9}{12}\right) = c$ Subtract $\frac{9}{12}$ by adding its inverse, $-\frac{9}{12}$.

$-\frac{5}{12} = c$

Likewise, to add or subtract mixed numbers with unlike denominators, first rename the fractions with a common denominator.

Examples

3 **Solve $b = 2\frac{5}{8} + 3\frac{11}{24}$.** Estimate: 3 + 3 = 6

$b = 2\frac{15}{24} + 3\frac{11}{24}$ Use the LCD of 8 and 24 to rename $\frac{5}{8}$ as $\frac{15}{24}$.

$b = 5\frac{26}{24}$

$b = 6\frac{2}{24}$ or $6\frac{1}{12}$ Simplify.

In Example 4, why is it necessary to rename $8\frac{10}{36}$ as $7\frac{46}{36}$?
So that there are enough 36ths to subtract from.

4 **Solve $8\frac{5}{18} - 6\frac{7}{12} = y$.** Estimate: 8 − 7 = 1

$8\frac{5}{18} - 6\frac{7}{12}$ ➡ $8\frac{10}{36} - 6\frac{21}{36}$ ➡ $7\frac{46}{36} - 6\frac{21}{36} = 1\frac{25}{36}$ Rename $8\frac{10}{36}$ as $7\frac{46}{36}$.

$1\frac{25}{36} = y$

5 **Solve $d = 3\frac{2}{3} - 5\frac{1}{6}$.** Estimate: 4 − 5 = -1

$d = 3\frac{2}{3} - 5\frac{1}{6}$

$d = 3\frac{4}{6} - 5\frac{1}{6}$ Find a common denominator.

$d = 3\frac{4}{6} + \left(-5\frac{1}{6}\right)$ Subtract $5\frac{1}{6}$ by adding its inverse, $-5\frac{1}{6}$.

$d = 3\frac{4}{6} + \left(-4\frac{7}{6}\right)$ $-5\frac{1}{6} = -4\frac{7}{6}$

$d = -1\frac{3}{6}$ or $-1\frac{1}{2}$

Chalkboard Examples

- *For Example 3*
  Solve $f = 5\frac{3}{4} + 6\frac{1}{2}$. $12\frac{1}{4}$
- *For Example 4*
  Solve $9\frac{1}{5} - 7\frac{3}{8} = y$. $1\frac{33}{40}$
- *For Example 5*
  Solve $d = 4\frac{1}{6} - 8\frac{1}{2}$. $-4\frac{1}{3}$

3 PRACTICE/APPLY

Checking the Concept

As students work on Exercises 3-10, discuss any differences in a chosen common denominator. Point out that there are many common denominators but only one LCD. Other common denominators may be used, however the numbers will be larger and the answers will need to be simplified.

Error Analysis

Watch for students who rename the denominator but not the numerator.
Prevent by using estimation. When the numerators are not renamed, the resulting sum is often less than one of the fractions.

Practice Masters Booklet, **p. 45**

Name ______________ Date ______________

Practice Worksheet 5-6

Rationals: Adding and Subtracting Unlike Fractions

Solve each equation. Write each solution in simplest form.

1. $\frac{1}{2} - \frac{1}{3} = x$ $\frac{1}{6}$	2. $y = \frac{3}{8} + \frac{1}{4}$ $\frac{5}{8}$	3. $z = \frac{7}{8} - \frac{5}{6}$ $\frac{1}{24}$
4. $\frac{5}{12} + \frac{1}{3} = r$ $\frac{3}{4}$	5. $\frac{13}{16} - \frac{7}{12} = s$ $\frac{11}{48}$	6. $\frac{2}{3} + \frac{1}{6} = t$ $\frac{5}{6}$
7. $\frac{7}{8} - \frac{7}{12} = a$ $\frac{7}{24}$	8. $\frac{1}{6} + \frac{1}{2} = b$ $\frac{2}{3}$	9. $c = \frac{7}{9} - \frac{3}{5}$ $\frac{8}{45}$
10. $\frac{7}{8} + \frac{3}{4} = d$ $1\frac{5}{8}$	11. $-\frac{3}{4} - \frac{13}{20} = m$ $-1\frac{2}{5}$	12. $n = \frac{1}{9} + \frac{2}{3}$ $\frac{7}{9}$
13. $k = -\frac{7}{8} - \left(-\frac{2}{3}\right)$ $-\frac{5}{24}$	14. $l = -\frac{2}{3} + \frac{3}{4}$ $\frac{1}{12}$	15. $-\frac{3}{4} - \frac{2}{3} = h$ $-1\frac{5}{12}$
16. $\frac{7}{8} + \frac{1}{2} = i$ $1\frac{3}{8}$	17. $\frac{5}{6} - \frac{5}{8} = j$ $\frac{5}{24}$	18. $-\frac{5}{6} + \frac{5}{8} = p$ $-\frac{5}{24}$
19. $q = -\frac{3}{4} - \left(-\frac{1}{2}\right)$ $-\frac{1}{4}$	20. $\frac{1}{3} + \frac{5}{7} = r$ $1\frac{1}{21}$	21. $\frac{5}{8} - \frac{9}{16} = s$ $\frac{1}{16}$
22. $\frac{11}{12} - \frac{1}{16} = t$ $\frac{41}{48}$	23. $\frac{1}{5} - \frac{1}{2} = v$ $-\frac{3}{10}$	24. $\frac{3}{4} - \left(-\frac{5}{6}\right) = w$ $1\frac{7}{12}$
25. $u = 3 - \frac{3}{8}$ $2\frac{5}{8}$	26. $x = 2\frac{1}{2} - 1\frac{3}{4}$ $\frac{3}{4}$	27. $y = -5 - \left(-2\frac{2}{3}\right)$ $-2\frac{1}{3}$
28. $3\frac{1}{3} - 2\frac{1}{2} = z$ $\frac{5}{6}$	29. $1\frac{1}{3} + 2\frac{1}{6} = a$ $3\frac{1}{2}$	30. $b = 3\frac{1}{8} - \frac{7}{8}$ $2\frac{1}{4}$
31. $c = \frac{27}{4} - \frac{29}{8}$ $3\frac{1}{8}$	32. $6\frac{3}{4} - 3\frac{5}{8} = d$ $3\frac{1}{8}$	33. $-6 - 2\frac{7}{8} = e$ $-8\frac{7}{8}$

Alternate Strategies: Reteaching the Lesson

Reteaching Activity

Using Models Use measuring cups and water to model addition and subtraction of unlike fractions, such as $\frac{1}{2} + \frac{1}{4}$ and $\frac{3}{4} - \frac{1}{2}$. Have students explain the importance of renaming unlike fractions to add and subtract.

Reteaching Masters Booklet, **p. 41**

Name ______________ Date ______________

Reteaching Worksheet 5-6

Rationals: Adding and Subtracting Unlike Fractions

To add or subtract fractions with unlike denominators, start by renaming each fraction. Use a common denominator so the new fractions will have like denominators. The most convenient common denominator is the least common multiple of the given denominators. This is called the **least common denominator (LCD).**

	List the multiples to find the LCD.	Rename each fraction. Use the LCD.	Add or subtract. Simplify if necessary.
$\frac{1}{9} + \frac{2}{6}$	9: 9, 18, 27, ... 6: 6, 12, 18, ... LCM: 18	$\frac{1}{9} = \frac{2}{18}$ $+\frac{2}{6} = \frac{6}{18}$	$\frac{1}{9} = \frac{2}{18}$ $+\frac{2}{6} = \frac{6}{18}$ $\frac{8}{18} = \frac{4}{9}$

Rename each pair of fractions using the given denominator. Then add or subtract. Write your answer as a fraction or mixed

Independent Practice

Homework Assignment	
Basic	15-29 odd, 30-37
Average	16-28 even, 30-37
Honors	22-37

4 CLOSE

Assessment Option

Modeling Write the numbers 1-12 on 3 by 5 cards. Have students draw 4 cards and form two fractions. Then have students add or subtract the fractions and write the solutions in simplest form.

Additional Answers

2. To add integers with the same sign, add their absolute values. The sum has the same sign as the integers. To add integers with different signs, subtract their absolute values. The sum has the same sign as the integer with the greater absolute value.
37. Sample answer: A carpet layer needs $12\frac{1}{2}$ square yards of carpet for one room and $18\frac{3}{4}$ square yards of carpet for another room. How much carpet does he need in all?

Enrichment Masters Booklet, **p. 41**

Name ______________ Date ______________

Enrichment Worksheet 5-6

Adding and Subtracting Fractions

Solve each problem. The first one is done for you.

1. $\frac{7}{14} + \frac{3}{14}$	1. $\frac{5}{7}$ I	9. $15\frac{3}{8} + 13\frac{1}{4}$	9. $28\frac{5}{8}$ L
2. $\frac{5}{6} + \frac{7}{8}$	2. $1\frac{17}{24}$ K	10. $5\frac{3}{4} + 6\frac{2}{3}$	10. $12\frac{5}{12}$ F
3. $\frac{3}{5} + \frac{7}{10} + \frac{1}{15}$	3. $1\frac{11}{30}$ U	11. $8 - 2\frac{2}{3}$	11. $5\frac{1}{3}$ E
4. $\frac{3}{8} - \frac{1}{8}$	4. $\frac{1}{4}$ A	12. $5\frac{5}{7} - 3\frac{1}{6}$	12. $2\frac{23}{42}$ N
5. $\frac{6}{10} - \frac{2}{5}$	5. $\frac{1}{5}$ G	13. $1\frac{5}{24} + \frac{11}{12}$	13. $2\frac{1}{8}$ O
6. $2\frac{2}{3} + \frac{3}{5}$	6. $3\frac{4}{15}$ D	14. $8\frac{1}{6} - 3\frac{5}{8}$	14. $4\frac{13}{24}$ T
7. $8\frac{1}{2} - 6\frac{1}{3}$	7. $2\frac{1}{6}$ H	15. $15\frac{11}{30} + 5\frac{4}{15}$	15. $20\frac{19}{30}$ C
8. $25\frac{1}{9} - 14\frac{5}{6}$	8. $10\frac{5}{18}$ B	16. $15 - 8\frac{2}{3}$	16. $6\frac{1}{3}$ S

Write the letter that is next to each solution above on the corresponding line shown below to complete the following question. The first problem is complete.

Did you hear about the football player who . . .

A S K E D H I S C O A C H T O
$\frac{1}{4}$ $6\frac{1}{3}$ $1\frac{17}{24}$ $5\frac{1}{3}$ $3\frac{4}{15}$ $2\frac{1}{6}$ $\frac{5}{7}$ $6\frac{1}{3}$ $20\frac{19}{30}$ $2\frac{1}{8}$ $\frac{1}{4}$ $20\frac{19}{30}$ $2\frac{1}{6}$ $4\frac{13}{24}$ $2\frac{1}{8}$

F L O O D T H E F I E L D
$12\frac{5}{12}$ $28\frac{5}{8}$ $2\frac{1}{8}$ $2\frac{1}{8}$ $3\frac{4}{15}$ $4\frac{13}{15}$ $2\frac{1}{6}$ $5\frac{1}{3}$ $12\frac{5}{12}$ $\frac{5}{7}$ $5\frac{1}{3}$ $28\frac{5}{8}$ $3\frac{4}{15}$

S O H E C O U L D G O I N
$6\frac{1}{3}$ $2\frac{1}{8}$ $2\frac{1}{6}$ $5\frac{1}{3}$ $20\frac{19}{30}$ $2\frac{1}{8}$ $1\frac{11}{30}$ $28\frac{5}{8}$ $3\frac{4}{15}$ $\frac{1}{5}$ $2\frac{1}{8}$ $\frac{5}{7}$ $2\frac{23}{42}$

A S A S U B ?
$\frac{1}{4}$ $6\frac{1}{3}$ $\frac{1}{4}$ $6\frac{1}{3}$ $1\frac{11}{30}$ $10\frac{5}{8}$

Checking for Understanding

Communicating Algebra

1. What is the first step in adding or subtracting fractions with unlike denominators? **Rename the fractions with a common denominator.**
2. State the rules for finding the sign of sums of positive and negative numbers. (Look in Lesson 2-3 to review these rules.) **See margin.**

Guided Practice

Find the LCD. Then find each sum or difference.

3. $\frac{1}{4} + \frac{3}{8}$ **8, $\frac{5}{8}$**
4. $\frac{5}{6} - \frac{1}{3}$ **6, $\frac{1}{2}$**
5. $\frac{2}{7} + \frac{2}{14}$ **14, $\frac{3}{7}$**
6. $\frac{7}{8} - \frac{2}{5}$ **40, $\frac{19}{40}$**
7. $\frac{5}{8} - \frac{1}{2}$ **8, $\frac{1}{8}$**
8. $\frac{9}{10} + \frac{5}{6}$ **30, $1\frac{11}{15}$**
9. $\frac{8}{12} - \frac{1}{3}$ **12, $\frac{1}{3}$**
10. $\frac{4}{5} + \frac{11}{15}$ **15, $1\frac{8}{15}$**

Complete.

11. $7\frac{2}{5} = 6\frac{■}{5}$ **7**
12. $2\frac{1}{9} = 1\frac{■}{9}$ **10**
13. $5\frac{8}{30} = 4\frac{■}{30}$ **38**
14. $6\frac{4}{12} = 5\frac{■}{12}$ **16**

Exercises

Independent Practice

Solve each equation. Write each solution in simplest form.

15. $\frac{6}{7} + \frac{11}{14} = c$ **$1\frac{9}{14}$**
16. $\frac{7}{8} - \frac{3}{10} = x$ **$\frac{23}{40}$**
17. $\frac{11}{10} - \frac{3}{5} = k$ **$\frac{1}{2}$**
18. $a = \frac{7}{6} + \frac{5}{18}$ **$1\frac{4}{9}$**
19. $-5 - 3\frac{1}{2} = j$ **$-8\frac{1}{2}$**
20. $-2 - (-4) = m$ **2**
21. $a = -7 - \left(-2\frac{3}{4}\right)$ **$-4\frac{1}{4}$**
22. $p = -\frac{3}{4} - \left(-\frac{1}{4}\right)$ **$-\frac{1}{2}$**
23. $3\frac{5}{7} - \left(-1\frac{1}{7}\right) = x$ **$4\frac{6}{7}$**
24. $b = 3\frac{1}{3} - 2\frac{1}{6}$ **$1\frac{1}{6}$**
25. $s = 6\frac{3}{4} - 3\frac{1}{2}$ **$3\frac{1}{4}$**
26. $4\frac{1}{3} - 2\frac{1}{2} = t$ **$1\frac{5}{6}$**
27. $c = -\frac{9}{5} - \left(-\frac{3}{5}\right)$ **$-1\frac{1}{5}$**
28. $r = -\frac{3}{11} - \frac{7}{11}$ **$-\frac{10}{11}$**
29. $8\frac{1}{5} - 2\frac{1}{4} = v$ **$5\frac{19}{20}$**

Mixed Review

Evaluate each expression if $c = 4.3$ and $d = 17.04$. (Lesson 5-4)

30. $c + d$ **21.34**
31. $c - d$ **-12.74**

Solve each equation. Write each solution in simplest form. (Lesson 5-5)

32. $n = \frac{23}{14} - \frac{5}{14}$ **$1\frac{2}{7}$**
33. $\frac{33}{12} + \frac{9}{12} = g$ **$3\frac{1}{2}$**
34. $x = \frac{4}{10} + \left(-\frac{3}{10}\right)$ **$\frac{1}{10}$**

Application

35. **Publishing** The length of a page in a yearbook is 10 inches. The top margir is $\frac{1}{2}$-inch and the bottom margin is $\frac{3}{4}$-inch. What is the length of the page inside the margins? **$8\frac{3}{4}$ inches**

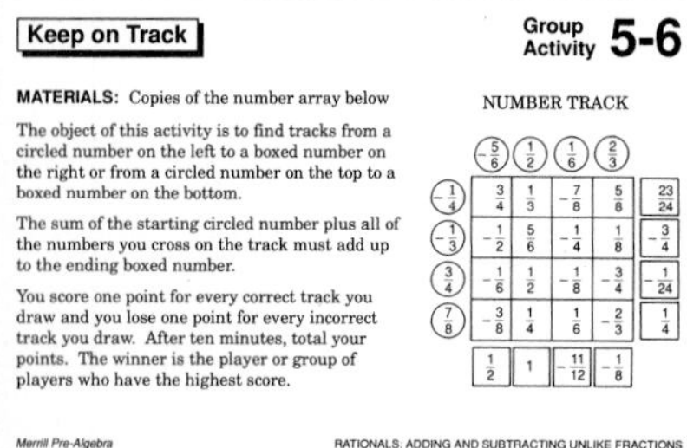

Critical Thinking

36. A rope is cut in half and one-half is used. Then one-fifth of the remaining rope is cut off and used. The piece left is 12 feet long. How long was the rope originally? **30 ft**

Wrap-Up

37. **Make Up a Problem** Write a problem in which you would add the mixed numbers $12\frac{1}{2}$ and $18\frac{3}{4}$. **See margin.**

Alternate Strategies: Extending the Lesson

Enrichment

Using Critical Thinking A unit fraction is a fraction that has a numerator of 1.

Express $\frac{1}{2}$ as the sum of three different unit fractions.

$$\frac{1}{3} + \frac{1}{4} + \frac{1}{12} = \frac{1}{2}$$

Cooperative Learning

Keep on Track — Group Activity **5-6**

MATERIALS: Copies of the number array below

The object of this activity is to find tracks from a circled number on the left to a boxed number on the right or from a circled number on the top to a boxed number on the bottom.

The sum of the starting circled number plus all of the numbers you cross on the track must add up to the ending boxed number.

You score one point for every correct track you draw and you lose one point for every incorrect track you draw. After ten minutes, total your points. The winner is the player or group of players who have the highest score.

NUMBER TRACK

	($-\frac{5}{6}$)	($\frac{1}{2}$)	($\frac{1}{6}$)	($\frac{2}{3}$)	
($-\frac{1}{4}$)	$\frac{3}{4}$	$\frac{1}{3}$	$-\frac{7}{8}$	$\frac{5}{8}$	$\frac{23}{24}$
($-\frac{1}{3}$)	$-\frac{1}{2}$	$\frac{5}{6}$	$-\frac{1}{4}$	$\frac{1}{8}$	$-\frac{3}{4}$
($\frac{3}{4}$)	$-\frac{1}{6}$	$\frac{1}{2}$	$-\frac{1}{8}$	$-\frac{3}{4}$	$-\frac{1}{24}$
($\frac{7}{8}$)	$-\frac{3}{8}$	$\frac{1}{4}$	$\frac{1}{6}$	$-\frac{2}{3}$	$\frac{1}{4}$
	$\frac{1}{2}$	1	$-\frac{11}{12}$	$-\frac{1}{8}$	

Merrill Pre-Algebra RATIONALS: ADDING AND SUBTRACTING UNLIKE FRACTIONS

Algebra in Action-Business

Stock Market Reports

Companies often are funded through the sale of shares of stock. The stock is purchased by individuals or groups in the hope that the price of the stock will rise and that the company will be profitable and pay dividends. Stock prices change daily. Rational numbers are used to show the increase or decrease in the price of a share of stock.

52-Week High	Low	Stock - Div	High	Low	Last	Chg.
24 7/8	17	ChWstes .16	23 1/2	23	23	– 1/4
23 7/8	17 7/8	Chspk .72	19 1/8	18 1/2	18 5/8	– 3/4
73 1/2	52 3/4	Chevrn 2.80	70	68 3/4	68 7/8	– 7/8
149	136 3/4	ChiMlw 6.00r	138 1/4	138 1/4	138 1/4	– 1/4
22 1/2	13	Chile n .34e	17 7/8	17 5/8	17 5/8	– 3/8
38 1/2	27 5/8	Chilis s	37 1/8	37	37	– 3/8
26 3/4	13 1/8	Chiqula .40	26 7/8	25 3/8	25 1/2	– 7/8
8 3/4	4 7/8	ChkFull .31t	7 7/8	7 3/4	7 3/4	....
42 7/8	30 1/8	ChrisCr 1.61t	32 1/4	31 1/8	31 3/8	– 5/8
16	13 1/4	ChCft pf 1.00	14 1/4	14 1/4	14 1/4	+ 1/4
13 1/2	8 1/4	Christn	12 3/4	12 5/8	12 5/8	– 1/4
27 1/8	14 1/2	Chryslr 1.20	16 5/8	16	16 1/8	– 1/4
51 3/8	34 1/8	Chubbs 1.32	46	44 7/8	45 1/8	– 5/8
4 5/8	1 3/8	Chyron	2	1 7/8	2	....
39 3/8	31 3/4	Cilcorp 2.46	33 3/4	33 1/2	33 1/2	– 3/8
35	22	CinnBel .76	24 1/4	24	24 1/8	....
32 3/8	27 1/8	CinGE 2.40	30 3/8	30	30	– 1/2
46	40	CinG pf 4.00	45	45	45	+1
99	93	CinG pf 9.30	94	93 1/2	94	+ 1/2
81	74 1/4	CinG pf 7.44	77 5/8	77 5/8	77 5/8	– 7/8
98	91 1/2	CinG pf 9.28	93 1/2	93 1/2	93 1/2	....
100 1/2	95	CinG pf 9.52	97	97	97	+1
21 7/8	15	CinMil .72	17 3/4	17 5/8	17 3/4	+ 1/8
13 5/8	4 1/2	CineOd	5 1/8	5	5 1/8	....
13 1/8	1	viCircK	1 1/4	1	1 1/8	....
28 7/8	18 5/8	CirClys .10	25 5/8	25 3/8	25 3/8	– 1/2
66 1/4	40	Circus	65	63	64	– 5/8
35 1/2	21 3/4	Citicorp 1.78	22 5/8	22	22 3/8	....
70	59	Citcp pf 6.00e	61 1/2	61 1/2	61 1/2	– 1/4
81 5/8	67 5/8	Citcp pf A 7.00e	69 1/8	69	69	– 1/4
25 1/2	22 1/4	Citcp pfC 2.28	23 7/8	23 1/4	23 1/4	– 1/4
36	23	CtzSCp 1.40	24 1/8	23 3/8	23 1/2	– 5/8
28	20	ClyNCs .64	20 5/8	20 1/8	20 1/8	– 3/8

The newspaper clipping at the right shows part of the stock market page. Listed are

- the name of the company (usually abbreviated);
- the high and low price for the past 52 weeks;
- the high, low, and closing price, in dollars, for the last business day;
- the change, in dollars, from the previous day's closing price.

A listing of $23\frac{1}{2}$ is read as $23\frac{1}{2}$ points and means $23.50. (A point is a dollar, so $\frac{1}{2}$ point is $0.50.)

Look at the shaded line, the stock of Chrysler (Chryslr). Its high for the year is $27\frac{1}{8}$ and its low is $14\frac{1}{2}$. It had a high of $16\frac{5}{8}$, a low of 16, and closed at $16\frac{1}{8}$ yesterday. It closed down $\frac{1}{4}\left(-\frac{1}{4}\right)$ from the day before. What did it close at the day before? $16\frac{3}{8}$

Answer each question for Chevron (Chevrn).

1. What is its high for the year? What is its low? How many points difference is there between the high and low? $73\frac{1}{2}$; $52\frac{3}{4}$; $20\frac{3}{4}$
2. What did it close at yesterday? What did it close at the day before? $68\frac{7}{8}$; 68

Complete the following.

3. Jean bought some shares of Fidelity Trust stock at $96\frac{1}{2}$. Fidelity Trust closed yesterday at $87\frac{5}{8}$. Write and solve an equation that shows what happened to Jean's investment. $96\frac{1}{2} + x = 87\frac{5}{8}$; lost $8\frac{7}{8}$
4. **Research** Choose a stock from a newspaper listing to follow for several days. Make a graph and then write a few sentences about your stock's activity. See students' work.

Applying Algebra to the Real World

Objective This optional page shows how algebra is used in the real world and also provides a change of pace.

Using Discussion

Ask students if they or their parents own any stock. Ask if anyone can explain what stock is and why some people choose stock as an investment. If possible, have a stock broker visit the class to explain how the stock market operates and to answer questions.

Using Communication

Have students examine the high and low stock prices for the last 52 weeks. Have each student choose a stock of his or her choice and write a paragraph explaining why, in the student's opinion, the stock has risen or fallen. Examples might be specific, such as Exxon stock falling as a result of the Alaskan oil spill, or fairly general, including such factors as low product demand or poor company management.

Activity

Using Charts (Materials: business section of the current newspaper)
Allow each student a hypothetical $10,000 to spend in the stock market. From the stock report in the newspaper, have each student set up a chart showing what stock or stocks he or she has "purchased," the number of shares purchased, and the purchase price per share. For several days, have students follow their stock, listing daily changes in the closing prices on the chart. One month later have each student determine individual profit or loss. Discuss what stock did well and if there was any way to predict success or failure.

5-Minute Check
(over Lesson 5-6)

Solve each equation. Write each solution in simplest form.

1. $\frac{7}{15} + \frac{3}{9} = y$ $\frac{36}{45} = \frac{4}{5}$
2. $g = -\frac{2}{3} - \frac{5}{9}$ $-\frac{11}{9}$ or $-1\frac{2}{9}$
3. $d = 7\frac{1}{4} + 11\frac{5}{6}$ $19\frac{1}{12}$
4. $-3\frac{3}{10} - (-6\frac{2}{5}) = v$ $-3\frac{1}{10}$
5. $t = -9 - (-5\frac{1}{4})$ $-3\frac{3}{4}$

Transparency 5-7 contains the 5-Minute Check and a teaching aid for this lesson.

1 FOCUS

The purpose of this lesson is to apply the techniques used in solving equations and inequalities involving integers to solving equations and inequalities involving rational numbers.

Motivating the Lesson

Use a catalog to select prices for merchandise. Then use the prices to make problems using decimals. For example, you have \$15 and want to buy a gold chain for \$7.82. Can you buy earrings that cost \$7.52? $x + \$7.82 \leq \$15$; $x \leq \$7.18$; no

2 TEACH

Using Models

Place two identical containers containing equal amounts of water on each pan of a two-pan scale. Use a measuring cup to remove $\frac{1}{3}$ cup of water from one container.

Discuss what must be done to get the scale to balance.

Checking Prerequisite Skills You may wish to review the addition and subtraction properties for equations and inequalities presented in Lessons 3-1, 3-2, and 3-7.

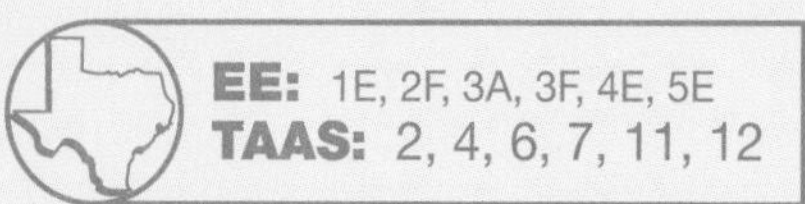
EE: 1E, 2F, 3A, 3F, 4E, 5E
TAAS: 2, 4, 6, 7, 11, 12

5-7 Solving Equations and Inequalities

Objective:
Solve equations and inequalities with rational numbers.

In 1989 the top two oil-producing states were Texas and Alaska. Together they produced 1372.2 million barrels of oil. How many barrels of oil were produced in Texas?

You know that the two states produced 1372.2 million barrels. From the graph, you know that Alaska produced 684.0 million barrels.

Let b represent the number of barrels, in millions, produced in Texas. Then the equation $b + 684.0 = 1372.2$ represents this problem.

$$b + 684.0 = 1372.2$$
$$b + 684.0 - 684.0 = 1372.2 - 684.0$$

1372.2 [−] 684.0 [=] 688.2

Estimate: $1400 - 700 = 700$

$$b = 688.2$$

Texas produced 688.2 million barrels of oil.

Compare with the estimate. Is the answer reasonable? **yes**

You can solve rational number equations using the same skills you used to solve equations in Chapters 1 and 3.

FYI
The United States has 590 million barrels of government-owned crude oil in reserve for an emergency. This is the largest reserve in the world.

Examples

Solve each equation. Check your solution.

1
$$x - 4.7 = 1.5$$
$$x - 4.7 + 4.7 = 1.5 + 4.7 \quad \text{Add 4.7 to each side.}$$
$$x = 6.2$$

Check: $x - 4.7 = 1.5$
$6.2 - 4.7 \stackrel{?}{=} 1.5$
$1.5 = 1.5$ ✓

Bell Ringer
Write two addition problems involving fractions that have a sum of $\frac{4}{9}$. Each fraction should have a different denominator.
Sample answer: $\frac{1}{3} + \frac{1}{9}$; $\frac{1}{4} + \frac{7}{36}$

Estimation Hint

Since $\frac{2}{3}$ is close to 1, and $\frac{5}{2}$ is $2\frac{1}{2}$, x must be about $1\frac{1}{2}$.

2

$x + \frac{2}{3} = \frac{5}{2}$

$x + \frac{2}{3} - \frac{2}{3} = \frac{5}{2} - \frac{2}{3}$ Subtract $\frac{2}{3}$ from each side.

$x = \frac{15}{6} - \frac{4}{6}$ The LCD of 2 and 3 is 6.

$x = \frac{11}{6}$ or $1\frac{5}{6}$

$x = 1\frac{5}{6}$

Check: $x + \frac{2}{3} = \frac{5}{2}$

$1\frac{5}{6} + \frac{2}{3} \stackrel{?}{=} \frac{5}{2}$

$\frac{11}{6} + \frac{4}{6} \stackrel{?}{=} \frac{5}{2}$

$\frac{15}{6} \stackrel{?}{=} \frac{5}{2}$

$\frac{5}{2} = \frac{5}{2}$ ✓

The solution is $1\frac{5}{6}$.

Likewise, rational number inequalities are solved using the same skills used for solving whole number and integer inequalities.

Examples

Solve each inequality.

3

$x + \frac{1}{4} > 3$

$x + \frac{1}{4} - \frac{1}{4} > 3 - \frac{1}{4}$ Subtract $\frac{1}{4}$ from each side.

$x > 2\frac{3}{4}$

Check: Try 3, a number greater than $2\frac{3}{4}$.

$x + \frac{1}{4} > 3$

$3 + \frac{1}{4} \stackrel{?}{>} 3$

$3\frac{1}{4} > 3$ ✓

Is $2\frac{3}{4}$ a solution? Why or why not? **No; $2\frac{3}{4} > 2\frac{3}{4}$ is false.**

The solution is $x > 2\frac{3}{4}$, all numbers greater than $2\frac{3}{4}$.

4 $14.29 + m \leq 8.73$

$m \leq 8.73 - 14.29$ Subtract 14.29 from each side.

$m \leq 8.73 + (-14.29)$ Subtract by adding the inverse.

$m \leq -5.56$ Check this solution.

Is -5.56 a solution? Why or why not? **Yes; $-5.56 \leq -5.56$ is true.**

The solution is $m \leq -5.56$, all numbers less than or equal to -5.56.

Chalkboard Examples

Solve each equation. Check your solution.

- *For Example 1*
  $t - 5.6 = 3.2$ 8.8
- *For Example 2*
  $x + \frac{2}{5} = \frac{3}{4}$ $\frac{7}{20}$

Solve each inequality.

- *For Example 3*
  $b + \frac{5}{9} > 7$ $6\frac{4}{9}$
- *For Example 4*
  $23.79 + g \leq 19.73$ -4.06

3 PRACTICE/APPLY

Checking the Concept

Have students work with a partner on Exercises 4-12. Monitor students as they explain to each other how they would solve each equation or inequality. After students have completed the exercises ask them how they would check their solutions.

Alternate Strategies: Reteaching the Lesson

Reteaching Activity

Using Problem Solving If students experience difficulty with determining the operation to be used, rewrite problems using whole numbers. Determine the operation, then solve the original problem. Encourage students to show a diagram illustrating fractions, if possible.

Reteaching Masters Booklet, p. 42

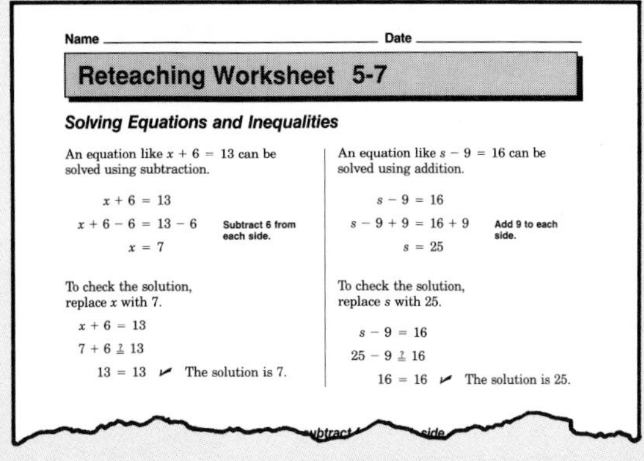

Name ______________ Date ______________

Reteaching Worksheet 5-7

Solving Equations and Inequalities

An equation like $x + 6 = 13$ can be solved using subtraction.

$x + 6 = 13$

$x + 6 - 6 = 13 - 6$ **Subtract 6 from each side.**

$x = 7$

To check the solution, replace x with 7.

$x + 6 = 13$

$7 + 6 \stackrel{?}{=} 13$

$13 = 13$ ✓ The solution is 7.

An equation like $s - 9 = 16$ can be solved using addition.

$s - 9 = 16$

$s - 9 + 9 = 16 + 9$ **Add 9 to each side.**

$s = 25$

To check the solution, replace s with 25.

$s - 9 = 16$

$25 - 9 \stackrel{?}{=} 16$

$16 = 16$ ✓ The solution is 25.

Error Analysis

Watch for students who choose the wrong operation.
Prevent by emphasizing the use of the operation that is opposite to the one in the problem.

Independent Practice

Homework Assignment	
Basic	13-39 odd, 40-49, 54, 55
Average	20-38 even, 40-50, 53-55
Honors	24-38 even, 40-55

Checking for Understanding

Communicating Algebra

1. Estimate the solution of the equation $n + 8.7 = 25.2$. about 16
2. Explain how you should solve the equation $y + 7\frac{1}{2} = 3\frac{3}{4}$. Subtract $7\frac{1}{2}$ from each side.
3. Explain how you should solve the inequality $y - 3\frac{1}{2} \geq -5\frac{1}{2}$. Add $3\frac{1}{2}$ to each side

Guided Practice

Explain how to solve each equation. Then solve.

4. $x + (-7) = 10$ 17
5. $y - 1.4 = -9.3$ -7.9
6. $14 = x + 7\frac{1}{2}$ $6\frac{1}{2}$
7. $-14.2 = t - 5$ -9.2
8. $r + 17\frac{1}{2} = 12\frac{3}{4}$ $-4\frac{3}{4}$
9. $m - \left(-7\frac{1}{2}\right) = -7\frac{1}{2}$ -15

Explain how to solve each inequality. Then solve.

10. $x + \frac{1}{2} > 5$ $x > 4\frac{1}{2}$
11. $a - 1.6 < 3.4$ $a < 5$
12. $y - 3 \leq \frac{5}{2}$ $y \leq 5\frac{1}{2}$

Exercises

Independent Practice

Solve each equation. Check your solution.

13. $t - 2.6 = 5.8$ 8.4
14. $s - 1.3 = 4.7$ 6.0
15. $x + 5 = \frac{1}{2}$ $-4\frac{1}{2}$
16. $b + 3\frac{1}{4} = 5$ $1\frac{3}{4}$
17. $y - 2.6 = 11.4$ 14
18. $p + 1.7 = -3.4$ -5.1
19. $b + 16.7 = -4.3$ -21
20. $a + \frac{3}{8} = 2\frac{1}{2}$ $2\frac{1}{8}$
21. $z - \frac{7}{8} = 3\frac{1}{4}$ $4\frac{1}{8}$
22. $m + \frac{3}{2} = \frac{7}{2}$ 2
23. $t - 2\frac{1}{8} = 3\frac{3}{8}$ $5\frac{1}{2}$
24. $n + 21.6 = 16.8$ -4.8

Solve each inequality. Check your solution.

25. $a + \frac{1}{2} > 4$ $a > 3\frac{1}{2}$
26. $d - \frac{2}{3} < \frac{7}{3}$ $d < 3$
27. $n - 5.7 < -10$ $n < -4.3$
28. $b - 1.6 \leq 4.3$ $b \leq 5.9$
29. $f + 2.8 \geq -7.3$ $f \geq -10.1$
30. $n + \frac{1}{4} \leq -2$ $n \leq -2$
31. $-3.5 + p > -7$ $p > -3.5$
32. $y - 6 \leq -8.5$ $y \leq -2.5$
33. $a - 7\frac{1}{2} \geq -8$ $a \geq -\frac{1}{2}$
34. $-5 + d > -\frac{11}{2}$ $d > -\frac{1}{2}$
35. $f - 2 \geq 6\frac{1}{4}$ $f \geq 8\frac{1}{4}$
36. $-2\frac{1}{3} \leq a - \frac{5}{6}$ $-1\frac{1}{2} \leq a$

Language Skill

Write using symbols.

37. x is less than or equal to -4.2. $x \leq -4.2$
38. The value of x is greater than 4.5. $x > 4.5$
39. The value of b is 3.78. $b = 3.78$

Practice Masters Booklet, **p. 46**

Name ______________________ Date ____________

Practice Worksheet 5-7

Solving Equations and Inequalities

Solve each equation. Check your solution.

1. $x + 7\frac{1}{2} = -8$ $-15\frac{1}{2}$
2. $y - 12 = -7\frac{1}{3}$ $4\frac{2}{3}$
3. $z - \left(-\frac{3}{4}\right) = 6\frac{1}{2}$ $5\frac{3}{4}$
4. $a - \frac{1}{6} = 2\frac{1}{3}$ $2\frac{1}{2}$
5. $b - 4.3 = 21.5$ 25.8
6. $c - \frac{4}{5} = 2\frac{1}{2}$ $3\frac{3}{10}$
7. $d + 2.4 = -15$ -17.4
8. $e + \frac{1}{3} = 7$ $6\frac{2}{3}$
9. $u - \frac{1}{4} = \frac{5}{4}$ $1\frac{1}{2}$
10. $v - 0.4 = 1.5$ 1.9
11. $54.7 + w = -6.72$ -61.42
12. $m + 4 = \frac{7}{8}$ $-3\frac{1}{8}$
13. $n - 1\frac{3}{4} = 3\frac{1}{6}$ $4\frac{11}{12}$
14. $p + \frac{7}{2} = -\frac{5}{4}$ $-4\frac{3}{4}$
15. $16\frac{4}{5} = 21\frac{3}{5} + q$ $-4\frac{4}{5}$

Solve each inequality. Check your solution.

16. $x + \frac{2}{3} > 7$ $6\frac{1}{3}$
17. $y + 5.2 \leq -1.4$ $y \leq -6.6$
18. $2.7 + z \geq 5.36$ $z \geq 2.66$
19. $a - 4\frac{2}{3} < -5\frac{1}{2}$ $a < -\frac{5}{6}$
20. $b - \frac{5}{6} > 3\frac{2}{3}$ $b > 4\frac{1}{2}$
21. $c + 3\frac{1}{5} \leq -8\frac{1}{2}$ $c \leq -11\frac{7}{10}$
22. $d + \frac{3}{4} > -2$ $d > -2\frac{3}{4}$
23. $e - 4\frac{2}{5} \leq -8\frac{1}{8}$ $e \geq -3\frac{29}{40}$
24. $-\frac{5}{6} + f < -\frac{3}{11}$ $f < \frac{37}{66}$
25. $\frac{7}{4} + m \leq \frac{17}{2}$ $m \leq 6\frac{3}{4}$
26. $-2.8 + n > -4.5$ $n > -1.7$
27. $w - 2.6 \leq 5.4$ $w \leq 8$
28. $-3 + u > -\frac{13}{5}$ $u > \frac{2}{5}$
29. $v - 3 \leq 7\frac{3}{4}$ $v \leq 10\frac{3}{4}$
30. $-4\frac{1}{3} \leq k - \frac{5}{6}$ $k \geq -3\frac{1}{2}$

Mixed Review

40. Evaluate the expression $10 + y$ if $y = -15$. (Lesson 2-3) -5

41. Find the width of a rectangle with area 240 square feet and length 30 feet. (Lesson 3-6) 8 ft

42. Evaluate $2x^3$ if $x = -2$. (Lesson 4-2) -16

Solve each equation. (Lessons 5-4, 5-5, 5-6)

43. $-3\frac{1}{5} + \frac{3}{5} = s$ $-2\frac{3}{5}$

44. $1\frac{3}{8} - 4\frac{1}{8} = t$ $-2\frac{3}{4}$

45. $3.67 - 0.74 = p$ 2.93

46. $a = \frac{1}{3} - \left(-\frac{2}{5}\right)$ $\frac{11}{15}$

47. $y = 4\frac{3}{4} - 5\frac{1}{6}$ $-\frac{5}{12}$

48. $c = -\frac{2}{7} + \frac{11}{8}$ $1\frac{5}{56}$

Applications **Write and solve an equation or inequality for each application.**

49. **Landscaping** Tom needed at least $5\frac{1}{3}$ pounds of grass seed for his lawn. He has $2\frac{1}{2}$ pounds. How much more does he need? $2\frac{1}{2} + x \geq 5\frac{1}{3}$; $2\frac{5}{6}$ lb

50. **Cooking** Serafina owes her friend Maria $2\frac{1}{2}$ cups of sugar and she needs $2\frac{1}{4}$ cups to bake cookies. How much sugar does she need to buy to repay Maria and bake the cookies? $2\frac{1}{2} + 2\frac{1}{4} = x$; $4\frac{3}{4}$ cups

51. **Driver's Education** The odometer on the car read 269.5 miles at the beginning of class. After class the odometer read 298.2 miles. How far was the car driven during class? 28.7 mi.
$269.5 + x = 298.2$

52. **Meteorology** At 2:00 P.M. the barometric pressure was 29.85 inches. It had dropped 0.28 inches from the previous reading. What was the previous reading? $29.85 = x - 0.28$; 30.13 inches

Connection

53. **Geometry** The sum of the measures of the angles in a triangle is 180°. If two of the angles measure 75.5° and 60.3°, what is the measure of the third angle? 44.2°

Critical Thinking

54. The sign ≥ can also mean *not less than*. What can the sign ≤ mean? not more than

Wrap-Up

55. Explain how the solutions of $x + 7 = -5$ and $x + 7 > -5$ differ. The solution of $x + 7 = -5$ is -12. The solution of $x + 7 > -5$ is all numbers greater than -12.

Writing Connection

Write one or more complete sentences to answer each question. See margin.

1. How do you know that 3.16 is greater than 3.158?
2. How do you know that $\frac{7}{16}$ is equal to $\frac{14}{32}$?
3. How do you know that -5 is a rational number?
4. How do you know that 3.5 is not the solution of $x + 1.5 = 6.0$?

4 CLOSE

Assessment Option

Speaking Tell what needs to be added to or subtracted from each equation or inequality to solve it.

1. $x + \frac{3}{4} = 2$ subtract $\frac{3}{4}$
2. $y - 2.4 = 2.4$ add 2.4
3. $m + 2\frac{1}{2} \leq 3\frac{1}{2}$ subtract $2\frac{1}{2}$

Additional Answers

Writing Connection

1. Rewrite 3.16 as 3.160. Then rewrite both decimals as fractions with like denominators: $3\frac{160}{1000}$ and $3\frac{158}{1000}$. Since 158 is less than 160, 3.158 is less than 3.16.
2. Multiply the numerator and denominator of $\frac{7}{16}$ by 2. The answer is $\frac{14}{32}$. Therefore, $\frac{7}{16}$ is equal to $\frac{14}{32}$.
3. The number -5 is a rational number because it can be expressed in the form of $\frac{a}{b}$, where *a* and *b* are integers and $b \neq 0$: $\frac{-5}{1}$.
4. If you solve the equation $x + 1.5 = 6.0$, you get $x = 4.5$. The answer, then, is 4.5 not 3.5.

Enrichment Masters Booklet, p. 42

Name ____________ Date ____________

Enrichment Worksheet 5-7

Solving Equations Involving Addition and Subtraction

Solve each equation.

1. $p + 5 = 8$ 3
2. $16 + a = 20$ 4
3. $d - 3\frac{2}{3} = 1\frac{1}{3}$ 5
4. $j + 2\frac{1}{2} = 9\frac{1}{2}$ 7
5. $8.2 + n = 14.2$ 6
6. $g - 5 = 3$ 8
7. $k + 1\frac{2}{3} = 5\frac{2}{3}$ 4
8. $s - 3 = 4\frac{2}{5}$ $7\frac{2}{5}$
9. $x + 2\frac{1}{2} = 5$ $2\frac{1}{2}$
10. $15 = w + 7$ 8
11. $r + 3.23 = 8.23$ 5
12. $2\frac{4}{5} = t - 4\frac{3}{5}$ $7\frac{2}{5}$
13. $7 + y = 11$ 4
14. $1.4 = x - 3.4$ 4.8
15. $n + 5.3 = 8.7$ 3.4
16. $g - 1\frac{2}{3} = 1\frac{1}{3}$ 3
17. $n + 7 = 12.23$ 5.23
18. $24 = x + 18$ 6
19. $\frac{5}{6} = y - \frac{5}{6}$ $1\frac{2}{3}$
20. $7 + y = 12$ 5
21. $t - 0.8 = 3.2$ 4
22. $1\frac{2}{3} = n + 1\frac{2}{3}$ 0

Match each solution above to the corresponding letter in the table below. Then place each letter on the appropriate blank at the bottom of the page to form the answer to this riddle.

Why didn't the man receive the basketballs?

A	B	C	D	E	H	I	K	N	O	S	U
7	3	5	0	4	$7\frac{2}{5}$	$2\frac{1}{2}$	3.4	$1\frac{2}{3}$	5.23	8	6

B E C A U S E   H I S
(1 2 3 4 5 6 7   8 9 10)

C H E C K   B O U N C E D
(11 12 13 14 15   16 17 18 19 20 21 22)

Alternate Strategies: Extending the Lesson

Enrichment

Using Cooperative Groups Have each student name a mixed number. Have students exchange numbers and write equations or inequalities with the number as the solution. Require that each problem use at least two fractions with unlike denominators.

Cooperative Learning

Inequality Maker Group Activity **5-7**

MATERIALS: Three dice

Each player must make an inequality from the numbers rolled on three dice. You score a point if your inequality solution includes an integer rolled on one die.

To begin, someone rolls three dice, and all players make two different mixed numbers from combinations of them. One of the digits will be the whole number, one will be the numerator of the fraction, and the last will be the denominator of the fraction.

Next, everyone writes an inequality using these two mixed numbers, a variable, addition and subtraction, and one of the inequality signs. All players then solve their inequality.

Lastly, one die is rolled to get an integer. When players' solution sets include this number, they score one point. The first to score five points wins.

Merrill Pre-Algebra SOLVING EQUATIONS AND INEQUALITIES

5-Minute Check
(over Lesson 5-7)

Solve each inequality. Check your solution.

1. $h - \frac{4}{5} \leq \frac{1}{4}$ $h \leq \frac{21}{20}$
2. $j + \frac{5}{6} > \frac{2}{3}$ $j > -\frac{1}{6}$
3. $-15.23 + t \leq -7$ $t \leq 8.23$
4. $r - 5\frac{1}{2} > -\frac{9}{2}$ $r > 1$
5. $m - 2.83 \leq -9$ $m \leq -6.17$

Transparency 5-8 contains the 5-Minute Check and a teaching aid for this lesson.

1 FOCUS

The purpose of this lesson is to introduce another strategy for problem solving and to establish a framework for working with sequences in the next lesson.

Motivating the Lesson

Ask students which they would rather have - \$1000 now, or 1 cent on the first day, 2 cents on the second day, 4 cents on the third day, and so on for 20 days.

2 TEACH

Mrs. Freeman gave a Pre-Algebra test. She posted the grading scale at the right. What score would a student receive if he missed six problems? 64%

-1 = 94%
-2 = 88%
-3 = 82%
-4 = 76%

3 PRACTICE/APPLY

Checking the Concept

Have students work in pairs. One student starts a pattern and the other gives hints until the correct pattern emerges. Then they reverse roles.

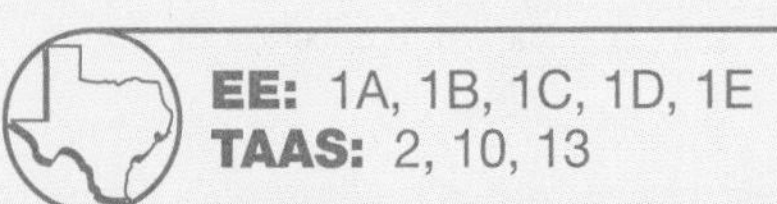

Problem Solving

5-8 Strategy: Look for a Pattern

Objective:
Solve problems by looking for a pattern.

Marguerite has part of a bus schedule. She wishes to take the bus to visit her grandmother but she cannot leave until after 1:00 P.M. What is the earliest time Marguerite can catch the bus?

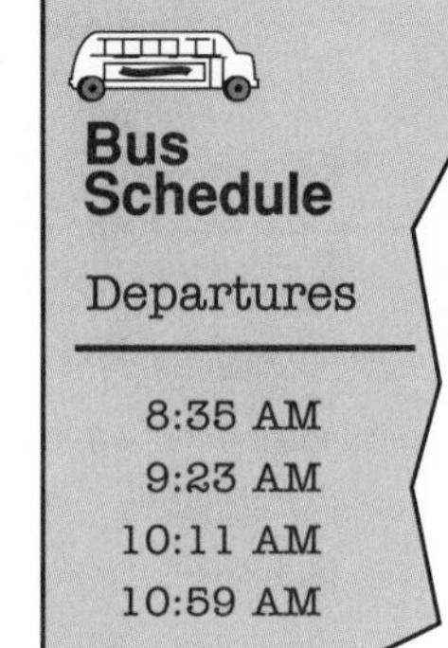

Bus Schedule
Departures
8:35 AM
9:23 AM
10:11 AM
10:59 AM

Explore The schedule shows several morning departure times. Marguerite needs to know the earliest departure time after 1:00 P.M.

Plan Since bus schedules often follow patterns, look for a pattern. Once you find a pattern, you can extend the schedule beyond 1:00 P.M.

Solve Notice that there are 48 minutes between each of the departure times.

8:35 +48 min. → 9:23 +48 min. → 10:11 +48 min. → 10:59

According to this pattern, the next scheduled departure would be 48 minutes after 10:59, or 11:47 P.M. The schedule would continue as follows.

11:47 +48 min. → 12:35 +48 min. → 1:23

Marguerite can catch the bus at 1:23 P.M.

What patterns can you observe in your classroom? **Sample answer: Class periods may be in a pattern.**

Examine You can estimate to check the reasonableness of your answer. Since there are about 50 minutes between departures, and the last known time is about 11:00, the next times should be about 11:50, 12:40, and 1:30. Therefore, the answer 1:23 seems reasonable.

Looking for, and then extending, patterns is a good problem-solving strategy. Sometimes the patterns are easy to see and sometimes they may be more hidden.

Checking for Understanding

Communicating Algebra

1. Use the pattern at the right to find 9999×5 and 9999×6. Explain your thinking. **49,995 and 59,994**

$9999 \times 1 = 9999$
$9999 \times 2 = 19{,}998$
$9999 \times 3 = 29{,}997$
$9999 \times 4 = 39{,}996$

2. Look at the pattern of numbers shown below.

   1 2 4 7

   Is the next number found by multiplying by 2? Why or why not? **No; $4 \times 2 \neq 7$.**

Bell Ringer

Solve the following equations or inequalities.

1. $x + \frac{4}{9} = 5$ $4\frac{5}{9}$
2. $y - 11.67 = 24.2$ 35.87

Reteaching Activity

Using Comparison Give students who are having trouble simple patterns to identify. For example, use the multiples of 3: 3, 6, 9, 12, 15, . . .
Have students find the difference between terms in the series. Continue with other simple patterns.

Exercises

Independent Practice

Solve. Look for a pattern.

1 × 1	=	1
11 × 11	=	121
111 × 111	=	12,321
1,111 × 1,111	=	1,234,321

3. Use the pattern at the right to find 11,111 × 11,111 and 111,111 × 111,111. **123,454,321 and 12,345,654,321**

4. At Fairview High School the bell rings at 8:05, 8:51, 8:55, 9:41, and 9:45 each weekday morning. When do the next three bells ring? **10:31, 10:35, 11:21**

5. Look at the quilt at the right. What color is the piece needed to complete the quilt? **red**

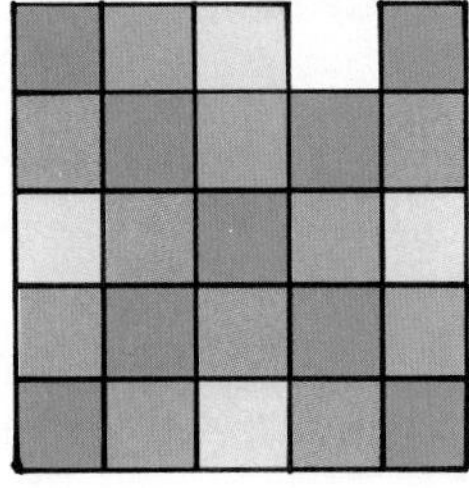

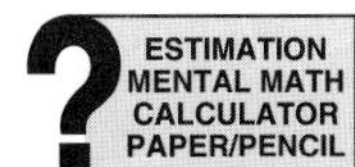

Solve. Use any strategy.

6. Two peaches and one pear cost $1.15. Three peaches and three pears cost $2.40. What is the cost of one peach? **35¢**

7. Willa is conditioning for the swim team. On the first day, she did 5 push-ups. The second day she did 6 push-ups. The third day she did 8 and on the fourth day she did 11. To continue this pattern, how many push-ups should she do on the fifth day, the sixth day, and the seventh day? On which day will she reach her goal of 40 push-ups? **15, 20, 26; 9th day**

8. Willa swam 1 lap on the first day. She swam 2 laps on the second day, 4 laps on the third day, and 8 laps on the fourth day. To continue this pattern, how many laps should she swim on the seventh day? **64 laps**

9. Ross travels south on his bicycle riding 8 miles per hour. One hour later, his friend Mason starts riding his bicycle from the same location. He travels south trying to catch up with Ross. If Mason rides 10 miles per hour for 3 hours, will he catch up with Ross? **no**

10. What is the sum of the first 50 odd numbers? **2500**

11. The Bulldogs have lost $\frac{2}{3}$ of their games. If they win their last four games, they will have won as many games as they lost. How many games have the Bulldogs won so far? **4 games won so far**

Critical Thinking

12. Jon is stacking oranges to form a triangular pyramid. Each orange touches three oranges below it as shown at the right. In order to have a pyramid with 6 layers, how many oranges should Jon put on the bottom layer? **21 oranges**

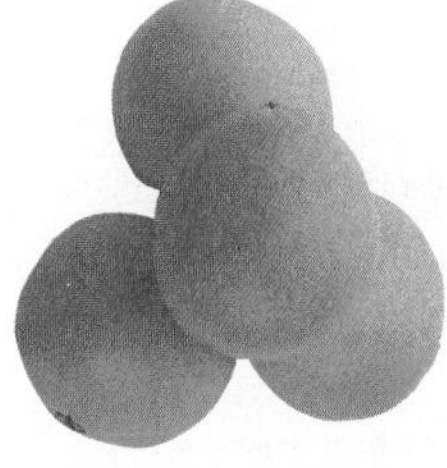

Wrap-Up

13. Suppose another student is having difficulty finding a pattern in a list of numbers. Write some hints you could give about how to find a pattern. **Sample answer: See if there is a common difference between terms.**

Error Analysis

Watch for students who become discouraged easily when looking for a pattern in a sequence.
Prevent by having students use a diagram. Also remind students that more than one arithmetic operation may be involved, and they should look for all four operations.

Independent Practice

Homework Assignment	
Basic	3-13
Average	3-13
Honors	3-13

4 CLOSE

Assessment Option

Speaking Have students brainstorm ways they look for a pattern.

Practice Masters Booklet, **p. 47**

Name ______________________ Date ____________

Practice Worksheet 5-8

Problem Solving Strategy: Look for a Pattern

Solve. Look for a pattern.

1. Ralph and Ella are playing a game called "Guess My Rule." Ralph has kept track of his guesses and Ella's responses in this table.

Ralph	0	1	2	3	4	5	6
Ella	10	9	8	7	6	5	4

Look for a pattern and predict Ella's response for the number 6. Describe this pattern. **Ella's response is Ralph's number subtracted from 10.**

2. Mollie is using the following chart to help her calculate prices for tickets.

Tickets	1	2	3	4
Price	$7.50	$12.50	$17.50	$22.50

A customer came in and ordered 10 tickets. How much should Mollie charge for this ticket order? **$52.50**

3. Brad needs to set up a coding system for files in the library using two-letter combinations. He has begun this table.

Letters	1	2	3	4	5
Combinations	1	4	9	16	25

1 LETTER	2 LETTERS	3 LETTERS	4 LETTERS
AA	AB BA BB AA	AA BC AB CA AC CB BA CC BB	AA BC DA AB BD DB AC CA DC AD CB DD BA CC BB CD

How many files can Brad code using the letters A, B, C, D, and E?

4. If the library has 400 items to code, how many letters will the librarian need if she uses Brad's system? **20 letters**

5. Billie needs to make a tower of soup cans as a display in a grocery store. Each layer of the tower will be in the shape of a rectangle. The length and the width of each layer will be one less than the layer below it.

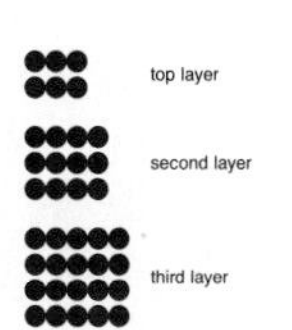

a. How many cans will be needed for the fifth layer of the tower? **42 cans**

b. How many total cans will be needed for a 10-layer tower? **570 cans**

Alternate Strategies: Extending the Lesson

Enrichment

If a painter can climb a ladder by going up one rung or two rungs, how many different ways can he reach the first rung? **1** The second rung? **2** The fifth rung? **8** Find a pattern and determine how many ways the painter can reach the twelfth rung. **Fibonacci sequence; 233 ways**

Cooperative Learning

Climb Those Stairs — Group Activity **5-8**

You and a partner will investigate how many blocks are needed to make staircases with increasing numbers of steps.

Consider a staircase of just one step. It is made from one square. Now draw a staircase with two steps, as shown below. It is made from three squares. If you draw a staircase of three steps, how many squares are needed? (6) How many squares would be needed to draw a staircase of 12 steps?

Look for a pattern in the number of squares needed by recording some information you know. Make a table with two columns, Number of Steps and Number of Squares, and your data for staircases of 1, 2, 3, 4, 5, and 6 steps. Do you see a pattern in the Number of Squares column? How could you determine the number of squares needed for 7 steps? Then for 8 steps? Write a sentence describing the pattern(s) you and your partner found.

Refer to the back of the card for more variations.

?

Merrill Pre-Algebra — PROBLEM-SOLVING STRATEGY: LOOK FOR A PATTERN

Lesson Notes 5-9

5-Minute Check
(over Lesson 5-8)

Solve. Use any strategy.

1. Four pencils and one pen cost $1.25 Two pencils and three pens cost $2.25. What is the cost of one pen? $0.65
2. Tamikka leaves from her house with some friends for the band competition. Traffic is heavy so they travel at 35 miles per hour. Tamikka's parents leave from their house one hour later. If they drive at 50 miles per hour for two hours, will they catch up with Tamikka? no

Transparency 5-9 contains the 5-Minute Check and a teaching aid for this lesson.

1 FOCUS

The purpose of this lesson is to use rational numbers in the development and explanation of arithmetic sequences.

Motivating the Lesson

Have students brainstorm a list of events that can be broken into equal parts.

2 TEACH

Using Discussion

Write two lists of sequences on the chalkboard or overhead. One list should contain arithmetic sequences while the other should not. Discuss with students the differences between the two lists to develop the definition of an arithmetic sequence.

EE: 1E, 2F, 3A, 3H
TAAS: 2, 6, 7, 12

5-9 Arithmetic Sequences

Objectives:
Find terms of arithmetic sequences.
Represent a sequence algebraically.

Key Terms:
sequence
term
arithmetic sequence
common difference

In 1990, the first class postage rate was 25¢ for the first ounce and 20¢ for each additional ounce. A chart showing the postage for weights up to 5 ounces is shown below. What was the cost for a 9-oz letter?

Weight	1 oz	2 oz	3 oz	4 oz	5 oz	6 oz	7 oz	8 oz	9 oz
Postage	$0.25	$0.45	$0.65	$0.85	$1.05	$1.25	$1.45	$1.65	$1.85

Look for a pattern in the chart. After the first ounce, each additional ounce costs an additional 20¢. By extending the chart, you can see that the cost for a 9-oz letter was $1.85.

A list of numbers in a certain order, such as 1, 2, 3, 4, … or 0.25, 0.45, 0.65, 0.85, … , is called a **sequence.** Each number is called a **term** of the sequence. When the difference between any two consecutive terms is the same, the sequence is called an **arithmetic sequence.** The difference is called the **common difference.**

Arithmetic Sequence: An arithmetic sequence is a sequence in which the difference between any two consecutive terms is the same.

FYI

The United States Postal Service has the world's largest vehicle fleet, 158,758 cars and trucks. The United States also ranks first in the average number of letters that each person mails, 635 letters per year.

Examples

State whether each sequence is arithmetic. Then write the next three terms of each sequence.

1 5, 6.5, 8, 9.5, …

Since the difference between any two consecutive terms is 1.5, the sequence is arithmetic.

The next three terms are 11, 12.5, and 14.

2 1, 3, 6, 10, 15, …

Since there is no common difference, the sequence is *not* arithmetic.

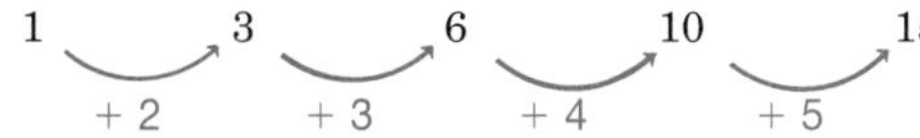

The next three terms are 21, 28, and 36.

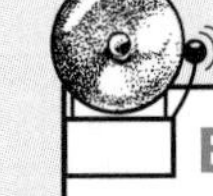

Bell Ringer

Find the pattern in the following sequence. State the next four letters. a, z, b, y, c, x, . . . d, w, e, v

Application

5-10 Adding and Subtracting Measures

Objectives:
Convert within the customary system.
Add and subtract measures.

Key Terms:
customary units
length
weight
capacity

Megan enjoys riding her bicycle cross country. Last fall she rode her bicycle from her home to Atlanta, a distance of 645 miles.

The *mile* is a unit of **length** commonly used in the United States. Other **customary units** of length are *inches*, *feet*, and *yards*.

The most weight that Megan carries in her backpack when bicycling is 10.5 pounds. Customary units of **weight** are *ounces*, *pounds*, and *tons*.

Megan always carries a 1-quart canteen of water when bicycling. In the customary system, **capacity** is measured using *fluid ounces*, *cups*, *pints*, *quarts*, and *gallons*.

These relationships make it possible to convert measures within the customary system.

The Customary System
1 foot (ft) = 12 inches (in.)
1 yard (yd) = 3 feet (ft)
1 mile (mi) = 5,280 feet (ft)
1 pound (lb) = 16 ounces (oz)
1 ton = 2,000 pounds (lb)
1 cup (c) = 8 fluid ounces (fl oz)
1 pint (pt) = 2 cups (c)
1 quart (qt) = 2 pints (pt)
1 gallon (gal) = 4 quarts (qt)

Examples

1 **27 in. = ■ ft.**

$\frac{27}{12} = 2\frac{3}{12}$ or $2\frac{1}{4}$

27 in. = $2\frac{1}{4}$ ft

You are changing from a smaller unit to a larger unit, so DIVIDE. Since 12 in. = 1 ft, divide by 12.

2 **10.5 lb = ■ oz**

10.5 [×] 16 [=] 168

10.5 lb = 168 oz

You are changing from a larger unit to a smaller unit, so MULTIPLY.

Since 1 lb = 16 oz, multiply by 16.

Bell Ringer

Write five arithmetic sequences.

Lesson Notes 5-10

5-Minute Check
(over Lesson 5-9)

Write the next three terms of each sequence.
1. 19, 13, 7, 1 **-5, -11, -17**
2. 6, 10, 11, 15, 16 **20, 21, 25**
3. 6.25, 5.5, 4.75, 4 **3.25, 2.5, 1.75**
4. 11, 8, 5, 2, **-1, -4, -7**
5. 58, 65, 72 **79, 86, 93**

Transparency 5-10 contains the 5-Minute Check and a teaching aid for this lesson.

1 FOCUS

The purpose of this lesson is to apply the concept of renaming fractions with unlike denominators to converting units within the customary system of measurement.

Motivating the Lesson

Bring in a box or can and ask students to state its characteristics or uses. As students express examples, write their answers in a 3-column table in terms of length, mass, or volume. Ask students to label each column.

2 TEACH

Using Manipulatives

Provide groups of students with rulers or yardsticks, scales, and measuring cups. Have them model several equivalent measurements.

Chalkboard Examples

- *For Example 1*
  32 in. = ■ ft $2\frac{2}{3}$ ft
- *For Example 2*
  14.5 lb = ■ oz 232 oz

EE: 1E, 4B
TAAS: 4, 11

Chalkboard Examples

- For Example 3
  3 ft 5 in.
  + 2 ft 8 in.
  6 ft 1 in.
- For Example 4
  9 gal 2 qt
  − 3 gal 3 qt
  5 gal 3 qt
- For Example 5
  Find the perimeter of the triangle shown at the right.
  21 ft 5 in.

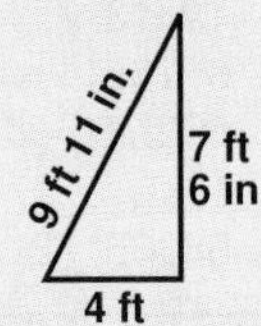

3 PRACTICE/APPLY

Checking the Concept

Have students complete Exercises 5-16 in cooperative groups. Give each group measuring cups, scales, and yardsticks to model problems.

Error Analysis

Watch for students who multiply when they should divide, and vice-versa, when changing from one unit to another.
Prevent by using diagrams. For example, draw rulers and a yardstick, emphasizing that there are three rulers for each yardstick, so there are three times as many feet as yards.

Practice Masters Booklet, **p. 49**

Name ______________________ Date ______________

Practice Worksheet 5-10

Application: Adding and Subtracting Measures

Add or subtract.

1. 8 lb 13 oz − 3 lb 5 oz = **5 lb 8 oz**
2. 3 gal − 1 gal 2 qt = **1 gal 2 qt**
3. 12 ft 8 in. − 6 ft 10 in. = **5 ft 10 in.**
4. 7 lb 3 oz + 3 lb 14 oz = **11 lb 1 oz**
5. 1 gal 2 qt + 3 gal 2 qt = **5 gal**
6. 5 ft 8 in. + 6 ft 11 in. = **12 ft 7 in.**
7. 1 yd 2 ft + 8 yd 1 ft = **10 yd**
8. 8 yd 1 ft − 2 ft = **7 yd 2 ft**
9. 5 gal 2 qt − 2 gal 3 qt = **2 gal 3 qt**

Find the perimeter.

10. (square) 1 yd 1 ft — **5 yd 1 ft**
11. (rectangle) 1 yd 2 ft; 2 ft — **4 yd 2 ft**
12. (triangle) 1 ft 11 in.; 2 ft 5 in.; 2 ft 8 in. — **7 ft**
13. (hexagon) 9 ft 11 in. — **59 ft 6 in.**
14. (parallelogram) 1 yd 1 ft; 2 yd 2 ft — **8 yd**
15. (rhombus) 3 yd 2 ft — **14 yd 2 ft**
16. 1 ft 7 in.; 3 ft 8 in.; 1 ft 5 in.; 2 ft 7 in.; 2 ft 9 in. — **12 ft**
17. 3 yd 1 ft; 2 yd; 3 yd; 4 yd 2 ft — **13 yd**
18. (pentagon) 2 ft 8 in. — **13 ft 4 in.**

Customary units can be added or subtracted. Sometimes it is necessary to rename measurements as shown in the following examples.

Examples

3

5 ft 8 in.	
+ 2 ft 6 in.	Add the units separately.
7 ft 14 in.	

↑ 14 in. = 1 ft 2 in.

7 ft 14 in. = 8 ft 2 in.

4

6 gal 1 qt
− 3 gal 3 qt

➡

5 gal 5 qt (6 and 1 crossed out, renamed 5 and 5)
− 3 gal 3 qt
2 gal 2 qt

Since 3 qt is greater than 1 qt, rename 6 gal 1 qt as 5 gal 5 qt. Then subtract.

Estimation Hint

THINK:
4 ft 10 in. is almost 5 ft; 5 ft 4 in. is a little more than 5 feet. The perimeter should be about 5 + 3 + 5 or 13 feet.

5 **Find the perimeter of the triangle shown at the right.**

To find the perimeter, add the measures of the sides.

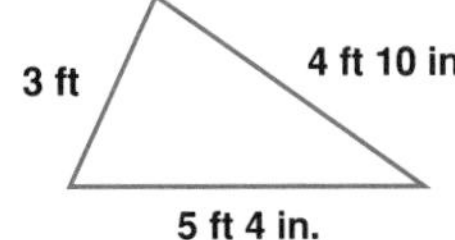

4 ft 10 in.
3 ft
+ 5 ft 4 in.
12 ft 14 in. = 13 ft 2 in.

The perimeter of the triangle is 13 ft 2 in.

Checking for Understanding

Communicating Algebra

1. Explain how to convert 20 inches to feet. **Divide 20 by 12.**
2. Explain how to convert 5 gallons to quarts. **Multiply 5 by 4.**
3. State the formula for the perimeter of a rectangle. $P = 2(\ell + w)$
4. If you know the measure of one side of a square, how would you find the perimeter? **Multiply by 4.**

Guided Practice

Complete.

5. 24 in. = ■ ft **2**
6. 12 ft = ■ yd **4**
7. 5 mi = ■ yd **8800**
8. 3 lb = ■ oz **48**
9. 6 tons = ■ lb **12,000**
10. 3 c = ■ fl oz **24**
11. 0.5 lb = ■ oz **8**
12. 96 yd = ■ ft **288**
13. 1.25 mi = ■ ft **6600**

Add or subtract.

14. 10 ft 3 in. + 5 ft 9 in. **16 ft**
15. 3 yd 2 ft + 8 yd 1 ft **12 yd**
16. 9 ft 4 in. − 7 ft 1 in. **2 ft 3 in.**

Alternate Strategies: Reteaching the Lesson

Reteaching Activity

Using Manipulatives Have three groups of students measure several items. Each group measures one characteristic (length, mass, or volume) and prepares a chart of equivalent measures. Then each group quizzes the others by giving a measurement and asking for it in a different unit of measure.

Reteaching Masters Booklet, **p. 44**

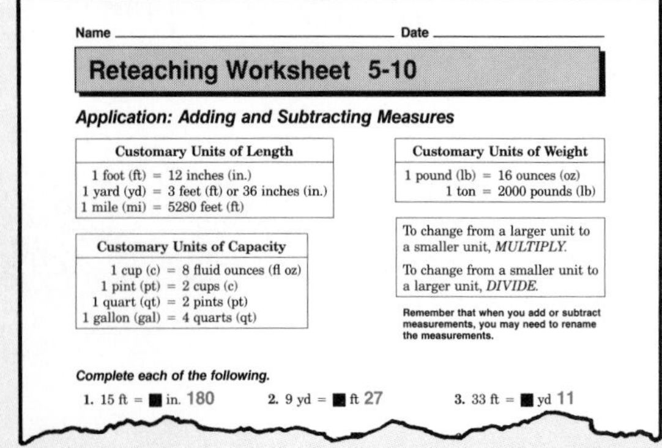
Name ______________________ Date ______________

Reteaching Worksheet 5-10

Application: Adding and Subtracting Measures

Customary Units of Length
1 foot (ft) = 12 inches (in.)
1 yard (yd) = 3 feet (ft) or 36 inches (in.)
1 mile (mi) = 5280 feet (ft)

Customary Units of Weight
1 pound (lb) = 16 ounces (oz)
1 ton = 2000 pounds (lb)

Customary Units of Capacity
1 cup (c) = 8 fluid ounces (fl oz)
1 pint (pt) = 2 cups (c)
1 quart (qt) = 2 pints (pt)
1 gallon (gal) = 4 quarts (qt)

To change from a larger unit to a smaller unit, *MULTIPLY.*

To change from a smaller unit to a larger unit, *DIVIDE.*

Remember that when you add or subtract measurements, you may need to rename the measurements.

Complete each of the following.

1. 15 ft = ■ in. 180
2. 9 yd = ■ ft 27
3. 33 ft = ■ yd 11

Exercises

Independent Practice

Add or subtract.

17. 6 lb 12 oz + 4 lb 8 oz **11 lb 4 oz**
18. 10 ft − 4 ft 6 in. **5 ft 6 in.**
19. 2 gal 3 qt + 4 gal 1 qt **7 gal**
20. 5 gal 3 qt − 2 gal 2 qt **3 gal 1 qt**
21. 7 lb 8 oz − 3 lb 13 oz **3 lb 11 oz**
22. 4 gal − 2 gal 3 qt **1 gal 1 qt**

Find the perimeter.

23. **16 ft**

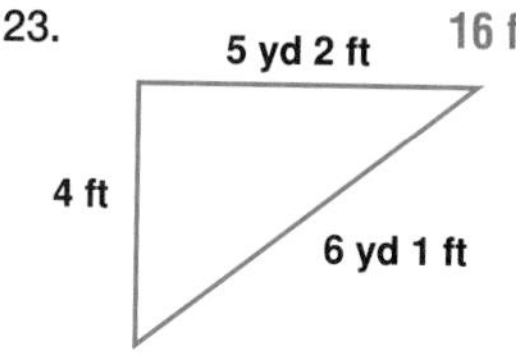

24. **34 ft 4 in.**

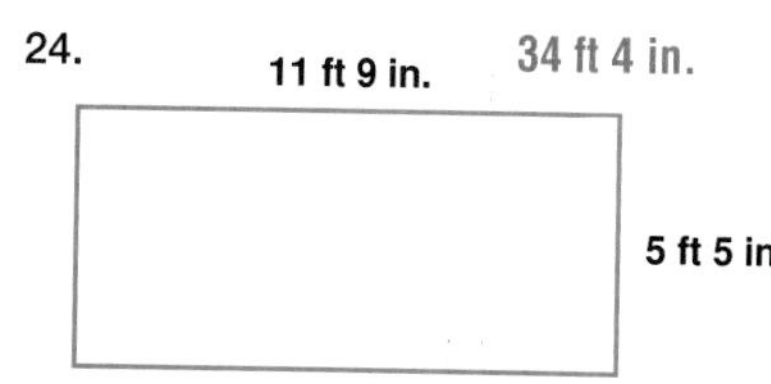

Applications

25. **Consumer Awareness** A small car weighs 1.2 tons. Find the weight of the car in pounds. **2400 pounds**

26. **Home Economics** A pitcher holds 3 quarts. How many 12-oz glasses can be filled from the pitcher? **8 glasses**

Connection

27. **Geometry** The perimeter of a triangle is 8 ft 10 in. The lengths of two sides are 3 ft 8 in. and 2 feet 9 in. Find the length of the third side. **2 ft 5 in.**

Mixed Review

28. Solve the inequality $-3p > 105$. (Lesson 3-8) $p < -35$
29. Write 3^{-2} using positive exponents. (Lesson 4-10) $\frac{1}{3^2}$
30. Solve the equation $b - 2\frac{3}{8} = 1\frac{1}{2}$. (Lesson 5-7) $3\frac{7}{8}$
31. Write the next three terms of the sequence 5, 4, 2, -1, -5. (Lesson 5-9) **-10, -16, -23**

Critical Thinking

32. Mr. Hiroshi has an office that he wants to panel. The office is a square, 11 feet 6 inches on a side and 8 feet high. If panelling comes in sheets 8 feet high by 4 feet wide, how many sheets of panelling will he need to buy? **12 sheets**

Wrap-Up

33. Explain in general how you would find the perimeter of any polygon. **Add the measures of the sides.**

Team Problem Solving

Mr. Cutter has a back yard that is 25 meters long and 10 meters wide. The path that Mr. Cutter's lawn mower cuts is 1 meter wide. If Mr. Cutter mows his lawn using the path shown, how far will he have walked when he is finished? **250 m**

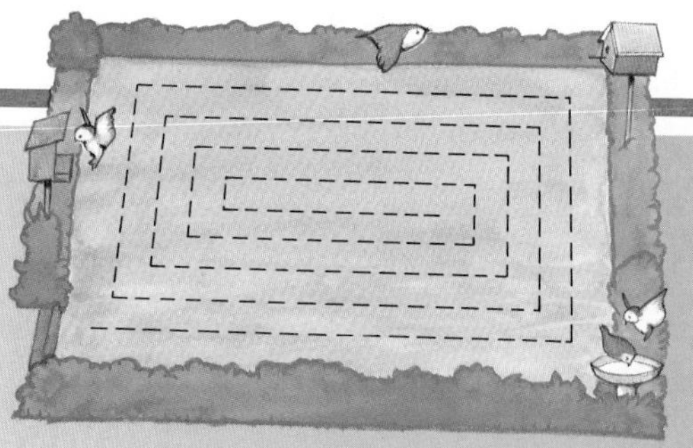

Independent Practice

Homework Assignment	
Basic	17-25 odd, 28-33
Average	18-26 even, 28-33
Honors	22-33

Chapter 5, Quiz B, (Lessons 5-6 through 5-10) is available in the Evaluation Masters Booklet, p. 43.

4 CLOSE

Assessment Option

Modeling Divide the class into three groups. Have each group perform different tasks; one group should weigh things, another group should measure the size of things, and another group should measure liquids. Then have them add or subtract the measures.

Enrichment Masters Booklet, **p. 44**

Name ______ Date ______

Enrichment Worksheet 5-10

Problem Solving: Measures

Solve each problem.

1. A flower bed is in the shape of a triangle. The sides measure 2.5 m, 3.5 m, and 4.25 m. What is the perimeter of the flower bed? 10.25 m
2. Mindy has a class picture that measures 10 inches by $8\frac{1}{2}$ inches. The wood on the frame she uses is $1\frac{1}{8}$ inches wide. What is the perimeter of the framed picture? 46 in.
3. The perimeter of a square is 140 m. Find the length of each side. 35 m
4. A regular octagon has a perimeter of 10 cm. Find the length of each side. 1.25 cm
5. A security guard walks around a building 115 feet long and 39 feet wide. If her strides average $2\frac{1}{2}$ feet in length, how many strides does she take each trip around? The perimeter is 308 feet and 308 ÷ 2.5 is about 123 strides. However, since she cannot walk exactly along the edge of the building, the number of strides will be greater than 123.
6. A regulation baseball diamond, 90 feet square, is laid out on a field 172 feet wide and 301 feet long. How much greater is the distance around the whole field than around the diamond? 586 ft
7. How many feet of chrome edging do you need to finish a table top 54 inches long and 30 inches wide? 14 ft

Alternate Strategies: Extending the Lesson

Enrichment

Using Tables Bring in a recipe book and have students choose a recipe that serves 6 people. Then have each student create a two-column table. The first column should contain the ingredients for the base recipe. Have students complete the second column with the amounts necessary to feed 200 people.

Cooperative Learning

Competitive Conversions Group Activity **5-10**

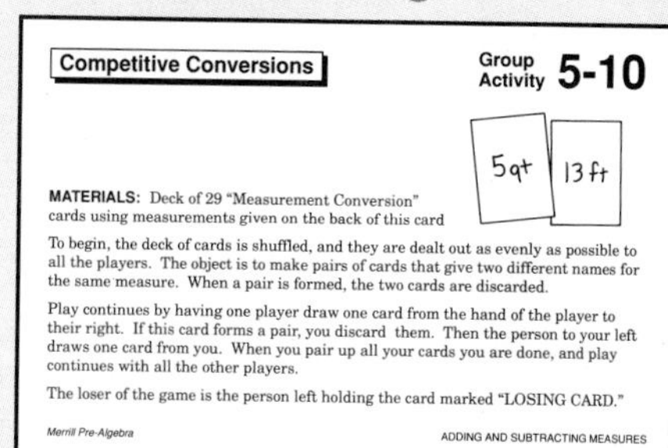

MATERIALS: Deck of 29 "Measurement Conversion" cards using measurements given on the back of this card

To begin, the deck of cards is shuffled, and they are dealt out as evenly as possible to all the players. The object is to make pairs of cards that give two different names for the same measure. When a pair is formed, the two cards are discarded.

Play continues by having one player draw one card from the hand of the player to their right. If this card forms a pair, you discard them. Then the person to your left draws one card from you. When you pair up all your cards you are done, and play continues with all the other players.

The loser of the game is the person left holding the card marked "LOSING CARD."

Merrill Pre-Algebra ADDING AND SUBTRACTING MEASURES

Using the Chapter Review

The Chapter Review is a comprehensive review of the concepts presented in this chapter. This review may be used to prepare students for the Chapter Test.

Alternate Review Strategy

To provide a brief in-class review, you may wish to read the following questions to the class and require a verbal response.

1. Give an example of a whole number; an integer; a rational number. possible answers: 2; -2; $\frac{1}{2}$
2. Explain how to rename $0.\overline{7}$ as a fraction. Let N = 0.777, multiply N by 10 because one digit repeats, subtract N from $10N$, and divide both sides by 9.
3. Round 8.05 to the nearest tenth. 8.1
4. Simplify $d = -4.8 + 1.95$. -2.85
5. Solve $\frac{5}{9} + \frac{7}{9}$ and give the solution in simplest form. $1\frac{1}{3}$
6. Explain how you should solve $g = \frac{3}{8} - \frac{2}{5}$. Rename the fractions with a common denominator. Then subtract numerators.
7. Explain how you should solve the inequality $x - 6\frac{2}{3} \geq -3\frac{1}{3}$. Add $6\frac{2}{3}$ to each side.
8. Solve. The city bus system issued a new schedule. Doug read the morning express bus schedule and found there were only four express bus times. The first three times were 6:25 A.M., 6:50 A.M., and 7:15 A.M. What time will the last express bus leave from Doug's stop? 7:40 A.M.
9. Is the sequence 19, 22, 25, 28 arithmetic? Explain your answer. yes, because the difference between each consecutive term is the same
10. Explain how to convert 15 yards to feet. multiply 15 by 3

Review

Language and Concepts

Choose the letter of the best word or words to complete each sentence.

1. To subtract a rational number, add its __?__ . e
2. To add fractions with __?__ , add the numerators. f
3. The decimal 0.333 . . . is an example of a __?__ . h
4. The closure property for addition states that the sum of any two rational numbers is a __?__ . g
5. __?__ are five properties of addition that apply to rational numbers. a, b, c, d, e

a. associative
b. closure
c. commutative
d. identity
e. inverse
f. like denominators
g. rational number
h. repeating decimal
i. terminating decimal
j. unlike denominators

Skills

Replace each ● with <, >, or = to make a true sentence. (Lesson 5-1)

6. 4.6 ● 3.9 >
7. -5.5 ● 1.6 <
8. $\frac{4}{5}$ ● $-\frac{4}{5}$ >
9. $7\frac{1}{2}$ ● $\frac{15}{2}$ =

Express each decimal as a fraction or mixed number in simplest form. (Lesson 5-2)

10. -0.6 $-\frac{3}{5}$
11. 0.85 $\frac{17}{20}$
12. -0.25 $-\frac{1}{4}$
13. 0.08 $\frac{2}{25}$
14. 1.4 $1\frac{2}{5}$
15. -2.36 $-2\frac{9}{25}$
16. 0.333 . . . $\frac{1}{3}$
17. 0.2727 . . . $\frac{3}{11}$
18. $2.\overline{4}$ $2\frac{4}{9}$

Round each decimal to the nearest whole number or dollar. (Lesson 5-3)

19. \$7.45 \$7
20. 9.621 10
21. \$2.50 \$3
22. 109.92 110

Estimate. (Lesson 5-3)

23. \$10.03 + \$5.84 \$16
24. 44.03 − 32.9 10
25. 20.3 + 59.7 + 62.8 140

All are properties of addition.

Name the property shown by each sentence. (Lesson 5-4)

26. 9.2 + (-9.2) = 0 inverse
27. (2 + 3.4) + (-5) = -5 + (2 + 3.4) comm.
28. -1.5 + 2.3 = 2.3 + (-1.5) comm.
29. 8.3 + (-6.1) is a rational number. closure

Solve each equation. (Lesson 5-4)

30. $p = 0.9 + 4.5$ 5.4
31. $s = 3.05 - 1.94$ 1.11
32. $w = 4.6 - 2.7$ 1.9
33. $h = -3.6 + 9.4$ 5.8
34. $5.8 - (-3.2) = q$ 9
35. $m = -1.8 + (-3.7)$ -5.5

Find the LCM for the denominators in each sum or difference. (Lesson 5-6)

36. $\frac{3}{4} + \frac{1}{8}$ 8
37. $\frac{5}{8} - \frac{1}{6}$ 24
38. $\frac{2}{5} - \frac{1}{6}$ 30
39. $\frac{3}{7} + \frac{1}{2}$ 14

Solve each equation. Write each solution in simplest form. (Lessons 5-5, 5-6)

40. $a = \frac{7}{9} + \frac{5}{9}$ $1\frac{1}{3}$
41. $\frac{27}{18} - \frac{9}{18} = h$ 1
42. $2\frac{3}{8} + 1\frac{5}{8} = p$ 4
43. $6 - 3\frac{3}{4} = a$ $2\frac{1}{4}$
44. $a = \frac{5}{9} - \frac{7}{18}$ $\frac{1}{6}$
45. $b = -\frac{1}{6} + \frac{1}{3}$ $\frac{1}{6}$
46. $-\frac{3}{5} - \frac{3}{10} = t$ $-\frac{9}{10}$
47. $1\frac{3}{5} + 6\frac{7}{8} = m$ $8\frac{19}{40}$

Explain how to solve each equation or inequality. Then solve. (Lesson 5-7)

48. $g - 1.4 = 8$ 9.4
Add 1.4 to each side.
49. $-3.6 = x - 9$ 5.4
Add 9 to each side.
50. $a + \frac{2}{3} < 2$ $1\frac{1}{3}$
Subtract $\frac{2}{3}$ from each side.

Write the next three terms of each sequence. Then state whether or not the sequence is arithmetic. Write *yes* or *no*. (Lesson 5-9)

51. 20, 23, 26, 29, . . . 32, 35, 38 yes
52. 8, 9, 12, 17, . . . 24, 33, 44 no

Add or subtract. (Lesson 5-10)

53. 5 gal 2 qt + 2 gal 3 qt = 8 gal 1 qt
54. 10 lb 15 oz + 8 lb 12 oz = 19 lb 11 oz
55. 10 yd − 2 yd 1 ft = 7 yd 2 ft

Applications and Problem Solving

56. A volleyball team has 6 members. Suppose each member shakes hands with every other member. How many handshakes take place? (Lesson 5-8) 15 handshakes

57. A rectangular field is 30 yd 1 ft wide and 75 yd 2 ft long. What is the perimeter of the field? (Lesson 5-10) 212 yd

Communicating Algebra

Is -3 a solution to the inequality $y - 4.5 < 0$? Write your answer in paragraph form. See margin.

Curriculum Connection

- **Language Arts** Research the Dewey Decimal System to find out how decimals are used to organize books in the library. See margin.

Read More About It

Burns, Marilyn. *The I Hate Math! Book.*
Luce, Marnie and A. B. Lerner. *Infinity, What is It?*
Wallace, G. David. *Money Basics.*

Additional Answers
Communicating Algebra
If -3 is substituted for y in the equation $y - 4.5 < 0$, the resulting inequality is $-7.5 < 0$. Since -7.5 is less than 0, this is a true statement, and -3 is a solution to the inequality.

Curriculum Connection
The Dewey Decimal System classifies literature by assigning numbers to different categories. The general category numbers are 000, 100, 200, . . . , 900. The books within a particular category are assigned numbers which may include decimals. For example, in the general category of social science (300), a certain book may have the number 387.236. This number distinguishes it from all others.

You may wish to use a Chapter Test (free-response format) as an additional chapter review. Two forms are provided in the Evaluation Masters Booklet as shown below.

Evaluation Masters Booklet, **p. 41**

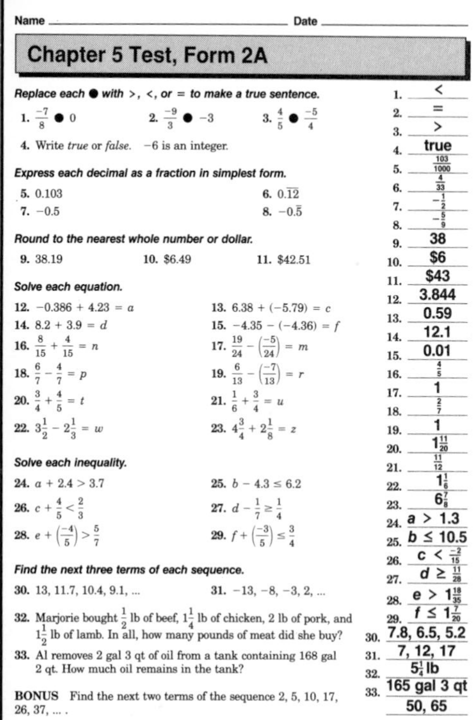

Name ______ Date ______

Chapter 5 Test, Form 2A

Replace each ● with >, <, or = to make a true sentence.

1. $\frac{-7}{8}$ ● 0
2. $\frac{-9}{3}$ ● −3
3. $\frac{4}{5}$ ● $\frac{-5}{4}$
4. Write *true* or *false*. −6 is an integer.

Express each decimal as a fraction in simplest form.

5. 0.103
6. $0.\overline{12}$
7. −0.5
8. $-0.\overline{5}$

Round to the nearest whole number or dollar.

9. 38.19
10. \$6.49
11. \$42.51

Solve each equation.

12. $-0.386 + 4.23 = a$
13. $6.38 + (-5.79) = c$
14. $8.2 + 3.9 = d$
15. $-4.35 - (-4.36) = f$
16. $\frac{8}{15} + \frac{4}{15} = n$
17. $\frac{19}{24} - \left(\frac{-5}{24}\right) = m$
18. $\frac{6}{7} - \frac{4}{7} = p$
19. $\frac{6}{13} - \left(\frac{-7}{13}\right) = r$
20. $\frac{3}{4} + \frac{4}{5} = t$
21. $\frac{1}{6} + \frac{3}{4} = u$
22. $3\frac{1}{2} - 2\frac{1}{3} = w$
23. $4\frac{3}{4} + 2\frac{1}{8} = z$

Solve each inequality.

24. $a + 2.4 > 3.7$
25. $b - 4.3 \le 6.2$
26. $c + \frac{4}{5} < \frac{2}{3}$
27. $d - \frac{1}{7} \ge \frac{1}{4}$
28. $e + \left(\frac{-4}{5}\right) > \frac{5}{7}$
29. $f + \left(\frac{-3}{5}\right) \le \frac{3}{4}$

Find the next three terms of each sequence.

30. 13, 11.7, 10.4, 9.1, ...
31. −13, −8, −3, 2, ...
32. Marjorie bought $\frac{1}{2}$ lb of beef, $1\frac{1}{4}$ lb of chicken, 2 lb of pork, and $1\frac{1}{2}$ lb of lamb. In all, how many pounds of meat did she buy?
33. Al removes 2 gal 3 qt of oil from a tank containing 168 gal 2 qt. How much oil remains in the tank?

BONUS Find the next two terms of the sequence 2, 5, 10, 17, 26, 37, ...

Answers: 1. < 2. = 3. > 4. true 5. $\frac{103}{1000}$ 6. $\frac{4}{33}$ 7. $-\frac{1}{2}$ 8. $-\frac{5}{9}$ 9. 38 10. \$6 11. \$43 12. 3.844 13. 0.59 14. 12.1 15. 0.01 16. $\frac{4}{5}$ 17. 1 18. $\frac{2}{7}$ 19. 1 20. $1\frac{11}{20}$ 21. $\frac{11}{12}$ 22. $1\frac{1}{6}$ 23. $6\frac{7}{8}$ 24. $a > 1.3$ 25. $b \le 10.5$ 26. $c < \frac{-2}{15}$ 27. $d \ge \frac{11}{28}$ 28. $e > 1\frac{18}{35}$ 29. $f \le 1\frac{7}{20}$ 30. 7.8, 6.5, 5.2 31. 7, 12, 17 32. $5\frac{1}{4}$ lb 33. 165 gal 3 qt BONUS: 50, 65

Evaluation Masters Booklet, **p. 42**

Name ______ Date ______

Chapter 5 Test, Form 2B

Replace each ● with >, <, or = to make a true sentence.

1. $\frac{7}{8}$ ● 0
2. $\frac{-9}{3}$ ● −3
3. $\frac{4}{5}$ ● $\frac{5}{4}$
4. Write *true* or *false*. −6 is a whole number.

Express each decimal as a fraction in simplest form.

5. 0.105
6. $0.\overline{16}$
7. −0.4
8. $-0.\overline{4}$

Round to the nearest whole number or dollar.

9. 38.91
10. \$8.50
11. \$12.09

Solve each equation.

12. $-0.386 + 8.46 = b$
13. $6.38 + (-7.31) = e$
14. $8.2 + 2.8 = g$
15. $-4.35 - (-4.34) = h$
16. $\frac{6}{15} + \frac{4}{15} = j$
17. $\frac{17}{24} - \left(\frac{-5}{24}\right) = k$
18. $\frac{6}{9} - \frac{2}{9} = q$
19. $\frac{6}{13} + \left(\frac{-7}{13}\right) = s$
20. $\frac{1}{4} + \frac{4}{5} = v$
21. $\frac{1}{6} + \frac{1}{4} = x$
22. $5\frac{1}{2} - 2\frac{2}{3} = y$
23. $4\frac{1}{4} + 2\frac{3}{8} = z$

Solve each inequality.

24. $a + 2.4 \le 5.3$
25. $b - 4.3 > 4.7$
26. $c - \frac{4}{5} \ge \frac{2}{3}$
27. $d + \frac{1}{7} < \frac{1}{4}$
28. $e + \left(\frac{-4}{5}\right) < \frac{5}{9}$
29. $f - \left(\frac{-3}{5}\right) \ge \frac{3}{4}$

Find the next three terms of each sequence.

30. 12, 13.7, 15.4, 17.1, ...
31. −10, −7, −4, −1, ...
32. Anthony bought $\frac{1}{2}$ lb of beef, $3\frac{1}{4}$ lb of chicken, 1 lb of pork, and $2\frac{1}{2}$ lb of lamb. In all, how many pounds of meat did he buy?
33. Hal removes 6 gal 3 qt of oil from a tank containing 168 gal 1 qt. How many gallons remain in the tank?

BONUS Find the next two terms of the sequence 65, 62, 57, 50, 41, 30, ...

Answers: 1. > 2. = 3. < 4. false 5. $\frac{21}{200}$ 6. $\frac{16}{99}$ 7. $-\frac{2}{5}$ 8. $-\frac{4}{9}$ 9. 39 10. \$9 11. \$12 12. 8.074 13. −0.93 14. 11 15. −0.01 16. $\frac{2}{3}$ 17. $\frac{11}{12}$ 18. $\frac{4}{9}$ 19. $-\frac{1}{13}$ 20. $1\frac{1}{20}$ 21. $\frac{5}{12}$ 22. $2\frac{5}{6}$ 23. $6\frac{5}{8}$ 24. $a \le 2.9$ 25. $b > 9$ 26. $c \ge 1\frac{7}{15}$ 27. $d < \frac{3}{28}$ 28. $e < 1\frac{16}{45}$ 29. $f \ge \frac{3}{20}$ 30. 18.8, 20.5, 22.2 31. 2, 5, 8 32. $7\frac{1}{4}$ lb 33. 161 gal 2 qt BONUS: 17, 2

Using the Chapter Test

This page may be used as a test or as an additional review. Two forms of a Chapter Test (multiple-choice format) are provided in the Evaluation Masters Booklet. One of the tests is shown below.

Evaluation Masters Booklet, **pp. 37-38**

Name ______________________ Date ____________

Chapter 5 Test, Form 1A

In Exercises 1–2, choose the best answer.

1. A rational number can be written as $\frac{a}{b}$, where a is __?__.
   A. a whole number B. a fraction C. an integer D. zero — 1. C
2. Name the set of numbers to which $\frac{-3}{5}$ belongs.
   A. whole numbers B. rationals C. integers D. odd numbers — 2. B

Replace each ● to make a true sentence.

3. $\frac{12}{-4}$ ● -3 A. $<$ B. $>$ C. $=$ D. cannot tell — 3. C
4. $\frac{-1}{2}$ ● $\frac{3}{100}$ A. $<$ B. $>$ C. $=$ D. cannot tell — 4. A
5. Express $0.\overline{12}$ as a fraction in simplest form.
   A. $\frac{12}{20}$ B. $\frac{4}{33}$ C. $\frac{3}{25}$ D. $\frac{12}{100}$ — 5. B
6. Express 0.55 as a fraction in simplest form.
   A. $\frac{11}{2}$ B. $\frac{55}{10}$ C. $\frac{50}{9}$ D. $\frac{11}{20}$ — 6. D
7. Round $36.86 to the nearest dollar.
   A. $36.90 B. $36.80 C. $37.00 D. $36.00 — 7. C
8. Estimate the sum $503 + $98 + $106 + $2.
   A. $600 B. $700 C. $800 D. $900 — 8. B
9. Round 34.638 to the nearest tenth.
   A. 34.6 B. 40.638 C. 34.7 D. 34.64 — 9. A
10. Name the property of addition shown by $8.6 + (-8.6) = 0$.
    A. Commutative B. Associative C. Identity D. Inverse — 10. D
11. Solve $r = -13.68 - (-14.7)$.
    A. -1.02 B. 1.02 C. -28.38 D. 28.38 — 11. B

Solve each equation.

12. $\frac{3}{11} + \frac{2}{11} = d$
    A. $\frac{5}{11}$ B. $\frac{1}{11}$ C. $\frac{3}{2}$ D. $\frac{2}{3}$ — 12. A
13. $\frac{-5}{13} + \left(\frac{-5}{13}\right) = f$
    A. $\frac{10}{13}$ B. $\frac{-10}{26}$ C. 0 D. $\frac{-10}{13}$ — 13. D

Name ______________________ Date ____________

Chapter 5 Test, Form 1A (continued)

Solve each equation.

14. $\frac{-6}{17} - \left(\frac{-8}{17}\right) = g$
    A. $\frac{-2}{17}$ B. $\frac{-14}{17}$ C. $\frac{2}{17}$ D. $\frac{14}{17}$ — 14. C
15. $\frac{1}{3} + \frac{3}{5} = h$
    A. $\frac{4}{8}$ B. $\frac{14}{15}$ C. $\frac{1}{5}$ D. $\frac{1}{2}$ — 15. B
16. $\frac{3}{8} - \frac{1}{10} = j$
    A. -1 B. $\frac{11}{40}$ C. $\frac{-2}{2}$ D. $\frac{24}{80}$ — 16. B

Solve each inequality.

17. $d + \frac{2}{3} < \frac{7}{3}$
    A. $d < 3$ B. $d < \frac{-5}{3}$ C. $d < \frac{5}{3}$ D. $d < -3$ — 17. C
18. $y - 5 > -8.3$
    A. $y > 13.3$ B. $y > -3.3$ C. $y > 3.3$ D. $y > -13.3$ — 18. B
19. $-4 + a > \frac{-13}{2}$
    A. $a > \frac{9}{2}$ B. $a > \frac{-17}{2}$ C. $a > \frac{5}{2}$ D. $a > \frac{-5}{2}$ — 19. D
20. Find the next term in the sequence 8, 2, −4, −10, ...
    A. −12 B. −14 C. −16 D. −20 — 20. C
21. Find the tenth term in the sequence 72, 66, 60, 54, ...
    A. 18 B. 30 C. 12 D. 24 — 21. A
22. Complete 5 ft = ■ in.
    A. 80 B. 50 C. 500 D. 60 — 22. D
23. Bill is filling water glasses as a party. Each glass holds 8 ounces of water. How many glasses can Bill fill with one gallon of water?
    A. 16 B. 8 C. 32 D. 20 — 23. A
24. Katy cut a piece from a large cheese wheel. The wheel weighed 50 lb before cutting and 37 lb 4 oz after cutting. How much did the piece of cheese weigh?
    A. 13 lb 12 oz B. 12 lb 12 oz C. 87 lb 4 oz D. 13 lb 4 oz — 24. B
25. A square trapdoor measures 2 ft 3 in. on each side. Find the perimeter of the trapdoor.
    A. 4 ft 6 in. B. 6 ft 9 in. C. 8 ft 3 in. D. 9 ft — 25. D

BONUS Each of 10 packages weighs 6 lb 9 oz. What is the total weight?
A. 66 lb B. 71 lb 2 oz C. 65 lb 10 oz D. 67 lb 6 oz — C

Test

Replace each ● with <, >, or = to make a true sentence.

1. $2\frac{3}{5}$ ● $2\frac{5}{8}$ <
2. 54.349 ● 54.36 <
3. 1.04 ● $1\frac{2}{50}$ =

Express each decimal as a fraction or mixed number in simplest form.

4. 0.72 $\frac{18}{25}$
5. 2.702 $2\frac{351}{500}$
6. $0.\overline{7}$ $\frac{7}{9}$
7. $-1.\overline{6}$ $-1\frac{2}{3}$

Name the property shown by each sentence. All are properties of addition.

8. $7.9 + 3.6 = 3.6 + 7.9$ comm.
9. $1.49 + 0 = 1.49$ iden.
10. $\frac{4}{5} + \left(-\frac{4}{5}\right) = 0$ inverse
11. $1\frac{2}{7} \div (-5)$ is a rational number. closure

Solve each equation.

12. $6.8 + 0.7 = m$ 7.5
13. $y = 15 - 8.7$ 6.3
14. $2.13 - 0.95 = s$ 1.18
15. $3.9 + 4.1 - 2.6 = h$ 5.4
16. $a = 1.6 - (-3.4)$ 5
17. $n = 4.5 - 8.6$ -4.1
18. $\frac{9}{16} + \frac{9}{16} = a$ $1\frac{1}{8}$
19. $2\frac{13}{15} - 1\frac{14}{15} = g$ $\frac{14}{15}$
20. $6\frac{1}{7} + \left(-2\frac{4}{7}\right) = h$ $3\frac{4}{7}$
21. $\frac{4}{5} - \frac{5}{10} = g$ $\frac{3}{10}$
22. $j = \frac{2}{3} + 3\frac{4}{5}$ $4\frac{7}{15}$
23. $-\frac{3}{5} - \frac{1}{10} = c$ $-\frac{7}{10}$

Solve each equation or inequality. Write the solutions in simplest form.

24. $h - \frac{7}{2} = 2\frac{1}{2}$ 6
25. $r - 6.8 = 10.2$ 17
26. $1.2 + s > 3$ $s > 1.8$
27. $a - 9 \leq 1.5$ $a \leq 10.5$

Write the next three terms of each sequence. Then state whether the sequence is arithmetic. Write *yes* or *no*.

28. 1, 1.2, 1.6, 2.2, . . . 3, 4, 5.2; no
29. 7, 14, 21, 28, . . . 35, 42, 49; yes

Solve.

30. Luisa plants $\frac{1}{4}$ of her garden in flowers, $\frac{1}{3}$ in tomatoes, and the rest in beans. How much of the garden is planted in beans? $\frac{5}{12}$
31. Write the first 5 terms in an arithmetic sequence with a common difference of 4. The first term is 20. 20, 24, 28, 32, 36
32. Find the sum of the whole numbers from 1 through 100. 5050
33. Estimate the perimeter of a triangle with sides 4.55 m, 6.81 m, and 9.27 m. 21 m

BONUS

True or *false*: $0.3 = \frac{1}{3}$. Write your answer in paragraph form. See Solutions Manual.

Test Generator Software is provided in both Apple and IBM formats. You may use this software to create your own tests, based on the needs of your students.

Academic Skills Test

Cumulative, Chapters 1-5

1. If $x = 9$ and $y = 18$, what is the value of $9y - 18x$?

   A 729
   (B) 0
   C -9
   D -243

2. If $a + 2.5 = 5.1$, what is the value of a?

   (A) 2.6
   B 3.6
   C 5.1
   D 7.6

3. Which equation is equivalent to $-14d = 98$?

   A $-14d \cdot (-14) = 98$
   B $-14d \div (-14) = 98$
   C $-14d \div (-14) = 98 \cdot (-14)$
   (D) $-14d \div (-14) = 98 \div (-14)$

4. Which is equivalent to 3^4?

   A 12
   B 64
   (C) 81
   D 243

5. Which is equivalent to $\frac{a^2}{a^4}$?

   (A) a^{-2}
   B a^2
   C a^6
   D a^8

6. If $m + 2.1 = 8$, what is the value of m?

   (A) 5.9
   B 6.9
   C 8
   D 10.1

7. Which number should come next in this pattern?

   1, 3, 7, 13, 21, . . .

   A 23
   B 29
   (C) 31
   D 35

8. A group of divers are at a depth of -20 m. If they descend 15 m more, at what depth will they be?

   A 5 m
   B -5 m
   C 35 m
   (D) -35 m

9. Sandy bowls in a league. Her handicap score is found using the formula:

   $$s = g + c$$

   where s is the handicap score, g is the game score, and c is the handicap. What was Sandy's game score if her handicap score is 186 and her handicap is 15?

   A 161
   (B) 171
   C 191
   D 201

10. Gladys bought grocery items for the following prices: \$1.39, \$2.89, 58¢, and \$1.19. The best estimate of the total cost is—

    A \$4
    B \$5
    (C) \$6
    D \$9

A Cumulative Review (free-response format) and Cumulative Test (multiple-choice format) are also provided in the Evaluation Masters Booklet as shown at the right.

Test Item	1	2	3	4	5	6	7	8	9	10
Lesson Number	1-2	3-1	3-3	4-2	4-10	5-7	5-9	2-5	3-5	5-3
TAAS Objective	2	2	2	1	2	2	2	7	2	10

Using the Academic Skills Test

This test familiarizes students with a standardized format while testing skills and concepts presented up to this point.

Evaluation Masters Booklet, **p. 44**

Name ______________________ Date ____________

Cumulative Review, Chapters 1-5

Evaluate each expression if a = 4 and b = 5. (Lesson 1–2)

1. $2 + 3 \cdot b$
2. $3 \cdot a - 2 \cdot b$

Name the property shown by each statement. (Lessons 1–3, 1–4)

3. $3(xy) = (3x)y$
4. $4(a + b) = 4a + 4b$

Compute. (Lessons 2–1, 2–5, 2–7, 2–8)

5. $|-12| - |3|$
6. $-4 - (-3)$
7. $8(-16)$
8. $-18 \div (-3)$

Solve. (Lessons 3–1 through 3–4)

9. $c + (-4) = 18$
10. $q - (-3) = 20$
11. $16x = -224$
12. $\frac{y}{-8} = 448$
13. Evaluate m^5, if $m = -3$. (Lesson 4–2)
14. Find the prime factorization of 1080. (Lesson 4–4)
15. Find the GCF of 24 and 40. (Lesson 4–5)
16. Find the LCM of 12 and 18. (Lesson 4–7)
17. Find the product $(-3y^2z)(5yz^3)$. (Lesson 4–9)
18. Find the quotient $10^8 \div 10^4$. (Lesson 4–10)

Express each decimal as a fraction in simplest form. (Lesson 5–2)

19. 0.36
20. $0.\overline{04}$

Solve each equation. (Lessons 5–4 through 5–6)

21. $\frac{2}{3} - \frac{7}{15} = a$
22. $\frac{3}{4} + \frac{3}{10} = b$
23. $4.3 - 2.86 = c$

Solve.

24. Ken read a story about a king who put grains of rice on the squares of a chessboard. He put 1 grain on the first square, 2 on the second square, 4 on the third, 8 on the fourth, and so on. How many grains did he place on the eighth square? (Lesson 5–8)
25. Rob's computer prints part one of a banner which is 4 ft 8 in. long. Mary's computer prints the other part which is 5 ft 7 in. long. How long is the entire banner? (Lesson 5–10)

1. **17**
2. **2**
3. **Assoc., Mult.**
4. **Distrib.**
5. **9**
6. **−1**
7. **−128**
8. **6**
9. **22**
10. **17**
11. **−14**
12. **−3584**
13. **−243**
14. $2^3 \cdot 3^3 \cdot 5$
15. **8**
16. **36**
17. $-15y^3z^4$
18. 10^4
19. $\frac{9}{25}$
20. $\frac{4}{99}$
21. $\frac{1}{5}$
22. $1\frac{1}{20}$
23. **1.44**
24. **128 grains**
25. **10 ft 3 in.**

Evaluation Masters Booklet, **p. 45**

Name ______________________ Date ____________

Cumulative Test, Chapters 1-5

Evaluate each expression if a = 5, b = 6, and m = −2.

1. $3a + b$ — A. 41 B. 21 C. 33 D. 31 — 1. **B**
2. m^4 — A. −16 B. 32 C. 40 D. 16 — 2. **D**

Name the property of addition shown by each statement.

3. $3 + 2 = 2 + 3$ — A. Commutative B. Associative C. Identity D. Inverse — 3. **A**
4. $4 + 0 = 4$ — A. Commutative B. Associative C. Identity D. Inverse — 4. **C**

Simplify.

5. $-12 + 8$ — A. −4 B. 20 C. −20 D. 4 — 5. **A**
6. $-9 - (-2)$ — A. 11 B. −11 C. 7 D. −7 — 6. **D**
7. $4(-15)$ — A. −19 B. 60 C. −60 D. −11 — 7. **C**
8. $14 \div (-2)$ — A. −7 B. 7 C. −16 D. 16 — 8. **A**

Solve.

9. $a + (-5) = 14$ — A. 9 B. −9 C. −19 D. 19 — 9. **D**
10. $b - (-4) = -3$ — A. 7 B. −7 C. −1 D. 1 — 10. **B**
11. $y \div (-6) = 120$ — A. 20 B. −20 C. −720 D. 720 — 11. **C**
12. $12x = -216$ — A. −18 B. 18 C. 2592 D. −2592 — 12. **A**
13. Find the prime factorization of 240. — A. $24 \cdot 10$ B. $16 \cdot 15$ C. $2^3 \cdot 3^2 \cdot 5$ D. $2^4 \cdot 3 \cdot 5$ — 13. **D**
14. Find the GCF of 16 and 20. — A. 2 B. 4 C. 80 D. 320 — 14. **B**
15. Find the product $(-2x^4y)(-3xy)$. — A. $6x^5y$ B. $6x^4y$ C. $-6x^4y$ D. $6x^5y^2$ — 15. **D**

Solve each equation.

16. $\frac{3}{4} - \frac{3}{8} = x$ — A. $\frac{3}{4}$ B. $\frac{6}{12}$ C. 0 D. $\frac{3}{8}$ — 16. **D**
17. $\frac{1}{3} + \frac{2}{5} = y$ — A. $\frac{3}{8}$ B. $\frac{11}{15}$ C. $\frac{1}{5}$ D. $\frac{7}{15}$ — 17. **B**
18. $8.1 - 3.65 = z$ — A. 4.55 B. 5.55 C. 4.45 D. 5.45 — 18. **C**
19. To make a flagpole, Guy welds a 6 ft 9 in. piece of pipe to a 4 ft 9 in. piece. How long is the flagpole? — A. 11 ft 6 in. B. 10 ft 9 in. C. 12 ft 3 in. D. 11 ft 9 in. — 19. **A**
20. Anna started reciting a sequence that began 4, 12, 20, 28, ... Name the next number in her sequence. — A. 32 B. 34 C. 36 D. 38 — 20. **C**

Rational Numbers: Multiplying and Dividing Patterns

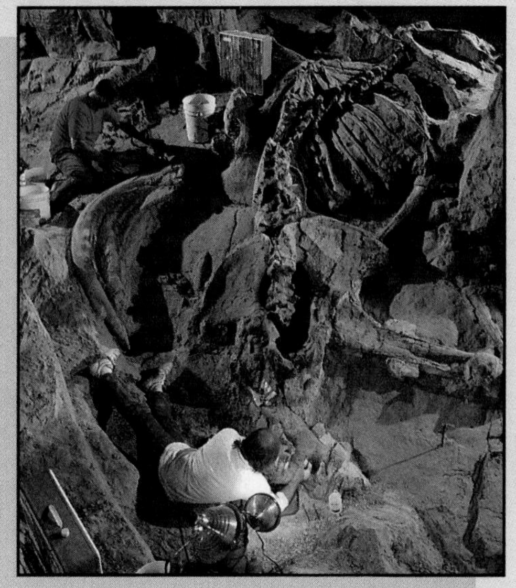

Previewing the Chapter

This chapter begins with a study of fractions expressed as terminating or repeating decimals. The emphasis is on estimating products and quotients and then on multiplying or dividing rational numbers. Students will learn to solve equations and inequalities that contain rational numbers and to use scientific notation to express large and small numbers. Students compare decimals and fractions and use algebra to find the terms of a geometric sequence.

Logic Students learn to use and differentiate between deductive and inductive reasoning.

Lesson (Pages)	Lesson Objectives	State/Local Objectives
6-1 (204-207)	6-1: Writing fractions as decimals.	1E, 2D, 3A
6-2 (209-210)	6-2: Estimating products and quotients.	1E, 2D, 3A, 4B
6-3 (211-214)	6-3: Multiplying fractions.	1E, 2D, 3A, 3D, 3H
6-4 (215-218)	6-4: Multiplying decimals.	1E, 2D, 3A, 3D, 3H
6-5 (219-221)	6-5: Multiplicative Inverses.	1E, 2D, 3A
6-6 (222-224)	6-6: Divide fractions.	1E, 2D, 3A, 3D, 3H
6-7 (225-227)	6-7: Divide decimals.	1E, 2D, 3A, 5E
6-8 (228-230)	6-8: Solving equations and inequalities.	1E, 2D, 3A, 3F
6-9 (231-232)	6-9: Identify examples of deductive and inductive reasoning.	1A, 1E
6-10 (233-235)	6-10A: Recognize and extend geometric sequences. 6-10B: Represent a geometric sequence algebraically.	1E, 2F
6-11 (237-239)	6-11: Write numbers in scientific notation.	1E, 2A, 2D, 3A
6-12 (240-242)	6-12: Compare rational numbers.	1E, 2A, 2D, 3A
6-13 (243-245)	6-13: Find the circumference of a circle.	1E, 3A, 4A, 4B, 4E

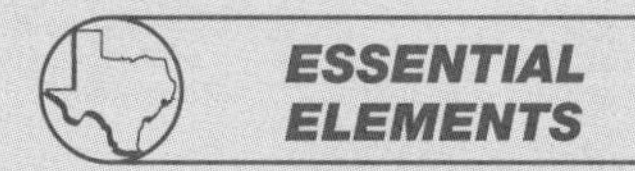

Organizing the Chapter

*You may want to refer to the **Course Planning Calendar** on Page T31.*

Planning Guide

Lesson (Pages)	Pacing Chart (in days) MINIMUM	STANDARD	ACCELERATED	Extra Practice (Student Edition)	Blackline Masters Booklets: Reteaching	Practice	Enrichment	Other Resources
6-1 (204-207)	1.5	1	1	p. 599, Set 6A	p. 45	p. 50	p. 45	Transparency 6-1 Group Activity Card 6-1
6-2 (209-210)	1	1	0.5	p. 599, Set 6B	p. 46	p. 51	p. 46	Transparency 6-2 Group Activity Card 6-2
6-3 (211-214)	1.5	1	1	p. 599, Set 6B	p. 47	p. 52	p. 47	Transparency 6-3 Group Activity Card 6-3
6-4 (215-218)	1.5	1	1	p. 599, Set 6B	p. 48	p. 53	p. 48	Transparency 6-4 Group Activity Card 6-4
6-5 (219-221)	1	1	1	p. 599, Set 6B	p. 49	p. 54	p. 49	Transparency 6-5 Group Activity Card 6-5
6-6 (222-224)	1	1	1	p. 599, Set 6B	p. 50	p. 55	p. 50	Transparency 6-6 Group Activity Card 6-6
6-7 (225-227)	1	1	1	p. 599, Set 6B	p. 51	p. 56	p. 51	Transparency 6-7 Group Activity Card 6-7
6-8 (228-230)	1	1	1	p. 600, Set 6C	p. 52	p. 57	p. 52	Transparency 6-8 Group Activity Card 6-8
6-9 (231-232)	1	1	0.5			p. 58		Transparency 6-9 Group Activity Card 6-9
6-10 (233-235)	1	1	1	p. 600, Set 6D	p. 53	p. 59	p. 53	Transparency 6-10 Group Activity Card 6-10
6-11 (237-239)	1	1	1	p. 599, Set 6A	p. 54	p. 60	p. 54	Transparency 6-11 Group Activity Card 6-11
6-12 (240-242)	1	1	1	p. 599, Set 6A	p. 55	p. 61	p. 55	Transparency 6-12 Group Activity Card 6-12
6-13 (243-245)	1	1	1	p. 600, Set 6C	p. 56	p. 62	p. 56	Transparency 6-13 Group Activity Card 6-13
Review (246-247)	1.5	1	1					Test Generator
Test (248)	1	1	1		Evaluation Masters, pp. 46-51			

Other Chapter Resources

Student Edition
Challenge, pp. 207, 214, 242
Exploration, p. 208
Reading Algebra, p. 218
Mid-Chapter Quiz, p. 227
Team Problem Solving, p. 230
Algebra in Action, p. 236
History, p. 245
Academic Skills Test, p. 249

Teacher Resource Package
Interdisciplinary Activity, p. 6
Application Worksheet, p. 21
Cooperative Problem Solving, p. 36
Multicultural Activity, p. 51
Fun Activities, p. 68
Technology Worksheets, pp. 6, 21, 36
Lab Manual, pp. 42-44
Quizzes(2), p. 52
Class Review Game

Software
Test Generator

available for Apple and IBM

Enhancing the Chapter

Some of the blackline masters for enhancing this chapter are shown below.

Applications, p. 21

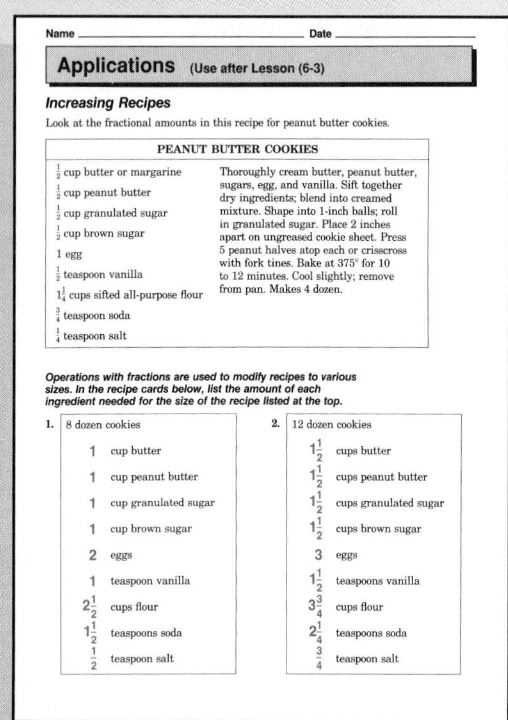

Name ______________________ Date ______________

Applications (Use after Lesson (6-3)

Increasing Recipes

Look at the fractional amounts in this recipe for peanut butter cookies.

PEANUT BUTTER COOKIES

$\frac{1}{2}$ cup butter or margarine
$\frac{1}{2}$ cup peanut butter
$\frac{1}{2}$ cup granulated sugar
$\frac{1}{2}$ cup brown sugar
1 egg
$\frac{1}{2}$ teaspoon vanilla
$1\frac{1}{4}$ cups sifted all-purpose flour
$\frac{3}{4}$ teaspoon soda
$\frac{1}{4}$ teaspoon salt

Thoroughly cream butter, peanut butter, sugars, egg, and vanilla. Sift together dry ingredients; blend into creamed mixture. Shape into 1-inch balls; roll in granulated sugar. Place 2 inches apart on ungreased cookie sheet. Press 5 peanut halves atop each or crisscross with fork tines. Bake at 375° for 10 to 12 minutes. Cool slightly; remove from pan. Makes 4 dozen.

Operations with fractions are used to modify recipes to various sizes. In the recipe cards below, list the amount of each ingredient needed for the size of the recipe listed at the top.

1. 8 dozen cookies
   1 cup butter
   1 cup peanut butter
   1 cup granulated sugar
   1 cup brown sugar
   2 eggs
   1 teaspoon vanilla
   $2\frac{1}{2}$ cups flour
   $1\frac{1}{2}$ teaspoons soda
   $\frac{1}{2}$ teaspoon salt

2. 12 dozen cookies
   $1\frac{1}{2}$ cups butter
   $1\frac{1}{2}$ cups peanut butter
   $1\frac{1}{2}$ cups granulated sugar
   $1\frac{1}{2}$ cups brown sugar
   3 eggs
   $1\frac{1}{2}$ teaspoons vanilla
   $3\frac{3}{4}$ cups flour
   $2\frac{1}{4}$ teaspoons soda
   $\frac{3}{4}$ teaspoon salt

The **Activity Masters Booklet** contains the page shown above.

Interdisciplinary Activity, p. 6

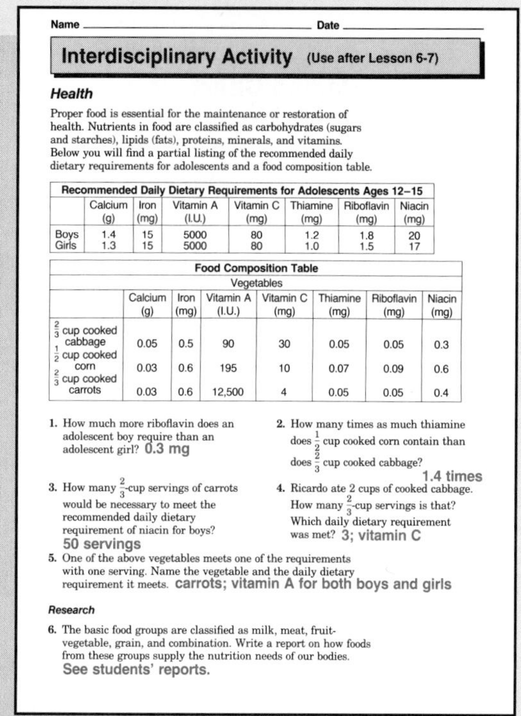

Name ______________________ Date ______________

Interdisciplinary Activity (Use after Lesson 6-7)

Health

Proper food is essential for the maintenance or restoration of health. Nutrients in food are classified as carbohydrates (sugars and starches), lipids (fats), proteins, minerals, and vitamins. Below you will find a partial listing of the recommended daily dietary requirements for adolescents and a food composition table.

Recommended Daily Dietary Requirements for Adolescents Ages 12–15							
	Calcium (g)	Iron (mg)	Vitamin A (I.U.)	Vitamin C (mg)	Thiamine (mg)	Riboflavin (mg)	Niacin (mg)
Boys	1.4	15	5000	80	1.2	1.8	20
Girls	1.3	15	5000	80	1.0	1.5	17

Food Composition Table Vegetables							
	Calcium (g)	Iron (mg)	Vitamin A (I.U.)	Vitamin C (mg)	Thiamine (mg)	Riboflavin (mg)	Niacin (mg)
$\frac{2}{3}$ cup cooked cabbage	0.05	0.5	90	30	0.05	0.05	0.3
$\frac{1}{2}$ cup cooked corn	0.03	0.6	195	10	0.07	0.09	0.6
$\frac{2}{3}$ cup cooked carrots	0.03	0.6	12,500	4	0.05	0.05	0.4

1. How much more riboflavin does an adolescent boy require than an adolescent girl? **0.3 mg**
2. How many times as much thiamine does $\frac{1}{2}$ cup cooked corn contain than does $\frac{2}{3}$ cup cooked cabbage? **1.4 times**
3. How many $\frac{2}{3}$-cup servings of carrots would be necessary to meet the recommended daily dietary requirement of niacin for boys? **50 servings**
4. Ricardo ate 2 cups of cooked cabbage. How many $\frac{2}{3}$-cup servings is that? Which daily dietary requirement was met? **3; vitamin C**
5. One of the above vegetables meets one of the requirements with one serving. Name the vegetable and the daily dietary requirement it meets. **carrots; vitamin A for both boys and girls**

Research

6. The basic food groups are classified as milk, meat, fruit-vegetable, grain, and combination. Write a report on how foods from these groups supply the nutrition needs of our bodies. **See students' reports.**

The **Activity Masters Booklet** contains the page shown above.

Models and Manipulatives

Students can practice multiplication and division of fractions by using a sheet of paper ($8\frac{1}{2} \times 11$) and measuring and cutting out squares of a specified fractional length. Pose the problem: "How many $3\frac{1}{8}$ in. squares can be cut from this sheet of paper?"

Follow up with, "Is there an easier way to do this using mathematics?"

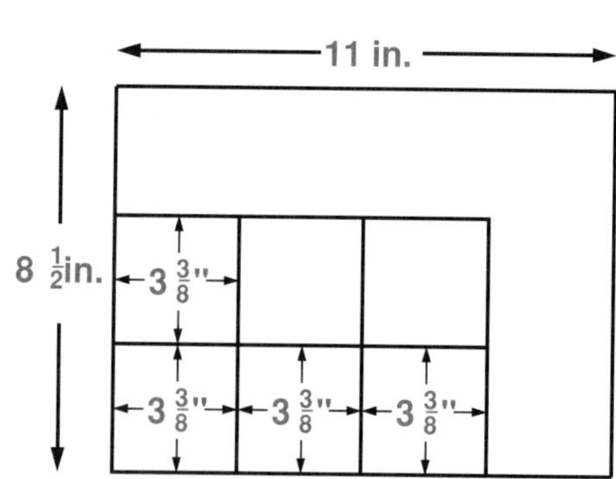

Multicultural Activity

Most countries in the world use the metric system for measurement. If the metric system is used, is there a need to know how to compute with fractions? Students could write or research possible answers.

Students could exchange recipes from their cultures that serve 6 and contain fractions and show how to make enough for the whole class.

Cooperative Learning

The following activity is provided in the **Activity Masters Booklet.**

Cooperative Problem Solving, p. 36

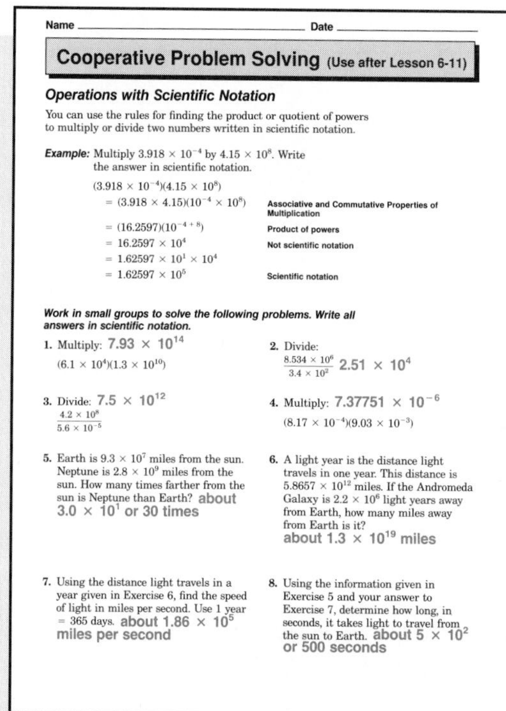

Name ______ Date ______

Cooperative Problem Solving (Use after Lesson 6-11)

Operations with Scientific Notation

You can use the rules for finding the product or quotient of powers to multiply or divide two numbers written in scientific notation.

Example: Multiply 3.918×10^{-4} by 4.15×10^{8}. Write the answer in scientific notation.

$(3.918 \times 10^{-4})(4.15 \times 10^{8})$	
$= (3.918 \times 4.15)(10^{-4} \times 10^{8})$	Associative and Commutative Properties of Multiplication
$= (16.2597)(10^{-4+8})$	Product of powers
$= 16.2597 \times 10^{4}$	Not scientific notation
$= 1.62597 \times 10^{1} \times 10^{4}$	
$= 1.62597 \times 10^{5}$	Scientific notation

Work in small groups to solve the following problems. Write all answers in scientific notation.

1. Multiply: 7.93×10^{14}
   $(6.1 \times 10^{4})(1.3 \times 10^{10})$
2. Divide: $\frac{8.534 \times 10^{6}}{3.4 \times 10^{2}}$ 2.51×10^{4}
3. Divide: 7.5×10^{12}
   $\frac{4.2 \times 10^{8}}{5.6 \times 10^{-5}}$
4. Multiply: 7.37751×10^{-6}
   $(8.17 \times 10^{-4})(9.03 \times 10^{-3})$
5. Earth is 9.3×10^{7} miles from the sun. Neptune is 2.8×10^{9} miles from the sun. How many times farther from the sun is Neptune than Earth? about 3.0×10^{1} or 30 times
6. A light year is the distance light travels in one year. This distance is 5.8657×10^{12} miles. If the Andromeda Galaxy is 2.2×10^{6} light years away from Earth, how many miles away from Earth is it? about 1.3×10^{19} miles
7. Using the distance light travels in a year given in Exercise 6, find the speed of light in miles per second. Use 1 year = 365 days. about 1.86×10^{5} miles per second
8. Using the information given in Exercise 5 and your answer to Exercise 7, determine how long, in seconds, it takes light to travel from the sun to Earth. about 5×10^{2} or 500 seconds

Cooperative Problem Solving

Problem A sweetheart decided to give his valentine a special gift for Valentine's Day. For each day in February, he would double the value of the present he gave her on the previous day. If he gave her a \$5 gift on February 1st, how much is the value of the gift on February 14th? Split students into groups of about three students. They should be able to explain in writing how they solved the problem and how they figured out that the 14th day the sweetheart's valentine would receive a gift worth $5(2^{14-1})$ or \$40,960.

Interactive Bulletin Board

Science Connection

Curious Facts

Largest

Smallest

mass of a bee hummingbird 3.5×10^{-3} pound

mass of earth 6.5856×10^{21} tons

Purpose Provide practice in using scientific notation.

How to Use It Have students use encyclopedias or the *Guinness Book of World Records* to find very large or very small numbers and to make or find a picture in a magazine to show their curious fact. Students should write the number in scientific notation. Each day a different student should bring their fact to the class, discuss it briefly, and add it to the bulletin board.

Outside Resources

Books/Periodicals
Mathematics for the Middle Grades (5-9), 1982 Yearbook, NCTM

Films/Videotapes
Dividing with Fractions—Reciprocals, Silver Burdett

Software
More Teasers From Tobbs, Sunburst

Technology

There are three pages in the ***Technology Masters Booklet*** that involve technology with concepts in this chapter. One page involves calculators and one page has a problem that can be solved using the BASIC program that is provided. Students should evaluate the information they obtain from running the program and solve a similar problem by extending the program.

Using the Chapter Opener

Transparency 6-0 is available in the Transparency Package. It provides a full-color visual and motivational activity that you can use to engage students in the mathematical content of the chapter.

Using Manipulatives

Have several fossils of plants and animals available for student examination. Ask students how they would tell how old the fossil is. Explain radiocarbon dating. Work with students to develop definitions for ***radioactive*** (emits radiation) and ***isotope*** (has the same number of protons as any other atom of the same element, but differs in number of neutrons and thus differs in atomic mass).

The half-life of carbon-14 is 5730 years.

CHAPTER OBJECTIVES

In this chapter you will learn to:

- compare and order rational numbers expressed as fractions and decimals
- multiply and divide rational numbers
- solve equations and inequalities with rational numbers
- find terms of a geometric sequence
- use deductive and inductive reasoning

Rationals: Multiplying and Dividing Patterns

Archaeologists can learn a lot studying animal fossils. One question they always have is, "When was this animal alive?" A good way to find out is to use radiocarbon dating.

All living things contain a radioactive isotope of carbon called carbon-14. When an animal dies, the carbon-14 in its body begins very slowly to change, or decay, into nitrogen-14. When we find the fossilized body many thousands of years later, some of the carbon-14 is still there. By comparing the amounts of carbon-14 and nitrogen-14 in the fossil, we can estimate how long ago the animal died. The graph shows the rate at which carbon-14 decays into nitrogen-14.

How long does it take for half of the carbon-14 to become nitrogen-14? (This is known as the half-life of carbon-14.)

5730 years

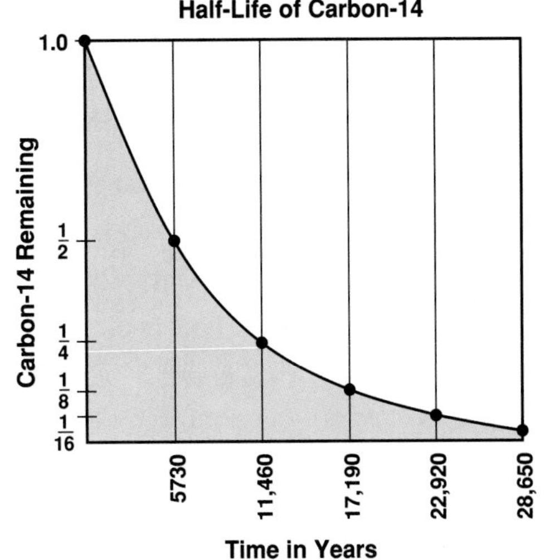

Class Project

Do research to find other methods that are used to estimate the age of objects, such as rocks, that are not suitable for carbon-14 dating.

Chemistry Connection

Earth science books and encyclopedias have information on dating Earth's materials. One common method of dating involves the use of index fossils. In this method, fossils of known organisms that existed for only a short geological time can be used to date rocks in which the fossils are found. Another common method is relative age, which uses the fact that, in general, rocks near Earth's surface are younger than rocks beneath them.

After researching, students may prepare and display posters showing various dating methods.

Looking Ahead

You may want to have the following materials available to use in this chapter.

Exploration, p. 208
calculator

Algebra in Action, p. 236
basketball
computer
spreadsheet software

5-Minute Check
(over Chapter 5)

Rename each decimal as a fraction or mixed number in simplest form.

1. 0.4 $\frac{2}{5}$
2. $1.\overline{6}$ $1\frac{2}{3}$
3. -2.45 $-2\frac{9}{20}$

Solve each equation.

4. $m = 3.9 - (-2.6)$ 6.5
5. $-4.1 + 5.7 = x$ 1.6

Transparency 6-1 contains the 5-Minute Check and a teaching aid for this lesson.

1 FOCUS

The purpose of this lesson is to use calculators to rename fractions as decimals.

Motivating the Lesson

Have students brainstorm a list of situations in which fractions are easy to use, such as measuring length. Make another list of situations in which decimals are more practical, such as working with money.

2 TEACH

Using Calculators

Have students determine decimal values for the six house parts in the lesson chart. Have students use calculators on half the calculations and paper and pencil on the other half. Discuss ease of comparison of the resulting decimals.

EE: 1E, 2D, 3A
TAAS: 1

6-1 Writing Fractions as Decimals

Objective:
Write fractions as terminating or repeating decimals.

Key Terms:
terminating
repeating

Much of the energy consumed in the United States is used for heating buildings. Some of this energy is lost because buildings lose heat through their exteriors. The chart below shows the fraction of heat lost from different parts of a house.

Part of House	Fraction of Total Heat Loss
Exterior walls	$\frac{1}{8}$
Ceiling	$\frac{3}{8}$
Doors	$\frac{1}{20}$
Windows	$\frac{3}{25}$
Basement	$\frac{2}{25}$
Air leakage	$\frac{1}{4}$

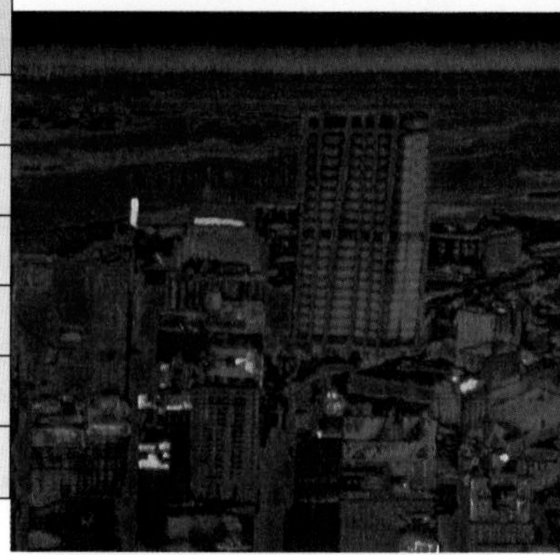

Which part accounts for the greatest heat loss? **ceiling**

It is sometimes more convenient to write numbers as decimals instead of fractions. One reason is that it is easier to compare with decimals. It may also be more convenient to use decimals when computing with a calculator.

Consider the fraction $\frac{1}{4}$. Remember that a fraction is another way of writing a division problem. So, $\frac{1}{4}$ means 1 ÷ 4. Divide using a calculator.

1 [÷] 4 [=] 0.25

Any fraction can be expressed as a decimal by dividing the numerator by the denominator.

$$\frac{1}{4} \Rightarrow \begin{array}{r} 0.25 \\ 4\overline{)1.00} \\ -8 \\ \hline 20 \\ -20 \\ \hline 0 \end{array}$$

Annex zeros to the numerator. 1 = 1.00

FYI

A thermogram is a photograph-like image of a building that shows areas that are emitting large amounts of heat. The red areas show maximum heat loss. Usually these are areas where more insulation is needed.

The fraction $\frac{1}{4}$ can be expressed as the decimal 0.25. Remember that a decimal like 0.25 is called a **terminating decimal** because the division ends or terminates when the remainder is zero.

Bell Ringer

Find the next problem that follows the same pattern.

$\begin{array}{r} 13 \\ \times 17 \\ \hline 221 \end{array}$ $\begin{array}{r} 25 \\ \times 25 \\ \hline 625 \end{array}$ $\begin{array}{r} 34 \\ \times 36 \\ \hline 1224 \end{array}$ $\begin{array}{r} 42 \\ \times 48 \\ \hline 2016 \end{array}$

Examples

1 **Express $\frac{2}{5}$ as a decimal.**

Use a calculator.

2 [÷] 5 [=] 0.4

$\frac{2}{5} = 0.4$

Use paper and pencil.

$\frac{2}{5}$ ➡ $5\overline{)2.0}$ = 0.4

2 **Express $2\frac{3}{8}$ as a decimal.**

Use a calculator.

$2\frac{3}{8} = 2 + \frac{3}{8}$

2 [+] 3 [÷] 8 [=] 2.375

$2\frac{3}{8} = 2.375$

Use paper and pencil.

Consider only $\frac{3}{8}$.

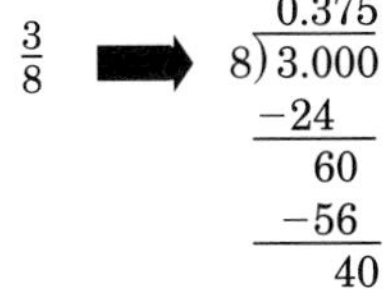

$\frac{3}{8}$ ➡ $8\overline{)3.000}$ = 0.375; −24, 60, −56, 40

$2 + 0.375 = 2.375$

An alternative strategy is to first write $2\frac{3}{8}$ as the improper fraction $\frac{19}{8}$. What decimal is equivalent to $\frac{19}{8}$? **2.375**

Not all fractions can be expressed as terminating decimals. Consider the fraction $\frac{1}{3}$. How can $\frac{1}{3}$ be expressed as a decimal? Use a calculator to divide.

1 [÷] 3 [=] 0.3333333

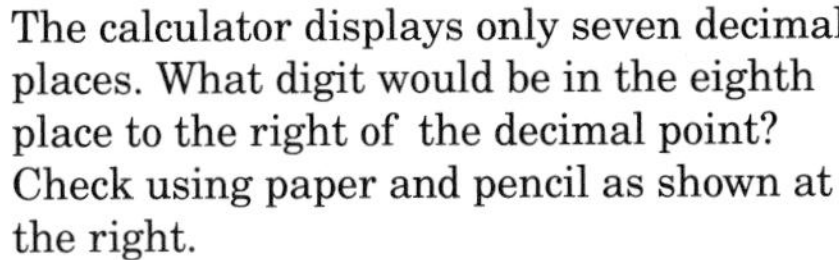

The calculator displays only seven decimal places. What digit would be in the eighth place to the right of the decimal point? Check using paper and pencil as shown at the right.

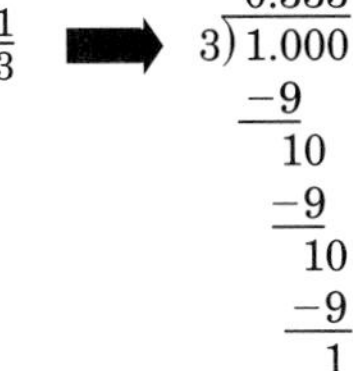

$\frac{1}{3}$ ➡ $3\overline{)1.000}$ = 0.333; −9, 10, −9, 10, −9, 1

Notice that the remainder after each step is 1. If you continue dividing, the pattern will repeat. Therefore, the digit 3 will be in the eighth place and will continue indefinitely.

Remember that a decimal like 0.333333 . . . , or $0.\overline{3}$, is called a **repeating decimal.**

Chalkboard Examples

- *For Example 1*
  Express $\frac{4}{5}$ as a decimal. 0.8
- *For Example 2*
  Express $1\frac{7}{8}$ as a decimal. 1.875
- *For Example 3*
  Express $\frac{2}{9}$ as a decimal. $0.\overline{2}$
- *For Example 4*
  Express $-3\frac{1}{9}$ as a decimal. $-3.\overline{1}$

Alternate Strategies: Reteaching the Lesson

Reteaching Activity

Using Models After modeling additional problems, have each student find a fraction-decimal equivalent. Have students make up a matching test using student problems. Have students take the test as a practice test.

Reteaching Masters Booklet, p. 45

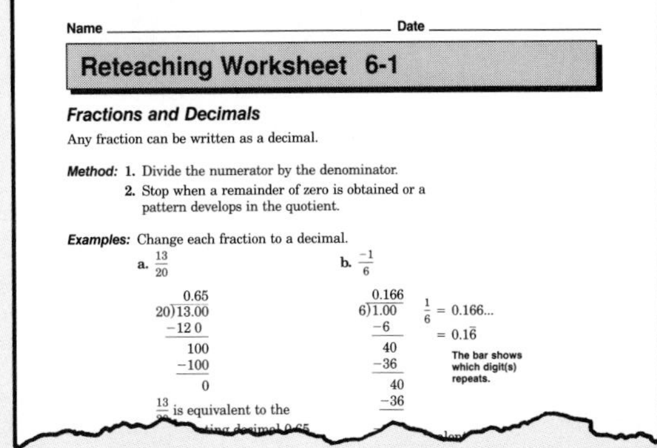

Name ______________ Date ______________

Reteaching Worksheet 6-1

Fractions and Decimals

Any fraction can be written as a decimal.

Method: 1. Divide the numerator by the denominator.
2. Stop when a remainder of zero is obtained or a pattern develops in the quotient.

Examples: Change each fraction to a decimal.

a. $\frac{13}{20}$ — $20\overline{)13.00}$ = 0.65; −12 0, 100, −100, 0

b. $\frac{-1}{6}$ — $6\overline{)1.00}$ = 0.166; −6, 40, −36, 40, −36

$\frac{1}{6} = 0.166...$
$= 0.1\overline{6}$

The bar shows which digit(s) repeats.

$\frac{13}{20}$ is equivalent to the

3 PRACTICE/APPLY

Checking the Concept

Have students use paper and pencil to work Exercises 10-19. Allow students to use a calculator to check their answers.

Error Analysis

Watch for students who divide the denominator by the numerator. **Prevent by** having students read the fraction as a division problem, emphasizing that the fraction is read from top to bottom.

Practice Masters Booklet, **p. 50**

Calculator Hint

Some calculators round answers and others truncate answers. *Truncate* means to cut off at a certain place-value position, ignoring the digits that follow. Does your calculator round or truncate?

Examples

3 Express $\frac{5}{9}$ as a decimal.

Use a calculator.

5 ÷ 9 = 0.5555556

The calculator rounds.

5 ÷ 9 = 0.5555555

The calculator truncates.

$\frac{5}{9} = 0.555\ldots$ or $0.\overline{5}$

Use paper and pencil.

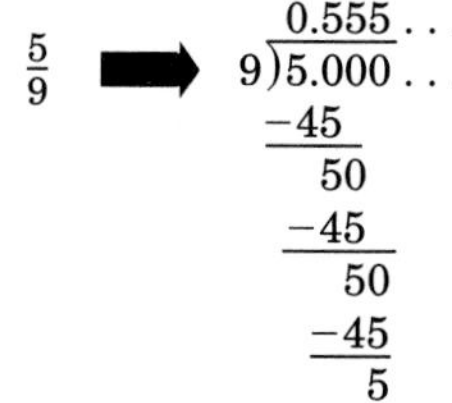

4 Express $-5\frac{2}{3}$ as a decimal.

Use a calculator.

$-5\frac{2}{3} = -(5 + \frac{2}{3})$

5 + 2 ÷ 3 = 5.6666667
+/- −5.6666667

$-5\frac{2}{3} = -5.666\ldots$ or $-5.\overline{6}$

Use paper and pencil.

Consider only $\frac{2}{3}$.

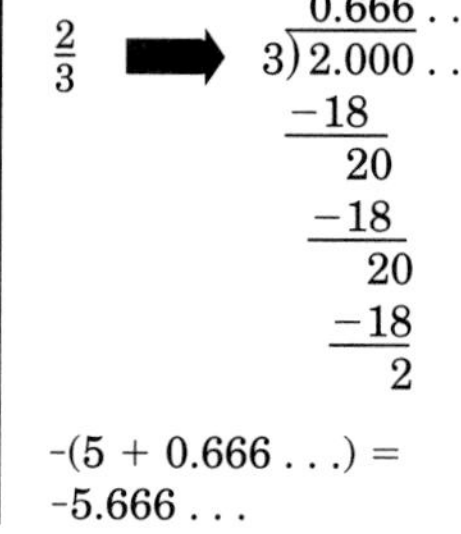

$-(5 + 0.666\ldots) = -5.666\ldots$

Checking for Understanding

1. Divide the numerator by the denominator.

Communicating Algebra

1. In your own words, explain how to express a fraction as a decimal.
2. Give two examples of fractions that can be expressed as terminating decimals. Give two examples that can be expressed as repeating decimals. Sample answers: $\frac{2}{5}, \frac{3}{4}; \frac{1}{3}, \frac{1}{6}$

Express each decimal using bar notation.

3. 0.85858585 . . . $0.\overline{85}$
4. 0.0023232323 . . . $0.00\overline{23}$
5. 0.833333333 . . . $0.8\overline{3}$

Write the first ten decimal places. See margin.

6. $0.1\overline{8}$
7. $0.\overline{846}$
8. $0.\overline{0528}$
9. $0.0\overline{528}$

Guided Practice

Express each fraction as a decimal. Use a bar to show a repeating decimal.

10. $\frac{1}{2}$ 0.5
11. $-\frac{1}{3}$ $-0.\overline{3}$
12. $-\frac{3}{4}$ −0.75
13. $\frac{1}{8}$ 0.125
14. $\frac{2}{3}$ $0.\overline{6}$
15. $-\frac{1}{6}$ $-0.1\overline{6}$
16. $\frac{5}{8}$ 0.625
17. $-2\frac{5}{6}$ $-2.8\overline{3}$
18. $\frac{2}{9}$ $0.\overline{2}$
19. $1\frac{7}{10}$ 1.7

Additional Answers

6. 0.1888888888
7. 0. 8468468468
8. 0.0528052805
9. 0.0528528528
50. Multiply 4.95 by 17 and divide by 8. The result is 42.075 which would round to $42.08.

Name ______________ Date ______________

Practice Worksheet 6-1

Fractions and Decimals

Express each fraction as a decimal. Use a bar to show a repeating decimal.

1. $\frac{4}{5}$ 0.8	2. $\frac{9}{25}$ 0.36	3. $6\frac{5}{20}$ 6.25
4. $\frac{9}{16}$ 0.5625	5. $\frac{8}{9}$ $0.\overline{8}$	6. $\frac{10}{11}$ $0.\overline{90}$
7. $\frac{17}{3}$ $5.\overline{6}$	8. $\frac{5}{12}$ $0.41\overline{6}$	9. $\frac{3}{11}$ $0.\overline{27}$
10. $\frac{7}{33}$ $0.\overline{21}$	11. $\frac{16}{45}$ $0.3\overline{5}$	12. $\frac{18}{25}$ 0.72
13. $5\frac{1}{9}$ $5.\overline{1}$	14. $\frac{2}{15}$ $0.1\overline{3}$	15. $\frac{8}{125}$ 0.064
16. $\frac{47}{333}$ $0.\overline{141}$	17. $\frac{97}{25}$ 3.88	18. $\frac{70}{999}$ $0.0\overline{700}$
19. $\frac{4}{9}$ $0.\overline{4}$	20. $-\frac{3}{4}$ -0.75	21. $\frac{5}{8}$ 0.625
22. $2\frac{8}{9}$ $2.\overline{8}$	23. $-1\frac{2}{3}$ $-1.\overline{6}$	24. $-\frac{7}{12}$ $-0.58\overline{3}$
25. $3\frac{7}{8}$ 3.875	26. $-\frac{5}{6}$ $-0.8\overline{3}$	27. $4\frac{3}{11}$ $4.\overline{27}$
28. $-\frac{19}{20}$ -0.95	29. $5\frac{11}{18}$ $5.6\overline{1}$	30. $-1\frac{19}{25}$ -1.76
31. $\frac{5}{33}$ $0.\overline{15}$	32. $-\frac{28}{45}$ $-0.6\overline{2}$	33. $3\frac{11}{12}$ $3.91\overline{6}$

Exercises

Independent Practice

Express each fraction as a decimal. Use a bar to show a repeating decimal.

20. $\frac{2}{5}$ 0.4
21. $\frac{7}{10}$ 0.7
22. $\frac{12}{25}$ 0.48
23. $-\frac{3}{8}$ −0.375
24. $\frac{11}{20}$ 0.55
25. $\frac{1}{9}$ $0.\overline{1}$
26. $\frac{3}{11}$ $0.\overline{27}$
27. $\frac{7}{18}$ $0.3\overline{8}$
28. $7\frac{3}{4}$ 7.75
29. $\frac{7}{16}$ 0.4375
30. $\frac{2}{3}$ $0.\overline{6}$
31. $2\frac{5}{9}$ $2.\overline{5}$
32. $\frac{7}{9}$ $0.\overline{7}$
33. $\frac{5}{9}$ $0.\overline{5}$
34. $\frac{10}{33}$ $0.\overline{30}$
35. $\frac{23}{45}$ $0.5\overline{1}$
36. $\frac{28}{45}$ $0.6\overline{2}$
37. $2\frac{9}{16}$ 2.5625
38. $-4\frac{5}{16}$ −4.3125
39. $\frac{31}{40}$ 0.775

Calculator

Exercises 40-43 give several different calculators' displays for 1 ÷ 6. What would each calculator display for 8 ÷ 9?

40. .16666666 .88888888
41. 0.1666666 0.8888888
42. 0.1666667 0.8888889
43. .17 .89

Mixed Review

44. State whether $\frac{-5r}{s}$ is a monomial. (Lesson 4-1) no
45. Find the product $(mn^3)(mp)(n^2p^2)$. (Lesson 4-9) $m^2n^5p^3$
46. *True* or *false:* $7.43 < 7.5$. (Lesson 5-1) true
47. Round 26.549 to the nearest tenth. (Lesson 5-3) 26.5

Solve each equation. (Lessons 5-5, 5-7)

48. $x = \frac{32}{21} - \frac{14}{21}$ $\frac{6}{7}$
49. $b - \frac{5}{8} < 3\frac{1}{2}$ $b < 4\frac{1}{8}$

Applications

50. **Consumer Awareness** Sarah bought $2\frac{1}{8}$ yards of fabric at $4.95 per yard. Explain how you could find the total cost using your calculator. See margin.
51. **Business** On Tuesday, XYZ stock fell $1\frac{5}{8}$ points. This means that the price of the stock dropped $\$1\frac{5}{8}$. Express this amount in dollars and cents. $1.625 or $1.63

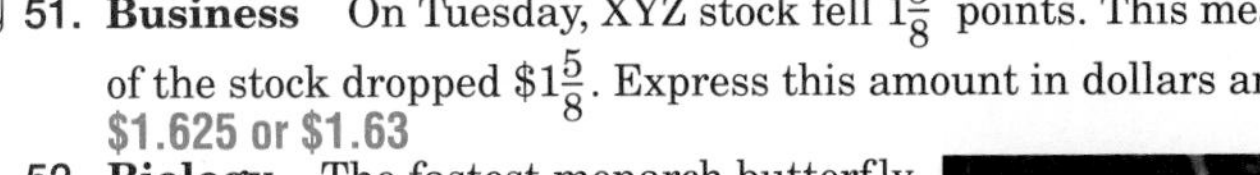

52. **Biology** The fastest monarch butterfly can fly $\frac{1}{3}$ mile in one minute. Express $\frac{1}{3}$ as a decimal rounded to the nearest hundredth. 0.33

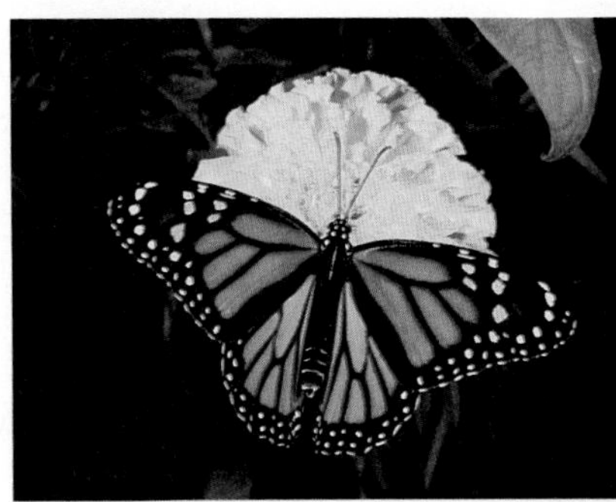

Critical Thinking

53. Find a terminating decimal that lies between $\frac{1}{3}$ and $\frac{5}{9}$ on a number line. Sample answer: $\frac{2}{5}$

Wrap-Up

54. Express $\frac{1}{11}, \frac{2}{11}, \ldots, \frac{10}{11}$ as decimals. Explain the pattern you have found. $0.\overline{09}, 0.\overline{18}, 0.\overline{27}, 0.\overline{36}, \ldots 0.\overline{90}$; The repeating digits are multiples of 9.

Enrichment

Are there decimals that neither terminate nor repeat? Consider the decimal 0.101001000100001000001 . . . . It is constructed by writing a 1 followed by a 0, then a 1 followed by two 0s. Certainly this decimal is well-defined in that you can determine the digit in any decimal place. Yet it is non-terminating, non-repeating. Can you write another decimal that is non-terminating, non-repeating?
Sample answer: 0.101101110 . . .

Independent Practice

Homework Assignment	
Basic	21-43 odd, 44-50, 53, 54
Average	24-42 even, 44-54
Honors	34-54

4 CLOSE

Assessment Option

Writing Express the following fractions as decimals. Use a calculator or paper and pencil.

1. $\frac{3}{10}$ 0.3
2. $\frac{5}{8}$ 0.625
3. $\frac{2}{9}$ $0.\overline{2}$
4. $1\frac{2}{5}$ 1.4

Enrichment Masters Booklet, **p. 45**

Name ______ Date ______

Enrichment Worksheet 6-1

Decimals in Sports

Many sports use decimals to show how well a team or player is doing statistically. You will need to change fractions to decimals to answer the questions below.

Solve each problem. Use a bar to show a repeating digit.

1. Cindy make 12 of 15 free throw attempts in the last basketball game. As a decimal, what was her success rate? 0.8
2. Andy carried the football eight times, but gained only five yards. How many yards per carry did he average? 0.625 yard
3. Julio plays shortstop and had only seven errors in the 105 times the baseball was hit to him. Express his error rate as a decimal. $0.0\overline{6}$
4. Fay's tennis team won six of nine games in May, but then won four and lost twenty the rest of the season. Use a decimal to show the fraction of games won during the entire season. $\frac{10}{33} = 0.\overline{30}$
5. Arnie putted only 25 times in his last round of golf (18 holes). As a decimal, what was his average number of putts per hole? 1.38 putts
6. Diana bowled 35 games last year and got a total of 203 strikes. How many strikes per game did she average? 5.8 strikes

A baseball pitcher's earned run average (ERA) is the number of runs allowed per nine-inning game. To compute this average, the number of earned runs is divided by the quotient of the number of innings pitched and 9.

Example: Find Alex's ERA if he allowed 5 earned runs in 18 total innings.

$5 \div \frac{18}{9} = 5 \div 2 = 2.5$ runs per game

7. Find Gregg's earned run average if he allowed 44 earned runs in 200 innings. 1.98 runs per game
8. What is Carla's earned run average if she allowed 35 earned runs in 150 innings? 2.1 runs per game

Alternate Strategies: Extending the Lesson

Enrichment

Using Models Have students create a fraction for each domino in a set except ones containing blanks. Then have students rename each fraction as a decimal. Ask students to look for a pattern to tell whether a fraction will be a terminating or repeating decimal.

Cooperative Learning

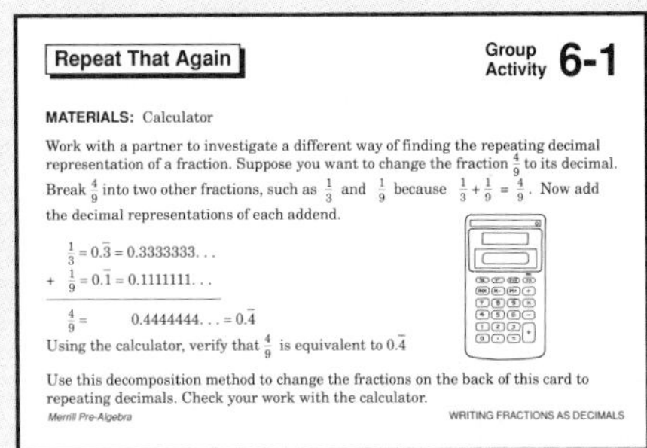

Repeat That Again Group Activity **6-1**

MATERIALS: Calculator

Work with a partner to investigate a different way of finding the repeating decimal representation of a fraction. Suppose you want to change the fraction $\frac{4}{9}$ to its decimal. Break $\frac{4}{9}$ into two other fractions, such as $\frac{1}{3}$ and $\frac{1}{9}$ because $\frac{1}{3} + \frac{1}{9} = \frac{4}{9}$. Now add the decimal representations of each addend.

$\frac{1}{3} = 0.\overline{3} = 0.3333333\ldots$

$+\ \frac{1}{9} = 0.\overline{1} = 0.1111111\ldots$

$\frac{4}{9} = \quad 0.4444444\ldots = 0.\overline{4}$

Using the calculator, verify that $\frac{4}{9}$ is equivalent to $0.\overline{4}$

Use this decomposition method to change the fractions on the back of this card to repeating decimals. Check your work with the calculator.

Merrill Pre-Algebra WRITING FRACTIONS AS DECIMALS

EXPLORATION:
Decimal Patterns

Objective Students will investigate patterns in terminating and repeating decimals.

1 FOCUS

Motivating the Exploration

List the ninths $\left(\frac{1}{9}, \frac{2}{9}, \frac{3}{9}, \ldots\right)$ on the chalkboard and ask students to rewrite each as a decimal.

2 TEACH

Using Charts

Have students create a 3-column chart. Then have them label the columns "Fraction," "Decimal," and "T or R" (for terminating or repeating).

3 PRACTICE/APPLY

Using Cooperative Groups

Have students add a column to their charts and label it "Prime Factorization of the Denominator." Have groups divide up the work for completing this column. Then have groups answer Exercise 2. Have each group test their findings on a unit fraction they have not already renamed.

4 CLOSE

Using Questioning

Have students rename multiples of fractions having denominators of 7, 13, and 17. Ask students the questions below.

- What is the most number of places that a fraction with a denominator of 7 can have in the repeat? 6 a denominator of 13? 12 of 17? 16

Have students write a generalization statement based on the answers.

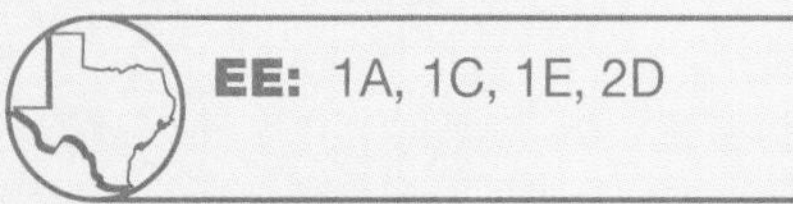
EE: 1A, 1C, 1E, 2D

Exploration
Decimal Patterns

Materials: calculator

Every fraction can be expressed as either a terminating or repeating decimal. In this Exploration, you will look for a pattern that will help you identify whether the decimal for a given fraction terminates or repeats.

Explore: Use a calculator to express each fraction $\frac{1}{2}, \frac{1}{3}, \frac{1}{4}, \ldots, \frac{1}{20}$ as a decimal.

Here are some examples.

▶ $\frac{1}{8}$ → 1 ÷ 8 = 0.125

The decimal terminates.

▶ $\frac{1}{12}$ → 1 ÷ 12 = 0.0833333

The decimal repeats.

Your Turn: **Express each fraction $\frac{1}{2}, \frac{1}{3}, \ldots, \frac{1}{20}$ as a decimal. Identify each decimal as terminating or repeating. Keep track of your results in a chart.** See Solutions Manual.

Analysis

1. Have you discovered a pattern? If so, write a sentence that describes it. See margin.
2. If you haven't discovered a pattern, try finding the prime factorization of each denominator. Look for a pattern in the prime factorizations. Write a sentence that describes the pattern. See margin.
3. Suppose one of your classmates predicts that $\frac{1}{30}$ can be expressed as a terminating decimal. Do you agree? Write a sentence that explains your reasoning. No. The prime factorization of 30 is 2 • 3 • 5; since it has a 3 as a factor, the decimal repeats.

SET-UP

Materials

- calculators

You may wish to use the Exploration worksheet provided on page 42 of the Lab Manual.

For Students Each student or group of students will need a calculator.

For the Overhead Projector You may wish to show the long division for $\frac{1}{17}$ and $\frac{1}{19}$ on the overhead to save time.

Additional Answers

1. Sample answer: The denominator of fractions greater than $\frac{1}{4}$ that terminate is a multiple of 5 or 8.
2. Sample answer: The denominator of fractions that terminate have prime factors of only 2 and /or 5.

6-2 Estimating Products and Quotients

Objective: Estimate products and quotients of rational numbers.

Key Term: compatible numbers

Marta solves this problem using a calculator.

56.3 [×] 1.25 [÷] 9.1 [=]

The display reads 77.335165.
Is this the correct answer? You can use estimation to determine if an answer is reasonable.

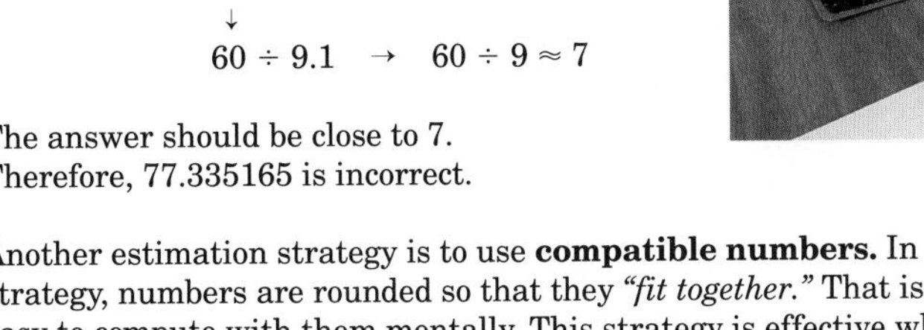

$$\begin{array}{r} 56.3 \\ \times\ 1.25 \end{array} \rightarrow \begin{array}{r} 60 \\ \times\ 1 \\ \hline 60 \end{array}$$ Round each factor to its greatest place-value position.

$60 \div 9.1 \rightarrow 60 \div 9 \approx 7$

What mistake might Marta have made? **She might have forgotten to enter the decimal point in 56.3.**

The answer should be close to 7.
Therefore, 77.335165 is incorrect.

Another estimation strategy is to use **compatible numbers.** In this strategy, numbers are rounded so that they *"fit together."* That is, it is easy to compute with them mentally. This strategy is effective when estimating the product of a fraction and a whole number. For example, estimate the product of $\frac{1}{3}$ and 11.

$\frac{1}{3} \times 11 = ■$ The denominator tells how many equal parts. THINK: What is $\frac{1}{3}$ of 11?

$\frac{1}{3} \times 12 = 4$ The nearest multiple of 3 is 12. 3 and 12 are compatible numbers.

The product of $\frac{1}{3}$ and 11 is about 4.

History Connection

One of the most common customary measurements, the mile, originated as an estimate. Historically, a mile was defined as the distance covered by a Roman soldier in 1000 double steps. Notice the similarity between the words *mile* and *mille*, meaning 1000.

Examples

Estimate each product.

1 $\frac{2}{5} \times 49$

$\frac{2}{5} \times 49 \rightarrow \frac{2}{5} \times 50$

THINK: $\frac{1}{5}$ of 50 is 10.
$\frac{2}{5}$ of 50 is 20.

$\frac{2}{5} \times 49$ is about 20.

2 $\frac{25}{49} \times 180$

THINK: $\frac{25}{49}$ is about $\frac{1}{2}$.

$\frac{25}{49} \times 180 \rightarrow \frac{1}{2} \times 180$

THINK: $\frac{1}{2}$ of 180 is 90.

$\frac{25}{49} \times 180$ is about 90.

Lesson Notes 6-2

5-Minute Check (over Lesson 6-1)

Express each fraction as a decimal. Use a bar to show a repeating decimal.

1. $\frac{3}{5}$ 0.6
2. $\frac{5}{8}$ 0.625
3. $\frac{31}{45}$ $0.6\overline{8}$
4. $-6\frac{4}{9}$ $-6.\overline{4}$

Transparency 6-2 contains the 5-Minute Check and a teaching aid for this lesson.

1 FOCUS

The purpose of this lesson is to extend estimation skills to the multiplication and division of rational numbers.

2 TEACH

Chalkboard Examples

Estimate each product.

- *For Example 1* $\frac{1}{3} \times 28$ about 10
- *For Example 2* $\frac{7}{27} \times 200$ about 50

Practice Masters Booklet, **p. 51**

Name ____________ Date ____________

Practice Worksheet 6-2

Estimating Products and Quotients

Estimate each product or quotient. Sample answers given.

1. 18.87 × 7.6 160	2. 3.19 × 2.6 9	3. 60.3 × 4.05 240
4. 28.9 × 6.6 210	5. 8.29 × 7.1 56	6. 9.7 × 89.7 900
7. 10.16 × 4.8 50	8. 9.6 × 9.6 100	9. 4.37 × 25.4 100
10. 47.56 ÷ 2.9 16	11. 10.4 ÷ 9.67 1	12. 6.82 ÷ 7.09 1
13. 29.61 ÷ 5.4 6	14. 56 ÷ 8.4 7	15. 80.3 ÷ 20.2 4
16. $16.25 ÷ 3.8 $4	17. $45 ÷ 8.75 $5	18. $27.50 ÷ 6.67 $4
19. $\frac{1}{3} \times 8$ 3	20. $\frac{1}{4} \times 15$ 4	21. $\frac{1}{5} \times 29$ 6
22. $\frac{2}{3} \times 13$ 8	23. $\frac{3}{4} \times 19$ 15	24. $\frac{3}{5} \times 26$ 15
25. $\frac{4}{9} \times 19$ 8	26. $\frac{5}{6} \times 35$ 30	27. $\frac{4}{7} \times 61$ 36
28. $\frac{7}{8} \times 73$ 63	29. $\frac{3}{11} \times 20$ 6	30. $\frac{10}{31} \times 66$ 20
31. $\frac{8}{19} \times 100$ 40	32. $\frac{11}{14} \times 30$ 22	33. $\frac{43}{50} \times 300$ 240

Bell Ringer

Express each fraction as a decimal.
1. four tenths 0.4
2. nine elevenths $0.\overline{81}$

Reteaching Masters Booklet, **p. 46**

Name ____________ Date ____________

Reteaching Worksheet 6-2

Estimating Products and Quotients

Multiplication Round each factor to its greatest place-value position. Do *not* change 1-digit factors. Then multiply.

$18.034 \rightarrow 20$; $\times\ 0.65 \rightarrow \times\ 0.7$; 14

Division Round the divisor to its greatest place-value position. Do *not* change 1-digit divisors. Round the dividend so it is a multiple of the divisor. Then divide.

$0.69\overline{)0.489}$ $\quad 0.7\overline{)0.49}$ = 0.7

Estimate each product or quotient. Sample answers given.

1.	2.	3.	4.	5.
2.7 × 8.1 = 24	9.32 × 6.5 = 63	3.06 × 19.1 = 60	8.53 × 4.86 = 45	75.61 × 1.09 = 80

EE: 1E, 2D, 3A, 4B
TAAS: 1, 8, 9, 10

3 PRACTICE/APPLY

Checking the Concept

After completing Exercises 2 and 4, have students do the actual multiplication and use the estimate to place the decimal point.

Error Analysis
Watch for students who have difficulty changing the dividend to a multiple of the divisor. **Prevent by** modeling several problems illustrating at least one in which the dividend is increased and one in which the dividend is decreased.

Independent Practice

Homework Assignment	
Basic	9-21 odd, 23-29
Average	8-22 even, 23-29
Honors	10-18 even, 20-29

4 CLOSE

Assessment Option

Writing Have students write about a situation where they had to estimate the product or quotient of rational numbers.

Enrichment Masters Booklet, **p. 46**

Name ______________________ Date ______________

Enrichment Worksheet 6-2

Estimating Fractional Products

Find the best estimate of the product from the list at the right. Write the corresponding letter to the right of each exercise.

1. A little more than $\frac{1}{3}$ of 1488 E
2. A little less than $\frac{3}{4}$ of 1635 I
3. A little less than $\frac{1}{5}$ of 462 C
4. A little more than $\frac{1}{7}$ of 1326 O
5. Very close to $\frac{2}{3}$ of 922 M
6. A little less than $\frac{5}{6}$ of 1871 H
7. A little less than $\frac{5}{8}$ of 1729 T
8. A little more than $\frac{1}{9}$ of 861 A
9. A little more than $\frac{5}{3}$ of 1298 F
10. Very close to $\frac{3}{7}$ of 2079 K
11. A little less than $\frac{1}{4}$ of 2866 U
12. A little more than $\frac{1}{10}$ of 1292 N
13. A little less than $\frac{1}{8}$ of 428 S
14. A little more than $\frac{2}{9}$ of 3549 R

A	100
C	90
E	500
F	2000
H	1500
I	1200
K	900
M	615
N	130
O	200
R	800
S	50
T	1000
U	700

Place the letters from the answers above on the blanks with the corresponding exercise number below them.

The best way to make a fire with two sticks is to ...

M	A	K	E		S	U	R	E		O	N	E		O	F
5	8	10	1		13	11	14	1		4	12	1		4	9

T	H	E	M		I	S		A		M	A	T	C	H
7	6	1	5		2	13		8		5	8	7	3	6

Will Rogers

Checking for Understanding

Communicating Algebra

1. Explain why estimation is an important step when computing answers with a calculator. See margin.

Guided Practice

Rewrite each problem as you would to estimate using rounding. Then estimate each product or quotient.

2. 4.61×1.9 $5 \times 2; 10$
3. $35 \div 7.3$ $35 \div 7; 5$
4. $5.8 \div 2.29$ $6 \div 2; 3$

Rewrite each problem as you would to estimate using compatible numbers. Then estimate each product.

5. $\frac{1}{3} \times 5$ $\frac{1}{3} \times 6; 2$
6. $\frac{8}{23} \times 9$ $\frac{1}{3} \times 9; 3$
7. $\frac{1}{2} \times 10\frac{1}{8}$ $\frac{1}{2} \times 10; 5$

Exercises

Independent Practice

Estimate each product or quotient. Sample answers given.

8. 15.93×9.8 160
9. 2.49×1.9 4
10. 59.1×2.09 120
11. $18.20 \div 2.7$ \$6
12. $27.26 \div 2.6$ 9
13. $8.1 \div 2.2$ 4
14. $\frac{1}{3} \times 5$ 2
15. $\frac{1}{4} \times 13$ 3
16. $\frac{1}{5} \times 24$ 5
17. $\frac{5}{6} \times 10$ 8
18. $\frac{2}{3} \times 16$ 10
19. $\frac{5}{9} \times 20$ 10
20. $\frac{9}{19} \times 120$ 60
21. $\frac{10}{14} \times 30$ 20
22. $\frac{31}{40} \times 200$ 150

Mixed Review

23. State the least prime number that is a factor of 91. (Lesson 4-4) 7
24. Find the twelfth term in the arithmetic sequence 99, 90, 81, 72, ... (Lesson 5-9) 0
25. Express $3\frac{3}{8}$ as a decimal. (Lesson 6-1) 3.375

Application

26. **Biology** A dolphin can swim at a speed of 37 mph. A human can swim about one-eighth as fast. About how fast can a human swim? about 5 mph

Connection

27. **Geometry** The formula for the area of a rectangle is $A = \ell w$, where ℓ is the length and w is the width. If the length is 5.8 meters and the width is 3.1 meters, is the area less than or greater than 20 square meters? less than

Critical Thinking

28. Choose the correct phrase: The product of a whole number and a fraction less than one is always (less than, greater than, equal to) the whole number. less than

Wrap-Up

29. Write a problem involving decimals whose estimated answer is 3. Sample answer: Estimate $35.9 \div 12.005$.

Additional Answer

1. in case a wrong key is entered or the decimal point is not entered

Cooperative Learning

Up or Down Group Activity **6-2**

MATERIALS: Calculator

You and your partner can win points by giving the closer estimate of a product.

To begin, think of a number between 1 and 10 with one decimal place. Your partner thinks of a number between 20 and 80 with one decimal place. Then each person should estimate the product of the numbers. Compute the actual product using a calculator. The player whose estimate is closer to the exact product scores one point.

Play continues until one person is five points ahead of the other.

EXAMPLE: The problem is 9.8×54.3. You round both numbers up and mentally compute $10 \times 55 = 550$. You know this is high so you guess 545. Your partner estimates the product as 10×50 or 500 and makes an actual guess of 525. Using a calculator you get the exact product of 532.14. Your partner is closer; therefore, your partner scores a point.

Merrill Pre-Algebra ESTIMATING PRODUCTS AND QUOTIENTS

6-3 Rationals: Multiplying Fractions

Objective:
Multiply fractions.

About $\frac{1}{3}$ of Earth's land can be used for farming. About $\frac{2}{5}$ of this farmland is used to grow grain crops. What part of Earth's land is used to grow grain?

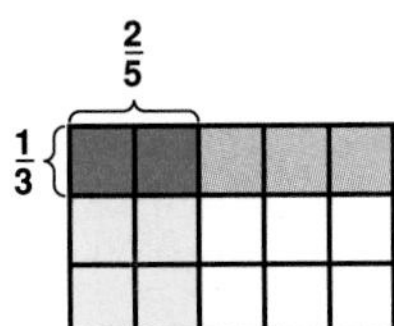

About $\frac{2}{5}$ of $\frac{1}{3}$, or $\frac{2}{15}$, of Earth's land is used to grow grain. You get the same result if you compute $\frac{2}{5} \cdot \frac{1}{3}$.

$$\frac{2}{5} \cdot \frac{1}{3} = \frac{2 \cdot 1}{5 \cdot 3}$$ Multiply the numerators. Multiply the denominators.

$$= \frac{2}{15}$$

Multiplying Fractions

In words: To multiply fractions, multiply the numerators and multiply the denominators.

In symbols: For fractions $\frac{a}{b}$ and $\frac{c}{d}$, where $b \neq 0$ and $d \neq 0$, $\frac{a}{b} \cdot \frac{c}{d} = \frac{ac}{bd}$.

FYI

Grain is one of the best sources of energy for people and animals. The eight most common grains are wheat, rice, corn, barley, sorghum, oats, rye, and millet.

Example

1 **Solve $x = \frac{5}{9} \cdot \frac{8}{15}$.**

Method 1

$x = \frac{5}{9} \cdot \frac{8}{15}$

$x = \frac{5 \cdot 8}{9 \cdot 15}$ Multiply.

$x = \frac{40}{135}$ or $\frac{8}{27}$ Simplify.

Method 2

$x = \frac{5}{9} \cdot \frac{8}{15}$

$x = \frac{\cancel{5}^{1}}{9} \cdot \frac{8}{\cancel{15}_{3}}$ The GCF of 5 and 15 is 5. Divide 5 and 15 by 5.

$x = \frac{1 \cdot 8}{9 \cdot 3}$ or $\frac{8}{27}$ Multiply.

Bell Ringer

Estimate each product or quotient.
1. 14.6×3.07 **45**
2. $\frac{3}{4} \times 11$ **9**
3. $10.25 \div 1.9$ **5**

Lesson Notes 6-3

5-Minute Check
(over Lesson 6-2)

Estimate each product or quotient.
1. 39.65×5.13 **200**
2. $\frac{1}{6} \times 37$ **6**
3. $798.67 \div 41$ **20**
4. $\frac{3}{8} \times 50$ **25**
5. $20.54 \div 2.6$ **7**

Transparency 6-3 contains the 5-Minute Check and a teaching aid for this lesson.

1 FOCUS

The purpose of this lesson is to use the concept of GCF to simplify multiplication of fractions.

Motivating the Lesson

Take a survey of the pets owned by members of the class. Write the results in fractional form on the chalkboard or overhead. For example, $\frac{6}{29}$ means that 6 out of 29 students own a certain type of pet. Predict the number of each type of pet in $\frac{1}{2}$, $\frac{1}{3}$, and $\frac{1}{4}$ of the class.

2 TEACH

Using Models

Use diagrams to model problems similar to the following. If $\frac{3}{5}$ of all fatal car accidents are caused by drinking, and teenagers are involved in $\frac{1}{3}$ of these, what fraction of fatal accidents are caused by teenagers drinking? $\frac{1}{5}$

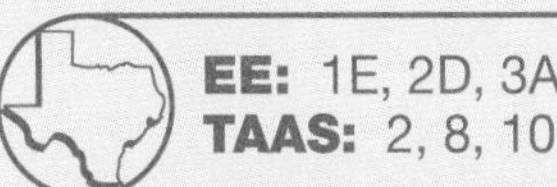

EE: 1E, 2D, 3A, 3D, 3H
TAAS: 2, 8, 10, 13

Chalkboard Examples

- *For Example 1*
  Solve $x = \frac{2}{7} \bullet \frac{3}{10}$ $\frac{3}{35}$

Solve each equation.

- *For Example 2*
  $5\frac{1}{4} \bullet (-1\frac{4}{7}) = c$ $-8\frac{1}{4}$
- *For Example 3*
  $x = \frac{2}{-5}\left(\frac{4}{-9}\right)$ $\frac{8}{45}$
- *For Example 4*
  $x = \left(\frac{3}{4}\right)^2$ $\frac{9}{16}$
- *For Example 5*
  $y = \left(\frac{2}{-7}\right)^2$ $\frac{4}{49}$

The multiplication skills that you have developed with integers and fractions can be used when you multiply negative fractions.

Examples

Solve each equation.

Estimation Hint

You can estimate to get a range for the product. In Example 2, the product is between 3(-4) and 4(-5); that is, between -12 and -20.

2 $3\frac{1}{2} \cdot \left(-4\frac{2}{3}\right) = c$ Estimate: 3(-5) = -15

$\frac{7}{2} \cdot \left(\frac{-14}{3}\right) = c$ Rename $3\frac{1}{2}$ as $\frac{7}{2}$ and $-4\frac{2}{3}$ as $\frac{-14}{3}$.

$\frac{7}{\cancel{2}_1} \cdot \left(\frac{\cancel{-14}^{-7}}{3}\right) = c$

$\frac{-49}{3} = c$ The product of two rational numbers with different signs is negative.

$-16\frac{1}{3} = c$ Compare with the estimate.

3 $x = -\frac{3}{4} \cdot \left(-\frac{5}{7}\right)$

$x = \frac{-3}{4} \cdot \left(\frac{-5}{7}\right)$

$x = \frac{-3(-5)}{4 \cdot 7}$ The product of two rational numbers with the same sign is positive.

$x = \frac{15}{28}$

The rules for exponents that were stated for whole numbers in Lesson 4-2 also hold for fractions. For example, the expression $\left(\frac{3}{4}\right)^2$ means $\frac{3}{4} \cdot \frac{3}{4}$.

Examples

Solve each equation.

What is the difference between $\left(-\frac{3}{4}\right)^2$ and $-\left(\frac{3}{4}\right)^2$?

$\left(-\frac{3}{4}\right)^2 = \left(-\frac{3}{4}\right)\left(-\frac{3}{4}\right)$

$-\left(\frac{3}{4}\right)^2 = -\left(\frac{3}{4}\right)\left(\frac{3}{4}\right)$

4 $x = \left(\frac{2}{3}\right)^2$

$x = \frac{2}{3} \cdot \frac{2}{3}$

$x = \frac{4}{9}$

5 $y = \left(-\frac{5}{6}\right)^2$

$y = \left(-\frac{5}{6}\right)\left(-\frac{5}{6}\right)$

$y = \frac{25}{36}$

Alternate Strategies: Reteaching the Lesson

Reteaching Activity

Using Problem Solving Use transparency overlays to illustrate multiplication. For example, illustrate $\frac{1}{4}$ of $\frac{1}{2}$ by drawing a rectangle, shading $\frac{1}{2}$ of it, then using darker shading for $\frac{1}{4}$ of the shaded half. $\frac{1}{8}$ of the entire rectangle has the dark shading. Have students illustrate $\frac{1}{4}$ of $\frac{2}{3}$, $\frac{1}{2}$ of $\frac{3}{4}$, and $\frac{1}{4}$ of $\frac{1}{3}$.

Reteaching Masters Booklet, **p. 47**

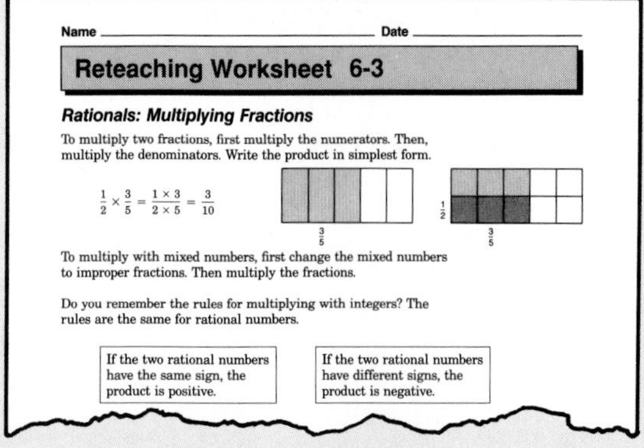

Name ______ Date ______

Reteaching Worksheet 6-3

Rationals: Multiplying Fractions

To multiply two fractions, first multiply the numerators. Then, multiply the denominators. Write the product in simplest form.

$\frac{1}{2} \times \frac{3}{5} = \frac{1 \times 3}{2 \times 5} = \frac{3}{10}$

To multiply with mixed numbers, first change the mixed numbers to improper fractions. Then multiply the fractions.

Do you remember the rules for multiplying with integers? The rules are the same for rational numbers.

If the two rational numbers have the same sign, the product is positive.	If the two rational numbers have different signs, the product is negative.

Checking for Understanding

Communicating Algebra

1. Explain how the model at the right shows the product of $\frac{2}{3}$ and $\frac{1}{4}$. What is the product? See margin; $\frac{1}{6}$

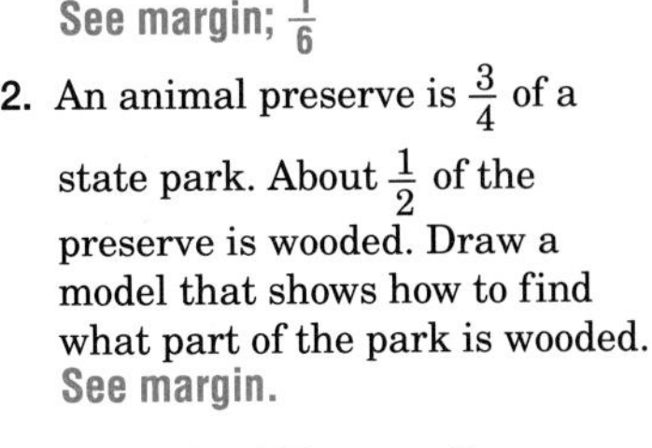

2. An animal preserve is $\frac{3}{4}$ of a state park. About $\frac{1}{2}$ of the preserve is wooded. Draw a model that shows how to find what part of the park is wooded. See margin.

3. What should be your first step when computing $5\frac{1}{4} \cdot 3\frac{1}{6}$? Express $5\frac{1}{4}$ as $\frac{21}{4}$ and $3\frac{1}{6}$ as $\frac{19}{6}$.

Guided Practice

State whether each product is positive or negative.

4. $-\frac{1}{2} \cdot 4$ −
5. $\frac{2}{3} \cdot \frac{3}{4}$ +
6. $2\frac{1}{2}(-3)$ −
7. $(-5)\left(-2\frac{1}{2}\right)$ +

Solve each equation. Write each solution in simplest form.

8. $\frac{1}{2} \cdot \frac{5}{6} = a$ $\frac{5}{12}$
9. $\frac{2}{3} \cdot \frac{9}{10} = b$ $\frac{3}{5}$
10. $\frac{8}{12} \cdot \frac{4}{6} = c$ $\frac{4}{9}$
11. $y = \frac{5}{6}(-2)$ $-\frac{5}{3}$
12. $r = 1\frac{2}{3} \cdot 2$ $\frac{10}{3}$
13. $2\frac{3}{4}\left(-\frac{4}{5}\right) = f$ $-\frac{11}{5}$

Exercises

Independent Practice

Solve each equation. Write each solution in simplest form.

14. $c = \frac{1}{2} \cdot \frac{2}{7}$ $\frac{1}{7}$
15. $r = -2\frac{1}{2}(-6)$ 15
16. $k = -\frac{5}{6}\left(-\frac{2}{5}\right)$ $\frac{1}{3}$
17. $d = -4\left(\frac{3}{8}\right)$ $-\frac{3}{2}$
18. $(-7)\left(-2\frac{1}{3}\right) = h$ $\frac{49}{3}$
19. $5\left(-3\frac{1}{2}\right) = x$ $-\frac{35}{2}$
20. $m = \left(-1\frac{1}{3}\right)\left(-\frac{3}{4}\right)$ 1
21. $\left(2\frac{1}{4}\right)\left(-\frac{4}{3}\right) = t$ −3
22. $j = \left(\frac{3}{4}\right)\left(-\frac{4}{3}\right)$ −1
23. $\left(-9\frac{3}{5}\right)\left(\frac{5}{12}\right) = y$ −4
24. $f = (-16)\left(-\frac{3}{8}\right)$ 6
25. $(-12)\left(-\frac{5}{6}\right) = c$ 10
26. $(-7)\left(-8\frac{1}{2}\right) = x$ $\frac{119}{2}$
27. $\left(3\frac{1}{6}\right)\left(-2\frac{1}{3}\right) = m$ $-\frac{133}{18}$
28. $\left(-8\frac{1}{3}\right)\left(2\frac{2}{5}\right) = k$ −20
29. $x = \left(\frac{1}{2}\right)^2$ $\frac{1}{4}$
30. $d = \left(-\frac{3}{4}\right)^2$ $\frac{9}{16}$
31. $\left(\frac{5}{8}\right)^2 = n$ $\frac{25}{64}$
32. $a = \left(-\frac{2}{3}\right)^2$ $\frac{4}{9}$
33. $\left(-\frac{4}{5}\right)^2 = y$ $\frac{16}{25}$
34. $2 \cdot \left(\frac{5}{6}\right)^2 = m$ $\frac{25}{18}$

Additional Answer

1. The part that is shaded yellow shows $\frac{2}{3}$ and the part that is shaded green is $\frac{1}{4}$ of $\frac{2}{3}$; $\frac{1}{6}$

2.

3 PRACTICE/APPLY

Checking the Concept

Have students solve Exercises 8-13 using both Method 1 and Method 2. Then have students state what the result means.

Error Analysis

Watch for students who use modified addition rules, finding a common denominator and multiplying only numerators in a multiplication problem.
Prevent by using estimates. Also, point out that finding a common denominator results in a correct answer, but the larger numbers must be simplified, and the problem takes longer to work.

Independent Practice

Homework Assignment	
Basic	15-37 odd, 43-52
Average	18-42 even, 43-52
Honors	22-34 even, 37-52

Practice Masters Booklet, **p. 52**

Name ______________ Date ______________

Practice Worksheet 6-3

Rationals: Multiplying Fractions

Solve each equation. Write each solution in simplest form.

1. $a = -\frac{5}{7} \cdot \frac{14}{15}$ $-\frac{2}{3}$
2. $\frac{6}{11}\left(-\frac{33}{34}\right) = b$ $-\frac{9}{17}$
3. $c = \left(-6\frac{2}{3}\right)\left(-\frac{15}{16}\right)$ $6\frac{1}{4}$
4. $x = 5\left(-\frac{1}{10}\right)$ $-\frac{1}{2}$
5. $\frac{1}{7} \cdot \frac{1}{8} = y$ $\frac{1}{56}$
6. $z = -5\left(-\frac{21}{25}\right)$ $4\frac{1}{5}$
7. $m = \left(-9\frac{1}{5}\right)\left(\frac{10}{23}\right)$ −4
8. $\left(-\frac{3}{4}\right)\left(-\frac{8}{9}\right) = n$ $\frac{2}{3}$
9. $p = 4\frac{1}{2} \cdot 8$ 36
10. $\left(-\frac{8}{9}\right)\left(\frac{9}{8}\right) = q$ −1
11. $-5\frac{1}{3} \cdot 1\frac{4}{5} = r$ $-9\frac{3}{5}$
12. $9\left(-3\frac{1}{3}\right) = s$ −30
13. $t = \left(7\frac{7}{8}\right)\left(-\frac{5}{9}\right)$ $-4\frac{3}{8}$
14. $l = \left(1\frac{1}{9}\right)\left(\frac{27}{40}\right)$ $\frac{3}{4}$
15. $\left(-\frac{36}{50}\right)\left(\frac{75}{48}\right) = h$ $-1\frac{1}{8}$
16. $a = \left(-\frac{1}{2}\right)^2$ $\frac{1}{4}$
17. $b = 3\left(\frac{4}{5}\right)^2$ $1\frac{23}{48}$
18. $c = -1\left(-\frac{3}{5}\right)^2$ $-\frac{9}{25}$

Evaluate each expression if $a = -\frac{1}{4}$, $b = \frac{5}{6}$, $c = -1\frac{1}{2}$, and $d = 2\frac{1}{3}$.

19. $4c$ −6
20. bd $1\frac{17}{18}$
21. $3b - 4a$ $3\frac{1}{2}$
22. $18b - 6c$ 24
23. $a + cd$ $-3\frac{3}{4}$
24. $9d + \frac{7}{8}$ $21\frac{7}{8}$
25. $a(c + 4)$ $-\frac{5}{8}$
26. $b(a + 8)$ $6\frac{11}{24}$
27. $d(b + 6)$ $15\frac{17}{18}$

4 CLOSE

Assessment Option

Modeling Have students model the following products.

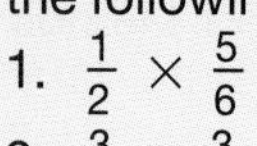

1. $\frac{1}{2} \times \frac{5}{6}$

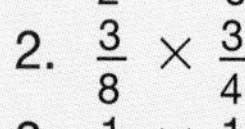

2. $\frac{3}{8} \times \frac{3}{4}$

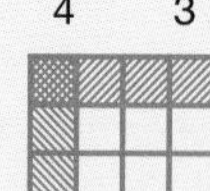

3. $\frac{1}{4} \times \frac{1}{3}$

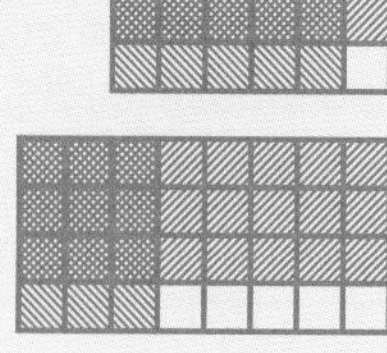

Additional Answer

52. Sample answer: Multiply the numerators and multiply the denominators. Simplify if necessary.

Enrichment Masters Booklet, **p. 47**

Name ______________________ Date ____________

Enrichment Worksheet 6-3

Visualizing the Distributive Property

Using the distributive property to estimate the product of fractions can be shown by using the area of a rectangle. For example, suppose you are working with this product:

$$3\frac{1}{2} \times 2\frac{1}{3}$$

This product is modeled by the rectangle at the right. The length is split into two parts, 3 units and $\frac{1}{2}$ unit. The width is split into 2 units and $\frac{1}{3}$ unit. The area of the rectangle is then divided into four parts.

	3	$\frac{1}{2}$
2	$2 \times 3 = 6$	$2 \times \frac{1}{2} = 1$
$\frac{1}{3}$	$3 \times \frac{1}{3} = 1$	$\frac{1}{6}$ ($\frac{1}{2} \times \frac{1}{3}$)

Now, find the area of each part. The area of the largest part is just 2×3, or 6.

The areas of the two next-largest rectangles are $2 \times \frac{1}{2}$, or 1, and $3 \times \frac{1}{3}$, or 1.

The area of the smallest rectangle is $\frac{1}{2} \times \frac{1}{3}$, or $\frac{1}{6}$.

Thus, the product is $6 + 1 + 1 + \frac{1}{6}$, or $8\frac{1}{6}$.

For each product, model the factors as the lengths of the sides of a rectangle and find the product.

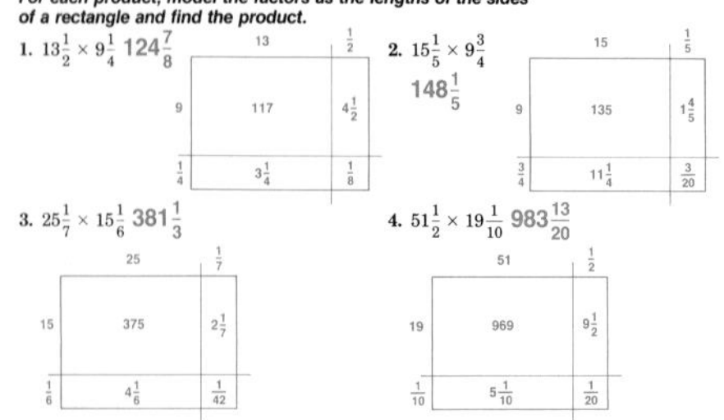

1. $13\frac{1}{2} \times 9\frac{1}{4}$ $124\frac{7}{8}$

	13	$\frac{1}{2}$
9	117	$4\frac{1}{2}$
$\frac{1}{4}$	$3\frac{1}{4}$	$\frac{1}{8}$

2. $15\frac{1}{5} \times 9\frac{3}{4}$ $148\frac{1}{5}$

	15	$\frac{1}{5}$
9	135	$1\frac{4}{5}$
$\frac{3}{4}$	$11\frac{1}{4}$	$\frac{3}{20}$

3. $25\frac{1}{7} \times 15\frac{1}{6}$ $381\frac{1}{3}$

	25	$\frac{1}{7}$
15	375	$2\frac{1}{7}$
$\frac{1}{6}$	$4\frac{1}{6}$	$\frac{1}{42}$

4. $51\frac{1}{2} \times 19\frac{1}{10}$ $983\frac{13}{20}$

	51	$\frac{1}{2}$
19	969	$9\frac{1}{2}$
$\frac{1}{10}$	$5\frac{1}{10}$	$\frac{1}{20}$

Evaluate each expression if $a = \frac{1}{2}$, $b = -\frac{2}{3}$, $x = 2\frac{1}{4}$, and $y = -1\frac{5}{6}$.

35. ax $\frac{9}{8}$
36. $2y$ $-\frac{11}{3}$
37. b^2 $\frac{4}{9}$
38. $by + \frac{1}{2}$ $\frac{31}{18}$
39. $3b - 4a$ -4
40. $a^2(x + 5)$ $\frac{29}{16}$
41. $y - (a + b)$ $-1\frac{2}{3}$
42. $x - ay$ $3\frac{1}{6}$

Mixed Review

43. Solve the equation $x = -15 + 5 + (-2)$. (Lesson 2-4) -12
44. Write $\frac{4a^2b}{12b^3}$ in simplest form. (Lesson 4-6) $\frac{a^2}{3b^2}$
45. Express -2.44 as a mixed number in simplest form. (Lesson 5-2) $-2\frac{11}{25}$
46. Simplify the expression $9.4d + 4.3d + 1.8d$. (Lesson 5-4) $15.5d$
47. Express $-5\frac{7}{15}$ as a decimal. (Lesson 6-1) $-5.4\overline{6}$
48. Estimate the product $\frac{1}{6} \times 23$. (Lesson 6-2) 4

Applications

49. **Home Economics** A recipe for 16 pancakes calls for $2\frac{1}{2}$ cups of flour. How much flour is needed to make one-half the recipe? $1\frac{1}{4}$ cups
50. **Carpentry** Four pieces of wood each $11\frac{3}{8}$ inches long are required to build a cabinet. If all four pieces are cut from one board and 1 inch is allowed for waste in cutting each piece, how long should the board be? $48\frac{1}{2}$ inches

Critical Thinking

51. Which point shown on the number line could be the graph of the product of the numbers graphed at A and B? D

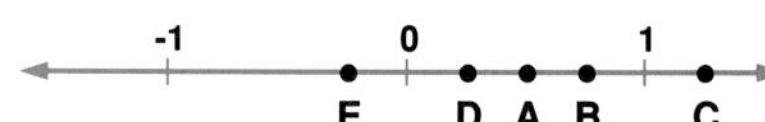

Wrap-Up

52. In your own words, explain how to multiply fractions. See margin.

Enrichment

Algebraic Fractions

Just as you can multiply rational numbers expressed as fractions, you can multiply algebraic fractions.

Find $\frac{a}{b} \cdot \frac{b}{c}$, where $b \neq 0$ and $c \neq 0$.

$\frac{a}{b} \cdot \frac{b}{c} = \frac{a \cdot \cancel{b}}{\cancel{b} \cdot c}$ The GCF of the numerator and denominator is *b*. Divide the numerator and denominator by *b*.

$= \frac{a}{c}$

How should you find the product $\frac{a^2}{b} \cdot \frac{b}{a}$? Divide the numerator and denominator by *ab*. The product is *a*.

Alternate Strategies: Extending the Lesson

Enrichment

Using Logical Reasoning Write the numbers $-4\frac{7}{8}$, $1\frac{1}{6}$, $-6\frac{3}{10}$, $\frac{2}{3}$ on the chalkboard.

1. Ask students to mentally determine which two will give the largest product. $-4\frac{7}{8}$ and $-6\frac{3}{10}$
2. Ask students to mentally determine which two will give the smallest product. $-6\frac{3}{10}$ and $\frac{2}{3}$

Cooperative Learning

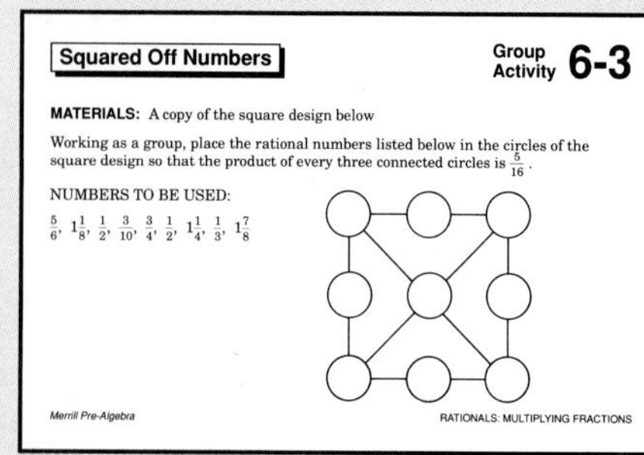

Squared Off Numbers Group Activity **6-3**

MATERIALS: A copy of the square design below

Working as a group, place the rational numbers listed below in the circles of the square design so that the product of every three connected circles is $\frac{5}{16}$.

NUMBERS TO BE USED:

$\frac{5}{6}$, $1\frac{1}{8}$, $\frac{1}{2}$, $\frac{3}{10}$, $\frac{3}{4}$, $\frac{1}{2}$, $1\frac{1}{4}$, $\frac{1}{3}$, $1\frac{7}{8}$

Merrill Pre-Algebra RATIONALS: MULTIPLYING FRACTIONS

6-4 Rationals: Multiplying Decimals

Objective:
Multiply decimals.

Juan is a member of a springboard diving team. Recently his team participated in a diving competition. Each dive that Juan performs is scored by several judges. The individual scores are totaled and then multiplied by a number called the degree of difficulty. This number is between 1 and 4.

The judges' scores for Juan's first dive are shown below. This dive had a 1.5 degree of difficulty. We can find his score for this dive as follows:

$6.5 + 7.0 + 6.5 + 5.5 + 7.0 = 32.5$ Add the scores.

$32.5 \times 1.5 = \blacksquare$ Multiply by the degree of difficulty.

Estimation is helpful in placing the decimal point in the product.

THINK: $32 \times 1 = 32$, $32 \times 2 = 64$ — Since 1.5 is between 1 and 2, 32 × 1.5 should be between 32 and 64.

$$\begin{array}{r} 32.5 \\ \times\ 1.5 \\ \hline 1625 \\ 325 \\ \hline 48.75 \end{array}$$

Multiply as with whole numbers.

Place the decimal point using the estimate.

What is the rule for locating the decimal point in a product? **Count the number of places after the decimal point in the factors. The product will have that number of places after the decimal point.**

Juan scored 48.75 points on his first dive. Notice that 48.75 is between 32 and 64.

Check using a calculator.

32.5 ⊠ 1.5 ⊟ 48.75 ✓ The solution checks.

Lesson Notes 6-4

5-Minute Check
(over Lesson 6-3)

Solve each equation. Write each solution in simplest form.

1. $d = \frac{1}{5} \cdot \frac{3}{4}$ $\frac{3}{20}$
2. $k = \frac{3}{-7} \cdot \left(\frac{4}{-9}\right)$ $\frac{4}{21}$
3. $(-8)\left(2\frac{1}{6}\right) = m$ $-17\frac{1}{3}$
4. $\left(\frac{3}{-5}\right)^2$ $\frac{9}{25}$
5. $\left(-2\frac{1}{7}\right)\left(4\frac{2}{5}\right)$ $9\frac{3}{7}$

Transparency 6-4 contains the 5-Minute Check and a teaching aid for this lesson.

1 FOCUS

The purpose of this lesson is to extend multiplication and estimation to multiplying rational numbers expressed as decimals.

Motivating the Lesson

Show students several meat labels. Read the weight of the meat and the price per pound. Ask students how they would determine the cost of the package of meat.

2 TEACH

Using Chalkboard Examples

Write the same problem horizontally three times on the chalkboard. After doing the number multiplication, have one student locate the decimal point by counting decimal places, another student locate the decimal point by estimating, and a third student by using a calculator. Discuss the advantages and disadvantages of each method.

Bell Ringer

Multiply using Method 2 on p. 211. Then check with Method 1.

1. $\frac{6}{11} \times \frac{33}{37}$ $\frac{6 \times 3}{1 \times 37} = \frac{18}{37}$
2. $\frac{4}{9} \times \frac{3}{8}$ $\frac{1 \times 1}{3 \times 2} = \frac{1}{6}$

EE: 1E, 2D, 3A, 3D, 3H
TAAS: 2, 8, 10, 13

Chalkboard Examples

Solve each equation.

- *For Example 1*
  $y = (8.4)(1.2)$ 10.08
- *For Example 2*
  $(-0.116)(0.05) = m$ -0.0058
- *For Example 3*
  $t = (1000)(7.8)$ 7800

3 PRACTICE/APPLY

Checking the Concept

Have students work in groups of three to solve Exercises 11-13. Have one student multiply numbers, another estimate the product, and the third student use the estimate to place the decimal point in the product. Students should rotate roles.

Error Analysis

Watch for students who count from left to right rather than from right to left to place the decimal point.
Prevent by having students estimate before multiplying.

Additional Answers

1. Sample answer: The number of decimal places in the product is the same as the sum of the number of decimal places in the factors.
3. Sample answer: Move the decimal point to the right the same number of places as the number of zeros.

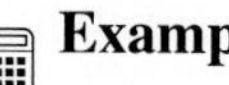

Examples

Solve each equation.

1 $y = (2.3)(3.5)$ Estimate: $2 \times 4 = 8$

$$\begin{array}{r} 2.3 \\ \times\ 3.5 \\ \hline 115 \\ 69 \\ \hline 8.05 \end{array}$$

or 2.3 [×] 3.5 [=] 8.05

$y = 8.05$ Compare with the estimate. The answer is reasonable.

2 $(-0.105)(0.03) = k$ Estimate: $-\frac{1}{10} \cdot \frac{3}{100} = -\frac{3}{1000}$

$$\begin{array}{r} -0.105 \\ \times\ \ 0.03 \\ \hline -0.00315 \end{array}$$

or 0.105 [+/−] [×] 0.03 [=] -0.00315

$-0.00315 = k$ Compare with the estimate.

Mental Math Hint

When multiplying by powers of 10 like 10, 100, 1000, . . . , you can easily find the product mentally. The decimal point is moved to the right the same number of places as the number of zeros in the power of 10.

3 $c = (100)(2.4)$ Estimate: $100 \cdot 2 = 200$

$$\begin{array}{r} 100 \\ \times\ 2.4 \\ \hline 400 \\ 200 \\ \hline 240.0 \end{array}$$

or 100 [×] 2.4 [=] 240

$c = 240$ Compare with the estimate.

Checking for Understanding

Communicating Algebra

1. State the rule for placement of the decimal point in multiplication. See margin.
2. Explain why you should make an estimate when using a calculator to multiply. to check that the answer is reasonable
3. In your own words, state how to find a product when one of the factors is 10, 100, 1000, ... See margin.

Use estimation to choose the correct product.

4. (1.3)(0.02); 0.260 or <u>0.026</u>
5. (0.04)(0.01); <u>0.0004</u> or 0.4000
6. (5.1)(0.8); 40.8 or <u>4.08</u>
7. (0.02)6; 0.012 or <u>0.12</u>

Alternate Strategies: Reteaching the Lesson

Reteaching Activity

Using Cooperative Groups Play a game of "Low Score Roll." Two cubes are needed, one numbered in tenths (0.1, 0.2, . . . , 0.6) and one numbered in hundredths. Each player, in turn, rolls the cubes and multiplies the numbers. Play for four rounds and add each player's scores. The player with the lowest score wins.

Reteaching Masters Booklet, p. 48

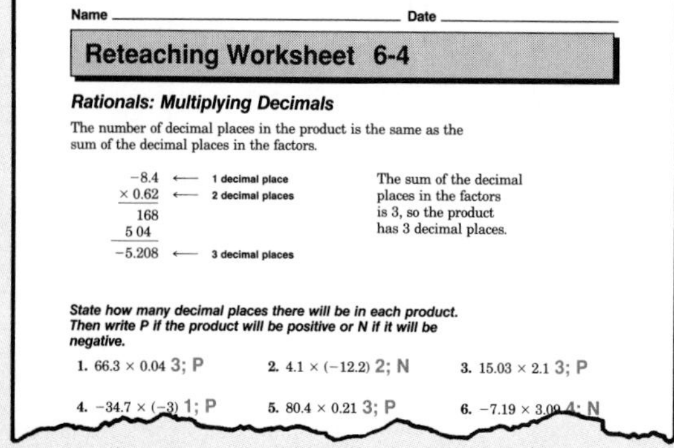

Name ______ Date ______

Reteaching Worksheet 6-4

Rationals: Multiplying Decimals

The number of decimal places in the product is the same as the sum of the decimal places in the factors.

$$\begin{array}{rl} -8.4 & \leftarrow \text{1 decimal place} \\ \times\ 0.62 & \leftarrow \text{2 decimal places} \\ \hline 168 & \\ 5\ 04 & \\ \hline -5.208 & \leftarrow \text{3 decimal places} \end{array}$$

The sum of the decimal places in the factors is 3, so the product has 3 decimal places.

State how many decimal places there will be in each product. Then write P if the product will be positive or N if it will be negative.

1. 66.3 × 0.04 3; P
2. 4.1 × (−12.2) 2; N
3. 15.03 × 2.1 3; P
4. −34.7 × (−3) 1; P
5. 80.4 × 0.21 3; P
6. −7.19 × 3.004 4; N

Guided Practice

State where the decimal point should be placed in each product.

8. $16 \cdot 4.7 = 752$ (^ after 75)
9. $3.62 \cdot 30 = 10860$ (^ after 108)
10. $(3.2)(7.5) = 2400$ (^ after 24)

Find each product.

11. $(9.16)(39)$ 357.24
12. $(0.118)(-4.8)$ -0.5664
13. $(12.8)(1.1)$ 14.08

Exercises

Independent Practice

Solve each equation.

14. $x = 6(3.2)$ 19.2
15. $z = (11.8)(5)$ 59
16. $w = -7(8.46)$ -59.22
17. $p = 2.4 \cdot 8.7$ 20.88
18. $r = (-5.03)(-6.1)$ 30.683
19. $m = (40.6)(0.9)$ 36.54
20. $(2.1)(0.6) = x$ 1.26
21. $0.98(-0.6) = k$ -0.588
22. $0.22 \cdot 0.008 = y$ 0.00176

Mental Math

Solve each equation mentally.

23. $(100)(11.6) = t$ 1160
24. $(1000)(7.2) = m$ 7200
25. $p = (12.79)(10)$ 127.9
26. $(0.02)(10) = y$ 0.2
27. $n = 10(-3.05)$ -30.5
28. $x = (-100)(-3.6)$ 360

Estimation

Estimate each product. Then compute with a calculator.

29. $(2.01)(1.5) = r$ 3.015
30. $0.082 \cdot 6.6 = y$ 0.5412
31. $(35.3)4.9 = t$ 172.97
32. $8.022(0.03) = s$ 0.24066
33. $(1.08)(4.75) = p$ 5.13
34. $0.035 \cdot 4.1 = k$ 0.1435
35. $d = 5.92 \cdot 0.47$ 2.7824
36. $g = (75.9)(0.372)$ 28.2348
37. $x = 9.0006(9.01)$ 81.095406
38. $w = (7.2)(3.5)(0.05)$ 1.26
39. $y = (0.23)(1.7)(0.04)$ 0.01564
40. $a = (81)(0.02)(1.5)$ 2.43

Evaluate each expression.

41. $2.5x$ if $x = 8$ 20
42. $3y^2$ if $y = 0.4$ 0.48
43. ab if $a = -1.5, b = 10$ -15
44. $r(s + t)$ if $r = 0.9, s = 4.2, t = 5.1$ 8.37
45. $(x + y)^2$ if $x = 0.4, y = -0.2$ 0.04
46. $(x + 4)(x - 2)$ if $x = 1.8$ -1.16

Mixed Review

47. Find the LCD for $\frac{1}{3b^2}$ and $\frac{7}{18b}$. $18b^2$ (Lesson 4-8)
48. Solve the equation $s = 5\frac{2}{3} - 1\frac{5}{6}$. $3\frac{5}{6}$ (Lesson 5-6)
49. **Social Studies** Tuy builds a model of the Pentagon for his social studies project. The length of each side is 10.7 inches. What is the total perimeter? (Lesson 5-10) 53.5 inches
50. Estimate $6.08 \times 3.99 \div 7.96$. (Lesson 6-2) 3

Independent Practice

Homework Assignment	
Basic	15-45 odd, 47-50
Average	16-46 even, 47-50
Honors	20-40 even, 41-50

Practice Masters Booklet, **p. 53**

Name ______ Date ______

Practice Worksheet 6-4

Rationals: Multiplying Decimals

Solve each equation.

1. $y = -8(4.2)$ 33.6
2. $x = (21.4)(3)$ 64.2
3. $(-4)(-9.37) = z$ 37.48
4. $(0.32)(-1.4) = a$ −0.448
5. $b = 50(8.3)$ 415
6. $c = 10(-15.82)$ −158.2
7. $(-21.04)(-4.2) = d$ 88.368
8. $e = (8.002)(0.4)$ 3.2008
9. $(-3.2)(-8.61) = f$ 27.552
10. $k = 400(-8.15)$ −3260
11. $(2.18)3.4 = z$ 7.412
12. $(-0.111)(0.12) = p$ −0.01332
13. $(3.15)(2.4) = r$ 7.56
14. $(-0.075)(-5.5) = s$ 0.4125
15. $(-26.2)9.4 = t$ −246.28
16. $v = 1.033(0.04)$ 0.04132
17. $u = (-1.01)(5.45)$ −5.5045
18. $w = -3.82(-0.34)$ 1.2988
19. $9.51(0.579) = x$ 5.50629
20. $4.0001(4.05) = y$ 16.200405
21. $z = (-38.6)(-45.6)$ 1760.16
22. $(-3.4)(5.2) = m$ −17.68
23. $n = (8.01)(1.01)$ 8.0901
24. $d = (5.07)(-4.8)$ −24.336
25. $(15.8)(12.07) = p$ 190.706
26. $q = (-1.4)(-23.56)$ 32.984
27. $(-41.77)(-0.93) = r$ 38.8461

4 CLOSE

Assessment Option

Speaking Ask students to state how the product of a decimal less than one and a decimal greater than one relates to the factors. The product will be between the factors.

Solve each equation. Write each solution in simplest form. (Lesson 6-3)

51. $d = (-3)\left(2\frac{1}{7}\right)$ $-6\frac{3}{7}$

52. $f = \left(-2\frac{1}{4}\right)\left(-\frac{1}{3}\right)$ $\frac{3}{4}$

Applications

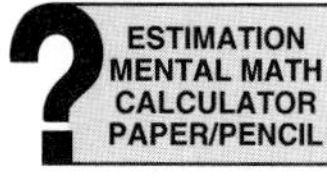

53. **Economics** When Emilio's baseball team visited Mexico, $1 in American money could be exchanged for 2702.7 pesos. If Emilio exchanged $25 in American money, how many pesos did he receive? 67,567 pesos (round *down* to the nearest peso)

54. **Home Economics** Suppose you are in charge of baking a ham for your family picnic. The directions tell you to cook the ham for 22 minutes per pound at 325°. The ham weighs 7.45 pounds. To the nearest minute how long should you bake the ham? 164 minutes

55. **Consumer Awareness** In a recent year, American consumers spent $0.8 billion for golf equipment. They spent four times more for athletic shoes than on golf equipment. How much did they spend for athletic shoes? $3.2 billion

Critical Thinking

56. Name two decimals whose sum is 2.4 and whose product is 1.44. 1.2, 1.2

Wrap-Up

57. Copy. Place a decimal point in each factor so that the product is correct. Sample answer: 4.93 × 1.7

493 × 17 = 8.381

Reading Algebra

The Metric System

During the 1790s, a group of French scientists developed a system of measurement called the metric system. Some basic units are the **meter** (length), **liter** (capacity), and the **gram** (mass). Other units are named by using *prefixes* with the basic units. The chart at the right shows how the prefixes relate to the powers of ten.

thousands	hundreds	tens	ones	tenths	hundredths	thousandths
kilo-	hecto-	deka-	basic unit	deci-	centi-	milli-

When the prefix *centi-* is added to *meter*, the result is *centimeter*. A *centimeter* is one-hundredth of a meter.

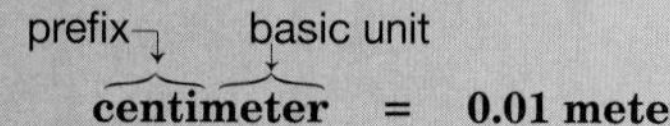

Name the metric unit equivalent to each measurement.

1. 0.001 meter millimeter
2. 1000 liters kiloliter
3. 100 grams hectogram
4. 0.1 meter decimeter
5. 10 liters dekaliter
6. 0.01 gram centigram
7. **Research** Use a dictionary to find the meaning of the prefixes *mega-* and *micro-*. one million; one millionth

Enrichment Masters Booklet, **p. 48**

Name ________________ Date ________________

Enrichment Worksheet 6-4

Multiplying by 0.1, 0.01, 0.001, and so on

Being able to multiply mentally by 0.1, 0.01, 0.001, and so on can be very helpful in real-world applications. In each of the situations below, the person is using this skill to make quick decisions. See how you would do in these jobs.

Marty works as an audit clerk for a company. His job is to see that the salespersons are meeting their goals. Each month the salespeople need to have at least 10% of their yearly goal (0.1 × Goal). Place a check (✓) next to the salepeople who made their goal and are in the 10% club.

Person	Goal	Sales	Met 10%
B. Cannon	$450,000	$53,338	✓
G. Danial	$320,000	$28,724	
H. Edward	$632,000	$57,154	
Q. Franke	$287,000	$31,532	✓
V. Howard	$723,000	$82,000	✓

Manny works as a quality control supervisor for a parts manufacturer. Her job is to detect machines that are turning out more than 1 rejected part in 100. (0.01 × Products). Place a check (✓) next to the machines that are not working up to expectations.

Machine	Products	Reject	Check
Molder	27,379	375	✓
Painter	33,248	283	
Buffer	28,106	197	
Cutter	46,449	452	
Grinder	83,115	728	

Monte works as an inspector for the Motor Vehicle Emissions-Testing Department. One test requires that no more than 1 part per thousand be dangerous hydrocarbons (0.001 × Total). Write *Pass* or *Fail* for each car.

License	Total	Hy-Carb	Pass/Fail
Y1234	347,667	48	Pass
A2279	426,892	257	Pass
B3658	127,225	182	Fail
QBB13	204,885	202	Pass
P1168	552,447	612	Fail

Milly works for a consumer advocate group, checking sales discount claims for accuracy. She uses 10% as a guide to determine quickly if discounts of 20%, 30%, and 40% are accurate. Find the amount off for these sales.

Percent Discount	Regular Price	Amount Off
10%	$47.50	$4.75
20%	$144.00	$28.80
30%	$75.00	$22.50
15%	$40.00	$6.00
40%	$120.00	$48.00

Alternate Strategies: Extending the Lesson

Enrichment

Business Connection Check a bank for current currency exchange rates. Write and solve problems using these rates. Keep the problems. Throughout the year, compare the rates. Have they changed? For what countries did the rate change? Graph this information to show trends in currency exchange.

Cooperative Learning

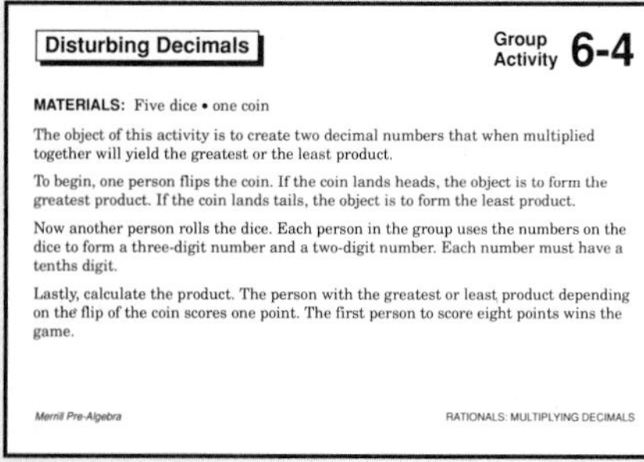

Disturbing Decimals Group Activity **6-4**

MATERIALS: Five dice • one coin

The object of this activity is to create two decimal numbers that when multiplied together will yield the greatest or the least product.

To begin, one person flips the coin. If the coin lands heads, the object is to form the greatest product. If the coin lands tails, the object is to form the least product.

Now another person rolls the dice. Each person in the group uses the numbers on the dice to form a three-digit number and a two-digit number. Each number must have a tenths digit.

Lastly, calculate the product. The person with the greatest or least product depending on the flip of the coin scores one point. The first person to score eight points wins the game.

Merrill Pre-Algebra RATIONALS: MULTIPLYING DECIMALS

6-5 Multiplicative Inverses

Objective:
Identify and use the properties of multiplication.

Key Terms:
multiplicative inverse
reciprocal

Tim and Hiro want to buy a surfboard together. Since Tim will be gone part of the summer, Hiro suggests that Tim pay only $\frac{1}{3}$ of the cost instead of $\frac{1}{2}$. If Tim pays $80, what is the total cost of the surfboard?

You can use an equation to solve this problem. Let c = total cost.

$\frac{1}{3}$ of total cost = 80

$$\frac{1}{3}c = 80$$

$$\frac{3}{1} \cdot \frac{1}{3}c = 80 \cdot \frac{3}{1}$$ Multiply each side of the equation by 3.

$$1c = 240$$ $\frac{3}{1} \cdot \frac{1}{3} = 1$

$$c = 240$$ $1c = c$

The surfboard costs $240.

When you multiplied $\frac{1}{3}$ by $\frac{3}{1}$, you used a property of rational numbers called the **inverse property of multiplication.** Two numbers whose product is 1 are **multiplicative inverses,** or **reciprocals,** of each other. For example, $\frac{1}{2}$ and 2 are multiplicative inverses because $\frac{1}{2} \cdot \frac{2}{1} = 1$.

In the same way, $-\frac{3}{2}$ and $-\frac{2}{3}$ are multiplicative inverses because $-\frac{2}{3} \cdot -\frac{3}{2} = 1$.

Are $-\frac{5}{8}$ and $\frac{8}{5}$ multiplicative inverses?
no; $-\frac{5}{8} \cdot \frac{8}{5} = -1$

Inverse Property of Multiplication

In words: The product of a number and its multiplicative inverse is 1.
In symbols: For every nonzero number $\frac{a}{b}$, where a, b ≠ 0, there is exactly one number $\frac{b}{a}$ such that $\frac{a}{b} \cdot \frac{b}{a} = 1$.

All the properties that were true for multiplication of integers are also true for multiplication of rationals. The properties for multiplication of rationals are summarized in the following chart.

Bell Ringer

Tell how many places to the left the decimal point needs to be moved.
1. 54.6 × 11.75 3
2. 0.057 × 0.86 5

5-Minute Check
(over Lesson 6-4)

Solve each equation.
1. $r = (-6.2)(5.9)$ -36.58
2. $x = (2.35)(100)$ 235
3. $(-0.045)(100) = m$ -4.5
4. $8(4.1) = k$ 32.8
5. $(-0.73)(-2.5) = p$ 1.825

Transparency 6-5 contains the 5-Minute Check and a teaching aid for this lesson.

1 FOCUS

The purpose of this lesson is to extend the properties of multiplication to multiplying rational numbers expressed as fractions.

Motivating the Lesson

Write numbers on cards. Write the numbers' multiplicative inverses on other cards. Give each student a card. Have students quietly find the person who has the number that, when multiplied by their number, equals 1.

2 TEACH

Using Models

Use tiles or diagrams to model examples of the commutative, associative, identity, inverse, and distributive properties.

EE: 1E, 2D, 3A
TAAS: 2

Chalkboard Examples

- *For Example 1*
  Compute $6 \times 3\frac{1}{2}$. **21**
- *For Example 2*
  Compute $\frac{1}{5} \times 10\frac{5}{8}$. $2\frac{1}{8}$

3 PRACTICE/APPLY

Checking the Concept

If any pairs in Exercises 4-7 are not multiplicative inverses, have students write the multiplicative inverses for both numbers.

Error Analysis

Watch for students who find the multiplicative inverse of a mixed number by inverting the fractional part of the number and ignoring the whole number part.
Prevent by emphasizing that the whole number and fractional parts of a mixed number together represent one unique number. That number can be renamed as an improper fraction.

Practice Masters Booklet, **p. 54**

Name ______________________ Date ______________

Practice Worksheet 6-5

Multiplicative Inverses

Name the multiplicative inverse of each rational number.

1. 7 $\frac{1}{7}$	2. -10 $-\frac{1}{10}$	3. 1 1	4. 0.6 $\frac{5}{3}$
5. $\frac{1}{3}$ 3	6. $\frac{1}{5}$ 5	7. $-\frac{1}{12}$ -12	8. $\frac{1}{10}$ 10
9. $-\frac{4}{3}$ $-\frac{3}{4}$	10. $\frac{2}{3}$ $\frac{3}{2}$	11. $-\frac{8}{7}$ $-\frac{7}{8}$	12. 1.5 $\frac{2}{3}$
13. $-\frac{3}{23}$ $-\frac{23}{3}$	14. $\frac{6}{41}$ $\frac{41}{6}$	15. $3\frac{1}{5}$ $\frac{5}{16}$	16. $-3\frac{3}{4}$ $-\frac{4}{15}$
17. $\frac{x}{z}$ $\frac{z}{x}$	18. $\frac{e}{f}$ $\frac{f}{e}$	19. $-\frac{a}{c}$ $-\frac{c}{a}$	20. $\frac{w}{y}$ $\frac{y}{w}$

Name the property shown by each statement. All properties are of multiplication.

21. $-2\left(-\frac{3}{7}\right)$ is a rational number.
    closure
22. $\left(\frac{5}{9}\right)\left(\frac{9}{5}\right) = 1$
    inverse
23. $\frac{1}{2}\left(\frac{1}{3} \cdot \frac{1}{4}\right) = \left(\frac{1}{2} \cdot \frac{1}{3}\right) \cdot \frac{1}{4}$
    associative
24. $1 \cdot 3\frac{2}{3} = 3\frac{2}{3}$
    identity
25. $1 = \left(-\frac{14}{15}\right)\left(-\frac{15}{14}\right)$
    inverse
26. $\frac{3}{2}\left(-\frac{5}{6}\right) = \left(-\frac{5}{6}\right)\frac{3}{2}$
    commutative
27. $-2\left(-\frac{2}{9} \cdot \frac{3}{8}\right) = \left[-2 \cdot \left(-\frac{2}{9}\right)\right]\frac{3}{8}$
    associative
28. $4 \times 5\frac{1}{2} = 4(5) + 4\left(\frac{1}{2}\right)$
    distributive

Solve.

29. A nickel is $\frac{1}{20}$ of a dollar. How many nickels are in a \$2 roll?
    40 nickels
30. Four pies are cut into sixths. How many pieces of pie are there?
    24 pieces

Properties of Multiplication	Examples
Closure Property For all rational numbers x and y, $x \cdot y$ is a rational number.	$-3 \cdot 4 = -12$ $\quad 3.2 \cdot 0.5 = 1.6$ $-\frac{2}{5} \cdot \frac{3}{4} = -\frac{3}{10}$
Commutative Property For all rational numbers x and y, $x \cdot y = y \cdot x$.	$-3(-5) = -5(-3)$ $0.2(0.3) = 0.3(0.2)$ $\frac{2}{3} \cdot \frac{1}{2} = \frac{1}{2} \cdot \frac{2}{3}$
Associative Property For all rational numbers x, y, and z, $(x \cdot y) \cdot z = x \cdot (y \cdot z)$.	$(-2 \cdot 3) \cdot 4 = -2(3 \cdot 4)$ $\left(-\frac{1}{4} \cdot \frac{2}{3}\right) \cdot \frac{1}{2} = -\frac{1}{4} \cdot \left(\frac{2}{3} \cdot \frac{1}{2}\right)$ $(-6.5 \cdot 9.3) \cdot 2.1 = -6.5 \cdot (9.3 \cdot 2.1)$
Identity Property For every rational number x, $x \cdot 1 = x$ and $1 \cdot x = x$.	$-7 \cdot 1 = -7$ $\quad 1 \cdot \frac{2}{3} = \frac{2}{3}$ $7.45 \cdot 1 = 7.45$
Inverse Property For every rational number $\frac{x}{y}$, $x, y \neq 0$, there is a unique rational number $\frac{y}{x}$ such that $\frac{x}{y} \cdot \frac{y}{x} = 1$.	$2 \cdot \frac{1}{2} = 1$ $\quad -\frac{2}{3}\left(-\frac{3}{2}\right) = 1$ $0.5\left(\frac{1}{0.5}\right) = 1$

What number has no multiplicative inverse? **0**

The distributive property is the only property of rationals that involves two operations. The operations are multiplication and addition.

Distributive Property	For all rational numbers, x, y, and z, $x \cdot (y + z) = x \cdot y + x \cdot z$.

You can use the distributive property to compute products mentally.

Examples

1 **Compute $4 \times 5\frac{1}{2}$.**

$4 \times 5\frac{1}{2} = 4\left(5 + \frac{1}{2}\right)$

THINK: 4 groups of 5 is 20. 4 groups of $\frac{1}{2}$ is 2.

$= 20 + 2$ or 22

2 **Compute $\frac{1}{3} \times 6\frac{3}{4}$.**

$\frac{1}{3} \times 6\frac{3}{4} = \frac{1}{3}\left(6 + \frac{3}{4}\right)$

THINK: $\frac{1}{3}$ of 6 is 2. $\frac{1}{3}$ of $\frac{3}{4}$ is $\frac{1}{4}$.

$= 2 + \frac{1}{4}$ or $2\frac{1}{4}$

Alternate Strategies: Reteaching the Lesson

Reteaching Activity

Using Connections Have students use the rule on page 211 to replace the numerator (n) and denominator (d) with numbers that make the following statements true.

1. $\frac{2}{3} \cdot \frac{n}{d} = 1$
2. $\frac{3}{4} \cdot \frac{n}{d} = 1$
3. $\frac{n}{d} \cdot \frac{5}{1} = 1$
4. $\frac{n}{d} \cdot \frac{1}{2} = 1$

Reteaching Masters Booklet, **p. 49**

Name ______________________ Date ______________

Reteaching Worksheet 6-5

Multiplicative Inverses

When dividing with fractions, you will use the reciprocal of a number.

Two numbers whose product is 1 are called **reciprocals.** The reciprocal is also called the **multiplicative inverse.**

The reciprocal of 4 is $\frac{1}{4}$ because $4 \times \frac{1}{4} = 1$.
The reciprocal of $\frac{1}{4}$ is 4 because $\frac{1}{4} \times 4 = 1$.
The reciprocal of $-\frac{4}{5}$ is $-\frac{5}{4}$ because $-\frac{4}{5} \times -\frac{5}{4} = 1$.

Write the reciprocal of each number.

1. $\frac{4}{5}$ $\frac{5}{4}$	2. $\frac{8}{3}$ $\frac{3}{8}$	3. $-\frac{2}{7}$ $-\frac{7}{2}$	4. $\frac{5}{6}$ $\frac{6}{5}$
5. 3 [illegible]	6. -7 [illegible]	7. [illegible] -8	8. [illegible]

Checking for Understanding

Communicating Algebra

1. Name two numbers that are multiplicative inverses of each other. **1. Sample answer: $\frac{1}{2}$, 2**
2. Write a number sentence that shows the commutative property of multiplication for rational numbers. **Sample answer: $\left(-\frac{1}{2}\right)\left(\frac{2}{3}\right) = \left(\frac{2}{3}\right)\left(-\frac{1}{2}\right)$**
3. What property allows you to compute $9 \times 3\frac{2}{3}$ as $9(3) + 9\left(\frac{2}{3}\right)$? **distributive**

Guided Practice

State which pairs of numbers are multiplicative inverses. Write *yes* or *no*.

4. $5, \frac{1}{5}$ **yes**
5. $-\frac{3}{4}, 1\frac{1}{3}$ **no**
6. $3\frac{3}{4}, \frac{15}{4}$ **no**
7. $0.5, 2$ **yes**

Exercises

Independent Practice

Name the multiplicative inverse of each rational number.

8. $\frac{2}{3}$ **$\frac{3}{2}$**
9. $-\frac{8}{9}$ **$-\frac{9}{8}$**
10. 7 **$\frac{1}{7}$**
11. 0.8 **$\frac{5}{4}$**
12. $2\frac{4}{5}$ **$\frac{5}{14}$**
13. -1 **-1**
14. $\frac{a}{b}$ **$\frac{b}{a}$**
15. $\frac{x}{y}$ **$\frac{y}{x}$**

Name the property shown by each statement. **All properties are of multiplication.**

16. $\left(2 \cdot \frac{5}{2}\right) \cdot \frac{3}{4} = \frac{3}{4}\left(2 \cdot \frac{5}{2}\right)$ **comm.**
17. $-5 \cdot \frac{4}{5}$ is a rational number. **closure**
18. $-1\frac{14}{17} \cdot 1 = -1\frac{14}{17}$ **identity**
19. $\left(-\frac{5}{6}\right)\left(-\frac{6}{5}\right) = 1$ **inverse**
20. $(-4 \cdot 5) \cdot \frac{1}{4} = [5 \cdot (-4)] \cdot \frac{1}{4}$ **comm.**
21. $10 \times 3\frac{1}{5} = 10(3) + 10\left(\frac{1}{5}\right)$ **dist.**

Mental Math

Compute.

22. $100 \times 2\frac{1}{2}$ **250**
23. $6 \times 2\frac{1}{3}$ **14**
24. $3\frac{1}{4} \times 8$ **26**
25. $3\frac{2}{5} \times 20$ **68**
26. $\frac{1}{2} \times 8\frac{1}{2}$ **$4\frac{1}{4}$**
27. $\frac{1}{4} \times 12\frac{1}{2}$ **$3\frac{1}{8}$**
28. $\frac{2}{3} \times 6\frac{3}{5}$ **$4\frac{2}{5}$**
29. $\frac{3}{4} \times 16\frac{2}{3}$ **$12\frac{1}{2}$**

Mixed Review

30. *True* or *false:* $\frac{11}{3} \geq 3\frac{2}{3}$. (Lesson 5-1) **true**
31. Find the product $\left(-\frac{1}{2}\right)(8)$. (Lesson 6-3) **$-4$**
32. Solve the equation $p = (-7.8)(0.04)$. (Lesson 6-4) **-0.312**
33. Evaluate $a(b + c)$ if $a = 4.1$, $b = 0.8$, and $c = 9.3$. (Lesson 6-4) **41.41**

Application

34. **Personal Finance** Marsha bought a dozen plates for $3.25 each and a dozen bowls for $1.25 each. Write two different expressions that Marsha can use to find the total cost. **12(3.25 + 1.25); 12 • 3.25 + 12 • 1.25**

Critical Thinking

35. What is the product of the first 10 terms of the sequence $\frac{1}{2}, \frac{2}{3}, \frac{3}{4}, \frac{4}{5}, \ldots$? **$\frac{1}{11}$**

Wrap-Up

36. Explain how multiplicative inverses and additive inverses differ. Give an example for each using $-\frac{5}{9}$. **See margin.**

Independent Practice

Homework Assignment	
Basic	9-29 odd, 30-36
Average	8-28 even, 30-36
Honors	10-20 even, 25-36

4 CLOSE

Assessment Option

Writing Have students write a description of how they would explain the concept of reciprocal to a younger student.

Additional Answer

36. The product of two multiplicative inverses is 1. The sum of two additive inverses is 0. For example, the multiplicative inverse of $-\frac{5}{9}$ is $-\frac{9}{5}$, and the additive inverse of $-\frac{5}{9}$ is $\frac{5}{9}$.

Enrichment Masters Booklet, **p. 49**

Alternate Strategies: Extending the Lesson

Enrichment

Using Cooperative Pairs Have students work with a partner to multiply two fractions using the distributive property. $3\frac{3}{5} \bullet 6\frac{1}{4}$

$$= \left(3 + \frac{3}{5}\right)\left(6 + \frac{1}{4}\right)$$
$$= 3\left(6 + \frac{1}{4}\right) + \frac{3}{5}\left(6 + \frac{1}{4}\right)$$
$$= (3 \cdot 6) + \left(3 \cdot \frac{1}{4}\right) + \left(\frac{3}{5} \cdot 6\right) + \left(\frac{3}{5} \cdot \frac{1}{4}\right)$$
$$= 18 + \frac{3}{4} + \frac{18}{5} + \frac{3}{20}$$
$$= 22\frac{1}{2}$$

Cooperative Learning

Less Is Better Group Activity **6-5**

Work in groups of three. Complete the following multiplication table together, using as few new multiplications as possible. One person must write out the multiplications your group used, another person must list the properties you used, and the other person must keep track of the order of the multiplications you used and the number of multiplications. The group that finishes with the least number of new multiplications performed is the winner.

×	12	10	2	$\frac{5}{4}$	$\frac{3}{4}$
12					9
10				$\frac{25}{2}$	
2					$\frac{3}{2}$
$\frac{5}{4}$	15		$\frac{5}{2}$	$\frac{25}{16}$	
$\frac{3}{4}$		$\frac{15}{2}$		$\frac{15}{16}$	$\frac{9}{16}$

Use the commutative and distributive properties of multiplication. For example, your group might decide to start by doing the problem 12 × 12. You might rewrite it using the distributive property as 12 (10 + 2) and perform 2 new multiplications. Then the answer for the problems 12 × 10 and 12 × 2 would be known, so they would not be new multiplications.

Merrill Pre-Algebra MULTIPLICATIVE INVERSES

Name ______________ Date ______________

Enrichment Worksheet 6-5

Data Bank

Each problem below has at least one important fact missing. Use the data bank at the right to find the additional information needed to solve the problems.

Data Bank

Total Area (including land and water)	
AK	589,757 sq mi
FL	58,560 sq mi
IN	36,291 sq mi
MN	84,068 sq mi
OH	41,222 sq mi
RI	1214 sq mi

Population (1990 Census)	
CA	About 11.5 times the Kansas population
FL	about 12,535,000
KS	about 2,485,000
KY	about 3,742,000
MO	about 5,163,000
NC	about 6,602,000
WI	about 360,000 less than Missouri

1. Delaware, the "First State," is also the nation's second smallest. Its area is about 1.69 times the area of Rhode Island. The area of Delaware is about how many square miles? **about 2052 sq mi**
2. Wyoming, the "Equality State," has the nation's smallest population. California had about 28,074,000 more people than Wyoming in 1990. What was the population of Wyoming in 1990? **about 503,500**
3. Tennessee, the "Volunteer State," had about 130,000 fewer residents than Wisconsin according to the 1990 Census. What was the population of Tennessee in 1990? **about 4,673,000**
4. Pennsylvania, the "Keystone State," has about 4358 more square miles of area than its neighboring state to the west. What is the area of Pennsylvania? **about 45,580 sq mi**
5. Texas, the "Lone Star State," is the second largest state in total area. The largest state, Alaska, has an area approximately 2.19 times the area of Texas. What is the area of Texas? **about 269,295 sq mi**
6. Minnesota, the "North Star State," has another nickname, "The Land of 10,000 Lakes." The land area of Minnesota is 79,289 square miles. If it does have 10,000 lakes, what is the approximate area of the average lake in Minnesota? **about 0.4779 sq mi**
7. Florida, the "Sunshine State," is the fourth largest in population, but only 22nd in land area. How many people per square mile live in Florida? Give your answer to the nearest whole number. **about 214 people**
8. Indiana, the "Hoosier State," has about 153 people per square mile according to the 1990 census. About how many people lived in Indiana in 1990? **about 5,552,523 people**

Lesson Notes 6-6

5-Minute Check
(over Lesson 6-5)

Compute.
1. $10 \times 4\frac{1}{5}$ 42
2. $7\frac{2}{3} \times 6$ 46
3. $\frac{3}{4} \times 8\frac{2}{5}$ $6\frac{3}{10}$
4. $\frac{1}{2} \times 6\frac{3}{4}$ $3\frac{3}{8}$

Transparency 6-6 contains the 5-Minute Check and a teaching aid for this lesson.

1 FOCUS

The purpose of this lesson is to use the concept of reciprocal, as developed in Lesson 6-5, and the techniques of multiplying fractions to form an algorithm for dividing fractions.

Motivating the Lesson

Inform students that a honeybee can produce $\frac{1}{10}$ of a pound of honey in its lifetime. Ask students how many honeybees it would take to produce a half pound of honey.

2 TEACH

Chalkboard Examples

Solve each equation.

- *For Example 1*
  $y = \frac{6}{7} \div \frac{3}{8}$ $2\frac{2}{7}$
- *For Example 2*
  $y = 7 \div \left(\frac{1}{-5}\right)$ -35
- *For Example 3*
  $a = \frac{12}{-5} \div \left(\frac{4}{-15}\right)$ 9
- *For Example 4*
  $b = -7\frac{1}{3} \div 1\frac{2}{9}$ -6

EE: 1E, 2D, 3A, 3D, 3H
TAAS: 2, 9

6-6 Rationals: Dividing Fractions

Objective:
Divide fractions.

LeRoy Freeman needs 3 cups of pineapple for a fruit salad. If every can of pineapple contains $\frac{3}{4}$ cup, how many cans should Mr. Freeman buy?

Will Mr. Freeman need more than 3 or less than 3 cans of pineapple?
more than 3

To decide how many cans are needed, divide 3 by $\frac{3}{4}$. Recall that dividing by a number is the same as multiplying by its multiplicative inverse.

$$3 \div \frac{3}{4} = 3 \cdot \frac{4}{3}$$

Dividing by $\frac{3}{4}$ is the same as multiplying by $\frac{4}{3}$.

$$= \frac{\overset{1}{\cancel{3}}}{1} \cdot \frac{4}{\underset{1}{\cancel{3}}}$$

$$= 4$$

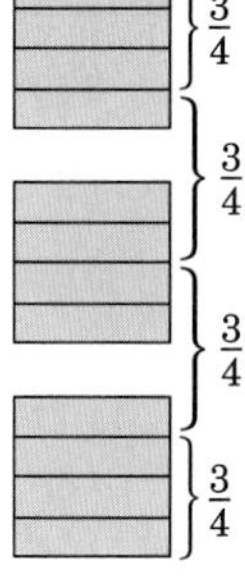

Mr. Freeman needs to buy 4 cans of pineapple. Compare with the model.

Division with Rational Numbers

In words: To divide by a rational number, multiply by its multiplicative inverse.

In symbols: For rational numbers $\frac{a}{b}$ and $\frac{c}{d}$, where $b, c, d \neq 0$,
$\frac{a}{b} \div \frac{c}{d} = \frac{a}{b} \cdot \frac{d}{c}$.

Example

1 **Solve $y = \frac{4}{5} \div \frac{2}{3}$.**

$y = \frac{4}{5} \div \frac{2}{3}$

$y = \frac{4}{5} \cdot \frac{3}{2}$ Dividing by $\frac{2}{3}$ is the same as multiplying by $\frac{3}{2}$.

$y = \frac{\overset{2}{\cancel{4}}}{5} \cdot \frac{3}{\underset{1}{\cancel{2}}}$ Divide 4 and 2 by 2.

$y = \frac{6}{5}$ or $1\frac{1}{5}$ Rename as a mixed number in simplest form.

Bell Ringer

Name the multiplicative inverse of the following numbers.
1. $\frac{4}{5}$ $\frac{5}{4}$ 2. $2\frac{8}{9}$ $\frac{9}{26}$ 3. 0.48 $\frac{25}{12}$

The division skills you have developed with integers and fractions can be used to divide with negative fractions.

Examples

Solve each equation.

2 $y = 3 \div \left(-\frac{1}{2}\right)$

$y = \frac{3}{1} \cdot \frac{-2}{1}$ Dividing by $-\frac{1}{2}$ is the same as multiplying by -2.

$y = -6$

3 $a = -\frac{10}{7} \div \left(-\frac{5}{14}\right)$

$a = -\frac{10}{7} \cdot \left(-\frac{14}{5}\right)$

$a = -\frac{\overset{2}{\cancel{10}}}{\underset{1}{\cancel{7}}} \cdot \left(-\frac{\overset{2}{\cancel{14}}}{\underset{1}{\cancel{5}}}\right)$

$a = 4$

4 $b = -3\frac{1}{2} \div 1\frac{3}{4}$

$b = -\frac{7}{2} \div \frac{7}{4}$

$b = -\frac{7}{2} \cdot \frac{4}{7}$

$b = -\frac{\overset{1}{\cancel{7}}}{\underset{1}{\cancel{2}}} \cdot \frac{\overset{2}{\cancel{4}}}{\underset{1}{\cancel{7}}}$

$b = -2$

Checking for Understanding

Communicating Algebra

1. State another name for *reciprocal.* **multiplicative inverse**
2. Complete the sentence: Dividing by any number, except zero, is the same as ■ . **multiplying by its reciprocal**
3. Name the multiplicative inverse of -3. $-\frac{1}{3}$

For Exercises 4-11, see margin.

Guided Practice

State a multiplication expression for each division expression. Then compute.

4. $\frac{2}{5} \div \frac{3}{4}$
5. $\frac{5}{6} \div \frac{10}{11}$
6. $-\frac{7}{9} \div \frac{2}{3}$
7. $\frac{13}{15} \div 6$
8. $5 \div \left(-1\frac{1}{3}\right)$
9. $2\frac{3}{5} \div 3\frac{6}{7}$
10. $5 \div 1\frac{9}{11}$
11. $7\frac{5}{9} \div (-8)$

Exercises

Independent Practice

Solve each equation. Write each solution in simplest form.

12. $a = 6 \div \left(-\frac{2}{3}\right)$ **-9**
13. $c = -10 \div \left(\frac{5}{2}\right)$ **-4**
14. $\frac{3}{4} \div \frac{2}{3} = t$ $\frac{9}{8}$
15. $h = 2\frac{1}{2} \div \frac{3}{4}$ $\frac{10}{3}$
16. $p = -3\frac{1}{5} \div 4\frac{2}{5}$ $-\frac{8}{11}$
17. $6\frac{1}{8} \div 4\frac{2}{3} = v$ $\frac{21}{16}$
18. $x = 10 \div (-2)$ **-5**
19. $-3 \div \left(\frac{2}{3}\right) = y$ $-\frac{9}{2}$
20. $\frac{3}{4} \div \frac{1}{2} = g$ $\frac{3}{2}$

3 PRACTICE/APPLY

Checking the Concept

Have students work in pairs to solve Exercises 4-11. Have students take turns verbalizing each exercise and monitor their responses.

Error Analysis
Watch for students who use the reciprocals of both fractions or the reciprocal of the dividend. **Prevent by** estimating or checking the quotient.

Independent Practice

Homework Assignment	
Basic	13-35 odd, 37-42, 45, 46
Average	18-36 even, 37-46
Honors	27-46

Additional Answers

4. $\frac{2}{5} \cdot \frac{4}{3}; \frac{8}{15}$
5. $\frac{5}{6} \cdot \frac{11}{10}; \frac{11}{12}$
6. $-\frac{7}{9} \cdot \frac{3}{2}; -1\frac{1}{6}$
7. $\frac{13}{15} \cdot \frac{1}{6}; \frac{13}{90}$
8. $\frac{5}{1} \cdot -\frac{4}{3}; -6\frac{4}{3}$
9. $\frac{13}{5} \cdot \frac{7}{27}; \frac{91}{135}$
10. $\frac{5}{1} \cdot \frac{11}{20}; 2\frac{3}{4}$
11. $\frac{68}{9} \cdot -\frac{1}{8}; -\frac{17}{18}$

Practice Masters Booklet, **p. 55**

Name ______________ Date ______________

Practice Worksheet 6-6

Rationals: Dividing Fractions

Solve each equation. Write each solution in simplest form.

1. $a = -8 \div (-12)$ $\frac{2}{3}$
2. $x = -15 \div \frac{3}{4}$ -20
3. $h = -\frac{3}{4} \div 3$ $-\frac{1}{4}$
4. $b = -5\frac{1}{2} \div \left(-2\frac{3}{4}\right)$ 2
5. $-8 \div \left(-\frac{4}{5}\right) = p$ 10
6. $c = 2\frac{1}{5} \div \left(-1\frac{7}{10}\right)$ $-1\frac{5}{17}$
7. $-1\frac{1}{9} \div 1\frac{17}{63} = d$ $-\frac{7}{8}$
8. $-10 \div \left(-5\frac{3}{4}\right) = k$ $1\frac{17}{23}$
9. $g = -\frac{1}{5} \div \frac{7}{8}$ $-\frac{8}{35}$
10. $-12\frac{1}{4} \div 4\frac{2}{3} = x$ $-2\frac{5}{8}$
11. $-5\frac{2}{7} \div \left(-\frac{3}{8}\right) = r$ $14\frac{2}{21}$
12. $-7\frac{3}{5} \div \left(-1\frac{9}{10}\right) = y$ 4
13. $6\frac{2}{3} \div \left(-\frac{10}{3}\right) = p$ -2
14. $-12\frac{1}{4} \div \left(-\frac{7}{8}\right) = k$ 14
15. $h = -5\frac{2}{3} \div \left(-2\frac{4}{15}\right)$ $2\frac{1}{2}$
16. $t = -1\frac{1}{2} \div \left(-\frac{3}{20}\right)$ 10
17. $b = \frac{5}{7} \div \left(-1\frac{1}{14}\right)$ $-\frac{2}{3}$
18. $-\frac{16}{17} \div \left(-1\frac{13}{51}\right) = p$ $\frac{3}{4}$
19. $c = -\frac{16}{15} \div \frac{64}{45}$ $-\frac{3}{4}$
20. $4\frac{6}{7} \div 1\frac{3}{14} = d$ 4
21. $-\frac{14}{11} \div \left(-\frac{16}{11}\right) = e$ $\frac{7}{8}$
22. $0 \div \left(-2\frac{15}{16}\right) = m$ 0
23. $n = 4 \div 6\frac{2}{3}$ $\frac{3}{5}$
24. $l = -10\frac{5}{6} \div (-6)$ $1\frac{29}{36}$

Alternate Strategies: Reteaching the Lesson

Reteaching Activity

Using Models Draw eight identical circles on the chalkboard or overhead. Divide each circle into fourths. Ask students how many groups of $\frac{3}{4}$ they see. 6 Have students write the division problem that represents this model. Repeat after dividing the circles into eighths.

Reteaching Masters Booklet, **p. 50**

Name ______________ Date ______________

Reteaching Worksheet 6-6

Rationals: Dividing Fractions

To divide by a rational number, multiply by its multiplicative inverse (its reciprocal).

$4 \div \frac{1}{2}$ is read "4 divided by $\frac{1}{2}$."

$4 \div \frac{1}{2}$ means "How many $\frac{1}{2}$s in 4?"

(1/2) (3/4) (5/6) (7/8) $4 \div \frac{1}{2} = 8$ **Think: 4 × 2 = 8**

8 halves

To divide mixed numbers, first rename the mixed numbers as fractions. Then, divide.

$-1\frac{1}{5} \div 2\frac{2}{5} = -\frac{6}{5} \div \frac{12}{5} = -\frac{6}{5} \times \frac{5}{12} = -\frac{30}{60} = -\frac{1}{2}$

4 CLOSE

Assessment Option

Writing Write a fraction or number on the board. Then have students write a division problem with that quotient. For example, write $\frac{4}{5}$ on the chalkboard and have students write a problem that will result in that answer, such as $\frac{1}{5} \div \frac{1}{4}$, or $2\frac{2}{3} \div 3\frac{1}{3}$.

Additional Answer

46. When you multiply a number by a rational number between 0 and 1, you are finding a part of the original number, thus the result will be smaller than the original number. When you divide a number by a rational number between 0 and 1, you are finding how many of those rational number parts are in the original number. Since the rational number is between 0 and 1, the result will be larger than the original number.

Enrichment Masters Booklet, **p. 50**

Name ______________________ Date ______________

Enrichment Worksheet 6-6

Dividing Fractions

When multiplying fractions, you multiply the numerators and multiply the denominators. What would happen if when dividing fractions you would divide the numerators and divide the denominators?

$$\frac{5}{8} \div \frac{1}{4} = \frac{5 \div 1}{8 \div 4} = \frac{5}{2} = 2\frac{1}{2}$$

When adding and subtracting fractions, you first change the fractions to like fractions. What would happen if when dividing fractions you change to like fractions before you divide?

$$\frac{2}{3} \div \frac{1}{4} = \frac{8}{12} \div \frac{3}{12} = \frac{8}{12} \times \frac{12}{3} = \frac{8}{3} = 2\frac{2}{3}$$

Find the quotient by dividing numerators and dividing denominators. Check each answer by using the traditional method.

1. $\frac{1}{6} \div \frac{1}{3}$ $\frac{1}{2}$
2. $\frac{5}{12} \div \frac{1}{4}$ $\frac{5}{3} = 1\frac{2}{3}$
3. $\frac{3}{8} \div \frac{3}{4}$ $\frac{1}{2}$
4. Will this method always produce the correct quotient? Explain. Yes; $\frac{A}{B} \div \frac{C}{D} = \frac{AD}{BC}$ and $\frac{A \div C}{B \div D} = \frac{A}{C} \div \frac{B}{D} = \frac{AD}{BC}$; therefore, $\frac{A}{B} \div \frac{C}{D} = \frac{A \div C}{B \div D}$
5. Give an example when this method may be more difficult than the traditional. Examples will vary. One possible answer is $\frac{3}{4} \div \frac{5}{3} = \frac{3 \div 5}{4 \div 3}$.

Find the quotient by first changing to like fractions. Check by using the traditional method.

6. $\frac{5}{6} \div \frac{3}{4}$ $\frac{10}{9} = 1\frac{1}{9}$
7. $\frac{4}{5} \div \frac{7}{10}$ $\frac{8}{7} = 1\frac{1}{7}$
8. $\frac{7}{8} \div \frac{11}{16}$ $\frac{14}{11} = 1\frac{3}{11}$
9. Will this method always produce the correct quotient? Explain. Yes; when you change to like fractions, you are not changing the value of either fraction or their quotient.
10. Name the method you like best and explain why. Answers will vary.

Solve each equation. Write each solution in simplest form.

21. $p = -\frac{5}{7} \div \frac{1}{14}$ -10
22. $2\frac{3}{4} \div \left(-\frac{3}{4}\right) = a$ $-\frac{11}{3}$
23. $-8 \div \left(-\frac{4}{3}\right) = h$ 6
24. $f = -\frac{3}{8} \div (-3)$ $\frac{1}{8}$
25. $c = 5\frac{5}{6} \div 2\frac{1}{3}$ $\frac{5}{2}$
26. $4\frac{2}{3} \div \left(-\frac{6}{7}\right) = d$ $-\frac{49}{9}$
27. $q = -2 \div \left(-\frac{1}{3}\right)$ 6
28. $s = -3\frac{1}{4} \div 2\frac{1}{6}$ $-\frac{3}{2}$
29. $-7\frac{1}{2} \div \left(1\frac{1}{5}\right) = n$ $-\frac{25}{4}$
30. $m = -\frac{16}{7} \div \left(-\frac{12}{35}\right)$ $\frac{20}{3}$
31. $a = \frac{21}{30} \div \left(-\frac{7}{15}\right)$ $-\frac{3}{2}$
32. $12\frac{1}{4} \div \left(-\frac{14}{3}\right) = j$ $-\frac{21}{8}$

Evaluate each expression.

33. $a \div b$, if $a = \frac{2}{3}$ and $b = 1\frac{1}{3}$ $\frac{1}{2}$
34. $r \div s$, if $r = -\frac{8}{9}$ and $s = \frac{7}{18}$ $-\frac{16}{7}$
35. $a^2 \div b^2$, if $a = -\frac{3}{4}$ and $b = 1\frac{1}{3}$ $\frac{81}{256}$
36. $m + n \div p$, if $m = \frac{2}{3}$, $n = 1\frac{1}{3}$, and $p = \frac{1}{9}$ $12\frac{2}{3}$

Mixed Review

37. Evaluate $2d^3$ if $d = 3$. (Lesson 4-2) 54
38. Round 44.005 to the nearest tenth. (Lesson 5-3) 44.0
39. **Personal Finance** Ana buys two pairs of shoes at a store that is having a "buy one pair, get the second for half price" sale. If the first pair of shoes costs \$35.98, the second pair costs \$29.98, and the tax is \$3.73, how much can Ana expect to pay? (Lesson 6-4) \$54.70
40. Name the multiplicative inverse of $-3\frac{1}{4}$. (Lesson 6-5) $-\frac{4}{13}$
41. Compute $\frac{1}{3} \times 1\frac{4}{5}$. (Lesson 6-5) $\frac{3}{5}$

Applications

42. **Home Economics** Mrs. Blair needs $8\frac{1}{4}$ cups of raisins to make 2 fruitcakes. A 15-ounce box of raisins contains $2\frac{3}{4}$ cups. How many boxes should Mrs. Blair buy? 3 boxes
43. **Publishing** A page of type is to be divided into three columns. If the page is $6\frac{3}{4}$ inches wide, how many inches wide is each column? $2\frac{1}{4}$ inches
44. **Carpentry** How many boards, each 2 feet 6 inches long, can be cut from a board 18 feet long? 7 boards

Critical Thinking

45. What is the quotient if the eighth term of the sequence $1, \frac{1}{2}, \frac{1}{4}, \frac{1}{8}, \ldots$ is divided by the ninth term? 2

Wrap-Up

46. A number is both multiplied and divided by the same rational number n, where $0 < n < 1$. Which is greater, the product or the quotient? Explain your reasoning. quotient; See margin.

Alternate Strategies: Extending the Lesson

Enrichment

Using Models Using a set of dominoes, have students express a problem with a quotient of 1, such as $\frac{1}{2} \div \frac{2}{4}$. Have students find two dominoes that can express a problem with a quotient of 2, such as $\frac{4}{3} \div \frac{2}{3}$. Ask students if division is commutative. Have students explain using the models.

Cooperative Learning

Distributing Division Group Activity **6-6**

You know there is a distributive property of multiplication over addition. Is there also a distributive property of division over addition? You will investigate that question in this activity.

Evaluate the expression $(50 + 15) \div 5$ in two ways.

Method One	Method Two
Distribute the division.	Add first.
$(50 \div 5) + (15 \div 5) = 10 + 3$	$(50 + 15) \div 5 = 65 \div 5$
$= 13$	$= 13$

With your partner, try another two or three examples. Make up your own division expressions. One of you can solve them using the distributive property, and the other can solve them by first adding.

Merrill Pre-Algebra RATIONALS: DIVIDING FRACTIONS

6-7 Rationals: Dividing Decimals

Objective:
Divide decimals.

The world outdoor sprint records in 1990 are shown in the graph. Carl Lewis ran 100 meters in 9.92 seconds. How many meters, on the average, did he run in 1 second? To find this rate, divide 100 by 9.92.

Estimation Hint

Estimate by rounding.
$100 \div 10 = 10$

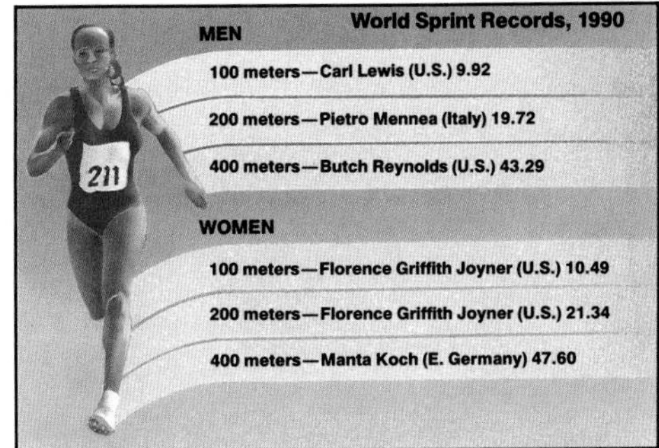

100 [÷] 9.92 [=] 10.080645

To the nearest hundredth, Carl Lewis ran an average of 10.08 meters in 1 second.

Let's review how this division is done. The division can be completed using paper and pencil more easily if the divisor, 9.92, is a whole number. Think of the fraction $\frac{100}{9.92}$.

$\frac{100}{9.92} \times \frac{100}{100} = \frac{10{,}000}{992}$

You can multiply by 100 mentally.
$100 \times 100 = 10{,}000$
$9.92 \times 100 = 992$

Since $\frac{100}{100} = 1$, the value of the fraction is unchanged. This becomes a division problem involving whole numbers.

$\frac{100}{9.92}$ ➡ $9.92\overline{)100.00}$ ➡ $992\overline{)10{,}000.000}$

$$\begin{array}{r} 10. \\ 9.92\overline{)100.00} \\ \underline{992} \\ 80 \\ \underline{0} \\ 80 \end{array} \qquad \begin{array}{r} 10.080 \\ 992\overline{)10{,}000.000} \\ \underline{992} \\ 80 \\ \underline{0} \\ 800 \\ \underline{0} \\ 8000 \\ \underline{7936} \\ 640 \end{array}$$

To the nearest hundredth, the quotient is 10.08. This matches the calculator result.

Bell Ringer

State a multiplication expression for each division expression.

1. $\frac{3}{7} \div \frac{4}{9}$ $\frac{3}{7} \times \frac{9}{4}$
2. $3\frac{6}{7} \div 2\frac{1}{11}$ $\frac{27}{7} \times \frac{11}{23}$

Lesson Notes 6-7

5-Minute Check
(over Lesson 6-6)

Solve each equation. Write each solution in simplest form.

1. $\frac{3}{5} \div \frac{6}{7} = k$ $\frac{7}{10}$
2. $5 \div \left(\frac{1}{-4}\right) = m$ -20
3. $x = \frac{15}{-8} \div (-3)$ $\frac{5}{8}$
4. $y = -7\frac{1}{2} \div \frac{5}{22}$ -33
5. $5\frac{1}{3} \div \left(-2\frac{2}{3}\right) = h$ -2

Transparency 6-7 contains the 5-Minute Check and a teaching aid for this lesson.

1 FOCUS

The purpose of this lesson is to apply the properties of equality to make division of decimals easier and to use estimation to check the reasonableness of the answers.

Motivating the Lesson

Present students with the following problem.
Sue earns $132.68 in a week in which she works 30.5 hours. What is Sue's hourly pay rate? $4.35

2 TEACH

Using Questioning

List decimal numbers on the chalkboard. For each, ask students what they would multiply the number by to make it a whole number.

EE: 1E, 2D, 3A, 5E
TAAS: 9, 10, 12, 13

Chalkboard Examples

Solve each equation.

- *For Example 1*
  $120 \div 1.2 = j$ **100**
- *For Example 2*
  $-0.0068 \div 0.004 = m$ **-1.7**

3 PRACTICE/APPLY

Checking the Concept

Divide students into groups of three to solve Exercises 7-9. For each exercise, have one student solve by moving the decimal point and dividing, one by using estimation, and one by using the calculator. Students should compare results and rotate roles.

Error Analysis

Watch for students who move the decimal point in the divisor but not in the dividend.
Prevent by having students write the multiplication by powers of ten for both the divisor and the dividend.

Practice Masters Booklet, **p. 56**

Name ____________________ Date ____________

Practice Worksheet 6-7

Rationals: Dividing Decimals

Solve each equation.

1. $0.102 \div (-0.51) = x$ **−0.2**
2. $-114 \div (-0.38) = y$ **300**
3. $896 \div 0.112 = z$ **8000**
4. $k = -0.545 \div (-10.9)$ **0.05**
5. $h = 3.66 \div 0.061$ **60**
6. $-0.0544 \div 0.017 = g$ **−3.2**
7. $-10.6 \div (-0.053) = m$ **200**
8. $n = 0.848 \div (-1.6)$ **−0.53**
9. $2.413 \div (-0.019) = a$ **−127**
10. $b = -4.03 \div (-62)$ **0.065**
11. $c = 0.3936 \div 0.48$ **0.82**
12. $d = -0.672 \div (-67.2)$ **0.01**
13. $0.2208 \div (-3.68) = e$ **−0.06**
14. $-332.5 \div 6.65 = f$ **−50**
15. $j = 0.225 \div (-0.015)$ **−15**
16. $-0.00001 \div (-0.001) = l$ **0.01**
17. $0.4405 \div 0.05 = i$ **8.81**
18. $z = -4.045 \div (-0.005)$ **809**

Examples

Solve each equation.

1 $50 \div 2.5 = a$ Estimate: $50 \div 2 = 25$

$2.5\overline{)50.0}$ Multiply both 2.5 and 50 by 10 to get a whole number divisor. or 50 ÷ 2.5 = 20

$25\overline{)500}$

$20 = a$ Compare with the estimate.

2 $-0.0078 \div 0.003 = y$ Estimate: $-8 \div 3 = -2\frac{2}{3}$

$0.003\overline{)0.0078}$ Multiply 0.003 and 0.0078 by 1000 to get a whole number divisor.

$$\begin{array}{r} -2.6 \\ 3\overline{)-7.8} \end{array}$$

The quotient is negative.

or

0.0078 +/− ÷ 0.003 = -2.6

$-2.6 = y$ Compare with the estimate.

Checking for Understanding

Communicating Algebra

1. What is the first step in preparing to divide two decimals? **Make an estimate.**
2. Explain why you should make an estimate when using a calculator to divide. **Check for reasonableness.**

Use estimation to choose the correct quotient.

3. $36 \div 1.2$; 3 or <u>30</u>
4. $4.5 \div 0.9$; <u>5</u> or 0.5
5. $1.6 \div 8$; 2 or <u>0.2</u>
6. $1.6 \div 0.8$; <u>2</u> or 0.2

Guided Practice

State where the decimal point should be placed in each quotient.

7. $0.48 \div 0.2 = 24$ **2‸4**
8. $25 \div 0.05 = 500$ **500‸**
9. $3.6 \div 0.04 = 90$ **90‸**
10. $0.012 \div 0.04 = 03$ **0‸3**
11. $0.0018 \div 0.2 = 9$ **‸009**
12. $0.56 \div 0.007 = 80$ **80‸**

Find each quotient.

13. $24 \div 0.3$ **80**
14. $0.3 \div 6$ **0.05**
15. $15.5 \div (-0.5)$ **−31**

Alternate Strategies: Reteaching the Lesson

Reteaching Activity

Using Groups of Two Before reteaching, determine exact causes of errors. Students may have trouble with the numerical division process, placing the decimal point, or rounding. Ask students to work a problem while you watch. Reteach, then pair up students and have them verbalize each step.

Reteaching Masters Booklet, **p. 51**

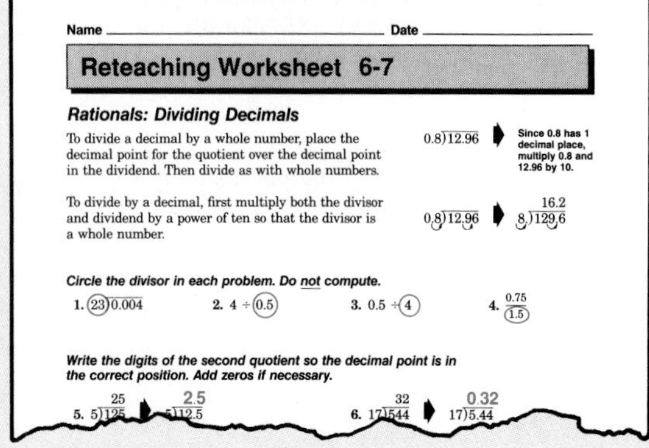
Name ____________________ Date ____________

Reteaching Worksheet 6-7

Rationals: Dividing Decimals

To divide a decimal by a whole number, place the decimal point for the quotient over the decimal point in the dividend. Then divide as with whole numbers.

$0.8\overline{)12.96}$ ➧ Since 0.8 has 1 decimal place, multiply 0.8 and 12.96 by 10.

To divide by a decimal, first multiply both the divisor and dividend by a power of ten so that the divisor is a whole number.

$0.8\overline{)12.96}$ ➧ $8\overline{)129.6}$ = 16.2

Circle the divisor in each problem. Do not compute.

1. $(23)\overline{)0.004}$
2. $4 \div (0.5)$
3. $0.5 \div (4)$
4. $\frac{0.75}{(1.5)}$

Write the digits of the second quotient so the decimal point is in the correct position. Add zeros if necessary.

5. $5\overline{)125}$ = 25 ➧ $5\overline{)12.5}$ = **2.5**
6. $17\overline{)544}$ = 32 ➧ $17\overline{)5.44}$ = **0.32**

Exercises

Independent Practice

Solve each equation.

16. $a = 0.128 \div 8$ 0.016
17. $r = 19.26 \div 6$ 3.21
18. $0.335 \div 5 = d$ 0.067
19. $y = 5.0 \div 0.25$ 20
20. $z = 2.25 \div 2.5$ 0.9
21. $-3.75 \div 0.25 = b$ -15
22. $1.69 \div (-1.3) = x$ -1.3
23. $-7.5 \div (-1.5) = m$ 5
24. $4.156 \div 0.4 = k$ 10.39

Estimation

Estimate each quotient. Then compute with a calculator. Round the quotient to the nearest tenth, if necessary.

25. $a = 5.98 \div 2.9$ 2.1
26. $1.98 \div 0.71 = p$ 2.8
27. $7.81 \div 5 = y$ 1.6
28. $z = 0.597 \div 0.25$ 2.4
29. $t = 93.702 \div 2.4$ 39.0
30. $a = 17.3 \div 5.2$ 3.3

Mixed Review

31. Solve the equation $-5x = -100$. (Lesson 3-3) 20
32. Simplify the expression $-\frac{4}{5}y + 2\frac{3}{5}y + 7\frac{1}{5}y$. (Lesson 5-5) 9y
33. Name the property shown by the sentence $8 \times 2\frac{1}{4} = 8(2) + 8\left(\frac{1}{4}\right)$. (Lesson 6-5) distributive property

Applications

34. **Sports** Cheryl competes in the 100-meter freestyle event at a swim meet. Her times in the previous five races were 53.53 s, 54.24 s, 54.82 s, 54.69 s, and 54.60 s. Find Cheryl's average time. 54.376 s

35. **Business** While taking inventory at The Builder's Store, a clerk measures a stack of table tops. If each top is 1.875 inches thick and the stack is 3 feet 9 inches high, how many table tops are in the stack? 24 table tops

Critical Thinking

36. Name two decimals whose sum is 2.7 and whose quotient is 2. 1.8, 0.9

Wrap-Up

37. Using the information in the chart at the beginning of the lesson, find the average number of meters Florence Griffith-Joyner ran in 1 second in the 100-meter event. 9.53 meters

Mid-Chapter Quiz

1. Express $\frac{2}{3}$ as a decimal. (Lesson 6-1) $0.\overline{6}$
2. Estimate $\frac{2}{3} \times 20$. (Lesson 6-2) 14
3. Explain how to compute $8 \times 3\frac{1}{4}$ using the distributive property. (Lesson 6-5) $8 \times 3 + 8 \times \frac{1}{4}$

Solve each equation. (Lesson 6-3, 6-4, 6-6)

4. $x = -2\frac{1}{2}(-8)$ 20
5. $0.008 \times 0.9 = y$ 0.0072
6. $a = -\frac{3}{8} \times 1\frac{1}{3}$ $-\frac{1}{2}$
7. $b = \left(\frac{4}{9}\right)^2$ $\frac{16}{81}$
8. $p = -2.5 \times 1.8$ -4.5
9. $\frac{3}{4} \div 1\frac{1}{3} = c$ $\frac{9}{16}$

Independent Practice

Homework Assignment	
Basic	17-29 odd, 31-37
Average	16-30 even, 31-37
Honors	21-24, 27-37
All	Mid-Chapter Review 1-9

Chapter 6, Quiz A (Lessons 6-1 through 6-7) is available in the Evaluation Masters Booklet, p. 52.

CLOSE

Assessment Option

Modeling Write decimal point division problems with blanks for numbers, such as xx.x)x.xxx. Then use number cards 0-9 to fill in the blanks and solve.

Alternate Strategies: Extending the Lesson

Enrichment

Consumer Connection Have students write problems giving total cost and number of units purchased and ask for the unit cost. For example, Mark buys 2.83 pounds of steak for \$16.95. What is the cost per pound? \$5.99 Have students use familiar purchases and make the problems realistic. Trade and solve.

Cooperative Learning

Point It Out Group Activity **6-7**

MATERIALS: Calculator

This activitiy is best done in pairs. The object of the activity is to correctly estimate the position of the decimal point in a quotient.

To begin, each person makes up a number between 1 and 100 with up to four digits after the decimal point. One person has the calculator. That person's number is the dividend. The other person's number is the divisor. Write the problem on a piece of paper.

The person with the calculator computes the answer and reads the digits out loud. The other person must tell between which two numbers the decimal point should be placed. If a correct answer is given, then this person scores one point and is given the calculator for the next problem.

The winner is the first person to score ten points.

Merrill Pre-Algebra RATIONALS: DIVIDING DECIMALS

Enrichment Masters Booklet, **p. 51**

Name ______ Date ______

Enrichment Worksheet 6-7

Decimal Hunt

Each of the sentences below is missing two parts, an operation symbol (+, −, ×, ÷) and a result. The missing results are given in the box at the right. Use guess and check to find the operations and the results that make each sentence true.

1. 12.35 ⊗ 4.16 = 51.376
2. 6.25 ⊕ 3.06 = 9.31
3. 38.052 ⊕ 12.6 = 3.02
4. 0.08 ⊕ 2.5 = 0.032
5. 21.45 ⊖ 13.237 = 8.213
6. 1.987 ⊗ 1.025 = 2.036675
7. 7.23 ⊕ 8.669 = 15.899
8. 30.68 ⊖ 12.228 = 18.452
9. 8.35 ⊗ 3.24 = 27.054
10. 2.3625 ⊕ 1.35 = 1.75

0.032
1.75
2.036675
3.02
8.213
9.31
15.899
18.452
27.054
51.376

Lesson Notes 6-8

5-Minute Check
(over Lesson 6-7)

Solve each equation.

1. $d = 0.207 \div 9$ **0.023**
2. $-2.55 \div (-0.15)$ **17**
3. $0.786 \div 1000 = t$ **0.000786**
4. $-6.3 \div 0.35 = x$ **-18**
5. $y = 1.088 \div (-0.64)$ **-1.7**

Transparency 6-8 contains the 5-Minute Check and a teaching aid for this lesson.

1 FOCUS

The purpose of this lesson is to provide students additional opportunities in solving equations and inequalities by including rational numbers in the solution sets.

Motivating the Lesson

List several sentences and have students tell whether they represent inequalities (The labor charge will be at least $72.00.) or equations (The total number of players is 11.). Have students add to each list.

2 TEACH

Using Problem Solving

Introduce the use of rational numbers in equations and inequalities by first solving problems using whole numbers. Replace the whole numbers with decimals and fractions and solve.

Chalkboard Examples

Solve each equation. Check your solution.

- *For Example 1*
  $\frac{x}{-4.3} = 2.7$ **-11.61**

EE: 1E, 2D, 3A, 3F
TAAS: 2, 8, 9

6-8 Solving Equations and Inequalities

Objective:
Solve equations and inequalities containing rational numbers.

You can apply the multiplication and division skills that you have learned for rational numbers to solve equations and inequalities containing rational numbers. Consider this problem.

On the first day Cherry Creek Limited stock was traded, it gained $4\frac{1}{8}$ points. The amount of gain was $\frac{1}{4}$ of its opening price. What was the stock price when it opened?

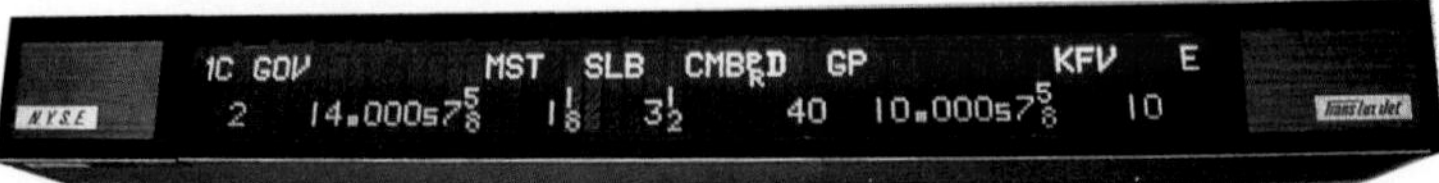

What is the product of a number and its multiplicative inverse? **1**

Let x = the opening price.

$$\frac{1}{4} \text{ of opening price} = 4\frac{1}{8}$$

$$\frac{1}{4}x = 4\frac{1}{8}$$

$$4 \cdot \frac{1}{4}x = 4 \cdot 4\frac{1}{8} \quad \text{4 and } \frac{1}{4} \text{ are multiplicative inverses.}$$

$$x = \frac{4}{1} \cdot \frac{33}{8}$$

$$x = \frac{33}{2} \text{ or } 16\frac{1}{2}$$

Cherry Creek Limited stock opened at $16\frac{1}{2}$ points or $16.50.

FYI

Two hundred years ago, stock brokers in New York City met underneath a buttonwood tree on Wall Street to transact their business. Today, this site on Wall Street is the location of the New York Stock Exchange.

Examples

Solve each equation. Check your solution.

1 $\frac{x}{-1.5} = 4.5$

$(-1.5)\frac{x}{-1.5} = (-1.5)4.5$ Multiply each side by -1.5.

$x = -6.75$

Check: $\frac{x}{-1.5} = 4.5$

$\frac{-6.75}{-1.5} \stackrel{?}{=} 4.5$ 6.75 [+/-] [÷] 1.5 [+/-] [=] 4.5

$4.5 = 4.5$ ✓

Bell Ringer

Make up a division problem in which you have to move the decimal point two units. **Possible answer: 8.95 ÷ 9.86**

2 $2.3x = -9.2$

$\frac{2.3x}{2.3} = \frac{-9.2}{2.3}$ Divide each side by 2.3.

9.2 [+/-] [÷] 2.3 [=] -4

$x = -4$

Check: 2.3 [×] 4 [+/-] = -9.2 ✓

In Example 3, why should you multiply by $\frac{6}{5}$? **$\frac{6}{5} \cdot \frac{5}{6} = 1$**

3 $\frac{5}{6}m = -\frac{2}{3}$

$\frac{6}{5} \cdot \frac{5}{6}m = \left(\frac{6}{5}\right)\left(-\frac{2}{3}\right)$ Multiply each side by $\frac{6}{5}$.

$m = -\frac{4}{5}$

Check: $\frac{5}{6}m = -\frac{2}{3}$

$\frac{5}{6}\left(-\frac{4}{5}\right) \stackrel{?}{=} -\frac{2}{3}$

$-\frac{2}{3} = -\frac{2}{3}$ ✓

Inequalities with rational numbers are solved using the same skills you developed for solving inequalities with integers.

Examples

Solve each inequality.

How can you check the solution of an inequality? **Replace the variable with a number from the solution.**

4 $\frac{a}{2.6} > 4.5$

$(2.6)\frac{a}{2.6} > (2.6)4.5$ Multiply each side by 2.6.

2.6 [×] 4.5 [=] 11.7

$a > 11.7$

Any number greater than 11.7 is a solution.

5 $\frac{c}{-2} \geq 3.6$

$(-2)\frac{c}{-2} \leq (-2)3.6$ Multiply each side by -2. Remember to reverse the order symbol.

$c \leq -7.2$

Any number less than or equal to -7.2 is a solution.

Checking for Understanding

Communicating Algebra

1. Explain how you would use a multiplicative inverse to solve $\frac{2}{3}x = 8$. **1. Multiply each side by $\frac{3}{2}$, the multiplicative inverse of $\frac{2}{3}$.**
2. Name the multiplicative inverse of $-\frac{4}{9}$. **$-\frac{9}{4}$**

Chalkboard Examples

- *For Example 2*
  $1.4y = -8.4$ **-6**
- *For Example 3*
  $\frac{3}{4}k = \frac{5}{-8}$ **$\frac{5}{-6}$**

Solve each inequality.

- *For Example 4*
  $\frac{m}{3.8} > 6.2$ **$m > 23.56$**
- *For Example 5*
  $\frac{r}{-5} \geq 2.9$ **$r \leq -14.5$**

3 PRACTICE/APPLY

Checking the Concept

After students have solved Guided Practice Exercises 3-11, have them check the results by substitution.

Alternate Strategies: Reteaching the Lesson

Reteaching Activity

Using Chalkboard Examples Have students rewrite Examples 1, 4, and 5 without using the fraction bar. Ask students how they would solve these if the number on the same side as the variable was a whole number. Have students use calculators to apply their responses to the rewritten examples.

Reteaching Masters Booklet, **p. 52**

Name ____________ Date ____________

Reteaching Worksheet 6-8

Solving Equations and Inequalities

One step in solving some equations is to multiply each side by the same number to get the variable by itself.

The number you multiply each side by is the reciprocal of the number that is multiplied times the variable.

$$-\frac{y}{5} = 8$$
$$-\frac{1}{5} \cdot y = 8$$
$$-\frac{5}{1} \cdot \left(-\frac{1}{5}\right) \cdot y = 8 \cdot \left(-\frac{5}{1}\right)$$
$$y = -40$$

Write the number you would multiply each side by in order to get the variable by itself.

1. $4n = 12$ **$\frac{1}{4}$**
2. $\frac{a}{2} = 50$ **$\frac{2}{1}$**
3. $-7t = 21$ **$-\frac{1}{7}$**
4. $-\frac{m}{6} = 2$ **-6**
5. $-35 < \frac{h}{7}$ **$\frac{7}{1}$**
6. $0.25b < 5$ **$\frac{1}{0.25}$ or 4**
7. $2.4 \leq -6x$ **$-\frac{1}{6}$**
8. $-\frac{c}{3} \geq -12$ **-3**

Practice Masters Booklet, **p. 57**

Name ____________ Date ____________

Practice Worksheet 6-8

Solving Equations and Inequalities

Solve each equation or inequality. Check your solution.

1. $-8a = -5.68$ **0.71**
2. $\frac{b}{4.2} = -5$ **-21**
3. $27.44 = -4.9c$ **-5.6**
4. $-\frac{d}{4} < -4.7$ **$d > 18.8$**
5. $-12.6 \leq 3e$ **$e \geq -4.2$**
6. $-5f > 35.5$ **$f < -7.1$**
7. $-125 = -\frac{5}{8}m$ **200**
8. $-2.3n = 0.805$ **-0.35**
9. $-\frac{t}{8.7} = -3.01$ **26.187**
10. $-8.4r \geq 5.88$ **$r \leq -0.7$**
11. $\frac{k}{1.5} < -4.5$ **$k < -6.75$**
12. $20.4 \leq -3.4l$ **$l \leq -6$**
13. $-18.24 = -6x$ **3.04**
14. $-\frac{z}{2.1} = -100$ **210**
15. $-1.27y = 0.0381$ **-0.03**
16. $\frac{r}{0.5} < -3.1$ **$r < -1.55$**
17. $-0.16s > -9.6$ **$s < 60$**
18. $-\frac{2}{3}t \leq -\frac{8}{9}$ **$t \geq 1\frac{1}{3}$**
19. $3.4j = 0.816$ **0.24**
20. $\frac{i}{7.4} = -0.5$ **-3.7**
21. $48.374 = -1.34w$ **-36.1**
22. $0.3u < -2.73$ **$u < -9.1$**
23. $-\frac{3}{4}v \geq -1\frac{11}{16}$ **$v \leq 2\frac{1}{4}$**
24. $0.025x \leq 5.25$ **$x \leq 210$**
25. $-\frac{z}{50.3} = 7.6$ **-382.28**
26. $-\frac{8}{9}k = -0.16$ **0.18**
27. $0.42y = -2.6166$ **-6.23**

Error Analysis

Watch for students who are confused by varied syntax when words are used.
Prevent by having students list as many word expressions as possible for each of several different mathematical expressions.

Independent Practice

Homework Assignment	
Basic	13-21 odd, 27-35
Average	14-22 even, 27-35
Honors	21-35

4 CLOSE

Assessment Option

Writing Have students work in pairs to create problems using equations and inequalities.

Additional Answer

34. Linda correctly answered $\frac{2}{3}$ of the questions on a quiz. If she answered more than 6 questions correctly, how many questions were on the quiz?

Enrichment Masters Booklet, **p. 52**

Name ______________________ Date ____________

Enrichment Worksheet 6-8

Multi-Step Problems

Solving an equation such as $5 + 3y = 17$ requires two steps. First, subtract 5 from each side of the equation. Then divide each side of the equation by 3.

$$5 + 3y = 17$$
$$-5 \quad\quad -5$$
$$\frac{3y}{3} = \frac{12}{3}$$
$$y = 4$$

Write the operation and number that would be used in each step of the following two-step equations. Use A for addition, S for subtraction, M for multiplication, and D for division.

	Equation	Step 1	Step 2	Solution
Example	$2y - 6 = 10$	A 6	D 2	$y = 8$
1.	$2a + 3.4 = 75.6$	S 3.4	D 2	$a = 36.1$
2.	$3.456 = 4b - 1$	A 1	D 4	$b = 1.114$
3.	$15 = 3.6 + \frac{c}{3}$	S 3.6	M 3	$c = 34.2$
4.	$0.4 = \frac{d}{12.6} + 2$	S 2	M 12.6	$d = -20.16$
5.	$7 - 0.87e = 8.4355$	S 7	D −0.87	$e = -1.65$
6.	$87 = 0.25f - 38.6$	A 38.6	D 0.25	$f = 502.4$

Write and solve a multi-step equation for each problem.

7. What are the length and width of a rectangular dog pen with a perimeter of 38 feet if the length is two feet less than twice the width? $2(2w - 2) + 2w = 38$; 7 ft by 12 ft

8. Apex Taxi charges $2.80 per mile plus $1.50 per passenger. How many miles did Mr. and Mrs. Kelly travel if the charge was $31? $3 + 2.8m = 31$; 10 mi

9. Alice earned a 5% commission for selling encyclopedias. How many dollars in sales did she have if she still needed $60 to buy a $100 radio? $0.05x + 60 = 100$; $800

Guided Practice

Explain how to solve each equation or inequality. Then solve. See margin.

3. $0.5x = 10$ 20
4. $1.1y = -2.2$ −2
5. $3.6 < 0.9c$ $4 < c$
6. $\frac{2}{3}x > 6$ $x > 9$
7. $-\frac{5}{6}y = \frac{3}{5}$ $-\frac{18}{25}$
8. $\frac{5}{8}t = 4$ $\frac{32}{5}$
9. $\frac{k}{1.5} = 1.1$ 1.65
10. $\frac{z}{-7} \leq 12$ $z \geq -84$
11. $-11t > 12\frac{1}{2}$ $t < -\frac{25}{22}$

Exercises

Independent Practice

Solve each equation or inequality. Check your solution.

12. $2a = -12$ −6
13. $-3y = 1.5$ −0.5
14. $\frac{x}{3} > -6$ −18

15. $-\frac{1}{4}c = 3.4$ −13.6
16. $\frac{x}{3.2} < -4.5$ $x < -14.4$
17. $-1.6n = 0.48$ −0.3
18. $\frac{n}{2} \geq -1.6$ $n \geq -3.2$
19. $\frac{1}{3}d = -0.36$ −1.08
20. $\frac{m}{2.3} = -5.2$ −11.96
21. $-\frac{3}{5}r \leq \frac{2}{3}$ $r \geq -1\frac{1}{9}$
22. $-7\frac{1}{2}x = 5\frac{1}{4}$ $-\frac{7}{10}$
23. $-2h > 4.6$ $h < -2.3$
24. $\frac{4}{5}y = \frac{3}{8}$ $\frac{15}{32}$
25. $\frac{x}{-2.5} \leq 3.2$ $x \geq -8$
26. $7x < 1\frac{4}{10}$ $x < \frac{1}{5}$

Mixed Review

27. Evaluate the expression $4[2(3 + 5) - 8]$. (Lesson 1-1) 32
28. Solve the inequality $f - 4.6 < -3.1$. (Lesson 5-7) $f < 1.5$
29. Evaluate the expression $x^2 \div y$ if $x = \frac{1}{2}$ and $y = -\frac{2}{3}$. (Lesson 6-6) $-\frac{3}{8}$
30. Solve the equation $y = 30.66 \div 7$. (Lesson 6-7) 4.38
31. **Measurement** The distance from Jeff's house to school is about 2000 feet. What part of a mile is this? (Lesson 6-7) about $\frac{2}{5}$

Applications

32. **Personal Finance** Alma has $24 to spend on cassette tapes. The CD and Tape Mart is selling tapes for $6.99. How many tapes can Alma buy? 3
33. **Personal Finance** Kioka earns 5¢ for every newspaper she delivers. She earns between $2.50 and $3.00 every day. What is the least number of newspapers Kioka delivers each day? What is the greatest number? 50, 60

Critical Thinking

34. **Make Up a Problem** Write a problem that can be solved using the inequality in Exercise 6. Sample answer in margin.

Wrap-Up

35. Write an equation that can be solved by multiplying by $\frac{3}{4}$. Sample answer: $\frac{4}{3}y = 10$

Team Problem Solving

The Absent-Minded Professor has two glasses of Sparkling Soda. The first is half full. The second glass, twice the size of the first glass, is one-quarter full. The professor fills both glasses with water and mixes the contents into a third container. What part of the final mixture is Sparkling Soda? $\frac{1}{3}$

230 *Rationals: Multiplying and Dividing Patterns*

Alternate Strategies: Extending the Lesson

Enrichment

Using Groups of Two Write inequalities with the variable on both sides of the inequality. Use models to solve. Work with a partner.

Cooperative Learning

Comparing To One Group Activity **6-8**

MATERIALS: Four 0-9 spinners

You and a partner will investigate the solutions to equations involving rational numbers. To begin, spin the four 0-9 spinners. If a zero turns up, you will needed to spin again until you get all nonzero numbers.

From these four digits, form two fractions, both of which are less than one (that is, in both fractions the numerator is less than the denominator). Using the two fractions, write an equation of the form $ax = b$, replacing the a and b with the fractions.

Now decide if the solution to the equation is less than 1 or greater than 1. Solving the equation using algebraic techniques will allow you to tell if your decision was correct.

Do five more of these equations. Write a short paragraph explaining when the value of x will be less than one and when it will be greater than one.

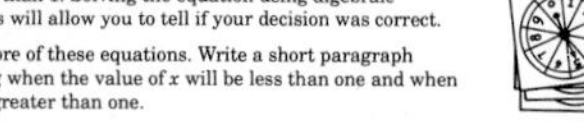

Merrill Pre-Algebra SOLVING EQUATIONS AND INEQUALITIES

6-9 Inductive and Deductive Reasoning

Objective:
Use deductive and inductive reasoning.

Key Terms:
inductive
deductive

Carla noticed that for the last six Thursdays her pre-algebra teacher, Mrs. Hodges, has given a pop quiz. So, Carla assumed that the next Thursday there would be a pop quiz in pre-algebra.

Carla used **inductive reasoning**. Inductive reasoning *makes* a rule after seeing several examples. Carla made a conclusion based on what happened in the past.

Example

1 The Italian scientist Galileo discovered that there was a relationship between the time of the swing back and forth of a pendulum and its length.

Time of Swing	Length of Pendulum
1 second	1 unit
2 seconds	4 units
3 seconds	9 units
4 seconds	16 units

How long do you think a pendulum with a swing of 5 seconds is?

Look at the pattern in the table. The measure of the pendulum is the square of the measure of time.

Apply inductive reasoning. A pendulum with a swing of 5 seconds would have a length of 5^2 or 25 units.

Let's return to Carla's pop quiz situation. Suppose her teacher does not give a pop quiz the next Thursday. Then the method of inductive reasoning did not work. Since inductive reasoning is based on past evidence only, it may sometimes fail.

At the beginning of the year, Carla's science teacher, Mr. Steiner, said he would give a quiz every Friday. Carla knows that if it is a Friday, there will be a quiz in science.

This is an example of **deductive reasoning**. Deductive reasoning *uses* a rule to make a conclusion or a decision.

FYI

Galileo (1564–1642) is sometimes called the father of modern experimental science. His father wanted him to be a medical doctor. However, his interest in mathematics led him to serve as professor of mathematics for 18 years at the University of Padua in Italy.

Example

2 All pentagons have five sides. The figure shown at the right has five sides. What can you conclude?

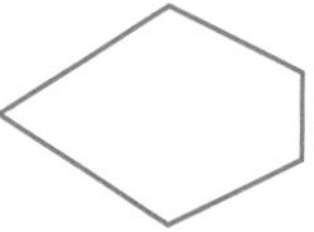

Use deductive reasoning to conclude that the figure is a pentagon.

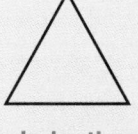

Bell Ringer

Solve the following equation and inequality.

1. $\frac{m}{5} = \frac{9}{10}$ $m = 4.5$
2. $\frac{5}{6}x > -10$ $x > -12$

Reteaching Activity

Using Problem Solving Choose a topic. Divide a piece of paper into two columns. Write inductive statements about the topic in column 1 and deductive statements in column 2. For example, the topic is a basketball game. Column 1: Al will make this shot. Column 2: If made, this foul shot will raise the score by 1 point.

Lesson Notes 6-9

5-Minute Check
(over Lesson 6-8)

Solve each equation or inequality. Check your solution.

1. $3x = -36$ **-12**
2. $\frac{y}{3} \geq -7.4$ $y \geq -22.2$
3. $\frac{2}{-3} m \leq \frac{1}{9}$ $m \geq \frac{1}{-6}$
4. $\frac{6}{7} c = \frac{3}{5}$ $c = \frac{7}{10}$

Transparency 6-9 contains the 5-Minute Check and a teaching aid for this lesson.

1 FOCUS

The purpose of this lesson is to distinguish between inductive and deductive reasoning and to use them to make predictions and draw conclusions.

2 TEACH

Chalkboard Examples

Determine whether each exercise is an example of inductive or deductive reasoning. Explain your reasoning.

- *For Example 1*
  What is the comparison of moist snow to water? How much water would you have with 42 inches of moist snow? **inductive; 7 inches**

moist snow	water
6 inches	1 inch
12 inches	2 inches
18 inches	3 inches
24 inches	4 inches

- *For Example 2*
  All triangles have three sides. The figure shown has three sides. What can you conclude? **deductive; The figure is a triangle.**

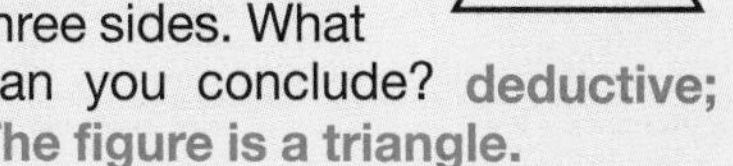

EE: 1A, 1E

3 PRACTICE/APPLY

Checking the Concept

After students solve Exercises 4-6, discuss whether inductive or deductive results are more reliable.

Error Analysis
Watch for students who are confused by the terms inductive and deductive. **Prevent by** reminding students that inductive reasoning starts with examples, and deductive reasoning starts with a rule.

Independent Practice

Homework Assignment	
Basic	7-16
Average	7-16
Honors	7-16

4 CLOSE

Assessment Option

Writing Have students work in pairs and write a deductive and inductive reasoning problem. Then have them exchange their problems and solve using inductive and deductive reasoning. Have the students tell which type of problem they are solving.

Practice Masters Booklet, **p. 58**

Name ______________ Date ______________

Practice Worksheet 6-9

Logic: Inductive/Deductive Reasoning

Use inductive reasoning to determine the next two numbers in each list.

1. 109, 110, 111, 112, ... 113, 114
2. 80, 75, 70, 65, ... 60, 55
3. 22, 32, 42, 52, 62, ... 72, 82
4. 1, 5, 11, 15, 21, 25, ... 31, 35
5. 2, 5, 4, 5, 6, 5, 8, 5, ... 10, 5
6. 2, 3, 5, 8, 12, 17, ... 23, 30
7. 8, 8, 10, 10, 12, 12, 14, ... 14, 16
8. 1, 4, 8, 13, 19, ... 26, 34
9. 1024, 512, 256, 128, 64, ... 32, 16
10. 16, 16, 16, 16, 16, ... 16, 16
11. 1, 2, 4, 5, 7, 8, ... 10, 11
12. 1, 0.5, 0, −0.5, −1, ... −1.5, −2
13. 1, 2, 3, 3, 4, 5, 6, 6, ... 7, 8
14. 1, 4, 9, 16, 25, 36, ... 49, 64
15. $\frac{1}{2}$, 1, 2, 4, 8, ... 16, 32
16. 1, 3, 6, 10, 15, ... 21, 28

Determine whether each exercise is an example of inductive or deductive reasoning. Explain your reasoning. See students' reasonings.

17. Numbers ending in zero are divisible by five. 25,893,690 is divisible by five. deductive
18. Everyone who came into the store today was wearing sunglasses. It is sunny today. inductive
19. Every student in class has a math book. This must be math class. inductive
20. Every triangle has 180° as the sum of its angle measures. Polygon *ABC* is a triangle. The sum of its angle measures must be 180°. deductive
21. If you are in first place, you will be able to go to the state tournament. You are in first place. You will be able to go to the tournament. deductive
22. It has rained every Monday for four weeks. Marsha says, "Tomorrow is Monday. I bet it will rain." inductive

Checking for Understanding

Communicating Algebra

1. In Example 1, suppose the time of the swing of the pendulum is 1.5 seconds. How long is the pendulum? 2.25 units
2. Which type of reasoning goes from a general rule to specific examples? deductive
3. How is the problem-solving strategy *look for a pattern* like inductive reasoning? It goes from examples to a rule.

Guided Practice

Determine whether each exercise is an example of *inductive* or *deductive* reasoning. Explain your reasoning. See students' work.

4. It has snowed every New Year's Day for the past four years. Akiko says it will snow on New Year's Day this year. inductive
5. The team that wins two more games will make the playoffs. Carter Junior High wins two more games, so they go to the playoffs. deductive
6. If the angles of a triangle have the same measure, the triangle is an equilateral triangle. The triangle shown at the right is an equilateral triangle. deductive

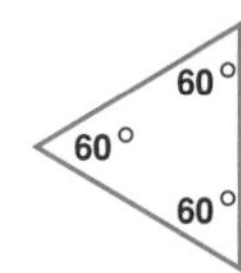

Exercises

Independent Practice

Determine whether each exercise is an example of *inductive* or *deductive* reasoning. Explain your reasoning. See students' work.

7. Patty noticed the school cafeteria served pizza on the last five Mondays. Patty decides that the cafeteria always serves pizza on Monday. inductive
8. Numbers whose last two digits are divisible by 4 are divisible by 4. So, 18,324 is divisible by 4. deductive
9. Band members are admitted free to all football games. Rachel plays flute in the band. She gets into every football game free. deductive
10. Every customer who came into Balmer's Clothing was wearing a raincoat. Mrs. Balmer decided it was raining. inductive

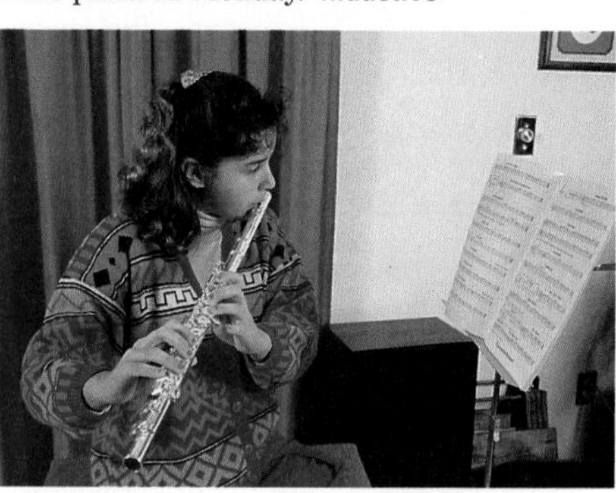

Use inductive reasoning to determine the next two numbers in each list.

11. 5, 10, 15, __?__ , __?__ 20, 25
12. 39, 33, 27, __?__ , __?__ 21, 15
13. 1, 10, 100, __?__ , __?__ 1000, 10,000
14. 6, 7, 9, 12, 16, __?__ , __?__ 21, 27

Critical Thinking

15. If you are not passing English, your parents will not let you go on the class field trip. You are not allowed to go on the field trip. Does this mean you did not pass English? Give reasons to support your answer. Not necessarily. There may be other reasons why you weren't allowed to go.

Wrap-Up

16. Explain the difference between inductive and deductive reasoning. Then give an example of each. See margin.

Additional Answer

16. Inductive reasoning uses examples to make a rule (specific to general). Deductive reasoning uses a rule to make a decision (general to specific). See students' examples.

Cooperative Learning

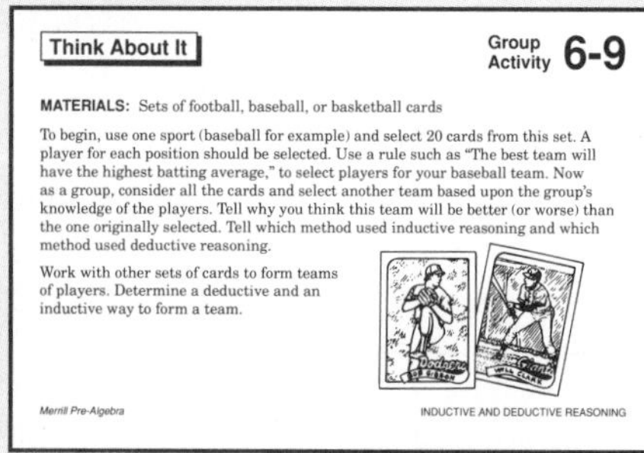

Think About It Group Activity **6-9**

MATERIALS: Sets of football, baseball, or basketball cards

To begin, use one sport (baseball for example) and select 20 cards from this set. A player for each position should be selected. Use a rule such as "The best team will have the highest batting average," to select players for your baseball team. Now as a group, consider all the cards and select another team based upon the group's knowledge of the players. Tell why you think this team will be better (or worse) than the one originally selected. Tell which method used inductive reasoning and which method used deductive reasoning.

Work with other sets of cards to form teams of players. Determine a deductive and an inductive way to form a team.

Merrill Pre-Algebra INDUCTIVE AND DEDUCTIVE REASONING

6-10 Geometric Sequences

Objectives:
Recognize and extend geometric sequences.
Represent a sequence algebraically.

Key Terms:
geometric sequence
common ratio

A certain golf ball, dropped from any height onto a hard surface will rebound 0.8 of the way back to its starting point. Suppose the ball is dropped from a height of 20 meters. The chart below shows its height after the first four bounces.

Bounce	1	2	3	4	5	6
Height (m)	20	16	12.8	10.24	8.192	?

× 0.8 × 0.8 × 0.8 × 0.8 × 0.8

How high will it bounce on the sixth bounce? Use your calculator.

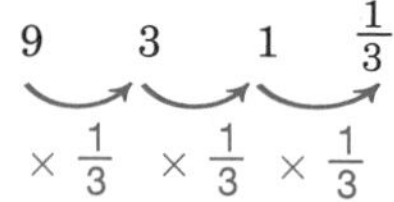

8.192 × 0.8 = 6.5536

Can a geometric sequence contain zero as a term? **no**

The successive heights form a sequence. When the terms of a sequence increase or decrease by a constant *factor,* the sequence is called a **geometric sequence**. The factor is called the **common ratio**. In the sequence shown above, the common ratio is 0.8.

Geometric Sequence

A geometric sequence is a sequence in which the ratio between any two successive terms is the same.

Examples

State whether each sequence is geometric. Then write the next three terms of each sequence.

1 $9, 3, 1, \frac{1}{3}, \ldots$

Since the common ratio is $\frac{1}{3}$, the sequence is geometric.

$9 \quad 3 \quad 1 \quad \frac{1}{3}$

$\times\frac{1}{3} \quad \times\frac{1}{3} \quad \times\frac{1}{3}$

The next three terms are $\frac{1}{9}$, $\frac{1}{27}$, and $\frac{1}{81}$.

2 -1, -1, -2, -6, -24, . . .

Since there is no common ratio, the sequence is *not* geometric.

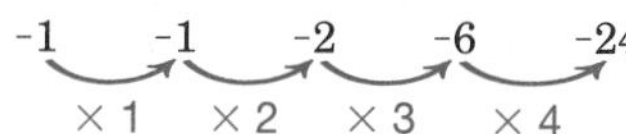

-1 -1 -2 -6 -24

×1 ×2 ×3 ×4

Are you using inductive or deductive reasoning when you find the terms? **inductive**

The next three terms are -120, -720, and -5040.

Bell Ringer

If today is Tuesday, what is the day before three days after tomorrow? **Friday**

Lesson Notes 6-10

5-Minute Check
(over Lesson 6-9)

Determine whether each exercise is an example of inductive or deductive reasoning.

1. Children ages 2 or younger get into the zoo free. Mr. Mitchel had to pay for his son, Mike. Mike must be older than 2 years. **deductive**
2. Every child walking to school had on a winter coat. Krista decided it must be cold outside. **inductive**

Transparency 6-10 contains the 5-Minute Check and a teaching aid for this lesson.

1 FOCUS

The purpose of this lesson is to introduce geometric sequences in a method parallel to the development of arithmetic sequences in Section 5-9.

Motivating the Lesson

Hold a ball up in the air. Ask students how many times they think the ball will bounce if it is dropped.

2 TEACH

Chalkboard Examples

State whether each sequence is geometric. Then write the next three terms of each sequence.

- *For Example 1*
  $4, 2, 1, \frac{1}{2} \ldots$ **geometric;** $\frac{1}{4}, \frac{1}{8}, \frac{1}{16}$
- *For Example 2*
  -6, -5, -3, 0, 4 . . . **not geometric; 9, 15, 21**

EE: 1E, 2F, 3A, 3H
TAAS: 2, 8, 9, 12

Chalkboard Examples

- *For Example 3*
  32, -8, 2, $\frac{1}{-2}$. . . geometric; $\frac{1}{8}$, $\frac{1}{-32}$, $\frac{1}{128}$
- *For Example 4*
  Use the expression $ar^{(n-1)}$ to find the sixth term of the sequence *when* $a = 4$, $r = 2$, and $n = 6$. 128
- *For Example 5*
  Find the height of the golf ball on page 233 after eight bounces. $a = 20$, $r = 0.8$, $n = 8$ about 4.2 meters

3 PRACTICE/APPLY

Checking the Concept

For each of the geometric sequences in Exercises 4-8, have students write the next three terms.

Practice Masters Booklet, **p. 59**

Name ______________ Date ______________

Practice Worksheet 6-10

Geometric Sequences

Write the next three terms of each sequence.

1. 2, 5, 8, 11, ... 14, 17, 20
2. 3, 9, 27, 81, ... 243, 729, 2187
3. $2\frac{2}{3}, 2, 1\frac{1}{3}, \frac{2}{3}, \ldots$ $0, -\frac{2}{3}, -1\frac{1}{3}$
4. 50, 46, 42, 38, ... 34, 30, 26
5. $\frac{2}{3}, \frac{2}{9}, \frac{2}{27}, \frac{2}{81}, \ldots$ $\frac{2}{243}, \frac{2}{729}, \frac{2}{2187}$
6. 2.8, 3.2, 3.6, 4, ... 4.4, 4.8, 5.2
7. 51, 44, 37, 30, ... 23, 16, 9
8. −45, −4.5, −0.45, −0.045, ... −0.0045, −0.00045, −0.000045
9. 1701, 567, 189, 63, ... $21, 7, 2\frac{1}{3}$
10. $\frac{1}{3}, \frac{1}{6}, \frac{1}{12}, \frac{1}{24}, \ldots$ $\frac{1}{48}, \frac{1}{96}, \frac{1}{192}$
11. 3.5, 7, 14, 28, ... 56, 112, 224
12. $\frac{2}{7}, \frac{6}{7}, 2\frac{4}{7}, 7\frac{5}{7}, \ldots$ $23\frac{1}{7}, 69\frac{3}{7}, 208\frac{2}{7}$
13. 88, −77, 66, −55, ... 44, −33, 22
14. 512, 64, 8, 1, ... $\frac{1}{8}, \frac{1}{64}, \frac{1}{512}$
15. −1, 5, −25, 125, ... −625, 3125, −15,625
16. 58, 45, 32, 19, ... 6, −7, −20
17. $18, -9, 4\frac{1}{2}, -2\frac{1}{4}, \ldots$ $1\frac{1}{8}, -\frac{9}{16}, \frac{9}{32}$
18. −12, −10, −8, −6, ... −4, −2, 0
19. $4, -1, \frac{1}{4}, -\frac{1}{16}, \ldots$ $\frac{1}{64}, -\frac{1}{256}, \frac{1}{1024}$
20. $\frac{3}{4}, -\frac{1}{2}, \frac{1}{3}, -\frac{2}{9}, \ldots$ $\frac{4}{27}, -\frac{8}{81}, \frac{16}{243}$
21. 10, 5, 0, −5, ... −10, −15, −20
22. $-24, -8, -2\frac{2}{3}, -\frac{8}{9}, \ldots$ $-\frac{8}{27}, -\frac{8}{81}, -\frac{8}{243}$
23. $3\frac{1}{2}, \frac{1}{2}, -2\frac{1}{2}, -5\frac{1}{2}, \ldots$ $-8\frac{1}{2}, -11\frac{1}{2}, -14\frac{1}{2}$
24. 6, −18, 54, −162, ... 486, −1458, 4374
25. 3, 4.5, 6, 7.5, ... 9, 10.5, 12
26. 8, −4, 2, −1, ... $\frac{1}{2}, -\frac{1}{4}, \frac{1}{8}$
27. 27, −18, 12, −8, ... $5\frac{1}{3}, -3\frac{5}{9}, 2\frac{10}{27}$
28. −1, 0.1, −0.01, 0.001, ... −0.0001, 0.00001, −0.000001

Example

State whether the sequence is geometric. Then write the next three terms.

3 8, -4, 2, -1, . . .

The common ratio is $-\frac{1}{2}$. The sequence is geometric.

$$8 \xrightarrow{\times\left(-\frac{1}{2}\right)} -4 \xrightarrow{\times\left(-\frac{1}{2}\right)} 2 \xrightarrow{\times\left(-\frac{1}{2}\right)} -1$$

The next three terms are $\frac{1}{2}$, $-\frac{1}{4}$, and $\frac{1}{8}$.

CONNECTION TO ALGEBRA

If we know the first term of a geometric sequence and the common ratio, we can find any other term of the sequence. Consider the sequence 2, 6, 18, 54, ...

Here's how to write an expression that represents a term in the sequence. The first term is 2; call the first term a. The common ratio is 3; call the common ratio r. Study this pattern.

1st term: a
2nd term: $a \cdot r$
3rd term: $a \cdot r \cdot r$ or ar^2
4th term: $a \cdot r \cdot r \cdot r$ or ar^3
. .
. .
. .
nth term: $a \cdot r^{n-1}$ The exponent is one less than the number of the term.

Because n represents any term, you can use this expression to find any term in the sequence.

Examples

4 **Use the expression ar^{n-1} to find the sixth term of the sequence 2, 6, 18, 54, . . .**

The first term, a, is 2, the common ratio is 3, and n is 6.

$ar^{(n-1)} = 2 \cdot 3^{6-1}$ or $2 \cdot 3^5$ $a = 2, r = 3, n = 6$

2 [×] 3 [y^x] 5 [=] 486

The sixth term is 486. You can check this answer by extending the sequence.

5 **Find the height of the golf ball on page 233 after 10 bounces.**

$ar^{(n-1)} = 20(0.8)^{(10-1)}$ $a = 20, r = 0.8, n = 10$

20 [×] 0.8 [y^x] 9 [=] 2.6843546

The height is about 2.7 meters.

Alternate Strategies: Reteaching the Lesson

Reteaching Activity

Using Cooperative Groups Have a student name a number. Have a second student multiply that number and give the second item in the sequence. Each following student must decide what factor was used and give the next sequence item. Rotate and repeat. Expand from whole numbers to other rational numbers.

Reteaching Masters Booklet, **p. 53**

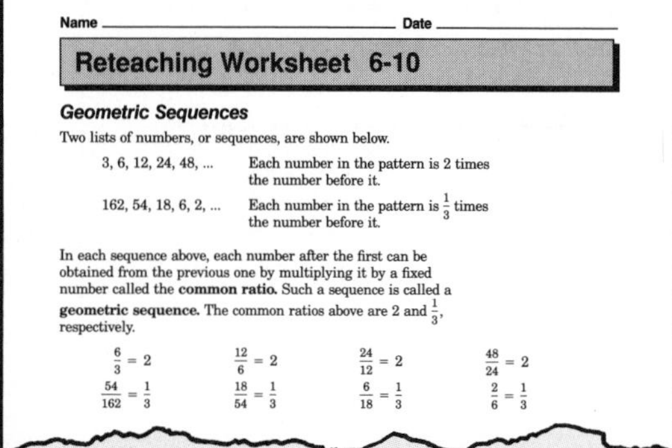

Name ______________ Date ______________

Reteaching Worksheet 6-10

Geometric Sequences

Two lists of numbers, or sequences, are shown below.

3, 6, 12, 24, 48, ... Each number in the pattern is 2 times the number before it.

162, 54, 18, 6, 2, ... Each number in the pattern is $\frac{1}{3}$ times the number before it.

In each sequence above, each number after the first can be obtained from the previous one by multiplying it by a fixed number called the **common ratio.** Such a sequence is called a **geometric sequence.** The common ratios above are 2 and $\frac{1}{3}$, respectively.

$\frac{6}{3} = 2$ $\frac{12}{6} = 2$ $\frac{24}{12} = 2$ $\frac{48}{24} = 2$

$\frac{54}{162} = \frac{1}{3}$ $\frac{18}{54} = \frac{1}{3}$ $\frac{6}{18} = \frac{1}{3}$ $\frac{2}{6} = \frac{1}{3}$

Checking for Understanding

Communicating Algebra

1. Give an example of a geometric sequence. Sample answer: 1, 2, 4, 8, . . .
2. Explain the difference between an arithmetic sequence and a geometric sequence. 2. Arithmetic—terms change by a constant sum or difference; Geometric—terms change by a constant factor
3. In the geometric sequence 8, -4, 2, -1, . . . , what is the *common ratio*? -0.5

Guided Practice

State whether each sequence is a geometric sequence. If so, state the common ratio.

4. 2, 4, 8, 16, . . . yes; 2
5. 2, 4, 6, 8, . . . no
6. $-5, 1, -\frac{1}{5}, \frac{1}{25}, \ldots$ 6. yes; $-\frac{1}{5}$
7. 24, 12, 6, 3, . . . yes; $\frac{1}{2}$
8. 9, 3, -3, -9, . . . no
9. $\frac{1}{2}, \frac{1}{4}, \frac{1}{8}, \frac{1}{16}, \ldots$ 9. yes; $\frac{1}{2}$

Exercises

Independent Practice

ESTIMATION
MENTAL MATH
CALCULATOR
PAPER/PENCIL

Write the next three terms of each sequence.

10. $\frac{1}{2}$, 1, 2, 4, . . . 8, 16, 32
11. 2, 3, 5, 8, 12, . . . 17, 23, 30
12. 8, 4, 2, 1, . . . $\frac{1}{2}, \frac{1}{4}, \frac{1}{8}$
13. 3, 7, 11, 15, . . . 19, 23, 27
14. 7, -14, 28, -56, . . . 112, -224, 448
15. $4\frac{1}{2}, 2\frac{1}{2}, \frac{1}{2}, -1\frac{1}{2}, \ldots$ 15. $-3\frac{1}{2}, -5\frac{1}{2}, -7\frac{1}{2}$
16. $18, -6, 2, -\frac{2}{3}, \ldots$ $\frac{2}{9}, -\frac{2}{27}, \frac{2}{81}$
17. $5, -\frac{5}{2}, \frac{5}{4}, -\frac{5}{8}, \ldots$ $\frac{5}{16}, -\frac{5}{32}, \frac{5}{64}$

Language Skill

18. Write the first five terms in a geometric sequence with a common ratio of $\frac{1}{2}$. The first term is 2. $2, 1, \frac{1}{2}, \frac{1}{4}, \frac{1}{8}$
19. Find the fourth term of a geometric sequence if $a = -5$ and $r = -2$. 40
20. Use the expression $ar^{(n-1)}$ to find the eighth term of the geometric sequence 16, 8, 4, . . . $\frac{1}{8}$

Mixed Review

21. Evaluate the expression $rs \div t$ if $r = 2.8$, $s = 0.5$, $t = 0.7$. (Lesson 6-7) 2

Solve each equation or inequality. (Lesson 6-8)

22. $\frac{k}{-1.3} = -4.7$ 6.11
23. $-\frac{7}{8}f > \frac{1}{3}$ $f < -\frac{8}{21}$

Applications

24. **Physics** A ball rebounds $\frac{2}{3}$ of its height after every fall. If it is dropped from a height of 48 feet, how high will it bounce at the end of the third bounce? 24. $14\frac{2}{9}$ ft

25. **Business** A certain automobile loses $\frac{3}{10}$ of its value every year. If Tina bought an automobile for $8400, what is the value at the end of three years? $2881.20

Critical Thinking

26. Find the value of x so that 3, x, 12, . . . is a geometric sequence. x = 6 or -6

Wrap-Up

27. Write the first four terms of a geometric sequence that has a common ratio of $-\frac{1}{3}$. Sample answer: 81, -27, 9, -3

Error Analysis

Watch for students who have difficulty remembering the difference between arithmetic and geometric sequences.
Prevent by listing several examples of sequences and having students identify sequence type.

Independent Practice

Homework Assignment	
Basic	11-19 odd, 21-27
Average	10-20 even, 21-27
Honors	15-27

4 CLOSE

Assessment Option

Speaking Name a ratio and the starting number for a geometric sequence. Then have the students give the next four numbers in the sequence.

Enrichment Masters Booklet, **p. 53**

Name ______________ Date ______________

Enrichment Worksheet 6-10

Applications of Geometric Sequences

Populations often grow according to a geometric sequence. If the population of a country grows at the rate of 2% per year, then the common ratio, r, is 1.02. To find the population of a city of 100,000 after 5 years of 2% growth, use the formula ar^{n-1}, where r is the common ratio and n is the number of years.

$$ar^{n-1} = 100{,}000 \times 1.02^{5-1} \quad a = 100{,}000;\ r = 1.02;\ n = 5$$
$$= 100{,}000 \times 1.02^4$$
$$\approx 108{,}243$$

After a few years, a small change in the annual growth rate can cause enormous differences in the population.

Assume that the nation of Grogro has a population of one million in 1990. Using a calculator, find the population of the country in the years 2000, 2050, and 2100 at growth rates of 1%, 3%, and 5% per year. Record your results in the table below.

	Population of Grogro			
	Growth Rate	Year 2000	2050	2100
1.	1%	1,093,685	1,798,709	2,958,215
2.	3%	1,304,773	5,720,003	25,075,956
3.	5%	1,551,328	17,789,701	204,001,612

Suppose we want to find the **total** distance a bouncing ball has moved. We need a formula for the **sum** of the terms of a geometric sequence. This is called a **geometric series.**

$$S_n = \frac{a - ar^n}{1 - r}$$

a = first term
r = common ratio ($r \neq 1$)
n = number of terms

Use the formula above to find each sum. Then check your answer by adding.

4. 5 + 10 + 20 + 40 + 80 155
5. 80 + 240 + 720 + 2160 + 6480 9680

Alternate Strategies: Extending the Lesson

Enrichment

Using Tables Draw 3 circles. Mark 2, 3, and 4 points, respectively, on the circles. Using straight lines, connect points in all possible ways. Make a table that shows the number of points and the number of regions formed. Predict the number of regions formed by 5 and 6 points.

Cooperative Learning

Geometrically Speaking Group Activity **6-10**

MATERIALS: 0-9 spinner

This activity works with geometric sequences. To begin, spin the spinner four times. Use these numbers to create a geometric sequence. One number needs to be the first term of the sequence (a). Two of the numbers will be the common ratio (r), one of which is the numerator of the ratio, and the other is the denominator of the ratio. The last number will indicate how many terms of the geometric sequence you are to determine.

After everyone has created one sequence, exchange papers and see if each of you can compute the indicated number of terms of the sequence given to you. As a group, check the accuracy of these computations.

Merrill Pre-Algebra GEOMETRIC SEQUENCES

Applying Algebra to the Real World

Objective This optional page shows how algebra is used in the real world and also provides a change of pace.

Using Discussion

If spreadsheet software is available, use a computer to demonstrate ease and speed of using a spreadsheet. Discuss how the formulas in the cells resemble algebraic expressions.

Using Manipulatives

Have students predict the number of times a basketball will bounce when dropped from a height of ten feet. Have students drop a basketball from ten feet, or from a height practical for their classroom. Measure the height of the first bounce and determine the common ratio. Write and complete a spreadsheet to check the accuracy of student predictions. Drop the ball again, count the bounces, and compare to the spreadsheet results. Discuss any differences.

Activity

Consumer Connection The Debate Club is selling fruit to raise money for a trip to Washington, D.C. The fruit is sold for $10.00 per box. Have students complete a spreadsheet to show the income for the first five days of the sale if daily totals for fruit sold were 12, 25, 14, 19, and 20 boxes. Students could also make up another spreadsheet that reports profit if the fruit cost the club $6.00 per box.

Algebra in Action-Computers

Spreadsheets

An electronic **spreadsheet** program is a computer application that allows users to prepare tables easily. Using a spreadsheet program, it is possible to project results, make calculations, and print almost anything that can be arranged in a table.

Spreadsheets can also be used as a tool to simulate experiments when the variables can be described algebraically. Consider the bouncing golf ball from page 233. We can use a spreadsheet to record the height of the ball after each bounce. The computer automatically performs the calculations. A sample printout is shown at the right.

BALL BOUNCE

	A	B
1	Initial Ht (m) =	20
2	Common Ratio =	0.8
3	HIT NUMBER	RETURN HT
4	1	20.000
5	2	16.000
6	3	12.800
7	4	10.240
8	5	8.192
9	6	6.554
10	7	5.243

In the printout, the vertical columns and the horizontal rows are combined and named to form **cells**. Each cell is identified by a row and column. Cell B6 shows the height 12.800 meters.

This spreadsheet was built so that the initial height can be changed by altering the value in cell B1. The common ratio can be changed by altering the value in B2. The remaining cells are determined by formulas. The computer does the calculations.

A4 + 1 means add 1 to the value in cell A4.

BALL BOUNCE

	A	B
1	Initial Ht (m) =	20
2	Common Ratio =	0.8
3	HIT NUMBER	RETURN HT
4	1	=B1
5	=A4+1	=B4*B2
6	=A5+1	=B5*B2
7	=A6+1	=B6*B2

B4 * B2 means multiply the value in cell B4 by the value in cell B2.

1. Explain the meaning of the formula in cell B6. **Multiply the value in cell B5 by the value in cell B2.**
2. A certain ball will return to a height that is 0.5 times the previous height. How would you modify the spreadsheet? **Change the value in B2 to 0.5.**
3. Suppose you wanted to investigate this question: If a ball is dropped from twice as high, will it bounce twice as many times? Describe how you could use a spreadsheet to answer this question. **Change B1 to 40 and run the program again. Compare the results.**

6-11 Scientific Notation

Objective:
Write numbers in scientific notation.

If you have ever visited Luray Caverns in Virginia or Carlsbad Caverns in New Mexico, you have probably wondered about the icicle-like structures that hang from the roof of the caves. These stalactites are formed as water containing limestone drips through the roof of the cave, one drop at a time.

Some stalactites are as old as 40,000 years. If one drop of water drips through the roof of the cave every second for 40,000 years, there would be about 1,262,304,000,000 drops. If each drop contained just 0.00001 g of limestone, 12,623,040 g of limestone would have formed. This is 12,623 kg or nearly 28,000 pounds.

Large numbers such as 1,262,304,000,000 and small numbers such as 0.00001 are difficult to use. It is easy to make mistakes by omitting zeros or having the decimal point in the wrong place. People who deal regularly with such numbers use **scientific notation.**

Scientific Notation — Numbers expressed in scientific notation are expressed as the product of a factor and a power of 10. The factor must be greater than or equal to 1 and less than 10.

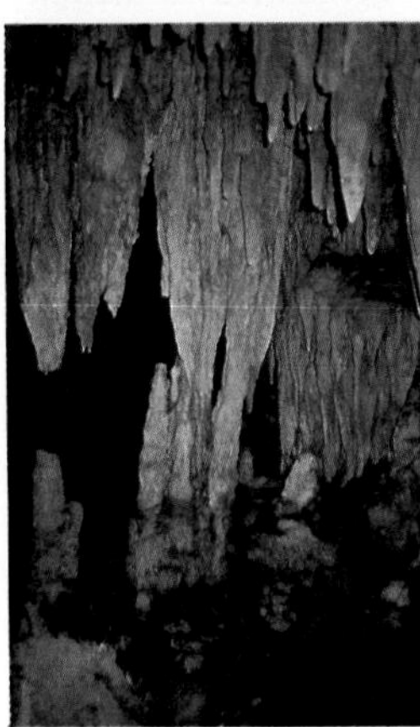

Examples

Express each number in standard form.

1 2.73×10^5

$2.73 \times 10^5 = 2.73 \times 100{,}000$
$= 273{,}000$

2.73000 five places

2 4.53×10^{-3}

$4.53 \times 10^{-3} = 4.53 \times \frac{1}{10^3}$
$= 4.53 \times \frac{1}{1000}$
$= 4.53 \times 0.001$
$= 0.00453$

Remember from Lesson 4-10 that $10^{-3} = \frac{1}{10^3}$.

004.53 three places

Bell Ringer
Write three geometric sequences and three arithmetic sequences.

Lesson Notes 6-11

5-Minute Check
(over Lesson 6-10)

Write the next three terms of each sequence.

1. $15, -5, \frac{5}{3}, \frac{5}{-9} \ldots$ $\frac{5}{27}, \frac{5}{-81}, \frac{5}{243}$
2. $\frac{1}{-2}, \frac{3}{2}, \frac{9}{-2}, \frac{27}{2} \ldots$ $\frac{81}{-2}, \frac{243}{2}, \frac{729}{-2}$
3. $-4, -2\frac{1}{2}, -1, \frac{1}{2} \ldots$ $2, 3\frac{1}{2}, 5$
4. $12, 3, \frac{3}{4}, \frac{3}{16} \ldots$ $\frac{3}{64}, \frac{3}{256}, \frac{3}{1024}$
5. $-3, -1, 1, 3 \ldots$ 5, 7, 9

Transparency 6-11 contains the 5-Minute Check and a teaching aid for this lesson.

1 FOCUS

The purpose of this lesson is to help students deal more easily with extremely large and extremely small numbers through the use of scientific notation.

Motivating the Lesson

Tell students that Saturn is 1 billion, 430 million kilometers from the sun, and the diameter of the planet is 121 thousand kilometers. Have students write these numbers in standard form.
1,430,000,000; 121,000

2 TEACH

Using Calculators

Guide students through the following keystrokes on the TI-30 Challenger calculator for Examples 1-2.

1. 2.73 [EE] 5 [INV] [EE] [=]
2. 4.53 [EE] 3 [+/-] [INV] [EE] [=]

Chalkboard Examples

Express each number in standard form.

- *For Example 1*
  3.75×10^4 37,500
- *For Example 2*
  8.39×10^{-3} 0.00839

EE: 1E, 2A, 2D, 3A
TAAS: 1

Chalkboard Examples

Express each number in scientific notation.

- *For Example 3*
  5000 5×10^3
- *For Example 4*
  817,000 8.17×10^5
- *For Example 5*
  -0.0001 -1×10^{-4}
- *For Example 6*
  0.0000429 4.29×10^{-5}
- *For Example 7*
  Use a calculator to express 0.000000034 in scientific notation. 3.4×10^{-8}
- *For Example 8*
  Write 2,413,027,000,000,000 in scientific notation.
  2.413027×10^{15}

3 PRACTICE/APPLY

Checking the Concept

Before students begin Independent Practice ask them to state how many decimal places and in what direction the decimal point will move in Exercises 11-16.

Practice Masters Booklet, **p. 60**

Name ______________________ Date ______________

Practice Worksheet 6-11

Scientific Notation

Express each number in standard form.

1. 8.2×10^3 8200	2. 6.4×10^2 640	3. 3.1×10^4 31,000
4. 9.03×10^{11} 903,000,000,000	5. -6.8×10^8 −680,000,000	6. 9.347×10^4 93,470
7. 1.5×10^{-1} 0.15	8. 7.3×10^{-3} 0.0073	9. 8.7×10^0 8.7
10. 2.9×10^{-2} 0.029	11. -3.07×10^{-4} −0.000307	12. -7.16×10^{-5} −0.0000716
13. 1.234×10^{-3} 0.001234	14. 5.008×10^4 50,080	15. -4.11×10^5 −411,000
16. -2.307×10^0 −2.307	17. 3.09×10^{-4} 0.000309	18. -1.4685×10^1 −14.685

Express each number in scientific notation.

19. 65,000,000 6.5×10^7	20. −9200 -9.2×10^3	21. 840,000 8.4×10^5
22. 0.0056 5.6×10^{-3}	23. 28,400,000 2.84×10^7	24. −5.65 -5.65×10^0
25. 5,620,800,000 5.6208×10^9	26. −0.00087 -8.7×10^{-4}	27. 769.5 7.695×10^2
28. 59,300 5.93×10^4	29. 9,000,000 9.0×10^6	30. −0.3054 -3.054×10^{-1}
31. 0.00001 1.0×10^{-5}	32. −8 -8.0×10^0	33. 89,000,000,000 8.9×10^{10}
34. −175 -1.75×10^2	35. 0.08792 8.792×10^{-2}	36. −31 -3.1×10^1
37. 0.0003141 3.141×10^{-4}	38. −1 -1.0×10^0	39. 6,801,700 6.8017×10^6
40. −5.001 -5.001×10^0	41. 1,000,000,000 1.0×10^9	42. 0.00000938 9.38×10^{-6}

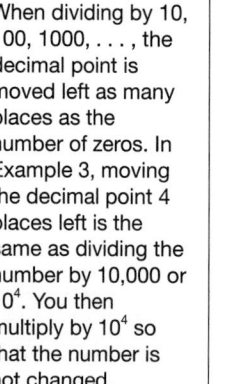

Mental Math Hint

When dividing by 10, 100, 1000, . . . , the decimal point is moved left as many places as the number of zeros. In Example 3, moving the decimal point 4 places left is the same as dividing the number by 10,000 or 10^4. You then multiply by 10^4 so that the number is not changed.

What is the relationship between the absolute value of the exponent and the number of places the decimal is moved?
They are equal.

Examples

Express each number in scientific notation.

3 20,000

$20,000 = 2 \times 10^4$ Move the decimal point 4 places to the left. Multiply by 10^4.

4 57,800,000

$57,800,000 = 5.78 \times 10^7$ Move the decimal point 7 places to the left. Multiply by 10^7.

5 -0.001

$-0.001 = -1 \times 10^{-3}$ Move the decimal point 3 places to the right. Multiply by 10^{-3}.

6 0.000623

$0.000623 = 6.23 \times 10^{-4}$ Move the decimal point 4 places to the right. Multiply by 10^{-4}.

Most scientific calculators allow you to compute with numbers in scientific notation. Example 7 shows how to enter a number in standard form and have the calculator express it in scientific notation. Example 8 shows how to enter a number that will not fit on the display screen in standard form.

Examples

7 Use a calculator to express 0.0000089 in scientific notation.

0.0000089 [EE] [=] 8.9 − 06

exponent of the power of ten

$0.0000089 = 8.9 \times 10^{-6}$

8 Enter 1,262,304,000,000 into a calculator.

First write the number in scientific notation.

$1,262,304,000,000 = 1.262304 \times 10^{12}$

Then enter the number.

1.262304 [EE] 12

The display shows 1.2623 12.

Alternate Strategies: Reteaching the Lesson

Reteaching Activity

Using Models Write numbers in standard form on a magnetic board or chalkboard. Use a magnet or a piece of masking tape as the decimal point. Have a student physically move the decimal to its new location. Have other students count places as the decimal is moved. Write the correct power of 10 by the new number.

Reteaching Masters Booklet, **p. 54**

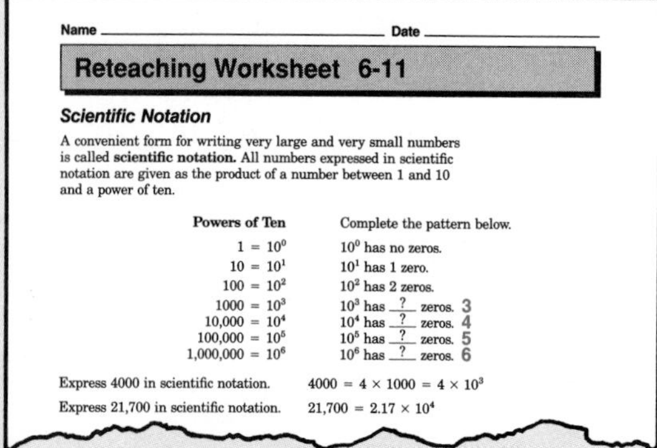

Name ______________________ Date ______________

Reteaching Worksheet 6-11

Scientific Notation

A convenient form for writing very large and very small numbers is called **scientific notation.** All numbers expressed in scientific notation are given as the product of a number between 1 and 10 and a power of ten.

Powers of Ten	Complete the pattern below.
$1 = 10^0$	10^0 has no zeros.
$10 = 10^1$	10^1 has 1 zero.
$100 = 10^2$	10^2 has 2 zeros.
$1000 = 10^3$	10^3 has _?_ zeros. 3
$10,000 = 10^4$	10^4 has _?_ zeros. 4
$100,000 = 10^5$	10^5 has _?_ zeros. 5
$1,000,000 = 10^6$	10^6 has _?_ zeros. 6

Express 4000 in scientific notation. $4000 = 4 \times 1000 = 4 \times 10^3$

Express 21,700 in scientific notation. $21,700 = 2.17 \times 10^4$

Checking for Understanding

Communicating Algebra

1. Explain why 23.8×10^4 is not written in scientific notation. $23.8 > 10$
2. Give an example of a number that is written in scientific notation. Sample answer: 5.43×10^2

Guided Practice

State where the decimal point should be placed in order to express each number in scientific notation. Then state the power of ten by which you should multiply.

3. 1‸59 10^2
4. 4‸6 10^1
5. 1‸800 10^3
6. 8‸5,000 10^4
7. 0.8‸5 10^{-1}
8. 0.002‸46 10^{-3}
9. 0.00005‸93 10^{-5}
10. 0.00001‸24 10^{-5}

Exercises

Independent Practice

Express each number in standard form.

11. 5.2×10^5 520,000
12. 3.9×10^3 3900
13. -6.1×10^4 -61,000
14. 1.23×10^{-2} 0.0123
15. -5.765×10^{-3} -0.005765
16. 7.02×10^0 7.02
17. the distance to the moon, 2.39×10^5 miles 239,000
18. the height of the Sears Tower, 1.454×10^3 feet 1454
19. the volume of a drop of liquid, 5×10^{-5} liter 0.00005

Express each number in scientific notation. 24. -4.976×10^{-3}

20. 820 8.2×10^2
21. 0.504 5.04×10^{-1}
22. -6100 -6.1×10^3
23. 97,000 9.7×10^4
24. -0.004976
25. 0.00623 6.23×10^{-3}
26. 5,000,000 5×10^6
27. 0.00000892 8.92×10^{-6}
28. 96 9.6×10^1
29. the diameter of a red blood cell, 0.0003 inch 3.0×10^{-4}
30. the distance to the sun, 93,000,000 miles 9.3×10^7

Mixed Review

31. Find the quotient $\frac{(-2)^4}{(-2)^2}$. (Lesson 4-10) 4
32. State whether the sequence 2, 4, 8, 16, . . . is an arithmetic sequence. (Lesson 5-9) no
33. Solve the inequality $\frac{t}{2.3} < -0.4$. (Lesson 6-8) $t < -0.92$
34. The people of Waynesburg, PA, celebrate July 26 as Rain Day, because it almost always rains on that day. Is this an example of inductive or deductive reasoning? (Lesson 6-9) inductive

Applications

35. **Physics** The speed of light in a vacuum is 29,979,280,000 centimeters per second. Explain how to enter this number into a calculator. 2.997928 EE 10

36. **Chemistry** An oxygen atom has a mass of 2.66×10^{-23} grams. Explain how to enter this number into a calculator. 2.66 EE -23

Critical Thinking

37. Use the associative and commutative properties of multiplication to compute $(2.72 \times 10^5)(3.25 \times 10^{-3})$. 8.84×10^2 or 884

Wrap-Up

38. Explain how the movement of the decimal point is related to expressing numbers in scientific notation. The number of places the decimal point is moved is the power of ten; moved left—positive exponent, moved right—negative exponent.

Error Analysis

Watch for students who change from scientific notation to standard form by adding the number of zeros indicated by the exponent to the end of the number. Example: $3.07 \times 10^3 = 307{,}000$

Prevent by having students move the decimal point the correct number of places, adding only what zeros are needed.

Independent Practice

Homework Assignment	
Basic	11-29 odd, 31-38
Average	12-30 even, 31-38
Honors	15-19, 25-38

4 CLOSE

Assessment Option

Speaking Ask students to interpret the following calculator displays.

1. 8.954 06 8,954,000
2. 5.319-05 0.00005319
3. 6.2359 01 62.359
4. 3.58-03 0.00358

Enrichment Masters Booklet, **p. 54**

Name ______________ Date ______________

Enrichment Worksheet 6-11

Scientific Notation

It is sometimes necessary to multiply and divide numbers in scientific notation.

The following rule is used to multiply numbers in scientific notation.

For any numbers a and b, and any numbers c and d,
$(c \times 10^a) \times (d \times 10^b) = (c \times d) \times 10^{a+b}$

Example: $(3 \times 10^4) \times (-5 \times 10^{-2}) = (3 \times -5) \times 10^{4+(-2)}$
$= -15 \times 10^2$
$= -1500$

The following rule is used to divide numbers in scientific notation.

For any numbers a and b, and any numbers c and d $(d \neq 0)$,
$(c \times 10^a) \div (d \times 10^b) = (c \div d) \times 10^{a-b}$

Example: $(30 \times 10^{-4}) \div (6 \times 10^2) = (30 \div 6) \times 10^{-4-2}$
$= 5 \times 10^{-6}$
$= 0.000005$

Multiply. Express the product or quotient in scientific notation.

1. $(2.7 \times 10^9) \times (3.1 \times 10^2)$ 8.37×10^{11}
2. $(6.1 \times 10^{-2}) \times (1.3 \times 10^5)$ 7.93×10^3
3. $(5.4 \times 10^{-3}) \div (1.8 \times 10^2)$ 3×10^{-5}
4. $(6.9 \times 10^{-3}) \div (0.3 \times 10^{-7})$ 2.3×10^5
5. $(1.1 \times 10^{-5}) \times (9.9 \times 10^{-1})$ 1.089×10^{-5}
6. $(4 \times 10^0) \div (10^{-2})$ 4×10^2

Solve. Write your answers in standard form.

7. The distance from Earth to the moon is about 2×10^5 miles. The distance from Earth to the sun is about 9.3×10^7 miles. How many times further is it to the sun than to the moon? 465
8. If each of the 3×10^4 people employed by Suny Motors earned 4×10^4 dollars last year, how much money did the company pay out to its employees? $1,200,000,000

Alternate Strategies: Extending the Lesson

Enrichment

Science Connection Use science books and encyclopedias to find uses of scientific notation. Write problems using these numbers. Example: More than 8.4×10^{11} drops of water flow over Niagra Falls per minute. There are 1.7×10^{21} molecules per drop. How many molecules per minute flow over the falls?

Cooperative Learning

Food For Thought Group Activity **6-11**

MATERIALS: Calculators

You are the head dietitian for your school district. The superintendent wants you to serve "Ice Cream Cookie Sundaes" for a treat. The ingredients for 6 people are as follows.

- 6 soft oatmeal cookies
- $\frac{1}{4}$ cup butterscotch topping
- $\frac{1}{5}$ cup chocolate topping
- $\frac{1}{3}$ cup caramel topping
- $1\frac{1}{2}$ small bananas
- $2\frac{7}{8}$ cups vanilla or chocolate ice cream
- $\frac{1}{6}$ cup peanuts

Determine how much of each ingredient is needed to serve the 12,000 students in your district. Compute the amounts and express the answers in scientific notation.

Merrill Pre-Algebra SCIENTIFIC NOTATION

Lesson Notes 6-12

5-Minute Check
(over Lesson 6-11)

Express each number in scientific notation.

1. 67,500 **6.75×10^4**
2. -2,768,000 **-2.768×10^6**
3. 0.0000945 **9.45×10^{-5}**
4. -800,230,000 **-8.0023×10^8**
5. -0.0071 **-7.1×10^{-3}**

Transparency 6-12 contains the 5-Minute Check and a teaching aid for this lesson.

1 FOCUS

The purpose of this lesson is to use decimals, fractions with like denominators, or a number line to compare rational numbers.

Motivating the Lesson

Ask students to find a number between 0.3 and $\frac{1}{3}$.

2 TEACH

Using Cooperative Groups

Have students work in groups of three. One student names two numbers, another locates the numbers on a number line, and the third names a number in between them. Start with whole numbers; advance to decimals, then to fractions, and finally, to a combination of fractions and decimals.

6-12 Comparing Rational Numbers

Objective:
Compare rational numbers.

Sometimes you need to determine which of two numbers is greater. A number line is sometimes a useful tool in comparing numbers. However, there are times when a number line is not convenient. Consider this problem.

After playing 21 baseball games, the Pittsburgh Pirates had won 14 games. During the same time, the New York Mets won 15 games out of 23. Which team has the better record?

Why is it inconvenient to compare $\frac{14}{21}$ and $\frac{15}{23}$ on a number line? **It is difficult to locate 21sts and 23rds.**

To solve this problem, compare $\frac{14}{21}$ and $\frac{15}{23}$. One way to compare these fractions is to express them as decimals and then compare the decimals.

$\frac{14}{21}$ ➡ 0.6666667 $\frac{15}{23}$ ➡ 0.6521739

In the hundredths place, 6 > 5.

Since 0.6666667 > 0.6521739, $\frac{14}{21} > \frac{15}{23}$.
The Pirates have the better record.

Another way to compare two rational numbers is to express them as equivalent fractions with like denominators.

Mental Math Hint

You can also compare fractions by using cross products.

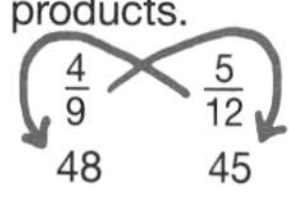

Since 48 > 45, $\frac{4}{9} > \frac{5}{12}$.

Examples

1 Replace each ● with <, >, or = to make a true sentence.

$\frac{4}{9}$ ● $\frac{5}{12}$

$\frac{16}{36}$ ● $\frac{15}{36}$ The common denominator is 36.

$\frac{16}{36} > \frac{15}{36}$ Since 16 > 15, $\frac{16}{36} > \frac{15}{36}$.

Therefore, $\frac{4}{9} > \frac{5}{12}$.

Bell Ringer

Write the following numbers in scientific notation.

1. 1,249,756,000 **1.249756×10^9**
2. 0.0000871 **8.71×10^{-5}**

EE: 1E, 2A, 2D, 3A
TAAS: 1

2 $\frac{2}{3}$ ● -0.5

Any positive number is graphed to the right of any other negative number on the number line.

Therefore, $\frac{2}{3} > -0.5$.

3 -0.8 ● $-\frac{2}{3}$

-0.8 ● $-\frac{2}{3}$

-0.8 ● $-0.6666\ldots$ Express $-\frac{2}{3}$ as a decimal.

In the tenths place, $-8 < -6$.

Therefore, $-0.8 < -\frac{2}{3}$.

4 35.9 ● 3.59×10^2

35.9 ● 3.59×10^2

35.9 ● 359 Express 3.59×10^2 in standard form.

$35.9 < 359$

Therefore, $35.9 < 3.59 \times 10^2$.

Checking for Understanding

Communicating Algebra

1. Compare the numbers that are graphed on the number line shown below. $-\frac{1}{5} < \frac{5}{6}$

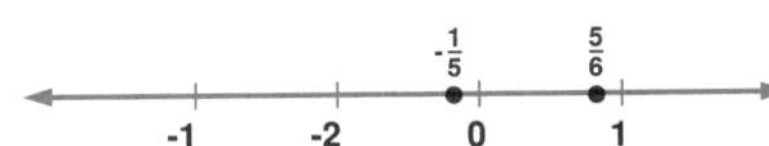

2. Using a number line, explain why $-1.5 < -1$. **-1.5 is graphed to the left of -1.**
3. In your own words, describe two different ways to compare $\frac{5}{8}$ and 0.4. **Compare $\frac{5}{8}$ and $\frac{4}{10}$; compare 0.625 and 0.4.**

Guided Practice

State the greater number for each pair.

4. <u>25.23</u>, 25.13
5. <u>-5.049</u>, -5.149
6. <u>63.024</u>, -63.028
7. <u>$1\frac{3}{5}$</u>, $1\frac{3}{6}$
8. <u>$-\frac{4}{5}$</u>, $-\frac{9}{10}$
9. 1.2×10^3, <u>1.2×10^4</u>

Chalkboard Examples

Replace each • with <, >, or = to make a true sentence.

- *For Example 1*
  $\frac{4}{7}$ • $\frac{5}{9}$ >
- For Example 2
  -0.24 • $\frac{3}{8}$ <
- *For Example 3*
  -0.5 • $\frac{3}{-4}$ >
- *For Example 4*
  214.5 • 2.145×10^3 <

3 PRACTICE/APPLY

Checking the Concept

After completing Exercises 4-9, have each student generate similar exercises for other students to solve.

Error Analysis

Watch for students who always identify the larger number as the one with more digits.
Prevent by writing the decimal numbers in a column, lining up the decimal points. Start comparing place values from the left.

Practice Masters Booklet, **p. 61**

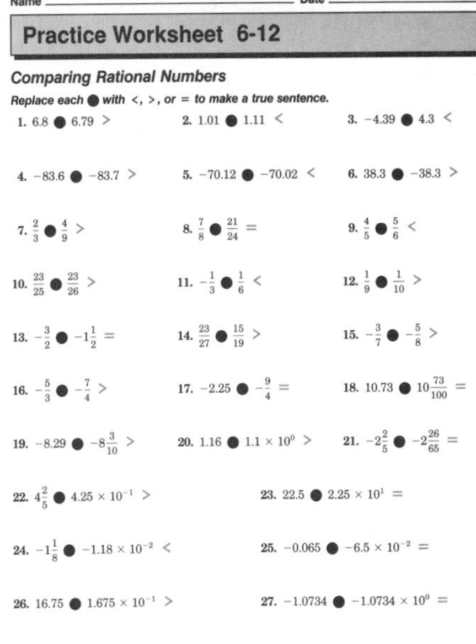
Name ______ Date ______

Practice Worksheet 6-12

Comparing Rational Numbers

Replace each ● with <, >, or = to make a true sentence.

1. 6.8 ● 6.79 >
2. 1.01 ● 1.11 <
3. -4.39 ● 4.3 <
4. -83.6 ● -83.7 >
5. -70.12 ● -70.02 <
6. 38.3 ● -38.3 >
7. $\frac{2}{3}$ ● $\frac{4}{9}$ >
8. $\frac{7}{8}$ ● $\frac{21}{24}$ =
9. $\frac{4}{5}$ ● $\frac{5}{6}$ <
10. $\frac{23}{25}$ ● $\frac{23}{26}$ >
11. $-\frac{1}{3}$ ● $\frac{1}{6}$ <
12. $\frac{1}{9}$ ● $\frac{1}{10}$ >
13. $-\frac{3}{2}$ ● $-1\frac{1}{2}$ =
14. $\frac{23}{27}$ ● $\frac{15}{19}$ >
15. $-\frac{3}{7}$ ● $-\frac{5}{8}$ >
16. $-\frac{5}{3}$ ● $-\frac{7}{4}$ >
17. -2.25 ● $-\frac{9}{4}$ =
18. 10.73 ● $10\frac{73}{100}$ =
19. -8.29 ● $-8\frac{3}{10}$ >
20. 1.16 ● 1.1×10^0 >
21. $-2\frac{2}{5}$ ● $-2\frac{26}{65}$ =
22. $4\frac{2}{5}$ ● 4.25×10^{-1} >
23. 22.5 ● 2.25×10^1 =
24. $-1\frac{1}{8}$ ● -1.18×10^{-2} <
25. -0.065 ● -6.5×10^{-2} =
26. 16.75 ● 1.675×10^{-1} >
27. -1.0734 ● -1.0734×10^0 =
28. $-\frac{2}{3}$ ● -6.66×10^{-1} <
29. 2.605×10^3 ● 0.002605 >

Alternate Strategies: Reteaching the Lesson

Reteaching Activity

Acting It Out Working in small groups, have each student write a fractional rational number on a card. Have students stand and arrange themselves in order, from the smallest to the largest fraction. Repeat, using decimals.

Reteaching Masters Booklet, **p. 55**

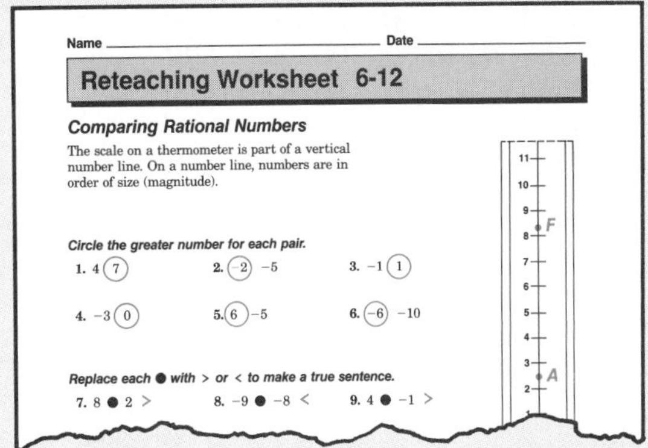
Name ______ Date ______

Reteaching Worksheet 6-12

Comparing Rational Numbers

The scale on a thermometer is part of a vertical number line. On a number line, numbers are in order of size (magnitude).

Circle the greater number for each pair.

1. 4 (7)
2. (-2) -5
3. -1 (1)
4. -3 (0)
5. (6) -5
6. (-6) -10

Replace each ● with > or < to make a true sentence.

7. 8 ● 2 >
8. -9 ● -8 <
9. 4 ● -1 >

Independent Practice

Homework Assignment	
Basic	11-23 odd, 28-35
Average	14-26 even, 28-35
Honors	21-35

4 CLOSE

Assessment Option

Speaking Have a student give two rational numbers to be compared. Then have another student compare them. Once this student is done, have the student give two more numbers to be compared and another student solve them. Continue around the room until each student has compared two numbers and has given two numbers to be compared.

Additional Answer

35.

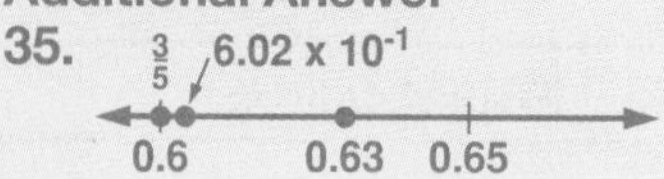

Enrichment Masters Booklet, **p. 55**

Name ____________ Date ____________

Enrichment Worksheet 6-12

Fraction Detective

The fifteen mixed numbers in the table at the right below belong in five groups with three numbers in each group. They have been scrambled. Your job is to use the clues below to place these numbers in their proper groups.

Clue 1: Each group has only one number less than 1.

Clue 2: In each group, the greatest number is the quotient of its middle number divided by its least number.

Clue 3: Group A contains both the greatest number and the least number of all fifteen.

Clue 4: $3\frac{3}{8}$ and $2\frac{1}{4}$ are in the same group—group B.

Clue 5: The greatest number in group C is the number closest to 3.

Clue 6: $1\frac{7}{8}$ and $\frac{4}{5}$ are in the same group—group D.

Clue 7: Group E has no number greater than 2.

$\frac{1}{2}$	$\frac{5}{6}$	$\frac{4}{5}$
$1\frac{1}{3}$	$\frac{3}{4}$	$\frac{2}{3}$
$3\frac{1}{5}$	$3\frac{3}{8}$	$1\frac{7}{8}$
$2\frac{1}{4}$	$2\frac{11}{32}$	$3\frac{1}{3}$
$1\frac{3}{5}$	$2\frac{2}{5}$	$6\frac{2}{3}$

Use the chart below to record your findings.

	A	B	C	D	E
Greatest	$6\frac{2}{3}$	$3\frac{3}{8}$	$3\frac{1}{5}$	$2\frac{11}{32}$	$1\frac{3}{5}$
Middle	$3\frac{1}{3}$	$2\frac{1}{4}$	$2\frac{2}{5}$	$1\frac{7}{8}$	$1\frac{1}{3}$
Least	$\frac{1}{2}$	$\frac{2}{3}$	$\frac{3}{4}$	$\frac{4}{5}$	$\frac{5}{6}$

Exercises

Independent Practice

ESTIMATION / MENTAL MATH / CALCULATOR / PAPER/PENCIL

Replace each ● with <, >, or = to make a true sentence.

10. 5.2 ● 5.18 >
11. 4.38 ● 4.48 <
12. -5.25 ● 5.2 <
13. -93.25 ● -93.35 >
14. -50.03 ● -50.13 >
15. 97.2 ● -96.23 >
16. $\frac{5}{9}$ ● $\frac{2}{3}$ <
17. $\frac{3}{8}$ ● $\frac{13}{25}$ <
18. $-\frac{2}{6}$ ● $\frac{7}{21}$ <
19. $-\frac{2}{3}$ ● $-\frac{1}{3}$ <
20. $\frac{25}{27}$ ● $\frac{17}{19}$ >
21. $-\frac{4}{5}$ ● $-\frac{5}{8}$ <
22. $1\frac{1}{8}$ ● 1.29 <
23. 107.58 ● $107\frac{58}{100}$ =
24. $-75\frac{3}{10}$ ● 75.29 <
25. $-2\frac{1}{2}$ ● -2.59 >
26. 1.27 ● 1.27×10^1 <
27. $5\frac{3}{5}$ ● 5.35×10^{-2} >

Mixed Review

28. Find the LCD of $\frac{5}{7x^2}$ and $\frac{9}{21x}$. (Lesson 4-9) $21x^2$
29. Solve the equation $r = -8\frac{3}{4} + 9\frac{7}{8}$. (Lesson 5-6) $1\frac{1}{8}$
30. State whether the sequence 16, 10, 4, -2, . . . is a geometric sequence. (Lesson 6-10) no
31. Express 0.024 in scientific notation. (Lesson 6-11) 2.4×10^{-2}

Applications

32. **Consumer Awareness** Zina found tennis balls priced at three for $4.69. At a second store they were priced at seven for $8.50. Which is the better buy?
33. **Sports** Use the information in the problem presented on page 240. Suppose the Pirates win two of their next three games and the Mets win all of their next three games. Which team has the better record? Mets

Critical Thinking

34. Find a fraction between $\frac{3}{4}$ and $\frac{4}{5}$. Explain how you found it.

Wrap-Up

35. Explain how to order $\frac{3}{5}$, 0.63, and 6.02×10^{-1} from least to greatest. Graph the numbers on a number line to show your solution. See margin.
$\frac{3}{5}$, 6.02×10^{-1}, 0.63

34. Sample answer: 0.77; Express $\frac{3}{4}$ and $\frac{4}{5}$ as decimals and name one between.

Enrichment

Density

How many rational numbers are there between $\frac{1}{3}$ and $\frac{1}{2}$? Would you guess *a few, many,* or *none?* If you express $\frac{1}{3}$ as 0.333 . . . and $\frac{1}{2}$ as 0.5, you can see that 0.4 falls between them. So does 0.41, 0.42, 0.43, and so on. In fact, there are infinitely many rational numbers between $\frac{1}{3}$ and $\frac{1}{2}$. The **density property** states that between any two rational numbers, no matter how close they may seem, there is at least one other rational number.

Alternate Strategies: Extending the Lesson

Enrichment

Sport Connection Use baseball averages for the current year and for previous years to rank players. Use almanacs and current newspapers or sports magazines to collect data.

Cooperative Learning

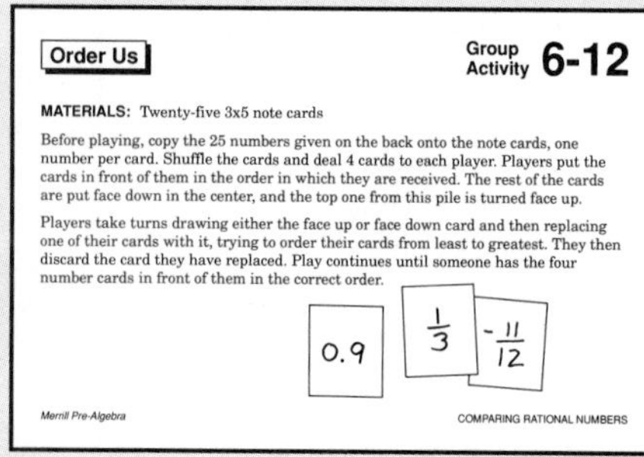
Order Us Group Activity **6-12**

MATERIALS: Twenty-five 3x5 note cards

Before playing, copy the 25 numbers given on the back onto the note cards, one number per card. Shuffle the cards and deal 4 cards to each player. Players put the cards in front of them in the order in which they are received. The rest of the cards are put face down in the center, and the top one from this pile is turned face up.

Players take turns drawing either the face up or face down card and then replacing one of their cards with it, trying to order their cards from least to greatest. They then discard the card they have replaced. Play continues until someone has the four number cards in front of them in the correct order.

0.9 $\frac{1}{3}$ $-\frac{11}{12}$

Merrill Pre-Algebra COMPARING RATIONAL NUMBERS

Application

6-13 Circles and Circumference

Objective:
Find the circumference of a circle.

Key Terms:
circle
center
radius
diameter
circumference

A favorite ride at amusement parks, the Ferris wheel is a power-driven, upright wheel with passenger cars mounted on the rim of the wheel. Each car is the same distance from the center. As the wheel turns, each car traces the path of a circle.

A **circle** is the set of all points in a plane that are the same distance from a given point in the plane. The given point is called the **center.** The distance from the center to any point on the circle is called the **radius (*r*).** The distance across the circle through its center is its **diameter (*d*).** The diameter of a circle is twice its radius, or $d = 2r$.

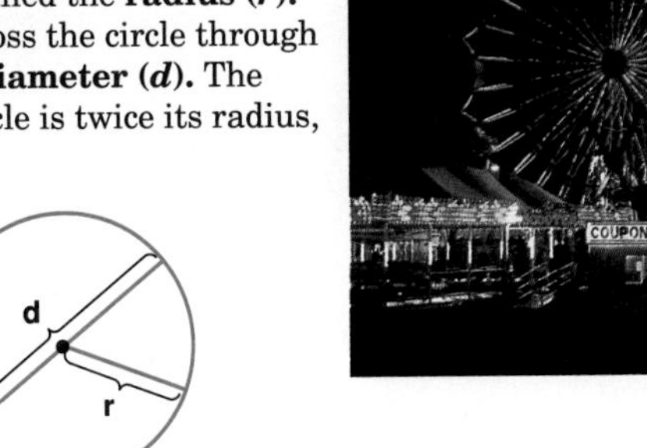

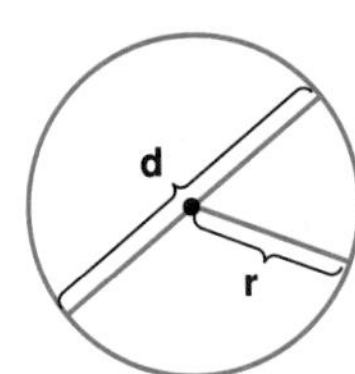

FYI

The Ferris wheel was invented by the American engineer G. W. Ferris for the 1893 World's Exposition in Chicago. The first Ferris wheel stood 250 feet tall and carried nearly 2000 passengers. Most modern Ferris wheels are only 45 feet tall.

The **circumference (*C*)** of a circle is the distance around the circle. Suppose a bicycle wheel makes one complete turn. The distance it travels is the same as the circumference of the wheel.

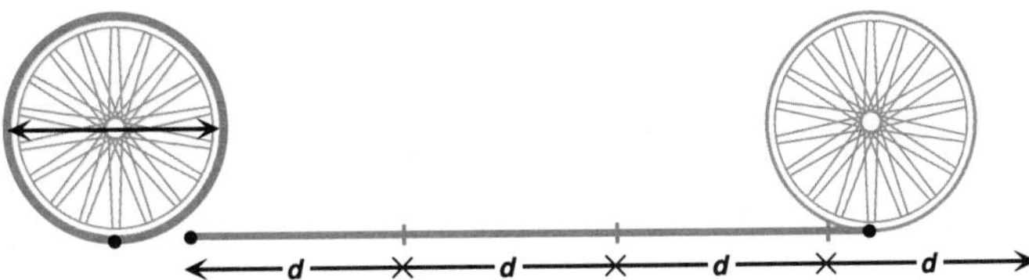

Notice in the drawing above that the circumference is a little more than three times the diameter of the wheel. In fact, the circumference of a circle is always 3.1415926 . . . times the diameter. The Greek letter π (pi) stands for this number. Although π is not a rational number, the rational numbers 3.14 and $\frac{22}{7}$ are two generally accepted approximations for π.

Circumference

In words: The circumference of a circle is equal to its diameter times π, or 2 times its radius times π.
In symbols: $C = \pi d$ or $C = 2\pi r$

Lesson Notes 6-13

5-Minute Check
(over Lesson 6-12)

Replace each ● with <, >, or = to make a true sentence.
1. $45.8 \bullet 0.458 \times 10^2$ =
2. $9.15 \times 10^{-4} \bullet 0.000920$ <
3. $4\frac{2}{5} \bullet 4.6$ <
4. $1\frac{2}{7} \bullet 1.196$ >
5. $-6\frac{3}{8} \bullet -6\frac{4}{7}$ >

Transparency 6-13 contains the 5-Minute Check and a teaching aid for this lesson.

1 FOCUS

The purpose of this lesson is to relate multiplication and division of rationals to the circumference of a circle.

Motivating the Lesson

If one is available, show students a hamster or gerbil in a cage with a wheel. Ask students how they would find out how far the animal runs on the wheel in a day.

2 TEACH

Using Manipulatives

Have small groups of students use string and rulers or metersticks to measure the circumference and diameter of several circular objects. Have students divide each circumference by its corresponding diameter and record the results. Compare their results to the value given for pi.

Bell Ringer

Which of the following numbers is greater?
1. 9.596, 9.597 9.597
2. $\frac{5}{7}, \frac{5}{8}$ $\frac{5}{7}$

EE: 1E, 3A, 4A, 4B, 4E
TAAS: 4, 11

Chalkboard Examples

Find the circumference of each circle. Use the given approximation for π.

- *For Example 1*
  $c = \pi d \quad \pi \approx \frac{22}{7}$
  diameter = 21 inches
  about 66 inches
- *For Example 2*
  $c = 2\pi r \quad \pi \approx 3.14$
  radius = 5.6 meters
  about 35.2 meters

3 PRACTICE/APPLY

Checking the Concept

After students complete Exercises 13-20, have them determine when it is more convenient to use $\frac{22}{7}$ for pi instead of 3.14.

Error Analysis

Watch for students who have difficulty distinguishing the parts of a circle.
Prevent by emphasizing the logical naming of some of the terms. "Circumference" sounds similar to "circle." "Radius" comes from a central point, as do other things that "radiate."

Practice Masters Booklet, **p. 62**

Name ______________ Date ______________

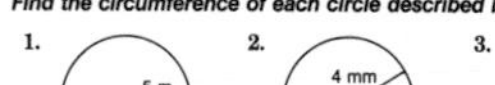

Practice Worksheet 6-13

Application: Circles and Circumference

Find the circumference of each circle described below.

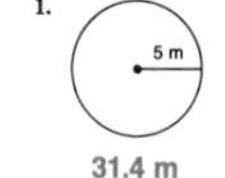
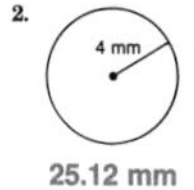

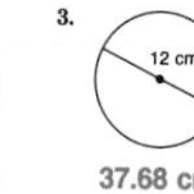
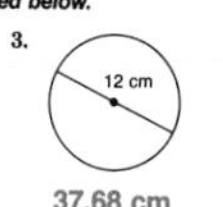
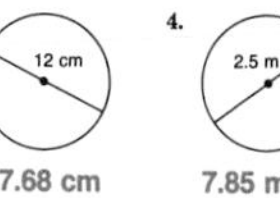

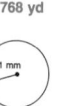

1. 5 m	2. 4 mm	3. 12 cm	4. 2.5 m
31.4 m	25.12 mm	37.68 cm	7.85 m
5. 2 ft	6. 1.2 yd	7. 9 mi	8. 20.5 m
12.56 ft	3.768 yd	56.52 mi	64.37 m
9. 7 in.	10. 8.1 mm	11. 10.4 mi	12. 11.2 cm
43.96 in. or 44 in.	50.868 mm	32.656 mi	70.336 cm

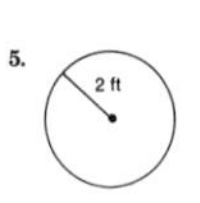
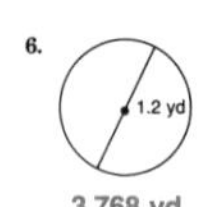
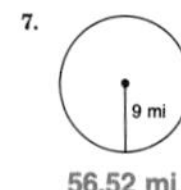
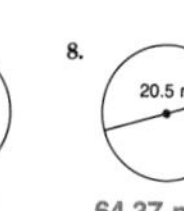
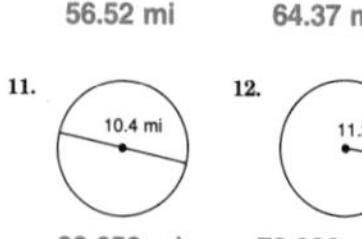

13. The diameter is 15.2 km. 47.728 km
14. The radius is 0.65 yd. 4.082 yd
15. The diameter is 0.5 ft. 1.57 ft
16. The radius is 3.75 in. 23.55 in.
17. The diameter is 25.6 cm. 80.384 cm
18. The radius is 12 mm. 75.36 mm

Why does $C = \pi d$ but $C \approx 3.14d$?
3.14 is an approximation for π.

Calculator Hint

π is such an important number in mathematics that it usually has its own key on a calculator. What is displayed on your calculator when you press $\boxed{\pi}$?

Examples

Find the circumference of each circle. Use the given approximation for π.

1 $C = \pi d \qquad \pi \approx \frac{22}{7}$

$C \approx \frac{22}{7} \cdot 14$

$C \approx 44$

The circumference is about 44 inches.

14 inches

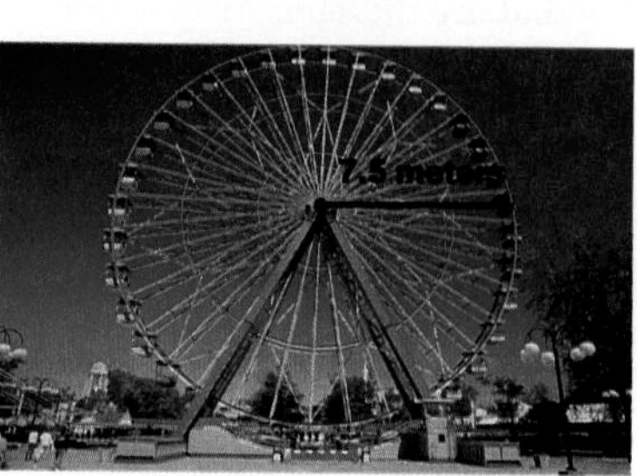

2 $C = 2\pi r \qquad \pi \approx 3.14$

$C \approx 2 \cdot 3.14 \cdot 7.5$

2 ⊠ 3.14 ⊠ 7.5 ⊟

The circumference is about 47.1 meters.

Checking for Understanding

1. Multiply the diameter times pi, or 2 times the radius times pi.

Communicating Algebra

1. In your own words, explain how to find the circumference of a circle.
2. Name two rational numbers that are approximations for π. **3.14, $\frac{22}{7}$**
3. If the radius of a circle is 8 inches, find the diameter. **16 inches**
4. If you know the diameter of a circle, how can you estimate the circumference? **Multiply the diameter by 3.**

For Exercises 5-12, value chosen for π may vary.

Guided Practice

State how to find the circumference of each circle described below.

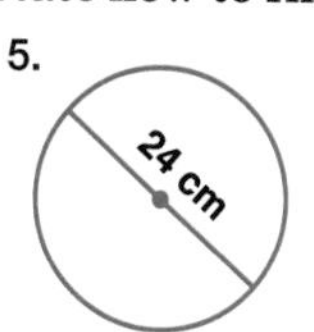
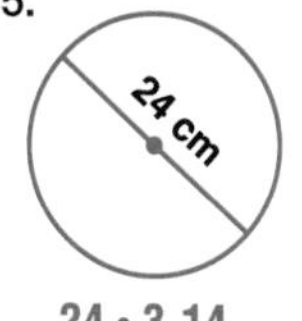
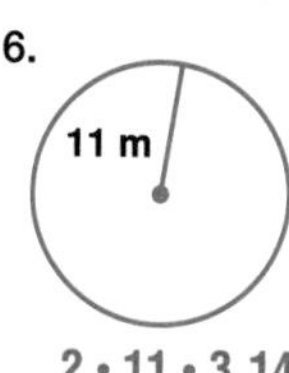
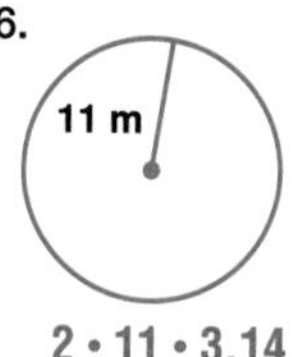
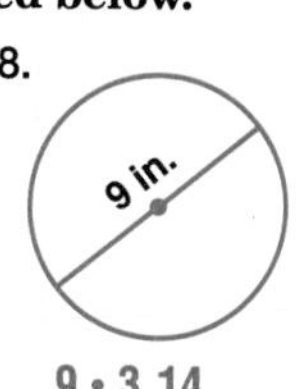

5. 24 cm — **24 • 3.14**
6. 11 m — **2 • 11 • 3.14**
7. $2\frac{1}{2}$ ft — **$2 \cdot 2\frac{1}{2} \cdot \frac{22}{7}$**
8. 9 in. — **9 • 3.14**
9. $d = 18$ **18 • 3.14**
10. $d = 15$ **15 • 3.14**
11. $r = 1.3$ **2 • 1.3 • 3.14**
12. $r = 21$ **$2 \cdot 21 \cdot \frac{22}{7}$**

Alternate Strategies: Reteaching the Lesson

Reteaching Activity

Using Connections Write the formula for circumference on the chalkboard or overhead. Ask students how to find pi if the circumference and diameter were known. **divide both sides by the diameter** Have students use calculators or computers to rename $\frac{22}{7}$ as a decimal.

Reteaching Masters Booklet, **p. 56**

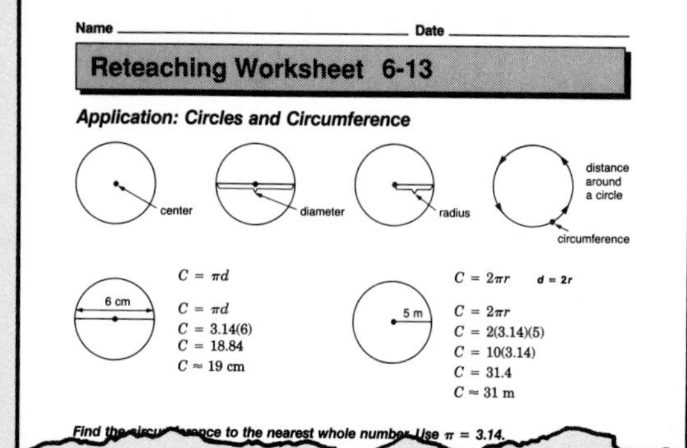
Name ______________ Date ______________

Reteaching Worksheet 6-13

Application: Circles and Circumference

center — diameter — radius — distance around a circle — circumference

$C = \pi d$ — $C = 2\pi r$ — $d = 2r$

6 cm: $C = \pi d$; $C = 3.14(6)$; $C = 18.84$; $C \approx 19$ cm

5 m: $C = 2\pi r$; $C = 2(3.14)(5)$; $C = 10(3.14)$; $C = 31.4$; $C \approx 31$ m

Find the circumference to the nearest whole number. Use π = 3.14.

Exercises For Exercises 13-20, value used for π may vary.

Independent Practice

Find the circumference of each circle described below.

13. 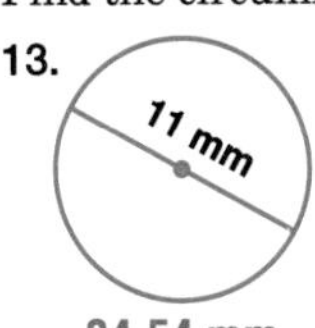

34.54 mm

14. 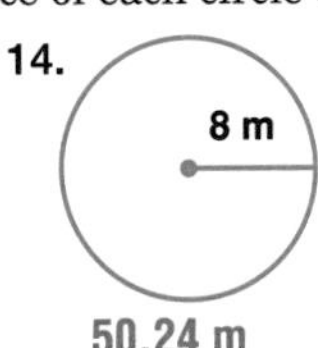

50.24 m

15. 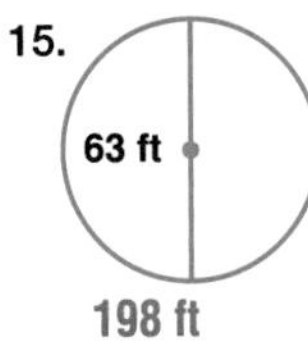

198 ft

16. 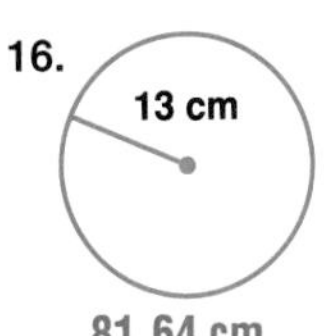

81.64 cm

17. The diameter is 16.4 km. **51.496 km**
18. The radius is 0.5 ft. **3.14 ft**
19. The radius is 14 yd. **88 yd**
20. The diameter is 3.5 in. **11 in.**

Mixed Review

21. Express -7000 in scientific notation. (Lesson 6-11) -7.0×10^3
22. Which is greater, $-\frac{2}{3}$ or $-\frac{4}{5}$? (Lesson 6-12) $-\frac{2}{3}$
23. Which is greater, 45.4 or 4.54×10^{-1}? (Lesson 6-12) **45.4**

Applications

24. **Recreation** A certain bicycle tire has a diameter of 26 inches. Find the distance the bicycle will travel in 10 rotations of the tire. **816.4 in.**
25. **Geography** The distance around the earth at the equator is about 25,000 miles. Find the approximate diameter of the earth at the equator. **about 7962 mi**

Critical Thinking

26. **Make Up a Problem** Write a problem that can be solved using the information in Exercise 19. **Sample answer in margin.**

Wrap-Up

27. Find a circular object and measure its diameter. Calculate the circumference and then measure to check your calculation. **See students' work.**

History

π

One of the great challenges faced by mathematicians was trying to find an exact value for π. As early as 240 B.C., Archimedes calculated π to four decimal places using a very clever method. His method was to draw two polygons, one inside and one outside a circle. By increasing the number of sides of the polygon, the circumference of the circle was *"trapped"* between the perimeters of the two polygons. Using a 96-sided polygon, he found that π was between 3.140 and 3.142.

Chinese mathematicians soon surpassed Archimedes' accomplishment. Father and son mathematicians, Tsu Ch'ung-Chih and Tsu Keng-Chih, drew polygons in a circle ten feet across. They calculated π to ten places as 3.1415929203. In Europe, π wasn't calculated to even seven decimal places until the 1600s, twelve hundred years after the Chinese.

Independent Practice

Homework Assignment	
Basic	13-27
Average	13-27
Honors	13-27

Chapter 6, Quiz B (Lessons 6-8 through 6-13) is available in the Evaluation Masters Booklet, p. 52.

4 CLOSE

Assessment Option

Modeling Bring in or obtain a variety of circular things such as plates, wheels, coasters, etc. Have students measure the diameter to find the circumference of each item.

Additional Answer

26. Sample answer: How much fence would be needed to enclose a circular horse pen with a radius of 14 yards?

Enrichment Masters Booklet, **p. 56**

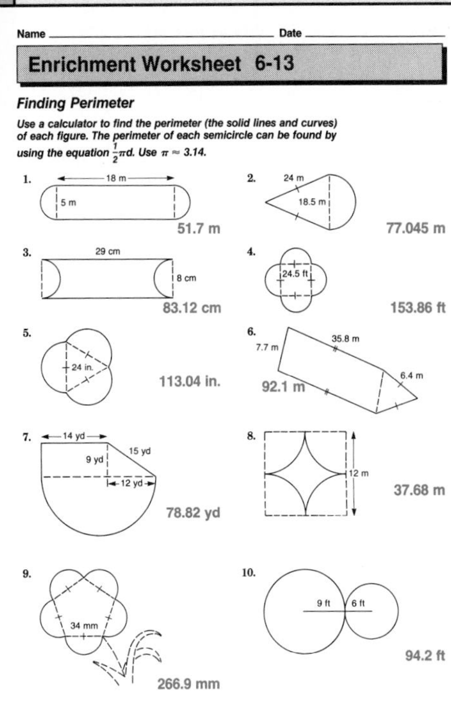
Name ______ Date ______

Enrichment Worksheet 6-13

Finding Perimeter

Use a calculator to find the perimeter (the solid lines and curves) of each figure. The perimeter of each semicircle can be found by using the equation $\frac{1}{2}\pi d$. Use $\pi \approx 3.14$.

Alternate Strategies: Extending the Lesson

Enrichment

Using Cooperative Groups Have small groups determine the answer to the following problem.

Two roads were built around Earth at the equator to form concentric circles. What would be the distance between the two road surfaces if the top road is 125 feet longer than the low road?

About 19.9 ft

Cooperative Learning

Curious Circumferences Group Activity **6-13**

In a small group, complete the following activity to discover an astounding fact about the distance around circles of different diameters.

Suppose you had a small plate and a bicycle tire. The diameter of the plate was 5 inches and the diameter of the tire was 30 inches. Compute the circumference of both the plate and the bicycle tire.

Pretend you had strings of these two lengths. Now suppose you added 9.42 inches to each string. If you put these new strings around the plate and the tire, how far outside each would the string be? You will be amazed when you compute the new diameters.

More amazing is the following: The diameter of Earth at the equator is about 8,000 miles. If you could put a string around Earth and then add 9.42 inches to this string, how far above the surface do you think the string would be? Change the diameter measurement to inches and do the computations to find the answer.

Merrill Pre-Algebra CIRCLES AND CIRCUMFERENCES

Using the Chapter Review

The Chapter Review is a comprehensive review of the concepts presented in this chapter. This review may be used to prepare students for the Chapter Test.

Alternate Review Strategy

To provide a brief in-class review, you may wish to read the following questions to the class.

1. What does the bar notation in $0.0\overline{528}$ mean? 528 repeats forever
2. Explain how you would estimate 4.82×3.16. 5×3
3. Explain how to solve $1\frac{4}{5} \cdot 2\frac{1}{3}$. $\frac{9}{5} \cdot \frac{7}{3} = \frac{63}{15} = 4\frac{1}{5}$
4. Where should the decimal point be placed in the product of $1.9 \times 3.42 = 6498$? 6.498
5. What is the multiplicative inverse of 8? $\frac{1}{8}$
6. Explain how to solve $2\frac{1}{2} \div 1\frac{2}{3}$. $\frac{5}{2} \cdot \frac{3}{5} = \frac{3}{2} = 1\frac{1}{2}$
7. State where the decimal point should be placed in the quotient of $2.884 \div 1.4 = 206$. 2.06
8. Explain how to solve $\frac{2}{5}k > 8$. Multiply each side by $\frac{5}{2}$, the multiplicative inverse of $\frac{2}{5}$.
9. Explain the difference between inductive and deductive reasoning. Inductive reasoning makes a rule after observing examples. Deductive reasoning uses a rule to make a conclusion.
10. Is 20, 10, 5, $\frac{5}{2}$ a geometric sequence? Explain your answer. yes; The common ratio is $\frac{1}{2}$.
11. Express 0.00000712 in scientific notation. 7.12×10^{-6}
12. Which is the greater number: -3.058 or -3.211? -3.058
13. If the diameter of a circle is 24 inches, what is the radius? 12 inches

Review

Language and Concepts

Choose the correct term to complete each sentence.

1. The fraction $\frac{1}{3}$ written as a decimal is an example of a (*terminating*, *repeating*) decimal.
2. The decimal 0.125 is an example of a (*terminating*, *repeating*) decimal.
3. Numbers like 2 and $\frac{1}{2}$, whose product is 1, are called (*reciprocals*, *integers*).
4. To find $2\frac{3}{4} \div 1\frac{1}{6}$, multiply $\frac{11}{4}$ by $\left(\frac{6}{7}, \frac{7}{6}\right)$.
5. $\frac{3}{4} \times \frac{4}{3} = 1$ is an example of the (*identity*, *inverse*) property of multiplication.

Skills

Express each fraction as a decimal. Use a bar to show repeating decimals. (Lesson 6-1)

6. $\frac{13}{25}$ 0.52
7. $4\frac{3}{4}$ 4.75
8. $\frac{5}{8}$ 0.625
9. $\frac{2}{9}$ $0.\overline{2}$

Estimate each product or quotient. (Lesson 6-2) Sample answers given.

10. $\frac{5}{9} \times 6\frac{1}{3}$ 3
11. $\frac{2}{3} \times 16$ 10
12. 9.6×2.02 20
13. $9\frac{5}{7} \times 12\frac{8}{9}$ 130

Solve each equation. Write each solution in simplest form. (Lesson 6-3, 6-4, 6-6, 6-7)

14. $\frac{37}{40} \cdot \frac{8}{12} = t$ $\frac{37}{60}$
15. $\left(-\frac{7}{8}\right)\left(2\frac{4}{7}\right) = x$ $-2\frac{1}{4}$
16. $(2.01)(0.04) = d$ 0.0804
17. $\frac{3}{5} \div \frac{13}{65} = y$ 3
18. $a = 2\frac{1}{9} \div 4$ $\frac{19}{36}$
19. $5\frac{10}{12} \div \left(-1\frac{2}{3}\right) = c$ $-3\frac{1}{2}$
20. $2.13 \div (-0.3) = a$ -7.1
21. $-1.4 \div (-7) = b$ 0.2
22. $4.498 \div (-1.73) = y$ -2.6

Compute using the distributive property. (Lesson 6-5)

23. $50 \times 3\frac{1}{2}$ 175
24. $8 \times 4\frac{3}{4}$ 38
25. $\frac{1}{2} \times 4\frac{1}{2}$ $2\frac{1}{4}$
26. $2\frac{1}{4} \times 12$ 27

Solve each equality or inequality. (Lesson 6-8)

27. $-3x = 2.4$ -0.8
28. $\frac{a}{6} = 0.12$ 0.72
29. $\frac{1}{4}d = 1.7$ 6.8
30. $7a > \frac{14}{15}$ $a > \frac{2}{15}$
31. $-4.95a \geq 89.1$ $a \leq -18$
32. $\frac{r}{23} < 5.7$ $r < 131.1$
33. $\frac{2x}{5} = -10$ -25
34. $2z > \frac{9}{2}$ $z > 2\frac{1}{4}$

Determine whether each sequence is a geometric sequence. Then write the next three terms. (Lesson 6-10)

35. 6.6, 5.7, 4.8, . . . no; 3.9, 3.0, 2.1
36. $\frac{1}{2}, \frac{1}{3}, \frac{1}{4}, \ldots$ no; $\frac{1}{5}, \frac{1}{6}, \frac{1}{7}$
37. 768, 192, 48, . . . yes; 12, 3, $\frac{3}{4}$
38. AN, OB, CP, QD, . . . no; ER, SF, GT, UH

Express each number in scientific notation. (Lesson 6-11)

39. 65,000 6.5×10^4 40. 198,000,000 1.98×10^8 41. 0.0021 2.1×10^{-3} 42. 0.00000743 7.43×10^{-6}

Replace each ● with <, >, or = to make a true sentence. (Lesson 6-12)

43. $\frac{6}{2}$ ● $\frac{12}{4}$ = 44. 2.67 ● 2.76 < 45. $\frac{3}{4}$ ● $\frac{2}{3}$ > 46. 1.33 ● 1.25 >

Find the circumference of each circle. (Lesson 6-13)

47.

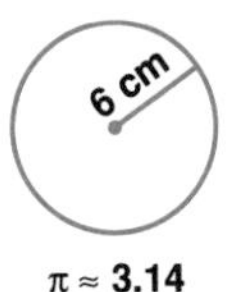

$\pi \approx 3.14$

37.68 cm

48.

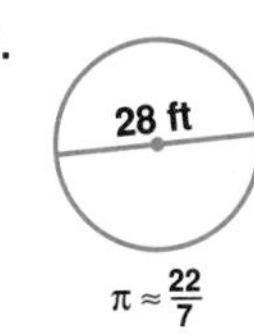

$\pi \approx 3.14$

7.536 m

49. 28 ft

$\pi \approx \frac{22}{7}$

88 ft

Applications and Logic

50. A wagon wheel has spokes that are each 0.5 meters long. What is the circumference of the wheel? (Lesson 6-13) 3.14 m

Determine whether each exercise is an example of inductive or deductive reasoning. (Lesson 6-9)

51. Numbers whose last 3 digits are divisible by 8 are divisible by 8. So, 31,816 is divisible by 8. deductive

52. Every student who came into the planetarium was wearing sunglasses. Professor Urban decided it was sunny outside. inductive

Communicating Algebra

In your own words, explain why zero is the only rational number that has no multiplicative inverse. There is no number that, multiplied by zero, is 1.

Curriculum Connection

- **Chemistry** Find the meaning of *Avogadro number.* How does it relate to the concepts in this chapter? See margin.
- **Current Events** Find examples of fractions in a newspaper or magazine. Find others that are decimals. Explain why each number was used. See students' work.

Read More About It

Luce, Marnie. *One is Unique.*

McHale, Thomas J. *Introductory Algebra: Programmed.*

Temple, Robert. *The Genius of China.*

Additional Answer
Chemistry Connection
There are 6.02×10^{23} particles in 1 mole. This quantity is known as Avogadro's number.
This number is expressed in scientific notation which was presented in Lesson 6-11.

You may wish to use a Chapter Test (free-response format) as an additional chapter review. Two forms are provided in the Evaluation Masters Booklet as shown below.

Evaluation Masters Booklet, **p. 50**

Name ____________ Date ____________

Chapter 6 Test, Form 2A

Express each fraction as a decimal.

1. $\frac{4}{9}$ 2. $\frac{1}{8}$ 3. $\frac{3}{16}$

Estimate the product or quotient.

4. $\frac{2}{3}(31)$ 5. $(3.97)(1.9)$ 6. $10.1 \div 2.03$

Solve each equation.

7. $\left(-2\frac{1}{5}\right)(5) = t$ 8. $(3.17)(1.02) = y$ 9. $-6(4.37) = z$

Name the property of multiplication shown by each statement.

10. $[-2 \cdot (-4)] \cdot 3 = -2(-4 \cdot 3)$ 11. $\frac{4}{5}m = 1$

Solve each equation or inequality.

12. $-\frac{2}{3} \div \left(-\frac{4}{5}\right) = a$ 13. $-21.06 \div (-8.1) = d$

14. $-\frac{1}{3}x = \frac{3}{5}$ 15. $3.5 > 7a$

Write the next term in each sequence.

16. 99, 33, 11, ... 17. $r, r^2, r^3, r^4, \ldots$

Write each number in scientific notation.

18. 403,000,000 19. 0.0000026

20. Write 6.34×10^4 in standard notation.

Replace each ● with >, <, or = to make a true statement.

21. $-\frac{4}{5}$ ● $\frac{1}{7}$ 22. 3.0643 ● 3.06043

23. Barbara is putting a fence around her circular flower garden. The garden is 6 feet across the center. How long is the fence?

24. Robbi estimates there are about 5.5 million characters in a dictionary she owns. Write this number in scientific notation.

25. Mal states that 1, 10, 2, 20, 3, 30, ... is not a geometric sequence. Why is he correct?

BONUS Find one-half of one-third of one-fourth of −48.

1. 0.4
2. 0.125
3. 0.1875
4. 20
5. 8
6. 5
7. −11
8. 3.2334
9. −26.22
10. Assoc.
11. Inver.
12. $\frac{5}{6}$
13. 2.6
14. $-1\frac{4}{5}$
15. $a < 0.5$
16. $3\frac{2}{3}$
17. r^5
18. 4.03×10^8
19. 2.6×10^{-6}
20. 63,400
21. <
22. >
23. 18.84 ft
24. 5.5×10^6
25. No common ratio

BONUS −2

Evaluation Masters Booklet, **p. 51**

Name ____________ Date ____________

Chapter 6 Test, Form 2B

Express each fraction as a decimal.

1. $\frac{7}{9}$ 2. $\frac{5}{8}$ 3. $\frac{5}{12}$

Estimate the product or quotient.

4. $\frac{2}{5}(31)$ 5. $(6.01)(3.9)$ 6. $15.01 \div 2.9$

Solve each equation.

7. $\left(-2\frac{1}{2}\right)(9) = t$ 8. $(3.17)(1.08) = y$ 9. $-8(5.73) = z$

Name the property of multiplication shown by each statement.

10. $[(-2)(-4)](8) = [(-4)(2)](8)$ 11. $\frac{4}{5}m = \frac{4}{5}$

Solve each equation or inequality.

12. $-\frac{2}{3} \div \left(-\frac{6}{7}\right) = a$ 13. $-50.4 \div 6.3 = d$

14. $-\frac{1}{3}x = \frac{4}{9}$ 15. $8.1 < 9y$

Write the next term in each sequence.

16. 88, 44, 22, ... 17. $2r, 2r^2, 2r^3, \ldots$

Write each number in scientific notation.

18. 40,300,000 19. 0.000000018

20. Write 6.05×10^5 in standard notation.

Replace each ● with >, <, or = to make a true statement.

21. $\frac{4}{5}$ ● $\frac{1}{7}$ 22. 2.0543 ● 2.05043

23. Adelle is putting a fence around her circular herb garden. The garden is 5 feet across the center. How long is the fence?

24. Sherry estimates there are about 200 million people living in her country. Write this number in scientific notation.

25. Flo states that 10, 20, 40, ... is a geometric sequence. Why is she correct?

BONUS Find one-half of one-third of one-sixth of 36.

1. 0.7
2. 0.625
3. $0.41\overline{6}$
4. 12
5. 24
6. 5
7. $-22\frac{1}{2}$
8. 3.4236
9. −45.84
10. Comm.
11. Ident.
12. $\frac{7}{9}$
13. −8
14. $-1\frac{1}{3}$
15. $y > 0.9$
16. 11
17. $2r^4$
18. 4.03×10^7
19. 1.8×10^{-8}
20. 605,000
21. >
22. >
23. 15.7 ft
24. 2.0×10^8
25. Common ratio is 2.

BONUS 1

Using the Chapter Test

This page may be used as a test or as an additional review. Two forms of a Chapter Test (multiple-choice format) are provided in the Evaluation Masters Booklet. One of the tests is shown below.

Evaluation Masters Booklet, **pp. 46-47**

Name ______________________ Date ______________

Chapter 6 Test, Form 1A

1. Express $\frac{2}{3}$ as a decimal.
   A. -0.6 B. 0.6 C. $-0.\overline{6}$ D. $0.\overline{6}$ — 1. **D**
2. Express $\frac{5}{16}$ as a decimal.
   A. 0.3125 B. 0.312 C. 5.16 D. 3 — 2. **A**
3. Estimate the product $\frac{1}{5}(16)$.
   A. 2 B. 3 C. 5 D. 80 — 3. **B**
4. Estimate the quotient $32 \div 3.1$.
   A. 96 B. 8 C. 12 D. 10 — 4. **D**
5. Solve $2\frac{1}{2} \cdot \frac{2}{3} = x$.
   A. $3\frac{3}{4}$ B. $1\frac{2}{3}$ C. 2 D. $1\frac{5}{6}$ — 5. **B**
6. Solve $3\frac{1}{5} \cdot 3\frac{3}{4} = y$.
   A. 12 B. 10 C. $9\frac{4}{20}$ D. $9\frac{1}{5}$ — 6. **A**
7. Solve $(9.6)(0.4) = w$.
   A. 10 B. 3.44 C. 3.84 D. 38.4 — 7. **C**
8. Solve $(3.6)(-1.1) = z$.
   A. -39.6 B. 4.7 C. -3.66 D. -3.96 — 8. **D**
9. Name the property of multiplication shown by $(3.6)(4.8) = (4.8)(3.6)$.
   A. Identity B. Associative C. Commutative D. Inverse — 9. **C**
10. Name the property of multiplication shown by $(3.6)n = 1$.
    A. Identity B. Associative C. Commutative D. Inverse — 10. **D**
11. Solve $-\frac{2}{3} \div \left(-\frac{3}{2}\right) = x$.
    A. 1 B. -1 C. $-\frac{4}{9}$ D. $\frac{4}{9}$ — 11. **D**
12. Solve $2\frac{1}{4} \div 1\frac{1}{4} = y$.
    A. $1\frac{4}{5}$ B. 2 C. $2\frac{13}{16}$ D. $\frac{5}{9}$ — 12. **A**
13. Solve $r = 36.48 \div 8.0$.
    A. 4.26 B. 4.06 C. 5.16 D. 4.56 — 13. **D**
14. Solve $t = 17.92 \div 5.6$.
    A. 4.7 B. 3.7 C. 3.2 D. 32.7 — 14. **C**

Name ______________________ Date ______________

Chapter 6 Test, Form 1A (continued)

15. Solve $\frac{2}{3}y = \frac{3}{7}$.
    A. $\frac{9}{14}$ B. $\frac{2}{7}$ C. $\frac{6}{7}$ D. $\frac{6}{14}$ — 15. **A**
16. Solve $\frac{x}{-3.2} < 12.8$.
    A. $x < -40.96$ B. $x > -40.96$ C. $x < -4$ D. $x > -4$ — 16. **B**
17. Use inductive reasoning to determine the next number.
    1, 11, 111, ...
    A. 121 B. 11 C. 1111 D. 1000 — 17. **C**
18. Write the next term of the sequence. 24, 12, 6, 3, ...
    A. 1 B. 1.5 C. 0.5 D. 0 — 18. **B**
19. Write the next term of the sequence. 8, −16, 32, −64, ...
    A. −80 B. 96 D. −128 D. 128 — 19. **D**
20. Express 23,700,000,000 in scientific notation.
    A. 2.37×10^{10} B. 2.37×10^{9} C. 23.7×10^{9} D. 2.37×10^{11} — 20. **A**
21. Replace ● with >, <, or = to make −3.059 ● −3.159 true.
    A. > B. < C. = D. Can't tell — 21. **A**
22. Replace ● with >, <, or = to make $\frac{2}{3}$ ● $\frac{3}{2}$ true.
    A. > B. < C. = D. Can't tell — 22. **B**
23. Mary gave a demonstration showing that a red blood cell is about 7.5×10^{-4} cm long. Write this number in standard form.
    A. 0.0075 B. 0.00075 C. 0.000075 D. 75,000 — 23. **B**
24. Helen bakes a pie having a diameter of 9 in. She puts a decoration around the circumference of the pie. How long is the decoration?
    A. 27.26 in. B. 14.13 in. C. 28.26 in. D. 254.34 in. — 24. **C**
25. Neil reads an estimate that there are about 10^{80} atoms in the universe. He decides to write this number in standard form. How many zeros will follow the 1 in his number?
    A. 81 B. 80 C. 79 D. 90 — 25. **B**

BONUS How many times larger than 2.4×10^4 is 2.4×10^6?
A. 2 B. 20 C. 100 D. 200 — **C**

Test

Express each fraction as a decimal. Use a bar to show repeating decimals.

1. $\frac{15}{12}$ 1.25
2. $\frac{17}{40}$ 0.425
3. $\frac{4}{9}$ $0.\overline{4}$
4. $\frac{17}{3}$ $5.\overline{6}$

Estimate each product or quotient.

5. $\frac{9}{10} \times 21$ 18
6. $16.542 \div 78$ 0.2
7. 28.6×7.6 240
8. $27\frac{5}{6} \div 3\frac{4}{5}$ 7

Solve each equation. Write each solution in simplest form.

9. $\frac{16}{3} \times \frac{18}{2} = n$ 48
10. $\frac{7}{12} \div \frac{2}{3} = y$ $\frac{7}{8}$
11. $4 \cdot 7.07 = n$ 28.28
12. $b = 62.9 \div 1000$ 0.0629
13. $f = 1.3 \div 1000$ 0.0013
14. $b = 13.98 \div 6$ 2.33
15. $p = 4\frac{1}{8} \cdot 5\frac{1}{3}$ 22
16. $\frac{14}{20} \div 2\frac{2}{5} = d$ $\frac{7}{24}$

Solve each inequality.

17. $2n \leq 7$ $n \leq \frac{7}{2}$
18. $\frac{p}{12} \geq -6$ $p \geq -72$
19. $-7s > 6.3$ $s > -0.9$
20. $7 < \frac{x}{-8}$ $-56 < x$

Determine whether each sequence is a geometric sequence. Then write the next three terms.

21. 17, 13, 18, 14, 19, . . . no; 15, 20, 16
22. 3, 9, 27, . . . yes; 81, 243, 729

Express each number in scientific notation.

23. 13,490,000 1.349×10^7
24. 0.00000674 6.74×10^{-6}
25. 0.00032 3.2×10^{-4}
26. 5810 5.81×10^3

Replace each ● with <, >, or = to make a true statement.

27. $\frac{1}{4}$ ● $\frac{3}{8}$ <
28. 4.6 ● 4.75 <
29. 9.5 ● 9.50 =
30. $\frac{12}{7}$ ● $\frac{5}{3}$ >

Find the circumference of each circle.

31.

$\pi \approx \frac{22}{7}$

132 ft

32.
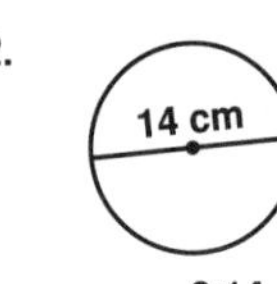

$\pi \approx 3.14$

43.96 in.

Determine whether the exercise is an example of inductive or deductive reasoning.

33. If you are a freshman, then you cannot attend the prom. Joni is a freshman. She is not allowed to attend the prom. deductive

BONUS

How do you know that $10 \div \frac{1}{2} > 10$? Sample answer: There would be more than 10 halves in 10.

Test Generator Software is provided in both Apple and IBM formats. You may use this software to create your own tests, based on the needs of your students.

Academic Skills Test

Cumulative, Chapters 1-6

1. What is the value of $y + (-7)$ if $y = 8$?

   A -56
   B -15
   C -1
   (D) 1

2. If $14 = w - (-20)$, what is the value of w?

   (A) -6
   B 6
   C 34
   D Not Here

3. If $\frac{h}{0.7} = -2.8$, what is the value of h?

   A -4
   B -2.8
   (C) -1.96
   D 0.7

4. What is the value of $3t^5$ if $t = 2$?

   A 7776
   (B) 96
   C 32
   D 30

5. How is the product $2 \cdot 2 \cdot 2 \cdot 2$ expressed in exponential notation?

   A 2^2
   B $2 \cdot 4$
   C 4^2
   (D) 2^4

6. Which number should come next in this pattern?

   0.5, 2, 3.5, 5, . . .

   A 8
   B 7.5
   C 7
   (D) 6.5

7. Jan plans to put a fence around a square garden that measures 12 feet by 12 feet. How many feet of fence will she need?

   A 144 ft
   B 96 ft
   (C) 48 ft
   D 24 ft

8. Carl bought a bike that cost $532.16. He paid for the bike in equal payments for 12 months. Estimate: the amount of each payment was between—

   A $10 and $20
   B $25 and $35
   (C) $40 and $50
   D $55 and $65

9. Lee is practicing for a 2500 meter run. He runs the distance twice a day for 5 days. How many kilometers has he run?

   (A) 25 km
   B 250 km
   C 25,000 km
   D Not Here

10. One red blood cell is about 7.5×10^{-4} centimeters long. What is another way to express this measure?

   A 0.000075 cm
   (B) 0.00075 cm
   C 0.0075 cm
   D 0.075 cm

A Cumulative Review (free-response format) and Cumulative Test (multiple-choice format) are also provided in the Evaluation Masters Booklet as shown at the right.

Test Item	1	2	3	4	5	6	7	8	9	10
Lesson Number	2-8	3-2	3-3	4-2	4-2	5-9	5-9	6-2	6-4	6-9
TAAS Objective	2	2	2	1	1	2	4	10	8	1

Using the Academic Skills Test

This test familiarizes students with a standardized format while testing skills and concepts presented up to this point.

***Evaluation Masters Booklet,* p. 53**

Name ______________ Date ______________

Cumulative Review, Chapters 1-6

Simplify. (Lessons 1–1, 2–5, 2–8)

1. $16 \div 4 + 4$ 2. $8 + 8 \div 2$ 3. $-8 - 15$
4. $-12 - (-12)$ 5. $-64 \div (-4)$

Solve. (Lessons 3–3, 3–4, 3–7, 3–8)

6. $-48 = 3c$ 7. $\frac{x}{16} = 12$
8. $x + 18 < 12$ 9. $-3y > -42$

Write the prime factorization of each number. (Lesson 4–4)

10. 128 11. 1225

12. Write the GCF of 24 and 40. (Lesson 4–5)
13. Write the LCM of 12 and 16. (Lesson 4–7)
14. Simplify $a^6 \cdot a \cdot a^{14}$. (Lesson 4–9)

Rename the number as a fraction in simplest form. (Lesson 5–2)

15. 0.08 16. $0.\overline{45}$

17. Solve $f - 3.7 < 5.2$. (Lesson 5–7)

Solve each equation. (Lessons 5–4, 6–3, 6–4, 6–6, 6–7)

18. $18 - 3.64 = t$ 19. $\frac{6}{8} \cdot \frac{20}{32} = w$ 20. $-\frac{24}{17} \div \frac{36}{34} = x$
21. $(8.36)(-0.16) = y$ 22. $-29.58 \div 3.4 = z$

23. Tony is waxing a dance floor shaped as a square 60 feet long on each side. Find the area of the floor. (Lesson 3–6)
24. Tony has two partially-full cans of floor wax. One contains 3 qt and the other contains 1 gal 3 qt. How much wax does he have altogether? (Lesson 5–10)
25. Marianne is the class treasurer. She divides $380.82 evenly among three accounts. How much does she put in each account? (Lesson 6–7)

Answers: 1. 8; 2. 12; 3. −23; 4. 0; 5. 16; 6. −16; 7. 192; 8. $x < -6$; 9. $y < 14$; 10. 2^7; 11. $5^2 \cdot 7^2$; 12. 8; 13. 48; 14. a^{21}; 15. $\frac{2}{25}$; 16. $\frac{5}{11}$; 17. $f < 8.9$; 18. 14.36; 19. $\frac{15}{32}$; 20. $-1\frac{1}{3}$; 21. −1.3376; 22. −8.7; 23. 3600 ft^2; 24. 2 gal 2 qt; 25. $126.94

***Evaluation Masters Booklet,* p. 54**

Name ______________ Date ______________

Cumulative Test, Chapters 1-6

1. Simplify $32 + 4 \cdot 3$.
   A. 384 B. 44 C. 108 D. 39 — 1. B
2. Simplify $-4 - (-12)$.
   A. −16 B. −8 C. 8 D. 16 — 2. C
3. Simplify $-60 \div 3$.
   A. −57 B. 20 C. −63 D. −20 — 3. D
4. Solve $8d = -48$.
   A. −6 B. −40 C. 6 D. −56 — 4. A
5. Solve $x + 14 < 10$.
   a. $x > 4$ B. $x < 4$ C. $x > -4$ D. $x < -4$ — 5. D
6. Solve $-3a < -36$.
   A. $a < -12$ B. $a > -12$ C. $a > 12$ D. $a < 12$ — 6. C
7. Write the prime factorization of 220.
   A. $2^2 \cdot 55$ B. $22 \cdot 10$ C. $2 \cdot 110$ D. $2^2 \cdot 5 \cdot 11$ — 7. D
8. Find the GCF of 24 and 32.
   A. 8 B. 2 C. 96 D. 16 — 8. A
9. Find the LCM of 12 and 30.
   A. 2 B. 60 C. 6 D. 72 — 9. B
10. Find the product $x^2 \cdot x^{12} \cdot x$.
   A. x^{15} B. x^{14} C. x^{24} D. x^{25} — 10. A
11. Express $0.\overline{36}$ as a fraction in simplest form.
   A. $\frac{36}{100}$ B. $\frac{9}{25}$ C. $\frac{4}{11}$ D. $\frac{36}{99}$ — 11. C
12. Solve $x - 2.6 > 3.4$.
   A. $x < -6$ B. $x > 6$ C. $x < 6$ D. $x > -6$ — 12. B
13. Solve $12 - 4.37 = d$.
   A. 8.63 B. 7.63 C. 8.62 D. 7.62 — 13. B
14. Solve $\frac{6}{14} \cdot \frac{28}{30} = n$. A. $\frac{168}{420}$ B. $\frac{2}{5}$ C. $\frac{14}{35}$ D. $\frac{7}{15}$ — 14. B
15. Solve $x = \frac{4}{5} \div \frac{15}{8}$. A. $\frac{32}{75}$ B. $\frac{3}{2}$ C. $\frac{2}{3}$ D. $\frac{1}{32}$ — 15. A
16. Solve $p = (4.37)(-0.12)$.
   A. 0.5244 B. −0.5244 C. −52.44 D. 6.03 — 16. B
17. Solve $31.356 \div 5.2 = y$.
   A. 63 B. 26.156 C. 6.3 D. 6.03 — 17. D
18. Kent is replacing a car's floor panel which is shaped like a square measuring 27 inches on a side. Find the area of the panel.
   A. 54 in^2 B. 108 in^2 C. 729 in^2 D. 243 in^2 — 18. C
19. The camp cook makes punch by mixing 3 gal 1 qt of apple juice, 2 qt of cherry juice, and 1 gal 3 qt of orange juice. How much punch does the cook mix?
   A. 4 gal 2 qt B. 5 gal 2 qt C. 5 gal 3 qt D. 6 gal — 19. B
20. Angeliki, the class treasurer, collected $4.85 from each of 30 students. How much did she collect altogether?
   A. $4.85 B. $124.55 C. $145.50 D. $1455.00 — 20. C

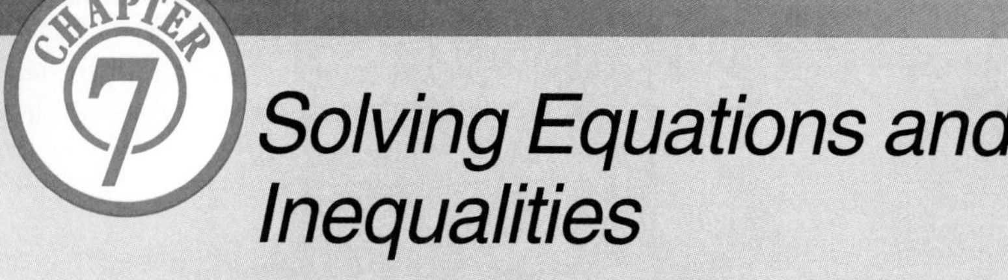

Solving Equations and Inequalities

Previewing the Chapter

This chapter relates solving problems by working backwards to solving equations, first with two steps and then with multiple steps. Since the steps used in solving equations reverses the steps in the order of operations, the two ideas can be coordinated and reinforced. Using algebra to translate verbal problems to equations and inequalities and then to solve them, students are able to see applications for the topics discussed. These topics include converting measures within the metric system.

Problem Solving Strategy Students will learn to solve problems by working backwards.

Lesson (Pages)	Lesson Objectives	State/Local Objectives
7-1 (252-253)	7-1: Solve a problem by working backwards.	1A, 1B, 1C, 1D, 1E
7-2 (255-258)	7-2: Solve equations that involve two operations.	1E, 2F, 3A, 3F, 3G, 3H, 4E
7-3 (259-261)	7-3: Solve verbal problems by translating them into two-step equations.	1D, 1E, 2F, 3A, 3F, 3G
7-4 (263-266)	7-4: Solve equations with variables on each side.	1E, 3A, 3F, 5E
7-5 (267-268)	7-5: Solve equations that involve more than two operations.	1E, 3A, 3F, 5E
7-6 (270-271)	7-6: Solve inequalities that involve more than one operation.	1E, 2F, 3A, 3F
7-7 (272-274)	7-7: Solve verbal problems involving rational numbers by translating them into inequalities.	1D, 1E, 3A, 3F
7-8 (275-277)	7-8: Convert measures within the metric system.	1E, 3A, 4B

Organizing the Chapter

*You may want to refer to the **Course Planning Calendar** on Page T31.*

Planning Guide

Lesson (Pages)	Pacing Chart (in days) MINIMUM	STANDARD	ACCELERATED	Extra Practice (Student Edition)	Blackline Masters Booklets: Reteaching	Practice	Enrichment	Other Resources
7-1 (252-253)	1	1	0.5			p. 63		Transparency 7-1 Group Activity Card 7-1
7-2 (255-258)	1.5	1	1	p. 603, Set 7A	p. 57	p. 64	p. 57	Transparency 7-2 Group Activity Card 7-2
7-3 (259-261)	1	1	1	p. 603, Set 7A	p. 58	p. 65	p. 58	Transparency 7-3 Group Activity Card 7-3
7-4 (263-266)	1.5	1	1	p. 603, Set 7A	p. 59	p. 66	p. 59	Transparency 7-4 Group Activity Card 7-4
7-5 (267-268)	1	1	0.5	p. 603, Set 7B	p. 60	p. 67	p. 60	Transparency 7-5 Group Activity Card 7-5
7-6 (270-271)	1	1	0.5	p. 603, Set 7B	p. 61	p. 68	p. 61	Transparency 7-6 Group Activity Card 7-6
7-7 (272-274)	1	1	1	p. 603, Set 7A	p. 62	p. 69	p. 62	Transparency 7-7 Group Activity Card 7-7
7-8 (275-277)	1	1	1	p. 604, Set 7C	p. 63	p. 70	p. 63	Transparency 7-8 Group Activity Card 7-8
Review (278-279)	1.5	1	1					Test Generator
Test (280)	1	1	1		Evaluation Masters, pp. 55-60			

Other Chapter Resources

Student Edition
Exploration, pp. 254, 262
Challenge, p. 258
Team Problem Solving, p. 261
Mid-Chapter Quiz, p. 266
Algebra in Action, p. 269
Career, p. 277
Academic Skills Test, p. 281

Teacher Resource Package
Interdisciplinary Activity, p. 7
Application Worksheet, p. 22
Cooperative Problem Solving, p. 37
Multicultural Activity, p. 52
Fun Activities, p. 69
Technology Worksheets, pp. 7, 22, 37
Lab Manual, pp. 45-47
Quizzes(2), p. 61
Class Review Game

Software
Test Generator

available for Apple and IBM

Enhancing the Chapter

Some of the blackline masters for enhancing this chapter are shown below.

Applications, p. 22

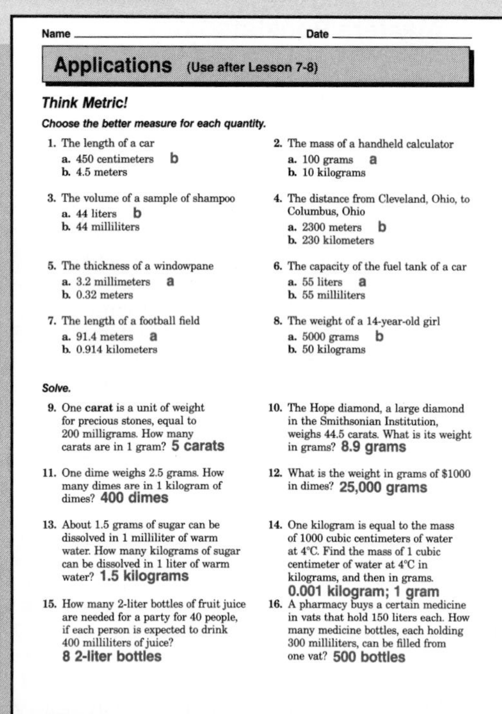

Name ____________________ Date ____________

Applications (Use after Lesson 7-8)

Think Metric!

Choose the better measure for each quantity.

1. The length of a car
   a. 450 centimeters **b**
   b. 4.5 meters
2. The mass of a handheld calculator
   a. 100 grams **a**
   b. 10 kilograms
3. The volume of a sample of shampoo
   a. 44 liters **b**
   b. 44 milliliters
4. The distance from Cleveland, Ohio, to Columbus, Ohio
   a. 2300 meters **b**
   b. 230 kilometers
5. The thickness of a windowpane
   a. 3.2 millimeters **a**
   b. 0.32 meters
6. The capacity of the fuel tank of a car
   a. 55 liters **a**
   b. 55 milliliters
7. The length of a football field
   a. 91.4 meters **a**
   b. 0.914 kilometers
8. The weight of a 14-year-old girl
   a. 5000 grams **b**
   b. 50 kilograms

Solve.

9. One **carat** is a unit of weight for precious stones, equal to 200 milligrams. How many carats are in 1 gram? **5 carats**
10. The Hope diamond, a large diamond in the Smithsonian Institution, weighs 44.5 carats. What is its weight in grams? **8.9 grams**
11. One dime weighs 2.5 grams. How many dimes are in 1 kilogram of dimes? **400 dimes**
12. What is the weight in grams of $1000 in dimes? **25,000 grams**
13. About 1.5 grams of sugar can be dissolved in 1 milliliter of warm water. How many kilograms of sugar can be dissolved in 1 liter of warm water? **1.5 kilograms**
14. One kilogram is equal to the mass of 1000 cubic centimeters of water at 4°C. Find the mass of 1 cubic centimeter of water at 4°C in kilograms, and then in grams. **0.001 kilogram; 1 gram**
15. How many 2-liter bottles of fruit juice are needed for a party for 40 people, if each person is expected to drink 400 milliliters of juice? **8 2-liter bottles**
16. A pharmacy buys a certain medicine in vats that hold 150 liters each. How many medicine bottles, each holding 300 milliliters, can be filled from one vat? **500 bottles**

The **Activity Masters Booklet** contains the page shown above.

Interdisciplinary Activity, p. 7

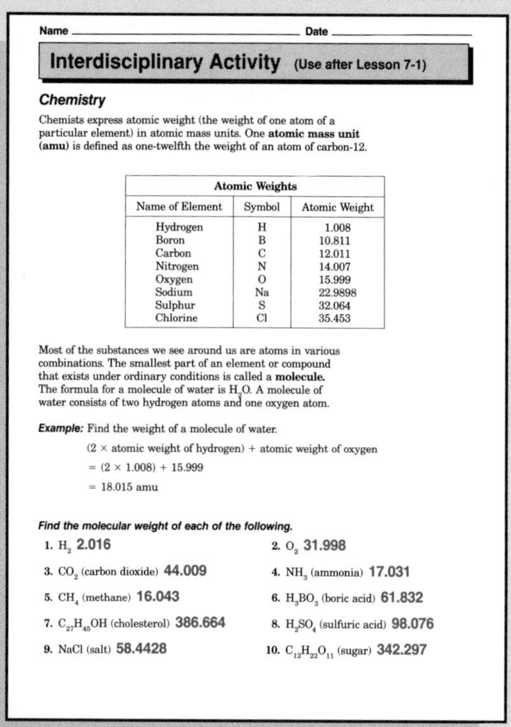

Name ____________________ Date ____________

Interdisciplinary Activity (Use after Lesson 7-1)

Chemistry

Chemists express atomic weight (the weight of one atom of a particular element) in atomic mass units. One **atomic mass unit (amu)** is defined as one-twelfth the weight of an atom of carbon-12.

Atomic Weights		
Name of Element	Symbol	Atomic Weight
Hydrogen	H	1.008
Boron	B	10.811
Carbon	C	12.011
Nitrogen	N	14.007
Oxygen	O	15.999
Sodium	Na	22.9898
Sulphur	S	32.064
Chlorine	Cl	35.453

Most of the substances we see around us are atoms in various combinations. The smallest part of an element or compound that exists under ordinary conditions is called a **molecule.** The formula for a molecule of water is H_2O. A molecule of water consists of two hydrogen atoms and one oxygen atom.

Example: Find the weight of a molecule of water.

(2 × atomic weight of hydrogen) + atomic weight of oxygen
= (2 × 1.008) + 15.999
= 18.015 amu

Find the molecular weight of each of the following.

1. H_2 **2.016**
2. O_2 **31.998**
3. CO_2 (carbon dioxide) **44.009**
4. NH_3 (ammonia) **17.031**
5. CH_4 (methane) **16.043**
6. H_3BO_3 (boric acid) **61.832**
7. $C_{27}H_{45}OH$ (cholesterol) **386.664**
8. H_2SO_4 (sulfuric acid) **98.076**
9. NaCl (salt) **58.4428**
10. $C_{12}H_{22}O_{11}$ (sugar) **342.297**

The **Activity Masters Booklet** contains the page shown above.

Models and Manipulatives

Students have been using order of operations in arithmetic but may not see the relationship between order of operations and order in solving equations. Discuss this relationship. Show that the order of operations is: 1) work inside parentheses, 2) evaluate exponents, 3) do multiplication and division, from left to right, and 4) do addition and subtraction, from left to right. The order of solving equations can use the order of operations backwards. For example, when solving $-3(x + 2^2) + 5 = -1$: **1)** subtract −5: $-3(x + 2^2) = -6$, **2)** divide by −3: $(x + 2^2) = 2$, **3)** evaluate exponent and remove parentheses: $x + 4 = 2$, and **4)** solve. $x = -2$

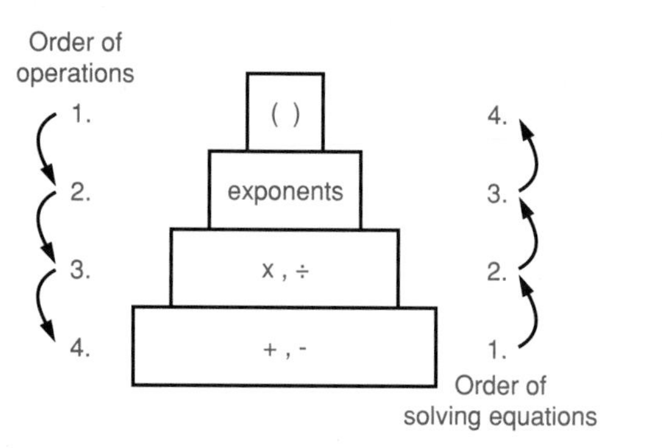

Multicultural Activity

One of the most amazing Hindu mathematicians is Srinarasa Ayengar Ramanujan, who possessed an exceptional ability to understand and explain pure mathematics, although he was untaught and untrained. He is best known for his contributions to number theory. He also found accurate approximations to π.

Have students research and write a paragraph on the contributions of other Hindu mathematicians or on the methods of early Hindu mathematicians. For example, one fact is that early Hindu addition was done from left to right, instead of right to left as we do it today.

Cooperative Learning

The following activity is provided in the **Activity Masters Booklet.**

Cooperative Problem Solving, p. 37

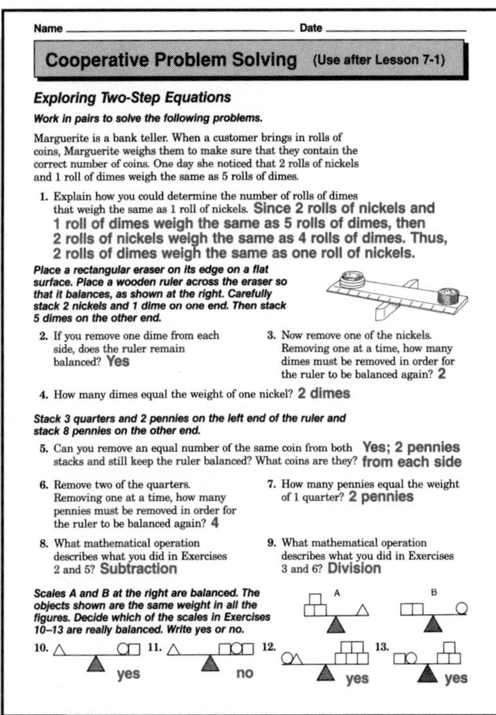

Name ______________ Date ______________

Cooperative Problem Solving (Use after Lesson 7-1)

Exploring Two-Step Equations

Work in pairs to solve the following problems.

Marguerite is a bank teller. When a customer brings in rolls of coins, Marguerite weighs them to make sure that they contain the correct number of coins. One day she noticed that 2 rolls of nickels and 1 roll of dimes weigh the same as 5 rolls of dimes.

1. Explain how you could determine the number of rolls of dimes that weigh the same as 1 roll of nickels. Since 2 rolls of nickels and 1 roll of dimes weigh the same as 5 rolls of dimes, then 2 rolls of nickels weigh the same as 4 rolls of dimes. Thus, 2 rolls of dimes weigh the same as one roll of nickels.

Place a rectangular eraser on its edge on a flat surface. Place a wooden ruler across the eraser so that it balances, as shown at the right. Carefully stack 2 nickels and 1 dime on one end. Then stack 5 dimes on the other end.

2. If you remove one dime from each side, does the ruler remain balanced? Yes
3. Now remove one of the nickels. Removing one at a time, how many dimes must be removed in order for the ruler to be balanced again? 2
4. How many dimes equal the weight of one nickel? 2 dimes

Stack 3 quarters and 2 pennies on the left end of the ruler and stack 8 pennies on the other end.

5. Can you remove an equal number of the same coin from both stacks and still keep the ruler balanced? What coins are they? Yes; 2 pennies from each side
6. Remove two of the quarters. Removing one at a time, how many pennies must be removed in order for the ruler to be balanced again? 4
7. How many pennies equal the weight of 1 quarter? 2 pennies
8. What mathematical operation describes what you did in Exercises 2 and 5? Subtraction
9. What mathematical operation describes what you did in Exercises 3 and 6? Division

Scales A and B at the right are balanced. The objects shown are the same weight in all the figures. Decide which of the scales in Exercises 10–13 are really balanced. Write yes or no.

10. yes
11. no
12. yes
13. yes

Cooperative Problem Solving

Have students work in groups of four to solve the following problem: A merchant sold two TVs for $360 each. She made 25% on the sale of one TV and lost 25% on the sale of the other TV. Did she make money, lose money, or break even on the sale of the two TVs? (Answer: She lost $48.)

Interactive Bulletin Board

Metric Connection

Metric Problems

1. Jan's rabbit weighs 2000 grams. How many kilograms does it weigh?

2. 14 m = ______ cm

3.

4.

Solutions
1.
2.
3.
4.

Purpose Provide practice with various types of metric problems.

How to Use It Write four or five problems on large pieces of construction paper and the answers on the strips of paper. Display problems and answers on a bulletin board and use strips of blank paper to cover the answers. Allow students to solve problems and check answers. Use with any type of measurement and change problems frequently.

Outside Resources

Books/Periodicals
The Ideas of Algebra, K-12, NCTM

Films/Videotapes
Equations in Algebra, International Films Bureau, Inc.

Manipulatives
Hands-on Equations Math Lab Kit, Educational Teaching Aids
Equations Game, Educational Teaching Aids

Software
The Factory, Sunburst

Technology

There are three pages in the ***Technology Masters Booklet*** that involve technology with concepts in this chapter. One page involves calculators and one page has a problem that can be solved using the BASIC program that is provided. Students should evaluate the information they obtain from running the program and solve a similar problem by extending the program.

Using the Chapter Opener

Transparency 7-0 is available in the Transparency Package. It provides a full-color visual and motivating activity that you can use to engage students in the mathematical content of the chapter.

Using Discussion

- Have students recall situations similar to the one in the Chapter Opener.
- Ask students if they have ever played a game where they had to name a number without going over the secret number or watched a TV game show where prices must be guessed without going over the actual price.
- The solution for the problem presented here can be found in the lesson opener on page 270.

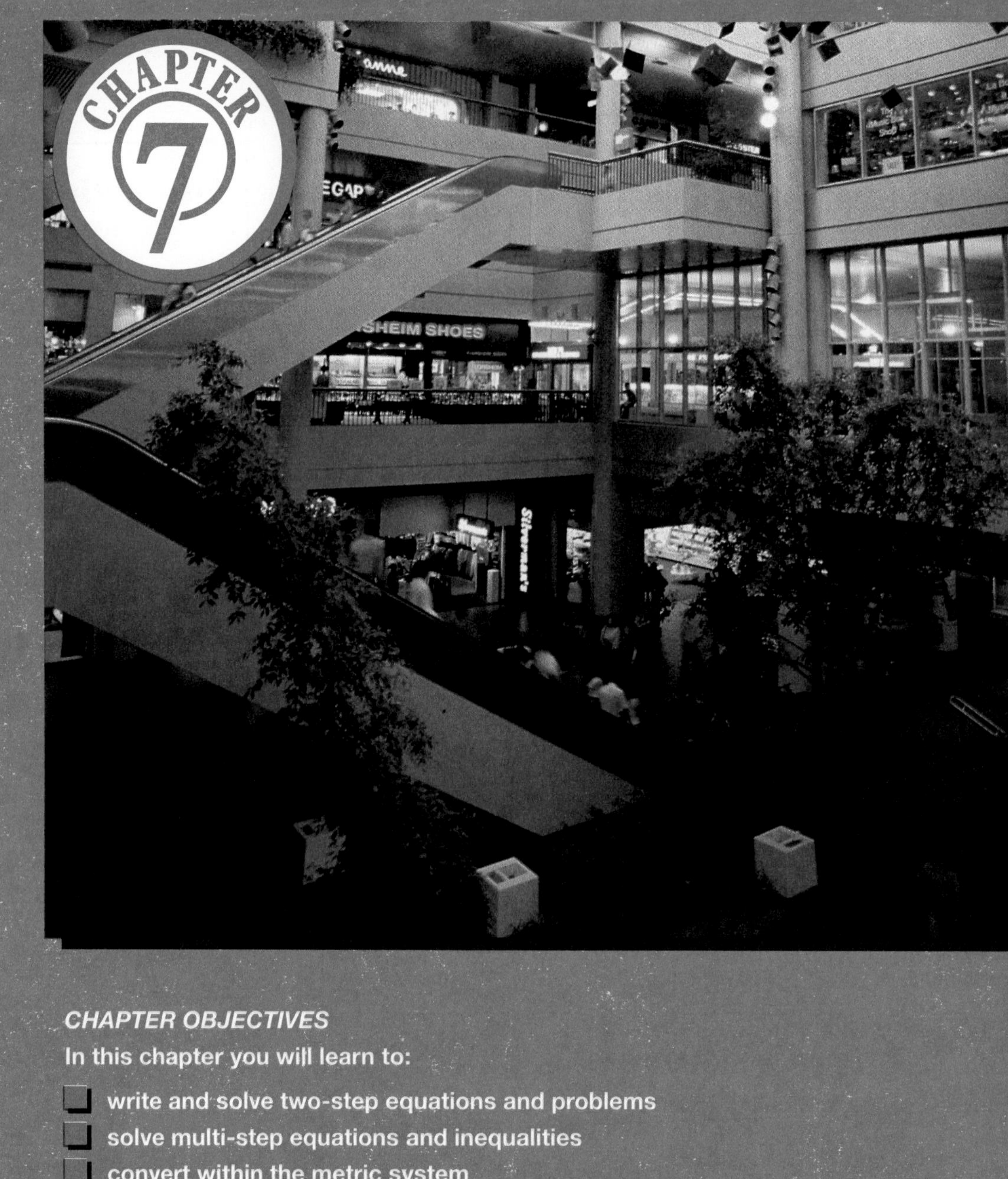

CHAPTER OBJECTIVES

In this chapter you will learn to:

- write and solve two-step equations and problems
- solve multi-step equations and inequalities
- convert within the metric system
- solve problems by using the work backwards strategy

Solving Equations and Inequalities

Math at the mall!—It's more than paying for your purchases and receiving correct change. Every time you make a tough buying decision, you are using mathematics.

Imagine that you need to buy a new pair of shoes, and you have \$90 to spend. However, you'd also like to buy two CDs. So you look at the shoes. The ones you really, really like cost \$70. Do you have enough to buy two CDs and the shoes you like?

When you make your decision, you are mentally solving this inequality.

Let x = cost of CDs
$2x + 70 \leq 90$

What's *your* buying decision?

Class Project
Collect advertisements from newspapers or magazines. Make up a situation similar to the one described above. Make a collage showing the situation. Include the inequality that describes it.

Consumer Connection

The class project may be done individually or in small groups. An option using small groups would be to have one student determine how much money group members can spend, and the other students use the ads to see who can spend the closest without going over the amount allowed. Display these as collages around a central money amount, including the inequality signs.

An option to using ads would be to use special interest catalogs.

Looking Ahead

You may want to have the following materials available to use in this chapter.

Exploration, p. 254
- cups*
- counters**
- mats***

Exploration, p. 262
- cups*
- counters**
- mats***

*You can use the Easy-to-Make manipulative provided on page 6 of the Lab Manual.

**You can use the Easy-to-Make manipulative provided on page 4 of the Lab Manual.

***You can use the Easy-to-Make manipulative provided on page 3 of the Lab Manual.

5-Minute Check
(over Chapter 6)

Solve each equation.

1. $(4)(-3\frac{5}{8}) = k$ $-14\frac{1}{2}$
2. $(-2.31)(-0.5) = m$ 1.155
3. $\frac{7}{9} \div \frac{2}{3} = x$ $1\frac{1}{6}$
4. $-1.596 \div 2.8 = y$ -0.57
5. $\frac{4}{7}a \leq \frac{8}{9}$ $a \leq 1\frac{5}{9}$

Transparency 7-1 contains the 5-Minute Check and a teaching aid for this lesson.

1 FOCUS

The purpose of this lesson is for students to understand that they can solve a problem by starting at the end and work backwards.

Motivating the Lesson

Ask students to explain how the TV game show "Jeopardy" works.

2 TEACH

Using Models While discussing the lesson example, use cards to model the problem. Also use the cards to model the examination of the solution. You may want to use cooperative groups.

Chalkboard Examples

Lisa took her sticker collection to Amy's house for the purpose of trading stickers. Lisa gave Amy half of the stickers she brought in exchange for 5 unusual stickers. Then Lisa gave Amy's little brother 2 stickers as a gift. If Lisa left Amy's house with 18 stickers, how many stickers did she bring to Amy's house? 30

EE: 1A, 1B, 1C, 1D, 1E
TAAS: 2, 10, 13

Problem Solving

7-1 Strategy: Work Backwards

Objective:
Solve problems by working backwards.

Willis brought some of his baseball cards to Tom's house for the purpose of trading cards. Willis traded Tom half of the cards he brought in exchange for two Jose Canseco cards. Then Willis gave Tom's little sister Mary 8 cards as a gift. If Willis left Tom's house with 48 baseball cards, how many cards did he bring to Tom's house?

In most problems, a set of conditions or facts is given and an end result must be found. However, this problem tells the result and asks for something that happened earlier. The strategy of working backwards can be used to solve this problem and similar problems. To use this strategy, start with the end result and *undo* each step.

Explore Willis had some baseball cards. He traded away half the cards. Then he received 2 cards and gave away 8 cards. In the end, he had 48 cards. The problem asks how many cards he had at the beginning.

Plan Since this problem gives the end result and asks for something that happened earlier, start with the result and work backwards. *Undo* each step.

Why is 8 added to 48, but 2 is subtracted from the result? **+8 is the inverse of −8; −2 is the inverse of +2.**

Solve

In the end Willis had 48 cards.	48
Undo the 8 cards that he gave to Mary. →	+ 8
	56
Undo the 2 cards that Tom gave to him. →	− 2
	54
Undo the half that he gave to Tom. →	× 2
	108

In the beginning Willis had 108 baseball cards.

Examine Assume that Willis started with 108 cards. After he gave Tom half his cards, he had 54 cards. Tom gave him 2 cards, so he had 54 + 2 or 56 cards. He gave Mary 8 cards, so he had 56 − 8 or 48 cards. In the end Willis had 48 cards, so the answer is correct.

Checking for Understanding

Guided Practice

Solve. Work backwards.

1. A certain number is multiplied by 3 and then 5 is added to the result. The final answer is 41. Find the number. 12
2. A certain number is divided by 5 and then 1 is subtracted from the result. The final answer is 32. Find the number. 165

Bell Ringer

The total cotton crop for the United States in 1988 was 6,938,000 bales. If the bales averaged 465 pounds and sold for 8.5¢ per pound, what was the value of the crop? Round your answer to the nearest million dollars and write it using scientific notation.
$\$2.74 \times 10^8$

Reteaching Activity

Consumer Connection Black out one price on a grocery cash register tape. Have students find that price.

3. A certain number is added to 13 and the result is multiplied by 5. The final answer is 125. Find the number. 12

4. Ursula is conditioning for soccer. She does 7 minutes of stretching exercises followed by 2 minutes of push-ups and 3 minutes of jumping jacks. Finally, she runs for 18 minutes. If Ursula finishes her run at 2:07 P.M., when did she start the stretching exercises? 1:37 P.M.

Exercises

Independent Practice

Solve. Use any strategy. Use mental math, estimation, or a calculator, as appropriate.

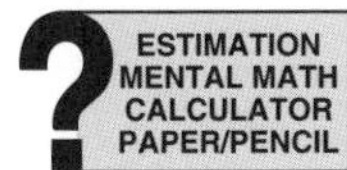

5. Zack was assigned some math exercises for homework. He did half the exercises in study hall. After school he did 5 more exercises. If he still has 13 exercises to do, how many exercises were assigned? 36 exercises

6. On Monday Buffy told a joke to 3 of her friends. On Tuesday each of those friends told 3 other friends the joke. On Wednesday each person who heard the joke on Tuesday told 3 other people. If this pattern continues, how many people will hear the joke on Saturday? 729 people

7. Samuel had some grapes. He gave half of his grapes to Chin. Chin then gave a third of his grapes to Rita. Rita gave a fourth of her grapes to Sue. If Sue has 9 grapes, how many grapes did Samuel have in the beginning? 216 grapes

8. Millie had some money. She baby-sat her nieces and earned \$15. She took all her money on a shopping trip and spent half of it on some new jeans. She spent another \$5 on some earrings. If she has \$32 left, how much did Millie have in the beginning? \$59

9. A certain bacteria doubles its population every 12 hours. After 3 full days, there are 1600 bacteria. How many bacteria were there at the beginning of the first day? 25 bacteria

10. The members of the camera club need to raise \$300 to buy some new equipment for a darkroom. They plan to sell 1000 school badges to encourage school spirit. If each badge costs the club 95¢, how much should the members charge for each badge in order to meet their goal? \$1.25

Wrap-Up

11. **Make Up a Problem** Write a problem that can be solved by working backwards. Trade problems with a friend and solve your friend's problem. See margin.

3 PRACTICE/APPLY

Checking the Concept

Have students work with a partner to solve Exercises 1-4.

Error Analysis
Watch for students who are confused with a problem. **Prevent by** encouraging the use of the guess-and-test strategy first.

Independent Practice

Homework Assignment	
Basic	5-11
Average	5-11
Honors	5-11

 CLOSE

Assessment Option

Speaking Have students explain how they know when to use the working backwards strategy.

Practice Masters Booklet, **p. 63**

Name ______ Date ______

Practice Worksheet 7-1

Problem Solving Strategy: Work Backwards

Solve. Work backwards.

1. Bus #17 runs from Apple Street to Ellis Avenue, making 3 stops in between. At Bonz Avenue, 2 people got off and 5 people got on the bus. At Crump Road, half the people on the bus got off and 4 people got on. At Dane Square, 3 people got off and 1 person got on. At the final stop, the remaining 12 people got off. How many people were on the bus when it left Apple Street? 17 people

2. Janette bought a share of stock in PRT Corporation. The first week, it increased in value 25%. During the second week, it decreased \$1.40 in value. The next week it doubled in value, so she sold it. She got \$27.20 for it. How much had she paid for it? \$12

3. Hector's mother sent him on two errands. She gave him \$5.00. He picked up clothes at the dry cleaners and later spent half the change on a loaf of bread. He returned 97¢ change to his mother. How much did the dry cleaning cost? \$3.06

4. Dawn baked cookies and gave $\frac{3}{4}$ of them to Penny. Penny gave back a dozen. Dawn ended up with 18 cookies. How many had she baked originally? 24 cookies

Solve. Use any strategy. Use mental math, estimation, or a calculator, as appropriate.

5. Guppies cost 20¢ less than swordtails. Three guppies and 4 swordtails cost \$2.83. How much do guppies cost? 29¢

6. A bus holds 40 people. At its first stop it picks up 8 people. At each stop after the first, 3 people get off and 7 get on. After which stop will the bus be full? 9th stop

7. Bjorn has 5 coins with a total value of 50¢. Not all of the coins are dimes. What are the coins? 1 quarter, 1 dime, 3 nickels

8. A certain number is added to 6 and the result is multiplied by 25. The final answer is 50. Find the number. −4

Additional Answer

11. Sample answer: I have \$1.50. I spent half of the money I had when I left home this morning for lunch and I lent Bill a dollar after lunch. How much money did I start with?

Cooperative Learning

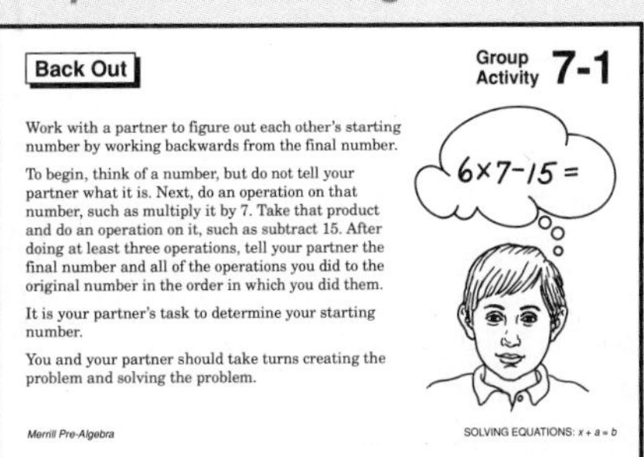

Back Out — Group Activity 7-1

Work with a partner to figure out each other's starting number by working backwards from the final number.

To begin, think of a number, but do not tell your partner what it is. Next, do an operation on that number, such as multiply it by 7. Take that product and do an operation on it, such as subtract 15. After doing at least three operations, tell your partner the final number and all of the operations you did to the original number in the order in which you did them.

It is your partner's task to determine your starting number.

You and your partner should take turns creating the problem and solving the problem.

Merrill Pre-Algebra — SOLVING EQUATIONS: $x + a = b$

EXPLORATION:
Two-Step Equations

Objective Students will use modeling to solve two-step equations.

1 FOCUS

Motivating the Exploration

Write the equations $27x + 43 = 97$ and $2x + 2 = 6$ on the chalkboard. Ask students how these two equations illustrate the solve a simpler problem strategy.

2 TEACH

Using Models

Model several examples of two-step equations for the class. Help students write the corresponding equations. Model the example for the entire class. Ask students to identify the two steps.

3 PRACTICE/APPLY

You may want to remind students how to model a zero pair.

Using Cooperative Groups

Divide the class into small groups. Circulate around the room as they model their problems. Have students check their answers by substituting them into the original equations.

Additional Answers

5. **Sample answer: You have the end result (the equation) and undo each operation to solve.**
6. **Just as different colored counters were used to represent negative integers, use a different colored cup to represent a variable with a negative coefficient.**

4 CLOSE

Writing Connection

Ask students to write a general rule for solving two-step equations.

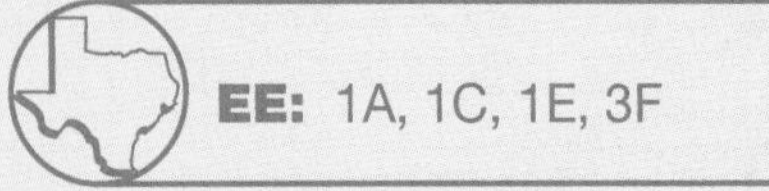

EE: 1A, 1C, 1E, 3F

Exploration

Two-Step Equations

Materials: cups, counters, mats

In this Exploration, you will use cups and counters as models for building and solving two-step equations.

▶ Consider the equation $2x + 2 = 6$. Let's use the model of the cups and counters to find all values of x for which $2x + 2 = 6$ is true. First, build the equation $2x + 2 = 6$.

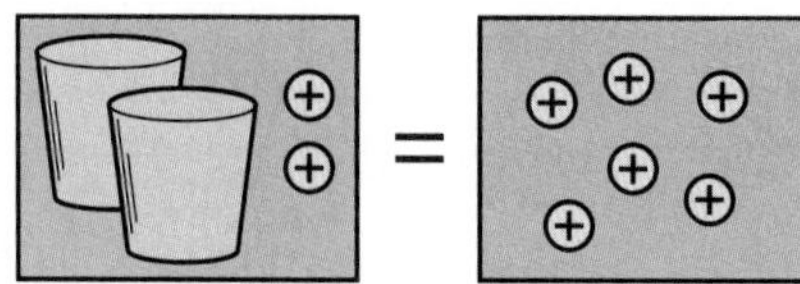

▶ How many counters are in each cup? To find this answer, first pair off and remove counters.

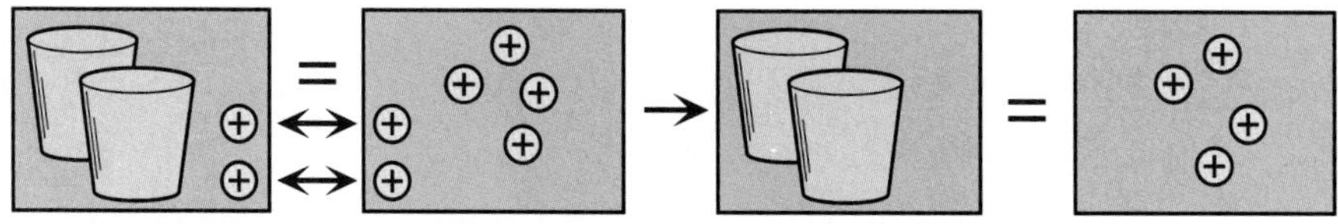

▶ Now your equation is $2x = 4$. Since there are two cups, match an equal number of counters with each cup. Therefore, each cup must contain two counters and $x = 2$.

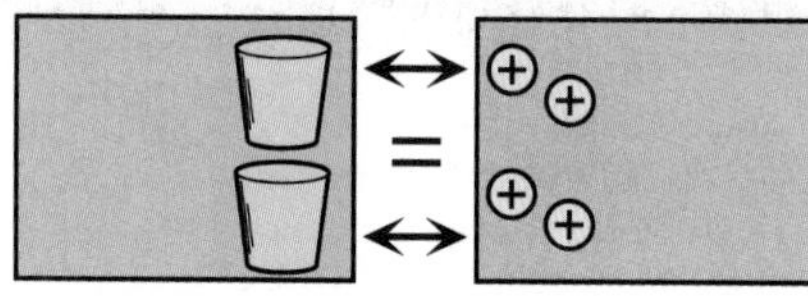

Your Turn: Model $2x + (-2) = 6$ and $2x + 2 = -4$. Add zero pairs as needed. See Solutions Manual.

Model each equation and solve. See Solutions Manual.

1. $2x + 3 = 13$ 5
2. $2x + (-2) = -4$ -1
3. $3x + 2 = -4$ -2
4. $3x + -2 = 4$ 2

Analysis

5. Explain how this model uses the work backwards strategy presented in Lesson 7-1. See margin.
6. Explain how you can use models to solve $-2x + 2 = 4$. See margin.

SET-UP

Materials

- Cups, Lab Manual, p. 6
- Counters, Lab Manual, p. 4
- Equation Mats, Lab Manual, p. 3

You may wish to use the Exploration worksheet provided on page 45 of the lab manual.

For Students Use two different colored counters to represent the positive and negative integers. Each group will need 16 positive counters and 6 negative counters.

HINT: Assemble the counters in sandwich bags with a twist-tie for convenient management.

For the Overhead Projector Use two different colors of bingo chips and transparent cups to model examples on the overhead.

7-2 Solving Two-Step Equations

Objective:
Solve equations that involve more than one operation.

Judi mailed some photographs to her cousin Misae. She paid \$1.25 to send them first-class. If the Post Office charges 25 cents for the first ounce and 20 cents for each additional ounce, how much did Judi's package weigh?

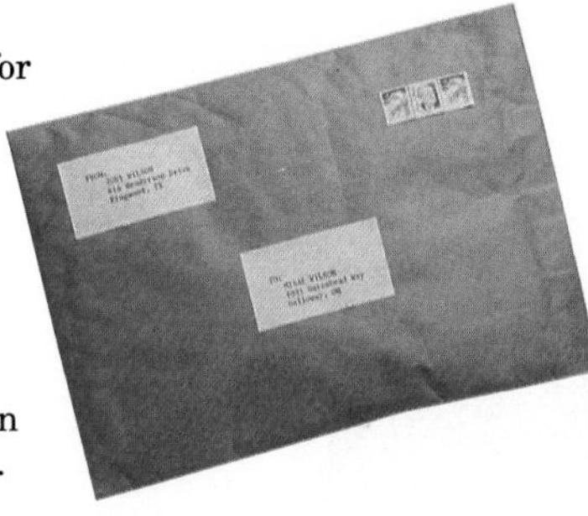

This problem can be solved by using the problem-solving strategy from Lesson 7-1 and the equation $25 + 20w = 125$. This equation contains more than one operation and is solved by undoing these operations.

$$25 + 20w = 125$$

$$25 - 25 + 20w = 125 - 25$$ First undo the addition. Subtract 25 from each side.

$$20w = 100$$

$$\frac{20w}{20} = \frac{100}{20}$$ Next undo the multiplication. Divide each side by 20.

$$w = 5$$

Check: $25 + 20w = 125$

$25 + 20 \cdot 5 \stackrel{?}{=} 125$ Replace w with 5.

$25 + 100 \stackrel{?}{=} 125$ Do the multiplication first.

$125 = 125$ ✓

There were 5 additional ounces, so Judi's package weighed 6 ounces.

Why do you compute the multiplication first? **order of operations**

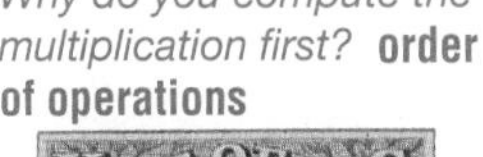

FYI

Benjamin Franklin was appointed the first American postmaster general in 1775. Nearly 80 years later, Congress issued the first postage stamps.

Example

1 Solve $-2k - 3 = 16$. Check your solution.

$-2k - 3 + 3 = 16 + 3$ Add 3 to each side.

$-2k = 19$

$\frac{-2k}{-2} = \frac{19}{-2}$ Divide each side by -2.

$k = -\frac{19}{2}$ or $-9\frac{1}{2}$

Check: $-2k - 3 = 16$

$-2\left(-\frac{19}{2}\right) - 3 \stackrel{?}{=} 16$ Replace k with $-\frac{19}{2}$.

$19 - 3 \stackrel{?}{=} 16$ Do the multiplication first.

$16 = 16$ ✓ The solution is $-\frac{19}{2}$ or $-9\frac{1}{2}$.

Bell Ringer

Each digit has been replaced by a different letter in the multiplication problem below. What two numbers were multiplied? **35 × 15**

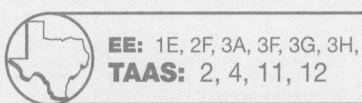

```
  AT
× IT
 IET
AT
TUT
```

Lesson Notes 7-2

5-Minute Check
(over Lesson 7-1)

1. Rupesh earned some money mowing lawns one month. He put half of his money into savings. With the rest, he spent \$15 on a new tape, \$6 to see a show, \$3 on food, and he still had \$24 left in his pocket. How much money did Rupesh earn mowing lawns? **\$96**

Transparency 7-2 contains the 5-Minute Check and a teaching aid for this lesson.

1 FOCUS

The purpose of this lesson is for students to understand that to solve two-step equations they should "undo" in an order that is the reverse of the order of operations.

Motivating the Lesson

Discuss with students situations that require two steps to reach a desired conclusion. For example, to check the oil in your car you must open the hood and then find the dipstick, or to drive a car you must first start it and then put it into gear.

2 TEACH

Using Discussion

Review the order of operations by listing them on the chalkboard. Have students take note of the operations you "undo" as you demonstrate how to solve the Chalkboard Examples. Discuss the order of the "undoing" and compare to the order of operations.

EE: 1E, 2F, 3A, 3F, 3G, 3H, 4E
TAAS: 2, 4, 11, 12

Chalkboard Examples

Solve each equation.

- *For Example 1*
  $-4m - 7 = 18.$
  $m = -6\frac{1}{4}$
- *For Example 2*
  $\frac{y}{-6} + 2 = -9$ $y = 66$
- *For Example 3*
  $\frac{d+5}{4} = -9.$ $d = -41$
- *For Example 4*
  $15 + 8x = 47.$ $x = 4$

3 PRACTICE/APPLY

Checking the Concept

Ask students to point out the errors in procedure in solving the equations below.

a) $5(r - 3) = 16$
$5r - 3 = 16$
5 not distributed over 3

b) $\frac{(b + 4)}{6} = 12$
$\frac{b}{6} = 8$
Should multiply each side by 6 first

Error Analysis

Watch for students who forget to divide by the coefficient of the variable.
Prevent by estimating and checking the solution.

Examples

Solve each equation.

2 $\frac{t}{-2} + 4 = -10$

$\frac{t}{-2} + 4 - 4 = -10 - 4$ Subtract 4 from each side.

$\frac{t}{-2} = -14$

$-2 \cdot \frac{t}{-2} = -2 \cdot (-14)$ Multiply each side by -2.

$t = 28$

Check: $\frac{t}{-2} + 4 = -10$

$\frac{28}{-2} + 4 \stackrel{?}{=} -10$ Replace t with 28.

$-14 + 4 \stackrel{?}{=} -10$ Do the division first.

$-10 = -10$ ✓ The solution is 28.

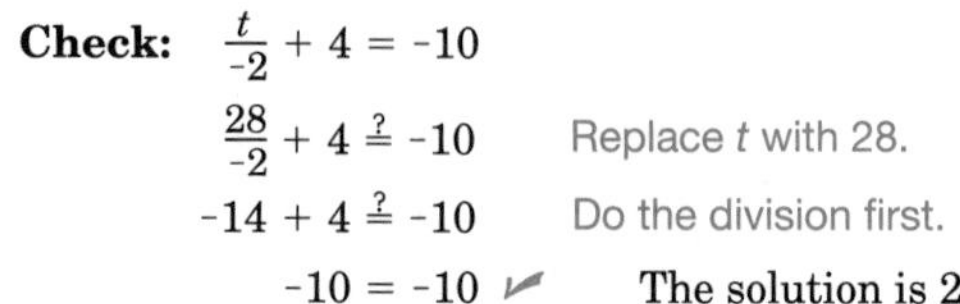

3 $\frac{b + 3}{10} = -4$

$10 \cdot \frac{(b + 3)}{10} = 10 \cdot (-4)$ Because $\frac{b+3}{10}$ means $(b + 3) \div 10$, undo the division first.

$b + 3 = -40$

$b + 3 - 3 = -40 - 3$ Subtract 3 from each side.

$b = -43$ Check the solution.

Many times, real-life situations can be described by two-step equations. Suppose your family wants to buy 15 square yards of carpeting for your family room. In addition to the cost of the carpet, there is a $40 installation charge. The total bill is $234.25. You want to find the price of one square yard of carpet.

Let p = price of one square yard of carpet.
The equation $15p + 40 = 234.25$ can be used to solve this problem.
You will learn more about writing equations in the next lesson.

Estimation Hint

THINK:
$15p + 40 \approx 240$
$15p \approx 200$

Since $15(10) = 150$ and $15(15) = 225$, the solution should be between 10 and 15.

Example

4 **Solve $15p + 40 = 234.25$.**

$15p + 40 = 234.25$ Subtract 40. Then divide by 15.

234.25 [−] 40 [=] [÷] 15 [=] 12.95

$p = 12.95$ Compare with the estimate. The answer is reasonable.

The price of the carpet is $12.95 per square yard.

Alternate Strategies: Reteaching the Lesson

Reteaching Activity

Using Models Use one cup, counters, and mats to model one-step problems. After these are mastered, add cups and model two-step problems.

Reteaching Masters Booklet, p. 57

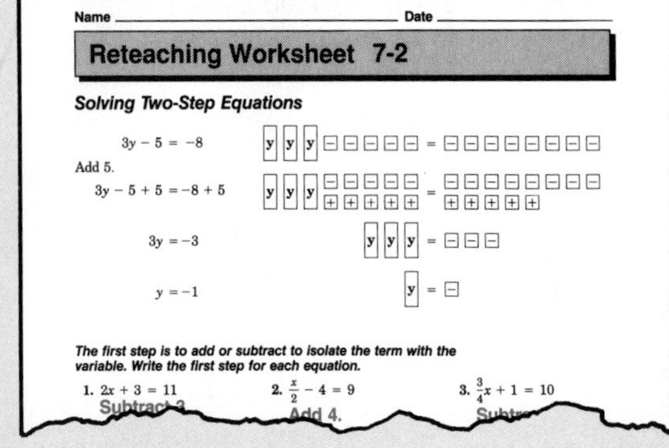

Name ______ Date ______

Reteaching Worksheet 7-2

Solving Two-Step Equations

$3y - 5 = -8$

Add 5.

$3y - 5 + 5 = -8 + 5$

$3y = -3$

$y = -1$

The first step is to add or subtract to isolate the term with the variable. Write the first step for each equation.

1. $2x + 3 = 11$ Subtract 3.
2. $\frac{x}{2} - 4 = 9$ Add 4.
3. $\frac{3}{4}x + 1 = 10$ Subtr...

Checking for Understanding

Communicating Algebra

Describe the first step you should take to solve each equation.

1. $5r - 6 = 27$
2. $2 + 5m = -19$
3. $\frac{z - 5}{-3} = 9$
4. Explain how you use the work backwards strategy to solve the equation $2x - 3 = 23$.

Complete the directions for solving each equation. Then solve each equation.

5. $2r - 7 = 1$ First add ■ to each side. Then divide each side by ■.
6. $\frac{y}{5} + 8 = 7$ First ■ 8 from each side. Then multiply each side by ■.
7. $4 - 2b = -8$ First subtract ■ from each side. Then ■ each side by -2.

Guided Practice

Name the first step you would take to solve each equation. Then solve each equation.

8. $3m - 4 = 11$
9. $4z - 7 = -15$
10. $3 + 5m = -22$
11. $\frac{a}{7} + 4 = 18$
12. $-\frac{x}{3} - 5 = -23$
13. $\frac{b}{4} - 19 = 17$
14. $\frac{k + 5}{4} = 9$
15. $\frac{n - 6}{-5} = 3$
16. $\frac{2m + 7}{5} = 9$

Exercises

Independent Practice

Solve each equation. Check your solution.

17. $-4y + 3 = 19$
18. $-8k - 21 = 75$
19. $9 - 4z = 57$
20. $12 - z = 28$
21. $-8 - t = -25$
22. $-36 = 24 - w$
23. $54 = 39 - x$
24. $-4 - y = 24$
25. $18 = 6 - y$
26. $\frac{b}{8} - 17 = 13$
27. $\frac{g}{12} - 4 = 7$
28. $8 = \frac{h}{-3} + 19$
29. $-12 + \frac{j}{4} = 9$
30. $13 + \frac{p}{-3} = -4$
31. $-3 = -31 + \frac{c}{6}$
32. $-3b + 5 = 20$
33. $4m + 3 = -73$
34. $47 = 12 - 7m$
35. $\frac{a}{7} + 21 = -12$
36. $\frac{d}{-6} - 17 = -8$
37. $\frac{x}{12} + 7 = 28$
38. $\frac{a + 3}{5} = -11$
39. $\frac{6 + c}{-13} = -3$
40. $\frac{d - 5}{7} = 14$

Mental Math

Solve each equation mentally.

41. $2x - 8 = 12$
42. $-4a + 4 = 0$
43. $\frac{n}{2} + (-3) = 5$

Language Skill

Translate each sentence into an equation.

44. Three times a number less sixteen equals twenty-five.
45. Twenty more than twice c is negative thirty.
46. The sum of fourteen and a number, divided by eight, equals five.
47. The quotient of a number and four, decreased by five, is seven.

Additional Answer

4. The order of operations to evaluate $2x - 3 = 23$ would be to multiply first then subtract. To solve the equation you would work backwards and undo the subtraction first then undo the multiplication.

Independent Practice

Homework Assignment	
Basic	17-47 odd, 48-55 57, 58
Average	18-46 even, 48-58
Honors	33-58

Practice Masters Booklet, **p. 64**

Name ______________ Date ______________

Practice Worksheet 7-2

Solving Two-Step Equations

Solve each equation. Check your solution.

1. $6x + 8 = 20$ 2
2. $-10 - k = 36$ −46
3. $15 = 7 - y$ −8
4. $15 + 4g = -33$ −12
5. $8 - z = 21$ −13
6. $-9x - 36 = 72$ −12
7. $4 - 5c = 64$ −12
8. $8h + 7 = -113$ −15
9. $15d - 21 = 564$ 39
10. $2x + 5 = 5$ 0
11. $14 = 27 - x$ 13
12. $44 = -4 + 8p$ 6
13. $3 + 6u = -63$ −11
14. $33 = 5i - 12$ 9
15. $19 = -3a - 5$ −8
16. $-21 - 15m = 219$ −16
17. $\frac{x}{12} - 15 = 31$ 552
18. $6 - 5j = -94$ 20
19. $-\frac{t}{5} - 3 = 17$ −100
20. $15 + \left(-\frac{b}{4}\right) = 29$ −56
21. $-\frac{k}{7} = 36$ −252
22. $\frac{b}{15} = -30$ −450
23. $-8 + \left(-\frac{c}{4}\right) = 48$ −224
24. $-2d + 7 = 13$ −3
25. $-\frac{e}{5} - 12 = -3$ −45
26. $9 = -\frac{m}{2} + 14$ 10
27. $-11 + \frac{z}{6} = 0$ 66
28. $\frac{t + 2}{3} = -5$ −17
29. $\frac{5 + r}{-2} = -6$ 7
30. $\frac{f - 6}{5} = 0$ 6
31. $\frac{s - 8}{-8} = -1$ 16
32. $-10 = \frac{a + 3}{3}$ −33
33. $-16 = \frac{c - 6}{-3}$ 54

Mixed Review

48. Name the operation that should be done first in the expression $15 \div 3 + 2 \cdot 9$. (Lesson 1-1) **$15 \div 3$**

49. *True* or *false*: $-3.54 < -3.51$. (Lesson 5-1) **T**

50. Round 12.556 to the nearest tenth. (Lesson 5-3) **12.6**

51. Find the perimeter of a rectangle with a length of 4 ft 3 in. and a width of 2 ft. (Lesson 5-10) **12 ft 6 in.**

52. Write $\frac{8}{11}$ as a decimal. (Lesson 6-1) **$0.\overline{72}$**

53. Find $\left(-\frac{2}{3}\right)^2$. (Lesson 6-3) **$\frac{4}{9}$**

54. Name the multiplicative inverse of $1\frac{5}{7}$. (Lesson 6-5) **$\frac{7}{12}$**

Application

55. **Nutrition** Big Jake claims that his new potato chips have about 8 calories a piece. If you eat c chips, you will have consumed $8c$ calories. A Big Jake Sub has about 700 calories. Together, a Big Jake Sub and chips have about $700 + 8c$ calories. How many chips can you eat with your Big Jake Sub if you want to consume 1100 calories? **50 chips**

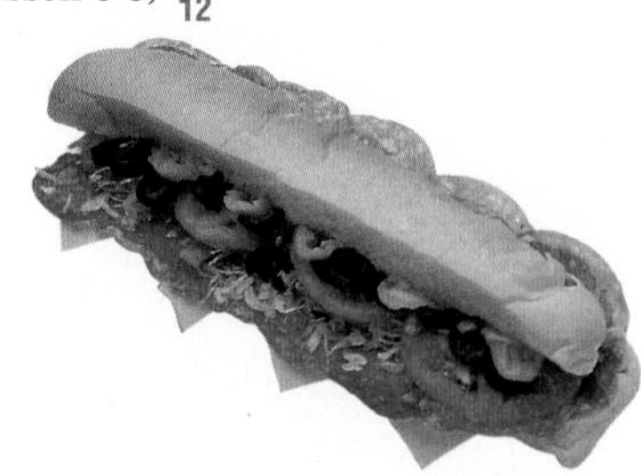

Connection

56. **Geometry** The area of a trapezoid can be found by multiplying the height and one-half the sum of the lengths of the bases. The formula is: $A = h \cdot \frac{1}{2}(b_1 + b_2)$. The area of the trapezoid at the right is 64 square inches. The trapezoid is 8 inches high and the length of one base is 7 inches. What is the length of the other base? **9 inches**

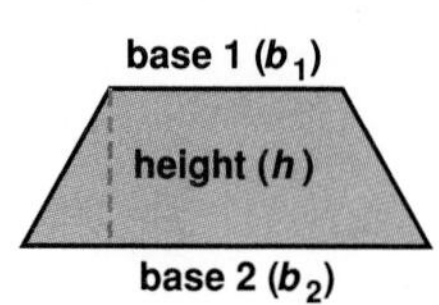

Critical Thinking

57. **Make Up a Problem** Write a two-step equation using the numbers 2, 3, and 6, in which the solution is $-\frac{1}{6}$. **Sample answer: $6x + 3 = 2$**

Wrap-Up

58. Briefly explain the general procedure for solving any two-step equation. **See margin.**

Challenge

Find the Equation

1. Find the missing values in the table below.

First Number	-2	-1	0	1	2	3	4	10	-10
Second Number	-7	-5	-3	-1	1	?	?	?	?

3 5 17 -23

2. How are the second numbers related to the first numbers? **Multiply the first number by 2, then subtract 3.**
3. If y is the second number and x is the first number, write an equation that represents the relationship between x and y. **$y = 2x - 3$**

4 CLOSE

Assessment Option

Modeling Have students use cups and counters to solve the following equations.

1. $2x + 4 = 8$ **$x = 2$**
2. $3x - 12 = -9$ **$x = 1$**
3. $2x + 6 = 8$ **$x = 1$**

Additional Answer

58. **The general procedure for solving any two-step equation is to undo operations in an order that is the reverse of the order of operations.**

Enrichment Masters Booklet, **p. 57**

Name ______________________ Date ______________

Enrichment Worksheet 7-2

Writing Word Problems

You have seen how using equations can help you solve word problems. Now it is your turn to write the word problems! When writers compose story problems, they usually have a particular type of equation in mind. Then they write about a situation which fits that equation. They try to make the story more interesting by inserting names and additional information that will help you understand the situation.

Here is a sample equation: $5 \times 3 + 2 = 17$

An author might think of this equation as showing 17 items separated into 5 groups of 3 items, with two items left over.

Here is one story that fits the equation.
Seventeen girls went on a canoeing trip. There were three girls in each canoe except the last one, which contained only two girls. How many canoes did they use?

Here is a second possible story.
Brad had some new baseball cards. He arranged them in 3 piles, with 5 cards in each pile. There were two cards left over. How many cards did Brad have in all?

Write a word problem for each of the following equations. **Answers will vary. Sample answers are given.**

1. $\frac{15 + 6}{7} = x$ **Jenny had 15 baby gerbils and 6 adult gerbils. She put them in different cages with 7 in each cage. How many cages did she use?**
2. $3 \times (6 + 4) = x$ **Three tables were set for an awards dinner. Six athletes and 4 parents were seated at each table. How many people attended the dinner?**
3. $19 - 5x = 9$ **Marty started with 19 flowers. He gave 5 of his friends each an equal number of flowers. He has 9 left. How many flowers did he give each friend?**
4. $6x + 3 = 45$ **The math club wants to buy 45 posters to decorate the math classrooms. The posters come in sets of 6, or separately. If they buy 3 posters separately, how many sets do they need?**

Alternate Strategies: Extending the Lesson

Enrichment

Consumer Connection At Pay-alot Rentals, the cost of renting a car is $52.00 per day. The first 75 miles driven are free, but any miles driven after that are 33¢ per mile. Susan needs the car for three days and only has $250.00 to spend. How many miles can she drive? **about 360 miles**

Cooperative Learning

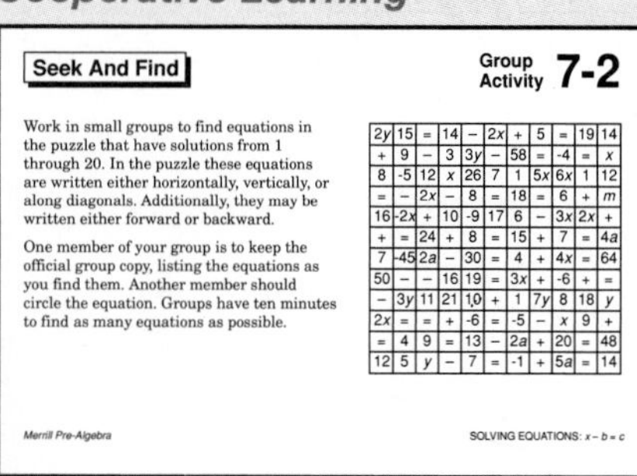

Seek And Find Group Activity **7-2**

Work in small groups to find equations in the puzzle that have solutions from 1 through 20. In the puzzle these equations are written either horizontally, vertically, or along diagonals. Additionally, they may be written either forward or backward.

One member of your group is to keep the official group copy, listing the equations as you find them. Another member should circle the equation. Groups have ten minutes to find as many equations as possible.

2y	15	=	14	–	2x	+	5	=	19	14
+	9	–	3	3y	–	58	=	-4	=	x
8	-5	12	x	26	7	1	5x	6x	1	12
=	–	2x	–	8	=	18	=	6	+	m
16	-2x	+	10	-9	17	6	–	3x	2x	+
+	=	24	+	8	=	15	+	7	=	4a
7	-45	2a	–	30	=	4	+	4x	=	64
50	–	–	16	19	=	3x	+	-6	+	=
–	3y	11	21	10	+	1	7y	8	18	y
2x	=	=	+	-6	=	-5	–	x	9	+
=	4	9	=	13	–	2a	+	20	=	48
12	5	y	–	7	=	-1	+	5a	=	14

Merrill Pre-Algebra SOLVING EQUATIONS: $x - b = c$

7-3 Writing Two-Step Equations

Objective:
Solve verbal problems by writing and solving equations.

Is 10 months a reasonable estimate? Why or why not? **No; 14 × 10 = 140, which is too much money.**

Jason wants to buy a portable CD player that costs $127. He has saved $57 from money he made by recycling. If he can save $14 per month, how long will it take him to save enough money to buy the CD player?

This problem can be solved by writing and solving a two-step equation.

Explore You know that Jason has $57 saved and that he can save $14 a month. You need to find out how many months it will take him to save enough money to buy the CD player. Let m = the number of months.

Plan In one month, he will have $57 + 1(14)$ dollars.
In two months, he will have $57 + 2(14)$ dollars.
In three months, he will have $57 + 3(14)$ dollars.
⋮
In m months, he will have $57 + m(14)$ dollars.

Solve $57 plus $14 a month for *m* months is $127.

$$57 + 14m = 127$$

$$57 + 14m = 127$$

$$57 - 57 + 14m = 127 - 57 \quad \text{Subtract 57 from each side.}$$

$$14m = 70$$

$$\frac{14m}{14} = \frac{70}{14} \quad \text{Divide each side by 14.}$$

70 [÷] 14 [=] 5

$$m = 5$$

It will take Jason 5 months to save enough money to buy the CD player.

Examine Is 5 times $14 plus $57 equal to $127? Yes

FYI

Aluminum recycling saves 95% of the energy needed to make aluminum from raw ore. In 1989 alone, the amount of energy saved was equal to 20 million barrels of oil.

Bell Ringer

Solve each equation.
1. $2y - 3 = 17$ **10**
2. $2k + 4 = -9$ **-6.5**
3. $\frac{p}{-4} + 7 = 5$ **8**
4. $\frac{m-3}{2} = 6$ **15**

Lesson Notes 7-3

5-Minute Check
(over Lesson 7-2)

Solve each equation. Check your solution.
1. $-b + 5 = 12$ **$b = -7$**
2. $3m + 5 = 17$ **$m = 4$**
3. $\frac{w+2}{7} = 3$ **$w = 19$**
4. $-8 + \frac{a}{3} = 6$ **$a = 42$**
5. $\frac{r-3}{4} = 7$ **$r = 31$**

Transparency 7-3 contains the 5-Minute Check and a teaching aid for this lesson.

1 FOCUS

The purpose of this lesson is to solve a verbal problem by translating it into a two-step equation and solving the equation.

Motivating the Lesson

Ask a student to give directions from his house to the house of another student in the class. Have the other student do the same. Ask the class if the second student worked backwards from the first students' directions.

2 TEACH

Using Discussion Using examples, have students identify what is asked, assign a variable, verbalize information, and write an equation from the verbalization. Emphasize that checking only determines that the computation is correct; it does not check for an incorrect equation.

EE: 1D, 1E, 2F, 3A, 3F, 3G
TAAS: 2, 10, 12, 13

Chalkboard Examples

- *For Example 1*
  It is 59° Fahrenheit outside. Using the formula $F = \frac{9}{5}C + 32$, what is the Celsius temperature? 15°C

3 PRACTICE/APPLY

Checking the Concept

After independently solving and checking Exercises 2-3, have students discuss the variables, equations, and solutions with another student.

Error Analysis

Watch for students who choose the incorrect operation(s).
Prevent by estimating the solution and then determining the operation(s) needed to arrive at a solution close to the estimate.

Practice Masters Booklet, **p. 65**

Name ______________________ Date ____________

Practice Worksheet 7-3

Problem Solving: Writing Two-Step Equations

Define a variable. Then write and solve an equation.

1. Find a number such that three times the number increased by 7 is 52. Let n = the number; $3n + 7 = 52$; 15
2. Five times a number decreased by 11 is 19. Find the number. Let n = the number; $5n - 11 = 19$; 6
3. Thirteen more than four times a number is −91. Find the number. Let n = the number; $4n + 13 = -91$; −26
4. Find a number such that seven less than twice the number is 43. Let n = the number; $2n - 7 = 43$; 25
5. The length of a rectangle is four times its width. Its perimeter is 90 m. Find its dimensions. Use $P = 2\ell + 2w$. Let w = width, then $4w$ = length; $90 = 2(4w) + 2w$; 9 m × 36 m
6. The total cost of a suit and a coat is $291. The coat cost twice as much as the suit. How much did the coat cost? Let s = the price of suit, then $2s$ = the price of coat; $2s + s = 291$; $194
7. In one season, Kim ran 18 races. This was four fewer races than twice the number of races Kelly ran. How many races did Kelly run? Let r = races run by Kelly; $18 = 2r - 4$; 11 races
8. The perimeter of a triangle is 51 cm. The lengths of its sides are consecutive odd integers. Find the lengths of all three sides. Let x = shortest side, then $x + 2$ and $x + 4$ are the remaining sides; $x + x + 2 + x + 4 = 51$; 15 cm, 17 cm, 19 cm
9. The length of a rectangle is 5 more than twice its width. Its perimeter is 88 feet. Find its dimensions. Use $P = 2\ell + 2w$. Let w = width, then $2w + 5$ = length; $88 = 2(2w + 5) + 2w$; 13 ft × 31 ft
10. Steve hit four more home runs than twice the number of home runs Larry hit. Together they hit 10 home runs. How many home runs did Steve hit? Let h = home runs hit by Larry, then $2h + 4$ = home runs hit by Steve; $h + 2h + 4 = 10$; 8 home runs

Science Connection

The Celsius (C) temperature scale is part of the metric system. In the United States, temperature is often measured using the Fahrenheit (F) scale.

There is one temperature that reads the same in both systems. Substitute *C* for *F* in the equation to find it. −40°

Example

1 **In a science lab, Seve needs to express 86° Fahrenheit in degrees Celsius. He remembers the formula for finding equivalent Fahrenheit temperatures when a Celsius temperature is known, $F = \frac{9}{5}C + 32$. What is the Celsius temperature?**

Explore You know the temperature in Fahrenheit and the formula for finding Fahrenheit. You need to find the Celsius temperature.

Plan Use the formula $F = \frac{9}{5}C + 32$ to write an equation.

$86 = \frac{9}{5}C + 32$ Replace *F* with 86.

Solve

$$86 = \frac{9}{5}C + 32$$

$$86 - 32 = \frac{9}{5}C + 32 - 32 \quad \text{Subtract 32 from each side.}$$

$$54 = \frac{9}{5}C$$

$$\frac{5}{9} \cdot 54 = \frac{5}{9} \cdot \frac{9}{5}C \quad \text{Multiply each side by } \frac{5}{9}.$$

$$30 = C$$

The equivalent Celsius temperature is 30°.

Examine Check to see if $86 = \left(\frac{9}{5} \cdot 30\right) + 32$.

Checking for Understanding

Communicating Algebra

1. A TV repairman charges $20 to come to the house. He then charges $30 an hour for the time spent on the job.
   a. Choose a variable to represent the number of hours the repairman takes to repair a TV. Let h = number of hours.
   b. Write an expression that represents the total cost to repair a TV. $30h + 20$
   c. Write an equation to determine the number of hours worked if the repair bill is $65. $30h + 20 = 65$
   d. What would be the first step in solving the equation you wrote in Exercise **1c**? Subtract 20 from each side.

Guided Practice

Define a variable and write an equation for each situation. Then solve.

2. If twice a number is subtracted from 8, the difference is 12. What is the number? Let n = number; $8 - 2n = 12$; −2
3. The population of Lafayette is 4800. Each year the population decreases by 35. In how many years will the population be 4520? Let y = number of years; $4800 - 35y = 4520$; 8 years

Alternate Strategies: Reteaching the Lesson

Reteaching Activity

Act It Out Bring to class a vest labeled "multiply/divide" and a jacket labeled "add/subtract". Show students that the normal order of operations is to put on the vest first (multiply/divide) and then the jacket (add/subtract). In solving an equation, to undo what was done to the variable, reverse order must be used.

Reteaching Masters Booklet, **p. 58**

Name ______________________ Date ____________

Reteaching Worksheet 7-3

Problem Solving: Writing Two-Step Equations

Example: The World Trade Center in New York City is 1350 feet tall. Suppose each floor is about 12.3 feet high. You ride the elevator from the top floor downward. How many floors have you passed when you drop below 120 feet?

Explore You could solve this problem by subtracting 12.3 feet until you reached 120 feet. The number of subtractions would be the number of floors. However, you can also use an equation.

Plan The total distance you descend is $12.3f$, where f is the number of floors. Thus, an equation for the problem is

$$1350 - 12.3f = 120$$

Solve By solving for f, you will find the number of floors. Check that the answer turns out to be 100 floors.

7-4 Variables on Each Side

Objective:
Solve equations with variables on each side.

Key Terms:
null set
empty set

Every day in the United States, about 215,000,000 canned drinks are consumed. Think back to yesterday or last week. Did you throw away an aluminum can?

By itself, one can may not be a problem, but think what would happen if all 215,000,000 cans were thrown away. There may soon be a shortage of many natural resources because these materials are now being buried as solid waste. One way to make the resources go further is to recycle them. Recycling not only helps the environment; it is also a source of spending money.

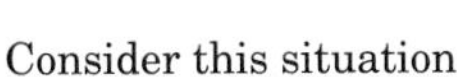

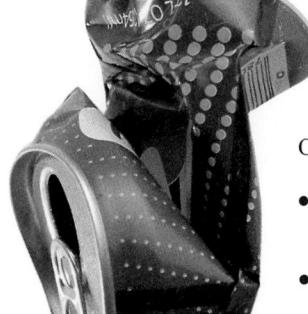

Consider this situation:

- Cash-For-Trash Recycling Center pays 42¢ per pound for 10 or more pounds of aluminum cans.
- Cash-Can Recycling Center pays a flat fee of 75¢ if the cans are washed, plus 37¢ per pound for 10 or more pounds of cans.

You may reason that for some weights you earn more at Cash-For-Trash, and for other weights you earn more at Cash-Can. Is there any weight that would earn the same amount at either place?

You can solve this problem by solving the following equation.

Let p = number of pounds of aluminum cans.

Cash-For-Trash		Cash-Can
$42p$	$=$	$37p + 75$

This equation is different from the equations in previous lessons because there is a variable on each side of the equation. To solve this type of equation, use the properties of equality to eliminate the variable from one side. The equation is solved on the next page.

FYI

On average, each American consumes 320 canned drinks per year. A recycled can appears on the shelf as a new can in about 4 months.

Lesson Notes 7-4

5-Minute Check
(over Lesson 7-3)

Define a variable. Then write and solve the equation.

1. Shyam sold the family car for \$200 more than half of the original price. If he sold the car for \$4,950, what was the original price? **\$9,500**
2. Erik scored 13 points higher than twice the lowest score on a science test. If he scored 87%, what was the lowest score on the test? **37%**

Transparency 7-4 contains the 5-Minute Check and a teaching aid for this lesson.

1 FOCUS

The purpose of this lesson is to apply the procedures used to solve a two-step equation to an equation with the variable on both sides of the equal sign.

Motivating the Lesson

Discuss the importance of recycling with your students. Emphasize how much time and money can be saved if everyone recycles.

2 TEACH

Working Backwards To show that this is not a new type of equation, start with an equation such as $4x + 12 = 16$. Add or subtract on both sides to get an equation such as $7x + 12 = 3x + 16$.

Bell Ringer

What is the first step in solving $3q + 2 = 11$? **Subtract 2 from each side.**

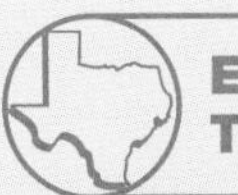

EE: 1E, 3A, 3F
TAAS: 2, 12

Chalkboard Examples

Solve each equation.

- *For Example 1*
  $5x + 3 = 3x - 7$ $x = -5$
- *For Example 2*
  $2f + 8 = 4.4f + 5.$ $f = 1.25$
- *For Example 3*
  $6x + 7 = 6x + 2$ 0
- *For Example 4*
  $3(y+1) - 3 = 3y$ set of all numbers

$$42p = 75 + 37p$$

$$42p - 37p = 75 + 37p - 37p$$ To eliminate $37p$ from the right side, subtract $37p$ from each side.

$$5p = 75$$ $42p - 37p = 5p$

$$\frac{5p}{5} = \frac{75}{5}$$ Divide each side by 5.

$$p = 15$$

Check: $42p = 75 + 37p$

$$42(15) \stackrel{?}{=} 75 + 37(15)$$ Replace p with 15.

$$630 \stackrel{?}{=} 75 + 555$$

$$630 = 630 \checkmark$$

If you recycle 15 pounds of aluminum cans, you would earn the same amount, $6.30, at either Cash-For-Trash or Cash-Can.

Examples

1 **Solve $8x - 3 = 1 + 6x$.**

$$8x - 3 = 1 + 6x$$

$$8x - 6x - 3 = 1 + 6x - 6x$$ Subtract $6x$ from each side.

$$2x - 3 = 1$$

$$2x - 3 + 3 = 1 + 3$$ Add 3 to each side.

$$2x = 4$$

$$\frac{2x}{2} = \frac{4}{2}$$ Divide each side by 2.

$$x = 2$$ Check this solution.

2 **Solve $3h + 9 = 4.5h + 5$.**

$$3h + 9 = 4.5h + 5$$

$$3h - 3h + 9 = 4.5h - 3h + 5$$ Subtract $3h$ from each side.

$$9 = 1.5h + 5$$

$$9 - 5 = 1.5h + 5 - 5$$ Subtract 5 from each side.

$$4 = 1.5h$$

$$\frac{4}{1.5} = \frac{1.5h}{1.5}$$ Divide each side by 1.5.

4 [÷] 1.5 [=] 2.6666667

$$2.6666667 = h$$

Calculator Hint

Use the Store and Recall keys to check solutions that involve decimals like 2.6666667.

Alternate Strategies: Reteaching the Lesson

Reteaching Activity

Using Models Use cups, counters, and mats to model problems with variables on each side of the equation. Start by using all positive counters, then use all negative counters, then use positive counters on one side and negative counters on the other side.

Reteaching Masters Booklet, p. 59

Name ______ Date ______

Reteaching Worksheet 7-4

Variables on Each Side of an Equation

When an equation has the variable on each side, the first step is to write an equivalent equation with the variable on just one side.

$$4a - 25 = 6a + 50$$

$$-6a + 4a - 25 = 6a + 50 + (-6a)$$ **Add $-6a$ to each side.**

$$-2a - 25 = 50$$

From this point, the equation is solved by first adding 25 to each side, and then dividing each side by -2.

1. Complete the solution of the equation in the example above.
   $-2a = 75$
   $a = -37.5$
2. Solve the equation in the example again. This time, first get the variable on the right side.
   $4a - 25 = 6a + 50$
   $-25 - 50 = 6a - 4a$
   $-75 = 2a$

Sometimes an equation has *no* solution. The solution set is the **null** or **empty set.** It is shown by the symbol { } or ∅.

Example

3 **Solve $5t + 7 = 5t + 3$.**

$$5t + 7 = 5t + 3$$

$$5t - 5t + 7 = 5t - 5t + 3 \quad \text{Subtract } 5t \text{ from each side.}$$

$$7 = 3$$

This sentence is *never* true. The solution set is ∅.

Other times, the solution of an equation may be all numbers.

Example

4 **Solve $2(x + 4) - 8 = 2x$.**

$$2(x + 4) - 8 = 2x$$

$$2x + 8 - 8 = 2x \quad \text{Distributive property}$$

$$2x = 2x \quad 8 - 8 = 0$$

$$\frac{2x}{2} = \frac{2x}{2} \quad \text{Divide each side by 2.}$$

$$x = x$$

This sentence is *always* true. The solution set is all numbers.

Checking for Understanding

Communicating Algebra

1. To solve $8a = 3a + 20$, ___?___ $3a$ from each side.
2. What is the first step you would take to solve $5y - 2 = -2y + 8$?
3. Name the property of equality that allows you to subtract a number from each side of an equation.

Guided Practice

Simplify each expression.

4. $7 + 9y + y$
5. $6d - d + 15$
6. $6m - 4m + 3$

Name the first two steps you should take to solve each equation. Then solve.

7. $3k + 10 = 2k - 21$
8. $4m - 9 = 5m + 7$
9. $8y - 6 = 5y + 12$
10. $x - 4 = 6x - 19$
11. $-3p + 8 = 2p - 2$
12. $-t + 10 = t + 4$

Additional Answers

7. Add -10 to each side; subtract $2k$ from each side.
8. Subtract 7 from each side; subtract $4m$ from each side.
9. Subtract $5y$ from each side; add 6 to each side.
10. Add 19 to each side; subtract x from each side.
11. Add $3p$ to each side; add 2 to each side.
12. Add t to each side; subtract 4 from each side.

3 PRACTICE/APPLY

Checking the Concept

Using cups, counters, and mats, have students model solutions to Exercises 4-6. Have students work in groups of three to solve Exercises 7-12, with two students naming and completing the first two steps and the third student solving.

Error Analysis

Watch for students who follow the regular order of operations in solving equations instead of the reverse order.

Prevent by using models and the distributive property.

Practice Masters Booklet, **p. 66**

Name ______________________ Date ______________

Practice Worksheet 7-4

Variables on Each Side of an Equation

Solve each equation. Check your solution.

1. $6n - 42 = 4n$ 21
2. $-3b = 96 + b$ -24
3. $6x = 2x - 8$ -2
4. $6r - 12 = 2r + 36$ 12
5. $21 - y = -87 - 2y$ -108
6. $-54 - 2v = -v + 21$ -75
7. $6 - 3y = y + 2$ 1
8. $2.4m + 24 = 6.4m$ 6
9. $7f + 18 = 4f - 33$ -17
10. $3k - 5 = 7k + 7$ -3
11. $7 + 6z = 8z - 13$ 10
12. $18d - 21 = 15d + 3$ 8
13. $12p = 6 - 3p$ $\frac{2}{5}$
14. $7j - 21 = 3 + j$ 4
15. $9 + 3k = 2k - 12$ -21
16. $-45m + 68 = 84m - 61$ 1
17. $25c + 17 = 5c - 143$ -8
18. $4 - 2x = -5x - 1$ $-1\frac{2}{3}$
19. $1.6 - n = 12.8 + 3n$ -2.8
20. $28 - 14z = -24 + 12z$ 2
21. $310s - 278 = 722 - 190s$ 2
22. $10 - h = 4h + 3$ $1\frac{2}{5}$
23. $23g - 500 = 73g - 32$ $-9\frac{9}{25}$
24. $2r - 21.6 = 3r + 36$ -57.6
25. $0.3x - 15 = 0.2x - 5$ 100

Independent Practice

Homework Assignment	
Basic	13-35 odd, 37-43
Average	14-36 even, 37-43
Honors	25-43
All	Mid-Chapter Quiz 1-8

4 CLOSE

Assessment Option

Speaking Have the students explain, in their own words, what the null or empty set is. (Possible answer: The solution set of an equation with no solution.)

Enrichment Masters Booklet, **p. 59**

Name ________________ Date ________________

Enrichment Worksheet 7-4

Tax Equations

In many states, you must pay taxes on the income you earn in that state. The table below is the 1988 tax table from the North Carolina state income tax form.

Tax Rates

If net taxable income is

over	but not over	The tax is
-0-	\$2000	3% of net taxable income
\$2000	\$4000	\$60 + 4% of amount over \$2000
\$4000	\$6000	\$140 + 5% of amount over \$4000
\$6000	\$10,000	\$240 + 6% of amount over \$6000
\$10,000		\$480 + 7% of amount over \$10,000

Example: Find the state income tax for 1988 for a North Carolina resident whose net taxable income was \$9000.

tax = \$240 + 6% of amount over \$6000
= 240 + 0.06(9000 − 6000)
= 240 + 0.06(3000)
= 420 The state income tax was \$420.

Example: Janine Eldridge paid \$1000 to the state of North Carolina in 1988 for state income taxes. Find her net taxable income to the nearest dollar.

Let x = the net taxable income. Since \$1000 > \$480, her taxable income was greater than \$10,000.

$$480 + 0.07(x - 10{,}000) = 1000 \qquad 0.07 = 7\%$$
$$480 + 0.07x - 700 = 1000$$
$$0.07x = 1220$$
$$x \approx 17{,}429$$

Her net taxable income was approximately \$17,429.

Solve. Use the tax rate table shown above.

1. Juan Ramos had a net taxable income of \$1900 in 1988. How much tax did he pay? \$57
2. Colleen Rath's net taxable income was \$19,000. How much tax did she pay? \$1110
3. What was the net taxable income of a person who paid \$300 in taxes? \$7000
4. What was the net taxable income of a person who paid \$3000 in taxes? \$46,000

Exercises

Independent Practice

Solve each equation. Check your solution.

13. $5x - 17 = 4x + 36$ 53
14. $10g = 11g - 48$ 48
15. $2f - 12 = 3f + 9$ -21
16. $y + 3 = 7y - 21$ 4
17. $6m - 2 = m + 13$ 3
18. $20c + 5 = 5c + 65$ 4
19. $18 + 4p = 6p + 11$ 3.5
20. $-3k + 10 = k + 3$ 1.75
21. $13 - t = -t + 7$ ∅
22. $3n + 7 = 7n - 13$ 5
23. $-9r = 20 - r$ -2.5
24. $4a - 9 = 6a + 7$ -8
25. $19b + 20 = 20 + 19b$ all numbers
26. $11h - 14 = 7 + 14h$ -7
27. $-43 - 3z = 2 - 6z$ 15
28. $0.5x - 7 = 0.3x + 1$ 40
29. $8z - 13 = 6z + 7$ 10
30. $7y + 7 = 3y - 5$ -3
31. $31 - 4b = 10b + 10$ 1.5
32. $2a - 1 = 3.5a - 3$ $1.\overline{3}$
33. $5x + 4 = 7x + 8$ -2
34. $6x + 17 = 4x - 31$ -24
35. $12x - 24 = -14x + 28$ 2
36. $8x - 4 = -10x + 50$ 3

Mixed Review

37. *True* or *false:* The sum of a positive and a negative integer is always positive. (Lesson 2-3) false
38. Solve the equation $n = \frac{14}{11} - \frac{9}{11}$. (Lesson 5-5) $\frac{5}{11}$
39. Which type of logical reasoning makes a rule after seeing several examples? (Lesson 6-9) inductive reasoning
40. Solve the equation $-5t - 30 = 25$. (Lesson 7-2) -11

Connection

41. **Age Problem** In three years, Joe's age will be 9 less than twice his present age. Solve the equation $x + 3 = 2x - 9$ to find Joe's age now. 12 years

Critical Thinking

42. The greater of two numbers is 7 more than the lesser. Three times the greater number is 5 more than 4 times the lesser number. Find the numbers. 16, 23

Wrap-Up

43. **Make Up a Problem** Write an equation with variables on each side whose solution is 5. Sample answer: $2x - 3 = x + 2$

Mid-Chapter Quiz

Solve each equation. (Lessons 7-2 and 7-4)

1. $2y - 3 = 17$ 10
2. $-k + 4 = -9$ 13
3. $4x + 3 = 11$ 2
4. $\frac{b}{4} + 7 = 2$ -20
5. $m + 3 = 7m - 21$ 4
6. $5x - 6 = 3x + 4$ 5

Solve. (Lesson 7-1)

7. Seth decides to give away his baseball cap collection. He gives one-fourth of his caps to Jovita. Then he gives one-half of the remaining caps to Karl. If he has 9 caps left, how many did he have in the beginning? 24 caps

Define a variable and write an equation. Then solve. (Lesson 7-3)

8. Three more than twice a number is equal to negative nine. Find the number.

8. Let n = number; $3 + 2n = -9$; -3

Alternate Strategies: Extending the Lesson

Enrichment

Consumer Connection The junior class is buying programs for a concert. One company charges \$30.00 plus 2¢ per program. Another company charges \$10.00 plus 4¢ per program. How many programs would they need to buy for the prices to be equal? 1000
If they need 600 programs, which price schedule is better? second

Cooperative Learning

Equation Builder Group Activity **7-4**

MATERIALS: Six 0-9 spinners

The object is to form an equation with a solution closest to a pre-selected number.

To begin, one player selects a number between -100 and +100. Next, all the spinners are spun to determine six numbers. Each player then uses these numbers to form an equation where there is a variable on each side of the equal sign ($2x - 31 = 62 - 4x$, for example). Each spun number may be used only one time.

The equations are then solved, and the person whose answer is closest to the selected number wins one point. In case of ties, all who tied score one point. The overall winner is the first to score eight points.

Merrill Pre-Algebra VARIABLES ON EACH SIDE

7-5 Solving Multi-Step Equations

Objective:
Solve equations that involve more than one operation.

A team's score in cross-country is the sum of the place numbers of the first five finishers. If five runners for a team finished in 2nd, 5th, 6th, 9th, and 12th place, the team's score is

$$2 + 5 + 6 + 9 + 12 = 34$$

Kristina and Ginnie are members of the Oswego cross-country team. In one meet Kristina finished three places ahead of Ginnie. Their combined score was 27. In what place did each girl finish?

How can you estimate the solution?

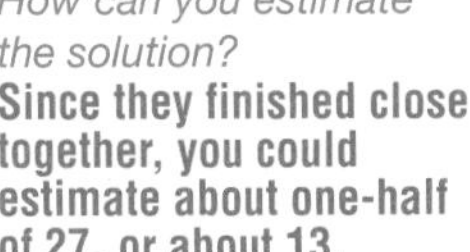

Since they finished close together, you could estimate about one-half of 27, or about 13.

You can solve this problem by using the techniques from the previous lessons.

Let k = Kristina's place. — Kristina finished three places ahead of Ginnie.
$k + 3$ = Ginnie's place.

Solve the equation $k + (k + 3) = 27$. — Their combined score was 27.

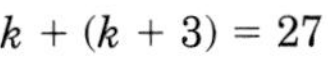

$k + (k + 3) = 27$	
$2k + 3 = 27$	Combine like terms.
$2k = 24$	Subtract 3 from each side.
$k = 12$	Divide each side by 2.

Kristina finished in 12th place. Ginnie finished in 15th place.

Example

1 **Solve $2k + 3(k + 1) = 6k - 3$.**

$2k + 3k + 3 = 6k - 3$	Distributive property
$5k + 3 = 6k - 3$	
$5k - 5k + 3 = 6k - 5k - 3$	Subtract $5k$ from each side.
$3 = k - 3$	
$3 + 3 = k - 3 + 3$	Add 3 to each side.
$6 = k$	

Check:

$2k + 3(k + 1) = 6k - 3$	
$2 \cdot 6 + 3(6 + 1) = 6 \cdot 6 - 3$	Replace k with 6.
$12 + 3(7) = 36 - 3$	
$12 + 21 = 33$	
$33 = 33$ ✓	

Bell Ringer

The sum of two consecutive even integers is equal to twice the integer between them. What are the numbers? **Any three consecutive integers starting with an even integer.**

EE: 1A, 3A, 3F, 5E
TAAS: 2, 12

Reteaching Masters Booklet, **p. 60**

Name ______________ Date ______________

Reteaching Worksheet 7-5

Solving Multi-Step Equations

When an equation includes parentheses, you often must first simplify the equation before you can solve it. Compare these examples.

$4(x - 6) = -44 + 3x$	$3(2x - 5x) = x + 45$
$4x - 24 = -44 + 3x$	$3(-3x) = x + 45$
$4x = -20 + 3x$	$-9x = x + 45$
$x = -20$	$-10x = 45$
	$x = -4.5$

1. Check the left example.
$4(-20 - 6) \stackrel{?}{=} -44 + 3(-20)$
$4(-26) \stackrel{?}{=} -44 - 60$
$-104 = -104$ ✓

2. Check the right example.
$3[2(-4.5) - 5(-4.5)] \stackrel{?}{=} -4.5 + 45$
$3(13.5) \stackrel{?}{=} 40.5$
$40.5 = 40.5$ ✓

3. Compare the first step in the two ... operations are used?

4. In the left example, what happens if you first divide both ...

Lesson Notes 7-5

5-Minute Check
(over Lesson 7-4)

Solve each equation. Check your solution.

1. $2x - 14 = 3x - 5$ **-9**
2. $6x + 5 = 4x - 7$ **-6**
3. $5m - 8 = 8m - 11$ **1**
4. $-7r + 5 = -2r - 30$ **7**
5. $8y - 3 = 5y + 9$ **4**

Transparency 7-5 contains the 5-Minute Check and a teaching aid for this lesson.

1 FOCUS

The purpose of this lesson is to apply all the previous equation solving procedures to solving equations with more than two steps.

2 TEACH

Chalkboard Examples

- *For Example 1*
Solve $x + 4(2x + 3) = 12x - 3$.
$x = 5$

Practice Masters Booklet, **p. 67**

Name ______________ Date ______________

Practice Worksheet 7-5

Solving Multi-Step Equations

Solve each equation. Check your solution.

1. $2(a + 4) = 3a - 1$ **9**	**2.** $3b + 2 = 6(3 - b)$ $\frac{16}{9}$
3. $-3(2c - 1) = 4(c + 5)$ $-\frac{17}{10}$	**4.** $3(d - 1) + 4 = -2d$ $-\frac{1}{5}$
5. $5(e + 3) = 4e + 8$ **−7**	**6.** $5(f + 2) = 2(3 - f)$ $-\frac{4}{7}$
7. $5(x + 1) = 5 + 12x$ **0**	**8.** $3(y - 4) = -2(y + 6)$ **0**
9. $7(g - 2) = 5(g + 4)$ **17**	**10.** $9(i + 2) = 3(i - 2)$ **−4**
11. $3 + 2(k + 1) = 3k + 6$ **−1**	**12.** $3l - 5 = 2(4l - 9)$ $\frac{13}{5}$
13. $4p + 3 = 6(p + 1) - 1$ **−1**	**14.** $2.5q + 8 = 6.5q - 4$ **3**
15. $5(r + 3) - 6 = 3(r - 2) - 9$ **−12**	**16.** $0.71 - 0.22s = 1.03 - 0.62s$ **0.8**
17. $\frac{5}{6}t + 4 = \frac{1}{6}t - 2$ **−9**	**18.** $\frac{4}{3}u - 6 = \frac{7}{3}u + 8$ **−14**
19. $\frac{5}{2}v - 4 = \frac{7}{2}v$ **−4**	**20.** $\frac{3}{4}w - 5 = \frac{1}{4}w - 1$ **8**
21. $13 - (x + 3) = 2(x - 2) + 5$ **3**	**22.** $5(z + 3) + 9 = 3(z - 2) + 6$ **−12**

3 PRACTICE/APPLY

Checking the Concept

Have students work with a partner to solve Exercises 3-10. One student states the steps while the other does the computations. Then, switch roles.

Independent Practice

Homework Assignment	
Basic	11-23 odd, 25-28, 30-32
Average	12-24 even, 25-32
Honors	17-32

Chapter 7, Quiz A (Lesson 7-1 through 7-5) is available in the Evaluation Masters Booklet, p. 61

4 CLOSE

Assessment Option

Speaking Have the students tell you each step in solving the following equations.

1. $2(s + 3) = 4s - 2$ $s = 4$
2. $12m - 5 = 3(2m - 1)$ $m = \frac{1}{3}$

Enrichment Masters Booklet, **p. 60**

Name ______________________ Date ______________

Enrichment Worksheet 7-5

Fractional Equations

To solve equations containing fractions, multiply both sides by the least common denominator. Then solve as usual.

Example: Solve $\frac{2x}{5} - \frac{x}{10} = 6$.

$$\frac{2x}{5} - \frac{x}{10} = 6 \quad \text{The least common denominator is 10.}$$
$$10\left(\frac{2x}{5}\right) - 10\left(\frac{x}{10}\right) = 10(6)$$
$$4x - x = 60$$
$$3x = 60$$
$$\frac{3x}{3} = \frac{60}{3}$$
$$x = 20$$

Solve each equation.

1. $\frac{3x}{2} - x = 1$ 2
2. $\frac{3x}{8} = \frac{x}{3} + \frac{4}{3}$ 32
3. $\frac{y}{6} - \frac{y}{4} = 5$ −60
4. $2a + \frac{a}{3} = \frac{a}{4} + 5$ $\frac{12}{5}$
5. $\frac{x-2}{3} = \frac{x+1}{4}$ 11
6. $\frac{x-1}{2} + \frac{x-2}{3} = 1$ $\frac{13}{5}$
7. $\frac{x-3}{5} - \frac{x+2}{15} + \frac{2}{3} = 0$ $\frac{1}{2}$
8. $\frac{x+4}{3} - 4 = \frac{x-11}{4}$ −1
9. $\frac{-d}{4} + d = \frac{1}{8}$ $\frac{1}{6}$
10. $\frac{x-7}{5} + 2 = \frac{x+8}{10}$ 2
11. $z + \frac{z}{4} = 14 - \frac{z}{2}$ 8
12. $\frac{y+3}{16} - \frac{y-4}{6} = \frac{1}{3}$ 5

Checking for Understanding

Communicating Algebra

1. Explain your strategy for estimating the equation $x + (x + 1) + (x + 2) = 99$. What is your estimate? 33
2. Solve the equation in Exercise 1. How does your solution compare with the estimate? 32

Guided Practice

State the steps you would take to solve each equation. Then solve each equation. See Solutions Manual.

3. $4x + 1 = 3x - 5$ -6
4. $7a - 6 = 19 + 2a$ -5
5. $4(s + 3) - 1 = 3(2s + 1) + 5$ 1.5
6. $7(x - 2) = 5(3x + 1) + 5$ -3
7. $5(b + 7) - 2 = 4(b + 3) + 5$ -16
8. $2.3n + 1 = 1.3n + 7$ 6
9. $\frac{5}{7}x - 4 = \frac{3}{7}x + 1$ $\frac{35}{2}$ or $17\frac{1}{2}$
10. $\frac{3}{4}m - 2 = \frac{1}{4}m + 7$ 18

Exercises

Independent Practice

Solve each equation. Check your solution.

11. $4(x + 5) = 2x + 12$ -4
12. $-5(y + 7) = 3y + 29$ -8
13. $a + 3 = 5(2a - 3)$ 2
14. $2m - 4 = 3(4m - 3)$ 0.5
15. $7 + 3(x + 1) = 2x + 9$ -1
16. $3(z + 5) = 5z + 7$ 4
17. $2(x - 3) + 5 = 3(x - 1)$ 2
18. $5b + 4 = 7(b + 1) - 3b$ 3
19. $3.5x + 6 = 1.5x$ -3
20. $\frac{5}{9}a + 7 = \frac{1}{9}a - 5$ -27
21. $\frac{4}{7}y - 8 = \frac{2}{7}y + 10$ 63
22. $\frac{7}{3}m + 3 = \frac{5}{3}m$ $-4\frac{1}{2}$
23. $-12 + 7(x + 3) = 4(2x - 1) + 3$ 10
24. $-8 + 5(3a - 2) = 4(2a + 1) + 6$ 4

Mixed Review

25. Use the formula $d = rt$ to find the time it takes a train to travel 434 miles at a rate of 62 mph. (Lesson 3.5) 7 hours
26. Write 0.000336 in scientific notation. (Lesson 6-11) 3.36×10^{-4}
27. Solve the equation $3r - 18 = -2r + 7$. (Lesson 7-4) 5

Connections

Statistics Use the information in the graph at the right to answer each question.

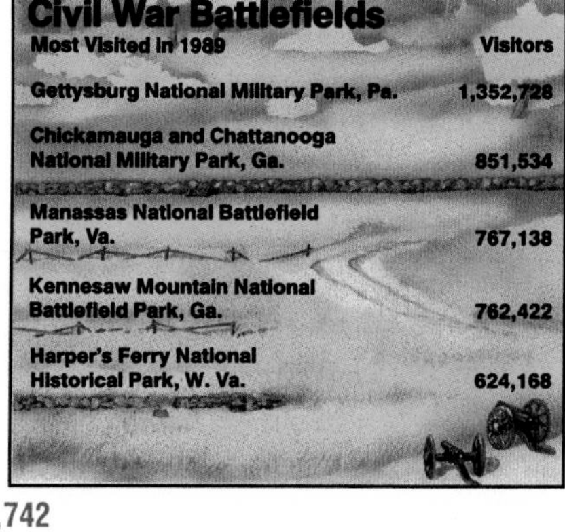

Civil War Battlefields
Most Visited in 1989
Visitors
Gettysburg National Military Park, Pa. 1,352,728
Chickamauga and Chattanooga National Military Park, Ga. 851,534
Manassas National Battlefield Park, Va. 767,138
Kennesaw Mountain National Battlefield Park, Ga. 762,422
Harper's Ferry National Historical Park, W. Va. 624,168

28. Let x represent the number of visitors to Harper's Ferry National Park. The expression $2x + 100{,}000$ is an estimate of the number of visitors at which park? Gettysburg
29. Let y represent the number of visitors to Manassas National Battlefield Park. Write an expression involving two operations that represents the number of visitors to Chickamauga and Chattanooga Military Park. $2y - 682{,}742$

Application

30. **Sports** The captain of a five-member cross-country team placed second in a meet. The other members placed in consecutive order but farther behind. The team score was 40. In what places did the other members finish? 8, 9, 10, 11

Critical Thinking

31. Consecutive integers are integers in counting order, such as 2, 3, 4. The sum of three consecutive integers is -57. Find the integers. -20, -19, -18

Wrap-Up

32. **Make Up a Problem** Write and solve a multi-step equation. Sample answer: $2(x - 3) + 1 = -3x$; 1

Alternate Strategies: Extending the Lesson

Enrichment

Business Connection Mr. Stokes had twelve coins, all nickels and dimes. They had a total value of 85¢. How many nickels did he have? How many dimes? 7 nickels, 5 dimes

Cooperative Learning

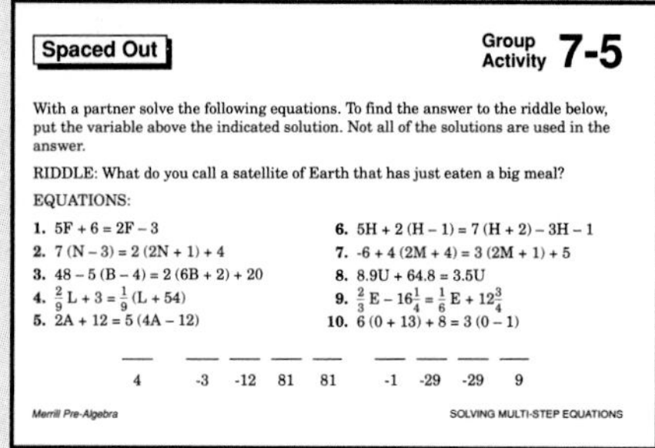

Spaced Out — Group Activity **7-5**

With a partner solve the following equations. To find the answer to the riddle below, put the variable above the indicated solution. Not all of the solutions are used in the answer.

RIDDLE: What do you call a satellite of Earth that has just eaten a big meal?

EQUATIONS:

1. $5F + 6 = 2F - 3$
2. $7(N - 3) = 2(2N + 1) + 4$
3. $48 - 5(B - 4) = 2(6B + 2) + 20$
4. $\frac{2}{9}L + 3 = \frac{1}{9}(L + 54)$
5. $2A + 12 = 5(4A - 12)$
6. $5H + 2(H - 1) = 7(H + 2) - 3H - 1$
7. $-6 + 4(2M + 4) = 3(2M + 1) + 5$
8. $8.9U + 64.8 = 3.5U$
9. $\frac{2}{3}E - 16\frac{1}{4} = \frac{1}{6}E + 12\frac{3}{4}$
10. $6(O + 13) + 8 = 3(O - 1)$

__   __ __ __ __   __ __ __ __

4   -3 -12 81 81   -1 -29 -29 9

Merrill Pre-Algebra — SOLVING MULTI-STEP EQUATIONS

Algebra in Action-Cooking

Boiling Point

In home economics class you learn that to hard-boil an egg, you place it in boiling water for 5 minutes. But if you try this in a city with a high altitude, such as Denver, after 5 minutes the egg is still runny. Why?

Water boils at 212°F at sea level. However, as the altitude increases, the air pressure drops. The lower air pressure causes water to boil at a lower temperature. Mathematically, for every 550 feet above sea level, the boiling point is lowered 1°F.

Find the boiling point of water at each multiple of 550 feet.

Altitude, in feet	0	550	1100	1650	2200	2750
Boiling Point, in °F	212	211	210	?	?	?
				209	208	207

You can use algebra to devise a formula for finding the boiling point.

$$\underbrace{\text{boiling point}} = \underbrace{212°\text{F}} \ \underbrace{\text{lowered by}} \ \underbrace{1°\text{F for every multiple of 550 feet}}$$

$$\begin{aligned} \text{boiling point} &= 212 - 1(\text{number of multiples of 550}) \\ &= 212 - 1\left(\frac{\text{altitude}}{550}\right) \\ &= 212 - \frac{A}{550} \quad \text{Let } A \text{ represent the altitude.} \end{aligned}$$

Therefore, the boiling point at Denver, where the altitude is 5280 feet above sea level, can be found as follows.

$$\begin{aligned} \text{boiling point} &= 212 - \frac{A}{550} \\ &= 212 - \frac{5280}{550} \quad \text{Replace } A \text{ with 5280.} \end{aligned}$$

212 [−] 5280 [÷] 550 [=] 202.4

The boiling point at Denver is 202.4°F.

Find the boiling point at each location.

1. Pike's Peak, 14,110 feet above sea level **186.3°**
2. Death Valley, 282 feet below sea level **212.5°**
3. your city or town **See students' work.**
4. **Research** Look in a cookbook or on a package of cake mix to find how altitude affects baking. **See margin.**

Applying Algebra to the Real World

Objective This optional page shows how algebra is used in the real world and also provides a change of pace.

Using Discussion

When discussing the development of the boiling point equation, be sure students understand that altitude has a reference point of sea level. Locations below sea level have a negative altitude, causing the boiling point to be higher than 212°F.

Social Studies Connection

Have students choose two areas of the world that have significantly different altitudes. Have them research these areas to find out what the natives commonly eat and how their food is prepared. Write a paragraph explaining how the difference in altitude of the two locations might affect what people eat and how it is prepared.

Activity

Have students investigate why pressurized suits are used in space. What might this have to do with pressure outside the body and boiling points of liquids? **If pressurized suits are not used, the pressure is so low that body temperature would cause a person's blood to boil.**

Additional Answers

4. Temperature must be increased for high altitudes.

Lesson Notes 7-6

5-Minute Check
(over Lesson 7-5)

Solve each equation. Check your solution.

1. $4(2x - 1) - 3 = 5(x - 5)$
   $x = -6$
2. $7(y - 3) - 2 = 3(2y - 5) + 4$
   $y = 12$
3. $\frac{4}{7}m + 5 = \frac{2}{7}m - 3$ $m = -28$

Transparency 7-6 contains the 5-Minute Check and a teaching aid for this lesson.

1 FOCUS

The purpose of this lesson is to apply strategies learned for multi-step equations to multi-step inequalities.

2 TEACH

Chalkboard Examples

- *For Example 1* $r < -4$
  Solve $19 - 8r > 43 - 2r$.
- *For Example 2* $d \geq 126.9$
  Solve $283.7 + 3d \geq 664.4$.

Practice Masters Booklet, **p. 68**

Name ______________ Date ______________

Practice Worksheet 7-6

Solving Multi-Step Inequalities

Solve each inequality.

1. $4x + 5 < 37$ $x < 8$
2. $7 + 8y \geq 71$ $y \geq 8$
3. $3z - 5 \leq 13$ $z \leq 6$
4. $-5a - 9 \geq 21$ $a \leq -6$
5. $3 - 9b < 30$ $b > -3$
6. $-7c + 4 > -10$ $c < 2$
7. $\frac{d}{4} + 1 < 3$ $d < 8$
8. $\frac{e}{-3} - 2 \leq 1$ $e \geq -9$
9. $2 + \frac{f}{5} < -15$ $f < -85$
10. $\frac{3x}{-5} + 1 > -14$ $x < 25$
11. $0.9r + 5 \leq 0.6r - 10$ $r \leq -50$
12. $-3.3 > \frac{s}{-10} - 3.5$ $s > -2$
13. $0.59 < \frac{t}{-8} + 0.7$ $t < 0.88$
14. $5(12 - 3w) \geq 15w + 60$ $w \leq 0$
15. $5 > 0.2(30 + u)$ $u < -5$
16. $6y - 29 < 5(7 - 2y)$ $y < 4$
17. $3x + 6 \geq 2x - 11$ $x \geq -17$
18. $11z + 5 \leq 8z - 28$ $z \leq -11$
19. $0.3a + 5.4 > 0.2 - a$ $a > -4$
20. $-9x + 8 \geq -x + 28$ $x \leq -\frac{5}{2}$
21. $1.2m + 0.3 \leq 0.2m + 2.1$ $m \leq 1.8$
22. $\frac{n}{-4} - \frac{1}{6} > \frac{2}{3}$ $n < -\frac{10}{3}$

7-6 Solving Multi-Step Inequalities

Objective:
Solve inequalities that involve more than one operation.

On page 251 you were presented with a situation that could happen to you while shopping at the mall.

Here is a summary of the problem.
- You have \$90 to spend.
- You want to buy shoes that cost \$70.
- You also want to buy two CDs.

Do you have enough money? You can find the answer by solving the inequality $2x + 70 \leq 90$, where x is the cost of one CD.

Why should you solve an inequality instead of an equation?
You only want to know if you have enough money. You don't need to spend exactly \$90.

$2x + 70 \leq 90$
$2x \leq 20$ Subtract 70 from each side.
$x \leq 10$ Divide each side by 2.

If you can find CDs that cost less than or equal to \$10, you can buy the shoes and two CDs.

Solving inequalities with more than one step or with variables on each side of the inequality requires you to apply the methods you have used to solve simple inequalities.

Examples

1 **Solve $13 - 6y > 49 - 2y$.**

$13 - 6y > 49 - 2y$
$13 - 6y + 2y > 49 - 2y + 2y$ Add $2y$ to each side.
$13 - 4y > 49$
$13 + (-13) - 4y > 49 + (-13)$ Add -13 to each side.
$-4y > 36$
$\frac{-4y}{-4} < \frac{36}{-4}$ Divide each side by -4.
$y < -9$ Any number less than -9 is a solution.

Why was the order symbol reversed? See page 114 for a review.
Divide by -4.

2 **Solve $605.7 + 2s \geq 754.41$.**

$605.7 + 2s \geq 754.41$ Subtract 605.7 from each side. Divide each side by 2.

754.41 [−] 605.7 [=] [÷] 2 [=] 74.355

$s \geq 74.355$

Any number greater than or equal to 74.355 is a solution.

Bell Ringer

State the first step in solving each equation.

1. $4 + n + 3n = 6 + n$ add n and $3n$
2. $2(r + 6) = 5r + 6$ distribute the 2 over $r + 6$

EE: 1E, 2F, 3A, 3F
TAAS: 2, 12

Reteaching Masters Booklet, **p. 61**

Name ______________ Date ______________

Reteaching Worksheet 7-6

Solving Multi-Step Inequalities

Suppose that you are to solve the inequality $13 - 6y > 49 - 2y$. You begin by solving the related equation $13 - 6y = 49 - 2y$, obtaining $y = -9$ as your answer.

You then know that the solution to the original inequality is either $y > -9$ or $y < -9$, but you are not sure which!

Sketching two number-line graphs can help you determine the correct solution.

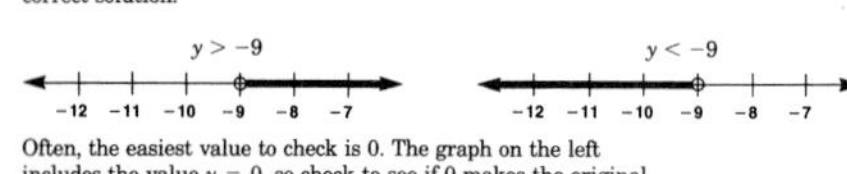

Often, the easiest value to check is 0. The graph on the left includes the value $y = 0$, so check to see if 0 makes the original inequality true.

$13 - 6y > 49 - 2y$

Checking for Understanding

Communicating Algebra

1. Explain how to check the solution for Example 2. See margin.
2. Explain why the solution of $-4x > 20$ is $x < -5$, not $x > -5$. You reverse the order symbol when you divide by -4.

Guided Practice

State the steps that are necessary to solve each inequality. Then solve each inequality. See margin.

3. $9x + 2 > 20$ $x > 2$
4. $4y - 7 < 21$ $y < 7$
5. $-7y + 6 < 48$ $y > -6$
6. $-5 < \frac{x}{4} - 7$ $8 < x$
7. $10y + 3 < 7y$ $-1 > y$
8. $\frac{m}{3} - 7 > 11$ $m > 54$

Exercises

Independent Practice

Solve each inequality.

9. $2a - 5 > 17$ $a > 11$
10. $-5d + 7 > -38$ $d < 9$
11. $7g - 3 \leq 46$ $g \leq 7$
12. $\frac{b}{-2} - 12 \leq 11$ $b \geq -46$
13. $\frac{z}{-3} - 4 > 27$ $z < -93$
14. $\frac{k}{5} + 36 \geq 51$ $k \geq 75$
15. $32 + 7t > 4$ $t > -4$
16. $5 + 9a < -19$ $a < -\frac{8}{3}$
17. $-12 + 11y < 54$ $y < 6$
18. $\frac{c}{4} + 7 < -6$ $c < -52$
19. $0.47 > \frac{t}{-9} + 0.6$ $1.17 < t$
20. $-2.2 < \frac{b}{-10} - 2.4$ $-2 > b$
21. $-18 \geq 3(k + 5)$ $-11 \geq k$
22. $2(k + 4) \leq 10$ $k \leq 1$
23. $-3(m - 2) > 12$ $m < -2$
24. $2k + 7 > k - 10$ $k > -17$
25. $0.8x + 6 > 0.5x - 9$ $x > -50$
26. $10y + 4 < 7y - 29$ $y < -11$
27. $3x + 5 > 7x + 4$ $x < 0.25$
28. $-5x + 3 < 3x + 23$ $x > -2.5$
29. $11y + 9 > 5y - 21$ $y > -5$

Language Skill

Translate each sentence into an inequality.

30. The sum of twice a number and 9 is less than 37. $2x + 9 < 37$
31. The difference of three times a number and 5 is greater than 16. $3n - 5 > 16$
32. Six more than the product of 3 and an integer is less than 39. $3y + 6 < 39$
33. Five less than half an integer is greater than sixteen. $\frac{1}{2}m - 5 > 16$

Mixed Review

34. Find the LCM of 18 and 4. (Lesson 4-7) 36
35. Solve the inequality $w - 3.8 \leq 9.4$. (Lesson 5-7) $w \leq 13.2$
36. Estimate $\frac{1}{7} \times 29$. (Lesson 6-2) about 4
37. *True* or *false:* $1.87 \geq 18.7 \times 10^{-1}$. (Lesson 6-13) true

Solve each equation. (Lessons 7-4 and 7-5)

38. $-3n - 9 = 15$ -8
39. $a + 7 = 13$ 6
40. $4(x - 1) + 7 = 5(-x + 6)$ 3

Application

41. **Hobbies** Glen has $10 to spend for two model airplanes and some supplies. The airplanes cost $3.49 each. Write an inequality that describes this situation. Then solve the inequality to find out how much Glen can spend on supplies. $2(3.49) + b \leq 10$; $b \leq 3.02$

Critical Thinking

42. The sum of the squares of two positive integers is 289. What are the integers? 8, 15

Wrap-Up

43. **Make Up a Problem** Write a problem that has $x \leq 13$ as the solution. See margin.

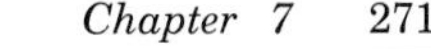

3 PRACTICE/APPLY

Checking the Concept

As students solve Exercises 9-29 ask what they did when you notice a step missing in their work.

Error Analysis

Watch for students who don't change the inequality sign when multiplying or dividing by a negative number.
Prevent by using a number line to review rules for working with inequalities.

Independent Practice

Homework Assignment	
Basic	9-33 odd, 34-43
Average	10-32 even, 34-43
Honors	21-43

4 CLOSE

Assessment Option

Speaking Ask students what problem-solving strategy they would use to answer Exercise 43.

Enrichment Masters Booklet, **p. 61**

Name ______ Date ______

Enrichment Worksheet 7-6

Conditional and Unconditional Inequalities

When the replacement set is the set of real numbers, the inequality $2x < 16$ is called a **conditional inequality** because it is true for at least one but not all values of the replacement set. Other examples of conditional inequalities are $x + 5 > 8$ and $2y - 6 < 10$.

If the replacement set is the set of real numbers, $x + 5 > x$ is true for every element of the replacement set. Such an inequality is called an **unconditional inequality.** Other examples of unconditional inequalities are $2x + 9 > 2x$ and $x - 7 < x$.

Solve each inequality. Then determine whether each inequality is conditional or unconditional.

1. $x - 2 > 4$ — $x > 6$; conditional
2. $3x - 2 < 2x + 4$ — $x < 6$; conditional
3. $4x + 5 \geq 4x$ — $5 \geq 0$; unconditional
4. $2(3x + 5) > 6x + 5$ — $10 > 5$; unconditional
5. $7y - 4 > 6 + 2y$ — $y > 2$; conditional
6. $8y - 3y > 5y - 10$ — $0 > -10$; unconditional
7. $5x \leq 10 + 2(3x - 4)$ — $x \geq -2$; conditional
8. $x < 7 + x$ — $0 < 7$; unconditional
9. $2c + 5 < 8 + 2c$ — $5 < 8$; unconditional
10. $6x + 3x - 1 < 8x + x$ — $-1 < 0$; unconditional
11. $2x + 3x \geq 4x + 1$ — $x \geq 1$; conditional
12. $7x + x + 10 \geq 8x$ — $10 \geq 0$; unconditional
13. $x + 8 < 8$ — $x < 0$; conditional
14. $8x < 5(2x + 4)$ — $x > -10$; conditional

Additional Answers

1. Substitute a number greater than 74.355 for *s* in the original inequality and evaluate.
43. Sample answer: Jay has $40. How much money can he spend on each of 3 gifts and have $1 left to pay for parking?

Cooperative Learning

Far Out Solutions — Group Activity **7-6**

MATERIALS: Four 0-9 spinners

One person spins the spinners to get four numbers that everyone will use to write multi-step inequalities. The inequalities must be of the form:

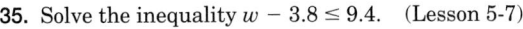

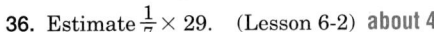

___ x (+ or −) ___ < ___ x (+ or −) ___

___ x (+ or −) ___ > ___ x (+ or −) ___

where the numbers spun are placed in the empty spots and x is the variable.

It is each player's challenge to write an inequality with a solution set that has its endpoint farthest from zero on the number line. The player who does so earns one point. The player with the most points after five rounds is the winner.

Merrill Pre-Algebra SOLVING MULTI-STEP INEQUALITIES

Lesson Notes 7-7

5-Minute Check
(over Lesson 7-6)

Solve each inequality.

1. $21 - 4t \le 29$ $t \ge -2$
2. $18 + 6m \ge -24$ $m \ge -7$
3. $-5.7 < \frac{a}{-20}$ $a < 114$
4. $13x - 8 \le 15x + 4$ $x \ge -6$
5. $9y - 5 > 5y + 11$ $y > 4$

Transparency 7-7 contains the 5-Minute Check and a teaching aid for this lesson.

1 FOCUS

The purpose of this lesson is to solve a verbal problem by translating it into an inequality and solving the inequality.

Motivating the Lesson

Write the test scores of a fictitious student on the chalkboard. Ask the class what score this student needs on the next test to raise the average by two percent.

2 TEACH

Using Tables

List the inequality symbols vertically on the chalkboard or overhead. As you discuss the examples have students write the phrases that suggest each symbol.

Chalkboard Examples

- *For Example 1*
  The auto mechanic charges \$15 to diagnose the problem. He then charges \$40 per hour to fix the problem. If he estimates that the total cost will be no more than \$155, how many hours can he work and still be within his estimate? $3\frac{1}{2}$ **hours**

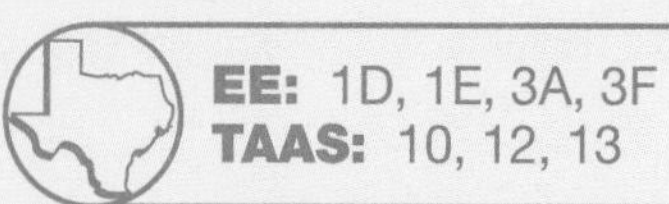

EE: 1D, 1E, 3A, 3F
TAAS: 10, 12, 13

Problem Solving

7-7 Writing Inequalities

Objective:
Write and solve inequalities involving rational numbers.

Katie has scores of 7.5, 6.9, and 6.7 in the all-around competition at a gymnastics meet. She has one more event. The leading opponent has completed the competition with an average score of 7.12. What must Katie score on her final trial if she is to win the competition?

Explore You must find Katie's fourth score so that her average score will be greater than 7.12.
Let s = Katie's fifth score.

Why might an estimate not be appropriate? **You need an exact answer to determine a winner.**

Plan

Katie's average	is greater than	average of the leader
$\frac{7.5 + 6.9 + 6.7 + s}{4}$	$>$	7.12

Solve

$$\frac{21.1 + s}{4} > 7.12$$

$$4 \cdot \frac{21.1 + s}{4} > 4 \cdot 7.12 \quad \text{Multiply each side by 4.}$$

$$21.1 + s > 28.48$$

$$21.1 - 21.1 + s > 28.48 - 21.1 \quad \text{Subtract 21.1 from each side.}$$

$$s > 7.38$$

Katie's score in the last event must be greater than 7.38.

Examine Check by substituting a score greater than 7.38 for s in the original inequality.

FYI
The events in the women's all-around include the floor exercise, the vault, the uneven bars, and the balance beam.

Problems containing the phrases *greater than* or *less than* can often be solved using inequalities. Other phrases that suggest inequalities are *at least, at most,* and *between.* Study the inequalities that correspond to each statement below.

The number x is *at least* 8.	$x \ge 8$	*At least 8* means 8 or greater.
The number y is *at most* 4.	$y \le 4$	*At most 4* means 4 or less.
A number z is *between* 7 and 9.	$7 < z < 9$	*Between 7 and 9* means greater than 7 and less than 9.

Bell Ringer

Order the numbers in each list from least to greatest and write two inequalities for each list.

1. -4.6, -4.9, -4.4, -4.7 **-4.9, -4.7, -4.6, -4.4; -4.9 < -4.4; -4.6 > -4.7**
2. $\frac{1}{2}, -\frac{1}{3}, \frac{2}{3}, -\frac{1}{2}, -\frac{2}{3}$
   $-\frac{2}{3}, -\frac{1}{2}, -\frac{1}{3}, \frac{1}{2}, \frac{2}{3}; \frac{1}{2} > -\frac{1}{3}; -\frac{2}{3} < -\frac{1}{3}$

Example

1 The owner of a lawn mower repair shop charges \$5 to diagnose the problem. He then charges \$30 per hour to fix the problem. If he estimates that the total cost will be no more than \$50, how many hours can he work and still be within his estimate?

Explore The total bill will be the diagnosis fee plus labor. No more than \$50 means the total will be less than or equal to \$50.

Plan Let h represent the number of hours of labor. Then $30h$ is the total charged for the labor.

diagnosis fee	plus	labor	is less than or equal to	\$50
5	+	$30h$	$\leq$	50

Solve

$$5 + 30h \leq 50$$

$$5 - 5 + 30h \leq 50 - 5 \quad \text{Subtract 5 from each side.}$$

$$30h \leq 45$$

$$\frac{30h}{30} \leq \frac{45}{30} \quad \text{Divide each side by 30.}$$

$$h \leq 1\frac{1}{2}$$

The owner can work no more than $1\frac{1}{2}$ hours to be within his estimate.

Examine Check by substituting times greater than, less than, and equal to $1\frac{1}{2}$ hours for h in the original inequality.

Checking for Understanding

Communicating Algebra **For each problem, answer the related questions.**

1. Jenny has scores of 87, 92, 89, and 97 on pre-algebra quizzes. There will be one more quiz this grading period. What must Jenny's fifth score be to have an average score of at least 90?
   a. What is asked?
   b. What does *at least 90* mean?
   c. What is the first operation that will be done to solve this problem?
   d. Write an inequality that represents this problem.

2. Nine less than six times a number is at most 33. What is the number?
   a. Write *nine less than six times a number* using symbols.
   b. What does *at most 33* mean?
   c. Write an inequality that represents this problem.
   d. How would you know if $7\frac{1}{2}$ is a member of the solution set?

3 PRACTICE/APPLY

Checking the Concept

After completing Guided Practice Exercises 3-8, solve and check each exercise. Remind students that checking confirms correct computation only; it is important to check reasonableness of the answer.

Error Analysis

Watch for students who have difficulty determining when to use > or ≥, and < or ≤.
Prevent by illustrating similar examples of each on the chalkboard for students to refer to as they are working problems.

Practice Masters Booklet, p. 69

Name ______________ Date ______________

Practice Worksheet 7-7

Problem Solving: Writing Inequalities

Write an inequality to solve each problem. Then solve each inequality.

1. Three times a number increased by 4 is at least 16. What is the number?
   Let n = the number; $3n + 4 \geq 16$; Any number greater than or equal to 4
2. Five less than a number is at most 11. What is the number?
   Let n = the number; $n - 5 \leq 11$; Any number less than or equal to 16
3. The sum of a number and 7 is less than 19. What is the number?
   Let n = the number; $n + 7 < 19$; Any number less than 12
4. Twice a number decreased by 9 is greater than 11. What is the number?
   Let n = the number; $2n - 9 > 11$; Any number greater than 10
5. The sum of two consecutive positive integers is less than 19. What are the integers? Let n = the lesser number, then $n + 1$ = the greater number; $n + n + 1 < 19$; Any number less than 9
6. The sum of two consecutive positive odd integers is at most 16. What are the integers? Let n = the lesser number, then $n + 2$ = the greater number; $n + n + 2 \leq 16$; Any number less than or equal to 7
7. Your test scores are 75, 93, 90, 82, and 85. What is the lowest score you can obtain on the next test to achieve an average of at least 86?
   Let t = next test score; $\frac{75 + 93 + 90 + 82 + 85 + t}{6} \geq 86$; 91
8. Juan spent at most \$2.50 on apples and oranges. He bought 5 apples at \$0.36 each. What is the most he spent on the oranges?
   Let p = the price of the oranges; $p + 5(0.36) \leq 2.50$; \$0.70
9. Three times a number increased by twice the number is greater than 125. What is the number?
   Let n = the number; $3n + 2n > 125$; Any number greater than 25
10. Five times a number decreased by 7 times the same number is at most 20. What is the number?
    Let n = the number; $5n - 7n \leq 20$; Any number greater than or equal to -10

Alternate Strategies: Reteaching the Lesson

Reteaching Activity

Using Groups of Two Have students work in pairs to write an "at least" problem, an "at most" problem, and a "between" problem. Trade and solve.

Reteaching Masters Booklet, p. 62

Name ______________ Date ______________

Reteaching Worksheet 7-7

Problem Solving: Writing Inequalities

There is one important difference between solving an equation and solving an inequality—whenever you multiply or divide both sides of an inequality by a negative number, you must reverse the inequality sign.

The puzzle below will give you practice solving inequalities.

Solve each inequality.

1. $4x - 7 < 17$
   $x < 6$
2. $10x + 18 \geq -72$
   $x \geq -9$
3. $12 > -14x - 2$
   $x > -1$
4. $\frac{x}{5} - 2 < 4$
   $x < 30$
5. $3x - 8 > 10$
   $x > 6$
6. $14 \leq 5x + 34$
   $x \geq -4$
7. $-\frac{x}{2} + 20 < 4$
   $x > 32$
8. $2x - 7 > x + 1$
   $x > 8$
9. $-28 \geq 12x - 4$
   $x \leq -2$
10. 6
11. $-10x - 2 \geq 8x$
12. $4x + 40$

Independent Practice

Homework Assignment	
Basic	9, 11, 13-17
Average	8, 10, 13-17
Honors	11-17

4 CLOSE

Assessment Option

Writing Have groups of three to four students write problems similar to Exercise 17.

Additional Answer

17. Sample answer: Mike is traveling 215 miles by bicycle. After 3 days, he wants to have no more than 175 miles left to travel. How many miles can he travel each of the first three days?

Enrichment Masters Booklet, **p. 62**

Name ____________ Date ____________

Enrichment Worksheet 7-7

Consecutive Integers and Inequalities

Consecutive integers follow one after another. For example, 4, 5, 6, and 7 are consecutive integers, as are −8, −7, −6. Each number to the right in the series is one greater than the one that comes before it. If x = the first consecutive integer, then $x + 1$ = the second consecutive integer, $x + 2$ = the third consecutive integer, $x + 3$ = the fourth consecutive integer, and so on.

Example: Find three consecutive positive integers whose sum is less than 12.

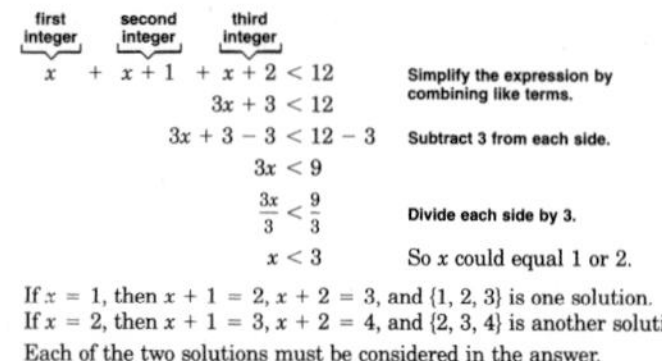

first integer, second integer, third integer

$x + x + 1 + x + 2 < 12$ — Simplify the expression by combining like terms.

$3x + 3 < 12$

$3x + 3 - 3 < 12 - 3$ — Subtract 3 from each side.

$3x < 9$

$\frac{3x}{3} < \frac{9}{3}$ — Divide each side by 3.

$x < 3$ — So x could equal 1 or 2.

If $x = 1$, then $x + 1 = 2$, $x + 2 = 3$, and {1, 2, 3} is one solution.
If $x = 2$, then $x + 1 = 3$, $x + 2 = 4$, and {2, 3, 4} is another solution.
Each of the two solutions must be considered in the answer.
The solution set is {1, 2, 3; 2, 3, 4}.

Solve. Give all possible solutions.

1. Find three consecutive positive integers whose sum is less than 15. {1, 2, 3; 2, 3, 4; 3, 4, 5}
2. Find two consecutive positive even integers whose sum is less than 10. {2, 4}
3. Find three consecutive positive integers such that the second plus four times the first is less than 21. {1, 2, 3; 2, 3, 4; 3, 4, 5}
4. Find three consecutive positive even integers such that the third plus twice the second is less than 26. {2, 4, 6; 4, 6, 8}

Guided Practice

Write an inequality for each situation.

3. You earn \$8 per hour plus a bonus of \$10. You wish to earn at least \$60. $8x + 10 \geq 60$
4. You can hike along the Appalachian Trail at 3 miles per hour. You will stop for an hour for a lunch break. You want to walk at least 18 miles. $3h + 1 \geq 18$
5. You buy some candy bars at 55 cents each plus one newspaper for 35 cents. You can spend no more than \$4. $55c + 35 \leq 400$
6. Four times a number increased by 4 is at least 16. What is the number? $4x + 4 \geq 16$
7. Twelve times a number decreased by $\frac{1}{20}$ of the number is less than 3250. What is the number? $12n - \frac{1}{20}n < 3250$

Exercises

Independent Practice

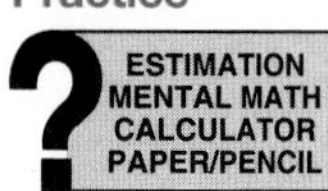

Write an inequality to solve each problem. Then solve each inequality.

8. Sue plans to spend no more than \$100.00 on blouses and one sweater. She buys 3 blouses at \$17 each. What is the most she can spend on the sweater? $3(17) + s \leq 100$; \$49
9. Cyril is going to buy a coat and a hat. The coat costs 3 times as much as the hat. He cannot spend more than \$120. What is the most he can spend for the coat? $3h + h \leq 120$; \$90
10. A stove and a freezer weigh at least 260 kg. The stove weighs 115 kg. What is the weight of the freezer? $f + 115 \geq 260$; 145 kg or greater
11. Tia is buying a new car. She can make a down payment of \$1,200. She wants to pay off the car in two years. She cannot afford monthly payments over \$250. What is the most she can pay for the car? $250(24) + 1200 \leq x$; \$7200

Challenge

12. If 4.05 times an integer is increased by 3.116, the result is between 13 and 25. What is the number? 3, 4, or 5

Mixed Review

13. Estimate $p = (-2.03)(0.6)$. (Lesson 6-4) -1.2

Solve each inequality. (Lesson 7-6)

14. $-4 < -2(b + 7)$ $-5 > b$
15. $3x - 14 \geq 2(3 - x)$ $x \geq 4$

Critical Thinking

16. Nancy has a stack of less than 50 pennies but more than one penny. When she divides the number of pennies by 2, there is 1 penny left over. There is also 1 penny left over when she divides by 3 or 7. How many pennies does she have? 43 pennies

Wrap-Up

17. **Make Up a Problem** Write a problem that would be solved using the inequality $215 - 3x \leq 175$. See margin.

Alternate Strategies: Extending the Lesson

Enrichment

Using Questioning Give students the problem $ay + bc \geq dy - bc$. Ask them if they are solving for y, do they need to know the values of a and d? Why? Yes, if you are dividing by a negative number $(a - d)$ the order symbol must be reversed.

Cooperative Learning

Clue Me In Group Activity **7-7**

MATERIALS: One die

Work with a partner to give clues and make guesses about a secret number. Mentally choose a number less than 50 and keep it a secret. Your partner will try to guess your number from clues you give. Clues must be inequalities that use two operations (×, ÷, +, and −), a variable, a number determined by rolling the die, and other numbers you choose to use. Your secret number must be a solution to the inequality you make, so your partner can solve the inequality and get a clue about your number. (For example, if your secret number is 30 and the number rolled is 6, you could write $2x - 6 < 55$ or $\frac{x}{10} + 4 > 6$ as a clue.) Roll the die to get a new number for each clue. Your partner should guess your number using the least number of clues.

Merrill Pre-Algebra WRITING INEQUALITIES

Application

7-8 Using the Metric System

Objective:
Convert measures within the metric system.

Key Terms:
meter
kilometer
gram
kilogram
liter

While on a family vacation in Canada, Chris noticed that the highway speed limit was 100! He reasoned that the speed limit couldn't be 100 miles per hour. Then he remembered that Canada uses the metric system of measurement. The metric system is also the system of measurement used by scientists in the United States.

The **meter** (m) is the basic unit of *length* in the metric system. All units of length in the metric system are defined in terms of the meter. The chart below shows how metric prefixes are related to decimal place-value positions.

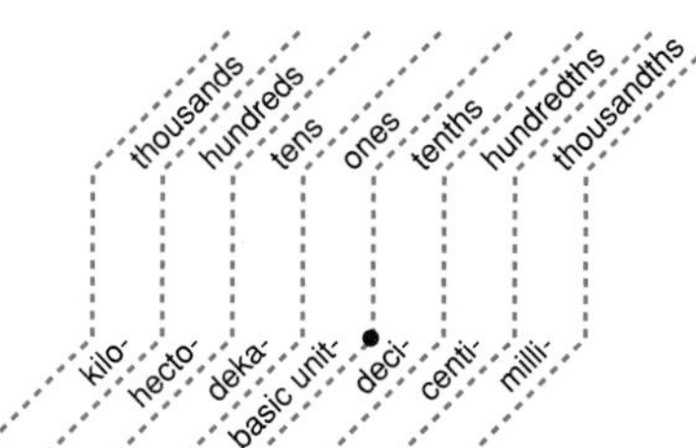

Note that each place value is 10 times the place value to its right.

Note that the value of each metric prefix is 10 times the value of the prefix to its right.

One **kilometer** (km) is 1000 meters. The speed limit that Chris noticed was 100 kilometers per hour, which is about 60 miles per hour.

Converting units within the metric system follows the same procedure as multiplying or dividing powers of ten. You may want to refer to Chapter 4 to review these procedures.

Larger units to smaller units: MULTIPLY →

Units of Length

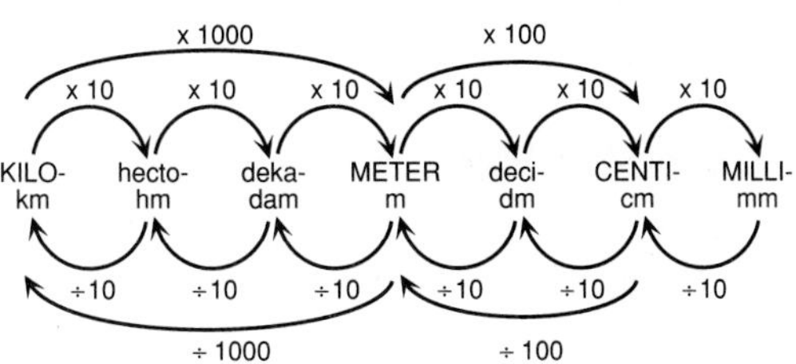

Smaller units to larger units: ← DIVIDE

Examples

Complete.

1 7 mm = ■ cm

Smaller to larger means fewer units. Divide by 10.

$7 \div 10 = 0.7$
7 mm = 0.7 cm

2 5.3 km = ■ m

Larger to smaller means more units. Multiply by 1000.

$5.3 \times 1000 = 5300$
5.3 km = 5300 m

Mental Math Hint

Remember, you can multiply or divide by a power of ten by moving the decimal point.

Bell Ringer

Write five inequalities in symbols and in words.

Lesson Notes 7-8

5-Minute Check
(over Lesson 7-7)

Write an inequality to solve each problem. Then solve each inequality.

1. The sum of two numbers is at most 48. If one number is 17, what is the other number? **31**
2. Sixteen times a number increased by $\frac{3}{4}$ of the number is less than 536. What is the number? **32**

Transparency 7-8 contains the 5-Minute Check and a teaching aid for this lesson.

1 FOCUS

The purpose of this lesson is to use equation-solving skills in unit conversion.

Motivating the Lesson

Have a "Guess the Size" contest. Place signs on several objects throughout your classroom asking students to guess the metric length, volume, or mass of the object.

2 TEACH

Using Models After discussing lesson examples, supply students with meter sticks, metric measuring cups, and balances with sets of weights. Have students model conversion problems.

Chalkboard Examples

Complete.

- *For Example 1*
  9mm = ■ cm **0.9 cm**
- *For Example 2*
  4.8 km = ■ m **4800 m**

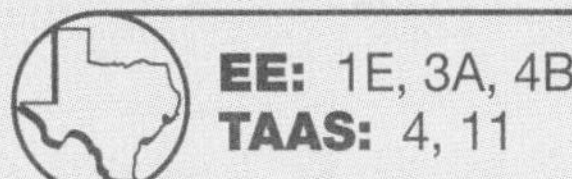

EE: 1E, 3A, 4B
TAAS: 4, 11

Chalkboard Examples

- For Example 3
  3 kg = ■ g 3000 g
- For Example 4
  20 mL = ■ L 0.020 L

3 PRACTICE/APPLY

Checking the Concept

After solving Exercises 5-7, ask students to check the reasonableness of their answers.

Error Analysis

Watch for students who don't move the decimal point the correct direction.
Prevent by having the student solve a simpler problem.

Practice Masters Booklet, **p. 70**

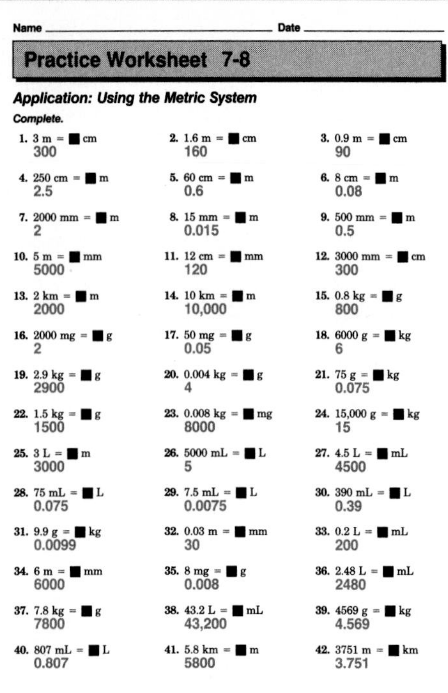

Name ______ Date ______

Practice Worksheet 7-8

Application: Using the Metric System

Complete.

1. 3 m = ■ cm 300	2. 1.6 m = ■ cm 160	3. 0.9 m = ■ cm 90
4. 250 cm = ■ m 2.5	5. 60 cm = ■ m 0.6	6. 8 cm = ■ m 0.08
7. 2000 mm = ■ m 2	8. 15 mm = ■ m 0.015	9. 500 mm = ■ m 0.5
10. 5 m = ■ mm 5000	11. 12 cm = ■ mm 120	12. 3000 mm = ■ cm 300
13. 2 km = ■ m 2000	14. 10 km = ■ m 10,000	15. 0.8 kg = ■ g 800
16. 2000 mg = ■ g 2	17. 50 mg = ■ g 0.05	18. 6000 g = ■ kg 6
19. 2.9 kg = ■ g 2900	20. 0.004 kg = ■ g 4	21. 75 g = ■ kg 0.075
22. 1.5 kg = ■ g 1500	23. 0.008 kg = ■ mg 8000	24. 15,000 g = ■ kg 15
25. 3 L = ■ m 3000	26. 5000 mL = ■ L 5	27. 4.5 L = ■ mL 4500
28. 75 mL = ■ L 0.075	29. 7.5 mL = ■ L 0.0075	30. 390 mL = ■ L 0.39
31. 9.9 g = ■ kg 0.0099	32. 0.03 m = ■ mm 30	33. 0.2 L = ■ mL 200
34. 6 m = ■ mm 6000	35. 8 mg = ■ g 0.008	36. 2.48 L = ■ mL 2480
37. 7.8 kg = ■ g 7800	38. 43.2 L = ■ mL 43,200	39. 4569 g = ■ kg 4.569
40. 807 mL = ■ L 0.807	41. 5.8 km = ■ m 5800	42. 3751 m = ■ km 3.751

The *mass* of an object is the amount of matter that it contains. The basic unit of mass in the metric system is the **gram** (g). Kilogram, gram, and milligram are related in a manner similar to kilometer, meter, and millimeter.

1 kg = 1000 g   1 g = 1000 mg

A pair of shoes has a mass of about 1 **kilogram** (kg).

Capacity is the amount of liquid or dry substance a container can hold. The basic unit of capacity in the metric system is the **liter** (L). Four average size water glasses hold about 1 liter. A liter and milliliter are related in a manner similar to meter and millimeter.

1 L = 1000 mL

Converting metric units of mass and capacity is similar to converting metric units of length.

Examples

Complete.

3 **8 kg = ■ g**

Larger to smaller means more units. Multiply by 1000.

$8 \cdot 1000 = 8000$
8 kg = 8000 g

4 **40 mL = ■ L**

Smaller to larger means fewer units. Divide by 1000.

$40 \div 1000 = 0.040$
40 mL = 0.040 L

Checking for Understanding

Communicating Algebra

1. Explain how to convert 6 meters to centimeters. **Multiply by 100.**
2. Explain how to convert 850 milliliters to liters. **Divide by 1000.**
3. Explain how to convert 3.9 grams to milligrams. **Multiply by 1000.**
4. Write a general rule for converting in the metric system. **See margin.**

Guided Practice

Complete.

5. 200 cm = ■ m 2
6. 3.2 kg = ■ g 3200
7. 9.4 L = ■ mL 9400

Exercises

Independent Practice

Complete. 13. 60,000

8. 4 m = ■ cm 400
9. 30 mm = ■ cm 3
10. 5 km = ■ m 5000
11. 500 cm = ■ m 5
12. 1200 mm = ■ m 1.2
13. 0.6 km = ■ cm

Alternate Strategies: Reteaching the Lesson

Reteaching Activity

Using Models Use the model below to show how to make unit conversions.

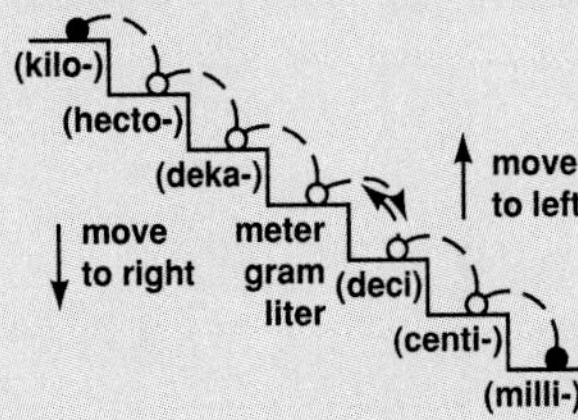

Reteaching Masters Booklet, **p. 63**

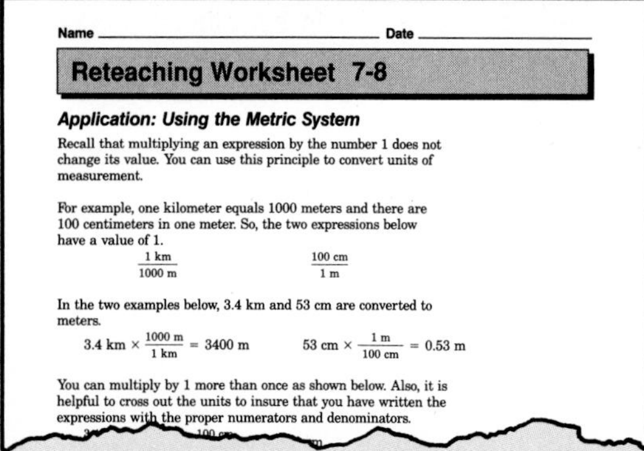

Name ______ Date ______

Reteaching Worksheet 7-8

Application: Using the Metric System

Recall that multiplying an expression by the number 1 does not change its value. You can use this principle to convert units of measurement.

For example, one kilometer equals 1000 meters and there are 100 centimeters in one meter. So, the two expressions below have a value of 1.

$\frac{1 \text{ km}}{1000 \text{ m}}$ $\frac{100 \text{ cm}}{1 \text{ m}}$

In the two examples below, 3.4 km and 53 cm are converted to meters.

$3.4 \text{ km} \times \frac{1000 \text{ m}}{1 \text{ km}} = 3400 \text{ m}$ $53 \text{ cm} \times \frac{1 \text{ m}}{100 \text{ cm}} = 0.53 \text{ m}$

You can multiply by 1 more than once as shown below. Also, it is helpful to cross out the units to insure that you have written the expressions with the proper numerators and denominators.

16. 0.32
21. 0.018
28. 3400
31. 10,600
34. 8500

14. 8 cm = ■ mm 80 15. 3 m = ■ mm 3000 16. 32,000 cm = ■ km
17. 5 kg = ■ g 5000 18. 3000 mg = ■ g 3 19. 2000 g = ■ kg 2
20. 6.7 g = ■ mg 6700 21. 18,000 mg = ■ kg 22. 1.9 kg = ■ g 1900
23. 7300 g = ■ kg 7.3 24. 0.006 kg = ■ mg 6000 25. 53 g = ■ kg 0.053
26. 5 L = ■ mL 5000 27. 2000 mL = ■ L 2 28. 3.4 L = ■ mL
29. 250 mL = ■ L 0.25 30. 7 mL = ■ L 0.007 31. 10.6 L = ■ mL
32. 350 mL = ■ L 0.35 33. 11 L = ■ mL 11,000 34. 8.5 L = ■ mL

Mixed Review

35. Find the next three terms in the arithmetic sequence 5, 2, -1, -4, . . . (Lesson 5-9) -7, -10, -13
36. Solve the equation $q = 3\frac{5}{6} + 1\frac{1}{3}$. (Lesson 6-6) $5\frac{1}{6}$
37. Solve the inequality $12 - 5y > 3y - 4$. (Lesson 7-6) $2 > y$
38. Translate into an inequality. *The sum of a number and two more than the number is at least 12.* (Lesson 7-6) $n + (n + 2) \geq 12$
39. The maximum load of a cargo elevator is 1600 pounds. If the current load is 1362 pounds, at most how many pounds can be added? (Lesson 7-7) $p \leq 238$

Application

40. **Consumer Awareness** Which has a greater capacity, a 2-liter bottle of cola or a six-pack of cans each containing 354 mL of the same cola? six-pack

Connection

41. **Geometry** The perimeter of a triangle is 1.6 meters. The length of the shortest side is 40 centimeters. Another side is 150 millimeters longer than the shortest side. Find the lengths of the other sides. 65 cm, 55 cm

Critical Thinking

42. Four volumes of International Recipes are in order on a shelf. The total pages of each volume are 5 cm thick. Each cover is 5 mm thick. A bookworm started eating at page 1 of Volume I and ate through to the last page of Volume IV. What distance did the bookworm cover? 13 cm

Wrap-Up

43. Explain how you use mental math skills to convert within the metric system. See margin.

Career

Laser Technician

Lasers have emerged as very valuable tools with applications ranging from very powerful cutting tools in industry to very delicate surgical instruments in medicine.

Laser technicians apply principles of laser engineering to the construction, testing, installation, and maintenance of laser devices. In the 1990s, the need for laser technicians is expected to grow 30%.

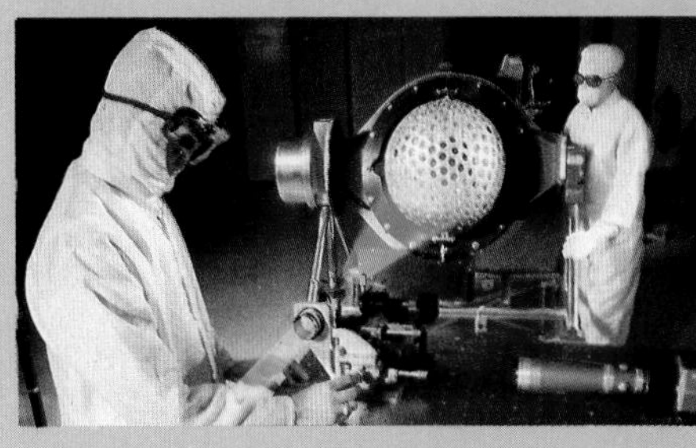

Independent Practice

Homework Assignment	
Basic	9-33 odd, 35-40, 42,43
Average	8-34 even, 35-43
Honors	22-43

Chapter 7, Quiz B (Lesson 7-6 through 7-8) is available in the Evaluation Masters Booklet, p. 61.

4 CLOSE

Assessment Option

Writing Have each student write two metric conversion problems. For example, 8 cm = ? mm. Then have them exchange their problems and solve the two they received from another student.

Additional Answers

4. To convert larger units to smaller units multiply by a power of 10. To convert smaller units to larger units divide by a power of 10.
43. The multiplication and division by powers of 10 is done by moving the decimal point.

Enrichment Masters Booklet, **p. 63**

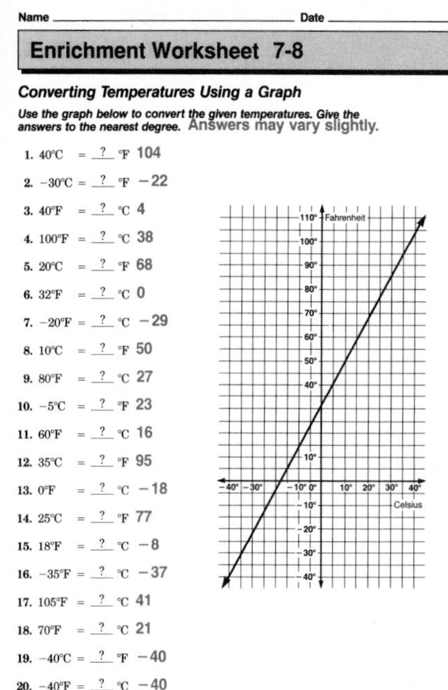

Name ______ Date ______

Enrichment Worksheet 7-8

Converting Temperatures Using a Graph

Use the graph below to convert the given temperatures. Give the answers to the nearest degree. Answers may vary slightly.

1. 40°C = ? °F 104
2. −30°C = ? °F −22
3. 40°F = ? °C 4
4. 100°F = ? °C 38
5. 20°C = ? °F 68
6. 32°F = ? °C 0
7. −20°F = ? °C −29
8. 10°C = ? °F 50
9. 80°F = ? °C 27
10. −5°C = ? °F 23
11. 60°F = ? °C 16
12. 35°C = ? °F 95
13. 0°F = ? °C −18
14. 25°C = ? °F 77
15. 18°F = ? °C −8
16. −35°F = ? °C −37
17. 105°F = ? °C 41
18. 70°F = ? °C 21
19. −40°C = ? °F −40
20. −40°F = ? °C −40

Alternate Strategies: Extending the Lesson

Enrichment

Using Models Using metric rulers, have students measure various objects in the class to the nearest cm. Have them convert each of these measurements to m and to mm.

Cooperative Learning

Measure Up Group Activity **7-8**

With a partner, find the following measurements for each person. Give the measures in both millimeters and meters.

Height: ______ Length of arm: ______ Circumference of head: ______
Length of foot: ______ Length of thumb: ______
Circumference of neck: ______ Span of fingers: ______
Distance from waist to floor: ______ Arm span: ______
Farthest distance you can jump: ______
Highest point you can touch without jumping: ______
Width of thinnest fingernail: ______ Distance around bicep: ______
Tell which of the two measurements is the most useful for each item.

Merrill Pre-Algebra USING THE METRIC SYSTEM

Using the Chapter Review

The Chapter Review is a comprehensive review of the concepts presented in this chapter. This review may be used to prepare students for the Chapter Test.

Alternate Review Strategy

To provide a brief in-class review, you may wish to read the following questions to the class and require a verbal response.

1. A certain number is multiplied by 4 and then 6 is added to the result. The final answer is 58. Find the number. 13
2. Explain how to solve $3y + 5 = 32$. Subtract 5 from each side. Divide each side by 3.
3. Ebony wants to buy a new sweater that costs $27. She has saved $15. She earns $4 per hour working at the grocery store. How many hours does she have to work to save enough money to buy the sweater? 3 hours
4. Name the first two steps you should take to solve $7a - 2 = 4a + 6$. Subtract $4a$ from each side. Add 2 to each side.
5. Solve $5(2m + 1) = 3m - 16$. $m = -3$
6. Solve $\frac{7}{9}x + 3 = \frac{5}{9}x + 7$. $x = 18$
7. Solve $-2r - 6 > 4$. $r \leq -5$
8. Write an inequality for six times a number decreased by four is at least 242. Then solve. $6x - 4 \geq 242$; $x = 41$
9. Explain how to convert 285 milliliters to liters. Divide by 1000.
10. Explain how to convert 5 meters to centimeters. Multiply by 100.

Review

Language and Concepts

Choose a word or symbol from the list at the right to correctly complete each statement.

customary system
divide
gram
liter
meter
metric system
multiply
$\varnothing$
$\neq$
$\leq$
$\geq$

1. To change larger units of measure to smaller units of measure, it is necessary to __?__ . multiply
2. To change smaller units of measure to larger units of measure, it is necessary to __?__ . divide
3. __?__ is the mathematical symbol that means the solution set is empty or null. $\varnothing$
4. The __?__ is based on powers of ten. metric system
5. The symbol __?__ means *at least*. $\geq$
6. The basic unit of capacity in the metric system is the __?__ . liter

Skills

Solve each equation. Check your solution. (Lessons 7-2, 7-4, 7-5)

7. $2x + 4 = -32$ -18
8. $3m + 8 = 71$ 21
9. $-2r + 8 = 24$ -8
10. $3y - 14 = 37$ 17
11. $6z - 1.6 = -5.2$ -0.6
12. $-2t - 1.5 = 1.3$ -1.4
13. $\frac{y}{3} - 6 = -9$ -9
14. $\frac{x}{5} + 3 = 6$ 15
15. $\frac{c + 8}{4} = 16$ 56
16. $5x - 4 = 4x + 3$ 7
17. $2y - 6 = 3y - 5$ -1
18. $7t + 6 = 3t - 14$ -5
19. $3(x + 2) = 12$ 2
20. $3(x - 5) = -6$ 3
21. $6(x + 2) - 4 = -10$ -3
22. $3x + 8 = 3x - 4$ $\varnothing$
23. $3(x + 2) - 6 = 3x$ all numbers
24. $4y + 8 = 15$ 1.75

Solve each inequality. (Lesson 7-6)

25. $2m + 1 < 9$ $m < 4$
26. $-3k - 4 \leq -22$ $k \geq 6$
27. $-2 \geq 10 - 2x$ $6 \leq x$
28. $1 - 3x > 7$ $x < -2$
29. $-3.2 + 14z < 15z$ $-3.2 < z$
30. $3(y - 2) > 5(y - 7)$ $14.5 > y$

Complete. (Lesson 7-8)

31. 5m = ■ cm 500
32. 3500 m = ■ km 3.5
33. 2900 g = ■ kg 2.9
34. 8.3 L = ■ mL 8300
35. 0.7 kg = ■ g 700
36. 1860 mL = ■ L 1.86

Applications and Problem Solving

Solve. Use the work backwards strategy. (Lesson 7-1)

37. Diana makes a salary of $250 a week. In addition to her weekly salary, she receives a bonus of $50 for every 25 boxes of books she sells. If she earned a total of $450 in salary and bonuses this week, how many boxes did she sell? **100 boxes**

38. Frank walks 10 blocks to work every day. It takes him between 15 to 20 minutes to get to work. At this rate, what is the least amount of time it would take for Frank to walk 50 blocks? **75 minutes**

Write and solve an equation. (Lesson 7-3)

39. Mr. Stinson bought a used boat for $30 more than half its original cost. He paid $150. What was the original cost? $\frac{c}{2} + 30 = 150$; $240

40. Mrs. Hawn bought a washing machine on sale. She paid $25 more than half of the regular price. She paid $265. What is the regular price? $\frac{r}{2} + 25 = 265$; $480

Use an inequality to solve each problem. (Lesson 7-7)

41. If 8 times a number is decreased by 2, the result is less than 15. What is the number? $8x - 2 < 15$; $x < \frac{17}{8}$

42. Linda plans to spend at most $85 on jeans and shirts. She bought 2 shirts for $15.30 each. How much can she spend on jeans? $2(15.30) + j \leq 85$; $54.40

Communicating Algebra

In your own words, briefly describe a general procedure for solving equations that have a variable on each side of the equal sign. **See margin.**

Curriculum Connection

- **Science** Do research on the relationship between balancing chemical equations and solving equations with a variable on both sides of the equal sign. **See margin.**
- **History** Do research to find out how Thomas Jefferson helped in the development of the metric system. **See margin.**
- **Language Arts** Write a composition titled *Math at the Mall.* **See students' work.**

Read More About It

Barr, George. *Entertaining with Number Tricks.*

Ecker, Michal W. *Getting Started in Problem Solving and Math Concepts.*

Luce, Marnie. *Zero is Something.*

You may wish to use a Chapter Test (free-response format) as an additional chapter review. Two forms are provided in the Evaluation Masters Booklet as shown below.

Evaluation Masters Booklet, **p. 59**

Name ________________ Date ________

Chapter 7 Test, Form 2A

1. A box of 90 map pins has twice as many red pins as blue, and half as many blue as black. How many pins are blue?
2. A balloon doubles its diameter every time 10 pounds of pressure are added. The diameter was 2 inches before 30 pounds of pressure were added. Find the balloon's present diameter.
3. Marcia read for 45 minutes, danced for 60 minutes, and rested for 20 minutes. At the end of her rest period, it was noon. At what time did she begin reading?

Solve each equation or inequality.

4. $3x + 8 = 23$
5. $6y - 12 = 30$
6. $\frac{a+4}{2} = 6$
7. $\frac{b}{4} + 5 = 2$
8. $-3m + 7 = 34$
9. $-6p - 15 = -63$
10. $\frac{y}{2} + 9 = 7$
11. $\frac{z}{3} - 10 = -8$
12. $x + 9 = 2x + 3$
13. $5a + 10 = 4a + 8$
14. $9b + 4 = 12b - 8$
15. $12c = 25c + 52$
16. $2.5d + 1 = 3d - 4$
17. $8f + 14 = 12f + 2$
18. $2(x + 5) = 20$
19. $4(y + 9) = 2(y + 21)$
20. $6(3a + 4) = 18(2a) + 6$
21. $\frac{b}{2} - 5 = \frac{b}{3} - 1$
22. $\frac{1}{2}(c - 6) = \frac{1}{4}c$
23. $7y + 2 < 30$
24. $-\frac{1}{2}m + 3 < 23$
25. $2p + 6 < 5p - 6$
26. $-3(x + 2) > 12$
27. $4y + 2 > 5y - 5$

Write and solve an inequality.

28. The sum of two consecutive integers is at least 13. Find the smaller integer.
29. If 5 times an integer is decreased by 17, the result is less than 63. Find the integer.

Complete.

30. 6 m = ■ cm
31. 8300 g = ■ kg
32. 5.2 L = ■ mL
33. 400 cm = ■ mm

BONUS A truck and its load weigh at least 65,000 lb. The empty truck weighs 41,000 lb. How heavy is one-half the load?

Answers: 1. 18; 2. 16 in.; 3. 9:55 A.M.; 4. 5; 5. 7; 6. 8; 7. −12; 8. −9; 9. 8; 10. −4; 11. 6; 12. 6; 13. −2; 14. 4; 15. −4; 16. 10; 17. 3; 18. 5; 19. 3; 20. 1; 21. 24; 22. 12; 23. $y < 4$; 24. $m > -40$; 25. $p > 4$; 26. $x < -6$; 27. $y < 7$; 28. $x \geq 6$; 29. $x < 16$; 30. 600; 31. 8.3; 32. 5200; 33. 4000; Bonus: $l \geq 12{,}000$ lb

Evaluation Masters Booklet, **p. 60**

Name ________________ Date ________

Chapter 7 Test, Form 2B

1. A box of 102 beads has twice as many red beads as black, and six more blue than black. How many beads are black?
2. An alga doubles its diameter every 6 hours. Its diameter was 3 inches 24 hours ago. Find the alga's present diameter.
3. Arthur read for 35 minutes, danced for 50 minutes, and rested for 30 minutes. At the end of his rest period, it was noon. At what time did he begin reading?

Solve each equation or inequality.

4. $3n + 8 = 20$
5. $6z + 12 = 30$
6. $\frac{p+4}{2} = 8$
7. $\frac{c}{4} - 6 = 20$
8. $-3t + 17 = 11$
9. $-6k - 15 = -57$
10. $\frac{h}{2} + 7 = 3$
11. $\frac{w}{3} - 10 = -60$
12. $h + 9 = 2h - 1$
13. $7b + 12 = 6b + 8$
14. $9d + 4 = 10d + 1$
15. $12c = 32c + 60$
16. $3.5q + 1 = 4q - 4$
17. $8x + 16 = 12x + 4$
18. $2(r + 5) = 24$
19. $4(y + 7) = 2(y + 41)$
20. $6(3d + 4) = 10(2d) + 6$
21. $\frac{b}{2} - 7 = \frac{b}{3} - 1$
22. $\frac{1}{3}(c - 6) = \frac{1}{9}c$
23. $6y + 8 < 32$
24. $-\frac{1}{2}m + 5 > 25$
25. $2n + 9 < 5n - 9$
26. $-2(f + 2) > 18$
27. $4w + 2 > 5w - 2$

Write and solve an inequality.

28. The sum of two consecutive integers is at least 19. Find the smaller integer.
29. If 8 times an integer is decreased by 12, the result is less than 44. Find the integer.

Complete.

30. 16 cm = ■ m
31. 4250 g = ■ kg
32. 7.1 L = ■ mL
33. 40 cm = ■ mm

BONUS A truck, its driver, and its load weigh at least 65,000 lb. The empty truck weighs 41,000 lb and the load weighs 23,815 lb. Find the weight of the driver.

Answers: 1. 24; 2. 48 in.; 3. 10:05 A.M.; 4. 4; 5. 3; 6. 12; 7. 104; 8. 2; 9. 7; 10. −8; 11. −150; 12. 10; 13. −4; 14. 3; 15. −3; 16. 10; 17. 3; 18. 7; 19. 27; 20. 9; 21. 36; 22. 9; 23. $y < 4$; 24. $m < -40$; 25. $n > 6$; 26. $f < -11$; 27. $w < 4$; 28. $n \geq 9$; 29. $n < 7$; 30. 0.16; 31. 4.25; 32. 7100; 33. 400; Bonus: $w \geq 185$ lb

Additional Answers

Communicating Algebra Isolate the variable on one side and follow the procedures for solving a two step equation.

Curriculum Connection - Science In balancing a chemical equation the same number of each kind of atom must be on each side of the arrow.

Curriculum Connection - History In 1790, the French Academy of Sciences developed the metric system. That same year, Secretary of State Thomas Jefferson, recommended that the United States use a decimal system of measurement. Congress rejected the idea.

Using the Chapter Test

This page may be used as a test or as an additional review. Two forms of a Chapter Test (multiple-choice format) are provided in the Evaluation Masters Booklet.

Evaluation Masters Booklet, **pp. 55-56**

Name ______________________ Date ______________

Chapter 7 Test, Form 1A

Write and solve an equation to find the unknown number.

1. Five times a number, plus 3, equals 48.
   A. 51 B. 10 C. 9 D. 45 — 1. C
2. A number divided by 3, minus 2, equals 14.
   A. 40 B. 36 C. 16 D. 48 — 2. D
3. Four times the sum of a number and 6 is 40.
   A. 4 B. 10 C. 44 D. 6 — 3. A
4. Solve $3n + 2 = 26$.
   A. 7 B. 8 C. 9 D. 6.5 — 4. B
5. Solve $-4m - (-2) = 6$.
   A. −2 B. 2 C. −1 D. 1 — 5. C
6. Solve $\frac{x}{3} + 2 = 12$.
   A. 10 B. 42 C. 36 D. 30 — 6. D
7. Jack has $30 and saves an additional $6 per week. Which equation would be used to find the number of weeks until he will have $96?
   A. $30 + w = 96$ B. $96 - w = 30$
   C. $30 + 6w = 96$ D. $6w - 30 = 96$ — 7. C
8. Jane buys $80 worth of non-taxable items and some other items taxable at 5%. Her total bill is $118.85. Which equation would be used to find the cost of the taxable items?
   A. $t + 0.05t + 80 = 118.85$ B. $t + 0.5t + 80 = 118.85$
   C. $t + 5t - 80 = 118.85$ D. $80 - 0.05t - t = 118.85$ — 8. A
9. Solve $4x - 8 = 3x - 1$.
   A. −7 B. 7 C. 9 D. −1 — 9. B
10. Solve $3y + 2 = 2y + 6$.
    A. −4 B. 8 C. 4 D. −8 — 10. C
11. Solve $15m + 3 = 18m - 3$.
    A. 2 B. 0 C. −2 D. 3 — 11. A
12. Solve $6y + 20 = -2y - 12$.
    A. 4 B. 8 C. −8 D. −4 — 12. D
13. Solve $3(a + 4) = 8a + 2$.
    A. 1.2 B. 2 C. 0.4 D. 3 — 13. B
14. Solve $7a - 3 = 5(a - 1)$.
    A. 0.25 B. 1 C. −1 D. 2 — 14. C

Name ______________________ Date ______________

Chapter 7 Test, Form 1A (continued)

15. Solve $x - 7 = 5(x - 11)$.
    A. −1 B. 12 C. 1 D. 3 — 15. B
16. Solve $4x - 2 > 10$.
    A. $x < 3$ B. $x > 3$ C. $x < 2$ D. $x > 2$ — 16. B
17. Solve $-4p - 5 < -25$.
    A. $p > 5$ B. $p < 5$ C. $p > 4$ D. $p < 7.5$ — 17. A
18. Solve $\frac{x}{2} - 2 < 2$.
    A. $x < 4$ B. $x < 6$ C. $x > 8$ D. $x < 8$ — 18. D
19. Michelle earns $7 per hour and gets a bonus of $20. She wants to work enough hours to earn at least $94. Which inequality would be used to find the number of hours?
    A. $7h - 20 \le 94$ B. $7h - 20 \ge 94$
    C. $7h + 20 \le 94$ D. $7h + 20 \ge 94$ — 19. D
20. Five times a number decreased by 8 is less than 92. Which inequality would be used to find the unknown number?
    A. $5n \div 8 < 92$ B. $5n + 8 < 92$
    C. $5n - 8 < 92$ D. $5n - 8 > 92$ — 20. C
21. Twice the sum of a number and 16 is greater than 46. Which inequality would be used to find the unknown number?
    A. $2(n + 16) > 46$ B. $n + 32 > 46$
    C. $2n + 16 < 46$ D. $2n - 16 > 46$ — 21. A

Complete.

22. 300 mg = ■ g
    A. 0.3 B. 3 C. 30 D. 0.03 — 22. A
23. 60,000 m = ■ km
    A. 6 B. 60 C. 600 D. 0.6 — 23. B
24. 5 m = ■ cm
    A. 0.05 B. 50 C. 500 D. 5000 — 24. C
25. Joe bought 5 full cartons of light bulbs and 6 extra bulbs. He has 726 bulbs. How many bulbs are there in one carton?
    A. 145 B. 150 C. 720 D. 144 — 25. D

BONUS A U.S. nickel weighs 5 grams. How many grams would $40 worth of nickels weigh?
A. 4000 B. 1125 C. 5000 D. 160 — A

Test

Solve each equation.

1. $4 - b = -2$ **6**
2. $3(p - 5) = 9$ **8**
3. $\frac{h}{-2} + 5 = -12$ **34**
4. $\frac{y}{3} - 17 = 8$ **75**
5. $8x - 3 = 13$ **2**
6. $10k - 31 = 11k + 76$ **-107**
7. $8p + 29 = 7p + 16$ **-13**
8. $3x + 5 = -2x + 10$ **1**
9. $6 - x = -3x + 10$ **2**
10. $-4y + 2 = 32$ **$-7\frac{1}{2}$**
11. $\frac{m + 5}{6} = -19$ **-119**
12. $\frac{5t - 9}{4} = 14$ **13**
13. $4(2y - 1) = -10(y - 5)$ **3**
14. $-2(3n - 5) + 3n = 2 - n$ **4**
15. $3(n + 5) - 6 = 3n + 9$ **all numbers**

Solve each inequality.

16. $-6a + 2 < 14$ **$a > -2$**
17. $2y + 1 \le -7$ **$y \le -4$**
18. $\frac{d}{-3} + 4 > -12$ **$d < 48$**

Complete.

19. 8.4 km = ■ m **8400**
20. 250 mL = ■ L **0.25**
21. 4 g = ■ mg **4000**
22. 18 cm = ■ m **0.18**

Solve. Work backwards.

23. Duane passes out rulers for a class exercise. He gives one half of the rulers to Todd, who will help to pass them out. He then gives one third of the remainder to Pat, who will pass them down her row. Duane has 12 rulers left. How many rulers did he start with? **36 rulers**

Write and solve an equation or inequality.

24. George plans to spend at most $40 for shirts and ties. He bought 2 shirts for $13.95 each. How much can he spend for ties? **$2(13.95) + t \le 40$; $12.10**
25. Juanita lost her tennis racquet. She bought a new one for $30. This is $6 less than three times the price of her old one. How much did she pay for her old racquet? **$30 = 3r - 6$; $12**

BONUS

A plumber charges $36 for the first hour of work and $16 for every half hour or any part of a half hour thereafter. Find the longest amount of time this plumber can work for Tim Evans without having the bill exceed $150. **4.5 hours**

Test Generator Software is provided in both Apple and IBM formats. You may use this software to create your own tests, based on the needs of your students.

Academic Skills Test

Cumulative, Chapters 1-7

1. Which expression is equivalent to $-14ab - 27ab$?

   A $-41ab$ **C** $13ab$
   B $-13ab$ **D** $41ab$

2. Which is equivalent to $a^5 \cdot a^2$?

   A $2a^{10}$ **C** $2a^7$
   B a^{10} **D** a^7

3. Which fraction is less than $\frac{5}{12}$?

   A $\frac{1}{2}$ **C** $\frac{3}{4}$
   B $\frac{5}{8}$ **D** $\frac{2}{6}$

4. If $6.0 = b - 2.2$, what is the value of b?

   A 8.2 **C** 4.8
   B 6.0 **D** 3.8

5. If $3.2y = 80$, what is the value of y?

   A 256 **C** 25
   B 76.8 **D** 2.5

6. Which equation is equivalent to $2y + 6 = 12$?

   A $2y = 12$
   B $2y + 6 - 6 = 12 - 6$
   C $2y + 1 = 2$
   D $2y + 6 - 6 = 12 + 6$

7. If $5y - 4 = 3y + 12$, what is the value of y?

   A 1
   B 2
   C 4
   D 8

8. 3542 runners entered the Merrill Marathon. 1054 runners did not finish the race. The number of runners that finished the race is between—

   A 3500 and 3600
   B 2400 and 2600
   C 2000 and 2200
   D 1900 and 2100

9. The labor charge for repairing a car is \$32.50 per hour. If it takes 2.5 hours to repair the car, what will be the charge for labor?

   A \$812.50
   B \$81.25
   C \$13.00
   D Not Here

10. George bought a used stereo for \$10 more than half its original cost. He paid \$150. What was the original cost?

    A \$70
    B \$85
    C \$280
    D \$310

A Cumulative Review (free-response format) and Cumulative Test (multiple-choice format) are also provided in the Evaluation Masters Booklet as shown at the right.

Test Item	1	2	3	4	5	6	7	8	9	10
Lesson Number	2-5	4-3	4-9	5-7	6-7	7-2	7-5	5-3	6-4	7-3
TAAS Objective	2	2	1	2	2	2	2	10	8	12

Using the Academic Skills Test

This test familiarizes students with a standardized format while testing skills and concepts presented up to this point.

***Evaluation Masters Booklet*, p. 62**

Name ____________ Date ____________

Cumulative Review, Chapters 1-7

1. Find the value of $12 \div 3 + 6 \div 2$. (Lesson 1–1) — 1. **7**
2. Solve $17a = 204$ by using the inverse operation. (Lesson 1–7) — 2. **12**
3. Simplify $|-4| + |8|$. (Lesson 2–1) — 3. **12**
4. Five plus a number equals −16. Find the number. (Lesson 2–9) — 4. **−21**
5. Solve $x - (-36) = -27$. (Lesson 3–2) — 5. **−63**
6. Solve $15y = -195$. (Lesson 3–3) — 6. **−13**
7. Charles begins at home, bicycles 2.7 miles to a church, then 2.4 miles to a library, and 3.2 miles back home. His route is shaped like a triangle. Find the perimeter. (Lesson 3–6) — 7. **8.3 mi**
8. Find the prime factorization of 810. (Lesson 4–4) — 8. $2 \cdot 3^4 \cdot 5$
9. Find the GCF of $15x$ and $40x^3$. (Lesson 4–5) — 9. **5x**
10. Find the LCM of 12 and 30. (Lesson 4–7) — 10. **60**
11. Find the product of $(m^3)(m)(m^5)$. (Lesson 4–9) — 11. m^9
12. Express 0.36 as a fraction in simplest form. (Lesson 5–2) — 12. $\frac{9}{25}$
13. Name the property of addition shown by $-2 + 4 = 2$. (Lesson 5–4) — 13. **Closure**
14. Solve $y = -16.43 - (-2.6)$. (Lesson 5–4) — 14. **−13.83**
15. Solve $\frac{5}{7} + \frac{2}{21} = c$. (Lesson 5–6) — 15. $\frac{17}{21}$
16. Derrick has pieces of rope measuring 5 ft 3 in., 6 ft 7 in., and 2 ft 10 in. Find the total length of the rope. (Lesson 5–10) — 16. **14 ft 8 in.**
17. Express $\frac{4}{11}$ as a decimal. Use a bar to show a repeating decimal. (Lesson 6–1) — 17. $0.\overline{36}$

Solve each equation. Write each solution in simplest form. (Lessons 6–3, 6–6, 6–8)

18. $q = -3\frac{1}{3}(-9)$ 19. $p = -4\frac{2}{5} \div 3\frac{2}{5}$ 20. $-\frac{3}{5}r = \frac{2}{3}$ — 18. **30** 19. $-1\frac{5}{17}$ 20. $-1\frac{1}{9}$
21. Express 3.46×10^{-3} in standard form. (Lesson 6–11) — 21. **0.00346**
22. Solve $-4y - 12 = -44$. (Lesson 7–2) — 22. **8**
23. A load of bricks costs \$0.30 per brick plus a \$10 delivery charge. Nikki paid a total bill of \$55 for her bricks. How many bricks did she buy? (Lesson 7–3) — 23. **150**
24. Solve $10m - 12 = 4m + 6$. (Lesson 7–4) — 24. **3**
25. Solve $4b - 12 < 36$. (Lesson 7–6) — 25. $b < 12$

***Evaluation Masters Booklet*, p. 63**

Name ____________ Date ____________

Cumulative Test, Chapters 1-7

1. Six added to a number equals −12. Find the number.
   A. 18 B. 6 C. −6 D. −18 — 1. **D**
2. Solve $x - (-24) = -31$.
   A. 55 B. −55 C. −7 D. 7 — 2. **B**
3. Solve $18y = -378$.
   A. −21 B. −360 C. −396 D. 21 — 3. **A**
4. A corner shelf is shaped like a triangle with sides measuring 15 in., 20 in., and 25 in. Find the perimeter of the shelf.
   A. 150 in. B. 120 in. C. 300 in. D. 60 in. — 4. **D**
5. Find the prime factorization of 36.
   A. $2^3 \cdot 3$ B. $2^2 \cdot 9$ C. $2^2 \cdot 3^2$ D. $2 \cdot 18$ — 5. **C**
6. Find the GCF of $20x^3$ and $25x^2$.
   A. $5x^2$ B. $100x^3$ C. $5x$ D. 5 — 6. **A**
7. Find the LCM of 18 and 30.
   A. 2 B. 3 C. 60 D. 90 — 7. **D**
8. Find the product of $(m^2)(m^3)(m)$.
   A. m B. m^5 C. m^6 D. m^7 — 8. **C**
9. Express 0.45 as a fraction in simplest form.
   A. $\frac{9}{100}$ B. $\frac{9}{20}$ C. $\frac{45}{100}$ D. $\frac{45}{99}$ — 9. **B**
10. Solve $y = -18.36 - (-4.1)$.
    A. −18.77 B. −14.26 C. 14.26 D. −22.46 — 10. **B**
11. Solve $c = \frac{4}{9} + \frac{5}{18}$. A. $\frac{1}{2}$ B. $\frac{9}{27}$ C. $\frac{1}{3}$ D. $\frac{13}{18}$ — 11. **D**
12. Add 6 ft 9 in. and 2 ft 6 in.
    A. 9 ft 5 in. B. 8 ft 3 in. C. 9 ft 3 in. D. 9 ft — 12. **C**
13. Express $\frac{3}{8}$ as a decimal.
    A. 0.375 B. 3.8 C. 2.333 D. 0.38 — 13. **A**
14. Solve $p = -3\frac{1}{3} - 2\frac{2}{3}$. A. −6 B. $-5\frac{1}{3}$ C. $5\frac{1}{3}$ D. 6 — 14. **A**
15. Solve $-5w - 12 = 18$.
    A. −4 B. −1.2 C. −6 D. 1.5 — 15. **C**
16. Express 4.04×10^2 in standard form.
    A. 404 B. 0.0404 C. 40.4 D. 400 — 16. **A**
17. Solve $-\frac{1}{3}x = \frac{2}{5}$. A. $-\frac{5}{6}$ B. $-1\frac{1}{5}$ C. $-\frac{2}{15}$ D. $-7\frac{1}{2}$ — 17. **B**
18. Solve $12m - 10 = 10m + 2$.
    A. −4 B. 4 C. 6 D. −6 — 18. **C**
19. Solve $3b - 2 > 13$.
    A. $b < 5$ B. $b > 5$ C. $b < 12$ D. $b > 12$ — 19. **B**
20. Mark buys lumber at \$1.25 per piece plus a delivery charge of \$15. He pays a total of \$77.50. How many pieces of lumber did he buy?
    A. 50 B. 100 C. 60 D. 40 — 20. **A**

Graphing Equations and Inequalities

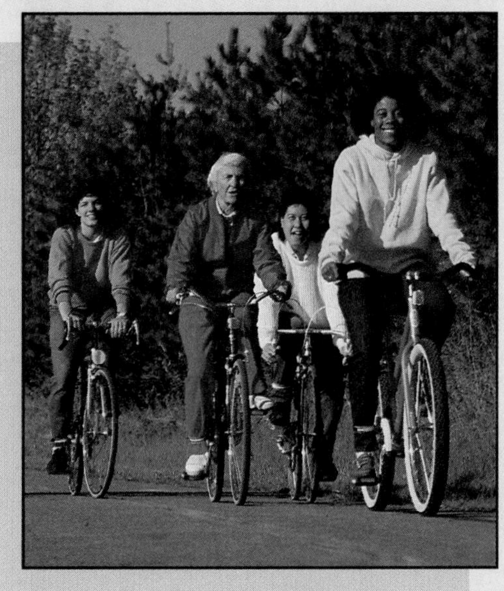

Previewing the Chapter

This chapter begins with the graph of a solution to an equation on a number line. Students then learn to graph inequalities on a number line. The natural extension to coordinate graphs and the concept of a linear equation follows. The slope of a line and its intercepts are discussed in the context of graphing. Students will solve systems of equations and inequalities by graphing them.

Problem Solving Strategy Students will learn to solve problems by drawing a graph.

Lesson (Pages)	Lesson Objectives	State/Local Objectives
8-1 (288-289)	8-1: Graph the solution of an equation on a number line.	1E, 3A, 3F, 6A
8-2 (290-292)	8-2: Graph the solution of an inequality on a number line.	1E, 3A, 3F, 6A
8-3 (294-296)	8-3: Identify the ordered pair of numbers associated with a point on a grid.	1A, 3A, 3F, 4E
8-4 (297-299)	8-4: Graph points in a coordinate system.	1E, 3A, 3F, 4E
8-5 (300-302)	8-5: Find solutions for equations with two variables.	1E, 2F, 3A, 4E, 6B
8-6 (303-305)	8-6: Graph linear equations on a coordinate system.	1E, 2F, 3A, 6B
8-7 (306-308)	8-7: Solve a problem by using a graph.	1A, 1B, 1C, 1D, 1E, 6B
8-8 (309-311)	8-8: Find the slope of a line.	1E, 3A, 5E, 6B, 6C
8-9 (312-313)	8-9: Graph a linear equation by using the x-intercept and y-intercept.	1E, 3A, 6B, 6C
8-10 (315-317)	8-10: Solve systems of linear equations by graphing.	1E, 3A, 6B, 6C, 6D
8-11 (319-321)	8-11: Graph linear inequalities on a coordinate system.	1E, 3A, 6B

Organizing the Chapter

You may want to refer to the ***Course Planning Calendar*** *on Page T31.*

Planning Guide

Lesson (Pages)	Pacing Chart (in days)			Extra Practice (Student Edition)	Blackline Masters Booklets			Other Resources
	MINIMUM	STANDARD	ACCELERATED		Reteaching	Practice	Enrichment	
8-1 (288-289)	1	1	0.5	p. 605, Set 8A	p. 65	p. 72	p. 65	Transparency 8-1 Group Activity Card 8-1
8-2 (290-292)	1	1	1	p. 605, Set 8A	p. 66	p. 73	p. 66	Transparency 8-2 Group Activity Card 8-2
8-3 (294-296)	1	1	1	p. 605, Set 8B	p. 67	p. 74	p. 67	Transparency 8-3 Group Activity Card 8-3
8-4 (297-299)	1	1	1	p. 605, Set 8B	p. 68	p. 75	p. 68	Transparency 8-4 Group Activity Card 8-4
8-5 (300-302)	1	1	1	p. 605, Set 8B	p. 69	p. 76	p. 69	Transparency 8-5 Group Activity Card 8-5
8-6 (303-305)	1	1	1	p. 606, Set 8B	p. 70	p. 77	p. 70	Transparency 8-6 Group Activity Card 8-6
8-7 (306-308)	1	1	1			p. 78		Transparency 8-7 Group Activity Card 8-7
8-8 (309-311)	1	1	1	p. 606, Set 8C	p. 71	p. 79	p. 71	Transparency 8-8 Group Activity Card 8-8
8-9 (312-313)	1	1	0.5	p. 606, Set 8C	p. 72	p. 80	p. 72	Transparency 8-9 Group Activity Card 8-9
8-10 (315-317)	1	1	1	p. 606, Set 8D	p. 73	p. 81	p. 73	Transparency 8-10 Group Activity Card 8-10
8-11 (319-321)	1	1	1	p. 605, Set 8B	p. 74	p. 82	p. 74	Transparency 8-11 Group Activity Card 8-11
Review	1.5	1	1					Test Generator
Test	1	1	1		Evaluation Masters, pp. 64-69			

Other Chapter Resources

Student Edition
Algebra in Action, p. 293
Biography, p. 296
Mid-Chapter Quiz, p. 305
Challenge, pp. 308, 321
Exploration, pp. 314, 318
Team Problem Solving, p. 317
Academic Skills Test, p. 325

Teacher Resource Package
Interdisciplinary Activity, p. 8
Application Worksheet, p. 23
Cooperative Problem Solving, p. 38
Multicultural Activity, p. 53
Fun Activities, pp. 70, 71
Technology Worksheets, pp. 8, 23, 38
Lab Manual, pp. 48-50
Quizzes(2), p. 70
Class Review Game

Software
Test Generator

available for Apple and IBM

Enhancing the Chapter

Some of the blackline masters for enhancing this chapter are shown below.

Applications, p. 23

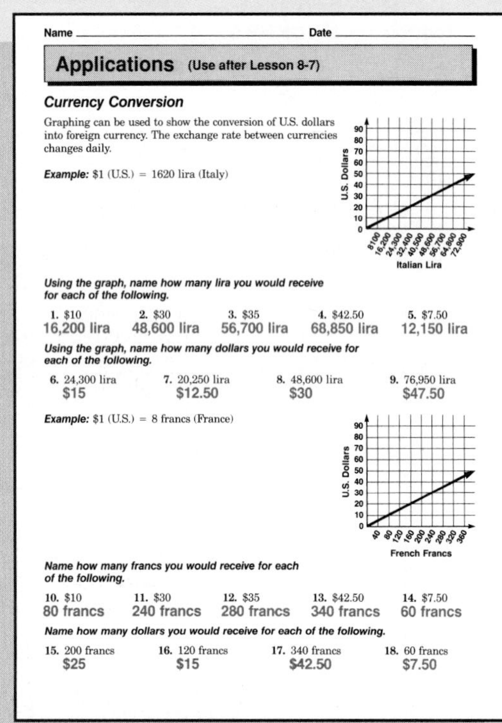

Name ______________________ Date ______________

Applications (Use after Lesson 8-7)

Currency Conversion

Graphing can be used to show the conversion of U.S. dollars into foreign currency. The exchange rate between currencies changes daily.

Example: \$1 (U.S.) = 1620 lira (Italy)

Using the graph, name how many lira you would receive for each of the following.

1. \$10 16,200 lira
2. \$30 48,600 lira
3. \$35 56,700 lira
4. \$42.50 68,850 lira
5. \$7.50 12,150 lira

Using the graph, name how many dollars you would receive for each of the following.

6. 24,300 lira \$15
7. 20,250 lira \$12.50
8. 48,600 lira \$30
9. 76,950 lira \$47.50

Example: \$1 (U.S.) = 8 francs (France)

Name how many francs you would receive for each of the following.

10. \$10 80 francs
11. \$30 240 francs
12. \$35 280 francs
13. \$42.50 340 francs
14. \$7.50 60 francs

Name how many dollars you would receive for each of the following.

15. 200 francs \$25
16. 120 francs \$15
17. 340 francs \$42.50
18. 60 francs \$7.50

The **Activity Masters Booklet** contains the page shown above.

Interdisciplinary Activity, p. 8

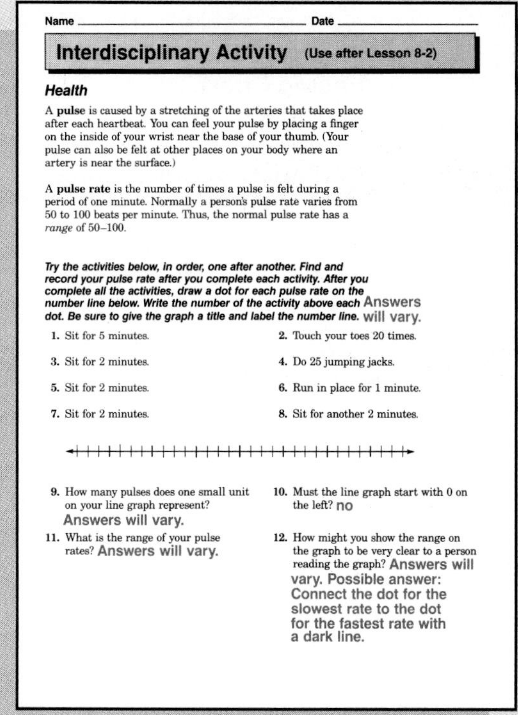

Name ______________________ Date ______________

Interdisciplinary Activity (Use after Lesson 8-2)

Health

A **pulse** is caused by a stretching of the arteries that takes place after each heartbeat. You can feel your pulse by placing a finger on the inside of your wrist near the base of your thumb. (Your pulse can also be felt at other places on your body where an artery is near the surface.)

A **pulse rate** is the number of times a pulse is felt during a period of one minute. Normally a person's pulse rate varies from 50 to 100 beats per minute. Thus, the normal pulse rate has a *range* of 50–100.

Try the activities below, in order, one after another. Find and record your pulse rate after you complete each activity. After you complete all the activities, draw a dot for each pulse rate on the number line below. Write the number of the activity above each dot. Be sure to give the graph a title and label the number line. Answers will vary.

1. Sit for 5 minutes.
2. Touch your toes 20 times.
3. Sit for 2 minutes.
4. Do 25 jumping jacks.
5. Sit for 2 minutes.
6. Run in place for 1 minute.
7. Sit for 2 minutes.
8. Sit for another 2 minutes.

9. How many pulses does one small unit on your line graph represent? Answers will vary.
10. Must the line graph start with 0 on the left? no
11. What is the range of your pulse rates? Answers will vary.
12. How might you show the range on the graph to be very clear to a person reading the graph? Answers will vary. Possible answer: Connect the dot for the slowest rate to the dot for the fastest rate with a dark line.

The **Activity Masters Booklet** contains the page shown above.

Models and Manipulatives

Students will locate an ordered pair on a coordinate axes. Reassign students to new seats by using masking tape on the floor to make the axes of a coordinate graph. As students enter the room, each one can be given an ordered pair and be asked to locate their new seat.

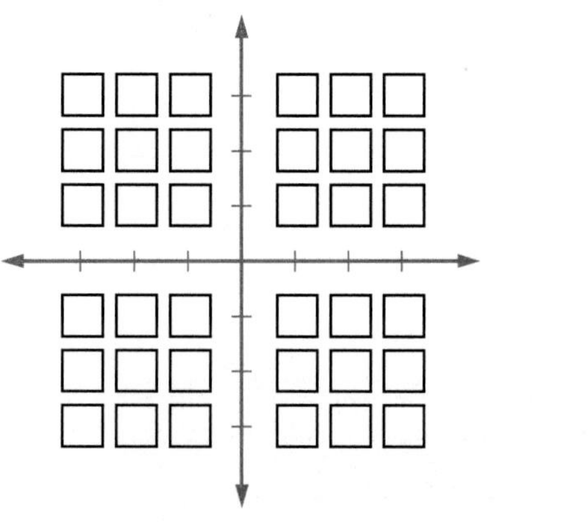

Multicultural Activity

Sehi Kowa (1642-1708), known as "the sacred mathematician", was a Japanese mathematician who did much to popularize and change the role of mathematics in Japan from an art form practiced by intellectuals to a science. Some of his accomplishments were to create a new mathematical notation system, the notation of a discriminant, a definition of the circumference of a circle, and he obtained a value of π correct to eighteen decimal places.

Have students research and write a paragraph on the contributions made by other Far Eastern mathematicians.

Cooperative Learning

The following activity is provided in the **Activity Masters Booklet.**

Cooperative Problem Solving, p. 38

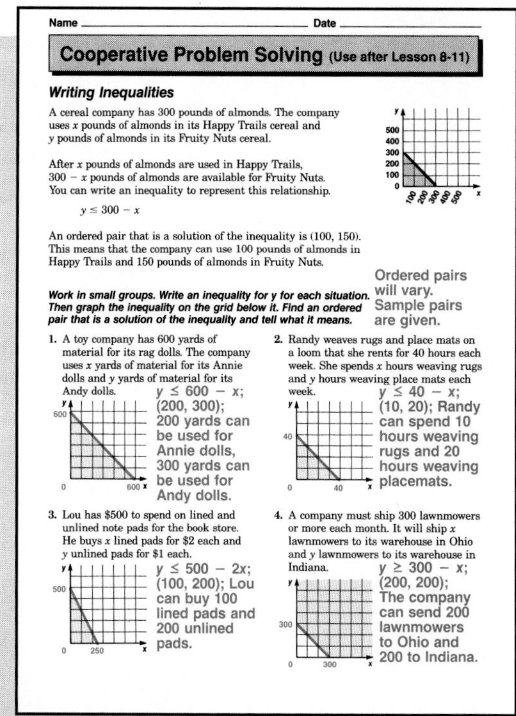

Name ______________________ Date ______________

Cooperative Problem Solving (Use after Lesson 8-11)

Writing Inequalities

A cereal company has 300 pounds of almonds. The company uses x pounds of almonds in its Happy Trails cereal and y pounds of almonds in its Fruity Nuts cereal.

After x pounds of almonds are used in Happy Trails, $300 - x$ pounds of almonds are available for Fruity Nuts. You can write an inequality to represent this relationship.

$$y \leq 300 - x$$

An ordered pair that is a solution of the inequality is (100, 150). This means that the company can use 100 pounds of almonds in Happy Trails and 150 pounds of almonds in Fruity Nuts.

Work in small groups. Write an inequality for y for each situation. Then graph the inequality on the grid below it. Find an ordered pair that is a solution of the inequality and tell what it means. Ordered pairs will vary. Sample pairs are given.

1. A toy company has 600 yards of material for its rag dolls. The company uses x yards of material for its Annie dolls and y yards of material for its Andy dolls. $y \leq 600 - x$; (200, 300); 200 yards can be used for Annie dolls, 300 yards can be used for Andy dolls.
2. Randy weaves rugs and place mats on a loom that she rents for 40 hours each week. She spends x hours weaving rugs and y hours weaving place mats each week. $y \leq 40 - x$; (10, 20); Randy can spend 10 hours weaving rugs and 20 hours weaving placemats.
3. Lou has $500 to spend on lined and unlined note pads for the book store. He buys x lined pads for $2 each and y unlined pads for $1 each. $y \leq 500 - 2x$; (100, 200); Lou can buy 100 lined pads and 200 unlined pads.
4. A company must ship 300 lawnmowers or more each month. It will ship x lawnmowers to its warehouse in Ohio and y lawnmowers to its warehouse in Indiana. $y \geq 300 - x$; (200, 200); The company can send 200 lawnmowers to Ohio and 200 to Indiana.

Cooperative Problem Solving

Have students work in groups of two to four. Make observations on the following problem. This should be used after students learn to graph a linear equation. Give students three pieces of graph paper and have them graph the following equations on the same coordinate axes. Then ask them to list all observations.

Sheet 1	Sheet 2	Sheet 3
$y = x$	$y = ^-x$	$y = 2x - 4$
$y = 2x$	$y = ^-2x$	$y = 2x + 4$
$y = 5x$	$y = ^-5x$	$y = 2x - 6$
$y = 8x$	$y = ^-8x$	$y = 2x + 8$

Interactive Bulletin Board

Statistics Connection

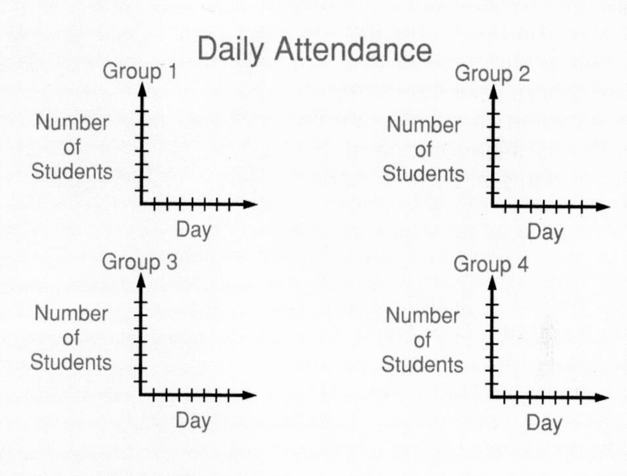

Purpose Provide practice in plotting ordered pairs.

How to Use It Divide students into four groups. Have each group determine and plot the daily attendance of a class in the school on a daily basis. The graph may not be a linear graph; but the practice will demonstrate the concept of plotting ordered pairs.

Outside Resources

Books/Periodicals
Professional Standards for Teaching Mathematics, NCTM

Films/Videotapes
Graphing Inequalities, Silver Burdet

Software
Green Globs and Graphing Equations, Sunburst

Technology

There are three pages in the ***Technology Masters Booklet*** that involve technology with concepts in this chapter. One page involves calculators and one page has a problem that can be solved using the BASIC program that is provided. Students should evaluate the information they obtain from running the program and solve a similar problem by extending the program.

Using the Chapter Opener

Transparency 8-0 is available in the Transparency Package. It provides a full-color visual and motivational activity that you can use to engage students in the mathematical content of the chapter.

Using Manipulatives

Have students place the upper right-hand corner of a piece of paper on the lower left-hand corner of the graph. Tell students to slide the paper to the right, keeping the top of their paper on the bottom line of the graph, until the corner is half way between 14 and 16. While keeping the right-hand edge at 15, have the students slide their paper up until the corner touches Jamie's graph. The top of their paper should now be a little over 22 on the left scale of the graph. Explain to students that they have just estimated how much money Jamie raised. Have students repeat the procedure to find how much money Kenji raised. **Kenji raised the most money; $28.**

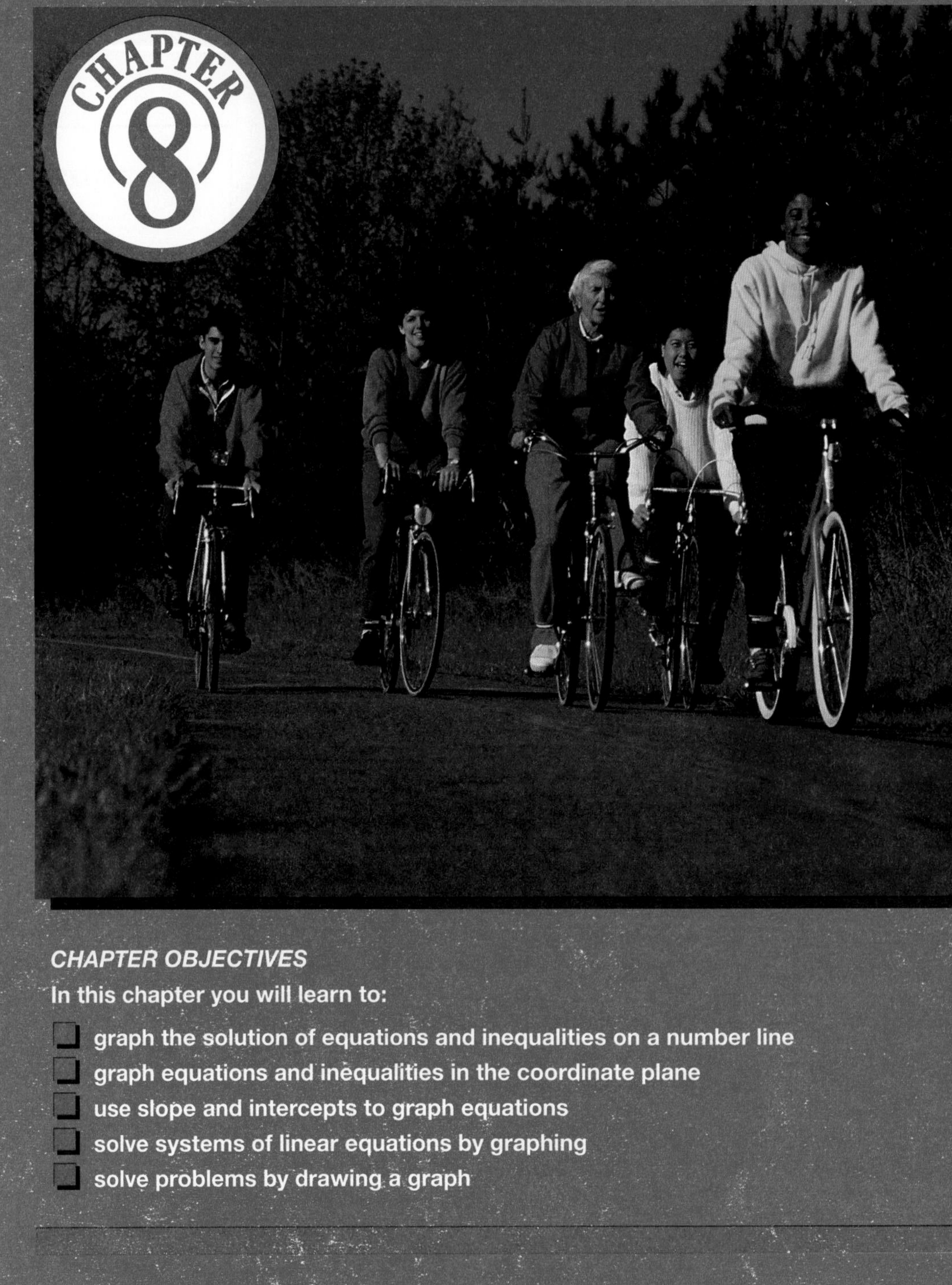

CHAPTER OBJECTIVES

In this chapter you will learn to:

- graph the solution of equations and inequalities on a number line
- graph equations and inequalities in the coordinate plane
- use slope and intercepts to graph equations
- solve systems of linear equations by graphing
- solve problems by drawing a graph

Graphing Equations and Inequalities

Imagine that your math class decides to participate in a Bike-A-Thon to raise money for a local charity. You all seek pledges; that is, promises from community businesses to give the Bike-A-Thon donations. Three of your classmates each convince a business to sponsor them for different amounts.

Jamie:	$1.50 for each kilometer
Kenji:	$2.00 for each kilometer
Enrique:	a $15 contribution

On the day of the Bike-A-Thon, Jamie rode 15 kilometers, Kenji rode 14 kilometers and Enrique rode 10 kilometers.

Explain how you can use the graph to determine who raised the most money. See margin.

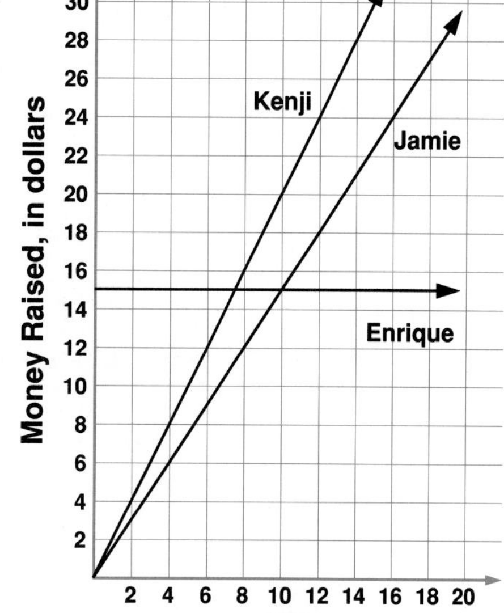

Bike-A-Thon Pledges

Language Connection

Class Project

Find examples of graphs in a newspaper or magazine. Write a paragraph that explains the purpose of the graph.

Language Connection

The purpose of a graph is to provide information at a glance. This information can show a performance history or a breakdown of a general category into its specific parts. *USA Today* is an excellent source for at least four 'creative' graphs a day.

Looking Ahead

You may want to have the following materials available to use in this chapter.

Algebra in Action, p. 289
- rectangular picture frames
- metric rulers
- scissors

Explorations, pp. 310, 314
- graphing calculators

Lesson Notes 8-1

5-Minute Check
(over Chapter 7)

Solve each equation or inequality.

1. $5m + 6 = 21$ 3
2. $6q + 13 = 29 - 2q$ 2
3. $12a - 4 < 44$ $a < 4$
4. $16y - 23 > -13 + 18y$ $y < -5$

Transparency 8-1 contains the 5-Minute Check and a teaching aid for this lesson.

1 FOCUS

The purpose of this lesson is to develop a procedure for graphing the solution set of an equation on a number line.

2 TEACH

Chalkboard Examples

- *For Example 1*
  Solve $x + 5 = -2$ and graph the solution. $x = -7$

-8 -7 -6 -5 -4 -3 -2 -1 0 1 2

Practice Masters Booklet, p. 71

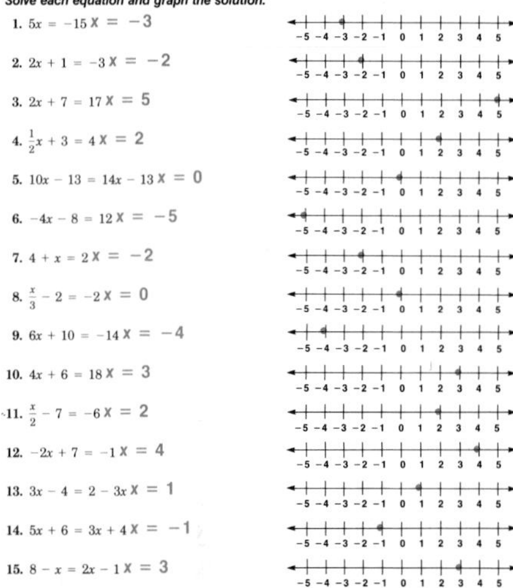

Name ______ Date ______

Practice Worksheet 8-1

Number Lines

Solve each equation and graph the solution.

1. $5x = -15$ $x = -3$
2. $2x + 1 = -3$ $x = -2$
3. $2x + 7 = 17$ $x = 5$
4. $\frac{1}{2}x + 3 = 4$ $x = 2$
5. $10x - 13 = 14x - 13$ $x = 0$
6. $-4x - 8 = 12$ $x = -5$
7. $4 + x = 2$ $x = -2$
8. $\frac{x}{3} - 2 = -2$ $x = 0$
9. $6x + 10 = -14$ $x = -4$
10. $4x + 6 = 18$ $x = 3$
11. $\frac{x}{2} - 7 = -6$ $x = 2$
12. $-2x + 7 = -1$ $x = 4$
13. $3x - 4 = 2 - 3x$ $x = 1$
14. $5x + 6 = 3x + 4$ $x = -1$
15. $8 - x = 2x - 1$ $x = 3$
16. $3 - 2x = x + 18$ $x = -5$
17. $3x + 11 = 17 + 5x$ $x = -3$

8-1 Equations and the Number Line

Objective:
Graph the solution of an equation on a number line.

Key Terms:
coordinate
graph

When you hear the word *graph,* what do you think of? You may think of a bar graph or a circle graph. The purpose of these graphs is to display data in a concise way. In algebra, we will study other kinds of graphs. These graphs will display data about equations and inequalities.

Let's start by assigning a number to each point on a line. The result is called a number line. Recall that the number is the coordinate of the point. The **coordinate** of a point tells its *distance* and *direction* from the 0-point of the line. The dot marking the point is called the **graph** of the number.

How would you use a number line to graph the number of United States Senators? Since there are 100 Senators, draw a number line and mark a dot on 100.

What do the arrowheads on each end of the number line indicate? **The line continues.**

You can also show the solution of an equation on a number line.

Examples

1 Solve $x + 3 = -1$ and graph the solution.

$$\begin{aligned} x + 3 &= -1 \\ x + 3 - 3 &= -1 - 3 \\ x &= -4 \end{aligned}$$

Check: $x + 3 = -1$

$-4 + 3 \stackrel{?}{=} -1$

$-1 = -1$ ✓

The solution is -4.

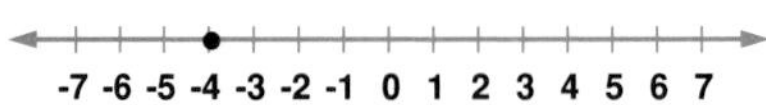

2 Solve $2x + 1 = 4$ and graph the solution.

$$\begin{aligned} 2x + 1 &= 4 \\ 2x + 1 - 1 &= 4 - 1 \\ 2x &= 3 \\ \frac{2x}{2} &= \frac{3}{2} \\ x &= \frac{3}{2} \end{aligned}$$

Check: $2x + 1 = 4$

$2(\frac{3}{2}) + 1 \stackrel{?}{=} 4$

$3 + 1 \stackrel{?}{=} 4$

$4 = 4$ ✓

The solution is $\frac{3}{2}$.

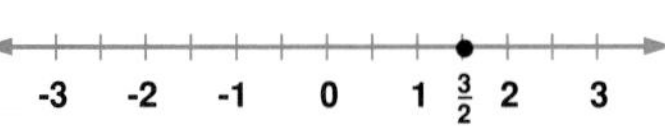

Bell Ringer

Name the integer that comes before and after these integers.

1. 8 7,9
2. -8 -9, -7
3. 0 -1,1
4. -13 -14, -12
5. -7069 -7070, -7068
6. -1099 -1100, -1098

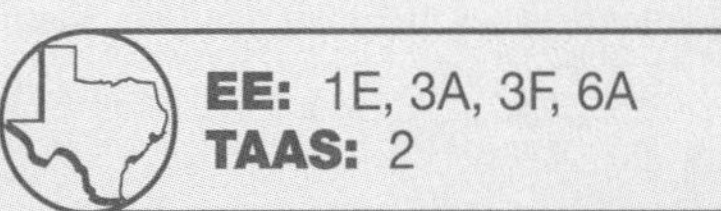

EE: 1E, 3A, 3F, 6A
TAAS: 2

Reteaching Masters Booklet, p. 64

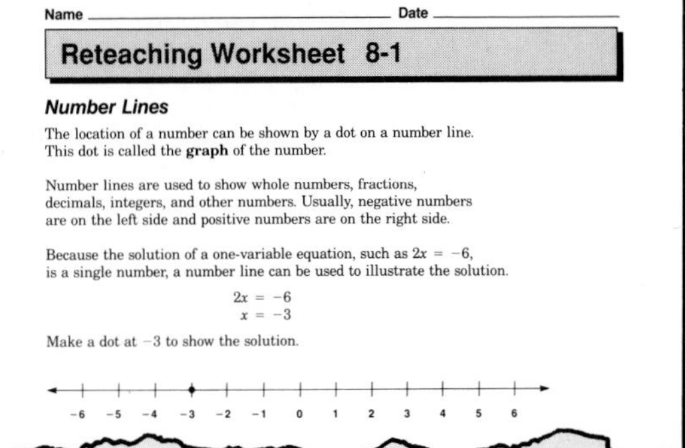

Name ______ Date ______

Reteaching Worksheet 8-1

Number Lines

The location of a number can be shown by a dot on a number line. This dot is called the **graph** of the number.

Number lines are used to show whole numbers, fractions, decimals, integers, and other numbers. Usually, negative numbers are on the left side and positive numbers are on the right side.

Because the solution of a one-variable equation, such as $2x = -6$, is a single number, a number line can be used to illustrate the solution.

$2x = -6$
$x = -3$

Make a dot at -3 to show the solution.

-6 -5 -4 -3 -2 -1 0 1 2 3 4 5 6

Checking for Understanding
For graphs to Exercises 1-8, see Solutions Manual.

Communicating Algebra

Draw a graph for each situation.

1. There are 435 members in the House of Representatives.
2. The low temperature last night was -5°F.
3. You wrote a check for \$10.50 yesterday.
4. You bought 6 tickets for the concert.
5. Gasoline costs \$1.29 per gallon.

Guided Practice

Solve each equation and graph the solution.

6. $x + 3 = 5$ **2**
7. $-5y = 10$ **-2**
8. $a + 5\frac{2}{3} = 9\frac{1}{3}$ **$3\frac{2}{3}$**

Exercises
For graphs to exercises 9-21, see Solutions Manual.

Independent Practice

Solve each equation and graph the solution.

9. $2x - 1 = 5$ **3**
10. $\frac{a}{3} = -1$ **-3**
11. $3x - 1 = 4$ **$\frac{5}{3}$**
12. $n + 3.5 = 4$ **0.5**
13. $y = -5 + -3$ **-8**
14. $2z - 6.5 = -1.5$ **2.5**
15. $x - 1.25 = 3.75$ **5**
16. $-7 + x = 9$ **16**
17. $2.5a = -15$ **-6**
18. $5y + 2y - 3 = 18$ **3**
19. $2a + a + 5 + 1 = 18$ **4**
20. $4x - 7 = 2x + 15$ **11**
21. $1 + 10x = 8x - 3$ **-2**

Choose the equation whose solution is graphed.

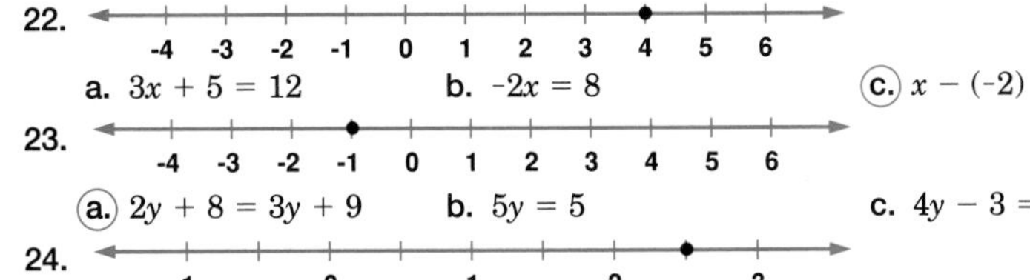

22. a. $3x + 5 = 12$ b. $-2x = 8$ **(c.)** $x - (-2) = 6$
23. **(a.)** $2y + 8 = 3y + 9$ b. $5y = 5$ c. $4y - 3 = 1$
24. -1 0 1 2 3
    a. $7 + m = 4.5$ b. $2m - (-2) = 3$ **(c.)** $6m = 15$

Mixed Review

25. Rewrite the expression $12 + (7 + m)$ using the associative property of addition. (Lesson 1-3) **$(12 + 7) + m$**
26. Write the next term in the geometric sequence 1, -3, 9, -27. . . . (Lesson 6-10) **81**
27. Write an inequality for the sentence: *The product of 6 and a number increased by 11 is at most 35.* (Lesson 7-6) **$6x + 11 \leq 35$**

Application

28. **Health** A thermometer can be thought of as a physical representation of a number line. A healthy person has a body temperature of 98.6° on a Fahrenheit thermometer. Graph this number on a number line. **See Solutions Manual.**

Critical Thinking

29. **Make Up a Problem** Write an equation whose solution is graphed on the number line below. Then write a different equation that has the same solution as the first equation. **Sample answers: $x + 2 = 2$; $3x = 0$**

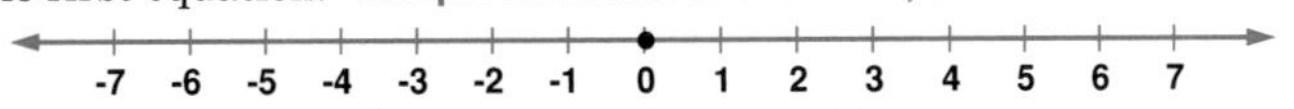

Wrap-Up

30. **Research** Find the coordinate for the normal body temperature on a Celsius thermometer. Then graph it on a number line. **37°C; See Solutions Manual for graph.**

- *For Example 2*
  Solve $3x + 2 = 6$ and graph the solution. $x = \frac{4}{3}$

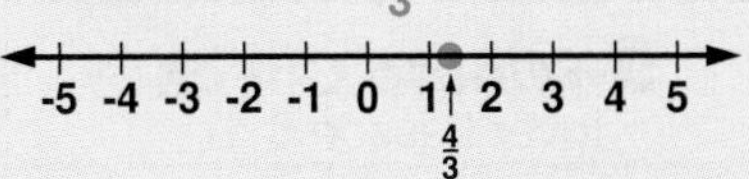

3 PRACTICE/APPLY

Checking the Concept

Writing Connection Have students give a written description of the graphs of Exercises 6-8.

Independent Practice

Homework Assignment	
Basic	9-23 odd, 25-30
Average	10-24 even, 25-30
Honors	15-21, 23-30

CLOSE

Assessment Option

Writing Have students write a description of the graph of the solution to an equation with one variable.

Enrichment Masters Booklet, **p. 64**

Name ______________________ Date ______________

Enrichment Worksheet 8-1

Density of Rational Numbers

Shown below is a portion of the number line containing all points from 0 to $\frac{1}{4}$. The coordinate of point F is $\frac{1}{8}$, which is half of $\frac{1}{4}$.

A B C D E F G H I J
0 $\frac{1}{16}$ $\frac{3}{32}$ $\frac{1}{8}$ $\frac{3}{16}$ $\frac{1}{4}$

The coordinate of point C is $\frac{1}{16}$, which is half of $\frac{1}{8}$.

Between any two rational numbers, there is an unlimited number of other rational numbers. This property is called the **density property** of rational numbers.

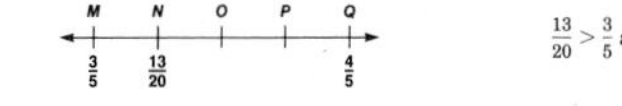

$\frac{13}{20} > \frac{3}{5}$ and $\frac{13}{20} < \frac{4}{5}$

The easiest point to locate between two given points is the point halfway between those two points. This point is half the sum of the two coordinates.

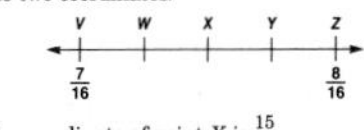

$\frac{1}{2}\left(\frac{7}{16} + \frac{8}{16}\right) \rightarrow \frac{1}{2}\left(\frac{15}{16}\right) \rightarrow \frac{15}{32}$

The coordinate of point X is $\frac{15}{32}$.

Using the number lines above, state the coordinates of each point. Assume that each point is halfway between the points to the left and right.

1. B $\frac{1}{32}$
2. D $\frac{5}{64}$
3. G $\frac{5}{32}$
4. I $\frac{7}{32}$
5. O $\frac{7}{10}$
6. P $\frac{3}{4}$
7. W $\frac{29}{64}$
8. Y $\frac{31}{64}$

Name the rational number that is halfway between the two given numbers on a number line.

9. $\frac{1}{2}$ and $\frac{3}{4}$ $\frac{5}{8}$
10. 0 and 5 $2\frac{1}{2}$
11. 4 and $5\frac{1}{4}$ $4\frac{5}{8}$
12. $1\frac{1}{2}$ and $\frac{5}{8}$ $1\frac{1}{16}$
13. $\frac{1}{2}$ and $\frac{2}{3}$ $\frac{7}{12}$
14. $\frac{7}{8}$ and $\frac{8}{9}$ $\frac{127}{144}$

Alternate Strategies: Extending the Lesson

Enrichment

Using Cooperative Groups Students write problems that can be translated into equations. Have groups exchange problems, translate them into equations, solve the equations, and graph the solutions.

Cooperative Learning

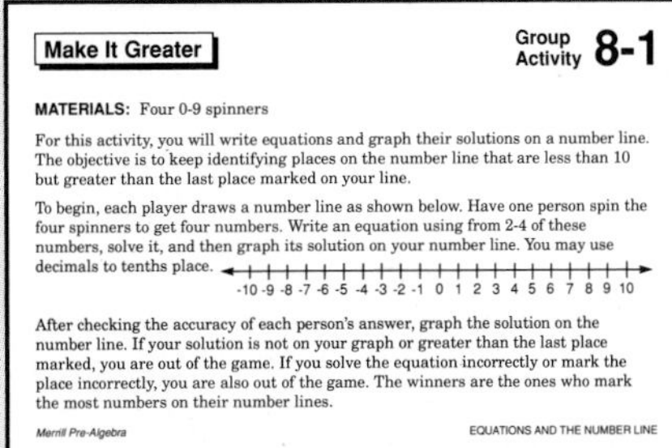

Make It Greater Group Activity **8-1**

MATERIALS: Four 0-9 spinners

For this activity, you will write equations and graph their solutions on a number line. The objective is to keep identifying places on the number line that are less than 10 but greater than the last place marked on your line.

To begin, each player draws a number line as shown below. Have one person spin the four spinners to get four numbers. Write an equation using from 2-4 of these numbers, solve it, and then graph its solution on your number line. You may use decimals to tenths place.

-10 -9 -8 -7 -6 -5 -4 -3 -2 -1 0 1 2 3 4 5 6 7 8 9 10

After checking the accuracy of each person's answer, graph the solution on the number line. If your solution is not on your graph or greater than the last place marked, you are out of the game. If you solve the equation incorrectly or mark the place incorrectly, you are also out of the game. The winners are the ones who mark the most numbers on their number lines.

Merrill Pre-Algebra EQUATIONS AND THE NUMBER LINE

5-Minute Check
(over Lesson 8-1)

Solve each equation and graph each solution.

1. $5x - 3 = 17$ $x = 4$
-2 0 2 4 6
2. $4m - 2.8 = 5.2$ $m = 2$
-4 -2 0 2 4

Transparency 8-2 contains the 5-Minute Check and a teaching aid for this lesson.

1 FOCUS

The purpose of this lesson is to develop a procedure for students to use when graphing an inequality on a number line.

Motivating the Lesson

Play "Graph my number" instead of "Guess my number." For example, say, "My number is graphed to the left of 3," or "My number is graphed either to the right of 9 or at 9." Then ask students to graph the number.

2 TEACH

Using Models Copy the chart below. Have students match the inequalities with the correct graph.

Inequality	Solution
$x > 1$	-2 -1 0 1 2 3 4
$y < -2$	-3 -2 -1 0 1 2 3
$a - 1 = -3$	-3 -2 -1 0 1 2 3
$b \leq 0$	-3 -2 -1 0 1 2 3
$z - 2 \geq 1$	-3 -2 -1 0 1 2 3

Chalkboard Examples

- *For Example 1*
  Solve $2y + 7 \leq 19$ and graph the solution. $y \leq 6$

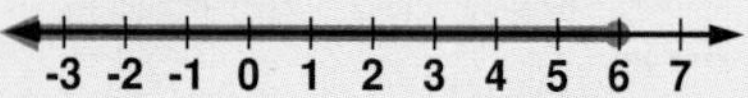

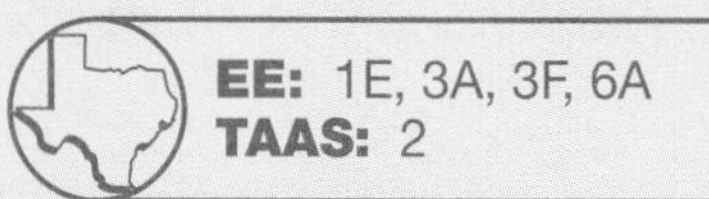

EE: 1E, 3A, 3F, 6A
TAAS: 2

8-2 Inequalities and the Number Line

Objective:
Graph the solutions of an inequality on a number line.

If a driver operates a car on an interstate highway at a speed that is greater than 65 mph, there is a risk of getting a speeding ticket. You can describe this situation algebraically by writing an inequality.

Suppose s represents the speed of the car. Then the inequality $s > 65$ is true for all values of s that are greater than 65. The solutions are graphed on the number line shown below.

Why is 65 not a solution of $s > 65$?
65 is not greater than 65.

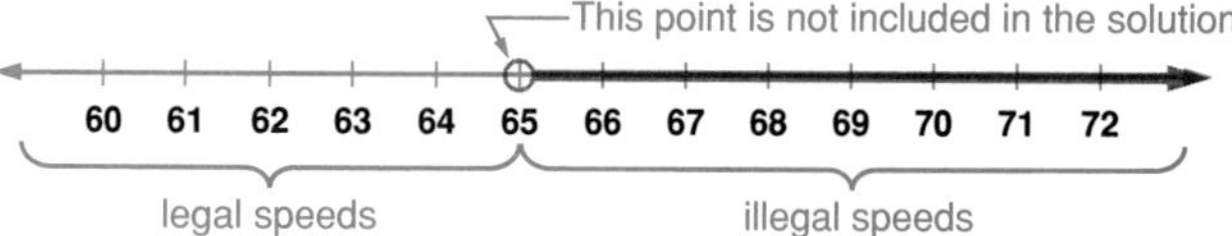

Now let's consider another situation. Suppose the driver always operates the car at speeds that are less than or equal to 65 mph. The inequality $s \leq 65$ describes these speeds. The graph of $s \leq 65$ is shown below.

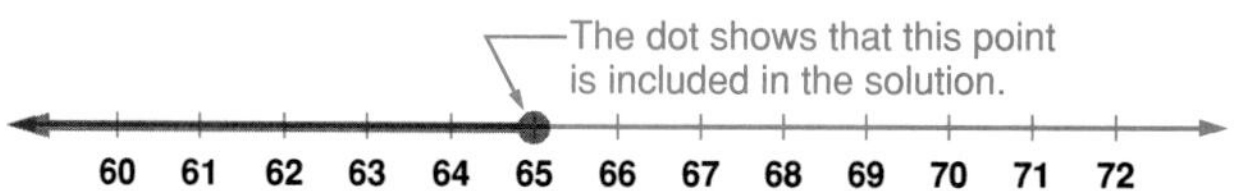

Just as you can solve and graph equations, you can solve and graph inequalities.

Examples

1 Solve $3x + 6 \leq 15$ and graph the solution.

$3x + 6 \leq 15$

$3x + 6 - 6 \leq 15 - 6$ Subtract 6 from each side.

$3x \leq 9$

$\frac{3x}{3} \leq \frac{9}{3}$ Divide each side by 3.

$x \leq 3$ The number 3 or any number less than 3 can be substituted for x to make $3x + 6 \leq 15$ a true statement.

-8 -7 -6 -5 -4 -3 -2 -1 0 1 2 3 4 5 6 7 8

How can you check your answer?
Substitute any number less than or equal to 3 for x in the original equation.

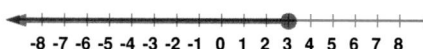

Bell Ringer

The Heel-N-Toe shoe store sells athletic socks for \$1.45 per pair. José can spend no more than \$10. How many pairs of socks can he buy? 6

2 **Solve $-3x - 2 > 10$ and graph the solution.**

$-3x - 2 > 10$

$-3x - 2 + 2 > 10 + 2$ Add 2 to each side.

$-3x > 12$

$\frac{-3x}{-3} < \frac{12}{-3}$ Divide each side by -3 and reverse the order symbol.

$x < -4$ Any number less than -4 is a solution.

Why do you need to reverse the order symbol when you divide by -3? **The order symbol is always reversed when dividing by a negative number.**

-10 -9 -8 -7 -6 -5 -4 -3 -2 -1 0 1 2 3 4 5 6 7 8 9 10

Notice that -4 is *not* a solution.

3 **Solve $3y - 4.7 \geq -3.2$ and graph the solution.**

$3y - 4.7 \geq -3.2$

$3y - 4.7 + 4.7 \geq -3.2 + 4.7$ Add 4.7 to each side.

$3y \geq 1.5$

$\frac{3y}{3} \geq \frac{1.5}{3}$ Divide each side by 3.

$y \geq 0.5$ Any number greater than or equal to 0.5 is a solution.

Is 0.4999 a solution? **no**

-2 -1 0 0.5 1 2

Checking for Understanding

For graphs to Exercises 1-5, see Solutions Manual.

Communicating Algebra

Draw a graph for each inequality.

1. He is more than 60 inches tall.
2. Juan spent less than \$5.50.
3. The flight of the glider lasted more than 15 minutes.
4. She drove at least 100 miles today.
5. Karen earned \$20 or more.

Guided Practice

Write an inequality that describes each graph.

6. **$x > 0$** (-7 -6 -5 -4 -3 -2 -1 0 1 2 3 4 5 6 7)

7. **$x < 1$** (-7 -6 -5 -4 -3 -2 -1 0 1 2 3 4 5 6 7)

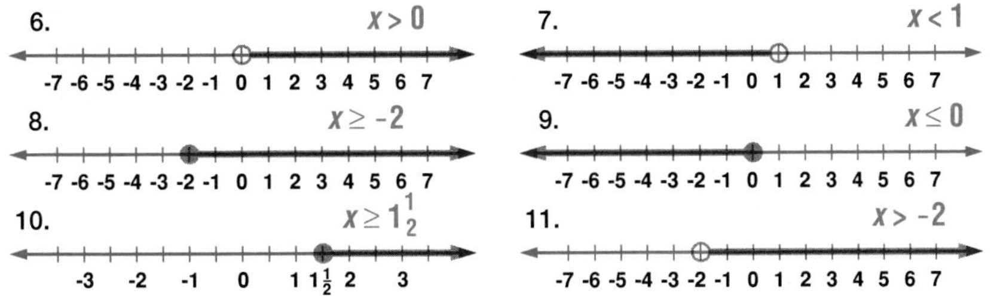

8. **$x \geq -2$** (-7 -6 -5 -4 -3 -2 -1 0 1 2 3 4 5 6 7)

9. **$x \leq 0$** (-7 -6 -5 -4 -3 -2 -1 0 1 2 3 4 5 6 7)

10. **$x \geq 1\frac{1}{2}$** (-3 -2 -1 0 1 $1\frac{1}{2}$ 2 3)

11. **$x > -2$** (-7 -6 -5 -4 -3 -2 -1 0 1 2 3 4 5 6 7)

Solve each inequality and graph the solution.

12. $n + 3 \geq 8$ **$n \geq 5$**
13. $a - 5 \leq -5$ **$a \leq 0$**
14. $b + 8 > 9$ **$b > 1$**

For graphs to Exercises 12-14, see Solutions Manual.

- *For Example 2*
  Solve $-4y - 3 > 9$ and graph the solution. **$y \leq -3$**

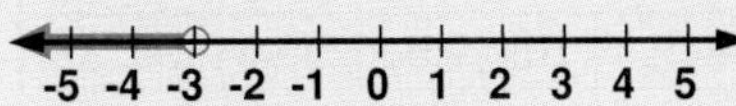

- *For Example 3*
  Solve $5m - 2.6 \geq 4.9$ and graph the solution. **$m \geq 1.5$**

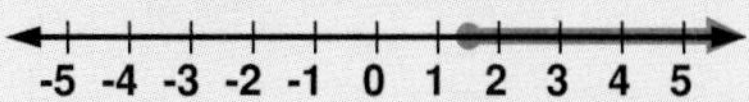

3 PRACTICE/APPLY

Checking the Concept

Using Manipulatives Write an inequality on several 3 × 5 cards. Prepare enough to distribute to half of the class. Graph the solution of each inequality on separate cards and distribute to the other half of the class. Have each student with an inequality card find the student with the corresponding graph of the solution to their inequality.

Error Analysis

Watch for students who are confused by the differences in graphing < and ≤, and > and ≥.

Prevent by emphasizing that the interior of the plotting point represents a number. If it is filled in, there is a number. If the point is not filled in, there is no number represented.

Practice Masters Booklet, **p. 72**

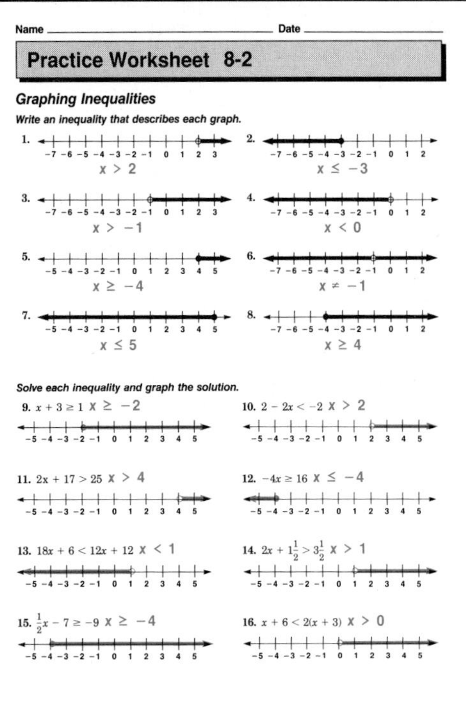

Name ______ Date ______

Practice Worksheet 8-2

Graphing Inequalities

Write an inequality that describes each graph.

1. $x > 2$
2. $x \leq -3$
3. $x > -1$
4. $x < 0$
5. $x \geq -4$
6. $x \neq -1$
7. $x \leq 5$
8. $x \geq 4$

Solve each inequality and graph the solution.

9. $x + 3 \geq 1$ $x \geq -2$
10. $2 - 2x < -2$ $x > 2$
11. $2x + 17 > 25$ $x > 4$
12. $-4x \geq 16$ $x \leq -4$
13. $18x + 6 < 12x + 12$ $x < 1$
14. $2x + 1\frac{1}{2} > 3\frac{1}{2}$ $x > 1$
15. $\frac{1}{2}x - 7 \geq -9$ $x \geq -4$
16. $x + 6 < 2(x + 3)$ $x > 0$

Alternate Strategies: Reteaching the Lesson

Reteaching Activity

Using Models Graph the solution to several simple inequalities on the chalkboard or overhead. Have students choose numbers from the unshaded and shaded parts of each graph and substitute them in the inequality to check that the solution is graphed correctly.

Reteaching Masters Booklet, **p. 65**

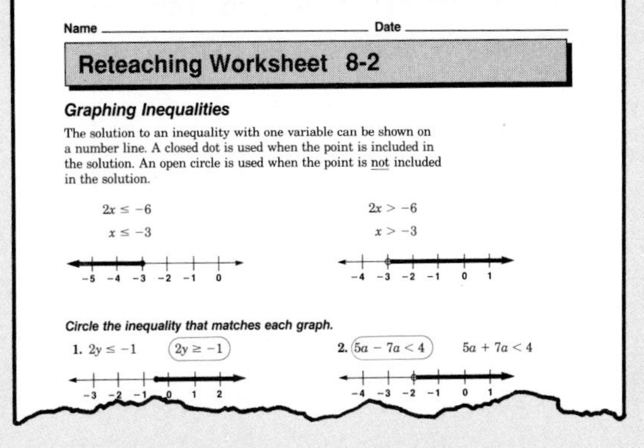

Name ______ Date ______

Reteaching Worksheet 8-2

Graphing Inequalities

The solution to an inequality with one variable can be shown on a number line. A closed dot is used when the point is included in the solution. An open circle is used when the point is not included in the solution.

$2x \leq -6$ / $x \leq -3$ (-5 -4 -3 -2 -1 0)

$2x > -6$ / $x > -3$ (-4 -3 -2 -1 0 1)

Circle the inequality that matches each graph.

1. $2y \leq -1$ ($2y \geq -1$)
2. ($5a - 7a < 4$) $5a + 7a < 4$

Independent Practice

Homework Assignment	
Basic	15-29 odd, 30-34, 36, 37
Average	16-20 even, 30-37
Honors	23-37, 30-37

4 CLOSE

Assessment Option

Speaking Have students state what the following graphs represent.

1. 

All numbers greater than or equal to negative two.

2. 

All numbers less than three.

Enrichment Masters Booklet, **p. 65**

Name ______________ Date ______________

Enrichment Worksheet 8-2

Compound Sentences

Example: $x > 3$ and $x \le 5$

Think: To be a solution, values must be both greater than 3 and less than or equal to 5.

Example: $x > 4$ or $x < 1$

Think: To be a solution, values need only be greater than 4 or less than 1.

Graph the solution set of each compound sentence.

1. $r \ge 0$ or $r \le 3$
2. $d > 3$ or $d < -3$
3. $m > 0$ and $m \le 3$
4. $x > 1$ and $x \le -1$ Ø
5. $b \ge 4$ and $b \le 4$
6. $q \ge 1$ or $q < -2$
7. $0 < p$ and $-3 < p$
8. $2 \le w$ or $-1 \ge w$
9. $x + 1 < 4$ and $x - (-1) > -1$
10. $-3 \le 2m + 1$ and $2m + 1 \le 7$
11. $r + 1 < 2r - 3$ and $2r - 3 < r + 2$
12. $2t + 1 > 7$ and $4t - 5 < 7$ Ø
13. $-3q - 2 < 1$ and $7 - 4q > -1$
14. $p + 2 \ge 4$ or $p + 5 \le 7$

Exercises

For graphs to Exercises 15-29, see Solutions Manual.

Independent Practice

Solve each inequality and graph the solution. 23. $m < -3$

15. $x - 1.3 < 2.7$ $x < 4.0$
16. $y + 2\frac{1}{2} \ge 4$ $y \ge 1\frac{1}{2}$
17. $2x - 1 \le 3$ $y \le 2$
18. $3y - 5 < 4$ $y < 3$
19. $3x + 3.2 > 4.7$ $x > 0.5$
20. $-3a \ge 18$ $a \le -6$
21. $5c > -20$ $c > -4$
22. $\frac{1}{2}a - 5 \ge -7$ $a \ge -4$
23. $-4m - 3\frac{2}{3} > 8\frac{1}{3}$
24. $13a - 12 > 11a + 4$ $a > 8$
25. $9r + 3 < 6r + 6$ $r < 1$
26. $8n + 10 > 7n + 5$ $n > -5$
27. $3(x + 6) > 2x + 12$ $x > -6$

Logical Reasoning

28. Graph the solutions for the compound inequality $y < -1$ or $y > 3$. Remember that an *or* sentence is true if either part is true.
29. Graph the solutions for the compound inequality $x > -5$ and $x \le 4$. An *and* sentence is true only if both parts are true.

Mixed Review

30. Simplify $|14| - |-9|$. (Lesson 2-1) 5
31. *True* or *false:* $-3\frac{1}{2} \ge -3.2$. (Lesson 6-12) false
32. **Business** A plumber charges $35 to make a house call. For each hour of labor, he charges $25. If he works 3 hours, how much will he charge? (Lesson 7-3) $110
33. Solve the equation $-3m - 3.5 = 14.5$ and graph the solution. (Lesson 8-1) -6; See the Solutions Manual for graph.

Applications

34. **Business** A bookstore makes a profit of $5 on each two-volume set of books sold. The owner of the store wants to make a profit of at least $150 on these books. How many sets of books should the owner sell to meet her goal? Write your answer as an inequality. $x \ge 30$
35. **Sports** Cecilia has a total score of 45.9 in five trials of a skating competition. The leading opponent has scores of 9.1, 8.7, 9.5, and 9.3 and has one more trial. What can you say about Cecilia's opponent's score in the last trial if Cecilia wins first place? Write your answer as an inequality. $x < 9.3$

Critical Thinking

36. Suppose there are fewer than 35 students in your math class. Explain why this graph is not an appropriate graph. There cannot be a negative number of students.

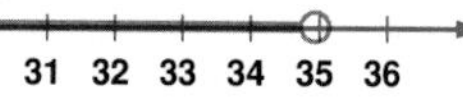

Wrap-Up

37. Devise a way to remember when to use a solid dot and when to use an open dot for the endpoint of the graph of an inequality. A solid dot is used when the number is included in the answer; an open dot when it is not.

Alternate Strategies: Extending the Lesson

Enrichment

Working in Pairs Have pairs of students work together to solve and graph more complicated inequalities, such as $6(s - 2) < 2s - 14$ or $-\frac{6}{7}s + \frac{2}{3} < 2$. $s < -\frac{1}{2}$; $s > -\frac{14}{9}$

Cooperative Learning

Watch Your Start — Group Activity **8-2**

MATERIALS: Five 0-9 spinners

For this activity, you will write inequalities and graph their solutions on the number line. The objective is to have your graphs start at a number between -20 and 20, and then have each new graph contain some numbers that were not included in the solution set of any of your other graphs.

To begin, each player draws a number line as shown below. Have one person spin the five spinners to get five numbers. Write an inequality using 2-5 of these numbers, solve it, and then graph its solution on your number line. You may use decimals to tenths place.

-20 -18 -16 -14 -12 -10 -8 -6 -4 -2 0 2 4 6 8 10 12 14 16 18 20

Solutions to these inequalities are then graphed on your respective number lines and are checked by others in the group. If your solution is incorrect, incorrectly graphed, or contains only numbers already graphed on your line, you are out of the game. The winner is the one who drops out last.

Merrill Pre-Algebra INEQUALITIES AND THE NUMBER LINE

Algebra in Action–Manufacturing

Tolerance

Parts used in automobiles must have very precise measurements or they will not work properly. However, it is impossible to produce parts with exact measurements. Thus, the dimensions of the parts must be between specified limits.

For example, a certain ball bearing that is specified to be 1 centimeter in diameter will work if it is only slightly larger or slightly smaller than 1 centimeter. The diameter may not differ from 1 centimeter by more than 0.001 centimeter. The 0.001 centimeter is called the **tolerance** of the ball bearing. The diameter of the ball bearing must be 1 ± 0.001 centimeter. That is, the diameter can vary between $1 + 0.001$ centimeter and $1 - 0.001$ centimeter. The acceptable diameter is shown by the following inequality.

$$1 - 0.001 \leq x \leq 1 + 0.001$$
$$0.999 \leq x \leq 1.001$$

The *tolerance interval* ranges from 0.999 cm to 1.001 cm.

That is, the least possible diameter is 0.999 cm, and the greatest possible diameter is 1.001 cm. The solution is graphed on the number line shown below.

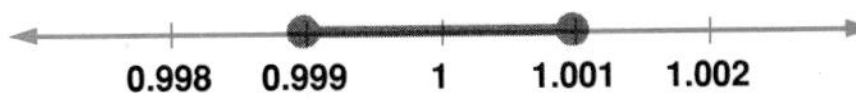

Write each expression as an inequality. Graph the solution. See Solutions Manual.

1. $x = 3 \pm 0.01$
2. $x = 5 \pm 0.003$
3. $x = 7 \pm 0.0002$
4. $y = 6 \pm 0.0015$
5. $y = 1 \pm 0.15$
6. $y = 2 \pm 0.003$
7. $r = 0.5 \pm 0.0001$
8. $r = 1.5 \pm 0.001$
9. $d = \frac{1}{2} \pm 0.0035$

10. **Chemistry** A chemical supply company guarantees the precision weighing of its products. They advertise that a certain product weighs 8 oz $\pm$ 0.03 oz. What is the tolerance interval? $7.97 \leq x \leq 8.03$

11. **Manufacturing** A pane of glass should be 26 inches wide by 32 inches long. The tolerance is $\frac{3}{16}$ inch. Find the tolerance interval for each dimension. $25\frac{13}{16} \leq w \leq 26\frac{3}{16}$; $31\frac{13}{16} \leq l \leq 32\frac{3}{16}$

Applying Algebra to the Real World

This optional page shows how algebra is used in the real world and also provides a change of pace.

Using Discussion

Ask students if they have tried on an item of clothing that fit, then tried on another item of the same size that did not fit. Discuss with students who cook how cooking measurements are not always precise. Then, ask students to list areas where measurements must be very precise. These may include topics such as production of a car or whether the football was carried far enough for a first down.

Using Communication

Many scientists believe that precision will be much greater when items can be manufactured in space. Have students write a paragraph on why tolerence intervals would be less in space. (Answers might include consistent temperatures, no atmospheric problems from corrosion, and reduction of friction.)

Activity

Materials rectangular picture frames, metric rulers, scissors

Using Cooperative Groups Provide each group with an empty picture frame. Using a metric ruler, have students determine the least and greatest possible length and width of the picture to be framed. Have them write length and width tolerence intervals as inequalities. Have students cut pieces of paper that match the greatest and least sizes that would fit the frame to confirm the tolerence intervals.

5-Minute Check
(over Lesson 8-2)

Solve each inequality and graph the solution.

1. $7x - 8 < 20$
   $x < 4$
2. $m + 1\frac{3}{4} \geq 6$
   $x \geq 4\frac{1}{4}$
3. $3y - 8 \geq -23$
   $y \geq -5$
4. $4(x - 8) > 3x - 29$
   $x > 3$

Transparency 8-3 contains the 5-Minute Check and a teaching aid for this lesson.

1 FOCUS

The purpose of this lesson is to extend the concept of graphing a point on a number line, where the coordinate is a single number, to graphing a point on a grid, where the coordinate is an ordered pair of numbers.

Motivating the Lesson

Bring in the game *Battleship* and start playing it with your students. Explain that the numbers and letters form an ordered pair and represent a location on the grid.

2 TEACH

Using Cooperative Groups Distribute a road map for your state or county to each group. Prepare a list of towns and cities for each group (or one list for everyone). Have students use the numerals across the top and the letters down the side to find ordered pairs that will locate the towns and cities you listed.

EE: 1E, 3A, 3F, 4E
TAAS: 2, 11

8-3 Ordered Pairs

Objective:
Identify the ordered pair of numbers associated with a point on a grid.

Key Term:
ordered pair

In 1791 President George Washington selected the site for the new capital that would be named in his honor. He chose a Frenchman, Pierre L'Enfant, to plan the city. The map at the right shows L'Enfant's design. Notice how the streets seem to form a grid pattern.

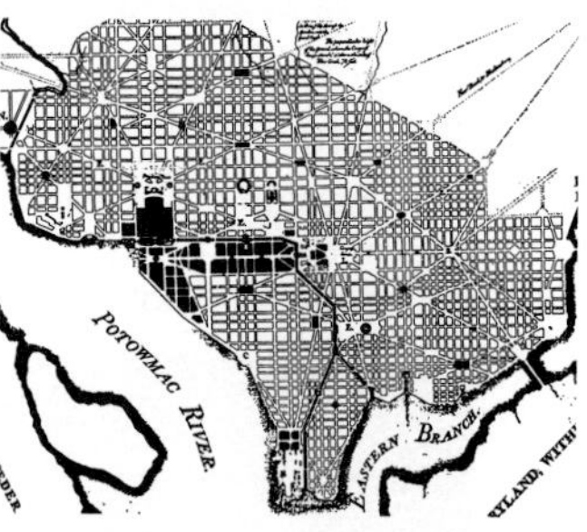

In mathematics, the location of any point on a grid can be indicated by an **ordered pair** of numbers. The grid below is a simplified version of the map of present-day Washington, D.C. To locate the Supreme Court on this grid, begin at 0, and move horizontally (east) 4 units. Then move vertically (north) 1 unit. The location of the Supreme Court is indicated by the ordered pair (4, 1).

Are the numbers in an ordered pair commutative? **no**

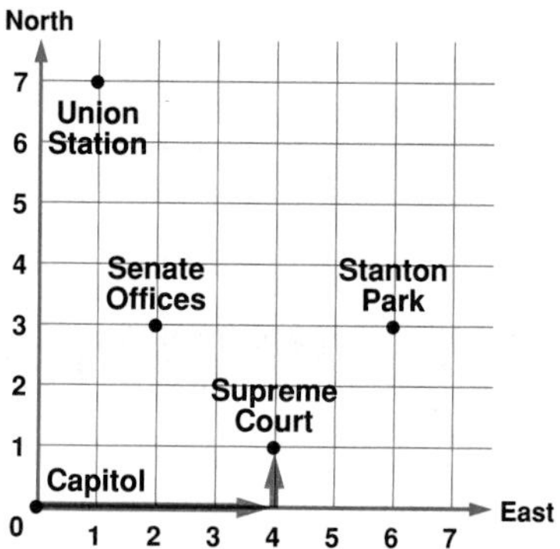

The location of any point on the grid can be indicated by the ordered pair (x, y), where x represents the number of horizontal units from 0 and y represents the number of vertical units from 0.

Bell Ringer

Ask the students how they would graph earning at least $6 on a number line. **A shaded dot at positive six and shade all numbers to the right of six.**

Examples

1 **Use the grid at the right to name the point for the ordered pair (3, 7).**

Move 3 units horizontally, then 7 units vertically.

The point for (3, 7) is *B*.

2 **Use the grid at the right to find the ordered pair for point *E*.**

Move 9 units horizontally, then 5 units vertically.

The ordered pair for point *E* is (9, 5).

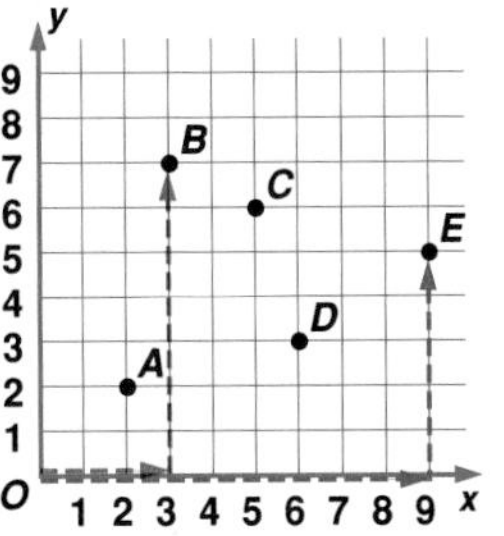

Checking for Understanding

Communicating Algebra

1. Locate Union Station on the grid on page 290. Name its ordered pair. (1, 7)
2. On this grid, what landmark is located at *O*? Capitol
3. If RFK Stadium were shown on the map, its ordered pair would be (24, 0). Describe its position with respect to the Capitol. 24 units east

Guided Practice

Use the map at the right to answer each question.

4. Which ordered pair indicates the location of Harding Pass? (8, 12)
5. Is (2, 10) the correct ordered pair for Willard Junction? no
6. Which ordered pair indicates the location of Red Clay Hill? (13, 9)
7. Is (3, 4) the correct ordered pair for Sun Valley Lookout Tower? yes
8. Which location does (8, 7) indicate? Thunder Point
9. Which ordered pair indicates the location of the forest service station? (1, 0)

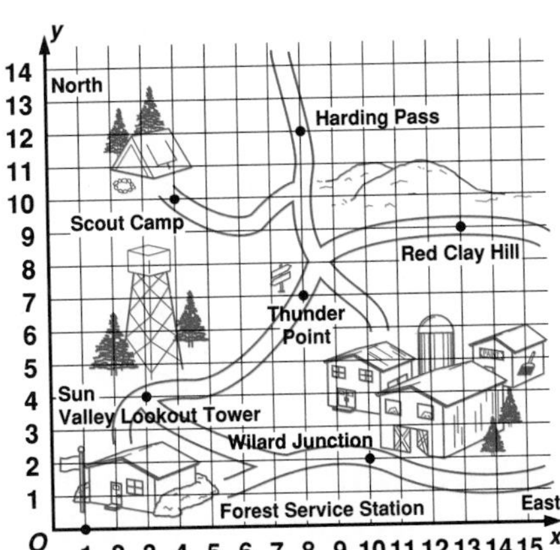

Exercises

Independent Practice

Use the grid at the right to name the point for each ordered pair.

10. (3, 4) D
11. (5, 1) Z
12. (1, 7) Q
13. (8, 2) F
14. (0, 2) J
15. (5, 6) L
16. (7, 5) M
17. (9, 3) C
18. (2, 0) K
19. (5, 9) Y

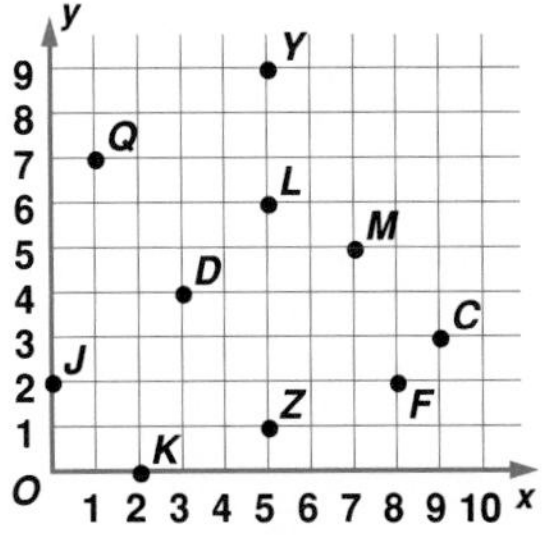

Chalkboard Examples

- *For Example 1*
  Use the grid at the right to find the name of the point for each ordered pair.
  a. (2,5) P
  b. (4,3) R
  c. (1,3) V

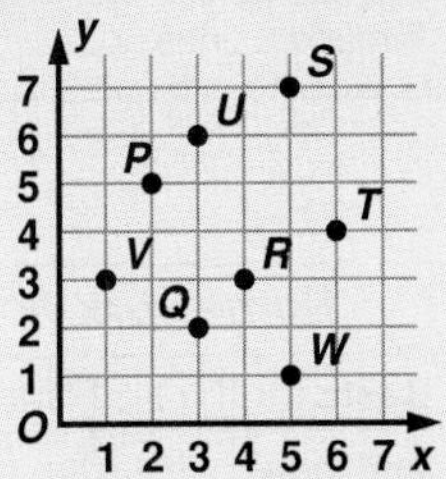

- *For Example 2*
  Use the grid above to find the ordered pair for each labeled point.
  a. Q (3,2) b. T (6,4) c. U (3,6)

3 PRACTICE/APPLY

Checking the Concept

Using Questioning Ask students what the difference is between the ordered pairs (3,2) and (2,3).

Practice Masters Booklet, **p. 73**

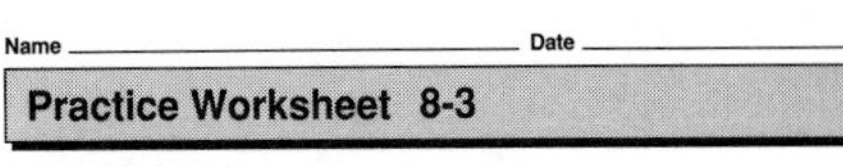

Name ____________ Date ____________

Practice Worksheet 8-3

Ordered Pairs

Use the grid below to name the point for each ordered pair. Write the letter directly below the ordered pair. After completing all the exercises, read the message formed by the letters.

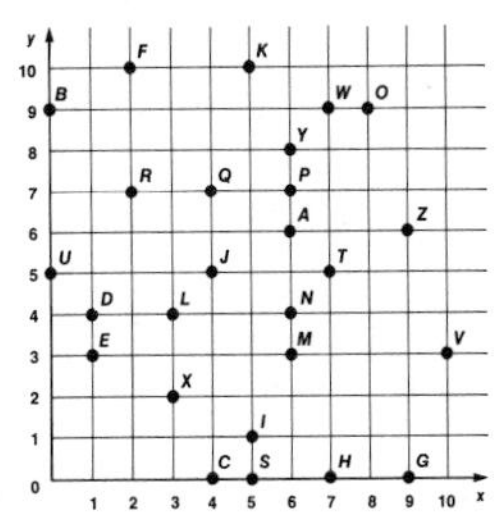

1. (9, 0) G 2. (2, 7) R 3. (6, 6) A 4. (6, 7) P 5. (7, 0) H 6. (5, 1) I 7. (6, 4) N 8. (9, 0) G
9. (5, 1) I 10. (5, 0) S 11. (6, 6) A 12. (9, 0) G 13. (8, 9) O 14. (8, 9) O 15. (1, 4) D
16. (7, 9) W 17. (6, 6) A 18. (6, 8) Y 19. (7, 5) T 20. (8, 9) O
21. (5, 0) S 22. (1, 3) E 23. (6, 4) N 24. (1, 4) D 25. (6, 6) A
26. (4, 0) C 27. (8, 9) O 28. (1, 4) D 29. (1, 3) E 30. (1, 4) D
31. (6, 3) M 32. (1, 3) E 33. (5, 0) S 34. (5, 0) S 35. (6, 6) A 36. (9, 0) G 37. (1, 3) E

Alternate Strategies: Reteaching the Lesson

Reteaching Activity

Working in Pairs Use dominoes to generate number pairs. Have one student pick up a domino and state an ordered pair. Have the other student locate and graph the point. An alternate activity would be for one student to pick up the domino and graph the point. The other student states the ordered pair of the graph.

Reteaching Masters Booklet, **p. 66**

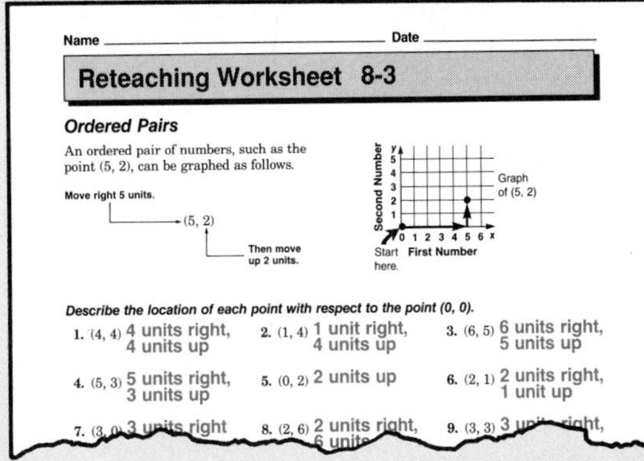

Name ____________ Date ____________

Reteaching Worksheet 8-3

Ordered Pairs

An ordered pair of numbers, such as the point (5, 2), can be graphed as follows.

Move right 5 units. (5, 2) Then move up 2 units.

Second Number; Graph of (5, 2); Start here. First Number

Describe the location of each point with respect to the point (0, 0).

1. (4, 4) 4 units right, 4 units up
2. (1, 4) 1 unit right, 4 units up
3. (6, 5) 6 units right, 5 units up
4. (5, 3) 5 units right, 3 units up
5. (0, 2) 2 units up
6. (2, 1) 2 units right, 1 unit up
7. (3, 0) 3 units right
8. (2, 6) 2 units right,
9. (3, 3) 3 units right,

Error Analysis

Watch for students who interchange the horizontal and vertical coordinates in an ordered pair.
Prevent by using arrows above the numbers in an ordered pair.

← ↑

For example, (-3,2) means 3 units to the left and 2 units up.

Independent Practice

Homework Assignment	
Basic	11-31 odd, 32-39
Average	10-30 even, 32-39
Honors	14-25, 32-39

4 CLOSE

Assessment Option

Writing Draw and label a grid on the chalkboard, plotting points on the graph and labeling them with letters. Then have the students write the coordinates of the points. For example, the coordinates of point A are (1,2).

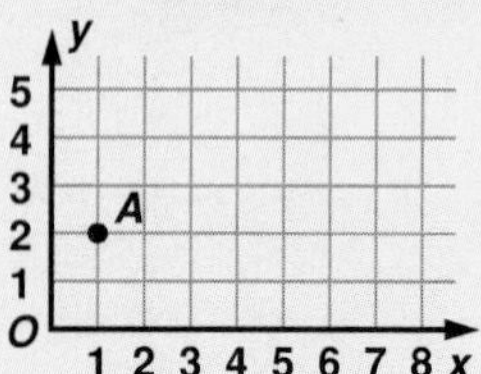

Enrichment Masters Booklet, **p. 66**

Name ______________________ Date ______________

Enrichment Worksheet 8-3

The Hidden Animal

Graph the following points. Join successive points by a line segment. When you finish, you will have a picture of an animal.

1. (3, 5) **2.** (1, 5) **3.** (−5, 4.5) **4.** (−6.5, 3) **5.** (−6.5, −2)

6. Start a new line segment.
(−6.5, 1), (−6, −0.5), (−6, −1.5), (−5.5, −4), (−5.5, −6), (−3, −6), (−3.5, −5), (−3.5, −1.5)

7. Start a new line segment.
(1.5, −0.5), (1, −1), (1.5, −3), (1.5, −6), (3.5, −6), (3, −5), (3, −1)

8. Start a new line segment.
(3, −2), (5, −4), (5, −5.5), (3.5, −5.5), (3.5, −4.5), (3, −4)

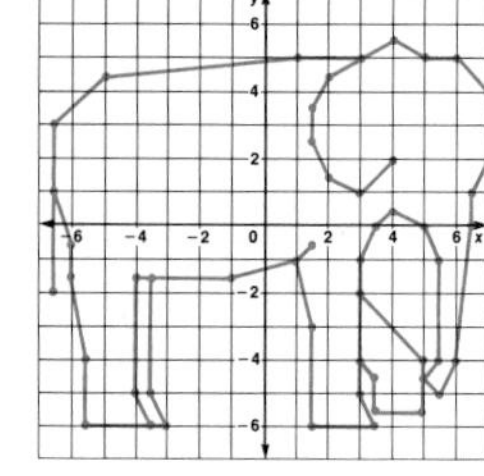

9. Start a new line segment.
(1, −1), (−1, −1.5), (−4, −1.5), (−4, −5), (−3.5, −6)

10. Start a new line segment.
(5, 5), (4, 5.5), (2, 4.5), (1.5, 3.5), (1.5, 2.5), (2, 1.5), (3, 1), (4, 2)

11. Start a new line segment.
(5, 5), (6, 5), (7, 4), (7, 2), (6.5, 1), (6.5, 0), (6, −4), (5.5, −5), (5, −4.5), (5.5, −4), (5.5, −1), (5, 0), (4, 0.5), (3.5, 0), (3, −1)

12. Suppose you multiply both coordinates of each ordered pair by 2 and graph the resulting ordered pairs on graph paper using the same scale on the axes as for the drawing above. How would the drawings compare? The new figure would be twice as large.

Use the grid to find the ordered pair for each labeled point.

20. W (1, 2)	21. R (4, 1)	22. A (3, 7)
23. P (8, 3)	24. S (2, 5)	25. I (5, 6)
26. G (7, 4)	27. B (9, 8)	28. N (3, 4)
29. E (6, 0)	30. X (0, 0)	31. H (0, 9)

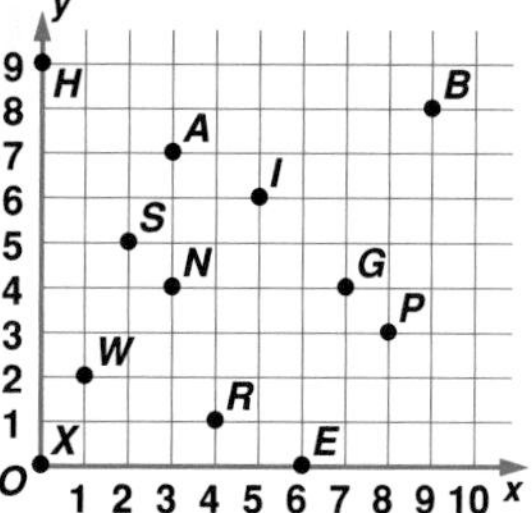

Mixed Review

32. Simplify the expression $-9ab - 13ab$. (Lesson 2-5) **$-22ab$**

33. Solve the equation $9(y + 3) = 4y - 13$. (Lesson 7-5) **-8**

34. Solve the equation $-4 + y = -3$ and graph the solution. (Lesson 8-1) **1**

35. Write an inequality for the graph: (Lesson 8-2) **$x > -2$**

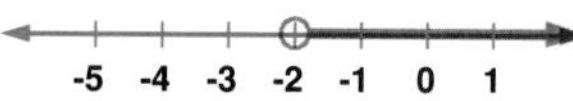

For graphs to Exercises 34 and 36-37, see Solutions Manual.

Connections

36. **Geometry** Graph (2, 1), (2, 4), and (5, 1) on a grid. Connect the points with line segments. What figure is formed? **triangle**

37. **Geometry** Using the ordered pairs from Exercise 36, multiply each number by 2. Graph the new ordered pairs. What figure is formed? **triangle**

Critical Thinking

38. Compare your figures from Exercises 36 and 37. Write a sentence that tells how the figures are the same. Write a sentence that tells how the figures are different. **The figures are both triangles of the same shape. The figures are different sizes.**

Wrap-Up

39. An example of an ordered pair in your daily life might be (put on your socks, put on your shoes). Write another ordered pair from your life. **Sample answer: (study, take test)**

Biography

Benjamin Banneker

Benjamin Banneker, the grandson of a black slave, was born a free man on a farm outside Baltimore, Maryland, in 1731. He was a brilliant student in mathematics and quickly excelled beyond the ability of his teachers. At the age of twenty, he built the nation's first American made clock. It was keeping perfect time when he died in 1806.

At the suggestion of Thomas Jefferson, Banneker was appointed to a three-man team charged with designing and building Washington, D.C. When Pierre L'Enfant resigned, taking all of the plans and maps with him, Banneker was able to reproduce the entire set of plans completely from memory. Washington, D.C., stands today as a monument to the genius of a self-educated, African-American, mathematician, Benjamin Banneker.

Alternate Strategies: Extending the Lesson

Enrichment

Draw a large grid on the chalkboard. Have students create a personalized ordered pair with their height in inches as the x-coordinate and their shoe size as the y-coordinate. Then have each student plot his or her ordered pair on the grid. Discuss how this information could be used by shoe manufacturers.

Cooperative Learning

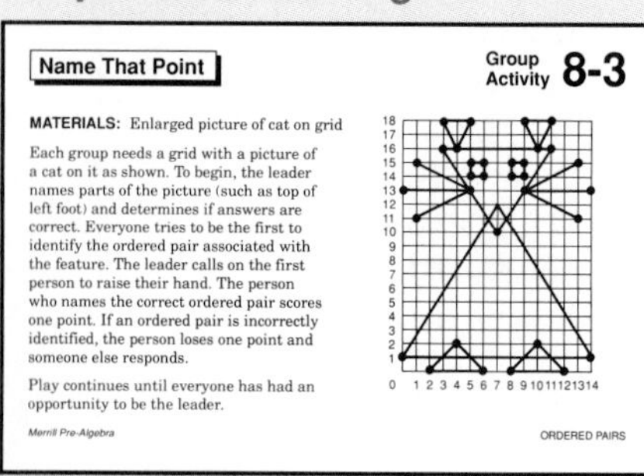

Name That Point Group Activity **8-3**

MATERIALS: Enlarged picture of cat on grid

Each group needs a grid with a picture of a cat on it as shown. To begin, the leader names parts of the picture (such as top of left foot) and determines if answers are correct. Everyone tries to be the first to identify the ordered pair associated with the feature. The leader calls on the first person to raise their hand. The person who names the correct ordered pair scores one point. If an ordered pair is incorrectly identified, the person loses one point and someone else responds.

Play continues until everyone has had an opportunity to be the leader.

Merrill Pre-Algebra ORDERED PAIRS

8-4 The Coordinate System

Objective:
Graph points in all four quadrants.

Key Terms:
coordinate system
x-axis
y-axis
origin
quadrant

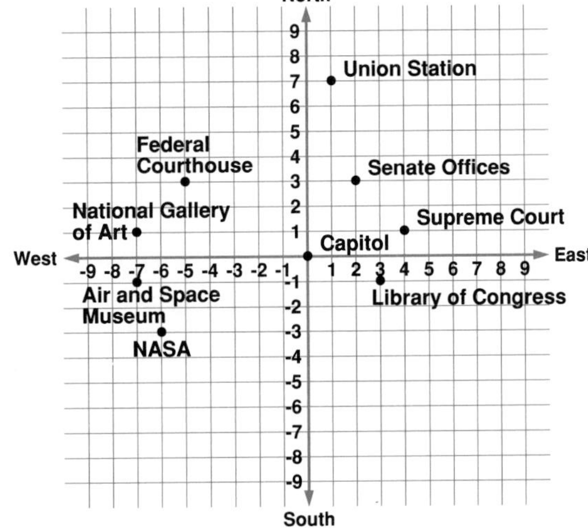

The map of Washington, D.C., can be extended to include the northwest, southwest, and southeast sections of the city. The location of the Library of Congress can be indicated by the ordered pair (3, -1). The location of the National Gallery of Art can be indicated by the ordered pair (-7, 1).

In mathematics, ordered pairs are used to locate points in a plane. A horizontal number line and a vertical number line intersect at their zero points to define a **coordinate system** for the plane. The horizontal number line is called the ***x*-axis;** the vertical number line is called the ***y*-axis.** The point where the two lines intersect is called the **origin.** The number lines separate the plane into four **quadrants.**

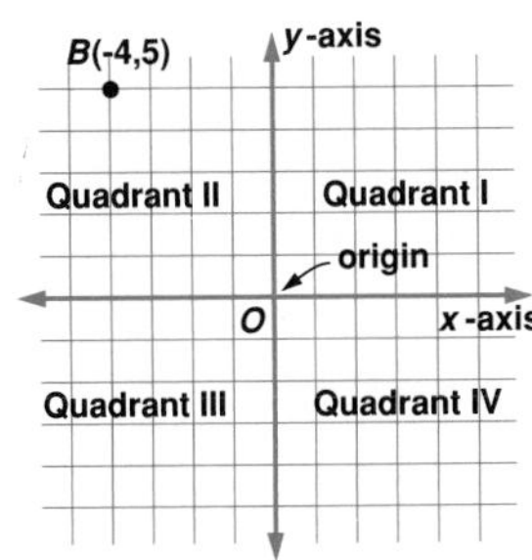

The numbers in an ordered pair are called coordinates. The *x-coordinate* of the ordered pair (-4, 5) is -4 and the *y-coordinate* is 5. The dot at (-4, 5) is the **graph** of point B.

The origin and the two axes do not lie in any quadrant. Axes is the plural of axis.

Geography Connection

To locate places on the surface of the Earth, geographers use a set of imaginary lines called latitude and longitude lines.
Latitude lines tell the location north or south of the equator. Longitude lines tell the location east or west of the prime meridian in Greenwich, England. For example, the location of the city of New Orleans, LA, is 30°N, 90°W.

Bell Ringer

Using the map on p. 291, ask the students the coordinates of the Scout Camp. (4,10)

Lesson Notes 8-4

5-Minute Check
(over Lesson 8-3)

Use the grid to find the ordered pair for each labeled point.

1. G (4,0)
2. D (3,4)
3. C (0,5)
4. B (4,7)
5. F (5,1)

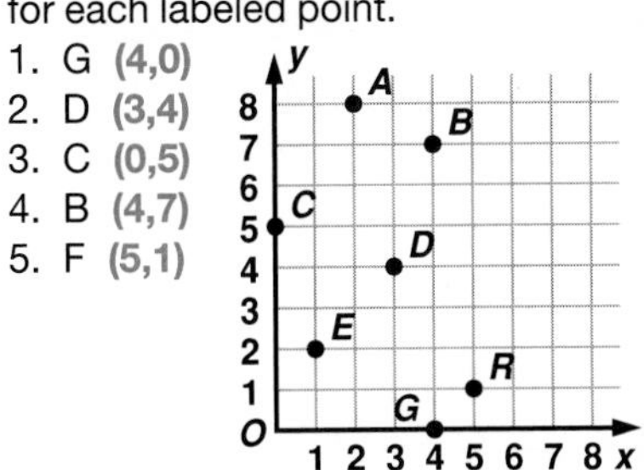

Transparency 8-4 contains the 5-Minute Check and a teaching aid for this lesson.

1 FOCUS

The purpose of this lesson is to extend the coordinate plane to include four quadrants.

Motivating the Lesson

Have students look at the map and give directions on how to go from the Capitol to the Air and Space Museum.

2 TEACH

Using Models Draw a coordinate system on the chalkboard or overhead and label the points shown below. Point out that the axes are really number lines that are perpendicular. Use the system below to answer the Chalkboard Examples on page 294.

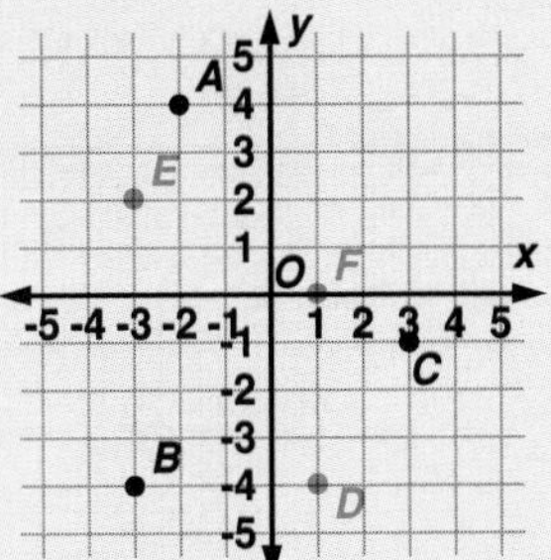

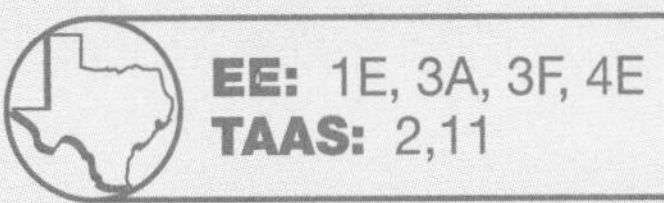

EE: 1E, 3A, 3F, 4E
TAAS: 2,11

Chalkboard Examples

Refer to the coordinate graph on page 293.

Find the coordinates of each point.

- *For Example 1.* A (-2, 4)
- *For Example 2.* B (-3, -4)
- *For Example 3.* C (3, -1)

Graph each point. (See grid.)

- *For Example 4.* D
- *For Example 5.* E
- *For Example 6.* F

3 PRACTICE/APPLY

Checking the Concept

Using Questioning Ask students the questions below.

- How do you know from the coordinates of a point which quadrant contains the point?
- How do you know when a point is on the x-axis? on the y-axis?

Practice Masters Booklet, **p. 74**

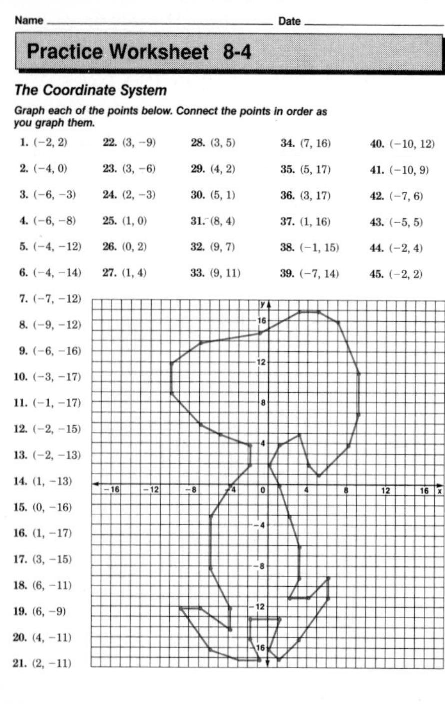
Name ______________________ Date ______________

Practice Worksheet 8-4

The Coordinate System

Graph each of the points below. Connect the points in order as you graph them.

1. (−2, 2)
2. (−4, 0)
3. (−6, −3)
4. (−6, −8)
5. (−4, −12)
6. (−4, −14)
7. (−7, −12)
8. (−9, −12)
9. (−6, −16)
10. (−3, −17)
11. (−1, −17)
12. (−2, −15)
13. (−2, −13)
14. (1, −13)
15. (0, −16)
16. (1, −17)
17. (3, −15)
18. (6, −11)
19. (6, −9)
20. (4, −11)
21. (2, −11)
22. (3, −9)
23. (3, −6)
24. (2, −3)
25. (1, 0)
26. (0, 2)
27. (1, 4)
28. (3, 5)
29. (4, 2)
30. (5, 1)
31. (8, 4)
32. (9, 7)
33. (9, 11)
34. (7, 16)
35. (5, 17)
36. (3, 17)
37. (1, 16)
38. (−1, 15)
39. (−7, 14)
40. (−10, 12)
41. (−10, 9)
42. (−7, 6)
43. (−5, 5)
44. (−2, 4)
45. (−2, 2)

Examples

1 Find the ordered pair for point *A*.

Think of a vertical line and a horizontal line passing through point A. Since the vertical line intersects the x-axis at -2, the x-coordinate is -2. Since the horizontal line intersects the y-axis at 3, the y-coordinate is 3.

So, the ordered pair for point A is (-2, 3).

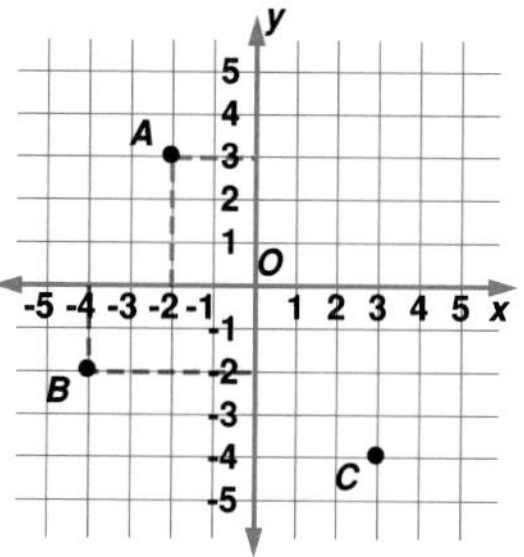

2 Find the ordered pair for point *B*.

The x-coordinate is -4. The y-coordinate is -2. The ordered pair for point B is (-4, -2).

In which quadrant is point A? point B? point C? 2; 3; 4

3 Find the ordered pair for point *C*.

The ordered pair for point C is (3, -4).

Remember that to graph a point means to place a dot at the point named by the ordered pair. This is sometimes called *plotting the point.*

Examples

4 Graph point *D*(3, -1).

Start at O. Move 3 units to the right. Then move 1 unit down to locate the point. Label the dot $D(3, -1)$.

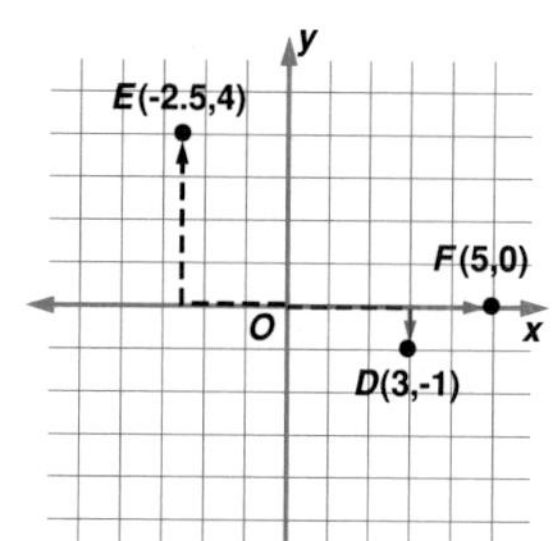

5 Graph point *E*(-2.5, 4).

Start at O. Move 2.5 units to the left. Then move 4 units up to locate the point. Label the dot $E(-2.5, 4)$.

In which quadrant is point F? none

6 Graph point *F*(5, 0).

Start at O. Move 5 units to the right. The graph is on the x-axis. Label the dot $F(5, 0)$.

Alternate Strategies: Reteaching the Lesson

Reteaching Activity

Using Writing Give students a four-quadrant graph with each letter of the alphabet located at a point somewhere on the graph. Give them a short, coded message by using the coordinates of the letters needed. After decoding the message, have each student write a coded message of his or her own. Trade and decode.

Reteaching Masters Booklet, **p. 67**

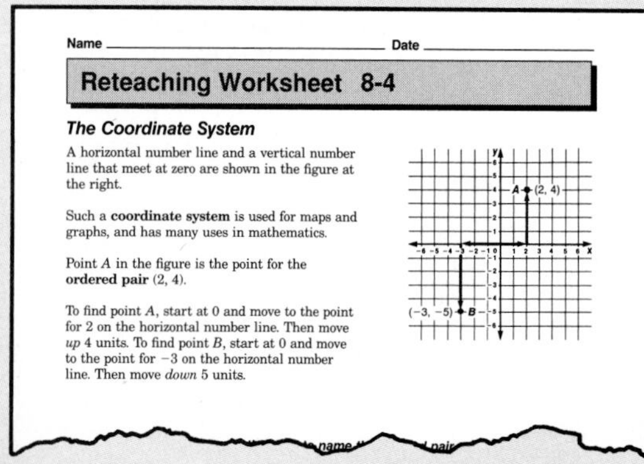
Name ______________________ Date ______________

Reteaching Worksheet 8-4

The Coordinate System

A horizontal number line and a vertical number line that meet at zero are shown in the figure at the right.

Such a **coordinate system** is used for maps and graphs, and has many uses in mathematics.

Point A in the figure is the point for the **ordered pair** (2, 4).

To find point A, start at 0 and move to the point for 2 on the horizontal number line. Then move *up* 4 units. To find point B, start at 0 and move to the point for −3 on the horizontal number line. Then move *down* 5 units.

Checking for Understanding 1. See margin.

Communicating Algebra

1. Explain how the quadrants in a coordinate plane are numbered.
2. Suppose the x-coordinate of an ordered pair is negative. In which quadrants might the point be graphed? Give two examples. 2, 3; (-2, 1), (-2, -1)
3. Suppose the y-coordinate of an ordered pair is positive. In which quadrants might the point be graphed? Give two examples. 1, 2; (1, 2), (-1, 2)

Guided Practice

5. $\frac{1}{2}$, -5, 4
7. -1, -4.7, 3

Name the x-coordinate and the y-coordinate of each ordered pair. Then tell which quadrant contains the graph of each ordered pair.

4. (-3, 2) -3, 2, 2
5. $\left(\frac{1}{2}, -5\right)$
6. (3, 8) 3, 8, 1
7. (-1, -4.7)
8. $\left(-\frac{2}{3}, 5\right)$ $-\frac{2}{3}$, 5, 2
9. (-2.25, 0) -2.25, 0, none
10. (0, -6) 0, -6, none
11. (0, 0) 0, 0, none

Exercises For graph to Exercises 12-23, see Solutions Manual.

Independent Practice

On graph paper, draw coordinate axes. Then graph and label each point.

12. $K(0, 7)$
13. $L(2, -8)$
14. $M(-5, -5)$
15. $N(-4, 7)$
16. $O(-1, 7)$
17. $P(3, 4)$
18. $Q(4, 3)$
19. $R(-4, -3)$
20. $A(-2.5, 4)$
21. $B\left(-1\frac{1}{2}, 6\right)$
22. $C(-3, 0)$
23. $D(5.5, 0.5)$

Logical Reasoning

Name the quadrant for the graph of (x, y) given each condition.

24. $x > 0, y < 0$ 4
25. $x < 0, y < 0$ 3
26. $x < 0, y > 0$ 2
27. $x > 0, y > 0$ 1

Mixed Review

28. Solve the equation $-7g = 84$. (Lesson 3-3) -12
29. Factor $28a^2b^3$ completely. (Lesson 4-5) $2 \cdot 2 \cdot 7 \cdot a \cdot a \cdot b \cdot b \cdot b$
30. Write $5\frac{7}{8}$ as a decimal. (Lesson 6-1) 5.875
31. Solve the inequality $-4m \leq 56$ and graph the solution. (Lesson 8-2) $m \geq -14$; See Solutions Manual for graph.

Application

32. **Physics** Paulo and Elise conducted an experiment to see how the mass of an object affected the distance a spring stretched. The data are shown in the table at the right. Graph the ordered pairs (mass, distance) in the coordinate plane. Use the x-axis for mass and the y-axis for distance. For graphs to Exercises 32-34, see Solutions Manual.

Stretching of a Spring

Mass	Distance
100 g	3 cm
200 g	6 cm
300 g	9 cm
400 g	12 cm
500 g	15 cm

Connections

33. **Geometry** Graph (2, 1), (2, 4), and (5, 1) in the coordinate plane. Connect the points with line segments. What figure is formed? triangle
34. **Geometry** Using the ordered pairs from Exercise 33, add 5 to each x-coordinate. Graph the new ordered pairs. What figure is formed? triangle

Critical Thinking

35. Compare your figures from Exercises 33 and 34. Write a sentence that tells how the figures are the same and how the figures are different. See margin.

Wrap-Up

36. Write two ordered pairs whose graph is in Quadrant III. Write two ordered pairs whose graph is *not* in Quadrant III. Sample answers: (-1, -2), (-3, -4); (1, 2), (-3, 4)

Independent Practice

Homework Assignment	
Basic	13-27 odd, 28-36
Average	12-26 even, 28-36
Honors	19-36

4 CLOSE

Assessment Option

Modeling Make a treasure map but do not tell the students where the treasure is. Have them find the treasure by laying a grid over your map and asking which quadrant the treasure is in. Then have them name coordinates until they land on the treasure.

Additional Answers

1. The quadrants are numbered from 1 to 4, starting in the upper right quadrant and moving counterclockwise.
35. The figures are triangles of the same size and shape. Their location on the coordinate plane is different.

Enrichment Masters Booklet, **p. 67**

Name ______ Date ______

Enrichment Worksheet 8-4

Polar Coordinates

In a rectangular coordinate system, the ordered pair (x, y) describes the location of a point x units from the origin along the x-axis and y units from the origin along the y-axis.

In a polar coordinate system, the ordered pair (r, θ) describes the location of a point r units from the pole on the ray (vector) whose endpoint is the pole and which forms an angle of θ with the polar axis.

The graph of (2, 30°) is shown on the polar coordinate system at the right below. Note that the concentric circles indicate the number of units from the pole.

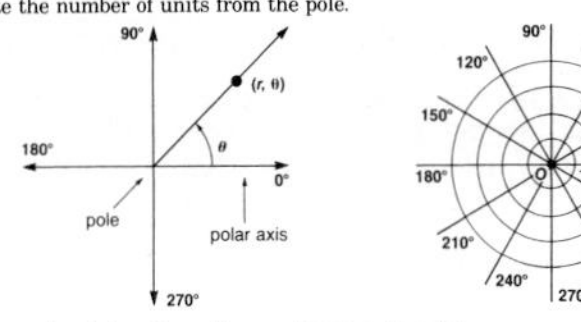

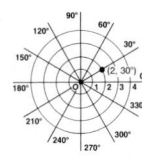

Locate each point on the polar coordinate system below.

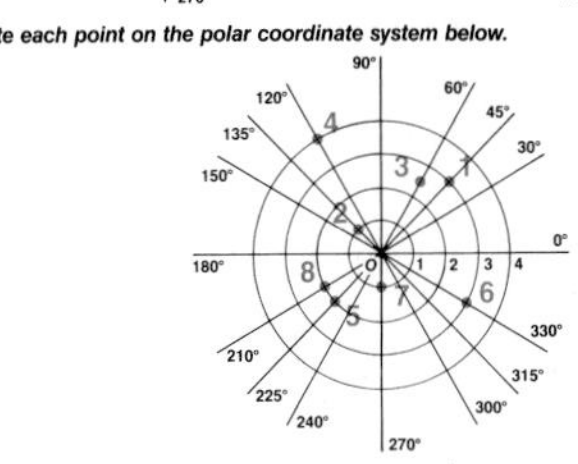

1. (3, 45°)
2. (1, 135°)
3. $(2\frac{1}{2}, 60°)$
4. (4, 120°)
5. (2, 225°)
6. (3, −30°)
7. (1, −90°)
8. (−2, 30°)

Alternate Strategies: Extending the Lesson

Enrichment

Art Connection Have each student draw a picture on a four-quadrant graph. Only straight lines are used. Turns are made only at integral points. Each student then writes, in order, coordinates for each point in the drawing. Have students exchange coordinates and re-create their partner's drawing.

Cooperative Learning

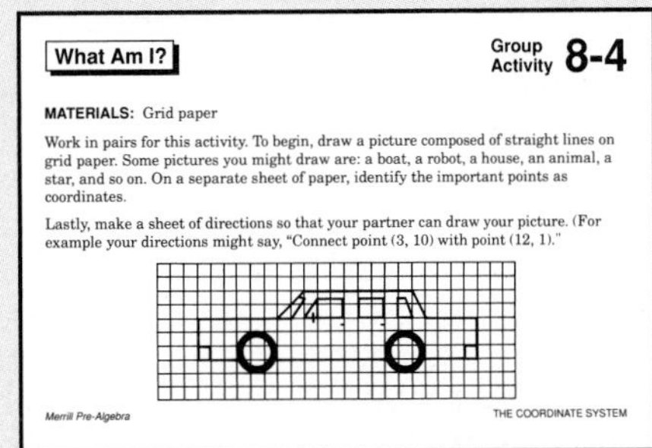

What Am I? Group Activity 8-4

MATERIALS: Grid paper

Work in pairs for this activity. To begin, draw a picture composed of straight lines on grid paper. Some pictures you might draw are: a boat, a robot, a house, an animal, a star, and so on. On a separate sheet of paper, identify the important points as coordinates.

Lastly, make a sheet of directions so that your partner can draw your picture. (For example your directions might say, "Connect point (3, 10) with point (12, 1).")

Merrill Pre-Algebra THE COORDINATE SYSTEM

5-Minute Check
(over Lesson 8-4)

On graph paper, draw coordinate axes. Then graph and label each point.

1. T (0,4)
2. M (-3,-2)
3. P (4,-1)
4. R (-1.5,3)
5. Q (3.5,0.5)

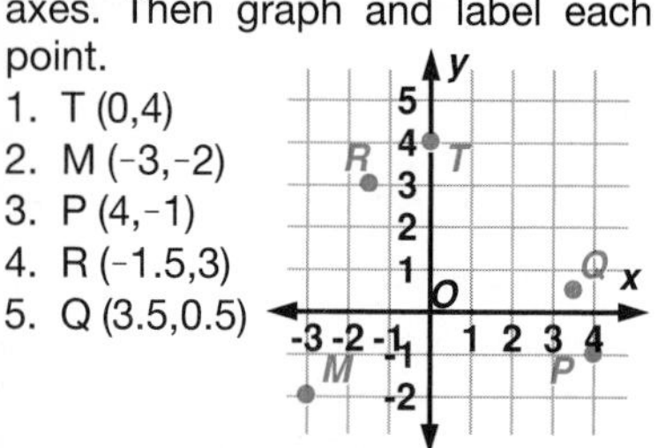

Transparency 8-5 contains the 5-Minute Check and a teaching aid for this lesson.

1 FOCUS

The purpose of this lesson is to set the stage for graphing lines in a coordinate plane.

Motivating the Lesson

Bring a recipe into class and work with students completing a chart for doubling it. Point out that the doubled recipe is dependent upon the original recipe.

2 TEACH

Using Discussion Stress that the values obtained for y in the second table depend on the values for x. In Example 2, explain that while the values chosen for x, (-1, 0, 1, 3), are arbitrary choices, it is generally good to choose a negative number, zero, and a positive number.

Chalkboard Examples

- *For Example 1*
  Which ordered pair, (5,15) or (6,20), is a solution of $y = 3x$? **(5,15)**
- *For Example 2*
  Find four solutions of $y = 4x - 6$. **(0, -6), (1, -2), (2,2), (3,6)**

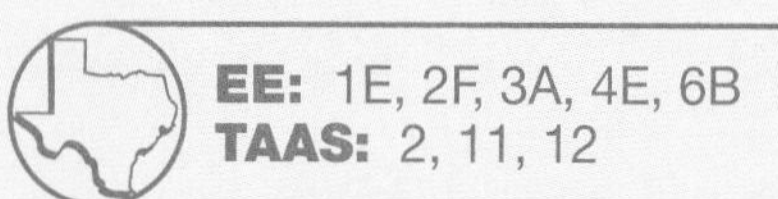

EE: 1E, 2F, 3A, 4E, 6B
TAAS: 2, 11, 12

8-5 Equations with Two Variables

Objective:
Find solutions for equations with two variables.

Forests serve as the only source of timber. Sometimes the production of timber conflicts with the need to conserve the environment and wildlife. In an effort to conserve both the forests and the wildlife, foresters replace the trees that have been cut down. About half of the seedlings planted survive until they are full grown.

Seedlings planted	One-half of seedlings planted	Full-grown trees
30 maples	$\frac{1}{2}(30)$	15
44 blue spruce	$\frac{1}{2}(44)$	22
46 aspen	$\frac{1}{2}(46)$	23

Suppose 50 pine seedlings were planted. How many would be expected to become full-grown trees? **25**

The chart above could be written algebraically.

Let x represent the number of seedlings planted. Then $\frac{1}{2}x$ represents one-half the seedlings planted.

Let y represent the number of full-grown trees.

You know that one-half of the seedlings survive until full grown. This relationship can be shown with the equation $y = \frac{1}{2}x$. This equation has two variables, x and y.

x	$\frac{1}{2}x$	y
30	$\frac{1}{2}(30)$	15
44	$\frac{1}{2}(44)$	22
46	$\frac{1}{2}(46)$	23

Recall that solving an equation means to replace the variable so a true sentence results. The solution for an equation with two variables consists of two numbers, one for each variable. Usually, the solution is expressed as an ordered pair.

FYI

The United States Congress has set aside about 155 forest areas to be managed and protected by the federal government. These national forests cover a total area of about 183 million acres, larger than the state of Texas.

Example

1 **Which ordered pair, (10, 20) or (8, 4), is a solution of $y = \frac{1}{2}x$?**

Substitute the values for x and y into the equation.

$y = \frac{1}{2}x$ — Replace x with 10 and y with 20.

$20 \stackrel{?}{=} \frac{1}{2} \cdot 10$

$20 \neq 5$

$y = \frac{1}{2}x$ — Replace x with 8 and y with 4.

$4 \stackrel{?}{=} \frac{1}{2} \cdot 8$

$4 = 4$ ✓

(10, 20) is *not* a solution. (8, 4) is a solution.

Bell Ringer

Plot a point in a coordinate plane and ask students to give three other points that will make a square. **Possible answer: (3,1), (0,1), (0, -2), (3, -2)**

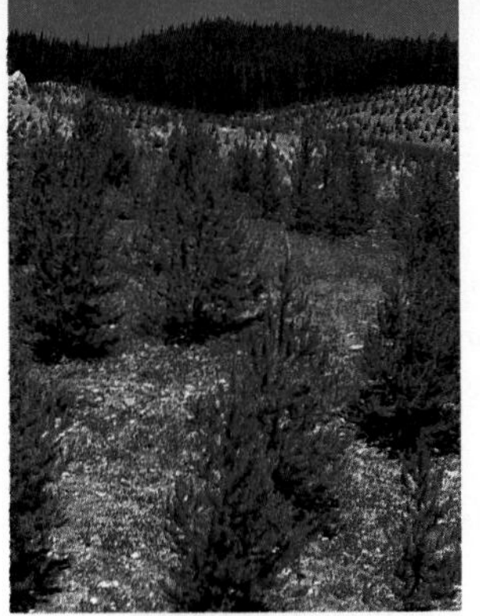

Examine

One way to check the solution is by working backwards. Graph the ordered pairs (30, 7) and (11, 3.2). The line that contains the points also contains (5, 2).

Another way to check is to see if the solution is reasonable. The sample tree grew a little more than 1 meter in 6 years. It needs to grow about 4 more meters until harvest. Therefore, it will be about 6×4 or 24 more years. Since $11 + 24 = 35$, a solution of 30 seems reasonable.

Checking for Understanding

Communicating Algebra

1. Explain why it is important to take the time to plan before you solve a problem. so that you can decide the best method to use

Use the graph in Example 1 to answer each question.

2. What was the height of the sample tree when it was planted? 1 m
3. What was the height of the tree 17 years after it was planted? 4.5 m
4. How many years did it take until the tree reached a height of 5 meters? 4. 19 years
5. What height would you expect the tree to reach after 31 years? over 7 m

Guided Practice

Name two ordered pairs (x, y) that can be used to graph the information in each problem.

6. David measures the heights of the steps going into his house. The 2nd step is 1 foot above ground. The 5th step is $2\frac{1}{2}$ feet above ground. What is the height of the 11th step? $(2, 1), (5, 2\frac{1}{2})$
7. Mrs. Madison drives at a constant rate for 6 hours. After $\frac{1}{2}$ hour she has driven 25 miles. After 2 hours she has driven 100 miles. How many miles does she drive in 6 hours? $(\frac{1}{2}, 25), (2, 100)$

Exercises

Independent Practice

Use a graph to solve each problem. Assume that the rate is constant in each problem. For graphs to Exercises 8-11, see Solutions Manual.

8. After 2 hours, Kaiyo checks the odometer in her car. She has traveled 160 kilometers. After 3 more hours, she has traveled a total distance of 400 kilometers. How many more hours will it take for Kaiyo to travel a total distance of 560 kilometers? 2 more hours
9. Larry used a chart to see if he was close to the average weight for his height. The chart gave a weight of 130 pounds for a male 60 inches tall. The average weight for a male 66 inches tall was 143 pounds. Larry is 6 feet in height. What should Larry's weight be? 156 lbs

3 PRACTICE/APPLY

Checking the Concept

Using Questioning Ask students to describe the graph of a line whose y-values decrease as the x-values increase.

Error Analysis

Watch for students who always assume they are given the value for x in an equation.

Prevent by having students talk through each problem. Have students ask themselves or a partner what information is given. Have students point to the axis where that information is represented, then read the corresponding horizontal or vertical value.

Alternate Strategies: Reteaching the Lesson

Reteaching Activity

Using Questioning Draw a graph of a linear equation on the chalkboard or overhead. Have students list the ordered pairs they can identify from the line.

Independent Practice

Homework Assignment	
Basic	8-13
Average	8-13
Honors	8-13

4 CLOSE

Assessment Option

Speaking Ask students in what types of situations they would draw a graph to solve a problem. Possible answer: when the problem involves a constant rate.

Additional Answer

13. Kelly's gas tank holds 10 gallons of gasoline. If she has a full tank, how many miles can she expect to go?

Practice Masters Booklet, **p. 77**

Name ________________ Date ________________

Practice Worksheet 8-7

Problem Solving Strategy: Draw a Graph

Use a graph to solve each problem. Assume that the rate is constant in each problem.

1. Mr. McCarthy drives at a constant rate for 5 hours. After 2 hours, he has driven 90 miles. After 4 hours, he has driven 180 miles. How many miles does he drive in 5 hours? 225 miles

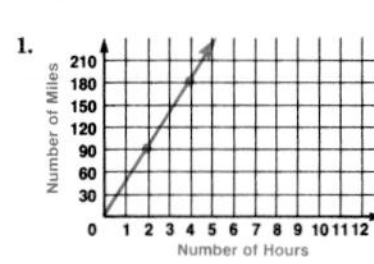

2. The interest Mary earned for \$80 was \$4. If she had deposited \$100, she would have earned \$5. How much would she earn for \$120? \$6

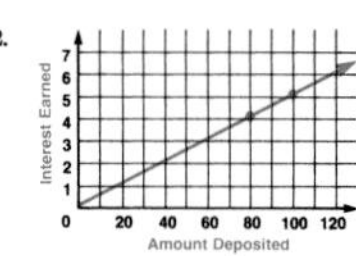

3. Larry earned \$150 for working $37\frac{1}{2}$ hours. He would have earned \$160 if he'd worked $2\frac{1}{2}$ hours more. What is Larry paid per hour? How much will he earn if he works 30 hours? \$4; \$120

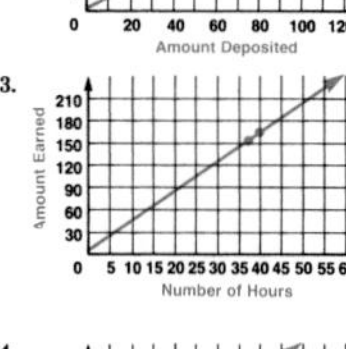

4. During a storewide sale, a TV which usually sells for \$450 is on sale for \$360. A stereo which usually sells for \$600 is on sale for \$480. What would the sale price be on a VCR which usually sells for \$500? \$400

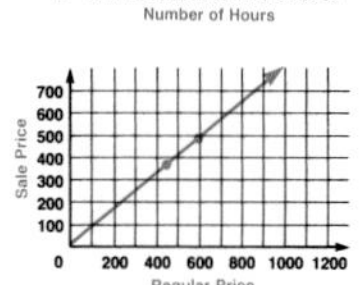

10. A temperature of 32° Fahrenheit corresponds to a temperature of 0° Celsius. A temperature of 100° Celsius corresponds to a temperature of 212° Fahrenheit. About what temperature in degrees Celsius corresponds to a temperature of 0° Fahrenheit? about −15°C

11. Diego cuts lawns during the summer to earn extra money. After working for $2\frac{1}{2}$ hours, Diego has earned \$10. After working for an additional $1\frac{1}{2}$ hours, Diego has earned a total of \$16. How much is Diego paid per hour? How much will Diego earn if he works a total of 6 hours? \$4 per hour; \$24

Decision Making

Solve using the graph and either mental math skills, estimation, or paper and pencil. Explain your method. See students' work.

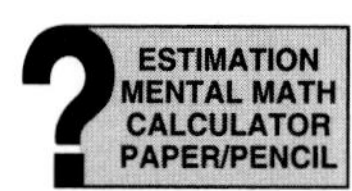

12. Kelly knows that her car can travel about 30 miles on one gallon of gasoline. The graph shows this relationship. Kelly has 6 gallons of gasoline in her car. She is starting on a 250-mile trip. Will she have to buy more gasoline sometime during her trip? If so, approximately when? yes; before driving 180 miles

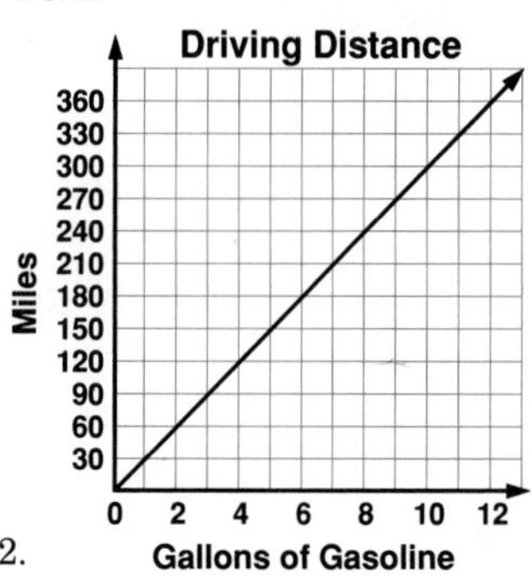

Wrap-Up

13. **Make Up a Problem** Write a problem that can be solved by using the graph for Exercise 12. See margin for sample answer.

Challenge

Parabolas

Not all equations are linear equations. Consider the equation $y = x^2$.

x	y
-3	9
-2	4
-1	1
0	0
1	1
2	4
3	9

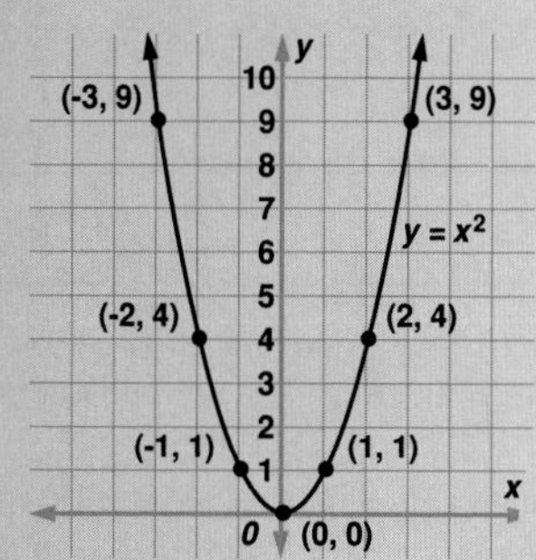

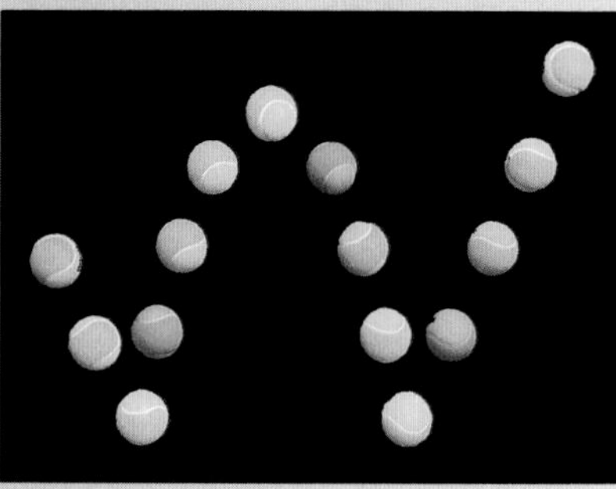

This curve is called a **parabola.** In real life, the path of a bouncing ball is a parabola. Research other areas of real-life where parabolas occur. Sample answers: path of rocket; sound wave

Alternate Strategies: Extending the Lesson

Enrichment

Science Connection Give students a data chart comparing altitude (feet) and temperature (°C). The altitudes are: 0, 1500, 6000, and 9000. The corresponding temperatures are 15, 5, −26, and −44. Have students graph the data and determine the temperature at 7000 feet from the ground. −32°C

Cooperative Learning

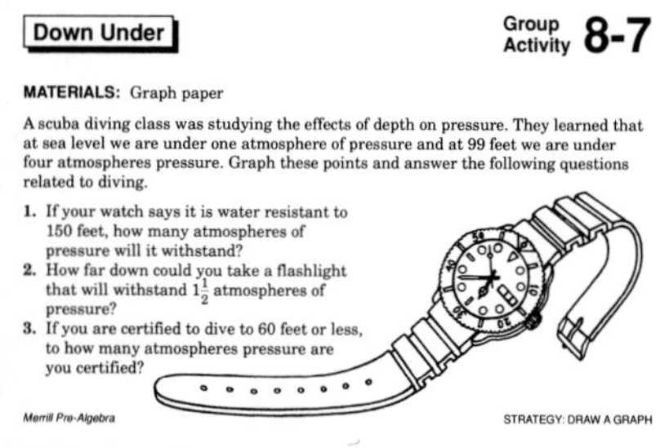

Down Under Group Activity **8-7**

MATERIALS: Graph paper

A scuba diving class was studying the effects of depth on pressure. They learned that at sea level we are under one atmosphere of pressure and at 99 feet we are under four atmospheres pressure. Graph these points and answer the following questions related to diving.

1. If your watch says it is water resistant to 150 feet, how many atmospheres of pressure will it withstand?
2. How far down could you take a flashlight that will withstand $1\frac{1}{2}$ atmospheres of pressure?
3. If you are certified to dive to 60 feet or less, to how many atmospheres pressure are you certified?

Merrill Pre-Algebra STRATEGY: DRAW A GRAPH

8-8 Slope

Objective:
Find the slope of a line.

Key Terms:
slope
change in y
change in x

Probably one of the most thrilling rides at an amusement park is the roller coaster. Imagine you are about to ride this one!

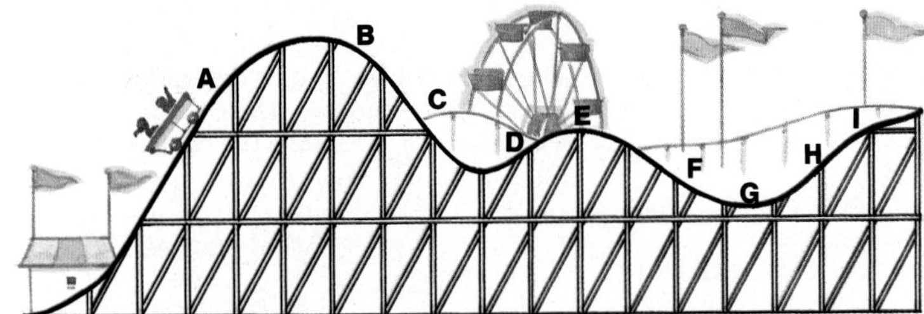

Let's compare position A with position D. In both cases, you are climbing. But at position A the climb is definitely steeper than at position D.

What about positions B and C? In both cases, you are dropping. At position C the drop is much steeper than at position B.

Think about what happens at position E. Here you are neither climbing nor dropping.

The steepness of the roller coaster depends on the vertical change and the horizontal change. It can be expressed as a ratio.

$$\text{steepness} = \frac{\text{vertical change}}{\text{horizontal change}}$$

Lines in a coordinate plane also have steepness. In mathematics, the steepness of a line is called its **slope.** The vertical change is called the **change in y,** and the horizontal change is called the **change in x.**

$$\text{slope} = \frac{\text{change in } y}{\text{change in } x}$$

The longest roller coaster in the world is The Beast at King's Island near Cincinnati, Ohio. It has reached a speed of 64.77 mph at the base of its 141-foot drop.

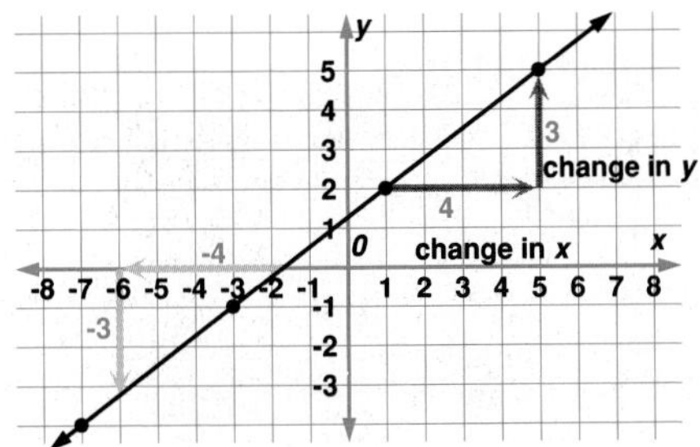

In Quadrant I, the change in y is 3 and the corresponding change in x is 4. Therefore, the slope of the line is $\frac{3}{4}$. Is the slope of the line the same in Quadrant III?

$$\frac{\text{change in } y}{\text{change in } x} = \frac{-3}{-4} \text{ or } \frac{3}{4}$$

The slopes are the same.

Bell Ringer

Have the students draw a line that contains the following points: (1, 4), (5,8), (-2,1).

Lesson Notes 8-8

5-Minute Check
(over Lesson 8-7)

Use a graph to solve the problem below. A logging truck can carry 20,000 pounds of logs from the forest to the mill. It takes $1\frac{1}{2}$ hours for the truck tomake a round trip from the logging site to the mill. How many pounds of logs will the truck be able to transport in a 6-hour day? **80,000 pounds**

Transparency 8-8 contains the 5-Minute Check and a teaching aid for this lesson.

1 FOCUS

The purpose of this lesson is to introduce the concept of slope.

Motivating the Lesson

Ask the students if they have ever been on a roller coaster. Talk about what happens when the roller coaster is steep. What else has a steepness? **a slide on a playground, a street or road, a ski slope**

2 TEACH

Using Models Use a geoboard as a model for the coordinate plane. You can use the Easy-to-Make Manipulative provided on page 9 of the Lab Manual. Let the peg in the lower lefthand corner represent the origin. Have students form line segments that have different slopes. Then have them find the slopes of their segments. Some examples are shown below.

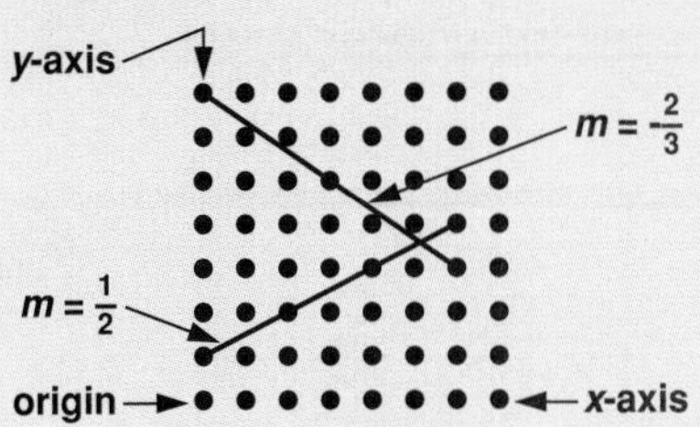

EE: 1E, 3A, 5E, 6B, 6C

Chalkboard Examples

Find the slope of the line that contains A(2,6) and B(-3,-8). $\frac{14}{5}$

3 PRACTICE/APPLY

Checking the Concept

Using Critical Thinking Ask students the questions below.

- Is it possible to tell if a line has a positive slope by looking at its graph? Explain. **yes, slants up to the right**
- Is it possible for a line to have a slope of zero? Explain. **yes, if y-coordinates are the same**
- What does a line with a zero slope look like? **horizontal**
- What does a line with no slope look like? **vertical**

Error Analysis

Watch for students who are not finding the correct slope.
Prevent by pointing out that when using the formula for slope, the "subtractions" for finding the changes in y and x must be done in the same order.

Practice Masters Booklet, **p. 78**

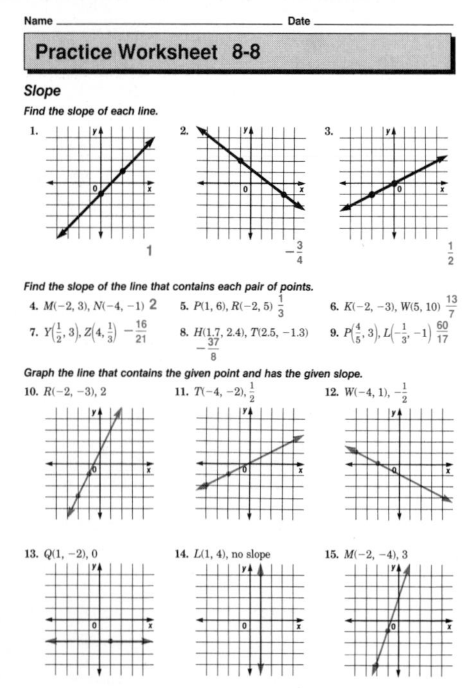

Name ______ Date ______

Practice Worksheet 8-8

Slope

Find the slope of each line.

1. 1
2. $-\frac{3}{4}$
3. $\frac{1}{2}$

Find the slope of the line that contains each pair of points.

4. M(−2, 3), N(−4, −1) 2
5. P(1, 6), R(−2, 5) $\frac{1}{3}$
6. K(−2, −3), W(5, 10) $\frac{13}{7}$
7. $Y(\frac{1}{2}, 3)$, $Z(4, \frac{1}{3})$ $-\frac{16}{21}$
8. H(1.7, 2.4), T(2.5, −1.3) $-\frac{37}{8}$
9. $P(\frac{4}{5}, 3)$, $L(-\frac{1}{3}, -1)$ $\frac{60}{17}$

Graph the line that contains the given point and has the given slope.

10. R(−2, −3), 2
11. T(−4, −2), $\frac{1}{2}$
12. W(−4, 1), $-\frac{1}{2}$
13. Q(1, −2), 0
14. L(1, 4), no slope
15. M(−2, −4), 3

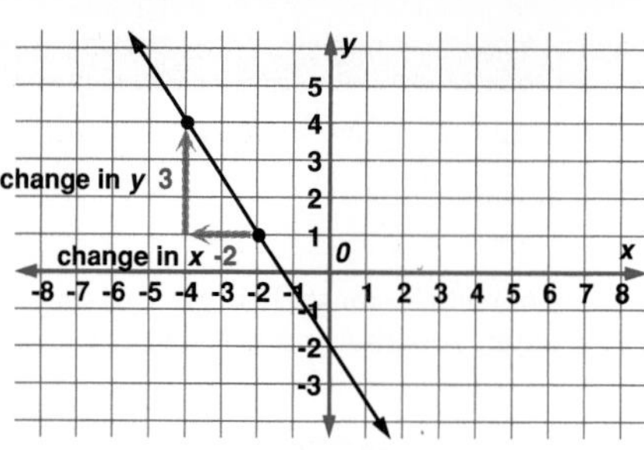

The slope of a line can also be negative. At the left the change in y is 3 and the corresponding change in x is -2. Therefore, the slope is $\frac{3}{-2}$ or $-\frac{3}{2}$.

Why is the slope of a horizontal line 0? **because the change in y is 0**
Why does a vertical line have no slope? **because the change in x is 0 and you cannot have 0 in the denominator**

The slope of a line can be determined by using the coordinates of any two points on the line. The change in y can be found by subtracting the y-coordinates. Likewise, the change in x can be found by subtracting the corresponding x-coordinates.

$$\text{slope} = \frac{\text{difference of } y\text{-coordinates}}{\text{difference of } x\text{-coordinates}}$$

Example

1 Find the slope of the line that contains $A(4, 3)$ and $B(-2, -5)$.

$$\text{slope} = \frac{\text{difference of } y\text{-coordinates}}{\text{difference of } x\text{-coordinates}}$$

$$\text{slope of line } AB = \frac{3 - (-5)}{4 - (-2)}$$

$$= \frac{8}{6} \text{ or } \frac{4}{3}$$

The slope is $\frac{4}{3}$.

Is the slope the same if you find $\frac{-5-3}{-2-4}$? **yes**

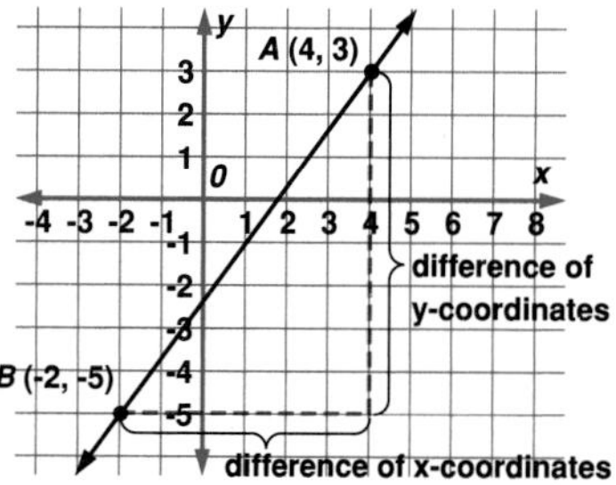

Checking for Understanding

Communicating Algebra

1. A, D, H, I; B, C, F

1. Using the drawing of the roller coaster, name all positions that represent a positive slope. Name all positions that represent a negative slope.
2. The slope of a line is 3. What does that mean? **See margin.**
3. On the drawing of the roller coaster, what is the slope at position G? **0**

Guided Practice

Find the slope of each line.

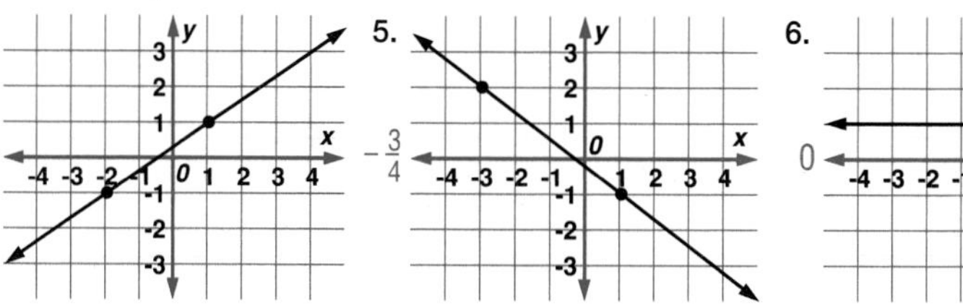

4. $\frac{2}{3}$
5. $-\frac{3}{4}$

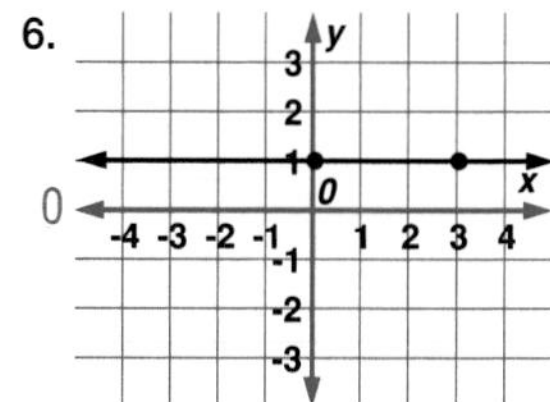

6. 0

Alternate Strategies: Reteaching the Lesson

Reteaching Activity

Using Chalkboard Examples On the chalkboard or overhead, draw lines that go through the origin and also the points: (2,2), (2,4), (4,2), (2,6), and (6,2). Have students determine and compare the slopes of the lines.

Reteaching Masters Booklet, **p. 70**

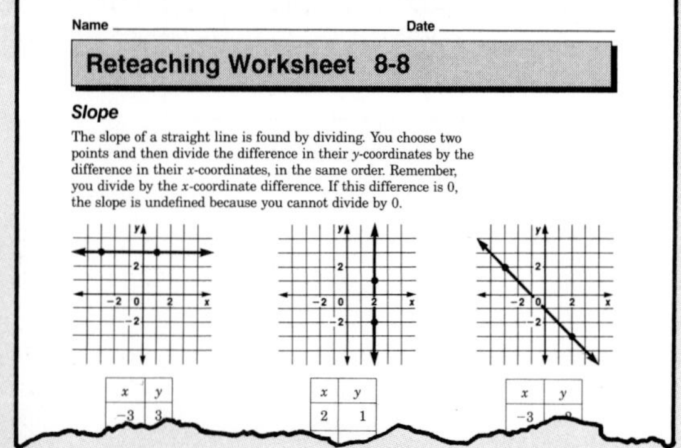

Name ______ Date ______

Reteaching Worksheet 8-8

Slope

The slope of a straight line is found by dividing. You choose two points and then divide the difference in their y-coordinates by the difference in their x-coordinates, in the same order. Remember, you divide by the x-coordinate difference. If this difference is 0, the slope is undefined because you cannot divide by 0.

Exercises

Independent Practice

Find the slope of the line that contains each pair of points.

7. $A(5, 3), B(-1, 1)$ $\frac{1}{3}$
8. $C(-3, 1), D(4, 5)$ $\frac{4}{7}$
9. $F(2, 3), G(-1, 3)$ 0
10. $L(-1, -2), M(2, -5)$ -1
11. $P(5, -2), Q(4, -3)$ 1
12. $R(7, 3), S(3, -9)$ 3
13. $Q(5, 6), S(2, -2)$ $2\frac{2}{3}$
14. $V(1, 0), X(-2, -3)$ 1
15. $A(5, -1), C(-3, -4)$ $\frac{3}{8}$
16. $S(-7, -3), T(-4, -5)$ $-\frac{2}{3}$
17. $C\left(\frac{3}{2}, 1\right), D\left(\frac{5}{2}, \frac{1}{2}\right)$ $-\frac{1}{2}$
18. $G\left(3, \frac{7}{2}\right), H\left(3, \frac{11}{2}\right)$ no slope

Mixed Review

19. Find the LCD of $\frac{5}{9x}$ and $\frac{2}{3x^3}$. (Lesson 4-9) $9x^3$
20. Simplify the expression $2(m + 3c) - 5c$. (Lesson 7-4) $2m + c$
21. If $r = -2$, what is the value of s in the equation $2r + s = 6$? (Lesson 8-5) 10
22. Graph the equation $y = \frac{1}{2}x - 1$. (Lesson 8-6) See Solutions Manual.

For graphs to Exercises 23-28, see Solutions Manual.

Challenge

Graph the line that contains the given point and has the given slope.

23. $M(0, 0); \frac{1}{2}$
24. $R(-1, 2); -\frac{1}{4}$
25. $T(3, 0); 0$
26. $D(-3, 1); 2$
27. $K(2, 5)$; no slope
28. $E(3, -4); -1$

Applications

29. **Science** An inclined plane is a slanted surface, which may be used for raising objects to higher places. Find the slope of the inclined plane pictured at the right. 0.1

30. **Surveying** A surveyor talks about slope in terms of *rise* and *run*. Use a surveyor's terms to define the slope of a line. Slope $= \frac{\text{rise}}{\text{run}}$

Connection

31. **Statistics** Line graphs are used to show changes in data over a period of time. The graph at the right shows how the Dow Jones Industrial Average changed from August 2 through November 1. Use the graph to answer each question.

Dow Jones Industrial Average

1500, 1450, 1400, 1350, 1300, 1250, 1200

9 23 6 20 4 18 1
Aug. Sept. Oct. Nov

a. During which week did the greatest increase occur? Oct. 25

b. How many weeks did the average decrease?

c. Name a week in which the average did not change. Aug. 30

31. b. 5 weeks

Critical Thinking

32. Explain how you can tell from just looking at the graph of a linear equation whether its slope is positive or negative. See margin.

Wrap-Up

33. Find a coordinate graph in the newspaper. Explain how your knowledge of slope can help you analyze the graph. See students' work.

Independent Practice

Homework Assignment	
Basic	7-17 odd,19-25, 30-33
Average	8-18 even, 19-25, 30-33
Honors	16-33

4 CLOSE

Assessment Option

Modeling Use two different colored dice. One is for x-values and the other for y-values. Roll both and create an ordered pair. Graph the point. Roll the cubes again and graph the point. What is the slope determined by the two points? Repeat as necessary. Answers may vary.

Additional Answers

2. The change in y is three times the change in x.
32. The slope is positive if the height of the line increases from left to right. The slope is negative if the height of the line decreases from left to right.

Enrichment Masters Booklet, **p. 70**

Name ______ Date ______

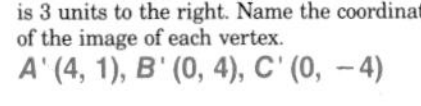

Enrichment Worksheet 8-8

Translations and Reflections

The lines on graph paper can help you draw slide images of figures.

1. Graph ΔABC with vertices $A(1, 1)$, $B(-3, 4)$, and $C(-3, -4)$. Drawn $\Delta A'B'C'$, the translation image of ΔABC, where the slide is 3 units to the right. Name the coordinates of the image of each vertex.
$A'(4, 1)$, $B'(0, 4)$, $C'(0, -4)$

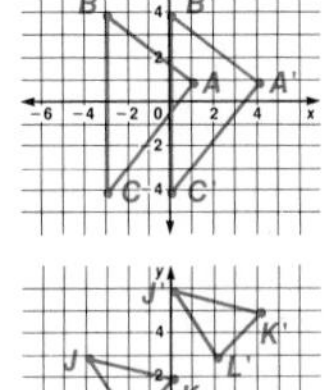

2. Draw ΔJKL with vertices $J(-4, 3)$, $K(0, 2)$, and $L(-2, 0)$. Let $\Delta J'K'L'$ be the image of ΔJKL under a slide of 4 units to the right and then a slide of 3 units up. Graph $\Delta J'K'L'$. Name the coordinates of the vertices of $\Delta J'K'L'$.
$J'(0, 6)$, $K'(4, 5)$, $L'(2, 3)$

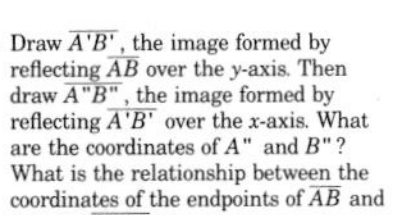

3. Draw $\overline{A'B'}$, the image formed by reflecting $\overline{AB}$ over the y-axis. Then draw $\overline{A''B''}$, the image formed by reflecting $\overline{A'B'}$ over the x-axis. What are the coordinates of A'' and B''? What is the relationship between the coordinates of the endpoints of $\overline{AB}$ and those of $\overline{A''B''}$?

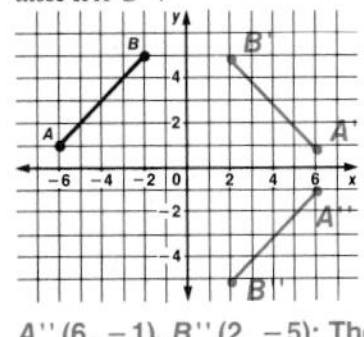

$A''(6, -1)$, $B''(2, -5)$; The coordinates of A'' and B'' have the opposite signs of A and B.

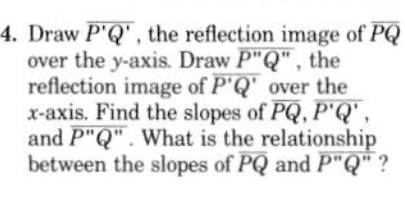

4. Draw $\overline{P'Q'}$, the reflection image of $\overline{PQ}$ over the y-axis. Draw $\overline{P''Q''}$, the reflection image of $\overline{P'Q'}$ over the x-axis. Find the slopes of $\overline{PQ}$, $\overline{P'Q'}$, and $\overline{P''Q''}$. What is the relationship between the slopes of $\overline{PQ}$ and $\overline{P''Q''}$?

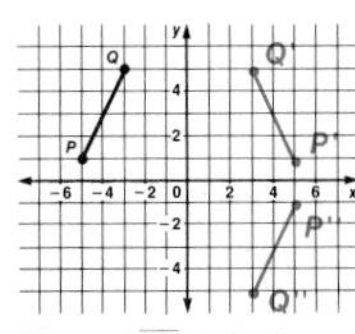

Slope of $\overline{PQ} = 2$; slope of $\overline{P'Q'} = -2$; slope of $\overline{P''Q''} = 2$; They are the same.

Alternate Strategies: Extending the Lesson

Enrichment

Using Discussion Have students graph several simple equations, such as $y = -2x + 4$, $y = 3x - 2$, and $y = 5x + 1$. Have students find the slope of each line. Discuss whether or not there is any relationship between this form of the equation and the slope of the line. Slopes: -2; 3; 5

Cooperative Learning

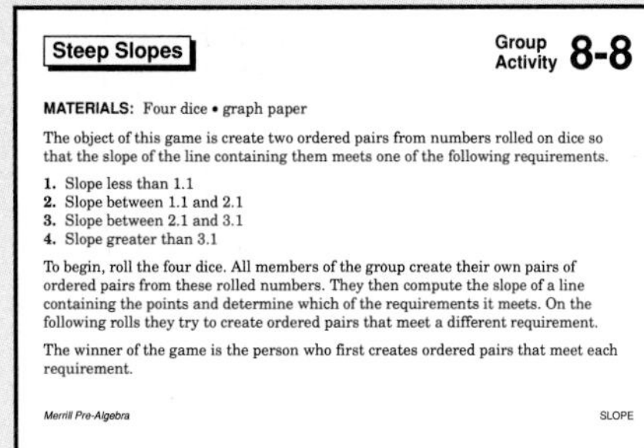

Steep Slopes Group Activity **8-8**

MATERIALS: Four dice • graph paper

The object of this game is create two ordered pairs from numbers rolled on dice so that the slope of the line containing them meets one of the following requirements.

1. Slope less than 1.1
2. Slope between 1.1 and 2.1
3. Slope between 2.1 and 3.1
4. Slope greater than 3.1

To begin, roll the four dice. All members of the group create their own pairs of ordered pairs from these rolled numbers. They then compute the slope of a line containing the points and determine which of the requirements it meets. On the following rolls they try to create ordered pairs that meet a different requirement.

The winner of the game is the person who first creates ordered pairs that meet each requirement.

Merrill Pre-Algebra SLOPE

Lesson Notes 8-9

5-Minute Check
(over Lesson 8-8)

Find the slope of the line that contains each pair of points.

1. C(-4,-2), D(5,3) $\frac{5}{9}$
2. P(1,4), Q(5,-2) $-\frac{3}{2}$
3. V(0,7), X(5,1) $-\frac{6}{5}$

Transparency 8-9 contains the 5-Minute Check and a teaching aid for this lesson.

1 FOCUS

The purpose of this lesson is to introduce the concept of an intercept and apply this idea to graphing a linear equation.

2 TEACH

Chalkboard Examples

Graph $y = -\frac{1}{4}x + 3$ by using the y-intercept and the x-intercept.
y- intercept is 3; x- intercept is 12.

***Practice Masters Booklet,* p. 79**

Name ______________ Date ______________

Practice Worksheet 8-9

Intercepts

Write the ordered pair describing the coordinates of each intercept.

1. x-intercept: 17 (17, 0)
2. y-intercept: 21 (0, 21)
3. x-intercept: $\frac{1}{5}$ $\left(\frac{1}{5}, 0\right)$
4. y-intercept: $\frac{3}{4}$ $\left(0, \frac{3}{4}\right)$
5. x-intercept: −6 (−6, 0)
6. y-intercept: −2.3 (0, −2.3)

Find the x-intercept and y-intercept for the graph of each equation.

7. $y = x - 7$ x-intercept: 7 y-intercept: −7
8. $y = 3x - 9$ x-intercept: 3 y-intercept: −9
9. $y = 5x + 10$ x-intercept: −2 y-intercept: 10
10. $y = 2x - 6$ x-intercept: 3 y-intercept: −6
11. $y = \frac{1}{2}x + 4$ x-intercept: −8 y-intercept: 4
12. $y = \frac{2}{3}x + 6$ x-intercept: −9 y-intercept: 6
13. $y = 4 - 2x$ x-intercept: 2 y-intercept: 4
14. $y = 12 - 6x$ x-intercept: 2 y-intercept: 12
15. $y = -7 + 3x$ x-intercept: $\frac{7}{3}$ y-intercept: −7

Use the x-intercept and y-intercept to graph each equation.

16. $y = 2x + 4$
17. $y = \frac{1}{2}x - 2$
18. $y = 0.5x + 1$

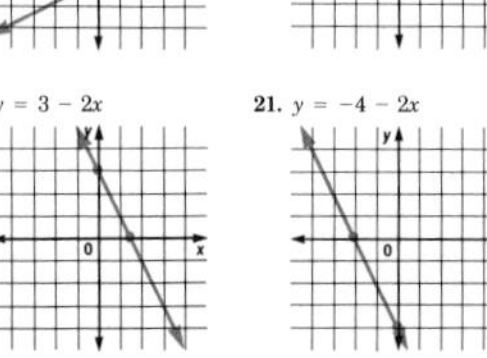

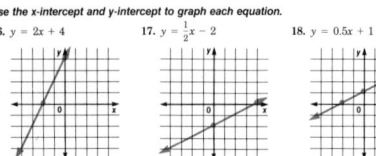

19. $y = -3 + 2x$
20. $y = 3 - 2x$
21. $y = -4 - 2x$

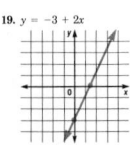

8-9 Intercepts

Objective:
Graph a linear equation by using the x-intercept and the y-intercept.

Key Terms:
x-intercept
y-intercept

When a defensive back intercepts a pass in football, he generally crosses the path of the ball on the way to the receiver.

In mathematics, the graph of a linear equation may cross either the x-axis, the y-axis, or both axes. The **x-intercept** is the x-coordinate of the point where the graph crosses the x-axis. The **y-intercept** is the y-coordinate of the point where the graph crosses the y-axis.

The equation is $y = -2x + 4$.

The ordered pair for the point on the y-axis is (0, 4). So the y-intercept is 4.

The ordered pair for the point on the x-axis is (2, 0). So the x-intercept is 2.

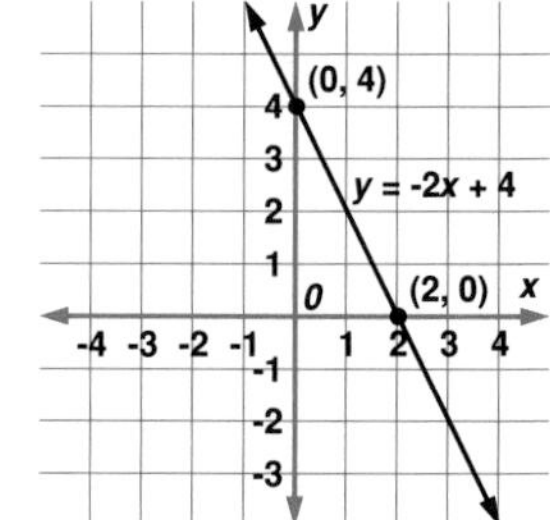

The y-intercept is the value of y when x is 0. The x-intercept is the value of x when y is 0. The y-intercept and x-intercept can be used to graph a linear equation.

Example

How many points determine a line? **2**

1 Graph $y = \frac{1}{2}x - 1$ by using the y-intercept and the x-intercept.

Find the y-intercept.
Find the value of y when $x = 0$.

$$y = \frac{1}{2}x - 1$$
$$y = \frac{1}{2}(0) - 1$$
$$y = -1$$

The y-intercept is -1.
The ordered pair is (0, -1).

Find the x-intercept.
Find the value of x when y = 0.

$$y = \frac{1}{2}x - 1$$
$$(0) = \frac{1}{2}x - 1$$
$$0 + 1 = \frac{1}{2}x - 1 + 1$$
$$1 = \frac{1}{2}x$$
$$2 = x$$

The x-intercept is 2.
The ordered pair is (2, 0).

Bell Ringer

What is the slope of the line determined by the following points?

1. (4,4) and (10,8) $\frac{2}{3}$
2. (-1,3) and (x,y) $\frac{3-y}{-1-x}$ or $\frac{y-3}{x-(-1)}$ or $\frac{y-3}{x+1}$

EE: 1E, 3A, 6B, 6C

***Reteaching Master Booklet,* p. 71**

Name ______________ Date ______________

Reteaching Worksheet 8-9

Intercepts

Each of the lines graphed at the right crosses the x- and y-axes. The point where a straight-line graph intersects an axis is called an **intercept** of the graph. (*Intersect* and *intercept* are words with similar meanings.)

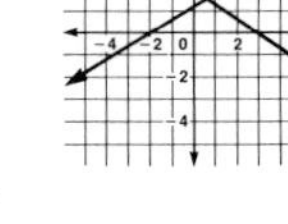

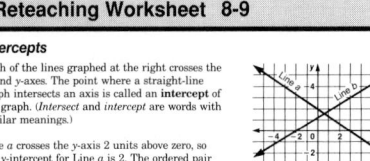

Line a crosses the y-axis 2 units above zero, so the y-intercept for Line a is 2. The ordered pair showing the location of this intercept is (0, 2). Notice that the x-value is zero.

The y-intercept is the value of an equation when x equals 0; the x-intercept is the value when y equals 0.

Write true or false for each.

1. The x-intercept for Line a is −3.
2. The y-intercept for Line b is 2. false

Graph the ordered pairs (0, -1) and (2, 0). Draw the line that contains the two points.

To test, you can graph a third point to see if it is on the line. For example, try $x = 4$. Then $y = \frac{1}{2}(4) - 1$ or 1. The ordered pair (4, 1) is on the line.

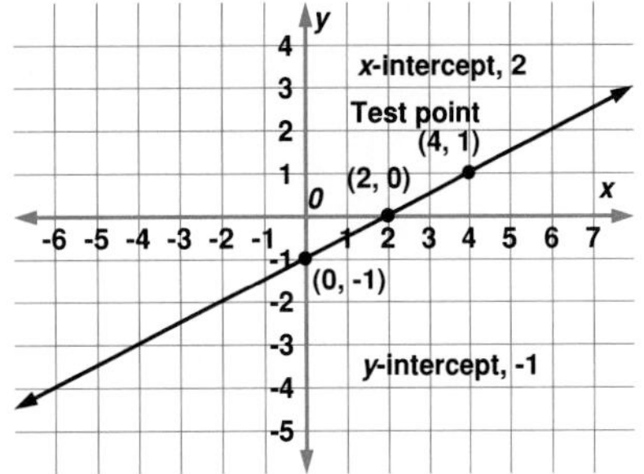

Checking for Understanding

For graphs to Exercises 1-2, see Solutions Manual.

Communicating Algebra

1. Graph the line that has an x-intercept of 3 and a y-intercept of -2.
2. Graph the line that has an x-intercept of -4 and a y-intercept of 1.
3. An x-intercept is 3. State the ordered pair describing its coordinates. **(3, 0)**
4. A y-intercept is -5. State the ordered pair describing its coordinates. **(0, -5)**

Guided Practice

Find the x-intercept and y-intercept for the graph of each equation.

5. $y = x - 3$ **3, -3**
6. $y = x + 5$ **-5, 5**
7. $y = -x - 2$ **-2, -2**
8. $y = 2x + 1$ **$-\frac{1}{2}$, 1**
9. $y = 3x - 4$ **$\frac{4}{3}$, -4**
10. $y = -5x + 6$ **$\frac{6}{5}$, 6**
11. $y = 2x - \frac{2}{3}$ **$\frac{1}{3}$, $-\frac{2}{3}$**
12. $y = 2 - 3x$ **$\frac{2}{3}$, 2**
13. $y = 7x - 4.2$ **0.6, -4.2**

Exercises

For graphs to Exercises 14-22, see Solutions Manual.

Independent Practice

Use the x-intercept and the y-intercept to graph each equation.

14. $y = x + 2$ **-2, 2**
15. $y = x - 1$ **1, -1**
16. $y = x + 3$ **-3, 3**
17. $y = 2x + 3$ **$-\frac{3}{2}$, 3**
18. $y = 3x - 6$ **2, -6**
19. $y = -5x + 10$ **2, 10**
20. $y = \frac{1}{2}x - 5$ **10, -5**
21. $y = 3 - 0.5x$ **6, 3**
22. $y = \frac{1}{3}x - 2$ **6, -2**

Mixed Review

23. Solve the equation $z = 37.2 \div 4$. (Lesson 6-7) **9.3**
24. Graph the equation $2x + y = 1$. (Lesson 8-6) **See Solutions Manual.**
25. Find the slope of the line that contains the points $P(7, -3)$ and $Q(-1, 4)$. (Lesson 8-8) **$-\frac{7}{8}$**

Application

26. **Business** Suppose you have an after-school baby-sitting service. You charge a flat fee of \$10 per week plus a fee of \$3 per hour. The equation $y = 3x + 10$ represents your earnings per week for one child. Graph this equation. Describe the y-intercept. **See Solutions Manual for graph; 10**

Critical Thinking Wrap-Up

27. Explain why you cannot graph the equation $y = 2x$ by using intercepts only. **See margin.**
28. Draw a graph of a line that has an x-intercept, but no y-intercept. **See Solutions Manual for sample answer.**

3 PRACTICE/APPLY

Checking the Concept

Using Questioning Ask students the questions below.

- What is the x-coordinate of any point on the y-axis?
- What is the y-coordinate of any point on the x-axis?

Error Analysis

Watch for students who interchange values for the x- and y- intercepts.
Prevent by emphasizing that the y-intercept crosses the y-axis, and the x-intercept crosses the x-axis.

Independent Practice

Homework Assignment	
Basic	15-21 odd, 23-28
Average	14-22 even, 23-28
Honors	18-28

4 CLOSE

Assessment Option

Writing Have students write a sentence or two describing the difference between an x-intercept and a y-intercept.

Enrichment Masters Booklet, p. 71

Name ____ Date ____

Enrichment Worksheet 8-9

Investments

The graph below represents two different investments. Line A represents an initial investment of \$30,000 with a bank paying passbook-savings interest. Line B represents an initial investment of \$5000 with a profitable mutual fund with dividends reinvested and capital gains accepted in shares. By deriving the equation, $y = mx + b$, for A and B, a projection of the future can be made.

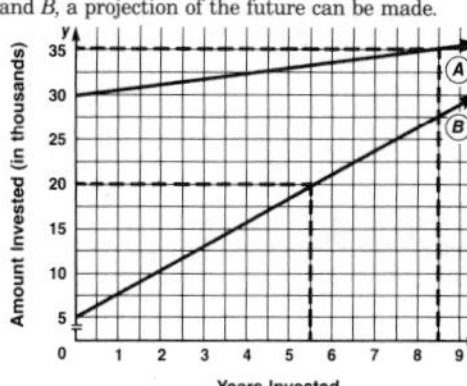

Solve.

1. The y-intercept, b, is the initial investment. Find b for each of the following.
   a. line A **30,000** b. line B **5000**
2. The slope of the line, m, is the rate of return. Find m for each of the following.
   a. line A **$\frac{35,000 - 30,000}{8.5 - 0} \approx 588$** b. line B **$\frac{20,000 - 5000}{5.5 - 0} \approx 2727$**
3. What are the equations of each of the following lines?
   a. line A **$y = 588x + 30,000$** b. line B **$y = 2727x + 5000$**

Answer each of the following, assuming that the growth of each investment continues in the same pattern.

4. What will be the value of the mutual fund after the 11th year? **$y = 2727(11) + 5000 = \$34,997$**
5. What will be the value of the bank account after the 11th year? **$y = 588(11) + 30,000 = \$36,468$**
6. When will the mutual fund and the bank account be of equal value? **$588x + 30,000 = 2727x + 5000 \rightarrow x \approx 11.7$ years**
7. In the long term, which investment has the greater payoff? **Mutual fund**

Additional Answer

27. The x-intercept and the y-intercept are both zero. The line, therefore, passes through the origin. Since two points are needed to graph a line, $y = 2x$ cannot be graphed using only the intercepts.

Cooperative Learning

On The Line Group Activity **8-9**

MATERIALS: Three 0-9 spinners

The object of this activity is to create equations of the form $y = ax + b$ or $y = ax - b$ whose intercepts meet one of the following requirements:

1. y-intercept less than or equal to -5
2. y-intercept between -1 and +4
3. x-intercept less than -2
4. x-intercept greater than 1
5. y-intercept positive and x-intercept negative

To begin, spin the three spinners. All members of the group will create their equations by using one of these numbers for a and a different one for b. Each person computes the intercepts from the created equation and determines which of the requirements it meets. On the following rolls each person tries to create equations that meet a different requirement.

The winner of the game is the first person to create one equation for each requirement.

Merrill Pre-Algebra INTERCEPTS

EXPLORATION
Slope

Objective Students will form conclusions by observing the physical relationships between the slopes of related linear functions.

1 FOCUS

The purpose of this exploration is to introduce students to the technology available and let them see geometry in algebra.

Motivating the Exploration

If students are not familiar with a graphing calculator, have them graph several linear functions on their calculator. This will help them feel more comfortable with the technology.

2 TEACH

Using Manipulatives

Give students the keystrokes to graph-related functions. Then ask them for conjectures about the related graphs as pertains to their slope.

3 PRACTICE/APPLY

Using Cooperative Groups

Have the students complete the activity in pairs. Circulate around the room as they graph the functions on the computer or calculator.

4 CLOSE

Writing Connection

Ask students to write a general rule for slopes of related graphs.

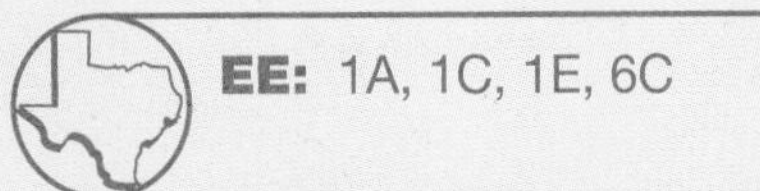

EE: 1A, 1C, 1E, 6C

Exploration
Slope

Materials: graphing calculator

In this Exploration, you will investigate several families of graphs to determine their characteristics.

▶ Consider the graphs of $y = 2x$, $y = -2x$, and $y = \frac{1}{2}x$.

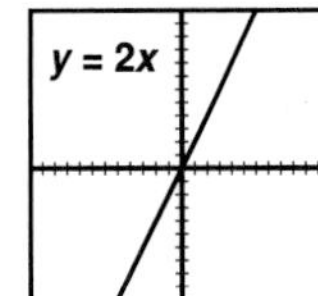

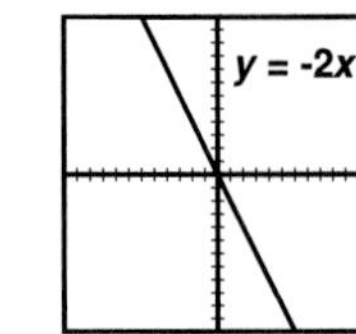

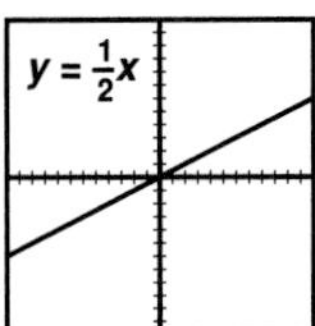

Alone the graphs may not appear to be related. But let's look at them together to discover some interesting patterns..

▶ Consider the graphs of $y = 2x$ and $y = -2x$. They appear to have the same steepness but in different directions.

Your Turn: Graph $y = 3x$ and $y = -3x$. Then graph $y = 1x$ and $y = -1x$. Describe the graphs. See Solutions Manual.

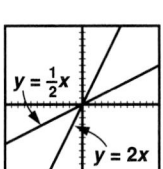

▶ Now consider the graphs of $y = 2x$ and $y = \frac{1}{2}x$. They appear to have different steepness but in the same direction.

Your Turn: Graph $y = 3x$ and $y = \frac{1}{3}x$. Then graph $y = 4x$ and $y = 2x$. Describe the graphs. See Solutions Manual.

Analysis

1. Write a sentence that explains the difference between the graphs of $y = 10x$ and $y = -10x$. $y = 10x$ has a positive slope; $y = -10x$ has a negative slope.
2. Write the equation of a line whose graph is between the graph of $y = 5x$ and $y = 1x$. Sample answer: $y = 4x$

Extension

3. Graph $y = 2x$, $y = 2x + 1$, $y = 2x + 2$, and $y = 2x + 3$. How are the graphs the same? How do they differ? The slopes are the same. The y-intercepts are different.

SET-UP

Materials

- computers or graphing calculators

You may wish to use the Exploration worksheet provided on page 48 of the Lab Manual.

For Students Each student or pair of students will need a graphing calculator or be stationed at a computer. If technology is not available, graph paper and pencil can be used.

For the Overhead Projector You can connect a computer to an overhead projection panel and complete the activity along with your students. Overhead projector graphing calculators are also available for this purpose.

8-10 Systems of Equations

Objective:
Solve systems of linear equations by graphing.

Key Term:
system of equations

The owner of any business, big or small, knows that in order to stay in business, the income from goods or services that are sold needs to balance with the cost of producing the goods or services. This is sometimes called the *break-even point*.

The break-even point can be found graphically. One equation is written to represent the income. Another equation is written to represent the cost. Then both equations are graphed. The point where the graphs intersect is the *break-even point*.

In mathematics, two equations with the same two variables form a **system of equations.** The solution of the system of equations is any ordered pair that is a solution of both equations. One way to solve a system of equations is by graphing.

Examples

1 **Use the graph at the right to solve the system of equations $y = x + 2$ and $y = 3x$.**

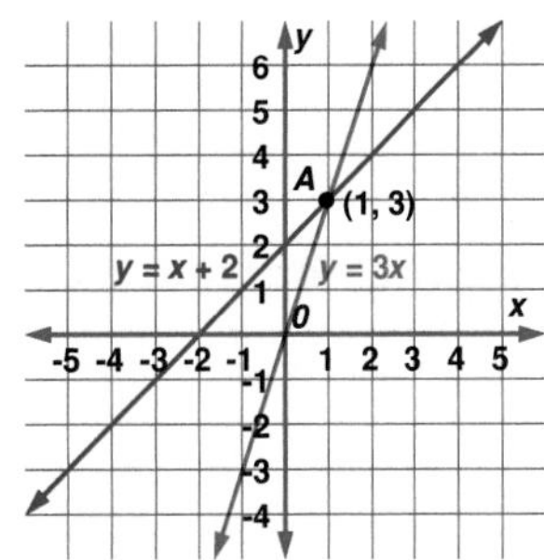

The graphs intersect at point A. Because point A is on the graph of each equation, the ordered pair for A is a solution of each equation. Thus, the solution of the system is (1, 3).

To check the solution, replace y in both equations with 3 and replace x in both equations with 1.

Check: $y = x + 2$ $\quad y = 3x$

$3 \stackrel{?}{=} 1 + 2$ $\quad 3 \stackrel{?}{=} 3(1)$

$3 = 3$ ✓ $\quad 3 = 3$ ✓

2 **Solve $x + y = 3$ and $y = 2x$ by graphing.**

Use intercepts to graph $x + y = 3$.

$x + 0 = 3$ Find the x-intercept.

$x = 3$

The ordered pair is (3, 0).

$0 + y = 3$ Find the y-intercept.

$y = 3$

The ordered pair is (0, 3).

Graph the points and draw the line that contains them.

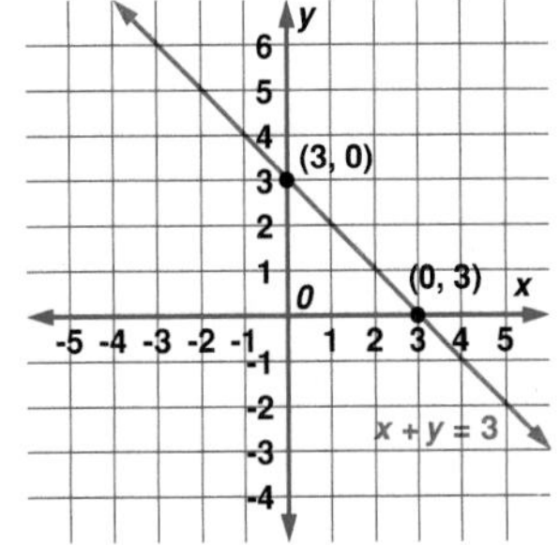

Bell Ringer

Graph $y = x + 1$ and $y = x + 4$. What do you notice about their slopes? **same** What does the graph look like? **parallel lines**

EE: 1E, 3A, 6B, 6C, 6D
TAAS: 2

Lesson Notes 8-10

5-Minute Check
(over Lesson 8-9)

Use the x-intercept and the y-intercept to graph each equation.

1. $y = 6 - x$ 2. $y = x - \frac{1}{2}$

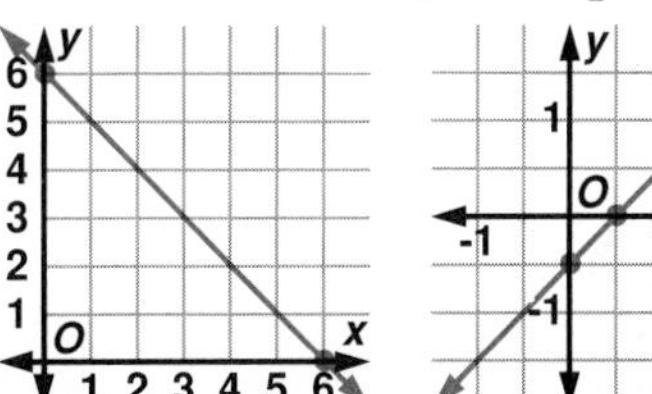

Transparency 8-10 contains the 5-Minute Check and a teaching aid for this lesson.

1 FOCUS

The purpose of this lesson is to provide students with a method for solving a system of two linear equations.

Motivating the Lesson

Tell students to use the guess-and-check strategy to solve this problem. *The sum of Mary and Joe's ages is 30. The difference in their ages is 2. What are Mary and Joe's ages?* **Mary is 16 and Joe is 14.**

2 TEACH

Using Connections Have students write equations to represent the first two statements in the problem above. Then have them graph both equations on the same coordinate system. Ask students for the coordinates of the intersection of the two lines. (16, 14) Remind students of the answer to the problem above. They should see the connection.

Chalkboard Examples

- *For Example 1*
Use the graph at the right to solve $y = x + 1$ and $y = 2x$.
(1,2)

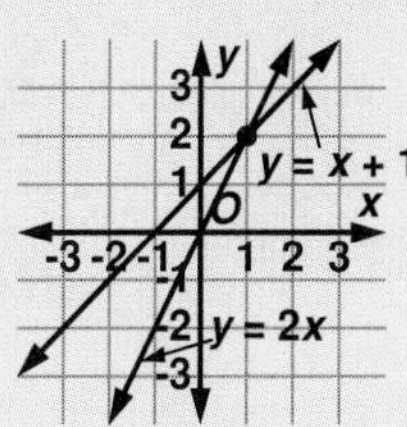

Chalkboard Examples

- *For Example 2*

Solve $x + y = 3$ and $y = x - 5$ by graphing. **(4, -1)**

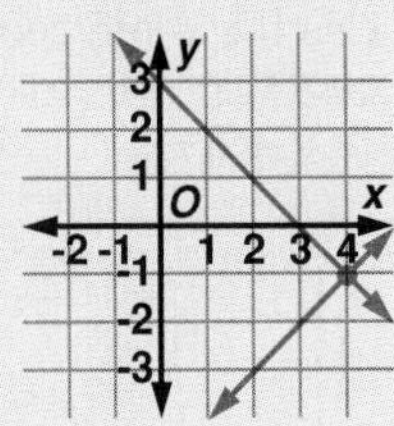

3 PRACTICE/APPLY

Checking the Concept

Using Critical Thinking Ask students to explain why the solution of a system of two linear equations with two variables is the point where the graphs of the equations intersect.

Error Analysis

Watch for students who have incorrect solutions because lines are inaccurately drawn.
Prevent by using a sharpened pencil and a straightedge.

Practice Masters Booklet, **p. 80**

Name ______ Date ______

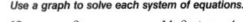

Practice Worksheet 8-10

Systems of Equations

The graphs of five equations are shown at the right. State the solution of each system of equations.

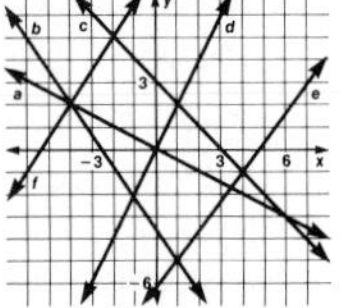

1. a and b $(-4, 2)$
2. c and d $(1, 2)$
3. c and e $(4, -1)$
4. b and d $(-1, -2)$
5. b and e $(1, -5)$
6. a and f $(-4, 2)$
7. c and f $(-2, 5)$
8. a and d $(0, 0)$
9. a and c $(6, -3)$
10. b and f $(-4, 2)$

Complete each table. Then graph the two equations in each exercise and state the solution as an ordered pair.

11. $x + y = 5$ (3, 2)

x	y
0	5
1	4
3	2
4	1

$x - y = 1$

x	y
7	6
5	4
3	2
1	0

12. $y = 2x + 6$ $(-1, 4)$

x	y
−2	2
−1	4
1	8
2	10

$y = x + 5$

x	y
−3	2
−1	4
0	5
2	7

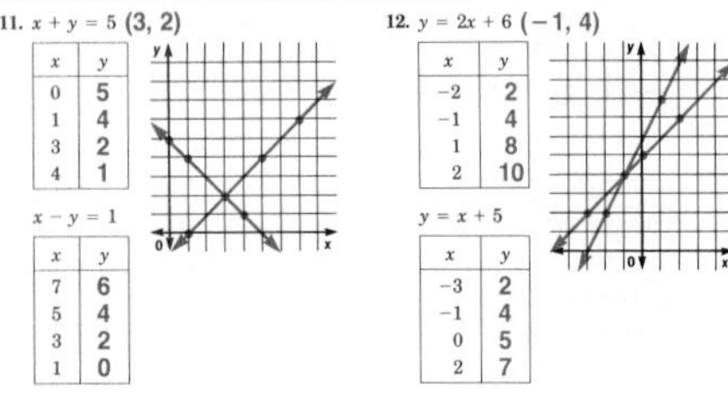

Use a graph to solve each system of equations.

13. $y - x = 2$, $x + y = 4$

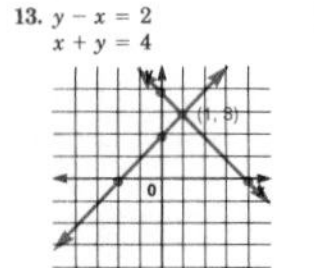

14. $2x + y = 4$, $y = 2x$

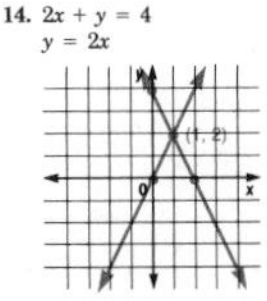

15. $2x - y = 3$, $x + y = 3$

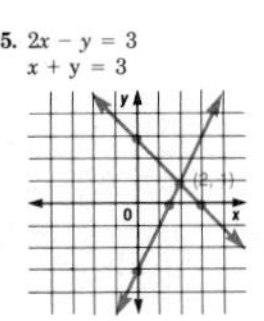

Use ordered pairs to graph $y = 2x$.

x	2x	y	(x, y)
-1	2(-1)	-2	(-1, -2)
0	2(0)	0	(0, 0)
1	2(1)	2	(1, 2)
2	2(2)	4	(2, 4)

Graph the points and draw the line that contains them.

The lines intersect at the point (1, 2). Therefore, the solution of the system of equations is (1, 2).

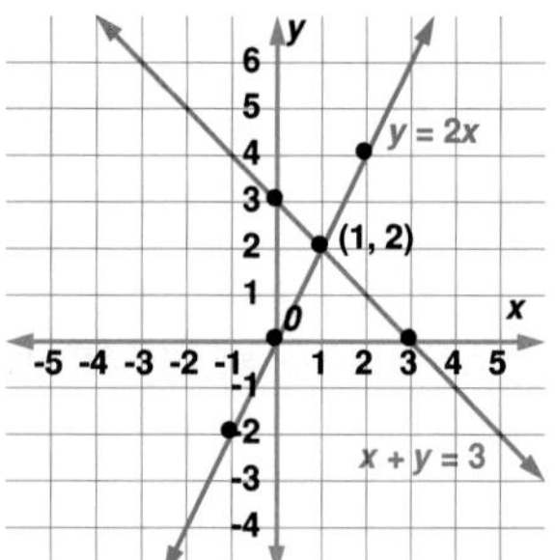

To check the solution, replace y in both equations with 2 and replace x in both equations with 1.

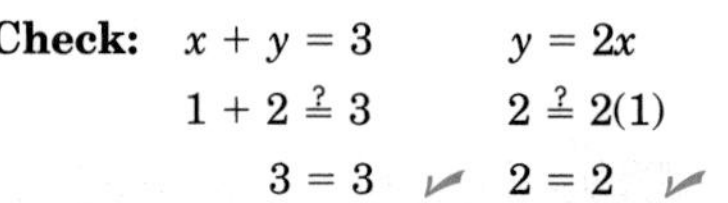

Check: $x + y = 3$ $\qquad$ $y = 2x$

$1 + 2 \stackrel{?}{=} 3$ $\qquad$ $2 \stackrel{?}{=} 2(1)$

$3 = 3$ ✓ $\qquad$ $2 = 2$ ✓

Checking for Understanding

Communicating Algebra

1. In business, the __?__ is where the costs of goods and services sold equals income. **break-even point**
2. Two equations with the same two variables form a __?__. **system of equations**
3. Explain why the ordered pair (2, -2) is not a solution of the system of equations $3x + 2y = 10$, $x + y = 0$. **(2, -2) is not a solution of $3x + 2y = 10$.**
4. Which ordered pairs are solutions of the equation $x + 2y = 7$? **a, c, d**
   a. (3, 2) **b.** (6, 1) **c.** (9, -1) **d.** (-1, 4)

Guided Practice

The graphs of several equations are shown at the right. State the solution of each system of equations.

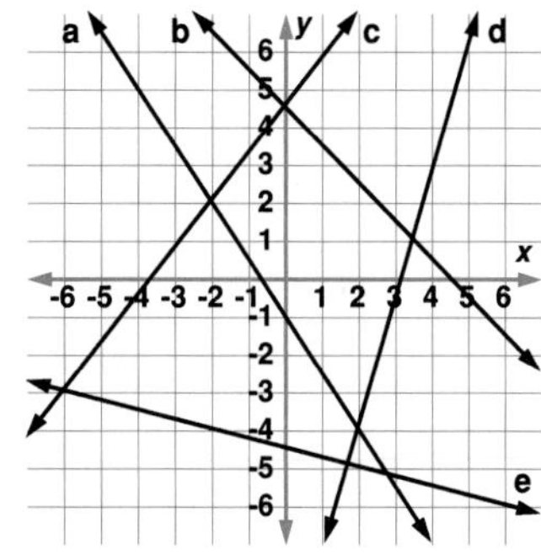

5. a and c **(-2, 2)**
6. b and c **(0, 4.5)**
7. c and e **(-6, -3)**
8. a and d **(2, -4)**
9. b and d **(3.5, 1)**
10. a and the y-axis **(0, -1)**
11. b and the x-axis **(4.5, 0)**

Alternate Strategies: Reteaching the Lesson

Reteaching Activity

Using Models Have students graph $y = 4x + 3$ on graph paper. Then tell them to choose a point on the line and a point not on the line and draw the line that goes through them. Have students write an equation for the new line and substitute the coordinates of the point on $y = 4x + 3$ into the new equation. Point out that any two equations form a system and the intersection of their graphs is the solution to the system.

Reteaching Masters Booklet, **p. 72**

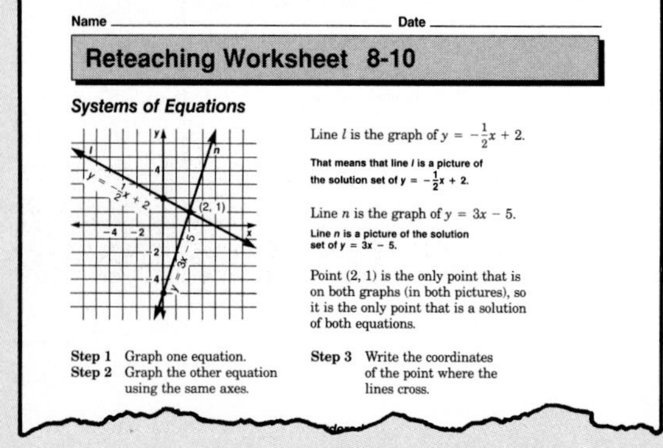

Name ______ Date ______

Reteaching Worksheet 8-10

Systems of Equations

Line l is the graph of $y = -\frac{1}{2}x + 2$.

That means that line l is a picture of the solution set of $y = -\frac{1}{2}x + 2$.

Line n is the graph of $y = 3x - 5$.

Line n is a picture of the solution set of $y = 3x - 5$.

Point (2, 1) is the only point that is on both graphs (in both pictures), so it is the only point that is a solution of both equations.

Step 1 Graph one equation.
Step 2 Graph the other equation using the same axes.
Step 3 Write the coordinates of the point where the lines cross.

Exercises

For graphs to Exercises 12-23, see Solutions Manual.

Independent Practice

Use a graph to solve each system of equations.

12. $y = 3x + 5$
    $y = x + 5$ (0, 5)
13. $y = x - 2$
    $y = 4x + 1$ (-1, -3)
14. $y = 4x$
    $y = -x$ (0, 0)
15. $y = x - 5$
    $y = -2x + 4$ (3, -2)
16. $x + y = 6$
    $y = 2x$ (2, 4)
17. $y - 4x = 3$
    $y = x$ (-1, -1)
18. $x = y + 7$
    $2x + y = 2$ (3, -4)
19. $y = \frac{1}{2}x$
    $x + 2y = 0$ (0, 0)
20. $2x + y = 8$
    $x - y = 4$ (4, 0)
21. $x + 3y = 5$
    $-x + y = 3$ (-1, 2)
22. $3x + y = 6$
    $4x + y = 7$ (1, 3)
23. $5y + 4x = 12$
    $3y - 4x = 4$ $(\frac{1}{2}, 2)$

Mixed Review

24. Solve the equation $7a + 2 = (-4)(a - 6)$. (Lesson 7-6) 2
25. **Science** Find the slope of the inclined plane pictured at right. (Lesson 8-8) $\frac{1}{2}$

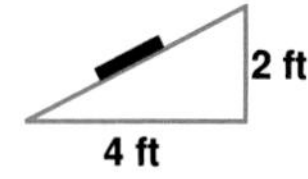

26. Graph $y = -3x + 2$ by using the x-intercept and the y-intercept. (Lesson 8-9) See Solutions Manual.

Application

27. **Business** The Murphy Company, a leading gadget maker, has fixed costs of \$900 per week. Each item produced by the company costs \$2 to manufacture and can be sold for \$5. If x is the number of gadgets produced each week, the cost of producing them can be represented by the equation $y = 900 + 2x$. The weekly income from selling the gadgets can be represented by $y = 5x$. Solve this system of equations by graphing. What is the company's *break-even point?* (300, 1500)

Critical Thinking

28. In this lesson, all of the systems have one solution. Is it possible for a system of two linear equations to have no solution or more than one solution? If so, draw a graph to show each situation. yes; See Solutions Manual for graphs.

Wrap-Up

29. Write a system of equations whose solution is (5, 8). Sample answers: $y = x + 3$; $y = 13 - x$

Team Problem Solving

Sometimes a graph is used to describe a series of events. This graph shows the height of a football above the ground from the time the ball was snapped for a field goal attempt.

Over which time periods did these events occur?

(a) The holder received the snap. B
(b) The ball was increasing in height. A, E
(c) The ball was kicked. D
(d) The ball lands in the stands behind the goal posts. G

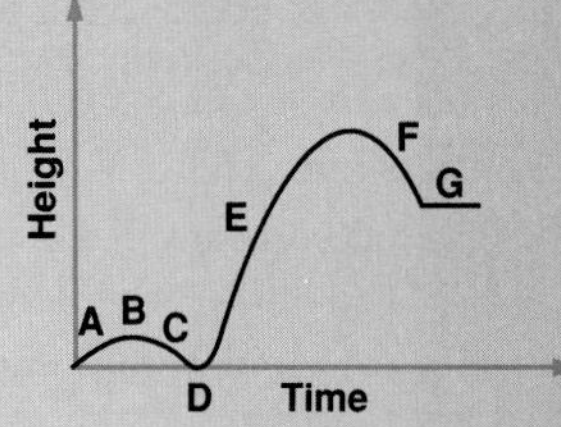

Draw a graph that shows how the speed of a skier changes as she waits for the ski lift, goes up the mountain, waits her turn, and skis down the mountain. See Solutions Manual.

Independent Practice

Homework Assignment	
Basic	13-23 odd, 24-29
Average	12-22 even, 24-29
Honors	18-29

4 CLOSE

Assessment Option

Writing Have students write the answer to the question below.

- What are the steps for finding the solution to a system of equations by graphing? Step 1: Graph both equations on the same coordinate system. Step 2: If the lines intersect, locate the point of intersection.

Enrichment Masters Booklet, **p. 72**

Name ____________ Date ____________

Enrichment Worksheet 8-10

Using Coordinates

1. Graph the points (1, 1), (4, 4), and (2, 4) on the coordinate system below. Connect the dots. Name the figure formed. triangle

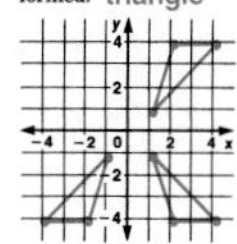

2. Multiply each y-coordinate by -1. Graph the points. How is this triangle related to the one in Exercise 1? It is a reflection over the x-axis.
3. Multiply each coordinate in Exercise 1 by -1. Graph the points.
4. What would you have to do to get the coordinates of a triangle in Quadrant II congruent to the ones in Exercises 1–3? Multiply each x-coordinate in Exercise 1 by -1.
5. Graph the points (3, 1), (2, 3), (4, 6), and (5, 4) on the coordinate plane at the right. Connect the dots. The figure formed is called a parallelogram.
6. Add 2 to both coordinates of each point and graph the new coordinates. Name the figure formed. parallelogram
7. Add -4 to the x-coordinate of each point in Exercise 5 and graph the new coordinates. Is this figure also a parallelogram? yes
8. Graph the points (5, −2), (6, −3), (5, −5), and (3, −3) on the coordinate plane at the right. Name the figure formed. trapezoid
9. Multiply both coordinates of each point in Exercise 8 by 2 and graph the new coordinates. This is an enlargement.
10. Multiply both coordinates of each point in Exercise 8 by $\frac{1}{2}$ and graph the new coordinates. This is a reduction.

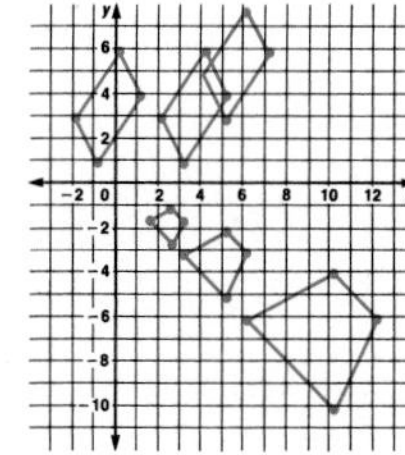

Alternate Strategies: Extending the Lesson

Enrichment

Consumer Awareness A club wants to sell bumper stickers. Manufacturer A will sell them the stickers for 22¢ each. Manufacturer B charges a \$50 flat rate plus 11¢ a sticker. Have students graph both plans. Discuss when one manufacturer would be cheaper than the other, and when they would be equal.

Cooperative Learning

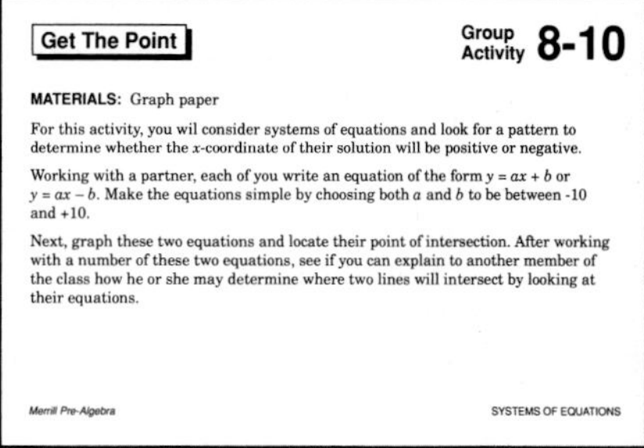

Get The Point Group Activity **8-10**

MATERIALS: Graph paper

For this activity, you wil consider systems of equations and look for a pattern to determine whether the x-coordinate of their solution will be positive or negative.

Working with a partner, each of you write an equation of the form $y = ax + b$ or $y = ax - b$. Make the equations simple by choosing both a and b to be between -10 and +10.

Next, graph these two equations and locate their point of intersection. After working with a number of these two equations, see if you can explain to another member of the class how he or she may determine where two lines will intersect by looking at their equations.

Merrill Pre-Algebra SYSTEMS OF EQUATIONS

EXPLORATION

Graphing Inequalities

Objective Students will be able to graph inequalities on the TI-81 graphing calculator and be able to complete an inequality based on the shaded area of the graph.

1 *FOCUS*

Motivating the Exploration

Give students the following key strokes for use on the TI-81.

[RANGE] [(-)] 10 [ENTER] 10 [ENTER] 1 [ENTER] [(-)] 10 [ENTER] 10 [ENTER] 1 [ENTER] [2nd] [QUIT]

This sets the axes ranges on their calculators to $(-10, 10)$ by $(-10, 10)$. Then have them graph $y < 3x + 4$ by entering the following keystrokes.

[2nd] [QUIT] [2nd] [DRAW] 1 [ENTER] [2nd] [DRAW] 7 [(-)] 10 [ALPHA] [,] 3 [X|T] [+] 4 [)] [ENTER]

2 *TEACH*

Using Manipulatives

You can use the Easy-to-Make Manipulative provided on page 26 of the Lab Manual to make an overlay of the TI-81 keyboard. Then you can use it on the overhead projector to help students locate the keys they need to press during this activity.

3 *PRACTICE/APPLY*

Using Cooperative Groups

Have the students complete the activity in pairs. Circulate around the room as they graph the functions on the calculator.

4 *CLOSE*

Writing Connection

Ask students to write a general rule for shading inequalities.

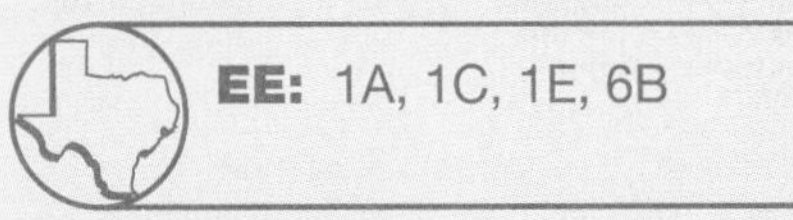

Exploration

Graphing Inequalities

Materials: TI-81 graphing calculator

In this Exploration, you will use a graphing calculator to investigate the graphs of inequalities.

▶ Consider the inequality $y < x + 4$. The graph of the inequality must show all of the points whose ordered pairs satisfy the inequality $y < x + 4$. Type the following keystroke sequence into your calculator.

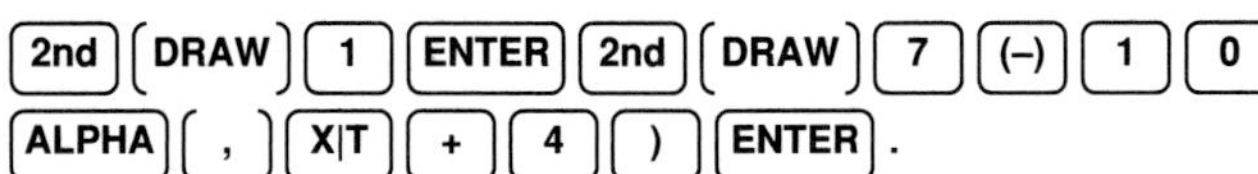

Notice that the graph is a shaded region. This indicates that all ordered pairs satisfy the inequality $y < x + 4$.

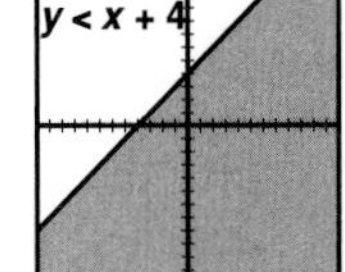

Your Turn: How does this differ from the graph of $y = x + 4$?

The graph of $y = x + 4$ is a line.

▶ Now consider the inequality $y > 2x - 1$. Type the following keystroke sequence into your calculator.

Once again, this graph is a shaded region. All ordered pairs satisfy the inequality $y > 2x - 1$.

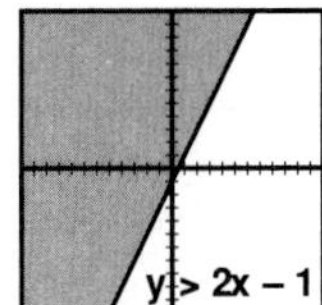

Your Turn: How does the graph of $y > 2x - 1$ differ from the graph of $y < x + 4$?

In $y > 2x - 1$, the region above the line is shaded.
In $y < x + 4$, the region below the line is shaded.

Application

1. The following keystroke sequence is used to graph the inequality y ● $x + 3$. Graph the inequality, then replace the ● with $<$ or $>$.

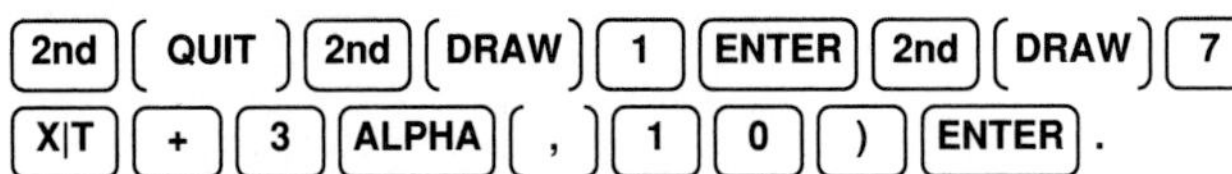

See Solutions Manual; >

SET-UP

Materials

- TI-81 graphing calculators

You may wish to use the Exploration worksheet provided on page 49 of the Lab Manual.

For Students Each student or pair of students will need a TI-81 graphing calculator. If technology is not available, graph paper and pencil can be used.

For the Overhead Projector You can use a TI-81 View-Screen™ and complete the activity along with your students.

8-11 Graphing Inequalities

Objective:
Graph linear inequalities.

Key Term:
boundary

The timberline separates a mountain into two regions. The region below the timberline can sustain tree growth. Above the timberline, the climate is too severe for tree growth.

The graph of a linear equation like $y = x + 1$ separates the coordinate plane into two regions, one above the line and one below the line. The line is called the **boundary** of the two regions. Point $A(2, 3)$ is on the line and $(2, 3)$ is a solution of $y = x + 1$.

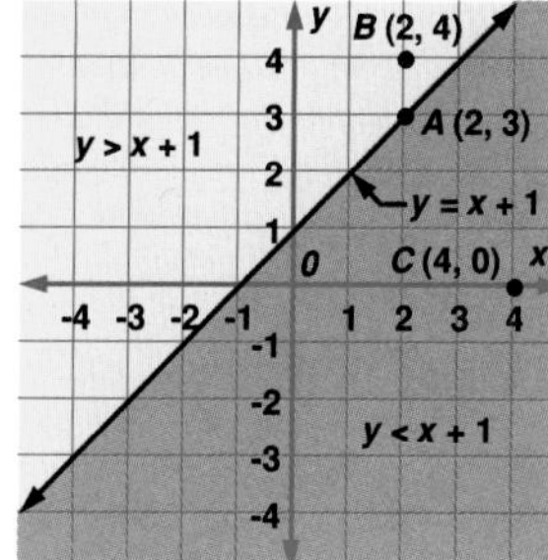

The graph of the inequality $y > x + 1$ is the region *above* the boundary line. Point $B(2, 4)$ is in this region and $(2, 4)$ is a solution of $y > x + 1$.

The graph of the inequality $y < x + 1$ is the region *below* the boundary line. Point $C(4, 0)$ is in this region and $(4, 0)$ is a solution of $y < x + 1$.

How is graphing inequalities on the coordinate plane similar to the way in which you graph inequalities on a number line? **Both graphs use shading to indicate the solution.**

Since the graph of an inequality must show *all* of the points whose coordinates are solutions of the inequality, you shade a region of the coordinate plane to graph an inequality. A dashed line is used when the boundary line is *not* part of the graph. A solid line is used when the boundary line is part of the graph. Two examples are shown.

FYI

At the timberline, or tree line, forests are replaced by low shrubs or no greenery at all. Temperature has the greatest effect on the location of the timberline, but soil, moisture, drainage, and sunlight are also factors.

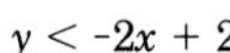

$y < -2x + 2$

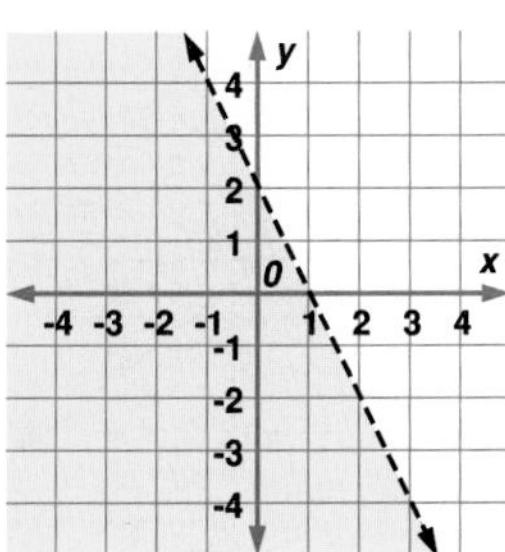

$y \geq x - 3$

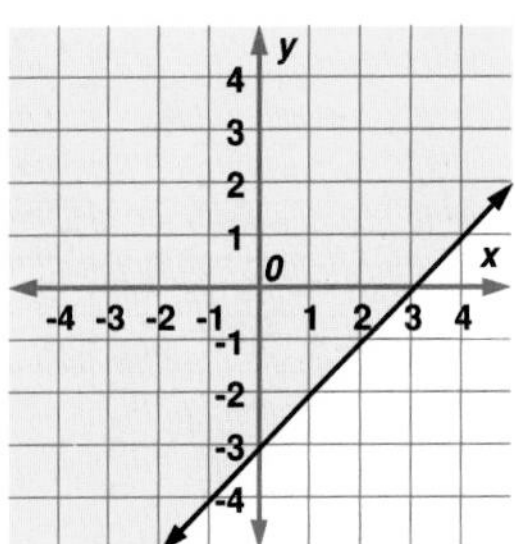

Lesson Notes 8-11

5-Minute Check
(over Lesson 8-10)

Use a graph to solve each system of equations.

1. $y = x + 1$
   $y = -x + 3$
2. $2x - y = 6$
   $x = y + 2$

(1, 2) (4, 2)

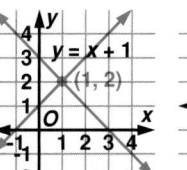

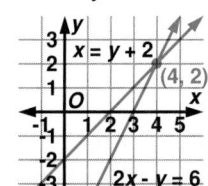

Transparency 8-11 contains the 5-Minute Check and a teaching aid for this lesson.

1 FOCUS

The purpose of this lesson is to introduce the procedures for graphing linear inequalities.

Motivating the Lesson

Discuss situations where shading is used. For example, a car visor, a baseball cap, sunglasses. Explain that in each case you shade the area you want to use.

2 TEACH

Using Charts Display the graph of $y = 2x - 3$ on the chalkboard or overhead. Have students create a chart with three columns. The heading of the columns should be $y < 2x - 3$, $y = 2x - 3$, and $y > 2x - 3$. Have students select points on the line and on either side of the line. Then have the students complete the chart by filling in each column with the coordinates of points that make the heading a true sentence.

Bell Ringer

The value of x is the same in both equations below. The two ink blots cover the same number. What is the value of x? **84**

$123 - x =$ ▇ $45 + x =$ ▇ **84**

39   **39**

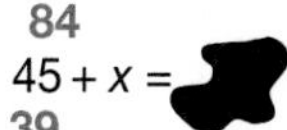

EE: 1E, 3A, 6B
TAAS: 2

Chalkboard Examples

Graph $y > -2x + 5$.

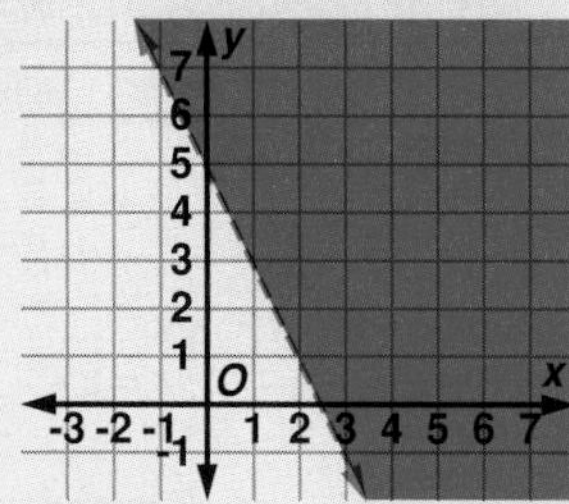

3 PRACTICE/APPLY

Checking the Concept

Using Questioning Ask students the following question.

- How do you determine which side of the boundary line to shade? **Choose a test point. Substitute its coordinates in the inequality. If the result is true, that side of the boundary is shaded.**

Error Analysis

Watch for students who have difficulty reading a graph.
Prevent by writing intervals on the horizontal axis and using a straightedge to read the graph.

Practice Masters Booklet, **p. 81**

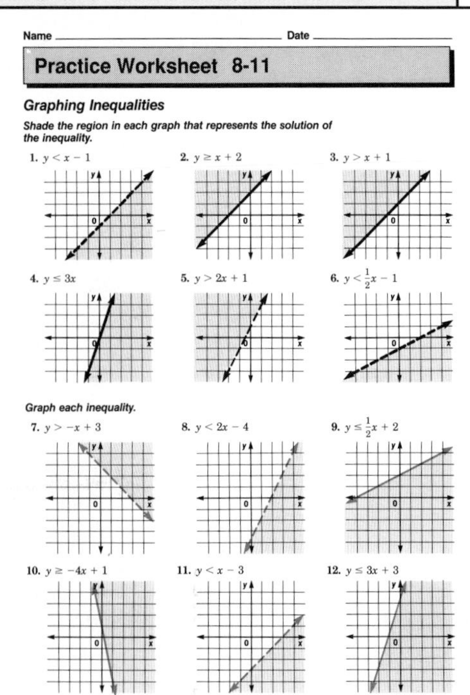

Name ______ Date ______

Practice Worksheet 8-11

Graphing Inequalities

Shade the region in each graph that represents the solution of the inequality.

1. $y < x - 1$
2. $y \geq x + 2$
3. $y > x + 1$
4. $y \leq 3x$
5. $y > 2x + 1$
6. $y < \frac{1}{2}x - 1$

Graph each inequality.

7. $y > -x + 3$
8. $y < 2x - 4$
9. $y \leq \frac{1}{2}x + 2$
10. $y \geq -4x + 1$
11. $y < x - 3$
12. $y \leq 3x + 3$

Example

1 **Graph $y > 2x - 3$.**

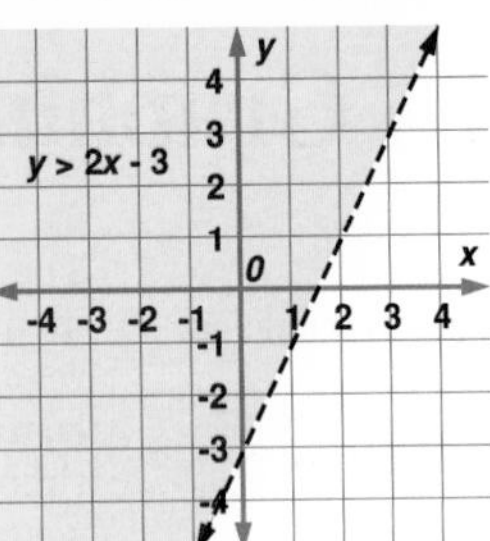

First graph $y = 2x - 3$. Draw a dashed line because the boundary line is not part of the graph of $y > 2x - 3$.

The graph is the region above the boundary. Shade this region.

Check: Choose a point in the region. Substitute its coordinates for x and y in the inequality. The origin is usually chosen because the coordinates of the ordered pair (0, 0) are easy to work with.

$y > 2x - 3$

$0 \overset{?}{>} 2(0) - 3$ Replace y with 0 and x with 0.

$0 > -3$ ✔ The inequality is true.

Since the resulting inequality is true, the shading is correct.

Checking for Understanding

Communicating Algebra

1. A line that separates the coordinate plane into two regions is called a __?__ line. **1. boundary**
2. Explain when a dashed line is used for the boundary line of the graph of an inequality. **See margin.**

If each inequality were graphed, would the boundary line be dashed or solid?

3. $y > x + 3$ **dashed**
4. $y \leq 3$ **solid**
5. $y < 5x$ **dashed**

Guided Practice

Copy each graph. Shade the region that represents the solution of the inequality.

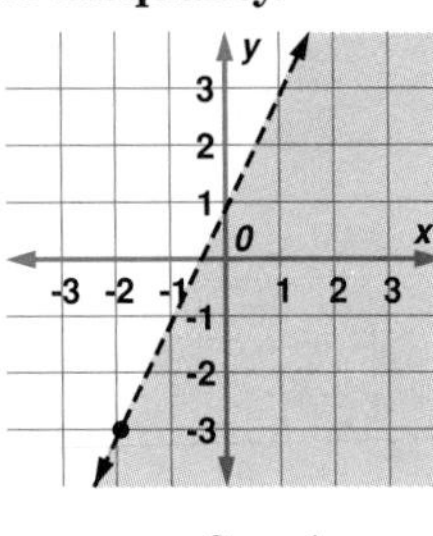

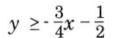

$y < 2x + 1$

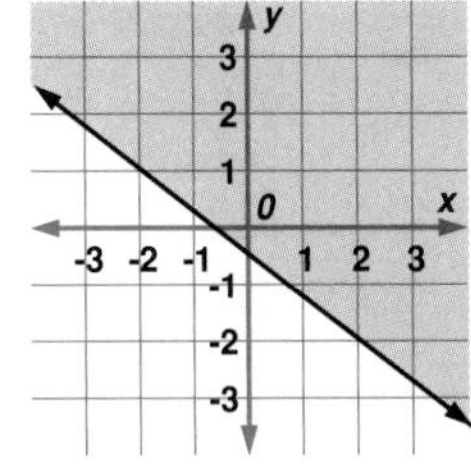

$y \geq -\frac{3}{4}x - \frac{1}{2}$

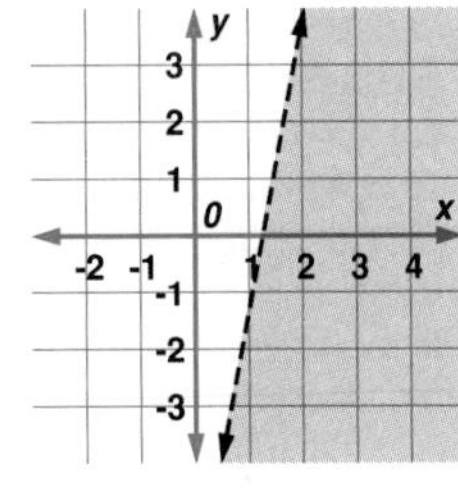

$y < 5x - 6$

Alternate Strategies: Reteaching the Lesson

Reteaching Activity

Comparing and Contrasting
Have students graph sets of similar inequalities, such as $y > 2x + 2$, $y \geq 2x + 2$, $y < 2x + 2$, and $y \leq 2x + 2$. Compare and contrast the graphs.

Reteaching Masters Booklet, **p. 73**

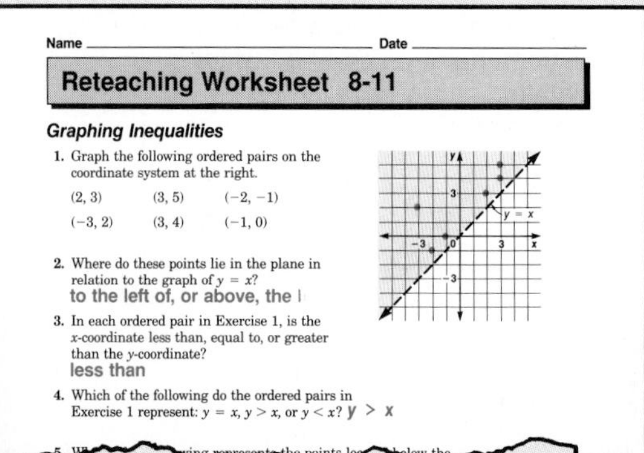

Name ______ Date ______

Reteaching Worksheet 8-11

Graphing Inequalities

1. Graph the following ordered pairs on the coordinate system at the right.
   (2, 3) (3, 5) (−2, −1)
   (−3, 2) (3, 4) (−1, 0)
2. Where do these points lie in the plane in relation to the graph of $y = x$?
   to the left of, or above, the l
3. In each ordered pair in Exercise 1, is the x-coordinate less than, equal to, or greater than the y-coordinate?
   less than
4. Which of the following do the ordered pairs in Exercise 1 represent: $y = x$, $y > x$, or $y < x$? $y > x$
5. W... the points l... below the

Exercises For graphs to Exercises 9-20, see Solutions Manual.

Independent Practice

Graph each inequality.

9. $y > x + 2$
10. $y \leq 2x$
11. $y > -3x - 3$
12. $y > -4x$
13. $y \leq -1$
14. $y \geq -\frac{1}{2}x + 3$
15. $y < \frac{1}{4}x - 2$
16. $y < -x - 1.5$
17. $y > -2x + 1$
18. $y < \frac{1}{3}x$
19. $y \geq x + 0.5$
20. $y \leq 1.5x - 0.5$

Mixed Review

21. Name the additive inverse of $-\frac{2}{3}$. (Lesson 5-1) $\frac{2}{3}$
22. Find the x-intercept and y-intercept for the graph of the equation $y = -x - 3$. (Lesson 8-9) **-3; -3**
23. Graph $y = -3x$ and $y = x - 8$. Then find the solution of the system of equations. (Lesson 8-10) **See Solutions Manual for graph; (2, -6)**

Application

24. **Consumer Awareness** Suppose you are shopping for cassettes and CDs at Music City. Cassettes cost \$7, CDs cost \$14, and you have \$28 to spend. First list all the combinations of cassettes and CDs you can purchase. Then graph the inequality $7c + 14d \leq 28$ where c is the number of cassettes and d is the number of CDs. **See Solutions Manual.**

Critical Thinking

25. **Make Up a Problem** Write an inequality whose graph has a solid boundary line. **Sample answer: $x + 3 \leq 5$**

Wrap-Up

26. Explain how you can check to see if you have shaded the correct region in the graph of an inequality. **See margin.**

Challenge

Systems of Inequalities

Consider the following system of inequalities.

$$y \geq x + 2$$
$$y \leq -2x - 1$$

To solve this system, you find the ordered pairs that satisfy *both* inequalities. One way is to graph each inequality and find the overlap of the two graphs.

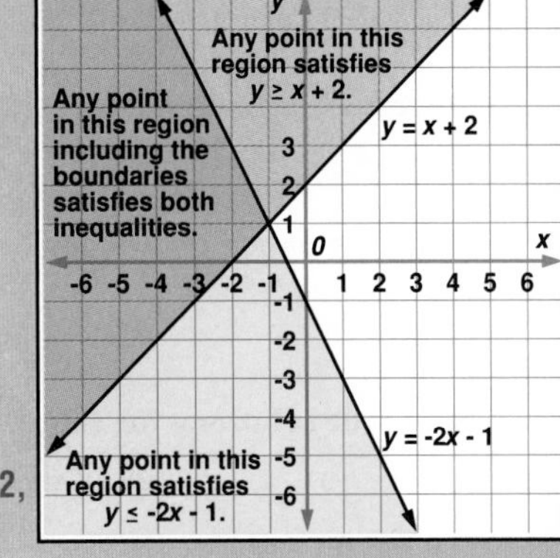

Solve each system of inequalities by graphing.

1. $y > x - 3$
   $y \leq -1$
2. $y > x + 2$
   $y < x - 3$ **For graphs to Exercises 1-2, see Solutions Manual.**

Independent Practice

Homework Assignment	
Basic	9-19 odd, 21-26
Average	10-20 even, 21-26
Honors	15-26

Chapter 8, Quiz B (Lessons 8-7 through 8-11) is available in the Evaluation Masters Booklet, p. 70.

4 CLOSE

Assessment Option

Speaking Write several in- equalities and their boundary lines on overhead transparencies without shading them. Then ask the students whether they need to shade above or below the line.

Additional Answers

2. A dashed line is used when the boundary line is not a part of the graph of the solution.
26. Select any point in the shaded region. Substitute the value of the x-coordinate into the equation and see if you get the corresponding value of the y-coordinate.

Enrichment Masters Booklet, **p. 73**

Name ______ Date ______

Enrichment Worksheet 8-11

Graphing Systems of Inequalities

Suppose you are given the following system of inequalities.

$y \geq x + 2$
$y \leq -2x - 1$

The solution of this system is the set of all ordered pairs that satisfy both inequalities. To find the solution, graph each inequality. The intersection of the graphs represents the solution.

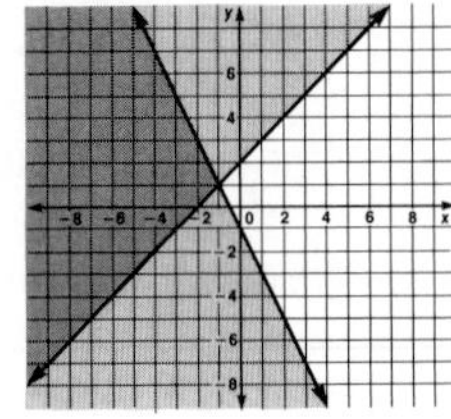

The graphs of the equations $y = x + 2$ and $y = -2x - 1$ are the boundaries of each region. The solution of the system is the region that contains ordered pairs that are solutions of *both* inequalities.

Solve each system by graphing.

1. $y \geq 2x + 1$, $y \leq -x + 1$
2. $y < -2$, $y - x > 1$
3. $y \geq x - 3$, $y \geq -x - 1$
4. $2y + x < 4$, $3x - y > 6$
5. $y > x + 1$, $y < x + 3$
6. $x \geq 1$, $y + x \leq 3$

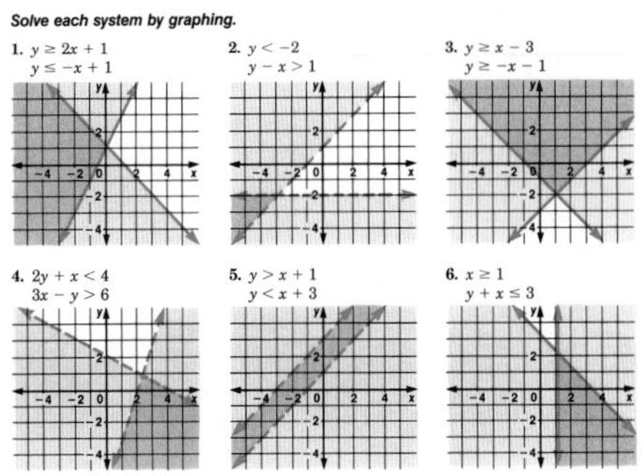

Alternate Strategies: Extending the Lesson

Enrichment

Using Cooperative Groups Have groups of students graph inequalities that contain absolute value. For example, $|y| \leq x - 1$. You may want to give them the hint that this inequality is equivalent to the following compound sentence.

$y \leq x - 1$ and $y \geq -x + 1$

You may then want to refer them to the Challenge feature above.

Cooperative Learning

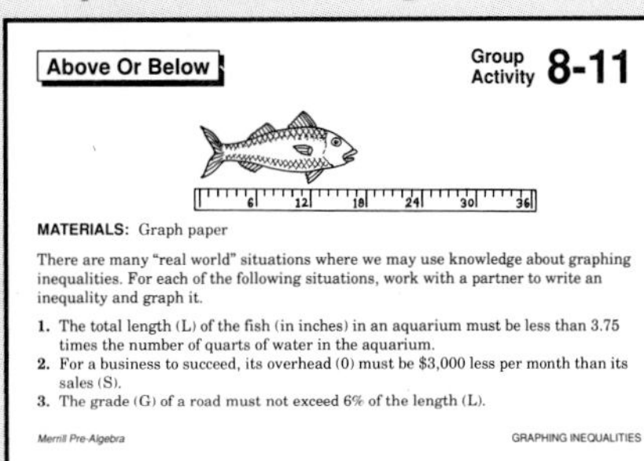

Above Or Below Group Activity **8-11**

MATERIALS: Graph paper

There are many "real world" situations where we may use knowledge about graphing inequalities. For each of the following situations, work with a partner to write an inequality and graph it.

1. The total length (L) of the fish (in inches) in an aquarium must be less than 3.75 times the number of quarts of water in the aquarium.
2. For a business to succeed, its overhead (O) must be \$3,000 less per month than its sales (S).
3. The grade (G) of a road must not exceed 6% of the length (L).

Merrill Pre-Algebra GRAPHING INEQUALITIES

Using the Chapter Review

The Chapter Review is a comprehensive review of the concepts presented in this chapter. This review may be used to prepare students for the Chapter Test.

Alternate Review Strategy

To provide a brief in-class review, you may wish to read the following questions to the class and require a verbal response.

1. Solve $x + 8 = -1$. $x = -9$
2. Solve $2x - 4 \geq 2$. $x \geq 3$
3. Describe how to graph the point (6,1). Move 6 units horizontally, and 1 unit vertically.
4. Which quadrant contains the ordered pair (-4,5)? Quadrant II
5. Give one solution for $y = x - 3$. Sample answer: (1,-2)
6. Explain the steps used to graph a linear equation.
   a. Find at least 4 solutions for the equation. Record each result as an ordered pair, (x,y).
   b. Graph these points.
   c. Draw the line that contains these points.
7. Name two ordered pairs (x,y) that can be used to graph the information in this problem. Mr. Banter drove at a constant rate for 8 hours. After 1 hour he had driven 57 miles. After 3 hours he had driven 171 miles. How many miles did he drive in 8 hours? (1, 57), (3, 171)
8. What is the formula for slope? slope $= \frac{\text{change in } y}{\text{change in } x}$
9. A y-intercept is -7. What is the ordered pair describing its coordinates? (0,-7)
10. What is the solution for a system of two equations that are graphed on the same coordinate plane? the point of intersection
11. How is the solution of an inequality shown on a graph? a dashed line if the line is not included in the answer, and shaded areas to show the graph that does satisfy the equation

Chapter 8 Review

Language and Concepts

Choose the letter of the correct word or words to complete each statement.

1. __?__ are graphed on a number line. c
2. __?__ are graphed on a coordinate plane. d
3. In the coordinate plane, the axes intersect at the __?__. e
4. When you graph an equation, all of the ordered pairs for the points on the line are __?__ of the equation. h
5. The coordinate of a point tells its distance and __?__ from the zero point of the line. a
6. The steepness of a line is called its __?__. g
7. Two equations with the same two variables form a __?__ of equations. i
8. The coordinate axes separate a plane into four __?__. f
9. In a coordinate system, the __?__ is a horizontal line. j
10. An equation whose graph is a straight line is called a __?__ equation. b

a. direction
b. linear
c. numbers
d. ordered pairs
e. origin
f. quadrants
g. slope
h. solutions
i. system
j. x-axis
k. y-axis

Skills

All graphs can be found in Solutions Manual.

Solve each equation and graph the solution. (Lesson 8-1)

11. $3y = -12$ -4
12. $x + 6 = 11$ 5
13. $h - 3 = -12$ -9
14. $3a - 7 = -10$ -1

Write an inequality that describes each graph. (Lesson 8-2)

15. $x \geq -5$
16. $x < 3$

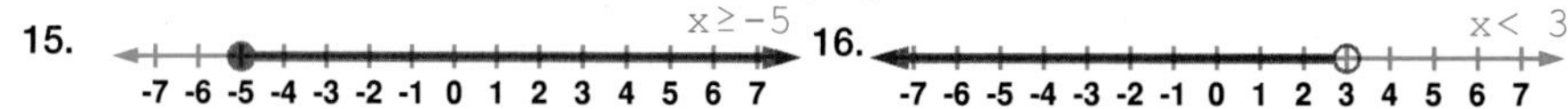

17. $x \leq 1$
18. $x < -4$

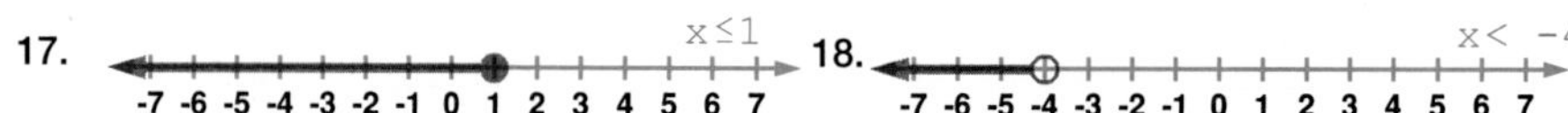

Solve each inequality and graph the solution. (Lesson 8-2)

19. $2a \geq -4$ $a \geq -2$
20. $4b - 5 < 7$ $b < 3$
21. $2x + 8 \geq -4$ $x \geq -6$
22. $a - 4 < -8$ $a < -4$

On graph paper, draw coordinate axes. Then graph and label each point. (Lessons 8-3, 8-4)

23. $A(6, 0)$
24. $P(1, -6)$
25. $C(-2, 3)$
26. $D(-3, -2)$

27. (0, 0), (1, $\frac{3}{2}$), (2, 3), (-2, -3) 28. (0, -3), (1, -7), (-1, 1), (2, -11)

Find four solutions for each equation. (Lesson 8-5)

27. $y = \frac{3}{2}x$
28. $y = -4x - 3$
29. $y = 5x - 3$
30. $y = 6x - 5$

29. (0, -3), (1, 2), (2, 7), (-1, -8) 30. (0, -5), (1, 1), (2, 7), (-1, -11)

Graph each equation. (Lesson 8-6)

31. $y = 3x - 1$ 32. $y = -5x - 2$ 33. $y = -3x - 4$ 34. $y = -4x + 18$

Find the slope of the line that contains each pair of points. (Lesson 8-8)

35. $A(-3, 4), B(-2, -2)$ -6 36. $C(-1, 0), D(5, -1)$ $-\frac{1}{6}$ 37. $F(6, 7), G(-4, 3)$ $\frac{2}{5}$

Use the x-intercept and y-intercept to graph each equation. (Lesson 8-9)

38. $y = x - 6$ 39. $y = -5 - x$ 40. $y = -3 + x$ 41. $y = -2x - 9$

Use a graph to solve each system of equations. (Lesson 8-10)

42. $y = x$, $y = 2 - x$ 43. $x + y = 6$, $x - y = 2$ 44. $y = x - 1$, $x + y = 11$

Graph each inequality. (Lesson 8-11)

45. $y < x - 2$ 46. $y \geq -2x + 1$ 47. $y > \frac{1}{2}x$ 48. $y \leq -x + 8$

Applications and Problem Solving

Solve by using a graph. Assume the rate is constant. (Lesson 8-7)

49. A cricket begins chirping when the temperature is about 37° Fahrenheit. When the temperature is 70° Fahrenheit, the cricket chirps about 132 times per minute. What is the approximate temperature when the cricket chirps 185 times per minute? 83°F; See Solutions Manual for graph.

Communicating Algebra

Explain how to determine if the ordered pair (3, -5) is a solution of the system of equations $2x + y = 1$, $x - y = 8$. Write your answer in paragraph form. Include a graph as part of your answer.
See Solutions Manual.

Curriculum Connection

- **Geography** Find the latitude and longitude of your town. Write your answer as an ordered pair. See student's work
- **Meteorology** An isobar is a curved line on a weather map that connects points with the same air pressure. What does an isotherm show? See margin.

Read More About It

Arnold, Caroline. *Charts and Graphs: Fun, Facts, and Activities.*

Catherall, Ed. *Investigating Mathematics: Graphs.*

Haber, Louis. *Black Pioneers of Science and Invention.*

Additional Answer
Meteorology Connection An isotherm is a line drawn on a weather map that connects points of equal temperature.

You may wish to use a Chapter Test (free-response format) as an additional chapter review. Two forms are provided in the Evaluation Masters Booklet as shown below.

Evaluation Masters Booklet, **p. 68**

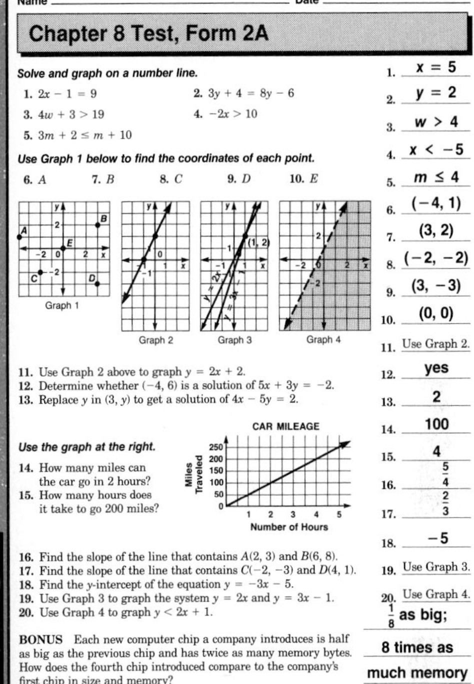

Name ______ Date ______

Chapter 8 Test, Form 2A

Solve and graph on a number line.

1. $2x - 1 = 9$
2. $3y + 4 = 8y - 6$
3. $4w + 3 > 19$
4. $-2x > 10$
5. $3m + 2 \leq m + 10$

Use Graph 1 below to find the coordinates of each point.

6. A 7. B 8. C 9. D 10. E

Graph 1 Graph 2 Graph 3 Graph 4

11. Use Graph 2 above to graph $y = 2x + 2$.
12. Determine whether $(-4, 6)$ is a solution of $5x + 3y = -2$.
13. Replace y in $(3, y)$ to get a solution of $4x - 5y = 2$.

Use the graph at the right.

14. How many miles can the car go in 2 hours?
15. How many hours does it take to go 200 miles?

CAR MILEAGE (Miles Traveled vs. Number of Hours)

16. Find the slope of the line that contains $A(2, 3)$ and $B(6, 8)$.
17. Find the slope of the line that contains $C(-2, -3)$ and $D(4, 1)$.
18. Find the y-intercept of the equation $y = -3x - 5$.
19. Use Graph 3 to graph the system $y = 2x$ and $y = 3x - 1$.
20. Use Graph 4 to graph $y < 2x + 1$.

BONUS Each new computer chip a company introduces is half as big as the previous chip and has twice as many memory bytes. How does the fourth chip introduced compare to the company's first chip in size and memory?

Answers: 1. $x = 5$ 2. $y = 2$ 3. $w > 4$ 4. $x < -5$ 5. $m \leq 4$ 6. $(-4, 1)$ 7. $(3, 2)$ 8. $(-2, -2)$ 9. $(3, -3)$ 10. $(0, 0)$ 11. Use Graph 2. 12. yes 13. 2 14. 100 15. 4 16. $\frac{5}{4}$ 17. $\frac{2}{3}$ 18. -5 19. Use Graph 3. 20. Use Graph 4. Bonus: $\frac{1}{8}$ as big; 8 times as much memory

Evaluation Masters Booklet, **p. 69**

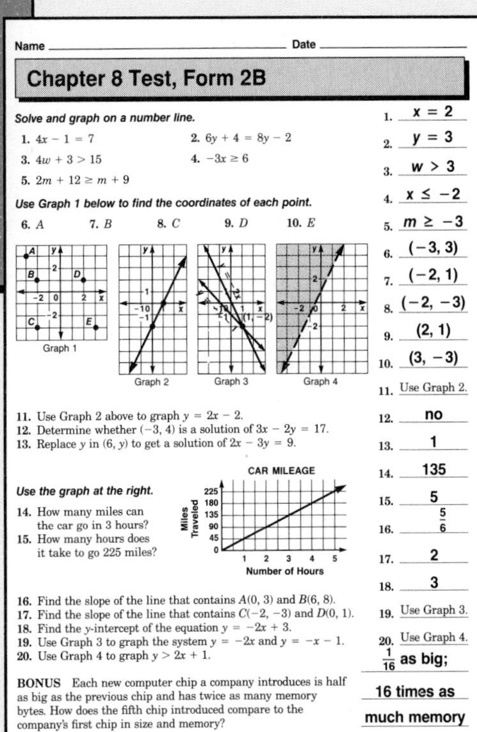

Name ______ Date ______

Chapter 8 Test, Form 2B

Solve and graph on a number line.

1. $4x - 1 = 7$
2. $6y + 4 = 8y - 2$
3. $4w + 3 > 15$
4. $-3x \geq 6$
5. $2m + 12 \geq m + 9$

Use Graph 1 below to find the coordinates of each point.

6. A 7. B 8. C 9. D 10. E

Graph 1 Graph 2 Graph 3 Graph 4

11. Use Graph 2 above to graph $y = 2x - 2$.
12. Determine whether $(-3, 4)$ is a solution of $3x - 2y = 17$.
13. Replace y in $(6, y)$ to get a solution of $2x - 3y = 9$.

Use the graph at the right.

14. How many miles can the car go in 3 hours?
15. How many hours does it take to go 225 miles?

CAR MILEAGE (Miles Traveled vs. Number of Hours)

16. Find the slope of the line that contains $A(0, 3)$ and $B(6, 8)$.
17. Find the slope of the line that contains $C(-2, -3)$ and $D(0, 1)$.
18. Find the y-intercept of the equation $y = -2x + 3$.
19. Use Graph 3 to graph the system $y = -2x$ and $y = -x - 1$.
20. Use Graph 4 to graph $y > 2x + 1$.

BONUS Each new computer chip a company introduces is half as big as the previous chip and has twice as many memory bytes. How does the fifth chip introduced compare to the company's first chip in size and memory?

Answers: 1. $x = 2$ 2. $y = 3$ 3. $w > 3$ 4. $x \leq -2$ 5. $m \geq -3$ 6. $(-3, 3)$ 7. $(-2, 1)$ 8. $(-2, -3)$ 9. $(2, 1)$ 10. $(3, -3)$ 11. Use Graph 2. 12. no 13. 1 14. 135 15. 5 16. $\frac{5}{6}$ 17. 2 18. 3 19. Use Graph 3. 20. Use Graph 4. Bonus: $\frac{1}{16}$ as big; 16 times as much memory

Using the Chapter Test

This page may be used as a test or as an additional review. Two forms of a Chapter Test (multiple-choice format) are provided in the Evaluation Masters Booklet.

Evaluation Masters Booklet, **pp. 64-65**

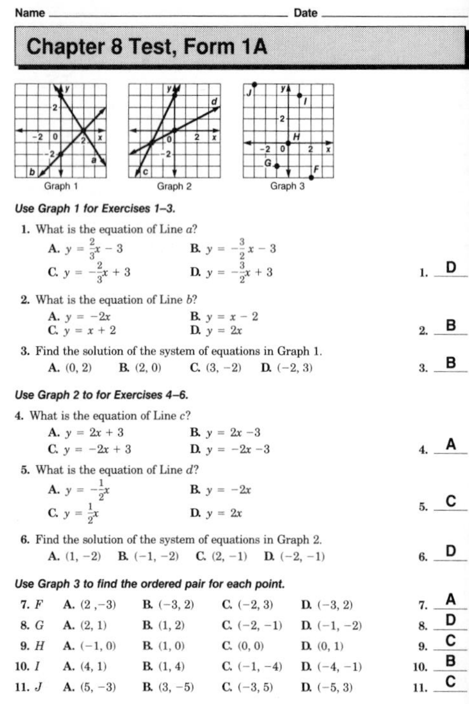

Name ______________________ Date ____________

Chapter 8 Test, Form 1A

Graph 1 Graph 2 Graph 3

Use Graph 1 for Exercises 1–3.

1. What is the equation of Line a?
   A. $y = \frac{2}{3}x - 3$ B. $y = -\frac{3}{2}x - 3$
   C. $y = -\frac{2}{3}x + 3$ D. $y = -\frac{3}{2}x + 3$ 1. D
2. What is the equation of Line b?
   A. $y = -2x$ B. $y = x - 2$
   C. $y = x + 2$ D. $y = 2x$ 2. B
3. Find the solution of the system of equations in Graph 1.
   A. (0, 2) B. (2, 0) C. (3, −2) D. (−2, 3) 3. B

Use Graph 2 to for Exercises 4–6.

4. What is the equation of Line c?
   A. $y = 2x + 3$ B. $y = 2x - 3$
   C. $y = -2x + 3$ D. $y = -2x - 3$ 4. A
5. What is the equation of Line d?
   A. $y = -\frac{1}{2}x$ B. $y = -2x$
   C. $y = \frac{1}{2}x$ D. $y = 2x$ 5. C
6. Find the solution of the system of equations in Graph 2.
   A. (1, −2) B. (−1, −2) C. (2, −1) D. (−2, −1) 6. D

Use Graph 3 to find the ordered pair for each point.

	A.	B.	C.	D.	
7. F	(2, −3)	(−3, 2)	(−2, 3)	(−3, 2)	7. A
8. G	(2, 1)	(1, 2)	(−2, −1)	(−1, −2)	8. D
9. H	(−1, 0)	(1, 0)	(0, 0)	(0, 1)	9. C
10. I	(4, 1)	(1, 4)	(−1, −4)	(−4, −1)	10. B
11. J	(5, −3)	(3, −5)	(−3, 5)	(−5, 3)	11. C

Name ______________________ Date ____________

Chapter 8 Test, Form 1A (continued)

12. Which is a solution of $2x - 3y = 5$?
    A. (4, 1) B. (1, 4) C. (−1, −4) D. (−4, 1) 12. A
13. Which is a solution of $3x - 2y = -12$?
    A. (3, −2) B. (−2, 3) C. (−3, 2) D. (2, −3) 13. B
14. Which is a solution of $4x + 2y = -8$?
    A. (−1, −2) B. (−2, 1) C. (1, 2) D. (−1, 2) 14. A

FUEL CONSUMPTION

Miles Traveled: 35, 70, 105, 140, 175, 210

Gallons of Fuel Used: 0, 1, 2, 3, 4, 5, 6

Use the graph above for Exercises 15–17.

15. How many gallons of fuel are needed to travel 140 miles?
    A. 3 B. 4 C. 5 D. 6 15. B
16. Find the least whole number of gallons needed to travel 100 miles.
    A. 1 B. 2 C. 3 D. 4 16. C
17. About how many gallons of fuel are needed to travel 190 miles?
    A. 4.5 B. 5 C. 5.5 D. 6 17. C
18. Find the slope of the line that contains $A(-2, 1)$ and $B(-1, 5)$.
    A. 4 B. 5 C. −4 D. −5 18. A
19. Find the slope of the line that contains $A(-3, 4)$ and $B(0, 1)$.
    A. −1 B. 1 C. 0 D. −2 19. A
20. Find the y-intercept of the equation $y = -4x + 6$.
    A. −4 B. 4 C. −6 D. 6 20. D

BONUS A cactus grows at a constant rate of 1.5 inches per year. In how many years will it be 20 inches high if it is 9.5 inches high now?
A. 8 B. 3 C. 7 D. 5 C

Test

All graphs can be found in Solutions Manual.

Solve each equation and graph the solution.

1. $y - 5 = -7$ **−2** 2. $a + 3 = 2$ **−1** 3. $-13 = h - 11$ **−2** 4. $3b - 3 = 6$ **3**

Solve each inequality and graph the solution.

5. $x + 8 \geq -3$ **$x \geq -11$** 6. $y - 1 \leq -6$ **$y \leq -5$** 7. $-2y \geq -3$ **$y \leq \frac{3}{2}$** 8. $\frac{y}{5} \geq -2$ **$y \geq -10$**

Use the grid at the right to find the ordered pair for each labeled point.

9. A **(10, 6)** 10. C **(2, 0)**
11. D **(1, 4)** 12. G **(3, 2)**

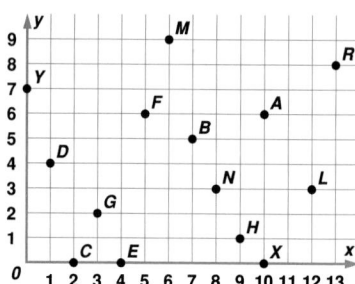

On graph paper, draw coordinate axes. Then graph and label each point.

13. $A(8, 9)$ 14. $B(-8, 9)$
15. $C(8, -9)$ 16. $D(-8, -9)$
17. $E(7, -6.5)$ 18. $F(5, -2.5)$
19. $G(0, -7)$ 20. $H(-5, 0)$

Find four solutions for each equation.

21. $y = x - 6$ 22. $y = x + 7$ 23. $y = 3x$ 24. $y = -4x$

21. (0, −6),(1, −5),(7, 1),(−1, −7) 22. (0, 7),(1,8),(−2, 5),(−8, −1) 23. (0, 0), (1, 3), (2, 6), (−1, −3) 24. (1, −4), (0, 0), (2, −8), (−1, 4)

Graph each equation.

25. $y = -3x + 1$ 26. $y = 3 - 4x$ 27. $y = -7x - 8$
28. $y = 9 - 8x$ 29. $y = 12 - 3x$ 30. $y = 5x$

Find the slope of the line that contains each pair of points.

31. $A(2, -3), B(-1, 0)$ **−1** 32. $C(-5, 6), D(-7, 8)$ **−1** 33. $E(4, 3), F(-5, 4)$ **$-\frac{1}{9}$**

Use the x-intercept and y-intercept to graph each equation.

34. $y = -x + 1$ 35. $y = -x - 2$ 36. $y = 2 - \frac{1}{2}x$

Use a graph to solve each system of equations.

37. $x + y = 8$
    $x - y = 8$
38. $x + 2y = 6$
    $-x + 3y = 4$

Graph each inequality.

39. $y \leq \frac{1}{2}x$ 40. $y < 3 - x$

BONUS See Solutions Manual.

Write equations, list solutions in a table, and draw a graph to illustrate the following relationship: The sum of two numbers is 42. Their difference is 18.

Test Generator Software is provided in both Apple and IBM formats. You may use this software to create your own tests, based on the needs of your students.

9-2 Proportions

Objectives:
Determine if a pair of ratios form a proportion. Solve proportions.

Key Terms:
proportion
cross products

Have you ever heard a statement like this on TV?

2 out of 3 Americans approve of the job the President is doing.

The ratio *2 out of 3* can be expressed as the fraction $\frac{2}{3}$. The statement means that $\frac{2}{3}$ of the people surveyed approve of the job the President is doing.

Hopefully, more than 3 people were surveyed. Suppose 300 people were surveyed. You can estimate that $\frac{2}{3}$ of 300, or 200 people, approve. Notice that the two fractions shown below are equivalent.

$$\frac{2}{3} = \frac{200}{300}$$

An equation stating that two ratios are equivalent is called a **proportion.** One way to determine if two ratios form a proportion is to check their **cross products.** In the proportion shown at the right, $2 \cdot 300$ and $3 \cdot 200$ are cross products.

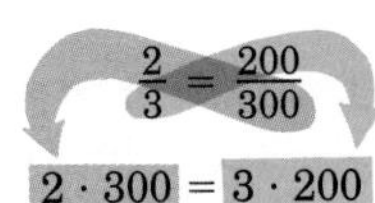

$$2 \cdot 300 = 3 \cdot 200$$

$$600 = 600$$

Property of Proportions

In words: The cross products of a proportion are equal.

In symbols: If $\frac{a}{b} = \frac{c}{d}$, then $ad = bc$. If $ad = bc$, then $\frac{a}{b} = \frac{c}{d}$.

Examples

Use cross products to determine whether each pair of ratios forms a proportion.

1 $\frac{2}{3}, \frac{8}{12}$

$2 \cdot 12 \stackrel{?}{=} 3 \cdot 8$ Property of Proportions

$24 = 24$

So, $\frac{2}{3} = \frac{8}{12}$.

2 $\frac{3.5}{8}, \frac{2.5}{4.6}$

8 ⊠ 2.5 ⊟ 20

3.5 ⊠ 4.6 ⊟ 16.1

$20 \neq 16.1$ So, $\frac{3.5}{8} \neq \frac{2.5}{4.6}$.

Bell Ringer

Name five ratios equivalent to 2:3.
4:6, 6:9, 8:12, 10:15, 12:18

Lesson Notes 9-2

5-Minute Check
(over Lesson 9-1)

Express each ratio as a fraction in simplest form.
1. 15 out of 115 $\frac{3}{23}$
2. 105:392 $\frac{15}{56}$
3. 132:275 $\frac{12}{25}$

Express each ratio as a unit rate.

4. \$128 for 16 tickets \$8/ticket
5. 412.5 miles in 7.5 hours 55 mph

Transparency 9-2 contains the 5-Minute Check and a teaching aid for this lesson.

1 FOCUS

The purpose of this lesson is to define a proportion and use the property of proportions to determine if ratios are equivalent and to solve a proportion.

Motivating the Lesson

Ask students to find the ratio relating each number to the previous number, and find the next three numbers in this sequence: 1, 5, 25. 5:1; 125, 625, 3125

2 TEACH

Using Discussion Use simple numerical examples (like $\frac{3}{4} = \frac{6}{8}$; $3 \times 8 = 4 \times 6$) to show equality of cross products.

Chalkboard Examples

Use cross products to determine whether each pair of ratios forms a proportion.

- *For Example 1*
  $\frac{4}{5}, \frac{12}{15}$ $60 = 60$
- *For Example 2*
  $\frac{2.1}{7}, \frac{1.4}{3.8}$ $7.98 \neq 9.8$

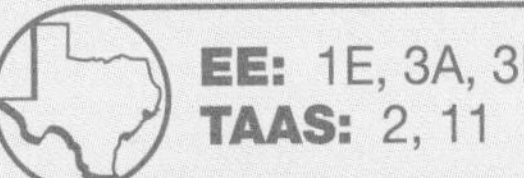

EE: 1E, 3A, 3I
TAAS: 2, 11

Chalkboard Examples

Solve each proportion.

- For Example 3
  $\frac{m}{16} = \frac{4}{32}$ $m = 2$
- For Example 4
  $\frac{9}{2.6} = \frac{3}{r}$ r is about 0.87

3 PRACTICE/APPLY

Checking the Concept

After students have solved Exercises 6-13, give them several cross products such as $4 \times 7 = 2 \times 14$, and have them write a proportion for each. Compare and contrast the resulting proportions.

Error Analysis

Watch for students who multiply numerators together and denominators together to get a cross product.

Prevent by emphasizing that the product is a "cross" (X) product and numbers are multiplied in that pattern.

Practice Masters Booklet, **p. 83**

Name ______________________ Date ______________

Practice Worksheet 9-2

Proportions

Replace each ■ with = or ≠ to make a true statement.

1. $\frac{4}{6}$ ■ $\frac{2}{3}$ =
2. $\frac{16}{4}$ ■ $\frac{20}{8}$ ≠
3. $\frac{21}{28}$ ■ $\frac{3}{4}$ =
4. $\frac{4}{5}$ ■ $\frac{12}{15}$ =
5. $\frac{21}{49}$ ■ $\frac{6}{14}$ =
6. $\frac{2.6}{4}$ ■ $\frac{16}{25}$ ≠

Solve each proportion.

7. $\frac{7}{16} = \frac{x}{32}$ 14
8. $\frac{y}{9} = \frac{4}{12}$ 3
9. $\frac{5}{a} = \frac{9}{27}$ 15
10. $\frac{18}{24} = \frac{6}{d}$ 8
11. $\frac{7}{4} = \frac{21}{x}$ 12
12. $\frac{15}{6} = \frac{n}{2}$ 5
13. $\frac{r}{10} = \frac{21}{7}$ 30
14. $\frac{4}{p} = \frac{8}{11}$ 5.5
15. $\frac{17}{50} = \frac{x}{25}$ 8.5
16. $\frac{c}{8} = \frac{32}{64}$ 4
17. $\frac{3.5}{150} = \frac{10.5}{a}$ 450
18. $\frac{f}{\$1.50} = \frac{7}{5}$ \$2.10
19. $\frac{8}{12} = \frac{b}{48}$ 32
20. $\frac{0.18}{0.09} = \frac{h}{0.06}$ 0.12
21. $\frac{0.25}{0.5} - \frac{m}{8}$ 4
22. $\frac{5}{2} = \frac{x}{4}$ 10
23. $\frac{15}{11} = \frac{a}{22}$ 30
24. $\frac{4.2}{c} = \frac{7}{12}$ 7.2
25. $\frac{1}{8} = \frac{2}{d}$ 16
26. $\frac{x}{6} = \frac{15}{18}$ 5
27. $\frac{0.4}{m} = \frac{2}{4.5}$ 0.9
28. $\frac{4}{11} = \frac{12}{x}$ 33
29. $\frac{2}{3} = \frac{0.8}{n}$ 1.2
30. $\frac{7}{12} = \frac{1.68}{b}$ 2.88
31. $\frac{f}{7.5} = \frac{1.9}{5.7}$ 2.5
32. $\frac{p}{36} = \frac{11.76}{35.28}$ 12
33. $\frac{n}{48} = \frac{5.22}{13.92}$ 18
34. $\frac{10}{2.4} = \frac{p}{2.64}$ 11
35. $\frac{85.8}{d} = \frac{70.2}{9}$ 11
36. $\frac{0.6}{1.1} = \frac{s}{8.47}$ 4.62

Mental Math Hint

Sometimes you can solve a proportion mentally by using equivalent fractions.

$$\frac{2}{3} = \frac{x}{27}$$

THINK: $3 \times 9 = 27$
$2 \times 9 = 18$
So, $x = 18$.

Cross products can also be used to solve proportions.

Examples

Solve each proportion.

3 $\frac{d}{24} = \frac{15}{60}$

$d \cdot 60 = 24 \cdot 15$ — Write the cross products.

$60d = 360$ — $24 \cdot 15 = 360$

$\frac{60d}{60} = \frac{360}{60}$ — Divide each side by 60.

$d = 6$

The solution is 6.

4 $\frac{12}{1.3} = \frac{5}{c}$

$12c = 1.3 \cdot 5$

1.3 [×] 5 [÷] 12 [=] 0.541666666

How is this similar to the paper-and-pencil method? **Multiply cross products, then divide.**

Therefore, c is about 0.54.

Checking for Understanding

Communicating Algebra

1. Name the property that enables you to determine whether two ratios are equivalent. **property of proportions**
2. Explain how to determine whether two ratios are equivalent. **See margin.**
3. Write the cross products for $\frac{2}{5} = \frac{0.02}{0.09}$. **2 • 0.09; 5 • 0.02**
4. Explain how to solve $\frac{x}{2.5} = \frac{3}{4}$ with a calculator. **Multiply 2.5 and 3; divide by 4.**
5. Explain how to solve $\frac{2}{5} = \frac{m}{35}$ mentally. **Think: $5 \times 7 = 35$, $2 \times 7 = 14$; $m = 14$**

Guided Practice

Replace each ■ with = or ≠ to make a true statement.

6. $\frac{2}{3}$ ■ $\frac{8}{12}$ =
7. $\frac{6}{15}$ ■ $\frac{3}{7}$ ≠
8. $\frac{8}{9}$ ■ $\frac{16}{17}$ ≠
9. $\frac{4}{5}$ ■ $\frac{12}{15}$ =

Solve each proportion.

10. $\frac{1}{5} = \frac{x}{35}$ 7
11. $\frac{1}{3} = \frac{6}{s}$ 18
12. $\frac{3}{a} = \frac{18}{24}$ 4
13. $\frac{m}{3} = \frac{14}{21}$ 2

Exercises

Independent Practice

Replace each ■ with = or ≠ to make a true statement.

ESTIMATION / MENTAL MATH / CALCULATOR / PAPER/PENCIL

14. $\frac{6}{4}$ ■ $\frac{21}{14}$ =
15. $\frac{8}{6}$ ■ $\frac{28}{22}$ ≠
16. $\frac{12}{8}$ ■ $\frac{40}{28}$ ≠
17. $\frac{7}{14}$ ■ $\frac{20}{45}$ ≠
18. $\frac{1.3}{2}$ ■ $\frac{16}{25}$ ≠
19. $\frac{2.1}{3.5}$ ■ $\frac{5}{7}$ ≠
20. $\frac{1.5}{2}$ ■ $\frac{1.8}{2.4}$ =
21. $\frac{0.5}{1.5}$ ■ $\frac{0.03}{0.09}$ =
22. $\frac{0.8}{1.6}$ ■ $\frac{4.3}{9}$ ≠
23. $\frac{1.3}{2}$ ■ $\frac{3.055}{4.7}$ =
24. $\frac{1.3}{2}$ ■ $\frac{16.25}{25}$ =
25. $\frac{8.6}{25.3}$ ■ $\frac{1}{3}$ ≠

Alternate Strategies: Reteaching the Lesson

Reteaching Activity

Using Groups of Two Have students take turns naming a fraction with a denominator of 2, 5, 10, 20, or 25. Improper fractions may be used. The other student uses a proportion to find the equivalent numerator if that fraction is expressed as a fraction with a denominator of 100.

Reteaching Masters Booklet, **p. 75**

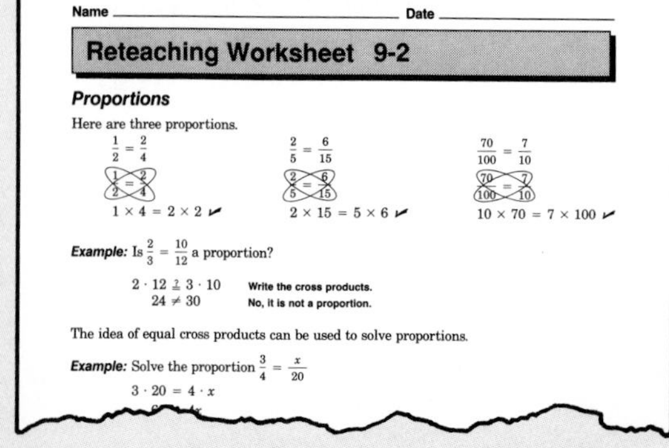

Name ______________________ Date ______________

Reteaching Worksheet 9-2

Proportions

Here are three proportions.

$\frac{1}{2} = \frac{2}{4}$ — $1 \times 4 = 2 \times 2$ ✓

$\frac{2}{5} = \frac{6}{15}$ — $2 \times 15 = 5 \times 6$ ✓

$\frac{70}{100} = \frac{7}{10}$ — $10 \times 70 = 7 \times 100$ ✓

Example: Is $\frac{2}{3} = \frac{10}{12}$ a proportion?

$2 \cdot 12 \stackrel{?}{=} 3 \cdot 10$ — Write the cross products.
$24 \neq 30$ — No, it is not a proportion.

The idea of equal cross products can be used to solve proportions.

Example: Solve the proportion $\frac{3}{4} = \frac{x}{20}$

$3 \cdot 20 = 4 \cdot x$

Solve each proportion.

26. $\frac{3}{7} = \frac{m}{49}$ **21**
27. $\frac{8}{6} = \frac{x}{27}$ **36**
28. $\frac{2}{5} = \frac{k}{35}$ **14**
29. $\frac{3}{39} = \frac{y}{13}$ **1**
30. $\frac{r}{3} = \frac{8}{15}$ **1.6**
31. $\frac{1}{2} = \frac{s}{7}$ **3.5**
32. $\frac{8}{6} = \frac{z}{14}$ **$18.\overline{6}$**
33. $\frac{18}{12} = \frac{24}{k}$ **16**
34. $\frac{s}{9.6} = \frac{7}{1.6}$ **42**
35. $\frac{7}{16} = \frac{x}{4.8}$ **2.1**
36. $\frac{5.1}{1.7} = \frac{7.5}{a}$ **2.5**
37. $\frac{1.6}{2.4} = \frac{3.4}{p}$ **5.1**

Mixed Review

38. Solve the equation $d = (-7)(3)(-1)$. (Lesson 2-7) **21**
39. Solve the equation $7x + 4(x - 3) = 9x + 2$. (Lesson 7-5) **7**
40. What do x and y represent in the ordered pair (x, y)? (Lesson 8-3) **See margin.**
41. Express the ratio 36:27 as a fraction in simplest form. (Lesson 9-1) **$\frac{4}{3}$**
42. Express the ratio $\frac{185 \text{ calories}}{5 \text{ grams}}$ as a unit rate. (Lesson 9-1) **$\frac{37 \text{ calories}}{\text{gram}}$**

Challenge

Solve each proportion.

43. $\frac{2a}{5} = \frac{12}{15}$ **2**
44. $\frac{0.28}{4n} = \frac{1.4}{4}$ **0.2**
45. $\frac{3}{2} = \frac{x + 1}{8}$ **11**
46. $\frac{1.5}{h - 3} = \frac{3}{14}$ **10**

Applications

47. **Cooking** A recipe calls for 3 cups of flour for 48 cookies. How much flour is needed for 72 cookies? Use the proportion $\frac{3}{48} = \frac{c}{72}$. **4.5 cups**
48. **Farming** A 5-acre field has a yield of 140 bushels of wheat. What yield can be expected for a 42-acre field? Use the proportion $\frac{140}{5} = \frac{b}{42}$. **1176 bushels**
49. **Consumer Awareness** Lauren's car averages 33 miles for each gallon of gasoline. How many gallons are needed for a trip of 313.5 miles? Use the proportion $\frac{33}{1} = \frac{313.5}{g}$. **9.5 gallons**

Critical Thinking

50. If three bakers can prepare 15 cakes in 1 hour, how long will it take six bakers working at the same rate to prepare 20 cakes? **40 minutes**

Wrap-Up

51. In your own words, write two examples in everyday life where proportions could be used. **See margin.**

Career

Actuary

Most states have laws requiring all drivers to have automobile insurance. Did you ever wonder who determines the cost of the insurance? An actuary does. Actuaries design insurance and pension plans for companies. They must make sure that the price charged for insurance will enable the company to pay all claims and expenses as they occur in the future. Employment for actuaries is expected to rise 35% or more through the 1990s as insurance sales increase and companies introduce new forms of insurance.

Alternate Strategies: Extending the Lesson

Enrichment

Health Connection Have each student take his or her pulse for 30 seconds. Have each student use a proportion to tell how many times his or her heart beats in one minute, one hour, and one day.

Cooperative Learning

Making Equal Group Activity **9-2**

In groups of two to four students, determine the missing terms of proportions.

To begin, think of three numbers to use in a proportion. All of the numbers should be less than 100. Each group member creates a proportion with the three numbers and a variable. Then exchange proportions with someone in your group and solve.

Compare answers. Did some of you get the same answer even though you did not start with exactly the same proportion? Discuss in your group why you think this can happen.

Repeat this activity twice to see if any members of the group get the same answer.

$$\frac{a}{b} = \frac{c}{d}$$

Merrill Pre-Algebra PROPORTIONS

Independent Practice

Homework Assignment	
Basic	15-37 odd, 38-42, 49-51
Average	14-36 even, 38-43, 48-51
Honors	32-51

4 CLOSE

Assessment Option

Modeling Have small groups of students use a set of dominoes. Each student draws two dominoes and determines if they form a proportion. If a blank domino is drawn the student determines the number needed to form a proportion.

Additional Answers

2. If the cross products of two ratios in a proportion are equal then the two ratios are equivalent.
40. x represents the x-coordinate and y represents the y-coordinate.
51. Sample answer: scale drawings and indirect measurement.

Enrichment Masters Booklet, p. 75

Name ______ Date ______

Enrichment Worksheet 9-2

Direct Variation

When the relationship between two quantities is such that when one quantity increases, the other increases, or when one quantity decreases, the other decreases, the quantities are said to **vary directly.**

Example: If 2 loaves of bread cost \$1.60, how much will 3 loaves of the same type of bread cost?

The number of loaves and the cost vary directly; that is, as the number of loaves increases, so does the cost.

$\frac{2 \text{ loaves}}{\$1.60} = \frac{3 \text{ loaves}}{x}$ **For direct variations, place like quantities directly across from each other in a proportion.**

$2x = 4.80$

$x = 2.40$

The cost for 3 loaves of bread is \$2.40.

Write a proportion to represent each situation. Then solve.

1. Three gallons of gasoline cost \$3.36. How much do 5 gallons cost? $\frac{3}{3.36} = \frac{5}{x}$; $x = 5.6$; \$5.60
2. At a rate of 50 mph, a car travels a distance of 600 miles. How far will the car travel at a rate of 40 mph if it is driven the same amount of time? $\frac{50}{600} = \frac{40}{x}$; $x = 480$; 480 miles
3. If the rent for 2 weeks is \$500, how much rent is paid for 5 weeks? $\frac{2}{500} = \frac{5}{x}$; $x = 1250$; \$1250
4. If 8 newspapers cost \$3.30, how much will 6 newspapers cost? $\frac{8}{3.20} = \frac{6}{x}$; $x = 2.40$; \$2.40
5. If 9 fully-loaded trucks carry a total of 140,400 pounds, how many pounds can 3 trucks carry? $\frac{9}{140,400} = \frac{3}{x}$; $x = 46,800$; 46,800 pounds
6. Twelve computer floppy disks can hold 16.8 million bytes of data. How many bytes will 20 floppy disks hold? $\frac{12}{16,800,000} = \frac{20}{x}$; $x =$ 28,000,000; 28 million bytes
7. If 12 computer floppy disks hold 16.8 million bytes of data, how many floppy disks are needed to hold 10 million bytes of data? $\frac{12}{16,800,000} = \frac{x}{10,000,000}$; $x \approx 7.14$; 8 disks are needed.
8. There are a total of 2100 calories in 5 candy bars (all the same kind). How many total calories are there in 3 dozen of these candy bars? $\frac{5}{2100} = \frac{36}{x}$; $x = 15,120$; 15,120 calories

EXPLORATION:

Capture-Recapture

Objective Students will use proportions to estimate a population.

1 FOCUS

Motivating the Exploration

Show students a photo of any large group, for example, a section of people at a football stadium or bees working on a honeycomb. Ask students how many people or bees are in the photo.

2 TEACH

Using Discussion

Using the same photo from the motivating exercise, ask students what procedures they would use to determine the number of subjects in the photo. Explain that this investigation is an example of statistical sampling methods used by naturalists in the field. Discuss why this is done.

3 PRACTICE/APPLY

Using Cooperative Groups

Divide the class into small groups. Circulate around the room as they model their problems. Use the problem below to apply the procedure to another situation.

Twenty birds are captured, banded, and then released back into a game preserve. Later, 29 are recaptured. Of these, 3 are banded. Estimate how many birds are in the game preserve. about 193

4 CLOSE

Writing Connection

Ask students to do research on endangered species and write a short composition on how the capture-recapture technique is being used to keep animals from becoming extinct.

Exploration

Capture-Recapture

Materials: small bowls, dried lima beans

Did you know that there is a way to estimate how many salmon are in Lake Ontario? Often naturalists want to know such a population but it would be impossible or impractical to make an actual count.

One method of estimating a population is the **capture-recapture** technique. In this exploration, you will model this technique using lima beans as "fish" and a bowl as "Lake Ontario."

Your Turn: Work in small groups to complete this activity.

- CAPTURE Fill a small bowl with dried lima beans. Grab a small handful of beans. Mark each bean with an X on both sides. Count the "tagged" beans and record this number. This number is the number *captured.*

  Return the "tagged" beans to the bowl and mix well.

- RECAPTURE Grab another small handful of beans. Count the total number of beans. This number is the number *recaptured.* Count the number of "tagged" beans. Record these numbers. This is sample A.

  Return all the beans to the bowl and mix.

- Repeat RECAPTURE nine more times, samples B through J. Find the total tagged and the total recaptured.

- Use the proportion shown below to estimate the number of lima beans in your bowl.

$$\frac{\text{original number captured}}{\text{number in bowl}} = \frac{\text{total tagged in samples}}{\text{total recaptured}}$$

Analysis 2. The estimate would be lower.

1. Why is it a good idea to base your prediction on several samples instead of just one sample? **Several samples give a better estimate.**
2. What would happen to your estimate if some of your tags fell off or wore off?
3. Count the number of beans in your bowl. How does your estimate compare to the actual number? **See students' work.**

330 *Proportion and Percent*

SET-UP

Materials

- small bowls
- 1 pound of dried lima beans

You may wish to use the Exploration worksheet provided on page 51 of the Lab Manual.

EE: 1A, 1C, 1E, 3I

For Students It is not necessary for each group to have an equal number. One pound of dried lima beans contains about 600 beans. If small bowls are not available, large plastic cups or coffee cans may be substituted.

For the Overhead Projector Use transparent tiles and "×" them with an overhead marker to model an example on the overhead.

Application

9-3 Using Proportions

Objective:
Use proportions to solve verbal problems.

Ralph Ramos is building a base for a television satellite dish. He needs 1.5 cubic yards of concrete. It takes 200 pounds of sand to make 4 cubic yards of concrete. How much sand does he need?

This problem can be solved using a proportion. In the proportion below, s represents the amount of sand needed to make 1.5 cubic yards of concrete.

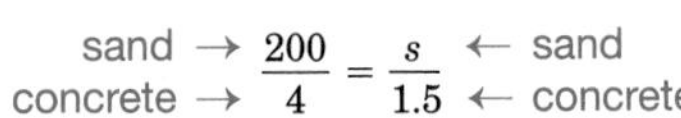

$$\text{sand} \rightarrow \frac{200}{4} = \frac{s}{1.5} \leftarrow \text{sand}$$
concrete → 4 … 1.5 ← concrete

Using a calculator, 200 [×] 1.5 [÷] 4 [=] 75

Mr. Ramos needs 75 pounds of sand.

Could you use the proportion $\frac{20}{16} = \frac{15}{w}$*?* **Yes.**

98 out of 100 homes in the United States own at least one television set.

Examples

1 **Bill Lee took a 96-mile trip to visit the Johnson Space Center. His car used 6 gallons of gasoline for the trip. How many gallons of gasoline would the car use for a 152-mile trip?**

$$\frac{96 \text{ miles}}{6 \text{ gallons}} = \frac{152 \text{ miles}}{x \text{ gallons}}$$ Notice that both rates compare miles to gallons.

$$\frac{96}{6} = \frac{152}{x}$$ Solve for x.

152 [×] 6 [÷] 96 [=] 9.5

$x = 9.5$

A trip of 152 miles would require 9.5 gallons of gasoline.

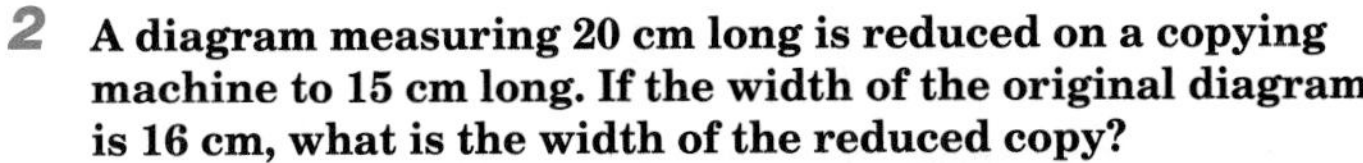

2 **A diagram measuring 20 cm long is reduced on a copying machine to 15 cm long. If the width of the original diagram is 16 cm, what is the width of the reduced copy?**

original length → $\frac{20}{15} = \frac{16}{w}$ ← original width
reduced length → … ← reduced width

$20 \cdot w = 16 \cdot 15$ Cross products are equal.

$20w = 240$

$\frac{20w}{20} = \frac{240}{20}$ Divide each side by 20.

$w = 12$ The width is reduced to 12 cm.

Bell Ringer

There are 375 students enrolled at South Middle School. Girls outnumber boys by 75. What is the ratio of boys to girls? 2:3

Lesson Notes 9-3

5-Minute Check
(over Lesson 9-2)

Solve each proportion.

1. $\frac{3}{11} = \frac{n}{33}$ $n = 9$
2. $\frac{y}{6} = \frac{32}{48}$ $y = 4$
3. $\frac{4.7}{x} = \frac{2}{8}$ $x = 18.8$
4. $\frac{12}{84} = \frac{2}{m}$ $m = 14$
5. $\frac{d}{3.2} = \frac{1.4}{6.4}$ $d = 0.7$

Transparency 9-3 contains the 5-Minute Check and a teaching aid for this lesson.

1 FOCUS

The lesson applies proportions to solving consumer and real-world applications of proportions.

2 TEACH

Using Discussion While demonstrating the examples, emphasize the importance of setting up the proportion correctly. The pattern established in the first ratio must be used in the second ratio. Use units to assure consistency.

Chalkboard Examples

- *For Example 1*
  Erla Yost drove 135 miles to visit the White House. Her car used 7.5 gallons of gasoline. How many gallons of gasoline would the car use for a 225-mile trip? 12.5 gallons
- *For Example 2*
  A picture measuring 25 cm long is enlarged on a copying machine to 30 cm long. If the width of the original picture is 15 cm, what is the width of the enlarged copy? 18 cm

EE: 1E, 3A, 3I
TAAS: 2, 10, 11, 13

Chalkboard Examples

- *For Example 3*
  Ms. Galvez paid $150 for 600 square feet of roofing. If she needs 240 square feet more, what is the extra cost? **$60**

3 PRACTICE/APPLY

Checking the Concept

After completing Exercises 5-10, have students compare the proportions. Using different proportions for the same exercise, find cross products and solve. Compare cross products and solutions.

Error Analysis

Watch for students who set up proportions incorrectly.
Prevent by writing units of numerators and denominators by each number.

Practice Masters Booklet, **p. 84**

Name ______________________ Date ______________

Practice Worksheet 9-3

Application: Using Proportions

Write a proportion that could be used to solve for each variable. Then solve.

1. 1 subscription for $21
   28 subscriptions for x dollars
   $\frac{1}{21} = \frac{28}{x}$; $x = 588$, $588
2. 20 ounces at $7
   17 ounces at x dollars
   $\frac{20}{7} = \frac{17}{x}$; $x = 5.95$, $5.95
3. 1 gallon of water weighs $8\frac{1}{3}$ pounds
   30 gallons of water weighs x pounds
   $\frac{1}{8\frac{1}{3}} = \frac{30}{x}$; $x = 250$, 250 pounds
4. 1 cm represents 3.5 km
   2.4 cm represents x km
   $\frac{1}{3.5} = \frac{2.4}{x}$; $x = 8.4$, 8.4 km
5. 5 liters at $15.25
   x liters at $33.55
   $\frac{5}{15.25} = \frac{x}{33.55}$; $x = 11$, $11
6. 3 packages of cheese for $7.17
   6 packages of cheese for x dollars
   $\frac{3}{7.17} = \frac{6}{x}$; $x = 14.34$, $14.34
7. 225 bushels for 3 acres
   x bushels for 9.6 acres
   $\frac{225}{3} = \frac{x}{9.6}$; $x = 720$, 720 bushels
8. 25 cm by 35 cm enlarged to 150 cm by x cm
   $\frac{25}{150} = \frac{35}{x}$; $x = 210$, 210 cm
9. 20 cm by 30 cm reduced to 12 cm by x cm
   $\frac{20}{12} = \frac{30}{x}$; $x = 18$, 18 cm
10. 64 ft of rope weighs 20 pounds
    28 ft of rope weighs x pounds
    $\frac{64}{20} = \frac{28}{x}$; $x = 8.75$, 8.75 pounds
11. $\frac{1}{4}$ in. represents 1 m
    5 in. represents x m $\frac{\frac{1}{4}}{5} = \frac{1}{x}$;
    $x = 20$, 20 m
12. 2 liters of orange juice at $3.58
    5 liters of orange juice at x dollars
    $\frac{2}{3.58} = \frac{5}{x}$; $x = 8.95$, $8.95
13. 2 tires at $240
    x tires at $1080
    $\frac{2}{240} = \frac{x}{1080}$; $x = 9$, 9 tires
14. 200 miles in 2.5 days
    x miles in 8 days
    $\frac{200}{2.5} = \frac{x}{8}$; $x = 640$, 640 miles
15. 450 km or 45 liters
    1500 km on x liters
    $\frac{450}{45} = \frac{1500}{x}$; $x = 150$, 150 liters
16. 3 shirts for $56.85
    x shirts for $132.65
    $\frac{3}{56.85} = \frac{x}{132.65}$; $x = 7$, 7 shirts
17. $\frac{1}{4}$ in. represents 1 ft
    x in. represents 25 ft
    $\frac{\frac{1}{4}}{1} = \frac{x}{25}$; $x = 6\frac{1}{4}$, $6\frac{1}{4}$
18. 5 hours for $53.75
    3 hours for x dollars
    $\frac{5}{53.75} = \frac{3}{x}$; $x = 32.25$, $32.25
19. 2.5 pounds of meat for 2 dogs
    x pounds of meat for 7 dogs
    $\frac{2.5}{2} = \frac{x}{7}$; $x = 8.75$, 8.75 pounds
20. 2 inches of rain in 2.5 hours
    3.6 inches of rain in x hours
    $\frac{2}{2.5} = \frac{3.6}{x}$; $x = 4.5$, 4.5 hours

Express $\frac{1}{4}$ as a decimal. Do you get the same result? **Yes.**

3 **Marcia draws a floor plan for the house she and her father will build. On her plans, $\frac{1}{4}$-inch represents 1 foot of the real house. If the house is to be 54 feet long, what is the length on her plans?**

$$\frac{\frac{1}{4}\text{ inch}}{x\text{ inches}} = \frac{1\text{ foot}}{54\text{ feet}} \rightarrow \frac{\frac{1}{4}}{x} = \frac{1}{54}$$

$$\frac{1}{4} \cdot 54 = 1x \qquad \text{Find the cross products.}$$

$$13\frac{1}{2} = x$$

The length 54 feet is represented by $13\frac{1}{2}$ inches on the plans.

Checking for Understanding

Communicating Algebra

1. In your own words, explain how to solve a proportion using a calculator. **Multiply the cross products, divide by the other number.**

Choose the proportion that could be used to solve each problem below.

2. If 2 liters of fruit juice costs $3.98, how much does 5 liters cost?
   (a.) $\frac{2}{\$3.98} = \frac{5}{d}$ b. $\frac{2}{\$3.98} = \frac{d}{5}$ c. $\frac{2}{5} = \frac{d}{\$3.98}$ d. $\frac{5}{d} = \frac{\$3.98}{2}$
3. If 64 feet of rope weighs 20 pounds, how much will 80 feet of the same kind of rope weigh?
   a. $\frac{p}{20} = \frac{64}{80}$ b. $\frac{80}{20} = \frac{64}{p}$ (c.) $\frac{64}{20} = \frac{80}{p}$ d. $\frac{64}{80} = \frac{p}{20}$
4. If a 10-pound turkey takes 4 hours to cook, how long will it take a 14-pound turkey to cook?
   a. $\frac{4}{10} = \frac{14}{h}$ (b.) $\frac{4}{10} = \frac{h}{14}$ c. $\frac{10}{20} = \frac{h}{4}$ d. $\frac{h}{10} = \frac{4}{14}$

Guided Practice

Write a proportion that could be used to solve for each variable. Then solve.

5. 40 ounces at $3.00
   25 ounces at x dollars $\frac{40}{3} = \frac{25}{x}$; $1.875
6. 3 liters at $7.00
   y liters at $6.20 $\frac{3}{7} = \frac{y}{6.20}$; 2.7 liters
7. 20 by 30 cm enlarged to 25 by x cm $\frac{20}{30} = \frac{25}{x}$; 37.5 cm
8. 16 by 24 cm reduced to 14 by x cm $\frac{16}{24} = \frac{14}{x}$; 21 cm
9. $\frac{1}{4}$ in. represents 1 ft
   3 in. represents x ft $\frac{\frac{1}{4}}{1} = \frac{3}{x}$; 12 ft
10. 1 cm represents 2.5 m
    2.5 cm represents x m
    $\frac{1}{2.5} = \frac{2.5}{x}$; 6.25 m

Exercises

Independent Practice

Write a proportion that could be used to solve for each variable. Then solve.

11. 250 bushels for 2 acres
    x bushels for 5 acres $\frac{250}{2} = \frac{x}{5}$; 625 bushels
12. 3 pounds for $15
    x pounds for $45 $\frac{3}{15} = \frac{x}{45}$; 9 pounds
13. 15 by 21 cm enlarged to 20 by x cm $\frac{15}{21} = \frac{20}{x}$; 28 cm
14. 5 liters at $6.15
    x liters at $8.00 $\frac{5}{6.15} = \frac{x}{8}$; 6.5 liters

Alternate Strategies: Reteaching the Lesson

Reteaching Activity

Using Models Not all populations are measured by capture-recapture. For certain types of populations, members in a certain area can be counted and a proportion used to predict the population in a larger area. Use dried lima beans on a desktop to model such a problem.

Reteaching Masters Booklet, **p. 76**

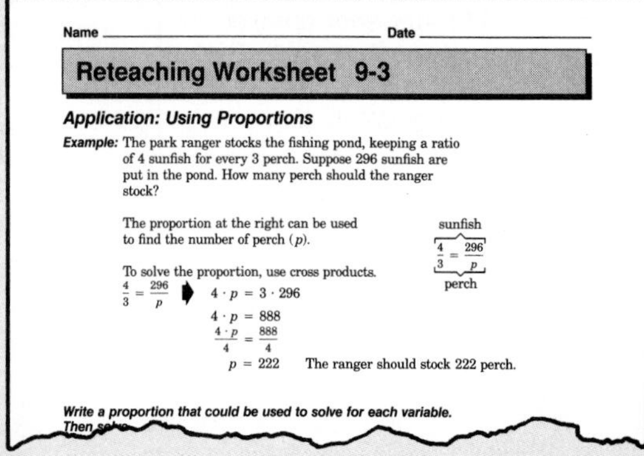

Name ______________________ Date ______________

Reteaching Worksheet 9-3

Application: Using Proportions

Example: The park ranger stocks the fishing pond, keeping a ratio of 4 sunfish for every 3 perch. Suppose 296 sunfish are put in the pond. How many perch should the ranger stock?

The proportion at the right can be used to find the number of perch (p).

sunfish
$\frac{4}{3} = \frac{296}{p}$
perch

To solve the proportion, use cross products.

$\frac{4}{3} = \frac{296}{p}$ ➧ $4 \cdot p = 3 \cdot 296$

$4 \cdot p = 888$

$\frac{4 \cdot p}{4} = \frac{888}{4}$

$p = 222$ The ranger should stock 222 perch.

Write a proportion that could be used to solve for each variable. Then solve.

16. Sample answer: (0, −3), (1, −1), (2, 1), (3, 3)

Mixed Review

15. Determine whether the following conjunction is true or false. *The product of 3x and 2x is 6x and the quotient of 8n and 2 is 4n.* (Lesson 3-9) **false**

16. Find four solutions of the equation $y = 2x - 3$. (Lesson 8-5)

17. Express as a unit rate: *6 inches of rain in 4 hours.* (Lesson 9-1) $\frac{1.5 \text{ inches}}{\text{hour}}$

18. Solve the proportion $\frac{r}{4} = \frac{6}{16}$. (Lesson 9-2) **1.5**

Applications

19. **Science** The ratio of weight on Earth to weight on the moon is 6:1. If you weigh 135 pounds on Earth, how much would you weigh on the moon? **22.5 pounds**

20. **Geography** The scale on a map is $\frac{1}{4}$ inch = 10 miles. On the map the distance from Pittsburgh to Philadelphia is about $6\frac{3}{4}$ inches. Estimate the actual distance between the two cities. **about 270 miles**

21. **Photography** In simple cameras, like the one at the right, light from an object passes through a lens and makes an image on film. The object and its image are always in proportion. This relationship between the object and its image can be expressed by the proportion

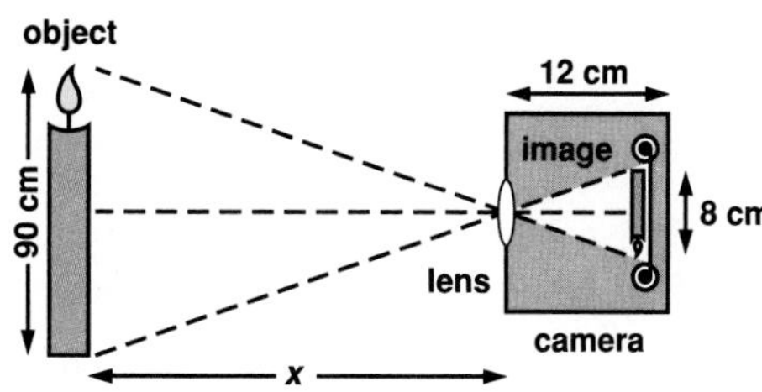

$$\frac{\text{image size}}{\text{object size}} = \frac{\text{image distance from lens}}{\text{object distance from lens}}.$$

Find the distance represented by x in the diagram. **135 cm**

22. **Consumer Awareness** Tai works 5 hours as a painter and earns \$53.25. If he works 8 hours, how much does he earn? **\$85.20**

23. **Cooking** A stew recipe uses 2 pounds of meat for 12 servings. How much is needed to make 9 servings? **1.5 pounds**

24. **Hobbies** The mast on a model ship is $6\frac{7}{8}$ inches tall. The scale of the model is $\frac{1}{8}$ inch = 1 foot. How tall is the mast on the real ship? **55 feet**

Critical Thinking

25. A 3-inch by 5-inch photograph is enlarged so that the area of the enlargement is 9 times the area of the photograph. Find the width and length of the enlargement. **9 inches, 15 inches**

Wrap-Up

26. **Make Up a Problem** Write a problem that can be solved using a proportion. **See margin.**

Independent Practice

Homework Assignment	
Basic	11-20, 25, 26
Average	13-22, 25, 26
Honors	15-26

4 CLOSE

Assessment Option

Modeling Divide the class into small groups. Put an unknown quantity of cut pieces of paper into brown bags (at least 50 in each bag) and give each group a bag. Have the students use the capture-recapture method to estimate the number of slips in the bag.

Additional Answer

26. Sample answer: One out of four students surveyed wore high-top athletic shoes. If there are 800 students, how many wear high-tops?

Enrichment Masters Booklet, **p. 76**

Name ______________________ Date ____________

Enrichment Worksheet 9-3

Inverse Variation

On a seesaw, the heavier person sits closer to the center; the lighter person sits farther away. If Marcia weighs 80 pounds and Carmen weighs 90 pounds, Carmen must sit closer to the center.

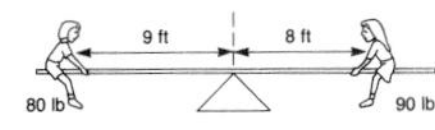

Notice that the product of weight times distance is the same on both sides. This is an illustration of **inverse variation.**

$80 \cdot 9 = 90 \cdot 8$
$720 = 720$
$w_1 \cdot d_1 = w_2 \cdot d_2$

The principle illustrated above is sometimes called the "law of the lever." Using the seesaw as a lever, the two girls could lift a small car. Place the seesaw so that 1 foot overhangs the center or point of leverage with 16 feet on the girls' side.

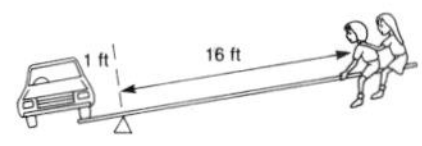

Then $x \cdot 1 = 16 \cdot 170$ The sum of the girls' weights is 170 pounds.
$x = 2720$

The girls could lift 2720 pounds.

Solve.

1. Greg weighs 150 pounds and sits 6 feet from the center of the seesaw. Miguel weighs 120 pounds. Where should Miguel sit in order to balance the seesaw? **7.5 feet**

2. How far from the center of the seesaw should John sit if he weighs 130 pounds and is trying to balance Tom, who weighs 85 pounds and is sitting 6.5 feet from the center? **4.25 feet**

3. Jennifer weighs 105 pounds and sits 5 feet from the center of the seesaw. Becky balances the seesaw when she sits 7 feet from the center. How much does Becky weigh? **75 pounds**

4. How much weight could two girls lift if they each weigh 104 pounds and are seated 12 feet from the point of leverage? Assume there is 5 feet on the opposite side of the point of leverage. **499.2 pounds**

Alternate Strategies: Extending the Lesson

Enrichment

Social Studies Connection Provide students with several different road maps. Using the scale and a proportion, have students find out what scale length represents 5 miles (or any distance of choice).

Cooperative Learning

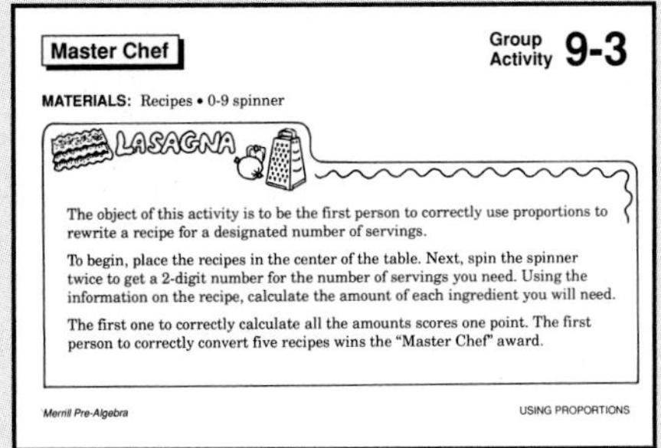

Master Chef Group Activity **9-3**

MATERIALS: Recipes • 0-9 spinner

LASAGNA

The object of this activity is to be the first person to correctly use proportions to rewrite a recipe for a designated number of servings.

To begin, place the recipes in the center of the table. Next, spin the spinner twice to get a 2-digit number for the number of servings you need. Using the information on the recipe, calculate the amount of each ingredient you will need.

The first one to correctly calculate all the amounts scores one point. The first person to correctly convert five recipes wins the "Master Chef" award.

Merrill Pre-Algebra USING PROPORTIONS

5-Minute Check
(over Lesson 9-3)

Write a proportion that could be used to solve for each variable. Then solve.

1. 5 gallons at \$6.50
   x gallons at \$11.70 **9 gallons**
2. $\frac{1}{2}$ inch represents 15 miles
   4 inches represents x miles
   120 miles
3. 8 by 12 cm enlarged to 10 by x cm. **15 cm**
4. 6 oranges for \$0.99
   x oranges for \$3.30
   20 oranges
5. 2 cm represents 5 meters
   7 cm represents x meters
   17.5 meters

Transparency 9-4 contains the 5-Minute Check and a teaching aid for this lesson.

1 FOCUS

The purpose of this lesson is to define percent, use a proportion to write a fraction as a percent, and solve percent problems.

Motivating the Lesson

Empty two rolls of pennies into a container. Take a handful of pennies out of the container and ask students how they would express the number missing from the container.

2 TEACH

Using Cooperative Groups

After defining the terms and demonstrating the examples, have students work in groups of three to solve the Chalkboard Examples. One student sets up the proportion, one writes the cross product, and the third student solves the equation using a calculator. Each student should take a different role for each problem.

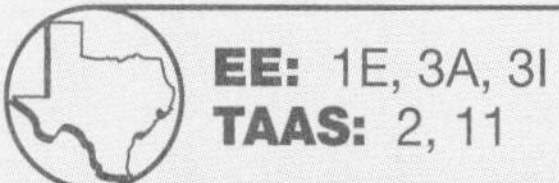

EE: 1E, 3A, 3I
TAAS: 2, 11

9-4 Using the Percent Proportion

Objectives:
Use the percent proportion to write fractions as percents.
Solve problems using the percent proportion.

Advertising is a \$61 billion industry in the United States. It encourages people to eat certain foods, drive certain cars, buy certain products, and so on. In order to gather information about the customers, advertisers often take surveys.

Key Terms:
percent
percentage
base
rate
percent proportion

The results of surveys are usually reported as fractions or percents. A **percent** is a ratio that compares a number to 100. Percent also means *hundredths,* or *per hundred.* The symbol for percent is %.

Suppose the SuperCola Company conducted a taste test of its product. Five hundred people were asked their preference for Brand A or Brand B. Of these people, 230 preferred Brand A. What percent is this?

Is $\frac{230}{500}$ greater than $\frac{1}{2}$ or less than $\frac{1}{2}$? **less than**

$\frac{230}{500} = \frac{x}{100}$ 230 out of 500 preferred Brand A.

$230 \cdot 100 = 500x$ Write the cross products.

230 [×] 100 [÷] 500 [=] 46

$x = 46$

So, $\frac{46}{100}$ or 46% preferred Brand A.

History Connection

Percents have been used for more than 2000 years to compute interest and taxes. The development of the % symbol started in the 15th century as an abbreviation for *per centum*. The current symbol probably comes from *PC°*, which became *p*, then $\frac{0}{0}$, and finally %.

In the proportion shown above, 230 is called the **percentage** (P). The number 500 is called the **base** (B). The ratio $\frac{46}{100}$ is called the **rate.**

$$\frac{230}{500} = \frac{46}{100} \rightarrow \frac{\text{Percentage}}{\text{Base}} = \text{Rate}$$

Note that the percentage, P, is a number that is compared to another number called the base, B.

If r represents the number per hundred, this equation can be rewritten as $\frac{P}{B} = \frac{r}{100}$. This proportion is called the **percent proportion.**

Bell Ringer

Name three situations where proportions could be used to solve problems. **Sample answer: Determining the range of a car with a full tank of gas and a mileage rating of 30 mpg.**

You can use the percent proportion to express fractions as percents and to solve percent problems.

Examples

1 Express $\frac{5}{8}$ as a percent.

$\frac{P}{B} = \frac{r}{100} \rightarrow \frac{5}{8} = \frac{r}{100}$ Replace P with 5 and B with 8.

$5 \cdot 100 = 8 \cdot r$ Find the cross products.

$\frac{500}{8} = \frac{8r}{8}$ Divide each side by 8.

$62\frac{1}{2} = r$

$\frac{5}{8}$ is equivalent to $62\frac{1}{2}\%$.

2 What number is 35% of 263?

Why should you replace r with 35? **$35\% = \frac{35}{100}$**

$\frac{P}{B} = \frac{r}{100} \rightarrow \frac{P}{263} = \frac{35}{100}$ Replace B with 263 and r with 35.

$P \cdot 100 = 263 \cdot 35$ Find the cross products.

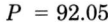

263 [×] 35 [÷] 100 [=] 92.05

$P = 92.05$

92.05 is 35% of 263.

3 The purchase price of a camera is \$84. The state tax rate is 5.5% of the purchase price. Find the total cost.

Is the total cost greater than \$84 or less than \$84? **greater than**

$\frac{P}{B} = \frac{r}{100} \rightarrow \frac{P}{84} = \frac{5.5}{100}$ Replace B with 84 and r with 5.5.

$P \cdot 100 = 84 \cdot 5.5$ Find the cross products.

84 [×] 5.5 [÷] 100 [=] 4.62

$P = 4.62$

The tax is \$4.62.

The total cost is \$84 + \$4.62 or \$88.62.

Chalkboard Examples

- *For Example 1*
  Express $\frac{3}{8}$ as a percent. $37\frac{1}{2}\%$
- *For Example 2*
  What number is 32% of 185? 59.2
- *For Example 3*
  The purchase price of a CD is \$16. The state tax rate is 5.5% of the purchase price. Find the total cost. \$16.88
- *For Example 4*
  School sweatshirts went on sale for \$18. This is 75% of the regular price. What is the regular price? \$24

Alternate Strategies: Reteaching the Lesson

Reteaching Activity

Statistics Connection Choose a topic, and survey the class to find out the fraction represented in each category. An example might be the number of students owning different types of pets. Using the percent proportion find, to the nearest percent, the percent equal to the fraction.

Reteaching Masters Booklet, **p. 77**

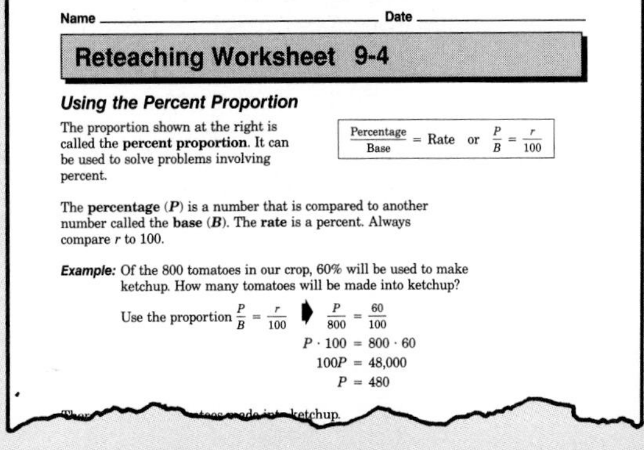
Name ____ Date ____

Reteaching Worksheet 9-4

Using the Percent Proportion

The proportion shown at the right is called the **percent proportion**. It can be used to solve problems involving percent.

$\frac{\text{Percentage}}{\text{Base}} = \text{Rate}$ or $\frac{P}{B} = \frac{r}{100}$

The **percentage** (*P*) is a number that is compared to another number called the **base** (*B*). The **rate** is a percent. Always compare *r* to 100.

Example: Of the 800 tomatoes in our crop, 60% will be used to make ketchup. How many tomatoes will be made into ketchup?

Use the proportion $\frac{P}{B} = \frac{r}{100}$ ➧ $\frac{P}{800} = \frac{60}{100}$

$P \cdot 100 = 800 \cdot 60$

$100P = 48{,}000$

$P = 480$

3 PRACTICE/APPLY

Checking the Concept

For the proportion $\frac{3}{4} = \frac{75}{100}$, have students identify percentage, base, and rate. Then ask them to state how they would solve the following proportions.

$\frac{x}{20} = \frac{40}{100}$ $\frac{3}{15} = \frac{x}{100}$ $\frac{5}{x} = \frac{20}{100}$

Error Analysis

Watch for students who write the decimal equivalent of the percent over 100 in the percent proportion.
Prevent by reminding students that "per cent" means *divided by 100.* Read the percent number and write what is read.

Practice Masters Booklet, **p. 85**

Name ______________________ Date ____________

Practice Worksheet 9-4

Using the Percent Proportion

Express each fraction as a percent.

1. $\frac{7}{25}$ 28% 2. $\frac{97}{100}$ 97% 3. $\frac{13}{50}$ 26% 4. $\frac{9}{4}$ 225%
5. $\frac{7}{8}$ 87.5% 6. $\frac{8}{5}$ 160% 7. $\frac{17}{20}$ 85% 8. $\frac{1}{50}$ 2%

Use a proportion to solve each problem.

9. What is 17% of 65? 11.05
10. Find 12.5% of 96. 12
11. What is 6% of 95? 5.7
12. Find 95% of 170. 161.5
13. Find 62.5% of 500. 312.5
14. What is 8% of 17.5? 1.4
15. 42 is what percent of 48? 87.5%
16. 9 is 15% of what number? 60
17. 13 is 5% of what number? 260
18. 24 is what percent of 32? 75%
19. 9% of 2000 is what number? 180
20. 80 is what percent of 300? $26\frac{2}{3}$%
21. 36 is what percent of 24? 150%
22. 76 is what percent of 40? 190%
23. What is 37.5% of 300? 112.5
24. 42 is 63% of what number? $66\frac{2}{3}$
25. 18 is 60% of what number? 30
26. 60 is 75% of what number? 80
27. Find 87.5% of 100. 87.5
28. 39 is 40% of what number? 97.5
29. 96 is what percent of 100? 96%
30. 56 is 1% of what number? 5600
31. Find 6.5% of 250. 16.25
32. 6 is what percent of 5? 120%

The percent proportion can also be used to find the base when the percentage and rate are given.

Is the regular price greater than $48 or less than $48? **greater than**

Example

4 **School jackets went on sale for $48. This is 60% of the regular price. What is the regular price?**

$\frac{P}{B} = \frac{r}{100} \rightarrow \frac{48}{B} = \frac{60}{100}$ Replace P with 48 and r with 60.

$48 \cdot 100 = B \cdot 60$ Find the cross products.

$\frac{4800}{60} = B$ Divide each side by 60.

$80 = B$

The regular price is $80.

In summary, there are three basic types of percent problems. Using the proportion $\frac{3}{4} = \frac{75}{100}$, you can see that the types are related as shown below.

Proportion $\frac{3}{4} = \frac{75}{100}$  **Word Form** 3 is 75% of 4.

$\frac{■}{4} = \frac{75}{100}$	What number is 75% of 4? Percentage	Find the percentage.
$\frac{3}{4} = \frac{■}{100}$	3 is what % of 4? Rate	Find the rate.
$\frac{3}{■} = \frac{75}{100}$	3 is 75% of what number? Base	Find the base.

Checking for Understanding

Communicating Algebra

1. A __?__ is a ratio that compares a number to 100. **percent**
2. Explain how to express a fraction as a percent. **Solve the proportion $\frac{a}{b} = \frac{x}{100}$ for x.**
3. Set up a proportion to find 16% of 90. $\frac{x}{90} = \frac{16}{100}$

Guided Practice

Express each fraction as a percent.

4. $\frac{31}{100}$ **31%** 5. $\frac{1}{25}$ **4%** 6. $\frac{3}{5}$ **60%** 7. $\frac{7}{20}$ **35%** 8. $\frac{3}{8}$ **37.5%**

Match each question with its corresponding proportion.

9. 48 is 60% of what number? **c** a. $\frac{48}{60} = \frac{r}{100}$
10. 48 is what percent of 60? **a** b. $\frac{P}{48} = \frac{60}{100}$
11. What number is 60% of 48? **b** c. $\frac{48}{B} = \frac{60}{100}$

Alternate Strategies: Extending the Lesson

Enrichment

Benito bought a package of batteries for $4.77. He received a $1.25 rebate from the manufacturer. What percent of Benito's final cost was the rebate? Round your answer to the nearest percent. **26%**

Cooperative Learning

Form Fits Group Activity **9-4**

The object of this activity is to determine the type of percent problem that must be solved. These are either percentage, rate, or base problems.

In groups of four or five, take turns making up and telling a problem to the others. The first one to correctly identify the problem as a percentage, rate, or base problem and to correctly solve it scores one point.

Play continues until everyone has three chances to be the problem maker. The person with the highest score wins the game.

EXAMPLES:

1. A nut mix contains 500 nuts. If 85 of them are pecans, what percent are pecans?
2. Twenty percent of a cereal is sugar. If the box weighs 19 ounces, how much sugar does it contain?
3. The state gasoline tax is 8.6%. You paid $1.74 in taxes when you bought gasoline. How many gallons of gasoline did you buy?

Merrill Pre-Algebra USING THE PERCENT PROPORTION

Identify each percentage, base, and rate. Then write a proportion and solve. See margin.

12. Find 7.5% of 405. 30.375
13. Find 81% of 32. 25.92
14. Twenty-eight is 20% of what number? 140
15. Sixteen is 40% of what number? 40
16. 19 is what percent of 76? 25%
17. 37 is what percent of 296? 12.5%

Exercises

Independent Practice

ESTIMATION / MENTAL MATH / CALCULATOR / PAPER/PENCIL

Express each fraction as a percent.

18. $\frac{2}{5}$ 40%
19. $\frac{7}{8}$ 87.5%
20. $\frac{3}{2}$ 150%
21. $\frac{15}{4}$ 375%
22. $\frac{9}{4}$ 225%

Use a proportion to solve each problem.

23. What is 40% of 60? 24
24. Find 37.5% of 80. 30
25. Twenty-one is 35% of what number? 60
26. Seventy-five is what percent of 250? 30%
27. Fifty-two is what percent of 80? 65%
28. Thirty-six is 45% of what number? 80

Mixed Review

29. **Personal Finance** Alison has developed a monthly budget for herself. She has allotted twice as much money for clothing as for eating out. If the total for both is $72, what is the most Alison can spend on eating out? (Lesson 7-7)

29. $24

30. Find the x-intercept and y-intercept for the graph of the equation $y = x - 4$. (Lesson 8-9) 4, -4
31. *True* or *false*: $\frac{7}{21} = \frac{0.5}{1.5}$. (Lesson 9-2) true
32. Write a proportion that could be used to solve for the variable x: *8 by 12 cm enlarged to 10 by x cm.* (Lesson 9-3) 15

Logical Reasoning

33. If $\frac{1}{3}$ is equivalent to $33\frac{1}{3}\%$, what percent is equivalent to $\frac{2}{3}$? $66\frac{2}{3}\%$
34. If 22.2% is equivalent to $\frac{2}{9}$, what number is equivalent to 44.4%? $\frac{4}{9}$

Applications

35. **Banking** Mika's savings account earned $9.48 in interest in one year. This is equal to $6\frac{1}{4}\%$ of his savings. What are his savings? $151.68
36. **Sports** Ten out of sixteen members of the softball team take the field. What percent of the team members are playing? 62.5%
37. **Consumer Awareness** The regular price of a CD is $12.98. Find the discount if the CD is marked 25% off. $3.25

Critical Thinking

38. Three 24-hour clocks show the correct time, 12 noon. One of the clocks is always correct, one loses a minute every 24 hours, and one gains a minute every 24 hours. How many hours will pass before all three clocks again show the correct time? 34,560 hours

Wrap-Up

39. **Research** Use newspaper articles or ads to help you create three percent problems. One of the problems should require finding the base, one should require finding the percentage, and one should require finding the rate. See margin.

Additional Answers

12. B, 405; r, 7.5; $\frac{7.5}{100} = \frac{p}{405}$
13. B, 32; r, 81; $\frac{81}{100} = \frac{x}{32}$
14. P, 28; r, 20; $\frac{28}{b} = \frac{20}{100}$
15. P, 16; r, 40; $\frac{16}{x} = \frac{40}{100}$
16. P, 19; B, 76; $\frac{19}{76} = \frac{x}{100}$
17. P, 37; B, 296; $\frac{37}{296} = \frac{r}{100}$

39. Sample Answers:
- The price of a coat was lowered 30%. The original price was $60. How much was the price lowered?
- Joe answered 40 out of 48 questions correctly on an exam. What percent did he answer correctly?
- Phil bought a ski jacket $30 off the regular price. This represented a 20% savings. What was the original price of the jacket?

Independent Practice

Homework Assignment	
Basic	19-27 odd, 29-36, 38, 39
Average	18-26 even, 29-39
Honors	22-28 even, 29-39

4 CLOSE

Assessment Option

Speaking Have two students name a percentage and a base. Have the class estimate what they think the rate will be. Then find the rate. Do this until the class has a concept of estimating the rate.

Enrichment Masters Booklet, **p. 77**

Name ______________________ Date ______________

Enrichment Worksheet 9-4

Relative Frequency

In an English language text, on the average, 1000 letters include the following number of particular letters.

E: 131	T: 105	O: 80
R: 68	I: 63	S: 61

The estimate of the likelihood of an event occurring is called **relative frequency.** It is equal to the number of successes divided by the number of trials. In the case of occurrence of letters, it is the number of times the letter occurs (a success) divided by the total number of letters (trials).

From the information above, write the relative frequency of each of the following letters as a decimal.

1. I 0.063
2. R 0.068
3. T 0.105
4. O 0.08
5. E 0.131
6. S 0.061

There are 913 letters in the article at the right. Use the relative frequencies found in Exercises 1–6 to determine the approximate number of times each of the following letters appears.

7. I 58
8. S 56
9. T 96
10. R 62
11. O 73
12. E 120

Find, to three decimal places, the actual relative frequency of each of the following letters in the article. Round answers to the nearest thousandth.

13. I 0.083
14. S 0.073
15. T 0.108
16. R 0.042
17. O 0.076
18. E 0.117

> *Music is Everybody's Language* was the theme of the special week set aside this month to recognize Music in Our Schools.
>
> Long interested in the attention given to learning about the importance of music in daily life, the sponsoring organization, Music Educators National Conference, consists of a membership of 64,000 music teachers. The influence of this organization has tremendously upgraded the acceptance of music by both students and parents for many years.
>
> All this brings to mind my own experience in Evening High School with the subject of music and its appreciation. As a student I had unfortunately selected two courses with a gap of one period between them. This was a catastrophe in night school because the valuable time was yours to use or waste, and those students attending this kind of schooling were definitely not attracted by waste. Therefore, after a bit of self-condemnation, I decided to take this elective course titled *Music Appreciation*. With my scant knowledge of music and an attentive ear, my curiosity was aroused to the point that I thought it might at least be fun—a sort of vacation.

19. How are the answers for Exercises 13–18 likely to compare with the combined results from ten similar-sized articles? They will be approximately the same.

Lesson Notes 9-5

5-Minute Check
(over Lesson 9-4)

Use a proportion to solve each problem.

1. What is 25% of $42? $10.50
2. 57 is 60% of what number? 95
3. Find 36% of $79. $28.44
4. Twenty-eight is 35% of what number? 80
5. What is 15% of 90? 13.5

Transparency 9-5 contains the 5-Minute Check and a teaching aid for this lesson.

1 FOCUS

The purpose of this lesson is to recognize the relationship between percents and decimals and use proportions to rename rational numbers.

Motivating the Lesson

Show students an item of interest to them, such as a CD. Ask them which they would rather do, have 25% taken off the price or $\frac{1}{5}$ taken off.

2 TEACH

Using a Table Suggest that students make an equivalence table of fractions, decimals, and percents for frequently used common fractions. Use multiples of $\frac{1}{2}, \frac{1}{3}, \frac{1}{4}, \frac{1}{5}$, and $\frac{1}{8}$.

EE: 1E, 3A, 3I, 5E
TAAS: 1, 2, 11, 12

9-5 Fractions, Decimals, and Percents

Objectives:
Express decimals as percents.
Express percents as fractions and decimals.

Julia wants to buy a new fishing reel. She finds two stores in which the reel is on sale. If the original price is the same at both stores, which store offers the better price?

To find the better price, you need to compare $\frac{1}{3}$ and 30%. One way to compare them is to express $\frac{1}{3}$ and 30% as decimals and compare the decimals.

$\frac{1}{3} = 1 \div 3$

1 ÷ 3 = 0.3333333

$\frac{1}{3} \approx 0.33$

$30\% = \frac{30}{100}$ Definition of percent

$= 0.30$

$30\% = 0.30$

Why is the approximation symbol, ≈, used? $\frac{1}{3} = 0.\overline{3}$; 0.33 is rounded.

Since 0.33 is greater than 0.30, Hoppy's Sporting Goods offers the better price.

You have learned how to express fractions as decimals and percents. Fractions, decimals, and percents are different names for the same number.

$\frac{40}{100}$ ↔ 0.40 ↔ 40%

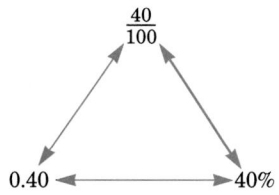

The following examples will help you express percents as fractions and decimals.

Bell Ringer

Write three fractions. Exchange and express each as a percent.

To express a decimal as a percent, first express the decimal as a fraction with a denominator of 100. Then, express the fraction as a percent. To express a fraction as a percent, first express the fraction as a decimal, then the decimal as a percent.

Examples

Mental Math Hint

In Examples 1-3, the decimal point was moved two places to the right as a result of multiplying by 100.

Express each decimal as a percent.

1 $0.53 \rightarrow \frac{53}{100} = 53\%$

2 $0.08 \rightarrow \frac{8}{100} = 8\%$

3 $0.259 \rightarrow \frac{259}{1000} = \frac{25.9}{100}$ Divide the numerator and denominator by 10.

$= 25.9\%$

Express each fraction as a percent.

4 $\frac{2}{3}$

2 [÷] 3 [=] 0.6666667

$\frac{2}{3} \approx 0.67 \rightarrow \frac{67}{100} = 67\%$

5 $\frac{5}{4}$

5 [÷] 4 [=] 1.25

$\frac{5}{4} = 1.25 \rightarrow \frac{125}{100} = 125\%$

The percent in Example 5 is greater than 100%. Why? $\frac{5}{4} > 1$

To express a percent as a fraction in simplest form, express the percent in the form $\frac{r}{100}$ and simplify. To express a percent as a decimal, rewrite the percent in the form $\frac{r}{100}$ and then express the fraction as a decimal.

Examples

Mental Math Hint

It is helpful to memorize the fraction-percent equivalents for halves, thirds, fourths, fifths, sixths, and eighths.

Write each percent as a fraction in simplest form.

6 5%

$5\% = \frac{5}{100}$

$= \frac{1}{20}$

7 $62\frac{1}{2}\%$

$62\frac{1}{2} = \frac{62\frac{1}{2}}{100}$ The fraction bar indicates division.

$= 62\frac{1}{2} \div 100$

$= \frac{\overset{5}{\cancel{125}}}{2} \times \frac{1}{\underset{4}{\cancel{100}}}$

$= \frac{5}{8}$

Chalkboard Examples

Express each decimal as a percent.

- *For Example 1*
  0.27 **27%**
- *For Example 2*
  0.05 **5%**
- *For Example 3*
  0.157 **15.7%**

Express each fraction as a percent.

- *For Example 4*
  $\frac{1}{3}$ **33%**
- *For Example 5*
  $\frac{6}{5}$ **120%**

Write each percent as a fraction in simplest form.

- *For Example 6*
  25% $\frac{1}{4}$
- *For Example 7*
  $32\frac{1}{2}\%$ $\frac{13}{40}$

Alternate Strategies: Reteaching the Lesson

Reteaching Activity

Using Cooperative Groups Have students work in groups of three. Have one student name a fraction, another student find the equivalent decimal and the third student find the equivalent percent. Rotate.

***Reteaching Masters Booklet,* p. 78**

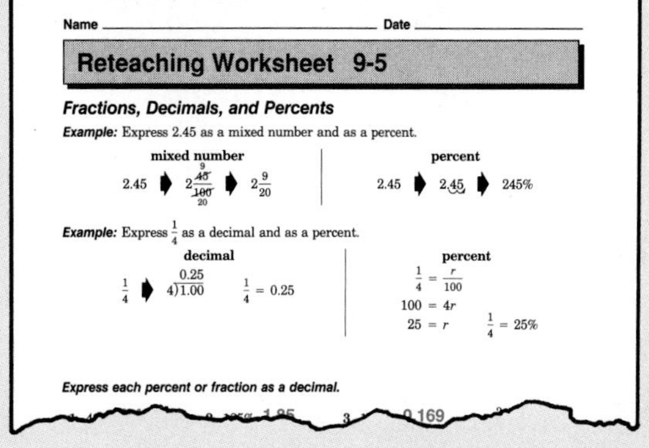
Name ______ Date ______

Reteaching Worksheet 9-5

Fractions, Decimals, and Percents

Example: Express 2.45 as a mixed number and as a percent.

mixed number: $2.45 \rightarrow 2\frac{\overset{9}{\cancel{45}}}{\underset{20}{\cancel{100}}} \rightarrow 2\frac{9}{20}$

percent: $2.45 \rightarrow 2.45 \rightarrow 245\%$

Example: Express $\frac{1}{4}$ as a decimal and as a percent.

decimal: $\frac{1}{4} \rightarrow 4\overline{)1.00}$ = 0.25; $\frac{1}{4} = 0.25$

percent: $\frac{1}{4} = \frac{r}{100}$; $100 = 4r$; $25 = r$; $\frac{1}{4} = 25\%$

Express each percent or fraction as a decimal.

Chalkboard Examples

Write each percent as a decimal.

- *For Example 8* 12% **0.12**
- *For Example 9* 175% **1.75**
- *For Example 10* 0.6% **0.006**

3 PRACTICE/APPLY

Checking the Concept

Ask students which Guided Practice Exercises they could do mentally and which exercises would require a calculator.

Error Analysis

Watch for students who have difficulty interpreting percents containing decimals.
Prevent by writing the decimal over 100; move the decimal point to the end of the numerator and the same number of pieces in the denominator, supplying zeros as needed.

Practice Masters Booklet, **p. 86**

Name ______________________ Date ______________

Practice Worksheet 9-5

Fractions, Decimals, and Percents

Express each decimal as a percent.

1. 0.5 50%	2. 2.72 272%	3. 0.65 65%
4. 0.08 8%	5. 15.7 1570%	6. 0.003 0.3%
7. 1.076 107.6%	8. 0.205 20.5%	9. 0.0125 1.25%

Express each fraction as a percent.

10. $\frac{3}{8}$ 37.5%	11. $\frac{5}{100}$ 5%	12. $\frac{7}{4}$ 175%
13. $\frac{7}{10}$ 70%	14. $\frac{13}{16}$ 81.25%	15. $\frac{7}{8}$ 87.5%
16. $\frac{1}{6}$ $16\frac{2}{3}$%	17. $\frac{11}{12}$ $91\frac{2}{3}$%	18. $\frac{5}{2}$ 250%
19. $\frac{3}{25}$ 12%	20. $\frac{3}{4}$ 75%	21. $\frac{6}{5}$ 120%
22. $\frac{4}{5}$ 80%	23. $\frac{1}{10}$ 10%	24. $\frac{5}{16}$ 31.25%

Express each percent as a fraction.

25. 46% $\frac{23}{50}$	26. 9% $\frac{9}{100}$	27. 65% $\frac{13}{20}$
28. 12.5% $\frac{1}{8}$	29. 24.6% $\frac{123}{500}$	30. $33\frac{1}{3}$% $\frac{1}{3}$
31. 62.5% $\frac{5}{8}$	32. $8\frac{1}{8}$% $\frac{13}{160}$	33. 2.5% $\frac{1}{40}$

Express each percent as a decimal.

34. 6% 0.06	35. 12% 0.12	36. 14.6% 0.146
37. 0.02% 0.0002	38. 33.3% 0.333	39. 0.75% 0.0075

Mental Math Hint

In Examples 8-10, the decimal point was moved two places to the left as a result of dividing by 100.

Examples

Write each percent as a decimal.

8 15% → $\frac{15}{100} = 0.15$

9 125% → $\frac{125}{100} = 1.25$

10 0.2% → $\frac{0.2}{100} = \frac{2}{1000}$
$= 0.002$

Checking for Understanding

For Exercises 1-4, see margin.

Communicating Algebra

1. Describe how to express a decimal as a percent.
2. Explain how to express a fraction as a percent.
3. Explain how to express a percent as a fraction.
4. Describe how to express a percent as a decimal.

Guided Practice

Express each decimal as a percent.

5. 0.36 **36%** 6. 0.7 **70%** 7. 0.475 **47.5%** 8. 0.003 **0.3%**

Express each fraction as a percent.

9. $\frac{31}{100}$ **31%** 10. $\frac{1}{25}$ **4%** 11. $\frac{9}{10}$ **90%** 12. $\frac{5}{4}$ **125%**

Express each percent as a fraction.

13. 60% $\frac{3}{5}$ 14. 87.5% $\frac{7}{8}$ 15. 32% $\frac{8}{25}$ 16. 0.05% $\frac{1}{2000}$

Express each percent as a decimal.

17. 28% **0.28** 18. 66.5% **0.665** 19. 80% **0.8** 20. 0.07% **0.0007**

Exercises

Independent Practice

Express each decimal as a percent.

21. 0.81 **81%** 22. 0.07 **7%** 23. 1.13 **113%** 24. 3.5 **350%**
25. 0.407 **40.7%** 26. 0.008 **0.8%** 27. 3.093 **309.3%** 28. 0.035 **3.5%**

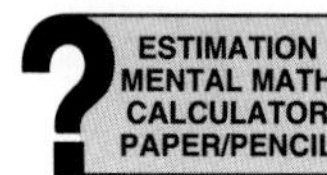

Express each fraction as a percent.

29. $\frac{1}{5}$ **20%** 30. $\frac{15}{16}$ **93.75%** 31. $\frac{9}{4}$ **225%** 32. $\frac{4}{3}$ **$133.\overline{3}$%**
33. $\frac{5}{8}$ **62.5%** 34. $\frac{5}{6}$ **$83.\overline{3}$%** 35. $\frac{7}{12}$ **$58.\overline{3}$%** 36. $\frac{3}{2}$ **150%**

Express each percent as a fraction.

37. 56% $\frac{14}{25}$ 38. 85% $\frac{17}{20}$ 39. 73% $\frac{73}{100}$ 40. 84.5% $\frac{169}{200}$
41. $66\frac{2}{3}$% $\frac{2}{3}$ 42. 81.25% $\frac{13}{16}$ 43. $16\frac{2}{3}$% $\frac{1}{6}$ 44. $21\frac{1}{4}$% $\frac{17}{80}$

Express each percent as a decimal.

45. 82% **0.82** 46. 47% **0.47** 47. 41% **0.41** 48. 97% **0.97**
49. 48.5% **0.485** 50. 18.4% **0.184** 51. 33.4% **0.334** 52. 0.09% **0.0009**

Additional Answers

1. Move the decimal point to the right two places.
2. Set up a proportion with the fraction as the first ratio and 100 as the denominator of the second ratio and solve for the numerator of the second ratio.
3. Write the percent in the form $\frac{r}{100}$ and simplify.
4. Move the decimal point two places to the left.

70. $30\% = \frac{3}{10}$, $26\% = \frac{13}{50}$, $21\% = \frac{21}{100}$, $17\% = \frac{17}{100}$, $6\% = \frac{3}{50}$

72. If the numerator is greater than the denominator, the fraction will be greater than 100%. If the numerator is less than 10 and the denominator is 1000 or greater, the fraction will be less than 1%.

Copy and complete each table.

	Fraction	Decimal	Percent
53.	$\frac{1}{8}$	0.125	12.5%
54.	$\frac{53}{100}$	0.53	53%
55.	$\frac{3}{16}$	0.1875	18.75%

	Fraction	Decimal	Percent
56.	$\frac{7}{20}$	0.35	35%
57.	$\frac{17}{100}$	0.17	17%
58.	$\frac{7}{4}$	1.75	175%

Mixed Review

59. Evaluate the expression $2r^2$ if $r = 7$. (Lesson 4-2) 98
60. Estimate $8.9 + 12.1 + 17.3$. (Lesson 5-3) 38
61. Solve the equation $\frac{x - 4}{9} = -3$. (Lesson 7-2) -23
62. Graph the inequality $y < -x + 3$. (Lesson 8-11) See Solutions Manual.
63. Express the ratio 11:55 as a fraction in simplest form. (Lesson 9-1) $\frac{1}{5}$
64. Solve the proportion $\frac{12}{s} = \frac{36}{9}$. (Lesson 9-2) 3

Use a proportion to solve each problem. (Lesson 9-4)

65. Eighteen is what percent of 90? 20%
66. Seventy-two is 60% of what number? 120

Applications

67. **Consumer Awareness** A computer game cartridge sells for \$39. On sale, the price is $33\frac{1}{3}\%$ less. What fraction of the original price is the sale price? $\frac{2}{3}$
68. **Sports** Gary made 16 out of 20 points after touchdowns. What percent did he make? 80%
69. **Meteorology** The Channel 10 meteorologist pointed to a spot on the state map that was marked .70" and said, "Down in Charlotte they received less than $\frac{3}{4}$ of an inch of rain." Was he correct? yes; 0.7 < 0.75

Connection

70. **Statistics** The circle graph at the right shows how a sample of people spend their vacations. Express each percent as a fraction in simplest form. See margin.

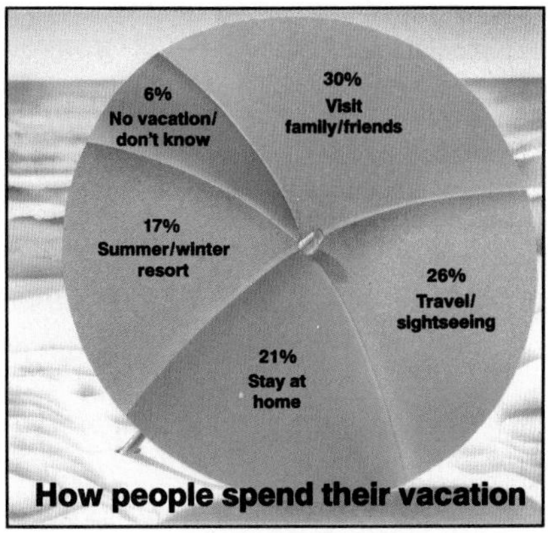

Critical Thinking

71. February the third is a *prime day* because the month and day (2/3) are represented by prime numbers. How many prime days are there in a leap year? 53 days

Wrap-Up

72. In your own words, explain how you can tell if a fraction will be greater than 100% or less than 1%. See margin.

Independent Practice

Homework Assignment	
Basic	21-57 odd, 59-67, 70-72
Average	22-58 even, 59-72
Honors	28-52 even, 53-72

Chapter 9, Quiz A (Lesson 9-1 through 9-5) is available in the Evaluation Masters Booklet, p. 79.

4 CLOSE

Assessment Option

Modeling Put 25 marbles in a bag. Have each student take a handful of marbles, and count how many they took. Then have students express the number as a fraction, a percent, and a decimal.

Enrichment Masters Booklet, **p. 78**

Name ______________ Date ______________

Enrichment Worksheet 9-5

Finding the Percent One Number is of Another

Solve. Use the circle graph.

1. How much money did Eric spend on all the camera equipment? \$520

Cost of Eric's Camera Equipment

Camera \$244.40
Camera Case \$31.20
Tripod \$46.80
Flash \$57.20
Wide-Angle Lens \$140.40

2. What percent of the total cost of the equipment did Eric spend on the camera? 47%
3. What percent of the total cost was spent on the camera case? 6%

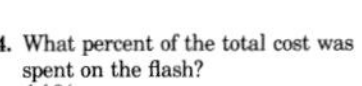

4. What percent of the total cost was spent on the flash? 11%
5. What percent of the total cost was spent on the wide-angle lens? 27%
6. What percent of the total cost was spent on the tripod? 9%
7. What percent of the total cost was spent on the camera case, tripod, and flash? 26%
8. The salesperson who sold Eric the equipment earned a $6\frac{1}{2}\%$ commission on the sale. How much was the commission? \$33.80

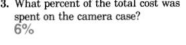

Alternate Strategies: Extending the Lesson

Enrichment

Writing Connection Have students write about the similarities and differences between fractions, decimals, and percents. Ask them to determine when each would be more appropriate to use in describing different everyday activities.

Cooperative Learning

Conversion Rummy Group Activity **9-5**

SETUP: Make a set of "Conversion Rummy" cards using the numbers given on the back of this card

Shuffle the cards and deal 6 to each player. Place the rest face down with the top card removed and placed face up to begin the discard pile.

Following the usual rules for rummy, play proceeds around the table with each person drawing a card from either pile. Players may keep the drawn card and discard another from their hands, or they may discard the new card. Players may never have more than 6 cards in their hands after a turn.

The object of the game is to get rid of all the cards in your hand by forming sets of three cards. All the cards in a set must name the same number. For example, cards with $\frac{1}{2}$, 0.5, and 50% would form a set. When you have a set, place it on the table in front of you. If someone else has a card that can be used in your set, he or she can place it there.

The first person to play all of his or her cards wins.

Merrill Pre-Algebra FRACTIONS, DECIMALS, AND PERCENTS

Lesson Notes 9-6

5-Minute Check
(over Lesson 9-5)

Copy and complete the table.

	Fraction	Decimal	Percent
1.	$\frac{1}{2}$	0.5	50%
2.	$\frac{4}{25}$	0.16	16%
3.	$\frac{1}{250}$	0.004	0.4%
4.	$\frac{3}{8}$	0.375	37.5%
5.	$\frac{49}{200}$	0.245	24.5%

Transparency 9-6 contains the 5-Minute Check and a teaching aid for this lesson.

1 FOCUS

The purpose of this lesson is to apply the skills used in the previous lesson to make a reasonable estimate of the answer to a percent problem.

Motivating the Lesson

Partially fill a glass with water. Ask students what percent of the glass is full or empty.

2 TEACH

Using Cooperative Groups

Have students work in groups of three to solve each of the examples, one using the fraction method, one the 1% method, and one the meaning of percent method. Compare and contrast results.

EE: 1E, 3A, 3I, 5E
TAAS: 2, 10, 11, 12

9-6 Percent and Estimation

Objective:
Estimate with percents.

During a pre-inventory sale Eastside Stereo put everything in the store on sale at 30% off. About how much would you save on a speaker that normally sells for $118?

To estimate means to find an answer that is close to the exact answer. The word *about* tells you that an exact answer is not required.

You can estimate the savings by rounding $118 to $120 and using any of the methods below.

Fraction Method	1% Method	Meaning of Percent Method
30% is nearly 33% or $\frac{1}{3}$ $\frac{1}{3}$ of $120 is $40 **Estimate:** $40	1% of $120 is $1.20 $1.20 rounds to $1 30 times $1 is $30 **Estimate:** $30	30% means: $30 for every $100 $3 for every $10 $30 + $3(2) is $36 **Estimate:** $36

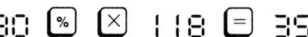

Calculator Hint

Use the % key to enter percents into the calculator. This key causes the percent to be replaced by its decimal equivalent.

Use a calculator to find the exact savings.

30 [%] [×] 118 [=] 35.4

The exact savings would be $35.40. Compared to the estimates, the answer is reasonable.

Examples

1 Estimate the percent that is shaded.

9 out of 20

$\frac{9}{20}$ is about $\frac{10}{20}$ or $\frac{1}{2}$.

$\frac{1}{2}$ = 50%

About 50% is shaded.

2 Estimate $300 less a discount of 22%.

22% is about 20% or $\frac{1}{5}$.

$\frac{1}{5}$ of $300 is $60.

300 − 60 = 240

$300 less a discount of 22% is about $240.

Bell Ringer

A photocopier reduces a picture that is 12 inches long to 10 inches in length. What would the length of the copy be if it is also reduced?
$8\frac{1}{3}$ inches

3 **Estimate how much Andy would save at Eastside Stereo on a receiver that normally sells for $248?**

1% of $248 is $2.48.
$2.48 rounds to $2.50.
30 times $2.50 is $75.

Andy would save about $75.00.

4 **Estimate 0.5% of 988.**

THINK
0.5% is half of 1%.
988 is about 1000.
1% means: 1 out of 100.
$1000 \div 100 = 10$
$\frac{1}{2}$ of 10 is 5.

0.5% of 988 is about 5.

5 **Estimate 107% of $42.**

THINK
107% is more than 100%,
so 107% of 42 is greater than 42.
107% is about 110%.
$110\% = 100\% + 10\%$
$42(100\% + 10\%) = 42 + 4.2$
$= 46.2$

107% of 42 is about 46.

Checking for Understanding

1. See margin. 2. $1.40 + 0.70 = $2.10

Communicating Algebra

1. In your own words, explain a method for estimating with percents.
2. Explain how you would estimate a 15% tip on a $14.50 meal.
3. Explain how you would estimate 25% of $98.95. $\frac{1}{4}$ of 100 = $25

Guided Practice

Estimate the percent.

4. 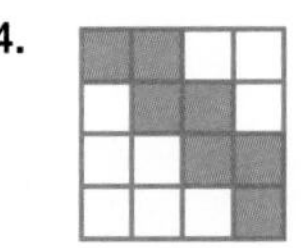 50 %

5. 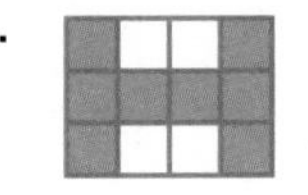 75 %

6. 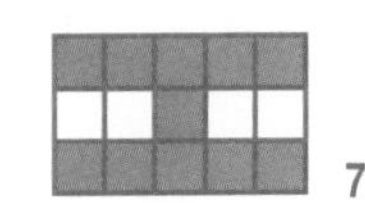 75 %

7. 6 out of 23 25% 8. 3 out of 40 10% 9. 41 out of 58 67% 10. $\frac{31}{25}$ 125%

Exercises

Independent Practice

Determine which is the best estimate.

11. 48% of 400 a. 2 b. 20 (c.) 200
12. 77% of 32 a. 2.4 (b.) 24 c. 240
13. $\frac{1}{4}$% of 800 a. 200 b. 20 (c.) 2
14. 125% of 1200 a. 15 b. 150 (c.) 1500

Alternate Strategies: Reteaching the Lesson

Reteaching Activity

Using Cooperative Groups Give small groups of students discount situations. Have them estimate to determine the better price. For example, a $300.00 bicycle is on sale for 30% off. The same bicycle can be bought at another store for $250.00, less a 10% discount. Which is the better buy?

Reteaching Masters Booklet, **p. 79**

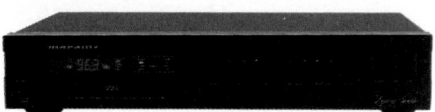

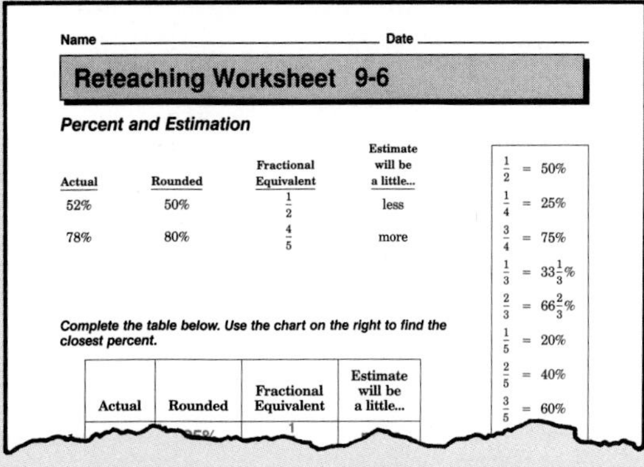

Name ______ Date ______

Reteaching Worksheet 9-6

Percent and Estimation

Actual	Rounded	Fractional Equivalent	Estimate will be a little...
52%	50%	$\frac{1}{2}$	less
78%	80%	$\frac{4}{5}$	more

$\frac{1}{2} = 50\%$
$\frac{1}{4} = 25\%$
$\frac{3}{4} = 75\%$
$\frac{1}{3} = 33\frac{1}{3}\%$
$\frac{2}{3} = 66\frac{2}{3}\%$
$\frac{1}{5} = 20\%$
$\frac{2}{5} = 40\%$
$\frac{3}{5} = 60\%$

Complete the table below. Use the chart on the right to find the closest percent.

Actual	Rounded	Fractional Equivalent	Estimate will be a little...

Chalkboard Examples

- *For Example 1*
  Estimate the percent that is shaded. **about 25%**

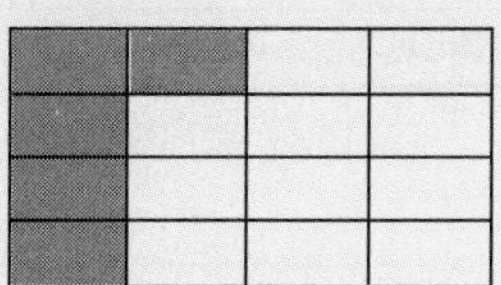

- *For Example 2*
  Estimate $210 less a discount of 32%.
  $\frac{1}{3}$ of 210 = 70 **about $140**
- *For Example 3*
  Estimate how much Mark would save at Pro Shop on a new bowling ball that normally sells for $128 if he would receive a 20% discount. **about $26**
- *For Example 4*
  Estimate 0.5% of 393. **about 2**
- *For Example 5*
  Estimate 111% of $57.
  about 63

3 PRACTICE/APPLY

Checking the Concept

Have students compare and contrast their answers to Exercises 4-14.

Error Analysis

Watch for students who use a fraction that is not close to the actual percent.
Prevent by having the student use a calculator to change the fraction to a decimal.

Additional Answer

1. Sample answer: Round the base to a convenient number and multiply by a common fraction that is almost equal to the percent.

Independent Practice

Homework Assignment	
Basic	11-43 odd, 45-50, 53-55
Average	12-44 even, 45-55
Honors	20-38 even, 39-55
All	Mid-Chapter Quiz 1-20

Additional Answer

47. $c > 2$ (number line from -2 to 5: open circle at 2, shaded to the right)

Practice Masters Booklet, **p. 87**

Name ______________________ Date ______________________

Practice Worksheet 9-6

Percent and Estimation

Determine which is the best estimate.

1. 19% of 50 a. 1 (b.) 10 c. 100
2. 76% of 240 a. 18 (b.) 180 c. 1800
3. $\frac{3}{4}$% of 90 (a.) 0.9 b. 9 c. 90
4. 193% of 800 a. 16 b. 160 (c.) 1600

Write the fraction, mixed number, or whole number you should use to estimate.

5. 35% $\frac{1}{3}$ 6. 67% $\frac{2}{3}$ 7. 24% $\frac{1}{4}$ 8. 78% $\frac{3}{4}$
9. 99% 1 10. $9\frac{3}{5}$% $\frac{1}{10}$ 11. 48% $\frac{1}{2}$ 12. $5\frac{1}{5}$% $\frac{1}{20}$
13. 123% $1\frac{1}{4}$ 14. 31.9% $\frac{1}{3}$ 15. 1.2% $\frac{1}{100}$ 16. $\frac{7}{8}$% $\frac{1}{100}$

Estimate.

17. 9% of 45 4.5 18. 47% of $35.95 18 19. 74% of 40 30
20. 26% of 64 16 21. 66% of $240 $160 22. $9\frac{5}{6}$% of 50 5
23. 98% of 75 75 24. $4\frac{3}{4}$% of $58 $3 25. 126% of 840 1050
26. 1.3% of 97 1 27. $\frac{7}{8}$% of 75 0.75 28. 0.9% of 1500 15

Estimate each percent.

29. 21 out of 60 $33\frac{1}{3}$% 30. 24 out of 50 50% 31. 21 out of 30 $66\frac{2}{3}$%
32. 7 out of 79 10% 33. 19 out of 80 25% 34. 9 out of 195 5%
35. 12 out of 81 $12\frac{1}{2}$% 36. 53 out of 79 $62\frac{1}{2}$% 37. 73 out of 82 $87\frac{1}{2}$%

Write the fraction, mixed number, or whole number you should use to estimate.

15. 27% $\frac{1}{4}$ 16. 75% $\frac{3}{4}$ 17. 65% $\frac{2}{3}$ 18. 97% 1 19. 36% $\frac{1}{3}$
20. 19% $\frac{1}{5}$ 21. $4\frac{1}{2}$% $\frac{1}{20}$ 22. 38% $\frac{1}{3}$ 23. 157% $1\frac{1}{2}$ 24. $10\frac{1}{5}$% $\frac{1}{10}$
25. 32.4% $\frac{1}{3}$ 26. 24.98% $\frac{1}{4}$ 27. $45\frac{4}{5}$% $\frac{1}{2}$ 28. 0.3% $\frac{1}{100}$ 29. $\frac{3}{8}$% $\frac{1}{100}$

Estimate. Sample answers given.

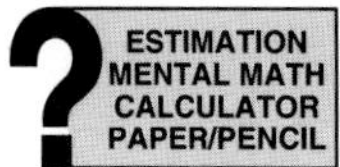

30. 78% of 20 15 31. 24% of 84 20 32. 9% of 32 3.2
33. 65% of 85 60 34. 48% of $23.95 $12 35. 98% of $5.50 $5.50
36. 1.5% of 135 2 37. 125% of 79 100 38. 0.6% of 205 1

Estimate each percent.

39. 6 out of 25 25% 40. 9 out of 17 50% 41. 19 out of 60 $33\frac{1}{3}$%
42. 62 out of 90 $66\frac{2}{3}$% 43. 7 out of 41 20% 44. 58 out of 179 $33\frac{1}{3}$%

Mixed Review

45. Determine whether the following problem is an example of inductive or deductive reasoning.
Jill noticed that in the last five basketball games José bounced the basketball three times before shooting a free throw. She concludes that he always bounces the ball three times before shooting a free throw. (Lesson 6-9) inductive
46. Solve the equation $3(z - 2) = -1 - 5z$. (Lesson 7-4) $\frac{5}{8}$
47. Solve the inequality $4c > c + 6$ and graph the solution. (Lesson 8-2) See margin.
48. Identify the percentage, base, and rate: *14 is 70% of what number?* (Lesson 9-4) 20
49. Express 0.827 as a percent. (Lesson 9-5) 82.7%
50. Express 38% as a fraction in simplest form. (Lesson 9-5) $\frac{19}{50}$

Connection

51. **Statistics** The graph at the right represents the five states with the most acres of farmland, including land used in livestock and dairy production. The total for the five states is 332.1 million acres. Estimate what percent of the total each state has.

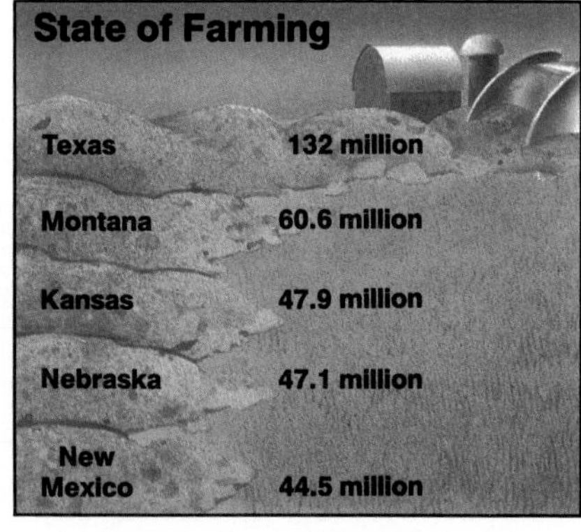

State	Percent Estimate
Texas	33%
Montana	20%
Kansas	17%
Nebraska	17%
New Mexico	15%

Applications

52. **Sports** Alice plays forward for the Millersport Falcons basketball team. In one game she made just over 80% of her 16 free throws. How many free throws did she make? **13 free throws**

53. **Consumer Awareness** The standard rate for tipping in a restaurant where all service is taken care of at your table is 15%. A quick way to mentally estimate 15% is to find 10% of the amount and then add one-half of the 10% amount. If the check totals $19.85, what tip should you leave? **$3**

Critical Thinking

54. The number 385 is the product of three consecutive primes, 5, 7, and 11. What three consecutive primes have a product of 12,673? **19, 23, 29**

Wrap-Up

55. **Research** The land area of Georgia is about 60% of the size of the land area of Great Britain. Find the size (in square miles) of Great Britain. Then estimate the size of Georgia. **Great Britain: 94,247 mi²; Georgia: about 54,000 mi²(58,876 mi²)**

Mid-Chapter Quiz

Express each ratio as a fraction in simplest form. (Lesson 9-1)

1. 20 to 12 $\frac{5}{3}$
2. 9 out of 15 $\frac{3}{5}$
3. 18:22 $\frac{9}{11}$

Express each ratio as a unit rate. (Lesson 9-1)

4. $3.84 for 3 gallons **$1.28/gallon**
5. 6 pounds gained in 8 weeks **0.75 pound/week**

Solve each proportion. (Lesson 9-2)

6. $\frac{1}{4} = \frac{n}{24}$ **6**
7. $\frac{21}{3} = \frac{63}{r}$ **9**
8. $\frac{a}{1.2} = \frac{3}{1.8}$ **2**

Write a proportion that could be used to solve for each variable. Then solve. (Lesson 9-3)

9. 2 pounds yields 5 servings. n pounds yields 7 servings. **2.8 pounds**
10. 9 gallons costs $12.15. n gallons costs $2.25. **$1\frac{2}{3}$ gallons**

Write a proportion to solve each problem. Then solve. (Lesson 9-4)

11. What number is 20% of 45? **9**
12. 21 is what percent of 56? **37.5%**

Express each fraction as a percent. (Lesson 9-4)

13. $\frac{88}{100}$ 88%
14. $\frac{1}{3}$ $33\frac{1}{3}$%
15. $\frac{7}{8}$ 87.5%

Express each percent as a decimal and as a fraction in simplest form. (Lesson 9-5)

16. 20% **0.2, $\frac{1}{5}$**
17. 0.8% **0.008, $\frac{1}{125}$**
18. 110% **1.1, $\frac{11}{10}$**

Estimate. (Lesson 9-6)

19. 52% of 18.9 **9**
20. 23.5% of $8.16 **$2**

4 CLOSE

Assessment Option

Speaking Ask students how the 1% method and the meaning of percent method are both similar to the work backwards strategy.

Enrichment Masters Booklet, **p. 79**

Name ______ Date ______

Enrichment Worksheet 9-6

Percent Puzzle

Solve each problem.

1. 8% of 75 **6**
2. 16% of 80 **12.8**
3. 20% of 85 **17**
4. 17% of 300 **51**
5. 40% of 170 **68**
6. 50% of 380 **190**
7. 75% of 160 **120**
8. $33\frac{1}{3}$% of 240 **80**
9. $62\frac{1}{2}$% of 72 **45**
10. 30% of 180 **54**
11. $66\frac{2}{3}$% of 210 **140**
12. 80% of 160 **128**
13. 110% of 60 **66**
14. 95% of 300 **285**
15. 150% of 75 **112.5**
16. 400% of 50 **200**

Answers
17 — R
120 — Y
54 — T
45 — G
6 — F
51 — A
128 — P
200 — O
112.5 — S
66 — I
140 — X
190 — H
12.8 — U
80 — N
68 — D
285 — E

Find the answer to each exercise above and note the letter next to it. Put this letter on the line or lines below that correspond to the exercise number.

HOW MUCH DID THE WORLD'S LARGEST PIZZA WEIGH?

E I G H T E E N
14 13 9 6 10 14 14 8

T H O U S A N D
10 6 16 2 15 4 8 5

S I X H U N D R E D
15 13 11 6 2 8 5 3 14 5

S I X T Y F O U R
15 13 11 10 7 1 16 2 3

P O U N D S
12 16 2 8 5 15

Alternate Strategies: Extending the Lesson

Enrichment

Consumer Connection Have students use newspaper or store ads that contain percentage discounts. If the sale price is given, have students estimate the regular price. If regular price is given, estimate the sale price.

Cooperative Learning

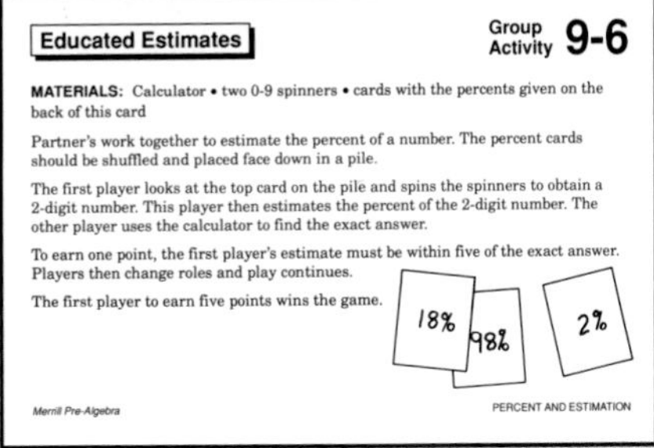

Educated Estimates Group Activity **9-6**

MATERIALS: Calculator • two 0-9 spinners • cards with the percents given on the back of this card

Partner's work together to estimate the percent of a number. The percent cards should be shuffled and placed face down in a pile.

The first player looks at the top card on the pile and spins the spinners to obtain a 2-digit number. This player then estimates the percent of the 2-digit number. The other player uses the calculator to find the exact answer.

To earn one point, the first player's estimate must be within five of the exact answer. Players then change roles and play continues.

The first player to earn five points wins the game.

Merrill Pre-Algebra PERCENT AND ESTIMATION

Lesson Notes 9-7

5-Minute Check
(over Lesson 9-6)

Write the fraction, mixed number, or whole number you should use to estimate.

1. 74% $\frac{3}{4}$
2. 123% $1\frac{1}{4}$
3. 65% $\frac{2}{3}$
4. 18% $\frac{1}{5}$
5. 41% $\frac{2}{5}$

Transparency 9-7 contains the 5-Minute Check and a teaching aid for this lesson.

1 FOCUS

The purpose of this lesson is to solve percent problems using equations instead of the percent proportion.

Motivating the Lesson

Ask students why, if they want to buy a CD that costs $12.95 and they have $13.00 they won't have enough money for the purchase? How can you estimate how much sales tax there is on an item?

2 TEACH

Using Connections

Write a percent proportion using the information about Jennifer Hall and solve. Then evaluate the percent equation ($P = R \cdot B$) using the same information.

EE: 1E, 3A, 3F, 3I
TAAS: 2, 11

9-7 Solving Percent Equations

Objective:
Translate percent problems into equations and solve.

Jennifer Hall buys a new home video game system that costs $195. In addition to the price of the video game system, she will have to pay a $5\frac{1}{2}\%$ state sales tax. That means that $5\frac{1}{2}$¢ tax is charged for each $1 of the purchase price. To find how much sales tax Jennifer pays, find 5.5% of $195.

Estimation Hint

THINK:
1% of $195 is $1.95.
1.95 rounds to $2.
5.5 × $2 is $11.

sales tax is 5.5% of $195

$t = 0.055 \cdot 195$ Write an equation. Write the percent as a decimal.

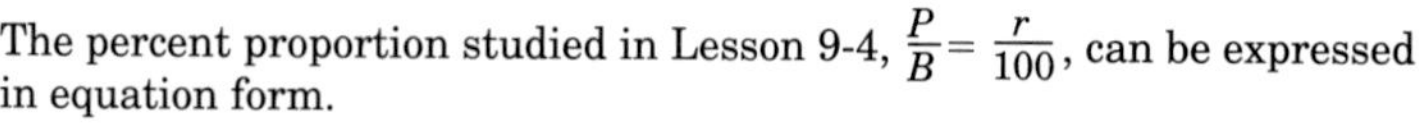

0.055 × 195 = 10.725

$t = 10.725$

Jennifer pays $10.73 in sales tax. Compare with the estimate, $11. The answer is reasonable.

CONNECTION TO ALGEBRA

The percent proportion studied in Lesson 9-4, $\frac{P}{B} = \frac{r}{100}$, can be expressed in equation form.

$$\frac{P}{B} = \frac{r}{100}$$

$$\frac{P}{B} \cdot B = \frac{r}{100} \cdot B \quad \text{Multiply each side by } B.$$

$$P = \frac{r}{100} \cdot B$$

Remember, the ratio $\frac{r}{100}$ is called the rate. Let R represent the decimal form of $\frac{r}{100}$.

$$P = R \cdot B \quad R = \frac{r}{100}$$

Percentage = Rate · Base

The form $P = R \cdot B$ is usually easier to use in problems where the rate and base are known, as in Example 1.

Bell Ringer

Would $50 be a good estimate for 48% of $95? Explain. Yes. Round 95 to 100 and 48% to $\frac{1}{2}$ and $\frac{1}{2}$ of 100 is 50.

Examples

1 **Find 28% of \$231.90.** Estimate: $\frac{1}{4}$ of \$240 is \$60.

What amount is 28% of \$231.90?

$P = 0.28 \cdot 231.9$ Write in $P = R \cdot B$ form. P represents the percentage.

0.28 ⊠ 231.9 ⊟ 64.932 Multiply.

$P = 64.932$

28% of \$231.90 is \$64.93. Compare with the estimate.

2 **13 is what percent of 65?** Estimate: $\frac{12}{60} = \frac{1}{5}$ or 20%.

$13 = R \cdot 65$ Write in $P = R \cdot B$ form. R represents the rate.

$13 = 65R$ Solve for R.

$\frac{13}{65} = \frac{65R}{65}$ Divide each side by 65.

13 ⊞÷ 65 ⊟ 0.2

$0.2 = R$

$20\% = R$ $0.2 = \frac{2}{10} = \frac{20}{100} = 20\%$

13 is 20% of 65. Compare with the estimate.

Is B greater than 42 or less than 42? Why?
greater than; 42 is $\frac{3}{5}$ of the number.

3 **42 is 60% of what number?** Estimate: 42 is $\frac{1}{2}$ of 84.

$42 = 0.6 \cdot B$ Write in $P = R \cdot B$ form. B represents the base.

$42 = 0.6B$ Solve for B.

$\frac{42}{0.6} = \frac{0.6B}{0.6}$ Divide each side by 0.6.

42 ⊞÷ 0.6 ⊟ 70

$70 = B$

42 is 60% of 70.

Checking for Understanding

Communicating Algebra

1. How do $\frac{r}{100}$ and R differ? How are they the same? **$\frac{r}{100}$ is a fraction, R is a decimal; both are rates.**
2. Explain why the percent proportion is sometimes easier to use than $P = R \cdot B$. **If the rate and base are known, you can simply multiply.**
3. If the rate is less than 100%, the percentage is (greater, <u>less</u>) than the base.

Guided Practice

Write in $P = R \cdot B$ form. Then solve. See margin.

4. 35 = 50% of ■ 5. 30% of ■ = 15 6. 25% of ■ = 17
7. 18 = ■ % of 60 8. 8 = ■ % of 64 9. 16 = ■ % of 64
10. 25 = ■ % of 75 11. ■ = 31% of 14 12. ■ = 16.5% of 60

Chalkboard Examples

- *For Example 1*
  Find 14% of \$163.40 **\$22.88**
- *For Example 2*
  18 is what percent of 45? **40%**
- *For Example 3*
  21 is 70% of what number? **30**

3 PRACTICE/APPLY

Checking the Concept

After completing Exercises 4-12, have students check solutions by using the percent proportion.

Error Analysis

Watch for students who have difficulty setting up percent equations. ***Prevent by*** having students use context and word clues to write what is written.

Additional Answers

4. $35 = 0.5B$; 70
5. $15 = 0.3B$; 50
6. $17 = 0.25B$; 68
7. $18 = 60R$; 30%
8. $8 = 64R$; 12.5%
9. $16 = 64R$; 25%
10. $25 = 75R$; $33\frac{1}{3}\%$
11. $P = 0.31 \cdot 14$; 4.34
12. $P = 0.165 \cdot 60$; 9.9

Reteaching Masters Booklet, **p. 80**

Name ________ Date ________

Reteaching Worksheet 9-7

Solving Percent Equations

A statement such as 50% of 16 is 8 can be written in two ways.

$\frac{50}{100} = \frac{8}{16}$ $50\% \cdot 16 = 8$

$\frac{r}{100} = \frac{P}{B}$ $R \cdot B = P$ $R = \frac{r}{100}$; Rate · Base = Percentage

The percent proportion on the left is equivalent to the corresponding equation on the right, with R being the decimal form of the ratio $\frac{r}{100}$. Problems involving percent can be solved using either the proportion or the equation.

Write both a percent proportion and an equation for each statement.

1. 25% of \$4.00 is \$1.00. $\frac{25}{1..}$ = $\frac{1}{..}$; 0.25 · 4 = 1
2. 10% of 78 is 7.8. $\frac{10}{..} = \frac{7.8}{78}$; 0.10 · 78...

Practice Masters Booklet, **p. 88**

Name ________ Date ________

Practice Worksheet 9-7

Solving Percent Equations

Solve.

1. Find 8% of 752. 60.16
2. 64 is what percent of 512? 12.5%
3. What number is 15% of \$80? \$12
4. 110 is what percent of 50? 220%
5. 92.5 is 25% of what number? 370
6. What percent of 2 is 8? 400%
7. $33\frac{1}{3}\%$ of what number is 30? 90
8. 7 is 10% of what number? 70
9. What number is $87\frac{1}{2}\%$ of 8? 7
10. What percent of 120 is 15? 12.5%
11. 32 is what percent of 24? $133\frac{1}{3}\%$
12. 125% of what number is 15? 12
13. \$10,000 is 110% of how many dollars? \$9090.91
14. What number is 19% of \$100? \$19
15. 4 is what percent of 6? $66\frac{2}{3}\%$
16. 14 is 28% of what number? 50
17. Find 200% of 115. 230
18. What number is 108% of \$650? \$702
19. 18 is 0.1% of what number? 18,000
20. What percent of 8 is 5? 62.5%
21. $87\frac{1}{2}\%$ of 64 is what number? 56
22. What number is $37\frac{1}{2}\%$ of 120? 45
23. What percent 160 is 4? 2.5%
24. \$50,000 is 40% of how many dollars? \$125,000
25. Find 0.1% of 250. 0.25
26. 49.2 is 102.5% of what number? 48
27. 2 is what percent of 125? 1.6%
28. What number is 40% of \$9? \$3.60

Independent Practice

Homework Assignment	
Basic	13-23 odd, 25-30, 33,34
Average	14-24 even, 25-34
Honors	20-34

4 CLOSE

Assessment Option

Modeling Give each student a cash register receipt with the total and tax not included. Have each find the correct total of the merchandise and the total after tax (use 5.5%).

Additional Answers

34. Sample answer: Marty bought a new stereo for $800. This was 85% of the original price. What was the original price?

Enrichment Masters Booklet, **p. 80**

Name ______________________ Date ______________

Enrichment Worksheet 9-7

Permillage

A fraction with a denominator of 100, such as $\frac{25}{100}$, can be thought of as 25 hundredths (0.25) or 25 percent.

A fraction with a denominator of 1000, such as $\frac{500}{1000}$, can be thought of as 500 thousandths (0.500) or 500 **per mill.** Per mill has been used for a long time, particularly by German merchants.

The symbol for percent is %; the symbol for per mill is ‰.

Write each permillage as a decimal.

1. 325‰ 0.325
2. 405‰ 0.405
3. 770‰ 0.77
4. 83‰ 0.083
5. 50‰ 0.05
6. 9‰ 0.009
7. 1200‰ 1.2
8. 1050‰ 1.05
9. 1000‰ 1

Write each of the following as a fraction in simplest form.

10. 500‰ $\frac{1}{2}$
11. 800‰ $\frac{4}{5}$
12. 750‰ $\frac{3}{4}$
13. 50‰ $\frac{1}{20}$
14. 80‰ $\frac{2}{25}$
15. 75‰ $\frac{3}{40}$
16. 5‰ $\frac{1}{200}$
17. 8‰ $\frac{1}{125}$
18. 7.5‰ $\frac{3}{400}$

Solve. Use a proportion.

19. 500‰ of $60 $30
20. 10‰ of $1000 $10
21. 750‰ of $200 $150
22. 250‰ of $7000 $1750
23. 5‰ of $50 $0.25
24. 1‰ of $400 $0.40

Exercises

Independent Practice

Solve.

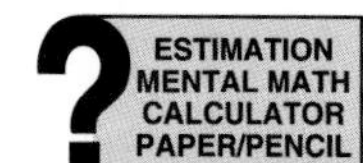

13. 19 is what percent of 76? 25%
14. 37 is what percent of 296? 12.5%
15. Find 4% of $6070. $242.80
16. Find 6% of $9.40. $0.56
17. 55 is what percent of 88? 62.5%
18. 88 is what percent of 55? 160%
19. $7030.50 is 107.5% of what amount? $6540
20. $54,000 is 108% of how many dollars? $50,000
21. What number is 25% of 500? 125
22. 20% of 65 is what number? 13
23. What percent of 12 is 6? 50%
24. 17 is what percent of 51? $33\frac{1}{3}$%

Mixed Review

25. Solve the inequality $\frac{c}{-3} + 11 \leq 5$. (Lesson 7-6) $c \geq 18$
26. Name the quadrant for the graph of (x, y) if $x < 0$ and $y > 0$. (Lesson 8-4) 2
27. Write $\frac{5}{4}$ as a percent. (Lesson 9-5) 125%
28. Estimate 75% of $19. (Lesson 9-6) $15

Applications

29. **Commission** Bob Ramirez earns 2% commission on all auto parts he sells. Last month he earned $974 in commissions. What were his sales? $48,700
30. **Consumer Awareness** Pauline purchased a blouse for $25.50 and a pair of jeans for $28. The sales tax rate in her state is 8%. How much change did Pauline receive from $70? $12.22
31. **Sports** The price of a girl's 10-speed mountain bike is $129. If the sales tax on the bike is $7.74, what is the sales tax rate? 6%
32. **Commission** A salesperson earns a 15% commission on each household appliance he sells. If he sells 6 toasters at $32 each, how much does he earn? $28.80

Critical Thinking

33. Use each of the digits 0-9 once to form two fractions that have a sum of 1. Sample answer: $\frac{148}{296} + \frac{35}{70}$

Wrap-Up

34. **Make Up a Problem** Write a problem that has 85% as the rate and uses $800 as either the base or percentage. See margin.

Team Problem Solving

All eight blocks look the same, but one of them is either lighter or heavier than the others. How can you find which one is different in three or fewer weighings? How can you tell if the block is lighter or heavier than the others? See Solutions Manual.

Alternate Strategies: Extending the Lesson

Enrichment

Consumer Connection Have students compute the tax rate for your locale. Have them use cash register tapes and compute the rate from the subtotal, the amount of tax, and the percent proportion.

Cooperative Learning

Percent Puzzle Group Activity **9-7**

MATERIALS: Twenty-four $2\frac{1}{2}$-inch squares cut from index cards

SETUP: The expressions given on the back of this card should be copied onto the squares.

Two players shuffle the cards and place them face up in a 5 by 5 array on the table. Leave a blank space in the lower right corner of the array. Take turns naming correct expressions of the form a% of $b = c$ (for example 20% of 200 = 40) by identifying expressions in the existing array or by moving one square into the blank space to form an expression. Record the expressions you have made. The game continues until no new expressions are made in 10 moves.

The person whose record has the most correct expressions wins. If you incorrectly identify an expression, you subtract one point from your final count.

10% of | 200= | 20

Merrill Pre-Algebra SOLVING PERCENT EQUATIONS

Application

9-8 Discount and Interest

Objective:
Solve problems involving discount and interest.

Key Terms:
discount
interest
principal
rate
time

Kelly Glaser works as a salesperson for Shoes Unlimited. One of his employee benefits is a 20% **discount** on any item be buys for himself. The regular price of a pair of cross-training athletic shoes is $58. What price must Kelly pay for the shoes?

You can find the sale price in one of two ways.

Method One

First, find the amount of discount.

20% of 58 = d

0.2 [×] 58 [=] 11.6

Kelly will save $11.60.

Then, subtract to find the discount price.

58 [−] 11.6 [=] 46.4

Method Two

First, subtract the percent discount from 100%.

Since 100% − 20% = 80%, Kelly will pay 80% of the original price.

Then, multiply to find the discount price.

0.8 [×] 58 [=] 46.4

Kelly will pay $46.40 for the shoes.

Estimation Hint

THINK:
$\frac{1}{5}$ of 60 is 12. The discount is about $12. The sale price is about $58 − $12 or $46.00.

Example

1 **Alyssa buys a CD that has been discounted to $11.24. If the regular price is $14.98, what is the rate of discount?**

14.98 [−] 11.24 [=] 3.74 Find the actual discount.

$R \cdot 14.98 = 3.74$ Use $R \cdot B = P$.

$$R = \frac{3.74}{14.98}$$

3.74 [÷] 14.98 [=] 0.2496662

$R = 0.2496662$ or about 0.25

The rate of discount is 25%.

What percent of the original price did Alyssa pay? **75%**

Sometimes you do not have enough money to buy something right away so you wait until you save what you need. A good way to save money is to deposit it in a savings account that pays interest.

Bell Ringer

What is the percentage if the rate is 22% and the base is 78? 17.16

Lesson Notes 9-8

5-Minute Check
(over Lesson 9-7)

Solve.
1. 93 is what percent of 310? 30%
2. 12 is 24% of what number? 50
3. Find 42% of 97. 40.74
4. 27 is what percent of 75? 36%
5. Find 85% of 90. 76.5

Transparency 9-8 contains the 5-Minute Check and a teaching aid for this lesson.

1 FOCUS

The purpose of this lesson is to use the percent equation to solve real-life percent problems.

Motivating the Lesson

Ask the class if anyone has a savings account. Ask students to tell the class what happens to their money if they leave it in the bank for a long time.

2 TEACH

Using Discussion

Build on the information offered by students in Motivating the Lesson. Discuss with students the difference between interest on savings and interest on a loan.

Using Calculators

Demonstrate Method One using a calculator and pressing the memory key after multiplying. You may want to remind students how to mentally rename a percent as a decimal before you multiply in Method Two.

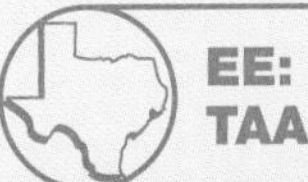

EE: 1E, 3A, 3F, 3I
TAAS: 2, 10, 11, 13

Chalkboard Examples

- *For Example 1*
  A shirt has been discounted to \$21.21. If the regular price is \$24.95, what was the rate of discount? **15%**
- *For Example 2*
  Alice has \$1500 in her savings account. The interest rate per year is $8\frac{1}{4}$%. If she does not deposit or withdraw any money, how much will be in her account after eight months? **\$1582.50**

3 PRACTICE/APPLY

Checking the Concept

After completing Exercises 7 and 8, have students find the total amount if the interest is on a loan and if the interest is on an investment.

Error Analysis

Watch for students who subtract interest or add discounts.
Prevent by writing "discount-subtract" and "interest-add" at the top of a sheet of paper and use this for reference until terms are remembered.

Practice Masters Booklet, **p. 89**

Simple **interest** (I) is calculated by finding the product of the **principal** (p), which is the amount in the account, the **rate** (r), which is a percent, and the **time** (t), which is given in years. This is expressed as the formula $I = prt$.

Example

2 **Mr. Wells deposited \$700 in his savings account. His account earns $6\frac{1}{4}$% interest annually. If he does not deposit or withdraw any money, how much will be in his account after nine months?**

First, find the amount of interest earned by using the simple interest formula.

$I = prt$ Replace p with 700, r with 0.0625,

$I = 700 \cdot 0.0625 \cdot \frac{9}{12}$ and t with $\frac{9}{12}$ since 9 months is $\frac{9}{12}$ year.

700 [×] 0.0625 [×] 9 [÷] 12 [=] 32.8125

$I = 32.8125$

The interest earned after nine months is \$32.81.

Then, add the interest to the savings: \$700 + \$32.81 = \$732.81.
After nine months the account will contain \$732.81.

The simple interest formula can also be used when you borrow money. In this situation, the principal is the amount borrowed.

Example

3 **Jean borrows \$560 to buy a trumpet. She is charged $12\frac{3}{4}$% simple interest per year. How much interest is Jean charged for 2 years?**

$I = prt$ Replace p with 560, r with 0.1275, and t with 2.

$I = 560 \cdot 0.1275 \cdot 2$

560 [×] 0.1275 [×] 2 [=] 142.8

Jean is charged \$142.80 interest after 2 years.

Checking for Understanding

Communicating Algebra

1. Describe two ways of finding the price of a \$90 item on sale at 30% off. **1. 90 − 0.3(90) or 0.7(90)**
2. Explain how to find the amount of interest \$100 would earn in one year if the annual interest rate was 8%. **Multiply 100 • 0.08 • 1.**
3. Discuss the differences between savings account interest and loan interest. **The bank pays you interest on a savings account; you pay the bank interest on a loan.**

Name ______________________ Date ______________

Practice Worksheet 9-8

Application: Discount and Interest

Find the discount or interest to the nearest cent.

1. \$500 television, 15% off **\$75**
2. \$155 bicycle, 20% off **\$31**
3. \$300 typewriter, 10% off **\$30**
4. \$35 watch, 15% off **\$5.25**
5. \$160 violin, $12\frac{1}{2}$% off **\$20**
6. \$125 set of golf clubs, 20% off **\$25**
7. \$1454 computer, 25% off **\$363.50**
8. \$15.96 compact disc, $33\frac{1}{3}$% off **\$5.32**
9. \$300 at 6% for 1 year **\$18**
10. \$750 at 8% for 6 months **\$30**
11. \$4000 at 10.5% for 6 months **\$210**
12. \$945 at 11% for 8 months **\$69.30**
13. \$1200 at 8.5% for 2 months **\$17**
14. \$30,000 at 12.5% for 25 years **\$93,750**
15. \$875 at 6% for 4 months **\$17.50**
16. \$7200 at 9.5% for 21 months **\$1197**

Find the discount rate.

17. \$30 fishing rod on sale for \$20 **$33\frac{1}{3}$%**
18. \$25 blouse on sale for \$12.50 **50%**
19. \$16 compact disc on sale for \$12 **25%**
20. \$12 tee-shirt on sale for \$8 **$33\frac{1}{3}$%**
21. \$30 jeans on sale for \$21 **30%**
22. \$40 sweatshirt on sale for \$27 **32.5%**
23. \$25 book bag on sale for \$14 **44%**
24. \$3.95 magazine on sale for \$3.16 **20%**
25. \$35 skirt on sale for \$28 **20%**
26. \$18 shirt on sale for \$12 **$33\frac{1}{3}$%**
27. \$50 sweatsuit on sale for \$31.25 **37.5%**
28. \$8 cassette tape on sale for \$7 **12.5%**

Alternate Strategies: Reteaching the Lesson

Reteaching Activity

Business Connection Contact a local bank to find out its interest rates on different savings accounts. Assume the interest is compounded annually. Set a hypothetical amount to deposit and determine the balance at the end of a year for each account.

Reteaching Masters Booklet, **p. 81**

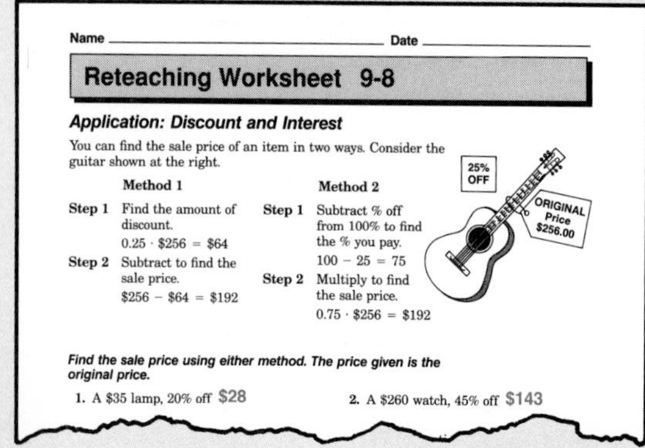

Name ______________________ Date ______________

Reteaching Worksheet 9-8

Application: Discount and Interest

You can find the sale price of an item in two ways. Consider the guitar shown at the right.

Method 1

Step 1 Find the amount of discount.
$0.25 \cdot \$256 = \$64$

Step 2 Subtract to find the sale price.
$\$256 - \$64 = \$192$

Method 2

Step 1 Subtract % off from 100% to find the % you pay.
$100 - 25 = 75$

Step 2 Multiply to find the sale price.
$0.75 \cdot \$256 = \$192$

Find the sale price using either method. The price given is the original price.

1. A \$35 lamp, 20% off **\$28**
2. A \$260 watch, 45% off **\$143**

Guided Practice	**Find the discount or interest to the nearest cent.**

4. \$345 stereo, 12% off **\$41.40**
5. \$210 suit, 5% off **\$10.50**
6. \$2500 at 12% for $2\frac{1}{2}$ years **\$750**
7. \$1860 at $7\frac{1}{2}$% for 15 months **\$174.38**

Exercises

Independent Practice

Find the discount or interest to the nearest cent.

ESTIMATION / MENTAL MATH / CALCULATOR / PAPER/PENCIL

8. \$22.75 blouse, 15% off **\$3.41**
9. \$37.65 sweatsuit, 20% off **\$7.53**
10. \$3 earrings, 30% off **\$0.90**
11. \$10,000 at 13% for 6 months **\$650**
12. \$100 at 6% for 8 months **\$4**
13. \$4000 at 13.5% for 21 months **\$945**
14. \$49.99 shoes, $33\frac{1}{3}$% off **\$16.66**
15. \$200 at 7% for 18 months **\$21**

Find the discount rate.

16. a \$15 tie on sale for \$10 **$33\frac{1}{3}$%**
17. an \$8 record on sale for \$6 **25%**
18. a \$25.50 skirt on sale for \$20 **20%**
19. a \$10 book now costs \$8.50 **15%**

Mixed Review

20. Solve the equation $3c = 72$ using the inverse operation. (Lesson 1-7) **24**
21. Graph the equation $2x + y = 5$. (Lesson 8-6) **See Margin.**
22. Estimate 24% of 80. (Lesson 9-6) **20**
23. Find 44% of \$156. (Lesson 9-7) **\$68.64**

Applications

24. **Entertainment** The regular price of football tickets is \$6 each. For the Homecoming game, tickets for the game were sold to alumni for \$4 each. What rate of discount did the alumni receive? **$33\frac{1}{3}$%**
25. **Finance** Tim's savings account earned \$30.72 interest in 6 months. The interest rate is $5\frac{3}{4}$%. How much was in his account to earn that amount of simple interest? **\$1068.52**
26. **Consumer Awareness** Maria bought a watch on sale for \$20. The regular price was \$25. What was the discount rate? **20%**

27. **Consumer Awareness** The regular price of a pair of jeans is \$45.95. If there is a 30% discount and a 6% sales tax (based on the discount price), how much do the jeans cost? **\$34.09**

Critical Thinking

28. The number 1729 can be written as the sum of two cubes, $10^3 + 9^3$. Find another pair of cubes whose sum is 1729. **$1^3 + 12^3$**

Wrap-Up

29. A sporting goods store advertises a \$5.50 golf glove on sale for \$5.00 and claims a 10% savings. Is this a true statement? If not, what is the discount rate? **no; ≈ 9%**

Independent Practice

Homework Assignment	
Basic	9-19 odd, 21-26, 29, 30
Average	10-18 even, 21-30
Honors	12-20 even, 21-30

4 CLOSE

Assessment Option

Modeling Bring in ads from newspapers or magazines that advertise a certain percent off sale or a percent off a particular garment. Give one to each student along with a price (actual or fictitious) for what they are to buy. Then have them calculate how much they will spend, including 5.75% sales tax, on their purchase.

Additional Answer

22.

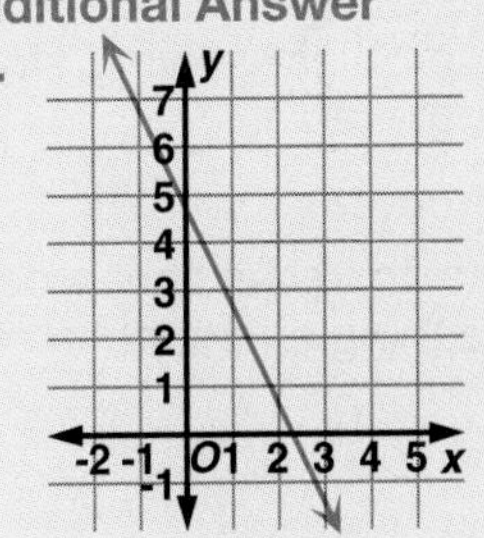

Enrichment Masters Booklet, **p. 81**

Name ____________ Date ____________

Enrichment Worksheet 9-8

Compound Interest

Interest may be paid annually (each year), semi-annually (twice a year), quarterly (four times a year), monthly (once a month), or daily.

Example: George had \$100 in an account for $1\frac{1}{2}$ years that paid 8% interest compounded semi-annually. What was the total amount in his account at the end of $1\frac{1}{2}$ years?

At the end of $\frac{1}{2}$ year: Interest: $\$100 \times 0.08 \times \frac{1}{2} = \$4.00$
New Principal: $\$100 + \$4 = \$104$

At the end of 1 year: Interest: $\$104 \times 0.08 \times \frac{1}{2} = \$4.16$
New Principal: $\$104 + \$4.16 = \$108.16$

At the end of $1\frac{1}{2}$ years: Interest: $\$108.16 \times 0.08 \times \frac{1}{2} = \$4.33$
New Principal: $\$108.16 + \$4.33 = \$112.49$

Find the total amount for each of the following.

	Principal	Rate	Time	Compounded	Total Amount
1.	\$200	6%	$1\frac{1}{2}$ years	semi-annually	\$218.55
2.	\$300	5%	2 years	semi-annually	\$331.15
3.	\$100	6%	1 year	quarterly	\$106.14
4.	\$500	8%	$\frac{3}{4}$ year	quarterly	\$530.60
5.	\$500	10%	4 months	monthly	\$516.88
6.	\$800	8%	$\frac{1}{4}$ year	monthly	\$816.10
7.	\$1000	8%	4 years	annually	\$1360.49
8.	\$700	6%	$1\frac{1}{2}$ years	semi-annually	\$764.91

Alternate Strategies: Extending the Lesson

Enrichment

Consumer Connection The regular price of a coat is \$320.00. It is on sale for 25% off. It doesn't sell and is put on clearance at 30% off the sale price. Does this new price differ from a sale price resulting from the regular price discounted 55%? If so, by how much? Why do the amounts differ? **yes; \$24; The base is less for 30% off.**

Cooperative Learning

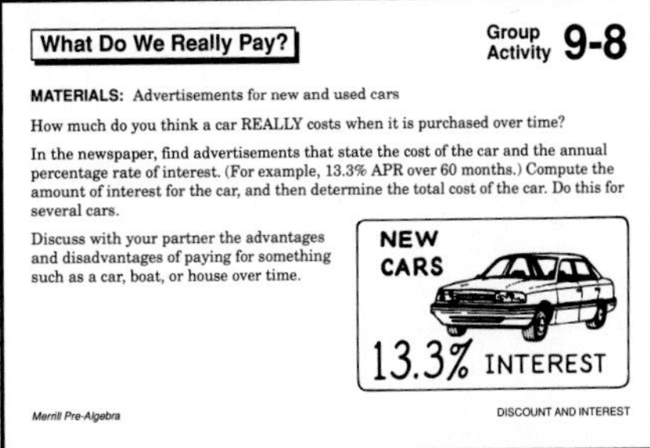

What Do We Really Pay? Group Activity **9-8**

MATERIALS: Advertisements for new and used cars

How much do you think a car REALLY costs when it is purchased over time?

In the newspaper, find advertisements that state the cost of the car and the annual percentage rate of interest. (For example, 13.3% APR over 60 months.) Compute the amount of interest for the car, and then determine the total cost of the car. Do this for several cars.

Discuss with your partner the advantages and disadvantages of paying for something such as a car, boat, or house over time.

NEW CARS
13.3% INTEREST

Merrill Pre-Algebra DISCOUNT AND INTEREST

Lesson Notes 9-9

5-Minute Check
(over Lesson 9-8)

Find the discount or interest to the nearest cent.

1. $28 jeans, 20% off **$5.60**
2. $54.95 coat, 15% off **$8.24**
3. $3000 at 12.5% for 18 months **$562.50**
4. $250 at 9% for 6 months **$11.25**
5. $15 CD at 25% off **$3.75**

Transparency 9-9 contains the 5-Minute Check and a teaching aid for this lesson.

1 FOCUS

The purpose of this lesson is to develop the problem-solving strategy of making a table.

Motivating the Lesson

Ask students to recall the procedures for graphing an equation of a line.

2 TEACH

Chalkboard Examples

Jarrett has $1.05 made up of five United States coins. He cannot make change for a dollar, 5¢, 10¢, 25¢, or 50¢. What five coins does Jarrett have? **3 dimes, 1 quarter, 1 half-dollar**

3 PRACTICE/APPLY

Checking the Concept

Use numbered slips of paper and a table to model Exercises 3 and 4.

Problem Solving

9-9 Strategy: Make a Table

Objective:
Solve problems by making a list.

Susan Lee has $1.15 made up of six United States coins. However, she cannot make change for a dollar, a half-dollar, a quarter, a dime, or a nickel. What six coins does Susan have?

Explore Susan has six coins equal to $1.15, but cannot make change for a dollar or any coin less than a dollar.

Why are there no pennies in the table? **You can't make change for a nickel** *What is the greatest number of nickels in the solution?* **1**

Plan Organize the data in a table. Try different combinations of six coins that make $1.15 until you find a group that does not include change for $1, 50¢, 25¢, 10¢, or 5¢.

Solve

This combination is *not* the solution because you could make change for a dollar or half-dollar. (→ row 3)

nickels	dimes	quarters	half-dollars	total
1	2	1	2	$1.50
1	2	2	1	$1.25
1	1	4	0	$1.15
⋮	⋮	⋮	⋮	⋮
0	4	1	1	$1.15

Examine Does this group satisfy all the requirements?

1. There are six coins in the group.
2. The coins have a value of $1.15.
3. You cannot make change for a dollar, half-dollar, quarter, dime, or nickel.

The solution is correct. Susan has 4 dimes, 1 quarter, and 1 half-dollar.

Checking for Understanding

1. It is a good way to organize data.

Communicating Algebra

1. Why is making a table a good strategy for solving problems?
2. Is making a table a good strategy for solving all problems? Why or why not? **No, not all problems involve data or counting.**

Guided Practice

Solve. Make a table.

3. How many ways can you make change for a $50-bill using only $5-, $10-, and $20-bills? **12**
4. How many ways can you add eight prime numbers to get a sum of 20? You may use a number more than once. **2**

Bell Ringer

Sam's Ski Shop had cross-country ski boots priced at $42. On January 5, the price went up 25%. On March 1, the boots went on sale at 25% off. Why is the sale price not $42? **The 25% taken off had a base of $52.50.**

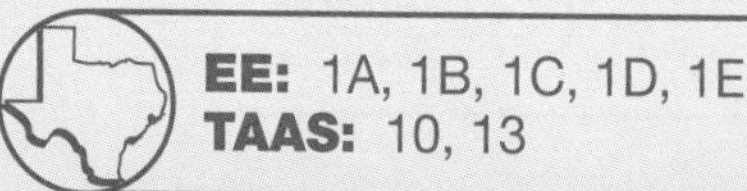

EE: 1A, 1B, 1C, 1D, 1E
TAAS: 10, 13

Reteaching Activity

Business Connection Alex invested $2000.00 at 6% compounded annually. He does not make any deposits or withdrawals and all interest is returned to the account. Make a table to show his balance at the end of four years.

Exercises

Independent Practice

ESTIMATION
MENTAL MATH
CALCULATOR
PAPER/PENCIL

Solve. Use any strategy.

5. Martin had 40 baseball cards. He traded 7 cards for 5 from Dani. He traded 3 more for 4 from Ted. He traded another 2 for 1 from Anita. Finally, he traded 11 more cards for 8 from Doug. How many baseball cards does Martin have now? **35 cards**

6. A penny, a nickel, a dime, and a quarter are in a purse. Without looking, Jorge picks up two coins. How many different amounts of money could he choose? **6¢, 11¢, 15¢, 26¢, 30¢, 35¢**

7. Bob wants to buy a set of tires for his ATV. Howe's Tire Company allows a 10% discount if a purchase is paid for within 30 days. An additional discount of 5% is also given if the account is paid for within 15 days. If Bob buys a set of tires that cost $180 and pays the entire amount at the time of purchase, how much does he pay for the tires? **$153.90**

8. Copy the figure at the right. Place the numbers 1 through 12 in the circles so that the sum of each of the six rows is 26.

7, 8, 3, 9, 6, 10, 4, 1, 12, 2, 11, 5

9. Carla is challenged to find her way through a maze. Each time she walks through a correct doorway, she receives $1. In each correct room, she is given a reward equal to the total she already has. The correct path passes through 8 doorways and 7 rooms. If Carla takes the correct path, how much money will she have at the end? **$255**

10. Mr. Ebin sold 100 shares of stock for $5975. When the price per share went down $5, he bought 200 more shares. When the price per share went back up $3, he sold 100 shares. How much did Mr. Ebin gain or lose in his transactions? **$800 gain**

Critical Thinking

11. The sum of two brothers' ages is 38. One brother is ten years older than the other. How old is each brother? **14 years; 24 years**

Wrap-Up

12. **Make Up a Problem** Write a problem that can be solved by making a table. **See margin.**

Writing Connection

Write one or more complete sentences to answer each question. **See margin.**

1. How do you know that the ratio 3 to 25 is the same as 12%?
2. How do you know that 50% of 90 is equal to 90% of 50?
3. How do you know that 101% of 50 is greater than 50?

Error Analysis

Watch for students who choose answers that do not satisfy all requirements.
Prevent by having students work in pairs and verbalize each step.

Independent Practice

Homework Assignment	
Basic	5-12
Average	5-12
Honors	5-12

4 CLOSE

Assessment Option

Writing Divide the class into small groups and have them write a problem that you can solve by making a table. Then exchange problems among groups and solve.

Practice Masters Booklet, **p. 90**

Name ____________ Date ____________

Practice Worksheet 9-9

Problem Solving Strategy: Make a Table

Solve. Make a table.

1. Kent Jones has $1.95 consisting of 7 U.S. coins. However, he cannot make change for a nickel or a half-dollar. What 7 coins does Kent have? **2 nickels, 1 dime, 1 quarter, 3 half-dollars**

2. A penny, nickel, dime, quarter, and half-dollar are in a purse. Without looking, Maria picks two coins. How many different amounts of money could she choose? What would be the total of these amounts? **10 amounts; $3.64**

3. Rita had 50 stamps in her collection. She traded 6 stamps for 4 from Jane. She traded 4 more for 5 from Mary. She traded another 5 for 3 from Norma. Finally, she traded 12 more stamps for 9 from Mike. How many stamps does Rita have now? **44 stamps**

4. Paul wants to buy a stereo system. The store allows a 15% discount if the purchase is paid for within 30 days. A 20% discount is given if the purchase is paid for within 10 days. If Paul pays $400 at the time of purchase, what was the original price of the stereo system? **$500**

5. Randall Burns bought 50 shares of stock for $2490. When the price per share went up $4, he sold 25 shares. Then the price per share went down $2, so he bought 100 more shares. When the price of the stock went back up $5, he sold 50 shares. How many shares of stock does he have now? How much is each share worth? **75 shares; $56.80**

6. Beth and Janeen both start their jobs at the same time. Beth's starting salary is $16,000 per year with a guaranteed $4000 pay raise per year for a 5-year period. Janeen's starting salary is $18,000 per year with a guaranteed $3000 pay raise per year for a 5-year period. Which person would be making more money during the fifth year? How much money would this person make during the five years? **Beth; $120,000**

Additional Answers

12. A paper route pays either 10¢ per paper or 50¢ a week plus 8¢ per paper. For what number of papers would you choose the second option?

Writing Connection

1. 12% means 12 out of 100 which can be simplified to 3 to 25.
2. 50% of 90 means $\frac{1}{2}$ of 90 which equals 45 and 90% of 50 means $0.9 \cdot 50$ which also equals 45.
3. The rate is greater than 100.

Cooperative Learning

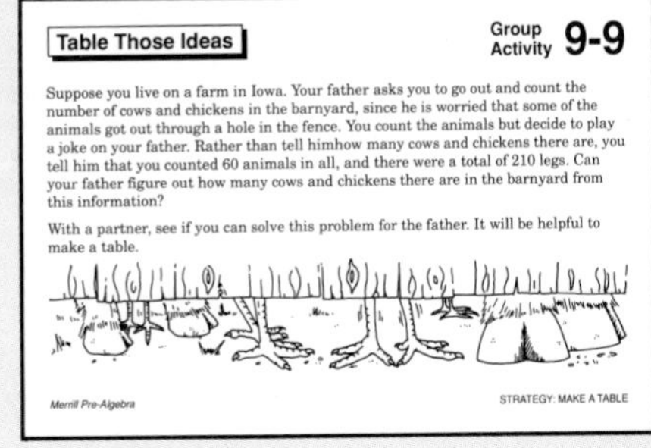

Table Those Ideas Group Activity **9-9**

Suppose you live on a farm in Iowa. Your father asks you to go out and count the number of cows and chickens in the barnyard, since he is worried that some of the animals got out through a hole in the fence. You count the animals but decide to play a joke on your father. Rather than tell himhow many cows and chickens there are, you tell him that you counted 60 animals in all, and there were a total of 210 legs. Can your father figure out how many cows and chickens there are in the barnyard from this information?

With a partner, see if you can solve this problem for the father. It will be helpful to make a table.

Merrill Pre-Algebra STRATEGY: MAKE A TABLE

5-Minute Check
(over Lesson 9-9)

Solve. Use any strategy. Abby bought a new car. The sticker price was $14,500. The car dealer came down 8% of the sticker price. Abby had to pay the 5.6% sales tax plus the discounted price. What was the final cost? **$14,087.04**

Transparency 9-10 contains the 5-Minute Check and a teaching aid for this lesson.

1 FOCUS

The purpose of this lesson is to use the percent proportion to find percent of change.

2 TEACH

Chalkboard Examples

The water level in Lake Anderson was 460 feet on June 1 and 410 feet on July 1. What was the percent of decrease? **about 10.9%**

Practice Masters Booklet, **p. 91**

Name ______________________ Date ______________

Practice Worksheet 9-10

Application: Percent of Change

Find the percent of change in the prices below. Round to the nearest whole percent.

1. old: $48.50 new: $38.80 **20%**	2. old: $15,000 new: $45,000 **200%**	3. old: $0.80 new: $1.08 **35%**
4. old: $19.95 new: $23.94 **20%**	5. old: $0.36 new: $0.60 **67%**	6. old: $50 new: $35 **30%**
7. old: $15,200 new: $14,212 **7%**	8. old: $150 new: $135 **10%**	9. old: $75 new: $85 **13%**
10. old: $20.00 new: $15.50 **23%**	11. old: $2880 new: $3500 **22%**	12. old: $3.00 new: $3.85 **28%**
13. old: $58.50 new: $37.50 **36%**	14. old $350 new: $311 **11%**	15. old: $325 new: $375 **15%**
16. old: $13.50 new: $8.00 **41%**	17. old: $52.25 new: $78.00 **49%**	18. old: $16 new: $22 **38%**
19. old: $135.00 new: $101.25 **25%**	20. old: $306.25 new: $350.00 **14%**	21. old: $84.00 new: $205.80 **145%**
22. old: $533 new: $260 **51%**	23. old: $1800 new: $1440 **20%**	24. old: $350 new: $329 **6%**
25. old: $75.11 new: $72.50 **3%**	26. old: $16.50 new: $13.55 **18%**	27. old: $9.75 new: $10.50 **8%**

Application

9-10 Percent of Change

Objective:
Find the percent of increase or decrease.

Last year, a new bicycle cost $120. This year, the same model costs $135. You can express this increase in price using percents.

To find the percent of increase, you can follow these steps.

Mental Math Hint

THINK: $\frac{15}{120} = \frac{1}{8}$

$\frac{1}{8} = 12.5\%$

Step 1 Subtract to find the amount of change.

$135 - 120 = 15$ The cost of the bicycle increased $15.

Step 2 Solve the percent proportion. Compare the amount of increase to the original amount.

$$\text{percentage} \rightarrow \frac{15}{120} = \frac{r}{100}\Big\}\text{ rate} \quad (\text{base} \rightarrow 120)$$

$15 \cdot 100 = 120r$ Find the cross products.

$1500 = 120r$ Divide each side by 120.

1500 [÷] 120 [=] 12.5

$r = 12.5$

The cost of the bicycle increased 12.5%.

The percent of decrease can be found in a similar way.

Example

1 When Andrea started bicycling last year, she completed the 5-mile course in 45 minutes. Now, she can complete the course in 40 minutes. Find the percent of decrease.

$45 - 40 = 5$ Find the amount of decrease.

$\frac{5}{45} = \frac{r}{100}$ Write the percent proportion. The original time is 45 minutes.

$5 \cdot 100 = 45r$ Find the cross products.

$500 = 45r$ Divide each side by 45.

500 [÷] 45 [=] 11.1111111

$r \approx 11.1$

The percent of decrease is about 11%.

Estimation Hint

THINK: $\frac{5}{45} = \frac{1}{9}$

Since $\frac{1}{9} > \frac{1}{10}$, the percent of decrease is greater than 10%.

Bell Ringer

State three advantages to making a table. **Possible answers: organize your thoughts, see what you have already done, and help you see a pattern.**

EE: 1E, 3A, 3I
TAAS: 2, 10, 11, 13

Reteaching Masters Booklet, **p. 82**

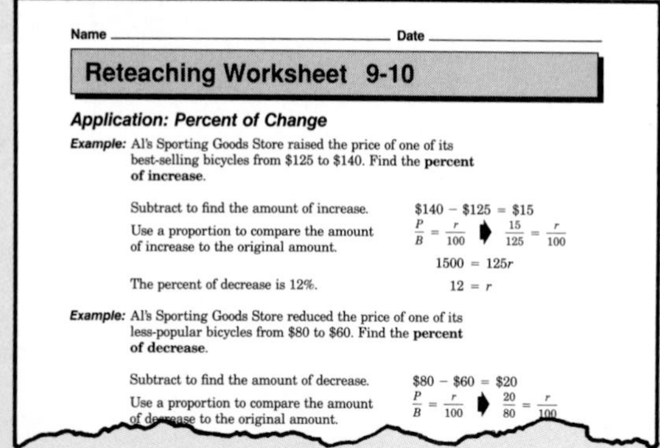

Name ______________________ Date ______________

Reteaching Worksheet 9-10

Application: Percent of Change

Example: Al's Sporting Goods Store raised the price of one of its best-selling bicycles from $125 to $140. Find the **percent of increase**.

Subtract to find the amount of increase. $\$140 - \$125 = \$15$

Use a proportion to compare the amount of increase to the original amount. $\frac{P}{B} = \frac{r}{100}$ ➧ $\frac{15}{125} = \frac{r}{100}$

$1500 = 125r$

The percent of decrease is 12%. $12 = r$

Example: Al's Sporting Goods Store reduced the price of one of its less-popular bicycles from $80 to $60. Find the **percent of decrease**.

Subtract to find the amount of decrease. $\$80 - \$60 = \$20$

Use a proportion to compare the amount of decrease to the original amount. $\frac{P}{B} = \frac{r}{100}$ ➧ $\frac{20}{80} = \frac{r}{100}$

Checking for Understanding

Communicating Algebra

1. What is the first step in finding the percent of change? Find the amount of change.
2. What part of the percent proportion do you solve for when finding a percent of change? rate
3. What is the name of the amount used as the base in the percent proportion when finding a percent of change? original amount

Guided Practice

Estimate the percent of increase or decrease in the prices below. Sample answers given.

4. old: $5 new: $6 20%
5. old: $12 new: $15 25%
6. old: $20 new: $18 10%
7. old: $14 new: $13 6%
8. old: $26 new: $20 25%
9. old: $0.49 new: $0.56 14%

Exercises

Independent Practice

ESTIMATION / MENTAL MATH / CALCULATOR / PAPER/PENCIL

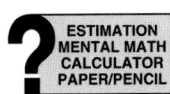

Find the percent of change in the prices below. Round to the nearest whole percent.

10. old: $65.00 new: $68.25 5%
11. old: $79.18 new: $74.00 7%
12. old: $62.00 new: $65.72 6%
13. old: $156.90 new: $194.55 24%
14. old: $139.40 new: $164.49 18%
15. old: $65.48 new: $60.24 8%
16. old: $475 new: $450 5%
17. old: $800 new: $835 4%
18. old: $615 new: $650 6%

Mixed Review

19. Find the slope of the line that contains the points $A(1,2)$ and $B(-3,0)$. (Lesson 8-8) $\frac{1}{2}$
20. Twenty-six is what percent of 130? (Lesson 9-7) 20%

Find the discount rate. (Lesson 9-8)

21. a $10 CD on sale for $8 20%
22. a $3.50 notebook on sale for $2.25 about 36%

Applications

23. **Economics** The Consumer Price Index (CPI) shows the relative costs of goods and services. If the CPI is 233.2 in April and 236.4 in May, what is the percent of increase? 1%
24. **Sports** At the start of wrestling season, Jorge weighed 150 pounds. At the end of the season, he weighed 144 pounds. What was the percent of change in his weight? 4% decrease
25. **Consumer Awareness** Last year the value of Patty's car was $6150. This year the value is $4920. What is the percent of change in the car's value? 20% decrease

Critical Thinking

26. A pair of hiking boots originally cost $42. The price was increased by 25%. The boots were sold later with the price reduced $\frac{1}{4}$. What was the final sales price? Explain why the final sales price is not $42. $39.38 The reduction was based on a greater base than the increase.

Wrap-Up

27. In your own words, explain how to find the percent of change. See margin.

3 PRACTICE/APPLY

Checking the Concept

Have students verbalize each step used to solve Guided Practice Exercises 4-9.

Independent Practice

Homework Assignment	
Basic	11-17 odd, 19-23, 26, 27
Average	10-14 even, 19-27
Honors	16-27

Chapter 9, Quiz B (Lesson 9-6 through 9-10) is available in the Evaluation Masters Booklet, p. 79.

4 CLOSE

Assessment Option

Speaking Use advertisements from newspapers or magazines that show a reduced price for an item (car, dress, shoes, etc.). Have the students tell you the steps in finding the percent of change for the item as you write each step on the board.

Enrichment Masters Booklet, **p. 82**

Name ______ Date ______

Enrichment Worksheet 9-10

Finance Charges

PREVIOUS BALANCE	TOTAL PURCHASES	PAYMENTS RETURNS & OTHER CREDITS	FINANCE *CHARGE	THIS IS YOUR NEW BALANCE	PAYMENTS OVERDUE	THIS IS YOUR MINIMUM PAYMENT
245.67	138.56	184.23	2.94	202.94		25.00

*ANNUAL PERCENTAGE RATE OF 15% COMPUTED ON THE AVERAGE DAILY BALANCE OF $235.19 .

Eileen Farrell received her monthly statement for her department store charge account. She left part of her balance unpaid last month. Her statement says that her finance charge is $2.94. This is computed on the annual rate of 15% on an average daily balance of $235.19. Is the charge correct?

Example: Compute the monthly finance charge for Eileen's unpaid balance. The annual percentage rate is 15%. To find the monthly rate, divide by 12.

Monthly rate: 15% ÷ 12 = 1.25% Compute 1.25% of $235.19.

$B \cdot R = P \rightarrow 235.19 \cdot 0.0125 = P$ 1.25% = 0.0125

$2.939875 = P$

$2.94 = P$ Round to the nearest cent.

The finance charge is $2.94. The statement is correct.

Find the monthly finance charge to the next cent on each average daily balance.

1. Balance: $165.00 Annual percentage rate: 18% $2.48
2. Balance: $231.00 Annual percentage rate: 15% $2.89
3. Balance: $713.00 Annual rate: 12% $7.13
4. Balance: $147.93 Annual rate: 15.5% $1.91
5. Balance: $419.60 Annual rate: 14% $4.90
6. Balance: $175.14 Annual rate: 16% $2.34
7. Balance: $450.00 Annual rate: 17% $6.38
8. Balance: $368.50 Annual rate: 18% $5.53
9. Balance: $250.50 Annual rate: $18\frac{1}{2}$% $3.86
10. Balance: $654.90 Annual rate: 12.5% $6.82

Additional Answer

27. Find the amount of change and divide by the original amount. Write the result as a percent.

Cooperative Learning

Why Are They Different? Group Activity **9-10**

MATERIALS: Two 0-9 spinners

Work together in groups of three or four to study percent of increase.

To begin, each member of the group should choose a 2-digit number with which to work. Someone should spin the two spinners to make another 2-digit number. The number formed by the digits on the spinners will be the *amount* of increase for this activity.

Using your own 2-digit number as the original amount, compute the *percent* of increase. Compare your results with other group members. Repeat the process three more times.

With a partner write a short paragraph explaining why all of the percent of increases were not the same.

Merrill Pre-Algebra PERCENT OF CHANGE

Using the Chapter Review

The Chapter Review is a comprehensive review of the concepts presented in this chapter. This review may be used to prepare students for the Chapter Test.

Alternate Review Strategy

To provide a brief in-class review, you may wish to read the following questions to the class and require a verbal response.

1. Express the ratio 22 out of 30 students as a fraction in simplest form. $\frac{11}{15}$
2. Solve the proportion $\frac{1}{2} = \frac{x}{24}$. $x = 12$
3. Explain what proportion you would use to solve this problem. If 2 yards of material make 6 scarves, how many yards of material are needed to make 24 scarves? $\frac{2}{x} = \frac{6}{24}$
4. What proportion would you use to solve 25 is 30% of what number? $\frac{25}{B} = \frac{30}{100}$
5. Express 45% as a decimal; as a fraction. 0.45, $\frac{9}{20}$
6. Estimate 73% of 78. $\frac{3}{4}$ of 80 = 60
7. Identify the percentage, rate, and base for $4 = 16\%$ of x. $p = 4, r = 16\%, b = x$
8. What is the simple interest formula? $I = prt$
9. Give an example of a problem that can be solved by making a table. Answers will vary.
10. What proportion would you use to find the percent of increase for this problem? A new TV cost $340 last year. This year that same TV costs $375. $\frac{35}{340} = \frac{r}{100}$

Review

Language and Concepts

Choose the correct term or number to complete each sentence.

base
rate
percentage
original
ratio
441
882
$\frac{2}{3}$
unit rate
discount
interest

1. A __?__ compares two numbers and can be written as follows: 2 out of 3, 2 to 3, 2:3, or $\frac{2}{3}$. ratio
2. In the equation $15\% \cdot \$22 = \$3.30$, the rate is __?__. 15%
3. A __?__ is an equation in the form $\frac{a}{b} = \frac{c}{d}$, which states that two ratios are equivalent. proportion
4. A ratio that has two measurements with different units of measure is called a __?__. rate
5. In the proportion $\frac{441}{882} = \frac{50}{100}$, the base is __?__. 882
6. To find the percent of increase or decrease, you compare the amount of change to the __?__. original
7. __?__ is equivalent to $66\frac{2}{3}\%$. $\frac{2}{3}$

Skills

Express each ratio as a fraction in simplest form. (Lesson 9-1)

8. 5 out of 6 $\frac{5}{6}$
9. 3 to 6 $\frac{1}{2}$
10. 15:10 $\frac{3}{2}$

Express each ratio as a unit rate. (Lesson 9-1)

11. 450 miles in 9 hours 50 mph
12. $12 in 1.5 hours $8/hour

Solve each proportion. (Lesson 9-2)

13. $\frac{1}{3} = \frac{n}{12}$ 4
14. $\frac{18}{48} = \frac{6}{y}$ 16
15. $\frac{2}{3} = \frac{x}{0.6}$ 0.4
16. $\frac{8}{2.5} = \frac{10.4}{c}$ 3.25

Write a proportion that could be used to solve for each variable. Then solve. (Lesson 9-3)

17. 4 pounds costs $89. 9 pounds costs n dollars $\frac{4}{89} = \frac{9}{n}$ $200.25
18. Al earns $160.95 in 37 hours. Al earns $26.10 in n hours. $\frac{160.95}{37} = \frac{26.10}{n}$ 6 hours

Express each fraction as a percent. (Lesson 9-4)

19. $\frac{7}{8}$ 87.5%
20. $\frac{9}{5}$ 180%
21. $\frac{2}{5}$ 40%
22. $\frac{3}{8}$ 37.5%
23. $1\frac{3}{50}$ 106%

Express each decimal as a percent. (Lesson 9-5)

24. 0.012 1.2%
25. 1.05 105%
26. 0.086 8.6%
27. 1.21 121%

Express each percent as a decimal and as a fraction in simplest form. (Lesson 9-5)

28. 25% $\frac{1}{4}$ 0.25
29. $33\frac{1}{3}\%$ $\frac{1}{3}$ $0.\overline{33}$
30. 8% $\frac{2}{25}$ 0.08
31. 23.5% $\frac{47}{200}$ 0.235
32. 38% $\frac{19}{50}$ 0.38

Estimate the percent. (Lesson 9-6) Sample answers given.

33. 12 out of 25 50% 34. 9 out of 26 $33\frac{1}{3}$% 35. 16 out of 50 30% 36. 28 out of 295 10%

Solve. (Lesson 9-7)

37. 120 is 60% of what number? 200
38. 50% of what number is 46? 92
39. $83\frac{1}{3}$% of 48 is what number? 40
40. What is 0.6% of 59? 0.354
41. 250 is what percent of 100? 2.50%
42. What percent of 400 is 2? 0.5%
43. 1.2% of what number is 0.06? 5
44. 450% of what number is 49.5? 11

Applications and Problem Solving

Find the amount of discount and the sale price of each item. (Lesson 9-8)

45. $50 jacket, 15% off $7.50, $42.50
46. $119.50 lamp, $\frac{1}{4}$ off $29.88, $89.62
47. $3.59 tennis balls, $\frac{1}{3}$ off $1.20, $2.39

Find the interest to the nearest cent. (Lesson 9-8)

48. $650 at 12% for 2 years $156
49. $1250 at 10% for 3 months $31.25

Find the percent of increase or decrease. (Lesson 9-10)

50. A $50 vase is now worth $87.50. 75% increase
51. Half-time intermission went from 15 to 12 minutes. 20% decrease

Solve. (Lesson 9-9)

52. Anne Zody buys a car for $100, sells it for $110, buys it back for $120, and sells it again for $130. How much does Ms. Zody make or lose? $20 gain

Communicating Algebra

In your own words, explain why 50% of 20 is not the same as $\frac{1}{2}$% of 20. See margin.

Curriculum Connection

- **Science** Find three examples of spirals in nature. See margin.
- **Geology** Two of the saltiest bodies of water are the Dead Sea and the Great Salt Lake. Determine how percents are used in describing how much salt is in salt water. See margin.

Read More About It

Charuhas, Mary S., et al. *Essential Mathematics for Life: Percents, Graphs, and Measurement.*

Gardner, Martin. *Perplexing Puzzles and Tantalizing Teasers.*

Schmitt, Lois. *Smart Spending: A Young Consumer's Guide.*

You may wish to use a Chapter Test (free-response format) as an additional chapter review. Two forms are provided in the Evaluation Masters Booklet as shown below.

Evaluation Masters Booklet, **p. 77**

Name ______________ Date ______________

Chapter 9 Test, Form 2A

Express each ratio as a fraction in simplest form.

1. 63 to 93
2. 14 out of 56

Express each ratio as a unit rate.

3. 202.5 miles in 9 hours
4. $495 for 30 tickets

5. Solve the proportion $\frac{k}{25} = \frac{3}{5}$.
6. Colleen's car averages 32 miles per gallon of gasoline. How many gallons are needed for a trip of 528 miles?
7. Three ounces of a perfume cost $105. How much do 7 ounces cost?

Express each value as a percent.

8. 0.4
9. $\frac{3}{5}$

10. What number is 28% of 425?
11. Six is what percent of 15?
12. Twelve is 25% of what number?

Express each percent as a fraction in simplest form.

13. 8%
14. 37.5%

Express each percent as a decimal.

15. 15%
16. 3.25%

17. Estimate a 15% tip on a restaurant bill of $39.95.
18. Estimate the 6% sales tax on a $635 refrigerator.
19. What percent of 6 is 24?
20. The price of a table is marked down from $180 to $120. Find the rate of discount.
21. Dave borrows $800 at a simple interest rate of 9.5% for 3 years. How much interest will he have to pay?
22. How many ways can you add four different prime numbers to total 25?
23. Last year, the tuition at a private college was $12,000. This year it will be $12,720. Find the percent of increase.

Find the percent of change from the old price to the new price.

24. Old: $46; new: $52.90
25. Old: $700; new: $784

BONUS A 600 gram candle burns off 35% of its weight. The remaining part of the candle is relit, and 20% of its weight is burned away. Find the weight of the remaining piece.

Answers: 1. $\frac{21}{31}$ 2. $\frac{1}{4}$ 3. 22.5 mph 4. $16.50 per ticket 5. 15 6. 16.5 gallons 7. $245 8. 40% 9. 60% 10. 119 11. 40% 12. 48 13. $\frac{2}{25}$ 14. $\frac{3}{8}$ 15. 0.15 16. 0.0325 17. $6.00 18. $40 19. 400% 20. $33\frac{1}{3}$% 21. $228 22. 2 23. 6% 24. 15% incr. 25. 12% incr. 312 grams

Evaluation Masters Booklet, **p. 78**

Name ______________ Date ______________

Chapter 9 Test, Form 2B

Express each ratio as a fraction in simplest form.

1. 66 to 96
2. 12 out of 72

Express each ratio as a unit rate.

3. 517.5 miles in 9 hours
4. $462.50 for 25 tickets

5. Solve the proportion $\frac{k}{35} = \frac{3}{5}$.
6. Maureen's car averages 28 miles per gallon of gasoline. How many gallons are needed for a trip of 350 miles?
7. Three ounces of a perfume cost $99. How much do 8 ounces cost?

Express each value as a percent.

8. 0.08
9. $\frac{7}{8}$

10. What number is 35% of 520?
11. Six is what percent of 48?
12. Twelve is 30% of what number?

Express each percent as a fraction in simplest form.

13. 12%
14. 62.5%

Express each percent as a decimal.

15. 6%
16. 40.5%

17. Estimate a 15% tip on a restaurant bill of $88.90.
18. Estimate the 5% sales tax on a $592 sound system.
19. What percent of 8 is 40?
20. The price of a table is marked down from $160 to $120. Find the rate of discount.
21. Raul borrows $600 at a simple interest rate of 8.5% for 2 years. How much interest will he have to pay?
22. How many ways can you add four different prime numbers to total 28?
23. Last year, the tuition at a private college was $13,500. This year it will be $14,175. Find the percent of increase.

Find the percent of change from the old price to the new price.

24. Old: $48; new: $53.76
25. Old: $700; new: $805

BONUS A 700 gram candle burns off 25% of its weight. The remaining part of the candle is relit, and 20% of its weight is burned away. Find the weight of the remaining piece.

Answers: 1. $\frac{11}{16}$ 2. $\frac{1}{6}$ 3. 57.5 mph 4. $18.50 per ticket 5. 21 6. 12.5 gallons 7. $264 8. 8% 9. 87.5% 10. 182 11. 12.5% 12. 40 13. $\frac{3}{25}$ 14. $\frac{5}{8}$ 15. 0.06 16. 0.405 17. $13.50 18. $30 19. 500% 20. 25% 21. $102 22. 1 23. 5% 24. 12% incr. 25. 15% incr. 420 grams

Additional Answers

Communicating Algebra

Sample answer: 50% of 20 means $\frac{1}{2}$ of 20 which is 10. $\frac{1}{2}$% means 0.5% or 0.005 and $0.005 \cdot 20 = 0.1$.

Curriculum Connection

Science There are spirals in pineapple scales, in rows of seeds of a sunflower, and in a chambered nautilus shell.

Geology In describing salinity, percent means the number of parts of dissolved salt per hundred parts of water.

Using the Chapter Test

This page may be used as a test or as an additional review. Two forms of a Chapter Test (multiple-choice format) are provided in the Evaluation Masters Booklet.

***Evaluation Masters Booklet,* pp. 73-74**

Name ______________________ Date ______________

Chapter 9 Test, Form 1A

1. Express the ratio 57 : 76 as a fraction in simplest form.
A. $\frac{9}{13}$ B. $\frac{19}{26}$ C. $\frac{3}{4}$ D. $\frac{57}{76}$ 1. C
2. Express the ratio 480 miles in 12 hours as a unit rate.
A. 0.25 mph B. 40 mph C. 42 mph D. 4 mph 2. B
3. Find the pair of ratios which form a proportion.
A. $\frac{3}{2}, \frac{9}{4}$ B. $\frac{3}{2}, \frac{4}{3}$ C. $\frac{2}{3}, \frac{4}{6}$ D. $\frac{2}{3}, \frac{4}{9}$ 3. C
4. Solve the proportion $\frac{x}{6} = \frac{9}{3}$.
A. 18 B. 27 C. 12 D. 21 4. A
5. Solve the proportion $\frac{5}{2a} = \frac{2}{4}$.
A. 10 B. 5 C. 20 D. 15 5. B
6. A soup recipe calls for 4 pounds of rice for 20 servings. How many pounds of rice are needed for 30 servings?
A. 4.5 B. 8 C. 6 D. 5 6. C
7. A fertilizer is spread at 40 pounds for 5000 square feet. How many pounds are needed for 12,500 square feet?
A. 100 B. 55 C. 312.5 D. 125 7. A
8. Express $\frac{2}{5}$ as a percent.
A. 2.5% B. 250% C. 0.4% D. 40% 8. D
9. What is 80% of 20?
A. 0.16 B. 16 C. 4 D. 0.04 9. B
10. Three is what percent of 15?
A. 45% B. 20% C. 5% D. 50% 10. B
11. Express 0.305 as a percent.
A. 0.305% B. 0.00305% C. 30.5% D. 3.05% 11. C
12. Express $\frac{3}{5}$ as a percent.
A. 60% B. 3.5% C. 6% D. 35% 12. A
13. Express 12% as a fraction in simplest form.
A. $\frac{12}{100}$ B. $\frac{12}{99}$ C. $\frac{3}{25}$ D. $\frac{4}{33}$ 13. C
14. Express 3.4% as a decimal.
A. 340 B. 0.034 C. 0.34 D. 3.4 14. B

Name ______________________ Date ______________

Chapter 9 Test, Form 1A (continued)

15. Estimate 21% of 250.
A. 5250 B. 45 C. 12 D. 50 15. D
16. 12 is what percent of 48?
A. 0.25% B. 25% C. 576% D. 4% 16. B
17. 15 is 30% of what number?
A. 50 B. 4.5 C. 2 D. 200 17. A
18. What number is 8% of 25?
A. 0.2 B. 312.5 C. 2 D. 20 18. C
19. Joni buys a swimsuit marked $50. She receives a 20% discount. Find the sale price of the swimsuit.
A. $45 B. $40 C. $30 D. $10 19. B
20. A $16 CD is on sale for $12. Find the discount rate.
A. 4% B. 20% C. 25% D. 40% 20. C
21. John has four identical boxes. He puts a penny in one box, a nickel in one, a dime in one, and leaves one empty. Jean picks three boxes. How many different amounts of money can Jean choose?
A. 3 B. 4 C. 8 D. 10 21. B
22. The value of a house changed from $140,000 to $168,000. Find the percent of increase.
A. 10% B. 14% C. 28% D. 20% 22. D
23. Bob weighed 220 pounds in January and 198 pounds in June. Find the percent of decrease.
A. 10% B. 22% C. 12% D. 20% 23. A
24. A $475 speaker is marked down to $380. Find the percent of decrease.
A. 15% B. 20% C. 30% D. 95% 24. B
25. A dealer buys a coin for $850 and sells it for $1190. Find the percent of increase.
A. 34% B. 340% C. 40% D. 20% 25. C

BONUS Jack buys a bike marked $400. He receives a 20% discount. Jack adds 10% to his cost and sells the bike. Find the final selling price.
A. $320 B. $352 C. $390 D. $340 B

Test

Express each ratio as a fraction in simplest form.

1. 14 to 28 $\frac{1}{2}$
2. 21:9 $\frac{7}{3}$
3. 8 out of 18 $\frac{4}{9}$

Solve each proportion.

4. $\frac{1}{a} = \frac{11}{22}$ 2
5. $\frac{3}{8} = \frac{y}{12}$ 4.5
6. $\frac{4}{3} = \frac{10}{w}$ 7.5
7. $\frac{6}{5} = \frac{f}{17.5}$ 21

Write a proportion that could be used to solve for each variable. Then solve.

8. 2 gallons costs $2.38, n gallons costs $10.71 $\frac{2}{2.38} = \frac{n}{10.71}$ 9 gallons
9. 6 packages costs 57¢, 4 packages costs n cents $\frac{6}{57} = \frac{4}{n}$ 38¢

Express each percent as a decimal and as a fraction in simplest form.

10. 1.2% 0.012, $\frac{3}{250}$
11. 105% 1.05, $\frac{21}{20}$
12. 7% 0.07, $\frac{7}{100}$

Express each decimal or fraction as a percent.

13. 0.37 37%
14. 0.061 6.1%
15. $\frac{31}{100}$ 31%
16. $\frac{19}{25}$ 76%

Estimate. Sample answers given.

17. 9% of 11 1.1
18. 35% of 150 50
19. 19% of 250 50
20. 250% of 48 125

Solve.

21. What number is 35% of 120? 42
22. 28% of 70 is what number? 19.6
23. 30 is what percent of 250? 12%
24. What percent of 32 is 8? 25%
25. 2.25 is 50% of what number? 4.5
26. 40% of what number is 35.8? 89.5

Find the sale price of each item.

27. $29.95 jeans, 25% off $22.46
28. $11.50 album, 15% off $9.78

Find the principal plus interest to the nearest cent.

29. $560 at 8% for 1 year $604.80
30. $4000 at 9.25% for 6 months $4185

Solve. Make a table.

31. How many 4-digit numbers can be made using the digits 1, 2, 3, and 4? Use each digit only once. 24 numbers

Find the percent of increase or decrease.

32. 40 tickets to 60 tickets 50% increase
33. a $440 canoe on sale for $396 10% decrease

BONUS

How do you know that 1% does not always mean $1? See margin.

Test Generator Software is provided in both Apple and IBM formats. You may use this software to create your own tests, based on the needs of your students.

Additional Answer

Bonus-1% only means $1 if the base is $100.

Academic Skills Test

Cumulative, Chapters 1-9

1. A group of divers needs to descend to a depth 3 times their present depth of -25 m. At what depth do they need to be?

   A 75 m
   B 28 m
   C -25 m
   D -75 m

2. Which is equivalent to $n^3 \cdot n^4$?

   A n^{12}
   B n^7
   C n^1
   D n^{-1}

3. Connie ordered computer equipment from a mail-order catalog. The components and prices were: a printer for \$300, a modem for \$150, and a disc drive for \$75. She added \$71.50 for tax, shipping, and handling. What was the total cost of Connie's order?

   A \$525.00 C \$767.50
   B \$596.50 D Not Here

4. Joe Smith decided to make storm windows instead of buying them. The materials for twelve storm windows cost \$72.48. He could buy storm windows for \$21.50 each. How much will he save per window by making them?

   A \$15.46 C \$93.98
   B \$50.98 D \$185.52

5. If $3x + 4(x + 1) = 5x - 8$, what is the value of x?

   A -6 C -2
   B -4.5 D 6

6. Sami plans to spend no more than \$50 on shirts and pants. He buys 2 shirts at \$15 each. Which inequality shows the most he can spend on pants?

   A $2 \cdot 15 - x \leq 50$
   B $2 \cdot 15 + x \geq 50$
   C $2 \cdot 15 + x \leq 50$
   D Not Here

7. Which is the ordered pair for point N?

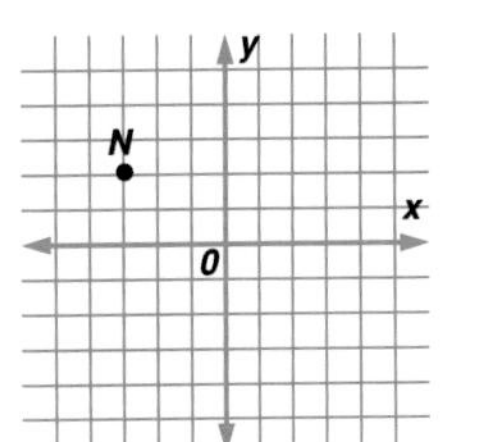

   A (2, -3)
   B (-2, 3)
   C (-3, 2)
   D (3, 2)

8. Which is a description of the graph of the equation $y = -3$?

   A The point (0, -3)
   B All points 3 units below the x-axis
   C All points 3 units left of the y-axis
   D The point (-3, 0)

9. A sweatshirt is on sale for \$15. This is 80% of the regular price. Which equation could be used to find the regular price?

   A $x = \frac{80}{100} \times 15$ C $15 = \frac{80}{100} \times x$
   B $x = \frac{20}{100} \times 15$ D $15 = \frac{20}{100} \times x$

10. A sweater that normally sells for \$35 is on sale at 25% off. The best estimate of the sale price is—

    A \$9 C \$32
    B \$26 D \$43

A Cumulative Review (free-response format) and Cumulative Test (multiple-choice format) are also provided in the Evaluation Masters Booklet as shown at the right.

Test Item	1	2	3	4	5	6	7	8	9	10
Lesson Number	2-6	4-3	5-4	6-4	7-6	7-8	8-3	8-6	9-4	9-6
TAAS Objective	8	2	6,7	9	2	2,4	2	2	11	10

Using the Academic Skills Test

This test familiarizes students with a standardized format while testing skills and concepts presented up to this point.

***Evaluation Masters Booklet*, p. 80**

Name ________________ Date ________________

Cumulative Review, Chapters 1-9

1. State the property of multiplication shown by (3)(2) = (2)(3). (Lesson 1–3)

Solve. (Lessons 2–4, 3–2)

2. $x = -7 + 6 + (-4)$
3. $a - (-8) = -15$
4. Find the LCM of 20 and 50. (Lesson 4–7)
5. Find the product $5^5 \cdot 5^3$ (Lesson 4–9)

Solve. (Lessons 5–4, 5–6, 5–7, 6–3, 6–4, 6–6, 6–7, 7–2, 7–4, 7–5)

6. $t = 357 - 8.38$
7. $w = \frac{7}{9} - \frac{1}{5}$
8. $t + 5.2 = 9.1$
9. $(15.5)(2.3) = y$
10. $x = \left(\frac{3}{5}\right)\left(\frac{12}{18}\right)$
11. $h = 15 \div \left(-\frac{1}{3}\right)$
12. $q = 7.21 \div 0.2$
13. $3b + 7 = 61$
14. $2w + 7 = 3w - 2$
15. $5(v + 7) = 6v + 31$
16. Complete 500 mm = ■ cm. (Lesson 7–8)
17. Is (2, −3) a solution of $y = 2x - 9$? (Lesson 8–5)
18. Find the slope of the line containing $A(6, 12)$ and $B(2, 8)$. (Lesson 8–8)
19. Find the y-intercept of the graph for $y = 2x + 9$. (Lesson 8–9)
20. Find the x-intercept of the graph for $y = 5x - 20$. (Lesson 8–9)
21. Solve the proportion $\frac{14}{w} = \frac{7}{9}$. (Lesson 9–2)
22. Express 1.26 as a percent. (Lesson 9–5)
23. Express 16.5% as a decimal. (Lesson 9–5)
24. Tim has a restaurant bill of \$19.87. He estimates a 15% tip. (Lesson 9–6)
25. Find the rate of discount if Al buys a \$30 hat for \$24. (Lesson 9–8)

Answers: 1. Comm. 2. −5 3. −23 4. 100 5. 5^8 6. 348.62 7. $\frac{26}{45}$ 8. 3.9 9. 35.65 10. $\frac{2}{5}$ 11. −45 12. 36.05 13. 18 14. 9 15. 4 16. 50 17. No 18. 1 19. 9 20. 4 21. 18 22. 126% 23. 0.165 24. \$3 25. 20%

***Evaluation Masters Booklet*, p. 81**

Name ________________ Date ________________

Cumulative Test, Chapters 1-9

1. State the property of multiplication shown by (3)(1) = 3.
   A. Associative B. Inverse C. Commutative D. Identity — 1. D

Solve each of the following.

2. $x = -8 - 6$ A. −14 B. −2 C. 14 D. 2 — 2. A
3. $a - (-4) = 12$ A. −8 B. 8 C. −16 D. 16 — 3. B
4. Find the LCM of 15 and 20.
   A. 300 B. 5 C. 60 D. 120 — 4. C
5. Find the product $3^4 \cdot 3^6 \cdot 3$.
   A. 3^{25} B. 3^{11} C. 3^{10} D. 3^{24} — 5. B

Solve each of the following.

6. $t - 3.7 = 4.6$ A. 0.9 B. 7.3 C. 1.1 D. 8.3 — 6. D
7. $x = \left(\frac{5}{9}\right)\left(\frac{18}{20}\right)$ A. $\frac{50}{81}$ B. 2 C. $\frac{1}{2}$ D. $\frac{2}{3}$ — 7. C
8. $z = 9.45 \div 2.1$ A. 4.05 B. 45 C. 0.45 D. 4.5 — 8. D
9. $2x + 4 = 3x + 7$ A. −3 B. 2.2 C. −2.2 D. 3 — 9. A
10. $4(a + 2) = 8a - 4$ A. 6 B. 0.5 C. 1.5 D. 3 — 10. D
11. Complete 6000 cm = ■ m.
    A. 60,000 B. 0.6 C. 6 D. 60 — 11. D
12. Which ordered pair is a solution of $y = 3x - 2$?
    A. (3, 11) B. (2, 6) C. (4, 10) D. (5, 12) — 12. C
13. Find the slope of the line that contains $A(4, 12)$ and $B(2, 4)$.
    A. −4 B. $-\frac{1}{4}$ C. $\frac{1}{4}$ D. 4 — 13. D
14. Find the x-intercept of the graph for $y = 3x + 6$.
    A. −2 B. 2 C. −9 D. 9 — 14. A
15. Find the y-intercept of the graph for $y = 3x - 9$.
    A. 3 B. −3 C. −9 D. 9 — 15. C
16. Solve the proportion $\frac{27}{y} = \frac{6}{8}$.
    A. 216 B. 36 C. 6 D. 26 — 16. B
17. Express 2.34 as a percent.
    A. 23.4% B. 0.0234% C. 2.34% D. 234% — 17. D
18. Express 0.1% as a decimal.
    A. 0.001 B. 0.01 C. 1 D. 10 — 18. A
19. Rene's restaurant bill is \$58. She estimates a 15% tip. How much is the tip?
    A. \$6 B. \$7 C. \$8 D. \$9 — 19. D
20. Find the discount rate if Ed buys a \$20 hat for \$5.
    A. 400% B. 25% C. 4% D. 75% — 20. D

Statistics and Graphs

Previewing the Chapter

This chapter introduces the student to the basic concepts of statistics. Students will learn to collect and organize data and then to display and analyze it. Measures of central tendency including mean, median, and mode, and measures of variation develop the ideas of range and interquartile range. Stem-and-leaf plots, box-and-whisker plots, and scatter plots are introduced as a means of displaying data and making conclusions based on these displays. Students will learn to recognize misleading statistics and to use samples to make predictions.

Problem Solving Strategy Students will learn to solve problems by first solving a simpler problem.

Lesson (Pages)	Lesson Objectives	State/Local Objectives
10-1 (363-365)	10-1: Gather and record data using a frequency table or histogram.	1E, 3A, 5D, 5E
10-2 (367-370)	10-2: Find the mean, median, and mode of a set of data.	1E, 3A, 5D, 5E, 5F
10-3 (371-373)	10-3A: Make a stem-and-leaf plot of a set of data. 10-3B: Make conclusions based on data displayed in a stem-and-leaf plot.	1E, 3A, 5D, 5E, 5F
10-4 (374-377)	10-4: Use measures of variation to compare data.	1E, 3A, 5D, 5E, 5F
10-5 (378-381)	10-5: Make a box-and-whisker plot of a set of data.	1E, 3A, 5D, 5E, 5F
10-6 (383-385)	10-6: Interpret data displayed in a scatter plot.	1E, 3A, 5D, 5E
10-7 (386-387)	10-7: Solve a problem by first solving a simpler problem.	1A, 1B, 1C, 1D, 1E
10-8 (388-390)	10-8: Use a sample to predict actions of a larger group.	1A, 3A, 3I, 5D, 5E
10-9 (391-393)	10-9: Recognize misleading statistics.	1A, 3A, 5D, 5E, 5F

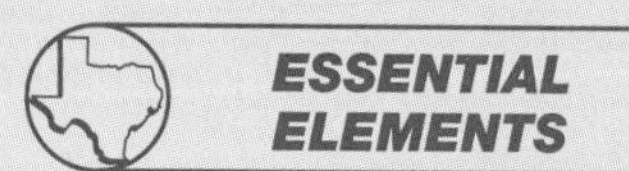

Organizing the Chapter

You may want to refer to the ***Course Planning Calendar*** *on Page T31.*

Planning Guide

Lesson (Pages)	Pacing Chart (in days) MINIMUM	STANDARD	ACCELERATED	Extra Practice (Student Edition)	Blackline Masters Booklets: Reteaching	Practice	Enrichment	Other Resources
10-1 (363-365)	1	1	1	p. 609, Set A	p. 83	p. 92	p. 83	Transparency 10-1 Group Activity Card 10-1
10-2 (367-370)	1.5	1	1	p. 609, Set B	p. 84	p. 93	p. 84	Transparency 10-2 Group Activity Card 10-2
10-3 (371-373)	1	1	1	p. 610, Set C	p. 85	p. 94	p. 85	Transparency 10-3 Group Activity Card 10-3
10-4 (374-377)	1.5	1	1	p. 609, Set B	p. 86	p. 95	p. 86	Transparency 10-4 Group Activity Card 10-4
10-5 (378-381)	1.5	1	1	p. 610, Set C	p. 87	p. 96	p. 87	Transparency 10-5 Group Activity Card 10-5
10-6 (383-385)	1	1	1	p. 610, Set C	p. 88	p. 97	p. 88	Transparency 10-6 Group Activity Card 10-6
10-7 (386-387)	1	1	0.5			p. 98		Transparency 10-7 Group Activity Card 10-7
10-8 (388-390)	1	1	1	p. 610, Set D	p. 89	p. 99	p. 89	Transparency 10-8 Group Activity Card 10-8
10-9 (391-393)	1	1	1	p. 610, Set D	p. 90	p. 100	p. 90	Transparency 10-9 Group Activity Card 10-9
Review (394-395)	1.5	1	1					Test Generator
Test (396)	1	1	1		Evaluation Masters, pp. 82-87			

Other Chapter Resources

Student Edition
Exploration, pp. 362, 382
Algebra in Action, p. 366
Challenge, p. 377
Mid-Chapter Quiz, p. 381
Team Problem Solving, p. 387
Career, p. 390
Academic Skills Test, p. 397

Teacher Resource Package
Interdisciplinary Activity, p. 10
Application Worksheet, p. 25
Cooperative Problem Solving, p. 40
Multicultural Activity, p. 55
Fun Activities, p. 73
Technology Worksheets, pp. 10, 25, 40
Lab Manual, pp. 54-56
Quizzes(2), p. 88
Class Review Game

Software
Test Generator

available for Apple and IBM

Enhancing the Chapter

Some of the blackline masters for enhancing this chapter are shown below.

Applications, p. 25

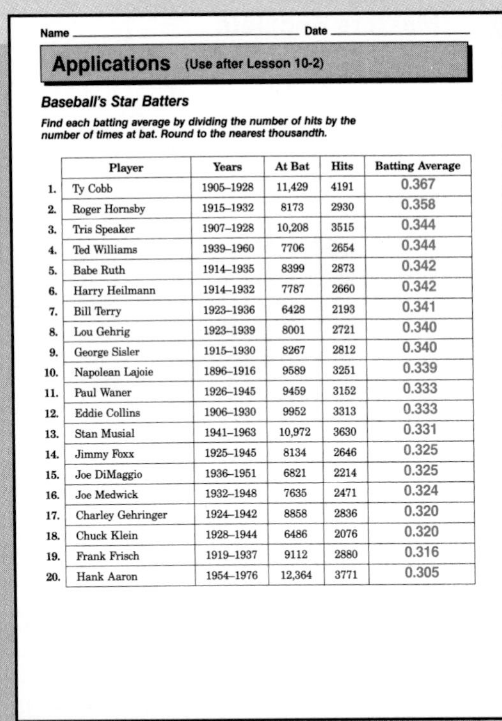

Name ______________________ Date ______________

Applications (Use after Lesson 10-2)

Baseball's Star Batters

Find each batting average by dividing the number of hits by the number of times at bat. Round to the nearest thousandth.

	Player	Years	At Bat	Hits	Batting Average
1.	Ty Cobb	1905–1928	11,429	4191	0.367
2.	Roger Hornsby	1915–1932	8173	2930	0.358
3.	Tris Speaker	1907–1928	10,208	3515	0.344
4.	Ted Williams	1939–1960	7706	2654	0.344
5.	Babe Ruth	1914–1935	8399	2873	0.342
6.	Harry Heilmann	1914–1932	7787	2660	0.342
7.	Bill Terry	1923–1936	6428	2193	0.341
8.	Lou Gehrig	1923–1939	8001	2721	0.340
9.	George Sisler	1915–1930	8267	2812	0.340
10.	Napolean Lajoie	1896–1916	9589	3251	0.339
11.	Paul Waner	1926–1945	9459	3152	0.333
12.	Eddie Collins	1906–1930	9952	3313	0.333
13.	Stan Musial	1941–1963	10,972	3630	0.331
14.	Jimmy Foxx	1925–1945	8134	2646	0.325
15.	Joe DiMaggio	1936–1951	6821	2214	0.325
16.	Joe Medwick	1932–1948	7635	2471	0.324
17.	Charley Gehringer	1924–1942	8858	2836	0.320
18.	Chuck Klein	1928–1944	6486	2076	0.320
19.	Frank Frisch	1919–1937	9112	2880	0.316
20.	Hank Aaron	1954–1976	12,364	3771	0.305

The **Activity Masters Booklet** contains the page shown above.

Interdisciplinary Activity, p. 10

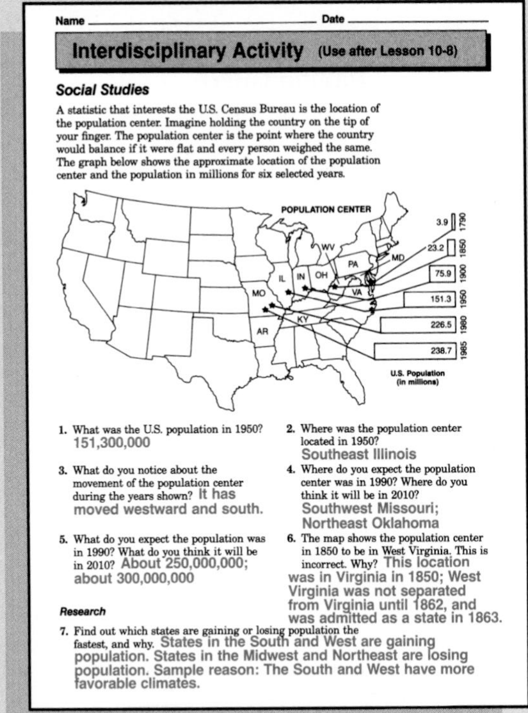

Name ______________________ Date ______________

Interdisciplinary Activity (Use after Lesson 10-8)

Social Studies

A statistic that interests the U.S. Census Bureau is the location of the population center. Imagine holding the country on the tip of your finger. The population center is the point where the country would balance if it were flat and every person weighed the same. The graph below shows the approximate location of the population center and the population in millions for six selected years.

1. What was the U.S. population in 1950? 151,300,000
2. Where was the population center located in 1950? Southeast Illinois
3. What do you notice about the movement of the population center during the years shown? It has moved westward and south.
4. Where do you expect the population center was in 1990? Where do you think it will be in 2010? Southwest Missouri; Northeast Oklahoma
5. What do you expect the population was in 1990? What do you think it will be in 2010? About 250,000,000; about 300,000,000
6. The map shows the population center in 1850 to be in West Virginia. This is incorrect. Why? This location was in Virginia in 1850; West Virginia was not separated from Virginia until 1862, and was admitted as a state in 1863.

Research

7. Find out which states are gaining or losing population the fastest, and why. States in the South and West are gaining population. States in the Midwest and Northeast are losing population. Sample reason: The South and West have more favorable climates.

The **Activity Masters Booklet** contains the page shown above.

Models and Manipulatives

Students will discuss histograms and the data used to develop them. Give each student a sticky note and have them print their first name on it. They would then be asked to stick it on the chalkboard under the number of letters in their first name. This makes a neat graph which could be compared to a histogram. A discussion of the data gathered would follow.

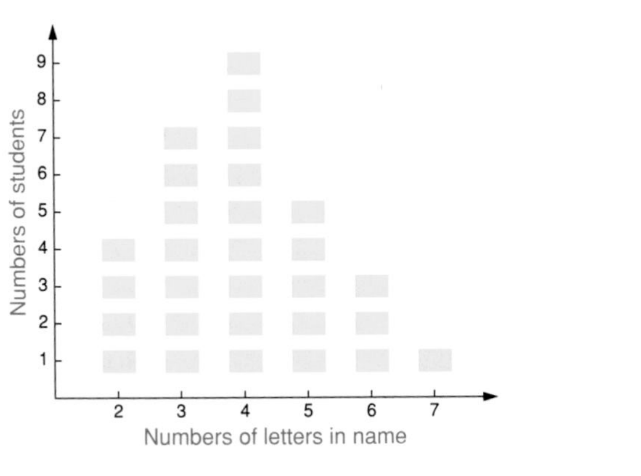

Multicultural Activity

David Blackwell is an honored black theoretician who has made many contributions to statistics, probability, game theory, set theory, dynamic programming, and information theory. He is noted for his rigor and clarity. He is also noted for his interest in *understanding* the areas of mathematics to which he has made contributions rather than doing research in these areas.

Have students research and write a paragraph on the contributions of other black mathematicians.

Cooperative Learning

The following activity is provided in the **Activity Masters Booklet.**

Cooperative Problem Solving, p. 40

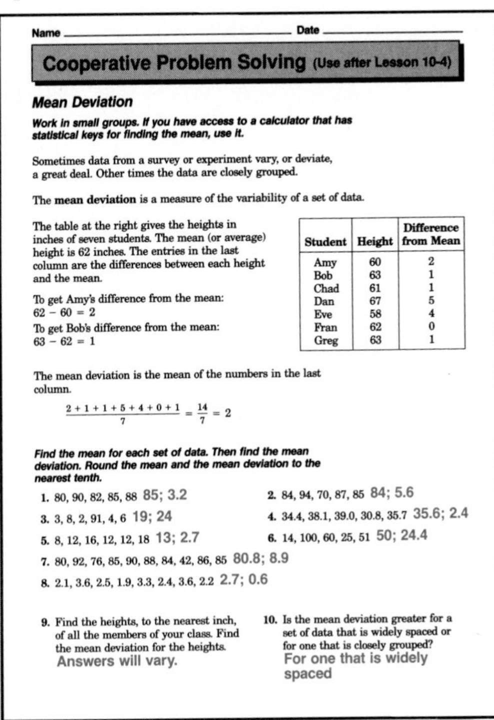

Name ____________________ Date ____________

Cooperative Problem Solving (Use after Lesson 10-4)

Mean Deviation

Work in small groups. If you have access to a calculator that has statistical keys for finding the mean, use it.

Sometimes data from a survey or experiment vary, or deviate, a great deal. Other times the data are closely grouped.

The **mean deviation** is a measure of the variability of a set of data.

The table at the right gives the heights in inches of seven students. The mean (or average) height is 62 inches. The entries in the last column are the differences between each height and the mean.

To get Amy's difference from the mean:
$62 - 60 = 2$

To get Bob's difference from the mean:
$63 - 62 = 1$

Student	Height	Difference from Mean
Amy	60	2
Bob	63	1
Chad	61	1
Dan	67	5
Eve	58	4
Fran	62	0
Greg	63	1

The mean deviation is the mean of the numbers in the last column.

$$\frac{2+1+1+5+4+0+1}{7} = \frac{14}{7} = 2$$

Find the mean for each set of data. Then find the mean deviation. Round the mean and the mean deviation to the nearest tenth.

1. 80, 90, 82, 85, 88 85; 3.2
2. 84, 94, 70, 87, 85 84; 5.6
3. 3, 8, 2, 91, 4, 6 19; 24
4. 34.4, 38.1, 39.0, 30.8, 35.7 35.6; 2.4
5. 8, 12, 16, 12, 12, 18 13; 2.7
6. 14, 100, 60, 25, 51 50; 24.4
7. 80, 92, 76, 85, 90, 88, 84, 42, 86, 85 80.8; 8.9
8. 2.1, 3.6, 2.5, 1.9, 3.3, 2.4, 3.6, 2.2 2.7; 0.6
9. Find the heights, to the nearest inch, of all the members of your class. Find the mean deviation for the heights. Answers will vary.
10. Is the mean deviation greater for a set of data that is widely spaced or for one that is closely grouped? For one that is widely spaced

Cooperative Problem Solving

Have students work in groups of three to four to discuss the following problem: It is often costly, time-consuming, and impossible to gather data from every student in the school or every person in a city. How could you pick a sample to make sure that the results would reflect the population that you wish to survey? The idea is to enable students to explore the idea of a random sample.

Interactive Bulletin Board

Statistics Connection

Topic: Height of Students

DATA

Height	Tally	Frequency
49-54	III	3
55-60	𝍸	5
61-66	𝍸 𝍸	10
67-72	𝍸 𝍸 III	13
73-78	𝍸	5

Mean ________
Median ________
Mode ________

Stem-and-Leaf Plot

4 | 9 9
5 | 2 1 9 8 7
6 | 1 1 2 4 6 8 9
7 | 3 4 5 6 8

Box-and-Whisker Plot

49 62 75

Purpose Provide practice in collecting, organizing, displaying, and analyzing data.

How to Use It Divide students into four groups. Have each group be responsible for the bulletin board for one week. Assign to each group a topic to be researched such as: the number of siblings each student in the school or class has, the height of the students in the school or class, the number of TVs sold by local appliance stores during a certain time period, etc. Have each group present the data by showing a frequency table, then by determining the mean, median, and mode of the data. Summarize the data by showing a stem-and-leaf plot and a box-and-whisker plot.

Outside Resources

Books/Periodicals
Misused Statistics: Straight Talk for Twisted Numbers, Marcel Dekker, Inc.
Teaching Statistics and Probability, 1981 Yearbook, NCTM

Films/Videotapes
Approximating and Estimating, Films Incorporated

Software
Interpreting Graphs, Sunburst
Safari Search, Sunburst

Technology

There are three pages in the ***Technology Masters Booklet*** that involve technology with concepts in this chapter. One page involves calculators and one page has a problem that can be solved using the BASIC program that is provided. Students should evaluate the information they obtain from running the program and solve a similar problem by extending the program.

Using the Chapter Opener

Transparency 10-0 is available in the Transparency Package. It provides a full-color visual and motivational activity that you can use to engage students in the mathematical content of the chapter.

Science Connection Show students a CD player or a picture of one and a picture of an old graphophone or phonograph. Ask how many students own CD players and if students know that they operate by use of lasers. Ask students to name other ways lasers are used to replace older technologies. Answers might include surgery, welding, and lighting.

Survey the class to find out how their spending on records, tapes, or CDs compares to a cost of $1.70 per week.

CHAPTER OBJECTIVES

In this chapter you will learn to:

- gather and record data
- describe data using measures of central tendency and measures of variation
- display data using stem-and-leaf, box-and-whisker, and scatter plots
- use statistics to predict and recognize misleading statistics
- solve problems by first solving a simpler problem

Statistics and Graphs

Do you know someone who owns a CD player? Today's compact disc player is certainly a long way from Alexander Graham Bell's 1876 graphophone or Thomas Alva Edison's 1877 phonograph. The laser beam and microcomputer of the CD player are virtually a quantum leap in technology from the stylus and diaphragm of Edison's original phonograph.

If you spend money like the "average" teenager, you probably spend about $1.70 per week on records, tapes, or CDs. How do you measure up against this statistic?

Consumer Connection

Class Project

Design a survey in which you ask classmates about their spending habits. Display the data in several kinds of graphs.

For each graph, write a paragraph in which you summarize the results of the survey.

Consumer Connection

When surveying the class, have students use very general categories, such as "recreation" instead of individually listing movies, ball games, and video games.

Review the use of circle, picture, line, and bar graphs.

Allow students freedom in displaying data. Some may choose to display collective data for the entire class. Some may choose to compare spending habits of boys and girls, or some may wish to compare several individuals.

Discuss the differences in the graphs. Show how circle graphs are especially useful for this type of data.

Looking Ahead

You may want to have the following materials available to use in this chapter.

Exploration, p. 382
tape measures
grid paper*

*You can use the Easy-to-Make Manipulative provided on page 7 of the Lab Manual.

EXPLORATION:
Gathering Data

Objectives Students will make appropriate decisions concerning taking a survey, develop appropriate survey questions, gather data through a survey, and analyze the results.

1 FOCUS

The purpose of this Exploration is to introduce students to statistics from an active point of view.

Motivating the Exploration

Ask students if they or their parents have ever been asked for their opinion on a particular issue or product.

2 TEACH

Using Discussion

Ask students to brainstorm reasons why they might be asked for their opinion. Discuss how advertisers try to convince people they need to buy a new product.

3 PRACTICE/APPLY

Using Cooperative Groups

Divide the class into groups of 4-6 students. Circulate around the room as they make decisions concerning writing and conducting the survey. Remind groups that they are looking for people who are most likely to buy their product because their advertising will be focused on these people.

4 CLOSE

Speaking Connection

This is an excellent opportunity for students to give an oral report using the materials from Exercise 3. Students may feel more comfortable if this is done cooperatively.

EE: 1A, 1C, 1E, 5D, 5E

Exploration

Gathering Data

Major advertisers, political parties, and media such as television and radio stations are concerned with **demographics,** the numbers that describe the characteristics of a population. Advertisers, for example, often find out about their public through surveys.

In this Exploration, you will find out about the students in your school by having some of them fill out a survey form. The pieces of information you will gather are called **data.** You will then analyze the data.

- Work in small groups. Pretend your group is an advertising company that has been hired to convince the students in your school to buy a new product.
- Decide what product you want to advertise.
- Decide how many people you want to survey. You probably cannot ask everyone's opinion, so use a smaller sample.
- Decide what questions to ask.
- Decide on the most effective way to gather the data.

Your Turn: **Write your survey and gather the data. Record the data from the surveys using a chart for each question.** See students' work.

Analysis See students' work.

1. Write a few sentences analyzing what you found out about the students in your school.
2. Explain how your advertising company can use the data to help convince students to buy your product.
3. Prepare a report, complete with charts and graphs, that summarizes your findings.

Extension See students' work.

4. Survey the cars in the teachers' parking lot. Determine what characteristics you will study, collect the data, and analyze it.

SET-UP

Materials

- Paper and pencil

You may wish to use the Exploration worksheet provided on page 54 of the Lab Manual.

10-1 Gathering and Recording Data

Objective:
Gather and record data using a frequency table or histogram.

Key Terms:
statistics
frequency table
sample
histogram

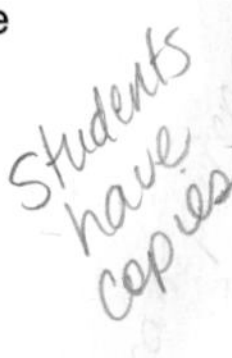

About how much television do students watch each week? **Statistics** involves collecting, analyzing, and presenting data such as this. To answer the question about television viewing, Andrea surveyed some students at her school. She recorded their responses, rounded to the nearest hour, on a **frequency table** as shown below.

Number of Hours Watched	Tally	Frequency
0-2	IIII	4
3-5	𝍸 III	8
6-8	𝍸 𝍸 𝍸 𝍸 II	22
9-11	𝍸 𝍸 𝍸 𝍸 𝍸 𝍸 II	32
12-14	𝍸 𝍸 𝍸 𝍸 𝍸 𝍸	30
15-17	IIII	4

Andrea did not survey every student; she surveyed a smaller group, or **sample.** She chose the students in the sample group randomly, so the sample is assumed to be representative of the larger group.

What does "randomly" mean?
without a set pattern

You can answer questions about the data by studying the frequency table.

Examples

1 How many hours of TV do the greatest number of students watch?

The greatest number of students (32) watch 9–11 hours per week. Almost as many (30) watch 12–14 hours.

2 How many people were surveyed for this sample?

$4 + 8 + 22 + 32 + 30 + 4 = 100$ The sum of the frequencies is the sample size.

One hundred people were surveyed.

3 What percent of the sample watch fewer than 12 hours?

$4 + 8 + 22 + 32$ or 66 people watch fewer than 12 hours. Compare 66 to the total (100). 66% watch fewer than 12 hours of TV per week.

4 Would Andrea have a representative sample if all 100 people she surveyed were involved in evening sports practices?

No, because the students sampled would not have as many hours available to watch TV.

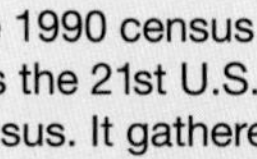

FYI

The 1990 census was the 21st U.S. census. It gathered information from the estimated 250 million people living in the U.S. Census data is used to determine, among other things, amounts of federal funding and the number of representatives to Congress.

Bell Ringer

The problem below is a famous mathematics code problem.

SEND
+MORE
MONEY

Each letter stands for a number. Determine what number each letter represents.

M Y E N D R S O
1 2 5 6 7 8 9 0

Lesson Notes 10-1

5-Minute Check
(over Chapter 9)

Solve.
1. $\frac{5}{16} = \frac{x}{144}$ $x = 45$
2. $\frac{4.3}{r} = \frac{2.5}{17.5}$ $r = 30.1$
3. 43% of \$62 **\$26.66**
4. 15 is what percent of 60? **25%**
5. 60 is 75% of what number? **80**

Transparency 10-1 contains the 5-Minute Check and a teaching aid for this lesson.

1 FOCUS

The purpose of this lesson is to introduce students to the process of gathering and recording data.

2 TEACH

Chalkboard Examples

Kevin surveyed his junior class to see how many hours each student studied per week. Use the chart below to answer the questions.

Study Hours per Week	Tally	Frequency
0-1	𝍸 𝍸 I	11
2-3	𝍸 𝍸 III	13
4-5	𝍸 𝍸 𝍸 𝍸 𝍸 𝍸 𝍸 𝍸 II	42
more than 5	𝍸 𝍸 𝍸 𝍸 𝍸 𝍸 IIII	34

- *For Example 1*
  How many hours do the greatest number of students study per week? **4-5**
- *For Example 2*
  How many people were surveyed for this sample? **100**
- *For Example 3*
  What percent of the sample study 4 or more hours per week? **76%**

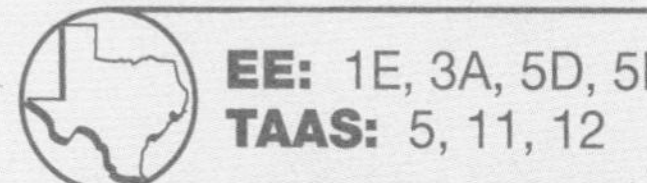

EE: 1E, 3A, 5D, 5E
TAAS: 5, 11, 12

Chalkboard Examples

- *For Example 4*
  Would Kevin have a representative sample if he surveyed only students with after-school jobs? **No because students sampled would not have as many hours available to study.**

3 PRACTICE/APPLY

Checking the Concept

Have students work in pairs and verbally answer Guided Practice Exercises 4-9. After completing Exercises 10-12, have each partner write additional statements. Trade and answer.

> ***Error Analysis***
>
> **Watch for** students who are careless when tallying.
> **Prevent by** comparing the frequency total to the number surveyed.

Practice Masters Booklet, **p. 92**

Name ______________________ Date ______________

Practice Worksheet 10-1

Gathering and Recording Data

The scores on an English test were 80, 95, 60, 75, 80, 70, 65, 70, 95, 45, 55, 60, 65, 90, 75, 65, and 80.

Score	Tally	Frequency
95	||	2
90	|	1
85		0
80	|||	3
75	||	2
70	||	2
65	|||	3
60	||	2
Below 60	||	2

1. Complete the frequency table for this set of data.
2. What is the highest score? 95
3. What is the lowest score? 45
4. What is the frequency of the score that occurred most often? 3
5. What is the frequency of the score that occurred least often? 0
6. How many scores are 75 or higher? 8
7. Write a sentence that describes the test-score data. Answers may vary. Sample answer: The test scores range from 45 to 95.

The scores on a mathematics test were 75, 80, 85, 70, 95, 80, 100, 95, 80, 60, 85, 85, 70, 90, 85, 80, 80, 75, 75, 50, 100, 85, 50, 95, and 80.

Score	Tally	Frequency
100	||	2
95	|||	3
90	|	1
85	~~||||~~	5
80	~~||||~~ |	6
75	|||	3
70	||	2
65		0
60	|	1
Below 60	||	2

8. Complete the frequency table for this set of data.
9. What is the highest score? 100
10. What is the frequency of the score that occurred most often? 6
11. How many scores are 90 or better? 6
12. If 70 is the lowest passing score, how many scores are not passing scores? 3
13. Write a sentence that describes the test-score data. Answers may vary. Sample answer: 88% of the students passed the test.

Another way to display the data from Andrea's frequency table is shown below. The graph is called a **histogram,** and it shows how the data are distributed.

In what way is a histogram a more effective display than a frequency table?
easier to compare and interpret data

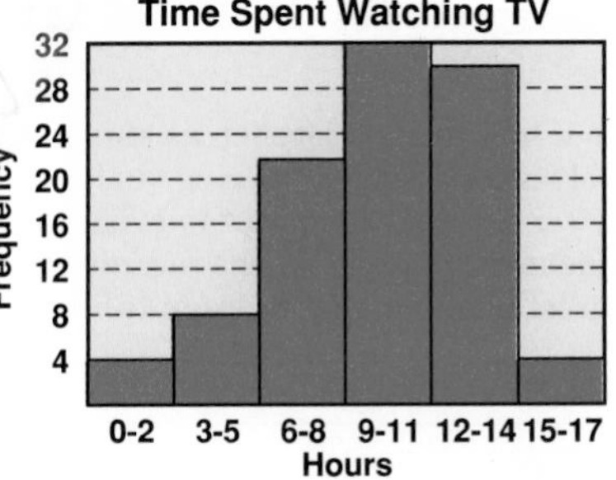

The width of the rectangular regions represents the time interval of the data. The height of the regions represents how many students are in the interval.

Checking for Understanding

For sample answers to Exercises 1-2, see margin.

Communicating Algebra

1. In your own words, describe a frequency table.
2. How are a frequency table and a histogram alike? How are they different?
3. When a sample is used, what does the surveyor need to consider? **The surveyor needs to consider whether the sample is representative of the larger group.**

Guided Practice

The frequency table below contains data from a favorite colors survey.

4. Copy the table and complete the frequency column.
5. What color was chosen most often? **blue**
6. What color was chosen least often? **purple**
7. How many people selected blue as their favorite color? **45**
8. How many people gave information for this survey? **100**

Favorite Color	Tally	Frequency
Yellow	~~||||~~ ~~||||~~ ||||	14
Orange	||||	4
Blue	~~||||~~ ~~||||~~ ~~||||~~ ~~||||~~ ~~||||~~ ~~||||~~ ~~||||~~ ~~||||~~ ~~||||~~	45
Purple	||	2
Green	~~||||~~ |||	8
Red	~~||||~~ ~~||||~~ ~~||||~~ ~~||||~~ ~~||||~~ ||	27

9. You would *not* make a histogram of the kind of data in this frequency table. Look at the information about histograms and tell what makes this data different from the kind of data in a histogram. **no intervals, not numerical**

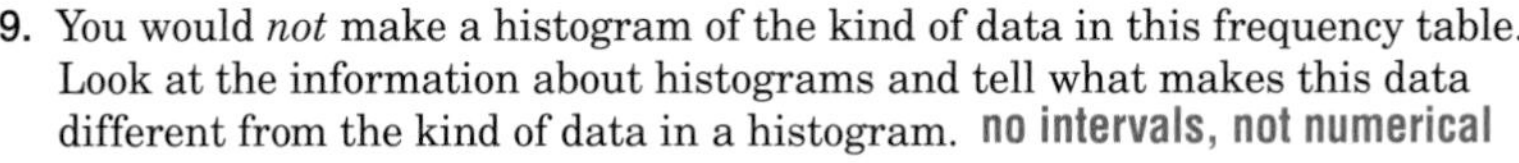

The Super Cola Company conducts a taste test. 800 people compare Super Cola to Brand X. 437 people prefer Super Cola. Which statements are true? Write *true* or *false*.

10. "Consumers prefer Super Cola 2 to 1." **false**
11. "Over 50% of the people surveyed prefer Super Cola." **true**
12. "More people always choose Super Cola over Brand X." **false**

Additional Answers

1. **A frequency table is a table for organizing numbers or items in a set of data.**
2. **A frequency table and a histogram are alike in the respect that they display data. The difference is that a frequency table shows how often single numbers occur while a histogram shows how often ranges of numbers occur.**

Reteaching Masters Booklet, **p. 83**

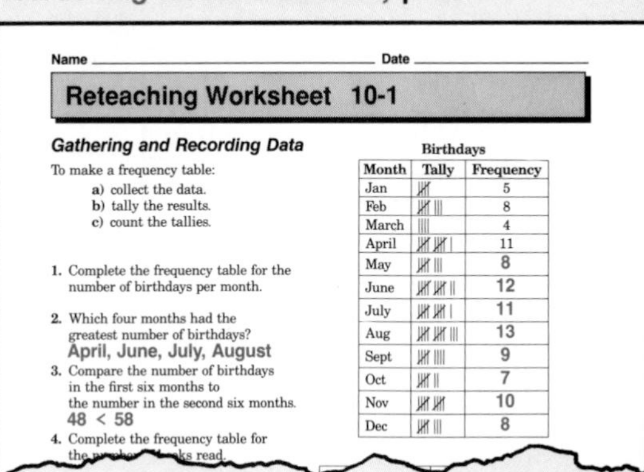

Name ______________________ Date ______________

Reteaching Worksheet 10-1

Gathering and Recording Data

To make a frequency table:
a) collect the data.
b) tally the results.
c) count the tallies.

1. Complete the frequency table for the number of birthdays per month.
2. Which four months had the greatest number of birthdays? April, June, July, August
3. Compare the number of birthdays in the first six months to the number in the second six months. 48 < 58
4. Complete the frequency table for the number of books read.

Birthdays

Month	Tally	Frequency
Jan	~~||||~~	5
Feb	~~||||~~ |||	8
March	||||	4
April	~~||||~~ ~~||||~~ |	11
May	~~||||~~ |||	8
June	~~||||~~ ~~||||~~ ||	12
July	~~||||~~ ~~||||~~ |	11
Aug	~~||||~~ ~~||||~~ |||	13
Sept	~~||||~~ ||||	9
Oct	~~||||~~ ||	7
Nov	~~||||~~ ~~||||~~	10
Dec	~~||||~~ |||	8

Exercises

Independent Practice

Refer to your completed frequency table of favorite colors on page 364.

13. What percent of people surveyed preferred red? **27%**
14. Would it be correct to say that 50% of the people surveyed preferred blue? **no**
15. Would it be correct to say that 50% of the people surveyed preferred either blue or orange? **no**

The scores on a 40-point test are given below. **16. See margin.**

38	35	40	36	29
27	35	31	33	35
35	38	40	38	29
27	35	34	31	34
35	27	31	30	31

16. Make a frequency table for the set of data.
17. What is the lowest score? **27**
18. What is the highest score? **40**
19. What is the frequency of the score that occurred most often? **6**
20. What is the frequency of the score that occurred least often? **1**
21. If 29 is the lowest passing score, how many scores are passing scores? **22**
22. Make a histogram for the set of data. **See Solutions Manual.**
23. Write a sentence that describes the test-score data. **Sample answer: the test scores range from 27 to 40, with 35 being the most common score.**

Mixed Review

24. An elevator goes up 9 floors, then down 14 floors. If it started on the sixth floor, what floor is it now on? (Lesson 2-9) **first floor**
25. Use a graph to solve the following system of equations: $x + 2y = 5$, $x - y = 2$. (Lesson 8-10) **See Solutions Manual for graph; (3, 1)**
26. Express as a rate: *115 revolutions in 10 seconds.* (Lesson 9-1) $\frac{\text{115 revolutions}}{\text{10 seconds}}$
27. Find the percent of change in taxes if the old taxes are $54.00 and the new taxes are $57.78. (Lesson 9-10) **7% increase**

Application

28. **Retail Sales** A women's clothing store conducted a survey that resulted in the frequency chart shown at the right.
    a. If the owner can only buy three colors of a certain item, what should they be? **black, teal, plum**
    b. If the store usually serves 300 customers a day, what percent sample did the owner use? **10%**
    c. What are some ways the owner could be certain the sample was representative of the customers? **Sample answers: conduct survey at different times of day, on different days of week; survey all age groups.**

Favorite Clothing Color

Color	Tally	No.
Brown	II	2
Black	~~IIII~~ II	7
Teal	~~IIII~~ III	8
Plum	~~IIII~~ I	6
Orange	III	3
Green	IIII	4

Critical Thinking

29. Quality control engineers survey the performance of products. A light bulb designed to give 1000 hours of light is lighted at midnight on July 1. It goes out at 9 A.M. on August 15. Did it last at least 1000 hours? How many hours did it last? **yes; 1089 hours**

Wrap-Up

30. Explain in a few sentences how to take a survey and make a frequency chart and histogram of your data. **See margin.**

Alternate Strategies: Extending the Lesson

Enrichment

Using Cooperative Groups Use all the words on page 363. Make a frequency table showing the total number of times each letter was used. Find the percent each letter is of the total number of letters. Compare this to the number of letters used in commercial word games like "Scrabble."

Cooperative Learning

To New Heights Group Activity **10-1**

How tall are the students in your pre-algebra class?

Record the heights of all your classmates. Then group the data in reasonable intervals. For example, you may want to use 2" intervals such as 4′10" to 5′, 5′ to 5′2", 5′2" to 5′4", and so on. Next, make a frequency table from which you can then make a histogram. Finally, answer the following questions about the data for your class:

1. What height interval is the most common?
2. What height interval is the least common?
3. What is the range of heights?
4. Is the frequency of the heights evenly spread across the range of heights?
5. Can you tell where the data for girls or boys lie in the histogram? How could you change the graph to show this?

Merrill Pre-Algebra GATHERING AND RECORDING DATA

Independent Practice

Homework Assignment	
Basic	13-22, 24-28a, 29, 30
Average	15-22, 24-30
Honors	16-30

4 CLOSE

Assessment Option

Modeling Divide the class into small groups. Have each group make a frequency table using a die. Have them roll the die 100 times and record the number rolled in the frequency table. Then make a histogram of this data.

Additional Answer

32. Factors to consider when taking a survey are asking appropriate questions, surveying a representative sample and recording the survey data in a frequency chart. To make a histogram of data, first choose a convenient interval of numbers based on the data, then make a frequency chart based on the intervals chosen. Draw and label the axes of the histogram and draw bars to show the frequency of each interval of data.

Enrichment Masters Booklet, **p. 83**

Name ______________ Date ______________

Enrichment Worksheet 10-1

Histograms

A histogram is a type of bar graph that displays the frequencies in a distribution of data that has been divided into equal intervals. Notice that there is no space between the bars. (A boundary grade, like 200 or 240, is included in the lower interval. 200 would be included in the 180–200 interval.)

Example: Weight of the players on the Mather Jr. High football team

Weight	Frequency
180–200	2
200–220	10
220–240	9
240–260	7
260–280	4
280–300	2

Use the graph to answer each of the following.

1. Give the histogram a name. **Weight of Players Mather Jr. High Football Team**
2. What does the vertical scale represent? **Number of players**
3. What does the horizontal scale represent? **Weight of the players**
4. How many weigh between 220 and 240? **9**
5. How many players are there on the team? **34**
6. How many weigh over 240 lb? **13**
7. How many weigh 227 lb? **Cannot be determined**

Make a histogram using the given data. **Check students' graphs.**

8. Grades in Mr. Miner's Math Class

Grade	Frequency
90–100	4
80–90	8
70–80	17
60–70	5
0–60	2

9. Grades in Mrs. Colburn's Math Class

Grade	Frequency
90–100	6
80–90	10
70–80	14
60–70	8
0–60	3

10. How many students in each class received a grade above 70? **Miner: 29; Colburn: 30**
11. How many students in each class had a grade of 60 or below? **Miner: 2; Colburn: 3**

Applying Algebra to the Real World

Objective This optional page shows how algebra is used in the real world and also provides a change of pace.

Using Questioning

Ask students how many of them have received a phone call from a person taking a survey. Did they ask how old you were or whether you were male or female? Why might they need to know the answers to these questions?

Using Logic

For each of the "no" answers for Exercises 6-12, have students name a location that would result in a "yes" answer. Make a list and discuss student responses.

Activity

Have students work in cooperative groups. Have each group choose a marketing topic for which class members would be a valid sample. Survey the class and display results in a frequency table. Ask students how they think results would differ if elementary students or parents had been surveyed.

Algebra in Action-Marketing

Market Data Surveys

Mary Felton is a market data collector. She collects information about the interests and tastes of different types of consumers. She enjoys surveying teenagers to find their tastes in music, clothing, colors, soft drinks, makeup, and sporting goods. From the information she collects, companies often make decisions about what products to manufacture, how to package them, and how to market them.

Mary works with samples of the population. At a basketball game, she tallied the soft drink preference of the fans who purchased soft drinks.

Soft Drink Purchases

Drink	Tally	No.
Cola	卌 卌 卌 卌 卌 卌 ||||	34
Diet Cola	卌 卌 卌 卌 卌 卌 卌 卌 卌 ||	47
Root Beer	卌 卌 卌 卌 卌 ||||	29
Lemon-Lime	卌 卌 卌 卌 卌 卌 卌 卌 卌 卌 卌 卌 ||	62
Orange	卌 卌 卌 卌 卌 卌 卌 |||	38
Grapefruit	卌 卌 卌 卌 卌 卌 卌 卌 卌 ||	47

2. See margin.

1. Copy and complete the table for her.
2. Would this be a good sample of the total high school population? Why or why not?
3. To find the favorite actor of a group of students, Mary surveyed every fifth person in a theater line. Why was this a poor sample? See margin.
4. Suppose your school has 2000 students in four grades. What advice could you give Mary to help her select a good sample of students for a general survey? See margin.
5. If Mary wanted to find people's choice for President before the election, should she survey people at a political party headquarters? Why or why not? no, because people at a political party headquarters will be biased toward their candidate

Would the following locations be good for a survey? Write *yes* or *no* and tell why.

	Survey	Location	
6.	favorite detergent	laundromat	yes; people who do laundry
7.	number of dogs	apartment building	no; dogs probably not allowed
8.	favorite carpet color	carpet store	yes; people buying carpet
9.	favorite singer	homes during a weekday	no; students not home
10.	favorite lunch	school cafeteria	yes, for kids; no, for general pop.
11.	favorite lunch	pizza parlor	no; mostly pizza eaters
12.	automobile owned	bus stop	no; many don't own auto

13. Write some survey items that might interest a compact disk manufacturer. Suggest locations where the survey could be taken. Sample answers: favorite musician or group, favorite type of music, age group of CD owners; music store, shopping center

Additional Answers

2. no; The survey does not take into account students who do not attend football games.
3. Every fifth person might not have been a student.
4. Sample equal numbers from each grade level.

10-2 Measures of Central Tendency

Objective:
Use mean, median, and mode as measures of central tendency.

Key Terms:
central tendency
mean
mode
median

Various brands of a radio with similar features have the following prices: $49, $49, $50, $50, $52, $52, $52, $55, $57, $60, and $62. What is the "average" price for such a radio?

In analyzing sets of data, researchers often try to find a number or other datum that can represent the whole set. These numbers or pieces of data are **measures of central tendency**. Three that we will study are the mean, the mode, and the median.

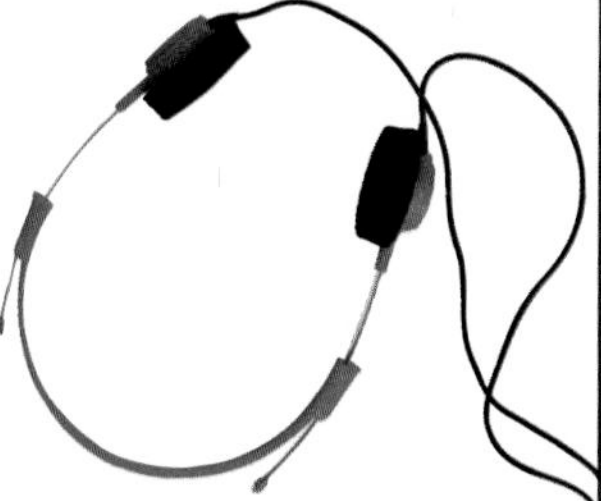

The **mean** is what people usually are talking about when they say "average." It is the arithmetic average of the data. For the prices above, the mean is

$$\frac{49 + 49 + 50 + 50 + 52 + 52 + 52 + 55 + 57 + 60 + 62}{11} = \frac{588}{11} \approx 53.454545$$

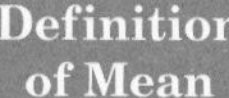

The mean price is about $53.45.

Notice that the mean does not have to be a member of the set of data.

Definition of Mean

The mean of a set of data is the sum of the data divided by the number of pieces of data.

Is it possible for the mode to be greater than the mean? **yes**

In the prices above, the price $52 appears the most number of times (three), so $52 is the **mode**. If there was another radio priced at $50, then $50 would also be a mode and the data would have two modes.

The mode is always a member of the set of data.

Definition of Mode

The mode of a set of data is the number or item that appears most often.

The **median** is simply the middle number when the data are in order.

49 49 50 50 52 [52] 52 55 57 60 62

The number in the middle is 52. The median price is $52.

If the number of data is even, then the set has two middle numbers. In that case the median is the mean of the two numbers. Consider the set of data 5, 7, 9, 11, 12, 15, 23, 26, 28, and 30. The middle numbers are 12 and 15. Their mean is found as follows:

$$(12 + 15) \div 2 = 27 \div 2 \text{ or } 13.5$$

The median is 13.5.

The median does not have to be a member of the set of data.

Bell Ringer

A clock gains 3.5 minutes each day. The clock was set correctly at noon. What time did it show at noon one week later? **12:24 P.M. and 30 seconds**

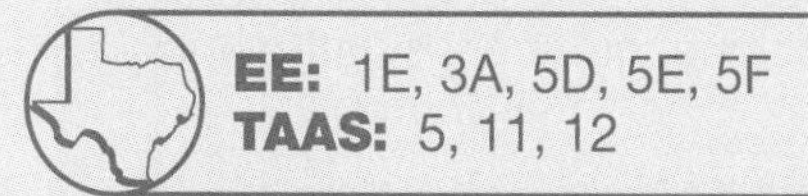

EE: 1E, 3A, 5D, 5E, 5F
TAAS: 5, 11, 12

Lesson Notes 10-2

5-Minute Check
(over Lesson 10-1)

The numbers of students in each homeroom at Johnson Park are listed below.

28	27	27	26	28
26	27	25	28	26
28	26	25	25	28

Use a frequency table for the set of data to answer the questions below.

1. What is the least number of students in a classroom? **25 students**
2. What is the frequency of the size that occurred most often? **5**
3. How many classrooms have fewer than 28 students? **10 classrooms**
4. How many classrooms were surveyed? **15 classrooms**

Transparency 10-2 contains the 5-Minute Check and a teaching aid for this lesson.

1 FOCUS

The purpose of this lesson is for students to understand the difference between the mean, median, and mode of a set of data.

Motivating the Lesson

Survey students for the following information.

- number of people in the family
- height of student
- age of student

Ask students to give a descriptive measure of each set of data.

2 TEACH

Using Discussion

From Motivating the Lesson, ask students the following questions about the data on students' height.

- How could you organize the data? **Sample answer: List heights from shortest to tallest.**
- What descriptions can you give using this data? **Sample answers: shortest height, tallest height, middle height, height that occurs most often, average height**

Chalkboard Examples

Organize the data. Then find the median, mode, and mean.

- *For Example 1*
  The following are test scores on a ten-question test in social studies: 6, 7, 6, 4, 5, 10, 2, 5, 8, 7, 4, 7, 9, 10, 4, 5, 7, 8, 5, 9, 6, 7, 2, 8, 6. **6, 7, 6.28**
- *For Example 2*
  In the ten games of basketball, Terron scored 12, 2, 6, 7, 14, 8, 5, 18, 9, and 10 points. **8.5, no mode, 9.1**

3 PRACTICE/APPLY

Checking the Concept

Have students work in groups of three to complete Exercises 4-9. Write "mean," "median," and "mode" on separate slips of paper. After ordering data, have each student draw a slip and find that measure of central tendency.

Error Analysis

Watch for students who interchange the terms mean, median, and mode.
Prevent by using a small set of data and illustrating each term. Have students keep these examples as models for other problems.

Definition of Median The median is the number in the middle when the data are arranged in order. When there are two middle numbers, the median is their mean.

Examples

Organize the data. Then find the median, mode, and mean.

1 Scores on a ten-question science quiz are given below.

3, 5, 7, 6, 8, 2, 9, 3, 7, 6, 5, 7, 7, 7, 8, 3, 2, 9, 9, 5, 8, 7, 2, 3, 5

One way to organize the data is to make a frequency table.

Score	Tally	Number
2	III	3
3	IIII	4
4		
5	IIII	4
6	II	2
7	~~IIII~~ I	6
8	III	3
9	III	3

The median is the middle number. There are 25 scores, so the 13th score is the median. The median score is 6.

The mode score is 7. Why? **It occurs more than any other score.**

To find the mean, add the scores and divide by 25. Use the frequency chart.

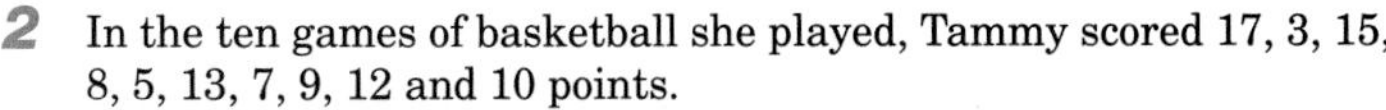

$$\frac{3(2) + 4(3) + 0(4) + 4(5) + 2(6) + 6(7) + 3(8) + 3(9)}{25} = 5.72$$

The mean score is 5.72.

2 In the ten games of basketball she played, Tammy scored 17, 3, 15, 8, 5, 13, 7, 9, 12 and 10 points.

Organize the data by putting them in order.

3, 5, 7, 8, 9, 10, 12, 13, 15, 17

Because there are ten pieces of data, the median is the mean of the 5th and 6th numbers.

$(9 + 10) \div 2 = 9.5$ The median is 9.5.

This data set has no mode because each piece of data occurs just once.

The mean is the sum of the data divided by 10.

$99 \div 10 = 9.9$ The mean is 9.9.

Which "average" do you think best represents Tammy's scores?

Computer Connection

You can use a data base program to organize data. Data base allows you to quickly sort data by categories and arrange the data in alphabetical or numerical order.

Alternate Strategies: Reteaching the Lesson

Reteaching Activity

Using Models Give students an odd number of different colored counters. Have students count the number of each color and list the data vertically from least to greatest. Ask them what number in their list occurred most often. Have them cross out the top and bottom numbers on their list. Continue this process until one number is left. Ask students what this number represents.

Reteaching Masters Booklet, p. 84

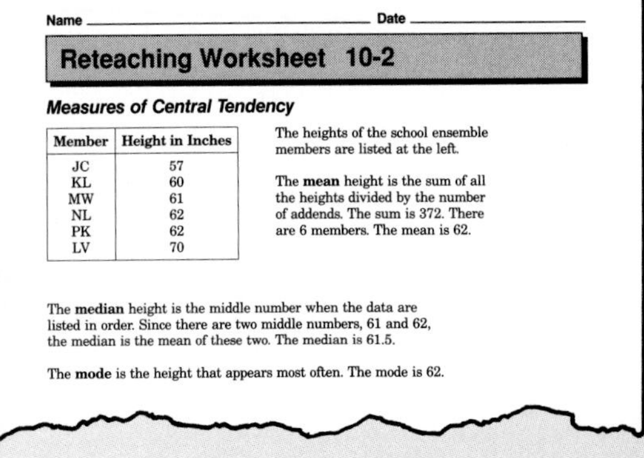

Name ______ Date ______

Reteaching Worksheet 10-2

Measures of Central Tendency

Member	Height in Inches
JC	57
KL	60
MW	61
NL	62
PK	62
LV	70

The heights of the school ensemble members are listed at the left.

The **mean** height is the sum of all the heights divided by the number of addends. The sum is 372. There are 6 members. The mean is 62.

The **median** height is the middle number when the data are listed in order. Since there are two middle numbers, 61 and 62, the median is the mean of these two. The median is 61.5.

The **mode** is the height that appears most often. The mode is 62.

Checking for Understanding

For sample answers to Exercises 1-3, see margin.

Communicating Algebra

1. In your own words, tell how to find the median of a set of data.
2. In your own words, tell how to find the mode of a set of data.
3. Describe the mean. How is it different from the median?

Guided Practice

List the data in each set from least to greatest. Then find the median, mode, and mean.

4. 5, 6, 9, 11, 2, 11, 40 9; 11; 12
5. 3.2, 1.5, 2.6, 1.5, 2.6, 4.8 2.6; 2.6 and 1.5; 2.7
6. 0.2, 0.4, 0.1, 0.6, 1.2, 1.1 0.5; none; 0.6
7. 4.5, 4.9, 4.7, 5.0, 4.7 4.7; 4.7; 4.76
8. 25.98, 30.00, 45.36, 25.00, 45.36 30.00; 45.36; 34.34
9. 105, 116, 125, 78, 78 105; 78; 100.4

Exercises

Independent Practice

Find the mean, median, and mode for each set of data. Round to the nearest tenth.

10. 36, 37, 41, 43, 43 40; 41; 43
11. 44, 48, 55, 56, 55, 68, 70 56.6; 55; 55
12. 2, 16, 21, 3, 8, 9, 8, 6, 7 8.9; 8; 8
13. 121, 130, 128, 126, 130, 121 126; 127; 121 and 130
14. 2.3, 3.6, 4.1, 3.6, 2.9, 3.0 3.3; 3.3; 3.6
15. 0.4, 1.6, 0.8, 0.9, 0.7, 1.1 0.9; 0.9; none

Use the data at the right to answer questions 16-25.

16. What is the mode? 155
17. What is the mean? 159.5
18. What is the median? 155

Heights of Students in Class

Name	Height (cm)
Martha	130
Mary	155
Tom	148
Gene	184
Chip	172
Meg	155
Dottie	162
Sean	155
Kim	165
Ali	173
Jesse	155

Suppose Jean enrolls in the class and her height is 135 cm. Without computing:

19. How will Jean affect the mean? lower
20. How will Jean affect the mode? no effect
21. How will Jean affect the median? no effect

Suppose Tim now joins the class. His height is 155 cm. Without computing:

22. How will Tim affect the mode? no effect
23. How will Tim affect the median? no effect
24. How will Tim affect the mean? raise
25. When both Jean and Tim join the class, what are the new mean, mode, and median? 157.2 155 155

Logical Reasoning

26. Think about all the problems you have worked in this lesson. Which is affected more by very large or very small numbers in a set of data, the mean, the median, or the mode? mean

Independent Practice

Homework Assignment	
Basic	10-24, 27-32, 37, 38
Average	14-34
Honors	16-38

4 CLOSE

Assessment Option

Modeling Survey the number of hours of television each student watched the night before and list the data on the chalkboard or overhead. Then have students find the mean, median, and mode of the set of data.

Additional Answers

1. Order the data and find the middle number or the average of the middle numbers.
2. Find the number that occurs most often.
3. The mean is the sum of the data divided by the number of items. It differs from the median in that it does not have to be a member of the set of data.

Practice Masters Booklet, **p. 93**

Name ______ Date ______

Practice Worksheet 10-2

Measures of Central Tendency

Find the mean, median, and mode for each set of data. Round to the nearest tenth, if necessary.

1. 2.5, 2.4, 2.9, 2.7, 2.4, 2.3, 2.4, 2.9, 2.3, 2.4 2.5; 2.4; 2.4
2. 1, 5, 8, 3, 10, 7, 8, 10, 3, 8, 6, 3, 4, 9 6.1; 6.5; 3 and 8
3. 70, 85, 90, 65, 70, 85, 100, 60, 55, 95, 85, 70, 75 77.3; 75; 70 and 85
4. 80, 70, 85, 90, 75, 75, 90 80.7; 80; 75 and 90
5. 7.0, 6.3, 7.5, 6.4, 8.9, 5.4, 7.9, 6.8 7.0; 6.9; none
6. 5, 7, 7, 9, 10, 10, 12 8.6; 9; 7 and 10

Use the data at the right for Exercises 7 – 12.

7. What is the mode? 60
8. What is the mean? 62
9. What is the median? 60

WEIGHTS OF STUDENTS IN CLASS

Name	Weight (kg)
Martha	49
Mary	60
Tom	58
Gene	73
Chip	67
Meg	60
Dottie	63
Sean	60
Kim	64
Ali	68
Jesse	60

Suppose Sonya enrolls in the class and her weight is 51 kg. Without computing, answer these questions.

10. How will Sonya affect the new mean? The new mean will be lower.
11. How will Sonya affect the new median? The median will not be affected, it will remain the same.

Suppose Hector now joins the class. His weight is 70 kg.

12. When both Sonya and Hector join the class, what are the new mode, mean, and median? 60; 61.8; 60

Mixed Review

27. Use the formula $F = \frac{9}{5}C + 32$ to find the equivalent Fahrenheit temperature for -25°C. (Lesson 7-8) -13°F
28. Solve the equation $n - 3.5 = -1$. Graph the solution. (Lesson 8-1) See margin.
29. **Cooking** A recipe that makes 8 muffins calls for 2 cups of flour. How much flour is needed to make 24 muffins? (Lesson 9-3) 6 cups
30. Refer to the frequency table on page 363. What percent of the sample watch fewer than 9 hours of television? (Lesson 10-1) 34%

Applications

31. **Sports** Julio bowled four games. His scores were 123, 108, 127, and 118. What is his mean score? 119

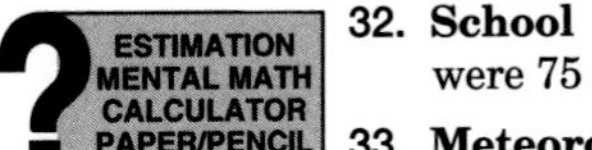

32. **School** Gary's mean score for three French tests is 77. His first two scores were 75 and 79. What was his other score? 77
33. **Meteorology** The high temperatures, in degrees Fahrenheit, for a week in May were 68, 70, 68, 66, 70, 74, and 72. Describe the temperatures using the mean, median, and mode. mean, 69.7; med., 70; mode, 68 and 70
34. **Business** At Wilcox Products, 7 employees earn \$20,000, 3 earn \$32,000, and 2 earn \$60,000. List the salaries of the employees on a frequency chart. Find the mean, median, and mode. Which measure of central tendency would you use to describe the "average" salary and why? See margin.
35. Use the column from a phone book shown at the right.
    - **a.** Make a tally of the last digits of the numbers. What is the mode? What is the median? 2; 4
    - **b.** Make a tally of the first digits of the numbers. What is the mode? What is the median? 8; 8
    - **c.** Is there a difference in parts **a** and **b**? yes Why or why not? See margin.

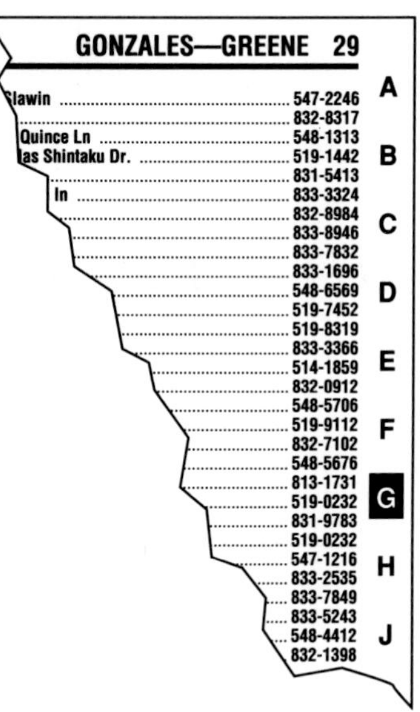

GONZALES—GREENE 29
lawin 547-2246
832-8317
Quince Ln 548-1313
las Shintaku Dr. 519-1442
831-5413
ln 833-3324
832-8984
833-8946
833-7832
833-1696
548-6569
519-7452
519-8319
833-3366
514-1859
832-0912
548-5706
519-9112
832-7102
548-5676
813-1731
519-0232
831-9783
519-0232
547-1216
833-2535
833-7849
833-5243
548-4412
832-1398
A
B
C
D
E
F
G
H
J

36. Here are Marilyn's test scores in mathematics for the semester: 78, 74, 85, 88, 93, 96, 98, and 100. If she needs a mean score of 90 to receive an A, what must she score on the final test? Write an inequality to solve this problem. $s \geq 98$

Critical Thinking

37. Construct a set of data with at least 7 items in which the mode, median, and mean are the same number. Sample answer: 1, 2, 3, 4, 4, 5, 6, 7

Wrap-Up

38. **Collect Data** For one hour while you are watching television or listening to the radio, record the length of each commercial break. Find the mean, median, and mode. Compare your results with three other people. Find the mean, median, and mode for the four sets of data. Write about your findings. See students' work.

Additional Answers

28. $n = 2.5$ (number line from -2 to 3 with point at 2.5)

34.

Salary	Frequency
\$20,000	7
\$32,000	3
\$60,000	2

mean: \$29,666.67
median: \$20,000.00
mode: \$20,000.00
Use median or mode to describe the "average" because the two \$60,000 salaries are twice as large as the mean.

35c. In less populated areas the first digit is the same and the last four digits are generated randomly.

Enrichment Masters Booklet, **p. 84**

Name ______________________ Date ______________

Enrichment Worksheet 10-2

Mean Variation

Mean variation is the average amount by which the data differ from the mean.

Example: The mean for the set of data at the right is 17. 12, 16, 27, 16, 14

Find the mean variation as follows.

Step 1 Find the difference between the mean and each item in the set.

17 − 12 = 5
17 − 16 = 1
27 − 17 = 10
17 − 16 = 1
17 − 14 = + 3

Step 2 Add the differences. 20

Step 3 Find the mean of the differences. This is the mean variation. $20 \div 5 = 4$

The mean variation is 4.

Find the mean variation.

1. 100, 250, 200, 175, 300
   The mean is 205.
   205 − 100 = 105
   250 − 205 = 45
   205 − 200 = 5
   205 − 175 = 30
   300 − 205 = 95
   Add the differences above.
   Then, divide by 5.
   The mean variation is 56.

2. 124, 128, 121, 123
   The mean is 124.
   124 − 124 = 0
   128 − 124 = 4
   124 − 121 = 3
   124 − 123 = 1
   Add the differences above.
   Then, divide by 4.
   The mean variation is 2.

For each set of data, find the mean and the mean variation.

3. 68, 43, 28, 25 41; 14.5
4. 13, 18, 22, 28, 35, 46 27; $9\frac{1}{3}$
5. 68, 25, 36, 42, 603, 16, 8, 18 102; 125.25
6. 79, 81, 85, 80, 78, 86, 84, 83, 75, 88 81.9; 3.3

Alternate Strategies: Extending the Lesson

Enrichment

Working Backwards Give an example of a set of data that might have the mean of 5. Give several other examples, such as data with a mean of 100 or \$5.50. Working in small groups, have one student give a mean and other students try to guess what the survey question might have been.

Cooperative Learning

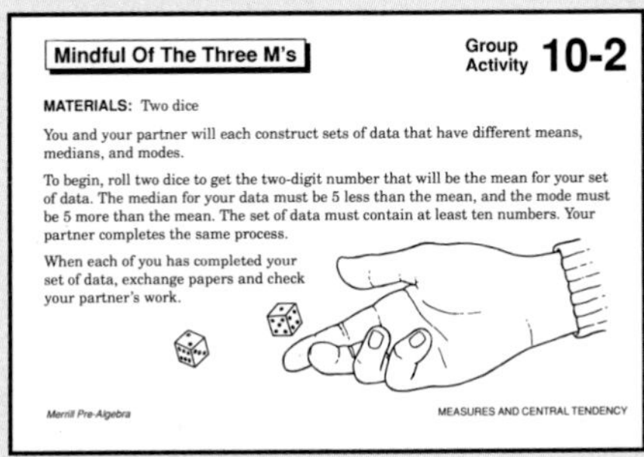

Mindful Of The Three M's Group Activity **10-2**

MATERIALS: Two dice

You and your partner will each construct sets of data that have different means, medians, and modes.

To begin, roll two dice to get the two-digit number that will be the mean for your set of data. The median for your data must be 5 less than the mean, and the mode must be 5 more than the mean. The set of data must contain at least ten numbers. Your partner completes the same process.

When each of you has completed your set of data, exchange papers and check your partner's work.

Merrill Pre-Algebra MEASURES AND CENTRAL TENDENCY

10-3 Stem-and-Leaf Plots

Objective:
Display and interpret data on stem-and-leaf plots.

Key Term:
stem-and-leaf plot

To improve its advertising, a local theatre conducts a survey to see which age group of people is most likely to attend a Saturday matinee. The ages of the 35 people surveyed are listed below.

12, 11, 22, 67, 56, 32, 35, 45, 46, 14, 14, 16, 33, 30, 41, 7, 9, 25, 8, 51, 43, 55, 42, 17, 67, 58, 30, 18, 14, 24, 25, 26, 29, 12, 13

One way to condense the data and make it more usable is to make a **stem-and-leaf plot**. The greatest place value of the data can be used for the *stem*. The next greatest place value forms the *leaves*. Follow these steps to construct a stem-and-leaf plot from the data above.

Step 1 Find the least and the greatest item of data.

The least is 7 and the greatest is 67.

Step 2 Find the stems.

The least number, 7, has a 0 in the tens place. The greatest number, 67, has a 6 in the tens place. Therefore, the stems are digits from 0 to 6.

Stem	Leaf
0	
1	
2	
3	
4	
5	
6	

Step 3 Put the leaves on the plot.

Record each of the data on the graph by pairing the units digit, or leaf, with the correct stem. For example, 25 is plotted by placing the units digit, 5, to the right of the stem 2.

Stem	Leaf
0	798
1	2144678423
2	254569
3	25300
4	56132
5	6158
6	77

Step 4 Arrange the leaves so they are ordered from least to greatest.

Step 5 Include an explanation of the data.

2|5 means age 25.

Stem	Leaf
0	789
1	1223444678
2	245569
3	00235
4	12356
5	1568
6	77

What is the mode of the data to the right? **14**

By just observing the stem-and-leaf plot above, you can tell that the largest age group attending the Saturday matinee is the 10–19 age group, because this row has the most leaves in it.

Bell Ringer
Write a set of data whose median is $5. **Sample answer: $2, $3, $5, $7, $11.**

Lesson Notes 10-3

5-Minute Check
(over Lesson 10-2)

Find the mean, median, and mode for each set of data. Round to the nearest tenth.

1. 32, 29, 45, 26, 31, 20, 19, 15, 35, 29, 38, 12, 11, 21, 25 **25.9, 26, 29**
2. 125, 143, 156, 185, 129 **147.6, 143, no mode**
3. 17, 92, 58, 16, 89, 54 **54.3, 56, no mode**
4. 6.3, 2.1, 5.3, 6.3, 2.0, 4.8, 5.1 **4.6, 5.1, 6.3**

Transparency 10-3 contains the 5-Minute Check and a teaching aid for this lesson.

1 FOCUS

The purpose of this lesson is to expand the ways of displaying data to include stem-and-leaf plots.

Motivating the Lesson

Bring a plant into the class. Ask students what relationship there is between the stem and leaves. Develop the concept that the leaves may be different but are off the same stem.

2 TEACH

Using Discussion

Ask students to name an integer between 10 and 50. List their responses and ask the following questions.

- How could these numbers be organized based on the digits they have in common? **group by tens digits**
- How could you arrange the numbers to make organizing them easier? **least to greatest**

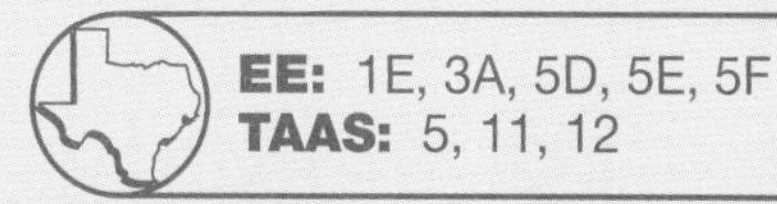

EE: 1E, 3A, 5D, 5E, 5F
TAAS: 5, 11, 12

Chalkboard Examples

- *For Example 1*
  Emily had the following test scores for the third grading period.
  Science: 92, 96, 80, 81, 75, 68, 88, 84, 89
  Math: 86, 62, 95, 96, 98, 78, 91, 97, 88
  Make a stem-and-leaf plot. In which subject did she have the better scores? **Math**
- *For Example 2*
  Here are the number of points scored by Larry Bird in ten games: 14, 28, 31, 18, 22, 27, 35, 41, 29, 23. Make a stem-and-leaf plot of the data. About how many points might you expect Bird to score in a game?

1	**4, 8**
2	**2, 3, 7, 8, 9**
3	**1, 5**
4	**1**

between 20 and 30 points

3 PRACTICE/APPLY

Checking the Concept

After completing the Guided Practice Exercises, have students explain their answers to Exercises 7 and 9.

***Practice Masters Booklet,* p. 94**

Name ________________ Date ________

Practice Worksheet 10-3

Stem-and-Leaf Plots

Thirty-five students took a ten-point quiz. The scores were: 7, 10, 7, 10, 6, 7, 2, 9, 3, 0, 10, 5, 8, 9, 7, 5, 9, 5, 3, 9, 8, 10, 10, 8, 6, 9, 7, 4, 5, 8, 5, 4, 7, 10, and 7.

1. Construct a stem-and-leaf plot for the data.

0	02334455555667777777888899999
1	000000

2. What was the highest score? **10**
3. What was the lowest score? **0**
4. What was the most common score? **7**
5. Make two or three statements about the data. **Answers may vary. Sample answer: More than half of the class scored 7 or better; the highest score was 10 and the lowest was 0.**

The ages of the first thirty people into a concert on Friday were: 19, 21, 24, 18, 20, 20, 19, 17, 20, 23, 18, 20, 21, 20, 24, 25, 22, 21, 25, 18, 19, 20, 21, 19, 22, 23, 17, 22, 25, and 23.

6. Construct a stem-and-leaf plot for the data.

1	778889999
2	000000111122233344555

7. How old was the oldest person? **25**
8. How young was the youngest person? **17**
9. What was the most common age? **20**
10. What might account for the limited range of years? **Answers may vary. Sample answer: It may have been a concert that attracted persons whose ages were 17 through 25, possibly a rock concert.**

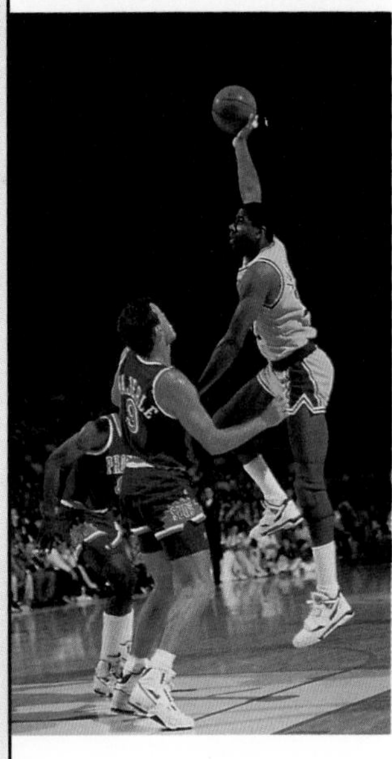

Examples

1 Mrs. Martin's ninth grade homeroom had the following test scores.

Mathematics	75, 93, 87, 56, 60, 73, 78, 69, 83, 89, 94, 97, 65, 73, 87
History	68, 73, 98, 87, 65, 64, 70, 73, 72, 78, 81, 83, 68, 57, 63

She made stem-and-leaf plots for the scores, and used the same stem for both sets of data.

Mathematics		History
6	5	7
9 5 0	6	3 4 5 8 8
8 5 3 3	7	0 2 3 3 8
9 7 7 3	8	1 3 7
7 4 3	9	8

6|5 means 56. 5|7 means 57.

The stem-and-leaf plot shows that, overall, the class scored better in mathematics.

2 Here are the number of points scored by Magic Johnson in ten games: 8, 30, 41, 27, 18, 22, 19, 37, 22, 26.
About how many points might you expect him to score in a game? Make a stem-and-leaf plot of the data.

The stems are 0, 1, 2, 3, and 4.

Magic Johnson's Points

0	8
1	8 9
2	2 2 6 7
3	0 7
4	1

4|1 means 41 points.

From the leaves, you could expect Magic to score between 20 and 29 points.

6. Sample answers: the greatest score, which class has better scores overall

Checking for Understanding

Communicating Algebra

1. When you make a stem-and-leaf plot, how do you know what to use for the stems and for the leaves? **See margin.**
2. Explain how a stem-and-leaf plot is similar to a horizontal bar graph or histogram. How is it different? **See margin.**
3. What are the stems for the following temperatures: 76, 83, 59, 71, 78? **5, 6, 7, 8**

Answer these questions about the stem-and-leaf plot in Example 1.

4. What were the highest and lowest history scores? **98, 57**
5. What is the median of the mathematics scores? **78**
6. What information can you gain from the plot?

Additional Answers

1. The stems represent the tens place and the leaves represent the units place.
2. It is similar to a horizontal bar graph because the more leaves a stem has the longer the line of leaves is. It is similar to a histogram because the stems are intervals of ten. It is different because there are no bars drawn.

***Reteaching Masters Booklet,* p. 85**

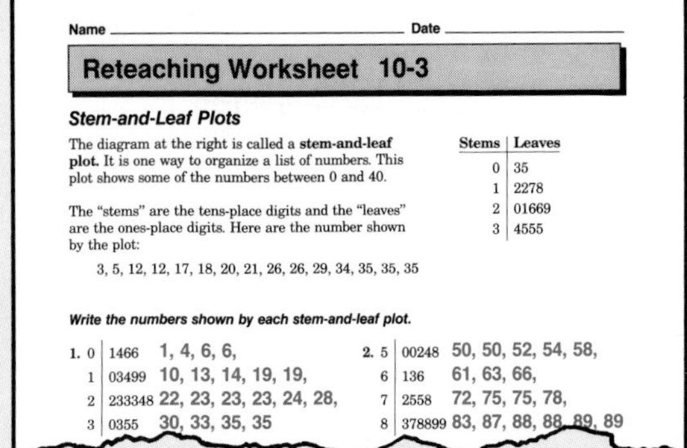

Name ________________ Date ________

Reteaching Worksheet 10-3

Stem-and-Leaf Plots

The diagram at the right is called a **stem-and-leaf plot.** It is one way to organize a list of numbers. This plot shows some of the numbers between 0 and 40.

The "stems" are the tens-place digits and the "leaves" are the ones-place digits. Here are the number shown by the plot:

3, 5, 12, 12, 17, 18, 20, 21, 26, 26, 29, 34, 35, 35, 35

Stems	Leaves
0	35
1	2278
2	01669
3	4555

Write the numbers shown by each stem-and-leaf plot.

1. 0	1466	1, 4, 6, 6,		2. 5	00248	50, 50, 52, 54, 58,
1	03499	10, 13, 14, 19, 19,		6	136	61, 63, 66,
2	233348	22, 23, 23, 23, 24, 28,		7	2558	72, 75, 75, 78,
3	0355	30, 33, 35, 35		8	378899	83, 87, 88, 88, 89, 89

Guided Practice

The heights (in inches) of members of a volleyball team are 64, 60, 72, 61, 73, 80, 68, 70, 65, 67, 70, and 80.

7. To make a stem-and-leaf plot of this data, what numbers will you use as stems? **6, 7, and 8**
8. Make a stem-and-leaf plot of the data. **See margin.**
9. What numbers are the leaves on the 8 stem? **0 and 0**
10. What percent of the heights are between 60 and 70 inches? Why do you think that is true? **50%; average ht. for age group < 70 inches**

Exercises

Independent Practice

The ages of the first twenty people into the museum on Saturday were 17, 9, 12, 25, 8, 39, 27, 14, 29, 40, 36, 8, 15, 41, 28, 29, 30, 31, 29, and 11.

11. Construct a stem-and-leaf plot for the data. **See margin.**
12. How old was the oldest person? **41**
13. How young was the youngest? **8**
14. What age group seemed most represented? **20s**
15. What might account for the limited span of years? **kind of museum**

Work with a partner to complete the following activity. **See students' work.**

16. Choose a topic and a group of people to gather numerical data about. Some examples are: basketball team—height, or class members—time it takes to get to school, or class members—number of hours of TV watched in a week.
17. Construct a stem-and-leaf plot for the data.
18. Make two or three statements about the data. (For example, most people in our class take between 10 and 20 minutes to get to school.)

Mixed Review

19. Find four solutions for the equation $y = -\frac{1}{2}x + 1$. (Lesson 8-5) **(0,1), (2,0), (4, −1), (−2, 2)**
20. Write $\frac{7}{8}$ as a percent. (Lesson 9-5) **$87\frac{1}{2}\%$**
21. Find the mean, median, and mode for the data set: 7, 2, 3, 9, 11, 8, 6, 3, 14. (Lesson 10-2) **7; 7; 3**

Applications

22. **Teaching** Mrs. Hunt taught English and Social Studies to the same class. The most recent test scores are plotted at the right. What was the highest grade in each subject? the lowest? In which subject did the class do better? Explain your answer. **See Solutions Manual.**

English		Social Studies
8 7	5	1 8
9 2 0	6	0 3 5 7
7 5 3 1	7	5 6 7 8 8 8 9
9 6 6 5 4 1	8	3 4 5 8 9
8 8 4 3	9	2 5

7|5 means 57. 5|1 means 51.

23. **Research** Find out the age at inauguration of all the presidents of the United States. Make a stem-and-leaf plot to display the data. Are the ages evenly distributed or clustered in the middle? **clustered**

Critical Thinking

24. Suppose you have seven coins in your pocket totaling $1. What is one possible combination of coins? (Hint: How can a stem-and-leaf plot or frequency chart help?) **sample answer: 50, 25, 5, 5, 5, 5, 5**

Wrap-Up

25. Give an example of data that might be represented on a stem-and-leaf plot. How would you use the plot to better understand the data? **Sample answer: hours of baby-sitting each month; plot can tell you whether or not you baby-sit about the same amount each month.**

Error Analysis

Watch for students who incorrectly construct a stem-and-leaf plot.
Prevent by having students check that the total number of leaves is the same as the original number of data items.

Independent Practice

Homework Assignment	
Basic	11-15, 19-22, 24, 25
Average	11-15, 19-25
Honors	11, 14, 16-25

4 CLOSE

Assessment Option

Speaking List the ages of each student's parents. Have students describe what a stem-and-leaf plot of this data would look like.

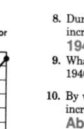

Additional Answers

8.

6	0 1 4 5 7 8
7	0 0 2 3
8	0 0

11.

0	8 8 9
1	1 2 4 5
2	5 7 8 9 9 9
3	0 1 6 9
4	0 1

Cooperative Learning

Random Numbers? Group Activity **10-3**

MATERIALS: A table of random numbers

Do tables of random numbers really produce numbers that are random? To help answer this question, you can use a stem-and-leaf plot.

You and your partner should choose any group of 100 digits on the table. From these digits, record the 50 two-digit numbers listed by reading the 100 digits in order.

Now, make a stem-and-leaf plot of these two-digit numbers. From this plot, answer the following questions.

1. What is the range of numbers?
2. Is there one group of numbers that is more frequent than the others?
3. Is there one group of numbers that is less frequent than the others?
4. What would you expect a stem-and-leaf plot of random numbers to look like?
5. Do you think the table you used lists two-digit numbers randomly?

Merrill Pre-Algebra STEM-AND-LEAF PLOTS

Enrichment Masters Booklet, **p. 85**

Name ______________________ Date ____________

Enrichment Worksheet 10-3

Statistical Graphs

Bar graphs and pictographs are used to compare quantities.
Line graphs are used to show changes.
Circle graphs compare parts to parts, or parts to the whole.

Solve. Use the pictograph.

Principal Languages of the World (to nearest fifty million)

🯅 = 100 million

Language	
English	🯅🯅🯅🯅
Hindi	🯅🯅½
Arabic	🯅½
Portuguese	🯅½
Chinese	🯅🯅🯅🯅🯅🯅🯅½
Russian	🯅🯅½
Spanish	🯅🯅½
French	🯅
Bengali	🯅½

1. How many people speak Portuguese? **150,000,000**
2. What is the ratio of people who speak Spanish to those who speak Russian? **1:1**
3. What three languages are each spoken by about 150 million people? **Arabic, Portuguese, Bengali**
4. How many fewer people speak Arabic than Hindi? **100,000,000**

Solve. Use the circle graph.

5. Which continent has the smallest population? **Australia**
6. How does the population of South America compare to that of Africa? **South America has about half as many people.**
7. About what is the population of Australia if the world's population is 4.6 billion? **About 13,800,000**

Australia 0.3%
Europe 15.1%
North Am. 8.3%
Asia 59.7%
South Am. 5.5%
Africa 10.9%

Population by Continent

Solve. Use the line graph.

8. During which ten-year period was the increase in the price of eggs greatest? **1940 – 1950**
9. What was the price of a dozen eggs in 1940? **16¢**
10. By what percent did the price of eggs increase from 1940 to 1950? **About 138%**
11. What was the increase in cents from 1930 to 1980? **33¢**

Lesson Notes 10-4

5-Minute Check
(over Lesson 10-3)

The first twenty-five sales Saturday morning at the jewelry counter of a local department store were: $26, $32, $15, $23, $54, $38, $9, $45, $22, $40, $14, $21, $16, $28, $24, $33, $7, $27, $19, $20, $42, $8, $59, $12, $29.
Use a stem-and-leaf plot for the data above to answer the questions below.

1. What was the largest amount spent? $59
2. What was the least amount spent? $7
3. What price range is most represented? 20s
4. What is the median price? $24

Transparency 10-4 contains the 5-Minute Check and a teaching aid for this lesson.

1 FOCUS

The purpose of this lesson is to introduce students to measures of variation in order to help them distinguish consistency among different sets of data.

Motivating the Lesson

Tell students that you are going to open a shoe store that sells only athletic shoes. Ask students what sizes you should order the most of, and least of, and why.

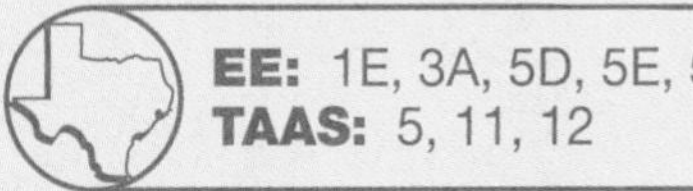

EE: 1E, 3A, 5D, 5E, 5F
TAAS: 5, 11, 12

10-4 Measures of Variation

Objective:
Use measures of variation to compare data.

Key Terms:
variation
range
interquartile range
upper quartile
lower quartile

Suppose you and a friend are in different Spanish classes, but have the same teacher. On a test, both classes have the same median score, the same mode score, and the same mean score. Does that mean that all the scores are the same? Not necessarily!

Here are the actual scores of the two classes:

First Period: 20, 28, 35, 38, 45, 50, 60, 60, 72, 75, 88, 89, 91, 96, 98

Second Period: 43, 45, 52, 54, 55, 56, 60, 60, 60, 68, 72, 75, 78, 81, 85

Using stem-and-leaf plots, we can see the differences quite easily.

First Period (2|0 means 20.)

Stem	Leaf
2	0 8
3	5 8
4	5
5	0
6	0 0
7	2 5
8	8 9
9	1 6 8

Second Period

Stem	Leaf
2	
3	
4	3 5
5	2 4 5 6
6	0 0 0 8
7	2 5 8
8	1 5
9	

For both classes the mode and median are both 60, and the mean is 63. But as you can see, the classes had quite different scores. What differs is the **variation** of the scores.

One measure of variation is called the **range**.

Definition of Range: The range of a set of numbers is the difference between the least and the greatest number in the set.

The ranges of the Spanish test scores are as follows.

First Period: 98 − 20 or 78 Second Period: 85 − 43 or 42

The grades of the first period class are more spread out, or dispersed, than those of the second period.

Another measure of variation is the **interquartile range.**

Definition of Interquartile Range: The interquartile range is the range of the middle half of the data.

Bell Ringer

State the lowest and highest numbers in the plot. lowest, 9, highest, 32

Stem	Leaf
0	9
1	1 2 4
2	3 3 3 9
3	1 2

2 | 3 means 23

To find the interquartile range, you must first find the middle half of the data. Here's how to find the interquartile range of the First Period scores. (See Example 2 for the Second Period scores.)

Step 1 Find the median of the data since the median separates the data into two halves.

20 28 35 38 45 50 60 [60] 72 75 88 89 91 96 98
Median

How could you use the stem-and-leaf plot to find the median and upper and lower quartiles? **Count the leaves to find the middle leaf, or median. Then find the middle leaf of the upper and lower half.**

Step 2 Find the median of the upper half. This number is called the **upper quartile**, indicated by UQ.

20 28 35 38 45 50 60 [60] 72 75 88 [89] 91 96 98
Median UQ

Step 3 Find the median of the lower half. This number is called the **lower quartile**, indicated by LQ.

20 28 35 [38] 45 50 60 [60] 72 75 88 [89] 91 96 98
LQ Median UQ
middle half of data

Step 4 The middle half of the data goes from 38 to 89. Subtract the lower quartile from the upper quartile.

$89 - 38 = 51$ The interquartile range of the scores is 51.

Examples

1 These are Kevin's scores on eight 25-point tests: 12, 15, 17, 20, 14, 18, 11, 21. Find the range and the interquartile range.

First order the scores. 11 12 14 15 17 18 20 21

The range is $21 - 11 = 10$.

The median is $(15 + 17) \div 2 = 16$.
The upper quartile is $(18 + 20) \div 2 = 19$.
The lower quartile is $(12 + 14) \div 2 = 13$.

Recall that when there are two middle numbers, the median is their mean.

Mental Math Hint

You can find the mean of pairs like 15 and 17 without dividing. Just think "what number is halfway between?" What is the mean of 14 and 18? of 5 and 10?

Notice how the median and quartiles are shown below.

11 12 ¦(13) 14 15 ¦(16) 17 18 ¦(19) 20 21

The interquartile range is $19 - 13$ or 6. The middle half of Kevin's scores varied by 6 points.

2 Find the interquartile range for the second period scores shown on page 374. Compare to the first period interquartile range.

43 45 52 [54] 55 56 60 [60] 60 68 72 [75] 78 81 85
LQ Median UQ

The interquartile range is $75 - 54$ or 21. Since the interquartile range is less for the second period class, its scores are more closely grouped around the median.

2 TEACH

Using Discussion

Write the numbers below on the chalkboard or overhead. Tell students they represent the mean daily temperatures for each of the last twelve months.

44, 49, 56, 66, 74, 82,
86, 86, 79, 68, 56, 48

Ask students the following questions.

- How would you find the lower 25% of these temperatures? **The lower 25% would be the three lowest temperatures.**
- How would you find any temperature extremes? **Subtract the low from the high.**
- How would you find the middle 50% of these temperatures? **Take away the three highest and three lowest temperatures.**

Chalkboard Examples

- *For Example 1*
  These are Adam's scores on eight 25-point quizzes: 7, 17, 24, 12, 22, 20, 14, 19. Find the range and interquartile range. **18, 8**
- *For Example 2*
  Find the interquartile range for the test scores shown for each class. Compare the two classes.
  Spanish II: 63, 82, 71, 65, 92, 86, 80, 95, 78, 89, 91. **91 − 71 = 20**
  Spanish III: 34, 81, 85, 90, 97, 54, 75, 79, 94, 78, 86. **90 − 75 = 15**
  Spanish III scores are more closely grouped around the median.

Alternate Strategies: Reteaching the Lesson

Reteaching Activity

Using Models List 26 test scores on the chalkboard. Make a stem-and-leaf plot of the data. Have students determine the median of the data. Then have them find the median of the upper half of the plot and circle it. Have students repeat this procedure for the lower half and find the difference of the two circled numbers.

Reteaching Masters Booklet, p. 86

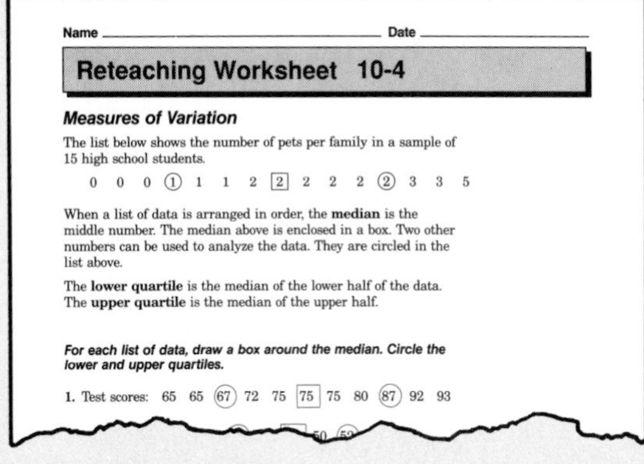
Name ______ Date ______

Reteaching Worksheet 10-4

Measures of Variation

The list below shows the number of pets per family in a sample of 15 high school students.

0 0 0 (1) 1 1 2 [2] 2 2 2 (2) 3 3 5

When a list of data is arranged in order, the **median** is the middle number. The median above is enclosed in a box. Two other numbers can be used to analyze the data. They are circled in the list above.

The **lower quartile** is the median of the lower half of the data.
The **upper quartile** is the median of the upper half.

For each list of data, draw a box around the median. Circle the lower and upper quartiles.

1. Test scores: 65 65 (67) 72 75 [75] 75 80 (87) 92 93

Checking for Understanding

Communicating Algebra

1. Name and describe the two measures of variation used in this lesson. **See margin.**
2. If a group of scores has a small interquartile range, what can you say about the scores? **grouped around the median**

Guided Practice

Given the set of data 5, 6, 9, 11, 24, 27, 29, find the following.

3. the range **24**
4. the median **11**
5. the upper and lower quartiles **27, 6**

Given the set of data 45, 47, 50, 51, 62, 68, 69, 72, 75, find the following.

6. the range **30**
7. the median **62**
8. the upper and lower quartiles **70.5; 48.5**
9. the interquartile range **22**

Use the data in the stem-and-leaf plot shown at the right.

10. What is the lowest rate? **40**
11. What is the highest rate? **81**
12. What is the range? **41**
13. What is the median? **67**
14. What are the upper and lower quartiles?
15. What is the interquartile range? **22**

14. **77, 55**

Words Typed Per Minute

4|0 means 40.

Stem	Leaf
4	02
5	159
6	3578
7	2378
8	01

Exercises

Independent Practice

Here are the final grades of the students in a French II class. 68, 70, 72, 75, 78, 80, 80, 82, 85, 89

16. What is the range of grades? **21**
17. What is the median grade? **79**
18. Did anyone receive the median grade? **no**
19. What are the upper and lower quartile grades? **82, 72**
20. What is the interquartile range? **10**
21. Write a paragraph describing the final grades. **See margin.**

The stem-and-leaf plots show the bowling average of Mary and Tanya for the first ten weeks of the league.

22. How do their medians compare? **same**
23. How do their ranges compare? **Mary's is greater.**
24. How do their interquartile ranges compare? **Tanya's is less.**
25. Which player is more consistent? Explain your answer. **Tanya; her scores are closer to her median most of the time; Mary's scores vary more game by game.**

Mary		Tanya
5	9	
3 2 1 1	10	3 5 6 8
9 8 8 7	11	0 0 3 5 7
9	12	2

5|9 means 95. 10|3 means 103.

3 PRACTICE/APPLY

Checking the Concept

Have students verbally solve Exercises 3-5, and find the interquartile range of the data. Have students independently solve Exercises 6-15.

Error Analysis

Watch for students who take one-fourth and three-fourths of the highest value in the data to find the quartiles.
Prevent by emphasizing the process of counting data and marking the points for the quartiles.

Independent Practice

Homework Assignment	
Basic	16-21, 26-29, 31, 32
Average	18-23, 26-29, 31, 32
Honors	22-32

Additional Answer

1. range; interquartile range The range is the difference between the least and the greatest number. The interquartile range is the range of the middle half of the data.

Practice Masters Booklet, **p. 95**

Name ____________ Date ____________

Practice Worksheet 10-4

Measures of Variation

Here are the weights, in pounds, of people in an aerobics class. 118, 112, 130, 106, 116, 146, 143, 129, 150, 132, 116, 118, 118, 109, 108, 114, 124, 126, 124, 113, 132, 136, 153, 127, 121, 134, 106, 129

1. What is the range of weights? 47 lb
2. What is the median weight? 124 lb
3. Did anyone actually have the median weight? yes
4. What are the upper and lower quartile weights? 132 lb; 115 lb
5. What is the interquartile range? 17 lb
6. Write a paragraph describing the weights. Include information about the whole aerobics class and about the middle half of the class. Answers may vary. Sample answer: The range is 47 lb and the median weight is 124 lb. The lightest person is 106 lb and the heaviest person is 153 lb. The middle half of the weights ranged from 115 lb to 132 lb.

The stem-and-leaf plots at the right show the test scores for Kyle and Matt during the first quarter.

7. How do their medians compare? Kyle's is greater.
8. How do their ranges compare? Matt's is greater.
9. How do their interquartile ranges compare? Matt's is less.
10. Which student is more consistent? Explain your answer. Matt; his interquartile range is less than Kyle's.

TEST SCORES FOR 1ST QUARTER

Kyle		Matt
8	4	0
6	5	9
40	6	5
50	7	0244589
5320	8	0
50	9	6

Mixed Review

26. Solve the equation $k - (-14) = 6$. (Lesson 3-2) **−8**
27. Identify the percentage, base, and rate: *Fourteen is 40% of what number?* (Lesson 9-4) **14; 35; $\frac{40}{100}$**
28. Make a stem-and-leaf plot of the following test scores: 75, 78, 92, 68, 81, 83, 95, 77, 61, 90, 88, 78. In what interval do most of the scores lie? (Lesson 10-3) **See Solutions Manual for plot; 70-79.**

Applications

29. **Meteorology** The table at the right lists the daily mean temperatures for San Francisco and Wichita. Construct stem-and-leaf plots for the temperatures of the two cities, using the same stem.
    a. How do the medians compare?
    b. How do the interquartile ranges compare?
    c. What conclusions can you draw from your answers to a and b?

Mean Daily Temperature (°F)		
Month	**San Francisco**	**Wichita**
January	49	30
February	52	35
March	53	44
April	55	56
May	58	66
June	61	76
July	62	81
August	63	80
September	64	71
October	61	59
November	55	44
December	49	34

29a. close
29b. Wichita's is greater.
29c. See margin.
30. See students' work.

30. **Research** Find the winning speeds at the Indianapolis 500 for the past 20 years. Find the median, range, and interquartile range. As a reporter, how would you write about the 1990 winning speed of 164 mph compared to the previous 20 years?

Critical Thinking

31. Produce a set of at least 10 pieces of data that has an interquartile range of zero. **4, 5, 6, 6, 6, 6, 6, 6, 6, 7, 8**

Wrap-Up

32. Explain how comparing the median, range, and interquartile range can help determine how consistent two sets of test scores are. **See margin.**

Challenge

Mean Variation

The mean variation of a set of data is the average amount each number differs from the mean. Suppose the high temperatures (°F) in Indianapolis on April 20 for the last 10 years have been:

70 65 45 80 55 62 81 50 74 48

Find the mean variation.

Step 1 Find the mean of the temperatures. **63**

Step 2 Find the difference between each of the 10 temperatures and the mean. **7, 2, 18, 17, 8, 1, 18, 13, 11, 15**

Step 3 Find the mean of the differences. **11**

What is the likelihood that this April 20 the temperature will be about 65°? **not very likely**
What is the likelihood that this April 20 the temperature will be within 11° of 65°? **very likely**

4 CLOSE

Assessment Option

Writing Have the students write a problem with a given range and interquartile range. For example, give the students a range of 67, and an interquartile range of 33, and have them create data that satisfy the measures.

Additional Answers

21. **Sample answer: The range and interquartile range are not very high so the scores do not vary much. The mean is 77.9 and half the class had a score of 80 or higher. The low interquartile range indicates that the middle half of the class was very close in ability.**

29c. **The middle temperature is about the same but the temperatures can be more extreme in Wichita.**

32. **The closer the median, range, and interquartile range of two sets of test scores are, the more consistent the two sets of test scores are.**

Enrichment Masters Booklet, **p. 86**

Name ____________________ Date ____________________

Enrichment Worksheet 10-4

Variance

Another way to measure the variation of a set of data is by computing the **variance.** The higher the variance is for a group of numbers, the more "spread out" the data will be.

The table below shows the price of the stock for two companies during one week.

	Mon.	Tues.	Wed.	Thur.	Fri.
Acme Computer Systems	$10	$7	$3	$8	$12
Baker Pencil Company	$7	$8	$7	$9	$9

1. What is the mean average price for the week for each company? **$8 for both companies**

Computing the variance will show which company's stock has the greater variation. To compute the variance, follow these steps:

Step 1 Subtract the mean from each number in the set.
Step 2 Multiply each difference in step 1 by itself.
Step 3 Add these differences.
Step 4 Divide the total by the number of members of the set.

Example: Find the variance for Acme Computer Systems.

$(10 - 8) \times (10 - 8) + (7 - 8) \times (7 - 8) + (3 - 8) \times (3 - 8) + (8 - 8) \times (8 - 8) + (12 - 8) \times (12 - 8)$
$= 4 + 1 + 25 + 0 + 16$
$= 46$

The variance is $46 \div 5$, or 9.2.

Solve.

2. Do you think the variance for Baker Pencil Company will be higher than the variance for Acme Computer Systems? Why? Compute the variance for Baker Pencil Company to see if you are correct. **No; the prices are closer together; 0.8**
3. Consolidated Airlines also had an average price last week of 48 per share, but its variance was 10.8. Give five stock prices that could give this variance. (Hint: Change only the Monday and Tuesday prices for Acme.) **Answers may vary. Sample answer: $11, $6, $3, $8, $12**
4. Sleepy Mattress Company's stock had an average price last week of $8 per share and a variance of 0. What was the price of shares each day last week? **$8 each day**
5. Are there any values that the variance cannot equal? If so, what are these values? **Yes; values less than zero**

Alternate Strategies: Extending the Lesson

Enrichment

Sports Connection Have students choose a sport or activity and brainstorm a list of ranges that could be determined from statistics about the sport. For example, in basketball, ranges involving the highest and lowest winning scores would be one possibility.

Cooperative Learning

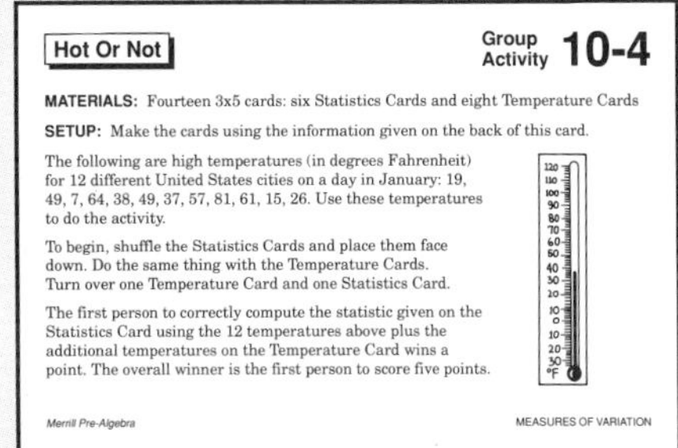

Hot Or Not — Group Activity **10-4**

MATERIALS: Fourteen 3x5 cards: six Statistics Cards and eight Temperature Cards

SETUP: Make the cards using the information given on the back of this card.

The following are high temperatures (in degrees Fahrenheit) for 12 different United States cities on a day in January: 19, 49, 7, 64, 38, 49, 37, 57, 81, 61, 15, 26. Use these temperatures to do the activity.

To begin, shuffle the Statistics Cards and place them face down. Do the same thing with the Temperature Cards. Turn over one Temperature Card and one Statistics Card.

The first person to correctly compute the statistic given on the Statistics Card using the 12 temperatures above plus the additional temperatures on the Temperature Card wins a point. The overall winner is the first person to score five points.

Merrill Pre-Algebra MEASURES OF VARIATION

Lesson Notes 10-5

5-Minute Check
(over Lesson 10-4)

Given the set of data 7, 11, 23, 14, 20, 17, 19, find the following.

1. the range **16**
2. the median **17**
3. the upper and lower quartile **11, 20**
4. the interquartile range **9**

Transparency 10-5 contains the 5-Minute Check and a teaching aid for this lesson.

1 FOCUS

The purpose of this lesson is to use measures of variation to construct box-and-whisker plots.

Motivating the Lesson

Show students a list of major league batting averages. Ask students what inconveniences they would anticipate if they were asked to make a frequency table or stem-and-leaf plot of the data.

2 TEACH

Using Discussion

Draw a box-and-whisker plot for the second period Spanish class scores on page 374. Discuss with the class the effects the plots have on interpreting the data.

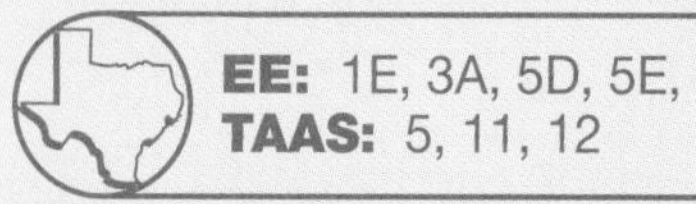

EE: 1E, 3A, 5D, 5E, 5F
TAAS: 5, 11, 12

10-5 Box-and-Whisker Plots

Objective:
Construct box-and-whisker plots.

Key Terms:
box-and-whisker plot
outliers

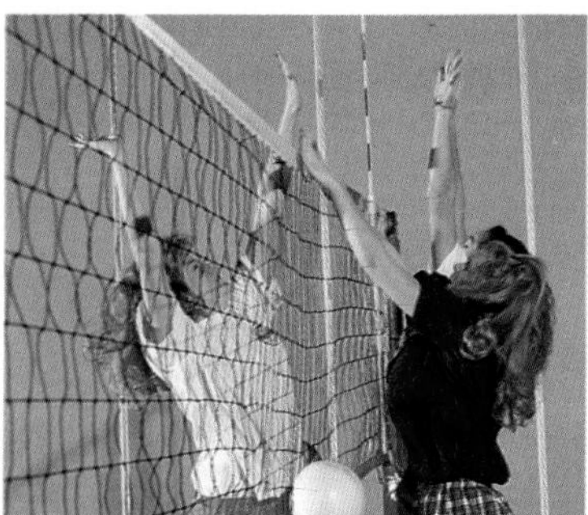

So far, you have made frequency tables and stem-and-leaf plots to *display* sets of data, and you have used measures of central tendency and measures of variation to *summarize* data. Now we will combine the ideas of summarizing and displaying data. A **box-and-whisker plot** summarizes data using the median, the upper and lower quartiles, and the *extreme* (highest and lowest) *values.*

How many girls are at least 6 feet tall? **2**

The heights of the eleven girls on the Towne High girls' volleyball team are displayed in the stem-and-leaf plot at the right. The median and quartiles are marked on the plot. The lower extreme is 59 inches, and the upper extreme is 74 inches.

Players' Heights

Stem	Leaf
5	9
6	3 [5] 7 8 [8] 8 9
7	[1] 2 4

5|9 means 59 inches.

Here's how to construct a box-and-whisker plot to display the data given above.

Step 1 Above a number line, mark points for the extreme, median, and quartile values.

From observing the box-and-whisker plot, would you expect the mean of these data to be greater or less than the median? **less than**

Step 2 Next, draw a *box* around the quartile values. Draw a vertical line through the median value. Finally, extend *whiskers* from each quartile to the extreme data points.

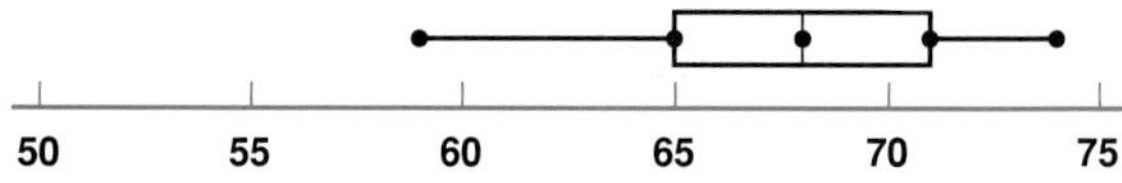

Thus, the box-and-whisker plot gives you five pieces of information about the data: lower extreme, lower quartile, median, upper quartile, and upper extreme.

Sometimes the data will have such great variation that one or both of the extremes will be far beyond the other data. Data that are more than 1.5 times the interquartile range from the quartiles are called **outliers.**

Bell Ringer

If the highest test score is 98 and the lowest test score is 55, what is the range? **43**

Examples

1 **Given the box-and-whisker plot below, answer these questions.**

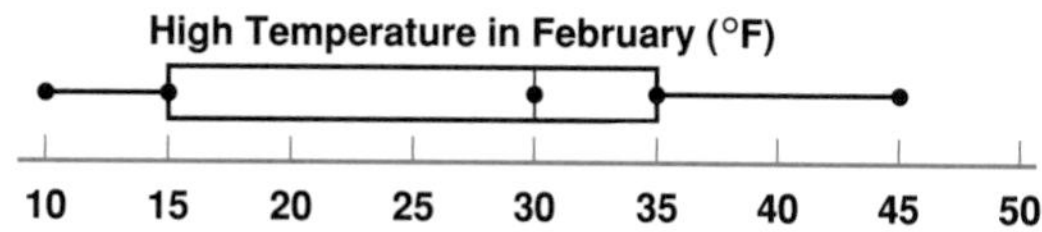

What was the highest temperature in February? 45°F

Exactly half of the days had highs over what temperature? 30°F

What fraction of the month had high temperatures less than 15°F? $\frac{1}{4}$

2 **Draw a box-and-whisker plot for the following test score data.**

20 60 | 66 70 [70] 70 76 | 80 100

Step 1 The median is 70; the upper quartile is (76 + 80) ÷ 2 or 78, and the lower quartile is (60 + 66) ÷ 2 or 63. Draw a box to show the median and the quartiles.

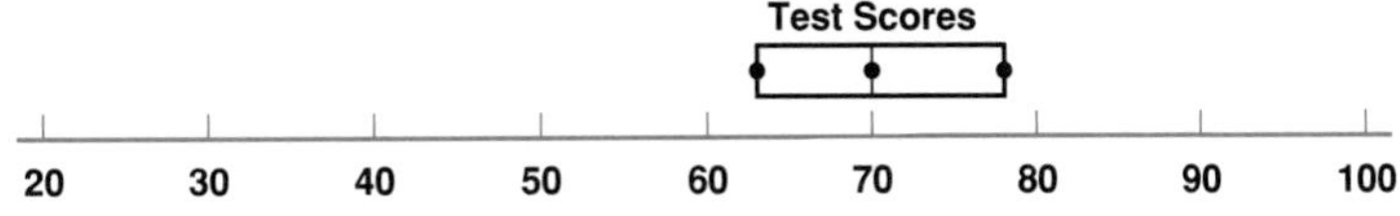

Step 2 The interquartile range is 78 − 63 or 15. So, data more than 1.5 times 15 from the quartiles are outliers.

$$1.5(15) = 22.5$$

Find the limits for the outlier.

Subtract 22.5 from the lower quartile.	63 − 22.5 = 40.5
Add 22.5 to the upper quartile.	78 + 22.5 = 100.5

So, 40.5 and 100.5 are the limits for outliers. There is one outlier in the data, 20. Plot the outlier with an asterisk. Draw the lower whisker to the lower extreme, 40.5, and the upper whisker to the upper extreme, 100.

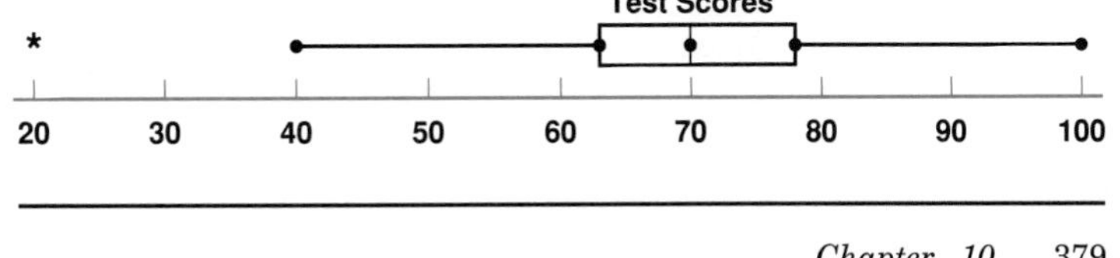

Alternate Strategies: Reteaching the Lesson

Reteaching Activity

Using Discussion Have students give the lowest number, lower quartile, median, upper quartile, and highest number from a set of data that is not in order. Then have them give the same information from a different set of data that is in order. Discuss the differences.

***Reteaching Masters Booklet,* p. 87**

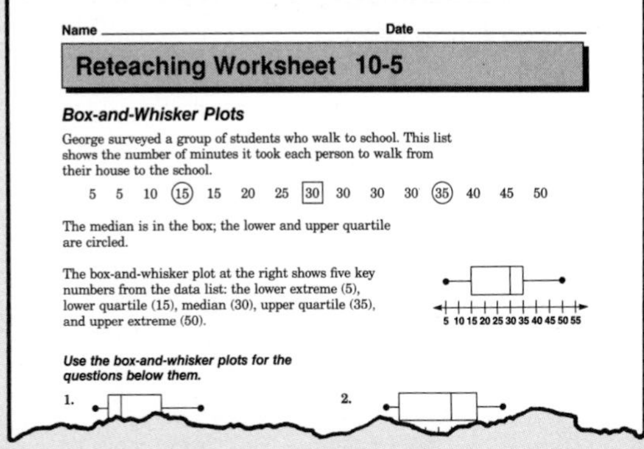

Name ______ Date ______

Reteaching Worksheet 10-5

Box-and-Whisker Plots

George surveyed a group of students who walk to school. This list shows the number of minutes it took each person to walk from their house to the school.

5 5 10 (15) 15 20 25 [30] 30 30 30 (35) 40 45 50

The median is in the box; the lower and upper quartile are circled.

The box-and-whisker plot at the right shows five key numbers from the data list: the lower extreme (5), lower quartile (15), median (30), upper quartile (35), and upper extreme (50).

5 10 15 20 25 30 35 40 45 50 55

Use the box-and-whisker plots for the questions below them.

1.

2.

Chalkboard Examples

- *For Example 1*
  Given the box-and-whisker plot, answer these questions.
  High Temperature in January

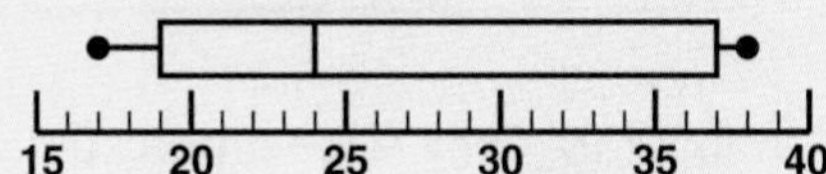

  a. What was the highest temperature in January? 38°F
  b. Exactly half of the days had highs over what temperature? 24°F
  c. What fraction of the month had high temperatures less than 17°F? $\frac{1}{4}$

- *For Example 2*
  a. Draw a box-and-whisker plot for the following test score data. 61, 64, 65, 66, 68, 70, 72, 77, 83, 84, 89

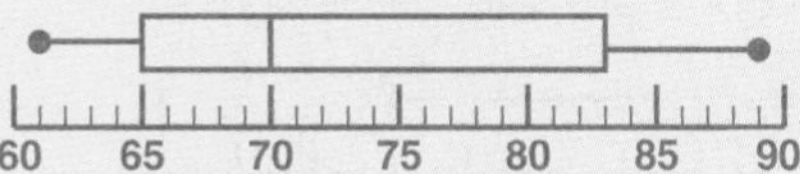

  b. Find the limits for the outliers. 47 and 101

3 PRACTICE/APPLY

Checking the Concept

Have students explain where they found their answers to Exercises 4-10.

Error Analysis

Watch for students who have difficulty mastering terminology associated with statistics.

Prevent by using flashcards or other models to review terms. Also give students an example and have them tell how each term relates to the example, if it does.

Independent Practice

Homework Assignment	
Basic	11-17, 25-28, 30, 31
Average	15-22, 25-28, 30, 31
Honors	18-31
All	Mid-Chapter Quiz 1-5

Chapter 10, Quiz A (Lessons 10-1 through 10-5) is available in the Evaluation Masters Booklet, p. 88.

4 CLOSE

Assessment Option

Speaking On the chalkboard or overhead, draw the box-and-whisker plot shown below. Then go around the room and have the students state facts from the plot. For example, the median is 7, there is an outlier at 0, the interquartile range is 3, etc.

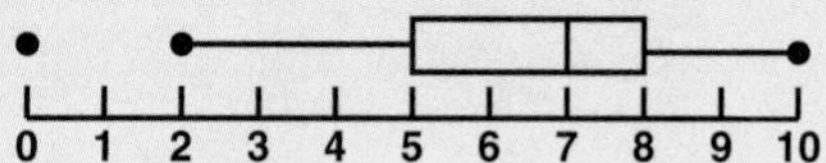

Practice Masters Booklet, **p. 96**

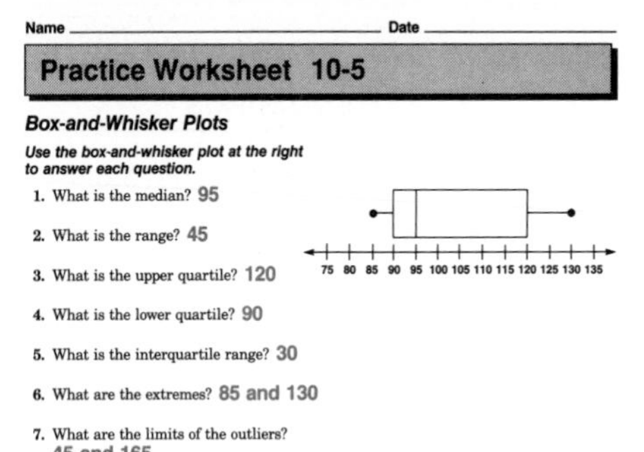

Name ______ Date ______

Practice Worksheet 10-5

Box-and-Whisker Plots

Use the box-and-whisker plot at the right to answer each question.

1. What is the median? 95
2. What is the range? 45
3. What is the upper quartile? 120
4. What is the lower quartile? 90
5. What is the interquartile range? 30
6. What are the extremes? 85 and 130
7. What are the limits of the outliers? 45 and 165
8. Are there any outliers? No

75 80 85 90 95 100 105 110 115 120 125 130 135

Use the box-and-whisker plot at the right to answer each question.

9. What is the median? 60
10. What is the range? 55
11. What is the upper quartile? 90
12. What is the lower quartile? 50
13. What is the interquartile range? 40
14. What are the extremes? 40 and 95
15. What are the limits of the outliers? 10 and 130
16. Are there any outliers? no

40 45 50 55 60 65 70 75 80 85 90 95 100

1. extremes, upper & lower quartiles, median

Checking for Understanding

Communicating Algebra

1. What five pieces of information can you learn from a box-and-whisker plot?
2. In your own words, describe an outlier. **See margin.**
3. How is the data shown on a box-and-whisker plot different from a stem-and-leaf plot? **It summarizes the data; stem-and-leaf lists *all* data.**

Guided Practice

Use the box-and-whisker plot shown below to answer each question.

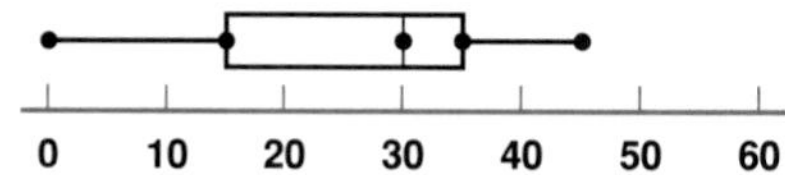

4. What is the median? **30**
5. What is the upper quartile? **35**
6. What is the lower quartile? **15**
7. What is the interquartile range? **20**
8. What are the extremes? **0, 45**
9. Are there outliers? **no**
10. What are the limits on the outliers? **−15, 65**

Exercises

Independent Practice

Use the box-and-whisker plot shown below to answer each question.

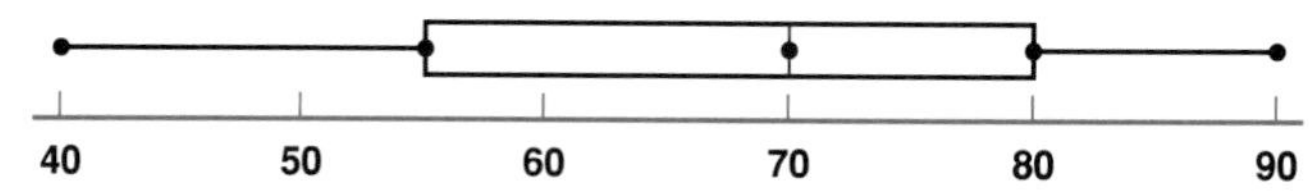

11. What is the median? **70**
12. What is the range? **50**
13. What is the upper quartile? **80**
14. What is the lower quartile? **55**
15. What is the interquartile range? **25**
16. What are the extremes? **40, 90**
17. What are the limits of the outliers? Are there any outliers? **17.5 and 117.5; no**

The box-and-whisker plot below represents last month's spending money for 31 students.

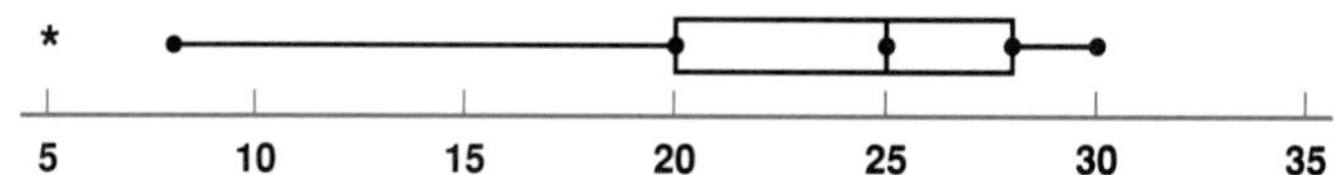

18. How many students spend less than $25 a month? **15**
19. How many students spend between $20 and $28? **15 or 16**
20. What is the range of spending money for the middle half of the students? (What is the interquartile range?) **$8**
21. What are the limits for the outliers? **8 and 40**
22. Would you expect the mean spending money to be greater or less than the median? Why? **less; more range in data less than 25**

Computers 23. If you used computer software to construct a box-and-whisker plot of the data on players' heights, describe the values that you would expect to enter. Then describe the values you would enter to construct a stem-and-leaf plot. **extremes, quartiles, and median; all values**

Logical Reasoning 24. Is it possible to have a box-and-whisker plot with only one whisker? Explain your answer. **Yes; if quartile is same value as all data above (or below) it.**

Mixed Review 25. Find the x-intercept and the y-intercept to graph the equation $y = 3 - 2x$. (Lesson 8-9) **$(\frac{3}{2}, 0)$, $(0, 3)$**

26. Find 85% of $165. (Lesson 9-7) **$140.25**

27. Find the range and median of the data set: 3, 4, 8, 8, 12, 14, 15, 15. (Lesson 10-4) **12; 10**

Applications 28. **Teaching** Mr. Stone has two classes of World History. He made a stem-and-leaf plot of the scores for the last test. Use the data to make a box-and-whisker plot. (Use the same number line for both; make one plot above the other.) What do the plots tell you about the classes? **See margin.**

29. **Research** Find the average temperatures each month for two cities of your choice. Make a box-and-whisker plot for each using the same number line. Write a paragraph comparing the year-round temperatures of the cities. **See students' work.**

Mr. Stone's History Classes

Third Period		Fifth Period
8 0	2	
8 5	3	
5	4	3 5
0	5	2 4 5 6
0 0	6	0 0 0 8
5 2	7	2 5 8
9 8	8	1 5
8 6 1	9	

0|2 means 20. 4|3 means 43.

Critical Thinking 30. In making a box-and-whisker plot of 23 scores with no outliers, Sarah found the median to be 70, the upper quartile to be 78, and the lower quartile to be 68. She then discovered four more scores: 100, 75, 69, and 67. When she added these to the data, what happened to the box-and-whisker plot? Hint: You may want to sketch the plots. **The box did not change. The score 100 is an outlier.**

Wrap-Up 31. How does a box-and-whisker plot separate the data into fourths? **The median separates the data into halves. The quartiles separate the halves into halves, which separates the data into fourths.**

Mid-Chapter Quiz

Use the data at the right to complete the following. **See margin.**

1. Make a frequency table for the data. (Lesson 10-1)
2. Find the mean, median, and mode. (Lesson 10-2)
3. Construct a stem-and-leaf plot. (Lesson 10-3)
4. Find the range and the interquartile range. (Lesson 10-4)
5. Construct a box-and-whisker plot. (Lesson 10-5)

Scores on a Mathematics Quiz

21	30	17	19	21
18	27	30	21	21
22	30	28	29	21
29	25	28	29	22
27	17	30	17	21

Additional Answers

1. lower extreme, lower quartile, median, upper quartile, and upper extreme

28. The scores of the fifth period class are more consistent.

Mid-Chapter Quiz

1.

Score	Frequency
17	3
18	1
19	1
21	6
22	2
25	1
27	2
28	2
29	3
30	4

2. mean = 24, median = 22, mode = 21

3.

Stem	Leaf
1	7 7 7 8 9
2	1 1 1 1 1 1 2 2
	5 7 7 8 8 9 9 9
3	0 0 0 0

4. range = 13, interquartile range = 8

5.

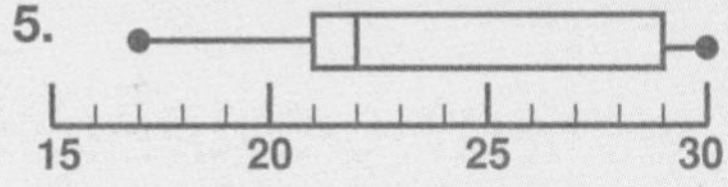

Enrichment Masters Booklet, **p. 87**

Name ______ Date ______

Enrichment Worksheet 10-5

Normal Curve

Before actually tossing a coin a number of times, there is a method for determining the probability that a certain number of times heads will result. For example, if you toss a coin 100 times, there is only about a 2.5% chance you will get over 60 heads.

The **normal curve** is a very useful tool when dealing with problems such as the one above. The curve is also called a *bell curve*. If a teacher says he grades "on a curve," he is probably referring to the normal curve.

The normal curve at the right shows the percent of the given data that will fall within a certain distance from the mean of the data. These distances are measured in units called *standard deviations*. We will use these units (without actually calculating them) in the exercises below. Also used will be the fact that if a coin is tossed 100 times, the standard deviation for the number of heads is 5 and the mean is 50.

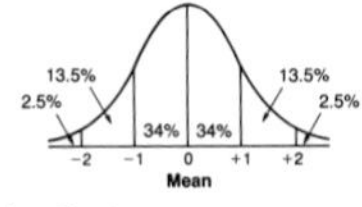

The 34% shown in the area under the curve between 0 and +1 is the percent chance that you will toss between 50 and 55 heads (mean + 1 standard deviation) when tossing the coin 100 times. The 2.5% shown in the area under the curve to the left of −2 is the percent chance that you will toss less than 40 heads (mean − 2 standard deviations) when tossing the coin 100 times.

Use the normal curve shown above to answer each question. The coin is tossed 100 times for each exercise.

1. What is the percent chance you will toss between 45 and 50 heads? 34%
2. What is the percent chance you will toss over 55 heads? 16%
3. What is the percent chance you will toss more than 60 heads? 2.5%
4. What is the chance you will toss less than 60 heads? 97.5%

If a coin is tossed 1000 times, the mean for the number of heads is 500 and the standard deviation is approximately 16.

Solve.

5. If a coin is tossed 1000 times, what is the percent chance you will get over 532 heads? 2.5%
6. If a coin is tossed 1000 times, there is a 16% chance you will get less than how many heads? 484 heads

Alternate Strategies: Extending the Lesson

Enrichment

Working Backwards Make up data for the following conditions.

a. The box is very short.
b. The box is very long.
c. The whiskers are very short.
d. The whiskers are very long.
e. The box is very short and the left whisker is longer than the right whisker.

Compare and contrast data.

Cooperative Learning

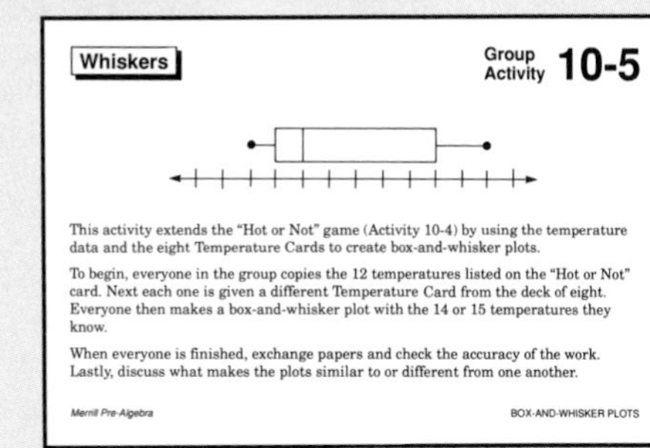
Whiskers — Group Activity 10-5

This activity extends the "Hot or Not" game (Activity 10-4) by using the temperature data and the eight Temperature Cards to create box-and-whisker plots.

To begin, everyone in the group copies the 12 temperatures listed on the "Hot or Not" card. Next each one is given a different Temperature Card from the deck of eight. Everyone then makes a box-and-whisker plot with the 14 or 15 temperatures they know.

When everyone is finished, exchange papers and check the accuracy of the work. Lastly, discuss what makes the plots similar to or different from one another.

Merrill Pre-Algebra — BOX-AND-WHISKER PLOTS

EXPLORATION

Scatter Plots

Objectives Students will complete a scatter plot and use it to determine if a relationship exists between two variables.

1 *FOCUS*

Motivating the Exploration

Ask students if there are some assumptions people make concerning physical characteristics. For example, tall people have big feet.

2 *TEACH*

Using Models

Record the height and shoe size of each student on the chalkboard or overhead. Ask students if they can see a pattern. Then plot the ordered pair for each student's height and shoe size as a point on a grid. Ask students if they notice a pattern on the grid.

3 *PRACTICE/APPLY*

Using Manipulatives

Have students copy the sample scatter plot on graph paper. Then have each student state his or her circumference and height in inches. Students should plot each ordered pair as it is stated.

4 *CLOSE*

Writing Connection

Ask students to write a brief report on who might be interested in the relationships they discovered.

Exploration

Scatter Plots

Materials: tape measures, graph paper

In this Exploration, you will try to determine whether there is any relationship between two given variables. You will use a **scatter plot** to plot the data.

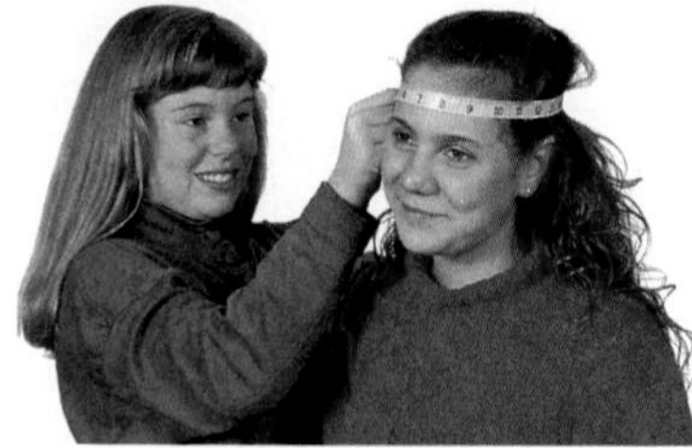

▶ Work with a partner. Measure the circumference of your partner's head, wrist, and neck in inches. Measure your partner's height in inches. Record these numbers.

▶ You will complete this part with the whole class. You will try to determine whether there is a relationship between the circumference of your head and your height. Write an ordered pair (circumference, height).

▶ Your teacher will instruct you how to display the data in a scatter plot. A sample is shown at the right. In this sample, the point shown represents a person whose head circumference is 21 inches and whose height is 60 inches.

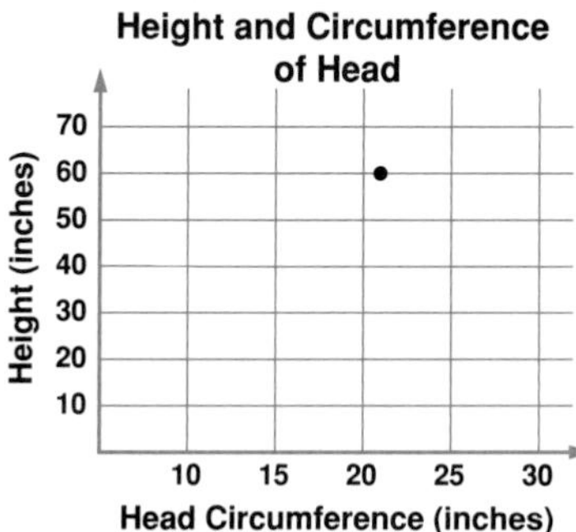

Your Turn: **Complete the scatter plot.**
See students' work.

Analysis See Solutions Manual.

1. Describe the scatter plot.
2. Is there a relationship between the head circumference and height? If so, write a sentence that describes the relationship. **Height is about 3 times circumference.**
3. In Chapter 8, you graphed linear equations on a coordinate plane. How is the scatter plot like those graphs? How does the scatter plot differ?
4. Why do you suppose this kind of graph is called a scatter plot?

Extension See Solutions Manual.

5. Using similar methods, determine if there is a relationship among the circumference of your head, wrist, neck, and your height.

SET-UP

Materials

- tape measures, graph paper

You may wish to use the Exploration worksheet provided on page 55 of the Lab Manual.

For Students Each pair of students will need a tape measure. If tape measures are not available, have students use string and measure the string with a ruler or yardstick.

For the Overhead Projector You can connect a computer to an overhead projection panel and plot the points along with your students. This can also be done using an overhead projector graphing calculator.

Additional Answer

3. **The scatter plot is similar to a graph of a linear equation because they both are a collection of points on a coordinate plane. The points of a scatter plot are not connected.**

10-6 Scatter Plots

Objective:
Interpret data displayed in a scatter plot.

Key Term:
scatter plot

Louise wants to know if there is a relationship between the grades earned on a test and the amount of time spent studying for the test. She collected the data shown in the chart.

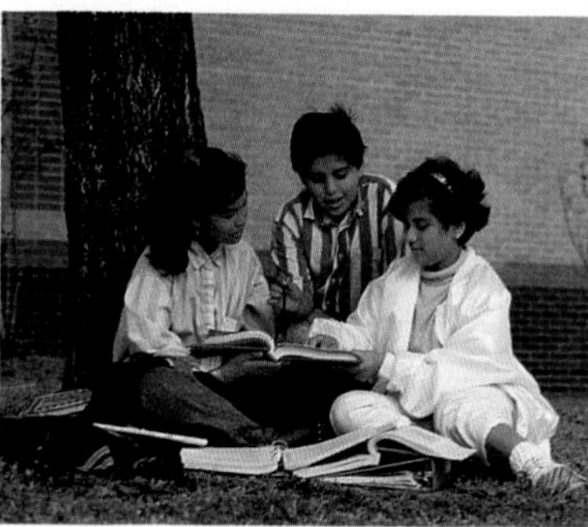

Student	Study Time	Test Score
Doug	10 min	65
Rebecca	15 min	68
Bradley	70 min	87
Justine	60 min	92
Allison	45 min	73
Tami	90 min	95
Mick	60 min	83
Montega	30 min	77
Christy	120 min	98

A **scatter plot** is a graph that shows the general relationship between two sets of data. To make a scatter plot of the study time data, draw a graph with Study Time along the horizontal axis and Test Scores along the vertical axis. Then plot points for each time and the corresponding score.

Relationship of Study Time to Test Scores

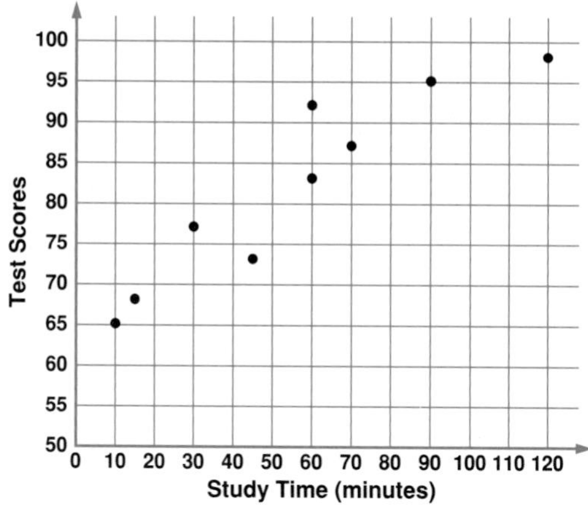

Why is this called a "positive" relationship? **The dots appear to form a line with a positive slope.**

From the scatter plot, you can see that there appears to be a relationship between test scores and time spent studying. In general, the more time spent studying, the higher the test score. This scatter plot shows a *positive* relationship.

Bell Ringer

If the interquartile range is 8 and the lower quartile is 24, what is the lowest possible extreme value? 12

Lesson Notes 10-6

5-Minute Check
(over Lesson 10-5)

Use the box-and-whisker plot shown to answer each question.

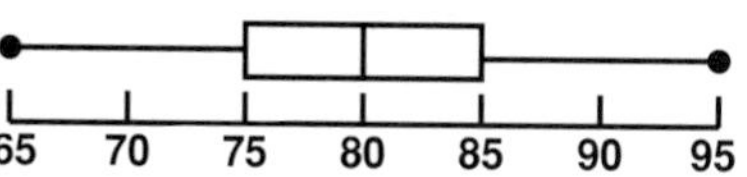

1. What is the median? 80
2. What is the upper quartile? 85
3. What is the lower quartile? 75
4. What is the interquartile range? 10
5. What are the limits on the outliers? 60 and 100

Transparency 10-6 contains the 5-Minute Check and a teaching aid for this lesson.

1 FOCUS

The purpose of this lesson is to give students experience in finding relationships between two sets of data by using a scatter plot.

Motivating the Lesson

From a pediatrician's office, obtain a blank height-weight graph and make a transparency from it. Ask students if they have ever seen such charts. Ask students if there is a relationship between weight and height while growing and what they expect a completed chart to look like.

2 TEACH

Using Models

Discuss what a scatter plot is and positive and negative relationships. Have each student write his or her height and shoe size on a piece of paper. Collect the papers, keeping boys' and girls' papers separated. Make scatter plots and discuss results.

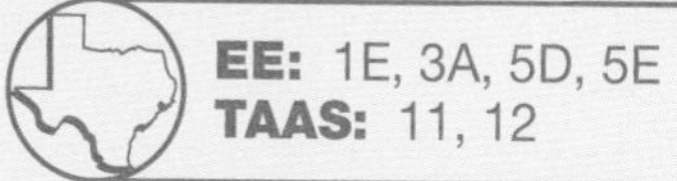

EE: 1E, 3A, 5D, 5E
TAAS: 11, 12

Chalkboard Examples

- *For Example 1*
  The scatter plot below shows the vocabulary of preschool children based on their ages.

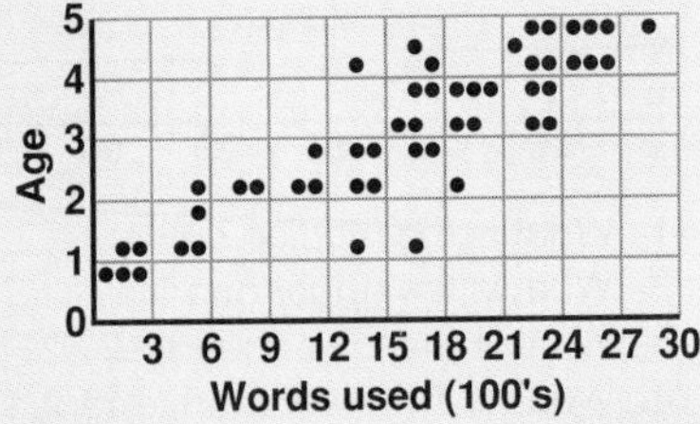

a. Can you make a general statement about the scatter plot? **As the age increases the vocabulary increases.**

b. What are some probable causes of the data that do not seem to fit? **speakers of other languages, developmentally disabled, etc.**

3 PRACTICE/APPLY

Checking the Concept

After students complete Exercises 3-11, have them relate other situations that would have positive, negative, or no relationship.

Practice Masters Booklet, **p. 97**

Name ______________________ Date ____________

Practice Worksheet 10-6

Scatter Plots

A scatter plot of physical activity and age is shown at the right.

1. What relationship (positive, negative, or none) does this data show between physical activity and age? **negative**
2. Where on the plot are the points showing the hours of physical activity as people grow older? **To the lower right of the plot**
3. What happens to the number of hours of physical activity as people grow older? **The number of hours decreases.**

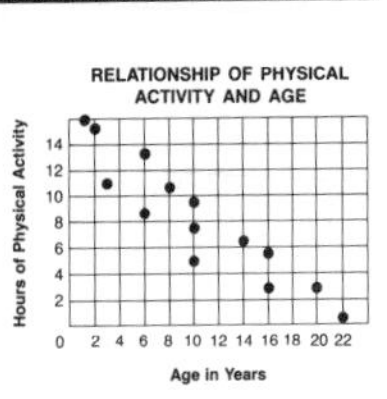

A scatter plot of hours worked and hourly wage is shown at the right.

4. What relationship does this data show between hours worked and hourly wage? **none**
5. How many people are shown on the plot? **14**

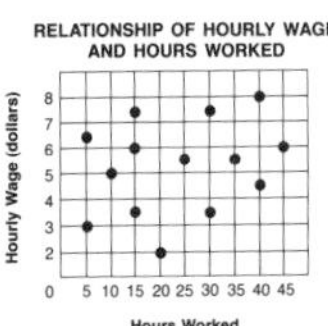

A scatter plot of assisted tackles and solo tackles for each player during a football season is shown at the right.

6. What relationship does this data show between assisted tackles and solo tackles? **positive**
7. What is the greatest number of assists shown on the plot? **64**
8. What is the least number of solo tackles shown on the plot? **3**

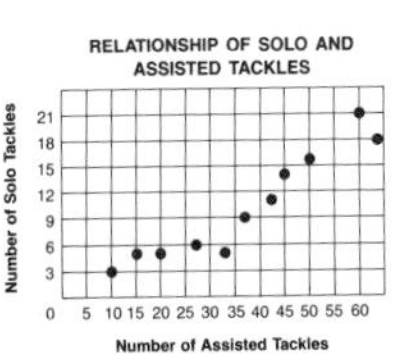

Example

1 The scatter plot shows the cost of cars on a used car lot based on the age of the cars.

What happens to the cost as the age increases? The cost goes down.

What can you say about the data that do not seem to fit? These could be cars that had some major problems or were in better-than-average condition.

Why is this called a "negative" relationship? **The dots appear to form a line with a negative slope.**

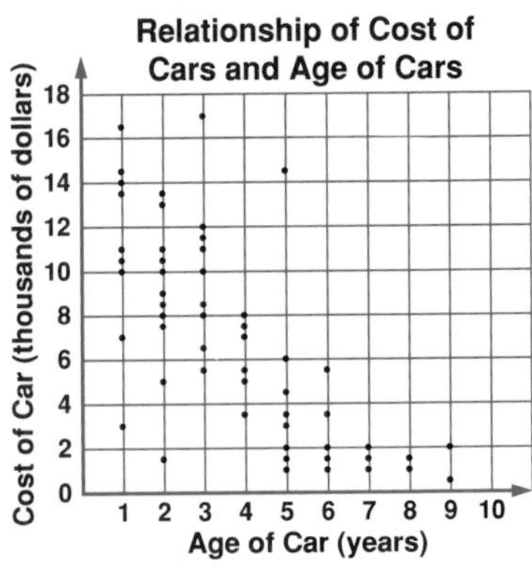

This scatter plot shows a *negative* relationship.

Checking for Understanding

Communicating Algebra

1. What is the major use of a scatter plot? **analyze relationships between data**
2. What do you think a scatter plot would look like if no relationship existed between the two sets of data? **points widely spread**

Guided Practice

3. none
4. negative
5. positive

What type of relationship, *positive, negative,* or *none,* is shown by each scatter plot?

3. 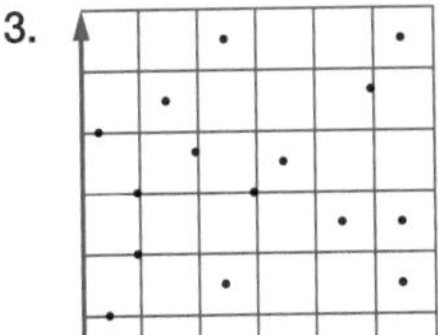

4. 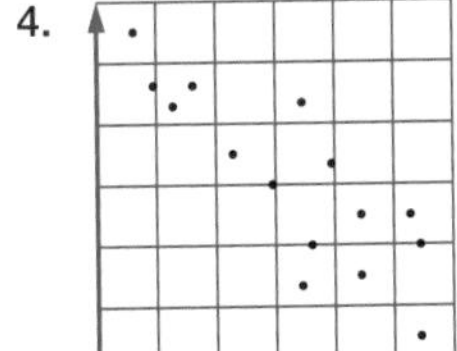

5. 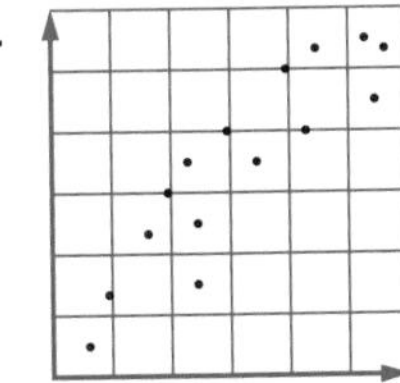

What relationship do you think a scatter plot of these data would show? Write *positive, negative,* or *none.* **9. negative 11. none**

6. outside temperature, sunburn **positive**
7. salary, years experience **positive**
8. outside temperature, frostbite **negative**
9. miles on odometer, cost of used car
10. hair color, weight **none**
11. month of birth, years of college

Exercises

Independent Practice

A scatter plot of height and weight for a class is shown at the right.

12. Does this data show a relationship between height and weight? **yes**
13. Where on the plot are the points for people who grew taller but not heavier?
14. Where are the points for people who grew heavier but not taller?

13. above most of the points 14. to the right of most points

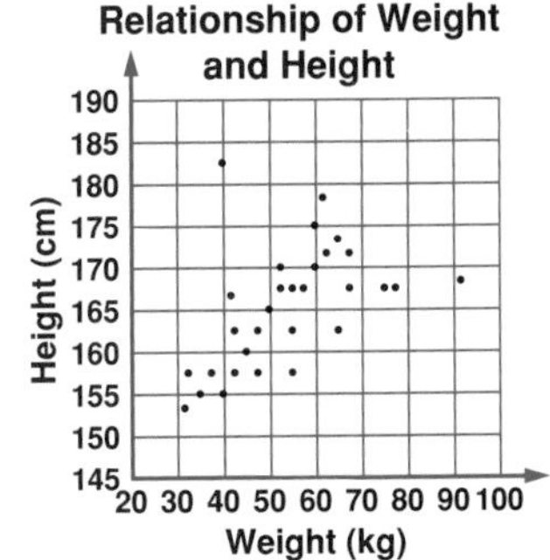

Alternate Strategies: Reteaching the Lesson

Reteaching Activity

Collecting and Interpreting Data

Working individually or in small groups, have students collect data from other students on the amount of time spent watching television per day and the amount of time spent on homework per day. Have them show results in a scatter plot and summarize any conclusions.

Reteaching Masters Booklet, **p. 88**

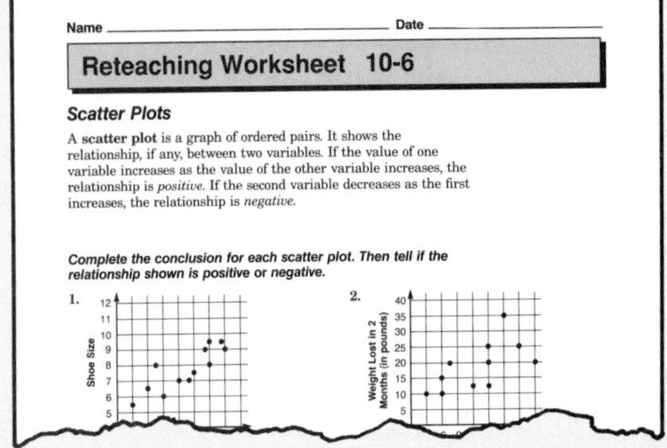
Name ______________________ Date ____________

Reteaching Worksheet 10-6

Scatter Plots

A **scatter plot** is a graph of ordered pairs. It shows the relationship, if any, between two variables. If the value of one variable increases as the value of the other variable increases, the relationship is *positive.* If the second variable decreases as the first increases, the relationship is *negative.*

Complete the conclusion for each scatter plot. Then tell if the relationship shown is positive or negative.

1. Shoe Size
2. Weight Lost in 2 Months (in pounds)

Juan wanted to find out whether there was any relationship between students' favorite classes and their best grades. He surveyed his class and used the data to construct the scatter plot at the right.

Relationship of Favorite Class to Best Grade

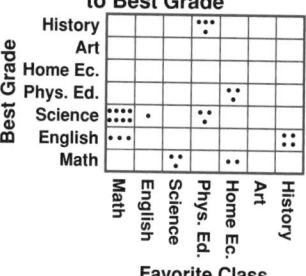

Best Grade: History, Art, Home Ec., Phys. Ed., Science, English, Math

Favorite Class: Math, English, Science, Phys. Ed., Home Ec., Art, History

15. Do the data appear to be related? **no**
16. Which class was the favorite of the most students? **math**
17. In which class did the most students receive their best grades? **science**
18. How many students are in the class? **31**

Mixed Review

19. Write $\frac{6x^2y}{27xy}$ in simplest form. (Lesson 4-6) $\frac{2x}{9}$
20. Find the upper and lower quartiles and the interquartile range of the data set: 38, 40, 41, 48, 52, 55, 56, 57, 61. (Lesson 10-4) **56; 41; 15**
21. Draw a box-and-whisker plot for the following bowling scores: 122, 185, 136, 139, 111, 142, 149, 133, 139, 157, 166, 153, 146. What are the extremes? (Lesson 10-5) **See Solutions Manual for plot; 111; 185.**

Applications

22. **Survey** As a class, record the number of boys and girls in each family. Use the data to make a scatter plot. Plot the number of boys on the horizontal axis and the number of girls on the vertical axis. Use your scatter plot to answer these questions. **See students' work.**
    a. Does there appear to be any relationship between the data in the scatter plot?
    b. How many families have three or more boys?
    c. How many families have three or fewer girls?
    d. How large is the largest family?
    e. What seems to be the mode?
23. **Medical Research** A research doctor used a scatter plot to compare the number of doses of a new antibiotic to severity of a disease. How could a scatter plot help the doctor reach a conclusion on how effective the antibiotic is? **If there is a negative relationship between the doses of the antibiotic and the severity of disease, the antibiotic is probably effective.**

Critical Thinking

24. A scatter plot of monthly ice cream sales and monthly water sports accidents in Wisconsin shows a positive relationship. Why would this be true? Does a positive relationship necessarily mean that one factor causes the other? Why or why not? **See margin.**

Wrap-Up

25. List two sets of data that could give a positive relationship on a scatter plot. List two sets that could give a negative relationship. List two sets that would show no relationship. **Sample answers: temperature and swimming pool attendance; cost of gasoline and vacation travel miles; temperature and cost of gasoline**

Error Analysis

Watch for students who have difficulty differentiating the relationship of a scatter plot.

Prevent by having students draw a line enclosing the majority of the plotted points. If the figure is an ellipse, have them draw a straight line through the long ends.

Independent Practice

Homework Assignment	
Basic	12-15, 19-22, 24, 25
Average	15-22, 24, 25
Honors	15-25

4 CLOSE

Assessment Option

Modeling Have students draw a generic scatter plot having a positive relationship.

Additional Answer

24. because both activities are dependent on warm weather; no; It could mean that the two factors have something in common.

Enrichment Masters Booklet, **p. 88**

Name ______________ Date ______________

Enrichment Worksheet 10-6

Growth Charts

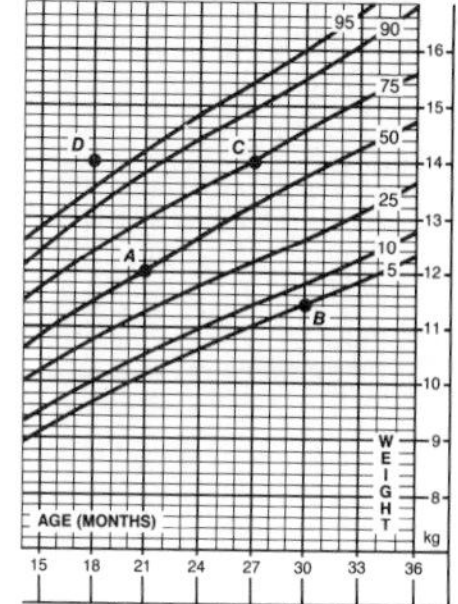

Scatter plots are often used by doctors to show parents the growth rates of their children. The horizontal scale of the chart at the right shows the ages from 15 to 36 months. The vertical scale shows weight in kilograms. One kilogram is about 2.2 pounds. The curved lines are used to show how a child's weight compares with others of his age.

Look at the point labeled A. It represents a 21-month-old who weighs 12 kilograms. It is located on the slanted line labeled 50. This means the child's weight is in the "50th percentile." In other words, 50% of all 21-month-olds weigh more than 12 kilograms and 50% weigh less than 12 kilograms.

The location of Point B indicates that a 30-month-old who weighs 11.4 kilograms is in the 5th percentile. Only 5% of 30-month-old children will weigh less than 11.4 kilograms.

Solve.

1. Look at the point labeled C. How much does the child weigh? How old is he? What percent of children his age will weigh more than him? **14 kg; 27 months; 25%**
2. Look at the point labeled D. What is the child's age and weight? What percent of children his age will weigh more than him? **18 months; 14 kg; less than 5%**
3. What is the 50th percentile weight for a child 27 months old? **13.2 kg**
4. How much weight would child B have to gain to be in the 50th percentile? **2.3 kg**
5. If child D did not gain any weight for four months, what percentile would he be in? **90th**
6. How much heavier is a $2\frac{1}{2}$-year-old in the 90th percentile than one in the 10th percentile? **3.7 kg**

Alternate Strategies: Extending the Lesson

Enrichment

Using Cooperative Groups Have groups of four students design an experiment to relate mathematics grades to English grades and also mathematics grades to science grades. Organize data by using scatter plots. Then, interpret the results.

Cooperative Learning

To Tell The Truth — Group Activity **10-6**

Is there a relationship between the amount of time students spend watching television and the amount of time they do homework? Investigate this question by collecting data and making a scatter plot.

To begin, ask each classmate how many hours (to the nearest half hour) of homework they do a day, Monday through Thursday. Also, ask each of them how many hours of television they watch on those days. Collect this data as pairs of information, and graph these data on a scatter plot. Use Hours of Studying as your horizontal axis and Hours of Television as your vertical axis.

When you have completed your scatter plot, consider the following questions.

1. Where do most of the data points fall?
2. Does there appear to be a positive or negative relationship between the number of hours spent studying and those spent watching television?

Merrill Pre-Algebra SCATTER PLOTS

Lesson Notes 10-7

5-Minute Check
(over Lesson 10-6)

1. Describe the scatter plot of two sets of data having a negative relationship. **The points slope down to the right.**

What relationship do you think a scatter plot of each pair of data below would show? Write positive, negative, or none.

2. month of birth, hair color **none**
3. oil reserves, number of cars being driven **negative**

Transparency 10-7 contains the 5-Minute Check and a teaching aid for this lesson.

1 FOCUS

The purpose of this lesson is to broaden problem-solving strategies to include solving a simpler problem.

Motivating the Lesson

Show the class a photo of a large crowd. Ask students how they would determine the number of people in the photo.

2 TEACH

Chalkboard Examples

Find the sum of the whole numbers from 1 to 50. **1275**

EE: 1A, 1B, 1C, 1D, 1E
TAAS: 10, 11, 13

Problem Solving

10-7 Strategy: Simplify the Problem

Objective:
Solve problems by first solving simpler problems.

When you make graphs of information, you are taking large amounts of data and presenting them in a simplified manner. This helps you and others who view the graph to understand the data.

Solving a simpler problem is a strategy that can be applied to other kinds of problems as well.

Finding the sum of the whole numbers from 1 to 200 could be a tedious task, even on a calculator. Here's how to simplify the problem and look for a pattern that will help you find the answer.

Explore The problem asks for the sum of the whole numbers from 1 to 200.

Plan First find the partial sums.

1, 2, 3, 4, 5, . . . , 196, 197, 198, 199, 200

2 + 199

1 + 200

Do this until you find a pattern that will allow you to solve the more difficult problem.

Solve

$1 + 200 = 201$
$2 + 199 = 201$
$3 + 198 = 201$
$\vdots$
$99 + 102 = 201$
$100 + 101 = 201$

There are 100 partial sums of 201.

$100 \times 201 = 20{,}100$

Examine Check to see if the pattern works for a small number of whole numbers. For example, try the numbers from 1 to 10.

$1 + 2 + 3 + 4 + 5 + 6 + 7 + 8 + 9 + 10 = 55$

Partial sums: $1 + 10, 2 + 9, 3 + 8, 4 + 7, 5 + 6$

There are 5 partial sums of 11: $5 \times 11 = 55$.

The pattern holds. So the answer 20,100 seems reasonable.

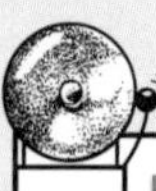

Bell Ringer

A garden 24 feet wide by 40 feet long is enclosed by a fence. The fence posts are placed 8 feet apart. One extra post is included for a gate. Find the number of fence posts. **17 fence posts**

Reteaching Activity

Using Discussion Discuss with students examples of when solving a simpler problem is used. Emphasize the importance of estimation in working all types of problems, and show through examples how estimation is an example of simplifying the problem.

Checking for Understanding

Guided Practice

Solve by first solving a simpler problem. 2., 4. Answers may vary.

1. Find the sum of the first 20 odd numbers. 400
2. What simpler problem(s) did you use to solve exercise 1?
3. How many cuts are needed to divide a long rod into 25 smaller pieces? 24
4. What simpler problem(s) did you use to solve exercise 3?

Exercises

Independent Practice

Solve. Use any strategy. Use mental math skills, estimation, or a calculator as appropriate.

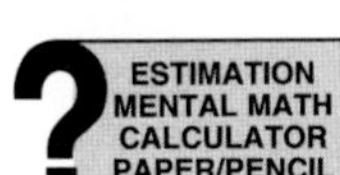

5. Unit 2 of a science book starts on page 126 and ends on page 241. How many pages are in the unit? 116 pages
6. The perimeter of a rectangle is 32 meters. Its area is 48 square meters. What are the dimensions of the rectangle? 12 meters by 4 meters
7. Chef Martino made a huge pan of lasagna for a banquet. He makes 6 cuts along the length of the rectangular pan and 10 cuts along the width. How many pieces does he have? 77 pieces
8. Find the sum of the first 100 *even* numbers. 10,100
9. Iona started with a certain amount of money. She spent half of her money. She earned $6 the next day. Later, she lost $\frac{1}{6}$ of her money, but she still had $15 left. How much money did she have in the beginning? $24
10. Fifteen points are marked on a circle. Line segments are drawn connecting every pair of points. How many segments are drawn? 105 segments
11. The original price of a pair of shoes was $56. The shoes were marked down 15% but didn't sell. Now, they are on final clearance at 30% off the sale price. If sales tax is 6%, what is the total cost of the shoes? $35.32
12. Elroy is on a diet. After 2 weeks on the diet, he weighs 173 pounds. After 4 weeks, he weighs 168 pounds. If he continues to lose weight at the same rate, what will he weigh after 10 weeks on the diet? 153 pounds
13. What is the total number of squares of any size shown in the checkerboard? (Hint: There are more than 64 squares.) 204 squares

Wrap-Up

14. Explain how working a simpler problem can sometimes help to solve a more difficult problem. Give some examples. See margin.

Team Problem Solving

In a town called Theirtown, there are 100,000 citizens. During the census, it was found that 45% of the males and 30% of the females were married to people from Theirtown. How many males and how many females live in Theirtown?
40,000 males; 60,000 females

3 PRACTICE/APPLY

Checking the Concept

After solving Exercises 5-13, have students check as many results as possible by using estimation.

Error Analysis
Watch for students who incorrectly solve a problem because they do not visualize it. **Prevent by** encouraging students to draw a diagram.

Independent Practice

Homework Assignment	
Basic	5-13 odd, 14
Average	6-14 even
Honors	9-14

4 CLOSE

Assessment Option

Speaking Ask students to explain how solving a simpler problem can save time.

Practice Masters Booklet, **p. 98**

Name ________________ Date ________

Practice Worksheet 10-7

Problem Solving Strategy: Solve a Simpler Problem

Solve. Use the solve-a-simpler-problem strategy.

1. Cliff heard a funny joke on the radio on Sunday. On Monday (day 1), he told the joke to Sarah, Rich, and Claire. These people each told the joke to 3 more people on day 2, who each told the joke to 3 more people on day 3. This pattern continued. How many people heard the joke on the 6th day? 729 people
2. How many days passed before at least 100 people had heard the joke? 4 days
3. By the end of day 6, how many people altogether had heard the joke? (Remember to count Cliff!) 1093 people
4. A summer camp has 7 buildings arranged in a circle. Paths must be constructed joining every building to every other building. How many paths are needed? 21 paths
5. In a basketball tournament, each team plays until it loses a game, then it is out of the tournament. If 64 teams are in the tournament at the start, how many games must be played to determine the tournament winner? 63 games
6. What is the total number of triangles of any size in the figure at the right? 26 triangles
7. Find the sum of the first 100 odd numbers. 10,000

Additional Answer

14. Sample answer: In solving a simpler problem, a pattern or shortcut may emerge that can be applied to the more difficult problem.

Cooperative Learning

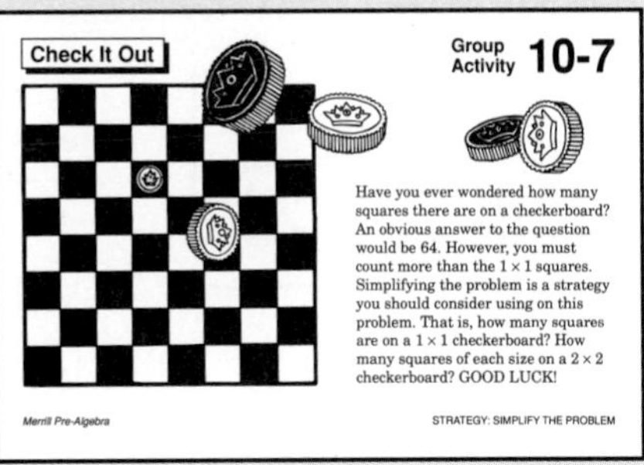
Check It Out

Group Activity 10-7

Have you ever wondered how many squares there are on a checkerboard? An obvious answer to the question would be 64. However, you must count more than the 1 × 1 squares. Simplifying the problem is a strategy you should consider using on this problem. That is, how many squares are on a 1 × 1 checkerboard? How many squares of each size on a 2 × 2 checkerboard? GOOD LUCK!

Merrill Pre-Algebra

STRATEGY: SIMPLIFY THE PROBLEM

Lesson Notes 10-8

5-Minute Check
(over Lesson 10-7)

The original price for a sweater was \$48. The sweater was marked down 20% but did not sell. Now the sweater is on final clearance at 40% off the sale price. If sales tax is 6%, what is the total cost of the sweater? **\$24.42**

Transparency 10-8 contains the 5-Minute Check and a teaching aid for this lesson.

1 FOCUS

The purpose of this lesson is to show students that statistics can be used to predict actions of a large group from the actions of a sample of the group.

Motivating the Lesson

Read the school menu for today. Ask students how the person who orders food for the cafeteria knows how much to order.

2 TEACH

Using Discussion

After discussing the examples, ask students to brainstorm a list of situations in their homes in which statistics are used to predict. Lists might include budgeting money, planning meals, or purchasing garden seed.

Chalkboard Examples

In a survey on favorite snack foods, 15 people out of 70 preferred soft pretzels. If there will be 7000 people at the stadium, how many soft pretzels should Terry stock? **1500 soft pretzels**

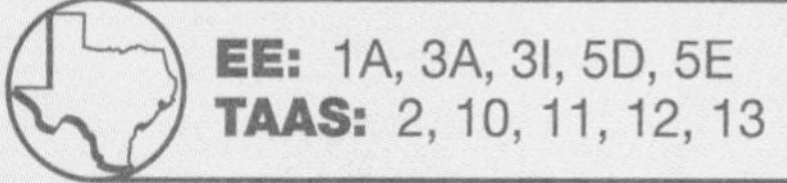

EE: 1A, 3A, 3I, 5D, 5E
TAAS: 2, 10, 11, 12, 13

Application

10-8 Using Statistics to Predict

Objective:
Use a sample to predict actions of a larger group.

Notice that this is an example of the problem-solving strategy, Simplify the Problem.

The 4-H Club will operate the soft drink booth at a big Fourth of July fireworks show at the stadium. Terry is in charge of ordering the soft drinks and needs to decide what kinds to order. She decided to *simplify the problem* and sampled a group of people at the school picnic. Because similar people would attend the show, she felt her sample would be representative. The bar graph shows the results of the survey.

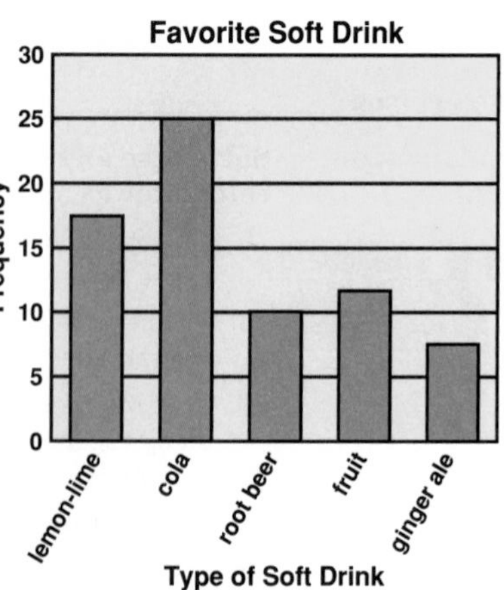

Terry estimates that every person at the stadium will buy one soft drink and she knows that the stadium holds about 7200 people. Using the results of the survey, she will order the drinks. Of the 72 people she surveyed, 12 chose a fruit drink. So she reasoned that $\frac{12}{72}$ or $\frac{1}{6}$ of her order should be fruit drink.

$$\frac{1}{6} \text{ of } 7200 = 1200$$

She could also have used a proportion to solve the problem.

$$\frac{12}{72} = \frac{x}{7200}$$

$(12)(7200) = 72x$

12 [×] 7200 [÷] 72 [=] 1200 $x = 1200$

Terry should order 1200 cans of fruit drink.

FYI

The four Hs in 4-H stand for head, heart, hands, and health. Members of 4-H do projects and activities to help the community. More than 80 countries have 4-H or similar programs.

Example

1 **How many bottles of cola should Terry order? 25 of 72 preferred cola.**

Method 1

$$\frac{25}{\cancel{72}_{1}} \cdot \cancel{7200}^{100} = 2500$$

Method 2

$$\frac{25}{72} = \frac{x}{7200}$$

$72x = (25)(7200)$

25 [×] 7200 [÷] 72 [=] 2500

$x = 2500$

She should order 2500 cans of cola.

Bell Ringer

A loaf of bread is ten inches long. How many cuts are necessary to cut it into twenty slices? **19 cuts**

Checking for Understanding

Communicating Algebra

1. Explain how a sample group survey can be used to predict the actions of a whole population. **See margin.**
2. What is the most important thing to consider in sampling? **that the sample group is representative of the larger group**

Guided Practice

Use the survey on favorite color to answer each question.

3. What is the size of the sample? **50**
4. What is the mode? **green**
5. What fraction chose blue? $\frac{3}{10}$
6. For 800 students, how many blue covers should the bookstore stock? **240**

Favorite Color	
Red	13
Green	17
Blue	15
Yellow	5

Use the sample data on yearbook price ranges to answer each question.

7. What is the size of the sample? **80**
8. If the price were less than $19, about how many would buy the yearbook? **42**
9. If there are 600 in the senior class, about how many would buy a yearbook that cost $18.50? **about 315**
10. About how many would buy at $16.95? **about 540**

Amount Willing to Pay for Yearbook	
no more than $15	8
no more than $17	30
no more than $19	32
no more than $21	10

Exercises

Independent Practice

The bookstore sells physical education uniforms. All incoming ninth grade students will need uniforms. There are 825 students starting ninth grade. Of these, 425 are girls. The uniforms come in four sizes: small, medium, large, and extra large. The students who run the store decide to survey about 50 girls to find out what size they wear. Using this information, they will order uniforms to sell.

ESTIMATION / MENTAL MATH / CALCULATOR / PAPER/PENCIL

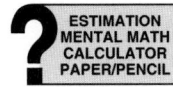

11. From an alphabetical list, the students survey every eighth girl. How many girls are surveyed? Is this a good sample? Why or why not?
12. Of the girls surveyed, 27 wear medium, 10 wear large, and 2 wear extra large. How many wear small? **14 girls**
13. For the 425 girls, how many uniforms of each size should be ordered?
14. The bookstore personnel estimated how much of each supply item would be needed during the year. They used the information in the chart below. They estimated based on 2450 students in the school and 10 months. Find the number of each item that should be ordered.
    a. paper b. pencils c. pens d. folders e. covers

11. 53 girls; yes; randomly taken
13. 112 small, 217 medium, 80 large, 16 extra large
a. 1,470,000 sheets
b. 24,500 pencils
c. 9800 pens
d. 4900 folders
e. 7350 covers

Supply Item	Amount Each Student Uses
Notebook paper	60 sheets per month
Pencils	1 per month
Pens	4 per school year
Pocket folders	2 per school year
Theme covers	3 per school year

3 PRACTICE/APPLY

Checking the Concept

If students need additional practice, then after answering Exercise 6, have them predict the number of other colors to stock.

Error Analysis

Watch for students who confuse the two methods.
Prevent by having students choose one method they feel comfortable with and use it exclusively.

Independent Practice

Homework Assignment	
Basic	11-13, 18-22
Average	14-16, 18-22
Honors	14-22

Additional Answer

1. A sample group survey can be used to predict by setting up and solving a proportion.

Practice Masters Booklet, **p. 99**

Name ______________ Date ______________

Practice Worksheet 10-8

Application: Using Statistics to Predict

Use the survey shown at the right to answer each question.

1. What is the size of the sample? **120**
2. What fraction of the sample chose KLAS as a favorite station? $\frac{1}{8}$
3. What is the ratio of KOOL listeners to KALM listeners? **8:7**
4. Suppose there are 15,880 people in the listening range of these stations. How many would you expect to listen to KRZY? **About 4500 people**
5. Suppose KLAS has 780 listeners. How many people would you predict listen to KOOL? **About 1664 people**

Favorite Radio Station	
KALM	28
KOOL	32
KLAS	15
KRZY	34
none	11

Use the poll shown at the right to answer each question.

6. What is the size of the sample? **63**
7. What fraction of the sample is in favor or strongly in favor of the bill? $\frac{1}{3}$
8. What fraction of the sample is strongly opposed to the bill? $\frac{1}{7}$
9. Suppose 12,600 people live in the city where the poll was taken. How many would you predict will be opposed or strongly opposed to the bill? **About 7400 people**
10. How many of the 12,600 people would you predict will have no opinion about the bill? **About 1000 people**

Popular Support of a Senate Bill	
Strongly in favor	3
In favor	18
Opposed	28
Strongly opposed	9
No opinion	5

Alternate Strategies: Reteaching the Lesson

Reteaching Activity

Using Models From a well-mixed bag of marbles of several different colors, draw a representative number of marbles and record the number of each color drawn. Given the number of marbles in the bag, predict the number of marbles of each color. Compare to the actual number. Discuss any differences.

Reteaching Masters Booklet, **p. 89**

Name ______________ Date ______________

Reteaching Worksheet 10-8

Application: Using Statistics to Predict

Mr. Niles takes a poll of 10 students in his class. Of the 10 students polled, 3 prefer to have the test today and 7 prefer to have the test tomorrow. The 10 students polled are a **sample** of all the students in the class. The results of the poll can be used to predict the number of students who prefer the test tomorrow.

There are 30 students in Mr. Niles's class. How many of these students prefer to take the test tomorrow?

Explore What is given? 10 students polled; 3 prefer to take the test today and 7 prefer tomorrow
What is asked? 30 students in the class; how many prefer the test tomorrow

Plan The sample is representative of the entire class. Set up a proportion to show two equivalent ratios. Let t represent the total number of students that prefer to take the test tomorrow.

15. The notebook paper comes in fillers of 50 sheets. How many fillers should be ordered? **29,400 fillers**

16. There are 10 fillers in a package and 10 packages in a case. How many cases need to be ordered? **294 cases**

17. **Collect Data** Make a frequency table showing hair color for students in your class. Use the data to predict the number of students in your school with each hair color. Choose a time and place to observe at least 50 students in your school and record their hair color. Compare that data to your predictions. Write about your findings. **See students' work.**

Mixed Review

18. Solve the equation $d = \frac{15}{8} - \frac{3}{8}$ and write the solution in simplest form. (Lesson 5-5) $1\frac{1}{2}$

19. Solve the proportion $\frac{3}{5} = \frac{t}{40}$. (Lesson 9-2) **24**

20. What relationship (*positive, negative,* or *none*) do you think a scatter plot of the following data would show: calorie intake, weight gained? (Lesson 10-6) **positive**

Critical Thinking

21. Refer to the situation at the beginning of the lesson. Terry buys her soft drinks at a cost of 6 for $1. If she sells all 7200 at 75¢ each, how much profit will the 4-H club make? **$4200**
If Terry sells only 90 percent of the drinks, what is the profit? **$3660**

Wrap-Up

22. Explain how sampling plays an important part in using statistics to predict. **See margin.**

Career

Weather Forecasting

It would be difficult to imagine watching the evening news without the statistics, graphs, and maps of the local meteorologist. The meteorologist you see forecasting the weather on TV is most likely an *operational* meteorologist. *Physical* meteorologists collect data on the chemical and electrical properties of the atmosphere. *Climatologists* concentrate to a greater degree on past and present climate data. They use the statistical data collected over time to plot trends in our climate.

Meteorologists receive their weather data from satellites, radar, high altitude balloons, and rockets. They use computers to analyze weather data and to generate graphs that not only assist in forecasting weather, but in preparing warnings and advisories. In addition to working for radio and television stations, meteorologists are employed by government agencies, the military, private industry, educational institutions, and airlines. Employment opportunities for meteorologists are expected to grow at least 25% by the year 2000.

4 CLOSE

Assessment Option

Speaking Have students name a job and a situation where statistics would be used as a predictor.

Additional Answer

22. Sample answer: Sampling can detect a new trend or a change in an old opinion. This could head off potential problems and save lots of money.

Enrichment Masters Booklet, **p. 89**

Name ____________ Date ____________

Enrichment Worksheet 10-8

Using Graphs to Predict

Use the graph at the right to answer the following questions.

Olympic Pole Vault Gold Medal Winning Heights

Height (feet); Olympic Year 1920–1980

Note: Olympics were not held in 1940 and 1944.

1. Estimate the height to the nearest foot that pole vaulters probably cleared in 1962. 16 ft
2. Estimate the year when 14 feet was cleared for the first time. 1930
3. Estimate the height to the nearest foot that pole vaulters probably cleared in 1966. 17 ft
4. Estimate the year when 18 feet was cleared for the first time. 1971
5. If the Olympics had been held in 1940, predict what the winning height would have been (to the nearest foot). 14 ft
6. Based on the trend from 1960 through 1980, would you predict the winning height in 1984 to be over or under 19 feet? over

Use the graph at the right to answer the following questions.

7. Based on the trend from 1977 through 1981, what level of savings would you predict for 1982? About $150 billion
8. How does your prediction for 1982 compare with the actual level of savings for 1982? About $15 billion too high
9. Based on the trend from 1981 through 1983, what level of savings would you predict for 1984? About $100 billion
10. The actual level of savings in 1984 was $156.1 billion. How does your prediction for 1984 compare with this actual level? About $55 billion too low

Alternate Strategies: Extending the Lesson

Enrichment

Science Connection Have students follow newspaper weather statistics for several days. From patterns developed, predict the weather for the following day. Compare to the weather service prediction and the actual weather. Discuss any differences.

Cooperative Learning

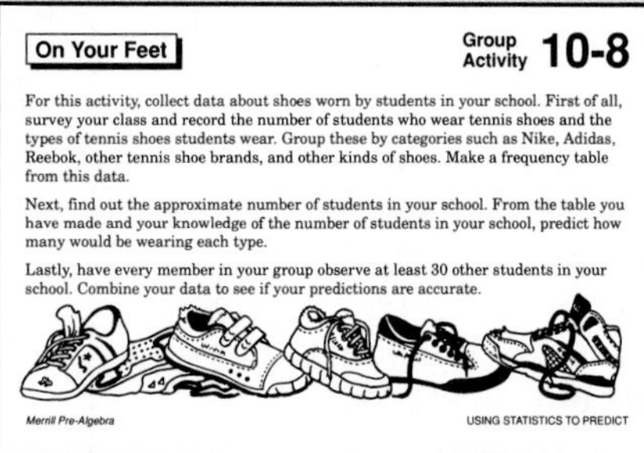

On Your Feet — Group Activity 10-8

For this activity, collect data about shoes worn by students in your school. First of all, survey your class and record the number of students who wear tennis shoes and the types of tennis shoes students wear. Group these by categories such as Nike, Adidas, Reebok, other tennis shoe brands, and other kinds of shoes. Make a frequency table from this data.

Next, find out the approximate number of students in your school. From the table you have made and your knowledge of the number of students in your school, predict how many would be wearing each type.

Lastly, have every member in your group observe at least 30 other students in your school. Combine your data to see if your predictions are accurate.

Merrill Pre-Algebra — USING STATISTICS TO PREDICT

10-9 Misleading Statistics

Objective:
Recognize when statistics are misleading.

Tom wants to convince his parents that his math grades are improving. He decides to make bar graphs that show his math grades for each grading period. Graphs A and B show Tom's grades. Although they display the same data, each graph gives a different impression.

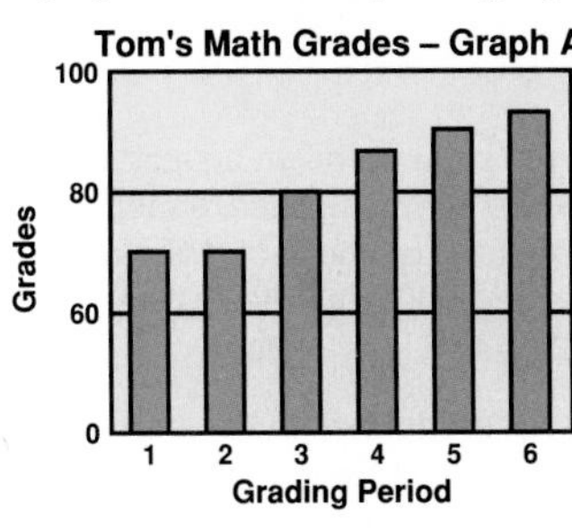

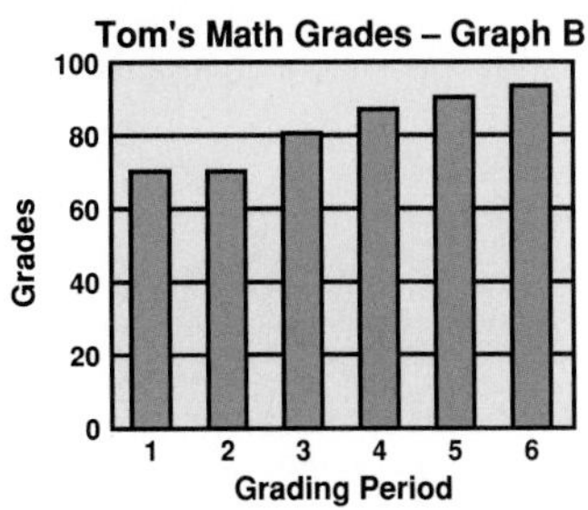

Which graph shows the greatest improvement in Tom's grades? Graph A does. However, it is misleading. Notice the vertical axis. The distance from 0 to 60 is the same as the distance from 60 to 80. This is an incorrect representation of the data and can lead to wrong conclusions.

To correct this graph, you can draw a broken line at the bottom of the vertical axis as shown at the right.

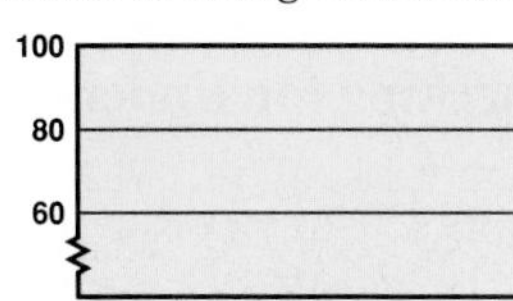

Example

1 The two graphs display the same ticket sales information for the Drexel Theater.

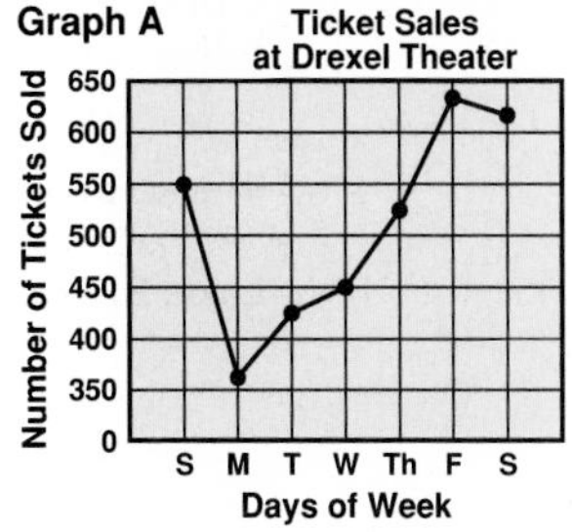

Is Graph A misleading? If so, why? Graph A is misleading because the distance between 0 and 350 is the same as the distance between 350 and 400 on the vertical axis.

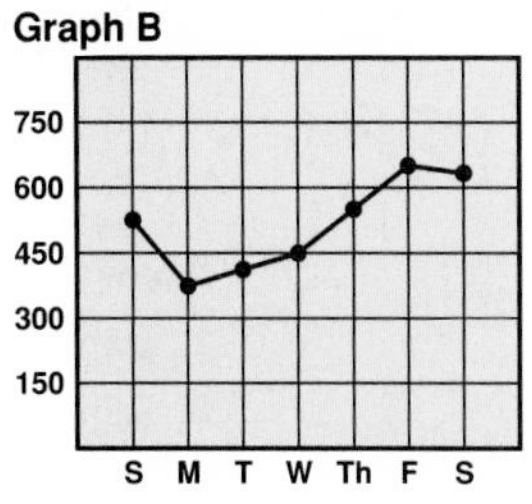

Is Graph B misleading? If so, why? Graph B is misleading because there is no title and there are no labels on either scale.

Lesson Notes 10-9

5-Minute Check
(over Lesson 10-8)

The ninth grade class officers decided to have a pizza party. They estimate one pizza would feed four students. There are a total of 240 students. The officers surveyed one homeroom to estimate how much of each kind of pizza to order.

Type of Pizza	Number of Students
pepperoni	12
cheese	4
sausage	8

1. How many students were surveyed? **24 students**
2. What fraction surveyed liked pepperoni pizza best? $\frac{1}{2}$
3. What fraction surveyed liked cheese pizza best? $\frac{1}{6}$
4. How many pepperoni pizzas need to be ordered? **30 pepperoni pizzas**
5. How many cheese pizzas need to be ordered? **10 cheese pizzas**

Transparency 10-9 contains the 5-Minute Check and a teaching aid for this lesson.

1 FOCUS

The purpose of this lesson is to examine graphs and measures of central tendency to determine if they misrepresent data.

Motivating the Lesson

Ask students to verbalize times when they were misled by information in written ads or television or radio commercials.

2 TEACH

Using Discussion

Tell students that you did a survey and 3 out of 4 students said that math was their favorite subject. Have students discuss what could be misleading about your survey.

EE: 1A, 3A, 5D, 5E, 5F
TAAS: 5, 11, 12

Bell Ringer

4 out of 11, 6 out of 17, and 8 out of 25. How many out of 30? **10**

Chalkboard Examples

- *For Example 1*
  Is the line graph below misleading? If so, why? yes; The distance between 0 and 50 is the same distance as the distance between 50 and 52.

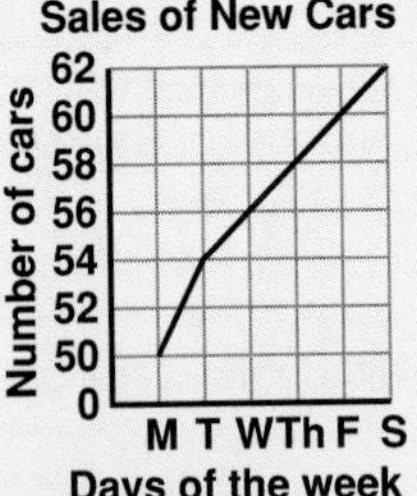

- *For Example 2*

Reading Scores	Number of Students
95% or higher	5
80-94%	37
70-79%	75
59-69%	58
below 59	65

Which "average" would the school board want to use? mode
Which "average" would school critics like to use? median or mean

Practice Masters Booklet, **p. 100**

Name ______________________ Date ____________

Practice Worksheet 10-9

Misleading Statistics

Salaries at the Homecraft Company are shown in the table at the right. Use the table to answer the following questions.

Salary	Number of Employees
$12,000	2
$18,000	6
$24,000	5
$28,000	2
$55,000	1
$79,000	1

1. What is the mode of the salaries? $18,000
2. What is the median salary? $24,000
3. What is the mean salary? $26,000
4. Which average would you use to attract new employees? mean
5. Suppose the person earning the $79,000 salary leaves the company. Find the new median and mean. Which was changed the most? $21,000, $22,687.50; mean

Bob and Carol went bowling. Their scores are shown in the table below. Use the table to answer the following questions. Round to the nearest tenth, if necessary.

	Game 1	Game 2	Game 3	Game 4	Game 5	Game 6
Bob	213	157	171	142	155	157
Carol	131	162	182	120	173	175

6. Find the range, mean, median, and mode for Bob's scores. 71; 165.8; 157; 157
7. Find the range, mean, median, and mode for Carol's scores. 62; 157.2; 167.5; none
8. Who had the better scores? Explain your answer. Answers may vary. Sample answer: Carol; she had the higher score in 4 of the 6 games.

The table at the right shows shoe sales for the month of March. Use the table to answer the following questions.

Size	Number Sold
5	3
$5\frac{1}{2}$	12
6	15
$6\frac{1}{2}$	5
7	4
$7\frac{1}{2}$	13
8	8
$8\frac{1}{2}$	2

9. Which was the most popular size? size 6
10. What was the median size sold? size $6\frac{1}{2}$
11. Which average would be most useful in deciding which sizes to order when the new styles come out? mode

Another way statistics can be misleading is by using the wrong average. Following are some guidelines for best use of the measures of central tendency.

- The mode can be used with either items or numbers. Use the mode when the most frequent item or number best represents the data.
- Very large or very small numbers affect the mean. Therefore, use the mean when the range is not great.
- Very large or very small numbers have little effect on the median. Therefore, use the median when the range is great.

Example

2 Employee salaries at an advertising agency are shown in the frequency table at the right. The mode and the median wage is $24,000. The mean wage is $30,815.

Salary	Number
$100,000	1
$75,000	2
$50,000	3
$24,000	15
$12,000	6

Which "average" best represents the data? Why? the median; because the range is great

Which "average" would the union want to use in its wage talks? Why? They might use the mode or median because it makes the current salaries look lower.

Which "average" would the factory owner use? Why? They might use the mean wage because it makes current salaries look higher.

Checking for Understanding

Communicating Algebra

1. What are some ways in which graphs can mislead? See margin.
2. When should the mean be used instead of the median? when there are no very small numbers or very large numbers

Which average, *mode, median,* or *mean,* would best describe the following? Explain each answer. For answers to Exercises 3-6, see margin.

3. eye color
4. height of the players on a basketball team
5. ages of persons in a theater
6. height of the fans at a game

Guided Practice

Linda Kline made two different line graphs showing the monthly sales for her bakery.

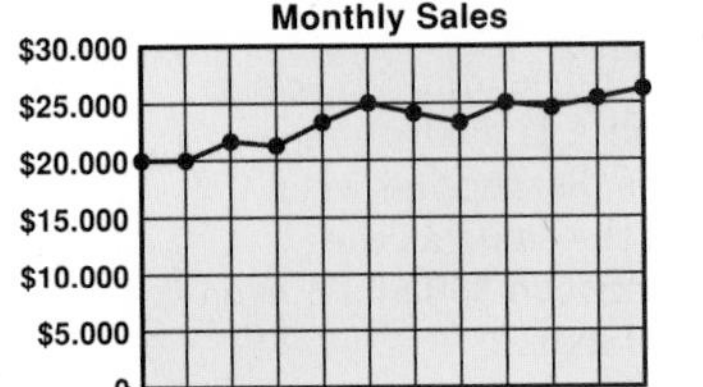

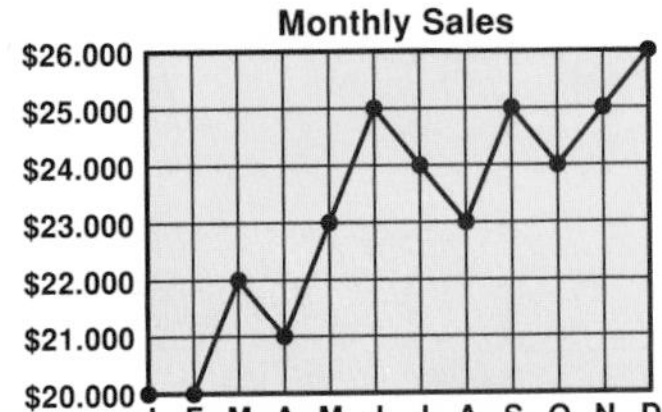

Answer each question about the graphs shown above. 7. different scale

7. Explain why these graphs made from the same data look different.
8. Which graph would she show to someone who wanted to buy her bakery? Explain.
9. Which graph would she show an employee who asked for a big raise? Explain.

8., 9. See margin.

Additional Answers

1. The units on the axes may not be uniformly marked or there may not be a title or labels.
3. mode
4. mean
5. median
6. mode or median

Reteaching Masters Booklet, **p. 90**

Name ______________________ Date ____________

Reteaching Worksheet 10-9

Misleading Statistics

The lists below show the amounts earned by high school students during summer vacation.

Group A: $30, $50, $100, $100, $100, $200, $600
Group B: $30, $40, $50, $50, $100, $100, $600

Use the two lists above for Exercises 1–5.

1. Describe your interpretation of the differences between the two lists.
   Answers will vary. Sample answer: More students in Group A made at least $100 during the summer.
2. The range of a list of data is the difference between the greatest and the least values. Find the range for each group.
   $570, $570
3. Find the median for each group.

Exercises

Independent Practice

The personnel manager of a local law firm made the following chart of its employees.

	Ana Sarafin	Doris Nethers	Jerry Anderson	Kimiko Chung	Brian Sommers
Age	29	32	35	38	31
Salary	\$47,000	\$13,000	\$25,500	\$66,000	\$34,700
Height (cm)	154	160	165	157	149
Favorite Entertainment	movies	theater	books	sports	sports

Use the chart to find the following. State the type of average you used.

10. average age 33; mean
11. average salary \$34,700; median
12. average height 157 cm; mean
13. average favorite entertainment sports; mode
14. How can you describe the "average" employee in this group? according to averages in Exercises 10-13

Mixed Review

15. Write 93,200 in scientific notation. (Lesson 6-11) 9.32×10^4
16. Find the mean, median, and mode for the data set: 2.4, 7.0, 3.8, 5.6, 4.1, 4.5. Round to the nearest tenth. (Lesson 10-2) 4.6; 4.3; none
17. Refer to the bar graph on page 388. How many cans of ginger ale should Terry order? (Lesson 10-8) 700 cans

Applications

Solve. State the type of average you used and why.

18. **Consumer Surveys** A survey at a grocery store showed that 5 people preferred Brand A, 15 people preferred Brand B, 27 people preferred Brand C, and 10 people preferred Brand D. Which brand did the "average" customer prefer? See margin.
19. **Real Estate** A subdivision has houses that are priced \$70,000, \$75,000, \$82,000, \$88,000, and \$150,000. Which price gives a better description of the houses in that subdivision? Why? \$82,000; median; \$150,000 is much larger than the other four prices

Critical Thinking

20. **Research** Find a graph in a magazine or newspaper. Redo the graph so that the data will appear to show different results. See students' work.

Wrap-Up

21. Describe two uses of statistics that can mislead the consumer. misleading graph, incorrect use of average

3 PRACTICE/APPLY

Checking the Concept

Ask students which two statistics they should check when determining which "average" to use. mode and range

Independent Practice

Homework Assignment	
Basic	10-13, 15-18, 20, 21
Average	12-21
Honors	12-21

Chapter 10, Quiz B (Lessons 10-6 through 10-9) is available in the Evaluation Masters Booklet, p. 88.

4 CLOSE

Assessment Option

Modeling Use other graphs from newspapers or magazines and ask the students if they are misleading or not.

Enrichment Masters Booklet, **p. 90**

Name ______________ Date ______________

Enrichment Worksheet 10-9

Using and Misusing Graphs

Use the graphs at the right. Complete the following to discover which graph is misleading.

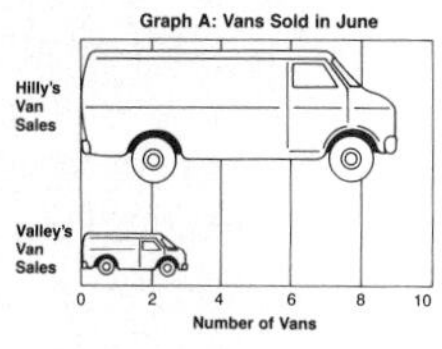

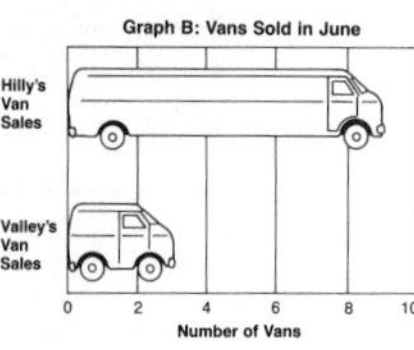

1. Do Graphs A and B give the same information on sales? Yes
2. Find the ratio of Hilly's sales to Valley's sales. 3:1
3. In Graph A, the Hilly van is about 2.5 cm high by 6 cm long. What is its area? 15 cm^2
4. The Valley van is about 0.75 cm high by 2 cm long. What is its area? 1.5 cm^2
5. In Graph B, both vans are about 1.5 cm high. The Hilly van is about 6 cm long. What is its area? 9 cm^2
6. The Valley van is about 2 cm long. What is its area? 3 cm^2
7. Compute the following ratios.
   Graph A: $\frac{\text{Area of Hilly}}{\text{Area of Valley}}$ $\frac{10}{1}$
   Graph B: $\frac{\text{Area of Hilly}}{\text{Area of Valley}}$ $\frac{3}{1}$
8. Compare the results of Exercises 2 and 7. Which graph is misleading? Explain your answer.
A; The actual number of vans sold by Hilly's is 3 times greater, but Graph A appears to show the sales as 10 times greater.

Use Graphs C and D to answer each question.

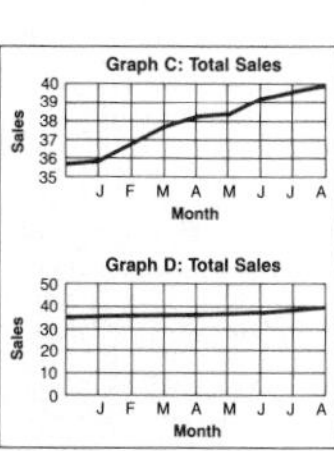

9. Which graph is easier to read? C
10. Compare the vertical scales. How do they differ? The units on Graph C increase by 1, while the units on Graph D increase by 10.
11. Which graph gives a better impression of the trend in sales? Explain. Sample answer: The sales increase is overstated by Graph C and understated by Graph D.

Additional Answers

8. The graph on the right because it looks like there is a dramatic rise in sales.
9. The graph on the left because it appears that sales are steady but not rising drastically enough to warrant a big raise.
18. The "average" customer preferred Brand C.

Cooperative Learning

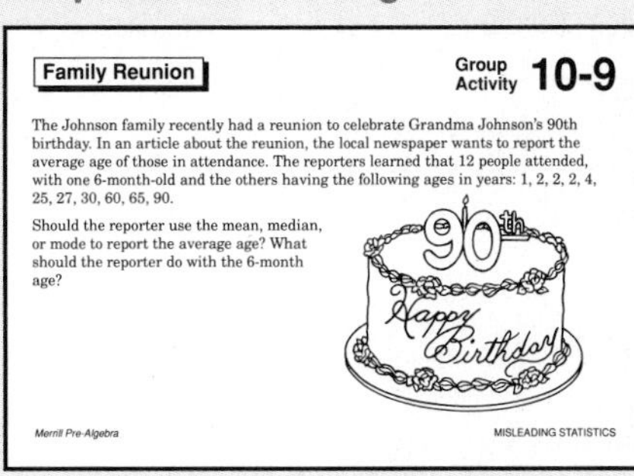

Family Reunion Group Activity **10-9**

The Johnson family recently had a reunion to celebrate Grandma Johnson's 90th birthday. In an article about the reunion, the local newspaper wants to report the average age of those in attendance. The reporters learned that 12 people attended, with one 6-month-old and the others having the following ages in years: 1, 2, 2, 2, 4, 25, 27, 30, 60, 65, 90.

Should the reporter use the mean, median, or mode to report the average age? What should the reporter do with the 6-month age?

Merrill Pre-Algebra MISLEADING STATISTICS

Review

Language and Concepts

Choose the correct term to complete each sentence.

1. The (median, mode) is the number or item that appears most often in a data set.
2. The (stem, leaf) of a stem-and-leaf plot is the greatest place value of the data.
3. Two *different* sets of data (can, cannot) have the same mean, median, and mode.
4. An (extreme value, outlier) in a box-and-whisker plot is any piece of data that is more than 1.5 times the interquartile range from the quartiles.

Skills

The table shows test scores for a biology class. Use the table to answer each question. (Lesson 10-1)

5. How many students are in the sample? 25
6. What scores occurred most often? 17–18
7. What scores occurred least often? 11–12
8. Would it be correct to say that 50% of the students scored at least 17? yes
9. Make a histogram of the data. See margin.

Score	Test Scores Tally	Frequency
19-20	𝍸	5
17-18	𝍸 IIII	9
15-16	𝍸	5
13-14	III	3
11-12	I	1
9-10	II	2

Find the mean, median, and mode for each set of data. (Lesson 10-2)

10. 156, 175, 212, 167, 628, 156
249, 171, 156
11. 2.6, 3.1, 6.8, 4.9, 5.7, 3.4, 4.3
4.4, 4.3, none

Use the stem-and-leaf plot to answer each question. (Lessons 10-3, 10-4)

12. What were the least and greatest movie attendance? 7, 78
13. What is the median of the data? 29
14. What are the lower and upper quartiles? 21, 34
15. What is the interquartile range? 13
16. What is the range of the data? 71

Movie Attendance

Stem	Leaf
0	7
1	7 9
2	1 5 5 8
3	0 0 2 4 5 9
4	
5	
6	
7	8

2|1 means 21.

Using the Chapter Review

The Chapter Review is a comprehensive review of the concepts presented in this chapter. This review may be used to prepare students for the Chapter Test.

Alternate Review Strategy

To provide a brief in-class review, you may wish to read the following questions to the class and require a verbal response.

1. Refer to the frequency chart on page 363. What percent of the sample watched 12 or more hours of TV per week? 34%
2. Mary's group received the following math test scores: 90, 92, 87, 95, 86. What was the median score? 90%
3. What are the stems for the following test scores: 98, 62, 85, 74, 43? 4, 5, 6, 7, 8, 9
4. Given the set of data 17, 11, 2, 31, 53, 29, 7, find the range and the median. 51, 17
5. What is the interquartile range for problem 4? 24
6. What information does the box in a box-and-whisker plot provide? upper and lower quartiles, median
7. What are three kinds of relationships shown by a scatter plot? positive, negative, none
8. Find the sum of the first 20 negative even integers. -420
9. Refer to the bar graph on page 388. How many cans of root beer should Terry order? 1000 cans
10. When should the mode be used for stating the average? when the most frequent item or number best represents the data

Use the box-and-whisker plot to answer each question. (Lesson 10-5)

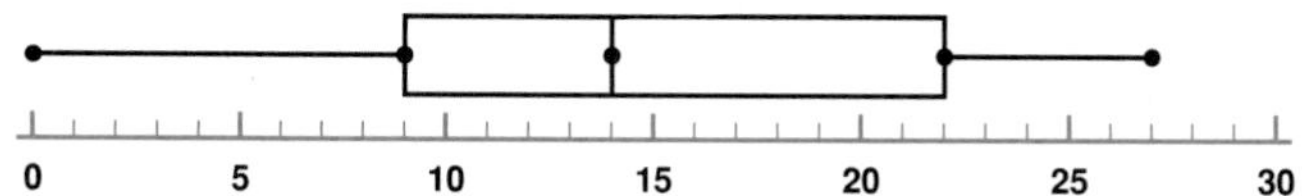

17. What is the median? 14
18. What is the upper quartile? 22
19. What is the lower quartile? 9
20. What is the interquartile range? 13
21. What are the extremes? 0, 27
22. Are there any outliers? no

Use the scatter plot to answer each question. (Lesson 10-6)

23. What kind of relationship, if any, is shown by the scatter plot? positive
24. What does the point shown in red represent? 185 lb, 6' 2" player

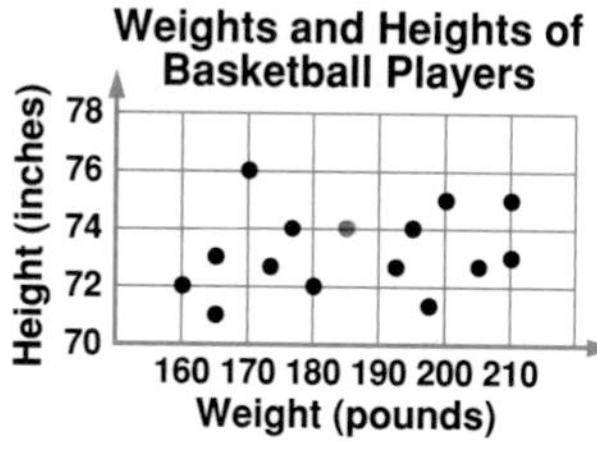

Applications and Problem Solving

25. The lockers in the hall outside Joanna's homeroom start with number 256 and end with number 375. How many lockers are in the hall? (Lesson 10-7) 120 lockers
26. In a sample, 25 of 75 students surveyed would choose a blue notebook cover. If 500 students buy notebook covers, how many blue covers should be ordered? (Lesson 10-8) 167 blue covers

Communicating Algebra

27. Describe three characteristics that should be part of every graph. titles, labels, and uniformly marked scales

Curriculum Connection

- **Consumer Awareness** Find at least two current ads for different brands of CD players. Determine which brand offers the better buy, technologically. See students' work.

Read More About It

James, Elizabeth. *What Do You Mean by "Average"?*

Robertson, Bruce. *How to Draw Charts and Diagrams.*

Additional Answers

9.

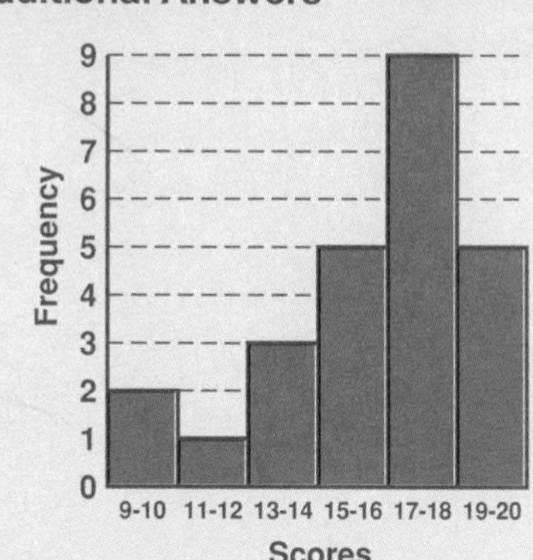

You may wish to use a Chapter Test (free-response format) as an additional chapter review. Two forms are provided in the Evaluation Masters Booklet as shown below.

Evaluation Masters Booklet, **p. 86**

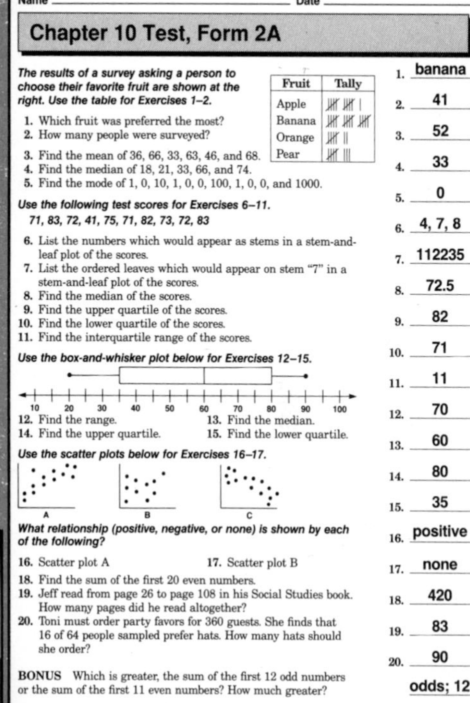

Name ________ Date ________

Chapter 10 Test, Form 2A

The results of a survey asking a person to choose their favorite fruit are shown at the right. Use the table for Exercises 1–2.

Fruit	Tally
Apple	卌 卌 |
Banana	卌 卌 卌
Orange	卌 ||
Pear	卌 |||

1. Which fruit was preferred the most? 1. banana
2. How many people were surveyed? 2. 41
3. Find the mean of 36, 66, 33, 63, 46, and 68. 3. 52
4. Find the median of 18, 21, 33, 66, and 74. 4. 33
5. Find the mode of 1, 0, 10, 1, 0, 0, 100, 1, 0, 0, and 1000. 5. 0

Use the following test scores for Exercises 6–11.
71, 83, 72, 41, 75, 71, 82, 73, 72, 83

6. List the numbers which would appear as stems in a stem-and-leaf plot of the scores. 6. 4, 7, 8
7. List the ordered leaves which would appear on stem "7" in a stem-and-leaf plot of the scores. 7. 112235
8. Find the median of the scores. 8. 72.5
9. Find the upper quartile of the scores. 9. 82
10. Find the lower quartile of the scores. 10. 71
11. Find the interquartile range of the scores. 11. 11

Use the box-and-whisker plot below for Exercises 12–15.

10 20 30 40 50 60 70 80 90 100

12. Find the range. 12. 70
13. Find the median. 13. 60
14. Find the upper quartile. 14. 80
15. Find the lower quartile. 15. 35

Use the scatter plots below for Exercises 16–17.

A B C

What relationship (positive, negative, or none) is shown by each of the following?

16. Scatter plot A 16. positive
17. Scatter plot B 17. none
18. Find the sum of the first 20 even numbers. 18. 420
19. Jeff read from page 26 to page 108 in his Social Studies book. How many pages did he read altogether? 19. 83
20. Toni must order party favors for 360 guests. She finds that 16 of 64 people sampled prefer hats. How many hats should she order? 20. 90

BONUS Which is greater, the sum of the first 12 odd numbers or the sum of the first 11 even numbers? How much greater? odds; 12

Evaluation Masters Booklet, **p. 87**

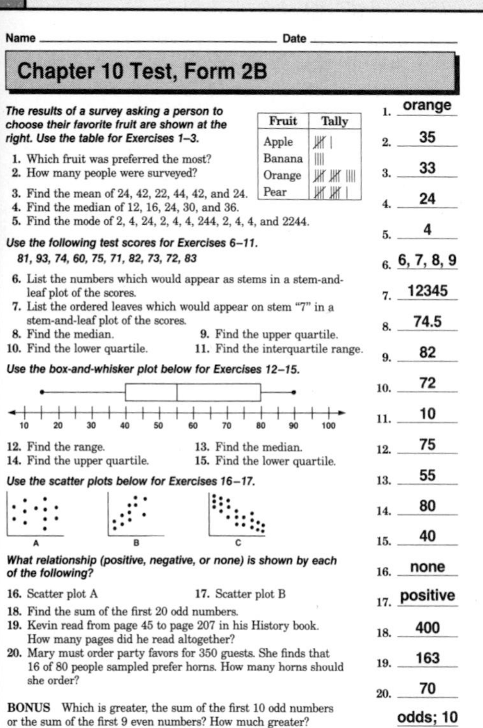

Name ________ Date ________

Chapter 10 Test, Form 2B

The results of a survey asking a person to choose their favorite fruit are shown at the right. Use the table for Exercises 1–3.

Fruit	Tally
Apple	卌 |
Banana	||||
Orange	卌 卌 ||||
Pear	卌 卌 |

1. Which fruit was preferred the most? 1. orange
2. How many people were surveyed? 2. 35
3. Find the mean of 24, 42, 22, 44, 42, and 24. 3. 33
4. Find the median of 12, 16, 24, 30, and 36. 4. 24
5. Find the mode of 2, 4, 24, 2, 4, 4, 244, 2, 4, 4, and 2244. 5. 4

Use the following test scores for Exercises 6–11.
81, 93, 74, 60, 75, 71, 82, 73, 72, 83

6. List the numbers which would appear as stems in a stem-and-leaf plot of the scores. 6. 6, 7, 8, 9
7. List the ordered leaves which would appear on stem "7" in a stem-and-leaf plot of the scores. 7. 12345
8. Find the median. 8. 74.5
9. Find the upper quartile. 9. 82
10. Find the lower quartile. 10. 72
11. Find the interquartile range. 11. 10

Use the box-and-whisker plot below for Exercises 12–15.

10 20 30 40 50 60 70 80 90 100

12. Find the range. 12. 75
13. Find the median. 13. 55
14. Find the upper quartile. 14. 80
15. Find the lower quartile. 15. 40

Use the scatter plots below for Exercises 16–17.

A B C

What relationship (positive, negative, or none) is shown by each of the following?

16. Scatter plot A 16. none
17. Scatter plot B 17. positive
18. Find the sum of the first 20 odd numbers. 18. 400
19. Kevin read from page 45 to page 207 in his History book. How many pages did he read altogether? 19. 163
20. Mary must order party favors for 350 guests. She finds that 16 of 80 people sampled prefer horns. How many horns should she order? 20. 70

BONUS Which is greater, the sum of the first 10 odd numbers or the sum of the first 9 even numbers? How much greater? odds; 10

Using the Chapter Test

This page may be used as a test or as an additional review. Two forms of a Chapter Test (multiple-choice format) are provided in the Evaluation Masters Booklet.

Evaluation Masters Booklet, **pp. 82-83**

Name ______________________ Date ____________

Chapter 10 Test, Form 1A

The results of a poll asking a person to choose their favorite brand of hand soap are shown in the table at the right. Use the table for Exercises 1 – 3.

Soap	Tally
Brand W	𝍸 𝍸 ||
Brand X	𝍸 𝍸 𝍸 |
Brand Y	𝍸 𝍸 ||
Brand Z	𝍸 𝍸 |

1. Which brand of soap was preferred the most? A. W B. X C. Y D. Z — 1. B
2. Which brand of soap was preferred the least? A. W B. X C. Y D. Z — 2. D
3. How many people preferred Brand X? A. 4 B. 13 C. 16 D. 21 — 3 C
4. Which measure is usually meant when a person says to find the "average?" A. mean B. median C. mode D. sum — 4. A
5. Find the median of 62, 63, 63, 64, 65, 70, and 71. A. 62 B. 63 C. 64 D. 65 — 5. C
6. Find the mean of 18, 20, 22, 25, and 30. A. 12 B. 22 C. 23 D. 115 — 6. C
7. Find the mode of 18, 20, 19, 18, 20, 18, 19, 19, 19, 20, and 21. A. 18 B. 19 C. 20 D. 21 — 7. B
8. Which number would not appear as a stem when drawing a stem-and-leaf plot? 80, 75, 72, 63, 75, 77, 78, 69 A. 5 B. 6 C. 7 D. 8 — 8. A
9. Which score appears most often in the stem-and-leaf plot at the right? 6 | 26678 A. 26 B. 62 C. 78 D. 66 — 9. D

Use the following exam scores for Exercises 10 – 12. 80, 84, 96, 88, 91, 96, 98

10. Find the range of the exam scores. A. 18 B. 88 C. 89 D. 622 — 10. A
11. Find the upper quartile of the exam scores. A. 88 B. 98 C. 91 D. 96 — 11. D
12. Find the lower quartile of the exam scores. A. 80 B. 84 C. 86 D. 88 — 12. B

Name ______________________ Date ____________

Chapter 10 Test, Form 1A (continued)

13. Brian is ordering ice-cream flavors for a large convention. In a random sample, he finds that 18 of 72 people asked prefer vanilla-flavored ice cream. If he must allow for 2000 servings, about how many vanilla-flavored ice creams should he order? A. 400 B. 500 C. 1000 D. 2000 — 13. B

Use the box-and-whisker plot below for Exercises 14 – 16.

20 30 40 50 60 70

14. Find the range. A. 55 B. 50 C. 45 D. 70 — 14. C
15. Find the median. A. 25 B. 30 C. 45 D. 55 — 15. C
16. Find the lower quartile. A. 25 B. 30 C. 40 D. 45 — 16. B

The scatter plot at the right shows the relationship between the price of 35 compact discs (CDs) and the number of years since each recording was originally released (on record, tape, or CD). Use the scatter plot for Exercises 17 – 19.

Price (in dollars) 6 8 10 12 14; Years Since Release 2 4 6 8 10

17. The relationship appears to be of what type? A. positive B. negative C. none D. quartile — 17. C
18. Find the years having the lowest prices. A. 0–2 B. 2–4 C. 4–6 D. 8–10 — 18. C
19. Find the years having the highest prices. A. 2–4 B. 4–6 C. 6–8 D. 8–10 — 19. D
20. Find the sum of the even numbers from 2 to 200. A. 10,000 B. 10,100 C. 20,200 D. 20,000 — 20. B

BONUS Two sets of school lockers on the second floor are numbered consecutively from 201 to 328 and from 406 to 500. If five lockers are broken, how many usable lockers are on the second floor? A. 216 B. 217 C. 218 D. 296 — C

CHAPTER 10 Test

For 1 and 7, see Solutions Manual.

Use the data in the temperature chart to complete the following.

High Temperature (°C) for Houston for a 20-day Period				
21	25	16	18	18
26	21	17	19	21
22	24	26	21	22
17	16	17	20	25

1. Make a frequency table of the data.
2. Find the range of the data. **10**
3. Find the mean of the data. **20.6**
4. Find the mode of the data. **21**
5. Find the median of the data. **21**
6. Make a stem-and-leaf plot of the data. Describe the distribution of the data. **See margin.**

Use the data in the television-viewing chart to complete the following.

Television Viewing Per Week

Age	Hours	Age	Hours
12	20	48	40
16	19	21	19
10	19	67	41
24	34	15	25
25	21	34	25
50	46	17	28
58	32	6	32
71	49	22	33
62	38	18	22
8	25	4	36

7. Make a scatter plot of the data.
8. Does there appear to be a positive, negative, or no relationship between age and number of hours of TV watched weekly? **positive**
9. Make a box-and-whisker plot of the hours. **9. See margin.**
10. What is the range of the hours? **30 hours**
11. What is the interquartile range? **15.5 hours**
12. What is the median number of hours of TV watched weekly? **30 hours**
13. What percent of the people surveyed watch more than 36 hours of TV per week? **25%**

Solve.

14. Find the sum of the first 50 odd numbers. How does this compare to the sum of the first 50 even numbers? **2500; 50 less**
15. Six out of 70 students surveyed at Midview School said they would like to start a Spanish club. The school's policy says there must be 30 interested students to start a new club. If there are 560 students in the school, predict how many students would be interested in a Spanish club. Is this enough to start a new club? **48 students; yes**

Use the graph to the right to complete the following. **16. uneven intervals on x-axis**

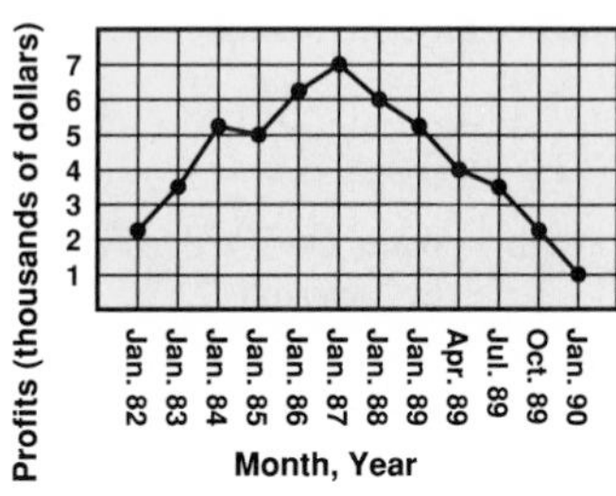

16. What is wrong with this graph?
17. If the graph were corrected, what could you say about the profits from 1987 to the present? **sharp decline**

Test Generator Software is provided in both Apple and IBM formats. You may use this software to create your own tests, based on the needs of your students.

Additional Answers

6.
1 | 6 6 7 7 7 8 8 9
2 | 0 1 1 1 1 2 2 4 5 5 6 6

The data is clustered between 16 and 26.

9.

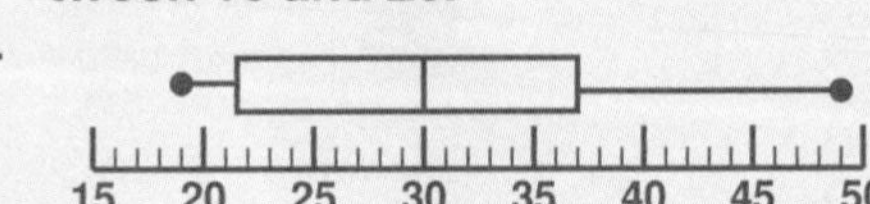

Academic Skills Test

Cumulative, Chapters 1-10

1. Which equation is equivalent to $1.8a = 36$?
   (A) $a = 36 \div 1.8$
   B $a = 36 - 1.8$
   C $1.8a - 1.8 = 36 - 1.8$
   D $1.8a = 36 \div 1.8$

2. If $\frac{n}{11} = 33$, what is the value of n?
   A 3 C 44
   B 22 (D) 363

3. Cindy needs $\frac{3}{4}$ cup of sliced almonds for a recipe. One bag contains about $1\frac{1}{2}$ cups. How much will be left?
   (A) $\frac{3}{4}$ cup
   B 1 cup
   C $1\frac{1}{4}$ cups
   D $2\frac{1}{4}$ cups

4. If $\frac{b}{456} = 1.2$, what is the value of b?
   A 38
   B 380
   (C) 547.2
   D 5472

5. A mail-order card company charges 50¢ for each greeting card plus a handling charge of $1.50. Which sentence could be used to find n, the number of cards ordered, if the total charge was $9?
   (A) $0.5n + 1.5 = 9$
   B $0.50n + 1.50n = 9$
   C $9 = 50n + 1.50$
   D $9 = (0.5 + 1.50)n$

6. Scott generally runs a mile in anywhere from 7.5 to 8.5 minutes. Which number line shows this range of times?

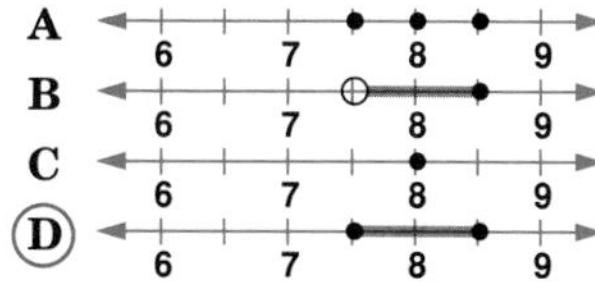

7. In a survey, 75 percent of the people surveyed like pizza. If 36 people were surveyed, which proportion will find n, the number who like pizza?
   A $\frac{75}{36} = \frac{n}{100}$ C $\frac{75}{100} = \frac{36}{n}$
   B $\frac{75}{n} = \frac{36}{100}$ (D) Not Here

8. The number of students in Sam's aerobics class increased from 15 to 24. What was the percent of increase?
   A 37.5% C 62.5%
   (B) 60% D 135%

9. The high temperatures for a week in April were 56°F, 58°F, 60°F, 63°F, 58°F, 62°F, and 70°F. What was the median temperature?
   A 58°F C 61°F
   (B) 60°F D 63°F

10. Chapter 10 of the book Milagros is reading starts on page 286 and ends on page 319. How long is the chapter?
    A 32 pages (C) 34 pages
    B 33 pages D Not Here

A Cumulative Review (free-response format) and Cumulative Test (multiple-choice format) are also provided in the Evaluation Masters Booklet as shown at the right.

Test Item	1	2	3	4	5	6	7	8	9	10
Lesson Number	1-7	3-4	5-6	6-7	7-3	8-2	9-4	9-10	10-2	10-7
TAAS Objective	2	2	7	2	12	2	2, 11	11	5	11

Using the Academic Skills Test

This test familiarizes students with a standardized format while testing skills and concepts represented up to this point.

Evaluation Masters Booklet, p. 89

Name ______________ Date ______________

Cumulative Review, Chapters 1-10

1. Simplify $3 \cdot 5 + 2 \div 2$. (Lesson 1–1)
2. Solve $y = -6 - 8$. (Lesson 2–5)
3. Find the perimeter of a square 12 meters on a side. (Lesson 3–6)
4. Evaluate x^4, if $x = -3$. (Lesson 4–2)
5. Find the LCM of 15 and 25. (Lesson 4–7)
6. Solve $x = -6.2 + 8.379$. (Lesson 5–4)
7. Subtract 11 ft 2 in. − 6 ft 5 in. (Lesson 5–10)
8. Express $\frac{2}{11}$ as a decimal. (Lesson 6–1)
9. Solve $(-4.07)(-6.3) = n$. (Lesson 6–4)
10. Express 0.24 in scientific notation. (Lesson 6–11)
11. Solve $3y + 4 = 40$. (Lesson 7–2)
12. Solve $6n - 6 = 5n + 1$. (Lesson 7–4)
13. Complete 3.6 m = ■ cm. (Lesson 7–8)
14. Name the quadrant that contains the graph of $(2, -7)$. (Lesson 8–4)
15. Find the slope of the line that contains $M(9, 10)$ and $N(6, 8)$. (Lesson 8–8)
16. Find the x-intercept for the graph of $y = x + 12$. (Lesson 8–9)
17. Solve $\frac{18}{12} = \frac{9}{y}$. (Lesson 9–2)
18. Express 3.6 as a percent. (Lesson 9–5)
19. Express 55% as a fraction. (Lesson 9–5)
20. What percent of 12 is 9? (Lesson 9–7)
21. Find the median of the scores 25, 35, 65, 40, and 25. (Lesson 10–2)
22. Find the mean of the scores 80, 85, 85, 90, and 95. (Lesson 10–2)
23. Find the mode of the scores 72, 80, 85, 85, 87, 90, 91, and 92. (Lesson 10–2)

Use the box-and-whisker plot below. (Lesson 10–5)

24. What is the median?
25. What is the upper quartile?

30 40 50 60 70 80 90

1. 16
2. −14
3. 48 m
4. 81
5. 75
6. 2.179
7. 4 ft 9 in.
8. $0.\overline{18}$
9. 25.641
10. 2.4×10^{-1}
11. 12
12. 7
13. 360
14. IV
15. $\frac{2}{3}$
16. −12
17. 6
18. 360%
19. $\frac{11}{20}$
20. 75%
21. 35
22. 87
23. 85
24. 60
25. 75

Evaluation Masters Booklet, p. 90

Name ______________ Date ______________

Cumulative Test, Chapters 1-10

1. Solve $y = -5 - (-8)$.
   A. 13 B. −13 C. 3 D. −3 1. C
2. Find the area of a square with 8-inch sides.
   A. 64 in² B. 16 in² C. 32 in² D. 8 in² 2. A
3. Evaluate x^3, if $x = -2$.
   A. 1 B. −5 C. −6 D. −8 3. D
4. Find the LCM of 10 and 20.
   A. 40 B. 200 C. 20 D. 2 4. C
5. Solve $x = -3.8 + 4.82$.
   A. 8.62 B. 1.02 C. −8.62 D. −1.02 5. B
6. Subtract 10 ft − 3 ft 8 in.
   A. 7 ft 4 in. B. 6 ft 8 in. C. 6 ft 4 in. D. 7 ft 8 in. 6. C
7. Express $\frac{1}{6}$ as a decimal.
   A. $0.1\overline{6}$ B. 1.6 C. $1.\overline{6}$ D. 0.16 7. A
8. Express 150 in scientific notation.
   A. 1.5×10^2 B. 0.15×10^3 C. 15×10^1 D. 1.5×10^{-2} 8. A
9. Solve $4m + 6 = 8m - 2$.
   A. −2 B. −1 C. 1 D. 2 9. D
10. Complete 250 cm = ■ m.
    A. 2500 B. 0.25 C. 25 D. 2.5 10. D
11. Name the quadrant that contains the graph of $(-5, -6)$.
    A. I B. II C. III D. IV 11. C
12. Find the slope of the line that contains $M(7, 10)$ and $N(5, -6)$.
    A. $\frac{1}{8}$ B. $-\frac{1}{8}$ C. −8 D. 8 12. D
13. Find the x-intercept for the graph of $y = x - 2$.
    A. 2 B. −2 C. −0.5 D. 0.5 13. A
14. Solve $\frac{10}{5} = \frac{x}{4}$.
    A. 2 B. 2.5 C. 0.125 D. 8 14. D
15. Express 40% as a fraction in simplest form.
    A. $\frac{40}{99}$ B. $\frac{4}{100}$ C. $\frac{2}{5}$ D. $\frac{1}{4}$ 15. C
16. What percent of 90 is 18?
    A. 20% B. 18% C. 0.2% D. 500% 16. A
17. Find the median of the scores 20, 30, 55, 40, and 20.
    A. 20 B. 30 C. 40 D. 55 17. B
18. Find the mean of the scores 70, 75, 85, 80, and 75.
    A. 70 B. 85 C. 75 D. 77 18. D

Use the box-and-whisker plot at the right.

19. What is the median?
    A. 20 B. 25 C. 35 D. 40 19. C
20. What is the lower quartile?
    A. 20 B. 25 C. 35 D. 40 20. B

10 20 30 40 50 60 70

Probability

Previewing the Chapter

This chapter begins with a study of the basic counting techniques necessary to figure out the probability of various events. Students will learn how to use tree diagrams and to apply the basic counting principles to permutations and combinations. The basic principles of probability are presented with a discussion of fair and unfair games, and models are used to simulate various events. The chapter closes with a study of probabilities of dependent and independent events, and finding probabilities of mutually exclusive events.

Problem Solving Strategy Students will learn to solve problems by making a model and using experiments to simulate events.

Lesson (Pages)	Lesson Objectives	State/Local Objectives
11-1 (400-402)	11-1: Use a tree diagram to count outcomes.	1E, 3A, 5A, 5B
11-2 (403-405)	11-2: Use the fundamental counting principle to count outcomes.	1E, 3A, 5A, 5B
11-3 (407-409)	11-3: Find permutations and combinations.	1E, 3A, 5B
11-4 (411-414)	11-4: Find the probability of a simple event.	1E, 3A, 5C
11-5 (415-416)	11-5: Solve a problem by first making a table.	1D, 1E, 3A, 5A, 5B, 5C
11-6 (418-420)	11-6: Find the probability of independent events.	1E, 3A, 5C
11-7 (421-423)	11-7: Find the probability of dependent events.	1E, 3A, 5C
11-8 (424-427)	11-8: Find the probability of mutually exclusive events.	1E, 3A, 5C
11-9 (429-431)	11-9: Investigate problems using simulation.	1A, 1B, 1C, 1D, 1E, 5A, 5D, 5E

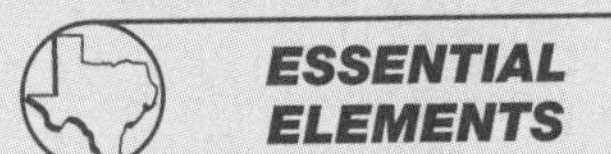

Organizing the Chapter

*You may want to refer to the **Course Planning Calendar** on Page T31.*

Planning Guide

Lesson (Pages)	Pacing Chart (in days)			Extra Practice (Student Edition)	Blackline Masters Booklets			Other Resources
	MINIMUM	STANDARD	ACCELERATED		Reteaching	Practice	Enrichment	
11-1 (400-402)	1	1	1	p. 611, Set A	p. 91	p. 101	p. 91	Transparency 11-1 Group Activity Card 11-1
11-2 (403-405)	1	1	1	p. 611, Set A	p. 92	p. 102	p. 92	Transparency 11-2 Group Activity Card 11-2
11-3 (407-409)	1	1	1	p. 611, Set B	p. 93	p. 103	p. 93	Transparency 11-3 Group Activity Card 11-3
11-4 (411-414)	1.5	1	1	p. 612, Set C	p. 94	p. 104	p. 94	Transparency 11-4 Group Activity Card 11-4
11-5 (415-416)	1	1	0.5		p. 95	p. 105	p. 95	Transparency 11-5 Group Activity Card 11-5
11-6 (418-420)	1	1	1	p. 612, Set C	p. 96	p. 106	p. 96	Transparency 11-6 Group Activity Card 11-6
11-7 (421-423)	1	1	1	p. 612, Set C	p. 97	p. 107	p. 97	Transparency 11-7 Group Activity Card 11-7
11-8 (424-427)	1.5	1	1	p. 612, Set C	p. 98	p. 108	p. 98	Transparency 11-8 Group Activity Card 11-8
11-9 (429-431)	1	1	1			p. 109		Transparency 11-9 Group Activity Card 11-9
Review (432-433)	1.5	1	1					Test Generator
Test (434)	1	1	1		Evaluation Masters, pp. 91-96			

Other Chapter Resources

Student Edition
Algebra in Action, p. 406
Exploration, pp. 410, 417, 428
Biography, p. 414
Mid-Chapter Quiz, p. 420
Team Problem Solving, p. 423
Challenge, p. 427
Academic Skills Test, p. 435

Teacher Resource Package
Interdisciplinary Activity, p. 11
Application Worksheet, p. 26
Cooperative Problem Solving, p. 41
Multicultural Activity, p. 56
Fun Activities, pp. 74-75
Technology Worksheets, pp. 11, 26, 41
Lab Manual, pp. 57-59
Quizzes(2), p. 97
Class Review Game

Software
Test Generator

available for Apple and IBM

Enhancing the Chapter

Some of the blackline masters for enhancing this chapter are shown below.

Applications, p. 26

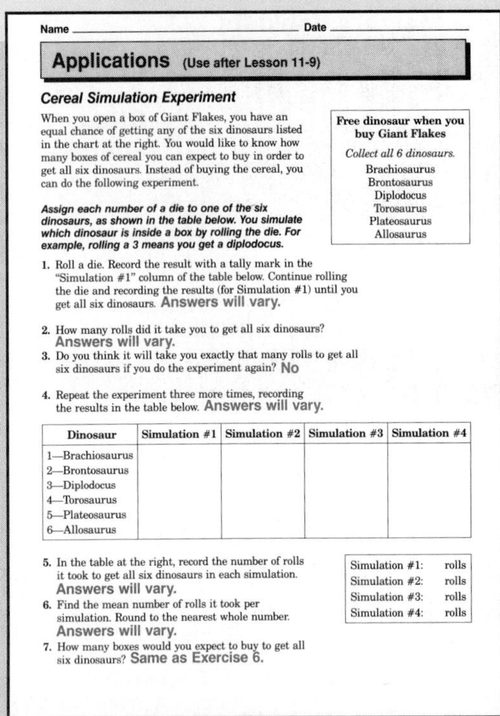

Name ______________________ Date ____________

Applications (Use after Lesson 11-9)

Cereal Simulation Experiment

When you open a box of Giant Flakes, you have an equal chance of getting any of the six dinosaurs listed in the chart at the right. You would like to know how many boxes of cereal you can expect to buy in order to get all six dinosaurs. Instead of buying the cereal, you can do the following experiment.

Free dinosaur when you buy Giant Flakes
Collect all 6 dinosaurs.
Brachiosaurus
Brontosaurus
Diplodocus
Torosaurus
Plateosaurus
Allosaurus

Assign each number of a die to one of the six dinosaurs, as shown in the table below. You simulate which dinosaur is inside a box by rolling the die. For example, rolling a 3 means you get a diplodocus.

1. Roll a die. Record the result with a tally mark in the "Simulation #1" column of the table below. Continue rolling the die and recording the results (for Simulation #1) until you get all six dinosaurs. **Answers will vary.**
2. How many rolls did it take you to get all six dinosaurs? **Answers will vary.**
3. Do you think it will take you exactly that many rolls to get all six dinosaurs if you do the experiment again? **No**
4. Repeat the experiment three more times, recording the results in the table below. **Answers will vary.**

Dinosaur	Simulation #1	Simulation #2	Simulation #3	Simulation #4
1—Brachiosaurus 2—Brontosaurus 3—Diplodocus 4—Torosaurus 5—Plateosaurus 6—Allosaurus				

5. In the table at the right, record the number of rolls it took to get all six dinosaurs in each simulation. **Answers will vary.**
6. Find the mean number of rolls it took per simulation. Round to the nearest whole number. **Answers will vary.**
7. How many boxes would you expect to buy to get all six dinosaurs? **Same as Exercise 6.**

Simulation #1:	rolls
Simulation #2:	rolls
Simulation #3:	rolls
Simulation #4:	rolls

The **Activity Masters Booklet** contains the page shown above.

Interdisciplinary Activity, p. 11

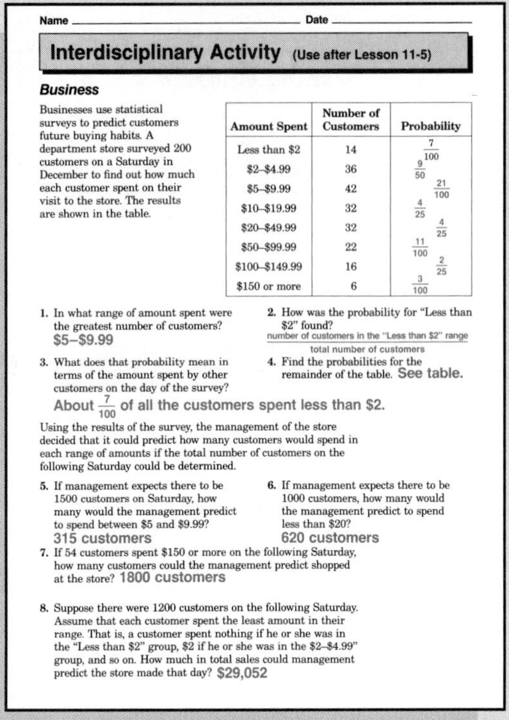

Name ______________________ Date ____________

Interdisciplinary Activity (Use after Lesson 11-5)

Business

Businesses use statistical surveys to predict customers future buying habits. A department store surveyed 200 customers on a Saturday in December to find out how much each customer spent on their visit to the store. The results are shown in the table.

Amount Spent	Number of Customers	Probability
Less than \$2	14	$\frac{7}{100}$
\$2–\$4.99	36	$\frac{9}{50}$
\$5–\$9.99	42	$\frac{21}{100}$
\$10–\$19.99	32	$\frac{4}{25}$
\$20–\$49.99	32	$\frac{4}{25}$
\$50–\$99.99	22	$\frac{11}{100}$
\$100–\$149.99	16	$\frac{2}{25}$
\$150 or more	6	$\frac{3}{100}$

1. In what range of amount spent were the greatest number of customers? **\$5–\$9.99**
2. How was the probability for "Less than \$2" found? $\frac{\text{number of customers in the "Less than \$2" range}}{\text{total number of customers}}$
3. What does that probability mean in terms of the amount spent by other customers on the day of the survey? **About $\frac{7}{100}$ of all the customers spent less than \$2.**
4. Find the probabilities for the remainder of the table. **See table.**

Using the results of the survey, the management of the store decided that it could predict how many customers would spend in each range of amounts if the total number of customers on the following Saturday could be determined.

5. If management expects there to be 1500 customers on Saturday, how many would the management predict to spend between \$5 and \$9.99? **315 customers**
6. If management expects there to be 1000 customers, how many would the management predict to spend less than \$20? **620 customers**
7. If 54 customers spent \$150 or more on the following Saturday, how many customers could the management predict shopped at the store? **1800 customers**
8. Suppose there were 1200 customers on the following Saturday. Assume that each customer spent the least amount in their range. That is, a customer spent nothing if he or she was in the "Less than \$2" group, \$2 if he or she was in the \$2–\$4.99" group, and so on. How much in total sales could management predict the store made that day? **\$29,052**

The **Activity Masters Booklet** contains the page shown above.

Models and Manipulatives

The possible outcomes of tossing two dice are shown on the chart at the right. Begin a discussion of probability with this chart and familiarize the students with the language involved in probability, as well as in counting the outcomes: equally likely, outcome, event, sample space, etc. The products and sums of the dice and their probabilities can give students a beginning look at fair and unfair games.

First die \ Second die	1	2	3	4	5	6
1	1,1	1,2	1,3	1,4	1,5	1,6
2	2,1	2,2	2,3	2,4	2,5	2,6
3	3,1	3,2	3,3	3,4	3,5	3,6
4	4,1	4,2	4,3	4,4	4,5	4,6
5	5,1	5,2	5,3	5,4	5,5	5,6
6	6,1	6,2	6,3	6,4	6,5	6,6

Multicultural Activity

Blaise Pascal was a French scientist known for his experiments on atmospheric pressure and significant findings in probability. At the age of 16 or 17, he had written an essay on conic sections which amazed Descartes since he could not believe it had been done by someone so young. At age 18, he invented the first calculating machine and began work in physics and mechanics. At age 31, a gambler, Chevalier de Méré, asked Pascal's help in establishing betting odds. Pascal was intrigued by the problem and discussed it with Pierre Fermet, one of the most brilliant mathematicians of the day. The result was the beginning of the theory of probability.

Have students research and write a paragraph on other French mathematicians.

Cooperative Learning

The following activity is provided in the **Activity Masters Booklet.**

Cooperative Problem Solving, p. 41

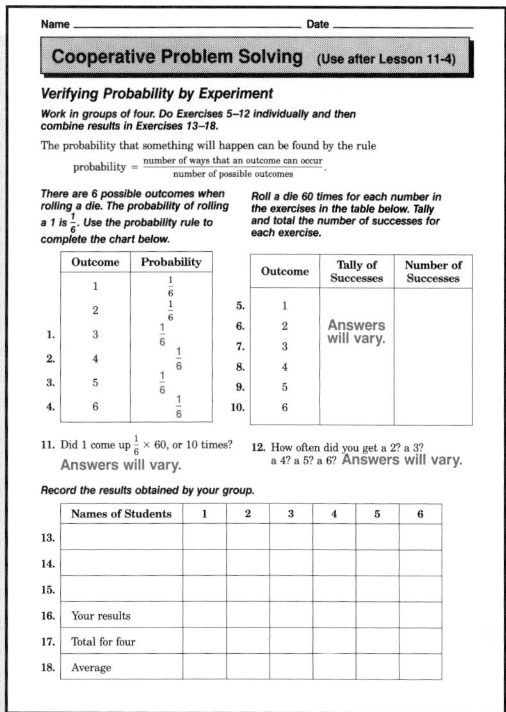

Name ______________________ Date ______________

Cooperative Problem Solving (Use after Lesson 11-4)

Verifying Probability by Experiment

Work in groups of four. Do Exercises 5–12 individually and then combine results in Exercises 13–18.

The probability that something will happen can be found by the rule

$$\text{probability} = \frac{\text{number of ways that an outcome can occur}}{\text{number of possible outcomes}}.$$

There are 6 possible outcomes when rolling a die. The probability of rolling a 1 is $\frac{1}{6}$. Use the probability rule to complete the chart below.

	Outcome	Probability
	1	$\frac{1}{6}$
	2	$\frac{1}{6}$
1.	3	$\frac{1}{6}$
2.	4	$\frac{1}{6}$
3.	5	$\frac{1}{6}$
4.	6	$\frac{1}{6}$

Roll a die 60 times for each number in the exercises in the table below. Tally and total the number of successes for each exercise.

	Outcome	Tally of Successes	Number of Successes
5.	1	Answers will vary.	
6.	2		
7.	3		
8.	4		
9.	5		
10.	6		

11. Did 1 come up $\frac{1}{6} \times 60$, or 10 times? Answers will vary.

12. How often did you get a 2? a 3? a 4? a 5? a 6? Answers will vary.

Record the results obtained by your group.

	Names of Students	1	2	3	4	5	6
13.							
14.							
15.							
16.	Your results						
17.	Total for four						
18.	Average						

Cooperative Problem Solving

Have students work in groups of four to figure out how many ways 3 students can be assigned to sit in 3 desks. Then have them make predictions from the information on how many ways 4 students could be arranged in 4 desks. One student could record the information as the other students act it out. They will need to discuss their observations and plan an easy way to record it.

Interactive Bulletin Board

Science Connection

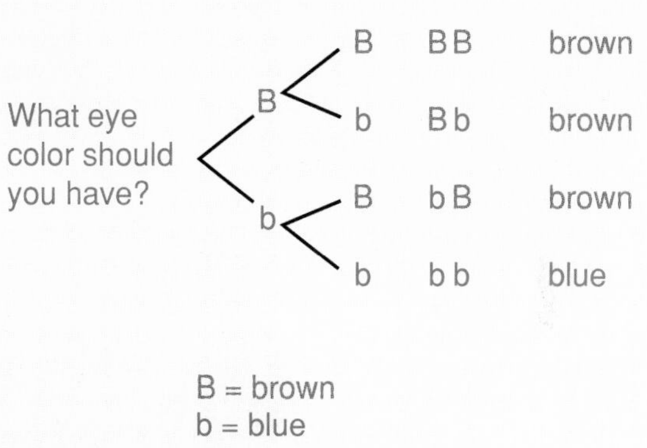

Purpose Provide practice in making tree diagrams for chosen situations.

How to Use It The theory of probability is used in the science of heredity, from the determination of obtaining flowers of a specified color to the determination of the color of the eyes of a person. It is also used in determining possible outcomes of various events from buying crackers to applications in geometry. Choose a situation such as the determination of the color of eyes of a person and use a tree diagram to show the possible outcomes. A different situation can be chosen on a periodic basis. The students could be assigned the determination of the situation to be discussed.

Outside Resources

Books/Periodicals
Probability, Thomas Y. Crowell Company
Teaching Statistics and Probability, 1981 Yearbook, NCTM

Films/Videotapes
Probability: An Introduction, BFA Educational Media
Probability, Films Incorporated

Software
Survival Math, Sunburst

Technology

There are three pages in the ***Technology Masters Booklet*** that involve technology with concepts in this chapter. One page involves calculators and one page has a problem that can be solved using the BASIC program that is provided. Students should evaluate the information they obtain from running the program and solve a similar problem by extending the program.

Using the Chapter Opener

Transparency 11-0 is available in the Transparency Package. It provides a full-color visual and motivating activity that you can use to engage students in the mathematical content of the chapter.

Using Graphs Discuss the meaning of the term "likelihood." Using the graph in the Chapter Opener, ask students how many people must be in the class for the likelihood of a shared birthday to be 75%. Predict the likelihood of a birthday being shared by two people in the class. Survey the class and find out how the survey results compare to the prediction.

CHAPTER OBJECTIVES

In this chapter you will learn to:

- count outcomes
- find permutations and combinations
- find probabilities of simple events and compound events
- solve problems by making a table
- use simulations to investigate problems

Probability

What are the chances that two Presidents of the United States share the same birthday? Considering that there are only 40 men in that group, you might think that the chances are pretty slim.

You may be surprised to know that in a group of only 24 people, the likelihood that two of them have birthdays on the same day is just about 50%, or one out of two. With 40, the likelihood is 85%!

So what about the group of presidents? Do any of them share a birthday? Two birthdays are shared!

- James Polk and Warren Harding were born on November 2.
- Andrew Johnson and Woodrow Wilson were born on December 29.

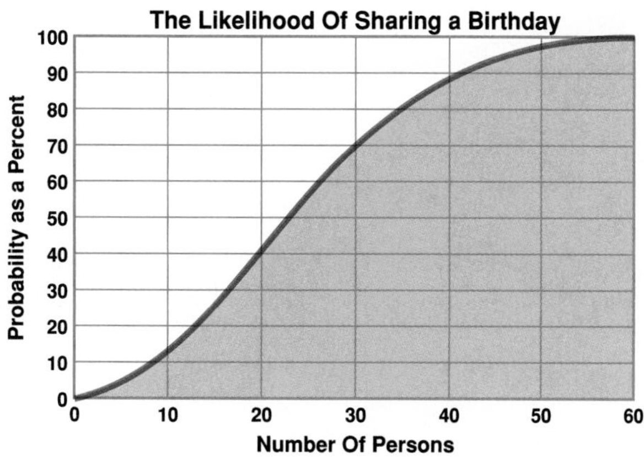

Class Project

Survey groups of 24 people in your school. Tally their birthdays.
Do 50% of your groups contain a shared birthday? Display your findings in a chart or graph.

Statistics Connection

Have students work in cooperative groups or groups of two to gather data for a predetermined number of groups of 24. Have each group graph or chart their data. Combine all data and have students graph or chart this collective data. Ask students if this graph or chart differs from individual group graphs or charts, and have them explain why.

Looking Ahead

You may want to have the following materials available to use in this chapter.

Algebra in Action, p. 406
- magnetic board
- magnetic letters
- magnetic numbers
- an atlas

Exploration, p. 410
- dice*

Exploration, p. 417
- paper bags
- colored golf tees

Exploration, p. 428
- computer

* You can use the Easy-to-Make Manipulative provided on page 17 of the Lab Manual.

Lesson Notes 11-1

5-Minute Check
(over Chapter 10)

Use the stem and leaf plot to answer each question.

0	6, 8
1	1, 5
2	
3	0, 2, 5, 6
4	7, 8
5	0, 0, 6

1. What is the median? **35**
2. What are the lower and upper quartiles? **13, 49**
3. What is the inter-quartile range? **36**
4. What is the range of the data? **50**
5. What is the mode? **50**

Transparency 11-1 contains the 5-Minute Check and a teaching aid for this lesson.

1 FOCUS

The purpose of this lesson is to draw tree diagrams and use them as a counting tool.

Motivating the Lesson

Show students a copy of a family tree. Ask how many students know their family trees. Ask how you would determine how many ancestors you have a given number of generations ago.

2 TEACH

Using Models Bring several different-colored shirts, socks, and slacks to class. Use illustrations and a tree diagram to model possible combinations.

Chalkboard Examples

- *For Example 1*
  Use a tree diagram to find all the possible outcomes in the situation described below. The school cafeteria serves two kinds of salads: chef and fruit salad. They also serve three beverages: milk, juice, and soda. Suppose you choose one salad and one beverage. How many possible choices are there? **6**

11-1 Counting Using Tree Diagrams

Objective:
Use a tree diagram to count outcomes.

Key Terms:
outcome
tree diagram
event

Beth, Juan, and Tim are running for Student Council president at Monroe High School. Kelly and Hiroshi are running for vice-president. How many possible combinations are there for president and vice-president?

You can draw a diagram to find the number of possible combinations or **outcomes**.

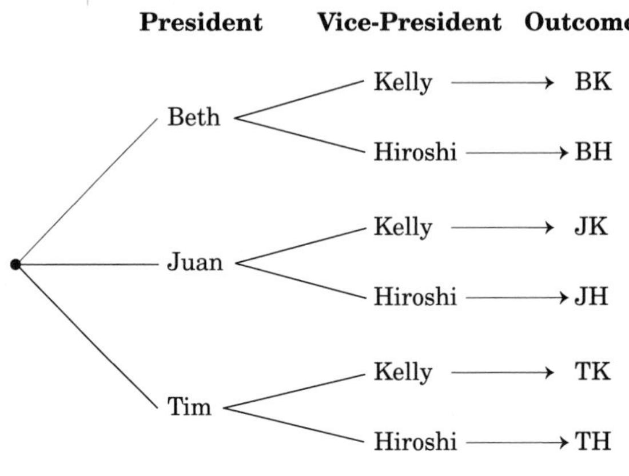

There are six possible outcomes.

The diagram above is called a **tree diagram**. You can use a tree diagram to list all the possible outcomes of other **events** like tossing a coin or rolling a die. For example, if you toss a penny and a nickel at the same time, a tree diagram can show the possible outcomes.

How does TH differ from HT? **First letter is for the penny; second letter is for the nickel.**

The possible outcomes are HH, HT, TH, and TT.
HH means heads on both coins.

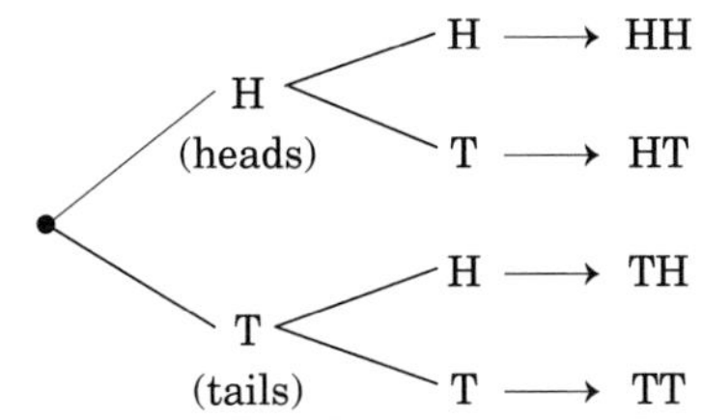

If you toss a penny, a nickel, and a dime, how many possible outcomes are there? **8 outcomes**

There are four possible outcomes.

Bell Ringer
Draw two different graphs that represent the same information.

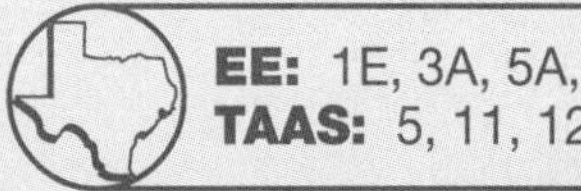

EE: 1E, 3A, 5A, 5B
TAAS: 5, 11, 12

Example

1 Use a tree diagram to find all the possible outcomes in the situation described below.

The Corner Sub Shop serves two types of sub sandwiches, a ham sub and a turkey sub. They also serve three beverages, milk, coffee, and soda. Suppose you choose one sub sandwich and one beverage. How many possible choices are there?

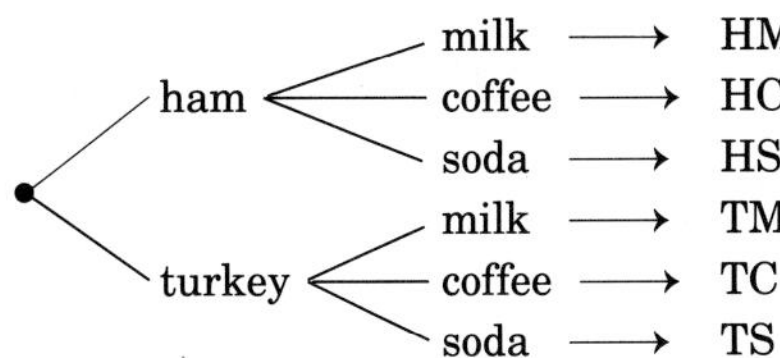

There are six possible choices, or outcomes.

Checking for Understanding

2. SR, SG, SW, MR, MG, MW, LR, LG, LW

Communicating Algebra

1. Explain how the tree diagram at the right can be used to count the different sweatshirts available at the school store. See margin.
2. List the outcomes illustrated in the tree diagram at the right.
3. Suppose you toss a penny and get heads. What is the event and what is the outcome? event; tossing a penny; outcome; heads

Size / **Color**

- small: red, gray, white
- medium: red, gray, white
- large: red, gray, white

Guided Practice

State the number of possible outcomes for each event.

4. tossing a quarter 2 outcomes

5. spinning the spinner 4 outcomes

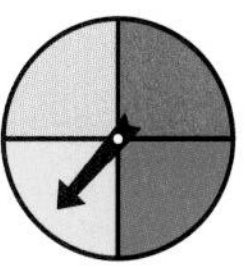

Refer to Example 1 above.

6. How many outcomes include a turkey sub? 3 outcomes
7. How many outcomes include milk? 2 outcomes
8. Include a pastrami sub with the sandwich choices and juice with the beverage choices. Draw the new tree diagram. What are the new outcomes? See Solutions Manual for tree diagram; HJ, TJ, PM, PC, PS, PJ

3 PRACTICE/APPLY

Checking the Concept

After completing Exercises 4-8, have students answer Exercises 6 and 7 for the diagram they drew for Exercise 8.

Error Analysis

Watch for students who do not list all possibilities.
Prevent by using models to determine all possible combinations.

Additional Answer

1. Extend the diagram to list the outcomes and count them.

Practice Masters Booklet, **p. 101**

Name ______ Date ______

Practice Worksheet 11-1

Counting Using Tree Diagrams

Draw a tree diagram for each exercise. Find the number of possible outcomes. Check students' diagrams.

1. The breakfast at Dion's Place has a choice of cereal, eggs, or french toast with a choice of milk or juice. 6
2. The lunch at Dion's Place has a choice of ham, turkey, or roast beef on rye or white bread with juice, milk, or tea. 18
3. Two dice are rolled. 36
4. Cheryl has a choice of a pink, red, or yellow blouse with white or black slacks for a school outfit. 6
5. Tina has a choice of a sports jersey in blue, white, gray, or black in sizes small, medium, or large. 12
6. Four coins are tossed. 16

Alternate Strategies: Reteaching the Lesson

Reteaching Activity

Using Models Using four students and four chairs, model the number of different ways the students can be seated. Confirm the solution with a tree diagram.

Reteaching Masters Booklet, **p. 91**

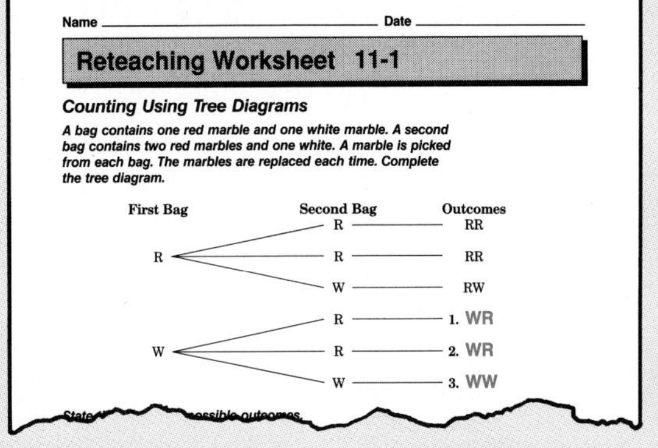

Name ______ Date ______

Reteaching Worksheet 11-1

Counting Using Tree Diagrams

A bag contains one red marble and one white marble. A second bag contains two red marbles and one white. A marble is picked from each bag. The marbles are replaced each time. Complete the tree diagram.

First Bag	Second Bag	Outcomes
R	R	RR
	R	RR
	W	RW
W	R	1. WR
	R	2. WR
	W	3. WW

Independent Practice

Homework Assignment	
Basic	9-15 odd, 17-20, 22, 23
Average	10-16 even, 17-23
Honors	13-23

4 CLOSE

Assessment Option

Modeling Using a set of pictures of related items, such as food or clothing, have each student draw a tree diagram to represent the possible outcomes of combining them.

Enrichment Masters Booklet, **p. 91**

Name ______________________ Date ______________

Enrichment Worksheet 11-1

Experimenting: Coin Tossing

1. Complete the tree diagram for tossing three coins at the same time.

First Coin	Second Coin	Third Coin	Results
heads	heads	heads	heads, heads, heads
		tails	heads, heads, tails
	tails	heads	heads, tails, heads
		tails	heads, tails, tails
tails	heads	heads	tails, heads, heads
		tails	tails, heads, tails
	tails	heads	tails, tails, heads
		tails	tails, tails, tails

You toss three coins at the same time. Express each probability as a fraction.

2. P(3 heads) $\frac{1}{8}$
3. P(2 heads, 1 tail) $\frac{3}{8}$
4. P(2 tails, 1 head) $\frac{3}{8}$
5. P(3 tails) $\frac{1}{8}$

Suppose you toss three coins 40 times each. Predict how many times you would expect to get each of the following results.

6. 3 heads 5
7. 2 heads, 1 tail 15
8. 2 tails, 1 head 15
9. 3 tails 5

10. Toss three coins 40 times each, and use tally marks to record the results in the table. Count the tally marks to get the number of times each result occurs. Answers will vary.

Results	Tally	Number
3 heads		
2 heads, 1 tail		
2 tails, 1 head		
3 tails		

11. Did each result occur exactly the number of times you predicted in Exercises 6–9? no

12. Does the probability of a result tell what *will actually happen* or what *will most likely happen?* what will most likely happen

Exercises

For tree diagrams to Exercises 9-16, see Solutions Manual.

Independent Practice

Draw a tree diagram for each exercise. Find the number of possible outcomes.

9. 12 outcomes
10. 24 outcomes

9. Each spinner is spun once.

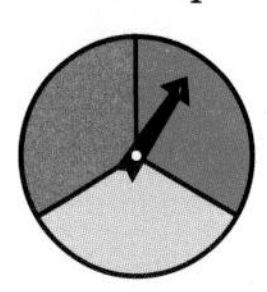

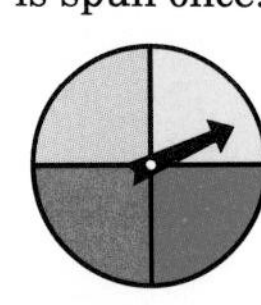

10. Each spinner is spun once.

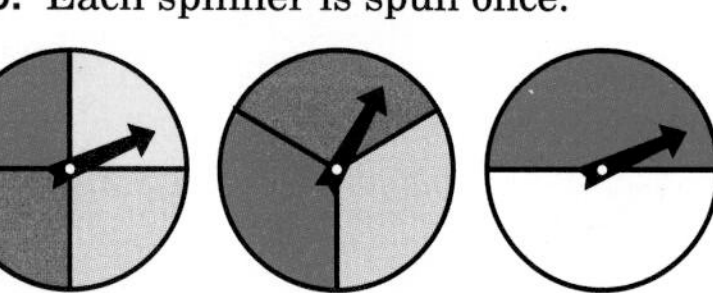

11. The continental breakfast at Homefire Inn has toast, muffin, or bagel with coffee, milk, or juice. 9 outcomes

12. Jean has a choice of a floral, plaid, or striped shirt with a choice of tan or white slacks. 6 outcomes

13. Cheerleading outfits come in 3 sizes, small, medium, and large. The letters come in 2 styles, script and block. The outfits come in 3 colors, blue, red, and green. 18 outcomes

14. Notebooks come in 4 colors, red, blue, green, and purple. They come in 2 sizes, 5-subject and 3-subject. 8 outcomes

15. Phones come in 2 styles, wall and desk. They come in 5 colors, white, black, mauve, red, and beige. 10 outcomes

16. There are 3 routes between Martin's house and the school. How many ways can Martin go from his house to the school and back home again? 9 outcomes

Mixed Review

17. Solve $\frac{a}{-8} = 12$. (Lesson 3-4) -96

18. Write the fraction you would use as an estimate for 21%. (Lesson 9-6) $\frac{1}{5}$

19. Which average, *mode, median,* or *mean,* would best describe hair color of a group of people? (Lesson 10-9) mode

Applications

20. See Solutions Manual for diagram; 12 outfits

20. **Travel** The French Club is taking a weekend trip to New Orleans. Each member can take one suitcase. Maureen finds two pairs of slacks, three tops, and two sweaters that are color-coordinated. Use a tree diagram to show how many three-piece outfits she can make for her trip.

21. **Business** Holiday Autorama found that customers preferred vans, station wagons, and sports cars in red, white, and gray. Use a tree diagram to show what kinds of vehicles they should keep in stock. See Solutions Manual.

Critical Thinking

22. The first round in the NBA playoffs is won when a team wins three of five games. Construct a tree diagram to show all possible outcomes for a playoff between the Mavericks (M) and the Lakers (L). See Solutions Manual.

Wrap-Up

23. Explain how to use a tree diagram to find all the possible outcomes of a situation involving two events. A tree diagram matches up all the possibilities in one event with the next event to give you all possible combinations, or outcomes.

Alternate Strategies: Extending the Lesson

Enrichment

Using a Diagram Use a tree diagram to solve. A friend tells you his telephone number. The exchange is the same as yours. The extension numbers are 1, 2, 3, and 3, but you don't remember the order. How many different arrangements are possible? 12 Would this change if all numbers differed? **Yes, there would be 24.**

Cooperative Learning

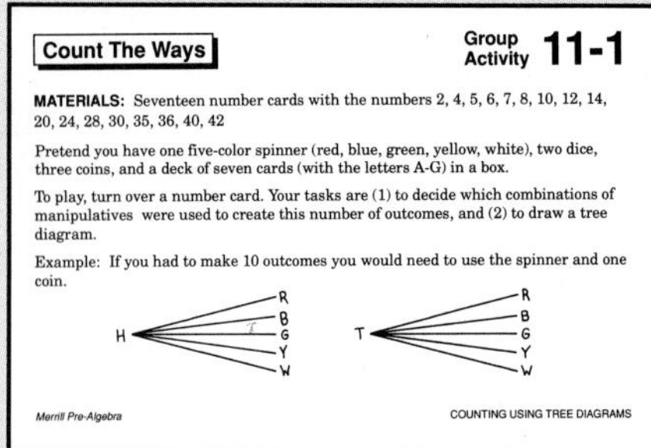

Count The Ways Group Activity **11-1**

MATERIALS: Seventeen number cards with the numbers 2, 4, 5, 6, 7, 8, 10, 12, 14, 20, 24, 28, 30, 35, 36, 40, 42

Pretend you have one five-color spinner (red, blue, green, yellow, white), two dice, three coins, and a deck of seven cards (with the letters A-G) in a box.

To play, turn over a number card. Your tasks are (1) to decide which combinations of manipulatives were used to create this number of outcomes, and (2) to draw a tree diagram.

Example: If you had to make 10 outcomes you would need to use the spinner and one coin.

Merrill Pre-Algebra COUNTING USING TREE DIAGRAMS

11-2 Counting Using Multiplication

Objective:
Use the Fundamental Counting Principle to count outcomes.

Key Term:
Fundamental Counting Principle

Andy Komer needs to buy a new clothes dryer. The Appliance Store carries two different brands, Centric (C) and Spin King (S). Each brand comes in two styles, gas (G) and electric (E). Each dryer comes in three colors, white (W), brown (B), and almond (A). Through the use of a tree diagram, Andy finds that he has 12 choices of dryers.

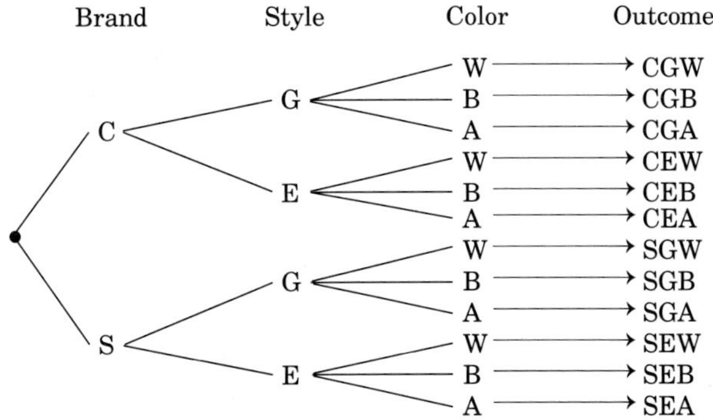

He notices that the product of the number of brands, styles, and colors, $2 \times 2 \times 3$, also equals 12. Multiplication is another way to find the number of possible outcomes. Andy's discovery is called the **Fundamental Counting Principle**.

Fundamental Counting Principle

If event M can occur in m ways and is followed by event N that can occur in n ways, then the event M followed by event N can occur in $m \cdot n$ ways.

The number of choices of dryers can be determined by using this principle.

$$\binom{\text{number of}}{\text{brands}} \times \binom{\text{number of}}{\text{styles}} \times \binom{\text{number of}}{\text{colors}} = \binom{\text{number of}}{\text{possible dryers}}$$

$$2 \times 2 \times 3 = 12$$

Examples

1 Two dice are rolled. How many outcomes are possible?

$$\binom{\text{number of outcomes}}{\text{for first die}} \times \binom{\text{number of outcomes}}{\text{for second die}} = \binom{\text{number of}}{\text{possible outcomes}}$$

$$6 \times 6 = 36$$

There are 36 possible outcomes.

Bell Ringer

Name one advantage to using a tree diagram to count outcomes. **Possible answer; It ensures all outcomes are listed.**

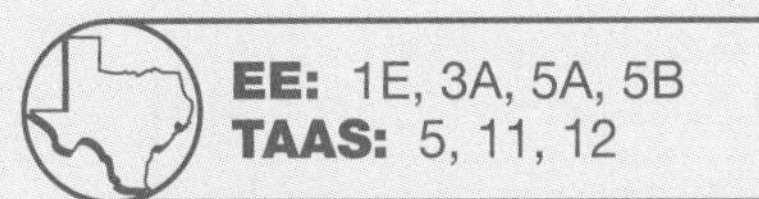

EE: 1E, 3A, 5A, 5B
TAAS: 5, 11, 12

Lesson Notes 11-2

5-Minute Check
(over Lesson 11-1)

Draw a tree diagram for each exercise. Find the number of possible outcomes.

1. A multiple choice test has four questions each with five possible responses. How many outcomes are possible for the four questions? **20**
2. The slippers come in two kinds of material: cotton and leather. The slippers come in four different colors: white, black, tan, and burgundy. How many outcomes are possible? **8**

Transparency 11-2 contains the 5-Minute Check and a teaching aid for this lesson.

1 FOCUS

The purpose of this lesson is to develop the Fundamental Counting Principle and use it to determine the number of outcomes.

Motivating the Lesson

Show students a sports schedule, and personalize the following for your school. If there are seven schools in your football league, and each school must play each other school once, how many league games must be played? A tree diagram may be used, but is not particularly practical. Why? **too many outcomes**

2 TEACH

Using Homework Have students use the tree diagrams they drew for Exercises 9-16 on page 402 to write multiplication problems that represent the number of outcomes.

Chalkboard Examples

- *For Example 1*
Three coins are tossed. How many outcomes are possible? **6**

Chalkboard Examples

- *For Example 2*
  Kim has three sweaters (purple, blue, red), two skirts (black and tan), and three blouses (white, yellow, and black). How many different three-piece outfits are possible? 18

3 PRACTICE/APPLY

Checking the Concept

Have students use tree diagrams to check Exercises 7 and 8.

Error Analysis

Watch for students who guess at solutions rather than systematically organizing the problem.
Prevent by having students begin with one item and explore all possibilities for that one item. Then proceed to the next item.

Practice Masters Booklet, **p. 102**

2 Rosa's Deli makes sandwiches for their customers. Customers have a choice of four types of meat (ham, turkey, pastrami, and corned beef), four types of cheese (cheddar, Swiss, mozzarella, and American), and four types of bread (white, wheat, rye, and sour dough). How many different sandwiches can be made with one type of meat, one type of cheese, and one type of bread?

$$\begin{pmatrix}\text{number of}\\ \text{choices for}\\ \text{meat}\end{pmatrix} \times \begin{pmatrix}\text{number of}\\ \text{choices for}\\ \text{cheese}\end{pmatrix} \times \begin{pmatrix}\text{number of}\\ \text{choices for}\\ \text{bread}\end{pmatrix} = \begin{pmatrix}\text{number of}\\ \text{possible}\\ \text{outcomes}\end{pmatrix}$$

$$4 \times 4 \times 4 = 64$$

There are 64 possible sandwiches.

Checking for Understanding

Communicating Algebra

1. Write a problem that corresponds to the tree diagram at the right. See margin.
2. Use the Fundamental Counting Principle to write a mathematical equation that corresponds to the tree diagram. $2 \times 2 \times 2 = 8$
3. What advantage does the Fundamental Counting Principle have over a tree diagram? faster, takes less space
4. In literature class, each student must choose one short story and one poem to read for homework. The students must choose from a list of g short stories and h poems. Write an algebraic expression for the number of possible outcomes. $g \times h$

heads — heads — heads / tails; tails — heads / tails
tails — heads — heads / tails; tails — heads / tails

Guided Practice

Use multiplication to answer each question.

5. Suppose there are only two types of cheese in Example 2. How many sandwiches are possible? $4 \times 2 \times 4 = 32$
6. Three dice are rolled. How many outcomes are possible? $6 \times 6 \times 6$ or $6^3 = 216$
7. Four coins are tossed. How many outcomes are possible? $2 \times 2 \times 2 \times 2$ or $2^4 = 16$
8. A quiz has five true and false questions. How many outcomes for giving answers to the five questions are possible? $2 \times 2 \times 2 \times 2 \times 2$ or $2^5 = 32$
9. Judy has 5 blouses, 6 skirts, and 4 scarves. How many three-piece outfits are possible? $5 \times 6 \times 4 = 120$

Exercises

Independent Practice

10. The spinner at the right is spun three times. How many outcomes are possible? 125 outcomes

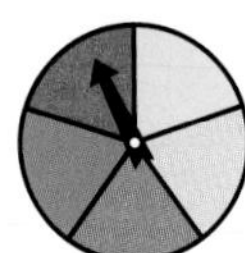

Name ______ Date ______

Practice Worksheet 11-2

Counting Using Multiplication

Use multiplication to answer each question.

1. Five coins are tossed. How many outcomes are possible? 32
2. Four dice are rolled. How many outcomes are possible? 1296
3. Two quarters are tossed. Then two dimes are tossed. How many outcomes are possible? 16
4. A penny, a nickel, and a dime are tossed. How many outcomes are possible? 8
5. If each spinner is spun once, how many outcomes are possible? 8

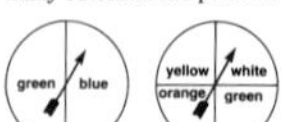
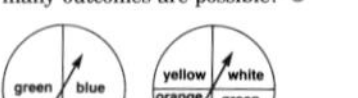

6. If each spinner is spun once, how many outcomes are possible? 24

7. If Alice has 3 skirts, 2 blouses, and 5 scarves, how many outfits are possible? 30
8. There are 4 quarterbacks and 6 centers on a football team that has 60 players. How many quarterback-center pairings are possible? 24
9. At an ice cream store, there are 31 flavors and 25 toppings. How many different ways are there to make an ice cream sundae? 775
10. A pizza shop has 6 meat toppings, 5 vegetable toppings, and 3 cheese toppings. How many different pizzas (one meat, one vegetable, and one cheese topping) can be made? 90

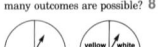

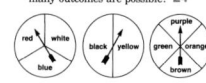

Alternate Strategies: Reteaching the Lesson

Reteaching Activity

Using Models Cut out ice cream cones and scoops and, by modeling a simple problem, develop the Fundamental Counting Principle.

Reteaching Masters Booklet, **p. 92**

Name ______ Date ______

Reteaching Worksheet 11-2

Counting Using Multiplication

To find the number of possible outcomes when two or more separate events are combined, multiply the number of outcomes for each event.

The three pointers below are each spun once.

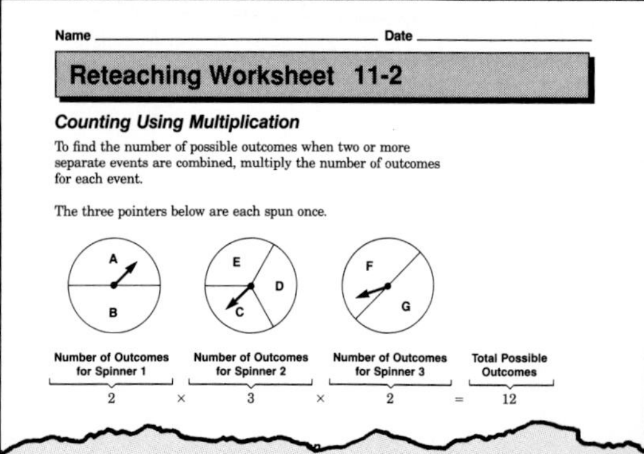

Number of Outcomes for Spinner 1		Number of Outcomes for Spinner 2		Number of Outcomes for Spinner 3		Total Possible Outcomes
2	×	3	×	2	=	12

11-4 Probability

Objective:
Find the probability of a simple event.

Key Terms:
probability
sample space

A weather forecaster says that there is a 70% chance of rain. What does this mean? It means that the probability of rain is 70%. **Probability** is the chance that some event will happen.

The symbol P(rain) is used to mean the probability that it will rain.

$$P(\text{rain}) = 70\% \text{ or } 0.7$$

On any given day, the probability of its raining or not raining is 100%. That means that P(rain) + P(no rain) equals 1. So, on a day when there is a 70% chance of rain, we know that the chance of no rain is 30%.

$$P(\text{no rain}) = 0.3$$

If you look out the window and see that it is already raining, the probability of rain is 100% (or 1). In that case, the probability of a completely sunny day is 0% (or 0).

Probability is also defined as the ratio of the number of ways that a certain outcome can occur to the number of possible outcomes.

Business Connection

Insurance companies use probability theory when they issue life insurance. The companies need to estimate how long the policy holder will live. This estimate of probability is called life expectancy.

Definition of Probability

$$\text{Probability} = \frac{\text{number of ways that a certain outcome can occur}}{\text{number of possible outcomes}}$$

The set of all possible outcomes is called the **sample space.** You can find the sample space in many ways. You already know how to make a list, construct a tree diagram, use the Fundamental Counting Principle, and use permutations and combinations to find a sample space.

Bell Ringer

Explain the difference between a permutation and a combination. Order matters in a permutation.

Lesson Notes 11-4

5-Minute Check
(over Lesson 11-3)

Find each value.

1. P (6, 3) 120
2. P (7, 4) 840
3. C (5, 2) 10
4. C (9, 3) 84
5. $\frac{5!\ 3!}{4!}$ 30

Transparency 11-4 contains the 5-Minute Check and a teaching aid for this lesson.

1 FOCUS

The purpose of this lesson is to introduce students to probability by using possible outcomes to create a ratio.

Motivating the Lesson

Give students some statements where the answers "probably" or "probably not" are appropriate. For example, are you going to be in school tomorrow, or will the football team win their next game. Discuss how sure they are of the event occurring.

2 TEACH

Using Models

Have students determine the sample space for each of the events below.

- tossing a coin H,T
- rolling a die 1, 2, 3, 4, 5, 6
- tossing a coin and rolling a die (H, 1), (H, 2), (H, 3), (H, 4), (H, 5), (H, 6), (T,1), (T, 2), (T, 3), (T, 4), (T, 5), (T, 6)

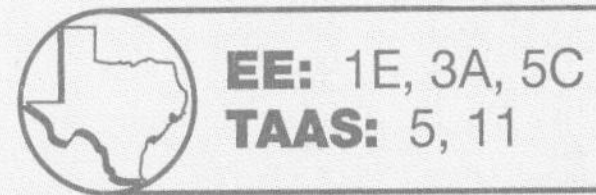

EE: 1E, 3A, 5C
TAAS: 5, 11

Chalkboard Examples

There are 5 blue markers, 6 red markers, 7 black markers, 2 purple markers, and 3 yellow markers in the marker bin. All the markers are the same size and shape. Suppose you reach into the bin and grab a marker without looking.

- *For Example 1*
  What is the probability that the marker chosen is black? $\frac{7}{23}$
- *For Example 2*
  What is the probability that the marker is either purple or yellow? $\frac{5}{23}$
- *For Example 3*
  What is the probability that the marker is green? Why? **0; There aren't any green markers.**

3 PRACTICE/APPLY

Checking the Concept

Have students express the probability in Exercises 4-13 as a fraction, a decimal, and a percent.

Error Analysis

Watch for students who incorrectly determine probability because they do not consider all possible outcomes.
Prevent by verbalizing a systematic list of outcomes.

Examples

There are 2 red pens, 3 blue pens, 1 black pen, and 4 green pens in a desk drawer. All the pens are the same size and shape. Suppose you open the drawer and grab a pen without looking. In other words, you are choosing the pen at random and each outcome is equally likely.

Estimation Hint

Use estimation to determine if P(blue) is less than or greater than $\frac{1}{2}$.

1 What is the probability that the pen chosen is blue?

The number of blue outcomes is 3. The number of possible outcomes is 2 + 3 + 1 + 4 or 10.

$$\text{Probability} = \frac{\text{number of ways that a certain outcome can occur}}{\text{number of possible outcomes}}$$

$$P(\text{blue}) = \frac{3}{10}$$

Can a probability be greater than 1? Why? **no; See margin.**

2 What is the probability that the pen chosen is either red or green?

$$P(\text{red or green}) = \frac{6}{10} \quad \frac{\text{number of red or green outcomes}}{\text{number of possible outcomes}}$$

Can a probability be less than 0? Why? **no; See margin.**

3 What is the probability that the pen is purple?

The probability is 0. Why? **There are no purple pens to choose from.**

Checking for Understanding

Communicating Algebra

1. What is a sample space? **the set of all possible outcomes**
2. In your own words explain what is meant by probability. Explain how to find the probability of an outcome. **See margin.**
3. Give an example of an outcome with a probability of 0.5. **Sample answer; heads on a coin**

Guided Practice

State the probability of each outcome.

4. The sun will rise tomorrow. **1**
5. A coin is tossed and shows tails. $\frac{1}{2}$
6. Your friend will live to be 300 years old. **0**
7. Today is Monday. **If Monday: 1, If not Monday: 0**

The spinner shown below is equally likely to stop in any one of the eight regions. It is spun once. Find the probability of each outcome.

8. a two $\frac{1}{8}$
9. an odd number $\frac{1}{2}$
10. not a seven $\frac{7}{8}$
11. a nine **0**
12. prime number $\frac{1}{2}$
13. a number less than four $\frac{3}{8}$

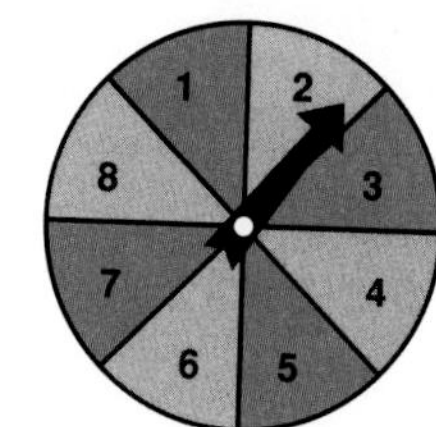

Alternate Strategies: Reteaching the Lesson

Reteaching Activity

Using Models Make or use a spinner divided into four equal sections, numbered 1, 2, 3, and 4. Find the probability of spinning each of the following: the 1, the 2, the 3, the 4, not the 1, an even number, an odd number, a prime number, and a composite number.
$\frac{1}{4}, \frac{1}{4}, \frac{1}{4}, \frac{1}{4}, \frac{3}{4}, \frac{1}{2}, \frac{1}{2}, \frac{1}{2}, \frac{1}{4}$

Reteaching Masters Booklet, **p. 94**

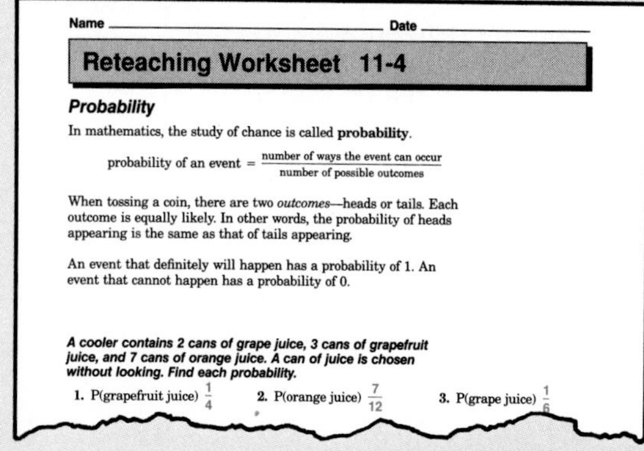
Name ______________ Date ______________

Reteaching Worksheet 11-4

Probability

In mathematics, the study of chance is called **probability**.

$$\text{probability of an event} = \frac{\text{number of ways the event can occur}}{\text{number of possible outcomes}}$$

When tossing a coin, there are two *outcomes*—heads or tails. Each outcome is equally likely. In other words, the probability of heads appearing is the same as that of tails appearing.

An event that definitely will happen has a probability of 1. An event that cannot happen has a probability of 0.

A cooler contains 2 cans of grape juice, 3 cans of grapefruit juice, and 7 cans of orange juice. A can of juice is chosen without looking. Find each probability.

1. P(grapefruit juice) $\frac{1}{4}$ 2. P(orange juice) $\frac{7}{12}$ 3. P(grape juice) $\frac{1}{6}$

Exercises

Independent Practice

There are 3 blue marbles, 6 red marbles, 2 green marbles, and 1 black marble in a bag. Suppose you select one marble at random. Find each probability.

14. $P(\text{blue})$ $\frac{1}{4}$
15. $P(\text{black})$ $\frac{1}{12}$
16. $P(\text{green})$ $\frac{1}{6}$
17. $P(\text{red})$ $\frac{1}{2}$
18. $P(\text{not green})$ $\frac{5}{6}$
19. $P(\text{blue or red})$ $\frac{3}{4}$
20. $P(\text{green or black})$ $\frac{1}{4}$
21. $P(\text{neither red nor green})$ $\frac{1}{3}$
22. $P(\text{yellow})$ 0
23. $P(\text{not orange})$ 1

Suppose you roll a die and toss a coin.

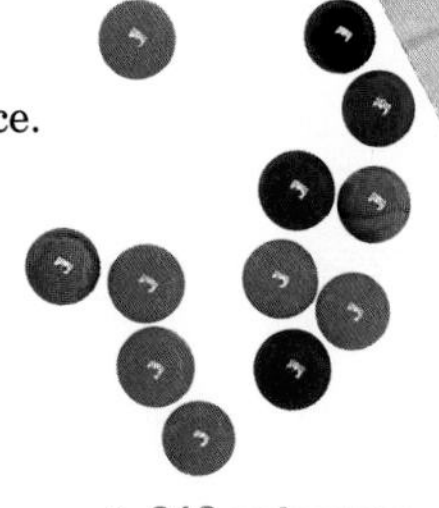

24. List all the members of the sample space. 24. 1H, 1T, 2H, 2T, 3H, 3T, 4H, 4T, 5H, 5T, 6H, 6T
25. What is $P(6, \text{tails})$? $\frac{1}{12}$
26. What is $P(5, \text{heads})$? $\frac{1}{12}$
27. What is $P(8, \text{tails})$? 0

Suppose you roll three dice.

28. How many outcomes are in the sample space? 216 outcomes
29. List three members of the sample space. Sample answers: 1, 1, 1; 1, 2, 3; 6, 5, 4
30. What is $P(6, 6, 6)$? $\frac{1}{216}$

Explain the meaning of each of the following. See margin.

31. $P(\text{heads}) = \frac{1}{2}$
32. $P(\text{red or green}) = \frac{1}{5}$

Mixed Review

33. Rename 0.88 as a fraction. (Lesson 5-2) $\frac{22}{25}$
34. Solve $18 - 7t \leq -3$. (Lesson 7-6) $t \geq 3$
35. Find the percent of increase if the old price of a bus ticket was \$0.60 and the new price is \$0.75. (Lesson 9-10) 25%
36. Draw a stem-and-leaf plot of the following temperatures: 54, 71, 58, 66, 64, 67, 58, 69, 63, 51, 70. (Lesson 10-3) See margin.
37. Find the value of $P(7, 2)$. (Lesson 11-3) 42

Applications

38. **Sports** A batter hits 0.300. What is the probability that she will get a hit next time at bat? What is the probability that she will not get a hit? 0.3; 0.7
39. **Sports** Jane averages two strikes every ten frames of bowling. What is the probability that she will get a strike in the first frame of the next game? $\frac{1}{5}$
40. **Space Exploration** What is the probability that humans will explore the moon on foot? What is the probability that humans will explore the sun on foot? 1; 0

Independent Practice

Homework Assignment	
Basic	15-31 odd, 33-43, 53, 54
Average	14-32 even, 33-43, 53, 54
Honors	33-54

Additional Answers

2. Sample answer: Probability is the mathematical likelihood that some event will happen. To find the probability of an outcome, divide the number of ways the outcome can occur by the number of possible outcomes.
31. Sample answer: A tossed coin will land heads up 50% of the time.
32. Sample answer: A red or green marble will be drawn out of a bag once for every five tries.
36.

Stem	Leaf
5	1 4 8 8
6	3 4 6 7 9
7	0 1

Practice Masters Booklet, **p. 104**

Name ______ Date ______

Practice Worksheet 11-4

Probability

There are 4 blue marbles, 5 red marbles, 1 green marble, and 2 black marbles in a bag. Suppose you select one marble at random. Find each probability.

1. P(black) $\frac{1}{6}$
2. P(blue) $\frac{1}{3}$
3. P(green) $\frac{1}{12}$
4. P(red) $\frac{5}{12}$
5. P(not blue) $\frac{2}{3}$
6. P(red or green) $\frac{1}{2}$
7. P(blue or black) $\frac{1}{2}$
8. P(neither red nor black) $\frac{5}{12}$
9. P(pink) 0
10. P(not purple) 1

Suppose you roll a die and spin the spinner.

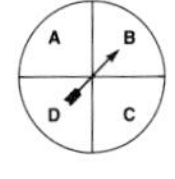

11. List all the members of the sample space.
1, A 2, A 3, A 4, A 5, A 6, A
1, B 2, B 3, B 4, B 5, B 6, B
1, C 2, C 3, C 4, C 5, C 6, C
1, D 2, D 3, D 4, D 5, D 6, D
12. What is P(1, A)? $\frac{1}{24}$
13. What is P(3, B)? $\frac{1}{24}$
14. What is P(6, C)? $\frac{1}{24}$
15. What is P(even number, D)? $\frac{1}{8}$
16. What is P(odd number, D)? $\frac{1}{8}$

Suppose you roll two dice.

17. How many outcomes are in the sample space? 36
18. What is P(5, 2)? $\frac{1}{36}$
19. What is P(6, 3)? $\frac{1}{36}$
20. What is P(even number, odd number)? $\frac{1}{4}$
21. What is P(both numbers are odd)? $\frac{1}{4}$

4 CLOSE

Assessment Option

Modeling Bring in a deck of cards. Have the students figure out the probabilities of a number of relationships among the cards. For example, what is the probability of picking:

1. a four $\frac{4}{52}$ or $\frac{1}{13}$
2. a facecard $\frac{12}{52}$ or $\frac{3}{13}$
3. a black card $\frac{26}{52}$ or $\frac{1}{2}$
4. the ace of spades $\frac{1}{52}$

Have each student select a card to test the probabilities.

Enrichment Masters Booklet, **p. 94**

Name ______________________ Date ______________

Enrichment Worksheet 11-4

Odds

The **odds** for an event can be found as follows.

odds *for* an event $= \frac{\text{number of ways that event can occur}}{\text{number of ways that event cannot occur}}$

If a die is rolled once, find the odds for a 4.

$\frac{1}{5}$ ▶ **A 4 can only occur in one way.** ▶ **The other events are 1, 2, 3, 5, and 6.**

The odds of rolling a 4 are $\frac{1}{5}$, or 1 to 5.

odds *against* an event $= \frac{\text{number of ways that event cannot occur}}{\text{number of ways that event can occur}}$

Find the odds for spinning each of the following.

1. for a 6 $\frac{1}{15}$
2. *not* for a 13 $\frac{15}{1}$
3. for a prime number $\frac{3}{5}$
4. for a 4, 8, or 12 $\frac{3}{13}$
5. *not* for an odd number $\frac{1}{1}$
6. for a 7 or 9 $\frac{1}{7}$
7. for an odd number less than 14 $\frac{7}{9}$
8. *not* for a number greater than 11 $\frac{11}{5}$

Two dice are rolled. Find the odds for each of the following.

9. for a sum of 6 $\frac{5}{31}$
10. for a sum of 2 or 10 $\frac{1}{8}$
11. *not* for a sum of 3 $\frac{17}{1}$
12. for matching numbers (doubles) $\frac{1}{5}$
13. for a sum of 7 and a 2 on one die $\frac{1}{17}$
14. for a sum of 10 and a 4 on one die $\frac{1}{17}$
15. *not* for a sum greater than 9 $\frac{5}{1}$
16. for a sum greater than 9 $\frac{1}{5}$

Challenge **All of the possible outcomes that can occur when a die is rolled twice are listed in the chart below. Find the probability of each outcome.**

1, 6	2, 6	3, 6	4, 6	5, 6	6, 6
1, 5	2, 5	3, 5	4, 5	5, 5	6, 5
1, 4	2, 4	3, 4	4, 4	5, 4	6, 4
1, 3	2, 3	3, 3	4, 3	5, 3	6, 3
1, 2	2, 2	3, 2	4, 2	5, 2	6, 2
1, 1	2, 1	3, 1	4, 1	5, 1	6, 1

41. 3, 5 $\frac{1}{36}$
42. not 2, 3 $\frac{35}{36}$
43. a sum of 5 $\frac{1}{9}$
44. a sum of 6 or 2 $\frac{1}{6}$
45. a sum of 12 $\frac{1}{36}$
46. a sum of 13 0
47. 2, 1 or 5, 3 $\frac{1}{18}$
48. both numbers odd $\frac{1}{4}$
49. the same number on both dice $\frac{1}{6}$
50. the first number is greater than the second number $\frac{15}{36}$
51. a sum greater than 9 $\frac{1}{6}$
52. a sum less than 15 1

Critical Thinking

53. In a box you have cards with the letters W, E, A, T, H, E, and R. What is the probability of drawing the letters W E T in order? (Hint: Find the total number of outcomes and the number of outcomes in which the letters W E T are drawn in order.) $\frac{1}{2520}$

Wrap-Up

54. Write a problem in which the answer will be a probability of 0.75. Sample answer: What is the probability of selecting a yellow marble out of a bag that contains 6 yellow marbles and 2 green marbles?

Biography

Blaise Pascal

Blaise Pascal was a French mathematician and physicist who lived from 1623 to 1662. Although he lived to be only 39 years old, he accomplished much in his short lifespan.

His father had wanted him to study ancient languages and denied him any books on mathematics. However, when he learned the first thirty-two theorems of Euclidean geometry at the age of 9, his father allowed him to study mathematics.

At 16 he published a book on the geometry of conic sections that far surpassed any work in this area since Apollonius in the third century B.C. When he was 19, he invented the ancestor of our pre-electronic calculating machines. However, it was too expensive to build at the time.

Pascal later corresponded with Pierre de Fermat, and together they became the founders of the modern theory of probability. Today, by applying the theory of probability, physicists can understand and develop theories about the atom.

Alternate Strategies: Extending the Lesson

Enrichment

Using Models Have students roll two dice and answer each of the following questions. How many different sums are possible? 11 Assuming the order of the dice is important, what is the probability the sum will be 6? $\frac{1}{6}$ 12? $\frac{1}{36}$ Roll the dice 36 times and compare the results to the probability.

Cooperative Learning

Have It Happen Group Activity **11-4**

MATERIALS: One five-color spinner • two dice • three coins • seven letter cards (with the letters A-G) • seventeen number cards from Activity 11-1

Using those tree diagrams you made for Group Activity 11-1 and the actual materials, calculate the probability of a particular event. The group takes turns making up events they want to occur. Some examples are: (1) red spin and tails, (2) number greater than 4, (3) 3 sixes, (4) vowel or yellow spin, and (5) consonant.

Everyone who correctly calculates the probability gets to take turns using the materials and trying to be the first to make that event occur. The first one to make the event occur scores one point.

The winner is the first person to score four points.

Merrill Pre-Algebra PROBABILITY

11-5 Make a Table

Objective:
Solve problems by making a table.

Parcheesi is a game that was first played in India. In this game 2 dice are rolled. A token can be put into play if a total of 5 is shown on the dice or if a 5 is shown on at least one of the dice. What is the probability that a token can be put into play in one roll of the dice (a favorable outcome)?

Explore There are 2 dice. You must find the probability of either rolling a total of 5 on both of the dice or rolling a 5 on at least one of the dice.

Is the probability of getting a token into play greater than or less than $\frac{1}{2}$?
less than $\frac{1}{2}$

Plan A table will help to find the number of favorable outcomes as well as the total number of outcomes. Using the information from the table, the probability can be determined.

Solve

Second Die

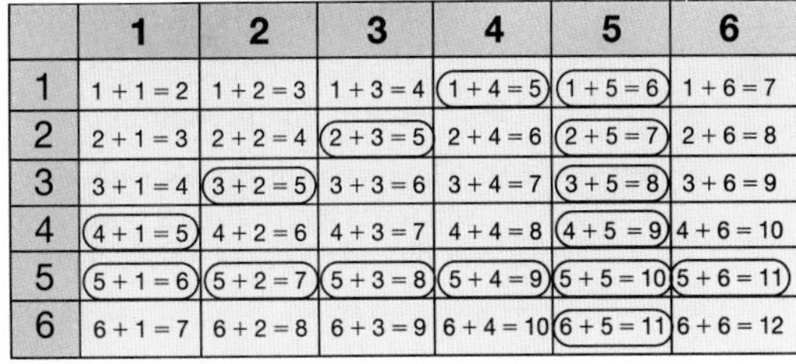

First Die	1	2	3	4	5	6
1	1 + 1 = 2	1 + 2 = 3	1 + 3 = 4	1 + 4 = 5	1 + 5 = 6	1 + 6 = 7
2	2 + 1 = 3	2 + 2 = 4	2 + 3 = 5	2 + 4 = 6	2 + 5 = 7	2 + 6 = 8
3	3 + 1 = 4	3 + 2 = 5	3 + 3 = 6	3 + 4 = 7	3 + 5 = 8	3 + 6 = 9
4	4 + 1 = 5	4 + 2 = 6	4 + 3 = 7	4 + 4 = 8	4 + 5 = 9	4 + 6 = 10
5	5 + 1 = 6	5 + 2 = 7	5 + 3 = 8	5 + 4 = 9	5 + 5 = 10	5 + 6 = 11
6	6 + 1 = 7	6 + 2 = 8	6 + 3 = 9	6 + 4 = 10	6 + 5 = 11	6 + 6 = 12

There are 4 ways of getting a total of 5 and 11 ways of getting a 5 on at least one die. This gives a total of 15 favorable outcomes. Since the sample space has 36 outcomes, the probability is $\frac{15}{36}$ or $\frac{5}{12}$.

Examine this solution.

Checking for Understanding

Communicating Algebra

1. How does the table above help you to solve the problem? It displays all possible outcomes so you can circle the ones that answer the problem.

Guided Practice

Use the table above to answer Exercises 2 and 3.

2. In many games where 2 dice are thrown, doubles (the same number showing on both dice) are important. What is the probability of throwing doubles? $\frac{1}{6}$
3. What is the probability that 2 dice will show a total less than 5? $\frac{1}{6}$
4. Make a table that can be used to solve probability problems about tossing two coins. See margin.

Bell Ringer
Brainstorm five probabilities involved with dice rolling. Sample answer: Probability of rolling a three twice in a row = $\frac{1}{36}$

Reteaching Activity
Using Cooperative Groups Have students make a table that can be used to solve probability problems about spinning a six-number, three-color spinner. Generate problems, and use the table to determine probabilities.

Lesson Notes 11-5

5-Minute Check
(over Lesson 11-4)

There are 6 white tees, 4 red tees, 3 green tees, and 2 blue tees in a bag. A tee is drawn at random. Find each probability.

1. P (red) $\frac{4}{15}$
2. P (white or green) $\frac{9}{15}$ or $\frac{3}{5}$
3. P (not blue) $\frac{13}{15}$
4. P (neither red nor blue) $\frac{9}{15}$ or $\frac{3}{5}$
5. P (orange) 0

Transparency 11-5 contains the 5-Minute Check and a teaching aid for this lesson.

1 FOCUS

The purpose of this lesson is to make tables and use them to solve problems.

Motivating the Lesson
Show students baseball statistics. Ask if there is a way to tell the probability of a player having an equal number of hits and errors during a game if there could be up to three of each.

2 TEACH

Chalkboard Examples

If two dice are rolled, what is the probability of rolling 7? $\frac{6}{36}$ or $\frac{1}{6}$

3 PRACTICE/APPLY

Checking the Concept
After completing Exercise 4, have students make up problems that can be solved using the table.

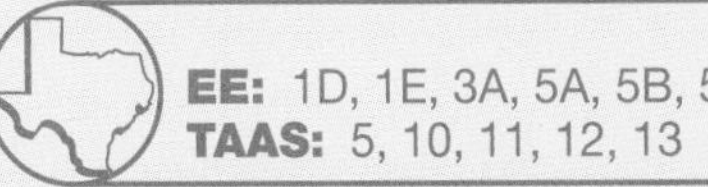
EE: 1D, 1E, 3A, 5A, 5B, 5C
TAAS: 5, 10, 11, 12, 13

Error Analysis
Watch for students who try to inappropriately use a table to solve a problem. **Prevent by** determining that the problem compares two items.

Independent Practice

Homework Assignment	
Basic	5-11 odd, 13-14
Average	6-10 even, 13-14
Honors	9-14

Chapter 11, Quiz A (Lessons 11-1 through 11-5) is available in the Evaluation Masters Booklet, p. 97.

CLOSE

Assessment Option

Speaking Have students explain when and how to create a table to solve a problem.

Practice Masters Booklet, **p. 105**

Name ______________ Date ______________

Practice Worksheet 11-5

Problem Solving: Make a Table

Solve. Use the make-a-table strategy.

1. Suppose you roll two dice. What is the probability that both will show 1? $\frac{1}{36}$

2. Suppose you roll two dice again. What is the probability that the sum of the numbers is 7? $\frac{1}{6}$

3. A game has the two spinners shown at the right. After spinning both spinners, what is the probability that the sum of the two numbers is less than 5? $\frac{1}{4}$

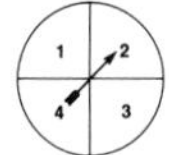

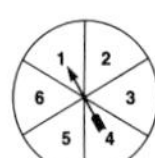

4. After spinning both spinners again, what is the probability that the sum of the two numbers is greater than 5? $\frac{7}{12}$

5. Fred's Fish Market charges $11.60 for 8 ounces of lobster meat. They charge $17.40 for 12 ounces. What would be the cost for two pounds of this lobster meat? $46.40

6. Suppose you toss two coins. What is the probability that one shows tails and the other shows heads? $\frac{1}{2}$

7. Suppose you toss three coins. What is the probability that each of the three coins shows a tail? $\frac{1}{8}$

Exercises

Independent Practice

Solve. Use any strategy.

5. If 2 coins are tossed, what is the probability that both coins show heads? $\frac{1}{4}$

6. In planning the big spring party, a chairperson is selected. The chairperson picks a person to head each of the 5 committees. Each person who heads a committee finds 6 people to work on his or her committee. How many people are helping to plan the spring party? **36 people**

7. Pablo collects postage stamps from foreign countries. Half of his stamps are from France. Half of the remaining stamps are from Japan. After setting aside the stamps from France and Japan, one fifth of the remaining stamps are from Spain. If there are 5 stamps from Spain, how many stamps does Pablo have altogether? **100 stamps**

8a. A tetrahedron is a 3-dimensional figure with 4 triangular faces the same size and shape. Assume there are 2 tetrahedron-shaped "dice" with a number from 1 to 4 marked on each face. The "dice" are rolled on the floor. What is the probability that the sum of the numbers facing the floor is 3? $\frac{1}{8}$

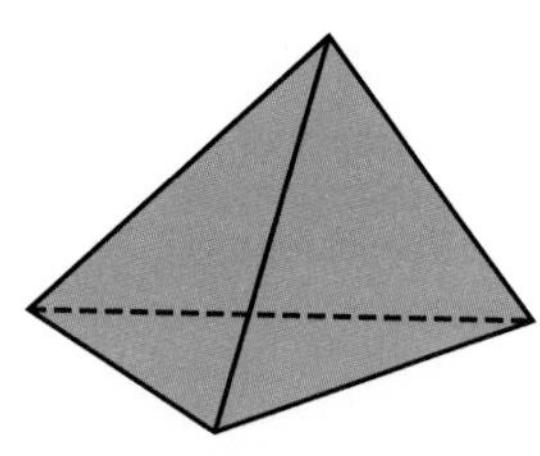

8b. What is the probability that the sum will be greater than 4? $\frac{5}{8}$

9. The owner of Rosa's Deli charges $1.80 for 10 ounces of pasta salad. She charges $2.16 for 12 ounces of the same pasta salad. At this rate, what would a pound of pasta salad cost? **$2.88**

10a. A game has 2 spinners as shown at the right. After spinning both spinners, what is the probability that the sum of the numbers is 8? $\frac{1}{8}$

10b. What is the probability that the sum is less than 8? $\frac{7}{16}$

Mixed Review

11. Find the mean, median, and mode for the data 12, 17, 9, 8, 20, 10, 15, 10, 9, 7, 10, 14, 6, 7. (Lesson 10-2) **11, 10, 10**

12. There are 7 blue marbles, 5 red marbles, and 3 yellow marbles in a bag. If you select one marble at random, what is the probability it will be blue? (Lesson 11-4) $\frac{7}{15}$

Critical Thinking

13. The product of three consecutive numbers is 10,626. Find the numbers. Use a calculator. **21, 22, 23**

Wrap-Up

14. Look at Exercises 5-13. List the Exercises you solved by using a table. How did a table help you to solve each of these exercises? **See students' work; A table displays all possible outcomes so you can select the ones that solve the problem.**

Additional Answer

4.

		Second Coin	
		H	T
First Coin	H	(H, H)	(H,T)
	T	(T, H)	(T, T)

Cooperative Learning

Crafty Cooking — Group Activity 11-5

Luigi, the Italian cook, needs grated cheese to make pizza for a birthday party. He has calculated that he needs 18 pounds of grated cheese. However, cheese only comes in 3-pound and 5-pound cans. How many cans of each size should he buy?

Try making a table to solve this problem. You might start by deciding to buy 0, 1, 2, etc. 5-pound cans and then determine the number of 3-pound cans necessary to buy 18 pounds of grated cheese.

Merrill Pre-Algebra PROBLEM SOLVING: MAKE A TABLE

Making Predictions

Materials: paper bags containing 10 colored golf tees

In this Exploration you will make predictions based on the results of an experiment.

Your Turn: Work with a partner to complete this experiment.

- Draw one golf tee from the bag, record its color, and replace it in the bag. Repeat this 10 times. See students' work.
- The term **relative frequency** means what fraction of the time a certain color was drawn. Calculate the relative frequency for each color golf tee. Express the relative frequency as a decimal. See students' work.
- Repeat both steps described above for twenty, thirty, forty, and fifty draws. See students' work.

Analysis

1. Is it possible to have a certain color tee in the bag and never draw that color? Is this situation likely to happen if you make only two draws? ten draws? fifty draws? yes; yes; possibly; no
2. Write a paragraph that describes how the relative frequencies changed as you increased the number of draws. See margin.
3. The **experimental probability** is an estimate based on the relative frequency you obtained in your experiment. Based on your experiment, what is the experimental probability of drawing each color tee? See students' work.
4. Predict the colors of the tees in your bag. Open the bag and check your prediction against the tees in the bag. See students' work.

EXPLORATION:
Making Predictions

Objectives Students will experiment with different-sized samples and make predictions.

1 FOCUS

The purpose of this Exploration is for students to use probability to determine whether samples drawn from a set (experimental probability) accurately reflect the theoretical probability.

2 TEACH

Using a Table

Have students make a table with three rows and five columns. Head the columns ten, twenty, thirty, forty and fifty. Tell students that for this to be a true experiment they should not peek inside their bag. You may need to remind students how to write a fraction as a decimal. To save time students should be allowed to use calculators.

3 PRACTICE/APPLY

Working With a Partner

Before students begin their experiments, have them determine their roles and how they are going to equally participate in each experiment.

Additional Answer

2. **Sample answer: As the number of draws increased, the experimental probability was closer to the theoretical probability.**

4 CLOSE

Writing Connection

Ask students to write a brief report about how the automobile insurance industry uses concepts of probability to determine insurance costs.

SET-UP

Materials

- paper bags, golf tees

You may wish to use the Exploration worksheet provided on page 58 of the Lab Manual.

For Students Each pair of students will need a paper bag containing ten golf tees.

HINT: Prepare the bags of golf tees ahead of time. Use no more than three different colors per bag and vary the number of individual colors per bag. For example, 1 red, 2 blue, 7 green and 2 red, 3 white, and 5 blue.

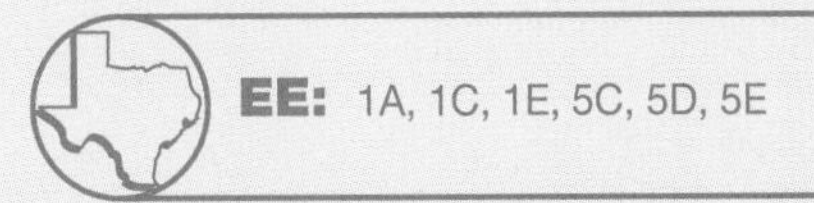

Lesson Notes 11-6

5-Minute Check
(over Lesson 11-5)

Solve. Use any strategy. A game has two spinners as shown.

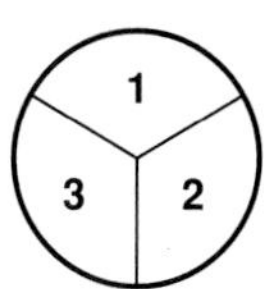

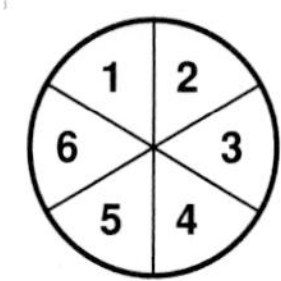

1. After spinning both spinners, what is the probability that the sum of the two spinners will be 5? $\frac{3}{18}$ or $\frac{1}{6}$
2. What is the probability that the sum of the two spinners will be greater than 4? $\frac{12}{18}$ or $\frac{2}{3}$
3. Refer to the table on page 415. What is the probability that the total sum of the 2 dice is greater than 5? $\frac{26}{36}$ or $\frac{13}{18}$

Transparency 11-6 contains the 5-Minute Check and a teaching aid for this lesson.

1 FOCUS

The purpose of this lesson is to introduce compound events and determine the probability of specific outcomes.

Motivating the Lesson

Have students make a list of characteristics of themselves that are independent of each other. Lists may include eye color, hair color or type, height, and weight.

2 TEACH

Chalkboard Examples

- *For Example 1*
  Erika selects, without looking, one button at random from each box. One box contains 4 white buttons and 5 black buttons. A second box contains 3 red buttons and 4 blue buttons. What is the probability that Erika will select one white and one blue button? $\frac{16}{63}$

11-6 Probability of Independent Events

Objective:
Find the probability of independent events.

Key Term:
independent event

Without looking, Poloma selects one ticket at random from each group of tickets. What is the probability that she will select a baseball ticket and a rock concert ticket?

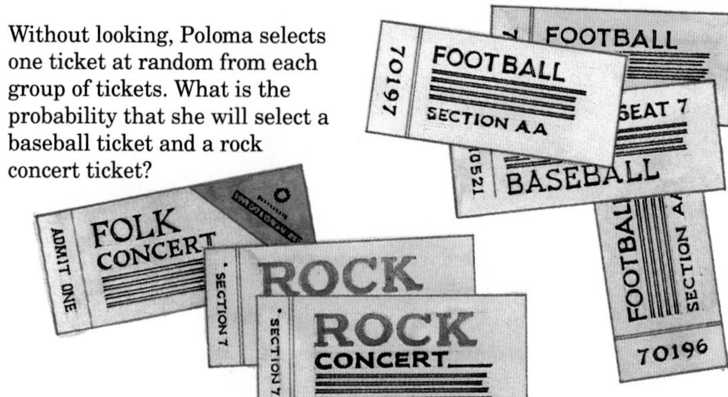

The ticket she chooses from the first group does not affect the ticket she chooses from the second group. We call these **independent events.** That is, the outcome of the one event does not affect the outcome of the other event.

Probability of Two Independent Events

The probability of two independent events can be found by multiplying the probability of the first event by the probability of the second event.

$$P(\text{A and B}) = P(\text{A}) \cdot P(\text{B})$$

$P(\text{baseball}) = \frac{1}{4}$ $\quad P(\text{rock concert}) = \frac{2}{3}$

$$P(\text{baseball and rock concert}) = P(\text{baseball}) \cdot P(\text{rock concert}) = \frac{1}{4} \cdot \frac{2}{3} = \frac{2}{12} \text{ or } \frac{1}{6}$$

The probability that the two events will occur is $\frac{1}{6}$.

FYI

Are you afraid to fly? Don't worry too much. The probability of being killed on a commercial airliner is only one in almost two million. There is a greater chance of being injured in your own bathtub—1 in 1028.

Examples

1 What is the probability that Poloma will select one football ticket and one rock concert ticket?

$P(\text{football}) = \frac{3}{4}$ $\quad P(\text{rock concert}) = \frac{2}{3}$

$$P(\text{football and rock concert}) = \frac{3}{4} \cdot \frac{2}{3} = \frac{6}{12} \text{ or } \frac{1}{2}$$

The probability that the two events will occur is $\frac{1}{2}$.

Bell Ringer

What is the maximum number of draws needed from a drawer of black and blue socks, to obtain a matching pair? 3

EE: 1E, 3A, 5C
TAAS: 5, 8, 11

2 Two dice are rolled. Find the probability that an even number is rolled on one die and a prime number is rolled on the other.

$P(\text{even number}) = \frac{1}{2}$ $\quad P(\text{prime number}) = \frac{3}{6}$ or $\frac{1}{2}$

$P(\text{even number and prime number}) = \frac{1}{2} \cdot \frac{1}{2}$

$= \frac{1}{4}$

The probability that the two events will occur is $\frac{1}{4}$.

How can the probability of three independent events be found? **Multiply the probabilities of the three events.**

Checking for Understanding

Communicating Algebra

1. What are independent events? **The outcome of one event doesn't affect the outcome of the other.**
2. Two positive numbers, each less than one, are multiplied. What is the relationship between the product and each of the numbers? **The product is less than each of the numbers.**

Guided Practice

The chart below lists the number and type of chocolates found in two boxes of candy. A milk chocolate is chosen at random. Then a dark chocolate is chosen at random. Find the probability of each outcome.

3. a milk chocolate with nuts and a dark chocolate with nuts $\frac{1}{21}$
4. a milk chocolate with nuts and a dark chocolate with fruit $\frac{1}{7}$
5. a plain milk chocolate and a dark chocolate with nuts $\frac{1}{42}$
6. a milk chocolate with fruit and a plain dark chocolate $\frac{3}{14}$

Boxes	Nuts	Fruits	Plain
Milk chocolate	4	6	2
Dark chocolate	2	6	6

Exercises

Independent Practice

Each spinner is spun once. Find each probability.

7. $P(1 \text{ and } A)$ $\frac{1}{20}$
8. $P(2 \text{ and } B)$ $\frac{3}{20}$
9. $P(3 \text{ and } C)$ $\frac{1}{20}$
10. $P(2 \text{ and } C)$ $\frac{1}{20}$
11. $P(1 \text{ and } B)$ $\frac{3}{20}$
12. $P(\text{an even number and a vowel})$ $\frac{1}{10}$
13. $P(\text{an odd number and a consonant})$ $\frac{2}{5}$

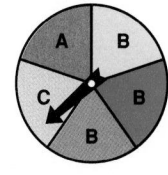

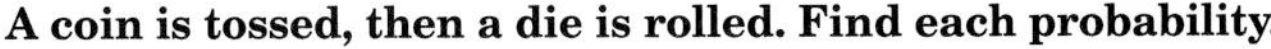

A coin is tossed, then a die is rolled. Find each probability.

14. $P(\text{heads and } 6)$ $\frac{1}{12}$
15. $P(\text{heads and number less than } 5)$ $\frac{1}{3}$
16. $P(\text{tails and } 5)$ $\frac{1}{12}$
17. $P(\text{tails and an odd number})$ $\frac{1}{4}$
18. $P(\text{heads and } 3)$ $\frac{1}{12}$
19. $P(\text{heads and a number greater than } 3)$ $\frac{1}{4}$
20. $P(\text{tails and 2 or } 3)$ $\frac{1}{6}$
21. $P(\text{tails and a prime number})$ $\frac{1}{4}$

One bag contains 3 red and 4 white balls. A second bag contains 6 yellow and 3 green balls. One ball is drawn from each bag. Find each probability.

22. $P(\text{red and yellow})$ $\frac{2}{7}$
23. $P(\text{red and green})$ $\frac{1}{7}$
24. $P(\text{white and green})$ $\frac{4}{21}$
25. $P(\text{white and yellow})$ $\frac{8}{21}$

- *For Example 2*
  Two dice are rolled. Find the probability that an even number is rolled on both die. $\frac{1}{4}$

3 PRACTICE/APPLY

Checking the Concept

After completing Exercises 3-6, ask students to explain why the rule for probability of independent events does not apply to choosing a milk chocolate with nuts and a plain milk chocolate.

Error Analysis

Watch for students who can't distinguish whether events are independent or not.
Prevent by asking if the second event depends on the first event.

Independent Practice

Homework Assignment	
Basic	7-25 odd, 26-29, 31, 32
Average	8-24 even, 26-32
Honors	10-20 even, 22-32
All	Mid-Chapter Quiz 1-8

Practice Masters Booklet, **p. 106**

Name ______ Date ______

Practice Worksheet 11-6

Probability of Independent Events

Each spinner is spun one. Find each probability.

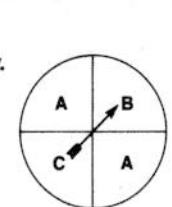

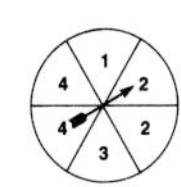

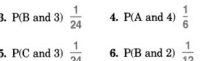

1. P(A and 1) $\frac{1}{12}$
2. P(C and 2) $\frac{1}{12}$
3. P(B and 3) $\frac{1}{24}$
4. P(A and 4) $\frac{1}{6}$
5. P(C and 3) $\frac{1}{24}$
6. P(B and 2) $\frac{1}{12}$
7. P(a consonant and odd number) $\frac{1}{6}$
8. P(a vowel and an even number) $\frac{1}{3}$
9. P(a consonant and prime number) $\frac{1}{4}$
10. P(a vowel and a number less than 3) $\frac{1}{4}$

A coin is tossed, then a die is rolled. Find each probability.

11. P(heads and 4) $\frac{1}{12}$
12. P(tails and 1) $\frac{1}{12}$
13. P(heads and an odd number) $\frac{1}{4}$
14. P(tails and an even number) $\frac{1}{4}$
15. P(tails and a number less than 4) $\frac{1}{4}$
16. P(heads and a number greater than 1) $\frac{5}{12}$
17. P(heads and 1 or 3) $\frac{1}{6}$
18. P(tails and a number less than 5) $\frac{1}{3}$

The spinner is spun twice. Find each probability.

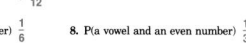

19. P(w and w) $\frac{1}{64}$
20. P(x and s) $\frac{1}{32}$
21. P(z and a) $\frac{1}{64}$
22. P(x and x) $\frac{1}{16}$
23. P(a vowel and a vowel) $\frac{1}{16}$
24. P(a consonant and a consonant) $\frac{9}{16}$
25. P(a vowel and a consonant) $\frac{3}{16}$
26. P(x and a vowel) $\frac{1}{16}$

Alternate Strategies: Reteaching the Lesson

Reteaching Activity

Using Tables Have students make a table with four columns and three rows. Head the columns with the sporting event tickets and head the rows with the concert tickets. Have students complete the cells and circle the ones containing both baseball and concert tickets. Then have them express the ratio of the number of circles to the total number of cells.

Reteaching Masters Booklet, **p. 96**

Name ______ Date ______

Reteaching Worksheet 11-6

Probability of Independent Events

To find the probability of two *independent* events, multiply the probability of the first event by the probability of the second event.

A jar contains 12 red bells and 12 silver bells. Pick one, replace it, and pick another. The probability of picking a silver bell twice is $\frac{1}{2} \times \frac{1}{2}$ or $\frac{1}{4}$.

Find each probability. Each item is replaced.

1. A box contains 10 red, 4 blue, and 4 white marbles. Choose a blue marble, then a red marble. $\frac{10}{81}$
2. A jar contains 6 cinnamon sticks and 8 licorice sticks. Choose a licorice stick twice. $\frac{16}{49}$
3. A box contains the names of 8 girls, 12 boys, and 1 teacher. Choose a boy,
4. A box contains the names of 8 girls and 8 boys. Choose a girl,

4 CLOSE

Assessment Option

Writing Divide the class into small groups. Have each group write a problem that involves independent events. Exchange problems and find the probability.

Enrichment Masters Booklet, **p. 96**

Name ____________ Date ____________

Enrichment Worksheet 11-6

Binomial Formula

The **Binomial Formula** can be used to calculate the probabilities of independent events when only two possible outcomes exist.

For example, if you take a multiple-choice test, there are ony two possible outcomes for each question—correct or incorrect. Assume you have no idea which choice is the correct answer, so you are just guessing. If there are five choices for each question, the probability of guessing any one answer correctly is $\frac{1}{5} = 0.2$. To find the probability of guessing exactly 3 of 4 questions correctly, use the binomial formula:

(number of questions; number of correct answers; P(correct answer); number of correct answers; P(incorrect answer); number of incorrect answers)

$$P(3 \text{ of } 4 \text{ correct}) = C(4, 3) \cdot (0.2^3) \cdot (0.8^1)$$
$$= 4 \cdot 0.008 \cdot 0.8$$
$$= 0.0256 \text{ or } 2.56\%$$

For a 10-question test with five choices for each question, find the probability of guessing each number of correct answers. Use a calculator and give your answers to the nearest whole-number percent.

1. 0 $C(10, 0)(0.2^0)(0.8^{10}) \approx 0.107 \approx 11\%$
2. 1 $C(10, 1)(0.2^1)(0.8^9) \approx 0.268 \approx 27\%$
3. 2 $C(10, 2)(0.2^2)(0.8^8) \approx 0.302 \approx 30\%$
4. 3 $C(10, 3)(0.2^3)(0.8^7) \approx 0.201 \approx 20\%$
5. 9 $C(10, 9)(0.2^9)(0.8^1) \approx 0.000004 \approx 0\%$
6. 10 $C(10, 10)(0.2^{10})(0.8^0) = 0.0000001 \approx 0\%$

Mixed Review

26. *True* or *false:* $\frac{9}{11} < \frac{5}{7}$. (Lesson 4-8) **false**
27. Express as a unit rate: *$3.00 for 12 doughnuts.* (Lesson 9-1) **25¢/doughnut**
28. Two dice are rolled. What is the probability that the sum of the numbers shown is equal to or less than 7? (Lesson 11-5) **$\frac{21}{36}$ or $\frac{7}{12}$**

Applications

29. **Clothing** On a rack in his closet, Amos has two green shirts, three red shirts, and four blue shirts. On another rack he has two blue slacks, two brown slacks, and two green slacks. Suppose Amos makes a selection from each rack without looking. What is the probability that he will have an all blue outfit? **$\frac{4}{27}$**
30. **Business** If 65% of a store's customers are men and 80% of the men have charge cards, what is the probability that a customer chosen at random is male and has a charge card? **0.52 or $\frac{13}{25}$**

Critical Thinking

31. The estimated probability that the Chargers will win a game is 0.7. The probability that the Colts will win is estimated as 0.6. If they do not play each other, what is the probability that they will both win? both lose? How do these two probabilities compare? Is this reasonable? **0.42; 0.12; Probability they both lose is less than probability they both win; yes**

Wrap-Up

32. Explain how to find the probability of two independent events. **Multiply the probability of the first event by the probability of the second event.**

Mid-Chapter Quiz

1. A diner serves three breakfasts (scrambled eggs, cereal, and pancakes) and two types of juice (orange and apple). Draw a tree diagram that illustrates the outcomes. (Lesson 11-1) **See Solutions Manual.**
2. For lunch Kelly can choose from six different sandwiches, three different beverages, and three different types of fruit. She picks one sandwich, one beverage, and one fruit. How many outcomes are possible? (Lesson 11-2) **54 outcomes**

Find each value. (Lesson 11-3)

3. 5! **120**
4. $P(7, 3)$ **210**
5. $C(9, 4)$ **126**

The first bag has 4 red marbles and 3 green marbles. The second bag has 5 blue marbles and 2 white marbles. (Lessons 11-4, 11-5)

6. A marble is picked at random from the first bag. Find *P*(green). **$\frac{3}{7}$**
7. A marble is picked at random from the second bag. Find *P*(orange). **0**
8. A marble is picked at random from each of the bags. Find *P*(red and white). **$\frac{8}{49}$**

Alternate Strategies: Extending the Lesson

Enrichment

Social Studies Connection Post a United States map. Have cooperative groups write probability problems relating independent information about the states. Trade and solve. For example, what is the probability that a state name begins with the letter "A" and the state borders the Gulf of Mexico?

Cooperative Learning

In The Bag Group Activity **11-6**

MATERIALS: Paper bag containing the following pieces from a set of pattern blocks: 3 triangles, 5 hexagons, 5 squares, 6 trapezoids, 7 rhombuses, a set of three cards with the numbers 2, 3, 4

Everyone first should calculate the probability of drawing one specific piece from the bag. Then he or she draws a piece from the bag, shows it to everyone, and returns it to the bag. Do this the number of times indicated on your card.

The other players calculate the probability of the pieces obtained by the first player.

The first player with the correct answer scores the point. Play continues until everyone has had one turn. The person with the most points wins.

Merrill Pre-Algebra PROBABILITY OF INDEPENDENT EVENTS

11-7 Probability of Dependent Events

Objective:
Find the probability of dependent events.

Key Term:
dependent event

Why is the probability on the second selection $\frac{1}{9}$ instead of $\frac{1}{10}$?
One card has already been drawn, leaving 9 cards in the deck.

FYI

Imagine that you play baseball and are considering a career in professional baseball immediately after you graduate. You had better be very good. The probability that you'll make it is less than 1%.

The band members sold magazines to help pay for new uniforms. Prizes are awarded to eight students who sold the most magazines. The prizes are three concert tickets and five movie tickets. Starting with the top salesperson, each of the top eight salespersons draws one ticket from a bag. Tina and Jose finished first and second. What is the probability that both Tina and Jose will draw concert tickets?

This is an example of **dependent events** because what Tina draws affects what Jose draws.

For Tina, $P(\text{concert}) = \frac{\text{number of concert tickets}}{\text{total number of tickets}} = \frac{3}{8}$.

Assume that Tina drew a concert ticket.

For Jose, $P(\text{concert})\ \frac{\text{number of concert tickets left}}{\text{number of tickets left}} = \frac{2}{7}$.

Therefore, $P(\text{concert tickets for both}) = \frac{3}{8} \cdot \frac{2}{7}$

$= \frac{6}{56}$ or $\frac{3}{28}$.

Examples

1 From a deck of 10 cards (5 ten-point cards, 3 twenty-point cards, and 2 fifty-point cards), Nancy needs to pick the 2 fifty-point cards to win a game. What is the probability that she will win?

First selection: $P(\text{fifty-point card}) = \frac{2}{10}$

Second selection: $P(\text{fifty-point card}) = \frac{1}{9}$

$P(\text{2 fifty-point cards}) = \frac{2}{10} \cdot \frac{1}{9}$

$= \frac{2}{90}$ or $\frac{1}{45}$

The probability that Nancy will draw 2 fifty-point cards is $\frac{1}{45}$.

2 If there were 3 fifty-point cards, 4 ten-point cards, and 3 twenty-point cards, what is the probability that Nancy will win the game described in Example 1?

First selection: $P(\text{fifty-point card}) = \frac{3}{10}$

Second selection: $P(\text{fifty-point card}) = \frac{2}{9}$

$P(\text{2 fifty-point cards}) = \frac{3}{10} \cdot \frac{2}{9}$

$= \frac{6}{90}$ or $\frac{1}{15}$

The probability that Nancy will draw 2 fifty-point cards is $\frac{1}{15}$.

Bell Ringer

Explain how to find the probability of two independent events. **Sample answer: Find the product of the probabilities of each event.**

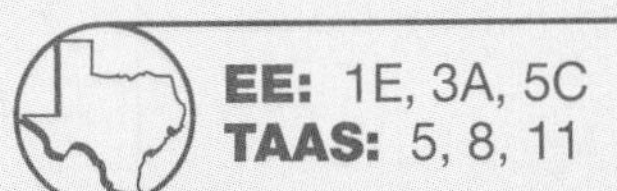

Lesson Notes 11-7

5-Minute Check
(over Lesson 11-6)

One bag contains 3 red marbles and 5 blue ones. A second bag contains 4 green and 6 white. A marble is drawn at random from each bag. Find each probability.

1. P(a red and a green) $\frac{12}{80}$ or $\frac{3}{20}$
2. P(a blue and a white) $\frac{30}{80}$ or $\frac{3}{8}$
3. P(a blue and a green) $\frac{20}{80}$ or $\frac{1}{4}$
4. P(a red and a white) $\frac{18}{80}$ or $\frac{9}{40}$

Transparency 11-7 contains the 5-Minute Check and a teaching aid for this lesson.

1 FOCUS

The purpose of this lesson is for students to become aware of the difference between independent and dependent events and the effect this difference has on the probability of compound events involving them.

Motivating the Lesson

Line up five students. Ask students what the probability is that (name) will be chosen. Remove the student from the line. Repeat for each of the remaining four students. Ask why the probabilities change.

2 TEACH

Chalkboard Examples

- *For Example 1*
  From a deck of 15 cards (8 ten-point cards, 4 twenty-point cards, and 3 fifty-point cards), Marla needs to pick two fifty-point cards to win. What is the probability that she will win? $\frac{6}{210}$ or $\frac{1}{35}$
- *For Example 2*
  If there are 5 fifty-point cards, 6 ten-point cards, and 4 twenty-point cards, what is the probability that Marla will win? $\frac{20}{210}$ or $\frac{2}{21}$

3 PRACTICE/APPLY

Checking the Concept

If practice is needed after completing Exercises 3-8, model similar problems using a set of pick-up sticks.

Error Analysis

Watch for students who incorrectly determine the second probability. **Prevent by** modeling the problems.

Additional Answers

1. Sample answer: Making two draws from a bag of marbles and not replacing the first marble drawn.
2. Events are independent when neither affects the other and dependent when the first event does affect the following event.

Practice Masters Booklet, **p. 107**

Name ______________ Date ______________

Practice Worksheet 11-7

Probability of Dependent Events

In a bag there are 4 red marbles, 5 white marbles, and 6 blue marbles. Once a marble is selected, it is not replaced. Find the probability of each outcome.

1. a red marble and then a white marble $\frac{2}{21}$
2. a blue marble and then a red marble $\frac{4}{35}$
3. 2 red marbles in a row $\frac{2}{35}$
4. 2 blue marbles in a row $\frac{1}{7}$
5. a red marble three times in a row $\frac{4}{455}$
6. a white marble three times in a row $\frac{2}{91}$
7. a blue marble, a white marble, and then a red marble $\frac{4}{91}$
8. a blue marble three times in a row $\frac{4}{91}$

Tracy makes up a deck of fifty cards. The cards are numbered from 1 to 10 and each number comes in five colors (orange, red, yellow, green, and blue). Tracy selects cards from the deck. Once a card is selected, it is not replaced. Find the probability of each outcome.

9. a 4 and then a 10 $\frac{1}{98}$
10. a 5 and then a 6 $\frac{1}{98}$
11. two 5's in a row $\frac{2}{245}$
12. three 7's in a row $\frac{1}{1960}$
13. a yellow and then a green $\frac{2}{49}$
14. a red and then a blue $\frac{2}{49}$
15. a 1, a 2, and then a 3 $\frac{5}{4704}$
16. a 10, an 8, and then a 6 $\frac{5}{4704}$
17. the orange 5, and then the red 1 $\frac{1}{2450}$
18. the red 5, and then the orange 1 $\frac{1}{2450}$
19. four 9's in a row $\frac{1}{46,060}$
20. four 1's in a row $\frac{1}{46,060}$

Checking for Understanding

Communicating Algebra

1. Give an example of dependent events. **See margin.**
2. Explain the difference between independent events and dependent events. **See margin.**

Guided Practice

Given the ten-card deck in Example 1, find the probability of each outcome.

3. 2 ten-point cards in a row $\frac{2}{9}$
4. 2 twenty-point cards in a row $\frac{1}{15}$
5. a ten-point card and then a twenty-point card $\frac{1}{6}$
6. a twenty-point card and then a fifty-point card $\frac{1}{15}$
7. a ten-point card and then a fifty-point card $\frac{1}{9}$
8. 3 twenty-point cards in a row $\frac{1}{120}$

Exercises

Independent Practice

In a bag there are 3 red marbles, 2 white marbles, and 4 blue marbles. Once a marble is selected, it is not replaced. Find the probability of each outcome.

9. a red marble and then a white marble $\frac{1}{12}$
10. a white marble and then a blue marble $\frac{1}{9}$
11. 2 white marbles in a row $\frac{1}{36}$
12. 2 blue marbles in a row $\frac{1}{6}$
13. a blue marble three times in a row $\frac{1}{21}$
14. 2 red marbles in a row $\frac{1}{12}$
15. a red marble, a white marble, and then a blue marble $\frac{1}{21}$
16. a white marble three times in a row **0**

Keith makes up a deck of forty cards. The cards are numbered from 1 to 10 and each number comes in four colors (orange, red, black, and blue). Keith selects cards from the deck. Once a card is selected, it is not replaced. Find the probability of each outcome.

17. a 5 and then a 9 $\frac{2}{195}$
18. a 10 and then a 7 $\frac{2}{195}$
19. two 7s in a row $\frac{1}{130}$
20. three 5s in a row $\frac{1}{2470}$
21. an orange and then a blue $\frac{5}{78}$
22. a red, a blue, and then an orange $\frac{25}{1482}$
23. a 4, a 5, and then a 6 $\frac{4}{3705}$
24. a 10, a 9, and then an 8 $\frac{4}{3705}$
25. the orange 10 and then the red 8 $\frac{1}{1560}$
26. four 6s in a row $\frac{1}{91,390}$

Mixed Review

27. Simplify $9x + (-14x) + 3x$. (Lesson 2-4) $-2x$
28. What type of relationship, *positive*, *negative*, or *none*, is shown by the scatter plot at the right? (Lesson 10-6) **positive**

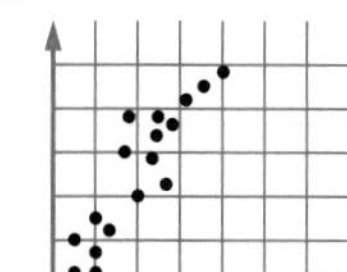

Alternate Strategies: Reteaching the Lesson

Reteaching Activity

Using Models Use a bag containing 5 blue and 3 green marbles. To emphasize the difference in dependent and independent events, model problems involving replacement and nonreplacement of items drawn from the bag.

Reteaching Masters Booklet, **p. 97**

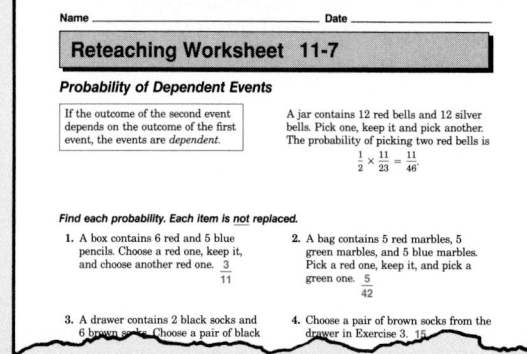

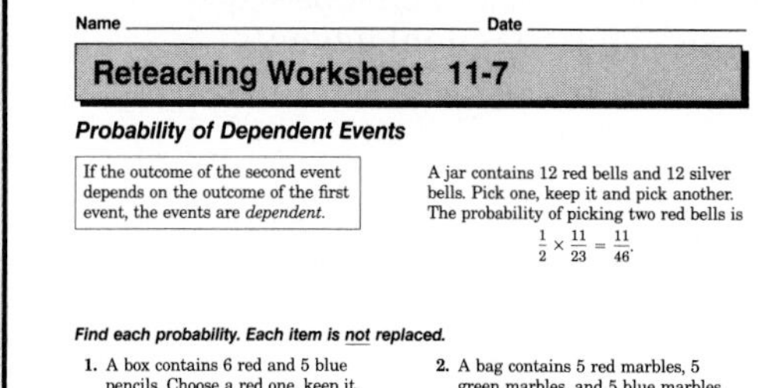

Name ______________ Date ______________

Reteaching Worksheet 11-7

Probability of Dependent Events

If the outcome of the second event depends on the outcome of the first event, the events are *dependent*.

A jar contains 12 red bells and 12 silver bells. Pick one, keep it and pick another. The probability of picking two red bells is $\frac{1}{2} \times \frac{11}{23} = \frac{11}{46}$.

Find each probability. Each item is not replaced.

1. A box contains 6 red and 5 blue pencils. Choose a red one, keep it, and choose another red one. $\frac{3}{11}$
2. A bag contains 5 red marbles, 5 green marbles, and 5 blue marbles. Pick a red one, keep it, and pick a green one. $\frac{5}{42}$
3. A drawer contains 2 black socks and 6 brown socks. Choose a pair of black
4. Choose a pair of brown socks from the drawer in Exercise 3. 15

29. Find the value of $C(6, 4)$. (Lesson 11-3) 15

30. A coin is tossed, then a die is rolled. Find P(heads and a number less than 3). (Lesson 11-6) $\frac{1}{6}$

Applications

31. **Business** A quality control inspector selects seventy samples from the conveyor. Thirty are defective. What is the probability that the next two selected are defective? $\frac{9}{49}$

32. **Clothing** Martin has five blue socks and eight black socks in his drawer. He picks one sock at random and then another. What is the probability that he will draw a pair of black socks? $\frac{14}{39}$

Critical Thinking

33. **Decision Making** Maria can't decide whether to go out or stay at home. If she goes out, she can go to dinner, to a school dance, to a concert, to a ball game, to a friend's house, or to a mall. She flips a coin to decide whether to go out or to stay home and then rolls a die to see which activity she will do if she goes out. What is the probability that she will go to the mall? $\frac{1}{12}$

Wrap-Up

34. Give an example that finds the probability of independent events and another example that finds the probability of dependent events. See margin.

Team Problem Solving

Rhonda buys six stamps. The postal clerk tears six stamps from a large sheet of stamps as shown.

Rhonda wonders how many different ways the clerk can tear off six attached stamps. Draw all the different formations of stamps. Be careful not to use the same figure that has been rotated. How many formations are there? See Solutions Manual; 35 formations

Independent Practice

Homework Assignment	
Basic	9-25 odd, 27-34
Average	10-26 even, 27-34
Honors	17-34

4 CLOSE

Assessment Option

Speaking Use a regular deck of playing cards and have students name outcomes. Then find the probability assuming once a card is chosen it is not replaced. For example, a student may want to find the probability of selecting a jack and then a queen. Have another student describe how to find that probability. Find the product of $\frac{4}{52}$ and $\frac{4}{51}$.

Enrichment Masters Booklet, **p. 97**

Name ______ Date ______

Enrichment Worksheet 11-7

Probability of Dependent Events

Look at the letters in the word MATHEMATICAL. If these letters were placed in a hat, what would be the probability of drawing a vowel and then, without replacing the vowel, drawing a consonant? These are **dependent events** since the letter selected on the first draw affects the probability for the second draw.

$P(\text{vowel, then consonant}) = \frac{5}{12} \cdot \frac{7}{11} = \frac{35}{132}$

Find the probability of drawing each of the following from the letters in MATHEMATICAL.

1. two M's $\frac{1}{66}$
2. two A's $\frac{1}{22}$
3. three A's $\frac{1}{220}$
4. three vowels $\frac{1}{22}$
5. five consonants $\frac{7}{264}$
6. the letters MATH in that order $\frac{1}{990}$

Now, think of using variables instead of numbers. This is very useful, since this is the way formulas are developed. Once a formula is found, it can be used for any numbers. Begin by examining the following problem.

Example: Three of ten socks in a box are blue. If socks are drawn without looking and not replaced, what is the probability of picking three blue socks in three drawings?

$\frac{3}{10} \cdot \frac{2}{9} \cdot \frac{1}{8} = \frac{6}{720}$, or $\frac{1}{120}$

7. If a box containing N socks has K blue ones, what is the probability of picking three blue socks in three drawings? $\frac{K}{N} \cdot \frac{K-1}{N-1} \cdot \frac{K-2}{N-2}$
8. If a box containing N socks has K blue ones, what is the probability of picking X blue socks in X drawings? $\frac{K}{N} \cdot \frac{K-1}{N-1} \cdot \frac{K-2}{N-2} \cdots \frac{K-(X-1)}{N-(X-1)}$
9. Use your formula from Exercise 7 to find the probability of picking three blue socks in three drawings from a box containing six socks, four of them blue. $\frac{4}{6} \cdot \frac{3}{5} \cdot \frac{2}{4} = \frac{1}{5}$
10. Use your formula from Exercise 8 to find the probability of picking four blue socks in four drawings from a box containing six socks, five of them blue. $\frac{5}{6} \cdot \frac{4}{5} \cdot \frac{3}{4} \cdot \frac{2}{3} = \frac{1}{3}$

Additional Answers

34. Sample answer: The probability of a tossed coin landing heads up and rolling a six on a die is an example of independent events. The probability of pulling two blue socks out of a drawer of blue and brown socks in only two tries is an example of dependent events.

Cooperative Learning

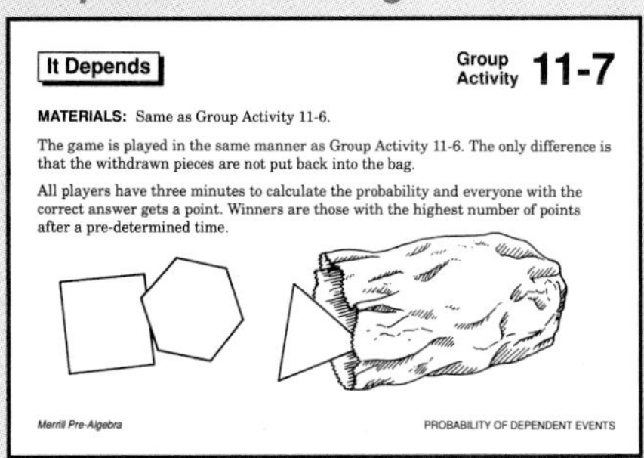

It Depends — Group Activity **11-7**

MATERIALS: Same as Group Activity 11-6.

The game is played in the same manner as Group Activity 11-6. The only difference is that the withdrawn pieces are not put back into the bag.

All players have three minutes to calculate the probability and everyone with the correct answer gets a point. Winners are those with the highest number of points after a pre-determined time.

Merrill Pre-Algebra PROBABILITY OF DEPENDENT EVENTS

Lesson Notes 11-8

5-Minute Check
(over Lesson 11-7)

Tom has a deck of cards that contains 5 blue cards, 3 red cards, and 2 yellow cards. Once a card is selected, it is not replaced. Find the probability of each outcome.

1. a blue card followed by a red card $\frac{15}{90}$ or $\frac{1}{6}$
2. two red cards in a row $\frac{6}{90}$ or $\frac{1}{15}$
3. a yellow, a blue, and then a red $\frac{30}{720}$ or $\frac{1}{24}$
4. a yellow and then a blue $\frac{10}{90}$ or $\frac{1}{9}$
5. three blue cards in a row $\frac{60}{720}$ or $\frac{1}{12}$

Transparency 11-8 contains the 5-Minute Check and a teaching aid for this lesson.

1 FOCUS

The purpose of this lesson is to determine whether two events are mutually exclusive and determine the probability of either or both events occurring.

Motivating the Lesson

Show students 4 white, 3 blue, and 5 red marbles. Place them into a box or paper bag. Tell students they have a choice of receiving 75¢ for drawing a blue marble in one draw, or receiving 25¢ for drawing a red marble on the first draw or a blue marble on the second draw. Discuss whether the prizes are fair.

2 TEACH

Using Discussion

Using examples, develop the concept of mutual exclusion, and the use of *and* and *or* in compound events. Be sure students know when to add and when to multiply probabilities.

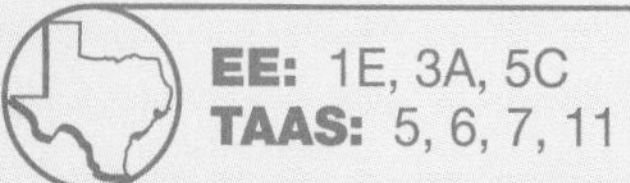

EE: 1E, 3A, 5C
TAAS: 5, 6, 7, 11

11-8 Adding Probabilities

Objective:
Find the probability of compound events by using addition.

Key Term:
mutually exclusive event

For a school bond election, people in the community were surveyed to determine whether they would work for the campaign, donate money, or do both. Of the sample, 15% were willing to work, 27% were willing to give money, and 8% were willing to do both. If a member of the community were selected at random, what is the probability that he or she would be willing to work *or* give money?

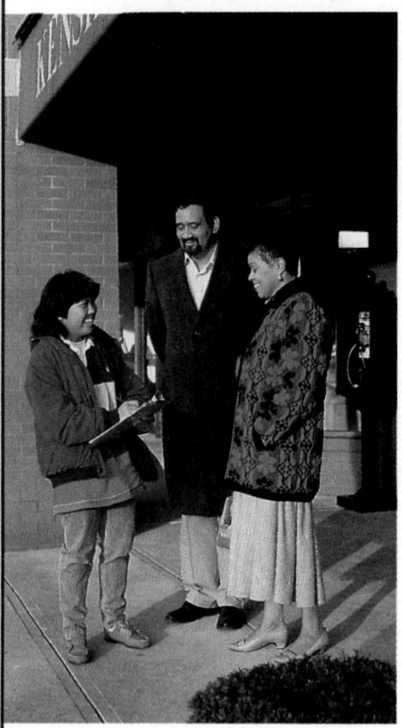

A similar example arises when throwing a die. What is the probability of throwing a 5 or a 6? In this case both events cannot happen at the same time. That is, the events are **mutually exclusive.**

When events A and B are mutually exclusive,
$P(\text{A or B}) = P(\text{A}) + P(\text{B})$.

$$P(5 \text{ or } 6) = P(5) + P(6) = \frac{1}{6} + \frac{1}{6} = \frac{2}{6} \text{ or } \frac{1}{3}$$

Event A is throwing a 5.
Event B is throwing a 6.

In the opening example both events can happen at the same time. That is, a person can work on the campaign *and* give money. They are not mutually exclusive events. In this case,

$$P(\text{A or B}) = P(\text{A}) + P(\text{B}) - P(\text{A and B}).$$

So, $P(\text{work or give money}) =$

$$P(\text{work}) + P(\text{give money}) - P(\text{work and give money}).$$

$$P(\text{work or give money}) = 0.15 + 0.27 - 0.8 \text{ or } 0.34$$

There is a 34% chance that a member of the community chosen at random would be willing to work or give money.

Example

1 A die is rolled. What is the probability of rolling a 2 or a prime number?

In this case the events are not mutually exclusive.

$$P(2 \text{ or prime}) = P(2) + P(\text{prime}) - P(2 \text{ and prime}) = \frac{1}{6} + \frac{3}{6} - \frac{1}{6} = \frac{3}{6} \text{ or } \frac{1}{2}$$

The probability of rolling a 2 or a prime number is $\frac{1}{2}$.

Why are the events in Example 1 not mutually exclusive? **2 is a prime number.**

Bell Ringer

State two events where the probability of both of them happening is $\frac{1}{4}$. **Sample answer: Rolling an even number on a number cube then rolling an odd number on the next roll.**

Notice that $P(\text{A or B}) = P(\text{A}) + P(\text{B}) - P(\text{A and B})$ can be used whenever an **or** situation occurs. However, when the events are mutually exclusive, $P(\text{A and B}) = 0$.

Do you think that the probability of the Yankees or the Red Sox winning is greater than or less than $\frac{1}{2}$? Why? **greater than $\frac{1}{2}$ because if you add 0.4 and 0.6 and subtract 0.2, the result will be greater than 0.5**

Examples

2 The probability that the Yankees will win their next game is 0.4. The probability that the Red Sox will win their next game is 0.6. The probability that they will both win is 0.4×0.6 or 0.24. What is the probability that one or the other will win? (They don't play each other.)

These are not mutually exclusive events.

Therefore, $P(\text{Yankees or Red Sox}) =$

$$P(\text{Yankees}) + P(\text{Red Sox}) - P(\text{Yankees and Red Sox}).$$

$$P(\text{Yankees or Red Sox}) = 0.4 + 0.6 - 0.24 \text{ or } 0.76.$$

The probability that the Yankees or the Red Sox will win is 0.76.

3 A bag contains six blue marbles and three red marbles. A marble is drawn, it is replaced, and another marble is drawn. What is the probability of drawing a red marble and a blue marble in either order?

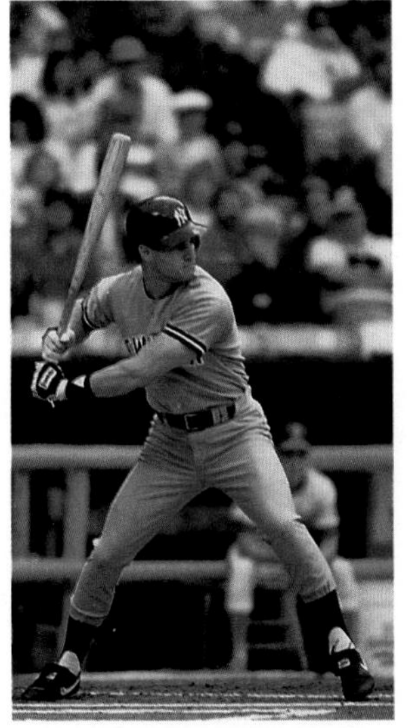

Consider two draws that are mutually exclusive.

$$P(\text{red and blue}) = P(\text{red}) \cdot P(\text{blue})$$
$$= \frac{3}{9} \cdot \frac{6}{9}$$
$$= \frac{18}{81} \text{ or } \frac{2}{9}$$

$$P(\text{blue and red}) = P(\text{blue}) \cdot P(\text{red})$$
$$= \frac{6}{9} \cdot \frac{3}{9}$$
$$= \frac{18}{81} \text{ or } \frac{2}{9}$$

$P(\text{red and blue in either order})$

$$= \frac{2}{9} + \frac{2}{9}$$
$$= \frac{4}{9}$$

The probability of drawing a red and blue is $\frac{4}{9}$.

Chalkboard Examples

- *For Example 1*
  A die is rolled. What is the probability of rolling a 6 or an even number? $\frac{3}{6}$ or $\frac{1}{2}$
- *For Example 2*
  A group of students was surveyed to determine how many want to play an instrument in the band, the orchestra, or in both. Of the sample, 50% want to play in the band, 35% want to play in the orchestra, and 15% are interested in playing in both. If a student was selected at random, what is the probability that he or she would be interested in playing in the band or in the orchestra? 70%
- *For Example 3*
  A bag contains 6 yellow golf balls and two white golf balls. A golf ball is picked. It is replaced and another golf ball is picked. What is the probability of picking a white golf ball and a yellow golf ball in either order? $\frac{6}{16}$ or $\frac{3}{8}$

Alternate Strategies: Reteaching the Lesson

Reteaching Activity

Using Models Use a spinner with four equal sections numbered 1, 2, 3, and 4. Have students find $P(1)$, $P(2)$, $P(1 \text{ or } 4)$, $P(2 \text{ or } 3)$, and $P(\text{odd number or even number})$. $\frac{1}{4}$, $\frac{1}{4}$, $\frac{1}{2}$, $\frac{1}{2}$, 1

Reteaching Masters Booklet, **p. 98**

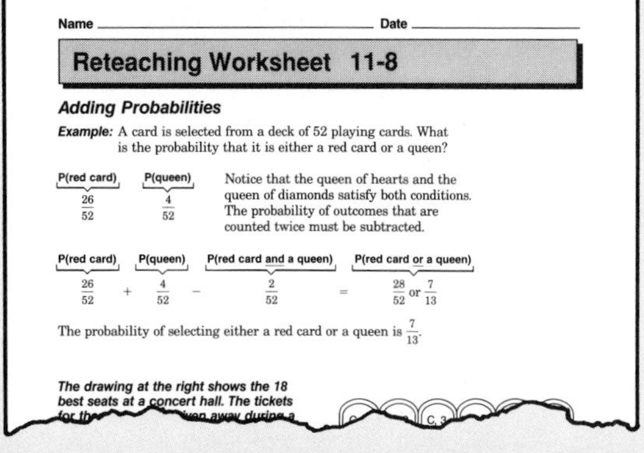

Name ________ Date ________

Reteaching Worksheet 11-8

Adding Probabilities

Example: A card is selected from a deck of 52 playing cards. What is the probability that it is either a red card or a queen?

P(red card) $\frac{26}{52}$ P(queen) $\frac{4}{52}$ Notice that the queen of hearts and the queen of diamonds satisfy both conditions. The probability of outcomes that are counted twice must be subtracted.

P(red card) $\frac{26}{52}$ + P(queen) $\frac{4}{52}$ − P(red card and a queen) $\frac{2}{52}$ = P(red card or a queen) $\frac{28}{52}$ or $\frac{7}{13}$

The probability of selecting either a red card or a queen is $\frac{7}{13}$.

The drawing at the right shows the 18 best seats at a concert hall. The tickets

3 PRACTICE/APPLY

Checking the Concept

Have students make up two problems where the answers are the answers to Exercises 9 and 10.

Error Analysis

Watch for students who have difficulty determining whether an event is mutually exclusive.
Prevent by using Venn diagrams.

Independent Practice

Homework Assignment	
Basic	11-23 odd, 24-29
Average	12-22 even, 24-29
Honors	16-29

Practice Masters Booklet, **p. 108**

Name ____________ Date ____________

Practice Worksheet 11-8

Adding Probabilities

A die is rolled.

1. What is P(3 or 5)? $\frac{1}{3}$
2. What is P(1 or 6)? $\frac{1}{3}$
3. What is P(4 or prime)? $\frac{2}{3}$
4. What is P(3 or prime)? $\frac{1}{2}$
5. What is P(even or odd)? 1
6. What is P(1 or odd)? $\frac{1}{2}$
7. What is P(even or prime)? $\frac{5}{6}$
8. What is P(odd or prime)? $\frac{2}{3}$
9. What is P(odd or greater than 3)? $\frac{5}{6}$
10. What is P(even or less than 6)? 1

A bag contains four blue marbles and six green marbles. A marble is drawn, it is replaced, and another marble is drawn.

11. What is P(blue)? $\frac{2}{5}$
12. What is P(green)? $\frac{3}{5}$
13. What is P(blue and then green)? $\frac{6}{25}$
14. What is P(green and then blue)? $\frac{6}{25}$
15. What is P(blue and green in either order)? $\frac{12}{25}$

A scarf is selected at random from a bag containing five white scarves, six red scarves, and four blue scarves.

16. What is P(red or blue)? $\frac{2}{3}$
17. What is P(white or blue)? $\frac{3}{5}$
18. What is P(red or white)? $\frac{11}{15}$
19. What is P(blue or not white)? $\frac{2}{3}$

A coin is tossed and a die is rolled.

20. What is P(tails or 4)? $\frac{7}{12}$
21. What is P(heads or prime)? $\frac{3}{4}$
22. What is P(tails or less than 3)? $\frac{2}{3}$
23. What is P(heads or even)? $\frac{3}{4}$

Checking for Understanding

Communicating Algebra

1. Explain what is meant by mutually exclusive events. Give an example of mutually exclusive events in your own life. For example, walking the dog and practicing the piano are mutually exclusive events. See margin.

2. Give an example of two events in your life that are not mutually exclusive. Sample answer: watch TV, eat a snack

Guided Practice

A die is rolled. Which probabilities represent mutually exclusive events?

3. P(3 or 4) yes
4. P(4 or even) no
5. P(3 or prime) no

A card is drawn from the cards below. Which events are not mutually exclusive?

1 2 3 4 5

6 7 8 9 0

6. 7 or odd no
7. 6 or prime yes
8. 9 or greater than 5 no

Suppose $P(A) = \frac{1}{2}$, $P(B) = \frac{1}{3}$, and A and B are mutually exclusive.

9. What is P(A and B)? $\frac{1}{6}$
10. What is P(A or B)? $\frac{5}{6}$

Exercises

Independent Practice

11. A coin is tossed and a die is rolled. What is P(heads or 3)? $\frac{2}{3}$
12. A die is rolled. What is P(even or less than 5)? $\frac{5}{6}$
13. One bag contains three red balls and four white balls. A ball is selected at random, replaced, and another ball is drawn. What is P(red on either draw)? $\frac{33}{49}$

A card is drawn from the cards at the right.

A B C D E F G

14. What is P(E or consonant)? $\frac{6}{7}$
15. What is P(A or vowel)? $\frac{2}{7}$

The chart shows the ages and gender of the students in Melissa's homeroom. A student is to be selected for student council.

Age	Male	Female
13	5	8
14	8	9

16. What is P(14 or female)? $\frac{5}{6}$
17. What is P(13 or male)? $\frac{7}{10}$

Additional Answers

1. Sample answers: Mutually exclusive events are events that cannot happen at the same time, for example, rolling a six on a number cube or rolling an odd number.

24.

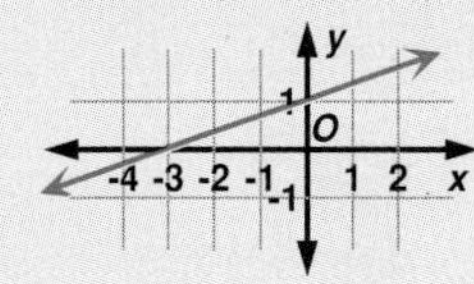

29. Sample answer: In a survey of 20 eighth graders, 9 volunteered to donate money to Special Olympics, 14 volunteered to work at the competition, and 19 said they would do both. What is the probability that a student chosen at random from this group is donating money or working at the competition?

The chart shows the number and types of chocolates in a box of candy. If a selection is made at random, find each of the following.

Chocolates	Nuts	Fruits	Plain
Light	5	3	7
Dark	7	2	6

18. P(light) $\frac{1}{2}$
19. P(dark or nut) $\frac{2}{3}$
20. P(light or fruit) $\frac{17}{30}$
21. P(dark or plain) $\frac{11}{15}$
22. P(fruit or plain) $\frac{3}{5}$
23. P(light or dark) 1

Mixed Review

24. Graph the equation $y = \frac{1}{3}x + 1$. (Lesson 8-6) See margin.
25. **Cooking** If a 6-pound beef roast takes 2 hours to cook, at this rate how long will a 9-pound beef roast take to cook? (Lesson 9-3) 3 hours
26. A bag of candy contains 6 peppermints and 4 jaw breakers. Without looking, you select two pieces. What is the probability of selecting two peppermints in a row? (Lesson 11-7) $\frac{1}{3}$

Application

27. **Business** An auto dealer finds that of the new cars returning for service, 70% need an oil change, 50% need lubrication, and 35% need both. What is the probability that a new car brought in for service needs either an oil change or a lubrication? 0.85

Critical Thinking

28. The Centerville High School volleyball team needs to beat both the Bulldogs and the Hawks to advance to the semifinals of the tournament. The coach believes that the probability of beating the Bulldogs is 0.6 and the probability of beating the Hawks is 0.7. She believes that the probability of beating at least one of them is 0.85. If these probabilities are valid, what is the probability of winning both games? 0.42

Wrap-Up

29. Make up a problem where the probability of one event is 0.45, the probability of another event is 0.70, and the probability of both events is 0.20. See margin.

Challenge

The referee tosses a coin. The probability of getting heads is $\frac{1}{2}$. Theoretically, this means that if the coin is tossed twice, heads will show once and if the coin is tossed four times, heads will show two times. This information can be graphed and the graph can be used to predict the number of heads for a given number of tosses.

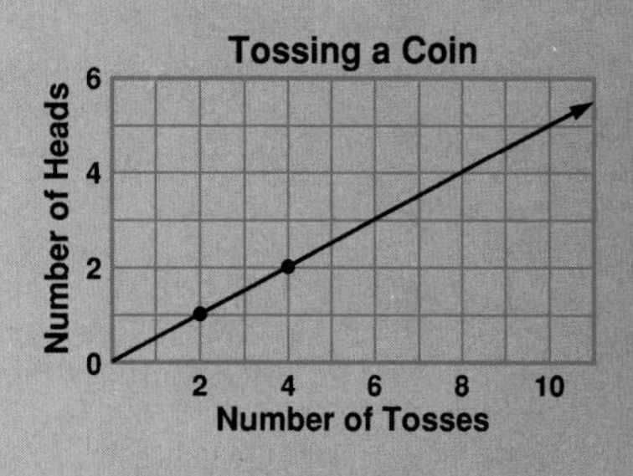

A die is rolled. Make a graph that shows how many times the die, in theory, should show 5 or 6. Use the graph to decide how many times a 5 or a 6, in theory, should show if the die is rolled 45 times. See Solutions Manual for graph; 15 times

4 CLOSE

Assessment Option

Speaking Have students state whether two events are mutually exclusive or not and explain why.

Enrichment Masters Booklet, **p. 98**

Name ____________ Date ________

Enrichment Worksheet 11-8

Adding Probabilities

You will need a map of the United States and a list of the 50 states to complete this worksheet.

Assume that the names of the 50 states are written on slips of paper and put into a hat, and each state has the same chance of being picked. Find the probability of selecting each of the following.

1. A state whose name begins with the letter A or the letter W $\frac{4}{50} + \frac{4}{50} = \frac{4}{25}$
2. A state whose name begins with the letter C or the letter N $\frac{3}{50} + \frac{8}{50} = \frac{11}{50}$
3. A state whose name begins with the letter S or a state whose name is two words $\frac{2}{50} + \frac{10}{50} - \frac{2}{50} = \frac{1}{5}$
4. A state whose name begins with the letter I or a state that is entirely east of the Mississippi River $\frac{4}{50} + \frac{26}{50} - \frac{2}{50} = \frac{14}{25}$
5. A state whose name is one syllable or a state whose name is more than two syllables $\frac{1}{50} + \frac{43}{50} = \frac{22}{25}$
6. A state with double letters (side by side) in its name or a state whose name begins with a vowel $\frac{9}{50} + \frac{12}{50} - \frac{1}{50} = \frac{2}{5}$
7. A state that borders on an ocean or a state whose name begins with the letter N $\frac{19}{50} + \frac{8}{50} - \frac{4}{50} = \frac{23}{50}$
8. A state whose name begins and ends with the same letter or a state that is larger in size than Texas $\frac{4}{50} + \frac{1}{50} - \frac{1}{50} = \frac{2}{25}$
9. A state that borders on the Pacific Ocean or a state that was one of the 13 original colonies $\frac{5}{50} + \frac{13}{50} = \frac{9}{25}$
10. A state that borders Wyoming or a state that borders Idaho $\frac{6}{50} + \frac{6}{50} - \frac{2}{50} = \frac{1}{5}$

Alternate Strategies: Extending the Lesson

Enrichment

Social Studies Connection Supply students with a list of state representatives, including name, sex, and political affiliation. If a representative is chosen at random, find P(man or a Republican), etc.

Cooperative Learning

Sweet Probabilities Group Activity 11-8

MATERIALS: Two bags of candy. One contains four flavors (any combination) to make 35 pieces. The other bag contains three flavors (any combination) to make 21 pieces • one note card with the words "same bag" • one note card with the words "different bags"

One group member draws a card telling him or her to use the same or different bags and draws two pieces of candy from the bag or bags. If one bag is indicated, the member may either replace the candy or draw two pieces without replacement.

The rest of the group then calculates the probability of the draw. When all have finished, the answers are compared and discussed. When all members understand how the correct probability is computed, the cards and bag are passed to the next member.

Merrill Pre-Algebra ADDING PROBABILITIES

EXPLORATION

Computer Simulation

Objective Students will realize how computers are used in experimental probability.

1 FOCUS

The purpose of this Exploration is to demonstrate to students how computers can be used to randomly generate numbers.

Motivating the Exploration

Ask each student to write a number from 1 to 9 on a sheet of paper. Tally the results. Discuss the mode and possible reasons for it or any noticeable pattern(s).

2 TEACH

Using Computers

The BASIC program below simulates writing a number from 1 to 9. Before you run the program, change the last number in line 10 to match the number of students in your class.

```
10 FOR W = 1 TO 30
20 LET N = INT(9*RND(X) + 1)
30 PRINT N
40 NEXT W
50 END
```

Compare the computer printout to the results of the students' responses. Ask students which experiment is more likely to have an even distribution of numbers.

3 PRACTICE/APPLY

Using Discussion

Have students answer the first two exercises orally and brainstorm reasons for the why or why not question.

4 CLOSE

Speaking Connection

Ask students to research other applications for computer simulations. Have each student give a brief report of his or her findings.

Exploration

Computer Simulation

Materials: computer

In this Exploration, you will use a computer to simulate the results of rolling a die and spinning a spinner.

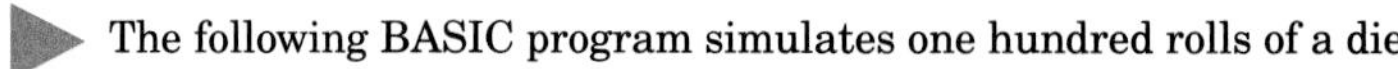

The following BASIC program simulates one hundred rolls of a die.

```
10  FOR R = 1 TO 100
20  LET D = INT(6*RND(X)+1)
30  PRINT D
40  NEXT R
50  END
```

Your Turn: Run the program shown above and record your results. See students' work.

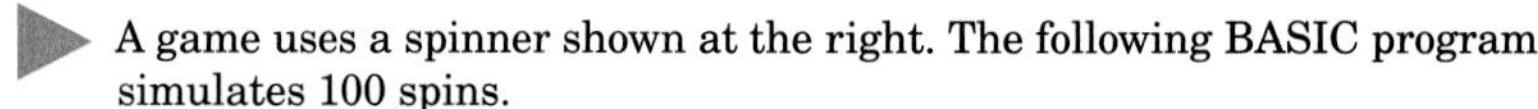

A game uses a spinner shown at the right. The following BASIC program simulates 100 spins.

```
10  FOR S = 1 TO 100
20  LET D = INT(8*RND(X)+1)
30  PRINT D
40  NEXT S
50  END
```

Your Turn: Run this program and record your results. See students' work.

Analysis

1. Look at the results from the simulation of rolling a die. Are the results similar to what you expected? Why or why not? See students' work.
2. Look at the results from the simulation of spinning the spinner. Are the results similar to what you expected? Why or why not? See students' work.
3. A local sports celebrity is planning a visit to Western Middle School. After she talks to all the students, 20 students will be selected at random to eat lunch with the guest. Design a computer simulation to choose the students. See Solutions Manual.
4. Describe a situation in which a computer simulation is preferred to actually rolling a die or spinning a spinner. any situation that requires a large number of trials

SET-UP

Materials

- computers or graphing calculators

You may wish to use the Exploration worksheet provided on page 59 of the Lab Manual.

EE: 1A, 1C, 1E, 5A, 5C, 5D, 5E

For Students Each student or pair of students should be stationed at a computer or calculator.

For the Overhead Projector You can connect a computer to an overhead projection panel and complete the activity along with your students. Overhead projector calculators can also be programmed for this purpose.

11-9 Strategy: Use a Simulation

Objective:
Investigate problems using simulation.

Key Term:
simulation

Have you ever been to a basketball game in which free throws decided the winner? Suppose your team is losing by one point when Sal steps to the foul line.

- If he misses the foul shot, your team loses.
- If he makes the foul shot, he gets one point and another try.
- If he makes the second shot, your team wins the game.

Suppose Sal has a record of making an average of three out of every four free throws. What is the probability that Sal scores 2 points and wins the game?

Why is it impractical to have a real player act it out?
A real player might tire after shooting many baskets.

One way to solve this problem is to do a **simulation**, that is, act it out. You might find a basketball player whose record of making free throws is three out of four. Have the player act out the problem.

How is the circle divided?
in fourths, $\frac{1}{4}$ for misses basket and $\frac{3}{4}$ for makes basket

A more efficient way is to make a model of the situation. For example, construct a spinner similar to the one shown at the right. Spin the spinner and record the results of several trips to the foul line.

A sample simulation for 25 trips to the foul line is shown in the chart below.

Misses the first shot (0 points)	Makes the first shot, misses the second (1 point)	Makes both shots (2 points)
𝍸 I	𝍸	𝍸 𝍸 IIII

Calculate the relative frequency for 0, 1, and 2 points.

0 points → $\frac{6}{25} = 24\%$
1 point → $\frac{5}{25} = 20\%$
2 points → $\frac{14}{25} = 56\%$

These are the relative frequencies for this simulation only.

Based on this simulation, the probability that Sal scores 2 points and wins the game is 56%.

Lesson Notes 11-9

5-Minute Check
(over Lesson 11-8)

The chart shows the ages and the gender of the students in John's math class. A student is to be selected for the math contest.

Age	Male	Female
14	5	10
15	8	7

1. What is P (15 or male)? $\frac{20}{30}$ or $\frac{2}{3}$
2. What is P (14 or female)? $\frac{22}{30}$ or $\frac{11}{15}$

The ticket office has 6 front-row seats, 8 second-row seats, and 10 third-row seats available.

3. What is P (front-row seat or second-row seat)? $\frac{14}{24}$ or $\frac{7}{12}$

Transparency 11-9 contains the 5-Minute Check and a teaching aid for this lesson.

1 FOCUS

The purpose of this lesson is to use simulations to determine experimental probabilities.

Motivating the Lesson

Ask students which would take less time to do – roll a die 100 times or run a computer program that simulates rolling die 100 times.

2 TEACH

Chalkboard Examples

Find the probability of at least three tails in the tossing of five coins. $\frac{2}{4}$ or $\frac{1}{2}$

simulation 1	H	T	T	T	T
simulation 2	T	H	H	T	T
simulation 3	H	H	T	H	T
simulation 4	H	T	H	H	H

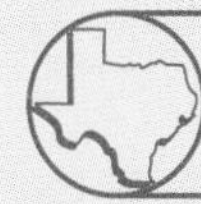

EE: 1A, 1B, 1C, 1D, 1E, 5A, 5D, 5E
TAAS: 5, 11, 12

Bell Ringer

Name two mutually exclusive events where the probability of one or the other occurring is $\frac{3}{4}$. **Sample answer: Spinning a specific number on a spinner with four equal sections and a tossed coin landing tails up.**

3 PRACTICE/APPLY

Checking the Concept

After completing Exercises 3-6, ask students to name other ways to simulate this situation. Answers might include using a coin or a die or number cube (counting whether the number is odd or even).

Error Analysis

Watch for students who carelessly estimate results.
Prevent by setting up a systematic method for recording results.

Additional Answers

1. Sample answer: A simulation is an imitation of a given problem.
2. Make the spinner so that there are two equal sections.
7. Sample answer: Rolling a die ten times with the result of 1, 2, 3, or 4 for shots from the floor. Rolling a die five times with a result of 1, 2, 3, 4, or 5 for free throws.

Practice Masters Booklet, **p. 109**

Name ____________ Date ____________

Practice Worksheet 11-9

Problem Solving Strategy: Use a Simulation

The diagram below shows a system of waterways that bring fresh water from a reservoir to a fish hatchery. Recently there have been many problems with beavers building dams across these waterways. For the last 30 days, each of the waterways has been closed about half of the time due to beaver dams.

What is the probability that the hatchery will still be able to get water even if some of the waterways are closed?

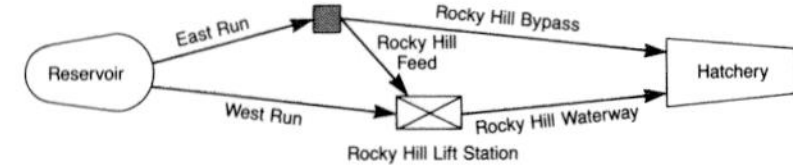

To simulate this situation, you need a procedure to determine if each of the five waterways is open or blocked. Since each waterway is closed about half of the time, you might toss a coin and note heads or tails, or roll a die and note an odd or even number.

Suppose you decide to toss a coin. Let heads mean the water is blocked and tails mean it is open. In the table below, Trial 1 has been completed for you.

1. Complete the table for the remaining trials. Answers will vary.

Trial	East Run	West Run	Rocky Hill Feed	Rocky Hill Bypass	Rocky Hill Waterway	Will Water Flow to the Hatchery?
1	T	H	H	T	H	Yes
2						
3						
4						
5						
6						
7						
8						
9						
10						

2. Conduct two more simulations of ten trials each. Based on thirty trials, what is the probability that the hatchery will still be able to get water even if some of the waterways are closed? Answers will vary; should be about $\frac{5}{8}$.

Example

1 The history quiz has ten true and false questions. Sharon wants to know if tossing a coin to decide the answers is a good strategy for taking the quiz. She would write T (true) if tails show and F (false) if heads show. Assume that the correct answers are F, T, T, T, T, T, F, T, T, F and that 7 or more correct answers are needed to pass the quiz.

Explore The quiz has ten questions. Tossing a coin is used to simulate writing the answers. Would Sharon pass using this strategy?

Plan Toss a coin and record the answer for each question. Check to see how many answers are correct. Repeat the simulation three times.

Solve

Answers	F	T	T	T	T	T	F	T	T	F
Simulation 1	T	(T)	(T)	F	F	F	T	(T)	(T)	(F)
Simulation 2	T	F	(T)	(T)	(T)	(T)	T	F	F	(F)
Simulation 3	(F)	(T)	F	(T)	(T)	F	(F)	F	F	T

Circle the correct answers. Since none of the simulations results in a passing grade, this is not a good way to take the quiz. Sharon decides to study for the quiz.

What other ways can you simulate true and false answers?
Sample answer: select a marble out of a bag with two marbles of different colors.

Examine Try some more simulations to confirm the results.

Checking for Understanding

Communicating Algebra

1. In your own words explain what a simulation is. See margin.
2. Will a simulation be exactly the same as the actual problem? Why?
3. Suppose Jake had gone to the foul line instead of Sal. Jake has a record of making one basket out of every two tries. How would you modify the spinner to simulate this situation? See margin.

Guided Practice

4. Conduct three simulations for the basketball situation on page 429. Write a sentence describing the results.

2. no; it is just a way of acting out the problem to predict what might happen

Exercises

Independent Practice

5. Conduct three more simulations for Example 1. Do your simulations back up Sharon's decision to study? See students' work.
6. Colin kicks extra points for the football team. He makes 75% of his attempts for extra points. How could you simulate the results of the next six attempts?
Sample answer: Use a spinner where one-fourth is "misses extra point" and three-fourths is "makes extra point."

Alternate Strategies: Reteaching the Lesson

Reteaching Activity

Using Computers Rewrite the Exploration program on page 428 to simulate 1000 rolls. Have students determine the probability of rolling a one or a two. Run the program and have students count the ones and twos.

7. Laneeda is a forward on the freshman basketball team. She usually makes $\frac{2}{3}$ of her shots from the field and $\frac{5}{6}$ of her free throws. If she averages 10 shots a game and 5 free throws, describe a simulation that could give her probable number of points in the next game. See margin.

8. Conduct your simulation for the situation in Exercise 7. Record your total from the simulation. Compare your total with those of your classmates. See students' work.

9. Mr. Namura runs a small gourmet restaurant. He has 12 tables. It is a popular restaurant and anyone wanting to eat at 6:00 on Saturday evening must have reservations. Mr. Namura knows that one out of six reservations usually does not show, so he takes reservations for 14 tables for 6:00. Describe a way to simulate the number of tables that will be filled at 6:00. Use a die and let a roll of 1 be a no show.

10. Conduct your simulation for Exercise 9 ten times. From your simulations, how many times is the restaurant overbooked? Are all 12 tables always filled? See students' work.

11. At a certain restaurant, prizes are given with children's meals. During the spring promotional, three different prizes are given at random. Estimate how many children's meals must be purchased in order to get all three prizes. See students' work.

12. Use simulation to test your estimate in Exercise 11. Conduct several simulations. Was your estimate big enough to ensure all three prizes at least 75% of the time? Do you think you could buy fewer meals and still be likely to get all three prizes? See students' work.

13. Game wardens can estimate the number of fish in a lake by capturing, marking, and releasing fish and then catching fish again after a few days. The warden caught, marked and released 150 fish on Monday. On Thursday she caught 300 fish and 15 of them were marked. How many fish did she estimate were in the lake? 3000 fish

Decision Making

14. Opal and Kara play offense for the junior varsity soccer team. Opal normally scores on one out of every four shots on goal, and Kara normally scores on one out of every six shots on goal. In a typical game, Opal makes seven shots on goal and Kara makes eleven shots on goal. The varsity coach wants one of the girls to play offense for the varsity team. If the coach's goal is to choose the girl who will most likely score more points for the team, which girl should she choose? Why? Kara; Opal: $\frac{1}{4}(7) = 1\frac{3}{4}$, Kara: $\frac{1}{6}(11) = 1\frac{5}{6} \rightarrow 1\frac{3}{4} < 1\frac{5}{6}$ so Kara is more likely to score the most points.

Critical Thinking

15. A football team plays 12 games during the season. A newspaper reporter predicts that the team has a 75% chance of winning each of its games. Devise and carry out a simulation that will determine the probability of the team winning three games in a row during the season. See margin.

Wrap-Up

16. Write a few sentences on why simulations are useful in probability. Simulations "act out" a situation and can be used to predict what will happen in the actual situation.

Independent Practice

Homework Assignment	
Basic	5-13 odd, 14-16
Average	6-14 even, 14-16
Honors	9-16

Chapter 11, Quiz B (Lessons 11-6 through 11-9) is available in the Evaluation Masters Booklet, p. 97.

4 CLOSE

Assessment Option

Modeling Use the BASIC programs in the Exploration and alter them slightly. Have the students run the programs for $R = 1$ to 50, $R = 1$ to 1000, and $R = 1$ to 10000. Is there a minimum number of times that the dice needs to be rolled or the spinner needs to be spun to get an accurate probability as a result? Yes.

Additional Answer

15. Sample simulation: Spin a spinner that has four equal sections. Spinning a 1, 2, or 3 means a win. Tally 25 groups of three spins as either three wins in a row or not.

Cooperative Learning

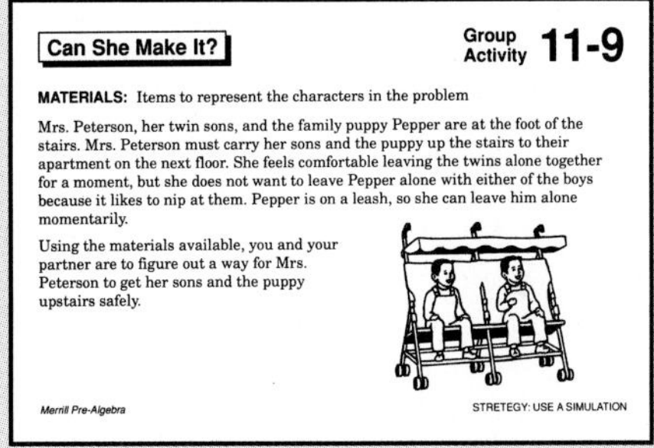

Can She Make It? Group Activity **11-9**

MATERIALS: Items to represent the characters in the problem

Mrs. Peterson, her twin sons, and the family puppy Pepper are at the foot of the stairs. Mrs. Peterson must carry her sons and the puppy up the stairs to their apartment on the next floor. She feels comfortable leaving the twins alone together for a moment, but she does not want to leave Pepper alone with either of the boys because it likes to nip at them. Pepper is on a leash, so she can leave him alone momentarily.

Using the materials available, you and your partner are to figure out a way for Mrs. Peterson to get her sons and the puppy upstairs safely.

Merrill Pre-Algebra STRETEGY: USE A SIMULATION

Using the Chapter Review

The Chapter review is a comprehensive review of the concepts presented in this chapter. This review may be used to prepare students for the Chapter Test.

Alternate Review Strategy

To provide a brief in-class review, you may wish to read the following questions to the class and require a verbal response.

1. Ginny has two sweaters (white and red) and three skirts (white, black, and red). How many different outfits can she put together? 6
2. What is the Fundamental Counting Principle? **If event *M* can occur in *m* ways and is followed by event *N* that can occur in *n* ways, then the event *M* followed by event *N* can occur in $m \cdot n$ ways.**
3. What is the difference between a permutation and a combination? **Order is important in a permutation but not in a combination.**
4. Explain how to find the value of $P(8,3)$. $8 \cdot 7 \cdot 6$
5. The names of six girls and seven boys are put into a hat. What is the probability that a boy's name will be randomly drawn? $\frac{7}{13}$
6. Refer to the table on page 415. What is the probability that two dice will show a total of 3 or 5? $\frac{6}{36}$ or $\frac{1}{6}$
7. How do you find the probability of two independent events? ***P* (event 1) · *P* (event 2)**
8. There are 3 chocolate chip cookies, 2 sugar cookies, and one oatmeal cookie in a bag. What is the probability that both Jim and Kyle, without looking, will pick a chocolate chip cookie? $\frac{1}{5}$
9. How do you find the probability of two mutually exclusive events? **Add the probability of event 1 with the probability of event 2.**
10. Give an example of when you might use a simulation. **Answers may vary but should be a situation where doing the actual event is not practical.**

Chapter 11 Review

Language and Concepts

Choose the correct term to complete each sentence.

1. In probability, spinning a spinner is called an (event, outcome).
2. If one event affects the outcome of another event, the events are (independent, dependent).
3. The fraction, $\frac{\text{number of ways a certain outcome can occur}}{\text{number of possible outcomes}}$, defines (probability, the Fundamental Counting Principle).
4. The set of possible outcomes is called a (factorial, sample space).
5. Getting an A in English and getting an A in algebra (are, are not) mutually exclusive events.

Skills

For diagrams to Exercises 6-7, see Solutions Manual.

Draw a tree diagram for each of the following. Find the number of possible outcomes. (Lesson 11-1)

6. Each spinner is spun once. 12 outcomes

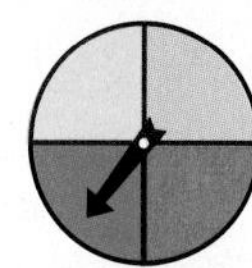
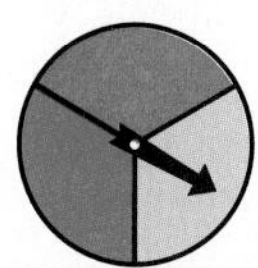

7. a choice of orange, tomato, or grapefruit juice with a choice of bacon or ham 6 outcomes

Answer each question. (Lesson 11-2)

8. A die is rolled and a coin is tossed. How many outcomes are possible? 12 outcomes
9. Four dice are rolled. How many outcomes are possible? 1296 outcomes

Find each value. (Lesson 11-3)

10. 9! 362,880
11. 0! 1
12. $P(8, 5)$ 6720
13. $C(8, 5)$ 56
14. Andy needs to pack three shirts for his trip. How many ways can he choose the shirts from the eight shirts in his closet? 56 ways
15. A baseball team has 13 players on the roster. How many ways can the coach pick the first three batters? 1716 ways

There are 4 black marbles, 2 yellow marbles, 3 green marbles, and 1 white marble in a bag. Find the probability of each outcome. (Lessons 11-4, 11-6, 11-7)

16. draw a yellow marble $\frac{1}{5}$
17. draw a green or a white marble $\frac{2}{5}$
18. draw a black, yellow, or green marble $\frac{9}{10}$
19. draw a white marble $\frac{1}{10}$

20. draw a yellow marble; replace it; draw a green marble $\frac{3}{50}$

21. draw a black marble; replace it; draw a white marble $\frac{1}{25}$

22. draw a green marble; do not replace it; draw a black marble $\frac{2}{15}$

23. draw a white marble; do not replace it; draw a white marble 0

Solve. (Lesson 11-8)

24. The probability that Vera will get an A in algebra is 0.8. The probability that Ned will get an A in algebra is 0.6. If the probability that both will get an A is 0.5, what is the probability that one or the other will get an A? 0.9

Application and Problem Solving

25. Two dice are rolled. What is the probability that the product of the numbers shown on the dice is 12? (Lesson 11-5) $\frac{1}{9}$

26. A certain restaurant gives out game cards. One out of six cards wins a small soft drink. Describe a simulation to predict how many soft drinks Ted will win with 14 game cards. (Lesson 11-9) See margin.

Communicating Algebra

See margin.

A bag has 3 red marbles, 4 yellow marbles, and 6 blue marbles. Two marbles are drawn at random. Explain the difference among the following probabilities.

a. the probability of drawing a red marble and then a blue marble if the first marble is replaced

b. the probability of drawing a red marble and then a blue marble if the first marble is not replaced

c. the probability of drawing a red marble and a blue marble in either order if the first marble is replaced

Curriculum Connection

- **Meteorology** Check the weather forecast. Find out the probability of precipitation in your community for tomorrow. See students' work.
- **History** Not only do some of the Presidents of the United States share a birthday, some also share a date of death. Report on this. John Adams, Thomas Jefferson, and James Monroe died on July 4.

Read More About It

Anno, Mitsumasa. *Socrates and the Three Little Pigs.*

Razzell, Arthur G. *Probability: The Science of Chance.*

Riedel, Manfred G. *Odds and Chances for Kids: A Look at Probability.*

You may wish to use a Chapter Test (free-response format) as an additional chapter review. Two forms are provided in the Evaluation Masters Booklet as shown below.

Evaluation Masters Booklet, **p. 95**

Name ______ Date ______

Chapter 11 Test, Form 2A

1. A store sells three brands of pens. Each brand comes in red, green, black, and blue ink. Kerry buys one of each brand and ink color. How many pens did Kerry buy?

Today's menu includes sandwiches with four choices of meat (ham, turkey, lamb, or beef) and three choices of bread (rye, white, or wheat).

2. How many sandwich choices include turkey?
3. If two meats must be combined in a single sandwich, how many possible choices are there?
4. Find the value of 8!.
5. Find the value of 0!.
6. Find the value of P(8, 3).
7. Find the value of C(8, 3).
8. In a 6-person race, gold and silver medals are awarded to the first two finishers. In how many ways can the medals be awarded?
9. If the probability of rain is 20%, what is the probability of no rain?
10. Find the probability of getting heads and an even number when tossing a coin and rolling a die at the same time.

A bag contains 8 red, 6 blue, 9 black, and 2 gray marbles. Find each of the following.

11. P(not blue)
12. P(green)

Two dice are rolled. Find the probability of each of the following.

13. A sum of 8
14. An even number on each die
15. Three dice are rolled. Find P(sum of 3).

Darla has written the numbers 1 to 8 on eight cards of the same size. She picks two cards at random, without replacing the first one. Find the probability of each of the following.

16. Drawing two odd-numbered cards
17. Drawing cards with numbers that are multiples of 3
18. Tom may buy a tape, an LP record, a single-play record, or a CD. Find the probability that he will buy either a tape or a CD.

Heather makes four out of five 10-foot putts. To simulate her chances of making a putt, she puts 40 marbles in a box. A red marble represents a made putt, and a blue means a missed putt. After a marble is drawn, it is replaced in the box.

19. How many red marbles does Heather need?
20. In 150 drawings, how many blue marbles can she expect?

BONUS Five coins are dropped on the floor. Find the probability that they will all land on heads.

1. 12
2. 3
3. 18
4. 40,320
5. 1
6. 336
7. 56
8. 30
9. 80%
10. $\frac{1}{4}$
11. $\frac{19}{25}$
12. 0
13. $\frac{5}{36}$
14. $\frac{1}{4}$
15. $\frac{1}{216}$
16. $\frac{3}{14}$
17. $\frac{1}{28}$
18. $\frac{1}{2}$
19. 32
20. 30

BONUS: $\frac{1}{32}$

Evaluation Masters Booklet, **p. 96**

Name ______ Date ______

Chapter 11 Test, Form 2B

1. A store sells two brands of pens. Each brand comes in red, green, black, and blue ink. Kevin buys one of each brand and ink color. How many pens did Kevin buy?

Today's menu includes sandwiches with four choices of meat (ham, turkey, lamb, or beef) and two choices of bread (rye or white).

2. How many sandwich choices include turkey?
3. If two meats must be combined in a single sandwich, how many possible choices are there?
4. Find the value of 0!.
5. Find the value of 5!.
6. Find the value of P(9, 3).
7. Find the value of C(9, 3).
8. In a 7-person race, gold and silver medals are awarded to the first two finishers. In how many ways can the medals be awarded?
9. If the probability of rain is 70%, what is the probability of no rain?
10. Find the probability of getting tails and a number less than 3 when tossing a coin and rolling a die at the same time.

A bag contains 8 red, 6 blue, 9 black, and 7 gray marbles. Find each of the following.

11. P(orange)
12. P(not blue)

Two dice are rolled. Find the probability of each of the following.

13. A sum of 10
14. A 4 on each die
15. Three dice are rolled. Find P(sum of 18).

Donna has written the numbers 1 to 6 on six cards of the same size. She picks two cards at random, without replacing the first one. Find the probability of each of the following.

16. Drawing two cards with numbers less than 4
17. Drawing an odd number and a number greater than 4
18. Tim may buy a tape, a LP record, or a CD. Find the probability that he will buy either a tape or a CD.

Heather makes three out of five 10-foot putts. To simulate her chances of making a putt, she puts 40 marbles in a box. A red marble represents a made putt, and a blue means a missed putt. After a marble is drawn, it is replaced in the box.

19. How many red marbles does Heather need?
20. In 140 drawings, how many blue marbles can she expect?

BONUS Six coins are dropped on the floor. Find the probability that they will all land on tails.

1. 8
2. 2
3. 12
4. 1
5. 120
6. 504
7. 84
8. 42
9. 30%
10. $\frac{1}{6}$
11. 0
12. $\frac{4}{5}$
13. $\frac{1}{12}$
14. $\frac{1}{36}$
15. $\frac{1}{216}$
16. $\frac{1}{5}$
17. $\frac{1}{10}$
18. $\frac{2}{3}$
19. 24
20. 56

BONUS: $\frac{1}{64}$

Additional Answers

26. Sample simulation: Roll a die 14 times. Every time a six is rolled, Ted wins a soft drink.

Communicating Algebra The events in a. are independent and the probability is found by multiplying the probabilities of each event. The events in b. are dependent (the probability of the second event will be greater because there are fewer marbles to choose from) and the probability is also found by multiplying the probabilities of each event. The events in c. are mutually exclusive and the probability is found by multiplying the probabilities of each event and doubling the result.

Using the Chapter Test

This page may be used as a test or as an additional review. Two forms of a Chapter Test (multiple-choice format) are provided in the Evaluation Masters Booklet.

Evaluation Masters Booklet, **pp. 91-92**

Name ______________________ Date ______________

Chapter 11 Test, Form 1A

1. Find the number of possible outcomes when a dime and a nickel are tossed.
   A. 2 B. 3 C. 4 D. 8 — 1. **C**
2. Abe, Betsy, and Charles are running for class president, and Doris, Ellen, and Frank are running for vice president. How many possible president-vice president combinations are possible?
   A. 6 B. 9 C. 27 D. 12 — 2. **B**
3. A multiple-choice test has 25 questions with four choices given for each. How many outcomes are possible?
   A. 100 B. 200 C. 29 D. 50 — 3. **A**
4. Today's menu has three choices of meat (ham, turkey, or beef) and four choices of bread (rye, white, wheat, or pumpernickel). How many sandwich choices include rye bread?
   A. 2 B. 3 C. 4 D. 12 — 4. **B**
5. Melvin has four pairs of pants and four shirts. How many different outfits are possible?
   A. 256 B. 16 C. 64 D. 8 — 5. **B**
6. Find the value of 5!.
   A. 5 B. 25 C. 120 D. 125 — 6. **C**
7. Find the value of P(5, 4).
   A. 9 B. 20 C. 60 D. 120 — 7. **D**
8. Find the value of C(5, 4).
   A. 5 B. 20 C. 60 D. 120 — 8. **A**
9. In a 7-person race, gold, silver, and bronze medals are awarded to the first three finishers. In how many ways can the medals be awarded?
   A. 210 B. 21 C. 10 D. 342 — 9. **A**
10. Valerie says the probability of rain is 40%. Find the probability of no rain.
    A. 60% B. 40% C. 20% D. 80% — 10. **A**

A bag contains 3 blue, 8 black, 5 red, and 2 yellow marbles.

11. Find P(red).
    A. $\frac{5}{240}$ B. $\frac{5}{11}$ C. $\frac{5}{18}$ D. $\frac{1}{4}$ — 11. **C**
12. Find P(not blue).
    A. $\frac{4}{9}$ B. $\frac{5}{6}$ C. $\frac{5}{12}$ D. $\frac{1}{6}$ — 12. **B**

Name ______________________ Date ______________

Chapter 11 Test, Form 1A (continued)

13. Find the probability of rolling two dice and getting a sum of 7.
    A. $\frac{7}{36}$ B. $\frac{1}{4}$ C. $\frac{1}{30}$ D. $\frac{1}{6}$ — 13. **D**
14. A box contains 26 cards. Each card has a different letter of the alphabet on it. Mark draws a card at random. What is the probability of drawing either A or B?
    A. $\frac{1}{13}$ B. $\frac{1}{2}$ C. $\frac{1}{26}$ D. $\frac{1}{24}$ — 14. **A**
15. Two dice are rolled. Find the probability for rolling an odd number on one die and an even number on the other.
    A. $\frac{1}{6}$ B. $\frac{1}{2}$ C. $\frac{1}{4}$ D. $\frac{1}{36}$ — 15. **C**
16. Kelly has ten cards numbered 1 to 10. What is the probability of picking two even-numbered cards one after the other, if the first card is not replaced?
    A. $\frac{2}{5}$ B. $\frac{2}{9}$ C. $\frac{1}{5}$ D. $\frac{1}{2}$ — 16. **B**
17. A bag contains 4 red, 20 blue, and 6 green marbles. Seth and Amy each pick one at random and keep it. What is the probability that they each select a red marble?
    A. $\frac{2}{300}$ B. $\frac{1}{15}$ C. $\frac{2}{145}$ D. $\frac{1}{870}$ — 17. **C**
18. Of the people asked to help in an election, 40% will work, 60% will donate money, and 20% will do both. Find the probability that a person chosen at random will either work or donate money, but not both.
    A. 40% B. 80% C. 120% D. 20% — 18. **B**

Fred usually makes three free throws of every five attempted. To simulate the probability of Fred's making two free throws in a row, Mabel puts 25 marbles in a bag, red for a basket and blue for a miss. After a marble is drawn and recorded, it is replaced.

19. How many red marbles will Mabel use?
    A. 9 B. 15 C. 12 D. 20 — 19. **B**
20. In 120 drawings, how many red marbles can Mabel expect to record?
    A. 45 B. 30 C. 72 D. 85 — 20. **C**

BONUS Two coins and a die are tossed. Find P(two heads and 6).
A. $\frac{1}{12}$ B. $\frac{1}{24}$ C. $\frac{1}{2}$ D. $\frac{1}{36}$ — **B**

Test

For tree diagrams to Exercises 1-2, see Solutions Manual.

Draw a tree diagram for each of the following. Find the number of possible outcomes.

1. a choice of floral or plaid wallpaper with a choice of beige or ivory paint **4 outcomes**
2. a choice of sweater in three colors (white, black, and navy) and in four sizes (small, medium, large, and extra large) **12 outcomes**

Answer each question.

3. A penny, a nickel, a dime, a quarter, and a half dollar are tossed. How many outcomes are possible? **32 outcomes**
4. Andy has 5 pairs of slacks, 6 shirts, and 3 sweaters. How many three-piece outfits are possible? **90 outfits**

Find each value.

5. 6! **720**
6. $\frac{6!2!}{4!0!}$ **60**
7. $P(10, 3)$ **720**
8. $C(12, 3)$ **220**
9. $C(7, 4)$ **35**

The spinner at the right is equally likely to stop in any one of the six regions. It is spun once. Find the probability of each outcome.

10. a 2 $\frac{1}{6}$
11. a number less than 5 $\frac{2}{3}$
12. an odd number $\frac{1}{2}$
13. a number greater than 6 **0**

A coin is tossed, then a die is rolled. Find the probability of each outcome.

14. tails and a 2 $\frac{1}{12}$
15. heads and a number less than 4 $\frac{1}{4}$

In a bag there are 4 red balls, 2 white balls, 3 black balls, and 1 green ball. Once a ball is selected, it is not replaced. Find the probability of each outcome.

16. a red ball and then a white ball $\frac{4}{45}$
17. 2 black balls in a row $\frac{1}{15}$

Answer each of the following.

18. The probability that the Bears will win their next game is 0.4. The probability that the Tigers will win their next game is 0.5. If the probability that both teams will win is 0.2, what is the probability that one or the other will win? **0.7**
19. Two dice are tossed. What is the probability that the positive difference between the two numbers is 1? $\frac{5}{18}$
20. A certain type of cereal advertises that there is a prize in each box. Actually there are six different prizes. Walt buys ten boxes hoping to get one of each of the prizes. Describe a way to simulate the situation. **See margin.**

BONUS

In a bag there are 3 red marbles, 2 white marbles, and 4 blue marbles. A marble is drawn and it is not replaced. A second marble is drawn. What is the probability that both marbles are the same color? $\frac{5}{18}$

Test Generator Software is provided in both Apple and IBM formats. You may use this software to create your own tests, based on the needs of your students.

Additional Answer

20. Sample simulation: Roll a die ten times.

Academic Skills Test

Cumulative, Chapters 1-11

1. Which fractions are in order from least to greatest?
   A $\frac{1}{2}, \frac{1}{3}, \frac{1}{4}$
   (B) $\frac{3}{5}, \frac{7}{10}, \frac{9}{12}$
   C $\frac{3}{4}, \frac{5}{8}, \frac{9}{10}$
   D $\frac{5}{6}, \frac{5}{8}, \frac{5}{12}$

2. If your heart beats about once every second, it will beat about 442,000,000 times in 15 years. How is this number expressed in scientific terms?
   A 4.42×10^{-8}
   B 44.2×10^{-7}
   C 442×10^{6}
   (D) 4.42×10^{8}

3. What is the solution for the inequality $3y - 5 > 2y + 8$?
   A $y < 3$ C $y < 13$
   B $y > 3$ (D) $y > 13$

4. Which is an equation of line ℓ?

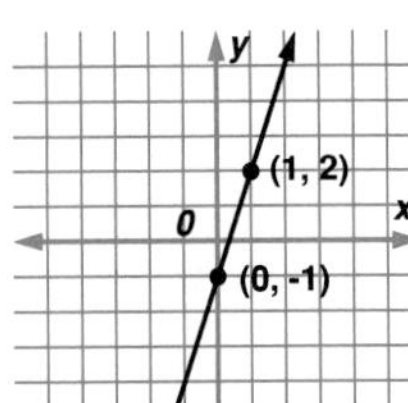

   A $y = -1$
   B $x - 1 = y$
   C $y = 3x$
   (D) $3x - 1 = y$

5. Which is the slope of the line in question 4?
   (A) 3 C $\frac{1}{2}$
   B 2 D $\frac{1}{3}$

6. The value of a certain car decreases by 20% after one year. To find the amount of decrease on a car originally costing \$12,500, multiply 12,500 by—
   A $\frac{1}{20}$ (C) $\frac{1}{5}$
   B $\frac{1}{4}$ D $\frac{4}{5}$

7. The frequency table below contains data about students' test scores on a 25-point test.

Number of Students	2	1	5	4	5	6	4	1
Score	18	19	20	21	22	23	24	25

   How many students had a score greater than 20?
   A 4 (C) 20
   B 5 D 25

8. Using the data in problem 7, what was the range of the test scores?
   (A) 7 points C 18 points
   B 8 points D 25 points

9. In how many different ways can all four students be arranged in a row?
   Sue Janet Marty Bill
   A 4 ways (C) 24 ways
   B 12 ways D 36 ways

10. A coin is tossed and a die is rolled. What is the probability of tossing tails and rolling a 5?
    (A) $\frac{1}{12}$ C $\frac{1}{4}$
    B $\frac{1}{10}$ D $\frac{1}{3}$

Using the Academic Skills Test

This test familiarizes students with a standardized format while testing skills and concepts presented up to this point.

A Cumulative Review (free-response format) and Cumulative Test (multiple-choice format) are also provided in the Evaluation Masters Booklet as shown at the right.

Test Item	1	2	3	4	5	6	7	8	9	10
Lesson Number	4-9	6-9	7-7	8-6	8-8	9-5	10-1	10-1	11-3	11-6
TAAS Objective	1	1	2	2	2	1	5	5	5	5

Evaluation Masters Booklet, **p. 98**

Name ______ Date ______

Cumulative Review, Chapters 1-11

1. Which symbol is read "less than?" (Lesson 1–10) — 1. <
2. Simplify $|-14| + |-3|$. (Lesson 2–1) — 2. 17
3. Solve $3x \le -63$. (Lesson 3–8) — 3. $x \le -21$
4. Find the LCM of 15 and 30. (Lesson 4–7) — 4. 30
5. Mel biked 9.9 miles to the park, 2.1 miles to a store, and 8.1 miles back home. Estimate how far he biked. (Lesson 5–3) — 5. 20 miles
6. Express $\frac{9}{32}$ as a decimal. (Lesson 6–1) — 6. 0.28125
7. Express 1,200,000,000 in scientific notation. (Lesson 6–11) — 7. 1.2×10^9
8. Beth donated half of her money to charity, gave \$3 to her sister, and had \$25 remaining. How much money did Beth have in the beginning? (Lesson 7–1) — 8. \$56
9. Solve $7a + 4 = 10a - 2$. (Lesson 7–4) — 9. 2
10. Write an inequality that describes the graph at the right. (Lesson 8–2) — 10. $x \le 1$
11. Find the x-intercept of the graph of $y = -5x + 12$. (Lesson 8–9) — 11. $2\frac{2}{5}$
12. A photo 36 cm long is reduced to 12 cm long. If the width of the original photo is 18 cm, what is the width of the reduced copy? (Lesson 9–3) — 12. 6 cm
13. Express 28% as a fraction in simplest form. (Lesson 9–5) — 13. $\frac{7}{25}$
14. 28 is what percent of 84? (Lesson 9–7) — 14. $33\frac{1}{3}\%$

For Exercises 17–19, use these scores: 63, 75, 78, 81, 85, 92, 92, 99, 100. (Lesson 10–2)

15. Find the mean score. — 15. 85
16. Find the mode of the scores. — 16. 92
17. A random sample of 600 boys indicates that 200 prefer blue, 300 prefer red, 30 prefer green, and 70 prefer other colors. Three thousand booklets will be distributed to male pupils. How many blue-covered booklets should be ordered? (Lesson 10–8) — 17. 1000
18. Find the value of 7! (Lesson 11–3) — 18. 5040
19. Find the value of P(9, 4). (Lesson 11–3) — 19. 3024
20. One bag contains 8 red and 3 white marbles. Another bag has 2 green and 6 black marbles. One marble is drawn from each bag. Find P(white and green). (Lesson 11–6) — 20. $\frac{3}{44}$

Evaluation Masters Booklet, **p. 99**

Name ______ Date ______

Cumulative Test, Chapters 1-11

1. Simplify $|-12| - |-3|$.
   A. −9 B. 9 C. −15 D. 15 — 1. B
2. Solve $-4x < -64$.
   A. $x < -16$ B. $x < 16$ C. $x > 16$ D. $x > -16$ — 2. C
3. Express $\frac{7}{16}$ as a decimal.
   A. 0.4375 B. 0.325 C. 2.2857 D. 0.4573 — 3. A
4. Express 1.03×10^{-3} in standard notation.
   A. 1030 B. 0.0103 C. 0.00103 D. 3.09 — 4. C
5. Solve $18a - 7 = 15a + 2$.
   A. −3 B. 3 C. 0.6 D. 4 — 5. B
6. Write an inequality that describes the graph at the right.
   A. $a \ge 3$ B. $b > 3$ C. $c \le 3$ D. $d < 3$ — 6. B
7. Find the slope of the line that contains A(8, 2) and B(7, 6).
   A. −8 B. 8 C. 4 D. −4 — 7. D
8. Find the y-intercept of $y = -2x + 5$.
   A. −2 B. 3 C. 5 D. −5 — 8. C
9. A photo 20 cm long is enlarged to 30 cm long. If the width of the original photo is 8 cm, what is the width of the enlargement?
   A. 12 cm B. 15 cm C. 16 cm D. 10 cm — 9. A
10. Express 45% as a fraction in simplest form.
    A. $\frac{9}{10}$ B. $\frac{45}{100}$ C. $\frac{9}{20}$ D. $\frac{45}{99}$ — 10. C
11. What percent of 72 is 18?
    A. 25% B. 4% C. 400% D. 40% — 11. A
12. Find the mean of the scores 63, 75, 78, 85, 90, 90, and 100.
    A. 581 B. 90 C. 83 D. 85 — 12. C
13. Find the median of the scores in Exercise 14.
    A. 581 B. 90 C. 83 D. 85 — 13. D
14. Desk calendars are printed in red, green, blue, and black. They come in small, medium, and large sizes. Find the number of possible combinations of color and size.
    A. 7 B. 15 C. 64 D. 12 — 14. D
15. Find the value of P(6, 3).
    A. 120 B. 20 C. 216 D. 18 — 15. A
16. Find the value of C(6, 3).
    A. 120 B. 20 C. 216 D. 18 — 16. B
17. One bag contains two red and four white rocks. Another bag contains three green and four black rocks. One rock is drawn from each bag. Find P(white and black).
    A. $\frac{16}{21}$ B. $\frac{8}{42}$ C. $\frac{8}{21}$ D. $\frac{2}{13}$ — 17. C

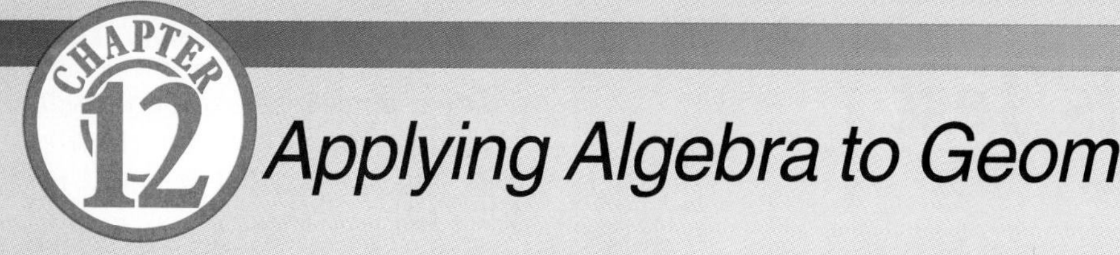

Applying Algebra to Geometry

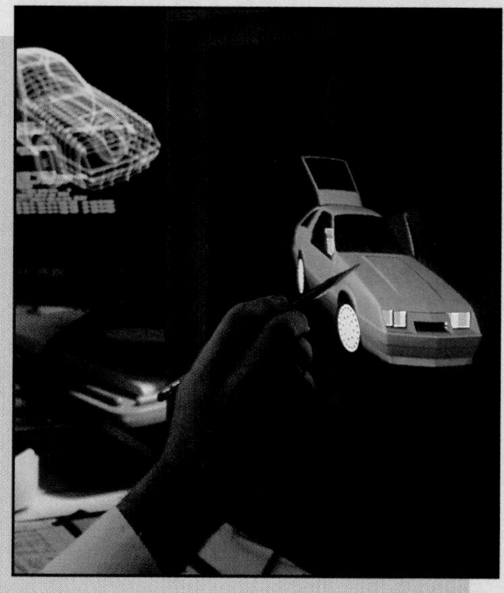

Previewing the Chapter

This chapter begins with the undefined geometric terms of point, line, and plane. Students learn to classify angles, triangles, and quadrilaterals and to study angle relationships resulting from parallel and intersecting lines. Applications to circle graphs combine the concepts of geometry to percents and angle measurement. The student is introduced to the properties of congruent and similar triangles, to the logic of conditional statements that lay a foundation for reading theorems in geometry, and to basic constructions. The chapter ends with an activity on tessellations and includes an exploration of translations, reflections, and rotations.

Logic The conditional statement is introduced. Students find the converse of a conditional and the truth value of both the conditional and the converse.

Lesson (Pages)	Lesson Objectives	State/Local Objectives
12-1 (438-441)	12-1A: Identify points, lines, planes, rays, segments, and angles.	1E, 3A, 4A
	12-1B: Classify angles as acute, right, or obtuse.	
12-2 (442-444)	12-2: Construct a circle graph based on raw data.	1E, 3A, 4A, 4E, 5D, 5E
12-3 (446-448)	12-3: Identify angle relationships.	1E, 3A, 4A, 4E
12-4 (449-451)	12-4: Identify the relationships of angles formed by two parallel lines and a transversal.	1E, 3A, 4A, 4E
12-5 (452-455)	12-5A: Construct congruent segments and angles using a compass and a straightedge.	1E, 3A, 4A
	12-5B: Bisect segments and angles.	
12-6 (456-458)	12-6A: Find the missing angle measure of a triangle.	1E, 3A, 4A, 4E
	12-6B: Classify triangles.	
12-7 (459-460)	12-7A: Identify a conditional and its parts.	1A, 1E
	12-7B: Write the converse of the conditional.	
12-8 (461-463)	12-8: Identify congruent triangles and corresponding parts of congruent triangles.	1E, 3A, 4A, 4E
12-9 (464-467)	12-9A: Identify corresponding parts of similar triangles.	1E, 3A, 4A, 4C, 4E
	12-9B: Find missing measures by using lengths of corresponding sides.	
12-10 (468-470)	12-10: Use proportions to solve problems involving similar triangles.	1D, 1E, 3A, 4A, 4C, 4E
12-11 (471-473)	12-11A: Find the missing angle measure of a quadrilateral.	1E, 3A, 4A, 4E
	12-11B: Classify quadrilaterals.	
12-12 (474-476)	12-12: Classify polygons.	1E, 3A, 4A, 4E

ESSENTIAL ELEMENTS

Organizing the Chapter

*You may want to refer to the **Course Planning Calendar** on Page T31.*

Planning Guide

Lesson (Pages)	Pacing Chart (in days)			Extra Practice (Student Edition)	Blackline Masters Booklets			Other Resources
	MINIMUM	STANDARD	ACCELERATED		Reteaching	Practice	Enrichment	
12-1 (438-441)	1.5	1	1	p. 612, Set A	p. 99	p. 110	p. 99	Transparency 12-1 Group Activity Card 12-1
12-2 (442-444)	1	1	1	p. 613, Set B	p. 100	p. 111	p. 100	Transparency 12-2 Group Activity Card 12-2
12-3 (446-448)	1	1	1	p. 613, Set C	p. 101	p. 112	p. 101	Transparency 12-3 Group Activity Card 12-3
12-4 (449-451)	1	1	1	p. 613, Set C	p. 102	p. 113	p. 102	Transparency 12-4 Group Activity Card 12-4
12-5 (452-455)	1.5	1	1	p. 614, Set D	p. 103	p. 114	p. 103	Transparency 12-5 Group Activity Card 12-5
12-6 (456-458)	1	1	1	p. 614, Set D	p. 104	p. 115	p. 104	Transparency 12-6 Group Activity Card 12-6
12-7 (459-460)	1	1	0.5			p. 116		Transparency 12-7 Group Activity Card 12-7
12-8 (461-463)	1	1	1	p. 614, Set D	p. 105	p. 117	p. 105	Transparency 12-8 Group Activity Card 12-8
12-9 (464-467)	1.5	1	1	p. 614, Set D	p. 106	p. 118	p. 106	Transparency 12-9 Group Activity Card 12-9
12-10 (468-470)	1	1	1	p. 614, Set D	p. 107	p. 119	p. 107	Transparency 12-10 Group Activity Card 12-10
12-11 (471-473)	1	1	1	p. 614, Set E	p. 108	p. 120	p. 108	Transparency 12-11 Group Activity Card 12-11
12-12 (474-476)	1	1	1	p. 614, Set E	p. 109	p. 121	p. 109	Transparency 12-12 Group Activity Card 12-12
Review (478-479)	1.5	1	1					Test Generator
Test (480)	1	1	1		Evaluation Masters, pp. 100-105			

Other Chapter Resources

Student Edition
Algebra in Action, p. 445
Mid-Chapter Quiz, p. 458
Exploration, pp. 464, 477
History, p. 470
Team Problem Solving, p. 476
Academic Skills Test, p. 481

Teacher Resource Package
Interdisciplinary Activity, p. 12
Application Worksheet, p. 27
Cooperative Problem Solving, p. 42
Multicultural Activity, p. 57
Fun Activities, p. 76
Technology Worksheets, pp. 12, 27, 42
Lab Manual, pp. 60-62
Quizzes(2), p. 106
Class Review Game

Software
Test Generator

available for Apple and IBM

Enhancing the Chapter

Some of the blackline masters for enhancing this chapter are shown below.

Applications, p. 27

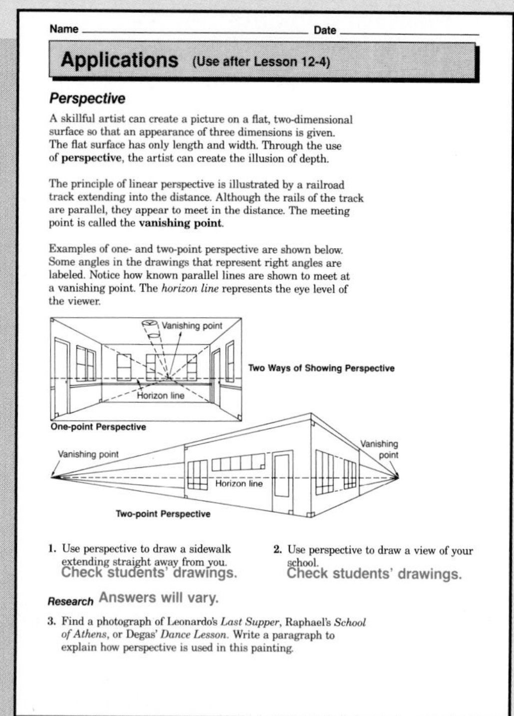

Name ______________ Date ______________

Applications (Use after Lesson 12-4)

Perspective

A skillful artist can create a picture on a flat, two-dimensional surface so that an appearance of three dimensions is given. The flat surface has only length and width. Through the use of **perspective**, the artist can create the illusion of depth.

The principle of linear perspective is illustrated by a railroad track extending into the distance. Although the rails of the track are parallel, they appear to meet in the distance. The meeting point is called the **vanishing point**.

Examples of one- and two-point perspective are shown below. Some angles in the drawings that represent right angles are labeled. Notice how known parallel lines are shown to meet at a vanishing point. The *horizon line* represents the eye level of the viewer.

1. Use perspective to draw a sidewalk extending straight away from you. Check students' drawings.
2. Use perspective to draw a view of your school. Check students' drawings.

Research Answers will vary.

3. Find a photograph of Leonardo's *Last Supper*, Raphael's *School of Athens*, or Degas' *Dance Lesson*. Write a paragraph to explain how perspective is used in this painting.

The **Activity Masters Booklet** contains the page shown above.

Interdisciplinary Activity, p. 12

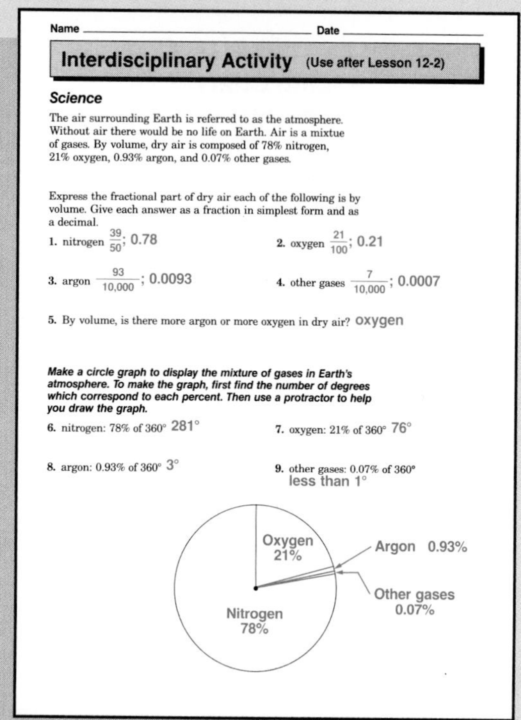

Name ______________ Date ______________

Interdisciplinary Activity (Use after Lesson 12-2)

Science

The air surrounding Earth is referred to as the atmosphere. Without air there would be no life on Earth. Air is a mixtue of gases. By volume, dry air is composed of 78% nitrogen, 21% oxygen, 0.93% argon, and 0.07% other gases.

Express the fractional part of dry air each of the following is by volume. Give each answer as a fraction in simplest form and as a decimal.

1. nitrogen $\frac{39}{50}$; 0.78
2. oxygen $\frac{21}{100}$; 0.21
3. argon $\frac{93}{10,000}$; 0.0093
4. other gases $\frac{7}{10,000}$; 0.0007
5. By volume, is there more argon or more oxygen in dry air? oxygen

Make a circle graph to display the mixture of gases in Earth's atmosphere. To make the graph, first find the number of degrees which correspond to each percent. Then use a protractor to help you draw the graph.

6. nitrogen: 78% of 360° 281°
7. oxygen: 21% of 360° 76°
8. argon: 0.93% of 360° 3°
9. other gases: 0.07% of 360° less than 1°

The **Activity Masters Booklet** contains the page shown above.

Models and Manipulatives

Most students are aware that the sum of the measure of the angles of a triangle is 180°. Make a chart of several quadrilaterals to see if a relationship exists for the sum of the angles of a quadrilateral. Use two protractors to show students that the sum of the central angles of a circle is 360°. Have students make any quadrilateral. Using a compass, have them draw the same size arc at each corner. Then have students tear off each corner and form a circle.

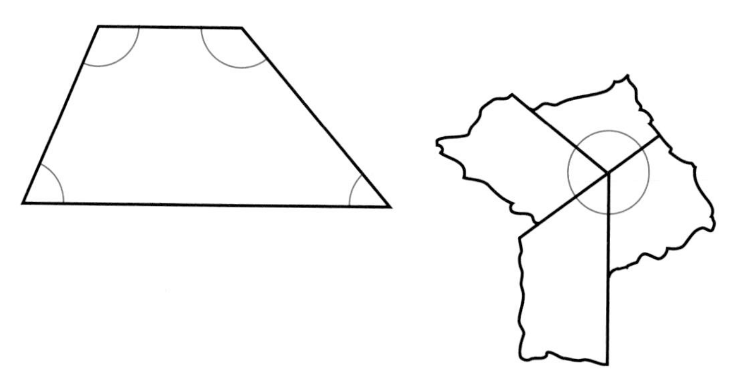

Limited English Proficiency (LEP) Activity

Review the vocabulary used in this chapter. Explain unfamiliar vocabulary such as translation, and parallel and intersecting lines. Research words that are different in other cultures. Have the students with limited English proficiency describe how the words differ. Explain how even though the terms may differ, the meaning and description remain the same.

Cooperative Learning

The following activity is provided in the **Activity Masters Booklet.**

Cooperative Problem Solving, p. 42

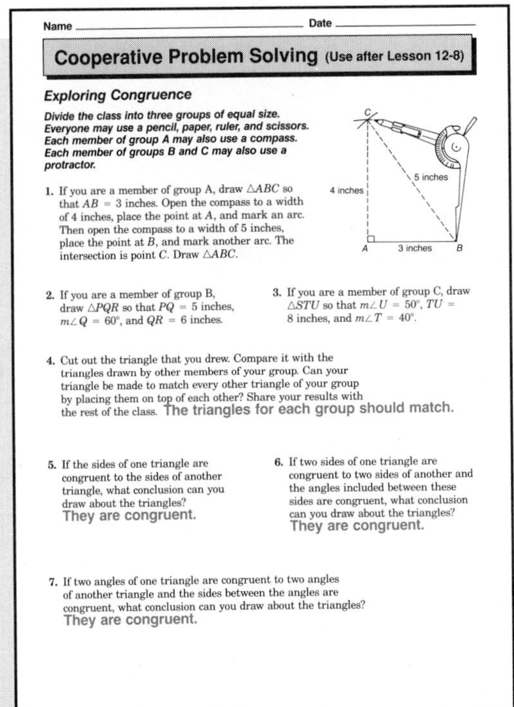

Name ______ Date ______

Cooperative Problem Solving (Use after Lesson 12-8)

Exploring Congruence

Divide the class into three groups of equal size. Everyone may use a pencil, paper, ruler, and scissors. Each member of group A may also use a compass. Each member of groups B and C may also use a protractor.

1. If you are a member of group A, draw $\triangle ABC$ so that $AB = 3$ inches. Open the compass to a width of 4 inches, place the point at A, and mark an arc. Then open the compass to a width of 5 inches, place the point at B, and mark another arc. The intersection is point C. Draw $\triangle ABC$.

2. If you are a member of group B, draw $\triangle PQR$ so that $PQ = 5$ inches, $m\angle Q = 60°$, and $QR = 6$ inches.

3. If you are a member of group C, draw $\triangle STU$ so that $m\angle U = 50°$, $TU = 8$ inches, and $m\angle T = 40°$.

4. Cut out the triangle that you drew. Compare it with the triangles drawn by other members of your group. Can your triangle be made to match every other triangle of your group by placing them on top of each other? Share your results with the rest of the class. The triangles for each group should match.

5. If the sides of one triangle are congruent to the sides of another triangle, what conclusion can you draw about the triangles? They are congruent.

6. If two sides of one triangle are congruent to two sides of another and the angles included between these sides are congruent, what conclusion can you draw about the triangles? They are congruent.

7. If two angles of one triangle are congruent to two angles of another triangle and the sides between the angles are congruent, what conclusion can you draw about the triangles? They are congruent.

Cooperative Problem Solving

Have students work in groups of two to four. Most students have trouble describing mathematically many of the figures they encounter. In groups, students will be asked to describe exactly in writing the properties that distinguish the following quadrilaterals: rectangle, square, parallelogram, rhombus, and trapezoid. Define what is meant by polygon and quadrilateral before beginning a discussion of the individual quadrilaterals.

Interactive Bulletin Board

Social Studies Connection

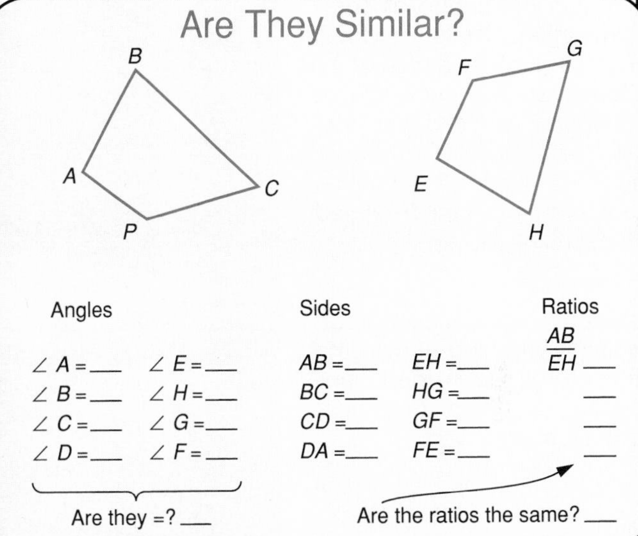

Purpose Provide practice recognizing quadrilaterals in everyday life.

How to Use It Have students bring in newspaper clippings or drawings they have created to show the concept of similar polygons. Each day a different student would bring his or her item to class and discuss it briefly and add it to the bulletin board. The discussion should include in what ways the sides are similar, what is the ratio of the sides, and how the respective angles are equal.

Outside Resources

Books/Periodicals
Geometry in the Mathematics Classroom, 36th Yearbook, NCTM

Films/Videotapes
Geometry—What's That? Coronet Media
Adventures in Perceptions, Association Films, Inc.

Software
The Geometric pre Supposer, Sunburst
Geometric Connectors: Transformations, Sunburst

Technology

There are three pages in the ***Technology Masters Booklet*** that involve technology with concepts in this chapter. One page involves calculators and one page has a problem that can be solved using the BASIC program that is provided. Students should evaluate the information they obtain from running the program and solve a similar problem by extending the program.

Using the Chapter Opener

Transparency 12-0 is available in the Transparency Package. It provides a full-color visual and motivating activity that you can use to engage students in the mathematical content of the chapter.

Career Connection

Some students have difficulty visualizing a computer simulation and understanding the scope of computer simulation. Have students contact a landscape architect or horticulturist, an architect, and a plastic surgeon and find out how computer simulations can help in planning their work. If possible, obtain a printout of a career-related computer simulation.

Writing Connection

Have students write a paragraph specifically explaining how the simulation described in the Chapter Opener can help designers build lighter, stronger cars.

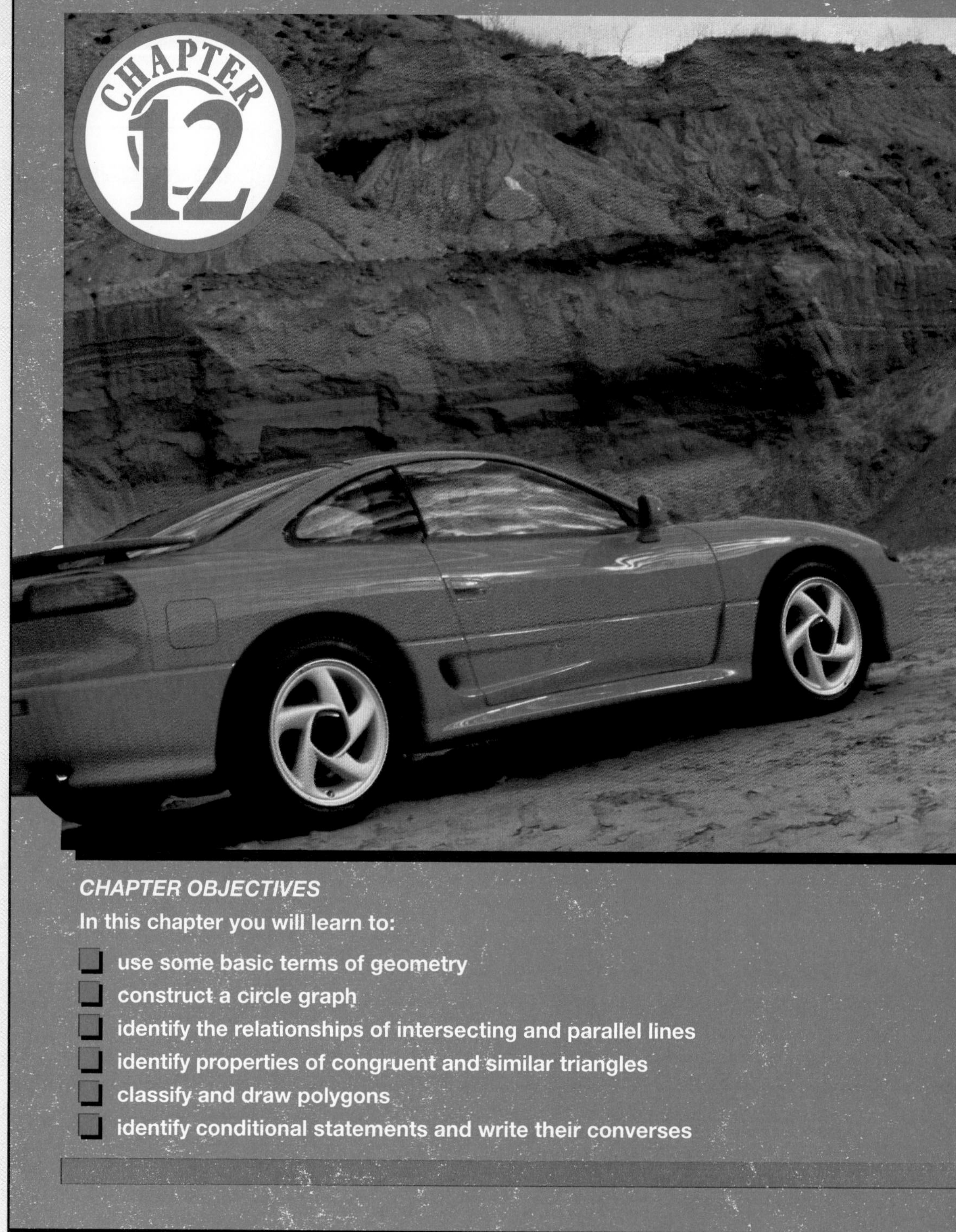

CHAPTER OBJECTIVES

In this chapter you will learn to:

- use some basic terms of geometry
- construct a circle graph
- identify the relationships of intersecting and parallel lines
- identify properties of congruent and similar triangles
- classify and draw polygons
- identify conditional statements and write their converses

Applying Algebra to Geometry

The new cars of the 1990s owe a lot to computers. After automotive designers have sketched several new car designs, promising designs are modeled in clay at a scale of 1 to 5. A three-dimensional scanner is run over the surface of each model, measuring and storing lengths, widths, and heights automatically. A computer accepts the measurements and projects three-dimensional images of the car on its screen.

Using the computer, the designer can investigate the car's structural strength. First it divides the car's entire surface into triangles. By shading each triangle, the computer shows the load on the car's surface at that location. The darker the shading, the bigger the load. That means today's designers can plan lighter, stronger cars than even the most experienced automotive designers of the past who worked without computer assistance.

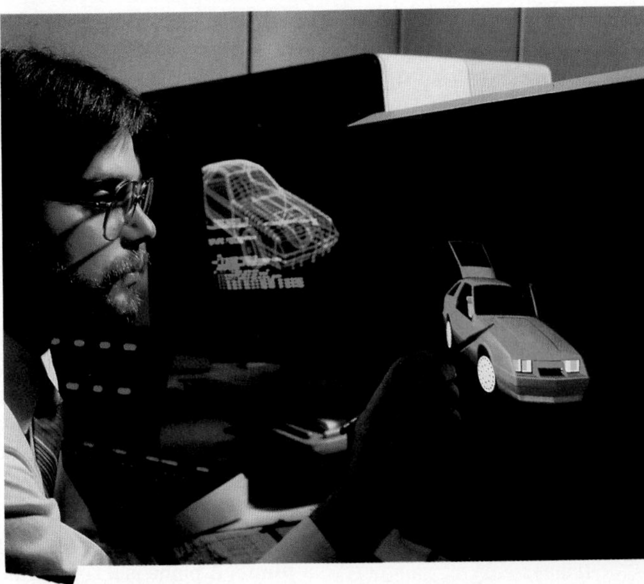

Language Connection

Class Project

Write letters to several automobile companies, asking for information about computer-aided design.

Write a report that summarizes the information.

Language Connection

To get current addresses for auto companies, contact local auto sales agencies. They will either have information on the simulations or can give you an address to contact. Contact both domestic and foreign-owned companies, and compare and contrast the information supplied.

Looking Ahead

You may want to have the following materials available to use in this chapter.

Algebra in Action, p. 445
- flashlight
- small plane mirror
- black construction paper
- modeling clay
- protractor
- unlined paper

Exploration, p. 464
- notebook paper
- scissors
- cardboard

Exploration, p. 477
- tracing paper
- cardboard
- scissors

Lesson Notes 12-1

5-Minute Check
(over Chapter 11)

Box A contains one blue marble and one green marble. Box B contains one green marble and one red marble. Box C contains one white marble and one green marble.

1. If a marble is drawn at random from each box, what is the probability that all three marbles are green? **$\frac{1}{8}$; 0.125**
2. What is the probability that exactly two marbles are green? **$\frac{3}{8}$; 0.375**

Transparency 12-1 contains the 5-Minute Check and a teaching aid for this lesson.

1 FOCUS

The purpose of this lesson is to identify basic geometric terms and use them to define and classify.

Motivating the Lesson

Show students a fishing reel with fishing filament. Ask students why the filament is called a line. Is it really a line?

2 TEACH

Using Transparencies

Using an overhead projector, list the new terms as covered in this lesson. On a separate transparency, give an example of each. After all terms have been covered, show examples in a different order and match each to the correct term.

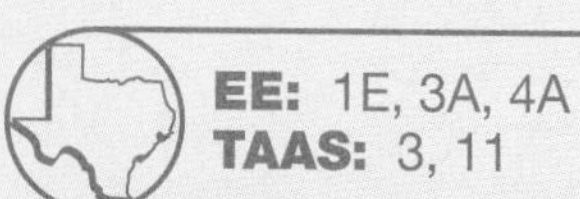

EE: 1E, 3A, 4A
TAAS: 3, 11

12-1 The Language of Geometry

Objectives:

Identify points, lines, planes, rays, segments, and angles.
Classify angles as acute, right, or obtuse.

Key Terms:

point
line
line segment
plane
ray
angle

Mr. Thompson uses a laser measuring device to detect bumps and hollows in his fields. This device sends signals to a land leveling machine which smooths the field to ensure even irrigation after the crop is planted.

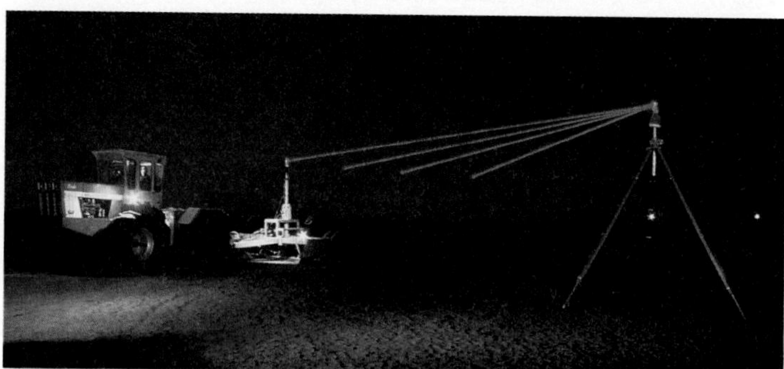

Science Connection

A lens can focus a laser to a point 0.0001 inch wide. When the beam is concentrated on such a small area, temperatures in excess of 10,000°F (5538°C) are produced.

The light from a laser is seen as a beam because it strikes and reflects off particles in the air. Each dust particle suggests a **point.** A point is a specific location in space, but the point itself has no size or shape. A point can be represented by a dot and named with a capital letter.

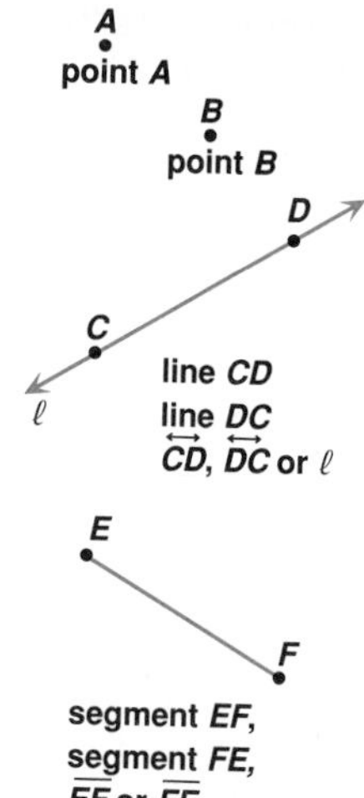

A laser beam travels in a straight line as can be seen in a collection of dust particles. In geometry, a **line** is a collection of points that extends indefinitely in two directions. Arrowheads are used to show that a line has no endpoints. A line can be named by a single lowercase letter or by using two points of the line.

The section of a laser beam that goes from the measuring device to the land leveler is a model of a **line segment.** A line segment is a part of a line containing two endpoints and all points between the endpoints. A line segment is named by its endpoints.

segment *EF*, segment *FE*, $\overline{EF}$ or $\overline{FE}$

Explain why the three points used to name a plane cannot lie on the same line.
If they lie on the same line, more than one plane is defined by that line.

Mr. Thompson's field, after leveling, is a model of a **plane.** A plane is a flat surface that has no boundaries. A plane can be named by any three points of the plane. (The three points must *not* lie on the same line.)

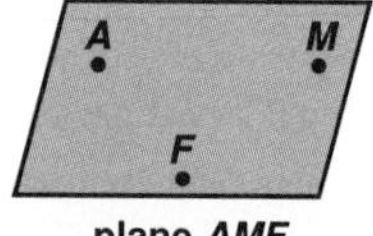

plane *AMF*

Bell Ringer

A coin is flipped, a die is rolled and a card is drawn from a deck of 52 playing cards. What is the probability of getting a head, a six, and a queen? $\frac{1}{156}$

The path of the laser beam is a model of a **ray.** A ray extends from one point indefinitely in one direction. A ray is named by using its endpoint first and then any other point on the ray.

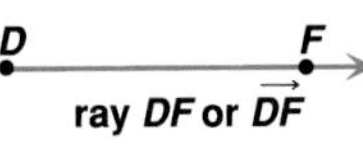

ray *DF* or $\overrightarrow{DF}$

Examples

1 Give three names for the line shown below.

There are three points labeled on the line. Any two can be used to name it. So we can name it $\overleftrightarrow{PQ}$, $\overleftrightarrow{QR}$, or $\overleftrightarrow{RP}$.

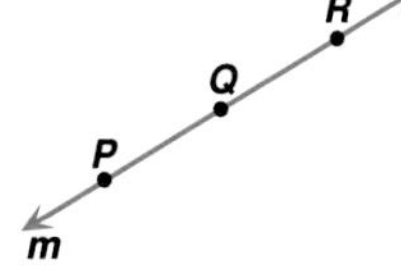

What is another name for the line that was not given? ***m, $\overleftrightarrow{QP}$, $\overleftrightarrow{RQ}$, or $\overleftrightarrow{PR}$***

2 Name two rays and three segments in the figure below.

Two of the rays are $\overrightarrow{AC}$ and $\overrightarrow{DB}$. Three of the segments are $\overline{AB}$, $\overline{BD}$, and $\overline{BC}$.

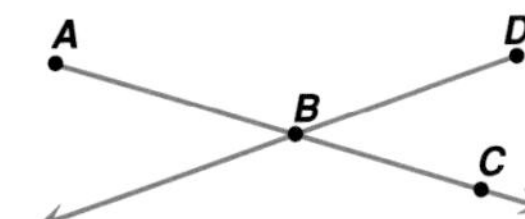

What is another name for $\overrightarrow{AC}$? ***$\overrightarrow{AB}$***
What segment was not named? ***$\overline{AC}$***

3 Give three names for the plane shown below.

There are four points labeled on the plane. Any three can be used to name it. So we can name it plane *EFG*, plane *FGH*, or plane *GHE*.

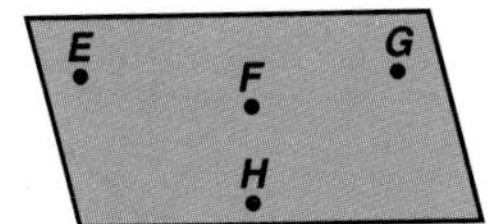

How many other ways are there to name the plane? **21 ways**

An **angle** is formed by two rays with a common endpoint called the **vertex.** The rays are called the **sides** of the angle. In the angle at the right, $\overrightarrow{QP}$ and $\overrightarrow{QR}$ form the sides of angle *PQR*. The vertex is point *Q*.

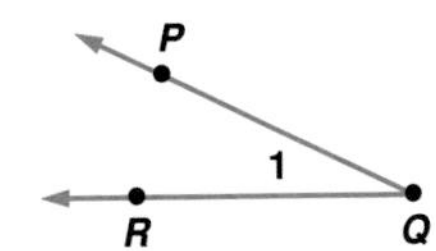

angle *PQR*, angle *RQP*, angle *Q*, ∠*PQR*, ∠*RQP*, ∠Q, or ∠1

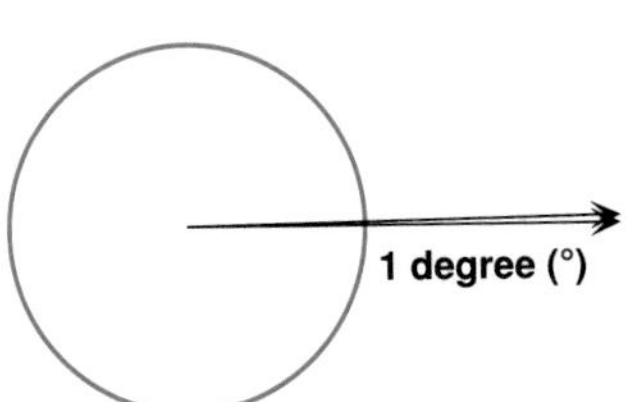

The most common unit of measure for angles is the **degree.** A circle can be separated into 360 arcs of the same length. An angle has a measurement of one degree if its vertex is at the center of the circle and its sides contain the endpoints of one of the 360 equal arcs.

Chalkboard Examples

- *For Example 1*
  Give three names for the line shown below. **$\overleftrightarrow{CE}$, $\overleftrightarrow{CD}$, $\overleftrightarrow{DE}$**

  C D E

- *For Example 2*
  Name three segments and two rays in the figure below.

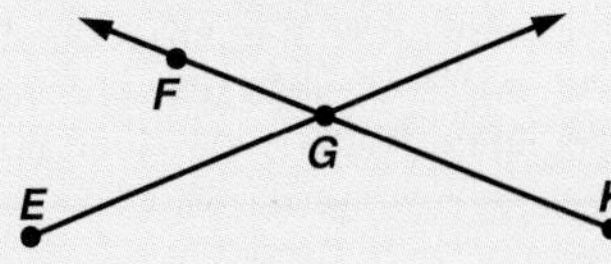

$\overrightarrow{KF}$, $\overrightarrow{EG}$, $\overline{FG}$, $\overline{GE}$, $\overline{GK}$

- *For Example 3*
  Give three names for the plane shown below.

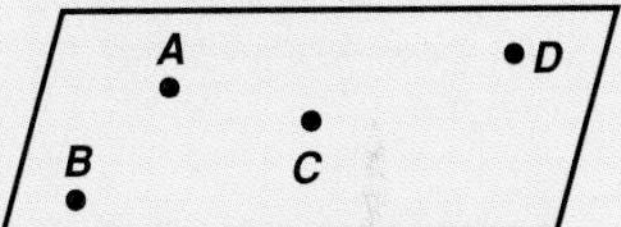

plane *ABC*, plane *ACD*, plane *BCD*

- *For Example 4*
  Find the measures of ∠*DEF* and ∠*GEH*.

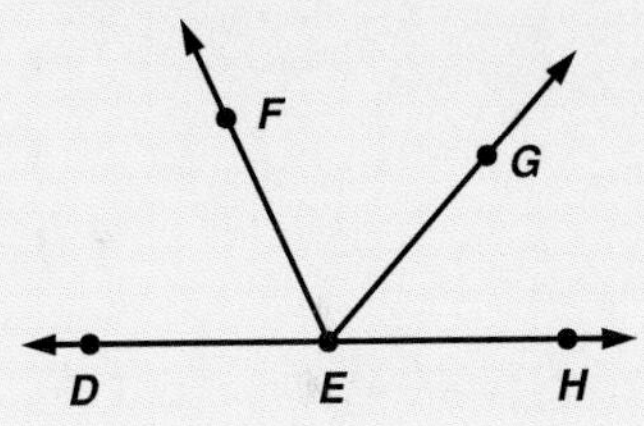

$m\angle FED = 115°$, $m\angle GEH = 48°$

Alternate Strategies: Reteaching the Lesson

Reteaching Activity

Working Backwards Have students play a game. Lesson terms are written on slips of paper and placed in a bag. As the terms are drawn, they are answers and students must give an appropriate question.

Reteaching Masters Booklet, p. 99

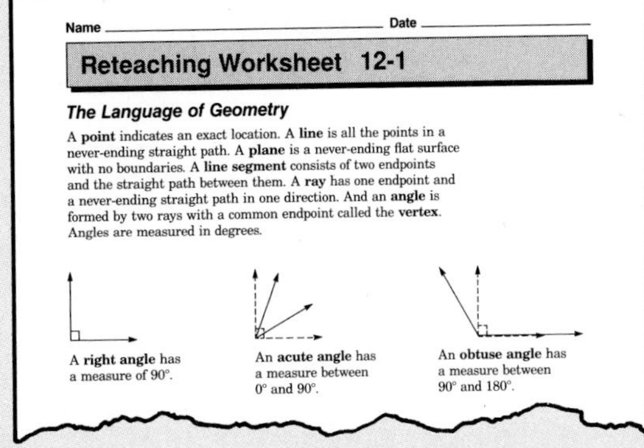

Name ______ Date ______

Reteaching Worksheet 12-1

The Language of Geometry

A **point** indicates an exact location. A **line** is all the points in a never-ending straight path. A **plane** is a never-ending flat surface with no boundaries. A **line segment** consists of two endpoints and the straight path between them. A **ray** has one endpoint and a never-ending straight path in one direction. And an **angle** is formed by two rays with a common endpoint called the **vertex**. Angles are measured in degrees.

A **right angle** has a measure of 90°.

An **acute angle** has a measure between 0° and 90°.

An **obtuse angle** has a measure between 90° and 180°.

3 PRACTICE/APPLY

Checking the Concept

Have students individually complete Exercises 5-10 then discuss answers collectively or in cooperative groups.

Error Analysis

Watch for students who read the wrong scale on a protractor.
Prevent by reminding students that if the angle is less than a right angle, its measure is less than 90°.

Additional Answers

2.

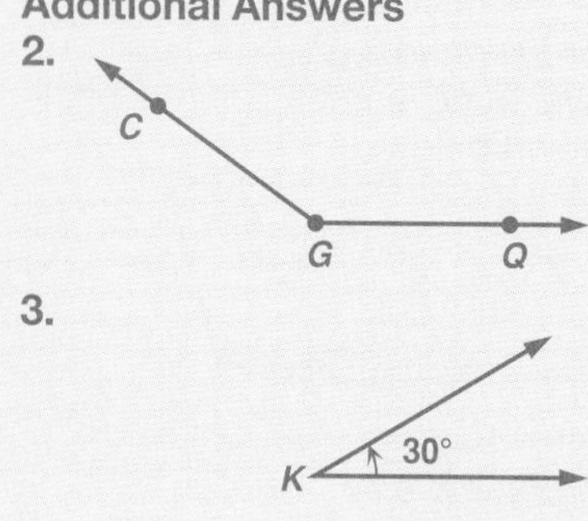

3. (angle of 30° with vertex K)

Practice Masters Booklet, **p. 110**

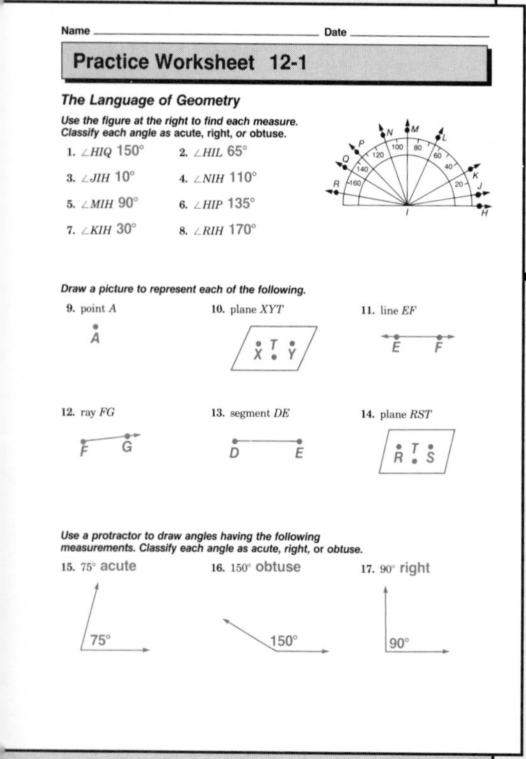

Name ______________ Date ______________

Practice Worksheet 12-1

The Language of Geometry

Use the figure at the right to find each measure. Classify each angle as acute, right, or obtuse.

1. ∠HIQ 150°
2. ∠HIL 65°
3. ∠JIH 10°
4. ∠NIH 110°
5. ∠MIH 90°
6. ∠HIP 135°
7. ∠KIH 30°
8. ∠RIH 170°

Draw a picture to represent each of the following.

9. point A
10. plane XYT
11. line EF
12. ray FG
13. segment DE
14. plane RST

Use a protractor to draw angles having the following measurements. Classify each angle as acute, right, or obtuse.

15. 75° acute
16. 150° obtuse
17. 90° right

You can use a **protractor** to measure angles.

- Place the center of the protractor on the vertex of the angle (B) with the straightedge along one ray ($\overrightarrow{BA}$).
- Use the scale that begins with 0 at $\overrightarrow{BA}$. Read where the ray ($\overrightarrow{BC}$) crosses this scale.

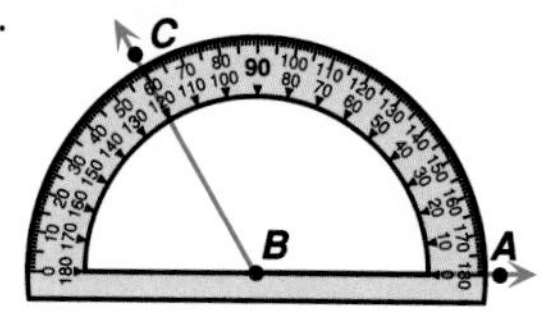

Say: The measure of angle ABC is 120 degrees.
Write: $m\angle ABC = 120°$

Example

Why is ∠V not a good way to name an angle? **Many angles share ∠V as a vertex.**

4 **Find the measure of ∠RVZ and ∠XVW.**

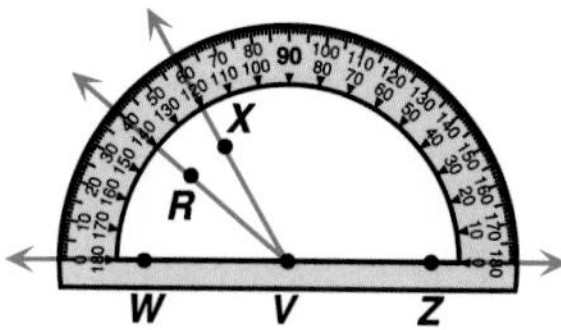

$m\angle RVZ = 140°$ Use the scale that begins with 0 at $\overrightarrow{VZ}$.
$m\angle XVW = 60°$ Use the scale that begins with 0 at $\overrightarrow{VW}$.

Angles are classified by degree measure.

Acute angles have measures greater than 0° and less than 90°.

Right angles have measures of 90°. The small square indicates that ∠JKL is a right angle.

Obtuse angles have measures greater than 90° but less than 180°.

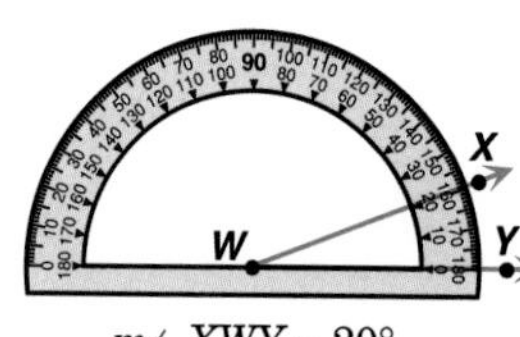

$m\angle XWY = 20°$

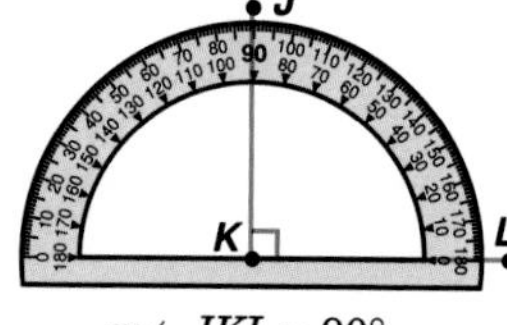

$m\angle JKL = 90°$

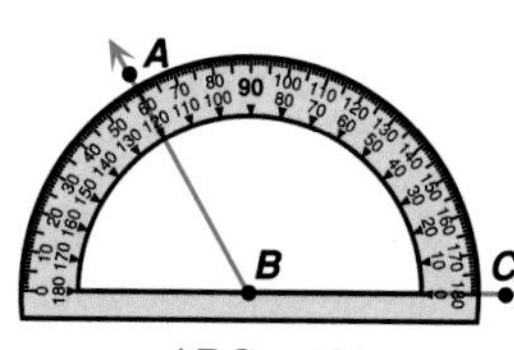

$m\angle ABC = 120°$

Checking for Understanding

Communicating Algebra

1. The line through points P and Q is named __?__. $\overleftrightarrow{PQ}$
2. Draw and label an obtuse angle with sides $\overrightarrow{GQ}$ and $\overrightarrow{GC}$. **See margin.**
3. Draw and label a 30° angle with vertex K. **See margin.**
4. Explain the difference between an obtuse angle and an acute angle. **4. An obtuse angle has a measure between 90° and 180°. An acute angle has a measure between 0° and 90°.**

Guided Practice
For Exercises 5-10, sample answers given.

Use the figure at the right to name an example of each term.

5. line $\overleftrightarrow{AE}$
6. obtuse angle ∠ACD
7. ray $\overrightarrow{CD}$
8. line segment $\overline{CE}$
9. acute angle ∠DCE
10. point A
11. Use a protractor to find the degree measure of ∠ECD. **27°**

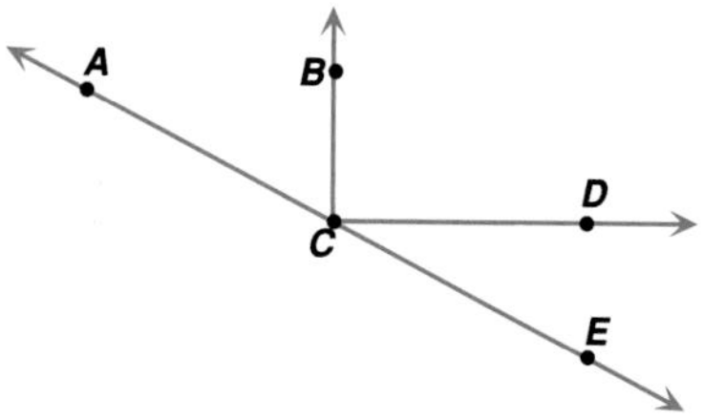

A, B, C, D, E (figure)

Additional Answers

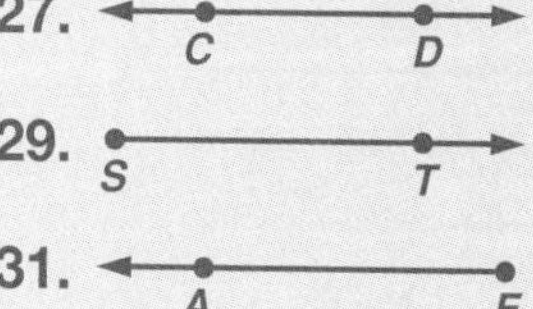

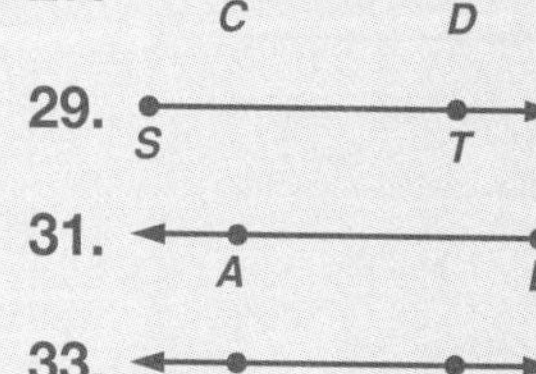

28. • F

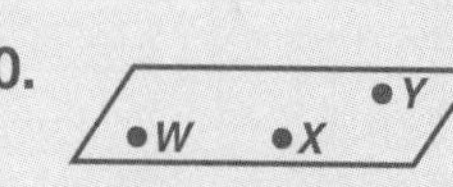

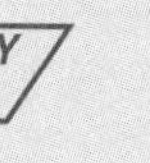

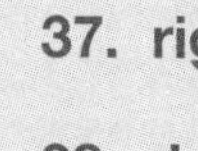

34. • M

35. acute
36. acute
37. right
38. obtuse
39. obtuse

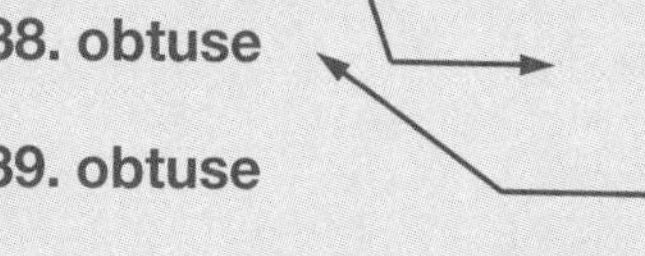

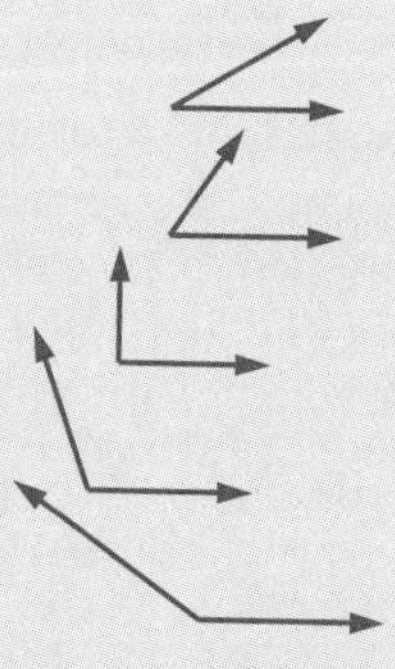

Determine whether each model suggests a point, line, or plane.

12. corner of a box point
13. guitar string line
14. meeting of two walls line
15. ice on an ice rink plane
16. cover of a book plane
17. sharp end of a thorn point

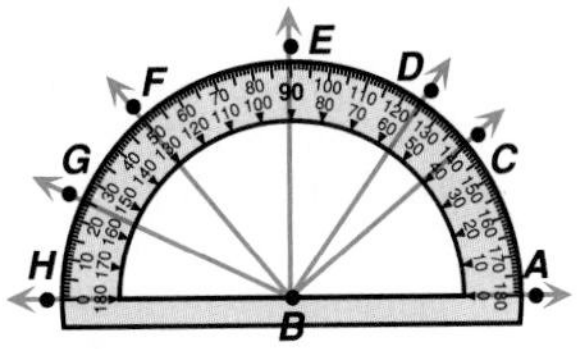

Use the figure at the left to find each measure. Classify each angle as *acute, right,* or *obtuse.*

18. $m\angle ABC$ 40°; acute
19. $m\angle CBH$ 140°; obtuse
20. $m\angle EBH$ 90°; right

Exercises

Independent Practice

Use the figure above to find each measure. Classify each angle as *acute, right,* or *obtuse.*

21. $m\angle GBH$ 25°; acute
22. $m\angle ABD$ 55°; acute
23. $m\angle FBH$ 50°; acute
24. $m\angle GBA$ 155°; obtuse
25. $m\angle ABE$ 90°; right
26. $m\angle DBH$ 125°; obtuse

Draw a picture to represent each of the following. For Exercises 27-34, see margin.

27. line *CD*
28. point *F*
29. ray *ST*
30. plane *WXY*
31. ray *EF*
32. plane *ABC*
33. line *GH*
34. point *M*

Use a protractor to draw angles having the following measurements. Classify each angle as *acute, right,* or *obtuse.* For Exercises 35-39, see margin.

35. 30°
36. 55°
37. 90°
38. 110°
39. 145°

Mixed Review

***True* or *false*.** (Lessons 1-10, 6-12)

40. $8(2) < 15$ false
41. $-38.12 > -38.22$ true
42. **Statistics** What fraction of people chose red as their favorite color? (Lesson 10-8) $\frac{2}{5}$

Favorite Color	
Blue	11
Red	12
Green	7

43. **Probability** Draw a tree diagram to determine the outcomes for tossing a coin three times. (Lesson 11-1) See margin.
44. **Probability** Suppose $P(A) = \frac{1}{3}$, $P(B) = \frac{1}{4}$, and A and B are mutually exclusive. What is P(A or B)? (Lesson 11-8) $\frac{7}{12}$

Application

45. **Photography** Cameras are often mounted on tripods to give stability. Why do tripods give stability? The three "pods" determine a plane.

Critical Thinking

46. ***True* or *false*.**
    a. The intersection of any two rays is always a point. false
    b. A line is part of a line segment. false

Wrap-Up

47. Use two pencils and your desk to model the concepts of point, line, plane, ray, and angle. See students' work.

Independent Practice

Homework Assignment	
Basic	21-39 odd, 40-47
Average	22-38 even, 40-47
Honors	28-34 even, 35-47

4 CLOSE

Assessment Option

Modeling Have each student use a protractor and find the measures of different angles. Have them measure angles that go both clockwise and counterclockwise. Also have them write the angle name and both rays.

Additional Answer

43.

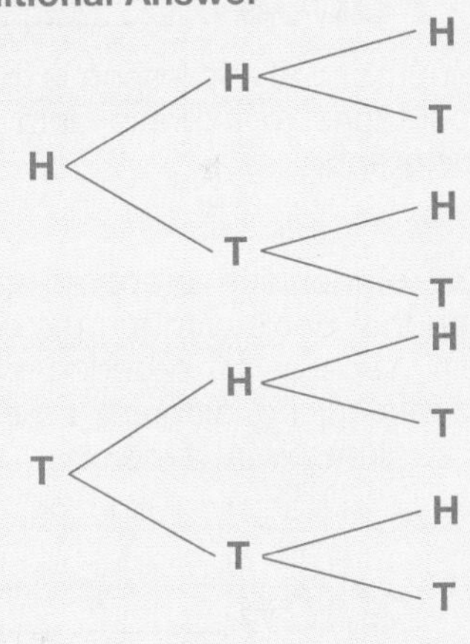

Enrichment Masters Booklet, **p. 99**

Name ______ Date ______

Enrichment Worksheet 12-1

Basic Geometric Terms: Word Search

R N B A S C V E S R E Q P O
G E O M E T R Y U D Z A H B
A T E J L S A I P T R U G T
T R I A N G L E P A M E H U
B A D V M X Y F L C A G B S
E P C P W I B L E F I L N E
L E T E S R E S M R D C O C
A Z U R U L Q V E H G I G W
C O M P L E M E N T A R Y H
I I L E A F O W T J N C L G
T D X N K R F E A M G L O E
R N T D M A X N R O L E P L
E E N I L Y Z L Y N E R Q G
V A U C S B P O L L K P I N
K S Q U A R E J H E M L J A
T A P L A N E N T O L E Y T
N S V A T C W U X Q R E S C
I K O R P U C T P V M R T E
O E Z Y Y A X S U B M O H R
P W Z A D J A C E N T A F S
S E G M E N T X Q W D G Z I

1. geometry
2. line
3. segment
4. plane
5. point
6. ray
7. angle
8. acute
9. right
10. obtuse
11. adjacent
12. complementary
13. supplementary
14. vertical
15. parallel
16. skew
17. perpendicular
18. triangle
19. polygon
20. rectangle
21. rhombus
22. square
23. trapezoid
24. circle

Alternate Strategies: Extending the Lesson

Enrichment

Using Models Have students look through magazines and newspapers and find pictured examples of each of the lesson terms.

Cooperative Learning

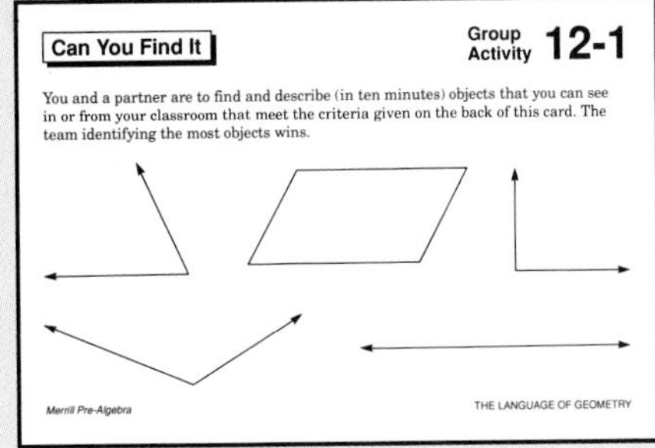
Can You Find It Group Activity **12-1**

You and a partner are to find and describe (in ten minutes) objects that you can see in or from your classroom that meet the criteria given on the back of this card. The team identifying the most objects wins.

Merrill Pre-Algebra THE LANGUAGE OF GEOMETRY

Lesson Notes 12-2

5-Minute Check
(over Lesson 12-1)

Draw a picture to represent each of the following.
1. line *LM*
2. plane *RST*
3. point *Q*
4. ray *DX*
5. line segment *XY*

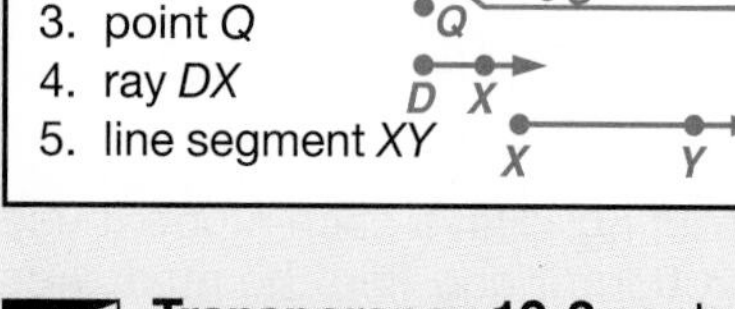

Transparency 12-2 contains the 5-Minute Check and a teaching aid for this lesson.

1 FOCUS

The purpose of this lesson is to use percentages to express data in a circle graph.

Motivating the Lesson

Show students a prepared circle graph that deals with a topic of interest, such as time budgeting or students taking different courses. Ask students what it means.

2 TEACH

Statistics Connection

Discuss the steps used in preparing a circle graph as the example is discussed. Survey the class according to telephone exchange or some other topic and express results in a circle graph.

EE: 1E, 3A, 4A, 4E, 5D, 5E
TAAS: 11,12

Application

12-2 Making Circle Graphs

Objective:
Make a circle graph from data.

Key Term:
circle graph

Thirty percent of Earth's surface is land. The other 70% is water. This information can be displayed in a circle graph. A **circle graph** is used to compare parts of a whole. Since 30% + 70% is 100%, the circle represents the whole surface of Earth.

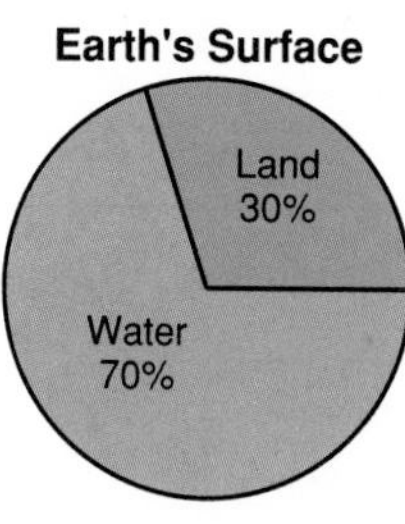

Check the sum of 108° and 252°. What should it be? **360°**

In Lesson 12-1, you learned that there are 360° in a circle.

30% of 360° is 108°. 70% of 360° is 252°.

Use your protractor to measure the angles in the circle graph. You should find that they measure 108° and 252°.

Sometimes you are given data that have not been expressed as a percent. Study the following example to find out how to make such a circle graph.

FYI

About 4 billion years ago, water from deep within Earth was released at Earth's surface through volcanic activity. This water began to accumulate to form the oceans. Today, the mass of the oceans is about 1.4×10^{24} g.

Example

1 **Make a circle graph to display the following data.**

Homework for April (in hours)	
Math	20
English	15
History	8
Science	5
Other	2

Step 1 Find the total number of hours.

20 + 15 + 8 + 5 + 2 = 50

Bell Ringer

Name five angle measures that are obtuse and five angle measures that are acute. **Answers will vary.**

Step 2 Find the ratio that compares the time spent on each subject to the total time.

Math: $\frac{20}{50} = 0.4$ Science: $\frac{5}{50} = 0.1$

English: $\frac{15}{50} = 0.3$ Other: $\frac{2}{50} = 0.04$

History: $\frac{8}{50} = 0.16$

Check the sum of the ratios. What should it be? **1.0**

Step 3 Find the number of degrees for each section of the graph.

Math: $0.4 \times 360° = 144°$ Science: $0.1 \times 360° = 36°$

English: $0.3 \times 360° = 108°$ Other: $0.04 \times 360° = 14.4°$

History: $0.16 \times 360° = 57.6°$

Check the sum of the degrees. What should it be? **360°**

Step 4 Draw a circle graph.

Use a compass to draw a circle and a radius as shown.

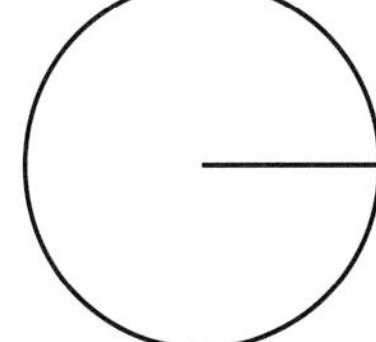

Start with the least number of degrees, in this case, 14.4°. Use your protractor to draw an angle of 14.4°.

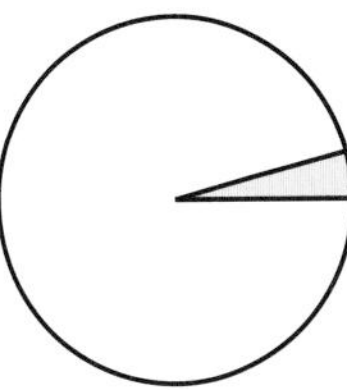

Repeat for the remaining sections. Label each section of the graph and give the graph a title.

0.4 = 40%

0.3 = 30%

0.16 = 16%

0.1 = 10%

0.04 = 4%

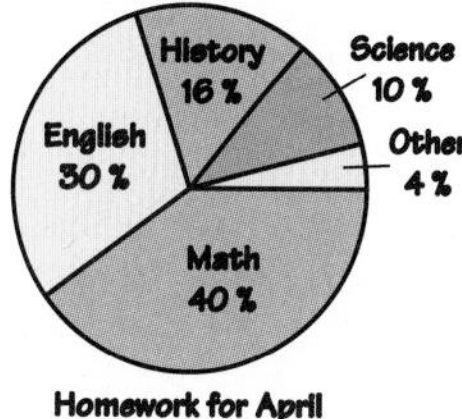

Checking for Understanding

Communicating Algebra

1. When is it appropriate to graph data in a circle graph? **See margin.**
2. Explain why it would not be appropriate to make a circle graph called "Population of the United States, 1900-2000." **See margin.**

Guided Practice

3. **Collect Data** Make a circle graph to represent your classmates' hair colors. **See students' work.**

Chalkboard Examples

- *For Example 1*

Make a circle graph to display the following data.

Students in each class	
Seniors	185
Juniors	105
Sophomores	115
Freshmen	95

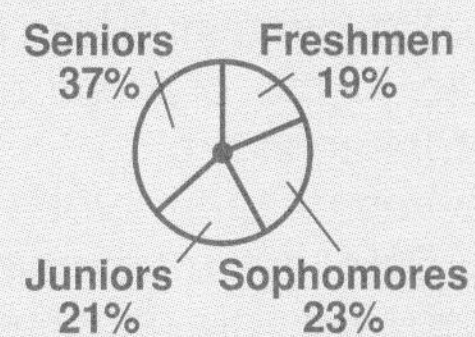

3 PRACTICE/APPLY

Checking the Concept

If additional practice is needed after completing the Exercise, repeat the exercise using eye color.

Error Analysis

Watch for students who use percents that do not total 100%.
Prevent by adding percents to check that they total 100%.

Practice Masters Booklet, **p. 111**

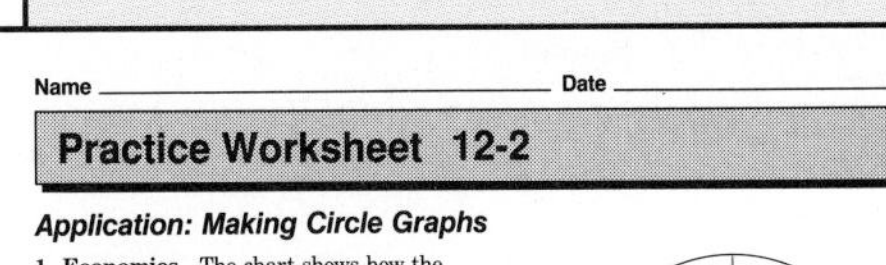

Name ____________ Date ____________

Practice Worksheet 12-2

Application: Making Circle Graphs

1. **Economics** The chart shows how the Lewis family spends their money. Make a circle graph to display the data.

How the Lewis Family Spends Their Money	
Housing	$10,500
Food	$7500
Clothing	$3000
Investments	$3000
Miscellaneous	$6000

Housing 35%, Food 25%, Miscellaneous 20%, 10% Clothing, 10% Investments

2. **Statistics** The chart shows how many hours are spent in daily activities. Make a circle graph to display the data.

Daily Activities	
Sleeping	8 hours
Eating	3 hours
School	6 hours
Homework	3 hours
Miscellaneous	4 hours

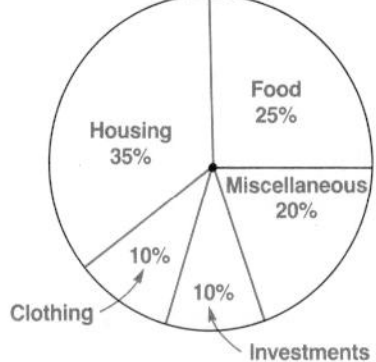

3. **Business** The chart shows four types of computers sold by a company in one year. Make a circle graph to display the data.

Computer Sales	
Educational	$2,000,000
Personal	$5,200,000
Business	$10,400,000
Scientific	$2,400,000

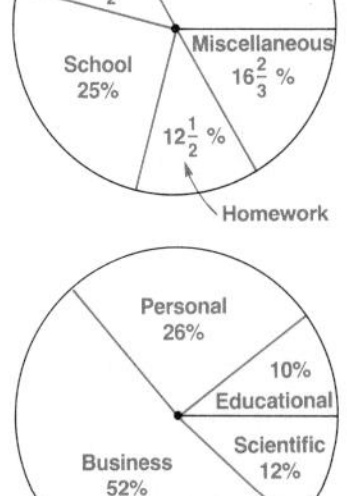

Alternate Strategies: Reteaching the Lesson

Reteaching Activity

Ecology Connection Have students make a circle graph showing the following information. The garbage in the United States consists of 42% paper products, 23% yard and food waste, 10% glass, 9% metal, 7% plastic, 9% other. Ask students which of these items could be recycled.

Reteaching Masters Booklet, **p. 100**

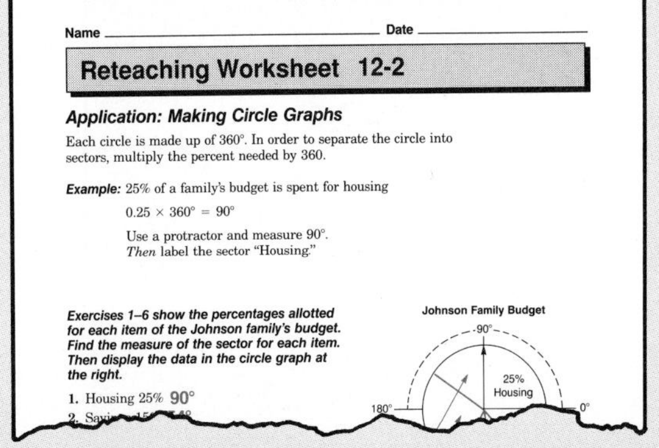

Name ____________ Date ____________

Reteaching Worksheet 12-2

Application: Making Circle Graphs

Each circle is made up of 360°. In order to separate the circle into sectors, multiply the percent needed by 360.

Example: 25% of a family's budget is spent for housing

0.25 × 360° = 90°

Use a protractor and measure 90°. *Then* label the sector "Housing."

Exercises 1–6 show the percentages allotted for each item of the Johnson family's budget. Find the measure of the sector for each item. Then display the data in the circle graph at the right.

1. Housing 25% 90°

Independent Practice

Homework Assignment	
Basic	4-10
Average	4-10
Honors	4-10

4 CLOSE

Assessment Option

Speaking Draw a circle graph with your students to display the following data. Have the students tell you each step in the process and the answer for each step.

A zoo has different types of animals. 50% are mammals, 25% are fish, 6% are insects, 10% are reptiles, and 9% are amphibians.

Additional Answers

1. Sample answer: When you want to compare parts of a whole.
2. Sample answer: There is nothing to compare.

4. 6.

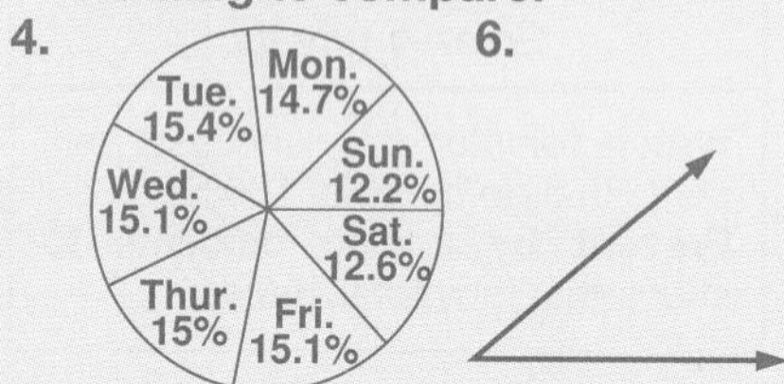

Enrichment Masters Booklet, **p. 100**

Name ______ Date ______

Enrichment Worksheet 12-2

Secants

A **secant** is a line that intersects a circle at exactly two points. $\overline{AB}$ and $\overline{BC}$ are secant segments.

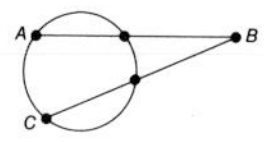

If two secant segments are drawn from a point outside a circle, then the product of the measures of one secant segment and its external part is equal to the product of the measure of the other secant segment and its external part.

Example:

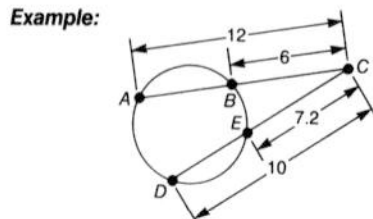

$AC \cdot BC = DC \cdot EC$
$(12)(6) = (10)(7.2)$
$72 = 72$

Substitute the measures from the diagram into the equation. Then multiply.

Find the length of the secant segment or its external part in each of the following.

1. $AC = 15, BC = 5, EC = 20$; Find DC. 3.75
2. $AC = 25, BC = 15, DC = 10$; Find EC. 37.5
3. $AC = 75, BC = 30, EC = 60$; Find DC. 37.5

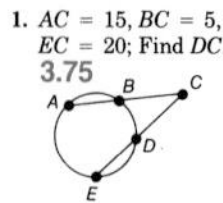

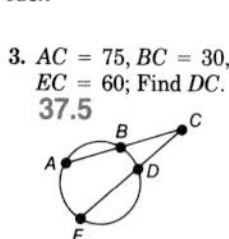

4. $AB = 7, AC = 15, AE = 8$; Find AD. 13.125
5. $AC = 20, AD = 9, AE = 25$; Find AB. 11.25
6. $BC = 20, AC = 30, EC = 8$; Find DC. 75

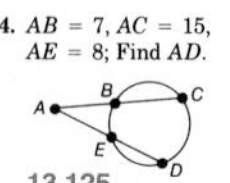

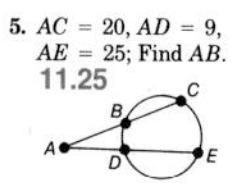

Exercises

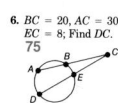

Independent Practice

4. **Statistics** The chart shows the average number of births per day in the United States. Make a circle graph to display the data. See margin.

Average U.S. Births Per Day	
Sunday	8,532
Monday	10,243
Tuesday	10,730
Wednesday	10,515
Thursday	10,476
Friday	10,514
Saturday	8,799

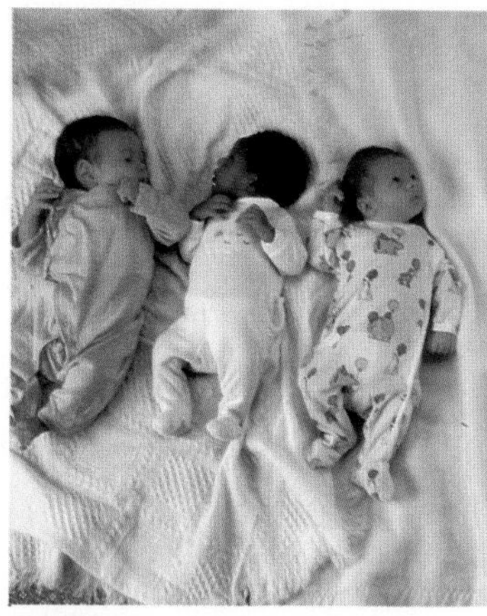

Mixed Review

5. **Statistics** What percent of the sample practice the piano more than 4 hours a week? (Lesson 10-1) $33\frac{1}{3}\%$

Piano Practice (hours)	Tally	Frequency
0-2	卌 卌	10
2-4	卌 卌 卌 卌 II	22
4-6	卌 卌 卌 I	16

6. Use a protractor to draw a 40° angle. Classify this angle as *acute, right,* or *obtuse.* (Lesson 12-1) See margin for drawing.; acute

Applications

Make a circle graph to display each set of data. For Exercises 7–8, see margin.

7. **Geography**

Areas (in square miles) of the Continents of the World	
Asia	17,012,000
Africa	11,785,000
North America	9,400,000
South America	6,883,000
Antarctica	5,100,000
Europe	4,071,000
Australia	2,966,000

8. **Biology**

Chemical Composition of the Human Body	
Oxygen	65%
Carbon	18%
Hydrogen	10%
Nitrogen	3%
Other	4%

Critical Thinking

9. Marcus had a pizza party. He had a large round pizza delivered for the occasion. He made four straight cuts from edge-to-edge to form 7 pieces. Make a drawing to show how he cut the pizza. See margin.

Wrap-Up

10. **Collect Data** Make a circle graph to represent how you spend an average 24-hour day. Include the following categories: school, sleep, eating, leisure, and miscellaneous. See students' work.

Additional Answers

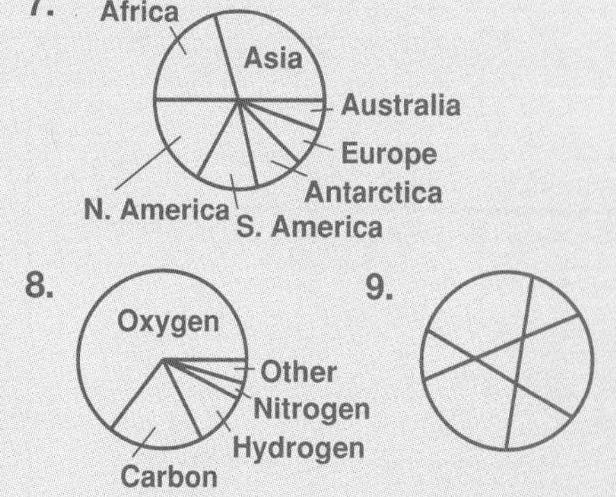

Cooperative Learning

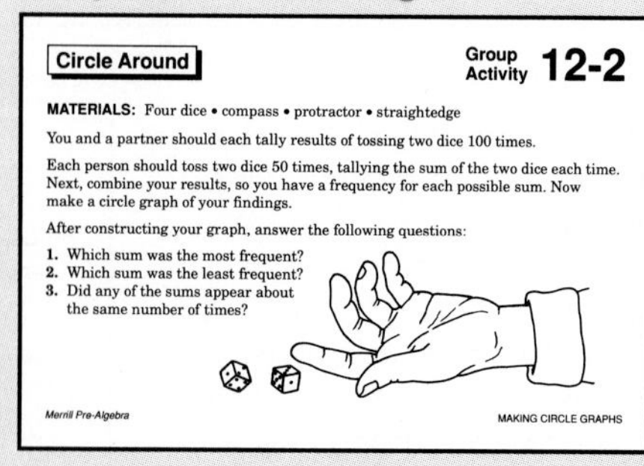
Circle Around Group Activity **12-2**

MATERIALS: Four dice • compass • protractor • straightedge

You and a partner should each tally results of tossing two dice 100 times.

Each person should toss two dice 50 times, tallying the sum of the two dice each time. Next, combine your results, so you have a frequency for each possible sum. Now make a circle graph of your findings.

After constructing your graph, answer the following questions:

1. Which sum was the most frequent?
2. Which sum was the least frequent?
3. Did any of the sums appear about the same number of times?

Merrill Pre-Algebra MAKING CIRCLE GRAPHS

Algebra in Action-Physics

Ray Optics

Light travels from the sun to Earth through a series of light waves. These light waves travel together in a straight line which, on a foggy day, can be seen in the form of a beam.

Light waves can be represented by rays. The rays show the direction the light is traveling. The study of light using ray diagrams is called **ray optics**.

When a ray of light strikes a flat reflecting object, such as a mirror, it bounces off the mirror in the same way a tennis ball bounces off the floor.

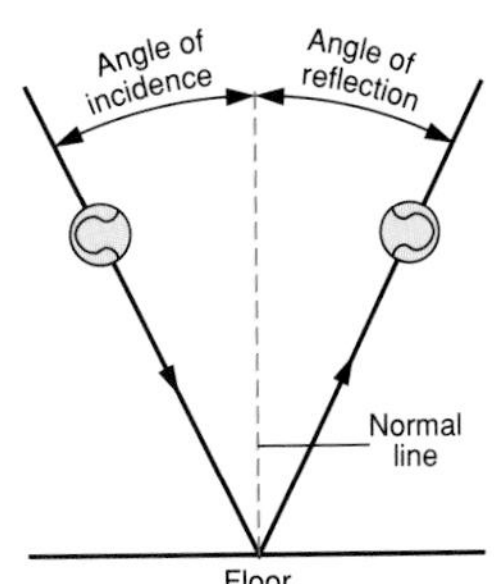

The angle a descending tennis ball makes with a line perpendicular to the floor (the *normal line*) is called the *angle of incidence.* The angle between the rebounding ball and the normal line is the *angle of reflection.*

When a ray of light is reflected off a mirror, it also forms an angle of incidence and an angle of reflection. These two angles have the same measure.

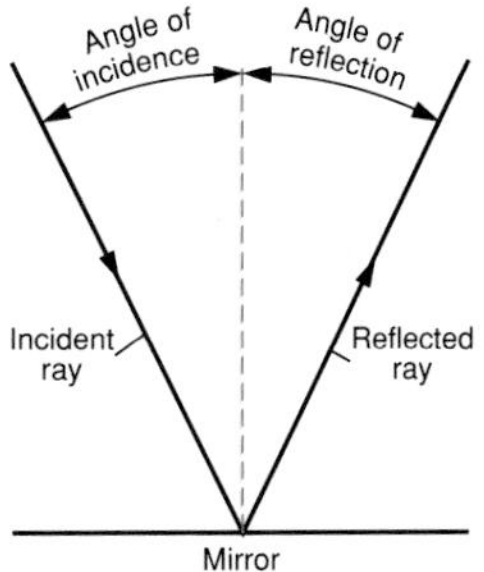

A ray of light strikes a mirror at a 53° angle to the normal line.

1. What is the measure of the angle of reflection? 53°
2. What is the measure of the angle between the incident ray and the reflected ray? 106°

Applying Algebra to the Real World

Objective This optional page shows how algebra is used in the real world and also provides a change of pace.

Science Connection

Radar is based on the fact that sound waves can be reflected, also. If the angle of incidence is 0° the angle of reflection will be 0°. The distance of the target can be determined by the length of time it takes the wave to return. Have students tell how bats and submarines use types of radar. Submarines use sonar to detect the presence and location of underwater objects. Bats are nocturnal and use a form of radar to locate food and obstacles.

Activity

Make a 5-mm slit in the center of the construction paper. Tape it over the flashlight lens. Place clay along one side of the unlined paper. Push the mirror into the clay so that the mirror is perpendicular to the paper. Draw a line perpendicular to the mirror on the paper. Draw 30° and 60° angles of incidence. Place the flashlight on one of these lines and mark the angle of reflection. Repeat for the other angle. Measure angles of reflection.

Physical Education Connection

Use the lesson to explain why, in general, right-handed batters tend to hit the ball to left field and left-handed batters tend to hit to right field. The angle at which a right-handed batter holds the bat gives an angle of incidence of the ball to the right and an angle of reflection to the left.

Lesson Notes 12-3

5-Minute Check
(over Lesson 12-2)

The city department of traffic control did a traffic survey of the intersection by Rose Hill School. Make a circle graph to display the data shown on the chart below.

Vehicles Passing by Intersection Each 15 Minutes	
car	65
bus	10
van	45
pickup	5
semi	15

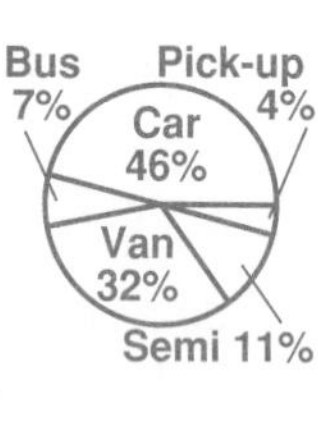

Transparency 12-3 contains the 5-Minute Check and a teaching aid for this lesson.

1 FOCUS

The purpose of this lesson is to develop angle relationships involving pairs of angles.

Motivating the Lesson

Show students road maps. Point out where roads intersect perpendicularly and where the intersections are not perpendicular. How are the angles formed related?

2 TEACH

Using Models

After discussing the new terms, have students match the terms to representative diagrams. Have students model and determine complementary and supplementary angles.

Chalkboard Examples

- *For Example 1*
  ∠*M* and ∠*N* are complementary. If ∠*M* = 63°, find ∠*N*. 27°

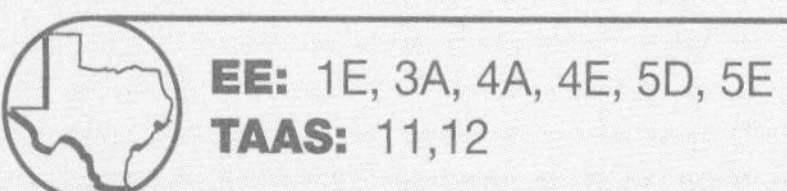

EE: 1E, 3A, 4A, 4E, 5D, 5E
TAAS: 11,12

12-3 Angle Relationships

Objective:
Identify angle relationships.

Key Terms:
vertical angles
congruent
perpendicular
adjacent angles
complementary
supplementary

Did you know that there is a place in the United States in which you can stand in four different states at once? The map shows that the boundaries of Arizona, New Mexico, Colorado, and Utah intersect in exactly one point.

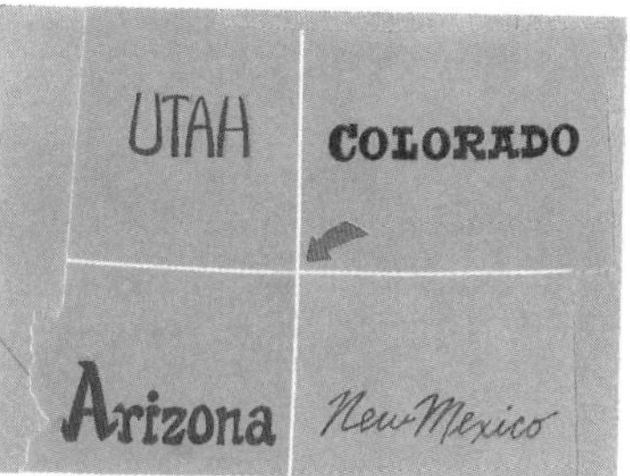

When two lines intersect, they form four angles with one point in common.

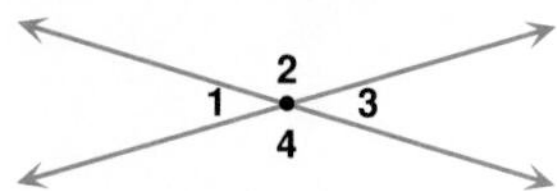

Name another pair of vertical angles shown in the figure. ∠**2 and** ∠**4**

Angles that are opposite to one another are called **vertical angles.** Angles 1 and 3, for example, are vertical angles. Vertical angles have the same measure. In other words, they are **congruent.**

If the vertical angles formed by two intersecting lines are right angles, the lines are said to be **perpendicular.**

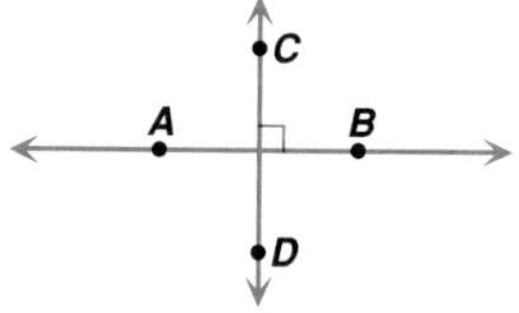

Line *AB* is perpendicular to line *CD*. This can be written $\overleftrightarrow{AB} \perp \overleftrightarrow{CD}$. The symbol ⊥ means *is perpendicular to.*

FYI

Cliff dwellers were native Americans who lived in the southwestern United States between 1000 and 1300. The most famous were the Anasazi, who built their homes in canyon walls, using sandstone blocks and mud mortar. As many as 1500 people could live in some of these dwellings.

Two angles are called **adjacent angles** if they have a common side, the same vertex, and do not overlap. In the diagram at the right, ∠1 and ∠2 are adjacent angles.

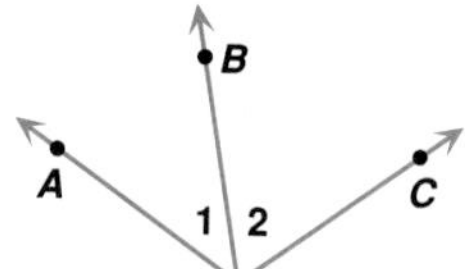

Two angles are **complementary** if the sum of their measures is 90°.

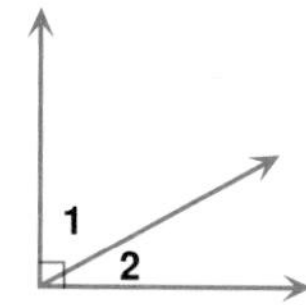

Two angles are **supplementary** if the sum of their measures is 180°.

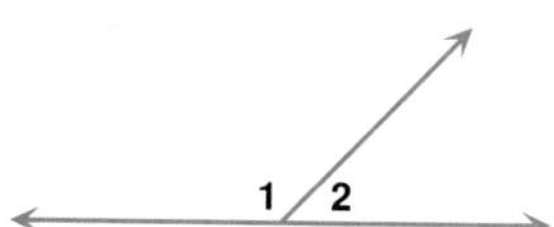

Bell Ringer

How many sections can a circle graph be divided into? **An infinite number. It would get too difficult to graph, however, if the graph would need to be divided many times.**

In geometry, we use the symbol $m\angle A$ to mean *the degree measure of angle A*. If $\angle A$ measures 50°, we write $m\angle A = 50°$.

Examples

1 Angles A and B are complementary. If $m\angle A = 35°$, find $m\angle B$.

Since $\angle A$ and $\angle B$ are complementary, $m\angle A + m\angle B = 90°$.

$$m\angle A + m\angle B = 90$$
$$35 + m\angle B = 90 \quad \text{Replace } m\angle A \text{ with 35.}$$
$$m\angle B = 55$$

The measure of $\angle B$ is 55°.

2 The angles shown below are supplementary. Find the measure of each angle.

$$m\angle PQR + m\angle RQT = 180°.$$
$$(x + 5) + (2x - 11) = 180$$
$$(x + 2x) + (5 - 11) = 180$$
$$3x - 6 = 180$$
$$3x = 186$$
$$x = 62$$

Why is 62° not the measure of one angle? **62 is the value of *x*.**

$\angle PQR$	$\angle RQT$
$x + 5 = 62 + 5$	$2x - 11 = 2(62) - 11$
$= 67$	$= 124 - 11$
	$= 113$
$m\angle PQR = 67°$	$m\angle RQT = 113°$.

Check: $67° + 113° = 180°$ The angles are supplementary.

Checking for Understanding

Communicating Algebra

Draw and label a diagram to show each of the following. For Exercises 1-4, see margin.

1. Angles ABC and CBD are adjacent angles.
2. Angles XYZ and AYC are vertical angles.
3. Angles XYZ and ZYW are adjacent, complementary angles.
4. Angles RST and TSW are adjacent, supplementary angles.

Guided Practice

Angles *M* and *P* are supplementary. Find $m\angle M$ when $\angle P$ has each measure.

5. 30° 150°
6. 120° 60°
7. 80° 100°
8. 175° 5°

Angles *A* and *B* are complementary. Find $m\angle A$ when $\angle B$ has each measure.

9. 30° 60°
10. 45° 45°
11. 50° 40°
12. 15° 75°

Chalkboard Examples

- *For Example 2*
The angles shown below are supplementary. Find the degree measure of each angle.

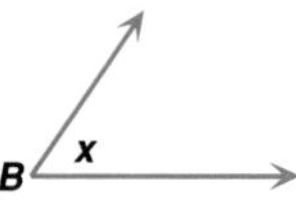

46°, 134°

3 PRACTICE/APPLY

Checking the Concept

After completing Exercises 4-12, check each by addition.

Error Analysis

Watch for students who have difficulty distinguishing between complementary and supplementary angles.
Prevent by writing the definition for each, using as reference until terms are mastered.

Practice Masters Booklet, **p. 112**

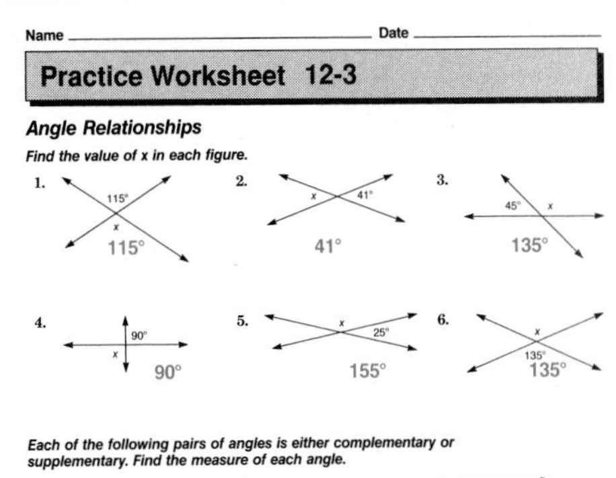

Name Date

Practice Worksheet 12-3

Angle Relationships

Find the value of x in each figure.

1. 115°
2. 41°
3. 135°
4. 90°
5. 155°
6. 135°

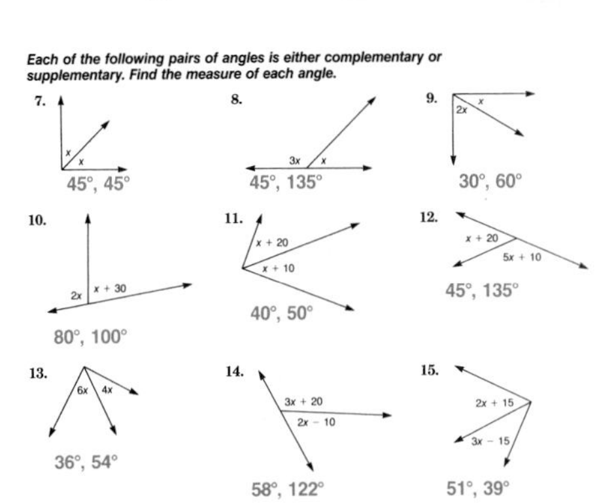

Each of the following pairs of angles is either complementary or supplementary. Find the measure of each angle.

7. 45°, 45°
8. 45°, 135°
9. 30°, 60°
10. 80°, 100°
11. 40°, 50°
12. 45°, 135°
13. 36°, 54°
14. 58°, 122°
15. 51°, 39°

Additional Answers

1.
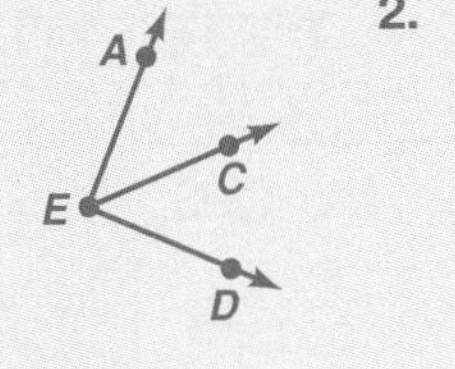

2. X Y A Z C

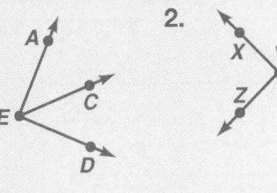

3.
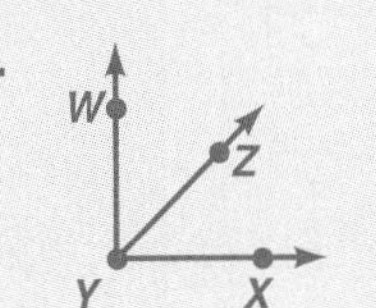

4.
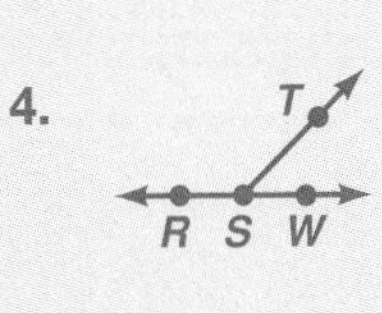

Reteaching Masters Booklet, **p. 101**

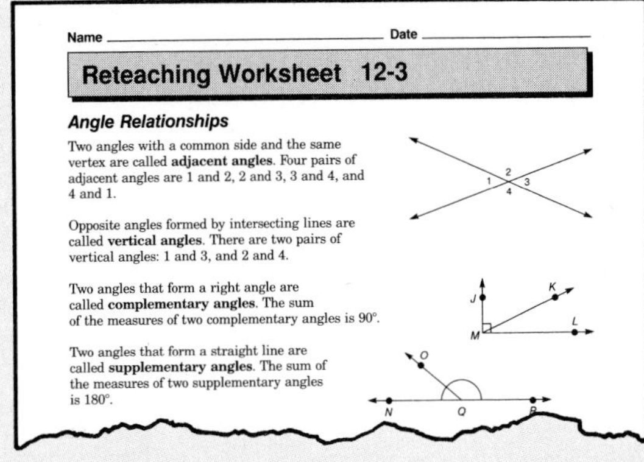

Name Date

Reteaching Worksheet 12-3

Angle Relationships

Two angles with a common side and the same vertex are called **adjacent angles**. Four pairs of adjacent angles are 1 and 2, 2 and 3, 3 and 4, and 4 and 1.

Opposite angles formed by intersecting lines are called **vertical angles**. There are two pairs of vertical angles: 1 and 3, and 2 and 4.

Two angles that form a right angle are called **complementary angles**. The sum of the measures of two complementary angles is 90°.

Two angles that form a straight line are called **supplementary angles**. The sum of the measures of two supplementary angles is 180°.

Independent Practice

Homework Assignment	
Basic	13-21 odd, 22-26, 28-30
Average	14-20 even, 22-30
Honors	18-30

4 CLOSE

Assessment Option

Speaking Have students work in pairs. Give each pair a magazine and have them find angle relationships in the pictures. Have each pair then tell the class all the relationships they found.

Additional Answers

26.

fruits and vegetables
breads and cereals
dairy
meat

28.

138°
42°
42°
138°

30.

55°

Enrichment Masters Booklet, **p. 101**

Name ______ Date ______

Enrichment Worksheet 12-3

Angle Relationships

Angles are measured in degrees (°). Each degree of an angle is divided into 60 minutes (′), and each minute of an angle is divided into 60 seconds (″).

$60' = 1°$

$60'' = 1'$

$67\frac{1}{2}° = 67°30'$

$70.4° = 70°24'$

$90° = 89°60'$

Two angles are complementary if the sum of their measures is 90°. Find the complement of each of the following angles.

1. 35°15′ 54°45′
2. 27°16′ 62°44′
3. 15°54′ 74°06′
4. 29°18′22″ 60°41′38″
5. 34°29′45″ 55°30′15″
6. 87°2′3″ 2°57′57″

Two angles are supplementary if the sum of their measures is 180°. Find the supplement of each of the following angles.

7. 120°18′ 59°42′
8. 84°12′ 95°48′
9. 110°2′ 69°58′
10. 45°16′24″ 134°43′36″
11. 39°21′54″ 140°38′6″
12. 129°18′36″ 50°41′24″
13. 98°52′59″ 81°7′1″
14. 9°2′32″ 170°57′28″
15. 1°2′3″ 178°57′57″

Exercises

Independent Practice

Find the value of x in each figure.

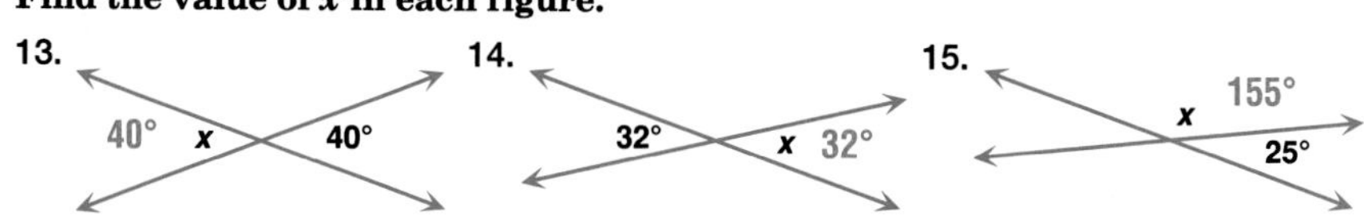

Each pair of angles is either complementary or supplementary. Find the degree measure of each angle.

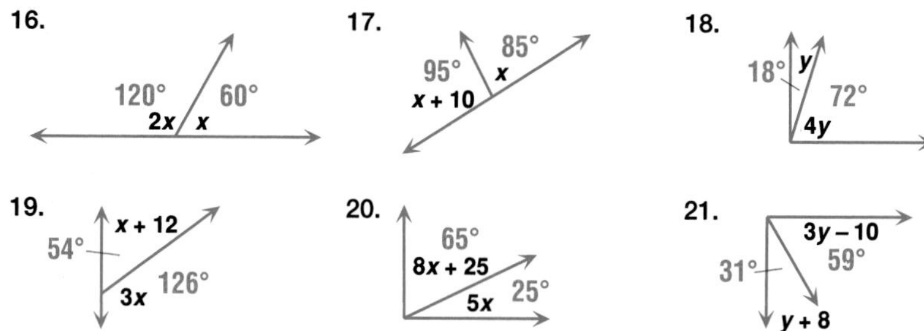

Mixed Review

22. Translate into an equation: *Seven times some number equals -28.* (Lesson 3-10) $7x = -28$

23. Jennifer scored 5 points less than twice the number of points she scored in the last basketball game. If she scored 12 points in the last game, how many points did she score in this game? (Lesson 7-3) 19 points

Find each value. (Lesson 11-3)

24. 6! 720

25. C(8, 3) 56

26. Suppose your daily food intake includes 25% fruits and vegetables, 40% breads and cereals, 20% meat, and 15% dairy products. Make a circle graph of this data. (Lesson 12-2) See margin.

Challenge

27. The measure of an angle is 26° more than three times the measure of the complement. Find the measure of the angle and the measure of the complement. 74°; 16°

Application

28. **City Planning** The Traverse City Street Commission is planning to have the curbs in the business district replaced. The construction company needs to know the angles of the street intersections ahead of time so they can build the forms that hold the cement. Two of the streets intersect at 42°. Draw a diagram of this intersection and label the angle measure of all four corners. See margin.

Critical Thinking

29. Find the measures of $\angle PQR$, $\angle RQS$, $\angle TQS$, and $\angle PQT$. 110°; 70°; 110°; 70°

P
R
2x + 10
Q
3x – 40
T
S

Wrap-Up

30. Use a protractor to draw adjacent, supplementary angles. One angle should measure 55°. See margin.

Alternate Strategies: Extending the Lesson

Enrichment

Using Models A rotating bracket for a hanging planter can get as close as 40° to the wall on either side. Over what angle can the planter be hung? 100°

Cooperative Learning

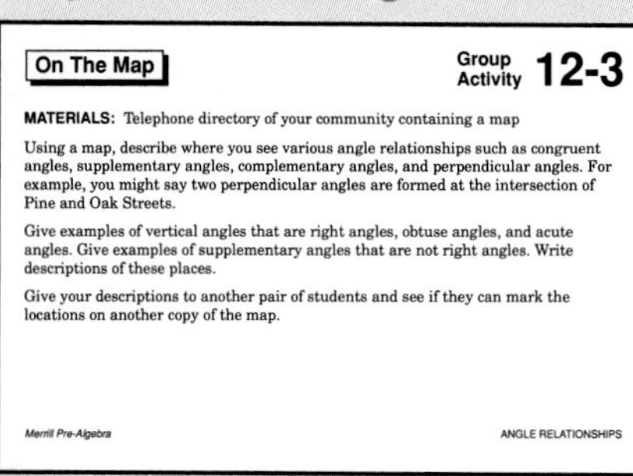
On The Map Group Activity **12-3**

MATERIALS: Telephone directory of your community containing a map

Using a map, describe where you see various angle relationships such as congruent angles, supplementary angles, complementary angles, and perpendicular angles. For example, you might say two perpendicular angles are formed at the intersection of Pine and Oak Streets.

Give examples of vertical angles that are right angles, obtuse angles, and acute angles. Give examples of supplementary angles that are not right angles. Write descriptions of these places.

Give your descriptions to another pair of students and see if they can mark the locations on another copy of the map.

Merrill Pre-Algebra ANGLE RELATIONSHIPS

12-4 Parallel Lines

Objective:
Identify the relationships of angles formed by two parallel lines and a transversal.

Key Terms:
parallel
transversal
interior angles
exterior angles
corresponding angles

The Bigtown Transit Authority is expanding its bus service. They need to check the angles of the corners at various intersections to make sure the turns will not be too sharp for the buses to make. The map at the right shows two parallel streets intersected by another street, forming eight angles. One angle measure is already known. How can the transit authority find the measure of the remaining seven angles without having to measure each one?

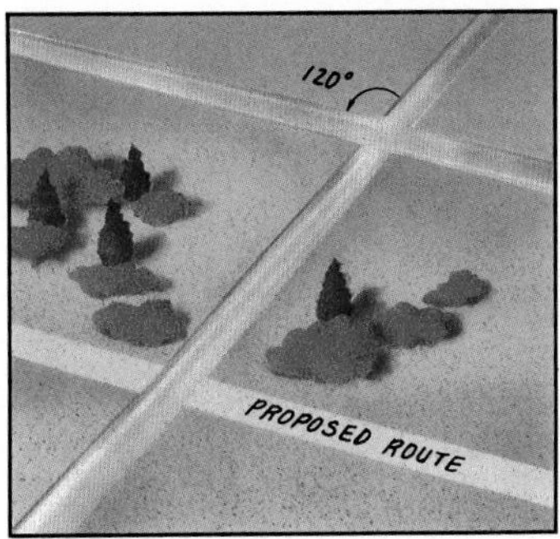

In geometry, we think of **parallel** lines as two or more lines in a plane that do not intersect. Parallel lines are *always* the same distance apart. In the figure below, line ℓ is parallel to line m, or $\ell \parallel m$. The symbol $\parallel$ means *is parallel to*.

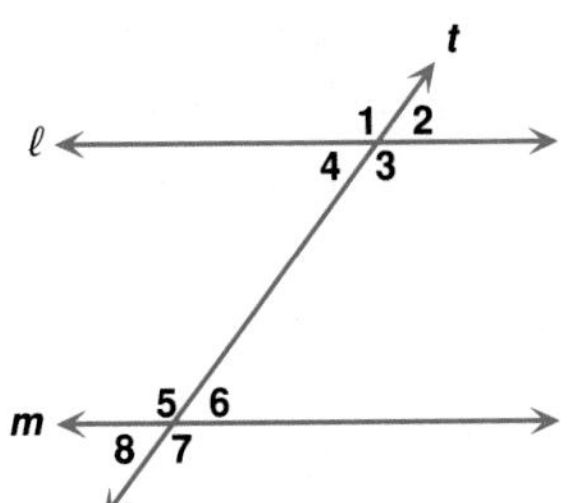

When a line, called a **transversal,** intersects two parallel lines, eight angles are formed. One way to classify these angles is as **interior angles** or **exterior angles.**

Interior angles: $\angle 3$, $\angle 4$, $\angle 5$, $\angle 6$
Exterior angles: $\angle 1$, $\angle 2$, $\angle 7$, $\angle 8$

When we study the relationship between the different angles, we can come up with further classifications.

- **alternate interior angles:** $\angle 4$ and $\angle 6$, $\angle 3$ and $\angle 5$
  Alternate interior angles are interior angles found on opposite sides of the transversal.
- **alternate exterior angles:** $\angle 1$ and $\angle 7$, $\angle 2$ and $\angle 8$
  Alternate exterior angles are exterior angles found on opposite sides of the transversal.
- **corresponding angles:** $\angle 1$ and $\angle 5$, $\angle 2$ and $\angle 6$, $\angle 3$ and $\angle 7$, and $\angle 4$ and $\angle 8$
  Corresponding angles are angles that hold the same position on two different parallel lines cut by a transversal.

Bell Ringer

Name five relationships between angles and draw a picture to represent each relationship. Sample answers: Angles can be supplementary, complementary, adjacent, vertical, or perpendicular. See students' drawings.

Lesson Notes 12-4

5-Minute Check
(over Lesson 12-3)

Each of the following pairs of angles is either complementary or supplementary. Find the degree measure of each angle.

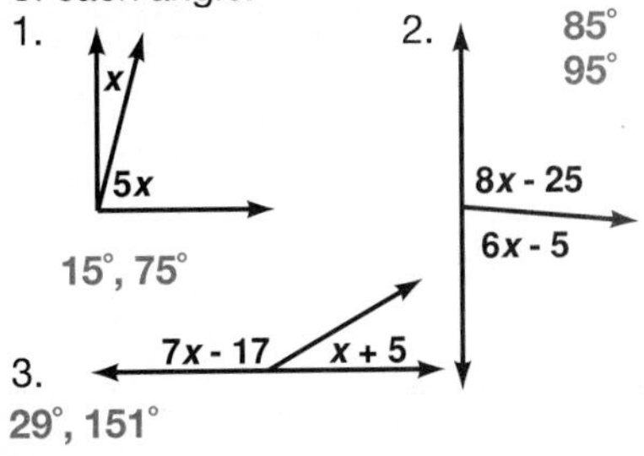

Transparency 12-4 contains the 5-Minute Check and a teaching aid for this lesson.

1 FOCUS

The purpose of this lesson is to introduce terms and use concepts regarding two parallel lines intersected by a transversal.

Motivating the Lesson

Show a picture of a football field. If a ball carrier crosses a yard line at a certain angle and does not turn, ask students where the defense needs to be when he is 10 yards downfield.

2 TEACH

Using Diagrams

Have students draw a diagram of two parallel lines intersected by a transversal. Using a protractor and working in cooperative groups, have them develop relationships between the angles formed.

EE: 1E, 3A, 4A, 4E
TAAS: 2, 3, 11

Chalkboard Examples

Refer to the diagram below. Classify each pair of angles.

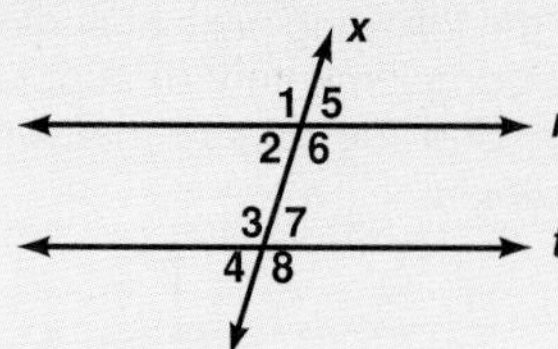

- *For Example 1*
  ∠1 and ∠8
  alternate exterior angles
- *For Example 2*
  ∠5 and ∠7
  corresponding angles

In the diagram above *r* is parallel to *t*. The measure of ∠3 is 108°.

- *For Example 3*
  Find *m*∠1. **108°**
- *For Example 4*
  Find *m*∠2. **72°**

3 PRACTICE/APPLY

Checking the Concept

After completing Exercises 4-9, have students work in cooperative groups to discuss any differences in naming lines or angles.

Practice Masters Booklet, **p. 113**

Name ______________________ Date ______________

Practice Worksheet 12-4

Parallel Lines

In the figure at the right, m is parallel to n. If the measure of ∠3 is 95°, find the measure of each angle below.

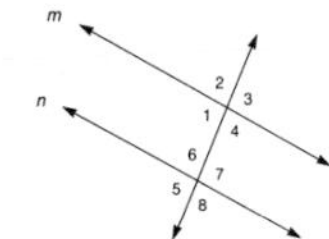

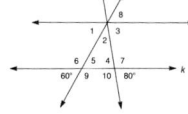

1. ∠1 95°	2. ∠4 85°
3. ∠5 95°	4. ∠6 85°
5. ∠7 95°	6. ∠8 85°
7. ∠2 85°	

In the figure at the right, l is parallel to k. Find the measure of each angle below.

8. ∠5 60°	9. ∠4 80°
10. ∠9 120°	11. ∠8 60°
12. ∠6 120°	13. ∠1 60°
14. ∠7 100°	15. ∠3 80°
16. ∠2 40°	17. ∠10 100°

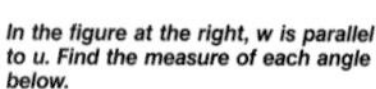

In the figure at the right, w is parallel to u. Find the measure of each angle below.

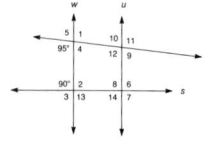

18. ∠1 95°	19. ∠2 90°
20. ∠3 90°	21. ∠12 95°
22. ∠10 85°	23. ∠11 95°
24. ∠13 90°	25. ∠7 90°
26. ∠6 90°	27. ∠8 90°
28. ∠9 85°	29. ∠14 90°
30. ∠5 85°	31. ∠4 85°

Examples

Refer to the diagram at the right. Classify each pair of angles.

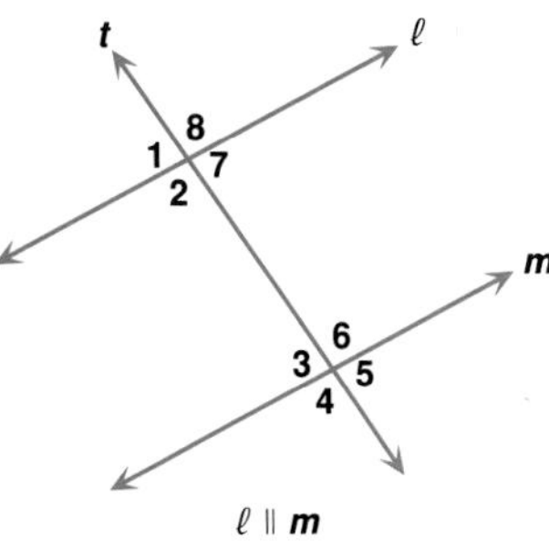

1 **∠1 and ∠5**

Since ∠1 and ∠5 are exterior angles on opposite sides of the transversal, they are alternate exterior angles.

2 **∠6 and ∠8**

∠6 and ∠8 are corresponding angles.

Use a protractor to measure the angles formed by the parallel lines shown above. You will find that certain angles have the same measure. These angle relationships are summarized below.

Parallel Lines Cut by Transversal

- Corresponding angles are congruent.
- Alternate interior angles are congruent.
- Alternate exterior angles are congruent.

Examples

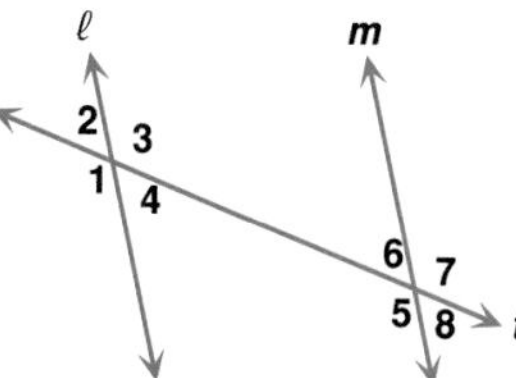

In the diagram at the right, ℓ is parallel to *m*. The measure of ∠5 is 120°.

3 **Find *m*∠1.**

∠1 and ∠5 are corresponding angles.

$m\angle 1 = m\angle 5$ Corresponding angles are congruent.

$m\angle 1 = 120$ Replace $m\angle 5$ with 120.

The measure of ∠1 is 120°.

4 **Find *m*∠4.**

∠1 and ∠4 are supplementary.

$m\angle 1 + m\angle 4 = 180$ The sum of the measures of two supplementary angles is 180°.

$120 + m\angle 4 = 180$ Replace $m\angle 1$ with 120.

$m\angle 4 = 60$

The measure of ∠4 is 60°.

Alternate Strategies: Reteaching the Lesson

Reteaching Activity

Music Connection In a marching band, a certain routine has a drummer crossing two yard lines at an angle of 75° to the line on her left. Have students draw a diagram and give the measure of all 8 angles formed.

Reteaching Masters Booklet, **p. 102**

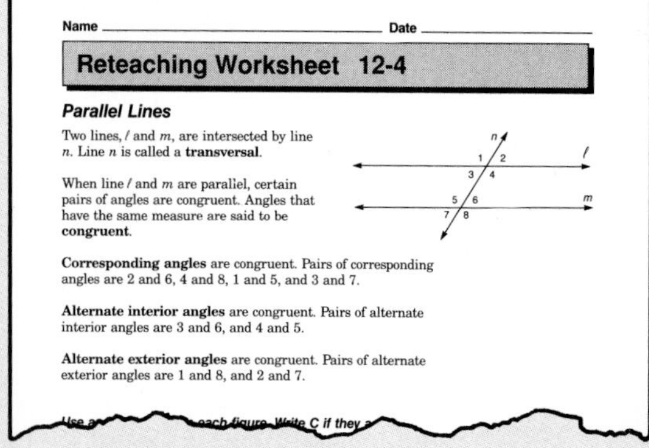
Name ______________________ Date ______________

Reteaching Worksheet 12-4

Parallel Lines

Two lines, *l* and *m*, are intersected by line *n*. Line *n* is called a **transversal**.

When line *l* and *m* are parallel, certain pairs of angles are congruent. Angles that have the same measure are said to be **congruent**.

Corresponding angles are congruent. Pairs of corresponding angles are 2 and 6, 4 and 8, 1 and 5, and 3 and 7.

Alternate interior angles are congruent. Pairs of alternate interior angles are 3 and 6, and 4 and 5.

Alternate exterior angles are congruent. Pairs of alternate exterior angles are 1 and 8, and 2 and 7.

Checking for Understanding

Communicating Algebra

1. In your own words, define parallel lines. See margin.
2. What is the relationship between any two corresponding angles? congruent
3. Draw parallel lines a and b intersected by transversal c. Label the interior angles formed 9, 10, 11, and 12. See margin.

Guided Practice

Refer to the diagram at the right to complete Exercises 4-9.

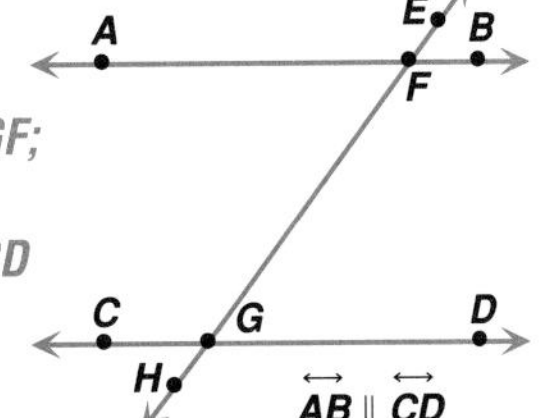

4. Name the transversal. $\overleftrightarrow{EH}$
5. Name the interior angles.
6. Name the exterior angles.
7. Name the pairs of alternate interior angles. $\angle BFG$ and $\angle CGF$; $\angle AFG$ and $\angle DGF$
8. Name the pairs of alternate exterior angles. $\angle EFA$ and $\angle HGD$; $\angle EFB$ and $\angle HGC$
9. Name the pairs of corresponding angles.

5. $\angle AFG$; $\angle BFG$; $\angle CGF$; $\angle DGF$
6. $\angle AFE$; $\angle BFE$, $\angle CGH$; $\angle DGH$
9. $\angle EFA$ and $\angle FGC$; $\angle BFE$ and $\angle DGF$; $\angle AFG$ and $\angle CGH$; $\angle BFG$ and $\angle DGH$

Exercises

Independent Practice

In the figure at the right, ℓ is parallel to m. If the measure of $\angle 1$ is 58°, find the measure of each angle.

10. $\angle 2$ 122°
11. $\angle 3$ 58°
12. $\angle 5$ 58°
13. $\angle 4$ 122°
14. $\angle 7$ 58°
15. $\angle 8$ 122°

Mixed Review

16. **Probability** If two dice are rolled, what is the probability that the sum is 7? (Lesson 11-5) $\frac{1}{6}$
17. Find the measure of the complement and supplement of a 16° angle. (Lesson 12-3) 74°; 164°

Application

18. **Public Service** The Bigtown Transit Authority is studying the street intersection on page 449. If a bus cannot make a turn at an angle that is less than 70°, can the Transit Authority provide service on the proposed route? Why or why not? no; Two of the angles on the route have a measure of only 60°.

Critical Thinking

19. In the figure at the right, $\ell \parallel m$. Find the measures of each of the eight angles formed when ℓ and m are cut by t. Four angle measures are 105°. The other four are 75°.

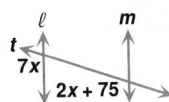

Wrap-Up

20. Explain the meaning of the statement "when parallel lines are cut by a transversal, angles that look equal are equal." When two parallel lines are cut by a transversal, there are two sets of four congruent angles. You can often tell by looking at the diagram, which angles are congruent.

Error Analysis

Watch for students who have difficulty finding pairs of alternate interior and exterior angles.
Prevent by reminding students that alternate means opposite, interior means inside, and exterior means outside.

Independent Practice

Homework Assignment	
Basic	10-20
Average	10-20
Honors	10-20

 CLOSE

Assessment Option

Writing Have students each draw and label two parallel lines and a transversal. Then have them write ten pairs of angles that are congruent and give the reason why they are congruent. Answers will vary.

Enrichment Masters Booklet, **p. 102**

Name ______ Date ______

Enrichment Worksheet 12-4

Parallel Lines

Given: line l parallel to line m;
line l perpendicular to line k;
$m\angle 1 = 40°$;
$m\angle 9 = 30°$

Find the measure of each angle.

1. $m\angle 1$ 40°
2. $m\angle 2$ 50°
3. $m\angle 3$ 30°
4. $m\angle 4$ 60°
5. $m\angle 5$ 40°
6. $m\angle 6$ 50°
7. $m\angle 7$ 30°
8. $m\angle 8$ 60°
9. $m\angle 9$ 30°
10. $m\angle 10$ 150°
11. $m\angle 11$ 30°
12. $m\angle 12$ 150°
13. $m\angle 13$ 90°
14. $m\angle 14$ 90°
15. $m\angle 15$ 90°
16. $m\angle 16$ 90°
17. $m\angle 17$ 50°
18. $m\angle 18$ 130°
19. $m\angle 19$ 50°
20. $m\angle 20$ 130°

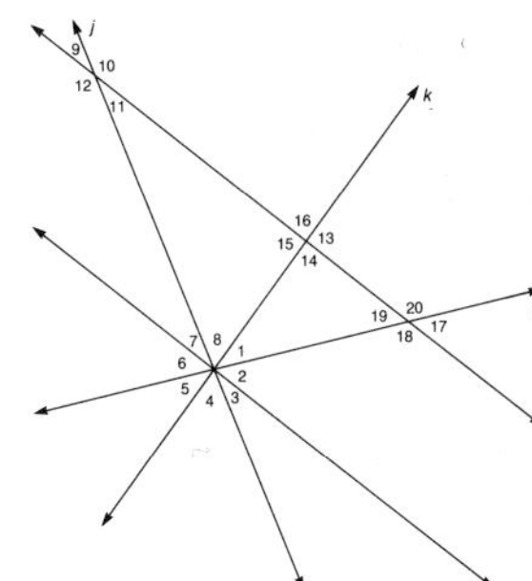

Additional Answers

1. Parallel lines are two or more lines in a plane that do not intersect.
3.

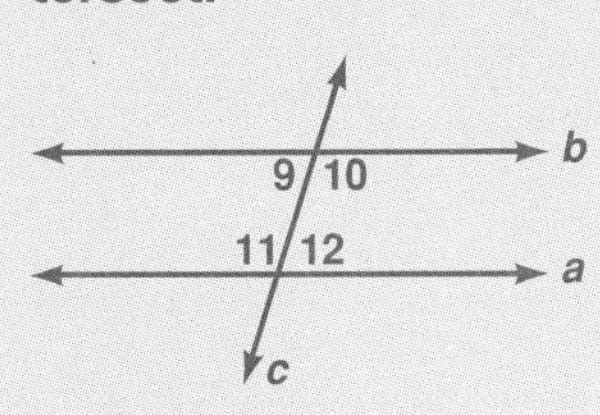

Cooperative Learning

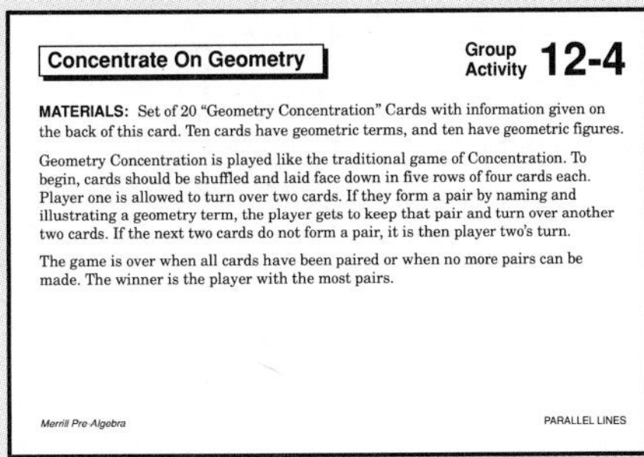

Concentrate On Geometry Group Activity **12-4**

MATERIALS: Set of 20 "Geometry Concentration" Cards with information given on the back of this card. Ten cards have geometric terms, and ten have geometric figures.

Geometry Concentration is played like the traditional game of Concentration. To begin, cards should be shuffled and laid face down in five rows of four cards each. Player one is allowed to turn over two cards. If they form a pair by naming and illustrating a geometry term, the player gets to keep that pair and turn over another two cards. If the next two cards do not form a pair, it is then player two's turn.

The game is over when all cards have been paired or when no more pairs can be made. The winner is the player with the most pairs.

Merrill Pre-Algebra PARALLEL LINES

5-Minute Check
(over Lesson 12-4)

In the figure below, c is parallel to d. If the measure of $\angle 1$ is 67°, find the measure of each angle.

1. $\angle 2$ 113°
2. $\angle 3$ 113°
3. $\angle 8$ 67°
4. $\angle 4$ 67°
5. $\angle 6$ 113°

Transparency 12-5 contains the 5-Minute Check and a teaching aid for this lesson.

1 FOCUS

The purpose of this lesson is to bisect and construct congruent line segments and angles using a compass and a straightedge.

Motivating the Lesson

Show a diagram of line segment AB. Have students solve the following. A is where (name) lives, and B is where (name) lives. Can we show exactly where they would meet if they start at the same time and walk along this segment at the same rate?

2 TEACH

Using Models

Using the overhead projector or chalkboard, model problems of each type, having students complete the constructions at the same time.

EE: 1E, 3A, 4A
TAAS: 3, 11

12-5 Constructing Segments and Angles

Objectives:
Construct congruent segments and angles using a compass and a straightedge.
Bisect segments and angles.

Key Terms:
straightedge
compass
bisect
midpoint
angle bisector

Segments and angles can be constructed using a straightedge and compass. A **straightedge** is any object that can be used to draw a straight line, such as an ID card, a piece of cardboard, or a ruler. A **compass** is used to draw a circle or part of a circle.

You can construct a line segment that has the same exact length as a given line segment by using a straightedge and a compass. Two line segments that have the same measure are said to be *congruent*.

Given $\overline{AB}$: A —— B

Step 1: Use a straightedge to draw $\overrightarrow{PS}$.

Step 2: Place the steel tip of the compass at A and the writing tip at B.

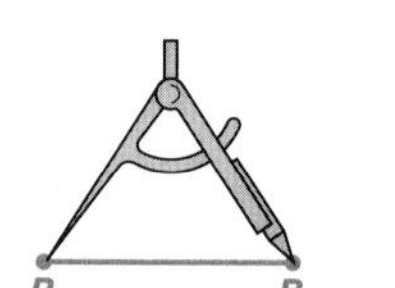

Step 3: Keep the same setting on the compass and place the steel tip at P. Draw an arc that intersects $\overline{PS}$ at Q.
$\overline{PQ}$ is congruent to $\overline{AB}$.

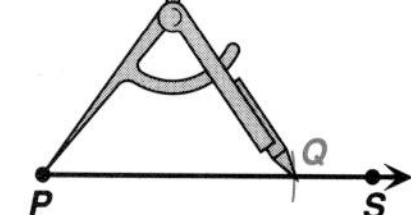

We can also use a compass and straightedge to **bisect** a line segment. Bisecting a segment means we draw a line segment through the **midpoint** of the given segment, forming two congruent segments.

Given $\overline{PQ}$: P —— Q

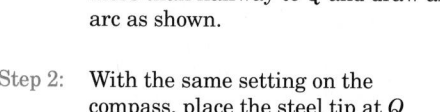

Step 1: Place the steel tip of the compass at P. Set the compass so the writing tip is more than halfway to Q and draw an arc as shown.

Step 2: With the same setting on the compass, place the steel tip at Q and draw an arc as shown. There must be two intersection points.

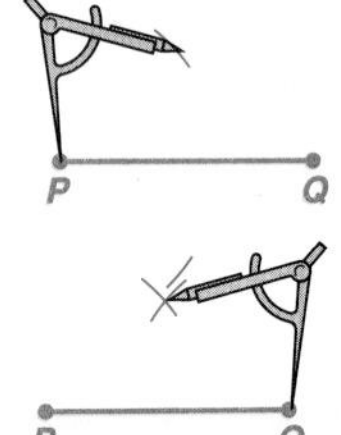

Step 3: With a straightedge, draw the line determined by the intersection points. This line bisects $\overline{PQ}$ at M, the midpoint of $\overline{PQ}$.
$\overline{PM}$ is congruent to $\overline{MQ}$.

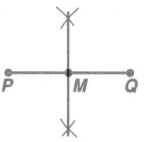

FYI

For over 200 years mathematicians tried to trisect an angle (divide an angle into three equal parts), using only a straightedge and a compass. In 1837 it was finally proved to be an impossible construction.

Bell Ringer

Name three properties of parallel lines. They are always the same distance apart, they have no points in common, they are in the same plane.

We can also construct congruent angles by using a compass and straightedge. Congruent angles have the same angle measure. Follow these steps for constructing $\angle TJK$ congruent to $\angle ABC$.

Given $\angle ABC$:

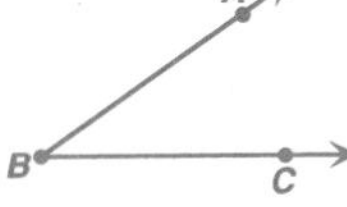

Step 1: Place the steel tip of the compass at B and draw an arc as shown. Label points R and S.

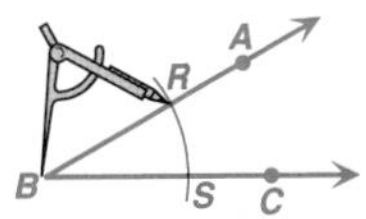

Step 2: Use a straightedge to draw $\overrightarrow{JK}$. Use the compass setting from Step 1 and construct an arc as shown. Label the intersection point M.

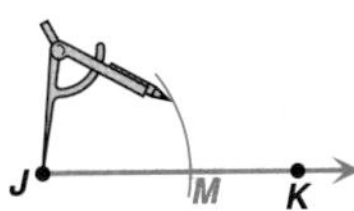

Step 3: Set the compass at points R and S as shown. Keep that setting and place the steel tip at M. Draw an arc as shown. Label the intersection point T.

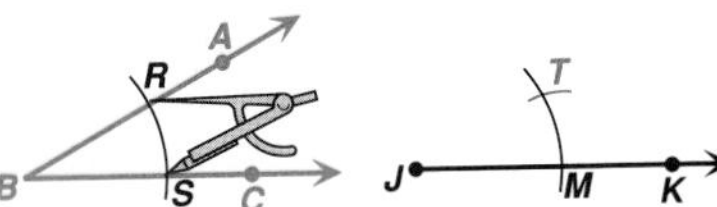

Step 4: With a straightedge, draw $\overrightarrow{JT}$. $\angle TJK$ is congruent to $\angle ABC$.

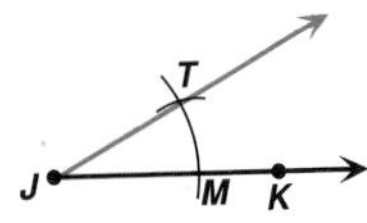

To bisect an angle, we construct a ray through the interior of the angle that forms two congruent angles. This ray is called the **angle bisector.**

Given $\angle RST$:

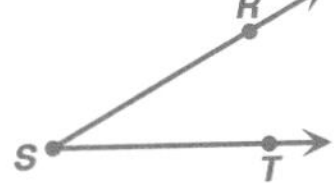

Step 1: Place the steel tip of the compass at S and draw an arc that intersects both sides of the angle. Use X and Y to name the points of intersection.

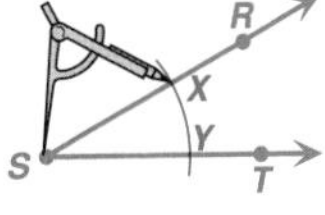

Step 2: Place the steel tip of the compass at X and draw an arc in the interior of $\angle RST$.

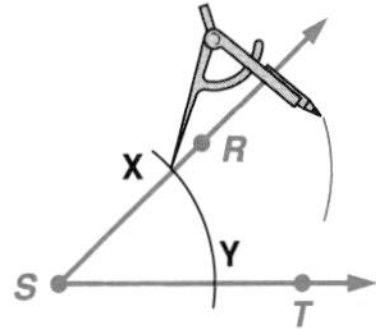

Chalkboard Examples

Draw a line segment. Using a straightedge and compass, draw another line segment that has the same measure.

Draw a line segment and label it $\overline{XZ}$. Bisect the line segment using a compass and straightedge.

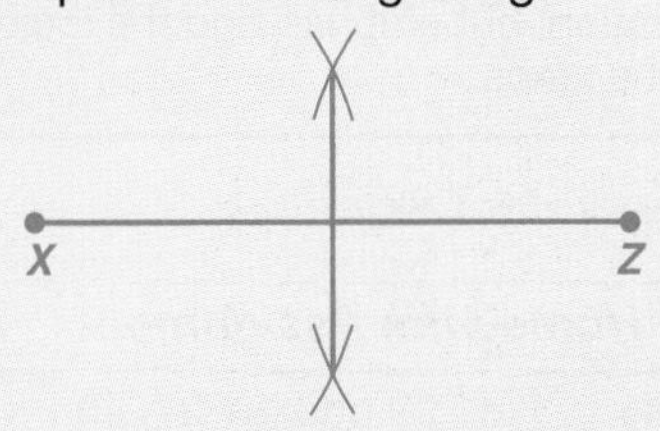

Use a protractor to draw $\angle A$ such that $m\angle A = 27°$. Then construct $\angle X$ such that $\angle X \cong \angle A$.

Use a protractor to draw $\angle QPR$ such that $m\angle QPR = 47°$. Use a compass and a straightedge to bisect QPR.

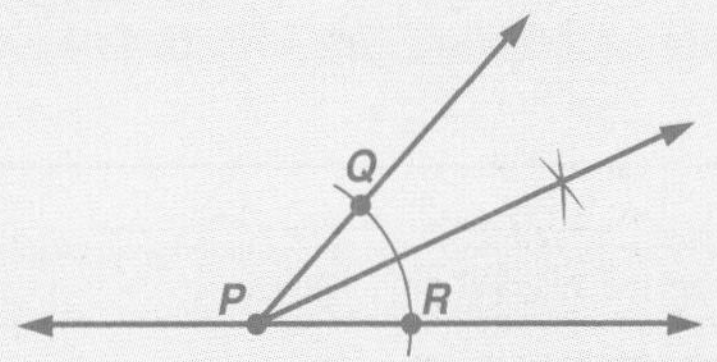

Alternate Strategies: Reteaching the Lesson

Reteaching Activity

Using Cooperative Groups Use a four-section spinner, each section labeled with a different construction. In turn, have each student spin. After each spin, have students complete the indicated construction. Have the first student to correctly complete the construction explain the steps to the other students.

Reteaching Masters Booklet, **p. 103**

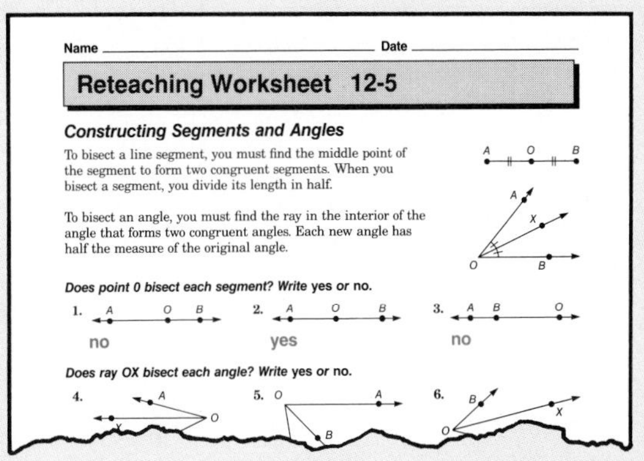

Name ______ Date ______

Reteaching Worksheet 12-5

Constructing Segments and Angles

To bisect a line segment, you must find the middle point of the segment to form two congruent segments. When you bisect a segment, you divide its length in half.

To bisect an angle, you must find the ray in the interior of the angle that forms two congruent angles. Each new angle has half the measure of the original angle.

Does point 0 bisect each segment? Write yes or no.

1. no
2. yes
3. no

Does ray OX bisect each angle? Write yes or no.

4.
5.
6.

3 PRACTICE/APPLY

Checking the Concept

After completing Exercises 4-9, have students bisect each segment and angle.

Error Analysis
Watch for students who have difficulty remembering the steps of a construction. **Prevent by** not emphasizing memorization, but emphasizing the logic of the steps.

Independent Practice

Homework Assignment	
Basic	11-29 odd, 31-37, 40
Average	10-26 even, 31-40
Honors	14-22 even, 27-40

Practice Masters Booklet, **p. 114**

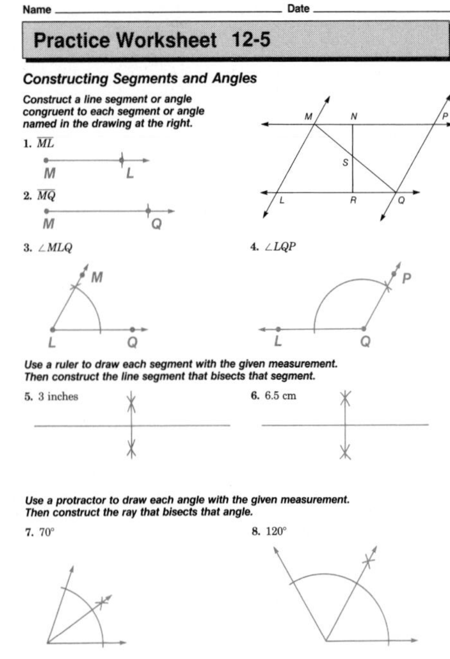

Name ______ Date ______

Practice Worksheet 12-5

Constructing Segments and Angles

Construct a line segment or angle congruent to each segment or angle named in the drawing at the right.

1. $\overline{ML}$
2. $\overline{MQ}$
3. $\angle MLQ$
4. $\angle LQP$

Use a ruler to draw each segment with the given measurement. Then construct the line segment that bisects that segment.

5. 3 inches
6. 6.5 cm

Use a protractor to draw each angle with the given measurement. Then construct the ray that bisects that angle.

7. 70°
8. 120°

Step 3: With the same setting on the compass, place the steel tip at Y and draw an arc that intersects the arc you drew in Step 2. Use W to name the point of intersection of the arcs.

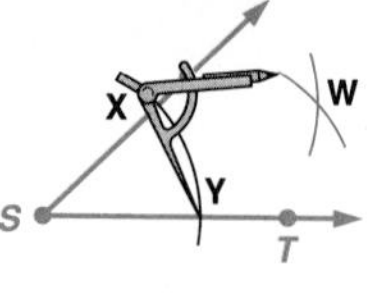

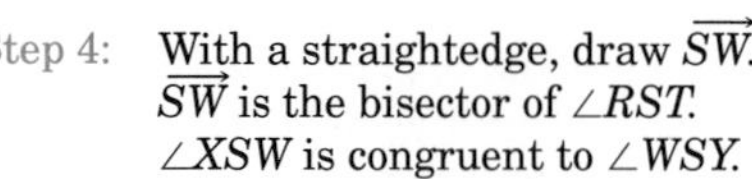

Step 4: With a straightedge, draw $\overrightarrow{SW}$. $\overrightarrow{SW}$ is the bisector of $\angle RST$. $\angle XSW$ is congruent to $\angle WSY$.

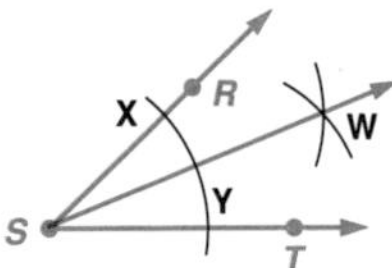

Checking for Understanding

Communicating Algebra

1. What tools, other than a sharp pencil and a piece of paper, are needed to do a geometric construction? straightedge; compass
2. In your own words, explain how you would construct a line segment congruent to a given line segment. See margin.
3. What point is always on the bisector of a line segment? midpoint

Guided Practice

Trace each segment. Then construct a segment congruent to it. For Exercises 4-6, see students' work.

4. ——— 5. ———— 6. ——————

Trace each angle. Then construct an angle congruent to it. For Exercises 7-9, see students' work.

7. 8. 9.

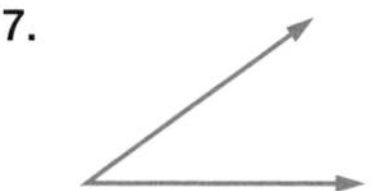

Exercises For Exercises 10-24, see students' work.

Independent Practice

Trace the drawing at the right. Then construct a line segment or angle congruent to each segment or angle named.

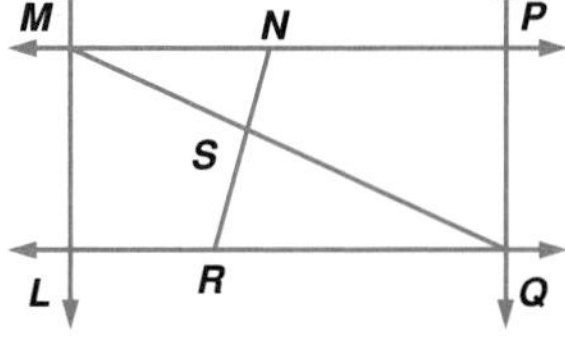

10. $\overline{LM}$ 11. $\overline{QR}$ 12. $\overline{SM}$
13. $\angle QML$ 14. $\angle NRQ$ 15. $\angle QSN$
16. $\overline{LR}$ 17. $\angle PMQ$ 18. $\overline{QS}$

Use a ruler to draw a segment with the given measurement. Construct a segment congruent to it. Then construct the line segment that bisects that segment.

19. 2 inches 20. 7.5 cm 21. 43 mm
22. $1\frac{5}{8}$ inches 23. $2\frac{3}{4}$ inches 24. 67 mm

Additional Answer

2. Sample answer: Construct a ray longer than the line segment. Put the metal tip of the compass at one end of the segment and the writing end of the compass at the other end of the segment. Keep the setting and construct an arc on the ray.

Use a protractor to draw each angle with the given measurement. Construct an angle congruent to it. Then construct the ray that bisects that angle. For Exercises 25-30, see students' work.

25. 60° **26.** 140° **27.** 47°

28. 163° **29.** 25° **30.** 104°

Mixed Review

31. Convert 32 inches into feet. (Lesson 5-10) $2\frac{2}{3}$ feet

32. Graph $y \le -2x + 1$. (Lesson 8-11) See margin.

33. **Statistics** Construct a stem-and-leaf plot of the heights (in inches) of members of a basketball team: 72, 70, 74, 66, 67, 71, 72, 66, 70, 69, 71, 66. (Lesson 10-3) See margin.

34. Two parallel lines are cut by a transversal. If an interior angle measures 64°, what is the measure of the alternate interior angle? (Lesson 12-4) 64°

Application

35. **Physics** The *center of mass* of an object is the point where the mass of the object is concentrated. If you have a flat triangular object like the one shown to the right, the center of mass is the intersection of three rays, each drawn from the vertex of one angle through the midpoint of the opposite side. Trace each triangle below and find its center of mass. See students' work.

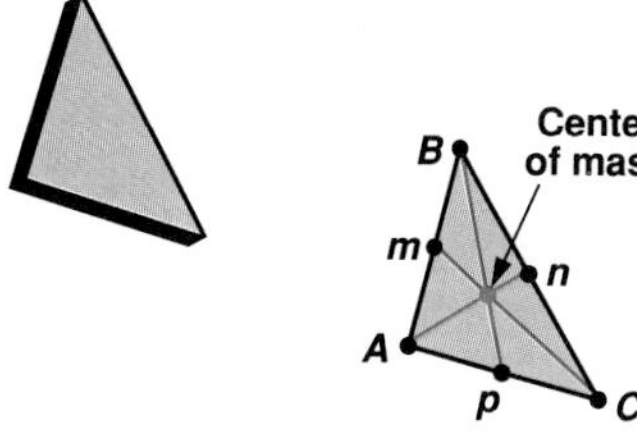

a.

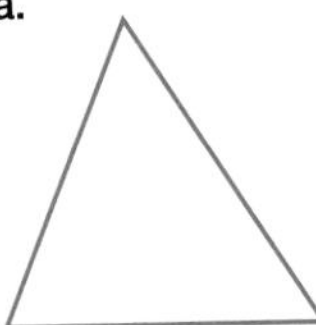

b.

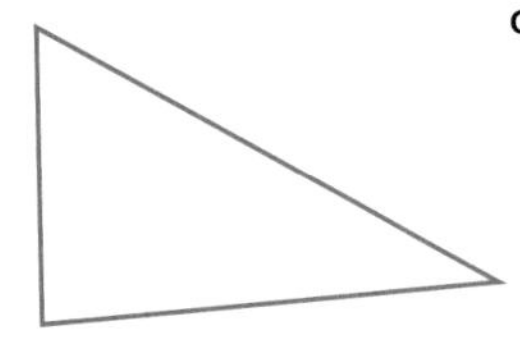

c.

Critical Thinking

Using the figure below, construct each of the following. For Exercises 36-40, see students' work.

36. a line segment that is twice as long as $\overline{MN}$

37. a line segment that is as long as the measure of $\overline{MN}$ plus the measure of $\overline{NQ}$

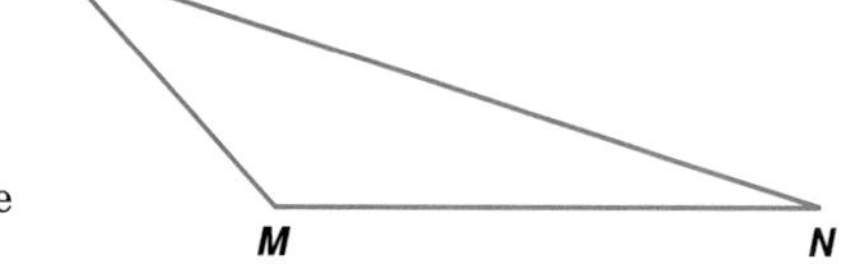

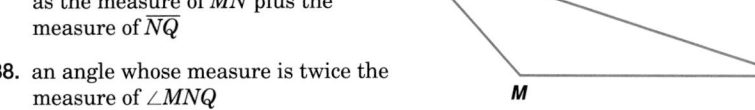

38. an angle whose measure is twice the measure of $\angle MNQ$

39. an angle whose measure is twice the measure of $\angle MNQ$ plus the measure of $\angle NQM$

Wrap-Up

40. Draw an obtuse angle. Construct an angle congruent to it. Then bisect the angle. What can you say about the two angles created? sample answers: congruent, acute, have same measure, adjacent, have the same vertex, share a side

4 CLOSE

Assessment Option

Modeling Have each student complete all four of the constructions described in the text by making their own segments and angles and copying them. Make sure they label each construction and write a mathematical statement to explain the construction (i.e. $\angle TJK \cong \angle ABC$).

Additional Answers

32.

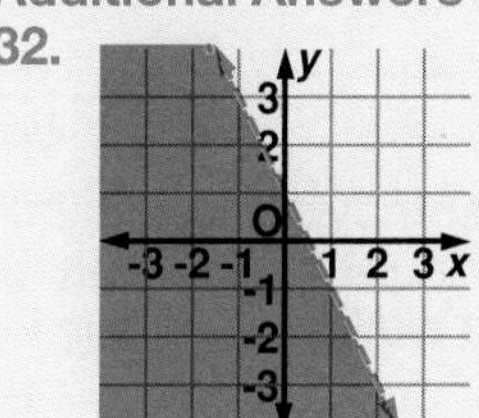

33.

6	6 6 6 7 9
7	0 0 1 1 2 2 4

Enrichment Masters Booklet, **p. 103**

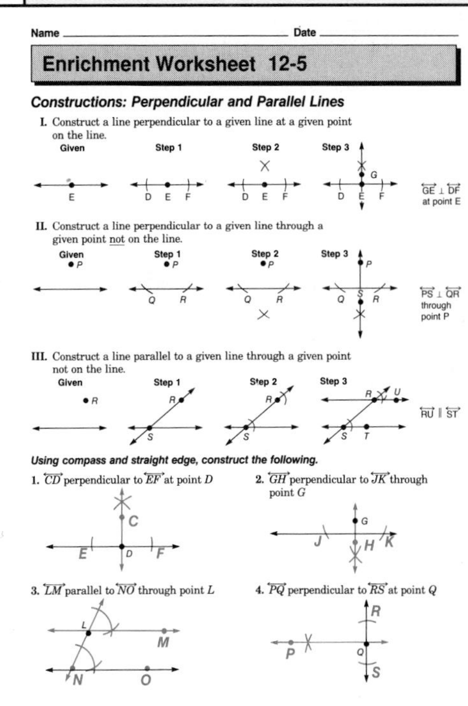

Name ______ Date ______

Enrichment Worksheet 12-5

Constructions: Perpendicular and Parallel Lines

I. Construct a line perpendicular to a given line at a given point on the line.

Given Step 1 Step 2 Step 3

$\overleftrightarrow{GE} \perp \overleftrightarrow{DF}$ at point E

II. Construct a line perpendicular to a given line through a given point not on the line.

Given Step 1 Step 2 Step 3

$\overleftrightarrow{PS} \perp \overleftrightarrow{QR}$ through point P

III. Construct a line parallel to a given line through a given point not on the line.

Given Step 1 Step 2 Step 3

$\overleftrightarrow{RU} \parallel \overleftrightarrow{ST}$

Using compass and straight edge, construct the following.

1. $\overleftrightarrow{CD}$ perpendicular to $\overleftrightarrow{EF}$ at point D

2. $\overleftrightarrow{GH}$ perpendicular to $\overleftrightarrow{JK}$ through point G

3. $\overleftrightarrow{LM}$ parallel to $\overleftrightarrow{NO}$ through point L

4. $\overleftrightarrow{PQ}$ perpendicular to $\overleftrightarrow{RS}$ at point Q

Alternate Strategies: Extending the Lesson

Enrichment

Writing Connection In his or her own words, have each student write the steps needed to construct a line segment. Trade steps with another student. Have that student follow the steps to see if he or she can construct a line segment from them. Discuss any problems. Repeat for the other three constructions.

Cooperative Learning

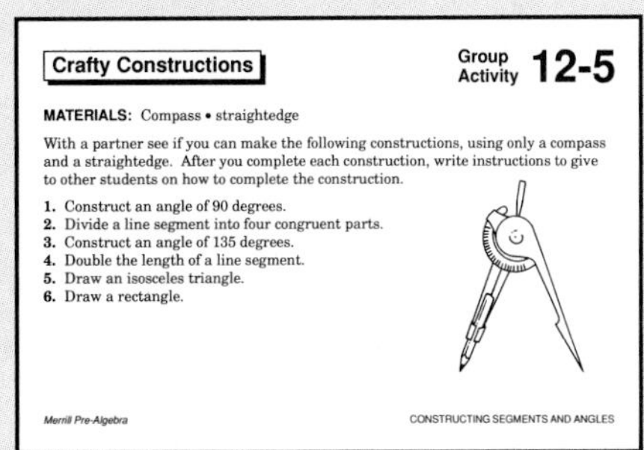

Crafty Constructions Group Activity **12-5**

MATERIALS: Compass • straightedge

With a partner see if you can make the following constructions, using only a compass and a straightedge. After you complete each construction, write instructions to give to other students on how to complete the construction.

1. Construct an angle of 90 degrees.
2. Divide a line segment into four congruent parts.
3. Construct an angle of 135 degrees.
4. Double the length of a line segment.
5. Draw an isosceles triangle.
6. Draw a rectangle.

Merrill Pre-Algebra CONSTRUCTING SEGMENTS AND ANGLES

5-Minute Check
(over Lesson 12-5)

Use a protractor to draw each angle with the given measurement. Construct an angle congruent to it. Then construct the ray that bisects that angle.

1. 50°
2. 135°

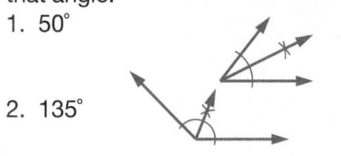

Transparency 12-6 contains the 5-Minute Check and a teaching aid for this lesson.

1 FOCUS

The purpose of this lesson is to classify triangles and to use the sum of the measures of the angles of a triangle to determine a missing angle.

Motivating the Lesson

Give each student a piece of paper cut into the shape of a triangle. Tell them to make a rectangle out of it by folding, only no folds can overlap. Then discuss the relationship between the angles of a triangle.

2 TEACH

Using Models Have students cut out a triangle and duplicate the lesson activity to determine the sum of the measures of angles of a triangle.

Chalkboard Examples

- *For Example 1*
  In $\triangle XYZ$, the measure of $\angle Y$ is 42° and the measure of $\angle Z$ is 53°. Find the measure of $\angle X$. **85°**

EE: 1E, 3A, 4A, 4E
TAAS: 2, 3, 11

12-6 Triangles

Objectives:
Find the missing angle measure of a triangle.
Classify triangles.

Key Terms:
triangle
vertices
acute
obtuse
right

In a plane, figures formed by three line segments, as shown, are called **triangles.** Triangles are named by their **vertices,** the endpoints of the line segments. The figure shown at the right is triangle *ABC*. Triangle *ABC* is written $\triangle ABC$.

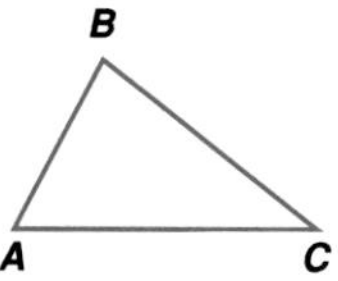

There are three angles in every triangle. There is also a unique relationship among the measures of these three angles. Try the following activity to try to discover the relationship.

1. Cut a large triangle out of a piece of paper. On one side label vertices *P*, *Q*, and *R*.
2. Fold the triangle so that point *P* lies on $\overline{QR}$ and the fold is parallel to the side. Label $\angle P$ as $\angle 2$.
3. Fold the triangle again so that points *Q* and *R* meet at the vertex of $\angle 2$. Label these angles $\angle 1$ and $\angle 3$.

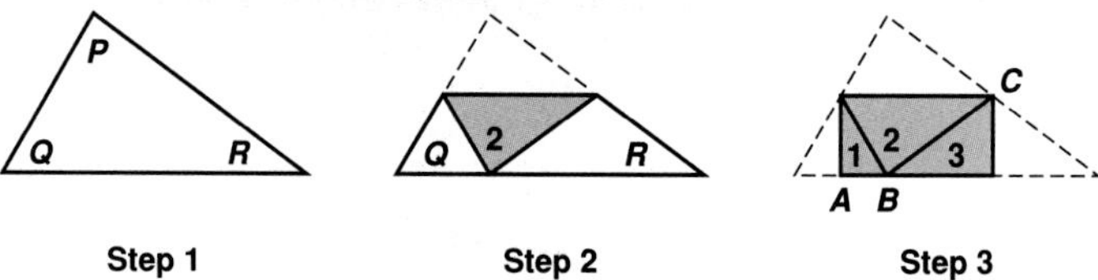

What do you notice about the relationship of $\angle 1$, $\angle 2$, and $\angle 3$?

The activity above will work with any triangle. You can also use a protractor to measure each angle. This activity suggests the following relationship.

Angles of a Triangle — The sum of the measures of the angles of a triangle is 180°.

Example

Estimation Hint

THINK:
$40 + 50 = 90$
$180 - 90 = 90$
$m\angle A$ is about 90°.

1 In $\triangle ABC$, the measure of $\angle B$ is 38° and the measure of $\angle C$ is 47°. Find the measure of $\angle A$.

$m\angle A + m\angle B + m\angle C = 180$ — The sum of the measures of the angles of a triangle is 180°.

$m\angle A + 38 + 47 = 180$ — Replace $m\angle B$ with 38 and $m\angle C$ with 47.

$m\angle A + 85 = 180$

$m\angle A = 95$ — The measure of $\angle A$ is 95°.

Bell Ringer

Construct an angle of 56° and bisect it.

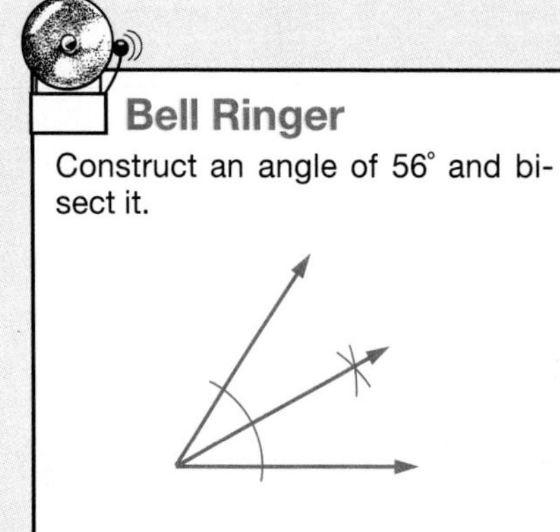

A triangle can be classified according to its angles.

What is the meaning of the red angle in the right triangle? The angle is a right angle.

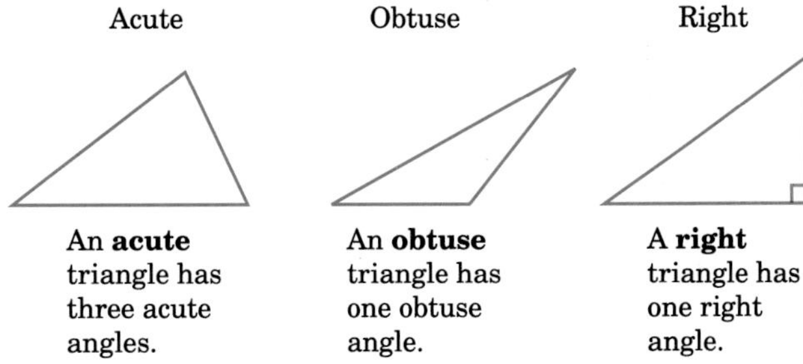

Checking for Understanding

1. Sample drawings in margin.

Communicating Algebra

1. Draw a sketch of an acute triangle, an obtuse triangle, and a right triangle.
2. Can a triangle have two right angles? Explain your answer. no, because the third angle would measure 0°

Guided Practice

Find the value of x. Then classify each triangle as *acute*, *right*, or *obtuse*.

3. 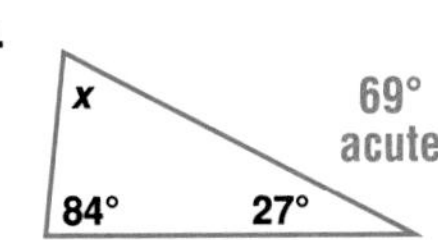

69° acute

4. 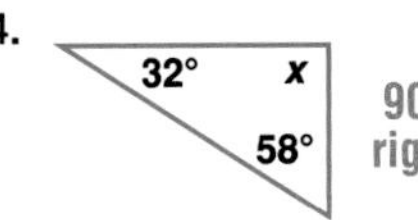

90° right

5. 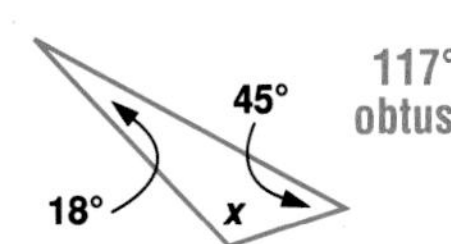

117° obtuse

Exercises

Independent Practice

Find the value of x. Then classify each triangle as *acute*, *obtuse*, or *right*.

6. 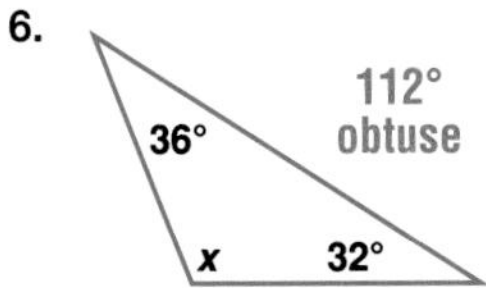

112° obtuse

7. 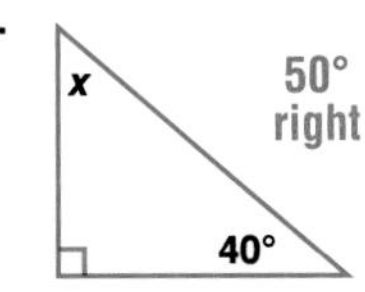

50° right

8. 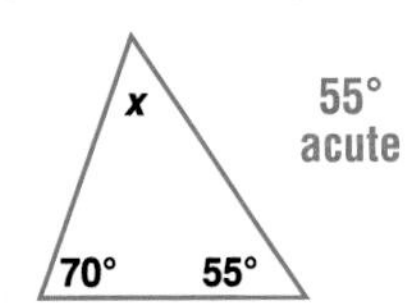

55° acute

Use the figure at the right to solve each of the following.

9. Find $m\angle 1$ if $m\angle 2 = 40$ and $m\angle 3 = 55$. 85
10. Find $m\angle 1$ if $m\angle 2 = 60$ and $m\angle 3 = 60$. 60
11. Find $m\angle 1$ if $m\angle 2 = 81$ and $m\angle 3 = 74$. 25
12. Find $m\angle 2$ if $m\angle 1 = 45$ and $m\angle 3 = 75$. 60
13. Find $m\angle 2$ if $m\angle 1 = 47$ and $m\angle 3 = 48$. 85

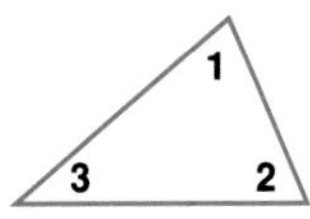

Mixed Review

14. **Probability** In a bag there are 4 red marbles and 8 white marbles. Once a marble is selected, it is not replaced. Find the probability of selecting two white marbles in a row. (Lesson 11-7) $\frac{14}{33}$
15. Use a ruler to draw a line segment 2.5 cm long. Construct a line segment that bisects that segment. (Lesson 12-5) See margin.

3 PRACTICE/APPLY

Checking the Concept

Before solving Exercises 3-5, have students use inspection to guess what type of triangle is used in each exercise. Ask students why this method may not be reliable. An angle with a measurement close to 90° may be assumed to be a right angle when it is not.

Independent Practice

Homework Assignment	
Basic	7-13 odd, 14-16, 19-22
Average	6-12 even, 14-16, 19-22
Honors	8-12 even, 14-22
All	Mid-Chapter Quiz 1-9

Chapter 12, Quiz A (Lesson 12-1 through 12-6) is available in the Evaluation Masters Booklet, p. 106.

Additional Answer

1.

15.

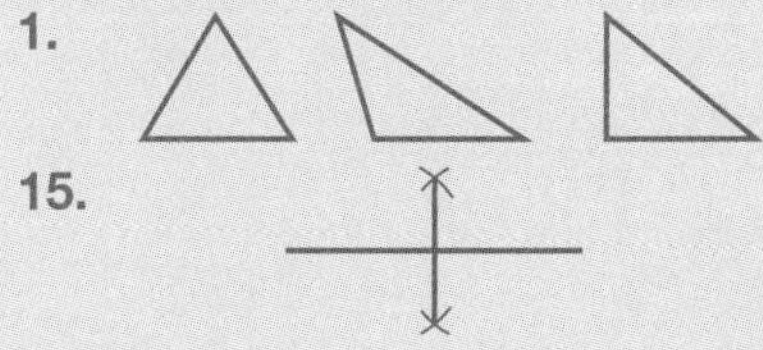

Reteaching Masters Booklet, **p. 104**

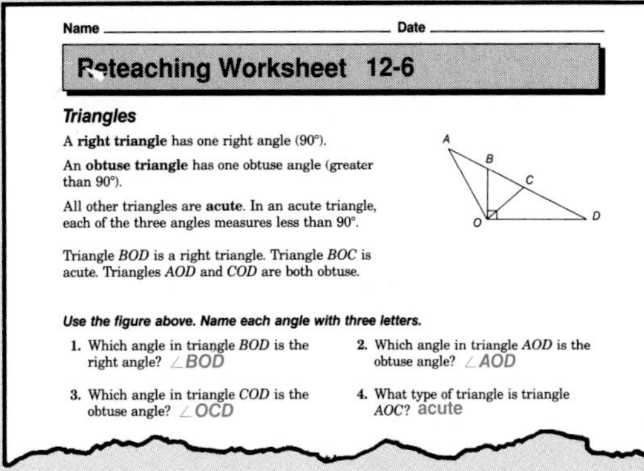

Name ______ Date ______

Reteaching Worksheet 12-6

Triangles

A **right triangle** has one right angle (90°).

An **obtuse triangle** has one obtuse angle (greater than 90°).

All other triangles are **acute**. In an acute triangle, each of the three angles measures less than 90°.

Triangle *BOD* is a right triangle. Triangle *BOC* is acute. Triangles *AOD* and *COD* are both obtuse.

Use the figure above. Name each angle with three letters.

1. Which angle in triangle *BOD* is the right angle? ∠BOD
2. Which angle in triangle *AOD* is the obtuse angle? ∠AOD
3. Which angle in triangle *COD* is the obtuse angle? ∠OCD
4. What type of triangle is triangle *AOC*? acute

Practice Masters Booklet, **p. 115**

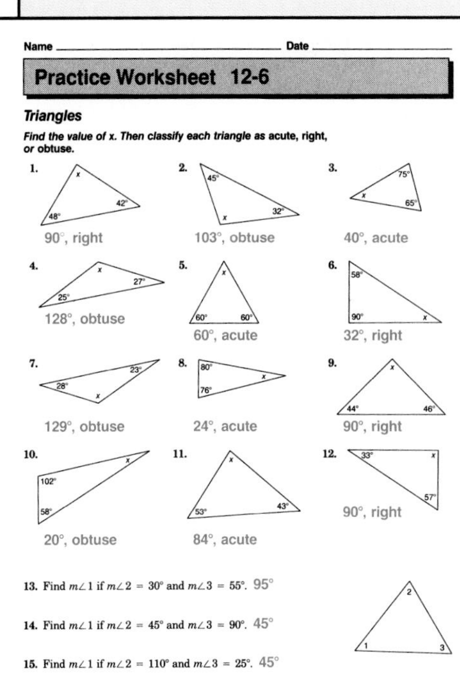

Name ______ Date ______

Practice Worksheet 12-6

Triangles

Find the value of x. Then classify each triangle as acute, right, or obtuse.

1. 90°, right
2. 103°, obtuse
3. 40°, acute
4. 128°, obtuse
5. 60°, acute
6. 32°, right
7. 129°, obtuse
8. 24°, acute
9. 90°, right
10. 20°, obtuse
11. 84°, acute
12. 90°, right
13. Find $m\angle 1$ if $m\angle 2 = 30°$ and $m\angle 3 = 55°$. 95°
14. Find $m\angle 1$ if $m\angle 2 = 45°$ and $m\angle 3 = 90°$. 45°
15. Find $m\angle 1$ if $m\angle 2 = 110°$ and $m\angle 3 = 25°$. 45°

4 CLOSE

Assessment Option

Modeling Have each student draw a triangle on a piece of paper and measure two of the angles. Write the measurements in the angle, then exchange papers among the students. Have each student find the measure of the missing angle without measuring, then have them use a protractor to check their answer.

Additional Answers

21. Yes, because their sum is 90°.

22. 
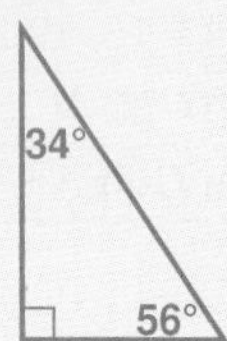

Enrichment Masters Booklet, p. 104

Name ______ Date ______

Enrichment Worksheet 12-6

Constructing Designs

Many designs can be made using geometric constructions. Two examples are stained glass rose windows found in churches and Pennsylvania Dutch hex designs found on barns.

Use your compass to draw a circle.

Then, without changing the compass setting, move the point to the circle. Draw a second circle.

Place the point on one of the points where the two circles intersect. Draw a circle. Repeat five more times.

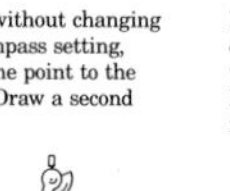

Use your compass and a straightedge to make a design like the one below. (HINT: See the design above.) Check students' drawings.

Challenge **Find the measures of the angles in each triangle.**

16. 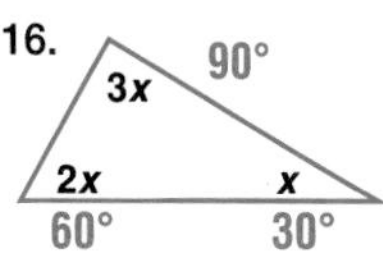

17. 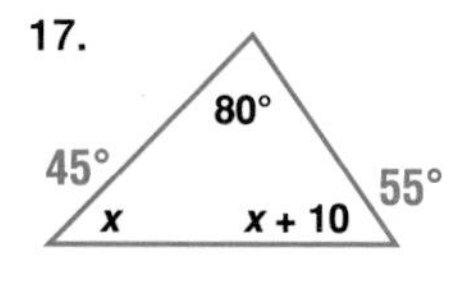

18. 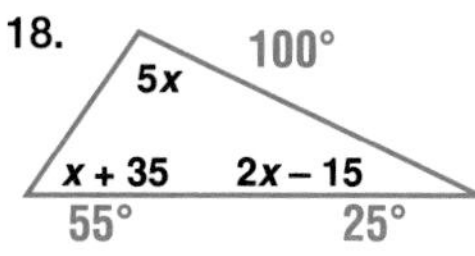

Applications

19. **Construction** Find the missing angle measure for the roof support shown at the right. 119°

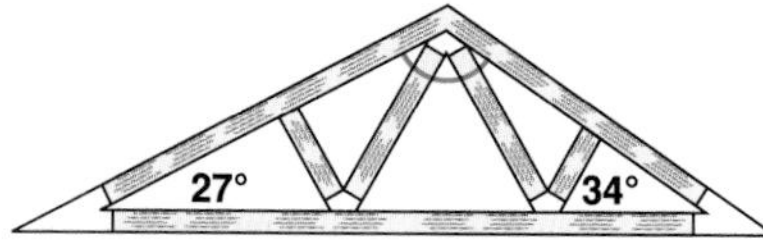

20. **Public Utilities** Brenda Sullivan works for the telephone company. One of her jobs is to attach a support cable to an upright telephone pole so that the cable makes a 20° angle with the pole. What angle does the cable have to make with the ground? Assume that the ground is level. 70°

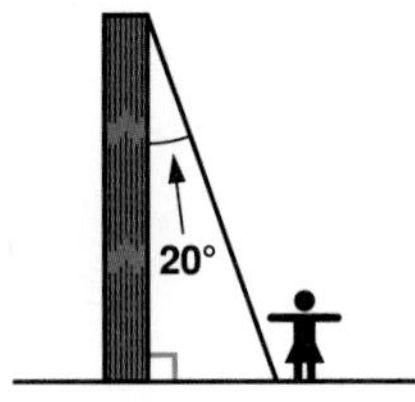

Critical Thinking

21. Are the acute angles of a right triangle complementary? Explain. See margin.

Wrap-Up

22. If one angle of a triangle measures 34° and another angle measures 56°, what is the measure of the third angle? Classify this triangle by its angles. Draw the triangle. 90°; right; See margin for drawing.

Mid-Chapter Quiz

Use a protractor to draw an angle with the given measurements. Classify each angle as *acute, right,* or *obtuse.* Then construct an angle congruent to one of your angles. (Lessons 12-1, 12-5) For Exercises 1-5, see students' work.

1. 60°
2. 115°
3. 85°
4. 150°
5. 20°

6. 17% of Foodtown's sales comes from the produce department. Find the measure of the produce department angle for a circle graph showing Foodtown's sales. (Lesson 12-2) about 61°

Find the measure of each angle using the following information. (Lesson 12-3)

7. $\angle A$ and $\angle B$ are complementary.
$m\angle A = x + 25$; $m\angle B = 2x - 10$
$m\angle A = 50°$; $m\angle B = 40°$

8. $\angle F$ and $\angle G$ are supplementary.
$m\angle F = 3x - 50$; $m\angle G = 2x - 20$
$m\angle F = 100°$; $m\angle G = 80°$

In the figure at the right, ℓ is parallel to m. If the measure of $\angle 3$ is 34°, find the measure of each angle. (Lesson 12-4)

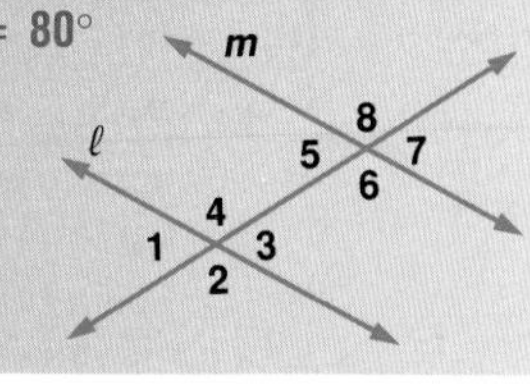

9. $\angle 1$ 34°
10. $\angle 4$ 146°
11. $\angle 5$ 34°
12. $\angle 6$ 146°
13. $\angle 8$ 146°

Alternate Strategies: Extending the Lesson

Enrichment

Writing Connection Have students write verbal problems using the angle measurements of each type of triangle. Trade and solve. Example problem: Sue pitched a triangular tent. The wall formed a 50° angle with the ground. The poles were perpendicular to the ground. What angle did the wall form with the pole?

Cooperative Learning

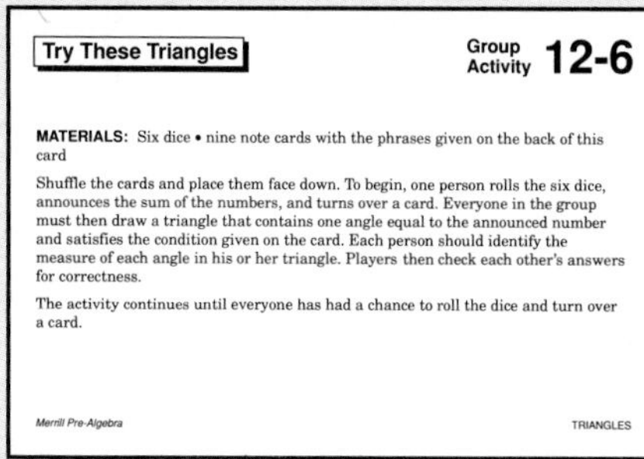

Try These Triangles Group Activity **12-6**

MATERIALS: Six dice • nine note cards with the phrases given on the back of this card

Shuffle the cards and place them face down. To begin, one person rolls the six dice, announces the sum of the numbers, and turns over a card. Everyone in the group must then draw a triangle that contains one angle equal to the announced number and satisfies the condition given on the card. Each person should identify the measure of each angle in his or her triangle. Players then check each other's answers for correctness.

The activity continues until everyone has had a chance to roll the dice and turn over a card.

Merrill Pre-Algebra TRIANGLES

12-7 Conditional Statements

Objectives:
Identify a conditional and its parts.
Write the converse of the conditional.

Key Terms:
conditional
converse

Miriam Frank writes copy for an advertising firm. She wrote the following slogan for Bob Dunn's campaign for city council. "If you want a booming city economy, vote for Dunn."

You can rewrite the slogan using the words *if* and *then.* "If you want a booming city economy, then you should vote for Dunn." A statement that can be written in *if-then* form is a **conditional.**

Conditionals have two parts.
- The part after *if* is the *hypothesis.*
- The part after *then* is the *conclusion.*

Examples

1 Identify the hypothesis and the conclusion in the slogan given above.

If you want a booming city economy, then you should vote for Dunn.
(hypothesis: If you want a booming city economy; conclusion: then you should vote for Dunn.)

2 Write a statement "All residents of Denver live in Colorado." in the form of a conditional.

If you are a resident of Denver, then you live in Colorado.
(hypothesis: If you are a resident of Denver; conclusion: then you live in Colorado.)

You can interchange the hypothesis and the conclusion of a conditional. The new statement is called the **converse** of the conditional.

Examples

3 Write the converse of the following conditional.

Conditional: If a triangle is a right triangle, then the triangle has two acute angles.

Converse: If a triangle has two acute angles, then the triangle is a right triangle.

4 In Example 3, determine whether each statement is true or false.

Conditional: A right triangle always has two acute angles. The conditional is true.

Converse: As shown in the drawing, an obtuse triangle also must have two acute angles. So, the converse is false.

acute angles
obtuse angle

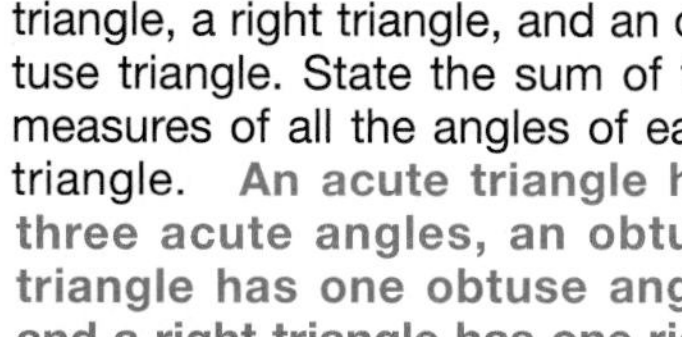
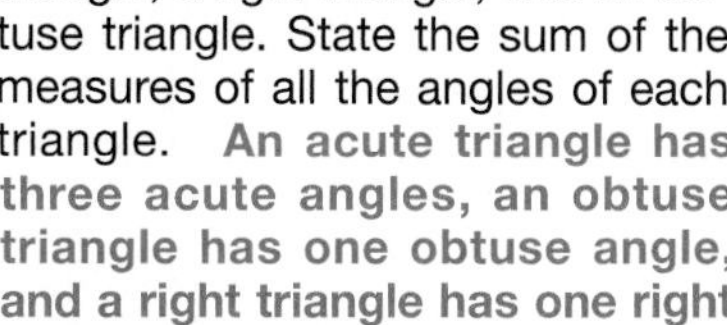

Bell Ringer

Describe how to define an acute triangle, a right triangle, and an obtuse triangle. State the sum of the measures of all the angles of each triangle. **An acute triangle has three acute angles, an obtuse triangle has one obtuse angle, and a right triangle has one right angle. All measure 180°.**

Reteaching Activity

Literature Connection Using a book of his or her choice, have each student choose statements and write each as a conditional and its converse. Tell if each conditional and converse is true or false.

Lesson Notes 12-7

5-Minute Check
(over Lesson 12-6)

Find the value of the missing angle. Then classify each triangle as acute, obtuse, or right.

1. Find $m\angle 1$ if $m\angle 2 = 35°$ and $m\angle 3 = 55°$. **90°, right**
2. Find $m\angle 1$ if $m\angle 2 = 43°$ and $m\angle 3 = 26°$. **111°, obtuse**
3. Find $m\angle 1$ if $m\angle 2 = 78°$ and $m\angle 3 = 52°$. **50°, acute**
4. Find $m\angle 2$ if $m\angle 1 = 61°$ and $m\angle 3 = 29°$. **90°, right**
5. Find $m\angle 2$ if $m\angle 1 = 39°$ and $m\angle 3 = 74°$. **67°, acute**

Transparency 12-7 contains the 5-Minute Check and a teaching aid for this lesson.

1 FOCUS

The purpose of this lesson is to write a conditional, including its parts, and its converse and determine the truth of each.

2 TEACH

Chalkboard Examples

- *For Example 1*
Identify the hypothesis and the conclusion in the slogan below.
The football coach was going over last week's game. He said, "If you want to win this week's game, the defense will need to be more aggressive."
hypothesis: If you want to win this week's game
conclusion: then the defense will need to be more aggressive.
- *For Example 2*
Write the statement "All residents of Chicago live in Illinois." in the form of a conditional.
If you are a resident of Chicago, then you live in Illinois.

EE: 1A, 1E

- *For Example 3*
  Write the converse of the following conditional.
  If a triangle is an obtuse triangle, then the triangle has one obtuse angle. **If a triangle has one obtuse angle, then the triangle is an obtuse triangle.**
- *For Example 4*
  In Example 3 determine whether each statement is true or false.
  conditional: true converse: true

3 PRACTICE/APPLY

Checking the Concept

After completing Exercises 3-5, have students write the converse of each.

Independent Practice

Homework Assignment	
Basic	6-15, 18, 19
Average	6-13, 16-19
Honors	8-19

4 CLOSE

Assessment Option

Speaking Have each student say a conditional statement and its converse. Then have them tell if each is true or false.

Practice Masters Booklet, **p. 116**

Name ____________ Date ____________

Practice Worksheet 12-7

Logic: Conditional Statements

Identify the hypothesis and the conclusion in each statement. Write the statement in the form of a conditional, if you need to.

1. (If a triangle is acute,) (then the degree measure of each angle is less than 90°.) — hypothesis; conclusion
2. (If a triangle is equilateral,) (then all of its sides are congruent.) — hypothesis; conclusion
3. (If she is on the all-star team,) (then she is famous.) — hypothesis; conclusion
4. (If the class has started,) (then the bell has rung.) — hypothesis; conclusion
5. (If a month has 30 days,) (then it is April.) — hypothesis; conclusion
6. (If a polygon has five sides,) (then it is a pentagon.) — hypothesis; conclusion
7. All triangles have three sides.
   (If a figure is a triangle,) (then it has three sides.) — hypothesis; conclusion
8. All obtuse angles have a measure greater than 90°.
   (If an angle is obtuse,) (then the angle has a measure greater than 90°.) — hypothesis; conclusion

Write the converse of each conditional. Then determine whether each statement (conditional and converse) is true or false.

9. If a month has only 28 days, then it is February.
   If the month is February, then it has only 28 days; true; false
10. If a triangle is an acute triangle, then the triangle has three acute angles.
    If a triangle has three acute angles, then it is an acute triangle; true; true
11. If a triangle is an isosceles triangle, then the triangle has two congruent sides.
    If a triangle has two congruent sides, then it is an isosceles triangle; true; false
12. If it is cold, then it is winter.
    If it is winter, then it is cold; false; false
13. If an angle measures less than 90°, then it is an acute angle.
    If an angle is an acute angle, then it measures less than 90°; true; true
14. If a quadrilateral is a square, then all four sides are congruent.
    If a quadrilateral has all four sides congruent, then it is a square; true; false

Checking for Understanding

Communicating Algebra

1. What are the two parts of a conditional? **hypothesis; conclusion**
2. Give an example of a conditional. Then write its converse.
   See Solutions Manual.

Guided Practice

Identify the hypothesis and the conclusion in each conditional.

3. If it is warm, then it is summer. **For Exercises 3-5, see Solutions Manual.**
4. If a polygon has three sides, then it is a triangle.
5. If a month has 31 days, then it is January.

Exercises

For Exercises 6-11, see Solutions Manual.

Independent Practice

Identify the hypothesis and the conclusion in each statement. Write the statement in the form of a conditional, if you need to.

6. If a triangle is a right triangle, then none of its angles are congruent.
7. It is morning if the sun is shining.
8. An angle that measures 90° is a right angle.

Write the converse of each conditional. Then determine whether each statement (conditional and converse) is true or false.

9. If an animal has four legs, then it is a cow.
10. If it is raining, the streets are wet.
11. When two lines intersect to form right angles, the lines are perpendicular.

Mixed Review

12. **Statistics** What is the median and range of the data in the box-and-whisker plot at the right? (Lesson 10-5) **20; 40**

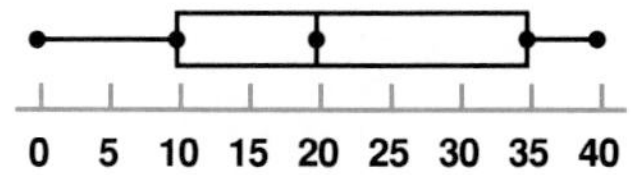

13. In $\triangle ABC$, the measure of $\angle B$ is 26° and the measure of $\angle C$ is 55°. Find the measure of $\angle A$. (Lesson 12-6) **99°**

Computer

In BASIC, an if-then statement is used to compare two numbers. If the condition is true, the computer follows the instructions given after the word *then*. If the condition is false, the computer goes to the next line.

Example: `10 IF 7 < 9 THEN GOTO 40` Since 7 is less than 9, the computer will go to line 40.

Determine whether the computer will go to line 40. Use the information in the chart at the right.

Inequality Symbols	
Algebra	**BASIC**
$<$	`<`
$>$	`>`
$\leq$	`<=`
$\geq$	`>=`
$\neq$	`<>`

14. `10 IF 15.8 < 16 THEN GOTO 40` **yes**
15. `10 IF 23 <> 23 THEN GOTO 40` **no**
16. `10 IF 3.2 <= 3.2 THEN GOTO 40` **yes**
17. `10 IF 9.16 >= 9.2 THEN GOTO 40` **no**

Critical Thinking

18. Shawn told his parents that if he earned an A in pre-algebra, he would be on the honor roll. Suppose Shawn is not on the honor roll. Does that mean that he did not earn an A in pre-algebra? Why or why not? **See Solutions Manual.**

Wrap-Up

19. Give an example of a conditional and its converse where the conditional is false and the converse is true. **Sample answer: If the month is February, then there are 28 days.**

Alternate Strategies: Extending the Lesson

Enrichment

Using Computers Discuss a simple computer program that contains an if-then clause. Follow the program step-by-step and determine how the conditional affects the outcome.

Cooperative Learning

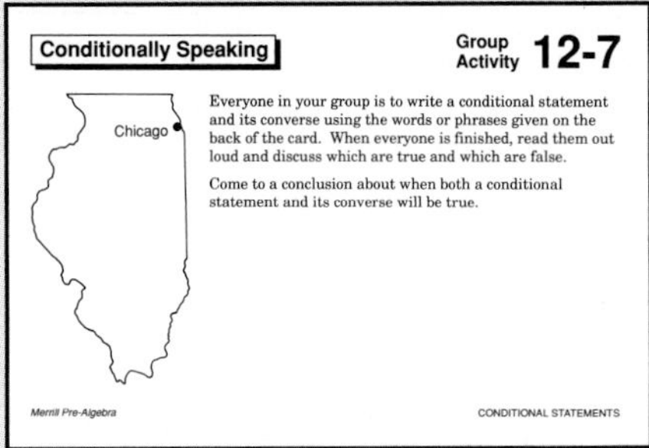
Conditionally Speaking Group Activity **12-7**

Everyone in your group is to write a conditional statement and its converse using the words or phrases given on the back of the card. When everyone is finished, read them out loud and discuss which are true and which are false.

Come to a conclusion about when both a conditional statement and its converse will be true.

Merrill Pre-Algebra CONDITIONAL STATEMENTS

12-8 Congruent Triangles

Objective:
Identify congruent triangles and corresponding parts of congruent triangles.

Key Terms:
congruent
corresponding parts

The roof supports of the Spaceship Earth geosphere at Epcot Center have the same size and shape. Figures that have the same size and shape are **congruent.**

Try the following activity to learn more about congruent figures.

1. On a piece of graph paper, draw two triangles like the ones below. Label the vertices as shown. Cut the triangles out.

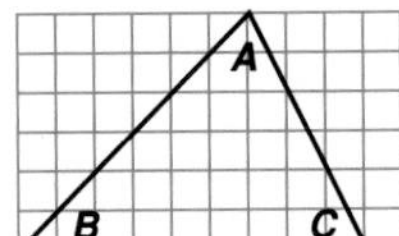

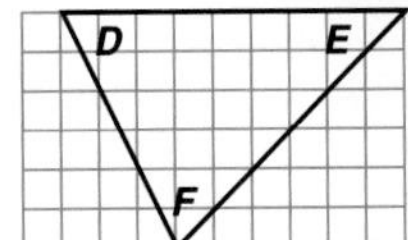

2. Put one triangle over the other so that parts with the same measures match up. Write down the pairs of angles and sides that match or correspond. Use the symbol $\longleftrightarrow$ which means *corresponds to.*

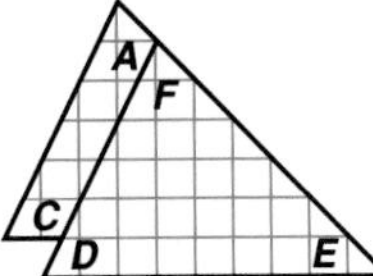

$\angle A \longleftrightarrow \angle F$	$\overline{AB} \longleftrightarrow \overline{FE}$
$\angle B \longleftrightarrow \angle E$	$\overline{BC} \longleftrightarrow \overline{ED}$
$\angle C \longleftrightarrow \angle D$	$\overline{AC} \longleftrightarrow \overline{FD}$

3. Place the triangles beside each other so that the corresponding parts are in the same positions.

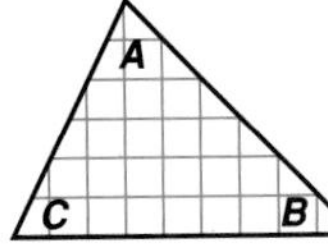

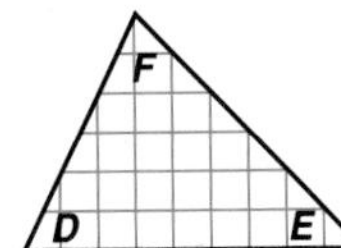

From the activity, you know that the **corresponding parts** have the same measure. Therefore, the corresponding parts are congruent. The symbol $\cong$ means *is congruent to.*

$\angle A \cong \angle F$	$\overline{AB} \cong \overline{FE}$
$\angle B \cong \angle E$	$\overline{BC} \cong \overline{ED}$
$\angle C \cong \angle D$	$\overline{AC} \cong \overline{FD}$

These relationships help to define congruent triangles.

Bell Ringer

Brainstorm ten conditional statements and then give their converses. **Answers will vary.**

Lesson Notes 12-8

5-Minute Check
(over Lesson 12-7)

Identify the condition and the conclusion in each statement. Write the statement in the form of a conditional, if you need to.

1. If it is cold outside, people wear warm coats.
   condition: If it is cold outside
   conclusion: then people wear warm coats.
2. If a figure has 4 sides, it is a rectangle.
   condition: If a figure has 4 sides
   conclusion: then it is a rectangle.

Transparency 12-8 contains the 5-Minute Check and a teaching aid for this lesson.

1 FOCUS

The purpose of this lesson is to identify congruent triangles and their corresponding parts.

Motivating the Lesson

Show pictures of identical twins. Why are they identical? **same characteristics**

2 TEACH

Using Models

Have students use the lesson activity to develop the meaning of congruence.

Chalkboard Examples

- *For Example 1*

If $\triangle MNP \cong \triangle RST$, name the congruent angles and sides.

$\angle M \cong \angle R$	$\overline{MP} \cong \overline{RT}$
$\angle N \cong \angle S$	$\overline{MN} \cong \overline{RS}$
$\angle P \cong \angle T$	$\overline{PN} \cong \overline{TS}$

EE: 1E, 3A, 4A, 4E
TAAS: 3, 11

Chalkboard Examples

- *For Example 2*

The corresponding parts of two congruent triangles are given. Write a congruency statement for the triangles.

$\angle ABC \cong \angle DBE$
$\angle A \cong \angle D$
$\angle C \cong \angle E$
$\overline{AC} \cong \overline{DE}$
$\overline{CB} \cong \overline{EB}$
$\overline{AB} \cong \overline{DB}$

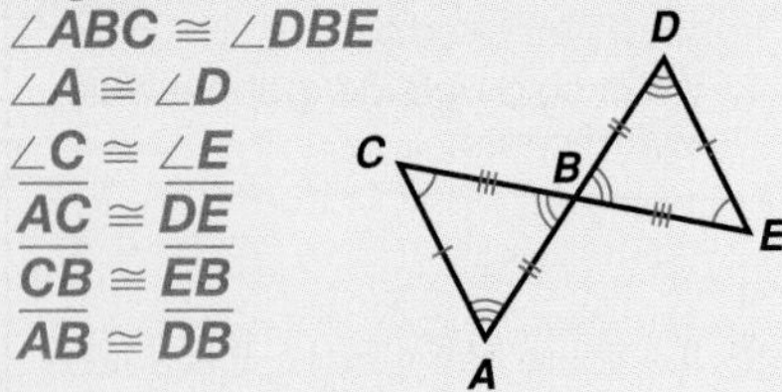

3 PRACTICE/APPLY

Checking the Concept

After completing Exercises 4-9, discuss solutions in cooperative groups.

Practice Masters Booklet, **p. 117**

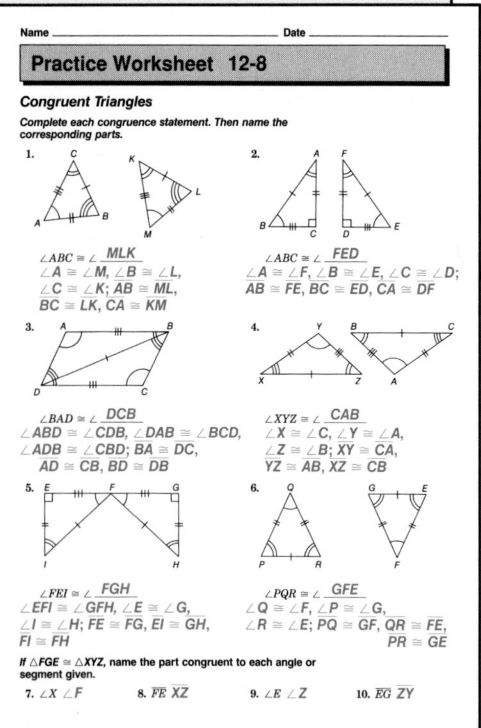

Name ______ Date ______

Practice Worksheet 12-8

Congruent Triangles

Complete each congruence statement. Then name the corresponding parts.

1. $\angle ABC \cong \angle$ MLK
$\angle A \cong \angle M$, $\angle B \cong \angle L$, $\angle C \cong \angle K$; $\overline{AB} \cong \overline{ML}$, $\overline{BC} \cong \overline{LK}$, $\overline{CA} \cong \overline{KM}$

2. $\angle ABC \cong \angle$ FED
$\angle A \cong \angle F$, $\angle B \cong \angle E$, $\angle C \cong \angle D$; $\overline{AB} \cong \overline{FE}$, $\overline{BC} \cong \overline{ED}$, $\overline{CA} \cong \overline{DF}$

3. $\angle BAD \cong \angle$ DCB
$\angle ABD \cong \angle CDB$, $\angle DAB \cong \angle BCD$, $\angle ADB \cong \angle CBD$; $\overline{BA} \cong \overline{DC}$, $\overline{AD} \cong \overline{CB}$, $\overline{BD} \cong \overline{DB}$

4. $\angle XYZ \cong \angle$ CAB
$\angle X \cong \angle C$, $\angle Y \cong \angle A$, $\angle Z \cong \angle B$; $\overline{XY} \cong \overline{CA}$, $\overline{YZ} \cong \overline{AB}$, $\overline{XZ} \cong \overline{CB}$

5. $\angle FEI \cong \angle$ FGH
$\angle EFI \cong \angle GFH$, $\angle E \cong \angle G$, $\angle I \cong \angle H$; $\overline{FE} \cong \overline{FG}$, $\overline{EI} \cong \overline{GH}$, $\overline{FI} \cong \overline{FH}$

6. $\angle PQR \cong \angle$ GFE
$\angle Q \cong \angle F$, $\angle P \cong \angle G$, $\angle R \cong \angle E$; $\overline{PQ} \cong \overline{GF}$, $\overline{QR} \cong \overline{FE}$, $\overline{PR} \cong \overline{GE}$

If $\triangle FGE \cong \triangle XYZ$, name the part congruent to each angle or segment given.

7. $\angle X$ $\angle F$
8. $\overline{FE}$ $\overline{XZ}$
9. $\angle E$ $\angle Z$
10. $\overline{EG}$ $\overline{ZY}$

Corresponding Parts of Congruent Triangles	If two triangles are congruent, their corresponding sides are congruent and their corresponding angles are congruent.

Note that when writing $\triangle ABC \cong \triangle FED$, the corresponding vertices are written in the same order. For example, A is the first vertex listed in the first triangle. Since F corresponds to A, F is the first vertex listed in the second triangle. Likewise, B corresponds to E and C corresponds to F.

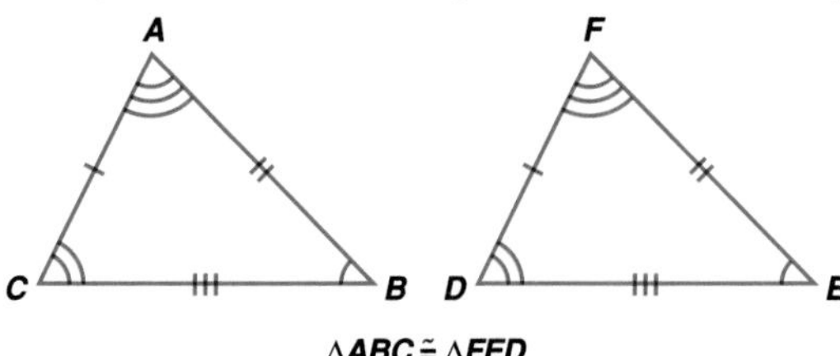

$\triangle ABC \cong \triangle FED$

Another way to show the corresponding parts is to use matching marks like those shown above in red.

Examples

1 **If $\triangle PQR \cong \triangle MLN$, name the congruent angles and sides.**

First, name the three pairs of congruent angles by looking at the order of the vertices.

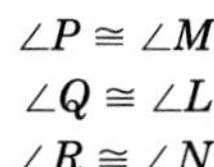

$\angle P \cong \angle M$
$\angle Q \cong \angle L$
$\angle R \cong \angle N$

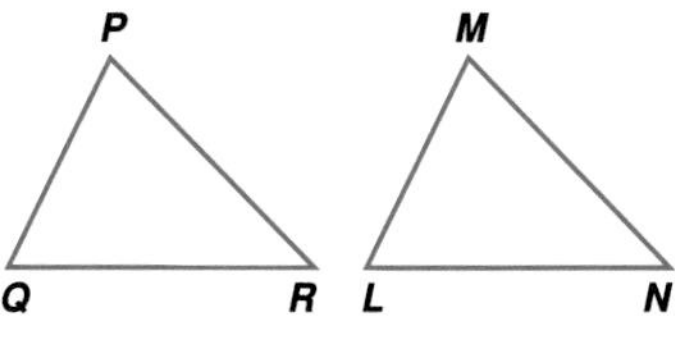

Now, draw the two triangles in the same position to confirm the corresponding sides. Name the three pairs of congruent sides.

$\overline{PQ} \cong \overline{ML}$, $\overline{QR} \cong \overline{LN}$, $\overline{PR} \cong \overline{MN}$

2 **The corresponding parts of two congruent triangles are given. Write a congruence statement for the triangles.**

$\angle I \cong \angle K$ $\quad \overline{IH} \cong \overline{KH}$
$\angle G \cong \angle J$ $\quad \overline{GH} \cong \overline{JH}$
$\angle GHI \cong \angle JHK$ $\quad \overline{GI} \cong \overline{JK}$

I, J, H, G, K

In this case, the congruence can be written by matching the vertices of the congruent angles. $\triangle IGH \cong \triangle KJH$

Alternate Strategies: Reteaching the Lesson

Reteaching Activity

Using Models Have students cut several different pairs of congruent triangles and mix them up. Then have students match each triangle to its congruent counterpart.

Reteaching Masters Booklet, **p. 105**

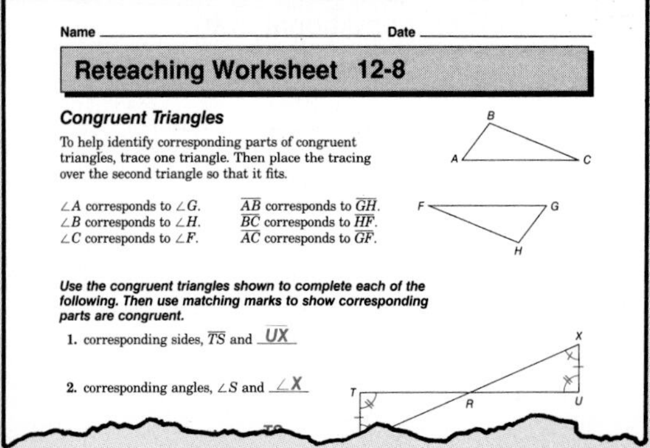

Name ______ Date ______

Reteaching Worksheet 12-8

Congruent Triangles

To help identify corresponding parts of congruent triangles, trace one triangle. Then place the tracing over the second triangle so that it fits.

$\angle A$ corresponds to $\angle G$. $\quad \overline{AB}$ corresponds to $\overline{GH}$.
$\angle B$ corresponds to $\angle H$. $\quad \overline{BC}$ corresponds to $\overline{HF}$.
$\angle C$ corresponds to $\angle F$. $\quad \overline{AC}$ corresponds to $\overline{GF}$.

Use the congruent triangles shown to complete each of the following. Then use matching marks to show corresponding parts are congruent.

1. corresponding sides, $\overline{TS}$ and $\overline{UX}$
2. corresponding angles, $\angle S$ and $\angle X$

Checking for Understanding 1. All corresponding parts are congruent.

Communicating Algebra

1. Explain what it means when two triangles are congruent.
2. In your own words, describe the corresponding parts of congruent triangles. See margin.
3. If $\triangle QRS \cong \triangle TUV$, name the angle that corresponds to $\angle R$. $\angle U$

Guided Practice

Use the congruent triangles at the right to complete Exercises 4-9.

4. $\overline{AB} \cong$ ■ $\overline{FE}$
5. $\angle E \cong$ ■ $\angle B$
6. $\angle C \cong$ ■ $\angle D$
7. $\overline{BC} \cong$ ■ $\overline{ED}$
8. $\overline{DF} \cong$ ■ $\overline{CA}$
9. $\angle D \cong$ ■ $\angle C$

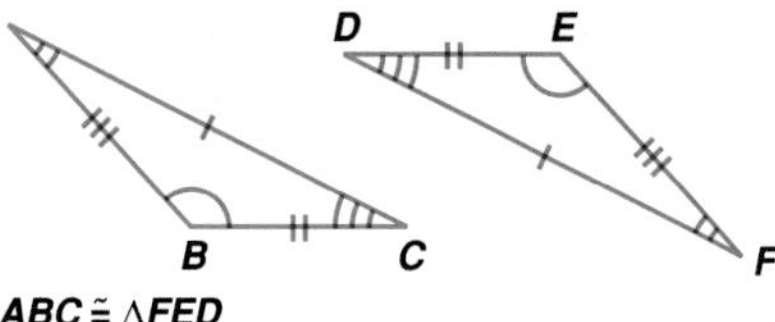

$\triangle ABC \cong \triangle FED$

Exercises

Independent Practice

Complete each congruence statement. Then name the corresponding parts.

10. △FED
11. △DEF
12. △ABC
13. △BAE

10.
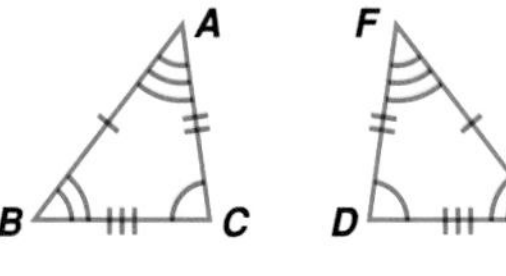
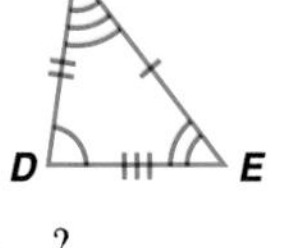

$\triangle ABC \cong \triangle$ __?__

11.
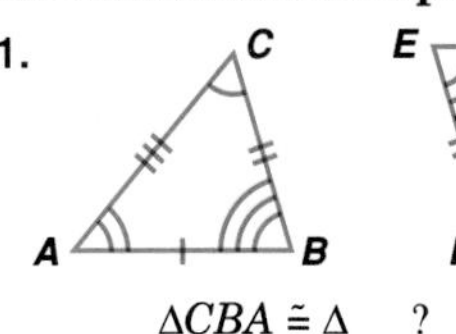

$\triangle CBA \cong \triangle$ __?__

12.

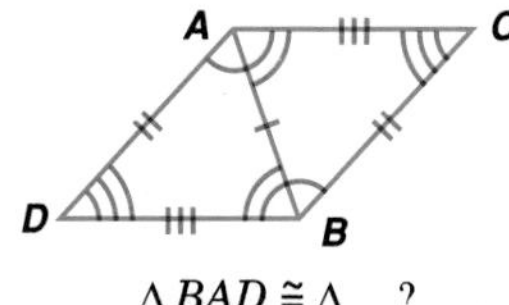

$\triangle BAD \cong \triangle$ __?__

13.

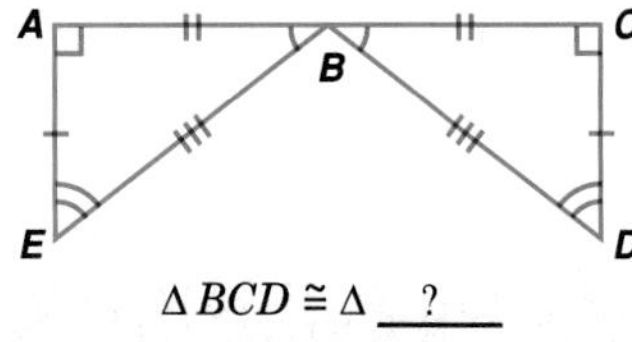

$\triangle BCD \cong \triangle$ __?__

If $\triangle BCA \cong \triangle GFH$, name the part congruent to each angle or segment given.

14. $\angle F$ $\angle C$
15. $\overline{BA}$ $\overline{GH}$
16. $\overline{FG}$ $\overline{CB}$
17. $\angle A$ $\angle H$
18. $\overline{AC}$ $\overline{HF}$

Mixed Review

19. Find the discount rate for a $40 sweater on sale for $34. (Lesson 9-10) 15%
20. **Probability** Three dice are rolled. How many outcomes are possible? (Lesson 11-2) 216
21. **Logic** Write as a conditional statement: *An angle that measures less than 90° is an acute angle.* (Lesson 12-7) See margin.

Connection

22. **Geometry** Two triangles are congruent and the perimeter of one triangle is 5 ft. What is the perimeter of the second triangle? 5 ft

Critical Thinking

23. If two triangles have congruent, corresponding angles, are the triangles congruent? Explain your answer by making a drawing. no; See margin for drawing.

Wrap-Up

24. Make a sketch of two congruent triangles. Label the triangles and write a congruence statement. See margin.

Independent Practice

Homework Assignment	
Basic	11-17 odd, 19-24
Average	10-18 even, 19-24
Honors	10, 12, 16-24

4 CLOSE

Assessment Option

Writing Draw and label two congruent triangles on the board or overhead. Have the students write the segments and angles that are congruent. Also have them write how the triangles are congruent. Answers will vary.

Additional Answers

2. Sample answer: The corresponding angles and sides have the same measure.
21. If an angle measures less than 90°, then it is an acute angle.

Enrichment Masters Booklet, **p. 105**

Additional Answers

23.
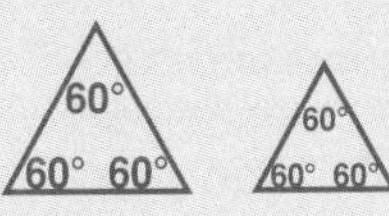

24.
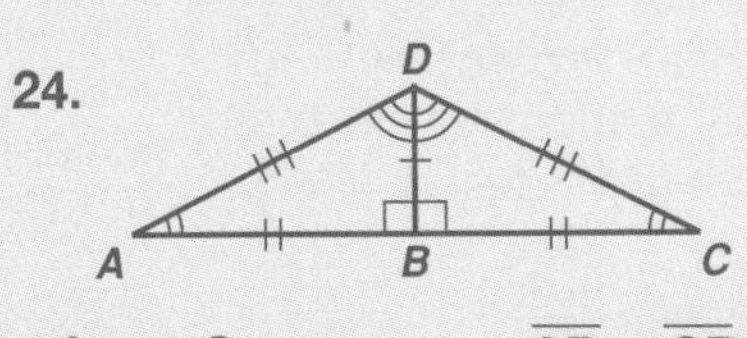

$\angle A \cong \angle C$ $\overline{AB} \cong \overline{CB}$
$\angle ABD \cong \angle CBD$ $\overline{DE} \cong \overline{DB}$
$\angle ADB \cong \angle CDB$ $\overline{AD} \cong \overline{CD}$

Cooperative Learning

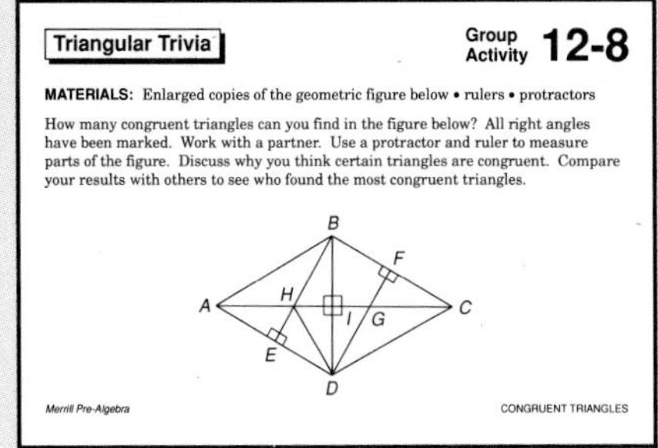
Triangular Trivia — Group Activity 12-8

MATERIALS: Enlarged copies of the geometric figure below • rulers • protractors

How many congruent triangles can you find in the figure below? All right angles have been marked. Work with a partner. Use a protractor and ruler to measure parts of the figure. Discuss why you think certain triangles are congruent. Compare your results with others to see who found the most congruent triangles.

Merrill Pre-Algebra — CONGRUENT TRIANGLES

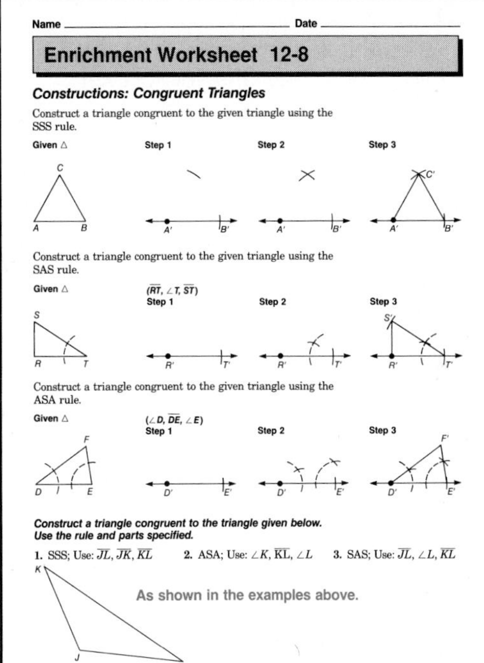
Name ______ Date ______

Enrichment Worksheet 12-8

Constructions: Congruent Triangles

Construct a triangle congruent to the given triangle using the SSS rule.

Given △ Step 1 Step 2 Step 3

Construct a triangle congruent to the given triangle using the SAS rule.

Given △ ($\overline{RT}$, ∠T, $\overline{ST}$) Step 1 Step 2 Step 3

Construct a triangle congruent to the given triangle using the ASA rule.

Given △ (∠D, $\overline{DE}$, ∠E) Step 1 Step 2 Step 3

Construct a triangle congruent to the triangle given below. Use the rule and parts specified.

1. SSS; Use: $\overline{JL}$, $\overline{JK}$, $\overline{KL}$ 2. ASA; Use: ∠K, $\overline{KL}$, ∠L 3. SAS; Use: $\overline{JL}$, ∠L, $\overline{KL}$

As shown in the examples above.

EXPLORATION

Translations

Objective Students will display the results of a translation.

1 FOCUS

In this exploration, students will be introduced to transformations and model translations.

Motivating the Exploration

If possible, wear to class a shirt, tie, etc., that illustrates a pattern that has been formed from a translation. Wallpaper patterns might also be used. Have students examine patterns and determine where it repeats. Then ask students if they can explain how the repeat was formed.

2 TEACH

Using Discussion

Before students begin the exploration, model the translation of a figure on a coordinate grid. Discuss the effect the movement has on the coordinates of the vertices.

3 PRACTICE/APPLY

Using Questioning

- Ask students to explain how they could check their answer to Exercise 1. **Sample answer: Model the translation on a coordinate grid and apply the distance formula.**
- Reflect $\triangle XYZ$ about YZ. Ask students to explain why this is not a translation. **Sample answer: In a translation all points move in one direction.**

Additional Answer

4. Sample answer:

4 CLOSE

Writing Connection

Have students write a definition for translation.

Exploration

Transformations

Materials: notebook paper, scissors, cardboard

Most of the technical art in this textbook was generated using a computer. The artist drew a figure and used a computer mouse to translate, reflect, or rotate the figure to the desired location.

In this Exploration, you will investigate a transformation called a translation.

Your Turn: Work with a partner as you complete this activity. **See students' work.**

▶ Cut a triangle out of a thin piece of cardboard. Label its angles 1, 2, and 3. Place the triangle on a piece of notebook paper as shown. Trace the triangle on the paper. Label the vertices so that the vertex of $\angle 1$ is X, the vertex of $\angle 2$ is Y, and the vertex of $\angle 3$ is Z.

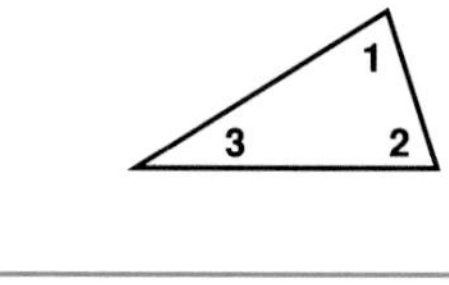

▶ Slide the cutout triangle to another place on the paper, making sure the common side of $\angle 2$ and $\angle 3$ is still aligned with a horizontal rule as shown. Trace the triangle. Label the vertices X', Y', and Z', so they correspond to the first triangle you drew.

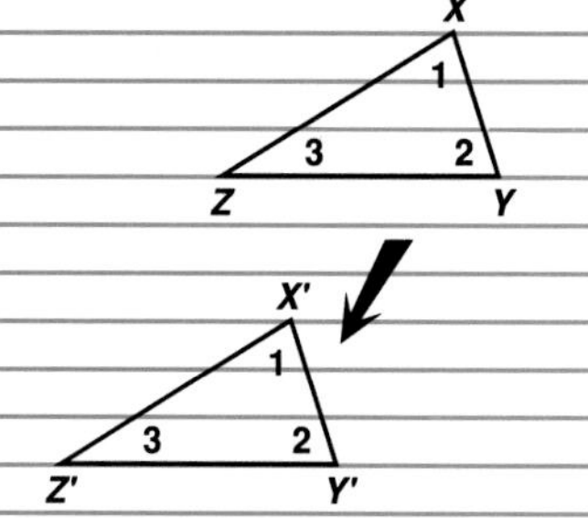

 Draw XX', YY', and ZZ'.

Analysis

1. Measure XX', YY', and ZZ'. What seems to be true about these segments? **congruent**
2. What kind of figure does quadrilateral $XX'Y'Y$ appear to be? Name two other figures of this type from your drawing. **parallelogram; $XX'Z'Z$; $YY'Z'Z$**
3. Write a congruence statement for the triangles you traced. **$\triangle XYZ \cong \triangle X'Y'Z'$**
4. Create a design by translating a figure. **See margin.**

SET-UP

Materials

- notebook paper, scissors, cardboard

You may wish to use the Exploration worksheet provided on page 60 of the Lab Manual.

For Students If scissors and cardboard are available, students can trace any object with a polygon-shaped base.

For the Overhead Projector You can model this exploration on the overhead as students follow along at the seats.

 **EE:** 1A, 1C, 1E, 4A

12-9 Similar Triangles

Objectives:
Identify corresponding parts of similar triangles.
Find missing measures by using lengths of corresponding sides.

Key Term:
similar

Rachel is on the yearbook staff at Wyandot Middle School. She must reduce the size of photographs to fit on the pages. The two photographs shown at the right have the same shape, but one is smaller than the other. Figures that have the same shape, but may differ in size are called **similar** figures.

Triangle *ABC* is similar to triangle *DEF*.

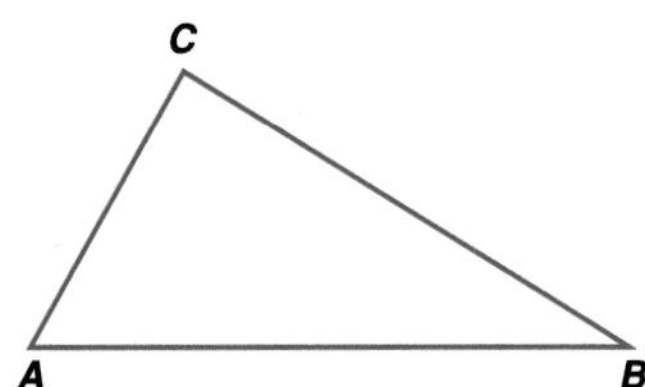

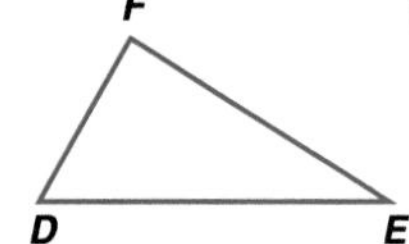

Say: Triangle *ABC* is similar to triangle *DEF*.

Write: $\triangle ABC \sim \triangle DEF$ The symbol $\sim$ means *is similar to.*

Use a protractor to measure each angle. Compare the measures of $\angle A$ and $\angle D$, $\angle C$ and $\angle F$, and $\angle B$ and $\angle E$. How do the measures of these angles compare?

Corresponding Angles of Similar Triangles

If two triangles are similar, then the angles of one triangle are congruent to the corresponding angles of the other triangle.

Remember that the converse of a conditional is formed by switching the hypothesis and the conclusion of the conditional.

The converse of the statement or conditional above is also true.

If the angles of one triangle are congruent to the corresponding angles of another triangle, then the triangles are similar.

Bell Ringer

If $\triangle STU \cong \triangle DEF$, name two angles and two segments of each triangle that are congruent.

Sample answer: $\overline{ST} \cong \overline{DE}$, $\overline{TU} \cong \overline{EF}$, $\angle S \cong \angle D$, $\angle T \cong \angle E$.

Lesson Notes 12-9

5-Minute Check
(over Lesson 12-8)

Complete each congruency statement.

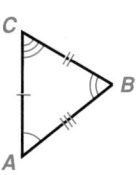

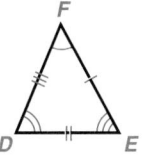

1. $\triangle ABC \cong$ $\triangle FDE$
2. $\angle A \cong$ $\angle F$
3. $AB \cong$ FD
4. $\angle C \cong$ $\angle E$
5. $\overline{BC} \cong$ $\overline{DE}$

Transparency 12-9 contains the 5-Minute Check and a teaching aid for this lesson.

1 FOCUS

The purpose of this lesson is to identify similar triangles and their corresponding parts and use proportions to solve problems involving similar triangles.

Motivating the Lesson

Show pictures of two similar objects, such as roses of different color. Ask students what is meant when we say that two items are similar. Some characteristics are the same and some are not.

2 TEACH

Using Models

Use an opaque projector to enlarge a triangle. Measure each side of the original triangle and one side of the enlarged triangle. Use a proportion to determine the length of the other sides. Check by measuring.

EE: 1E, 3A, 4A, 4C, 4E
TAAS: 2, 3, 11

Chalkboard Examples

- *For Example*

Find the value of x.

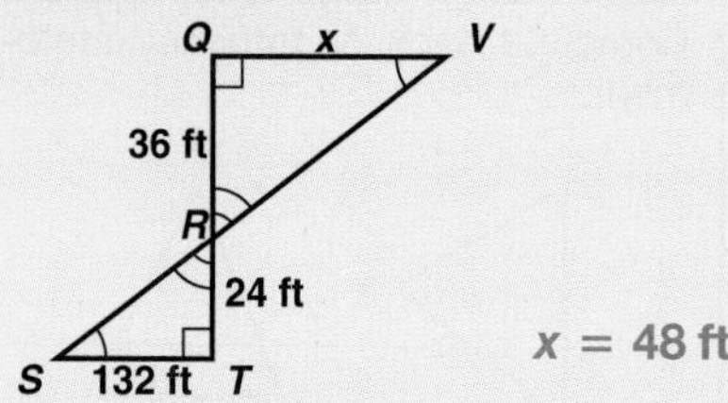

$x = 48$ ft

3 PRACTICE/APPLY

Checking the Concept

If additional practice is needed after completing Exercises 4-6, tell students that segment $RT = 15$ m and ask them to find the length of segment ST.

Error Analysis

Watch for students who set up proportions incorrectly.
Prevent by labeling each part of the proportion and checking labels of corresponding parts of the fractions.

Practice Masters Booklet, **p. 118**

Name ______________ Date ______________

Practice Worksheet 12-9

Similar Triangles

Use the similar triangles at the right to answer Exercises 1–3.

1. List three proportions for $\triangle ABC$ and $\triangle EFG$. $\frac{x}{5} = \frac{8}{10}, \frac{x}{6} = \frac{8}{12}, \frac{5}{6} = \frac{10}{12}$
2. What side corresponds to $\overline{AB}$? *EF*
3. Find the value of x. 4 in.

Find the value of x in each pair of similar triangles.

4. 5
5. 18
6. 10 m
7. 8 ft
8. 7 m
9. 12 m

Compare the measures of the corresponding sides of the similar triangles below by writing their ratios. The corresponding sides are $\overline{LN}$ and $\overline{RT}$, $\overline{MN}$ and $\overline{ST}$, and $\overline{LM}$ and $\overline{RS}$.

$\triangle LMN \sim \triangle RST$

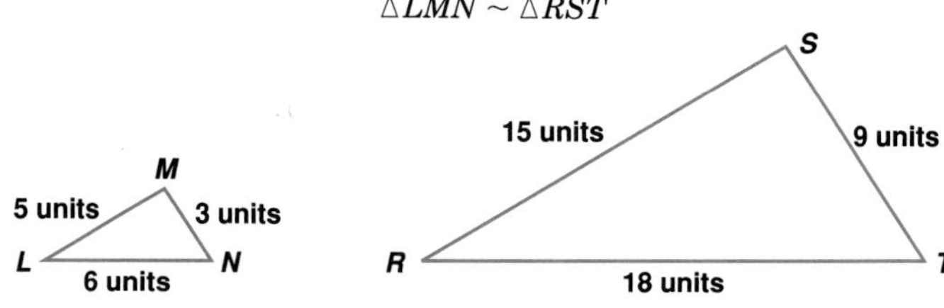

The notation $m\,\overline{LN}$ means the measure of $\overline{LN}$.

$\frac{m\,\overline{LN}}{m\,\overline{RT}} = \frac{6 \text{ units}}{18 \text{ units}}$ or $\frac{1}{3}$ $\quad \frac{m\,\overline{MN}}{m\,\overline{ST}} = \frac{3 \text{ units}}{9 \text{ units}}$ or $\frac{1}{3}$ $\quad \frac{m\,\overline{LM}}{m\,\overline{RS}} = \frac{5 \text{ units}}{15 \text{ units}}$ or $\frac{1}{3}$

Notice that the ratios are equivalent. So, the corresponding sides are proportional to each other. This example suggests the following property.

Corresponding Sides of Similar Triangles: If two triangles are similar, then their corresponding sides are proportional.

Is the converse of the conditional above true also? **yes**

Proportions can be used to find the measures of the sides of similar triangles when some measures are known.

Example

1 **Find the value of x.**

$\angle A \cong \angle D$, $\angle B \cong \angle E$, and $\angle ACB \cong \angle DCE$.

So, $\triangle ABC \sim \triangle DEC$ because their corresponding angles are congruent.

Which angles are vertical angles?
How are vertical angles related?
$\angle ECD$ and $\angle BCA$
$\angle ECD \cong \angle BCA$

$\frac{m\,\overline{BC}}{m\,\overline{EC}} = \frac{m\,\overline{AB}}{m\,\overline{DE}}$ Corresponding sides of similar triangles are proportional.

$\frac{7.5}{12} = \frac{15}{x}$

$7.5 \cdot x = 12 \cdot 15$ Cross multiply.

$7.5x = 180$

$\frac{7.5x}{7.5} = \frac{180}{7.5}$

180 ÷ 7.5 = 24

$x = 24$

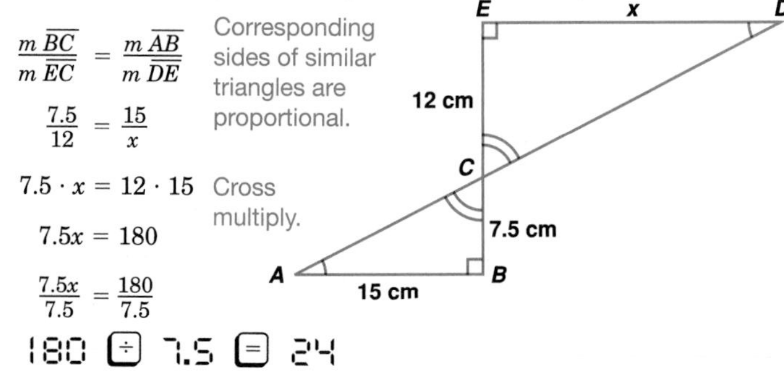

Alternate Strategies: Reteaching the Lesson

Reteaching Activity

Using Models Using a road map, form a triangle by connecting three points of interest. Measure all three sides. Using the scale and a proportion, determine the land measure of all three sides.

Reteaching Masters Booklet, **p. 106**

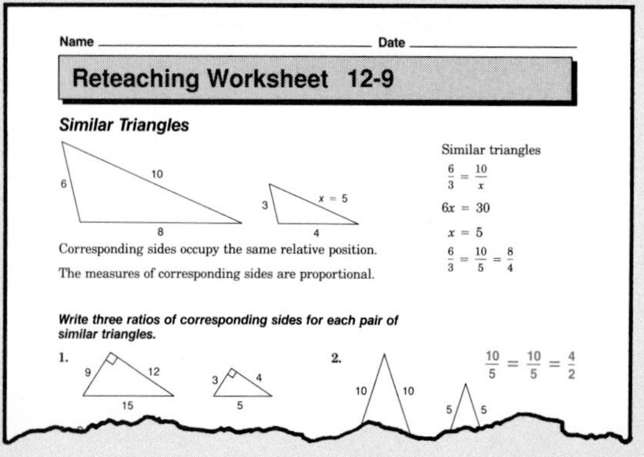
Name ______________ Date ______________

Reteaching Worksheet 12-9

Similar Triangles

Similar triangles
$\frac{6}{3} = \frac{10}{x}$
$6x = 30$
$x = 5$
$\frac{6}{3} = \frac{10}{5} = \frac{8}{4}$

Corresponding sides occupy the same relative position.
The measures of corresponding sides are proportional.

Write three ratios of corresponding sides for each pair of similar triangles.

1.
2. $\frac{10}{5} = \frac{10}{5} = \frac{4}{2}$

1. Corresponding sides are proportional or corresponding angles are congruent.

Checking for Understanding

Communicating Algebra

1. How do you know if two triangles are similar to each other? See margin.
2. Explain how to determine the corresponding parts of similar triangles.
3. Are congruent triangles also similar triangles? Explain. Yes; the corresponding sides are in the proportion 1:1.

Guided Practice

Use the similar triangles at the right to answer Exercises 4-6.

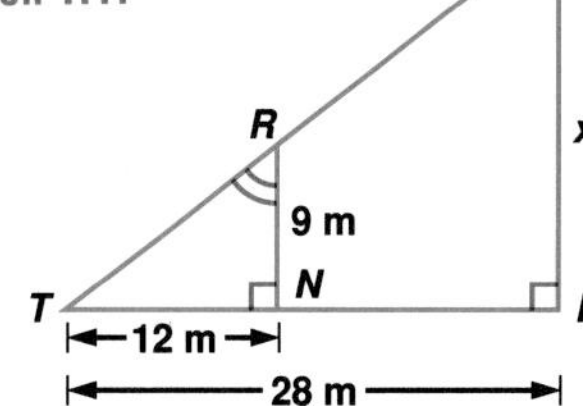

4. List three proportions for $\triangle NRT$ and $\triangle MST$. $\frac{m\overline{RN}}{m\overline{SM}}$; $\frac{m\overline{NT}}{m\overline{MT}}$; $\frac{m\overline{RT}}{m\overline{ST}}$
5. What side corresponds to $\overline{SM}$? $\overline{RN}$
6. Find the value of x. 21 m

Exercises

Independent Practice

Use the similar triangles at the right to answer Exercises 7-9.

7. List three proportions for $\triangle PQR$ and $\triangle STU$. $\frac{m\overline{PQ}}{m\overline{ST}}$; $\frac{m\overline{PR}}{m\overline{SU}}$; $\frac{m\overline{RQ}}{m\overline{UT}}$
8. What side corresponds to $\overline{PQ}$? $\overline{ST}$
9. Find the value of x. 3 cm

P, Q, R, x, 6 cm; S, T, U, 1 cm, 2 cm

Find the value of x in each pair of similar triangles.

10. 15 ft

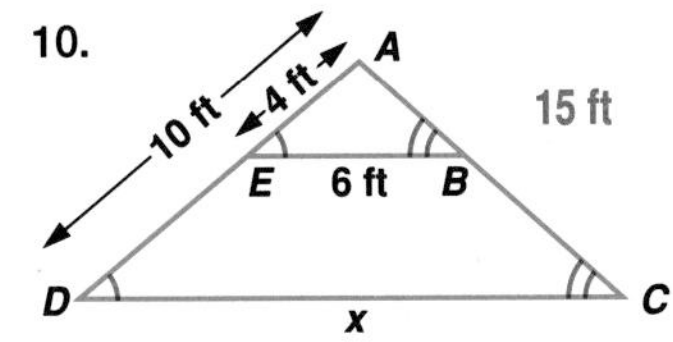

11.

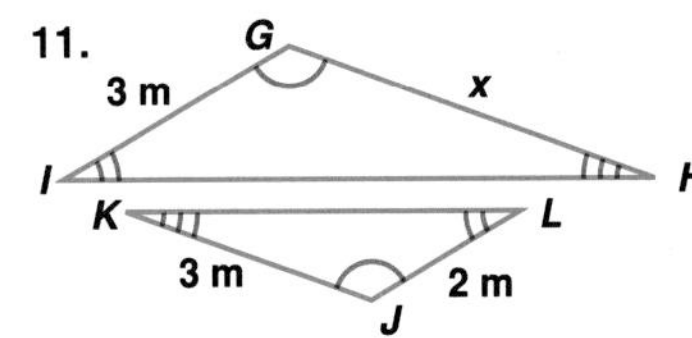

Mixed Review

12. What is the probability that it is 98°F at the North Pole? (Lesson 11-4)
13. Are the two triangles in Exercise 11 congruent? Why or why not? (Lesson 12-8) no; Sides are not congruent.

Application

14. **Civil Engineering** The city of Marion plans to build a bridge across Pine Lake. Use the information in the diagram at the right to find the distance across Pine Lake. 121 m

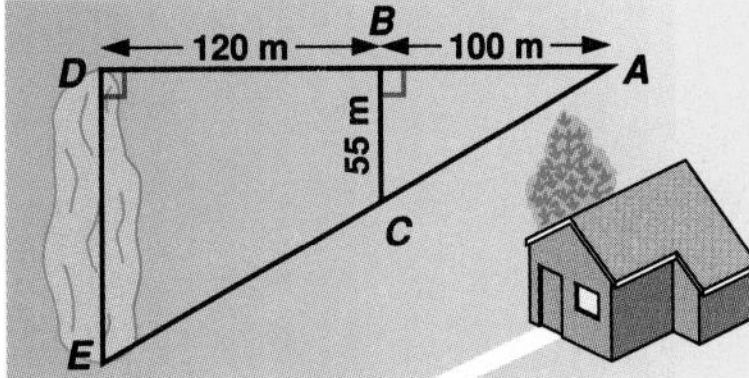

Critical Thinking

15. A photo negative is 1.5 cm wide by 2.2 cm long. The print is made 6 cm wide. How many times greater is the area of the print than the area of the negative? 16 times

Wrap-Up

16. **Make Up a Problem** Write a problem involving the use of similar triangles. See margin.

Independent Practice

Homework Assignment	
Basic	7-16
Average	7-16
Honors	7-16

4 CLOSE

Assessment Option

Modeling Make two or more similar triangles out of cardboard. Then translate them onto a piece of paper making a figure. Try to fill a paper with similar triangles or make a design.

Additional Answers

2. Sample answer: The corresponding angles will have the same measure and the corresponding sides will be proportional to each other.
16. Sample answer: Find the length of the other ladder in the drawing below.

Enrichment Masters Booklet, **p. 106**

Name ______ Date ______

Enrichment Worksheet 12-9

Scale Drawings

Scale drawings are very important in construction projects. Architects make *models* of the project that is being built. In a model, the lengths of the lines drawn are in direct proportion to the lengths of beams, walls, and so on in the final product. These drawings are said to be drawn *to scale.*

Example: Find the actual length of each side of the triangle.

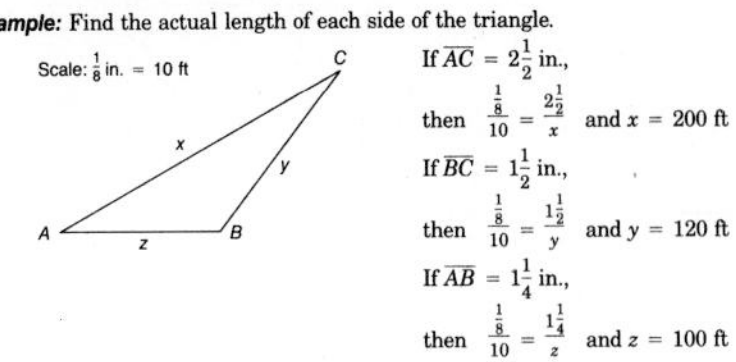

If $\overline{AC} = 2\frac{1}{2}$ in., then $\frac{\frac{1}{8}}{10} = \frac{2\frac{1}{2}}{x}$ and $x = 200$ ft

If $\overline{BC} = 1\frac{1}{2}$ in., then $\frac{\frac{1}{8}}{10} = \frac{1\frac{1}{2}}{y}$ and $y = 120$ ft

If $\overline{AB} = 1\frac{1}{4}$ in., then $\frac{\frac{1}{8}}{10} = \frac{1\frac{1}{4}}{z}$ and $z = 100$ ft

Using the scale 1 in. = 40 mi, draw lines to represent the following lengths.

1. 70 mi 1.75 in.
2. 100 mi 2.5 in.

Using the scale $\frac{1}{8}$ in. = 1 ft, draw lines to represent the following lengths.

3. 16 ft 2 in.
4. 20 ft 2.5 in.

Measure the following triangles to find the length of each side if the scales are as given.

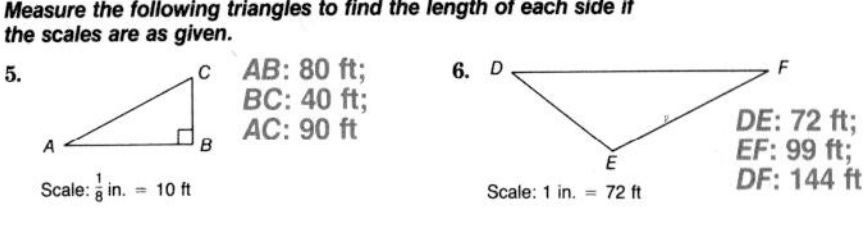

5. AB: 80 ft; BC: 40 ft; AC: 90 ft
6. DE: 72 ft; EF: 99 ft; DF: 144 ft

Alternate Strategies: Extending the Lesson

Enrichment

Comparing and Contrasting Have students consider the following conditional. If two triangles are congruent, then they are similar. Write the converse of this conditional. Tell whether the conditional and its converse are true or false and why.

Cooperative Learning

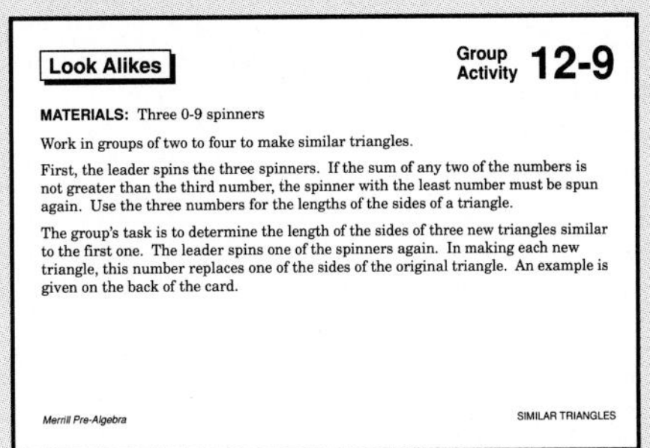

Look Alikes Group Activity **12-9**

MATERIALS: Three 0-9 spinners

Work in groups of two to four to make similar triangles.

First, the leader spins the three spinners. If the sum of any two of the numbers is not greater than the third number, the spinner with the least number must be spun again. Use the three numbers for the lengths of the sides of a triangle.

The group's task is to determine the length of the sides of three new triangles similar to the first one. The leader spins one of the spinners again. In making each new triangle, this number replaces one of the sides of the original triangle. An example is given on the back of the card.

Merrill Pre-Algebra SIMILAR TRIANGLES

Lesson Notes 12-10

5-Minute Check
(over Lesson 12-9)

Name the corresponding sides and angles for the pair of similar triangles.

1.

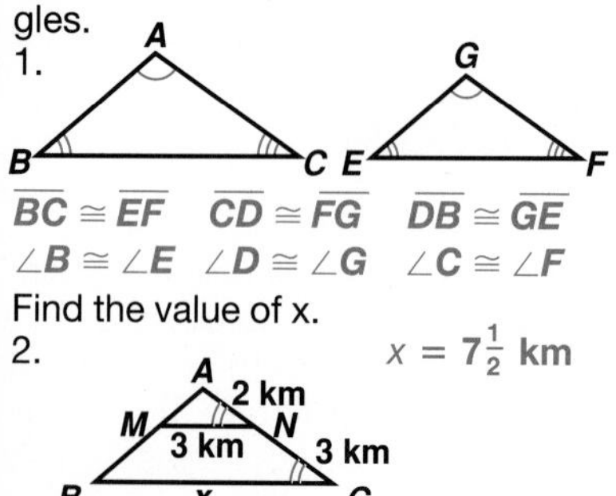

$\overline{BC} \cong \overline{EF}$ $\overline{CD} \cong \overline{FG}$ $\overline{DB} \cong \overline{GE}$
$\angle B \cong \angle E$ $\angle D \cong \angle G$ $\angle C \cong \angle F$

Find the value of x.

2. $x = 7\frac{1}{2}$ km

Transparency 12-10 contains the 5-Minute Check and a teaching aid for this lesson.

1 FOCUS

The purpose of this lesson is to indirectly measure by using proportions derived from similar triangles.

2 TEACH

Using Models

Have students cut similar triangles from construction paper. Measure all three sides of the smaller triangle and one side of the larger. Use a proportion to determine the lengths of the other two sides. Check by measuring.

Chalkboard Examples

- *For Example 1*
  Use similar triangles to find the distance across the pond.
  $x = 105$ m

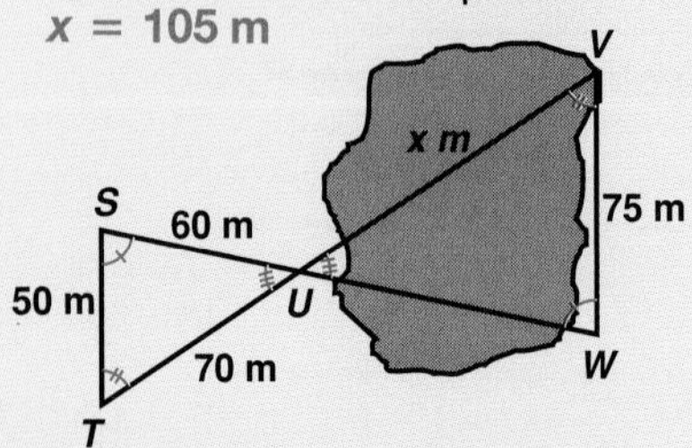

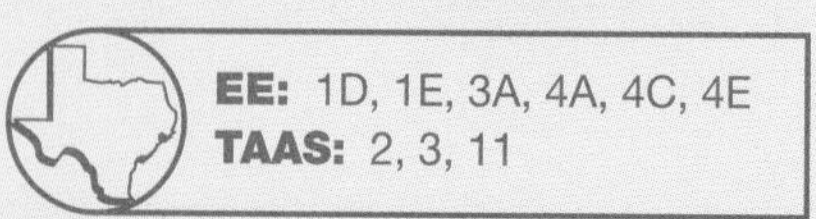

EE: 1D, 1E, 3A, 4A, 4C, 4E
TAAS: 2, 3, 11

Application

12-10 Indirect Measurement

Objective:
Use proportions to solve problems involving similar triangles.

In ancient Egypt, mathematicians used a technique called *shadow reckoning* to determine the heights of tall objects, such as the pyramids. Shadow reckoning is based on the principle of similar triangles. The height of a staff and the length of its shadow is proportional to the height of an object and the length of its shadow.

How do you know the two triangles are similar? **Triangles have congruent angles.**

You can use the same technique today by using a meterstick as your "staff". If the shadow of your meterstick is 0.7 meters and the shadow of a tree is 3.5 meters, you have enough information to find the height of the tree.

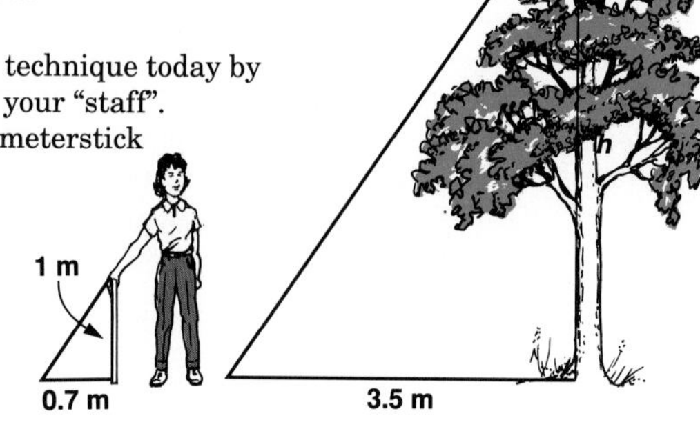

What is another proportion that could be used? $\frac{0.7}{1} = \frac{3.5}{h}$

shadow of stick → $\frac{0.7}{3.5} = \frac{1}{h}$ ← height of stick
shadow of tree → ← height of tree

$0.7 \times h = 3.5 \times 1$ Cross multiply. Cross products are equal.

$\frac{0.7h}{0.7} = \frac{3.5}{0.7}$ Divide each side by 0.7.

$h = 5$ The tree is 5 meters tall.

Example

1 Use similar triangles to find the distance across the river.

$\triangle TSR \sim \triangle QVR$ Corresponding angles are congruent.

$\frac{m\,\overline{RT}}{m\,\overline{RQ}} = \frac{m\,\overline{ST}}{m\,\overline{VQ}}$

$\frac{10}{16} = \frac{20}{x}$

$10 \cdot x = 20 \cdot 16$

$10x = 320$

$\frac{10x}{10} = \frac{320}{10}$

$x = 32$

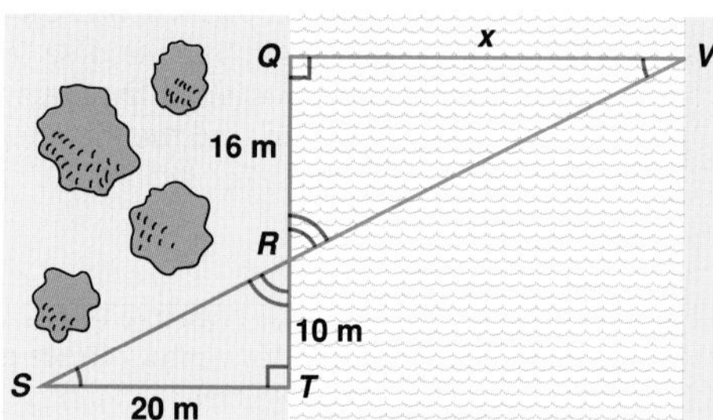

Bell Ringer

Name something that similar triangles and congruent triangles have in common. Then name a difference between them. **Answers will vary. Poss. Ans.: Their angles have the same measure; their segments have different measures.**

Checking for Understanding

Communicating Algebra

1. Liz wants to enlarge an embroidery pattern. She connects the centers of three flowers in the pattern to form a triangle. The sides of the triangle measure 3, 4, and 5 centimeters. Liz wants the longest distance between two flowers in the enlargement to be 12 centimeters. Where should Liz place the third flower in the enlargement?

   a. What side corresponds to the longest side of the enlargement? $\overline{AC}$

   b. What question is implied ? See margin.

   c. What assumption is made? See margin.

   d. What can be done to solve this problem? Set up a proportion.

   e. Draw and label a sketch to illustrate the enlargement. See margin.

   f. State a proportion you would use to find the length of the shortest side of the enlargement. $\frac{5}{12} = \frac{3}{x}$

Guided Practice

Write a proportion to find each missing measure x. Then find x.

2.

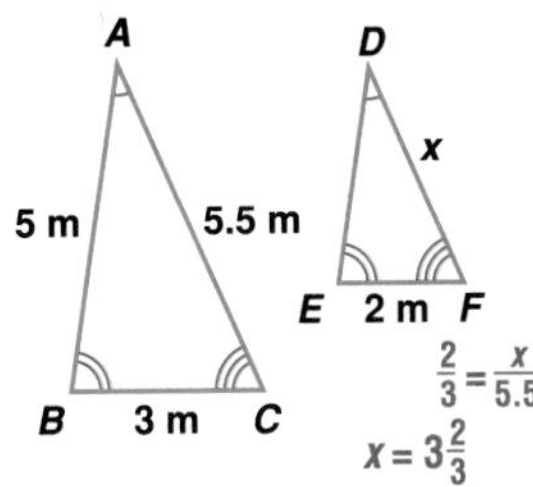

$\frac{2}{3} = \frac{x}{5.5}$

$x = 3\frac{2}{3}$

3.

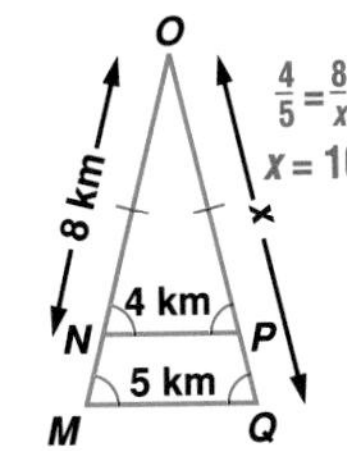

$\frac{4}{5} = \frac{8}{x}$

$x = 10$

Exercises

Independent Practice

Write a proportion to find each missing measure x. Then find x.

4.

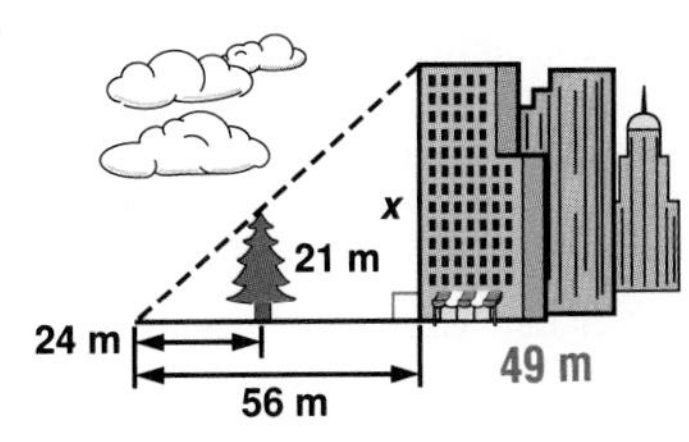

5.

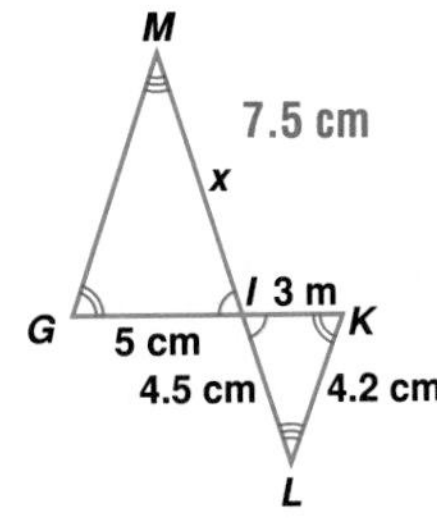

Mixed Review

6. Name two ways a graph can be misleading. (Lesson 10-9) See margin.

7. Find x. (Lesson 12-9) 2.7 ft

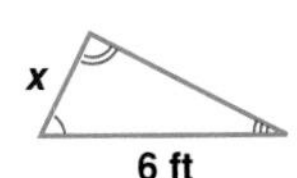

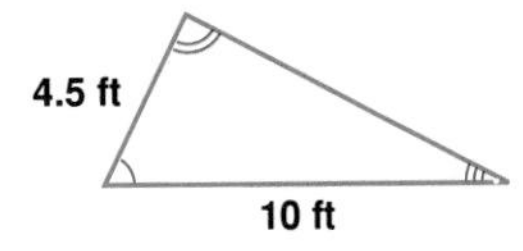

3 PRACTICE/APPLY

Checking the Concept

After completing Exercises 2 and 3, discuss solutions in cooperative groups.

Error Analysis
Watch for students who use proportions from triangles that are not similar. **Prevent by** measuring angles to assure similarity.

Independent Practice

Homework Assignment	
Basic	4-11, 14, 15
Average	5-12, 14, 15
Honors	6-15

Practice Masters Booklet, **p. 119**

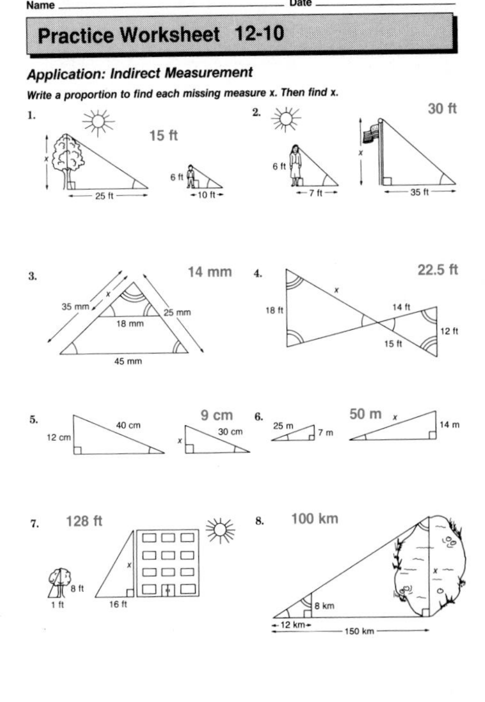

Name ________ Date ________

Practice Worksheet 12-10

Application: Indirect Measurement

Write a proportion to find each missing measure x. Then find x.

1. 15 ft
2. 30 ft
3. 14 mm
4. 22.5 ft
5. 9 cm
6. 50 m
7. 128 ft
8. 100 km

Alternate Strategies: Reteaching the Lesson

Reteaching Activity

Using Measurement Have students go outside on a sunny day. Use a meter stick and the length of its shadow and the length of the shadow of some tall object to determine the height of the taller object.

Reteaching Masters Booklet, **p. 107**

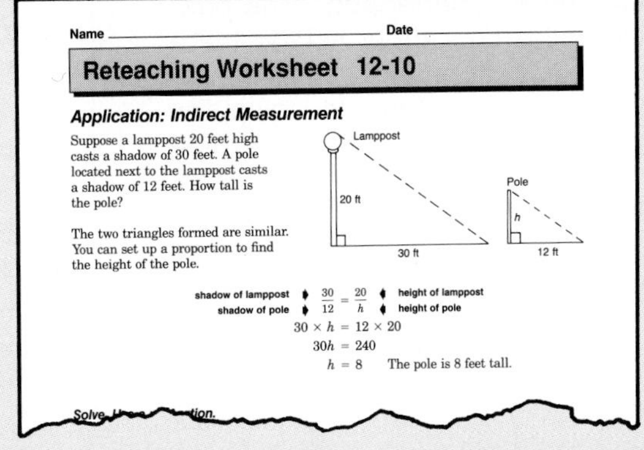

Name ________ Date ________

Reteaching Worksheet 12-10

Application: Indirect Measurement

Suppose a lamppost 20 feet high casts a shadow of 30 feet. A pole located next to the lamppost casts a shadow of 12 feet. How tall is the pole?

The two triangles formed are similar. You can set up a proportion to find the height of the pole.

shadow of lamppost → $\frac{30}{12} = \frac{20}{h}$ ← height of lamppost
shadow of pole → ← height of pole

$30 \times h = 12 \times 20$

$30h = 240$

$h = 8$ The pole is 8 feet tall.

Solve ... tion.

4 CLOSE

Assessment Option

Writing Have the students write a proportion with a variable. Then have them find the value of the variable and make a drawing of similar triangles with the same measures for segments.

Additional Answers

1b. What are the other two distances?

1c. The enlargement forms a similar triangle.

1e.

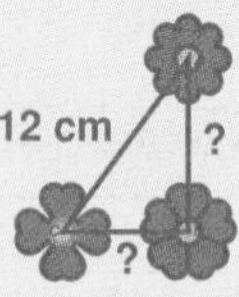

6. No titles or labels; using different scales.

14. Sample answer: No measuring tools are used to measure the missing length.

Enrichment Masters Booklet, **p. 107**

Name ______________________ Date ______________

Enrichment Worksheet 12-10

Nine-Point Circle

The **nine-point circle**, or **Feuerbach circle**, is a circle on which the following nine points lie. This holds true for any triangle.

Points 1, 2, and 3: the midpoints of the sides of the triangle

Points 4, 5, and 6: the points where the altitudes intersect the sides of the triangle

Points 7, 8, and 9: the midpoints of the segments that join the vertices of the triangle to the point of intersection (orthocenter) of the altitudes

Construct the nine-point circle for $\triangle ABC$ as follows.

Step 1 Construct the perpendicular bisectors of the sides. Locate the midpoints of $\overline{AB}$, $\overline{BC}$, and $\overline{AC}$. Label these points 1, 2, and 3.

Step 2 Label the intersection of the perpendicular bisectors D (circumcenter).

Step 3 Construct a line from each vertex perpendicular to the opposite side. Label the points where these altitudes meet the sides 4, 5, and 6. Label the point of intersection of the altitudes O.

Step 4 Construct the midpoints of $\overline{OA}$, $\overline{OB}$, and $\overline{OC}$. Label these points 7, 8, and 9.

Step 5 Draw $\overline{OD}$. Construct the midpoint of $\overline{OD}$. Label it F.

Step 6 Draw the nine-point circle with center F and radius $F1$. Points 1, 2, 3, 4, 5, 6, 7, 8, and 9 will lie on the circle.

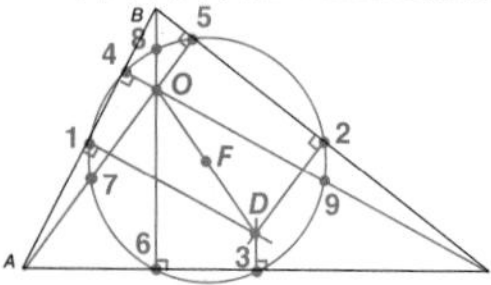

Give the name of the point of intersection for the following in relationship to triangles.

1. perpendicular bisectors circumcenter
2. altitudes orthocenter
3. The line determined by point O (orthocenter) and point D (circumcenter) is a special line. Do research and find the name of this line. Euler's Line

Applications

8. **Crafts** Mark wants to cut a triangular patch to make an emblem. The pattern for the emblem is a triangle with sides 8, 8, and 10 centimeters. If Mark wants to make the longest side of the emblem 25 centimeters, how long should the other sides be? **20 cm; 20 cm**

9. **Geography** On a map, the length from Cleveland to New York is 7 cm, from Cleveland to Atlanta is 10 cm, and from New York to Atlanta is 13 cm. If on a larger map the length from Cleveland to New York is 17.5 cm, what are the other two lengths? **Cleveland to Atlanta: 25 cm; New York to Atlanta: 32.5 cm**

10. Find the length of Kingly Lake. **2.7 mi**

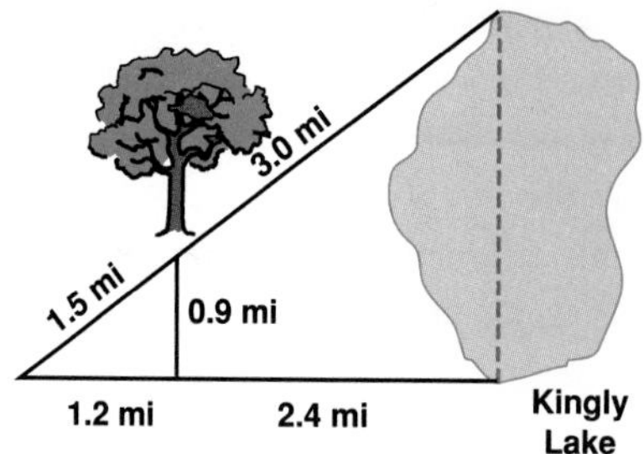

11. Find the length of the brace. **2.6 ft**

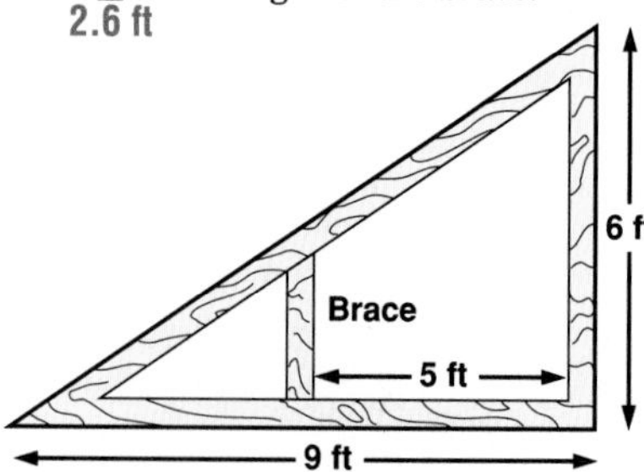

12. Find the length of Cedar Lane. **about 5.1 km**

Cedar Lane
Walnut Avenue
4 km
Oak Street
1 km
3.5 km
Maple Drive

13. Find the distance across the pond from point A to point B. **$10\frac{2}{3}$ m**

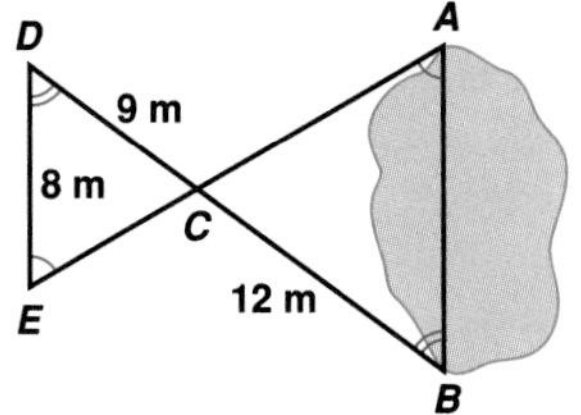

Critical Thinking

14. Written Exercises 8-13 above are examples of indirect measurement. Explain why it is called indirect measurement. **See margin.**

Wrap-Up

15. Explain how you could use indirect measurement to determine the height of your school building. **Sample answer: Measure the shadow of a meterstick and the school building. Set up a proportion.**

History

African Observers of the Universe

In the Republic of Mali in West Africa, there is a people called the Dogons who have an extremely complex knowledge of astronomy.

They are especially knowledgeable in the Sirius star system. Sirius is the brightest star in the sky. Without the use of a telescope, they have observed and studied the elliptical orbit of Sirius' small companion star, Sirius B, and have plotted its course and trajectory from the thirteenth century to the present.

Modern astronomy, with its most advanced observatories, has confirmed that Sirius B is in fact in orbit around Sirius. The fact that the Dogons have known this for 700 years, just on the basis of the naked eye, is truly amazing.

Alternate Strategies: Extending the Lesson

Enrichment

Geometry Connection The principles learned about similar triangles also apply to other similar figures. Have students solve the following problem. A photo is to be enlarged to four times its present area. By what number would its length and width be multiplied to quadruple the area of the photo? **2**

Cooperative Learning

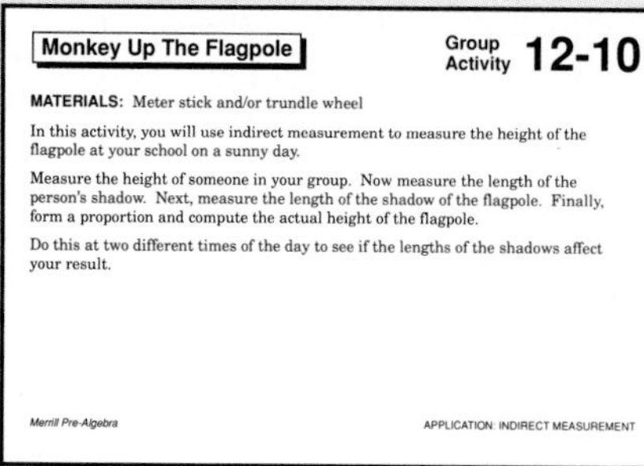

Monkey Up The Flagpole Group Activity **12-10**

MATERIALS: Meter stick and/or trundle wheel

In this activity, you will use indirect measurement to measure the height of the flagpole at your school on a sunny day.

Measure the height of someone in your group. Now measure the length of the person's shadow. Next, measure the length of the shadow of the flagpole. Finally, form a proportion and compute the actual height of the flagpole.

Do this at two different times of the day to see if the lengths of the shadows affect your result.

Merrill Pre-Algebra APPLICATION: INDIRECT MEASUREMENT

12-11 Quadrilaterals

Objectives:
Find the missing angle measure of a quadrilateral.
Classify quadrilaterals.

Key Terms:
quadrilateral
trapezoid
parallelogram
rectangle
rhombus
square

Geometric figures are often used to make patterns for quilts. All of the figures used to make the design in the quilt shown at the right are four-sided figures called **quadrilaterals.**

Just as with triangles, there is a relationship among the measures of the angles of a quadrilateral. Try the following activity.

1. Draw a quadrilateral. Label its vertices *A, B, C,* and *D.*
2. Use a protractor to find the measure of each angle.
3. Find the sum of the angle measures.
4. Repeat steps 1-3 with other quadrilaterals.
5. Select one of the quadrilaterals and draw $\overline{AC}$. Note that two triangles are formed.

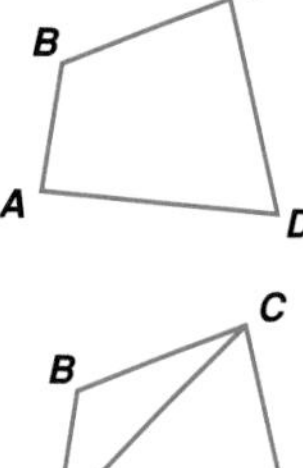

Since the sum of the measures of the angles of a triangle is 180°, what is the sum of the measures of the angles of the two triangles?

The activity above will work with any quadrilateral. This activity suggests the following relationship.

Angles of a Quadrilateral	The sum of the measures of the angles of a quadrilateral is 360°.

Example

1 Find the measures of the angles in the quadrilateral.

The sum of the measures of the angles is 360°.

$$75 + 40 + x + x = 360$$
$$115 + 2x = 360$$
$$2x = 245$$
$$x = 122\frac{1}{2}$$

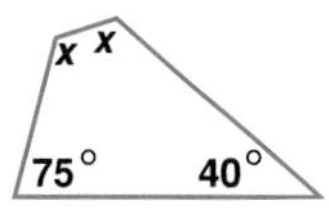

The measures of the angles are 75°, 40°, $122\frac{1}{2}$°, and $122\frac{1}{2}$°.

Bell Ringer

Name a situation where you could use indirect measurement.
Answers will vary.

Lesson Notes 12-11

5-Minute Check
(over Lesson 12-10)

Write a proportion to find the missing measure *x*. Then find *x*.

1. A 9-foot ladder touches the side of a building $7\frac{1}{2}$ feet above the ground. At what height would the top of a 16-foot ladder touch the building if both ladders form the same angle with the ground? **$13\frac{1}{3}$ ft**
2. At a certain time of the day, a flagpole casts a shadow 20.4 meters long. A parking meter nearby casts a shadow 2 meters long. The top of the parking meter is 1.5 meters above the ground. Find the height of the flagpole. **15.3 m**

Transparency 12-11 contains the 5-Minute Check and a teaching aid for this lesson.

1 FOCUS

The purpose of this lesson is to classify quadrilaterals according to their sides and find the missing angle measure in a quadrilateral.

Motivating the Lesson

Draw different quadrilaterals on note cards. Have a student pick a card without showing it to anyone else and describe it to the class. Have one student try to draw the figure at the board as the other describes it. Repeat until the cards are done.

2 TEACH

Using Models

Have students complete the lesson activity using different types of quadrilaterals.

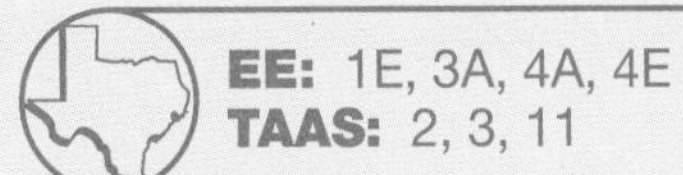

EE: 1E, 3A, 4A, 4E
TAAS: 2, 3, 11

Chalkboard Examples

- *For Example 1*
  Find the measures of the angles in the quadrilateral shown below. $x = 130°$

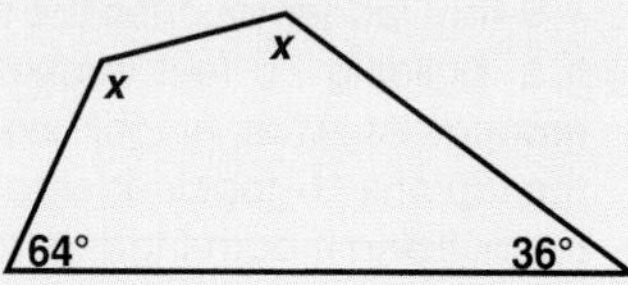

3 PRACTICE/APPLY

Checking the Concept

After completing Exercises 4-6, have students use a calculator to check answers.

Error Analysis

Watch for students who do not determine missing angles correctly. **Prevent by** writing all calculations or using a calculator to check.

Practice Masters Booklet, **p. 120**

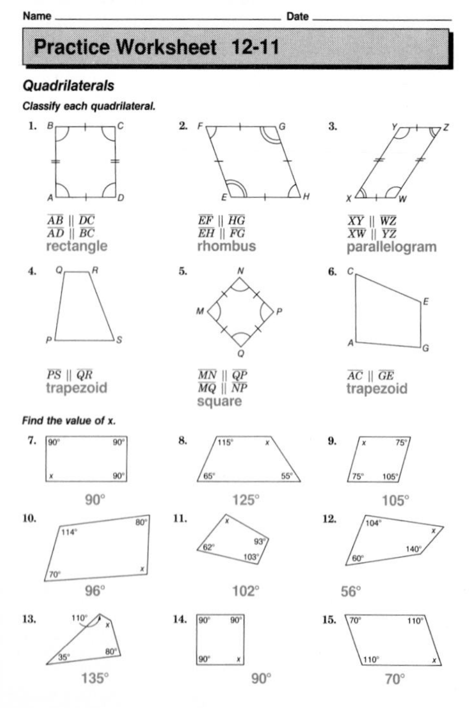

Name ______________ Date ______________

Practice Worksheet 12-11

Quadrilaterals

Classify each quadrilateral.

1. $\overline{AB} \parallel \overline{DC}$, $\overline{AD} \parallel \overline{BC}$ rectangle
2. $\overline{EF} \parallel \overline{HG}$, $\overline{EH} \parallel \overline{FG}$ rhombus
3. $\overline{XY} \parallel \overline{WZ}$, $\overline{XW} \parallel \overline{YZ}$ parallelogram
4. $\overline{PS} \parallel \overline{QR}$ trapezoid
5. $\overline{MN} \parallel \overline{QP}$, $\overline{MQ} \parallel \overline{NP}$ square
6. $\overline{AC} \parallel \overline{GE}$ trapezoid

Find the value of x.

7. 90°, 90°, 90°, x — 90°
8. 115°, x, 65°, 55° — 125°
9. x, 75°, 75°, 105° — 105°
10. 114°, 80°, 70°, x — 96°
11. x, 62°, 93°, 103° — 102°
12. 104°, x, 140°, 60° — 56°
13. 110°, x, 35°, 80° — 135°
14. 90°, 90°, 90°, x — 90°
15. 70°, 110°, 110°, x — 70°

There are also special kinds of quadrilaterals. They can be classified by the relationship of their sides and angles. Some of the well-known members of the quadrilateral family and their definitions are shown in the chart below.

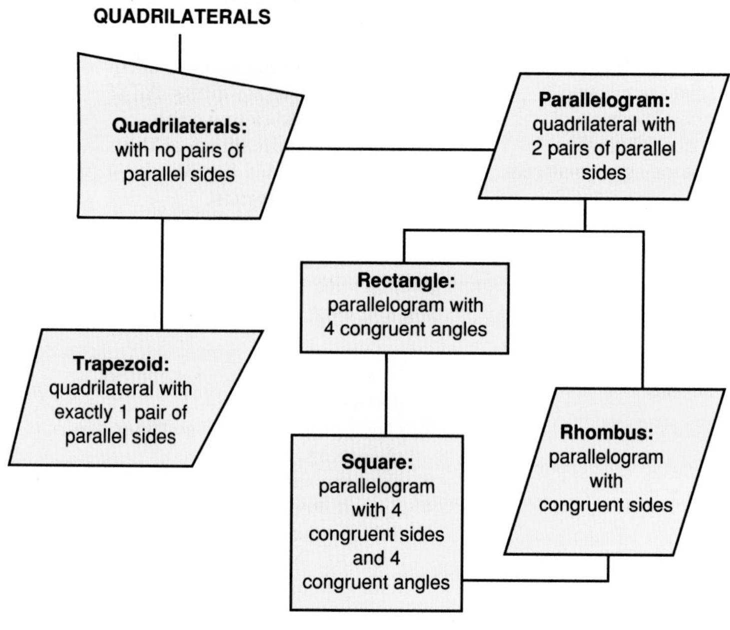

Checking for Understanding

Communicating Algebra

1. Which quadrilaterals have all four sides congruent? rhombus, square
2. Which quadrilaterals have two pairs of parallel sides? parallelogram, rhombus, square, rectangle
3. Which quadrilaterals have all four angles congruent? rectangle, square

Guided Practice

Find the value of x.

4.

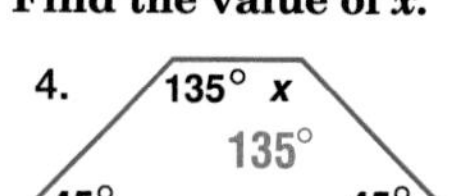

5.

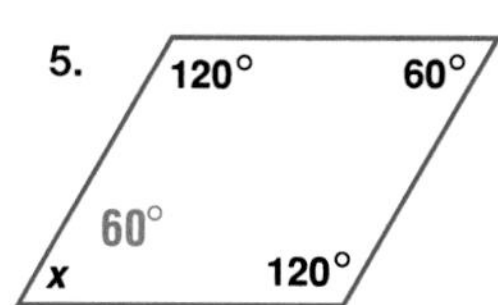

6.

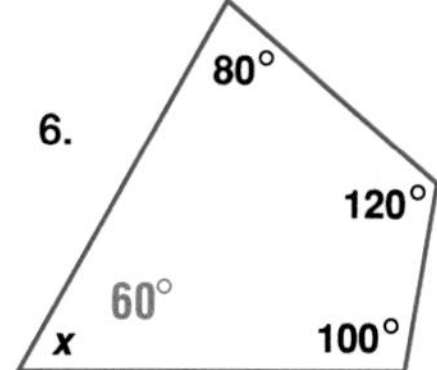

Classify each quadrilateral.

7. 8. 9.

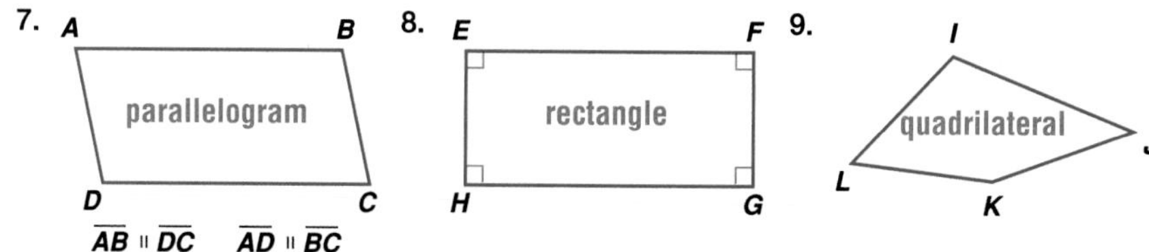

Alternate Strategies: Reteaching the Lesson

Reteaching Activity

Physical Education Connection
Have students measure one angle on a home plate at a baseball diamond then determine the other angles.

Reteaching Masters Booklet, **p. 108**

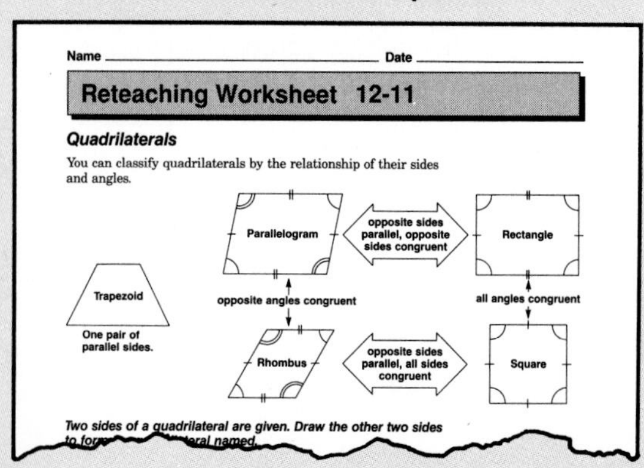

Name ______________ Date ______________

Reteaching Worksheet 12-11

Quadrilaterals

You can classify quadrilaterals by the relationship of their sides and angles.

Two sides of a quadrilateral are given. Draw the other two sides

Exercises

Independent Practice

Classify each quadrilateral.

10. 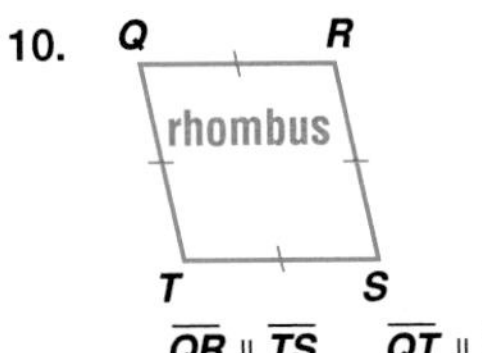

11. 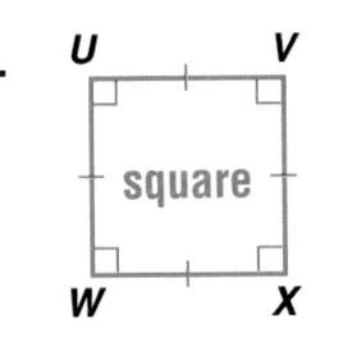

12. 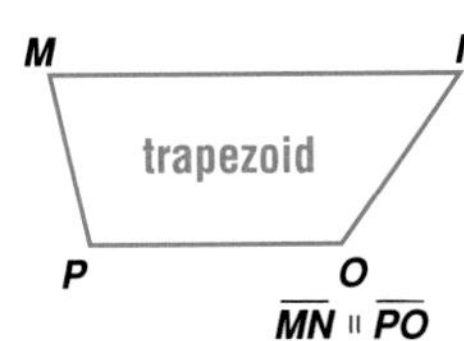

Find the value of x.

13. 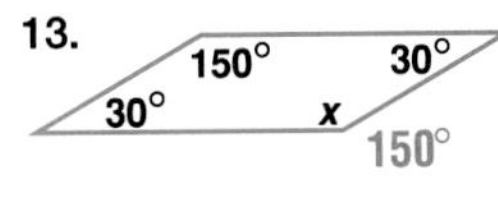

14. 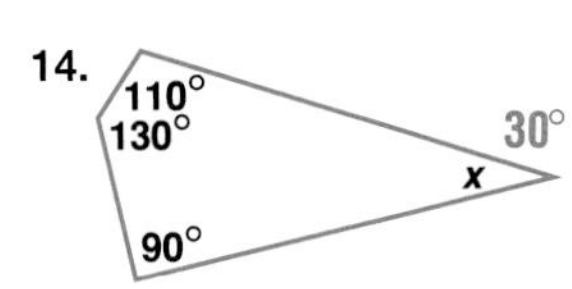

15. 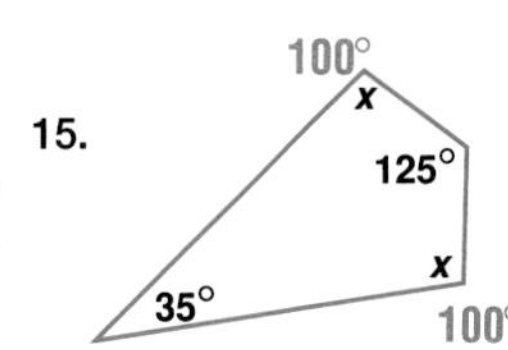

Logical Reasoning

Determine whether each statement is *always, sometimes,* or *never* true.

16. A rectangle is a parallelogram. always
17. A rectangle is a square. sometimes
18. A rhombus is a square. sometimes
19. A trapezoid is a parallelogram. never
20. A square is a parallelogram. always
21. A square is a rhombus. always

Mixed Review

22. Solve $a = \frac{-95}{5}$. (Lesson 2-8) −19
23. Factor 98 completely. (Lesson 4-4) 2 • 7 • 7
24. If $\angle A$ and $\angle B$ are complementary and $m\angle A = 70°$. Find $m\angle B$. (Lesson 12-3) 20°
25. Ed measures the shadow of an evergreen tree to be 8 feet and his shadow to be 3 feet. If Ed is 6 feet tall, how tall is the tree? (Lesson 12-10) 16 ft

Challenge

26. The measures of the four angles of a quadrilateral are $x - 15$, $x + 35$, $x + 20$, and x. Find each measure. 65°; 115°, 100°, 80°

Application

27. **Sports** The center portion of the main frame of the bicycle shown at the right is a trapezoid. Find x. 108°

Critical Thinking

28. Make a Venn diagram showing the relationship among members of the quadrilateral family. See margin.

Wrap-Up

29. Fold a sheet of paper in half and draw a trapezoid. Keep the paper folded and cut out two congruent trapezoids. Use your trapezoids to form a parallelogram. Then form a different parallelogram. See margin.

Independent Practice

Homework Assignment	
Basic	11-21 odd, 22-25, 27-29
Average	10-20 even, 22-29
Honors	12, 14, 18-29

4 CLOSE

Assessment Option

Writing Put the six types of quadrilaterals listed on page 472 on index cards. Go around the room and have the students draw a card. Then have them physically draw whatever quadrilateral is listed on the card, making sure it is different from any quadrilateral that has already been drawn.

Additional Answers

28.

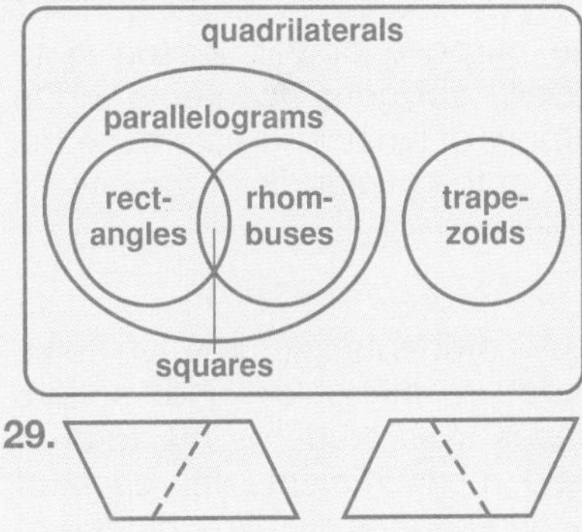

29.

Enrichment Masters Booklet, **p. 108**

Name ______________________ Date __________

Enrichment Worksheet 12-11

Polygons and Diagonals

A **diagonal** of a polygon is any segment that connects two non-consecutive vertices of the polygon. In each of the following polygons, all possible diagonals are drawn.

Example:

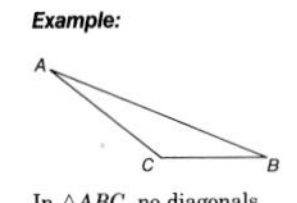

In $\triangle ABC$, no diagonals can be drawn. Why?

Example:

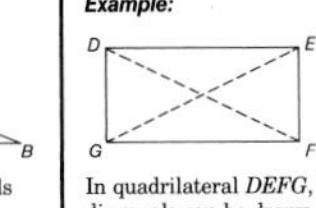

In quadrilateral *DEFG*, 2 diagonals can be drawn.

Example:

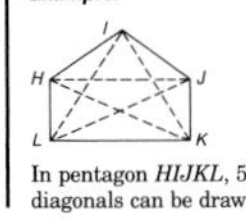

In pentagon *HIJKL*, 5 diagonals can be drawn.

Complete the chart below and try to find a pattern that will help you answer the questions that follow.

Polygons	Number of Sides	Number of Diagonals From One Vertex	Total Number of Diagonals
triangle	3	0	0
quadrilateral	4	1	2
pentagon	5	2	5
hexagon	6	1. 3	9
heptagon	7	2. 4	14
octagon	8	3. 5	20
nonagon	9	4. 6	27
decagon	10	5. 7	35

Find the total number of diagonals that can be drawn in a polygon with the given number of sides.

6. 6 9
7. 7 14
8. 8 20
9. 9 27
10. 10 35
11. 11 44
12. 12 54
1. 15 90
14. 20 170
15. 50 1175
16. 75 2700
17. n $\frac{n^2 - 3n}{2}$

Alternate Strategies: Extending the Lesson

Enrichment

Using Analysis Have students list each type of quadrilateral. For each, have them name the minimum number of angles that need to be measured so that the remaining angles can be determined. any parallelogram, 1; trapezoid, 2; no parallel sides, 3

Cooperative Learning

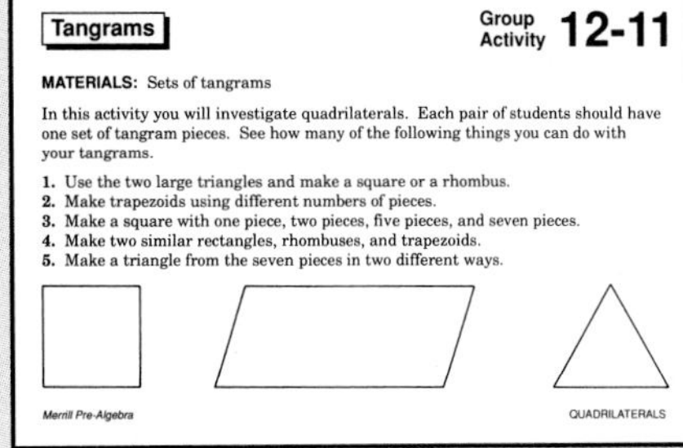

Tangrams Group Activity **12-11**

MATERIALS: Sets of tangrams

In this activity you will investigate quadrilaterals. Each pair of students should have one set of tangram pieces. See how many of the following things you can do with your tangrams.

1. Use the two large triangles and make a square or a rhombus.
2. Make trapezoids using different numbers of pieces.
3. Make a square with one piece, two pieces, five pieces, and seven pieces.
4. Make two similar rectangles, rhombuses, and trapezoids.
5. Make a triangle from the seven pieces in two different ways.

Merrill Pre-Algebra QUADRILATERALS

Lesson Notes 12-12

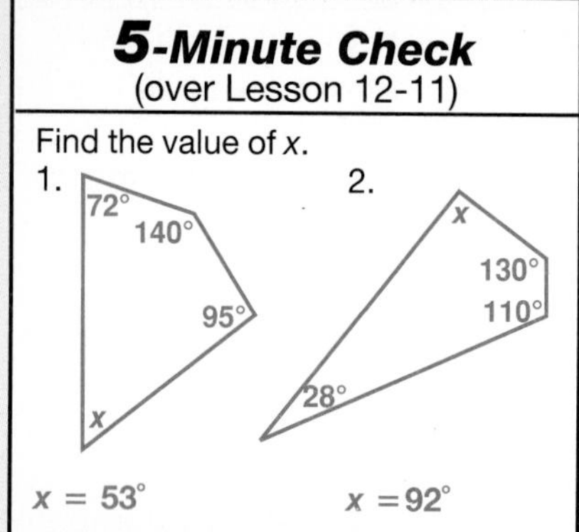

Transparency 12-12 contains the 5-Minute Check and a teaching aid for this lesson.

1 FOCUS

The purpose of this lesson is to classify polygons according to the number of sides and determine the sum of the measures of the interior angles.

Motivating the Lesson

Show students pictures of items made in triangular and square shapes. Ask students the total of angle measurements for each of the two shapes. Show a picture of the Pentagon in Washington, D.C. Ask for the total measurement of its angles.

2 TEACH

Using Models

Have students cut models of 3 to 6-sided polygons and measure the angles. Total each set of measurements. Divide each figure into triangles and confirm the total.

EE: 1E, 3A, 4A, 4E
TAAS: 2, 3, 11

12-12 Polygons

Objectives:
Classify polygons.
Determine the sum of the measures of the interior angles of a polygon.

Key Terms:
polygon
sides
vertices
regular polygon
equilateral
diagonal

The honeycomb shape of a beehive is a common example of a six-sided figure found in nature. The six-sided figure is a simple closed figure.

A simple closed figure can be traced in a continuous path without tracing any point other than the starting point more than once.

A **polygon** is a simple, closed figure formed by three or more line segments called **sides.** These sides are all in one plane and meet only at their endpoints. These points of intersection are called **vertices** (plural of **vertex**).

Polygons are classified by the number of sides. Some of the more common polygons are shown below.

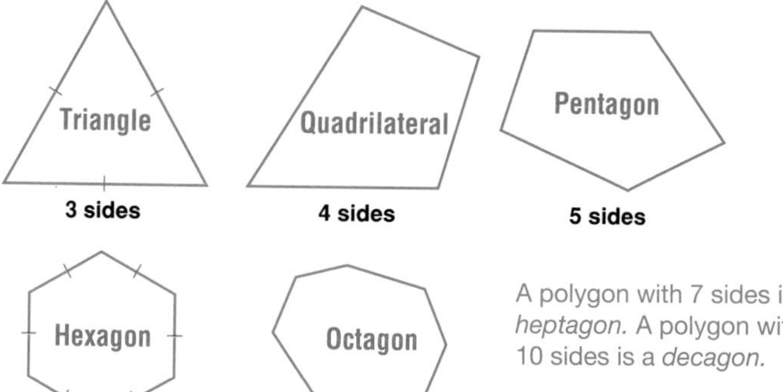

What would you call a polygon with n sides? ***n*-gon**

A polygon with 7 sides is a *heptagon.* A polygon with 10 sides is a *decagon.*

A **regular polygon** is a polygon that has all sides congruent and all angles congruent. The triangle and hexagon above are examples of regular polygons. The regular triangle is called an **equilateral** triangle. A regular quadrilateral is a square.

Bell Ringer

Name three things that a rhombus, a rectangle, and a square have in common. **Answers will vary. Poss. Ans.: They are all parallelograms, they are all quadrilaterals, their angles' sum is 180°.**

A **diagonal** of a polygon is a line segment that joins two nonconsecutive vertices. In each of the following polygons, all possible diagonals from one vertex are shown.

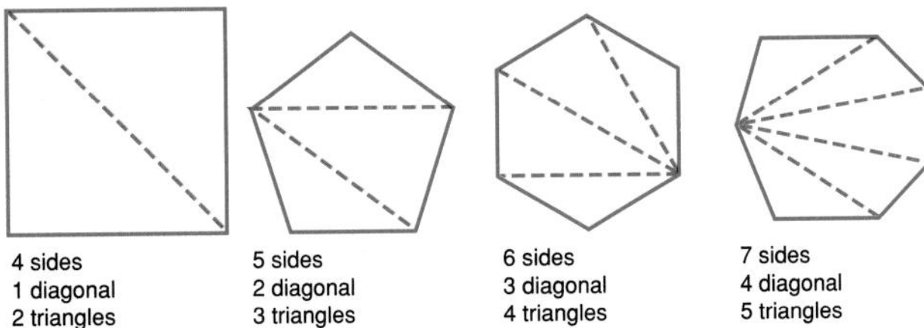

Notice that the number of triangles is equal to the number of sides minus two. You can use diagonals and the property of the sum of the angles of a triangle to determine the sum of the measures of the angles of any polygon without using a protractor.

If a polygon has n sides, then the sum of the degree measures of its angles is $(n - 2)180$.

Examples

1 Find the sum of the measures of the angles of a pentagon.

A pentagon has five sides. Therefore, $n = 5$.

$(n - 2)180 = (5 - 2)180$ Replace n with 5.

$= 3 \cdot 180$ or 540

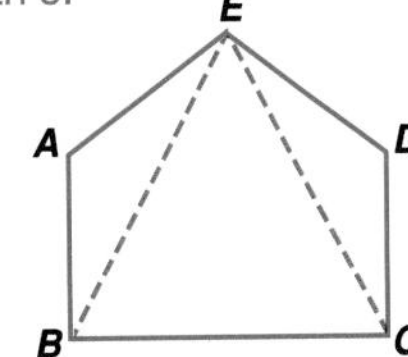

Check by drawing a pentagon and drawing the diagonals. There are three triangles. The solution checks.

The sum of the measures of the angles of a pentagon is 540°.

2 Find the sum of the measures of the angles of an octagon.

An octagon has eight sides. Therefore, $n = 8$.

$(n - 2)180 = (8 - 2)180$ Replace n with 8.

$= 6 \cdot 180$ or 1080 Check this solution.

The sum of the measures of the angles of an octagon is 1080°.

Checking for Understanding

Communicating Algebra

1. In your own words, explain what a regular polygon is. **See margin.**
2. Draw a hexagon and its diagonals. **See margin.**
3. What is the relationship between the number of sides in a polygon and the number of triangles formed by the diagonals? **The number of triangles is equal to the number of sides minus two.**

Chalkboard Examples

- *For Example 1*
  Find the sum of the measures of the angles of a hexagon. 720°
- *For Example 2*
  Find the sum of the measures of the angles of a 7-sided quadrilateral. 900°

3 PRACTICE/APPLY

Checking the Concept

Before completing Exercises 4-6, discuss the importance of the term "appears." Emphasize that sometimes measurements must be made because a polygon may appear regular but may not be.

Additional Answers

1. A regular polygon is a polygon with all sides and all angles congruent.
2.

19.

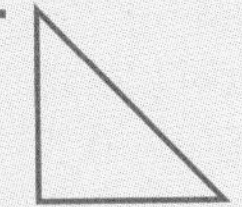

Practice Masters Booklet, **p. 121**

Name ____________ Date ____________

Practice Worksheet 12-12

Polygons

Find the sum of the measures of the angles of each polygon.

1. quadrilateral 360°	2. pentagon 540°	3. octagon 1080°
4. 12-gon 1800°	5. 18-gon 2880°	6. 20-gon 3240°
7. 30-gon 5040°	8. 45-gon 7740°	9. 75-gon 13,140°

Find the perimeter of each regular polygon.

10. triangle with sides 25 centimeters long 75 cm
11. pentagon with sides 11 millimeters long 55 mm
12. octagon with sides 15 feet long 120 ft
13. quadrilateral with sides 12.4 meters long 49.6 m
14. hexagon with sides 28.5 millimeters long 171 mm
15. decagon with sides 2.5 inches long 25 in.
16. heptagon with sides 10.75 feet long 75.25 ft
17. 12-gon with side 3.25 yards long 39 yd
18. 25-gon with sides 6 inches long 150 in.
19. 100-gon with sides 9 centimeters long 900 cm

Alternate Strategies: Reteaching the Lesson

Reteaching Activity

Using Models Obtain a copy of pictures or diagrams of road signs from the Bureau of Motor Vehicles. Identify the shape of each and determine the sum of its angle measurements.

Reteaching Masters Booklet, **p. 109**

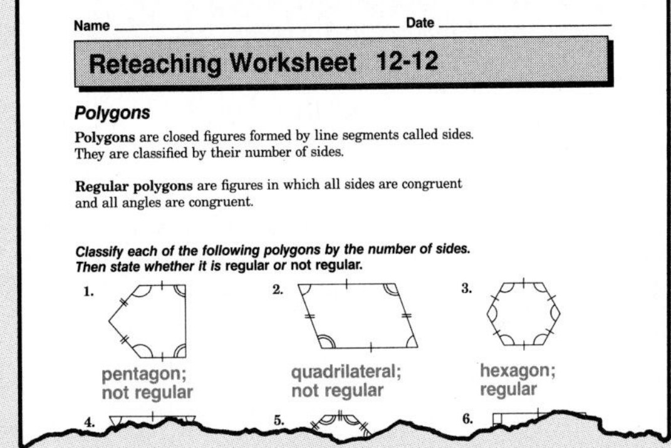
Name ____________ Date ____________

Reteaching Worksheet 12-12

Polygons

Polygons are closed figures formed by line segments called sides. They are classified by their number of sides.

Regular polygons are figures in which all sides are congruent and all angles are congruent.

Classify each of the following polygons by the number of sides. Then state whether it is regular or not regular.

1. pentagon; not regular
2. quadrilateral; not regular
3. hexagon; regular
4.
5.
6.

Error Analysis

Watch for students who assume that regular and irregular polygons have different sums of their angles. **Prevent by** modeling regular and irregular polygons.

Independent Practice

Homework Assignment	
Basic	7-15 odd, 17-23
Average	8-16 even, 17-23
Honors	11-23

Chapter 12, Quiz B (Lesson 12-7 through 12-12) is available in the Evaluation Masters Booklet, p. 106.

4 CLOSE

Assessment Option

Speaking Go around the room and have the students think of some object and state the shape of the object. For example, a pentagon is inside a star, a notebook is a quadrilateral, the Pentagon is a pentagon, a stop sign is an octagon. Have each student say one object and its shape.

Enrichment Masters Booklet, **p. 109**

Guided Practice

Classify each polygon below and determine whether it appears to be *regular* or *not regular*.

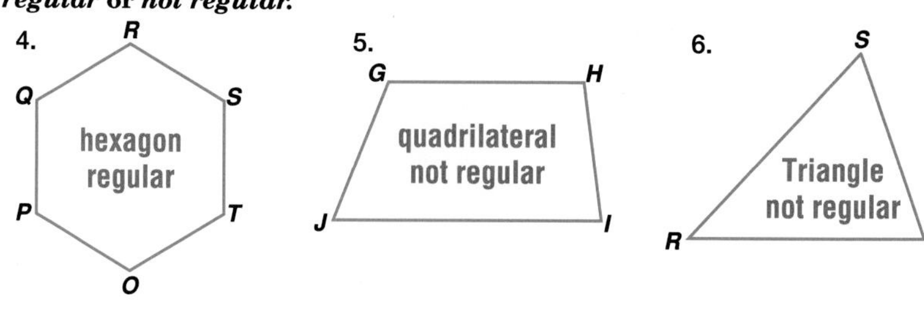

Exercises

Independent Practice

Find the sum of the measures of the angles of each polygon.

7. hexagon **720°**
8. heptagon **900°**
9. decagon **1440°**
10. 25-gon **4140°**
11. 50-gon **8640°**
12. 100-gon **17,640°**

Find the perimeter of each regular polygon.

13. triangle with sides 30 feet long **90 ft**
14. pentagon with sides 25 inches long **125 in.**
15. quadrilateral with sides 16.7 meters long **66.8 m**
16. hexagon with sides 34.5 meters long **207 m**

Mixed Review

17. **Statistics** Find the mean, median, and mode of the following data: 0.5, 0.7, 0.3, 0.4, 0.4, 0.6, 1.6, 0.4, 0.8, 0.3. (Lesson 10-2) **0.6, 0.45, 0.4**
18. **Probability** A coin is tossed, then a die is rolled. Find *P*(tails and 6). (Lesson 11-6) $\frac{1}{12}$
19. Using a protractor, draw a right triangle. (Lesson 12-6) **See margin.**
20. *True* or *false*: A rectangle is a parallelogram with all angles congruent. (Lesson 12-11) **true**

Application

21. **Manufacturing** The S & D Company has an order from a flooring company for tiles to be cut in the shape of regular hexagons. At what angle should the cutting machine be set so that the measure of each angle of each tile is identical? **120°**

Critical Thinking

22. Trace the dot pattern shown at the right. Without lifting your pencil from the paper, draw four line segments that connect all the points.

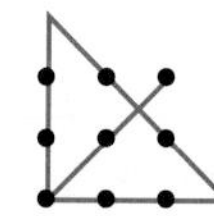

23. Explain why a square is a regular polygon. **See margin.**

Team Problem Solving

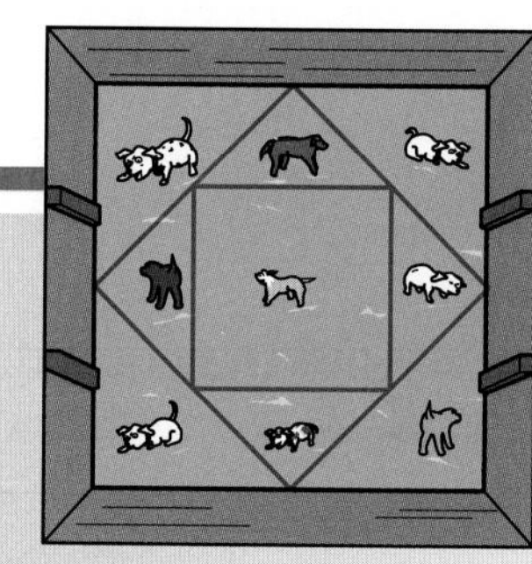

Mrs. O'Grady buys a square building to use as a dog kennel. She thinks that she can house 9 dogs in this kennel in the formation shown at the right. However, she feels it would be best if there were a fence to separate the dogs. She calls in the fencing company and asks them to build two fences in the shape of squares so that no two dogs share the same area. The fencing company is confused. Can you help?

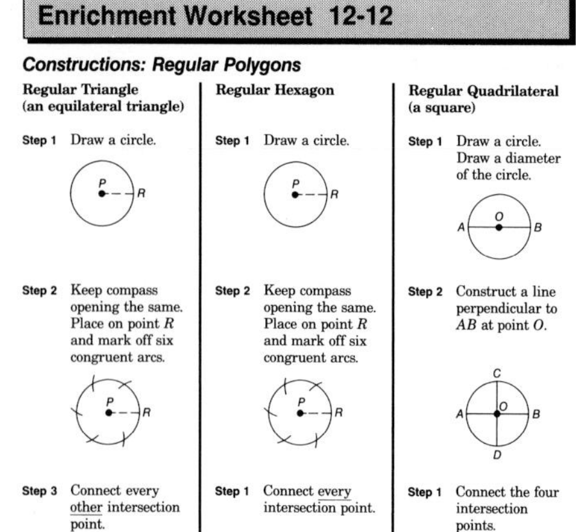

Name ______ Date ______

Enrichment Worksheet 12-12

Constructions: Regular Polygons

Regular Triangle (an equilateral triangle)	Regular Hexagon	Regular Quadrilateral (a square)
Step 1 Draw a circle.	Step 1 Draw a circle.	Step 1 Draw a circle. Draw a diameter of the circle.
Step 2 Keep compass opening the same. Place on point *R* and mark off six congruent arcs.	Step 2 Keep compass opening the same. Place on point *R* and mark off six congruent arcs.	Step 2 Construct a line perpendicular to *AB* at point *O*.
Step 3 Connect every other intersection point.	Step 1 Connect every intersection point.	Step 1 Connect the four intersection points.
Figure *RST* is a regular triangle.	Figure *RUSVTW* is a regular hexagon.	Figure *ADBC* is a regular quadrilateral.

Complete each construction.

1. a regular quadrilateral **See example above.**
2. a regular hexagon **See example above.**

Alternate Strategies: Extending the Lesson

Enrichment

Using Models Construct a regular hexagon. Use a compass to draw a circle. Measure its radius with the compass. Keep the length set; place both ends on the circle and make an arc. Place the point on the arc. Repeat. Continue around the circle. Connect with chords. Measure and total angles. Check mathematically.

Cooperative Learning

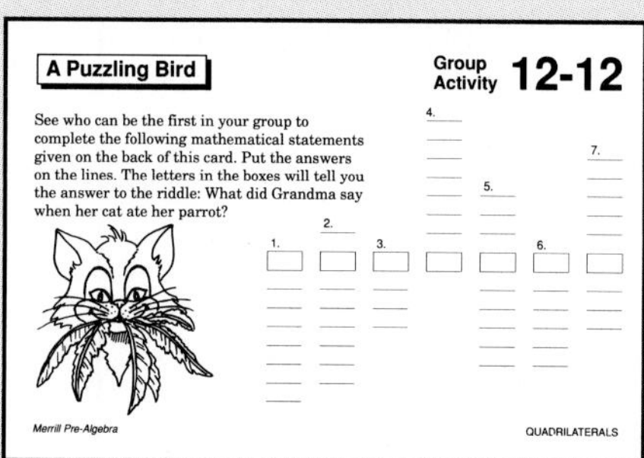

A Puzzling Bird Group Activity **12-12**

See who can be the first in your group to complete the following mathematical statements given on the back of this card. Put the answers on the lines. The letters in the boxes will tell you the answer to the riddle: What did Grandma say when her cat ate her parrot?

Merrill Pre-Algebra QUADRILATERALS

Tessellations

Materials: tracing paper, cardboard, scissors

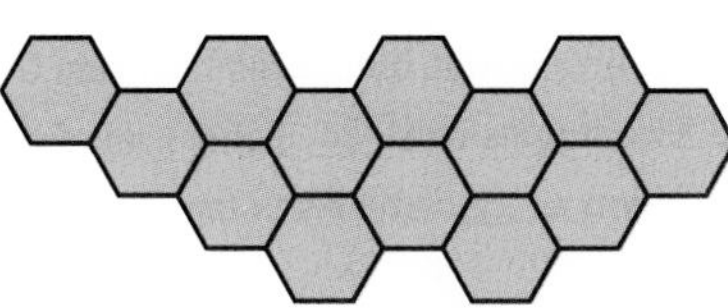

The repetitive pattern of regular polygons shown at the right is an example of a **tessellation.** In a tessellation, the polygons fit together with no holes or gaps.

In this Exploration, you will investigate tessellations with regular polygons.

Your Turn: Work with a partner.

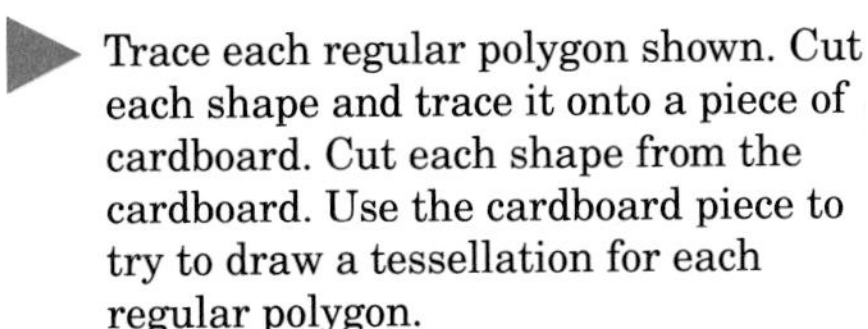

- Trace each regular polygon shown. Cut each shape and trace it onto a piece of cardboard. Cut each shape from the cardboard. Use the cardboard piece to try to draw a tessellation for each regular polygon.

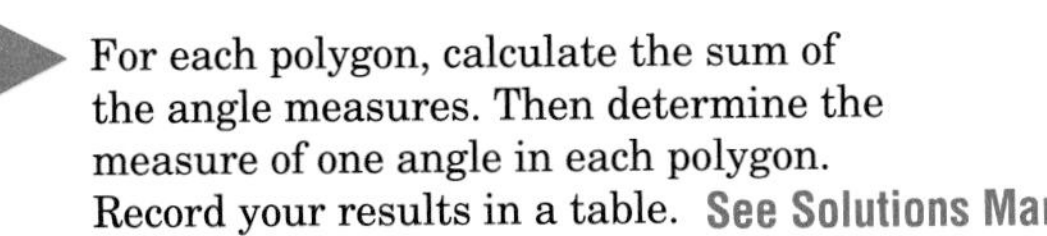

- For each polygon, calculate the sum of the angle measures. Then determine the measure of one angle in each polygon. Record your results in a table. See Solutions Manual.

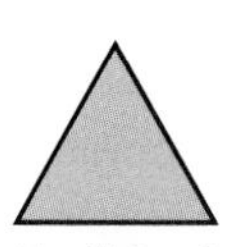

Equilateral Triangle

Square

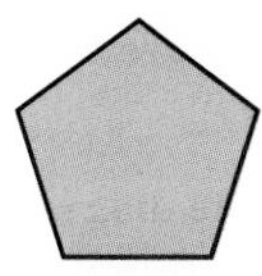

Regular Pentagon

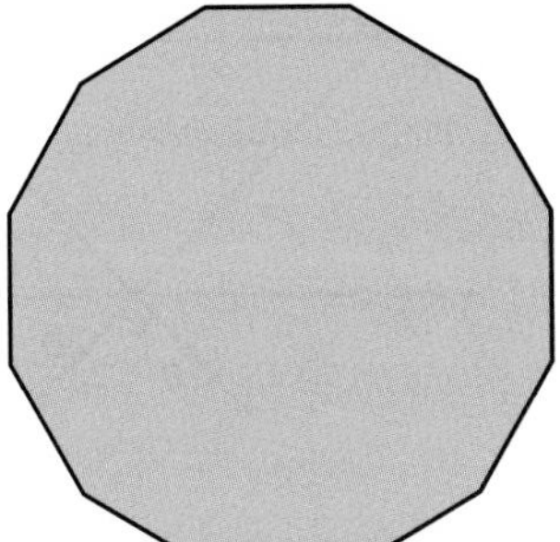

Regular Dodecagon

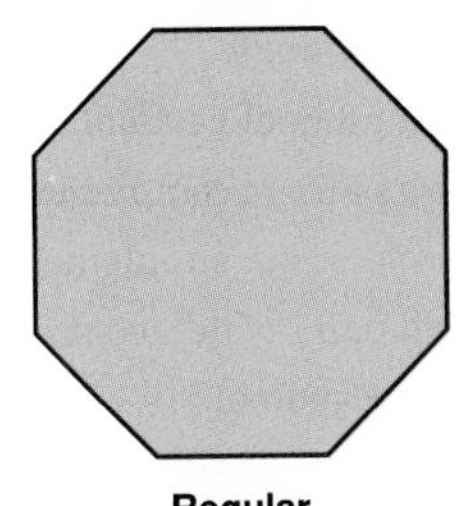

Regular Octagon

Analysis

1. How can you tell from the measure of one angle whether or not a polygon will tessellate? See margin.
2. Try to make tessellations from the combinations below. See students' work.
   a. square and octagon
   b. square, triangle, and hexagon
   c. square, triangle, and dodecagon
   d. another combination you choose
3. Describe a pattern similar to the one in Exercise 1 that tells whether a combination of polygons will tessellate. See margin.

EXPLORATION

Tessellations

Objective Students will recognize a tessellation.

1 FOCUS

This exploration allows the student to make connections between the measure of one angle of a polygon and whether the polygon tessellates.

Motivating the Exploration

Show students a honeycomb or a picture of a honeycomb. Ask students to describe the pattern.

2 TEACH

Using Models

Trace a regular hexagon on the chalkboard or overhead. Show students how to calculate the sum of the angle measures of other regular polygons by drawing all the diagonals possible from one vertex. Have students count the number of triangles formed and multiply by 180.

3 PRACTICE/APPLY

Using Tables

Have students make a table with four columns headed Name of Polygon, Sum of Angles, Measure of One Angle, and Does the Polygon Tessellate?. Tell students to include the hexagon in their table.

Using Models

Suggest that students look at the angles formed when two shapes are put together. For example, if a square is to be part of a tessellation, what kind of angle must be formed? right angle

4 CLOSE

Using Models

Have students try to find a pentagon that tessellates.

SET-UP

Materials

- tracing paper, cardboard, scissors

You may wish to use the Exploration worksheet provided on page 61 of the Lab Manual.

For Students Some students may benefit from tracing the shapes, cutting several out, and putting them together.

Additional Answers

1. **If the measure of the angle is a multiple of 30, the polygon will tessellate.**
3. **Sample answer: If the measure of the sum of the angles in the combination of polygons is a multiple of 120, the combination of polygons will tessellate.**

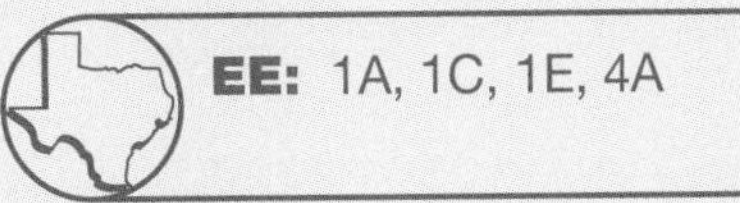

Using the Chapter Review

The Chapter Review is a comprehensive review of the concepts presented in this chapter. This review may be used to prepare students for the Chapter Test.

Alternate Review Strategy

To provide a brief in-class review, you may wish to read the following questions to the class and require a verbal response.

1. What is the difference between a line segment and a ray? A line segment has 2 end points, a ray has only 1 end point.
2. How many degrees make up a circle graph? 360°
3. What are vertical angles? Angles that are opposite to one another.
4. If the measure of one interior angle is 65°, what is the measure of the alternate interior angle? 65°
5. What does bisecting a line segment mean? To draw a line segment through the midpoint of the given segment forming two congruent segments.
6. Find the $m\angle 3$ if $m\angle 1$ is 17° and $m\angle 2$ is 82°. 81°
7. Give the statement "All 3-sided figures are triangles." in the form of a conditional. If a figure has 3 sides, then it is a triangle.
8. If $\triangle DEF \cong \triangle AMK$, name the side congruent to $\overline{EF}$. $\overline{MK}$
9. If $\triangle CBD \sim \triangle GEF$ and $\angle B \sim \angle E$, what side is similar to $\overline{DC}$? $\overline{FG}$
10. What is the height of a chimney if a meter stick casts a 0.5 m shadow and the chimney casts a 4 m shadow? 8 m
11. What is a rhombus? A parallelogram with 4 congruent sides.
12. How are polygons classified? By the number of sides.

Review

Language and Concepts

Choose the correct letter to complete each sentence.

1. An angle that measures between 0° and 90° is _?_ . b
2. Two angles are _?_ if the sum of their measures is 90°. h
3. When a _?_ intersects two parallel lines, the corresponding angles are congruent. g
4. When a line is perpendicular to another line, the angles formed are _?_ angles. f
5. An angle that measures between 90° and 180° is _?_ . a
6. A parallelogram with four congruent sides is a _?_ . e
7. Two angles are _?_ if the sum of their measures is 180°. i

a. obtuse
b. acute
c. vertical
d. trapezoid
e. rhombus
f. right
g. transversal
h. complementary
i. supplementary

Skills

Draw a picture to represent each of the following. (Lesson 12-1) For Exercises 8-11, see margin.

8. point C
9. $\overrightarrow{XY}$
10. plane GHI
11. $\overleftrightarrow{RS}$

Refer to the diagram at the right to name each of the following. (Lessons 12-1, 12-3, 12-4) Sample answer given.

12. two obtuse angles $\angle JIF$; $\angle BCE$
13. two acute angles $\angle KIJ$; $\angle ECD$
14. a right angle $\angle FCK$
15. two pairs of vertical angles See margin.
16. two pairs of complementary angles See margin.
17. two pairs of supplementary angles See margin.
18. two pairs of adjacent angles See margin.
19. a transversal $\overleftrightarrow{BH}$
20. two pairs of alternate interior angles See margin.
21. two sets of corresponding angles $\angle JIF$ and $\angle ICE$; $\angle HFG$; $\angle FCE$
22. Trace $\angle IFC$ shown above. Construct an angle congruent to it. (Lesson 12-5)
23. Trace $\overline{IF}$ shown above. Construct a segment congruent to it. (Lesson 12-5)

For Exercises 22-23, see students' work.

Use the figure at the right to solve. (Lesson 12-6)

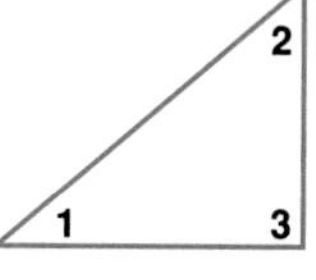

24. Find $m\angle 1$ if $m\angle 2 = 50°$ and $m\angle 3 = 80°$. 50°
25. Find $m\angle 2$ if $m\angle 1 = 72°$ and $m\angle 3 = 66°$. 42°

If $\triangle XYZ \cong \triangle ABC$, name the part congruent to each angle or segment.

26. $\angle X$ $\angle A$
27. $\angle B$ $\angle Y$
28. $\overline{YZ}$ $\overline{BC}$
29. $\overline{AC}$ $\overline{XZ}$

Additional Answers

8. • C

9.

10.

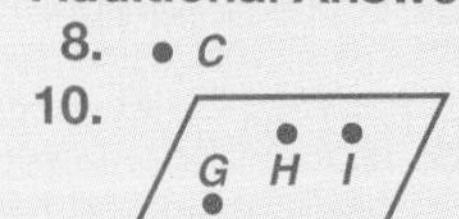

11.

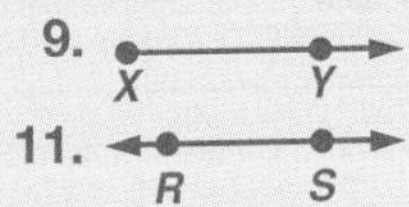

15. $\angle JIK$, $\angle FIC$; $\angle FCE$, $\angle ACB$
16. $\angle FCE$, $\angle ECD$; $\angle ICA$, $\angle ACB$
17. $\angle FIJ$, $\angle JIK$; $\angle HFG$, $\angle HFI$
20. $\angle GFC$, $\angle ACB$; $\angle FIC$, $\angle ICA$

Find the value of x in each pair of similar triangles. (Lesson 12-9)

30. 8m

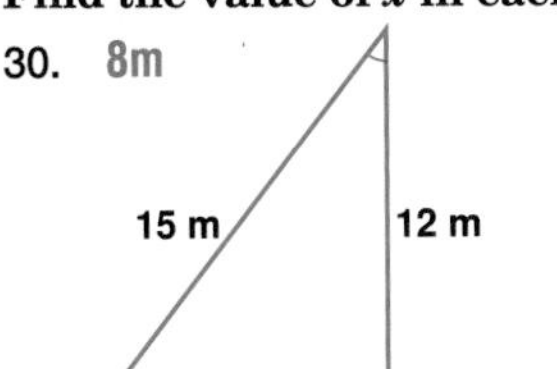

10 m
x

31. 18ft

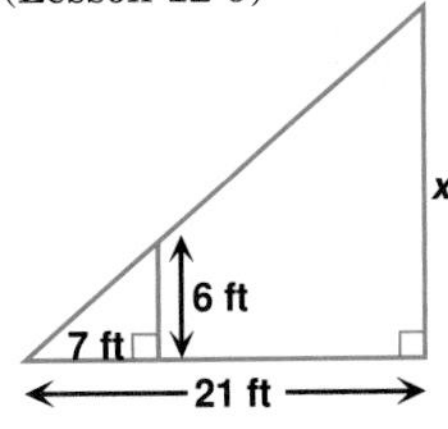

32. Find the value of x in the figure at the right. (Lesson 12-11) $55°$

33. Find the sum of the degree measures of the angles of a hexagon. (Lesson 12-12) $720°$

125° 55° x
55° 125°

Applications and Problem Solving

34. Make a circle graph to display the data in the chart. See margin. (Lesson 12-2)

Water Use in the U.S.	
Agriculture	36%
Public Water	8%
Utilities	33%
Industry	23%

35. A 6-foot ladder touches the side of a building at a point 5 feet above the ground. At what height would a 15-foot ladder touch the building if it makes the same angle with the building as the shorter ladder? (Lesson 12-10) 12.5 ft

Write the converse of each conditional. Then determine whether each statement (conditional and converse) is *true* or *false*. (Lesson 12-7)

36. If an angle measures 90°, then it is a right angle. See margin.

37. If Mrs. Clark lives in Boston, then Mrs. Clark lives in a city. See margin.

Communicating Algebra

In your own words, describe the relationship between two congruent polygons. See margin.

Curriculum Connection

- **Biology** Research why honeycombs are made in the shape of regular hexagons. See margin.

Read More About It

Frieder, David. *Clear and Simple Geometry.*
Laithwaite, Eric. *Shape: The Purpose of Forms.*
Zaslavsky, Claudia. *Africa Counts.*

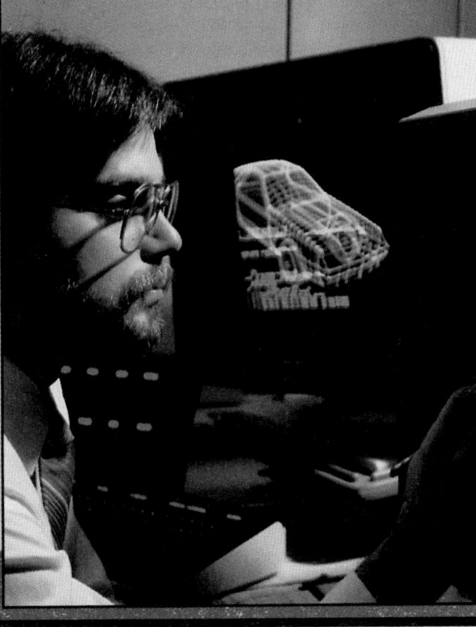

You may wish to use a Chapter Test (free-response format) as an additional chapter review. Two forms are provided in the Evaluation Masters Booklet as shown below.

Evaluation Masters Booklet, **p. 104**

Name ______ Date ______

Chapter 12 Test, Form 2A

1. What is the name of the figure at the right? — 1. line
2. The measure of angle C is 60°. Classify $\angle C$. — 2. acute
3. Find the number of degrees for the section of a circle graph that would represent 20%. — 3. 72°
4. Angles A and B are supplementary and $m\angle A = 12°$. Find $m\angle B$. — 4. 168°
5. Angles C and D are vertical and $m\angle C = 65°$. Find $m\angle D$. — 5. 65°

In the figure at the right, line l is parallel to line m. Use the figure for Exercises 6 and 7.

6. If $m\angle 1 = 80°$, find $m\angle 3$. — 6. 100°
7. If $m\angle 4 = 80°$, find $m\angle 5$. — 7. 80°
8. If point M bisects $\overline{PQ}$ and $m\overline{PQ} = 62$ cm, find $m\overline{PM}$. — 8. 31 cm
9. If the measure of angle DAB at the right is 70° and $\overrightarrow{AC}$ bisects $\angle DAB$, what is $m\angle CAB$? — 9. 35°
10. In $\triangle ABC$, $m\angle A = 48°$ and $m\angle B = 26°$. Find $m\angle C$. — 10. 106°
11. Write the converse of the statement *If the measure of an angle is 112°, then the angle is obtuse.*
11. If an angle is obtuse, then its measure is 112°.
12. If $\triangle ABC \cong \triangle XYZ$, what segment is congruent to $\overline{ZY}$? — 12. $\overline{BC}$

In the figure at the right, $\triangle ABC \sim \triangle FGH$. Use the figure for Exercises 13 and 14.

13. If $m\overline{AB} = 20$ cm, $m\overline{FG} = 15$ cm, and $m\overline{BC} = 28$ cm, find $m\overline{GH}$. — 13. 21 cm
14. If $m\angle A = 50°$ and $m\angle B = 45°$, find $m\angle H$. — 14. 85°
15. On a small scale map, the length from Boston to New York City is 12 cm, and from New York City to Washington, D.C. the length is 13 cm. On a larger map, the length from Boston to New York City is 18 cm. Find the length from New York City to Washington, D.C. on the larger map. — 15. 19.5 cm
16. What is the sum of the measures of the angles of a quadrilateral? — 16. 360°
17. Find the measure of $\angle D$ in the figure at the right. — 17. 70°
18. Classify a polygon having eight sides. — 18. octagon
19. Find the sum of the measures of the angles of a polygon having ten sides. — 19. 1440°
20. Owen draws two similar 4-sided designs. The smaller one has two short sides each measuring 6 inches and two long sides each measuring 9 inches. The larger design has two short sides each measuring 15 inches. Find the length of the long sides of the larger design. — 20. 22.5 in.

BONUS The perimeter, in feet, of a square is the same as the sum of the measures of the angles of a pentagon. Find the length of one side of the square. — 135 ft

Evaluation Masters Booklet, **p. 105**

Name ______ Date ______

Chapter 12 Test, Form 2B

1. What is the name of the figure at the right? — 1. angle
2. The measure of angle C is 90°. Classify $\angle C$. — 2. right
3. Find the number of degrees for the section of a circle graph that would represent 35%. — 3. 126°
4. Angles A and B are supplementary and $m\angle A = 74°$. Find $m\angle B$. — 4. 106°
5. Angles C and D are vertical and $m\angle C = 37°$. Find $m\angle D$. — 5. 37°

In the figure at the right, line l is parallel to line m. Use the figure for Exercises 6 and 7.

6. If $m\angle 1 = 100°$, find $m\angle 5$. — 6. 100°
7. If $m\angle 3 = 80°$, find $m\angle 6$. — 7. 80°
8. If point M bisects $\overline{PQ}$ and $m\overline{PQ} = 24$ cm, find $m\overline{PM}$. — 8. 12 cm
9. If the measure of angle DAB at the right is 64° and $\overrightarrow{AC}$ bisects $\angle DAB$, what is $m\angle CAB$? — 9. 32°
10. In $\triangle ABC$, $m\angle A = 63°$ and $m\angle B = 28°$. Find $m\angle C$. — 10. 89°
11. Write the converse of the statement *If the measure of an angle is 75°, then the angle is acute.*
11. If an angle is acute, then its measure is 75°.
12. If $\triangle ABC \cong \triangle XYZ$, what segment is congruent to $\overline{AC}$? — 12. $\overline{XY}$

In the figure at the right, $\triangle ABC \sim \triangle FGH$. Use the figure for Exercises 13 and 14.

13. If $m\overline{AB} = 30$ cm, $m\overline{FG} = 20$ cm, and $m\overline{BC} = 36$ cm, find $m\overline{GH}$. — 13. 24 cm
14. If $m\angle A = 48°$ and $m\angle B = 45°$, find $m\angle H$. — 14. 87°
15. On a small scale map, the length from Boston to New York City is 12 cm, and from New York City to Washington, D.C. the length is 13 cm. On a larger map, the length from Boston to New York City is 27 cm. Find the length from New York City to Washington, D.C. on the larger map. — 15. 29.25 cm
16. Find the measure of $\angle D$ in the figure at the right. — 16. 115°
17. What is the sum of the measures of the angles of a quadrilateral? — 17. 360°
18. Classify a polygon having five sides. — 18. pentagon
19. Find the sum of the measures of the angles of a polygon having nine sides. — 19. 1260°
20. Meghan draws two similar 4-sided designs. The smaller one has two short sides each measuring 6 inches and two long sides each measuring 9 inches. The larger design has two short sides each measuring 21 inches. Find the length of the long sides of the larger design. — 20. 31.5 in.

BONUS The perimeter, in feet, of a square is the same as the sum of the measures of the angles of a hexagon. Find the length of one side of the square. — 180 ft

Additional Answers

34.

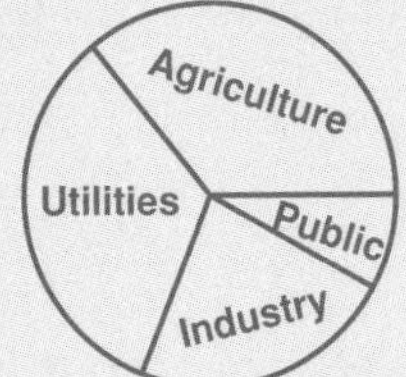

36. If an angle is a right angle, then it measures 90°. cond. – true; conv. – true

37. If Mrs. Clark lives in a city, then she lives in Boston. cond. – true; conv.– false

Communicating Algebra
The corresponding angles and sides are congruent.

Curriculum Connection
Regular hexagons are the strongest structure. They distribute the weight and do not collapse.

Using the Chapter Test

This page may be used as a test or as an additional review. Two forms of a Chapter Test (multiple-choice format) are provided in the Evaluation Masters Booklet.

Evaluation Masters Booklet, **pp. 100-101**

Name ______________________ Date ____________

Chapter 12 Test, Form 1A

1. What is the name for the figure shown at the right?
   A. segment B. ray C. angle D. line 1. B
2. The measure of angle A is 92°. Classify angle A.
   A. acute B. straight C. obtuse D. right 2. C
3. Find the number of degrees for the section of a circle graph that would represent 60%.
   A. 120° B. 240° C. 540° D. 216° 3. D
4. The pair of angles shown in the figure at the right are supplementary. Find x.
   4x + 35 2x − 5
   A. 25 B. 35 C. 75 D. 45 4. A

In the figure at the right, line ℓ and line m are parallel. Use the figure for Exercises 5 and 6.

5. If $m\angle 1 = 100°$, find $m\angle 3$.
   A. 160° B. 120° C. 100° D. 80° 5. C
6. If $m\angle 4 = 80°$, find $m\angle 5$.
   A. 100° B. 80° C. 120° D. 160° 6. B
7. If point M bisects $\overline{PQ}$ and $m\overline{PQ} = 20$ cm, find $m\overline{PM}$.
   A. 30 cm B. 40 cm C. 20 cm D. 10 cm 7. D
8. If $m\angle BAD = 120°$ and $\overline{AC}$ bisects $\angle BAD$, what is $m\angle CAD$?
   A. 120° B. 60° C. 240° D. 180° 8. B
9. In $\triangle ABC$, $m\angle A = 18°$ and $m\angle B = 25°$. Find $m\angle C$.
   A. 36° B. 137° C. 143° D. 130° 9. B
10. Write the converse of the statement *If it rains, then I get wet.*
    A. I will get wet if it rains.
    B. If I do not get wet, then it will not rain.
    C. If it does not rain, then I will not get wet.
    D. If I get wet, then it rains. 10. D
11. If $\triangle ABC \cong \triangle XZY$, which segment is congruent to $\overline{AC}$?
    A. $\overline{XY}$ B. $\overline{XZ}$ C. $\overline{YZ}$ D. $\overline{AB}$ 11. A

Name ______________________ Date ____________

Chapter 12 Test, Form 1A (continued)

12. If $\triangle LMN \cong \triangle VWX$, which angle is congruent to $\angle N$?
    A. $\angle W$ B. $\angle V$ C. $\angle M$ D. $\angle X$ 12. D

In the figure at the right, △ABC ~ △FGH. Use the figure for Exercises 13 and 14.

13. If $m\overline{AB} = 10$ cm, $m\overline{FG} = 15$ cm, and $m\overline{BC} = 16$ cm, find $m\overline{GH}$.
    A. 18 cm B. 20 cm C. 24 cm D. 12 cm 13. C
14. If $m\angle A = 80°$, $m\angle B = 20°$, and $m\angle F = 80°$, find $m\angle G$.
    A. 80° B. 20° C. 100° D. 60° 14. B
15. A photograph measuring 4 inches by 6 inches is enlarged to 12 inches by 18 inches. In the original photo, a tree's image is 1.5 inches high. Find the height of the tree's image in the enlargement.
    A. 4 in. B. 4.5 in. C. 9.5 in. D. 6 in. 15. B
16. Whitney sees an aerial photograph of her house and the pond behind her house. The images of her house and the pond are 6 cm and 9 cm wide, respectively. She knows that her house is 35 feet wide. Find the width of the pond.
    A. 44 ft B. 52.5 ft C. 62.5 ft D. 70 ft 16. B
17. Which quadrilateral does not have two pairs of parallel sides?
    A. trapezoid B. rectangle C. rhombus D. square 17. A
18. Quadrilateral $ABCD$ is shown at the right. Find $m\angle D$.
    A. 300° B. 240° C. 130° D. 60° 18. C
19. Classify a polygon having six sides.
    A. decagon B. hexagon C. pentagon D. octagon 19. B
20. Find the sum of the measures of the angles of a polygon having seven sides.
    A. 1260° B. 490° C. 700° D. 900° 20. D

BONUS The perimeter, in centimeters, of an equilateral triangle is the same as the sum of the measures of the angles of a pentagon. Find the length of one side of the triangle.
A. 180 cm B. 540 cm C. 360 cm D. 500 cm A

Test

Match the letter of each figure to its most exact description.

1. line segment c
2. complementary angles i
3. obtuse angle a
4. vertical angles g
5. supplementary angles e
6. perpendicular lines j
7. parallel lines h
8. acute triangle d
9. regular quadrilateral b
10. rhombus k
11. right triangle l
12. ray f

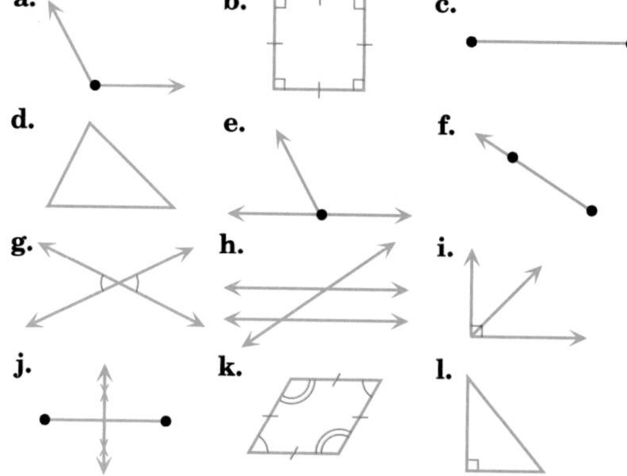

13. Find the value of x. Then classify it as *acute, right* or *obtuse.* 125°; obtuse

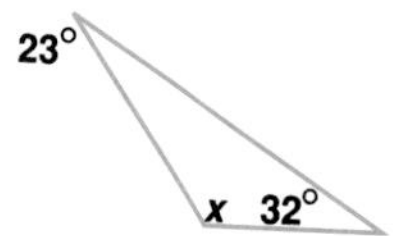

14. Find the value of x. 100°

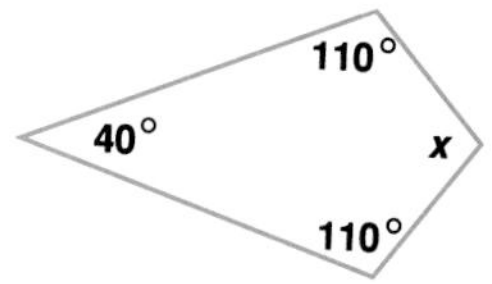

15. In the figure at the right, $\triangle XYR \cong \triangle TSR$. Name the congruent angles and sides. $\angle X, \angle T; \angle Y, \angle S; \angle XRY, \angle TRS; \overline{XR}, \overline{TR}; \overline{SR}, \overline{YR}; \overline{XY}, \overline{TS}$

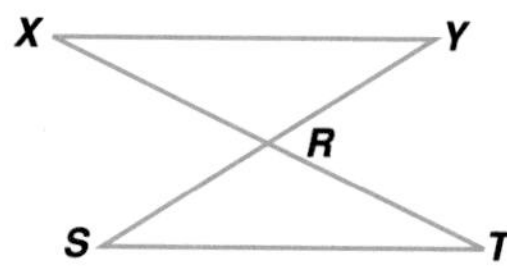

16. An angle of a circle graph represents \$30 out of a total of \$120. What should the measure of the angle be? 90°
17. Mara is 5 feet 6 inches tall. She notices that her shadow is 4 feet long and the shadow of a nearby tree is 24 feet long. How tall is the tree? 33 feet

Write the converse of the following statement.

18. If the sum of the measures of two angles is 180°, then the angles are supplementary. If two angles are supplementary, the sum of their measures is 180°.

Find the sum of the measures of the angles of each polygon.

19. quadrilateral 360°
20. decagon 1440°

BONUS

In your own words, explain why a triangle cannot have two right angles. See margin.

Test Generator Software is provided in both Apple and IBM formats. You may use this software to create your own tests, based on the needs of your students.

Additional Answer

Bonus—Sample answer: A triangle cannot have two right angles because the third angle would measure 0°.

Academic Skills Test

Cumulative, Chapters 1-12

1. Lois wants to cut a piece of ribbon that is $5\frac{1}{2}$ feet long into strips that are 8 inches long for some awards. How many inches are equivalent to $5\frac{1}{2}$ feet?

   A $16\frac{1}{2}$ inches C 55 inches
   B 44 inches (D) 66 inches

2. Which equation is equivalent to $4n - 4 = 3n + 10$?

   (A) $4n - 4 - 3n = 10$
   B $4n + 3n = 10 - 4$
   C $4n = 10 - 4$
   D $7n = 10 + 4$

3. Which ordered pairs are solutions for $y = 2x - 3$?

   (A) (-3, -9), (2, 1), (4, 5)
   B (-3, 0), (-1, -5), (3, 3)
   C (-3, 3), (-2, 1), (-1, -1)
   D (-2, -7), (-1, 1), (0, -3)

4. As a team, the Wildcats made 24 shots in 40 times at the freethrow line. Which expression could be used to find the percent of shots the team made?

   A $\frac{16}{40} \times 100$ C $\frac{40}{24} \times 100$
   (B) $\frac{24}{40} \times 100$ D Not Here

5. The high temperatures (in °F) for January 15th during the past 10 years are: 15°, 18°, 25°, 38°, 6°, 25°, 10°, 30°, 18°, and 25°. What is the mode of these temperatures?

   A 18° (C) 25°
   B 21.5° D Not Here

6. What is the median of the test scores shown in the stem-and-leaf plot below?

   6 | 0 means 60

   6 | 0 5 6 8
   7 | 0 0 7 9 9
   8 | 3 4 7
   9 | 2 2 4 5 8

   A 38
   (B) 79
   C 79 and 92
   D 80

7. The fastest two of six runners will qualify for the final race. How many different combinations of two qualifiers are possible?

   A 2 (C) 15
   B 12 D 30

8. Mr. Garza has 4 black ties, 3 gray ties, 2 blue ties, and 1 brown tie in his closet. If he selects one tie without looking, what is the probability that it will be blue?

   A $\frac{1}{10}$ C $\frac{1}{4}$
   (B) $\frac{1}{5}$ D $\frac{1}{2}$

9. The shaded region represents part of—

   A an angle
   B a line
   C a ray
   (D) a plane

10. $\triangle QRS$ is similar to $\triangle XYZ$. What is the length of $\overline{RQ}$?

   A 16
   (B) 18
   C 20
   D 22

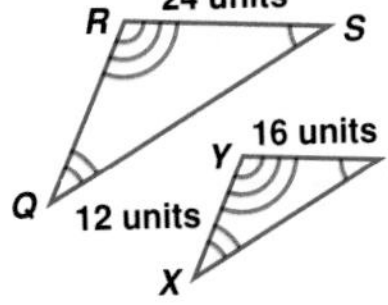

Using the Academic Skills Test

This test familiarizes students with a standardized format while testing skills and concepts presented up to this point.

Evaluation Masters Booklet, **p. 107**

Name ______ Date ______

Cumulative Review, Chapters 1-12

1. Evaluate $6y$, if $y = 9$. (Lesson 1–2)
2. Simplify $|-5| + |5|$. (Lesson 2–1)
3. Solve $-3x > 327$. (Lesson 3–8)
4. Find the GCF of 18 and 32. (Lesson 4–5)
5. Add 5 lb 7 oz + 9 lb 9 oz. (Lesson 5–10)
6. Solve $d = 9.66 \div 3.45$. (Lesson 6–7)
7. Find the circumference of a circle with a radius of 8 m. Use $\pi \approx 3.14$. (Lesson 6–13)
8. Solve $8m - 5 = 27$. (Lesson 7–2)
9. Solve $9x - 7 > 47$. (Lesson 7–6)
10. Find the slope of the line that contains $X(9, 6)$ and $Y(6, 4)$. (Lesson 8–8)
11. Find the y-intercept of the graph of $y = x - 12$. (Lesson 8–9)
12. Express 0.36% as a decimal. (Lesson 9–5)
13. 9 is what percent of 54? (Lesson 9–7)
14. Find the mean of 50, 70, 75, 75, and 85. (Lesson 10–2)
15. Find the interquartile range for the scores 20, 25, 35, 40, 45, 55, and 60. (Lesson 10–4)
16. Twenty of 80 people surveyed preferred oranges. Marnie expects 2400 people. How many oranges should Marnie supply? (Lesson 10–8)
17. Four coins are tossed. How many outcomes are possible? (Lesson 11–2)
18. Find the value of 6!. (Lesson 11–3)
19. Find the value of P(10, 5). (Lesson 11–3)
20. Two dice are rolled. Find the probability of rolling a 4 and a multiple of 3. (Lesson 11–6)
21. Classify angle X if $m\angle A = 116°$. (Lesson 12–1)
22. Find the number of degrees in a section of a circle graph representing 35%. (Lesson 12–2)
23. Angles A and B are complementary and $m\angle A = 34°$. Find $m\angle B$. (Lesson 12–3)
24. In triangle ABC, $m\angle A = 45°$ and $m\angle B = 53°$. Find $m\angle C$. (Lesson 12–6)
25. Lisa draws two similar triangles. One triangle has sides of 12, 15, and 10 cm. The longest side of the second triangle is 22.5 cm long. Find the length of the shortest side of the second triangle. (Lesson 12–10)

Answers:
1. 54
2. 10
3. $x < -109$
4. 2
5. 15 lb
6. 2.8
7. 50.24 m
8. 4
9. $x > 6$
10. -
11. −12
12. 0.0036
13. $16\frac{2}{3}\%$
14. 71
15. 30
16. 600
17. 16
18. 720
19. 30,240
20. $\frac{1}{18}$
21. obtuse
22. 126°
23. 56°
24. 82°
25. 15 cm

Evaluation Masters Booklet, **p. 108**

Name ______ Date ______

Cumulative Test, Chapters 1-12

1. Evaluate $2x$, if $x = -3$.
   A. 1 B. −23 C. −5 D. −6 1. D
2. Solve $-42 > -6x$.
   A. $x > 7$ B. $x > -7$ C. $x < -7$ D. $x < 7$ 2. A
3. Add 7 lb 9 oz + 2 lb 8 oz.
   A. 10 lb 7 oz B. 10 lb 1 oz C. 9 lb 1 oz D. 10 lb 3. B
4. Find the circumference of a circle with a radius of 5 m. Use $\pi \approx 3.14$.
   A. 78.5 m B. 8.14 m C. 31.4 m D. 15.7 m 4. C
5. Solve $5y - 2 = 13$.
   A. 2.2 B. −2.2 C. −3 D. 3 5. D
6. Solve $5x - 2 < 8$.
   A. $x > -2$ B. $x < -2$ C. $x < 2$ D. $x > 2$ 6. C
7. Find the slope of the line that contains $X(4, 2)$ and $Y(8, 3)$.
   A. $\frac{1}{4}$ B. 4 C. $-\frac{1}{4}$ D. −4 7. A
8. Find the x-intercept for the graph of $y = -x + 3$.
   A. −3 B. 3 C. $\frac{1}{3}$ D. 2 8. B
9. Express 0.5% as a decimal.
   A. 0.005 B. 0.05 C. 50 D. 0.0005 9. A
10. What percent of 8 is 32?
   A. 25% B. 250% C. 400% D. 4% 10. C
11. Find the mean of the scores 55, 70, 75, 75, and 75.
   A. 20 B. 72.5 C. 70 D. 75 11. C
12. Find the interquartile range for the scores 20, 25, 35, 40, 45, 50, and 60.
   A. 40 B. 10 C. 50 D. 25 12. D
13. Three coins are tossed. How many outcomes are possible?
   A. 12 B. 6 C. 8 D. 9 13. C
14. Find the value of 7!.
   a. 5040 B. 49 C. 2401 D. 1 14. A
15. Find the value of P(9, 4).
   A. 126 B. 6561 C. 3024 D. 36 15. C
16. The measure of angle A is 86°. Classify angle A.
   A. straight B. right C. acute D. obtuse 16. C
17. Find the number of degrees in a section of a circle graph representing 30%.
   A. 330° B. 108° C. 54° D. 30° 17. B
18. Angles A and B are supplementary and $m\angle A = 26°$. Find $m\angle B$.
   A. 154° B. 164° C. 26° D. 64° 18. A
19. In triangle ABC, $m\angle A = 28°$ and $m\angle B = 56°$. Find $m\angle C$.
   A. 124° B. 276° C. 56° D. 96° 19. D
20. Frank draws two similar triangles. One triangle has sides of 8, 9, and 10 cm. The shortest side of the second triangle is 20 cm long. Find the length of the longest side of the second triangle.
   A. 26 cm B. 28 cm C. 25 cm D. 22 cm 20. C

A Cumulative Review (free-response format) and Cumulative Test (multiple-choice format) are also provided in the Evaluation Masters Booklet as shown at the right.

Test Item	1	2	3	4	5	6	7	8	9	10
Lesson Number	5-10	7-5	8-5	9-7,8	10-2	10-4	11-3	11-4	12-1	12-9
TAAS Objective	4	2	2	11	5	5	5	5	3	3

Measuring Areas and Volume

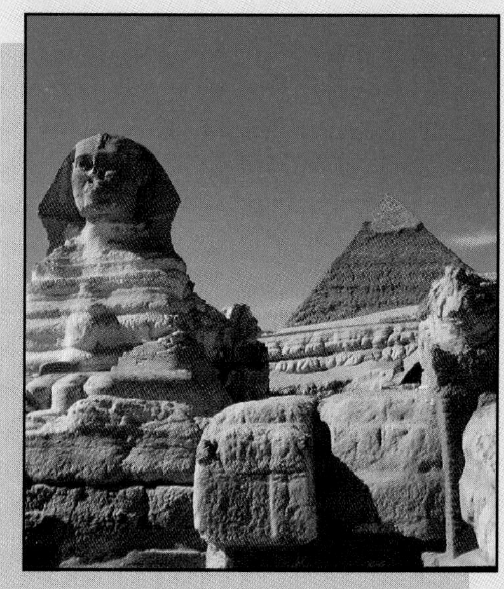

Previewing the Chapter

This chapter begins with a study of the area of parallelograms, triangles, trapezoids, and circles. The formulas are derived, relating the concepts of algebra and geometry. Finding the surface area of prisms, cylinders, pyramids, and cones extends these concepts to three-dimensional figures. Students will also learn to find the volume of these figures. The chapter includes a discussion of measurement and the use of significant digits to indicate precision.

Problem Solving Strategy Students will learn to solve problems by making a model or drawing.

Lesson (Pages)	Lesson Objectives	State/Local Objectives
13-1 (484-487)	13-1: Find the area of parallelograms and triangles.	1E, 3A, 3H, 4A, 4B, 4E
13-2 (488-490)	13-2: Find the area of trapezoids.	1E, 3A, 3H, 4A, 4B, 4E
13-3 (492-493)	13-3: Find the area of circles.	1E, 3A, 3H, 4A, 4B, 4E
13-4 (495-497)	13-4: Find the surface area of triangular and rectangular prisms.	1E, 3A, 3H, 4A, 4B, 4E
13-5 (498-500)	13-5: Find the surface area of circular cylinders.	1E, 3A, 3H, 4A, 4B, 4E
13-6 (501-504)	13-6A: Identify pyramids. 13-6B: Find the area of pyramids and cones.	1E, 3A, 3H, 4A, 4B, 4E
13-7 (506-508)	13-7: Find the volume of prisms.	1E, 3A, 3H, 4A, 4B, 4E
13-8 (509-510)	13-8: Find the volume of circular cylinders.	1E, 3A, 3H, 4A, 4B, 4E
13-9 (511-514)	13-9: Find the volume of pyramids and cones.	1E, 3A, 3H, 4A, 4B, 4E
13-10 (515-517)	13-10: Use precision and significant digits to describe a measurement.	1E, 3A, 4B
13-11 (518-519)	13-11: Solve a problem by making a model or drawing.	1A, 1B, 1C, 1D, 1E, 4B

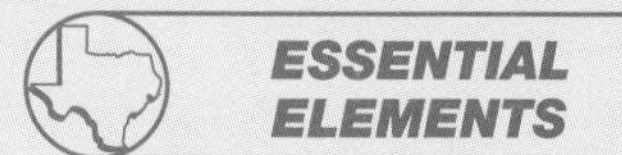

Organizing the Chapter

*You may want to refer to the **Course Planning Calendar** on Page T31.*

Planning Guide

Lesson (Pages)	Pacing Chart (in days) MINIMUM	STANDARD	ACCELERATED	Extra Practice (Student Edition)	Blackline Masters Booklets: Reteaching	Practice	Enrichment	Other Resources
13-1 (484-487)	1.5	1	1	p. 615, Set A	p. 110	p. 122	p. 110	Transparency 13-1 Group Activity Card 13-1
13-2 (488-490)	1	1	1	p. 615, Set A	p. 111	p. 123	p. 111	Transparency 13-2 Group Activity Card 13-2
13-3 (492-493)	1	1	0.5	p. 615, Set A	p. 112	p. 124	p. 112	Transparency 13-3 Group Activity Card 13-3
13-4 (495-497)	1	1	1	p. 615, Set B	p. 113	p. 125	p. 113	Transparency 13-4 Group Activity Card 13-4
13-5 (498-500)	1	1	1	p. 615, Set B	p. 114	p. 126	p. 114	Transparency 13-5 Group Activity Card 13-5
13-6 (501-504)	1.5	1	1	p. 615, Set B	p. 115	p. 127	p. 115	Transparency 13-6 Group Activity Card 13-6
13-7 (506-508)	1	1	1	p. 616, Set C	p. 116	p. 128	p. 116	Transparency 13-7 Group Activity Card 13-7
13-8 (509-510)	1	1	0.5	p. 616, Set C	p. 117	p. 129	p. 117	Transparency 13-8 Group Activity Card 13-8
13-9 (511-514)	1.5	1	1	p. 616, Set C	p. 118	p. 130	p. 118	Transparency 13-9 Group Activity Card 13-9
13-10 (515-517)	1	1	1		p. 119	p. 131	p. 119	Transparency 13-10 Group Activity Card 13-10
13-11 (518-519)	1	1	0.5			p. 132		Transparency 13-11 Group Activity Card 13-11
Review (520-521)	1.5	1	1					Test Generator
Test (522)	1	1	1		Evaluation Masters, pp. 109-114			

Other Chapter Resources

Student Edition
Team Problem Solving, p. 490
Algebra in Action, p. 491
Explorations, pp. 494, 505
Mid-Chapter Quiz, p. 504
Career, p. 514
Academic Skills Test, p. 523

Teacher Resource Package
Interdisciplinary Activity, p. 13
Application Worksheet, p. 28
Cooperative Problem Solving, p. 43
Multicultural Activity, p. 58
Fun Activities, p. 77
Technology Worksheets, pp. 13, 28, 43
Lab Manual, pp. 63-65
Quizzes(2), p. 115
Class Review Game

Software
Test Generator

available for Apple and IBM

Enhancing the Chapter

Some of the blackline masters for enhancing this chapter are shown below.

Applications, p. 28

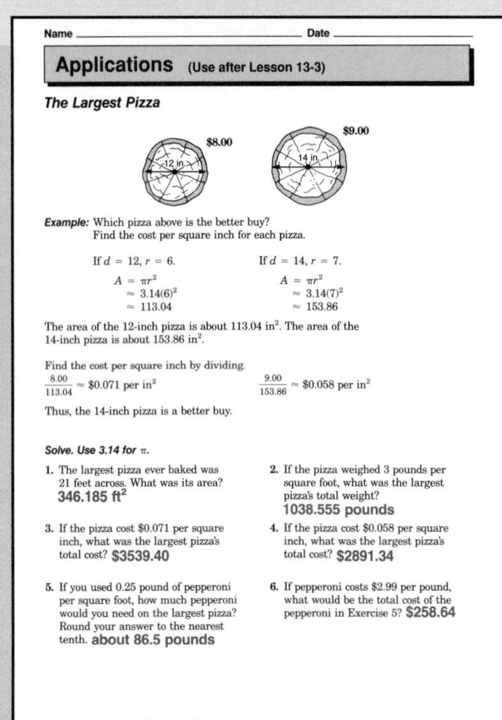

Name ________ Date ________

Applications (Use after Lesson 13-3)

The Largest Pizza

$8.00 12 in. $9.00 14 in.

Example: Which pizza above is the better buy?
Find the cost per square inch for each pizza.

If $d = 12$, $r = 6$.
$A = \pi r^2$
$\approx 3.14(6)^2$
≈ 113.04

If $d = 14$, $r = 7$.
$A = \pi r^2$
$\approx 3.14(7)^2$
≈ 153.86

The area of the 12-inch pizza is about 113.04 in^2. The area of the 14-inch pizza is about 153.86 in^2.

Find the cost per square inch by dividing.
$\frac{8.00}{113.04} \approx \$0.071$ per in^2 $\frac{9.00}{153.86} \approx \$0.058$ per in^2

Thus, the 14-inch pizza is a better buy.

Solve. Use 3.14 for π.

1. The largest pizza ever baked was 21 feet across. What was its area? **346.185 ft^2**
2. If the pizza weighed 3 pounds per square foot, what was the largest pizza's total weight? **1038.555 pounds**
3. If the pizza cost \$0.071 per square inch, what was the largest pizza's total cost? **\$3539.40**
4. If the pizza cost \$0.058 per square inch, what was the largest pizza's total cost? **\$2891.34**
5. If you used 0.25 pound of pepperoni per square foot, how much pepperoni would you need on the largest pizza? Round your answer to the nearest tenth. **about 86.5 pounds**
6. If pepperoni costs \$2.99 per pound, what would be the total cost of the pepperoni in Exercise 5? **\$258.64**

The **Activity Masters Booklet** contains the page shown above.

Interdisciplinary Activity, p. 13

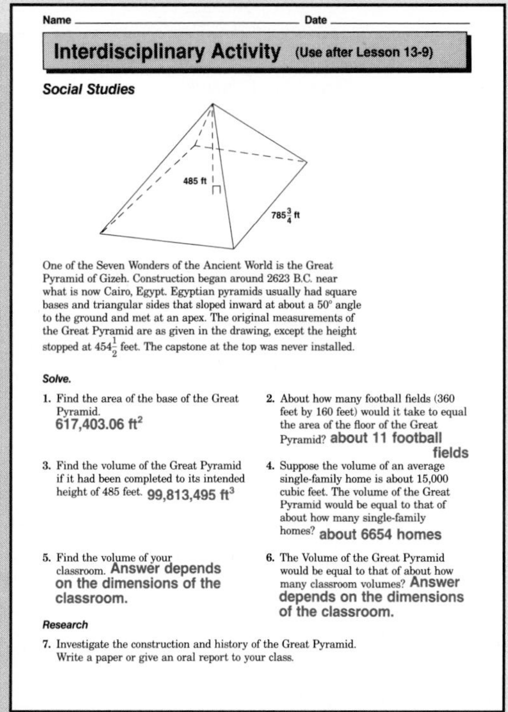

Name ________ Date ________

Interdisciplinary Activity (Use after Lesson 13-9)

Social Studies

485 ft $785\frac{3}{4}$ ft

One of the Seven Wonders of the Ancient World is the Great Pyramid of Gizeh. Construction began around 2623 B.C. near what is now Cairo, Egypt. Egyptian pyramids usually had square bases and triangular sides that sloped inward at about a 50° angle to the ground and met at an apex. The original measurements of the Great Pyramid are as given in the drawing, except the height stopped at $454\frac{1}{2}$ feet. The capstone at the top was never installed.

Solve.

1. Find the area of the base of the Great Pyramid. **617,403.06 ft^2**
2. About how many football fields (360 feet by 160 feet) would it take to equal the area of the floor of the Great Pyramid? **about 11 football fields**
3. Find the volume of the Great Pyramid if it had been completed to its intended height of 485 feet. **99,813,495 ft^3**
4. Suppose the volume of an average single-family home is about 15,000 cubic feet. The volume of the Great Pyramid would be equal to that of about how many single-family homes? **about 6654 homes**
5. Find the volume of your classroom. **Answer depends on the dimensions of the classroom.**
6. The Volume of the Great Pyramid would be equal to that of about how many classroom volumes? **Answer depends on the dimensions of the classroom.**

Research

7. Investigate the construction and history of the Great Pyramid. Write a paper or give an oral report to your class.

The **Activity Masters Booklet** contains the page shown above.

Models and Manipulatives

The use of geoboards, graph paper, and paper figures enable a student to visualize the areas of parallelograms, triangles, and trapezoids. An alternative to finding the formula of a trapezoid in terms of triangles, would be to copy a trapezoid and join it to the original to form a parallelogram. This helps to show why triangles and trapezoids are divided by two (memory aid). Paper figures can be used to show how 6 equilateral triangles can represent a regular hexagon.

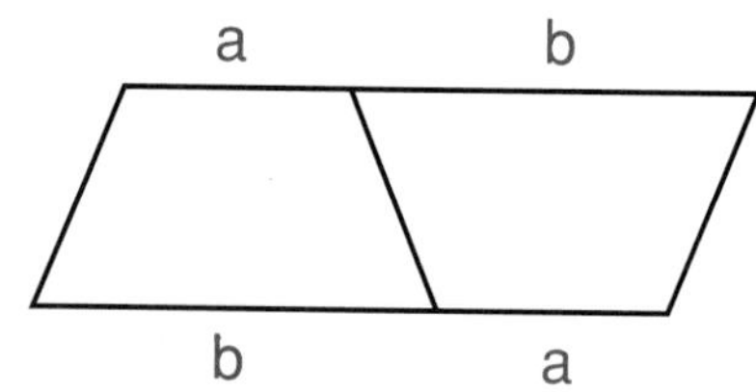

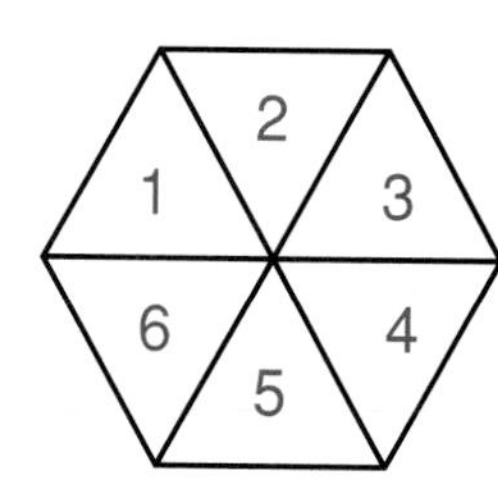

Multicultural Activity

Albrecht Durer (1471–1528), a German painter, engraver, and designer, was a great artist during the Renaissance Period. His woodcuts revolutionized the methods of his time by scientifically studying the art of perspective drawing. He projected in his woodcuts a grid that was able to show a 3-dimensional object projected into two dimensions. Although he was not a mathematician, he gave an excellent example of the trisection of an arbitrary angle and an approximate construction of a regular nonagon. He used mathematics in his perspective drawings which is the system that makes flat surface objects and persons actually appear three-dimensional.

Have students research and write a paragraph on the contributions of German mathematicians.

Cooperative Learning

The following activity is provided in the **Activity Masters Booklet.**

Cooperative Problem Solving, p. 43

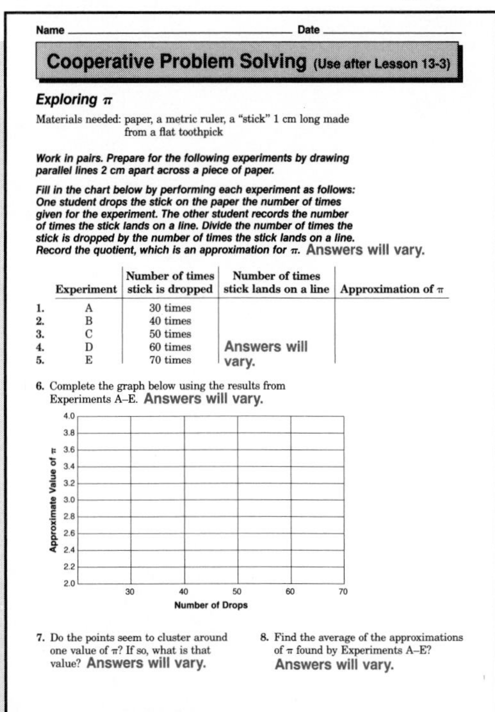

Name ______ Date ______

Cooperative Problem Solving (Use after Lesson 13-3)

Exploring π

Materials needed: paper, a metric ruler, a "stick" 1 cm long made from a flat toothpick

Work in pairs. Prepare for the following experiments by drawing parallel lines 2 cm apart across a piece of paper.

Fill in the chart below by performing each experiment as follows: One student drops the stick on the paper the number of times given for the experiment. The other student records the number of times the stick lands on a line. Divide the number of times the stick is dropped by the number of times the stick lands on a line. Record the quotient, which is an approximation for π. **Answers will vary.**

	Experiment	Number of times stick is dropped	Number of times stick lands on a line	Approximation of π
1.	A	30 times		
2.	B	40 times		
3.	C	50 times		
4.	D	60 times	**Answers will**	
5.	E	70 times	**vary.**	

6. Complete the graph below using the results from Experiments A–E. **Answers will vary.**

7. Do the points seem to cluster around one value of π? If so, what is that value? **Answers will vary.**

8. Find the average of the approximations of π found by Experiments A–E? **Answers will vary.**

Cooperative Problem Solving

Have students work in groups of three or four to determine a formula to find the area of a regular hexagon. They must present it orally to the class. They need to figure out what is needed to solve this problem and can present it with unknown quantities. Explain that a regular hexagon has 6 sides and all sides are of equal length. Sample answers:

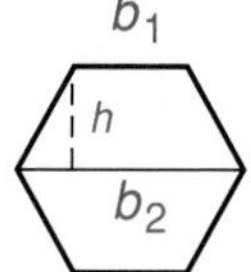

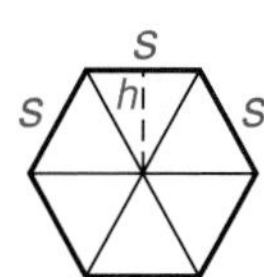

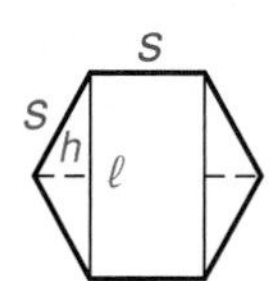

Interactive Bulletin Board

Manufacturing Connection

Three-dimensional shapes used to package food items

Shape <u>cylinder</u>

Food item package <u>canned good</u>

3–D Figure

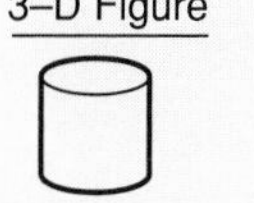

height <u>h</u>

radious <u>r</u>

circumferance <u>$2\pi r$</u>

Surface area <u>$2\pi r^2 + 2\pi rh$</u>

Volume <u>$\pi r^2 h$</u>

Opened-up Figure

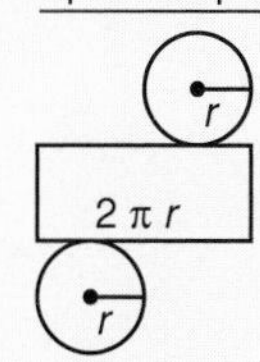

Purpose Provide practice in determining surface area and volume.

How to Use It Divide students into four groups. Have each group be responsible for the bulletin board for one week. Assign each group a container to be researched such as prism, cylinder, cone, or pyramid. Have each group determine how this item is used in packaging food goods. Make an opened-up diagram and 3-dimensional figure of each out of cardboard or construction paper to represent the food item to be placed on the bulletin board. Have each group present the data by discussing the surface area, volume, and also why the manufacturer used the container. The manufacturer may have to be contacted to determine why the container was used; it may be because the size of the container minimized the cost.

Outside Resources

Books/Periodicals
Curriculum and Evaluation Standards for School Mathematics, NCTM

Films/Videotapes
Mathematics of the Honeycomb, Moody Institute of Science.

Software
Perimeter, Area, and Volume, Gamco

Technology

There are three pages in the ***Technology Masters Booklet*** that involve technology with concepts in this chapter. One page involves calculators and one page has a problem that can be solved using the BASIC program that is provided. Students should evaluate the information they obtain from running the program and solve a similar problem by extending the program.

Using the Chapter Opener

Transparency 13-0 is available in the Transparency Package. It provides a full-color visual and motivational activity that you can use to engage students in the mathematical content of the chapter.

Using Measurements

How accurate were the builders of your school building? Using tape measures, measure the length of the sides of your classroom or school. Determine if walls that are to be the same length actually are the same length. How much error is there? Using a square, check the angles where walls, floor, and ceiling join. Are these angles exactly right angles?

CHAPTER OBJECTIVES

In this chapter you will learn to:

- find the area of polygons and circles
- find the surface area of prisms, cylinders, pyramids, and cones
- find the volume of prisms, cylinders, pyramids, and cones
- solve problems by making a model or drawing

Measuring Area and Volume

Engineers and builders in ancient Egypt, around 3000 B.C., pioneered many aspects of mathematics, and for good reasons. Their land experienced yearly floods, during which the Nile River's waters covered farmland for weeks. Every year after the waters drained away, farm boundaries had to be remeasured. It's no wonder that Egyptians were pioneers in many aspects of mathematics, particularly in measurement.

Khufu's Great Pyramid at Gizeh is evidence of the impressive mathematical skill of the Egyptians.

History Connection

Class Project

Choose one of these topics: history of mathematics, history of building, or archaeology. Research some of the important developments in your topic. Make a time line of those developments.

History Connection

Have students use encyclopedias and books on the history of mathematics, architecture, or archaeology to research developments on the chosen topic. After completing the time lines, have students who researched the same topic compare time lines and discuss similarities and differences. An option to individual time lines would be for those students who chose the same topic to work as a cooperative group to compile a collective time line.

Looking Ahead

You may want to have the following materials available to use in this chapter.

Algebra in Action, p. 491
- yard sticks or tape measures

Exploration, p. 494
- unlined paper
- ruler
- compass
- thumb tacks or straight pins

Exploration, p. 505
- 5 × 8 index cards
- tape
- rice
- grid paper*

*You can use the Easy-to-Make Manipulative provided on page 7 of the Lab Manual.

Lesson Notes 13-1

5-Minute Check
(over Chapter 12)

In the figure below, *a* is parallel to *b*. If the measure of ∠2 is 98°, find the measure of each angle below.

1. ∠1 **82°**
2. ∠4 **82°**
3. ∠5 **82°**
4. ∠7 **98°**
5. ∠6 **98°**

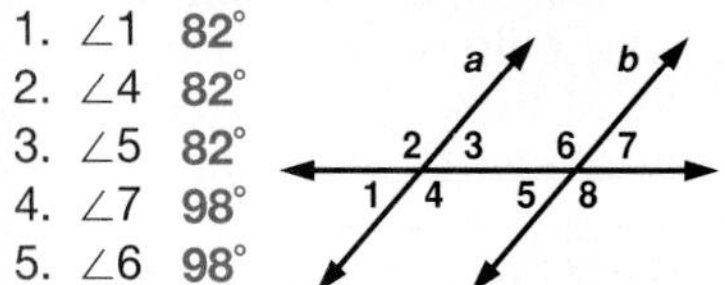

Transparency 13-1 contains the 5-Minute Check and a teaching aid for this lesson.

1 FOCUS

The purpose of this lesson is to develop and use formulas for areas of parallelograms and triangles.

Motivating the Lesson

Remove the bottom from a rectangular box, and tack the bottom to a bulletin board. Hold the box up to the bottom, and change the box's shape to a parallelogram. Ask students if the area changes.

2 TEACH

Using Models Have students use graph paper to model several areas of parallelograms and triangles. Determine each area mathematically, then check by counting squares on the graph paper.

EE: 1E, 3A, 3H, 4A, 4B, 4E
TAAS: 2, 3, 4, 10, 11, 13

13-1 Area: Parallelograms and Triangles

Objective:
Find the area of parallelograms and triangles.

Key Terms:
area
base
height
altitude

If you were driving from Memphis, Tennessee, to the Great Smoky National Park in Gatlinburg, Tennessee, you might use a road map similar to the one shown below. The map has been separated into congruent, nonoverlapping squares to aid you in finding certain cities.

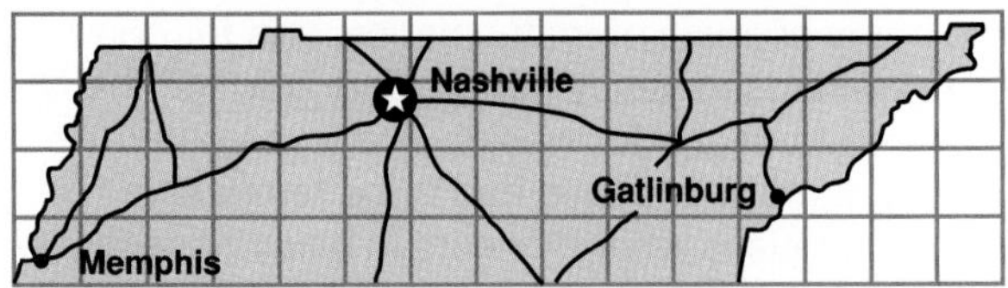

If the area of each square on the map of Tennessee is about 1000 square miles, what is an estimate of the area of Tennessee?
about 40,000 mi²

The surface covered by the squares is the **area** of the region. Area is measured by the number of units that it takes to cover the region exactly. Two common units of measure for area are the square centimeter (cm^2) and the square inch (in^2).

You can calculate the area of a rectangle by multiplying the measure of the length, or **base,** and the measure of the width, or **height.**

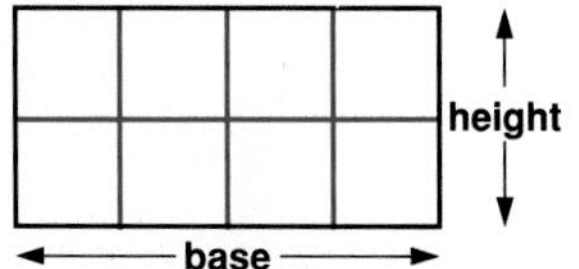

The rectangle shown at the left has a base of 4 units and a height of 2 units. The area is 8 square units.

History Connection

There is evidence that, as long ago as 2000 B.C., the Babylonians used some of the formulas we use today for measuring area, including formulas for the area of a rectangle and a right triangle.

A rectangle is a special kind of parallelogram. It should not be surprising to learn that finding the area of a parallelogram is closely related to finding the area of a rectangle.

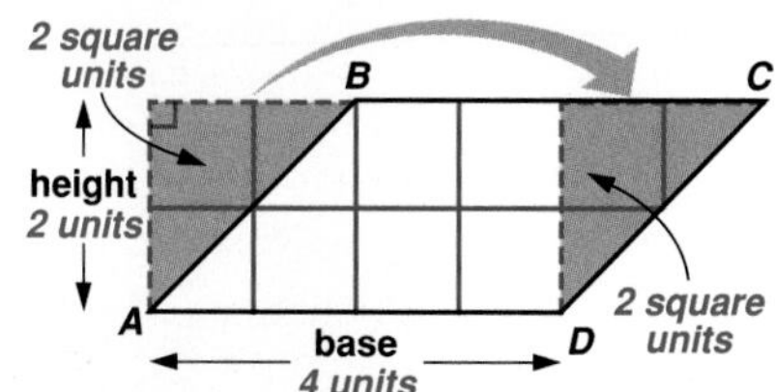

Parallelogram *ABCD* is made from the rectangle by moving the shaded triangle.

The areas of the parallelogram and the rectangle above are both 8 square units. This suggests that you can find the area of a parallelogram by multiplying the measures of the base and the height.

Area of a Parallelogram

If a parallelogram has a base of b units and a height of h units, then the area (A) is $b \cdot h$ square units.

$$A = bh$$

Bell Ringer

Draw three different rectangles that have an area of 20 square units.
Sample answer:

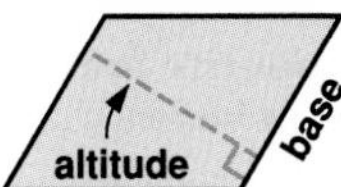

The base can be any side of the parallelogram. The height is the length of an **altitude,** a line segment perpendicular to the base with endpoints on the base and the side opposite the base.

Example

1 Find the area of the parallelogram.

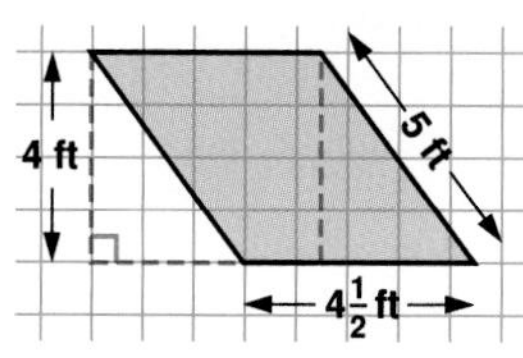

The base is $4\frac{1}{2}$ ft long. The height is 4 ft.

$A = bh$ Formula for area of a parallelogram

$A = 4\frac{1}{2} \cdot 4$ Replace b with $4\frac{1}{2}$ and h with 4.

$A = 18$

The area is 18 ft^2.

Notice that the diagonal and sides of a parallelogram form two triangles of the same size. You can use this fact to find the area of a triangle.

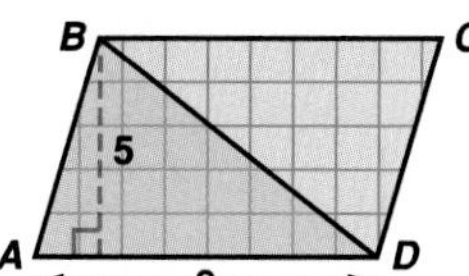

The area of the parallelogram at the left is $8 \cdot 5$ or 40 square units. The area of each triangle is one half the area of the parallelogram. So, each triangle has an area of 20 square units.

Area of a Triangle

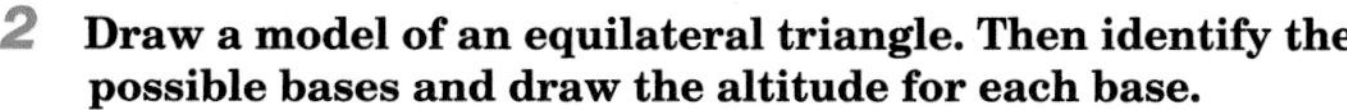

If a triangle has a base of b units and a height of h units, then the area (A) is $\frac{1}{2} \cdot b \cdot h$ square units.

$$A = \frac{1}{2}bh$$

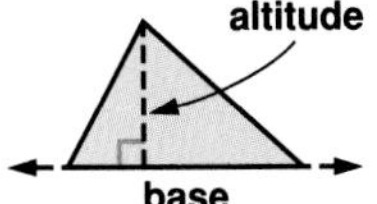

Any one of the sides of a triangle can be used as a base. The height is the length of the corresponding altitude, a line segment perpendicular to the base from the opposite vertex.

Example

2 Draw a model of an equilateral triangle. Then identify the possible bases and draw the altitude for each base.

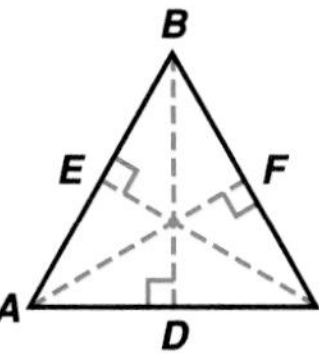

base		altitude
$\overline{AC}$	with	$\overline{BD}$
$\overline{AB}$	with	$\overline{CE}$
$\overline{BC}$	with	$\overline{AF}$

Chalkboard Examples

- *For Example 1*
  Find the area of the parallelogram that has a base of 6 feet and a height of $2\frac{1}{2}$ feet. 15 ft^2
- *For Example 2*
  Identify the possible bases for the equilateral triangle below. Identify the altitude for each base.

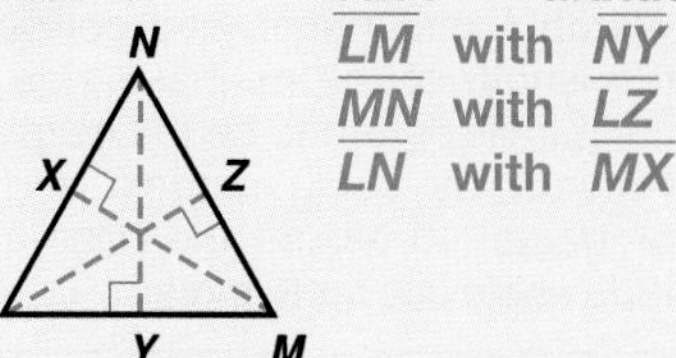

base		altitude
$\overline{LM}$	with	$\overline{NY}$
$\overline{MN}$	with	$\overline{LZ}$
$\overline{LN}$	with	$\overline{MX}$

- *For Example 3*
  Identify the possible bases for the obtuse scalene triangle below. Then identify the altitude for each base.

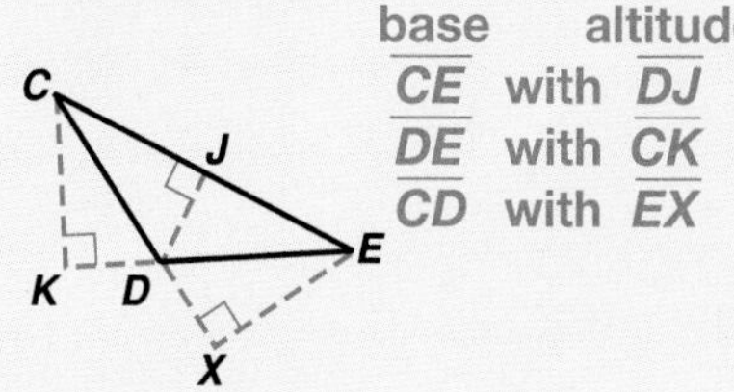

base		altitude
$\overline{CE}$	with	$\overline{DJ}$
$\overline{DE}$	with	$\overline{CK}$
$\overline{CD}$	with	$\overline{EX}$

Find the area of each triangle.

- *For Example 4*

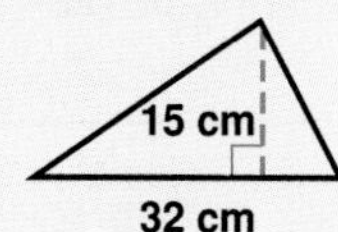

240 cm^2

- *For Example 5*

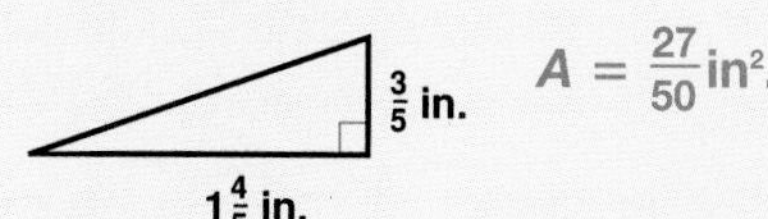

$A = \frac{27}{50}$in^2.

Alternate Strategies: Reteaching the Lesson

Reteaching Activity

Using Models Work in cooperative groups of three. Give each group some corregated cardboard with a piece of quarter-inch graph paper attached. Using tacks and string, have a student make a parallelogram or triangle on the graph paper. Have another student name base and altitude, and the third student determine the area.

Reteaching Masters Booklet, **p. 110**

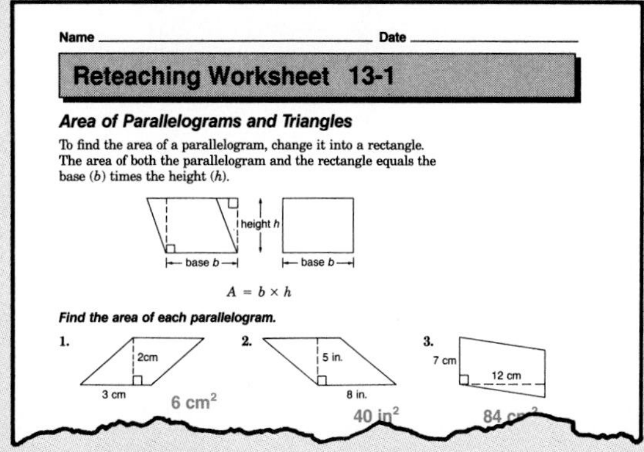

Name ______ Date ______

Reteaching Worksheet 13-1

Area of Parallelograms and Triangles

To find the area of a parallelogram, change it into a rectangle. The area of both the parallelogram and the rectangle equals the base (b) times the height (h).

height h base b base b

$A = b \times h$

Find the area of each parallelogram.

1. 2cm, 3 cm — 6 cm^2
2. 5 in., 8 in. — 40 in^2
3. 7 cm, 12 cm — 84 cm^2

3 PRACTICE/APPLY

Checking the Concept

After completing Exercises 7-9, have students explain an alternate way of determining area for Exercise 8. The length of the other set of parallel sides can be the base.

Error Analysis

Watch for students who consider the length of the nonbase side of the parallelogram to be the height. **Prevent by** using models and a protractor to assure the base-altitude angle is a right angle.

Practice Masters Booklet, **p. 122**

Name ______________ Date ______________

Practice Worksheet 13-1

Area of Parallelograms and Triangles

Find the area of each figure.

1. 4 m, 5 m, 3 m — 6 m²
2. 12 cm, 10 cm, 12 cm — 120 cm²
3. 24 m, 24 m, 20 m, 24 m — 240 m²
4. 8 ft, 11 ft, 13 ft — 104 ft²
5. 1.9 mm, 3.2 mm, 1.3 mm, 4.9 mm — 3.185 mm²
6. 4.0 cm, 3.7 cm, 3.2 cm, 4.0 cm — 5.92 cm²
7. 2 m, 2.3 m, 2.3 m — 4.6 m²
8. $\frac{5}{16}$ in., $\frac{5}{8}$ in., 1 in. — $\frac{5}{16}$ in²
9. 4.0 m, 2.9 m, 3.2 m, 3.6 m — 4.64 m²

Find the area of each figure described below.

10. parallelogram: base, 10 cm; height, 8 cm — 80 cm²
11. parallelogram: base, $2\frac{3}{4}$ ft; height, $1\frac{1}{2}$ ft — $4\frac{1}{8}$ ft²
12. triangle: base, 14 cm; height, 10 cm — 70 cm²
13. triangle: base, 8.6 m; height, 6.5 m — 27.95 m²
14. rectangle: length, $4\frac{2}{3}$ yd; width, $3\frac{3}{7}$ yd — 16 yd²
15. rectangle: length, 12.5 cm; width, 9.25 cm — 115.625 cm²

Examples

3 **Draw a model of an obtuse triangle. Then identify the possible bases and draw the altitude for each base.**

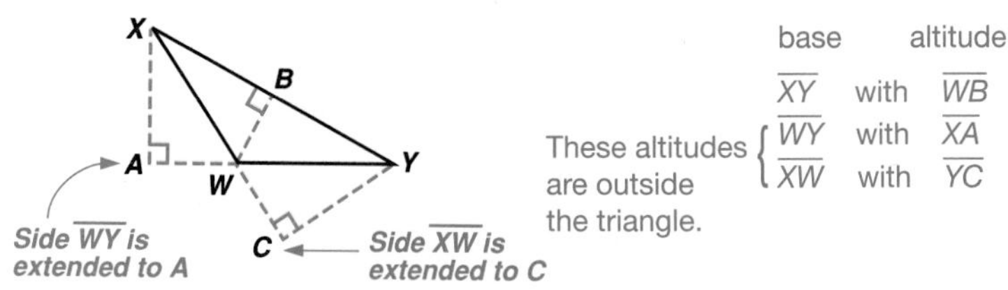

Side $\overline{WY}$ is extended to A
Side $\overline{XW}$ is extended to C

Estimation Hint

THINK:
$30 \times 20 = 600$
$\frac{1}{2}$ of 600 is 300.

Find the area of each triangle.

4

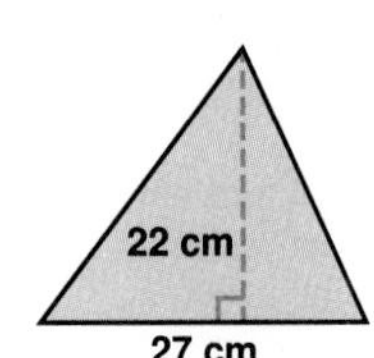

$A = \frac{1}{2}bh$

$A = \frac{1}{2} \cdot 27 \cdot 22$ Replace b with 27 and h with 22.

0.5 ⊠ 27 ⊠ 22 ⊟ 297

$A = 297$

The area is 297 cm².

5

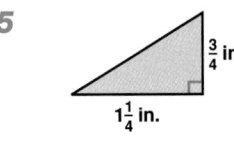

$\frac{3}{4}$ in.
$1\frac{1}{4}$ in.

In a right triangle, two of the altitudes are sides of the triangle.

$A = \frac{1}{2}bh$

$A = \frac{1}{2} \cdot 1\frac{1}{4} \cdot \frac{3}{4}$

$A = \frac{1}{2} \cdot \frac{5}{4} \cdot \frac{3}{4}$

$A = \frac{15}{32}$

The area is $\frac{15}{32}$ in².

Checking for Understanding

Communicating Algebra

1. In your own words, describe area. the number of square units that cover a region
2. Name two common units that are used to measure area. in², cm²
3. Describe the altitude of a triangle. a line segment ⊥ to the base, with endpoints on the base and the opposite vertex

State the formula used to find the area of each figure.

4. rectangle $A = \ell w$
5. parallelogram $A = bh$
6. triangle $A = \frac{1}{2}bh$

Guided Practice

7. 5 cm; 4 cm; $5 \cdot 4$; 20 cm²
8. 5 cm; 3 cm; $5 \cdot 3$; 15 cm²
9. 20 cm; 17 cm; $\frac{1}{2} \cdot 20 \cdot 17$; 170 cm²

State the measures of the base and height, and how to find the area of each figure. Then find each area.

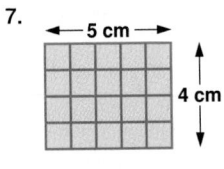

7. 5 cm, 4 cm
8. 5 cm, 3 cm
9. 20 cm, 17 cm

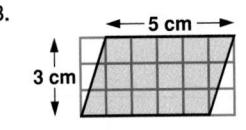

Additional Answers

10. base		altitude	11. base		altitude	12. base		altitude
$\overline{PQ}$	with	$\overline{RV}$	$\overline{AB}$	with	$\overline{CF}$	$\overline{HJ}$	with	$\overline{GK}$
$\overline{PR}$	with	$\overline{QT}$	$\overline{AC}$	with	$\overline{BD}$	$\overline{GJ}$	with	$\overline{GH}$
$\overline{QR}$	with	$\overline{PS}$	$\overline{BC}$	with	$\overline{AE}$	$\overline{GH}$	with	$\overline{GJ}$

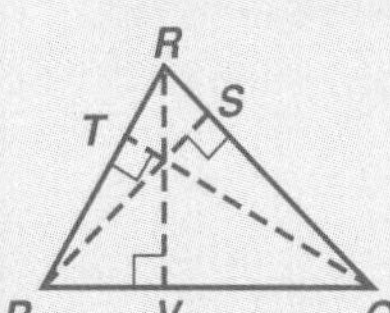

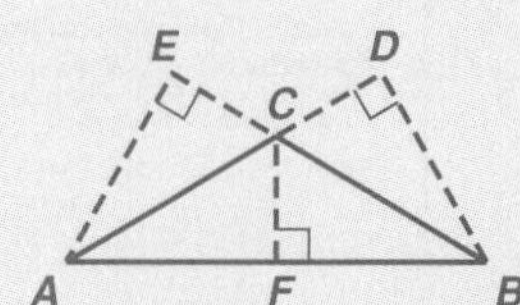

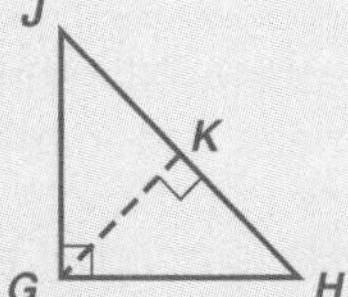

Exercises

Independent Practice

Draw a model of each triangle. Then identify the possible bases and draw a model of the height for each base. See margin.

10. acute scalene
11. obtuse isosceles
12. right isosceles

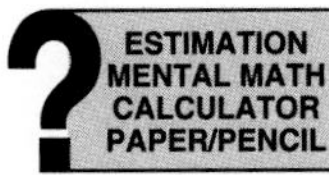

Find the area of each figure.

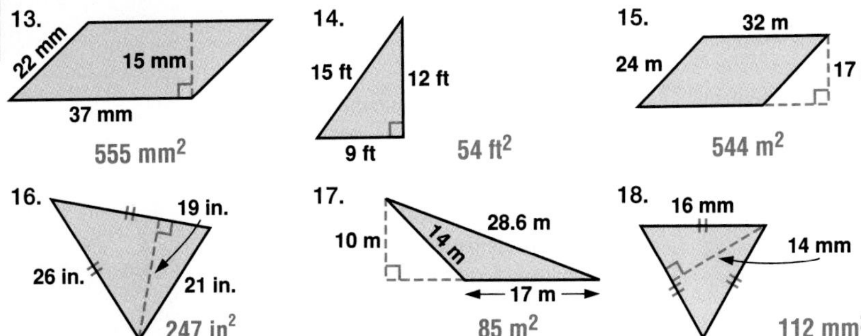

13. 555 mm²
14. 54 ft²
15. 544 m²

16. 19 in., 26 in., 21 in. 247 in²
17. 10 m, 14 m, 28.6 m, 17 m 85 m²
18. 16 mm, 14 mm 112 mm²

Find the area of each figure described below.

19. parallelogram; base, 12 cm; height, 18 cm 216 cm²
20. parallelogram; base $3\frac{1}{4}$ ft; height, 2 ft $6\frac{1}{2}$ ft²
21. triangle; base, 10 in.; height 7 in. 35 in²
22. triangle; base, 0.8 km; height, 2 km 0.8 km²
23. rectangle; length, $2\frac{1}{2}$ in.; width, $1\frac{1}{4}$ in. $3\frac{1}{8}$ in²
24. rectangle; length, 11 yd; width, 25 yd 275 yd²

Mixed Review

25. Solve $g = -12 + 16$. (Lesson 2-4) 4
26. *True* or *false:* $\frac{5}{9} > \frac{3}{5}$. (Lesson 4-8) false
27. **Probability** A multiple choice quiz has 5 questions with 4 possible answers for each. How many outcomes are possible? (Lesson 11-2) 4^5 or 1024 outcomes
28. **Geometry** Use a protractor to draw an angle having a measure of 115°. Classify this angle as *acute, right,* or *obtuse.* (Lesson 12-1) Obtuse; see margin for drawing.

Applications

29. **Gardening** A triangular rose garden has a base of 5 meters and a height of 3 meters. If each rose plant needs at least 0.5 m² of space, how many roses can be planted in this garden? 15
30. **Geography** The state of Tennessee as shown in the map on page 484 is shaped almost like a parallelogram. The distance along the north boundary is 447 miles and the north-south distance is 116 miles. Estimate the area of the state. The actual area is 42,144 mi².

Critical Thinking

31. What is the effect on the area of a square if the length of the sides is doubled? What is the effect on the area of a triangle if both the base and height are doubled? area quadrupled

Wrap-Up

32. In your own words, explain how the areas of a rectangle, a parallelogram, and a triangle are related. See margin.

Alternate Strategies: Extending the Lesson

Enrichment

Working Backwards Given the area and length of the base of a parallelogram, use models to determine the length of the nonbase sides and the altitude. Repeat for an isosceles triangle.

Cooperative Learning

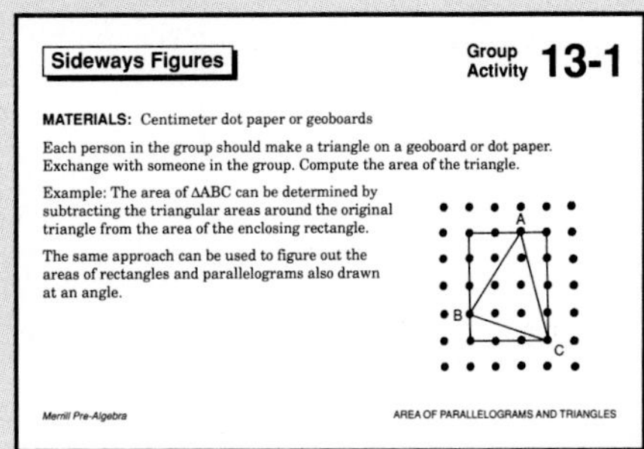
Sideways Figures — Group Activity 13-1

MATERIALS: Centimeter dot paper or geoboards

Each person in the group should make a triangle on a geoboard or dot paper. Exchange with someone in the group. Compute the area of the triangle.

Example: The area of ΔABC can be determined by subtracting the triangular areas around the original triangle from the area of the enclosing rectangle.

The same approach can be used to figure out the areas of rectangles and parallelograms also drawn at an angle.

Merrill Pre-Algebra — AREA OF PARALLELOGRAMS AND TRIANGLES

Independent Practice

Homework Assignment	
Basic	13-23 odd, 25-29, 31, 32
Average	14-24 even, 25-32
Honors	14-18 even, 22-32

4 CLOSE

Assessment Option

Modeling Make triangles from 1 × 1 squares. Have the class work in pairs and make different triangular shapes and find their areas. Have them draw the shapes and label the base and height of each figure.

Additional Answers

28.

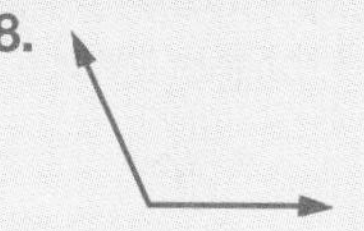

32. Sample answer: Since a triangle can be formed by cutting a rectangle or a parallelogram in half, the area of a triangle is one-half the area of the rectangle or parallelogram having the same base and height.

Enrichment Masters Booklet, **p. 110**

Name ______ Date ______

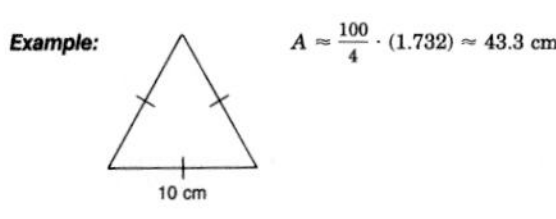
Enrichment Worksheet 13-1

Area of an Equilateral Triangle

The area of an equilateral triangle is the product of one-fourth of the square of a side times the square root of 3 (which is approximately 1.732).

$A = \frac{s^2}{4}(\sqrt{3})$

or $A \approx \frac{s^2}{4} \cdot (1.732)$

Example: $A \approx \frac{100}{4} \cdot (1.732) \approx 43.3$ cm² (10 cm)

Find the area of each equilateral triangle. Round each answer to the nearest tenth.

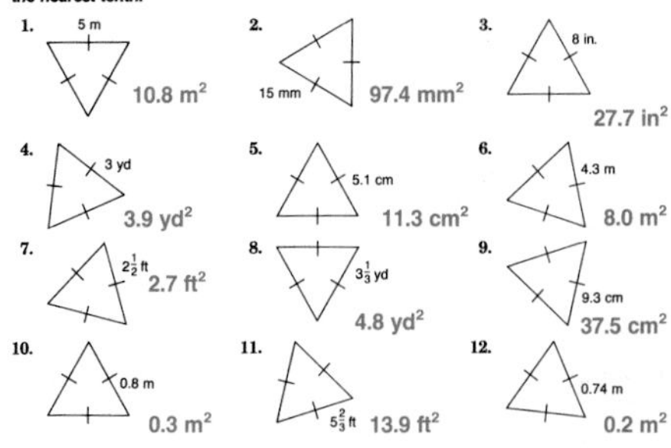

1. 5 m — 10.8 m²
2. 15 mm — 97.4 mm²
3. 8 in. — 27.7 in²
4. 3 yd — 3.9 yd²
5. 5.1 cm — 11.3 cm²
6. 4.3 m — 8.0 m²
7. $2\frac{1}{2}$ ft — 2.7 ft²
8. $3\frac{1}{3}$ yd — 4.8 yd²
9. 9.3 cm — 37.5 cm²
10. 0.8 m — 0.3 m²
11. $5\frac{2}{3}$ ft — 13.9 ft²
12. 0.74 m — 0.2 m²

Lesson Notes 13-2

5-Minute Check
(over Lesson 13-1)

Find the area of each figure described below.

1. triangle; base 8 yd; height 6 yd **24 yd²**
2. triangle; base 2.6 km; height 4km **5.2 km²**
3. parallelogram; base $6\frac{2}{3}$ ft; height $4\frac{1}{2}$ ft **30 ft²**
4. parallelogram; base 7.4 cm; height 9 cm **66.6 cm²**
5. rectangle; length $5\frac{1}{2}$ in.; width $2\frac{2}{5}$ in. **$13\frac{1}{5}$ in.²**

Transparency 13-2 contains the 5-Minute Check and a teaching aid for this lesson.

1 FOCUS

The purpose of this lesson is to develop and use a formula for finding the area of a trapezoid.

Motivating the Lesson

Hold up a picture frame and ask students what shape is used for each side of the frame. How does it differ from a rectangle?

2 TEACH

Using Models Using graph paper, have students model finding the area of a trapezoid by dividing it into two triangles, finding the area of each, and adding.

Chalkboard Examples

Name the bases and an altitude for each trapezoid.

- *For Example 1*

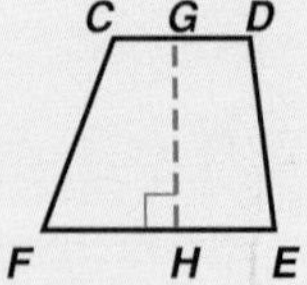

bases $\overline{CD}$ and $\overline{FE}$
altitude $\overline{GH}$

- *For Example 2*

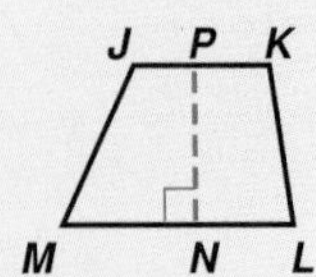

bases $\overline{JK}$ and $\overline{ML}$
altitude $\overline{NP}$

13-2 Area: Trapezoids

Objective:
Find the area of trapezoids.

Key Term:
base

The design of the College Park Pyramids in Indianapolis is based on a quadrilateral called a trapezoid.

Remember, a trapezoid is a quadrilateral with exactly two parallel sides called the **bases.** The height of a trapezoid is the distance between the bases. Like a parallelogram, an altitude is a segment perpendicular to both bases, with endpoints on the base lines. The length of the altitude is called the height.

Examples

Name the bases and an altitude of each trapezoid.

1

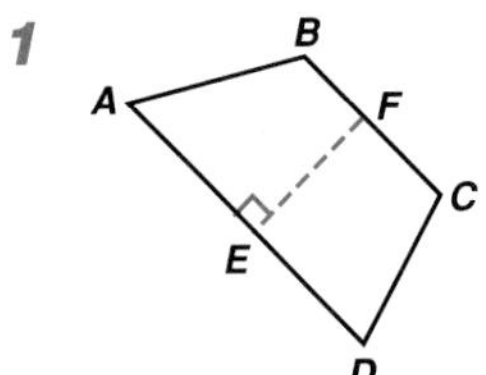

Sides $\overline{BC}$ and $\overline{AD}$ are the bases. $\overline{FE}$ is an altitude.

2

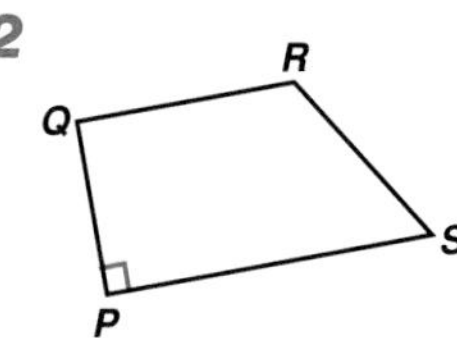

Sides $\overline{QR}$ and $\overline{PS}$ are the bases. $\overline{QP}$ is an altitude.

The area of a trapezoid can be found using the area of a triangle. The diagonal, $\overline{BD}$, separates the trapezoid shown below into two triangles. So, the area of the trapezoid is the sum of the areas of the triangles.

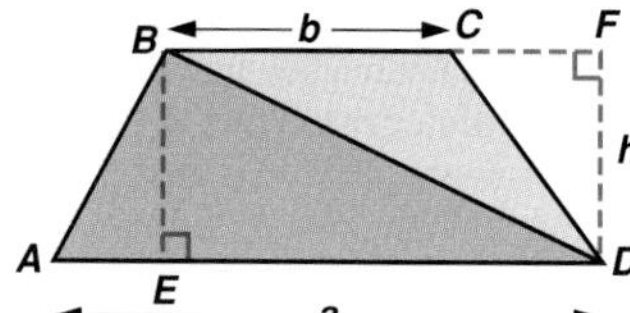

The two triangles are $\triangle ABD$ and $\triangle BCD$. The altitudes of these triangles, $\overline{BE}$ and $\overline{FD}$, are congruent. Both are h units long. The base of $\triangle ABD$ is $\overline{AD}$, a units long. The base of $\triangle BCD$ is $\overline{BC}$, b units long.

Area of trapezoid $ABCD$ = area of $\triangle ABD$ + area of $\triangle BCD$

$$= \frac{1}{2}ah + \frac{1}{2}bh$$

$$= \frac{1}{2}h(a + b)$$ Distributive property

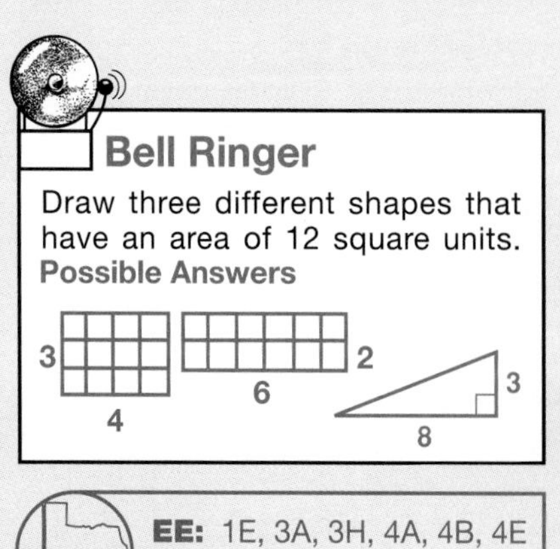

EE: 1E, 3A, 3H, 4A, 4B, 4E
TAAS: 2, 3, 4, 11

Area of a Trapezoid

If a trapezoid has bases of a units and b units and a height of h units, then the area (A) of the trapezoid is $\frac{1}{2} \cdot h \cdot (a + b)$ square units.

$$A = \frac{1}{2}h(a + b)$$

Example

3 Find the area of the trapezoid.

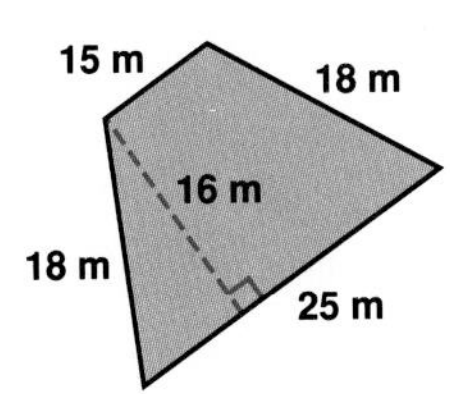

$A = \frac{1}{2}h(a + b)$ a is 15, b is 25, and h is 16.

$A = \frac{1}{2} \cdot 16(15 + 25)$

$A = \frac{1}{\cancel{2}_1} \cdot \cancel{16}^{8} \cdot 40$

$A = 320$

The area is 320 m^2.

Checking for Understanding

Communicating Algebra

Use the figure at the right for Exercises 1 and 2.

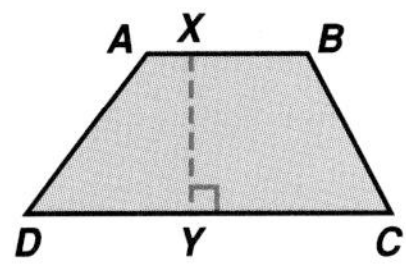

1. Name the bases of trapezoid $ABCD$. $\overline{AB}$, $\overline{DC}$
2. Name an altitude of trapezoid $ABCD$. $\overline{XY}$
3. In your own words, state how to find the area of a trapezoid. See margin.
4. Draw and label a trapezoid with bases $\overline{RS}$ and $\overline{TV}$. See margin.

Guided Practice

State the measures of the bases and altitude. Then find each area.

5. 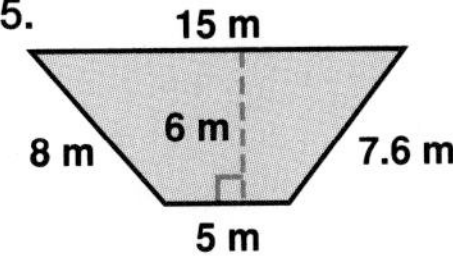

15 m, 5 m, 6 m, 60 m^2

6. 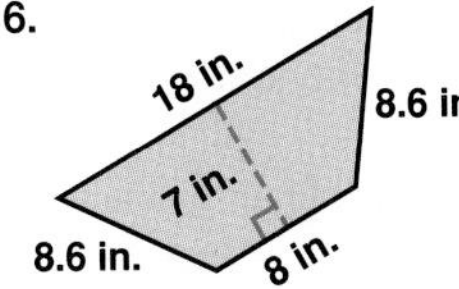

8 in., 18 in., 7 in., 91 in.^{2}

7. 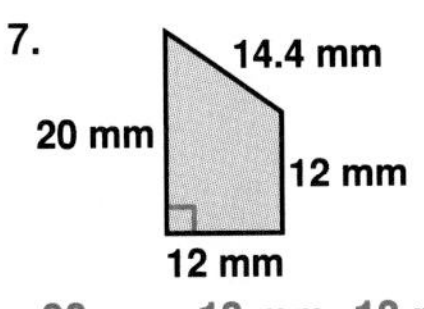

20 mm, 12 mm, 12 mm, 192 mm^2

Exercises

Independent Practice

Find the area of each trapezoid described below.

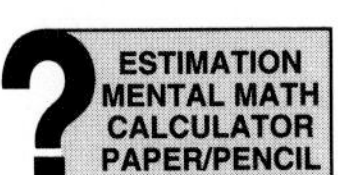

	base (a)	base (b)	height
8.	9 cm	24 cm	12 cm
9.	26 in.	14 in.	15 in.
10.	4.7 cm	5.9 cm	2 cm

	base (a)	base (b)	height
11.	12 ft	8 ft	7 ft
12.	0.3 km	0.5 km	0.2 km
13.	5.3 m	1.72 m	8.4 m

8. 198 cm^2 9. 300 in^2 10. 10.6 cm^2 11. 70 ft^2 12. 0.08 km^2 13. 29.484 m^2

- *For Example 3*
  Find the area of the trapezoid.

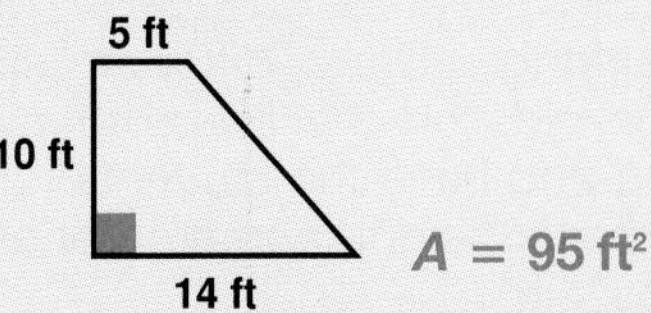

$A = 95$ ft^2

3 PRACTICE/APPLY

Checking the Concept

Before finding the areas of Exercises 5-7, have students explain why the nonbase sides can't be used as bases.

Error Analysis

Watch for students who average the bases incorrectly.
Prevent by having students verbalize each step.

Independent Practice

Homework Assignment	
Basic	9-13 odd, 14-18, 21, 22
Average	8, 10, 14-22
Honors	10, 12, 14-22

Practice Masters Booklet, **p. 123**

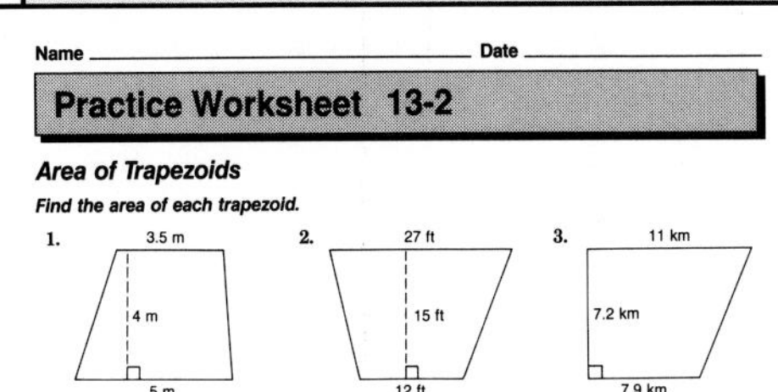
Name ______ Date ______

Practice Worksheet 13-2

Area of Trapezoids

Find the area of each trapezoid.

Find the area of each trapezoid described below.

	base (a)	base (b)	height	
4.	8.2 m	8 m	4.6 m	37.26 m^2
5.	$10\frac{1}{2}$ ft	6 ft	$4\frac{1}{2}$ ft	$37\frac{1}{8}$ ft^2
6.	12.3 cm	8 cm	6.1 cm	61.915 cm^2
7.	64 mm	40 mm	20 mm	1040 mm^2
8.	24 mi	14 mi	15 mi	285 mi^2
9.	18 yd	10 yd	8 yd	112 yd^2
10.	36.0 cm	24.2 cm	8.4 cm	252.84 cm^2
11.	16.7 m	7.7 m	16.2 m	197.64 m^2
12.	13.7 km	4.6 km	5.4 km	49.41 km^2
13.	24 in.	16 in.	11 in.	220 in^2
14.	18.4 m	12.9 m	10.1 m	158.065 m^2

Alternate Strategies: Reteaching the Lesson

Reteaching Activity

Using Models As in Lesson 13-1, work in cooperative groups of three. Give each group some corregated cardboard with quarter-inch graph paper attached. Using tacks and string, have a student make a trapezoid on the graph paper. Have another student name bases and altitude, and the third student determine the area.

Reteaching Masters Booklet, **p. 111**

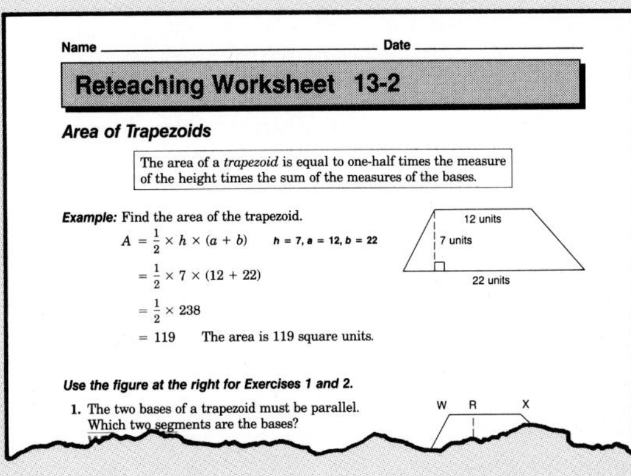
Name ______ Date ______

Reteaching Worksheet 13-2

Area of Trapezoids

The area of a *trapezoid* is equal to one-half times the measure of the height times the sum of the measures of the bases.

Example: Find the area of the trapezoid.

$A = \frac{1}{2} \times h \times (a + b)$ $h = 7, a = 12, b = 22$

$= \frac{1}{2} \times 7 \times (12 + 22)$

$= \frac{1}{2} \times 238$

$= 119$ The area is 119 square units.

Use the figure at the right for Exercises 1 and 2.

1. The two bases of a trapezoid must be parallel. Which two segments are the bases?

4 CLOSE

Assessment Option

Speaking Draw different sized trapezoids on the board or overhead and have the students name the base, height, and area of each trapezoid.

Additional Answers

3. Sample answer: Multiply the sum of the bases by the height and divide by 2.
4. 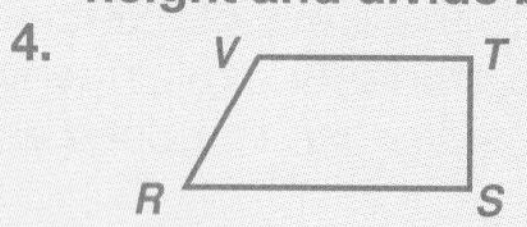

21. 

22. Sample answer: The formula for the area of a trapezoid is the formula for the sum of the areas of two triangles.

Enrichment Masters Booklet, **p. 111**

Name ______ Date ______

Enrichment Worksheet 13-2

Area of a Regular Polygon

The area of a regular polygon is equal to one-half the product of the **apothem** and the **perimeter**. The apothem is the distance from the center of the polygon to a side. The perimeter is the sum of the lengths of all of the sides.

Example:

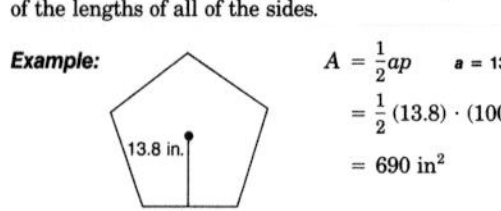

$A = \frac{1}{2}ap \quad a = 13.8, p = 100$

$= \frac{1}{2}(13.8) \cdot (100)$

$= 690 \text{ in}^2$

Find the area of each regular polygon.

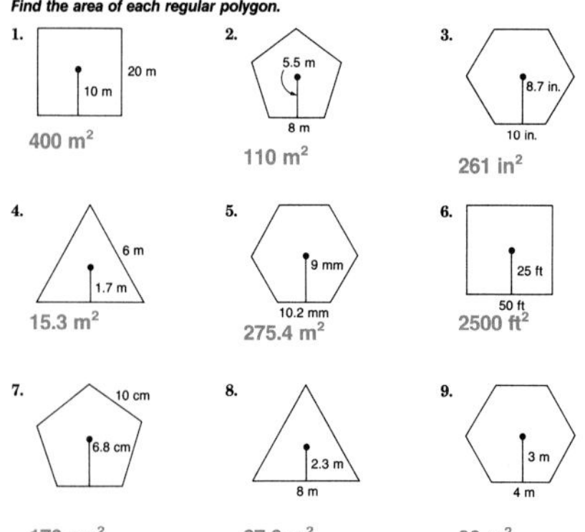

Mixed Review

14. Express 44,010,000 in scientific notation. (Lesson 6-11) 4.401×10^7
15. If $m\angle T = 54°$, find the measure of its supplement. (Lesson 12-3) 126°
16. Using the formula $A = \frac{1}{2}bh$, find the area of a triangle that has a base of 8 inches and a height of 7 inches. (Lesson 13-1) 28 in²

Applications

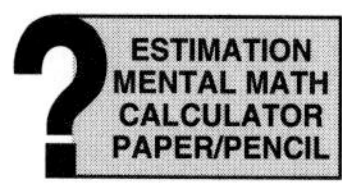

17. **Architecture** The side of a building is in the shape of a trapezoid. The base of the building is 400 feet wide. The top is 150 feet wide. The building is 500 feet tall. If the side is completely glass-paned, how much glass is used? 137,500 ft²
18. **Agriculture** A parcel of farmland, in the shape of a trapezoid, has been divided into two fields as shown in Figure 1. Which field has the greater area? How much greater? Field A; 1870 m²

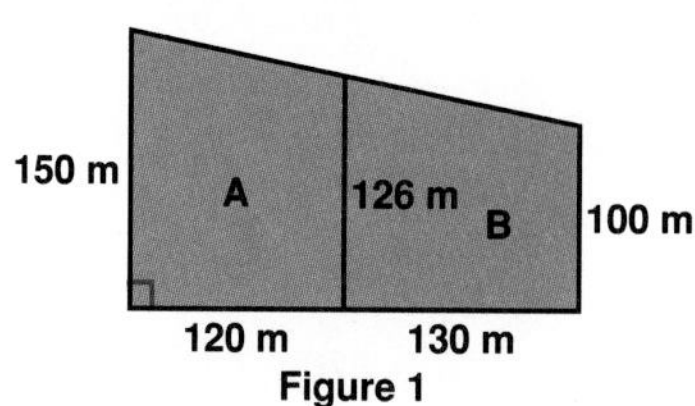

Figure 1

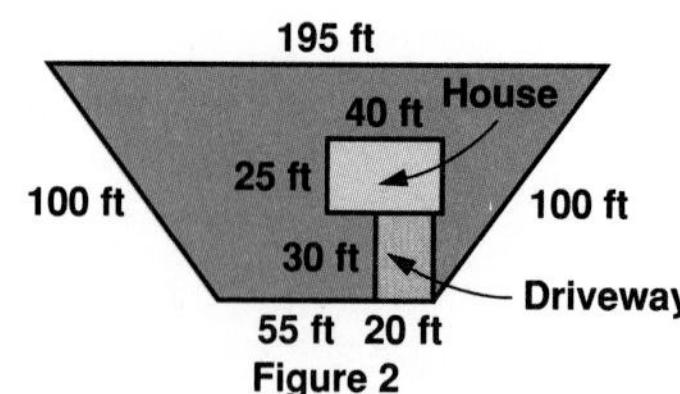

Figure 2

19. **Home Care** David Ling wants to re-seed his lawn. A diagram of his lot is shown in Figure 2. Before he buys the seed, he needs to know the area of the lawn. The lot is 85 feet deep. Calculate the number of square feet of lawn to be seeded. 9875 ft²
20. **Geography** The state of Wyoming is shaped like a trapezoid. Use the information on the map to estimate the area of the state. The actual area is 97,809 mi².

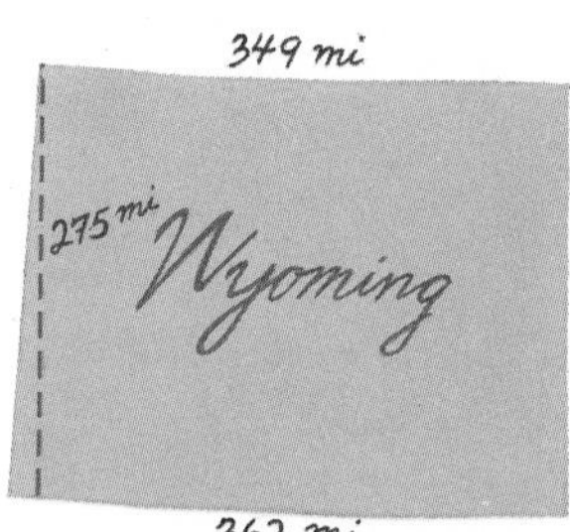

Critical Thinking

21. When a diagonal is drawn in a trapezoid, will one of the triangles formed always be an obtuse triangle? Will one always be an acute triangle? If not, draw a counterexample. See margin.

Wrap-Up

22. In your own words, tell how the formula for the area of a trapezoid is related to the formula for the area of a triangle. See margin.

Team Problem Solving

Someone has covered square *ABCD* with eight smaller squares, all the same size. The square marked 8 was the last square placed.

- Here is your challenge. Number the squares in the order they were placed. See drawing.
- Make a puzzle similar to this one to share with your friends. See students' work.

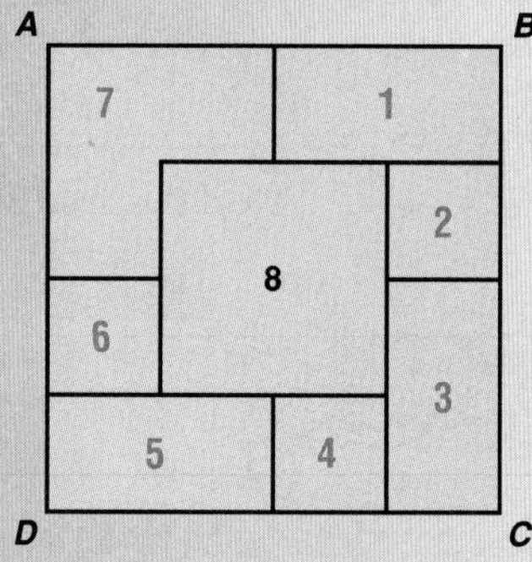

Alternate Strategies: Extending the Lesson

Enrichment

Career Connection A carpenter makes a picture frame from two sets of identical isosceles trapezoids. He cuts the trapezoids from a 2-inch wood strip. How many square inches of wood are in a frame for an 8 in. × 10 in. picture? 88 in.²

Cooperative Learning

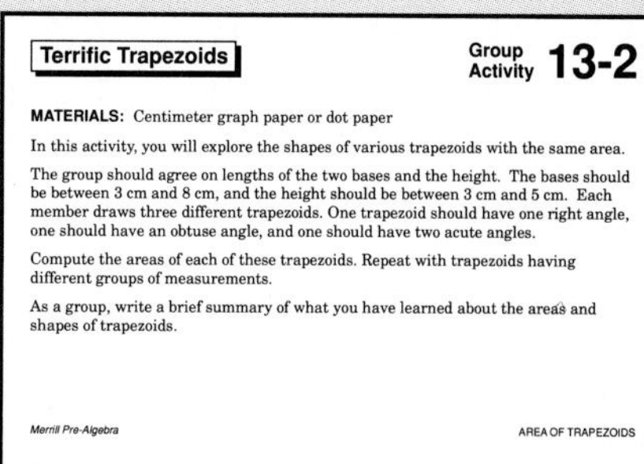

Terrific Trapezoids Group Activity **13-2**

MATERIALS: Centimeter graph paper or dot paper

In this activity, you will explore the shapes of various trapezoids with the same area.

The group should agree on lengths of the two bases and the height. The bases should be between 3 cm and 8 cm, and the height should be between 3 cm and 5 cm. Each member draws three different trapezoids. One trapezoid should have one right angle, one should have an obtuse angle, and one should have two acute angles.

Compute the areas of each of these trapezoids. Repeat with trapezoids having different groups of measurements.

As a group, write a brief summary of what you have learned about the areas and shapes of trapezoids.

Merrill Pre-Algebra AREA OF TRAPEZOIDS

Algebra in Action-Design

Interior Design

The library at Sam Houston High School needs new carpeting. An interior designer has selected the carpet and measured the room. A drawing of the room is shown below. All the corners are right angles.

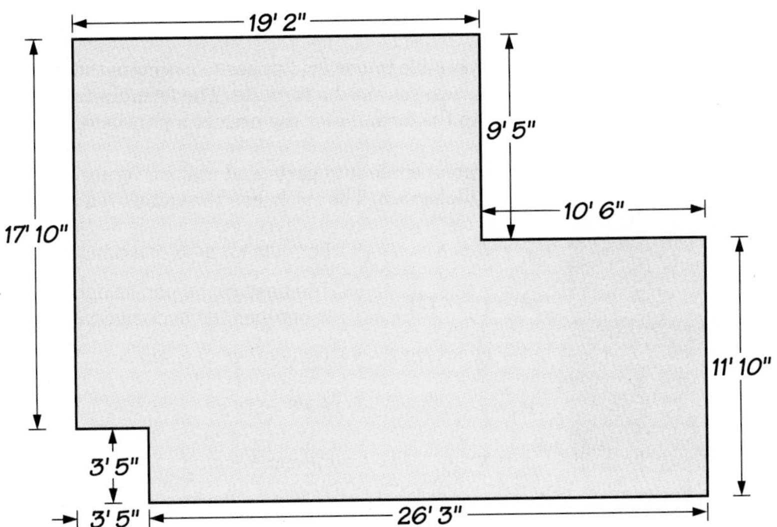

Work in a team to answer the following questions.

1. How could you find the area to be carpeted?
2. The carpeting can be purchased on a 12-foot wide roll or in square-foot pieces. How much carpeting will be needed if it is bought in the square-foot pieces? **556 squares**
3. If the carpeting is bought from a 12-foot wide roll, how much carpeting must be purchased? **about 49 ft**
4. The square-foot pieces cost $35 per dozen. The carpet on the roll costs $28 per square yard. Based on price, would you choose to buy the square pieces or the carpet from the roll? Why? **square pieces; costs less**

1. **Divide the room into smaller sections (squares and rectangles) and find the areas.**

Chapter 13 491

Applying Algebra to the Real World

Objective This optional page shows how algebra is used in the real world and also provides a change of pace.

Using Discussion After the teams of students have completed Questions 1-4, discuss the results. If students differ, have each team explain how their answer was obtained.

Career Connection A painter is hired to paint the room illustrated. If the walls are 10 feet tall, doors and windows are ignored, and one gallon of paint covers 400 square feet, how may gallons of paint are needed? 3

Activity

Assuming one gallon of paint will cover 400 square feet, measure your classroom and determine the amount of paint needed to paint the room. Allow for doors, windows, and the chalkboard.

5-Minute Check
(over Lesson 13-2)

Find the area of each trapezoid described below. **1. 175 cm²**

	base (*a*)	base (*b*)	height
1.	7 cm	18 cm	14 cm
2.	42 in.	14 in.	12 in.
3.	6.5 cm	3.4 cm	6 cm

2. 336 in.² **3. 29.7 cm²**

Transparency 13-3 contains the 5-Minute Check and a teaching aid for this lesson.

1 FOCUS

The purpose of this lesson is to develop and use a formula for finding the area of a circular region.

2 TEACH

Chalkboard Examples

Find the area of the circle. Round your answer to the nearest whole number.

6 cm

A ≈ 28 cm²

Practice Masters Booklet, **p. 124**

Name ____________ Date ____________

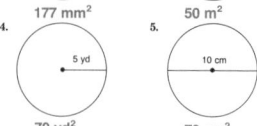

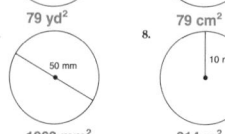

Practice Worksheet 13-3

Area of Circles

Find the area of each circle shown or described below. Round answers to the nearest whole number.

1. 15 mm — 177 mm²
2. 4 m — 50 m²
3. 32 cm — 804 cm²
4. 5 yd — 79 yd²
5. 10 cm — 79 cm²
6. 8 in. — 201 in²
7. 50 mm — 1963 mm²
8. 10 m — 314 m²
9. 39 mm — 1194 mm²
10. 9.8 cm — 75 cm²
11. 5.5 m — 95 m²
12. 1.4 m — 6 m²
13. radius, 4.9 cm — 75 cm²
14. diameter, 7 km — 38 km²
15. radius, $2\frac{1}{2}$ ft — 20 ft²
16. diameter, 4.2 mm — 14 mm²
17. radius, 5 yd — 79 yd²
18. diameter, $8\frac{1}{2}$ in. — 57 in²

13-3 Area: Circles

Objective:
Find the area of circles.

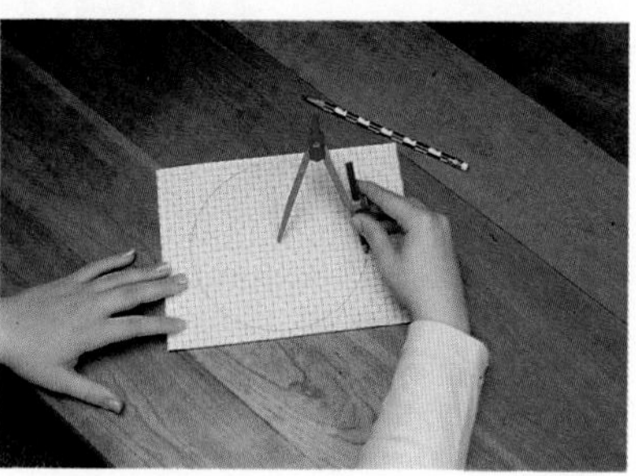

Can you think of a way to estimate the area of a circle? Here's a hint. First use a compass to draw a circle on grid paper. Count the squares contained completely within the circle. Include in your estimate the squares that are partially contained within the circle.

It is not always possible to use grid paper to estimate the area of a circle. In these cases, you need a formula. The formula for the area of a circle is related to the formula for the area of a parallelogram.

Separate a circle into parts and make a figure that looks like a parallelogram. The circle has the same area as that figure.

$A = b \times h$ Formula for area of a parallelogram

$A = \left(\frac{1}{2} \times C\right) \times r$ The base of the parallelogram is one-half the circumference.

$A = \frac{1}{2} \times (2\pi r) \times r$ Remember, $C = 2\pi r$.

$A = \pi \times r \times r$ $\frac{1}{2} \cdot 2 = 1$

$A = \pi r^2$ The formula is $A = \pi r^2$.

Area of a Circle

If a circle has a radius of r units, then the area (A) is $\pi \cdot r \cdot r$ or $\pi \cdot r^2$ square units.

$$A = \pi r^2$$

Example

1 Find the area of the circle. Round your answer to the nearest whole number.

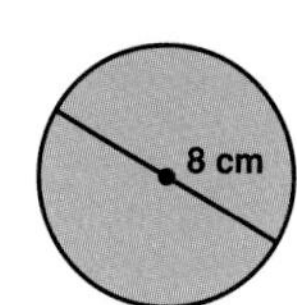

$A = \pi r^2$ Formula for area of a circle

$A = \pi \cdot 4^2$ Since the radius is one-half the diameter, $r = \frac{1}{2}(8)$ or 4.

π × 4 x² = 50.265482

$A \approx 50$ Compare with the estimate.

The area is about 50 cm².

Estimation Hint

You can estimate the area of a circle by squaring the radius and multiplying by 3. Thus the area of the circle in Example 1 is about 4 × 4 × 3 or 48 cm².

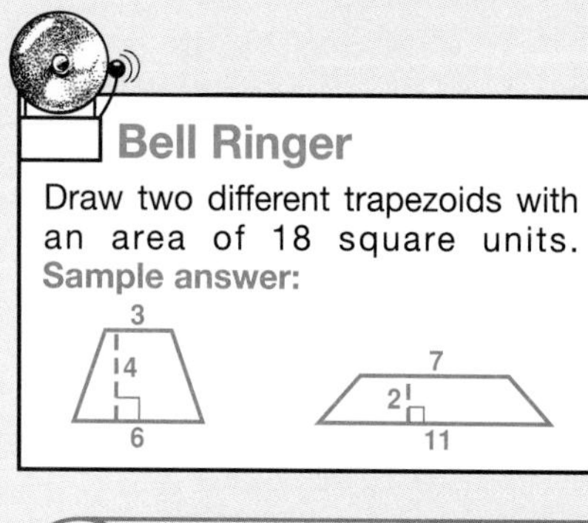

Bell Ringer

Draw two different trapezoids with an area of 18 square units.
Sample answer:

EE: 1E, 3A, 3H, 4A, 4B, 4E
TAAS: 2, 3, 4, 10, 11, 13

Reteaching Masters Booklet, **p. 112**

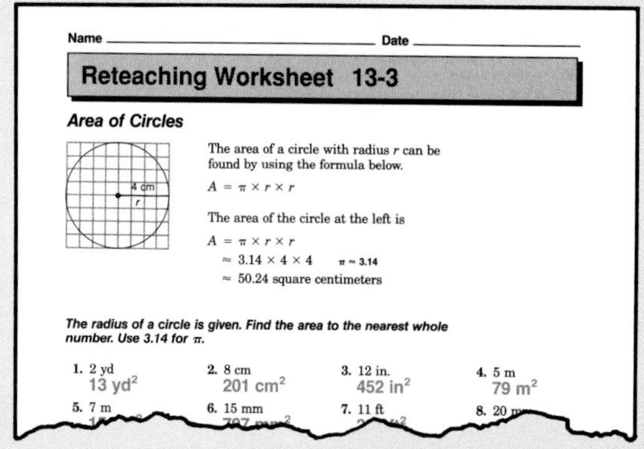

Name ____________ Date ____________

Reteaching Worksheet 13-3

Area of Circles

The area of a circle with radius r can be found by using the formula below.

$A = \pi \times r \times r$

The area of the circle at the left is

$A = \pi \times r \times r$
$\approx 3.14 \times 4 \times 4$ $\pi \approx 3.14$
≈ 50.24 square centimeters

The radius of a circle is given. Find the area to the nearest whole number. Use 3.14 for π.

1. 2 yd — 13 yd²
2. 8 cm — 201 cm²
3. 12 in. — 452 in²
4. 5 m — 79 m²
5. 7 m
6. 15 mm
7. 11 ft
8. 20 m

Checking for Understanding

Communicating Algebra

1. Estimate the area of the circle shown at the right by counting squares and by using the Estimation Hint on page 492. How do the estimates compare?
   Sample answer: about 48 square units

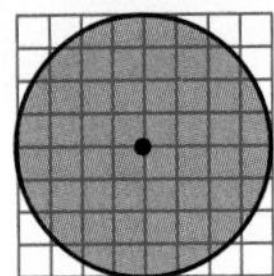

2. State the formula for finding the area of a circle. Square the radius and multiply times π.

Guided Practice

Tell how you should find the area of each circle. Then find each area.

3. radius, 3 cm
   $3 \cdot 3 \cdot \pi$; 28.3 cm^2
4. diameter, 10 ft
   $5 \cdot 5 \cdot \pi$; 78.5 ft^2
5. radius, 3.5 mi
   $3.5 \cdot 3.5 \cdot \pi$; 38.5 mi^2

Exercises

Answers are calculated using $\boxed{\pi}$.

Independent Practice

Find the area of each circle shown or described below. Round answers to the nearest whole number.

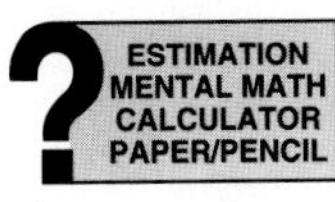

6. 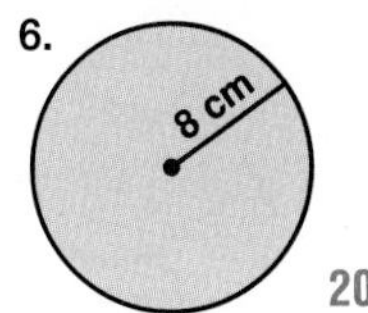

201 cm^2

7. 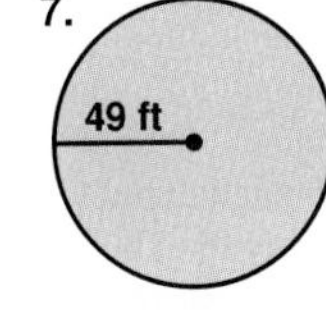

7543 ft^2

8. 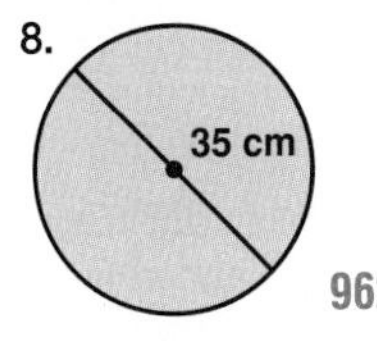

962 cm^2

9. radius, 16 cm 804 cm^2
10. diameter, 8 m 50 m^2
11. radius, 7 yd 154 yd^2
12. diameter, 42 in. 1385 in^2
13. radius, 5.2 km 85 km^2
14. radius, $3\frac{1}{2}$ in. 38 in^2

Mixed Review

15. **Sports** A 4-person relay team ran a race in 232 seconds. What was the average time for each person? (Lesson 1-9) 58 seconds
16. Using the formula $A = \frac{1}{2}h(a + b)$, find the area of a trapezoid with bases of 4 cm and 9 cm and a height of 6 cm. (Lesson 13-2) 39 cm^2

Applications

17. **Horticulture** A gardener for a park district has to prepare three circular gardens for planting. One garden has a diameter of 12 feet, one has a radius of 8 feet, and the third has a diameter of 20 feet. If each bag of peat moss can cover 160 square feet of topsoil, how many bags of peat moss will he need?
    4 bags
18. **History** Stonehenge, an ancient monument in England, may have been used as a calendar. The stones are arranged in a circle 30 meters in diameter. Find the area of the circle. about 707 m^2

Critical Thinking

19. The area and circumference of a circle have the same measure. Find the radius. 2 units

Wrap-Up

20. In your own words, explain how to find the area of a circle if you know its diameter. Divide the diameter by two, square the result, and multiply times π.

3 PRACTICE/APPLY

Checking the Concept

Using Critical Thinking Why is the height of the parallelogram on page 492 equal to r? Sample answer: Because the parallelogram is constructed from pieces of the circle.

Error Analysis

Watch for students who are not able to distinguish between the radius and the diameter.
Prevent by relating the term radius to the term radiate, coming from a central point.

Independent Practice

Homework Assignment

Basic	7-13 odd, 15-17, 19, 20
Average	6-10 even, 15-20
Honors	12-20

4 CLOSE

Assessment Option

Modeling Using circular objects such as plates, hats or coins, have students measure the diameter to find the radius. Then find the area of each circle.

Enrichment Masters Booklet, **p. 112**

Name ______________ Date ______________

Sector of a Circle

The **sector** of a circle is the region bounded by two radii and the arc of the circle. The area of a sector is a fractional part of the area of the circle.

$A = \frac{n}{360} \times \pi \times r^2$ where n is the degree measure of the central angle

Example:

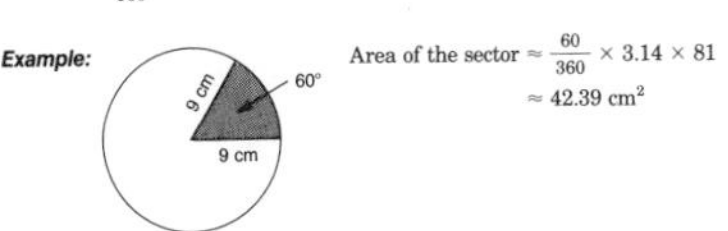

Area of the sector $\approx \frac{60}{360} \times 3.14 \times 81$
$\approx 42.39\ cm^2$

Find the area of each sector. Use 3.14 for π.

1. 12 cm, 45°, 12 cm — 56.52 cm^2
2. 12 cm, 30°, 12 cm — 37.68 cm^2
3. 12 cm, 60°, 12 cm — 75.36 cm^2
4. 6 cm, 90°, 6 cm — 28.26 cm^2
5. 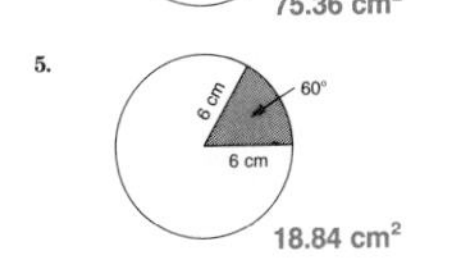

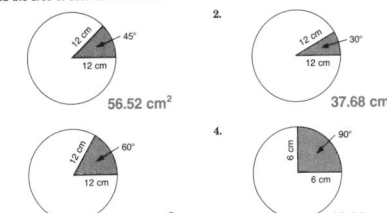

18.84 cm^2
6. 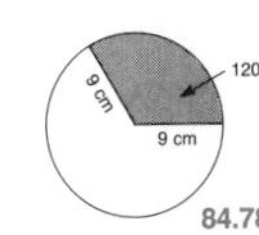

84.78 cm^2

Alternate Strategies: Extending the Lesson

Enrichment

Physical Education Connection Have students measure the foul line in the gymnasium as the diameter of a circle. Find the area of the circle. Estimate the area occupied by an average basketball player. At any one time, how many players could stand in the circle?

Cooperative Learning

Closing In On Circles — Group Activity 13-3

MATERIALS: Compass • straightedge • centimeter graph paper

With a partner, draw a circle with a radius 3 cm long on graph paper. Next draw one triangle inside the circle so that its vertices touch the circle. Draw another triangle outside so that its sides touch the circle.

Estimate the area of each triangle. Compute the difference in these areas.

Now, do the same thing using squares. Does the difference in areas get larger or smaller than the difference in areas for the triangles? Estimate the area of the circle. Which areas, the triangles or the rectangles, are closer to the area of the circle?

What do you think would happen if you used hexagons or octagons? Research how ancient mathematicians computed the area of the circle.

Merrill Pre-Algebra — AREA OF CIRCLES

EXPLORATION

Area and Probability

Objective Students will use the problem–solving strategy of using a simulation to explore the connection between probability and the area of irregular figures.

1 FOCUS

In this Exploration, students will find the area of irregular figures by applying their knowledge of proportion and probability.

2 TEACH

Using Discussion

Before groups begin dropping their objects, have students determine a rule for what constitutes landing "in" the regions, for example, if the point of the object is in. After the experiment, discuss why they needed to make 10 drops.

3 PRACTICE/APPLY

Using Models

You may want to provide cups in which to place the objects before they are dropped. You may also want to have students place their papers in a shallow box to lessen the chance of tacks bouncing away.

Additional Answer

4. Sample answer: Draw a six-inch square. Then draw a small circle within the square. Conduct an experiment similar to the one in Your Turn. Some variations may be to drop cotton balls, and blindfold the person dropping them.

4 CLOSE

Using Discussion

In Exercise 4, have students discuss the relationship between the area of the pond and the area of the field. Discuss how this is related to the probability of a dry landing.

Exploration

Area and Probability

Materials: unlined paper, ruler, compass, thumb tacks or straight pins

In this Exploration you will investigate the relationship between the area of irregular figures and probability.

Your Turn: Work in small groups to complete this activity. See students' work.

- Draw a 6-inch square on your paper. Within the square, draw a figure with an irregular shape. Hold 20 thumb tacks about 3 inches above the paper and drop them onto the paper.
- Count the number of thumb tacks that landed within the square. (Include those thumb tacks that landed in the figure.) Then count the number that landed only in the figure. This is sample A.
- Repeat nine more times for samples B through J. Find the total within the square and the total within the figure.

Analysis

1. The experimental probability that a thumb tack landed only in the figure is given by the ratio $\frac{\text{total within figure}}{\text{total within square}}$. Based on your findings, calculate the probability. See students' work.
2. The probability is also related to the area of the figure. Use the proportion below to estimate the area of the figure. See students' work.
$$\frac{\text{total within figure}}{\text{total within square}} = \frac{\text{area of figure}}{\text{area of square}}$$
3. Devise a way to determine whether your answer is reasonable. Sample answer: Draw a grid on the shape and count the squares.
4. Suppose a skydiver parachutes onto a square field that contains a pond. Assume there is an equal chance of landing at any point within the field. Design a model to help estimate the probability that the diver has a dry landing. See margin.

SET-UP

Materials

- unlined paper, ruler, compass, thumbtacks or straight pins

You may wish to use the Exploration worksheet provided on page 63 of the Lab Manual.

For Students Have students trace a coin or counter for Exercise 4 if compasses are not available.

For the Overhead Projector You can model this Exploration on the overhead dropping one centimeter square tiles or cubic centimeters.

EE: 1A, 1C, 1E, 4B, 5A, 5D

13-4 Surface Area: Prisms

Objective:
Find the surface area of triangular and rectangular prisms.

Key Terms:
prism
base
rectangular prism
face
surface area
triangular prism

In Lessons 13-1, 13-2, and 13-3, you found the area of two-dimensional shapes. However, most of the shapes you use in everyday life have three dimensions, length, width, and height.

Rectangular regions ABCD and EFGH are bases. Could another pair of regions be the bases of this rectangular prism?
Yes; any two parallel rectangles.

In geometry, solids such as the box in the photo are called **prisms.** A prism is a solid figure that has two parallel congruent sides, called **bases**. A prism is classified by the shape of its bases. The prism shown at the right is a **rectangular prism.**

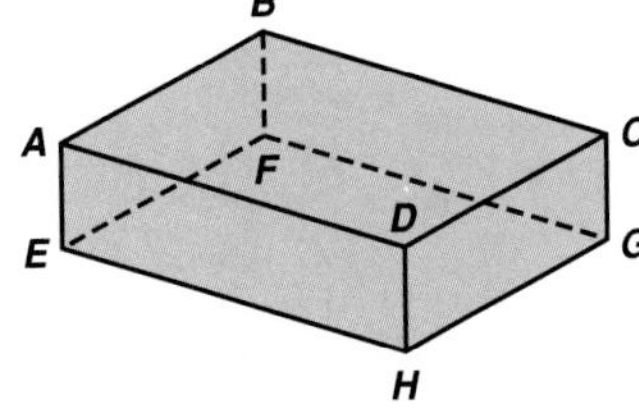

If you "open up" or "unfold" a rectangular prism, you will see the rectangular regions or **faces** that make up the surface of the prism. The **surface area** of a prism is the sum of the areas of its faces.

There are six faces in a rectangular prism.

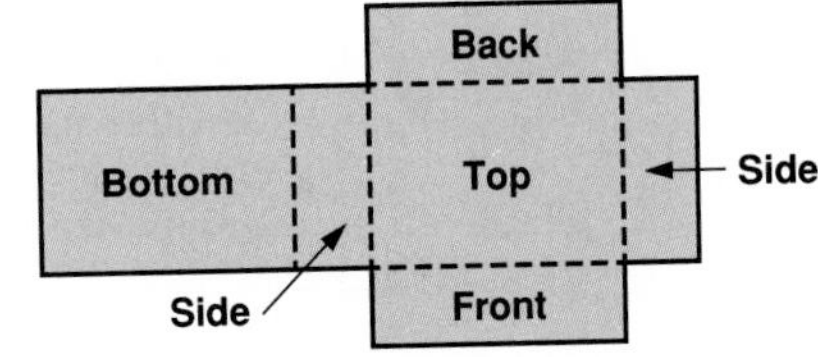

Example

1 **Find the surface area of a rectangular prism if the length is 0.8 m, the width is 0.5 m, and the height is 0.4 m.**

Use the formula $A = \ell w$ to find the area of each face.

How can you use the properties of a rectangle to find the dimensions that are not marked?
Parallel sides have the same measure.

Front or Back 0.8 ⊠ 0.4 ⊟ 0.32

Top or Bottom 0.8 ⊠ 0.5 ⊟ 0.4

Sides 0.5 ⊠ 0.4 ⊟ 0.2

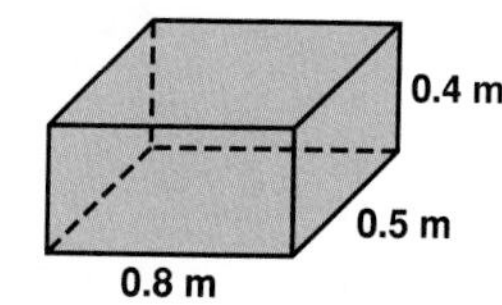

2 ⊠ 0.32 ⊞ 2 ⊠ 0.4 ⊞ 2 ⊠ 0.2 ⊟ 1.84

The surface area is 1.84 m^2.

Bell Ringer
What is the diameter of a circle if the area is 28.26 square meters?
6 meters

Lesson Notes 13-4

5-Minute Check
(over Lesson 13-3)

Find the area of each circle described below.
1. radius 9 cm $A \approx 254.5$ cm^2
2. diameter 24 cm $A \approx 452.4$ cm^2
3. diameter 6 ft $A \approx 28.3$ ft^2
4. radius 2.4 m $A \approx 18.1$ m^2
5. diameter 3 yd $A \approx 7.1$ yd^2

Transparency 13-4 contains the 5-Minute Check and a teaching aid for this lesson.

1 FOCUS

The purpose of this lesson is to develop and use a procedure for finding the lateral and the total surface areas of a prism.

Motivating the Lesson

Show students a light-diffracting prism, or a picture of one. Ask students if any of them have used such a prism before, and if anyone knows the characteristics of a prism.

2 TEACH

Using Cooperative Groups

Give cooperative groups of students models of different prisms. From the models, develop a list of characteristics of a prism. **2 congruent parallel bases connected by rectangles** Have students measure and find the surface area of each.

Chalkboard Examples

- *For Example 1*
  Find the surface area of a rectangular prism if the length is 12 cm, the width is 6 cm, and the height is 4 cm. **288 cm^2**

EE: 1E, 3A, 3H, 4A, 4B, 4E
TAAS: 2, 3, 4, 10, 11, 13

Chalkboard Examples

- *For Example 2*
  Find the surface area of the triangular prism shown below.

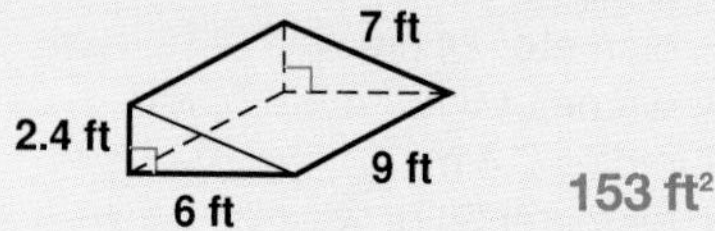

153 ft²

3 PRACTICE/APPLY

Checking the Concept

Show students a drawing of a hexagonal prism. Have students determine how many faces it has. Ask students to develop a formula that tells the number of faces a prism has based on the number of sides of the base. $F = E + 2$

Error Analysis

Watch for students who do not include the area of all sides.
Prevent by systematically listing all sides.

Practice Masters Booklet, **p. 125**

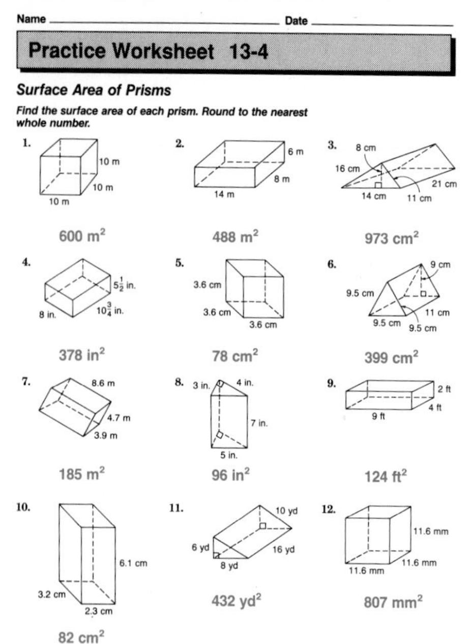

Name ______________________ Date ____________

Practice Worksheet 13-4

Surface Area of Prisms

Find the surface area of each prism. Round to the nearest whole number.

1. 10 m, 10 m, 10 m — 600 m²
2. 6 m, 8 m, 14 m — 488 m²
3. 8 cm, 16 cm, 14 cm, 11 cm, 21 cm — 973 cm²
4. $5\frac{1}{2}$ in., 8 in., $10\frac{3}{4}$ in. — 378 in²
5. 3.6 cm, 3.6 cm, 3.6 cm — 78 cm²
6. 9 cm, 9.5 cm, 11 cm, 9.5 cm, 9.5 cm — 399 cm²
7. 8.6 m, 4.7 m, 3.9 m — 185 m²
8. 3 in., 4 in., 7 in., 5 in. — 96 in²
9. 2 ft, 4 ft, 9 ft — 124 ft²
10. 6.1 cm, 3.2 cm, 2.3 cm — 82 cm²
11. 10 yd, 6 yd, 16 yd, 8 yd — 432 yd²
12. 11.6 mm, 11.6 mm, 11.6 mm — 807 mm²

In the prism at the right, △LMN is one base. What is the other? Why are these the bases? Does a base always need to be on the "bottom?"
△*PQR;* they are parallel congruent sides; no.

A prism is named by the shape of its bases. The parallel bases of the prism at the right are shaped like triangles, so it is called a **triangular prism.** Name something in everyday life that is the shape of a triangular prism. Sample answer: a tent

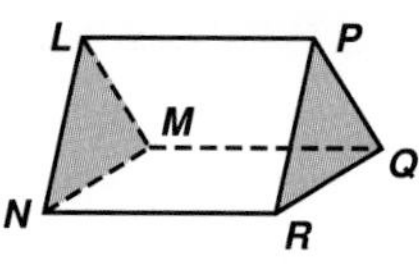

Example

2 **Find the surface area of the triangular prism shown below.**

There are five faces in a triangular prism.

Use the formula $A = \frac{1}{2}bh$.

Front Face $\frac{1}{2} \cdot 4 \cdot 3 = 6$

Back Face $\frac{1}{2} \cdot 4 \cdot 3 = 6$

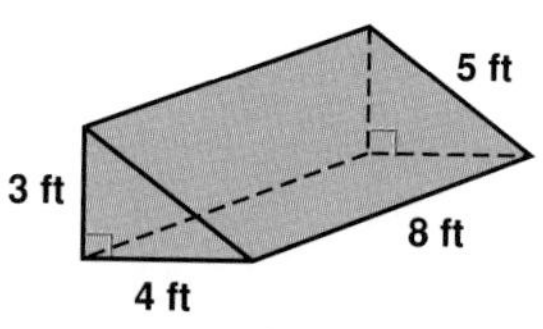

Use the formula $A = \ell w$.

Side $8 \cdot 5 = 40$
Side $8 \cdot 4 = 32$
Side $8 \cdot 3 = 24$
Total............................108

The surface area of the triangular prism is 108 ft².

Checking for Understanding

Communicating Algebra

1. A prism is named by its __?__. bases
2. A cube is a rectangular prism. Describe its faces. squares
3. Explain why surface area is important when you giftwrap a package. You are covering all the surfaces with paper.

Name each prism shown below. Justify your answer.

4. 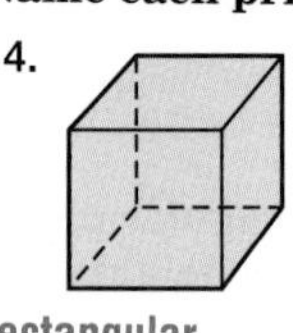
rectangular prism

5. 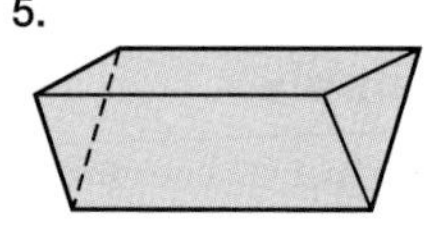
triangular prism

6. 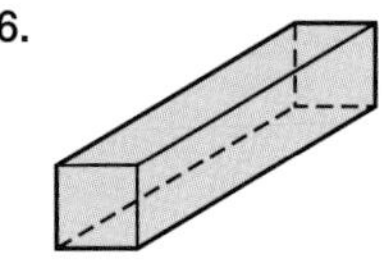
rectangular prism

Guided Practice

Explain how to find the surface area of each prism. Then find the surface area.

7. 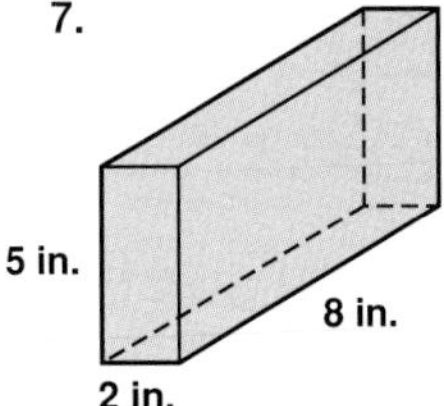

8. 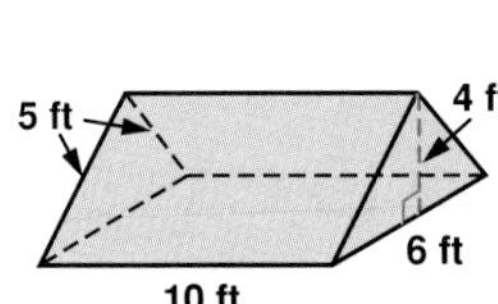

9. 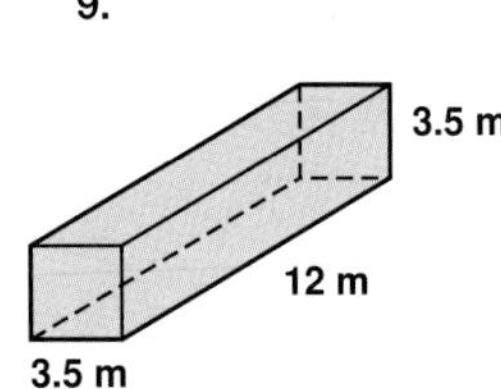

For answers to Exercises 7-9, see margin.

Alternate Strategies: Reteaching the Lesson

Reteaching Activity

Using Models Using the following pattern, have students make a triangular prism. Measure and calculate the area. Confirm the area using graph paper.

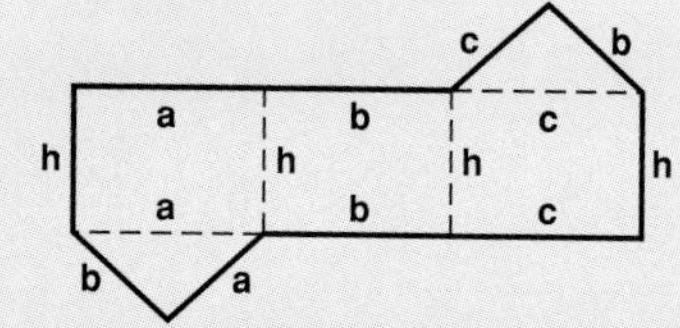

Reteaching Masters Booklet, **p. 113**

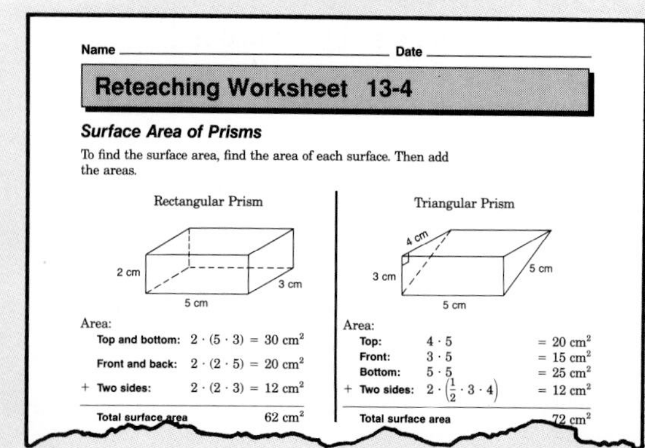

Name ______________________ Date ____________

Reteaching Worksheet 13-4

Surface Area of Prisms

To find the surface area, find the area of each surface. Then add the areas.

Rectangular Prism (2 cm, 3 cm, 5 cm)

Area:
- **Top and bottom:** $2 \cdot (5 \cdot 3) = 30$ cm²
- **Front and back:** $2 \cdot (2 \cdot 5) = 20$ cm²
- \+ **Two sides:** $2 \cdot (2 \cdot 3) = 12$ cm²

Total surface area 62 cm²

Triangular Prism (4 cm, 3 cm, 5 cm, 5 cm)

Area:
- **Top:** $4 \cdot 5 = 20$ cm²
- **Front:** $3 \cdot 5 = 15$ cm²
- **Bottom:** $5 \cdot 5 = 25$ cm²
- \+ **Two sides:** $2 \cdot \left(\frac{1}{2} \cdot 3 \cdot 4\right) = 12$ cm²

Total surface area 72 cm²

Exercises

Independent Practice

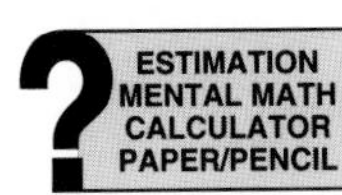

Find the surface area of each prism. Round to the nearest whole number.

10. 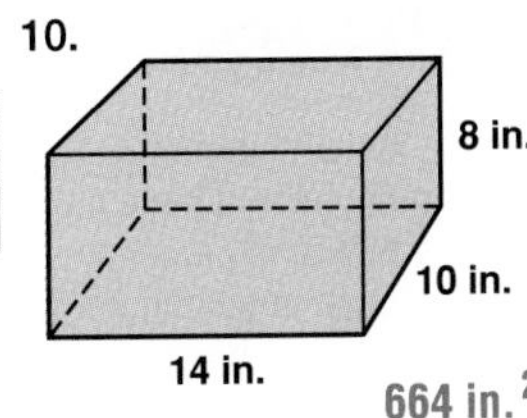

664 in.^{2}

11. 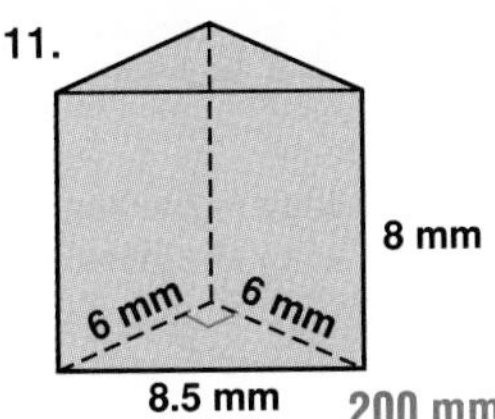

200 mm^2

12. 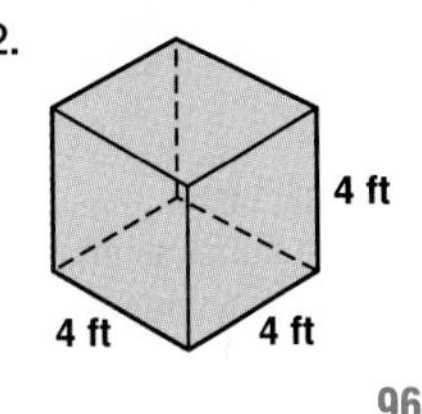

96 ft^2

Mixed Review

13. Solve $\frac{h}{-4} = 19$. (Lesson 3-4) -76

14. **Probability** What is the probability of correctly guessing the answer on one true-false question on a quiz? (Lesson 11-4) $\frac{1}{2}$

15. Using the formula $A = \pi r^2$, find the area of a circle that has a diameter of 14 cm. (Lesson 13-3) about 154 cm^2

Applications

16. **Woodworking** Paula is building a storage chest as a project in woodworking class. To help her plan the project, Paula made the scale drawing shown at the right. When the chest is completed, she intends to use a stain for the outside finish. If a can of stain will cover 30 ft^2, how many cans of stain will Paula need? 1

3 ft
FRONT 2 ft
TOP $1\frac{1}{2}$ ft $1\frac{1}{2}$ ft
Side A BACK Side B 2 ft
BOTTOM $1\frac{1}{2}$ ft
3 ft

17. **Interior Design** A rectangular room is 12.5 ft long by 8 ft high by 10 ft wide. How much wallpaper is needed to cover the walls, not taking into account doorways or windows? 360 ft^2

18. **Make Up a Problem** Write a situation in which you would need to know the surface area of a prism. See margin.

Challenge

19. Suppose a piece of paper $8\frac{1}{2}$ in. by 11 in. will be used to make a prism. Could the prism have a surface area of 95 in^2? Explain your answer. No; the surface area could not be more than the area of the paper.

Critical Thinking

20. Draw all the possible patterns that can be folded into a cube. (One is [cross-shaped pattern].) See Solutions Manual.

Wrap-Up

21. Write an explanation of surface area that would help a younger student understand what surface area is. See margin.

Independent Practice

Homework Assignment	
Basic	10-17, 20, 21
Average	11-18, 20, 21
Honors	11-21

4 CLOSE

Assessment Option

Modeling Have the students make a prism out of paper and give the prism measurements. Then have them exchange prisms with another student and find the total surface area.

Additional Answers

7. $2(5 \cdot 2) + 2(2 \cdot 8) + 2(5 \cdot 8)$
8. $2\left(\frac{1}{2} \cdot 4 \cdot 6\right) + (6 \cdot 10) + 2(5 \cdot 10)$
9. $4(3.5 \cdot 12) + 2(3.5)^2$
18. Sample answer: If you were building a toy chest you would need to know the surface area in order to buy enough wood.
21. Sample answer: Surface area is the amount of wrapping paper needed to cover a box without any overlap.

Enrichment Masters Booklet, **p. 113**

Name ______ Date ______

Enrichment Worksheet 13-4

Euler's Formula

Leonhard Euler (oi'ler), 1707–1783, was a Swiss mathematician who is often called the father of topology. He also studied perfect numbers and produced a proof to show that there is an infinite number of primes. He also developed the following formula, relating the number of vertices, the number of faces, and the number of edges of a *polyhedron*.

Euler's formula: $V + F = E + 2$
V = number of vertices
F = number of faces
E = number of edges

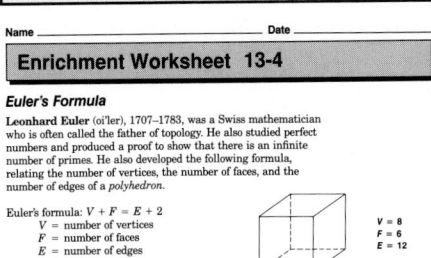

For a cube, $8 + 6 = 12 + 2$.

Another name for a cube is **hexahedron**.

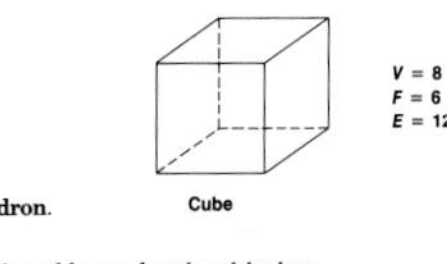

Cube

Use Euler's formula to find the number of faces of each polyhedron.

1. tetrahedron; $V = 4, E = 6$ 4 faces
2. octahedron; $V = 6, E = 12$ 8 faces

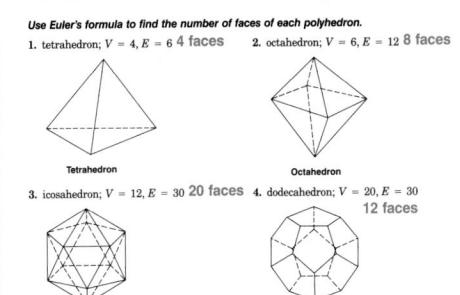

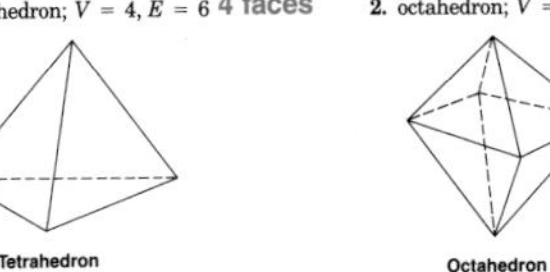
Tetrahedron
Octahedron

3. icosahedron; $V = 12, E = 30$ 20 faces
4. dodecahedron; $V = 20, E = 30$ 12 faces

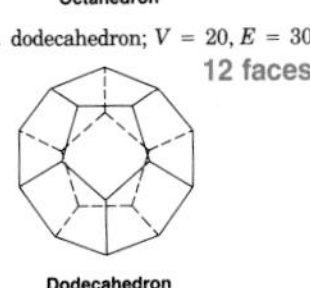
Icosahedron
Dodecahedron

The suffix -hedron comes from the Greek language meaning "face." Find the meaning of each of the following prefixes.

5. hexa- six
6. tetra- four
7. octa- eight
8. icosa- twenty
9. dodeca- twelve

Alternate Strategies: Extending the Lesson

Enrichment

Home Economics Connection A boy wants to make a triangular tent that has a floor 6 ft wide and 7 ft long and is 4 ft tall. The sides measure 5 ft from top to bottom. It also has flaps to cover both ends. How much fabric is needed? 136 sq. ft.

Cooperative Learning

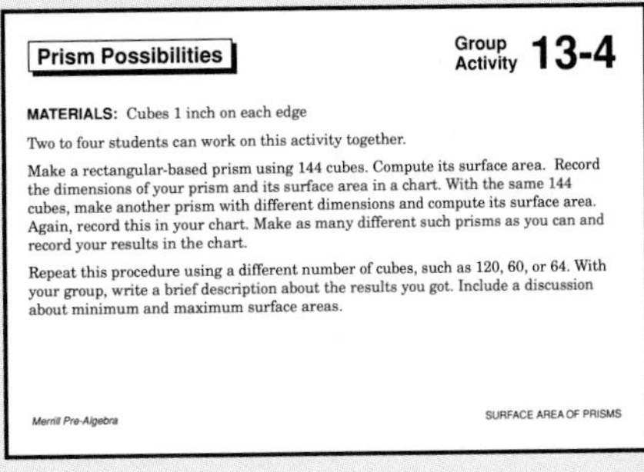

Prism Possibilities Group Activity **13-4**

MATERIALS: Cubes 1 inch on each edge

Two to four students can work on this activity together.

Make a rectangular-based prism using 144 cubes. Compute its surface area. Record the dimensions of your prism and its surface area in a chart. With the same 144 cubes, make another prism with different dimensions and compute its surface area. Again, record this in your chart. Make as many different such prisms as you can and record your results in the chart.

Repeat this procedure using a different number of cubes, such as 120, 60, or 64. With your group, write a brief description about the results you got. Include a discussion about minimum and maximum surface areas.

Merrill Pre-Algebra SURFACE AREA OF PRISMS

Lesson Notes 13-5

5-Minute Check
(over Lesson 13-4)

Find the surface area of each prism. Round to the nearest whole number.

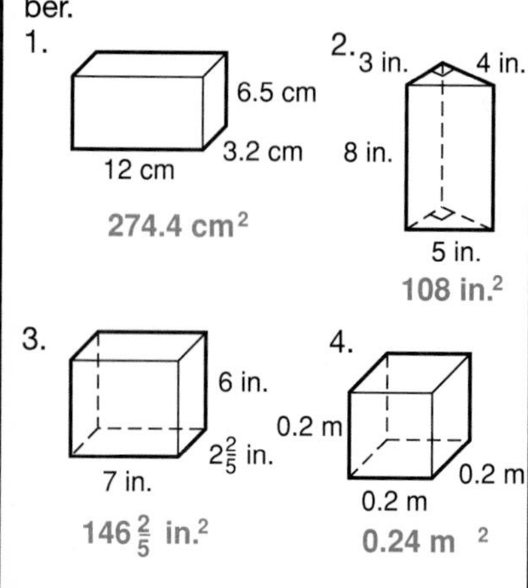

Transparency 13-5 contains the 5-Minute Check and a teaching aid for this lesson.

1 FOCUS

The purpose of this lesson is to develop and use a procedure for finding the surface area of a circular cylinder.

Motivating the Lesson

Show students pictures of a rocket, a tanker truck, a silo, and an oil storage tank. Ask what the items have in common.

2 TEACH

Using Models Have cooperative groups of students write 1 in.-12 in. on slips of paper and place them in a bag. Draw a number for the height and another number for the radius of a cylinder. Construct the cylinder and determine its surface area.

EE: 1E, 3A, 3H, 4A, 4B, 4E
TAAS: 2, 3, 4, 10, 11, 13

13-5 Surface Area: Cylinders

Objective:
Find the surface area of circular cylinders.

Key Term:
circular cylinder

Many foods are packaged in recyclable cans. These cans are examples of cylinders. A cylindrical container is relatively easy to manufacture and, once filled, can be sealed so the contents are airtight. In addition to food, cylindrical containers are also used to store water, oil, and grain.

Most of the cylinders we see are called **circular cylinders.** The bases of a circular cylinder are two parallel, congruent circular regions. In this textbook, when we say cylinder assume we are talking about a circular cylinder.

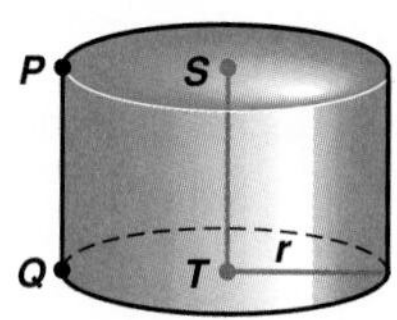

An altitude is any perpendicular line segment joining the two bases. $\overline{ST}$ and $\overline{PQ}$ are altitudes.

If you open the top and bottom of a cylinder and then make a vertical cut in the curved surface, you could lay the cylinder flat in the same way you did with a rectangular prism. You would then have a pattern for making that cylinder.

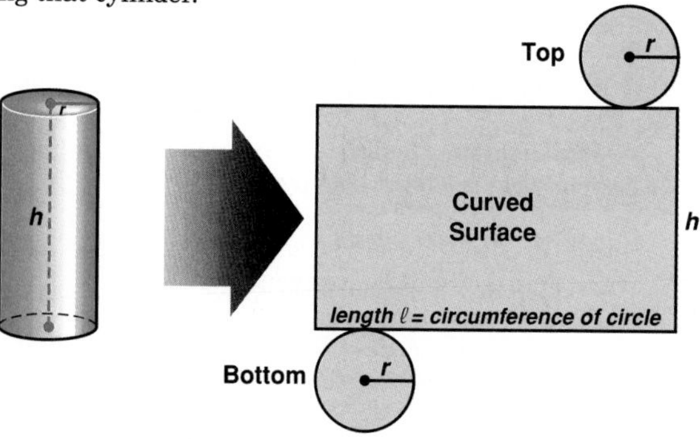

From the diagram above, you can see that:

1. The bases of the cylinder are congruent circular regions.
2. The curved surface of the cylinder opens to form a rectangular region.
3. The width of the rectangle is the height of the cylinder.
4. The length of the rectangle is the circumference of a base.

Why is the length of the rectangle the same as the circumference of a base? **It "wraps" completely around the circular base.**

You can use these observations to find the surface area of a circular cylinder.

Bell Ringer

Draw a picture of a rectangular prism, a triangular prism, and a square prism.

Example

1 **Find the surface area of a cylinder if the radius of a base is 7 cm and the height is 30 cm.**

Top or Bottom Base

$A = \pi r^2$ Area of a circle

$A = \pi \cdot 7^2$

[π] [×] 7 [x²] [=] 153.93804

$A \approx 153.9$

The areas of the bases are both about 153.9 cm^2.

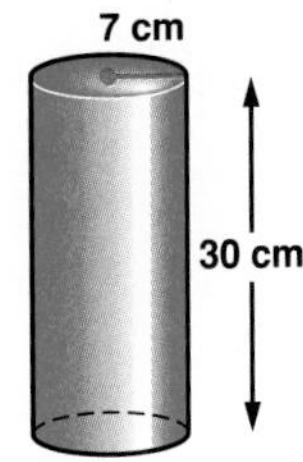

Curved Surface

$A = \ell w$ Area of a rectangle

$A = 2\pi r \cdot h$ Replace ℓ with the expression for the circumference of a circle.

$A = 2 \cdot \pi \cdot 7 \cdot 30$

2 [×] [π] [×] 7 [×] 30 [=] 1319.4689

$A \approx 1319.5$

The area of the curved surface is about 1319.5 cm^2.

Add to find the total surface area.

2 [×] 153.9 [+] 1319.5 [=] 1627.3

The surface area is about 1627.3 cm^2.

Checking for Understanding

Communicating Algebra

1. A circular cylinder has __?__ bases. 2, or circular
2. State the formula you should use to find the area of the bases of a cylinder. πr^2

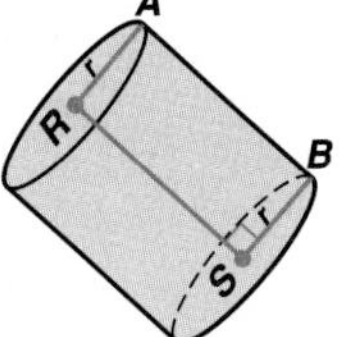

Use the figure shown at the right. 3. circle R and circle S; $\overline{AB}$ and $\overline{RS}$

3. Name the bases and two altitudes.
4. Explain how to find the curved surface area. $2\pi r$ times the length of $\overline{AB}$ Then explain how to find the total surface area. Find 2 times πr^2; add to the curved surface area.

Guided Practice

Explain how to find the surface area of each cylinder. Then find the surface area.

5. 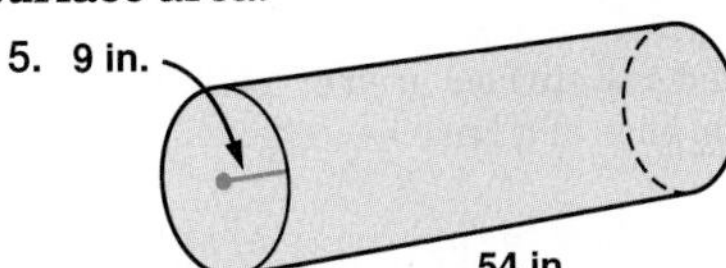

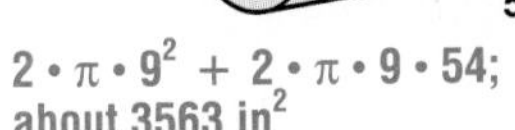

$2 \cdot \pi \cdot 9^2 + 2 \cdot \pi \cdot 9 \cdot 54$; about 3563 in^2

6. 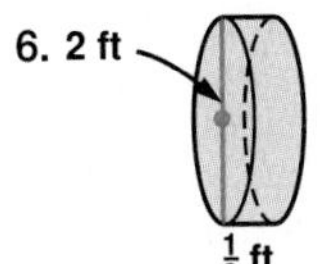

$2 \cdot \pi \cdot 1^2 + 2 \cdot \pi \cdot 1 \cdot 0.5$; about 9.4 ft^2

Chalkboard Examples

- *For Example 1*
  Find the surface area of a cylinder if the radius of a base is 5 cm and the height is 26 cm.
  $A \approx 973.9$ cm^2

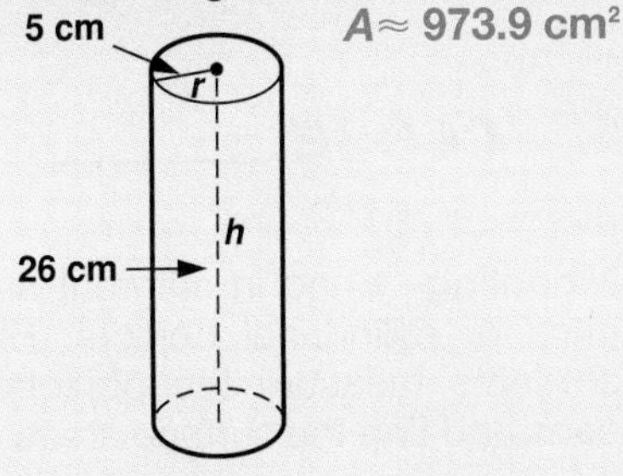

3 PRACTICE/APPLY

Checking the Concept

Using Discussion Display the BASIC program below on the overhead. Ask students to explain what happens in steps 40 and 50. Then have students use the program to check their answers to Exercises 5-10.

```
10 LET PI = 3.141592654
20 INPUT R
30 INPUT H
40 C = 2*PI*R
50 A = 2*PI*R^2+C*H
60 PRINT "THE TOTAL AREA
   = ";A
70 END
```

Practice Masters Booklet, **p. 126**

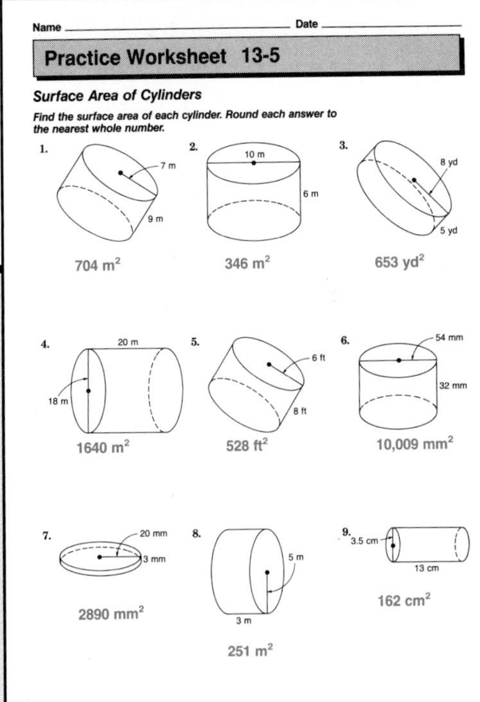

Name ________ Date ________

Practice Worksheet 13-5

Surface Area of Cylinders

Find the surface area of each cylinder. Round each answer to the nearest whole number.

1. 7 m, 9 m — 704 m^2
2. 10 m, 6 m — 346 m^2
3. 8 yd, 5 yd — 653 yd^2
4. 20 m, 18 m — 1640 m^2
5. 6 ft, 8 ft — 528 ft^2
6. 54 mm, 32 mm — 10,009 mm^2
7. 20 mm, 3 mm — 2890 mm^2
8. 5 m, 3 m — 251 m^2
9. 3.5 cm, 13 cm — 162 cm^2

Alternate Strategies: Reteaching the Lesson

Reteaching Activity

Using Measurements Ignoring irregularities in shape, have students determine the number of square inches of sheet aluminum needed to make an aluminum beverage can.

Reteaching Masters Booklet, **p. 114**

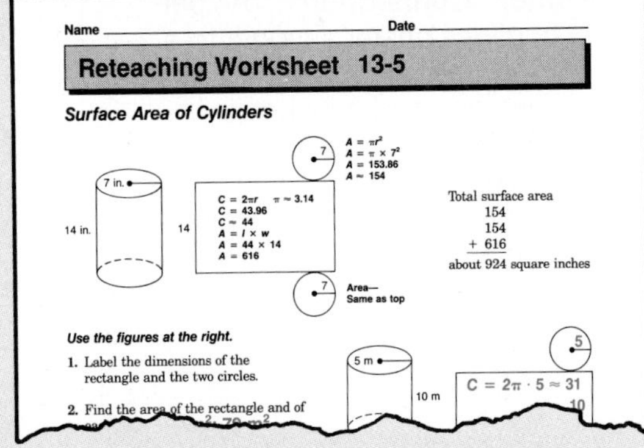

Name ________ Date ________

Reteaching Worksheet 13-5

Surface Area of Cylinders

7 in. 14 in.

$A = \pi r^2$
$A = \pi \times 7^2$
$A = 153.86$
$A \approx 154$

$C = 2\pi r$ $\pi \approx 3.14$
$C = 43.96$
$C \approx 44$
$A = l \times w$
$A = 44 \times 14$
$A = 616$

Area— Same as top

Total surface area
154
154
+ 616
about 924 square inches

Use the figures at the right.

1. Label the dimensions of the rectangle and the two circles.
2. Find the area of the rectangle and of ...

5 m 10 m $C = 2\pi \cdot 5 \approx 31$

Independent Practice

Homework Assignment	
Basic	7-15, 18, 19
Average	6-8, 10-16, 18, 19
Honors	8-19

4 CLOSE

Assessment Option

Modeling Bring in different sized cans or cylindrical objects. Have students measure the objects or cans and find the surface areas.

Enrichment Masters Booklet, **p. 114**

Name ______________________ Date ______________

Enrichment Worksheet 13-5

Approximations of π (pi)

Prior to the seventeenth century, approximations for π (pi) were calculated using geometric techniques. These techniques involved the ratio of the circumference of a circle to its diameter.

However, in about 1658, the English mathematician Wallis proved that π equals the following product of an infinite number of fractions.

(A) $\pi = 4 \times \left(\frac{2}{3} \times \frac{4}{3} \times \frac{4}{5} \times \frac{6}{5} \times \frac{6}{7} \times \frac{8}{7} \times \frac{8}{9} \times \ldots\right)$

In 1674, the German mathematician Leibniz proved the following.

(B) $\pi = 4 \times \left(1 - \frac{1}{3} + \frac{1}{5} - \frac{1}{7} + \frac{1}{9} - \frac{1}{11} + \ldots\right)$

An approximation of π, to twenty-five decimal places, is given below.

3.1415926535897932384626433 ...

Use method (A) to compute approximations of π. Express your answer as a fraction and as a decimal with five decimal places.

1. $4 \times \left(\frac{2}{3} \times \frac{4}{3}\right)$ $\frac{32}{9} \approx 3.55556$
2. $4 \times \left(\frac{2}{3} \times \frac{4}{3} \times \frac{4}{5}\right)$ $\frac{128}{45} \approx 2.84444$
3. $4 \times \left(\frac{2}{3} \times \frac{4}{3} \times \frac{4}{5} \times \frac{6}{5}\right)$ $\frac{768}{225} \approx 3.41333$
4. $4 \times \left(\frac{2}{3} \times \frac{4}{3} \times \frac{4}{5} \times \frac{6}{5} \times \frac{6}{7}\right)$ $\frac{4608}{1575} \approx 2.92571$
5. $4 \times \left(\frac{2}{3} \times \frac{4}{3} \times \frac{4}{5} \times \frac{6}{5} \times \frac{6}{7} \times \frac{8}{7} \times \frac{8}{9} \times \frac{10}{9} \times \frac{10}{11}\right)$ $\frac{29{,}491{,}200}{9{,}823{,}275} \approx 3.00218$

Use method (B) to compute approximations of π. Express your answer as a fraction in simplest form and as a decimal with five decimal places.

6. $4 \times \left(1 - \frac{1}{3}\right)$ $\frac{8}{3} \approx 2.66667$
7. $4 \times \left(1 - \frac{1}{3} + \frac{1}{5}\right)$ $\frac{52}{15} \approx 3.46667$
8. $4 \times \left(1 - \frac{1}{3} + \frac{1}{5} - \frac{1}{7}\right)$ $\frac{304}{105} \approx 2.89524$
9. $4 \times \left(1 - \frac{1}{3} + \frac{1}{5} - \frac{1}{7} + \frac{1}{9}\right)$ $\frac{1052}{315} \approx 3.33968$
10. $4 \times \left(1 - \frac{1}{3} + \frac{1}{5} - \frac{1}{7} + \frac{1}{9} - \frac{1}{11} + \frac{1}{13} - \frac{1}{15} + \frac{1}{17}\right)$ $\frac{2{,}490{,}548}{765{,}765} \approx 3.25237$
11. Which expression gives the more accurate approximation of π, Exercise 5 or Exercise 10? Exercise 10 (Ex. 5: difference of $\approx$ 0.14; Ex. 10: difference of $\approx$ 0.11)

Exercises

Independent Practice

Find the surface area of each cylinder. Round each answer to the nearest whole number. Answers are calculated using $\boxed{\pi}$.

7. 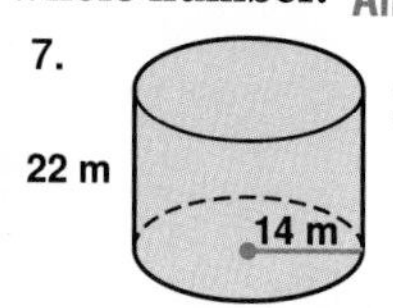

3167 m^2

8. 7 cm, 2.5 cm — 132 cm^2

9. 434 ft^2
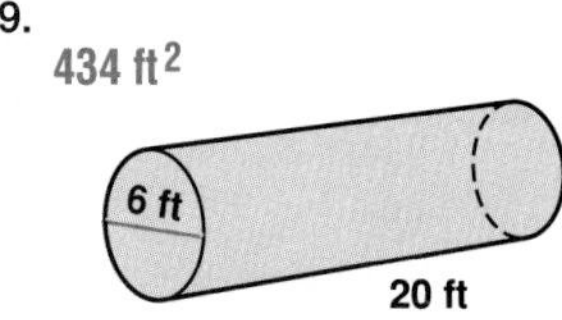

10. 4084 cm^2
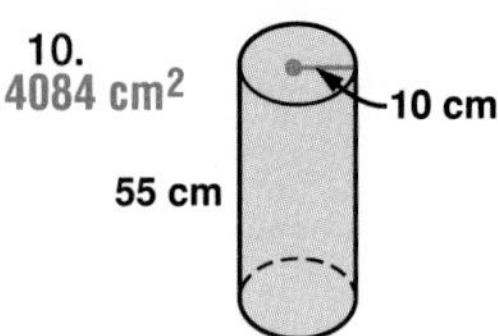

Mixed Review

11. Express as a unit rate: *\$1.62 for 18 pounds.* (Lesson 9-1) \$0.09/pound
12. Find the surface area of the prism shown at the right. (Lesson 13-4) 310 cm^2

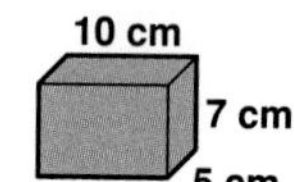

13. Identify the hypothesis and the conclusion in the statement: *If a polygon has six sides, then it is a hexagon.* (Lesson 12-7) hypothesis–If . . . conclusion–then . . .

Applications

14. **Engineering** A water storage tank has a cylindrical shape. If the radius of the base is about 20 feet and the tank is 60 feet high, what is the area of the curved surface? 7540 ft^2
15. **Business** The ABC Company has been hired to paint the tank described in Exercise 14. How many gallons of paint would be needed to apply one coat of paint to the tank if one gallon of paint covers about 450 square feet? 17 gallons
16. How much would the paint cost if one coat is applied to the tank in Exercise 14 and one gallon of paint costs \$10? How much would the paint cost if two coats are applied? \$170; \$340

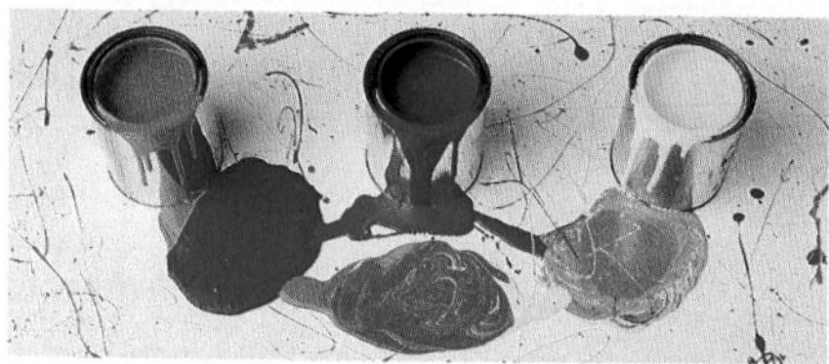

Challenge

17. Use algebra to show how steps 2, 3, and 4 on page 498 lead to the formula $2\pi rh$ for the curved surface area of a circular cylinder.
$A = \ell w;\ w = h;\ \ell = 2\pi r;\ A = 2\pi r \cdot h$
18. Show how to derive a formula for finding the total surface area of a circular cylinder. Area of base $= \pi r^2$; there are 2 bases; area of curved surface $= 2\pi rh$; $A = 2\pi rh + 2\pi r^2$

Critical Thinking

19. Explain how you can find the surface area of a circular cylinder if you know its height and the circumference of a base. See margin.

Wrap-Up

20. In your own words, explain how to find the total surface area of a circular cylinder. Find the area of the base (πr^2); multiply by 2; add the area of the curved surface ($2\pi rh$).

Alternate Strategies: Extending the Lesson

Enrichment

Consumer Connection A girl wants to give a poster as a gift to a friend. She rolls the poster into a tube 2 feet long and 2 inches in diameter. Find the amount of wrapping paper she needs to buy to wrap the poster, including enclosing the ends. about 160 square inches

Cooperative Learning

Make It Smaller — Group Activity **13-5**

MATERIALS: Calculators • two 0-9 spinners

The object of this activity is to form a cylinder that will have the smaller surface area.

To begin, two spinners are spun to give numbers for the radius of the base of a cylinder and its height. If a zero is obtained, that spinner must be spun again. Each member of the group uses one number for the height and the other number for the radius of the cylinder. Each member then computes the surface area for his or her cylinder using calculators.

The group should do this activity several times, comparing results after each time. As a group, write a statement about how the radius and height of a cylinder affect its surface area.

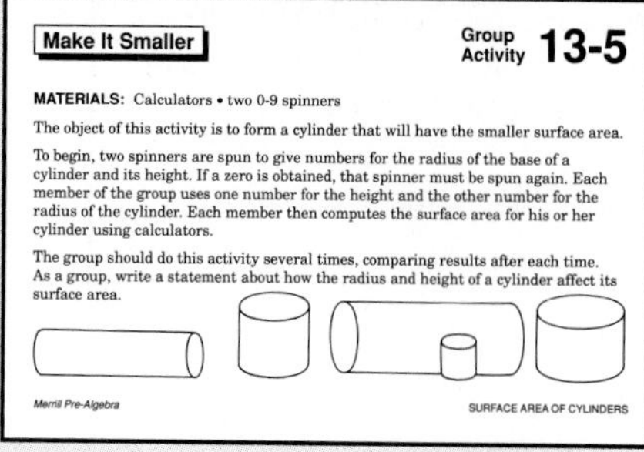

Merrill Pre-Algebra SURFACE AREA OF CYLINDERS

13-6 Surface Area: Pyramids and Cones

Objective:
Find the surface area of pyramids and cones.

Key Terms:
pyramid
vertex
square pyramid
lateral surface
slant height
circular cone

The pyramids of Egypt were built as burial tombs for the pharaohs and their relatives. The Great Pyramid at Gizeh, built about 2600 B.C. is one of the "Seven Wonders of the Ancient World." It measures 776 feet on each side of the square base and is about 450 feet high.

In geometry, **pyramids**, like prisms, are named by the shape of their base. A pyramid has only one base. All the other faces of a pyramid intersect at a point called the **vertex**. The pyramid shown below is a **square pyramid**.

A square pyramid has 5 faces. The base is a square. There are four triangular sides.

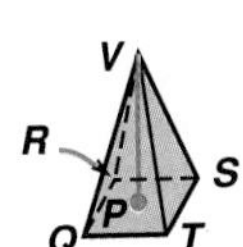

The altitude, $\overline{VP}$, is perpendicular to the base at its center.

If the base of a pyramid were shaped like a pentagon, how many faces would the pyramid have? Would the sides still be shaped like triangles? **6; yes**

The surface area of a pyramid can be found by adding the areas of the faces of the pyramid. In the diagram below, a square pyramid has been "unfolded" to help you identify the regions that make up the pyramid.

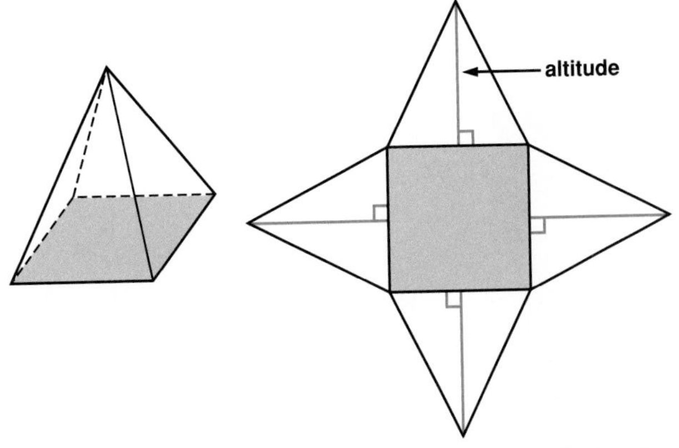

FYI

More than 2 million stone blocks, each weighing between 2 tons and 150 tons, were used in the construction of the Great Pyramid of Gizeh. To this day, historians have difficulty explaining how the blocks were transported from the quarries to the building site.

The unshaded regions of the square pyramid (the four sides) make up the **lateral surface** of the pyramid. As you can see, all of the sides are triangles. Because the base is a square region, the triangles are all congruent and their altitudes all have the same length. The length of any one of these altitudes is called the **slant height** of the pyramid.

Lesson Notes 13-6

5-Minute Check
(over Lesson 13-5)

Find the surface area of each cylinder. Round each answer to the nearest whole number.

1. 2.

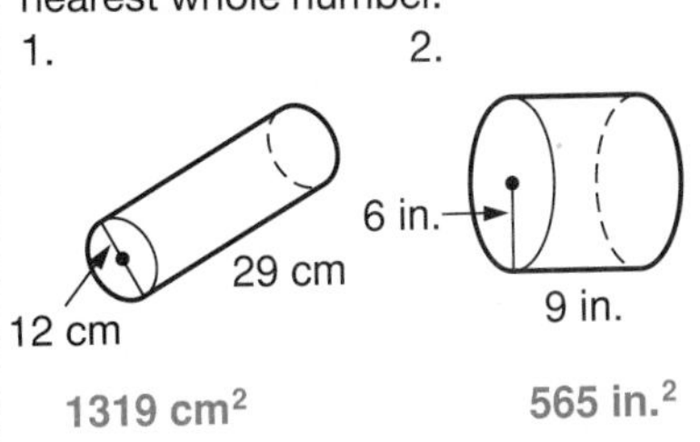

1319 cm² **565 in.²**

Transparency 13-6 contains the 5-Minute Check and a teaching aid for this lesson.

1 FOCUS

The purpose of this lesson is to develop and use procedures for finding the lateral and total surface areas of a pyramid and a cone.

Motivating the Lesson

Bring in or make a pyramid and a circular cone. Take them apart and ask the students how they would find the surface area.

2 TEACH

Using Models Discuss the lesson explanation and examples. Have students use construction paper to model triangular and hexagonal pyramids. Find lateral and total surface area of each.

Bell Ringer

In your own words, describe how to find the surface area of a cylinder.
Sample answer: $2\pi r^2 + \pi d \cdot h$

EE: 1E, 3A, 3H, 4A, 4B, 4E
TAAS: 2, 3, 4, 10, 11, 13

Chalkboard Examples

- *For Example 1*
  Find the surface area of the square pyramid shown below.

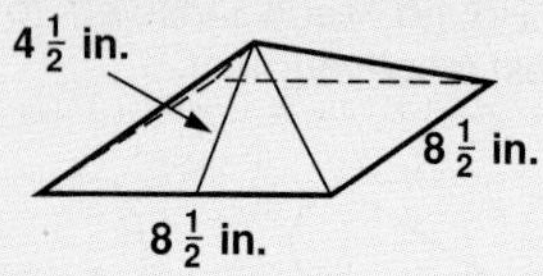

148.75 in.^{2}

- *For Example 2*
  Find the surface area of the circular cone shown below. Round to the nearest hundredth.

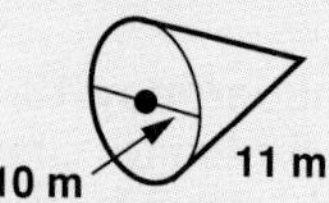

251.33 m^2

Estimation Hint

The area of the base is between 7 × 7 and 8 × 8 or about 56 in^2.

The area of each side is about one-half of 42 or 21 in^2. Since there are 4 sides, the area of the sides is about 84 in^2.

The total surface area is about 56 + 84 or 140 in^2.

Example

1 Find the surface area of the square pyramid shown at the right.

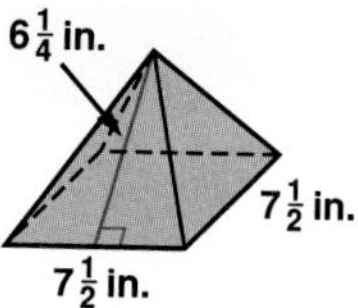

Base	**Each Triangular Side**
$A = lw$	$A = \frac{1}{2}bh$
$A = 7\frac{1}{2} \cdot 7\frac{1}{2}$	$A = \frac{1}{2} \cdot 7\frac{1}{2} \cdot 6\frac{1}{4}$
$A = 56\frac{1}{4}$ or 56.25	$A = 23\frac{7}{16}$ or 23.4375

Add to find the total surface area.

area of base	+	area of four triangular surfaces	=	surface area
56.25	+	4 × 23.4375	=	150

The surface area is 150 in^2. Compare with the estimate.

In this textbook, when we say *cone*, assume we are talking about a circular cone.

A cone is another three-dimensional shape that appears in everyday life as the cone for some ice cream cones, a support for cotton candy, or some paper drinking cups. Most of the cones that we see are called **circular cones** because the base is a circular region.

The base is a circular region with radius *r*. The altitude, $\overline{VP}$, is perpendicular to the base at its center.

In the following diagram, a cone has been opened and unrolled to help you identify the regions that make up the cone.

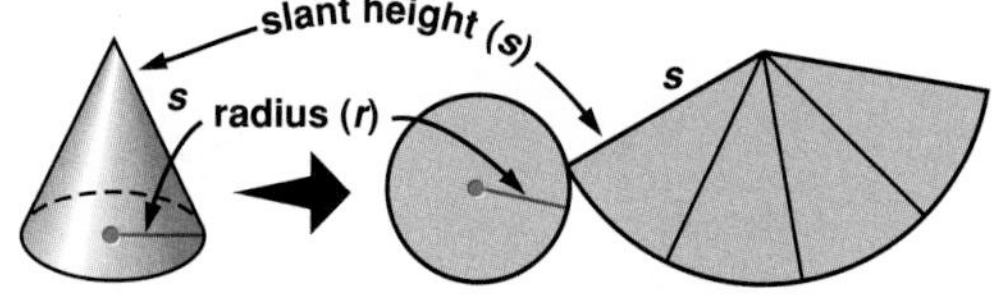

The curved edge is the length of the circumference of the base.

The base of the cone is a circular region, with area πr^2. The lateral surface can be cut into sections to form a parallelogram. The base of the parallelogram is half the circumference of the cone or $\frac{1}{2} \cdot 2\pi r$. Its height is the slant height of the cone, s. So the area of the lateral surface is $A = \pi rs$.

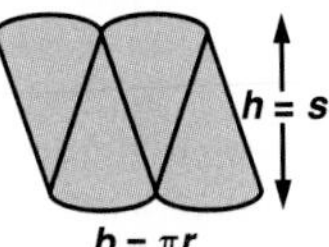

Alternate Strategies: Reteaching the Lesson

Reteaching Activity

Using Models Have students construct a pyramid by cutting out four equilateral triangles and a square whose sides are the same length as the sides of the triangles. Have students remove one of the triangular sides and measure the height of the pyramid and an altitude of the triangle. Then have them compare results.

Reteaching Masters Booklet, p. 115

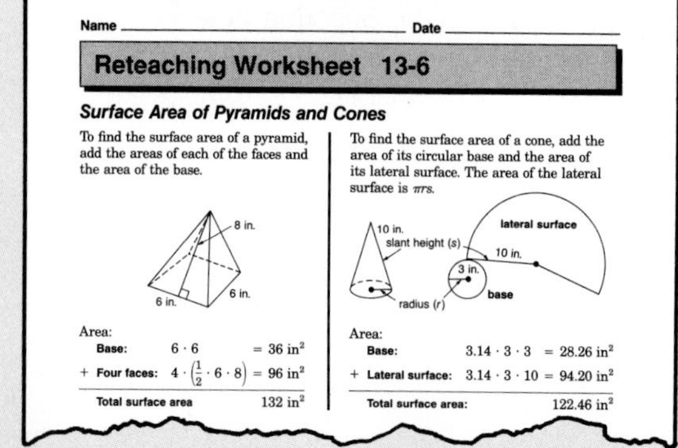

Name ________ Date ________

Reteaching Worksheet 13-6

Surface Area of Pyramids and Cones

To find the surface area of a pyramid, add the areas of each of the faces and the area of the base.

To find the surface area of a cone, add the area of its circular base and the area of its lateral surface. The area of the lateral surface is πrs.

Area:

Base:	6 · 6	= 36 in^2
+ Four faces:	$4 \cdot (\frac{1}{2} \cdot 6 \cdot 8)$	= 96 in^2
Total surface area		132 in^2

Area:

Base:	3.14 · 3 · 3	= 28.26 in^2
+ Lateral surface:	3.14 · 3 · 10	= 94.20 in^2
Total surface area:		122.46 in^2

Example

2 Find the surface area of the circular cone shown below. Round to the nearest hundredth.

Base	**Lateral Surface**
$A = \pi r^2$	$A = \pi rs$
$A = \pi \cdot 2 \cdot 2$	$A = \pi \cdot 2 \cdot 6$
π × 2 × 2 =	π × 2 × 6 =
$A \approx 12.57$	$A \approx 37.70$

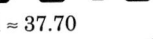

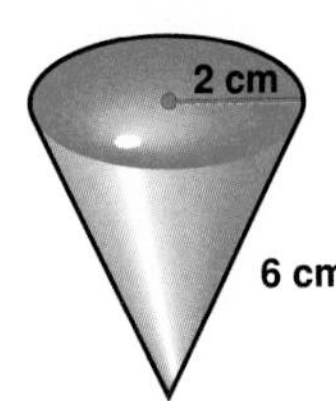

Find the total surface area by adding.

base + lateral surface = surface area

12.57 + 37.70 = 50.27

The surface area is about 50.27 cm^2.

Checking for Understanding

Communicating Algebra

1. Describe a square pyramid. See margin.
2. In your own words, tell the meaning of slant height. See margin.
3. How do you find the area of a triangular side of a pyramid? Multiply $\frac{1}{2}$ times the base times the height of the triangle.

Guided Practice

Name each shape. Then tell how many surfaces the figure has.

4. 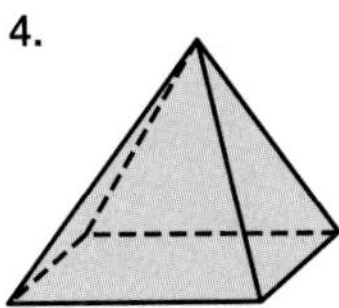
rectangular pyramid; 5 surfaces

5. 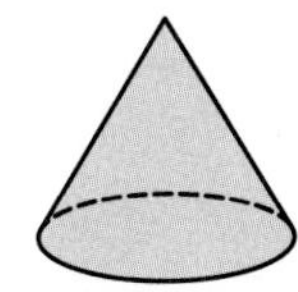
circular cone; 2 surfaces

6. 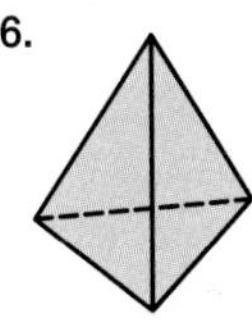
triangular pyramid; 4 surfaces

Exercises

Answers are calculated using π.

Independent Practice

Find the surface area of each pyramid or cone. Round each answer to the nearest tenth.

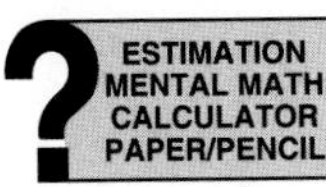

7. 799.4 m^2
8. 11,899 cm^2
9. 51.6 ft^2
10. 417.8 in^2
11. 115.5 ft^2
12. 593.8 m^2

7. 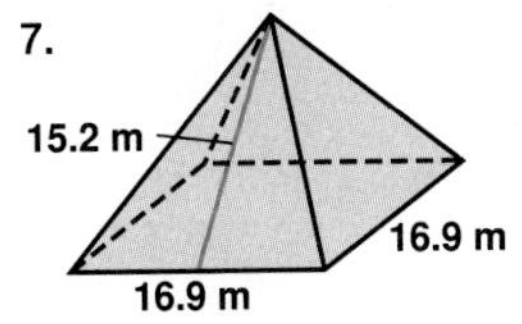

8. 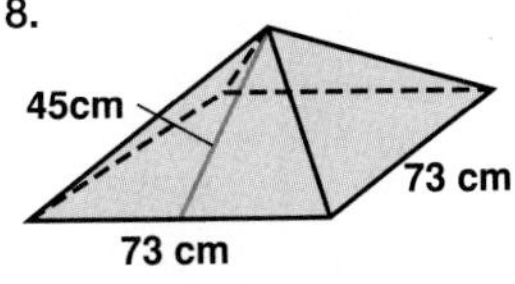
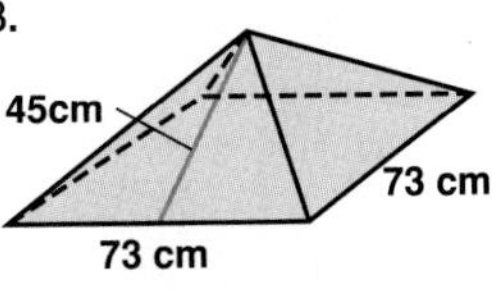

9. 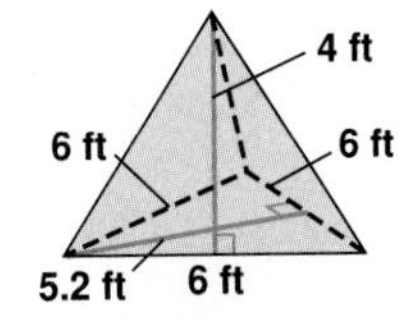

10. 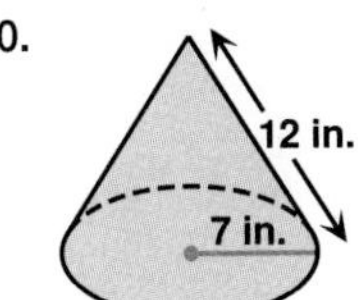

11. 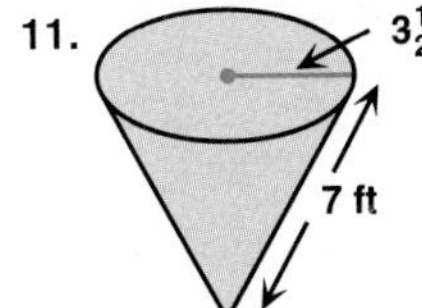

12. 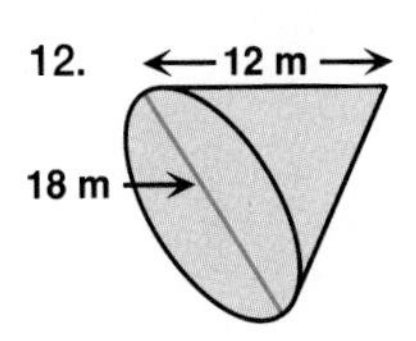

3 PRACTICE/APPLY

Checking the Concept

After completing Exercises 4-6, have students work in groups of two to verbalize how they would find the total surface area.

Error Analysis

Watch for students who have difficulty distinguishing between a triangular prism and a pyramid.
Prevent by reminding students that any prism must have a pair of parallel bases.

Independent Practice

Homework Assignment	
Basic	7-11 odd, 13-18
Average	8-12 even, 13-18
Honors	10-18
All	Mid-Chapter Quiz 1-8

Practice Masters Booklet, **p. 127**

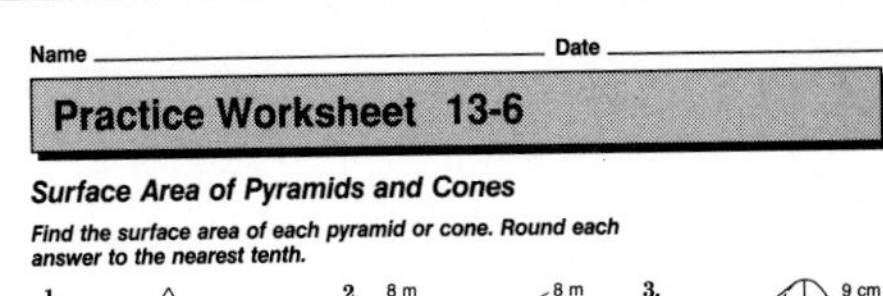
Name ________ Date ________

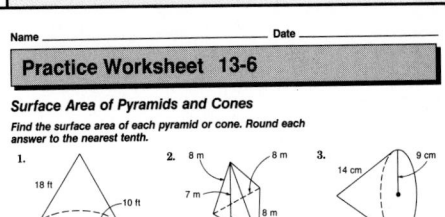

Practice Worksheet 13-6

Surface Area of Pyramids and Cones

Find the surface area of each pyramid or cone. Round each answer to the nearest tenth.

1. 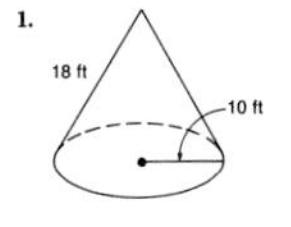

879.7 ft^2

2. 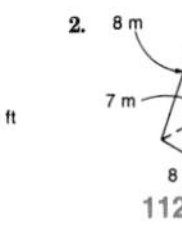

112 m^2

3. 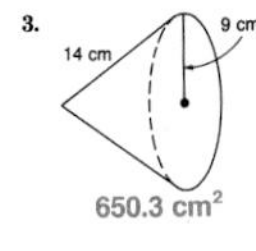

650.3 cm^2

4. 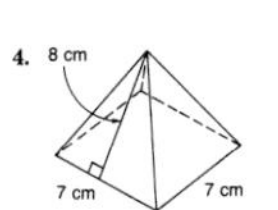

161 cm^2

5. 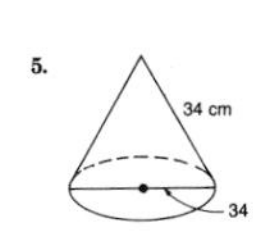

2723.7 cm^2

6. 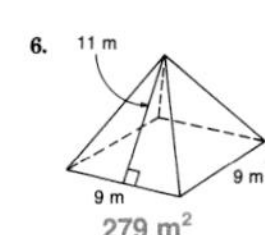

279 m^2

7. 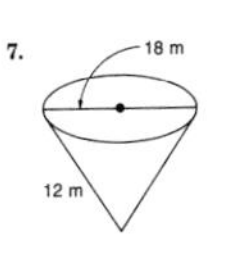

593.8 m^2

8. 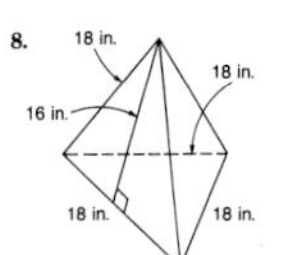

576 in^2

9. 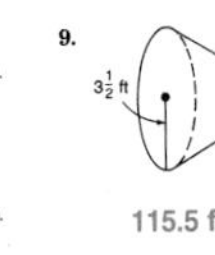

115.5 ft^2

Additional Answers

1. A square pyramid has a square base and four triangular sides.
2. Slant height is the length of the altitude of a triangular side of a pyramid.

Chapter 13, Quiz A (Lesson 13-1 through 13-6) is available in the Evaluation Masters Booklet, p. 115.

4 CLOSE

Assessment Option

Modeling Have each student make a pyramid or cone out of construction paper. Then exchange figures with another student and find the surface area.

Additional Answers

17. Sample answer: The height of a pyramid and cone is shorter than the slant height.
18. Sample answer: Pyramids have one base and prisms have two parallel bases. Pyramids have triangular sides and prisms have rectangular sides.

Enrichment Masters Booklet, **p. 115**

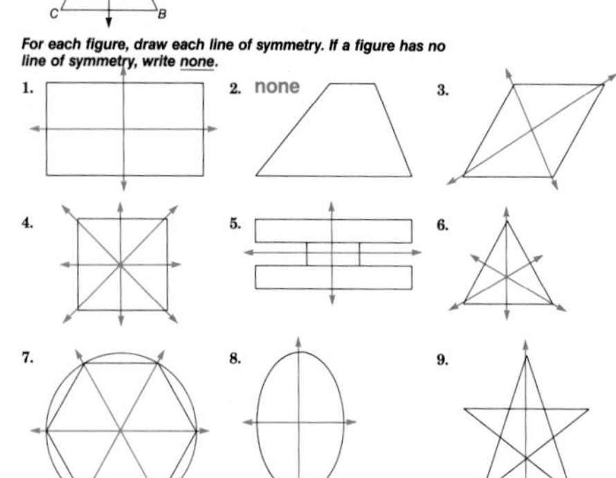

Name ______ Date ______

Enrichment Worksheet 13-6

Line Symmetry

Some geometric figures can be folded in half so that one part will fit exactly on the other. This property is called **line symmetry**. Figures that have line symmetry are often used in designs ranging from building plans to corporate logos.

When a figure is folded, the fold is part of a straight line. Thus, it is referred to as line of symmetry. The figure is symmetrical with respect to that line.

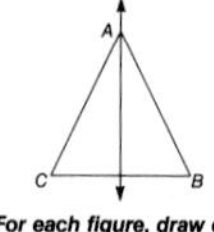

This isosceles triangle is symmetrical with respect to a line that is perpendicular to its base. Notice that if the triangle is folded on this line, point *B* would coincide exactly with point *C*.

For each figure, draw each line of symmetry. If a figure has no line of symmetry, write none.

1. 2. none 3.
4. 5. 6.
7. 8. 9.

Mixed Review	
	13. Write the next three terms of the sequence 1.23, 1.36, 1.49, 1.62, ... (Lesson 5-9) **1.75, 1.88, 2.01**

14. In the triangle shown at the right, find the value of x. (Lesson 12-9) **7.5 m**

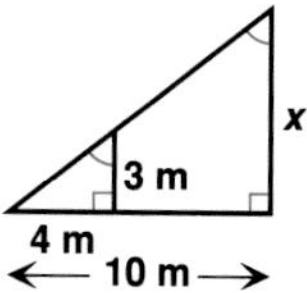

15. Find the surface area of a circular cylinder with a radius of 5 cm and a height of 12 cm. (Lesson 13-5) **about 534 cm²**

Application

16. **Manufacturing** The B & P Company is planning to manufacture paper cups. One of the designs being considered is shown at the right.

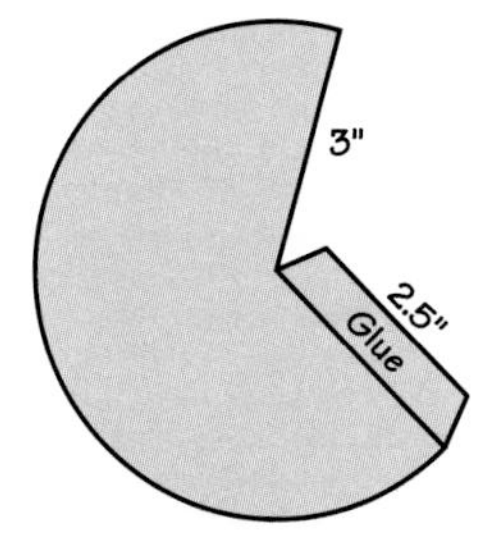

a. Name the shape of the finished cup.
b. What is the slant height of the cup?
c. If the diameter of the circle at the top of the finished cup is 2 inches, find the approximate lateral area.
d. About how many square inches of paper are needed to make each cup?

16. a. circular cone; b. 3 in.; c. about 9.4 in²; d. 9.4 in² used, some additional wasted

Critical Thinking

17. How does the height of a pyramid differ from its slant height? How does the height of a cone differ from its slant height? **See margin.**

Wrap-Up

18. Write a few sentences describing the difference between prisms and pyramids. **See margin.**

Mid-Chapter Quiz

Find the area of each figure. (Lessons 13-1, 13-2, 13-3)

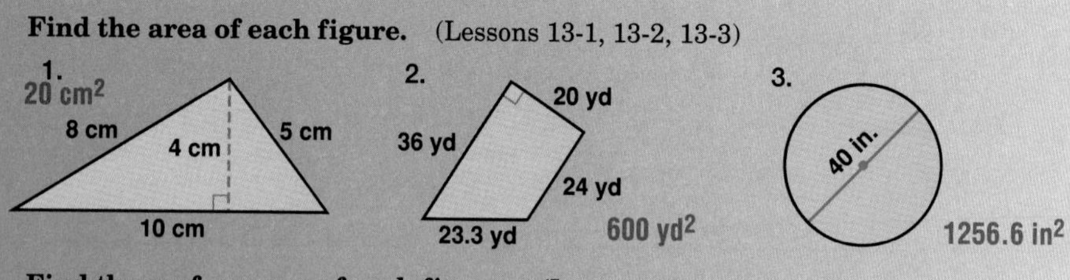

Find the surface area of each figure. (Lessons 13-4, 13-5, 13-6)

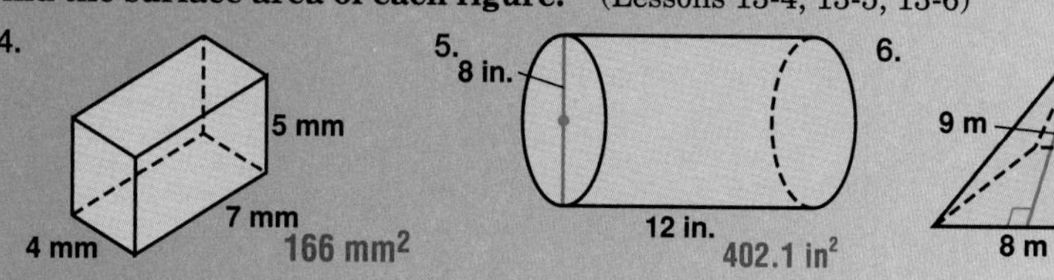

Solve.

7. A parallelogram has a base of 9 cm and a height of 4.5 cm. What is the combined area of two of these parallelograms? **81 cm²**

8. How much paper would be used to make an open paper cone with a diameter of 5 inches and a slant height of 6 inches? **47.1 in²**

Alternate Strategies: Extending the Lesson

Enrichment

Find the area of a sector of each circle given the measurements of its radius and central angle. Use $A = \frac{n}{360} \times \pi r^2$ where n is the degree measure of the central angle.

1.

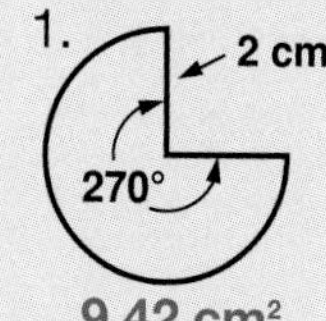

9.42 cm²

2.

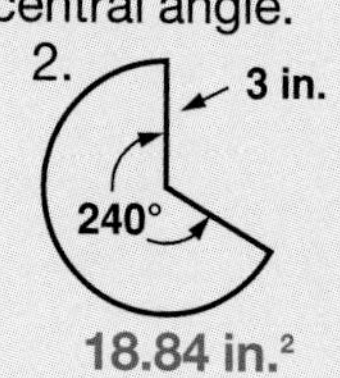

18.84 in.²

Cooperative Learning

Line Them Up Group Activity **13-6**

MATERIALS: Note cards

In this activity, group members compare the surface areas of pyramids or cones.

A person who is "it" decides if the solids used will be pyramids or cones. Then the other members choose two numbers between 15 and 40, not more than 10 apart. Each member writes the numbers on the front of a note card, identifying one as the slant height and the other as the radius of the circle or the side of the square base.

Each member then computes the surface area of their solid and writes it on the back of their card. When everyone is finished, the cards are put face up on the table. The person who is "it" must place the cards in order so the surface areas go from smallest to largest. He or she gets one point for each card that is placed correctly.

Repeat until each person in the group has been "it." The player with the most points after one round wins the game.

Merrill Pre-Algebra SURFACE AREA OF PYRAMIDS AND CONES

Exploration

Volume

Materials: 5 × 8 index cards, tape, rice, grid paper

In this Exploration, you will investigate volume by making containers of different shapes and comparing how much each container holds.

Your Turn: Work in small groups to complete this activity. See students' work.

- Use the 5 × 8 cards to make three containers: one circular, one square, and one triangular. Use tape to hold the tubes together. Then tape one end of each container to another card so the container has a bottom, but no lid. The base of each figure has a perimeter of 8 inches. Each figure is 5 inches high.

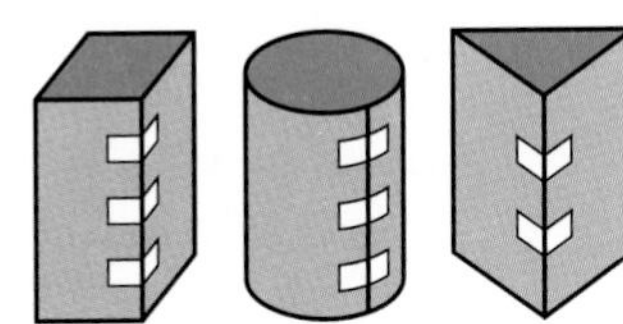

- Estimate which container will hold the most rice and which will hold the least.
- Fill one container with rice. Then pour the rice into another container. Does the rice fill this container? Is there too much rice? Continue this activity until you can determine which container holds the most rice and which holds the least. circular, most; triangular, least
- Trace each of the bases onto grid paper. Estimate the area of each base. triangular, about $2\frac{1}{2}$ in^2; square, 4 in^2; circular, about 5 in^2

Analysis

1. Based on the results of your activity, does there seem to be a relationship between the area of each base and the amount of rice the container will hold? If so, explain your reasoning. The greater the base area, the greater the volume.
2. Test your hypothesis by repeating the above activity for several containers with square or rectangular bases. The height of each container should be 5 inches. See students' work.
3. Make a cone-shaped paper cup. Then make a cylinder with the same height and base as the cone. Devise an experiment to compare the volumes of the cone and the cylinder. The cone holds about $\frac{1}{3}$ as much as the cylinder. See students' work.

SET-UP

Materials

- 5×8 index cards, tape, rice, grid paper

You may wish to use the Exploration worksheet provided on page 64 of the Lab Manual.

For Students Each group of students will need about one pound of rice and six 5 × 8 index cards. You may wish to substitute 3 × 5 index cards and use one-half pound of rice per group.

HINT: Assemble the rice in large sandwich bags with a twist-tie for convenient management. You may also want to provide each group with a shallow box and have students conduct their experiments inside it to keep rice from spilling onto the floor.

EE: 1A, 1C, 1E, 4B

EXPLORATION
Volume

Objective Students will be introduced to the concept of volume through modeling.

1 FOCUS

This Exploration allows the student to compare volumes of containers having the same height but different shaped bases.

Motivating the Exploration

On the chalkboard or overhead, draw a circle with circumference of 12 inches, a square with sides 3 inches long, and a triangle with sides 3, 4, and 5 inches. Ask students which one has the greatest area.

2 TEACH

Using Models

Demonstrate how to make the containers by taping only the 5-inch side. To make the cylinder, roll the card up several times to help it stay round. Fold a card in half twice to make the square prism. The triangular prism requires two folds of a card. You may want groups to work with the rice inside of a shoe box to contain any that is spilled. If materials are not available for small group work, demonstrate the Your Turn for the entire class.

3 PRACTICE/APPLY

Using Models

Groups can use the Easy-to-Make Manipulative found on page 22 of the Lab Manual for Exercise 3. The accompanying cylinder should be $2\frac{1}{8}$ inches high with a diameter of $2\frac{3}{8}$ inches.

4 CLOSE

Writing Connection

Have students write a paragraph that summarizes the results of Exercises 1-2.

Lesson Notes 13-7

5-Minute Check
(over Lesson 13-6)

Find the surface area of each figure. Use $\pi \approx 3.14$ and round answers to the nearest tenth.

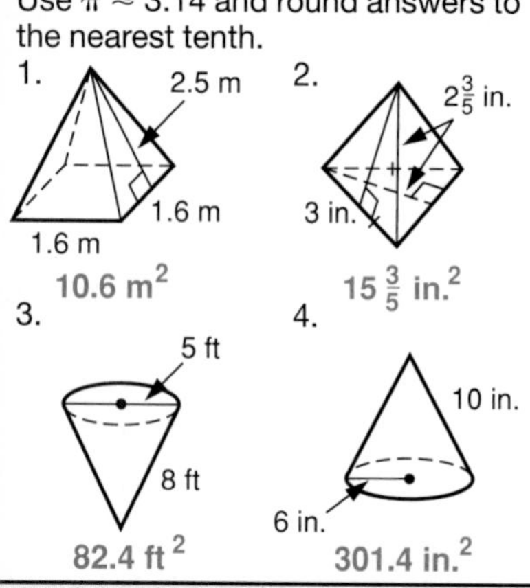

Transparency 13-7 contains the 5-Minute Check and a teaching aid for this lesson.

1 FOCUS

The purpose of the lesson is to develop and use a formula for finding the volume of a rectangular prism.

2 TEACH

Using Models Using different hollow prisms, have students measure the dimensions in cm and determine each volume. Using rice and a metric measuring cup, confirm the volume.

Chalkboard Examples

- *For Example* 1
  A rectangular prism formed by stacking centimeter cubes is shown below. Find the volume of the prism.

$V = 45\text{ cm}^3$

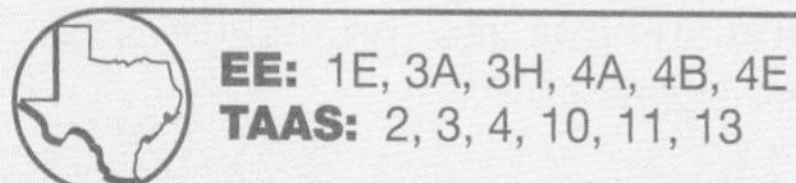

13-7 Volume: Prisms

Objective:
Find the volume of prisms.

Key Term:
volume

Have you or anyone you know ever tried a puzzle like the one shown at the right? Puzzles such as this can provide hours of fun and challenge. The pieces in this puzzle are small cubes, fastened together to make the larger cube. This puzzle is a model for finding the volume of a prism.

Volume is the number of cubic units needed to fill a space. Two common units of measure for volume are the cubic centimeter (cm^3) and the cubic inch (in^3).

You can count the cubes in the puzzle shown above as follows.

The bottom layer has $3 \cdot 3$ or 9 cubes.
The middle layer has $3 \cdot 3$ or 9 cubes.
The top layer has $3 \cdot 3$ or 9 cubes.
$9 + 9 + 9 = 27$

The volume of the puzzle is 27 cubic units.

You could also find the volume of the puzzle cube by multiplying.

$V = 3 \cdot 3 \cdot 3$ or 27

This example suggests that the volume of a rectangular prism can be found by multiplying length times width times height.

Volume of a Rectangular Prism

If a rectangular prism has a length of ℓ units, a width of w units, and a height of h units, then the volume (V) is $\ell \cdot w \cdot h$ cubic units.

$$V = \ell wh$$

Example

1 A rectangular prism formed by stacking centimeter cubes is shown below. Find the volume of the prism.

Would you get the same answer if you multiplied the area of the base by the height?
yes

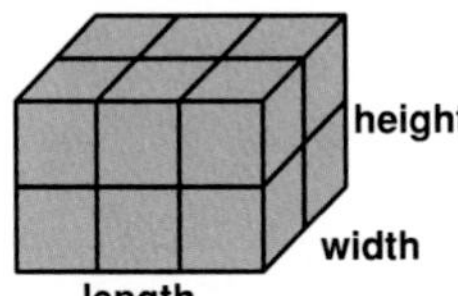

$V = \ell wh$
$V = 3 \cdot 2 \cdot 2$
$V = 12$

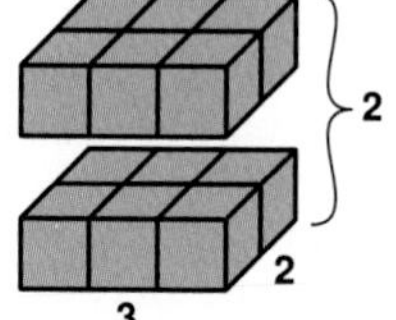

The volume is 12 cm^3.

There are 6 cubes in a layer. There are 2 layers. So, there are $6 \cdot 2$ or 12 centimeter cubes.

Bell Ringer

In your own words explain how to find the surface area of a square pyramid. **Sample answer: Find the area of one lateral surface, multiply by four and add the area of the base.**

Not all prisms are rectangular. Three other types are shown below.

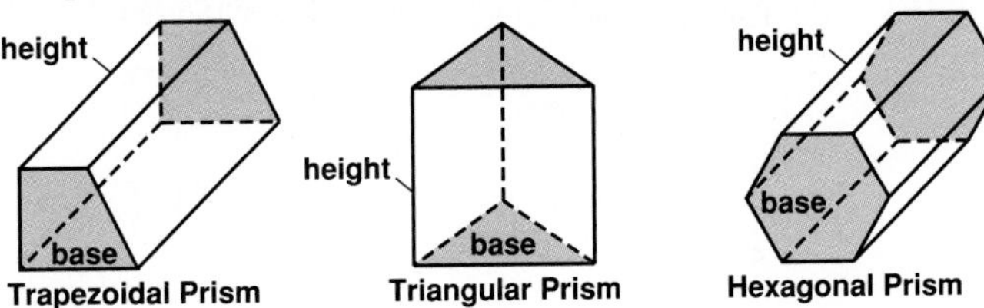

In Example 1 you can see that the volume is equal to the area of the base times the height. In fact, the volume of any prism can be found by multiplying the area of the base times the height.

Volume of a Prism

If a prism has a base area of B square units and a height of h units, then the volume (V) is $B \cdot h$ cubic units.

$$V = Bh$$

Examples

How could you find the height of a prism if you know the area of the base and the volume? **Divide the volume by the area of the base.**

2 Find the volume of the rectangular prism.

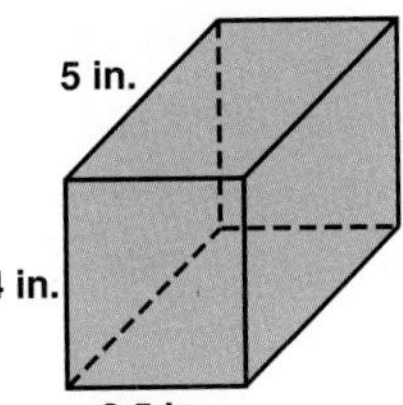

$V = Bh$ — Formula for volume of a prism

$V = \ell wh$ — Since the base of the prism is a rectangle, $B = \ell w$.

$V = 5 \cdot 3.5 \cdot 4$ — Replace ℓ with 5, w with 3.5 and h with 4.

$V = 70$

The volume is 70 in^3.

3 Find the volume of the triangular prism.

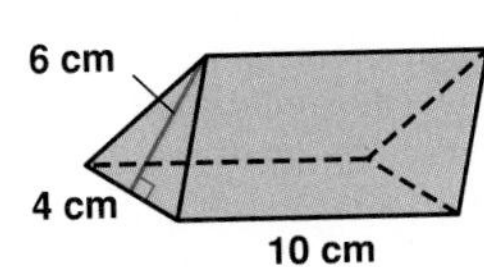

$V = Bh$ — Formula for volume of a prism

$V = \left(\frac{1}{2} \cdot 4 \cdot 6\right)10$ — The base of the prism is a triangle. The area of the triangle is $\frac{1}{2} \cdot 4 \cdot 6$.

$V = 12 \cdot 10$

$V = 120$

The volume is 120 cm^3.

Checking for Understanding

Communicating Algebra

1. In the formula $V = Bh$, B represents the __?__ and h represents the __?__. **base, height**
2. Volume is a __?__-dimensional measure. **3**
3. Draw a model of a rectangular prism. **See students' work.**

- *For Example 2*
  Find the volume of the rectangular prism.

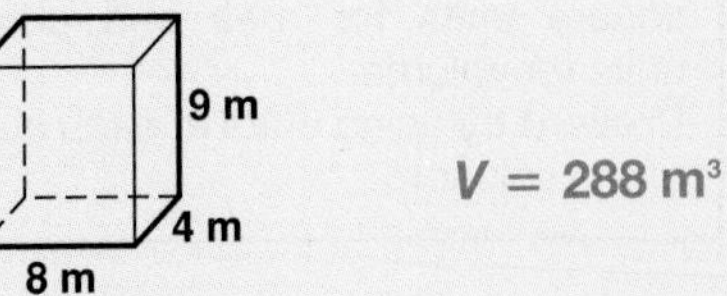

$V = 288\ m^3$

- *For Example 3*
  Find the volume of the triangular prism.

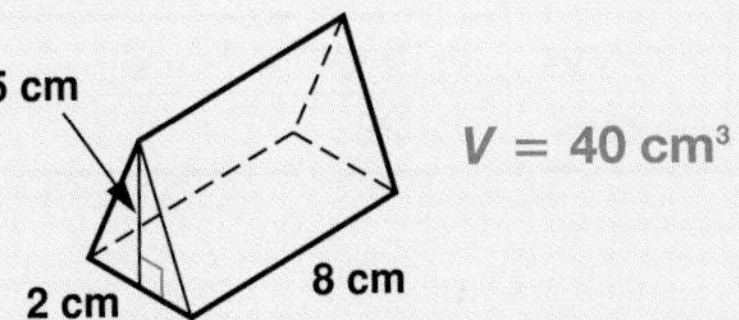

$V = 40\ cm^3$

3 PRACTICE/APPLY

Checking the Concept

Using Questioning Ask students what kind of units would be used to express the following situations.

- the perimeter of a base of a prism m
- the lateral surface area of a prism m^2
- the total surface area of a prism m^2
- the volume of a prism m^3

Practice Masters Booklet, **p. 128**

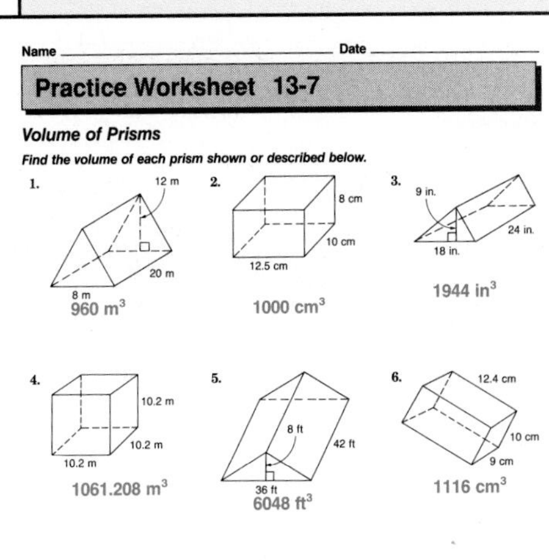

Name ____ Date ____

Practice Worksheet 13-7

Volume of Prisms

Find the volume of each prism shown or described below.

1. 12 m; 8 m; 20 m — 960 m^3
2. 8 cm; 10 cm; 12.5 cm — 1000 cm^3
3. 9 in.; 18 in.; 24 in. — 1944 in^3
4. 10.2 m; 10.2 m; 10.2 m — 1061.208 m^3
5. 8 ft; 42 ft; 36 ft — 6048 ft^3
6. 12.4 cm; 10 cm; 9 cm — 1116 cm^3
7. rectangular prism; length, 6 yd; width, 5 yd; height, 3 yd — 90 yd^3
8. rectangular prism; length, 16.5 mm; width, 8.4 mm; height, 3.2 mm — 443.52 mm^3
9. triangular prism; base of triangle, 6 m; altitude, 4 m; prism height, 3 m — 36 m^3
10. area of base, 15 in^2; height, 6 in. — 90 in^3
11. area of base, 72.5 m^2; height, 17.6 m — 1276 m^3

Alternate Strategies: Reteaching the Lesson

Reteaching Activity

Using Models Have students use one-inch cubes and empty rectangular boxes to model volume problems. Check by measuring and calculating.

Reteaching Masters Booklet, **p. 116**

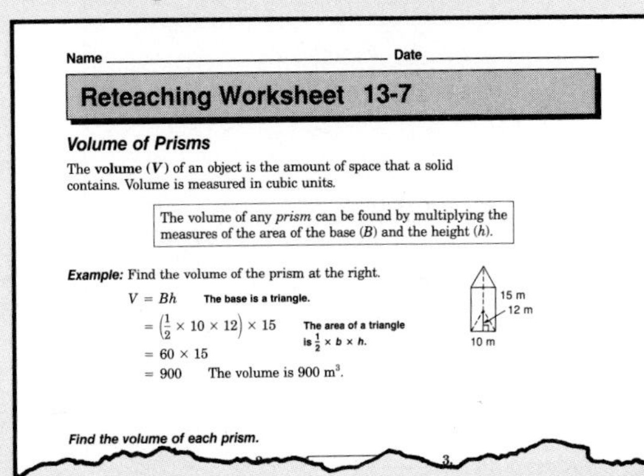

Name ____ Date ____

Reteaching Worksheet 13-7

Volume of Prisms

The **volume** (V) of an object is the amount of space that a solid contains. Volume is measured in cubic units.

The volume of any *prism* can be found by multiplying the measures of the area of the base (B) and the height (h).

Example: Find the volume of the prism at the right.

$V = Bh$ — The base is a triangle.

$= \left(\frac{1}{2} \times 10 \times 12\right) \times 15$ — The area of a triangle is $\frac{1}{2} \times b \times h$.

$= 60 \times 15$

$= 900$ — The volume is 900 m^3.

15 m; 12 m; 10 m

Find the volume of each prism.

Error Analysis

Watch for students who don't use square units for area and cubic units for volume.
Prevent by using units at each step of the solution.

Independent Practice

Homework Assignment	
Basic	7-15 odd, 17-19, 21, 22
Average	8-16 even, 17-22
Honors	12-22

CLOSE

Assessment Option

Speaking Ask students to develop a way to remember the kind of unit used in a given situation.

Enrichment Masters Booklet, **p. 116**

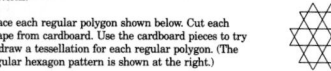

Name ________________ Date ________

Enrichment Worksheet 13-7

Tessellations

A **tessellation** is a repetitive pattern using one or more geometric shapes. The shapes fit together without holes or gaps. The word *tessellate* comes from the Latin word for tile. Tessellations are sometimes called tiling patterns.

Trace each regular polygon shown below. Cut each shape from cardboard. Use the cardboard pieces to try to draw a tessellation for each regular polygon. (The regular hexagon pattern is shown at the right.)

1. Which regular polygons tessellate? triangle, square, hexagon

Can you make tessellations from the following combinations?

2. square and octagon Yes
3. square, triangle, and hexagon Yes
4. square, triangle, and dodecagon Yes

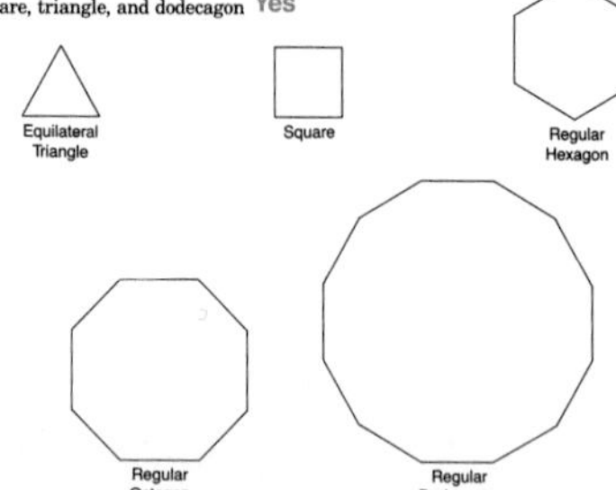

Guided Practice

Name each prism and explain how to find the volume. Then find the volume. For Exercises 4-6, see margin.

4. 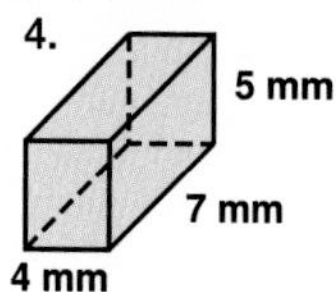

5. 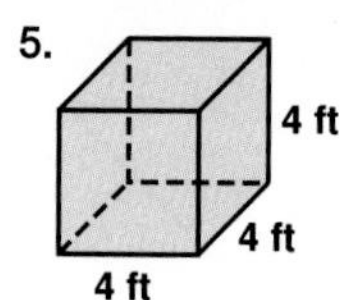

6. 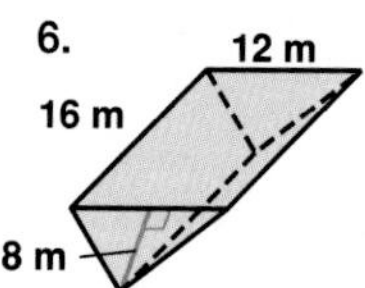

Exercises

Independent Practice

Find the volume of each prism shown or described below.

7. 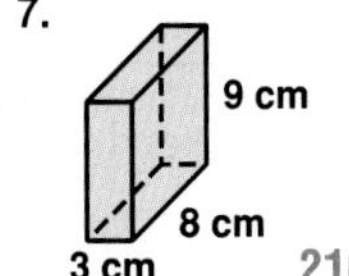

216 cm^3

8. 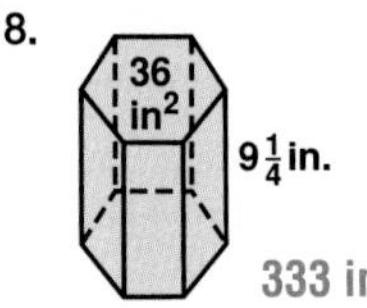

333 in^3

9. 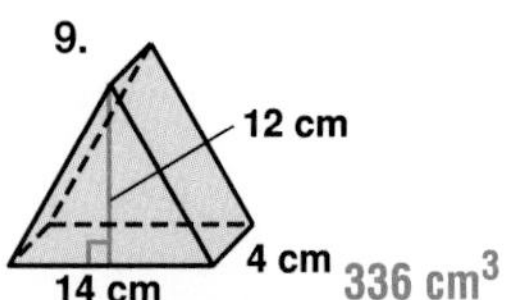

336 cm^3

10. rectangular prism: length, 4 m; width, 7 m; height 9 m 252 m^3
11. rectangular prism: length, 8 ft; width, 10 ft; height, 15 ft 1200 ft^3
12. rectangular prism: length, 16.2 cm; width, 9 cm; height, 1.24 cm 180.792 cm^3
13. triangular prism: base of triangle, 5 cm; altitude, 5 cm; prism height, 5 cm 62.5 cm^3
14. triangular prism: base of triangle, $2\frac{1}{2}$ ft; altitude, 1 ft; prism height, 2 ft 2.5 ft^3
15. area of base, 17 cm^2; height, 15 cm 255 cm^3
16. area of base, 75 in^2; height, 28 in. 2100 $in.^3$

Mixed Review

17. **Statistics** Find the mean, median, and mode for the data set: 3, 8, 11, 6, 9, 11, 12, 6, 7, 4, 11. (Lesson 10-2) 8, 8, 11
18. Using the formulas $A = \pi r^2$ and $A = \pi rs$, find the surface area of a cone that has a radius of 3 m and a slant height of 5 m. (Lesson 13-6) about 75 m^2

Applications

19. **Manufacturing** A leading manufacturer of sugar cubes packs a rectangular box so that there are six cubes along one edge, eleven cubes along a second edge, and three cubes along the third edge. How many sugar cubes are in the box? 198
20. **Pets** A rectangular fish tank is 30 in. long by 16 in. wide by 12 in. high. If the tank is filled to a height of 10 in., what is the volume of water in the tank? 4800 in^3

21. $1 \times 1 \times 48$, $1 \times 2 \times 24$, $1 \times 3 \times 16$, $1 \times 4 \times 12$, $1 \times 6 \times 8$, $2 \times 2 \times 12$, $2 \times 3 \times 8$, $2 \times 4 \times 6$, $3 \times 4 \times 4$

Critical Thinking

21. List all the possible combinations of whole number dimensions of a rectangular prism that result in a volume of 48 cm^3.

Wrap-Up

22. **Make Up a Problem** Write a problem that can be solved by finding volume. See margin.

Additional Answers

4. rectangular; $4 \cdot 5 \cdot 7$; 140 mm^3
5. cube; 4^3; 64 ft^3
6. triangular; $\frac{1}{2} \cdot 12 \cdot 8 \cdot 16$; 768 m^3
22. Sample answer: A tin of chocolate chips has a square base that is 3 cm on each edge. The height of the canister is 8 cm. If a chip has a volume of 0.5 cm^3, how many chips does the tin hold?

Cooperative Learning

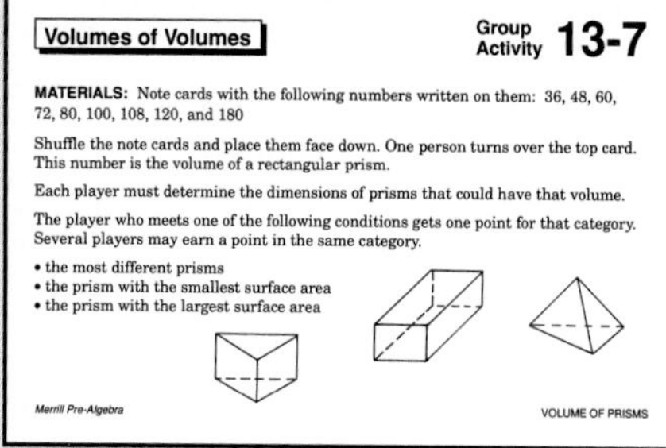
Volumes of Volumes Group Activity **13-7**

MATERIALS: Note cards with the following numbers written on them: 36, 48, 60, 72, 80, 100, 108, 120, and 180

Shuffle the note cards and place them face down. One person turns over the top card. This number is the volume of a rectangular prism.

Each player must determine the dimensions of prisms that could have that volume.

The player who meets one of the following conditions gets one point for that category. Several players may earn a point in the same category.

- the most different prisms
- the prism with the smallest surface area
- the prism with the largest surface area

Merrill Pre-Algebra VOLUME OF PRISMS

13-9 Volume: Pyramids and Cones

Objective:
Find the volume of pyramids and cones.

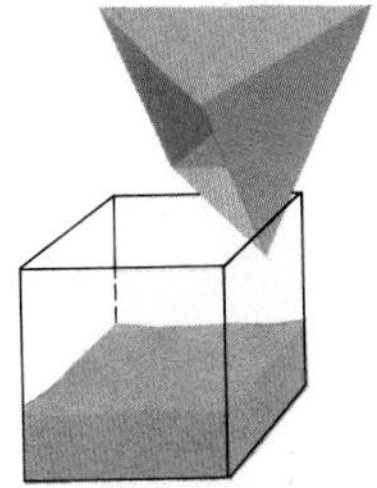

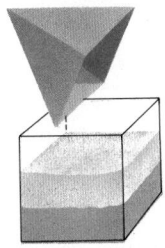

You probably have conducted experiments in science classes to find out how something works or to prove that a hypothesis is true. Gene and his friends conducted this experiment to find out if there was a relationship between the volume of a pyramid and a prism that it "fit" inside.

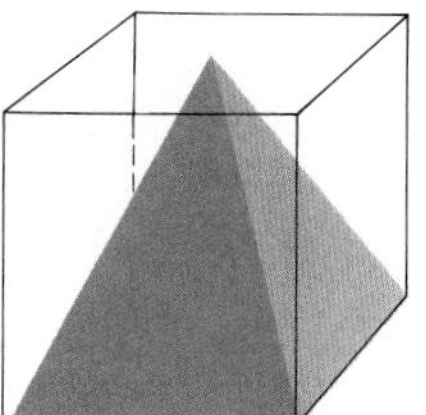

Here are the conditions.

1. The base of the pyramid and the base of the prism are congruent.
2. The altitude of the pyramid is congruent to the altitude of the prism.

You can see that the volume of the pyramid is less than the volume of the prism. The students used the models and colored sand to find out how the volumes compared.

As you can see from the drawings, three pyramids full of sand filled the prism. This suggests that the volume of the pyramid is one-third the volume of the prism.

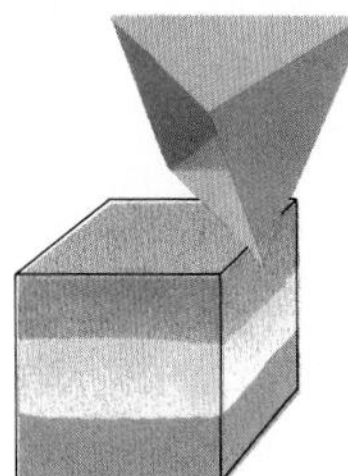

Since the formula for the volume of the prism is $V = Bh$, the volume of the pyramid would be equal to $\frac{1}{3}Bh$.

Volume of a Pyramid

If a pyramid has a base of B square units and a height of h units, then the volume (V) is $\frac{1}{3} \cdot B \cdot h$ cubic units.

$$V = \frac{1}{3}Bh$$

Calculator Hint

Recall that 3 and $\frac{1}{3}$ are multiplicative inverses. An easy way to enter $\frac{1}{3}$ into your calculator is to enter 3 and press the [1/x] key.

Example

1 Find the volume of the pyramid.

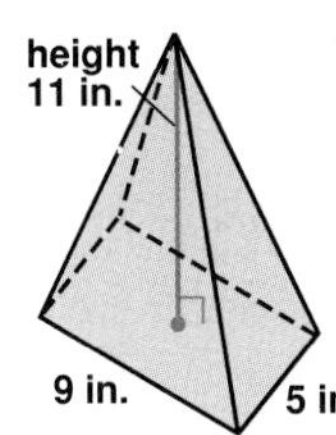

$V = \frac{1}{3}Bh$ — Formula for volume of a pyramid

$V = \frac{1}{3}\ell wh$ — Replace B with ℓw.

$V = \frac{1}{3} \cdot 9 \cdot 5 \cdot 11$ — Replace ℓ with 9, w with 5, and h with 11.

3 [1/x] [×] 9 [×] 5 [×] 11 [=] 165

The volume is 165 in^3.

Bell Ringer

What measurements do you need to find the volume of a cylinder? **The radius of the base and the height.**

Lesson Notes 13-9

5-Minute Check
(over Lesson 13-8)

Find the volume of each cylinder. Round decimal answers to the nearest tenth.

1. radius, 2 m; height, 8 m **100.5 m^3**
2. radius, 3.2 cm; height, 10.5 cm **337.8 cm^3**
3. radius, $2\frac{1}{2}$ in.; height, 12 in. **235.6 $in.^3$**

Find the value of h.

4. $V = \pi r^2 h$; $V = 508.9$ mm^3, $\pi = 3.14$, $r = 9$ mm **$h = 2$ mm**
5. $V = \pi r^2$; $V = 1021\frac{3}{7}$ ft^3, $\pi = \frac{22}{7}$; $r = 5$ ft **$h = 13$ ft**

Transparency 13-9 contains the 5-Minute Check and a teaching aid for this lesson.

1 FOCUS

The purpose of this lesson is to develop and use procedures for finding volumes of a pyramid and a cone.

Motivating the Lesson

Show a picture of the pyramids in Egypt. Those that have been opened have contained a tremendous number of artifacts. How did the Egyptians know how big to build the pyramids?

2 TEACH

Using Models Using rice or water and models similar to those in the lesson, show the class the relationship between the volume of a pyramid and a cone.

Chalkboard Examples

- *For Example 1*
  Find the volume of the pyramid.
  $V = 672.8$ cm^3

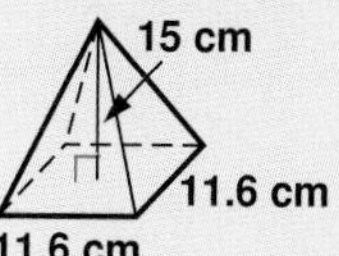

EE: 1E, 3A, 3H, 4A, 4B, 4E
TAAS: 2, 3, 4, 10, 11, 13

Chalkboard Examples

- *For Example 2*
  Find the volume of the cone to the nearest tenth.
  $V \approx 37.7 \text{ cm}^3$

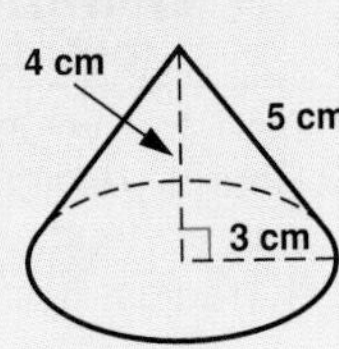

3 PRACTICE/APPLY

Checking the Concept

After completing Exercises 3-5, have students find the volume of a square pyramid with a base 3.54 inches on a side, and a cone that has a radius of 2 in., if both have a height of 4 in. Ask what they notice about the bases and volumes. **If the areas of the bases of a pyramid and cone are equal, the volumes are equal.**

Error Analysis

Watch for students who use the slant height instead of the altitude when determining the volume of a pyramid or cone.
Prevent by modeling the determination of area and volume.

It makes sense to predict that the volume of a cone and a cylinder might be related in the same way as the volume of a pyramid and a prism. Here is an experiment to check that prediction.

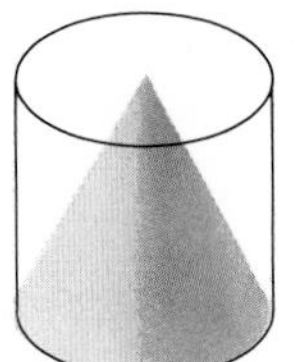

The conditions are similar.

1. The base of the cone and the base of the cylinder are congruent.
2. The altitude of the cone is congruent to the altitude of the cylinder.

By using the models and colored sand, it is easy to perform an experiment like the one done earlier for prisms and pyramids.

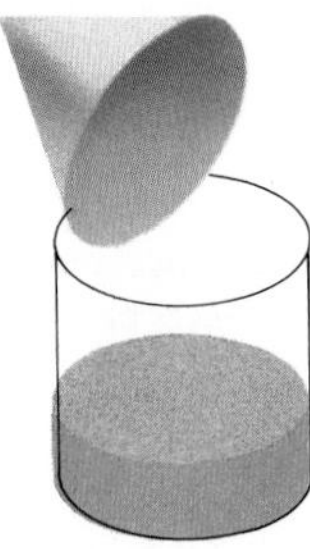

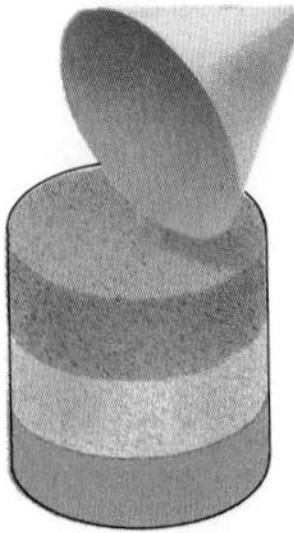

You can see that the cylinder was filled by three cones of sand. So, the volume of the cone appears to be one-third of the volume of the cylinder.

Volume of a Cone

If a cone has a radius of r units and a height of h units, then the volume (V) is $\frac{1}{3} \cdot \pi \cdot r^2 \cdot h$.

$$V = \frac{1}{3}\pi r^2 h$$

Estimation Hint

THINK: $\frac{1}{3} \times 3.14$ is a little greater than 1.

$3^2 \cdot 8 = 9 \cdot 8$ or 72

The volume should be a little greater than 72 m^3.

Example

2 Find the volume of the cone to the nearest tenth.

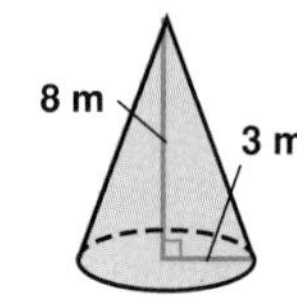

$V = \frac{1}{3}\pi r^2 h$ Formula for volume of a cone

$V = \frac{1}{3} \cdot \pi \cdot 3^2 \cdot 8$ Replace r with 3 and h with 8.

3 [1/x] [×] [π] [×] 3 [x²] [×] 8 [=] 75.398224

$V \approx 75.4$

The volume is about 75.4 m^3.

Alternate Strategies: Reteaching the Lesson

Reteaching Activity

Science Connection The command module of a rocket is basically cone-shaped. Have students use reference materials to find the dimensions of a command module and approximate its volume.

Reteaching Masters Booklet, p. 118

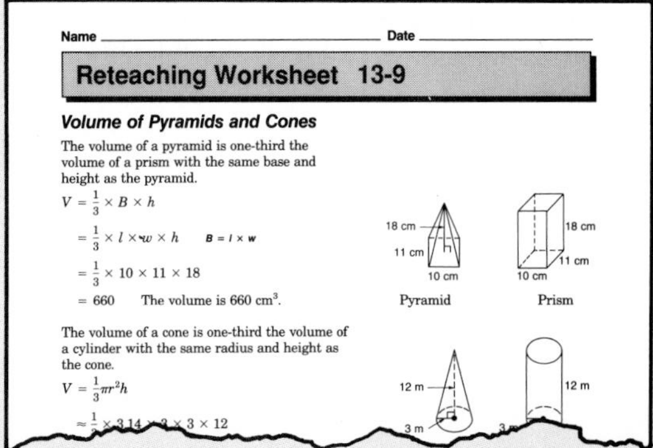

Name ______ Date ______

Reteaching Worksheet 13-9

Volume of Pyramids and Cones

The volume of a pyramid is one-third the volume of a prism with the same base and height as the pyramid.

$V = \frac{1}{3} \times B \times h$

$= \frac{1}{3} \times l \times w \times h$ $B = l \times w$

$= \frac{1}{3} \times 10 \times 11 \times 18$

$= 660$ The volume is 660 cm^3.

The volume of a cone is one-third the volume of a cylinder with the same radius and height as the cone.

$V = \frac{1}{3}\pi r^2 h$

$\approx \frac{1}{3} \times 3.14 \times 3 \times 3 \times 12$

Checking for Understanding

Communicating Algebra

1. State the formula for finding the volume of a pyramid. Then tell what each variable represents. See margin.
2. State the formula for finding the volume of a cone. Then tell what each variable represents. See margin.

Guided Practice

Explain how to find the volume of each pyramid or cone shown. Then find the volume.

3. 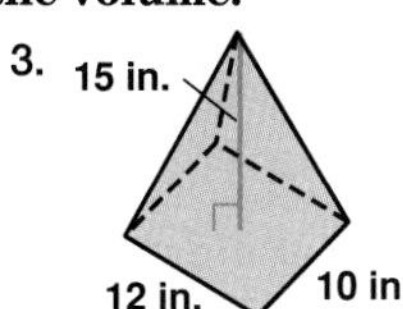

4. 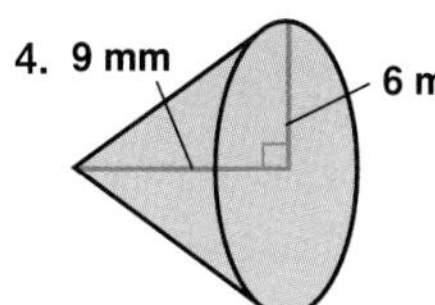

5. 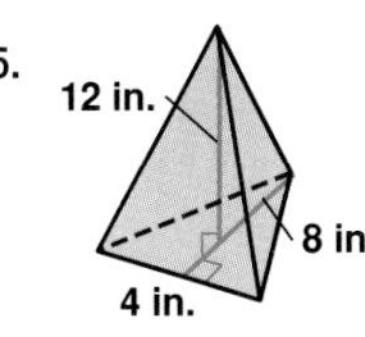

3. $\frac{1}{3} \cdot 12 \cdot 10 \cdot 15$; 600 in^3; 4. $\frac{1}{3} \cdot \pi \cdot 6^2 \cdot 9$; 339.3 mm^3; 5. $\frac{1}{3} \cdot \frac{1}{2} \cdot 4 \cdot 8 \cdot 12$; 64 in^3

Exercises

Independent Practice

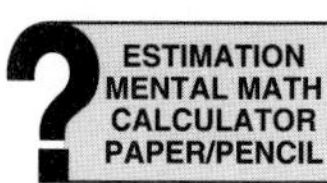

Find the volume of each pyramid or cone. Round decimal answers to the nearest tenth.

6. 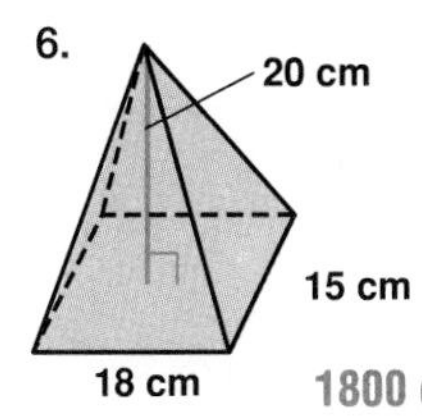

1800 cm^3

7. 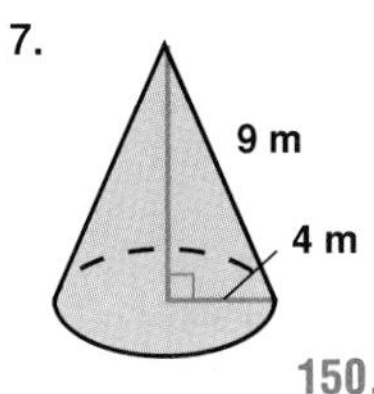

150.8 m^3

8. 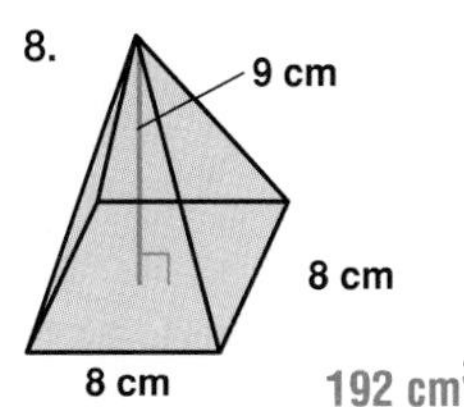

192 cm^3

9. 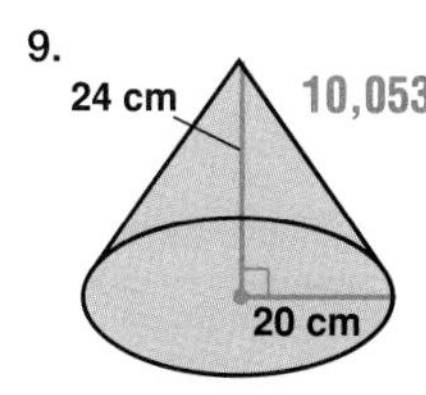

10,053.1 cm^3

10. 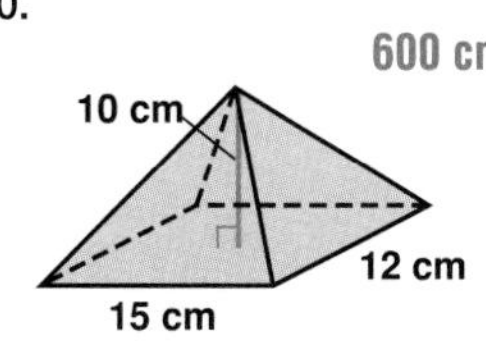

600 cm^3

11. 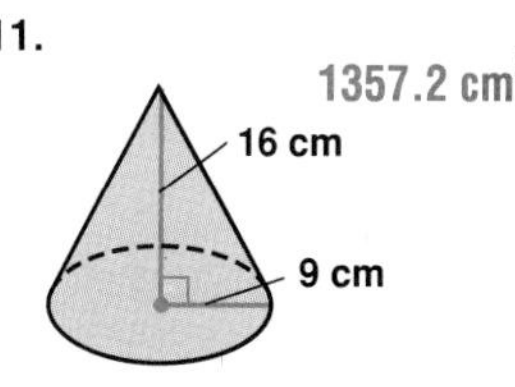

1357.2 cm^3

12. rectangular pyramid; length, 9 in.; width, 7 in.; height, 18 in. 378 in^3
13. square pyramid; length, 5 cm; height, 6 cm 50 cm^3
14. circular cone; radius, 3 ft; height, 14 ft 131.9 ft^3
15. circular cone; radius, 10 m; height, 18 m 1885.0 m^3

Mixed Review

16. **Probability** What is $P(A \text{ or } B)$ if $P(A) = \frac{1}{4}$ and $P(B) = \frac{2}{3}$ and A and B are mutually exclusive? (Lesson 11-8) $\frac{11}{12}$
17. Find the sum of the measures of the angles of a regular pentagon. (Lesson 12-12) 540°
18. Using the formula $V = \pi r^2 h$, find the volume of a circular cylinder that has a radius of 8 inches and a height of 13 inches. (Lesson 13-8) about 2614 in^2

Independent Practice

Homework Assignment	
Basic	7-15 odd, 16-20, 24, 25
Average	6-14 even, 16-21, 24, 25
Honors	10-14 even, 16-25

Practice Masters Booklet, **p. 130**

Name ______ Date ______

Practice Worksheet 13-9

Volume of Pyramids and Cones

Find the volume of each pyramid or cone. Round decimal answers to the nearest tenth.

1. 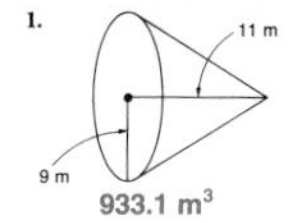

933.1 m^3

2. 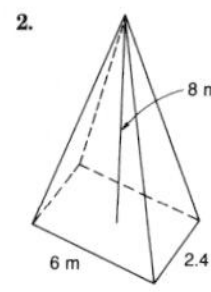

38.4 cm^3

3. 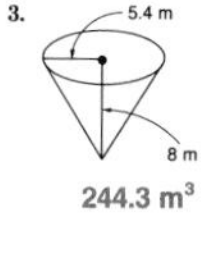

244.3 m^3

4. 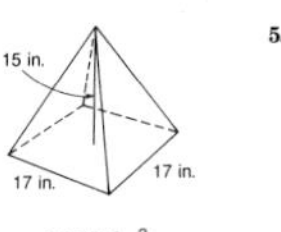

1445 in^3

5. 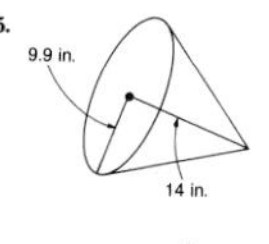

1436.9 in^3

6. 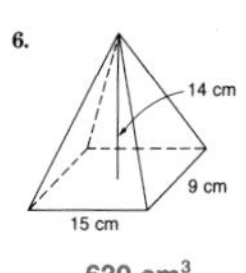

630 cm^3

7. rectangular pyramid; length, 8 cm; width, 7 cm; height, 9 cm
168 cm^3

8. square pyramid; length, 25 mm; height, 30 mm
6250 mm^3

9. circular cone; radius, 12 yd; height, 18 yd
2714.3 yd^3

Additional Answers

1. The formula for the volume of a pyramid is $V = \frac{1}{3}Bh$. V represents volume, B represents the area of the base, and h represents the height.
2. The formula for the volume of a cone is $V = \frac{1}{3}\pi r^2 h$. V represents volume, r represents the radius of the base, and h represents the height.

4 CLOSE

Assessment Option

Speaking Draw several pyramids and cones on the board or overhead projector. Have the students state measures for the base and height. Then find the volume of each figure.

Enrichment Masters Booklet, **p. 118**

Name ______________ Date ______________

Enrichment Worksheet 13-9

Using Area and Volume

Solve. Use 3.14 for π.

1. Mrs. Bartlett wants to put carpeting in a room that is 15 feet long and 12 feet wide. How many square feet of carpeting does she need? 180 ft^2
2. Tom is making a cover for a box 4.5 feet long and 23 inches wide. What will be the area of the cover, in square feet? 8.625 ft^2
3. How many 2 inches by 3 inches tickets can be cut from a 2 foot by 3 foot sheet of paper? 144 tickets
4. What is the area of the top of a tree stump that is 42 cm in diameter? 1384.74 cm^2
5. Mrs. Stabile has a one-story house that is 32 feet wide and 48 feet long. She plans to build an addition 12 feet by 16 feet. What will the total floor area of the house be then? 1728 ft^2
6. How many cubic meters of dirt must be removed when digging for the foundation of a building if the excavation is 32 m long, 12 m wide, and 8 m deep? 3072 m^3
7. Mr. Mendez has a whirling sprinkler for watering his lawn. The sprinkler waters a circle with a radius of 12 m. Find the area of the lawn that he can water at one time. 452.16 m^2
8. A cylindrical storage tank has a diameter of 6 m and a height of 5 m. What is the volume of the storage tank? 141.3 m^2
9. In Mr. Curin's living room there is a circular mirror with a diameter of 18 inches. What is the area of the mirror? 254.34 in^2
10. Find the cost of cementing a driveway 9 m by 16 m at $48 per square meter. $6912

Applications

19. **Food Service** The diameter of the rim of an ice cream cone is 2 inches and the height of the cone is 6 inches. If the cone is filled even with the rim with soft ice cream, what is the volume of the ice cream? **about 6.3 in^3**

20. If the cone in Exercise 19 is filled to a height of 3 inches above the top of the cone, in the shape of a cone, about how much ice cream is there above the cone? How much ice cream is there all together? **about 3.1 in^3; about 9.4 in^3**

Challenge

Find the volume, to the nearest tenth, of each figure shown below.

21. 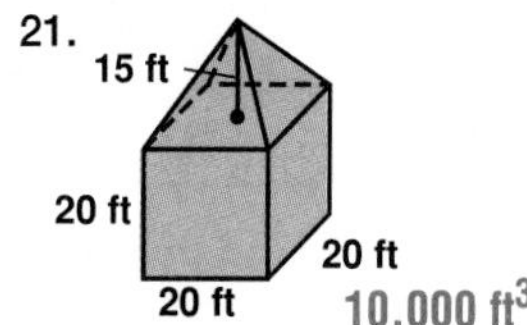

10,000 ft^3

22. 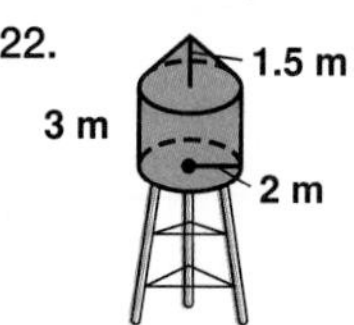

44.0 m^3

23. 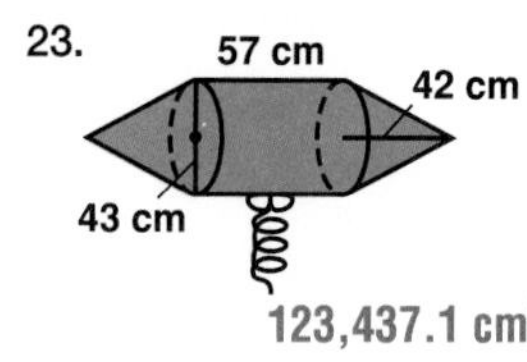

123,437.1 cm^3

Critical Thinking

24. Suppose you double the height of a cone. How does the volume change? Suppose you double the radius of the base. How does the volume change? **The volume doubles; the volume quadruples.**

Wrap-Up

25. In your own words, explain the relationship between the volumes of pyramids and prisms and between the volumes of cones and cylinders. **The volume of a pyramid is one-third the volume of a prism with the same base and height. The volume of a cone is one-third the volume of a cylinder with the same base and height.**

Career

Computer-Aided Design Technician

Computer-Aided Design (CAD) technicians use computers plus graphics printers and plotters to produce blueprints, schematics, and drawings for a variety of fields. Many technicians work for architectural and engineering firms to produce construction blueprints of buildings. Others work for automotive designers, technical illustrators, and other companies that require product design and detailed technical drafting.

A CAD technician should have the ability to concentrate on details and be accurate. The outlook for opportunities in CAD design is excellent through the 1990s.

Alternate Strategies: Extending the Lesson

Enrichment

Consumer Connection Which of the following holds more ice cream in the cone itself? **left: 7.85 cu in.; right: 6.28 cu in.**

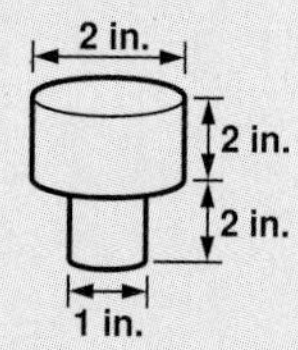

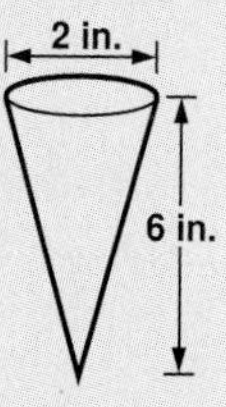

Cooperative Learning

Know It All Group Activity **13-9**

MATERIALS: A coin • two 0-9 spinners • four cards (Prism (square base), Pyramid (square base), Cone, and Cylinder)

The leader of each group flips the coin to determine if everyone in the group will compute the surface area (heads) or volume (tails) of a solid.

Next the leader picks a card from the deck to determine which solid they will use. Lastly, the leader spins the two spinners, one to determine the radius of the circle or the side of the square base, and the other to determine the height (for volume) or slant height (for surface area) of the solid. The leader must make sure that the slant height is greater than the radius of the circle or half the side of the square.

All group members then compute the volume or surface area for the solid with the given dimensions.

Merrill Pre-Algebra VOLUME OF PYRAMIDS AND CONES

Application

13-10 Precision and Significant Digits

Objective:
Use precision and significant digits to describe a measurement.

Key Terms:
precision
significant digits

Have you ever heard someone say that all measurements are approximate? What they mean is that no measurement can be any more exact than the scale the object is being measured with. The micrometer shown at the right is used by machinists to make measurements that need to be very precise. The micrometer can measure to the nearest 0.001 inch.

When you measure the length of a paper clip, you might use a metric ruler. Measuring to the nearest millimeter (0.1 of a centimeter) is all the precision you can expect.

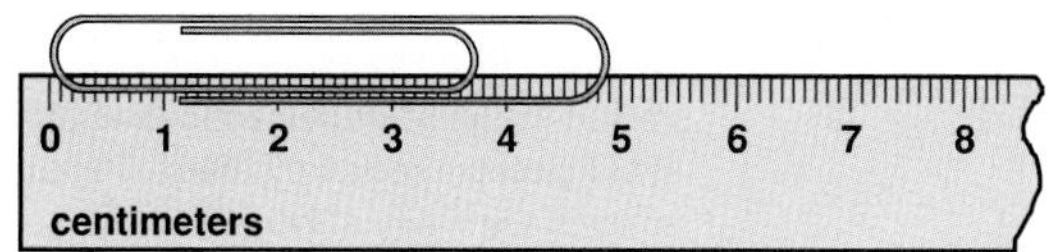

When you say that the length of the paper clip is 4.9 cm, you are really stating two things.

1. The unit being used (the precision unit) is 0.1 cm.
2. The number you selected for the measure is closer to 4.9 than it is to 4.8 or 5.0.

The **precision** of a measurement depends on the unit of measure. To improve the precision of a measurement, you must choose a measuring instrument that provides smaller units of measure. For example, a measurement obtained using a bathroom scale that reads to the nearest 0.5 kg would not be as precise as a measurement obtained using a balance scale that reads to the nearest 0.005 kg.

The digits you record when you measure are **significant.** These digits indicate the precision of the measurement.

Example

1 **The length of a piece of copper tubing is given as 43.58 cm. What can you tell from this information?**

a. The unit of measure is 0.01 cm.
b. The measurement is not exact. However, you can be reasonably certain that the actual length is between 43.57 cm and 43.59 cm.
c. There are four significant digits.

Bell Ringer

What is the ratio of the volume of a pyramid to the volume of a rectangular prism having the same dimensions? 1:3

Lesson Notes 13-10

5-Minute Check
(over Lesson 13-9)

Find the volume of each pyramid or cone. Round answers to the nearest tenth.

1. rectangular pyramid; length 4 m; width 6 m; height 11 m 88 m^3
2. rectangular pyramid; length 27 ft; width 16 ft; height 75 ft 10,800 ft^3
3. square pyramid; length 11.6 cm; height 15 cm 672.8 cm^3
4. circular cone; radius 3 m ; height 9 m 84.8 m^3
5. circular cone; radius 3 ft; height 14 ft 131.9 ft^3

Transparency 13-10 contains the 5-Minute Check and a teaching aid for this lesson.

1 FOCUS

The purpose of this lesson is to introduce the concepts of precision and significant digits and explain how they are related to a given measurement.

Motivating the Lesson

Show students a bathroom scale and a kitchen scale. Which would you use to measure the weight of an orange? Why?

2 TEACH

Chalkboard Examples

- *For Example 1*
  The length of a piece of electrical wire is given as 61.75 meters. What can you tell from this information?
  a. **Unit of measure is 0.01 meters.**
  b. **The measurement is not exact but the actual length is between 61.74 m and 61.76 m.**
  c. **There are 4 significant digits.**

EE: 1E, 3A, 4B
TAAS: 4

Analyze each measurement.

- *For Example 2*
  20.70 inches
  a. Actual length is closer to 20.70 in. than to 20.69 in. or 20.71 in.
  b. The unit of measure is 0.01 in.
  c. There are 4 significant digits.
- *For Example 3*
  0.006 kilograms
  a. The actual mass is closer to 0.006 kg than to 0.005 kg or 0.007 kg.
  b. The unit of measure is 0.001 kg.
  c. There is one significant digit.
- *For Example 4*
  The sides of a triangle measure 14.13 cm, 6.2 cm, and 7.341 cm. What is its perimeter? **27.7 cm**
- *For Example 5*
  The length of a rectangle is 15.28 cm and the width is 4.7 cm. What is the area of the rectangle? **72 cm²**

Practice Masters Booklet, **p. 131**

Name ______ Date ______

Practice Worksheet 13-10

Application: Precision and Significant Digits

For each measurement, give the measurements between which the actual length lies.

1. 237 mm 236 mm, 238 mm	2. 75 cm 74 cm, 76 cm	3. 9.5 m 9.4 m, 9.6 m	4. 23.3 mm 23.2 mm, 23.4 mm
5. 1.75 in. 1.74 in., 1.76 in.	6. 4.0 yd 3.9 yd, 4.1 yd	7. 11 ft 10 ft, 12 ft	8. 81.63 cm 81.62 cm, 81.64 cm
9. 5.25 mi 5.24 mi, 5.26 mi	10. 15.50 in. 15.49 in., 15.51 in.	11. 0.02 km 0.01 km, 0.03 km	12. 49.29 mm 49.28 mm, 49.30 mm
13. 8.6 m 8.5 m, 8.7 m	14. 100.2 km 100.1 km, 100.3 km	15. 9.70 cm 9.69 cm, 9.71 cm	16. 0.004 km 0.003 km, 0.005 km

Calculate. Round to the correct number of significant digits.

17. 16.81 cm + 7.9 cm 24.7 cm	18. 19.561 mm − 4.9 mm 14.7 mm
19. 13.2 m + 16.4 m 29.6	20. 8.027 mm − 4.81 mm 3.22 mm
21. 24.28 g + 6.7 g + 2.1075 g 33.1 g	22. 721.2 m + 24.3 m − 7.8 m 737.7 m
23. 3.5 ft + 2.25 ft + 1.75 ft 7.5 ft	24. 116.1 mm + 31.2 mm − 4.6 mm 142.7 mm
25. 4.261 mm × 3.7 16 mm	26. 23.73 cm × 2.91 69.1 cm
27. 506.7 km × 4.552 2306 km	28. 73.75 mi ÷ 5.6 13 mi
29. 90.2 kg ÷ 0.234 385	30. 201.95 mm ÷ 5.126 39.40 mm

Examples

Analyze each measurement.

2 10.50 inches

a. The actual length is closer to 10.50 in. than to 10.49 in. or 10.51 in.
b. The unit of measure is 0.01 in.
c. There are four significant digits. The zero in the hundredths place is significant.

3 0.003 kilograms

a. The actual mass is closer to 0.003 kg than to 0.002 kg or 0.004 kg.
b. The unit of measure is 0.001 kg.
c. There is one significant digit. The zeros in 0.003 are used to show only the place value of the decimal and are not counted as significant digits.

The result of a computation involving a measurement can be no more precise than the least precise measurement involved. Scientists usually round sums and differences of measures to the *same precision* as the least precise measurement. Products and quotients are rounded to the *same number of significant digits* as the least precise measurement.

Examples

In Example 4, which measurement is least precise? Why? **5.8 cm; 0.1 > 0.01 or 0.001**

4 **The sides of a triangle measure 12.26 cm, 5.8 cm, and 2.125 cm. What is its perimeter?**

12.26 cm + 5.8 cm + 2.125 cm = 20.185
2 decimal places; 1 decimal place; 3 decimal places

Round to 20.2 cm since the least precise measurement has 1 decimal place.

The perimeter of the triangle is 20.2 cm.

In Example 5, which measurement is least precise? Why? **5.1 cm, 0.1 > 0.01**

5 **The length of a rectangle is 12.63 cm and the width is 5.1 cm. What is the area of the rectangle?**

12.63 [×] 5.1 [=] 64.413
4 significant digits; 2 significant digits

Round to 64 cm since 64 has 2 significant digits.

The area of the rectangle is 64 cm^2.

Checking for Understanding

Communicating Algebra

1. "All measurements are approximate" means __?__.
2. When you say that the length of a pencil is 15.6 cm, you are stating that the actual length is between __?__ and __?__. **15.5 cm; 15.7 cm**
3. The precision of a measurement depends on __?__. **the unit of measure**

1. A measurement cannot be any more exact than the scale it is measured with.

Alternate Strategies: Reteaching the Lesson

Reteaching Activity

Using Cooperative Groups Use rulers with both metric and customary units, balances, and a container that measures metric volume. Have one student in a group make a measurement, and other students tell the number of significant digits used, the unit of measurement, and the meaning of the measurement.

Reteaching Masters Booklet, **p. 119**

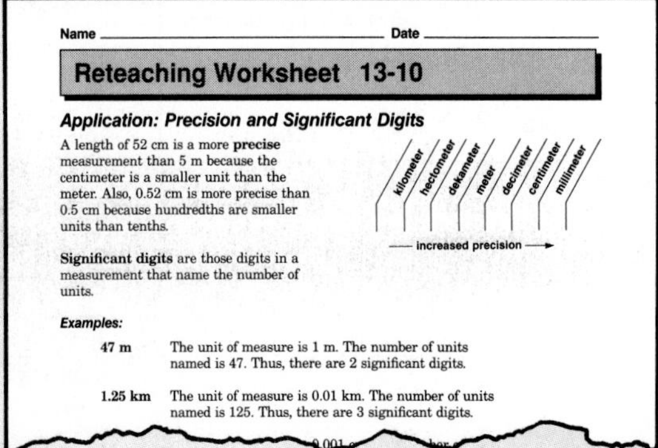

Name ______ Date ______

Reteaching Worksheet 13-10

Application: Precision and Significant Digits

A length of 52 cm is a more **precise** measurement than 5 m because the centimeter is a smaller unit than the meter. Also, 0.52 cm is more precise than 0.5 cm because hundredths are smaller units than tenths.

Significant digits are those digits in a measurement that name the number of units.

Examples:

47 m The unit of measure is 1 m. The number of units named is 47. Thus, there are 2 significant digits.

1.25 km The unit of measure is 0.01 km. The number of units named is 125. Thus, there are 3 significant digits.

Guided Practice **Tell how many significant digits each measurement has. Then tell the unit of measure.**

4. 7.5 m 2; 0.1 m
5. 21.25 ft 4; 0.01 ft
6. 107.50 mm 5; 0.01 mm
7. 0.007 kg 1; 0.001 kg
8. 4.0 mi 2; 0.1 mi
9. 0.7403 m 4; 0.0001 m

Exercises

Independent Practice **For each measurement, give the measurements between which the actual length lies.** See margin.

10. 146 cm
11. 63 mm
12. 3.6 cm
13. 18.2 m
14. 2.59 in.
15. 3.0 m
16. 4.90 m
17. 10 ft

Calculate. Round to the correct number of significant digits. 21. 84.47 m

18. 14.38 cm + 5.7 cm + 3.9082 cm 24.0 cm
19. 15.273 L − 8.2 L 7.1 L
20. 127.2 g + 42.3 g − 5.7 g 163.8 g
21. 29.307 m + 4.23 m + 50.93 m
22. 5.372 cm · 4.8 26 cm
23. 29.78 km ÷ 3.7 8.0 km
24. 4.397 cm × 2.4 11 cm
25. 50.3 kg ÷ 0.2937 171 kg

Mixed Review

26. Graph the equation $x + 2y = 4$. (Lesson 8-6) See margin.
27. Using the formula $A = bh$, find the area of a parallelogram that has a base of 7 meters and a height of 5 meters. (Lesson 13-1) $35\ m^2$
28. Name the pairs of alternate interior angles in the diagram at the right. (Lesson 12-4) ∠2 and ∠6; ∠3 and ∠7

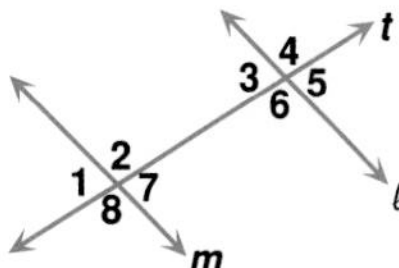

29. Using the formula $V = \frac{1}{3}Bh$, find the volume of a pyramid with a rectangular base, 7 in. by 3 in., and a height of 8 in. (Lesson 13-9) $56\ in^3$

Applications

30. **Measurement** Sam and Della both correctly measure the same piece of metal using different measuring instruments. Sam says the length is 12.3 cm. Della says the length is 123.4 mm. Which measurement is more precise? Why? 123.4 mm; 0.1 mm < 0.1 cm
31. **Measurement** Arrange the following measurements in order of precision, from most to least precise. 0.40 mm, 40 mm, 0.4 mm, 0.0004 mm 0.0004 mm, 0.40 mm, 0.4 mm, 40 mm
32. **Masonry** How high is a stack of 25 bricks, if each brick is 3.75 inches thick? Round to reflect the proper precision. 94 in.

Critical Thinking

33. If 56.7 represents the sum of two measurements that have been rounded to the nearest tenth, what is the least possible and the greatest possible number that was rounded? 56.65; 56.74$\overline{9}$

Wrap-Up

34. Write a few sentences about what precision is and why it is important in measurement. See margin.

3 PRACTICE/APPLY

Checking the Concept

After completing Exercises 6-9, have students verbalize the purpose of each zero and whether it is significant or not.

Independent Practice

Homework Assignment	
Basic	11-25 odd, 26-31, 33, 34
Average	10-24 even, 26-34
Honors	14, 16, 20-34

4 CLOSE

Assessment Option

Writing and Speaking Have a student pick a number from one to ten. Next have each student write a number that contains that many significant digits. Go around the room and have each student then read their number out loud.

Additional Answers

10. 145 cm & 147 cm
11. 62 mm & 64 mm
12. 3.5 cm & 3.7 cm
13. 18.1 m & 18.3 m
14. 2.58 in. & 2.60 in.
15. 2.9 m & 3.1 m
16. 4.89 m & 4.91 m
17. 9 ft & 11 ft

Enrichment Masters Booklet, **p. 119**

Name ______ Date ______

Enrichment Worksheet 13-10

Tolerance

The amount that a measurement may vary from the desired size is called the **tolerance** of the measurement.

A dimension of 12.000 in. ± 0.001 in. is read twelve inches plus or minus 0.001 inch and means that the measurement cannot differ by more than 0.001 in. from the basic dimension. The tolerance is ±0.001 in. and the **tolerance interval** is 11.999 in. to 12.001 in.

State the tolerance interval for each of the following blueprint measurements.

1. 3.447 in. ± 0.001 in. 3.446 in. to 3.448 in.
2. 2.6320 in. ± 0.0002 in. 2.6318 in. to 2.6322 in.
3. 0.720 in. ± 0.005 in. 0.715 in. to 0.725 in.
4. 4.516 in. ± 0.021 in. 4.495 in. to 4.537 in.
5. 3.0000 in. ± 0.0025 in. 2.9975 in. to 3.0025 in.
6. 6.329 in. ± 0.002 in. 6.327 in. to 6.331 in.

The specification for a particular bolt is 3.000 in. ± 0.002 in. State whether each of the following sizes is acceptable.

7. 2.999 in. yes
8. 3.002 in. yes
9. 3.011 in. no
10. 3.003 in. no
11. 2.997 in. no
12. 3.001 in. yes
13. 3.000 in. yes
14. 3.010 in. no

The desired size of a machine part is stated as 1.005 in. ± 0.003 in. State whether each of the following sizes is acceptable.

15. 1.002 in. yes
16. 1.001 in. no
17. 1.000 in. no
18. 1.004 in. yes

Solve.

19. A chemical supply company guarantees the precision weighing of its products. They advertise that Product Y weighs 8 oz ± 0.03 oz. What is the tolerance interval? 7.97 oz to 8.03 oz

Additional Answer

34. Sample answer: Precision tells how closely two measurements agree when measured with the same instrument. It is important in measuring because the more precise a measurement is the closer it is to the exact measure.

Cooperative Learning

How Significant Is It? Group Activity **13-10**

MATERIALS: Calculators • "Significant Operations" cards with expressions given on the back of this card

Shuffle the "Significant Operations" cards and place them face down. When the top card is turned over, players use their calculators to do the computation. They then must write the answer rounded to the correct number of significant digits.

After everyone has done this, players with the correct answer get one point each. Play continues with the next card being drawn from the pile. After all cards have been played, the game is over. The player with the most points is the winner.

Merrill Pre-Algebra PRECISION AND SIGNIFICANT DIGITS

Lesson Notes 13-11

5-Minute Check
(over Lesson 13-10)

Calculate. Round to the correct number of significant digits.

1. 315.2 g + 61.5 g − 240.3 g **136 g**
2. 2.050 kg ÷ 0.25 kg **8.2 kg**
3. 56.348 L − 6.039 L **50.31 L**
4. 9.87 cm × 0.008 cm **0.08 cm**
5. 43.901 m + 2.08 m + 60.05 m **106 m**

Transparency 13-11 contains the 5-Minute Check and a teaching aid for this lesson.

1 FOCUS

The purpose of this lesson is to add making a model or drawing to the student's problem-solving strategies.

Motivating the Lesson

Ask students what they do first when given complicated directions to a location. Why might drawing a map be helpful?

2 TEACH

Using Groups of Two Have students work with a partner to try to solve the lesson example without using a diagram. Then allow the students to use a diagram and discuss comparative ease of solution.

Chalkboard Examples

The school steps need to be replaced. There are five steps each step measuring 0.5 feet high, 1 foot deep, and 20 feet long. How much concrete will be needed to replace these steps? **150 ft³**

EE: 1A, 1B, 1C, 1D, 1E, 4B
TAAS: 10, 11, 13

Problem Solving

13-11 Strategy: Make a Model or Drawing

Objective:
Solve problems by making a model or drawing.

Lee's Masonry makes concrete steps for new homes. The steps for one home are to be 5 feet long, with three steps. Each step will be 0.5 foot high and 1 foot wide. How much concrete will be needed?

Without a drawing, it is difficult to determine how to find the volume. A model or drawing can help you solve problems like this one, as well as many other problems, especially problems involving geometry.

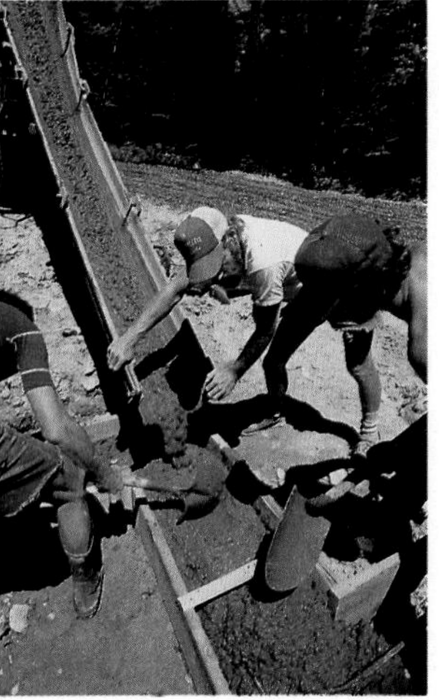

Explore You know some of the dimensions of the steps. You need to find the volume of the steps.

Plan After making a labeled drawing of the steps using the information you have, the problem becomes clearer. Notice that the steps can be divided into three rectangular prisms. You know how to find the volume of each prism. You can find the total volume by adding.

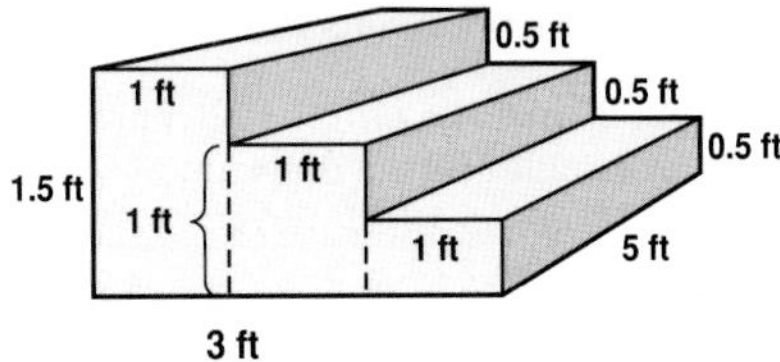

Solve

Volume of lowest step $= \ell wh$
$= 5 \cdot 1 \cdot 0.5$
$= 2.5$

Volume of middle step $= \ell wh$
$= 5 \cdot 1 \cdot 1$
$= 5$

Volume of highest step $= \ell wh$
$= 5 \cdot 1 \cdot 1.5$
$= 7.5$

Total volume $= 2.5 + 5 + 7.5 = 15$

It will take 15 cubic feet of concrete to make the steps.

How many cubic feet would a 4th step add to the total volume? **10 ft³**

Examine Notice that the steps can be divided into three different rectangular prisms.

Volume of bottom layer $= 5 \cdot 3 \cdot 0.5 = 7.5$
Volume of middle layer $= 5 \cdot 2 \cdot 0.5 = 5$
Volume of top layer $= 5 \cdot 1 \cdot 0.5 = 2.5$
Total volume $= 7.5 + 5 + 2.5 = 15$

Since the volume using either method is 15 ft^3, the answer checks.

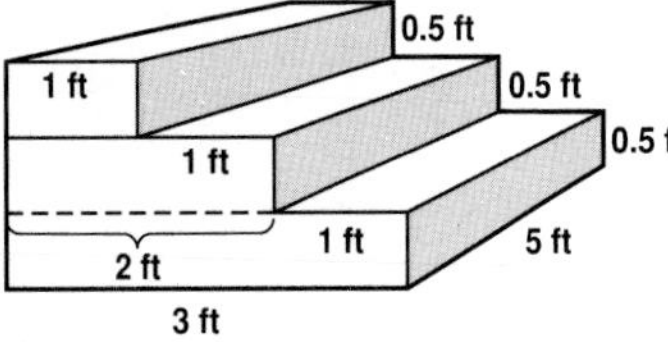

Bell Ringer

Write two numbers, each with five significant digits. **Sample answer: 10, 922**

Reteaching Activity

Using Diagrams Have students use a diagram to help solve the following problem. A silo 30 ft high has a diameter of 14 ft. It is topped with a cone that is 6 ft high. How much silage can the silo hold? **about 4926 ft³**

Checking for Understanding

See margin for drawings.

Guided Practice

Solve Exercises 1 and 2 by making a model or drawing.

1. There are 2 tiles. One is in the shape of a square and the other is in the shape of an equilateral triangle. The sides of the square are congruent to the sides of the triangle. The tiles are put together to form a pentagon. If one side of the triangle is 20 cm long, what is the perimeter of the pentagon? **100 cm**
2. A painting 15 cm by 25 cm is bordered by a matting that is 3 cm wide. The frame around the matting is 2 cm wide. What is the area of the picture including the frame and matting? **875 cm^2**

Communicating Algebra

3. Describe the model or drawing you used for Exercise 1. How did it help you solve the problem? **See students' work.**
4. Describe the model or drawing you used for Exercise 2. How did it help you solve the problem? **See students' work.**

Exercises

Independent Practice

ESTIMATION
MENTAL MATH
CALCULATOR
PAPER/PENCIL

Solve. Use any strategy.

5. A rectangular swimming pool is 4 meters wide and 10 meters long. A concrete walkway is poured around the pool. The walkway is 1 m wide and 0.1 m deep. What is the volume of the concrete? **3.2 m^3**
6. A circular track has a diameter of 400 feet. Candy starts out jogging around the track at a rate of 600 feet per minute. One minute later, Andrea starts jogging at the same place. She goes in the same direction and jogs at 700 feet per minute. Will Andrea pass Candy on the first, second, third, or fourth quarter of the track? **2nd**
7. A nonagon is a polygon with 9 sides. How many different diagonals can be drawn in a nonagon? **27**
8. Half of a garden is planted in corn. Half the remaining garden is planted in strawberries. A third of the part not planted in corn or strawberries is planted in tomatoes. If 6 m^2 is planted in tomatoes, what is the area planted in corn? **36 m^2**
9. The owner of Newland Dairy Farm plans to put a fence around the pasture behind the new dairy barn. The pasture is rectangular and measures 200 ft by 800 ft. The fence is only needed on three sides of the pasture because the barn will serve as one of the shorter sides. If a fence post is needed at every corner and at every 10 ft along the sides, how many posts are needed? **181 posts**
10. Alex has 36 identical cubes. Each edge of a cube is 1 in. long. How can Alex arrange the cubes to have the smallest surface area? **3 × 3 × 4**
11. A circular fountain has a diameter of 8 feet. A flower garden is planted around the fountain. If the garden extends 12 feet beyond the fountain, what is the area of the garden? **about 754.0 ft^2**

Wrap-Up

12. **Make Up a Problem** Write a problem from your everyday life that can be solved using a model or drawing. Solve the problem. **See students' work.**

3 PRACTICE/APPLY

Checking the Concept

After completing Exercises 1 and 2, have several students sketch their drawings on the chalkboard. Discuss how different representations may be effective as long as necessary information is included.

Independent Practice

Homework Assignment	
Basic	5-12
Average	5-12
Honors	5-12

Chapter 13, Quiz B (Lesson 13-7 through 13-11) is available in the Evaluation Masters Booklet, p. 115.

4 CLOSE

Assessment Option

Modeling Have the students arrange furniture in a room on paper. Give them measurements for the room and for every piece of furniture. Give the room doors, windows, vents, and other common obstacles.

Practice Masters Booklet, **p. 132**

Name ______ Date ______

Practice Worksheet 13-11

Problem Solving Strategy: Make a Model or Drawing

Solve by making a model or drawing.

1. Rita collects miniature lamps. She is building a shelf around the 15 feet by 18 feet family room to display them. How many feet of shelving will she need? **66 ft**
2. Twelve boxes of detergent are to be placed in a carton. Each box is 8 inches by 3 inches by 11 inches. How much space must the carton contain? Give possible dimensions of the carton. **3168 in^3; Sample dimensions: 8 in. × 36 in. × 11 in., 16 in. × 18 in. × 11 in., 24 in. × 12 in. × 11 in., 32 in. × 9 in. × 11 in.**
3. 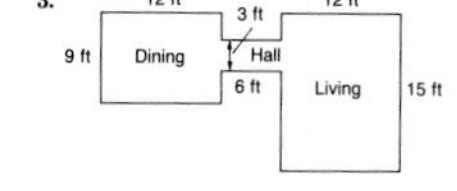

The dining room, living room, and hall areas are to be carpeted. How much will it cost if the carpet is priced at \$12.89 per square yard? **\$438.26**
4. The town playground is to have a hedge planted around it. The playground is in the shape of a pentagon with 2 sides of 40 feet, 2 sides of 60 feet, and one side of 70 feet. The bushes will be planted every 5 feet. How many bushes will be needed? **54 bushes**
5. A cord of wood is equivalent to 128 cubic feet and is described as a stack 4 feet by 4 feet by 8 feet. Herman and his son cut, split, and sell wood. They have a stack 16 feet by 6 feet by 12 feet. How many cords of wood do they have ready for sale? **9 cords of wood**
6. Javier wants to dig a circular swimming pool. It will have a diameter of 20 feet and a depth of 6 feet. How much dirt must he remove? **about 1884 ft^3**

Additional Answers

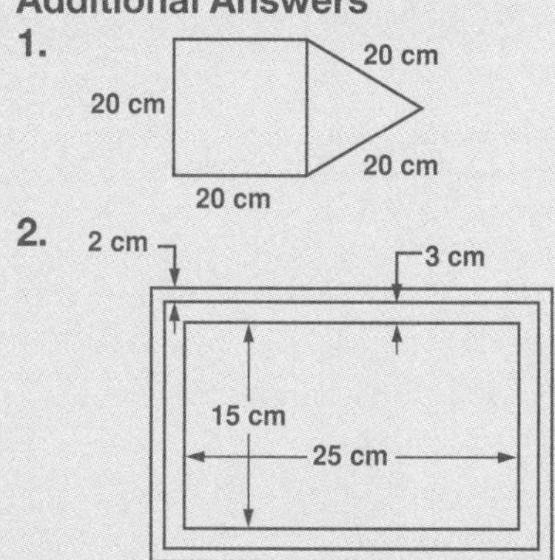

Cooperative Learning

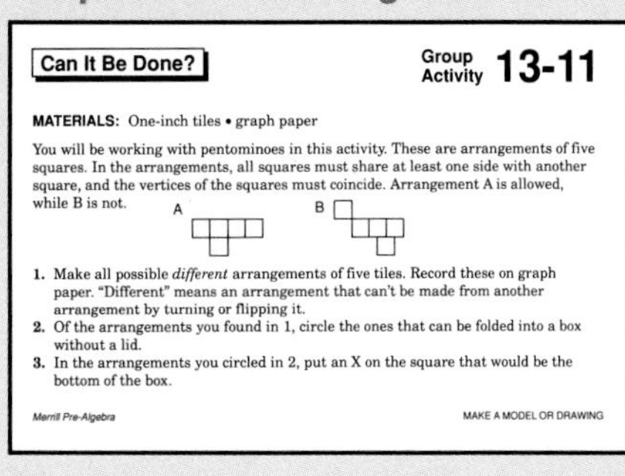

Can It Be Done? Group Activity **13-11**

MATERIALS: One-inch tiles • graph paper

You will be working with pentominoes in this activity. These are arrangements of five squares. In the arrangements, all squares must share at least one side with another square, and the vertices of the squares must coincide. Arrangement A is allowed, while B is not.

1. Make all possible *different* arrangements of five tiles. Record these on graph paper. "Different" means an arrangement that can't be made from another arrangement by turning or flipping it.
2. Of the arrangements you found in 1, circle the ones that can be folded into a box without a lid.
3. In the arrangements you circled in 2, put an X on the square that would be the bottom of the box.

Merrill Pre-Algebra MAKE A MODEL OR DRAWING

Using the Chapter Review

The Chapter Review is a comprehensive review of the concepts presented in this chapter. This review may be used to prepare students for the Chapter Test.

Alternate Review Strategy

To provide a brief in-class review, you may wish to read the following questions to the class and require a verbal response.

1. What is the area of a triangle with a base of 16 inches and a height of 9 inches? 72 in.^{2}
2. What is the area of a trapezoid with a height of 4 cm and the bases measuring 7 cm and 5 cm? 24 cm^2
3. Find the area of a circle with a diameter of 9 feet. $A \approx 63.6$ ft^2
4. Describe the faces of a triangular prism. There are 2 triangular faces and 3 rectangular faces.
5. If a circular cylinder was laid flat, the length of the curved surface would equal the _?_ of the circular top or bottom. circumference
6. How do you find the surface area of a square pyramid? area of base + area of four triangular surfaces
7. What is the formula for finding the volume of a rectangular prism? $V = \ell wh$
8. Explain how to find the volume of a cylinder with a diameter of 1.8 cm and a height of 6 cm. $\pi(0.9)^2(6)$
9. Explain how to find the volume of a circular cone with a diameter of 10 m and a height of 20 m. $V = \frac{1}{3}\pi(5)^2(20)$
10. Tell how many significant digits 0.0307 m has. 3
11. The Snyders want to carpet their dining room, living room, and hallway. The dining room is 12 × 14 ft, the living room is 16 × 18 ft, and the hallway is 4 × 8 ft. How many square feet of carpeting do the Snyders need to order? 488 ft^2

Review

Language and Concepts

Answers are calculated using π.

Choose the correct term to complete each sentence.

altitude
cubic centimeter
precision
pyramid
square centimeter
surface area
volume

1. The _?_ is a common unit of measure for area. cm^2
2. The _?_ is a common unit of measure for volume. cm^3
3. The _?_ of a solid is the sum of the areas of its faces. surface area
4. _?_ is the amount of space that a solid contains. volume
5. The _?_ of a parallelogram is a segment perpendicular to the bases with endpoints on the bases. altitude
6. A _?_ is named by the shape of its base. pyramid
7. The smaller the unit of measure, the greater the degree of _?_ of a measurement. precision

Skills

Find the area of each figure. (Lesson 13-1)

8. $3\frac{15}{16}$ in.^{2}

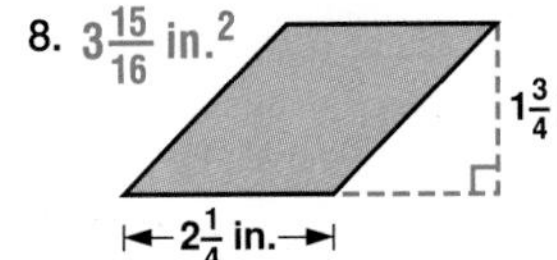

9. 82.5 in.^{2}

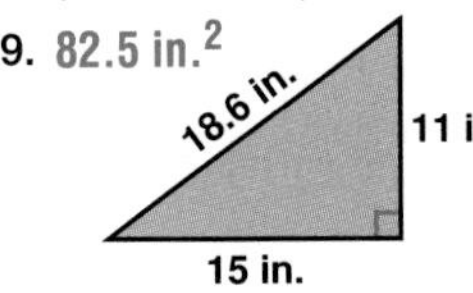

10. 1.19 m^2

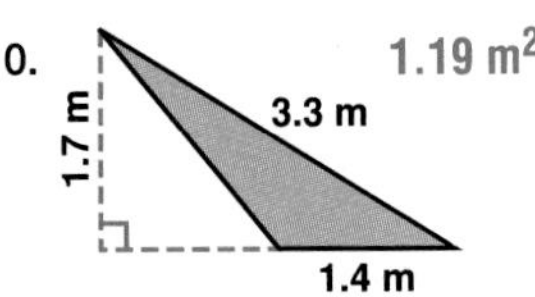

Find the area of each trapezoid. (Lesson 13-2)

11. 221 m^2

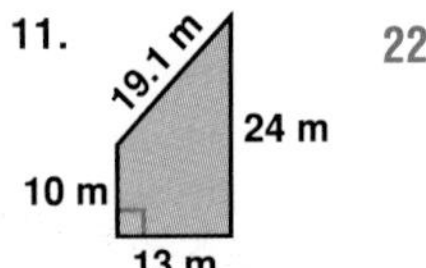

12. 476 mm^2

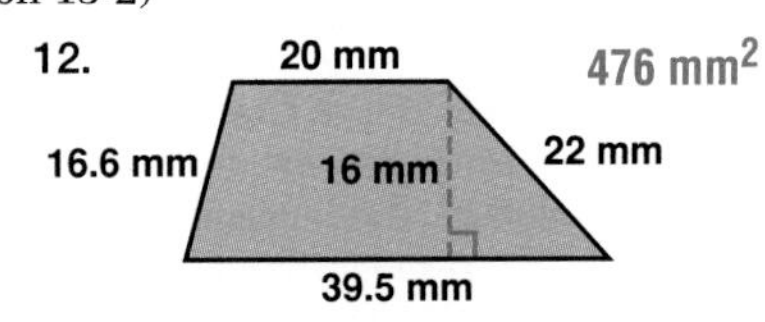

Find the area of each circle described below. Round decimal answers to the nearest tenth. (Lesson 13-3)

13. radius, 9 mi 254.5 mi^2
14. diameter, 4.2 m 13.9 m^2

Find the surface area of each prism. (Lesson 13-4)

15. 2840 m^2

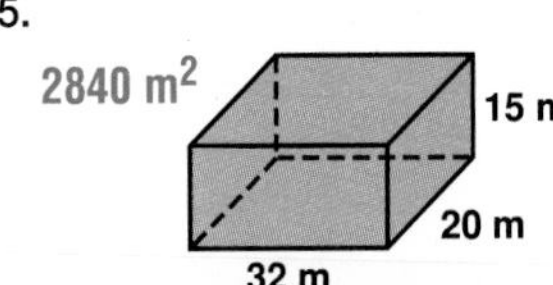

16. 6 cm^2

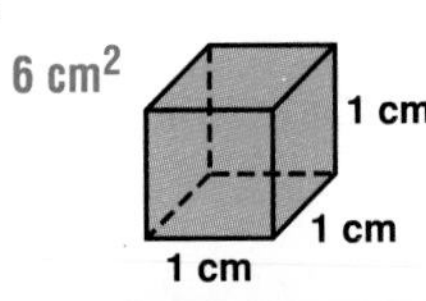

17. $3\frac{3}{8}$ ft^2

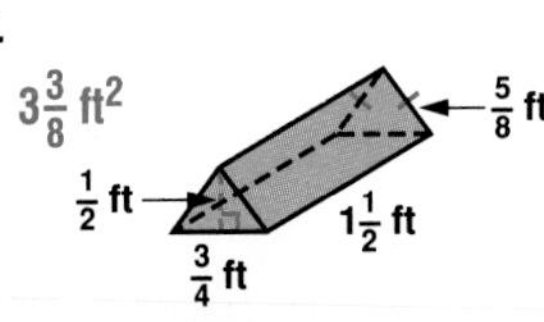

Find the surface area of each cylinder described below. Round each answer to the nearest whole number. (Lesson 13-5)

18. height, 2.3 m; radius 1 m **$21\ m^2$**
19. height, 41 cm; diameter, 40 cm **$7665\ cm^2$**

Find the surface area of each figure described below. Round decimal answers to the nearest tenth. (Lesson 13-6)

20. a pyramid with base 10 in. by 10 in. and slant height $8\frac{1}{4}$ in. **$265\ in^2$**
21. a cone with radius 1 m and slant height 2 m **$9.4\ m^2$**

Find the volume of each figure described below. Round decimal answers to the nearest tenth. (Lessons 13-7, 13-8, 13-9)

22. triangular prism: base of triangle, 5 cm; height, 3.4 cm; prism height, 12 cm **$102\ cm^3$**
23. hexagonal prism: area of base, 166.25 in^2; height, 20 in. **$3325\ in^3$**
24. rectangular prism: length, 4 m; width, 4 m; height, 16 m **$256\ m^3$**
25. cylinder: radius, 7 ft; height, 18 ft **$2770.9\ ft^3$**
26. cylinder: diameter, 10 m; height, 22 m **$1727.9\ m^3$**
27. rectangular pyramid: length, 8 m; width, 9 m; height, 21 m **$504\ m^3$**
28. cone: radius, 6 in.; height, 11 in. **$414.7\ in^3$**

Applications and Problem Solving

Determine the number of significant digits in each measurement. (Lesson 13-10)

29. 600 ft **1**
30. 84.0 cm **3**
31. 53.005 m **5**
32. 64 yd **2**

Solve by making a drawing. (Lesson 13-11)

33. The radius of a circular flower garden and its border is 2.8 meters. Without the border, the radius is 2.3 meters. Find the area of the border. **$8.0\ m^2$**

Communicating Algebra

In your own words, describe how to find the volume of a cone. **Find the volume of a cylinder with the same dimensions and divide by 3.**

Curriculum Connection

- **History** Write a brief report on how the Egyptian pyramids were constructed and the tools that were used. **See students' work.**

Read More About It

Holton, Jean Laity. *Geometry: A New Way of Looking at Space.*
McCauley, David. *Pyramid.*
Razzell, Arthur G. and K.G.O. Watts. *Circles and Curves.*

You may wish to use a Chapter Test (free-response format) as an additional chapter review. Two forms are provided in the Evaluation Masters Booklet as shown below.

Evaluation Masters Booklet, **p. 113**

Name ____________ Date ____________

Chapter 13 Test, Form 2A

Find the area of each figure. Use $\pi \approx 3.14$.

1. 5 cm, 6 cm
2. 3 m, 5 m, 4 m
3. 6 in., 5 in., 4 in., 6 in., 12 in.
4. 6 cm
5. 13.6 cm, 13.6 cm
6. 16 mm

Find the surface area of each figure. Use $\pi \approx 3.14$.

7. 6 in., 4.2 in.
8. 4 cm, 5 cm, 14 cm
9. 64 mm, 27 mm
10. 1.2 ft, 1.6 ft, 1.6 ft

Find the volume of each figure. Round decimal answers to the nearest tenth. Use $\pi \approx 3.14$.

11. 4 in., 8 in.
12. 5 ft, 5 ft, 5 ft
13. 4 cm, 6 cm, 11 cm
14. 4 cm, 9 cm

15. Find the volume of a triangular pyramid: base area, 42 in^2; height, 12 in.
16. Find the volume of a rectangular prism: length, 6 m; height, 4 m; width, 2 m
17. Find the area of a circle 600 yards in diameter. Use $\pi = 3.14$.
18. Kate cuts out a paper quadrilateral with sides measuring 4.35 cm, 2.8 cm, 4.457 cm, and 3.15 cm. Calculate the perimeter of the quadrilateral. Round your answer to the correct number of significant digits.
19. Peter freezes a 2.5-inch thick slab of ice shaped like a rectangle 30 feet wide and 48 feet long for use as a skating area. Find the volume of the ice.
20. Alice has a polished-stone paperweight shaped like a cube measuring 2.4 inches on an edge. Find the volume of Alice's paperweight.

BONUS Tom cuts a square having 4-inch sides out of a circle having a 9-inch diameter. Find the area of the remaining piece. Use $\pi = 3.14$.

Answers:
1. $30\ cm^2$
2. $6\ m^2$
3. $36\ in^2$
4. $113.04\ cm^2$
5. $184.96\ cm^2$
6. $200.96\ mm^2$
7. $135.648\ in^2$
8. $292\ cm^2$
9. $7714.98\ mm^2$
10. $6.4\ ft^2$
11. $134.0\ in^3$
12. $125\ ft^3$
13. $132\ cm^3$
14. $452.2\ cm^3$
15. $168\ in^3$
16. $48\ m^3$
17. $282{,}600\ yd^2$
18. 14.8 cm
19. $300\ ft^3$
20. $13.824\ in^3$

$47.585\ in^2$

Evaluation Masters Booklet, **p. 114**

Name ____________ Date ____________

Chapter 13 Test, Form 2B

Find the area of each figure. Use $\pi \approx 3.14$.

1. 5 cm, 7 cm
2. 6 m, 10 m, 8 m
3. 6 in., 5 in., 4 in., 6 in., 11 in.
4. 5 cm
5. 15.4 mm, 15.4 mm
6. 18 cm

Find the surface area of each figure. Use $\pi \approx 3.14$.

7. 5 in., 4.2 in.
8. 4 cm, 5 cm, 12 cm
9. 64 mm, 25 mm
10. 1.5 ft, 1.6 ft, 1.6 ft

Find the volume of each figure. Round decimal answers to the nearest tenth. Use $\pi \approx 3.14$.

11. 4 in., 7 in.
12. 7 ft, 7 ft, 7 ft
13. 4 cm, 6 cm, 12 cm
14. 4 cm, 12 cm

15. Find the volume of a triangular pyramid: base area, 45 in^2; height, 15 in.
16. Find the volume of a rectangular prism: length, 8 m; height, 4 m; width, 3 m
17. Find the area of a circle 800 feet in diameter. Use $\pi = 3.14$.
18. Li cuts out a paper trapezoid having sides measuring 4.338 mm, 2.82 mm, 4.007 mm, and 3.25 mm. Calculate the perimeter of the trapezoid. Round your answer to the correct number of significant digits.
19. Ivan freezes a 3.5-inch thick slab of ice shaped like a rectangle 20 feet wide and 45 feet long for use as a skating area. Find the volume of the ice to the nearest tenth.
20. Jacob has a polished-stone paperweight shaped like a cube measuring 2.3 inches on an edge. Find the volume of Jacob's paperweight.

BONUS Eve cuts a circle having a 5-inch diameter out of a square having an edge of 9 inches. Find the area of the remaining piece. Use $\pi = 3.14$.

Answers:
1. $35\ cm^2$
2. $24\ m^2$
3. $34\ in^2$
4. $78.5\ cm^2$
5. $237.16\ mm^2$
6. $254.34\ cm^2$
7. $105.19\ in^2$
8. $256\ cm^2$
9. $6986.5\ mm^2$
10. $7.36\ ft^2$
11. $117.2\ in^3$
12. $343\ ft^3$
13. $144\ cm^3$
14. $602.9\ cm^3$
15. $225\ in^3$
16. $96\ m^3$
17. $502{,}400\ ft^2$
18. 14.42 mm
19. $262.5\ ft^3$
20. $12.167\ in^3$

$61.375\ in^2$

Using the Chapter Test

This page may be used as a test or as an additional review. Two forms of a Chapter Test (multiple-choice format) are provided in the Evaluation Masters Booklet.

Evaluation Masters Booklet, **pp. 109-110**

Name ______________________ Date ____________

Chapter 13 Test, Form 1A

Find the area of each figure shown or described below. Use $\pi \approx 3.14$. Round decimal answers to the nearest tenth.

1. (figure: 6 m, 13.4 m, 12 m) A. 226.1 m² B. 18m² C. 72 m² D. 36 m² 1. D
2. (figure: 10 in., 7 in., 6 in., 8 in., 12 in.) A. 33 in² B. 720 in² C. 66 in² D. 132 in² 2. C
3. (figure: 12 cm) A. 452.2 cm² B. 144 cm² C. 113.0 cm² D. 75.4 cm² 3. A
4. Parallelogram: base, 15 cm; height, 21 cm A. 157.5 cm² B. 989.1 cm² C. 315 cm² D. 105 cm² 4. C
5. Rectangle: length, 12.5 in.; width, 3.25 in. A. 40.6 in² B. 13.5 in² C. 20.3 in² D. 37.3 in² 5. A
6. Circle: diameter, 18 in. A. 113.0 in² B. 254.3 in² C. 1017.4 in² D. 56.5 in² 6. B

Find the surface area of each figure shown or described below. Use $\pi \approx 3.14$. Round decimal answers to the nearest tenth.

7. (figure: 10 in., 5 in.) A. 500 in² B. 785 in² C. 207 in² D. 314 in² 7. D
8. (figure: 2 cm, 3 cm, 5 cm) A. 43 cm² B. 86 cm² C. 62 cm² D. 30 cm² 8. C
9. Cube: edge, 10 cm A. 1000 cm² B. 600 cm² C. 60 cm² D. 100 cm² 9. B
10. Square pyramid: slant height, 10 cm; edge of base, 6 cm A. 96 cm² B. 156 cm² C. 120 cm² D. 70 cm² 10. B
11. Cone: slant height, 8 cm; radius of base, 3 cm A. 210.4 cm² B. 94.2 cm² C. 103.6 cm² D. 75.4 cm² 11. C

Find the volume of each figure shown or described. Use $\pi \approx 3.14$. Round decimal answers to the nearest tenth.

12. Rectangular prism: length, 15 m; width, 8 m; height, 12 m A. 45.21.6 m³ B. 25 m³ C. 792 m³ D. 1440 m³ 12. D

Name ______________________ Date ____________

Chapter 13 Test, Form 1A (continued)

13. Cylinder: diameter, 10 in.; height, 10 in. A. 785 in³ B. 3140 in³ C. 1000 in³ D. 250 in³ 13. A
14. Pyramid: area of base: 23 in² height, 6 in. A. 1058 in³ B. 138 in³ C. 3.2 in³ D. 46 in³ 14. D
15. (figure: 18 ft, 6 ft) A. 226.1 ft³ B. 678.2 ft³ C. 2034. 7 ft³ D. 648 ft³ 15. B
16. (figure: 5 cm, 6 cm, 15 cm) A. 450 cm³ B. 150 cm³ C. 225 cm³ D. 112.5 cm³ 16. C
17. Javier applies lead came around pieces of machine-cut stained glass. One piece of glass is shaped like a rectangle 25.03 cm long and 12.374 cm wide. Find the perimeter of the glass. Round to the correct number of significant digits. A. 37.4 cm B. 74.8 cm C. 74.808 cm D. 74.81 cm 17. D
18. Quyen's refrigerator is shaped like a rectangular prism that is 34 inches high, 26 inches wide, and 15 inches deep. Find the volume of the refrigerator to the nearest whole number. A. 12,360 in³ B. 13,260 in³ C. 4420 in³ D. 3568 in³ 18. B
19. Dean pours concrete support posts shaped like cylinders with a radius of 9 inches and a height of 48 inches. Find the volume of one post. Use $\pi \approx 3.14$ and round to the nearest tenth. A. 6104.2 in³ B. 4069.4 in³ C. 12,208.3 in³ D. 2713.0 in³ 19. C
20. Rosita paints the entire surface of a metal can to match the decor of her living room. The can is shaped like a cylinder with a radius of 3 inches and a height of 9 inches. Find the surface area of the can. Use $\pi \approx 3.14$ and round to the nearest tenth. A. 226.1 in² B. 678.2 in² C. 84.7 in² D. 254.3 in² 20. A

BONUS Jeff makes a model of a rocket. For the body, he uses a hollow cylindrical paper tube that is 15 inches long and has a diameter of 2 inches. For the nose cone, he uses a cardboard cone with a 2-inch diameter and a slant height of 3 inches. Find the total surface area of the assembled rocket model. Use $\pi \approx 3.14$ and round to the nearest tenth. A. 282.6 in² B. 34.5 in² C. 103.6 in² D. 109.9 in² C

Test

Find the area of each figure. Answers are calculated using [π].

1. 244.77 cm²

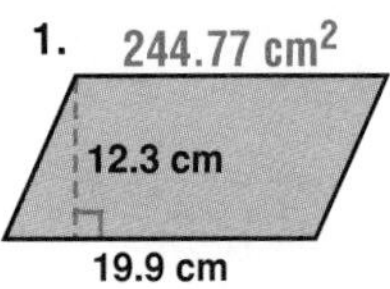

2. 30 in.²

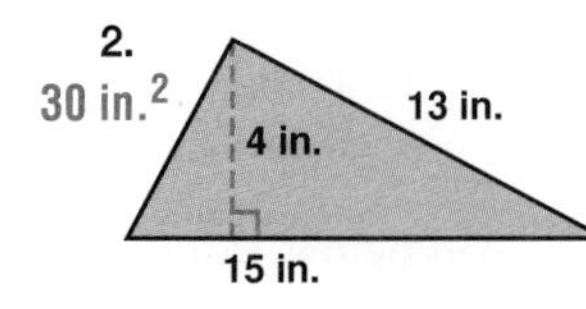

3. 28.2 cm²

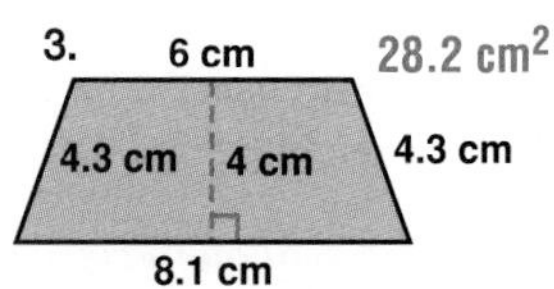

Find the area of each circle described below. Round decimal answers to the nearest tenth.

4. radius, 5 km 78.5 km²
5. radius, 1.5 cm 7.1 cm²
6. diameter, 42 in. 1385.4 in²

Find the surface area of each figure described below. Round decimal answers to the nearest tenth.

7. a rectangular prism with base 25 cm by 8 cm and height 3.4 cm 624.4 cm²
8. a cylinder with radius 2 in. and height $7\frac{1}{2}$ in. 119.4 in²

Find the volume of each figure described below. Round decimal answers to the nearest tenth.

9. a cone with radius 8 cm and height 5 cm 335.1 cm³
10. a rectangular prism with length 7.1 m, width 4.5 m, and height 9.3 m 297.1 m³
11. a rectangular pyramid with length 12 cm, width 15 cm, and height 20 cm 1200 cm³

12. 13. 14.

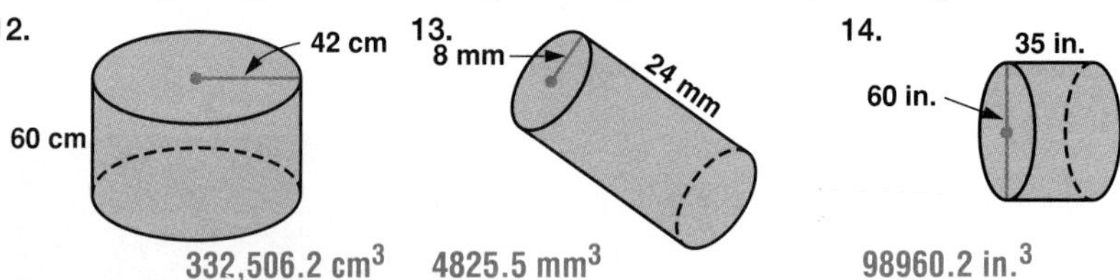

12. 332,506.2 cm³ 13. 4825.5 mm³ 14. 98960.2 in.³

Determine the number of significant digits in each measurement.

15. 0.008 ft 1
16. 87.496 m 5
17. 24,000 mi 2
18. 8.090 cm 4

Solve.

19. A cylindrical can of soup has a 3-in. diameter and a 5-in. height. What is the approximate area of the label that covers the side of the can? 47.1 in²
20. A circular part of a square field 600 m by 600 m is irrigated. The irrigated part has a radius of 300 m. If the circle is completely contained within the square, find the amount of the field that is not irrigated. 77,256.7 m²

BONUS

Explain why the area of a parallelogram is not doubled when the base and height are doubled. See margin.

Additional Answer

Bonus The area of a parallelogram is not doubled when the base and height are doubled because the area is quadrupled. $(2\ell)(2w) = 4\ell w$

Test Generator Software is provided in both Apple and IBM formats. You may use this software to create your own tests, based on the needs of your students.

Academic Skills Test

Cumulative, Chapters 1-13

1. Which is equivalent to $\frac{1}{6} \times \frac{1}{6}$?

   A 2^{-6} C 6^{2}
   (B) 6^{-2} D 2^{6}

2. Using the formula $F = \frac{9}{5}C + 32$, which temperatures are approximately equivalent?

   (A) 30°C, 86°F
   B 30°C, -1°F
   C 10°C, 42°F
   D 10°C, 34°F

3. Which number line shows the solution of the equation $y = |-2|$?

   A 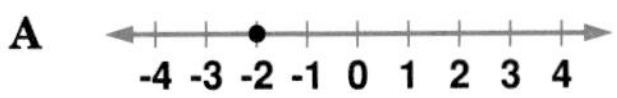

   B -4 -3 -2 -1 0 1 2 3 4

   C -4 -3 -2 -1 0 1 2 3 4

   (D) -4 -3 -2 -1 0 1 2 3 4

4. On a trip, the Garcias drive 104 miles in 2 hours. If they continue at the same rate, which proportion will give *t*, the total time in hours, for a 550-mile trip?

   A $\frac{104}{2} = \frac{t}{550}$ C $\frac{2}{t} = \frac{550}{104}$
   (B) $\frac{104}{2} = \frac{550}{t}$ D $\frac{t}{2} = \frac{550}{446}$

5. Ellen's science scores were 73, 84, 78, 76, and 84. What is the mean (average) of these scores?

   (A) 84 C 78
   B 79 D 77

6. When a six-sided number cube is rolled, what is the probability of rolling a 5 or an even number?

   A $\frac{1}{6}$ (C) $\frac{2}{3}$
   B $\frac{1}{2}$ D $\frac{5}{6}$

7. Which shows a step in constructing an angle congruent to a given angle?

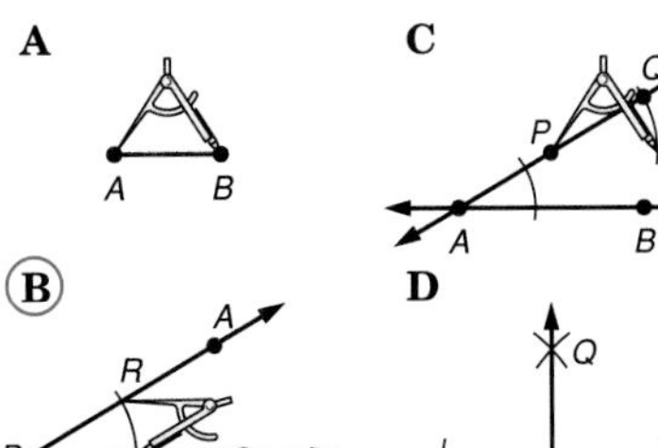

   (B) D

8. Which figure must contain exactly two acute angles?

   A a parallelogram
   B a rectangle
   (C) an acute triangle
   D an obtuse triangle

9. What is the area of the trapezoid?

   A 45 ft^2
   B 64 ft^2
   C 96 ft^2
   (D) 112 ft^2

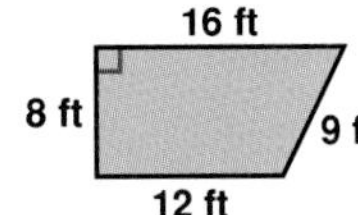

10. What is the volume of the triangular prism?

   A 3600 cm^3
   B 4800 cm^3
   C 30,000 cm^3
   (D) 36,000 cm^3

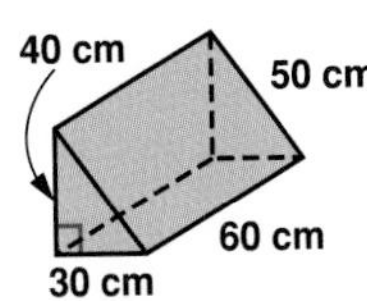

Using the Academic Skills Test

This test familiarizes students with a standardized format while testing skills and concepts presented up to this point.

A Cumulative Review (free-response format) and Cumulative Test (multiple-choice format) are also provided in the Evaluation Masters Booklet as shown at the right.

Test Item	1	2	3	4	5	6	7	8	9	10
Lesson Number	4-10	7-9	8-1	9-3	10-1	11-4	12-5	12-6	13-2	13-7
TAAS Objective	1	2	2	2,11	5	5	3	3	4	4

Evaluation Masters Booklet, **p. 116**

Name ______ Date ______

Cumulative Review, Chapters 1-13

1. Translate *nine less a number* into an algebraic expression. (Lesson 1–8) — 1. $9 - n$
2. Solve $n = -12 + 25$. (Lesson 2–4) — 2. 13
3. Solve $y - (-7) = 34$. (Lesson 3–2) — 3. 27
4. Find the LCM for $4a$, $6a$, and $18a$. (Lesson 4–7) — 4. $36a$
5. Solve $w = 23.5 + (-7.26)$. (Lesson 5–4) — 5. 16.24
6. Solve $q = 0.444 \div 0.37$. (Lesson 6–7) — 6. 1.2
7. Solve $3a + 4 = 4a - 3$. (Lesson 7–4) — 7. 7
8. Find the slope of the line that contains the points $X(2, 2)$ and $Y(5, 11)$. (Lesson 8–8) — 8. 3
9. Express 0.5% as a fraction in simplest form. (Lesson 9–5) — 9. $\frac{1}{200}$
10. Paula buys a $75 tire and receives a 15% discount. Find the cost of the tire. (Lesson 9–8) — 10. $63.75

Roger's typing scores are 63, 65, 66, 66, 75, 77, 78, 83, and 93. Find each average. (Lesson 10–2)

11. mode 12. mean 13. median — 11. 66 12. 74 13. 75
14. Maria, Li, and Fred are running for class president and Tom, Keli, Miquel, and Don are running for vice president. How many president-vice president pairings are possible? (Lesson 11–2) — 14. 12
15. Henri must pick 5 of 7 classes being offered. How many ways can Henri arrange a schedule? (Lesson 11–3) — 15. 2520
16. Sasha has 8 antique spoons. She uses 4 in a window display. How many combinations are possible? (Lesson 11–3) — 16. 70
17. Write a name for the figure at the right. (Lesson 12–1) [A B] — 17. $\overrightarrow{BA}$
18. Classify an angle having a measure of 12 degrees. (Lesson 12–1) — 18. acute
19. Aimee must represent 20% on a circle graph. How many degrees are in the measure of the section? (Lesson 12–2) — 19. 72°
20. In triangle *XYZ*, the measure of angle *Y* is 16° and the measure of angle *Z* is 81°. Find the measure of angle *X*. (Lesson 12–6) — 20. 83°

Find the area of each figure described below. (Lessons 13–1 through 13–3)

21. Parallelogram: base, 8 cm; height, 6 cm — 21. 48 cm^2
22. Triangle: base, 24 ft; height, 18 ft — 22. 216 ft^2
23. Trapezoid: base (*a*), 21 in.; base (*b*), 12 in.; height, 18 in. — 23. 297 in^2
24. Circle: radius, 12 ft (Use $\pi \approx 3.14$.) — 24. 452.16 ft^2
25. Joyce owns a cone-shaped planter that is 18 inches high and has a diameter of 20 inches. Find the volume of the planter. Use $\pi \approx 3.14$. (Lesson 13–9) — 25. 1884 in^3

Evaluation Masters Booklet, **p. 117**

Name ______ Date ______

Cumulative Test, Chapters 1-13

Solve each equation.

1. $n = -17 - 18$ A. 1 B. −1 C. 35 D. −35 — 1. D
2. $y - (-8) = -12$ A. −20 B. 20 C. −4 D. 4 — 2. A
3. $w = -3.6 + (-17.63)$ A. 14.03 B. −14.03 C. −21.23 D. 21.23 — 3. C
4. $q = 0.5 \div 0.25$ A. 20 B. 0.2 C. 0.5 D. 2 — 4. D
5. $5a + 4 = 3a - 2$ A. −3 B. 3 C. 0.75 D. −1 — 5. A
6. Express 0.3% as a decimal.
   A. 0.03 B. 0.003 C. 30 D. 0.3 — 6. B
7. Velma buys a $68 pair of shoes. She receives a 15% discount. How much did she pay for the shoes?
   A. $56.50 B. $54.40 C. $57.80 D. $53 — 7. C

Antonio's bowling scores were 145, 145, 153, 153, 153, 157, and 165. Find each average.

8. mode A. 145 B. 153 C. 157 D. 165 — 8. B
9. mean A. 145 B. 153 C. 157 D. 165 — 9. B
10. Mary and Emilio are running for class president and Tom, Keli, and Juanita are running for vice president. How many president-vice president pairings are possible?
   A. 4 B. 5 C. 6 D. 12 — 10. C
11. John has 6 old watches. How many combinations of 3 are possible?
   A. 9 B. 18 C. 20 D. 120 — 11. C
12. Name the figure at the right. [A B C D]
   A. $\overrightarrow{AB}$ B. $\overleftrightarrow{CA}$
   C. $\overleftarrow{DB}$ D. $\overline{AC}$ — 12. B
13. Classify an angle having a measure of 120°.
   A. obtuse B. straight C. right D. acute — 13. A
14. Reggie must represent 60% on a circle graph. Find the number of degrees for this section of the graph.
   A. 60° B. 216° D. 300° D. 180° — 14. B
15. In triangle *ABC*, the measure of angle *A* is 46° and the measure of angle *B* is 52°. Find the measure of angle *C*.
   A. 62° B. 98° C. 262° D. 82° — 15. D

Find the area of each figure described.

16. Parallelogram: base, 18 cm; height, 10 cm
   A. 180 cm^2 B. 90 cm^2 C. 28 cm^2 D. 60 cm^2 — 16. A
17. Triangle: base, 62 m; height, 40 m
   A. 142 m^2 B. 2480 m^2 C. 1240 m^2 D. 204 m^2 — 17. C
18. Trapezoid: base (*a*), 12 in.; base (*b*), 10 in.; height, 15 in.
   A. 74 in^2 B. 165 in^2 C. 330 in^2 D. 66 in^2 — 18. B
19. Circle: diameter, 10 in. (Use $\pi \approx 3.14$.)
   A. 39.25 in^2 B. 31.4 in^2 C. 314 in^2 D. 78.5 in^2 — 19. D
20. Roger has a cone-shaped trophy that is 12 inches high and has a radius of 6 inches. Find the volume of the trophy. Use $\pi \approx 3.14$.
   A. 72 in^3 B. 1356.48 in^3 C. 452.16 in^3 D. 432 in^3 — 20. C

Applying Algebra to Right Triangles

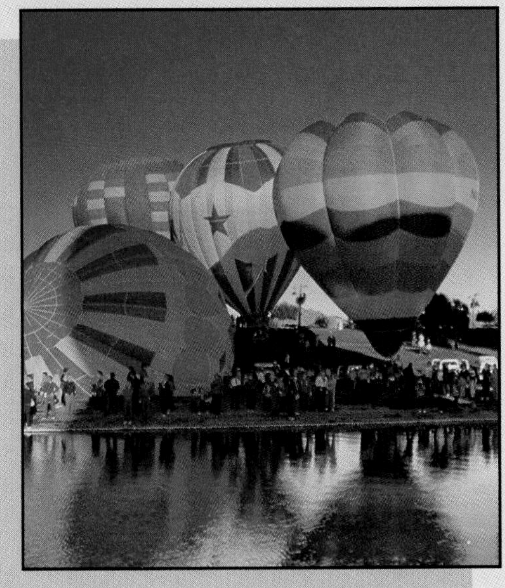

Previewing the Chapter

This chapter explores the properties of square roots and squares. The algebraic concept is fostered by solving quadratic equations of the form $x^2 = n$. Irrational numbers are represented in the context of the Pythagorean Theorem. Students learn to use the theorem and are introduced to the trigonometric ratios of sine, cosine, and tangent to solve problems involving right triangles.

Problem Solving Strategy Students will learn to solve problems by using Venn diagrams.

Lesson (Pages)	Lesson Objectives	State/Local Objectives
14-1 (526-528)	14-1: Find square roots of squares.	1E, 3A, 3E, 4E
14-2 (529-530)	14-2: Approximate square roots.	1E, 3A, 3E
14-3 (531-532)	14-3: Use a Venn diagram to solve a problem.	1A, 1B, 1C, 1D, 1E, 2D
14-4 (533-536)	14-4A: Identify types of numbers.	1E, 2D, 3A, 3E
	14-4B: Solve equations by finding square roots.	
	14-4C: Simplify square roots.	
14-5 (537-540)	14-5: Use the Pythagorean Theorem to find the length of the side of a right triangle.	1E, 3A, 3E, 4A, 4D
14-6 (542-544)	14-6: Solve problems using the Pythagorean Theorem.	1D, 1E, 3A, 3E, 4D, 4E
14-7 (545-547)	14-7: Find missing measures in 30°-60° and 45°-60° right triangles.	1E, 3A, 3E, 4A, 4D, 4E
14-8 (548-549)	14-8A: Find the tangent of an angle.	1E, 3A, 3I, 4A, 4E
	14-8B: Find the measure of an angle using the tangent ratio.	
14-9 (550-552)	14-9A: Find the sine and cosine of a number.	1E, 3A, 3I, 4A, 4E
	14-9B: Find the measure of an angle using the sine and cosine ratio.	
14-10 (554-557)	14-10: Solve problems by using the trigonometric ratios.	1D, 1E, 3A, 3I, 4A, 4E

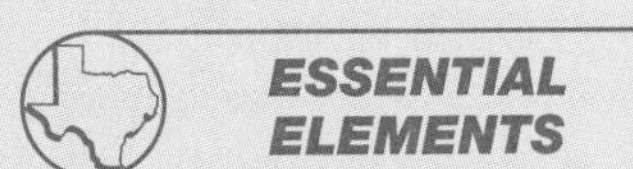

Organizing the Chapter

*You may want to refer to the **Course Planning Calendar** on Page T31.*

Planning Guide

Lesson (Pages)	Pacing Chart (in days)			Extra Practice (Student Edition)	Blackline Masters Booklets			Other Resources
	MINIMUM	STANDARD	ACCELERATED		Reteaching	Practice	Enrichment	
14-1 (526-528)	1	1	1	p. 614, Set A	p. 120	p. 133	p. 120	Transparency 14-1 Group Activity Card 14-1
14-2 (529-530)	1	1	0.5	p. 614, Set A	p. 121	p. 134	p. 121	Transparency 14-2 Group Activity Card 14-2
14-3 (531-532)	1	1	0.5			p. 135		Transparency 14-3 Group Activity Card 14-3
14-4 (533-536)	1.5	1	1	p. 614, Set B	p. 122	p. 136	p. 122	Transparency 14-4 Group Activity Card 14-4
14-5 (537-540)	1.5	1	1	p. 615, Set C	p. 123	p. 137	p. 123	Transparency 14-5 Group Activity Card 14-5
14-6 (542-544)	1	1	1	p. 615, Set C	p. 124	p. 138	p. 124	Transparency 14-6 Group Activity Card 14-6
14-7 (545-547)	1	1	1	p. 615, Set D	p. 125	p. 139	p. 125	Transparency 14-7 Group Activity Card 14-7
14-8 (548-549)	1	1	0.5	p. 615, Set D	p. 126	p. 140	p. 126	Transparency 14-8 Group Activity Card 14-8
14-9 (550-552)	1	1	1	p. 615, Set D	p. 127	p. 141	p. 127	Transparency 14-9 Group Activity Card 14-9
14-10 (554-557)	1.5	1	1	p. 615, Set D	p. 128	p. 142	p. 128	Transparency 14-10 Group Activity Card 14-10
Review (558-559)	1.5	1	1					Test Generator
Test (560)	1	1	1		Evaluation Masters, pp. 118-123			

Other Chapter Resources

Student Edition
Exploration, p. 541
Mid-Chapter Quiz, p. 544
Team Problem Solving, p. 552
Algebra in Action, p. 553
History, p. 557
Academic Skills Test, p. 561

Teacher Resource Package
Interdisciplinary Activity, p. 14
Application Worksheet, p. 29
Cooperative Problem Solving, p. 44
Multicultural Activity, p. 59
Fun Activities, pp. 78-79
Technology Worksheets, pp. 14, 29, 44
Lab Manual, pp. 66-68
Quizzes(2), p. 124
Class Review Game

Software
Test Generator

available for Apple and IBM

Enhancing the Chapter

Some of the blackline masters for enhancing this chapter are shown below.

Applications, p. 29

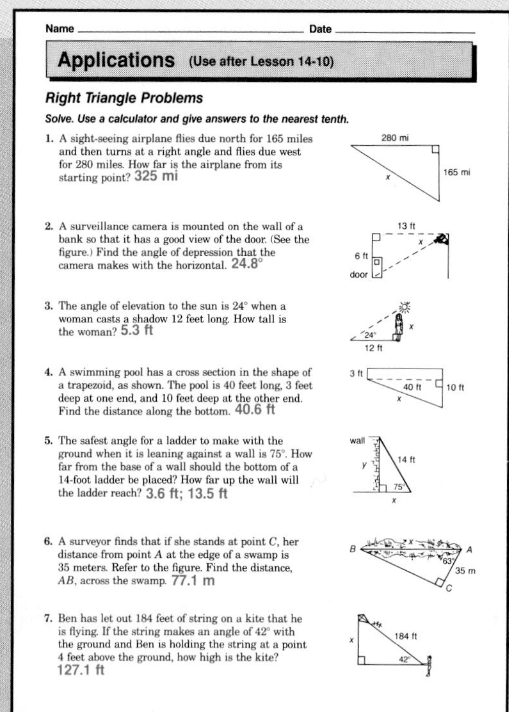

Name ______________________ Date ______________

Applications (Use after Lesson 14-10)

Right Triangle Problems

Solve. Use a calculator and give answers to the nearest tenth.

1. A sight-seeing airplane flies due north for 165 miles and then turns at a right angle and flies due west for 280 miles. How far is the airplane from its starting point? 325 mi
2. A surveillance camera is mounted on the wall of a bank so that it has a good view of the door. (See the figure.) Find the angle of depression that the camera makes with the horizontal. 24.8°
3. The angle of elevation to the sun is 24° when a woman casts a shadow 12 feet long. How tall is the woman? 5.3 ft
4. A swimming pool has a cross section in the shape of a trapezoid, as shown. The pool is 40 feet long, 3 feet deep at one end, and 10 feet deep at the other end. Find the distance along the bottom. 40.6 ft
5. The safest angle for a ladder to make with the ground when it is leaning against a wall is 75°. How far from the base of a wall should the bottom of a 14-foot ladder be placed? How far up the wall will the ladder reach? 3.6 ft; 13.5 ft
6. A surveyor finds that if she stands at point C, her distance from point A at the edge of a swamp is 35 meters. Refer to the figure. Find the distance, AB, across the swamp. 77.1 m
7. Ben has let out 184 feet of string on a kite that he is flying. If the string makes an angle of 42° with the ground and Ben is holding the string at a point 4 feet above the ground, how high is the kite? 127.1 ft

Interdisciplinary Activity, p. 14

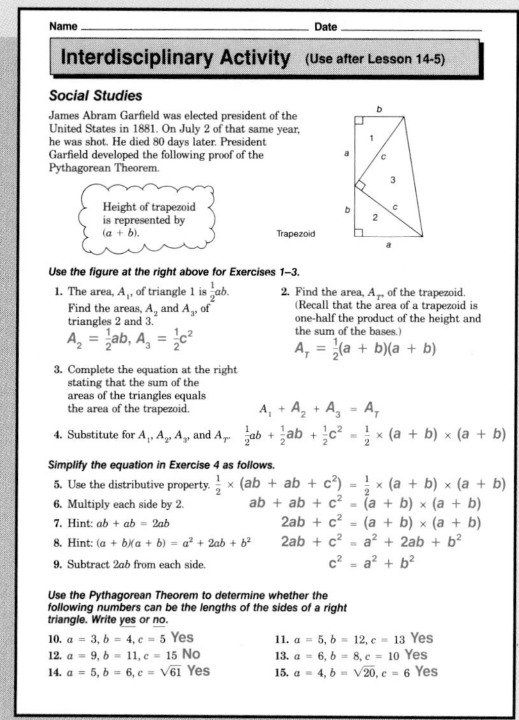

Name ______________________ Date ______________

Interdisciplinary Activity (Use after Lesson 14-5)

Social Studies

James Abram Garfield was elected president of the United States in 1881. On July 2 of that same year, he was shot. He died 80 days later. President Garfield developed the following proof of the Pythagorean Theorem.

Use the figure at the right above for Exercises 1–3.

1. The area, A_1, of triangle 1 is $\frac{1}{2}ab$. Find the areas, A_2 and A_3, of triangles 2 and 3. $A_2 = \frac{1}{2}ab$, $A_3 = \frac{1}{2}c^2$
2. Find the area, A_T, of the trapezoid. (Recall that the area of a trapezoid is one-half the product of the height and the sum of the bases.) $A_T = \frac{1}{2}(a + b)(a + b)$
3. Complete the equation at the right stating that the sum of the areas of the triangles equals the area of the trapezoid. $A_1 + A_2 + A_3 = A_T$
4. Substitute for A_1, A_2, A_3, and A_T. $\frac{1}{2}ab + \frac{1}{2}ab + \frac{1}{2}c^2 = \frac{1}{2} \times (a + b) \times (a + b)$

Simplify the equation in Exercise 4 as follows.

5. Use the distributive property. $\frac{1}{2} \times (ab + ab + c^2) = \frac{1}{2} \times (a + b) \times (a + b)$
6. Multiply each side by 2. $ab + ab + c^2 = (a + b) \times (a + b)$
7. Hint: $ab + ab = 2ab$ $\quad 2ab + c^2 = (a + b) \times (a + b)$
8. Hint: $(a + b)(a + b) = a^2 + 2ab + b^2$ $\quad 2ab + c^2 = a^2 + 2ab + b^2$
9. Subtract $2ab$ from each side. $c^2 = a^2 + b^2$

Use the Pythagorean Theorem to determine whether the following numbers can be the lengths of the sides of a right triangle. Write yes or no.

10. $a = 3, b = 4, c = 5$ Yes
11. $a = 5, b = 12, c = 13$ Yes
12. $a = 9, b = 11, c = 15$ No
13. $a = 6, b = 8, c = 10$ Yes
14. $a = 5, b = 6, c = \sqrt{61}$ Yes
15. $a = 4, b = \sqrt{20}, c = 6$ Yes

The **Activity Masters Booklet** contains the page shown above.

The **Activity Masters Booklet** contains the page shown above.

Models and Manipulatives

Use the sides of a right triangle to construct three squares on graph paper to show how $a^2 + b^2 = c^2$. Use $a = 3$, $b = 4$, and $c = 5$. First, cut b^2 into three 2×2 squares and two 1×2 rectangles. Then use these five pieces and a^2 to cover c^2 as shown.

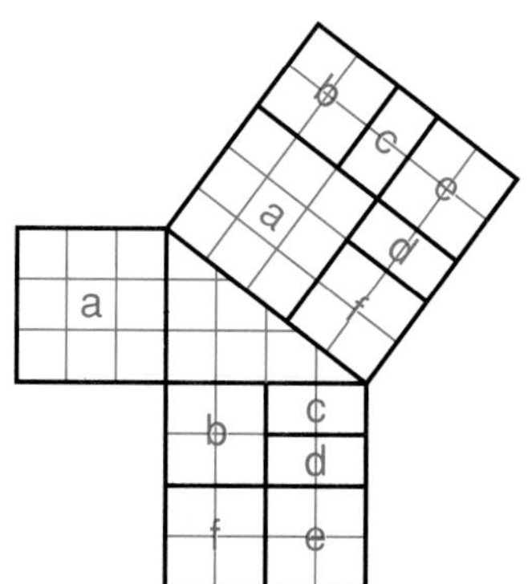

Limited English Proficiency Activity

Have students work backwards to determine the length of one side of a square. Use graph paper or tiles to represent 5^2. Then have students count the number of smaller squares on any side. Construct a two-column table. List the perfect squares below in one column and have students complete the other column ($\sqrt{\ }$) by finding the length of one side of a square with areas of: 121, 36, 64, 81.

Cooperative Learning

The following activity is provided in the **Activity Masters Booklet.**

Cooperative Problem Solving, p. 44

Name ______________ Date ______________

Cooperative Problem Solving (Use after Lesson 14-3)

Music Hath Charms

Work in small groups. Conduct a survey of your class to determine how many of your classmates enjoy rock music, rhythm and blues, and country-western music.

Use a Venn diagram like the one at the right to help you organize your data. The total of the numbers in the top left circle should be the number of students who like rock music; the total in the top right circle should be the number who like rhythm and blues; and the total in the bottom circle should be the number who like country-western.

A D B E G F C H

Which groups are represented by the following regions?

1. A Students who enjoy rock, but not rhythm and blues and not country-western
2. B Students who enjoy rhythm and blues, but not rock and not country-western
3. C Students who enjoy country-western, but not rock and not rhythm and blues
4. D Students who enjoy rock and rhythm and blues, but not country-western
5. E Students who enjoy rock and country-western, but not rhythm and blues
6. F Students who enjoy rhythm and blues and country-western, but not rock
7. G Students who enjoy all three types of music
8. That part of H not in any circle Students who do not enjoy any of the three types of music
9. What should the total of all the numbers in the rectangle represent? The number of students in the class

Use your Venn diagram to answer the following. Answers will vary.

10. How many students enjoy rock music, but not rhythm and blues and not country-western?
11. How many students enjoy both rhythm and blues and country-western, but not rock?
12. How many students enjoy all three types of music?
13. How many do not like any of the three types?
14. How many enjoy rock and country-western, but not rhythm and blues?
15. How many enjoy country-western, but not rock and not rhythm and blues?
16. How many enjoy rhythm and blues, but not rock and not country-western?
17. How many students enjoy both rock and rhythm and blues, but not country-western?

Cooperative Problem Solving

Have students work in groups of two to four to write a short report about what they discover in the pattern below.

$\sqrt{9} \times \sqrt{9} = \square$ $(\sqrt{9})^2 = \square$ $\sqrt{9^2} = \square$

$\sqrt{4} \times \sqrt{4} = \square$ $(\sqrt{4})^2 = \square$ $\sqrt{4^2} = \square$

$\sqrt{2} \times \sqrt{2} = \square$ $(\sqrt{2})^2 = \square$ $\sqrt{2^2} = \square$

$\sqrt{n} \times \sqrt{n} = \square$ $(\sqrt{n})^2 = \square$ $\sqrt{n^2} = \square$

Interactive Bulletin Board

Social Studies Connection

Topic: *How many students are currently taking a foreign language or computer class or both?*

Venn Diagram

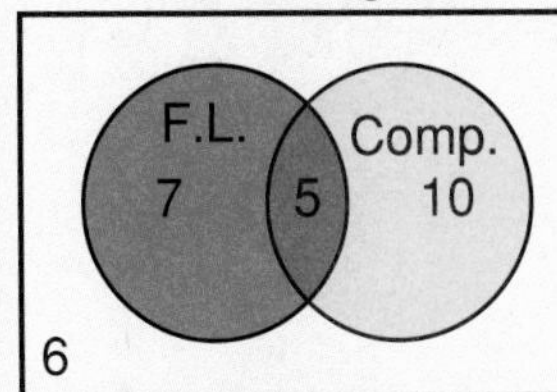

Total students polled	______
Foreign language	______
Computer class	______
Both	______
Neither	______

Purpose Provide practice in using Venn diagrams.

How to Use It Divide students into about four major groups. Have each group be responsible for the bulletin board for one week by polling a separate class on an interest of the class and generating a Venn diagram from the data obtained. One possible topic area could be: How many students are currently taking a foreign language, computer class, or both. Have each group present the data by discussing their Venn diagram and how they obtained the numbers used.

Outside Resources

Books/Periodicals
The vanHiele Model of Thinking in Geometry Among Adolescents, NCTM

Films/Videotapes
Possibly So, Pythagoras, International Film Bureau, Inc.

Software
The Geometric Supposer: Triangles, Sunburst

Technology

There are three pages in the ***Technology Masters Booklet*** that involve technology with concepts in this chapter. One page involves calculators and one page has a problem that can be solved using the BASIC program that is provided. Students should evaluate the information they obtain from running the program and solve a similar problem by extending the program.

Using the Chapter Opener

Transparency 14-0 is available in the Transparency Package. It provides a full-color visual and motivating activity that you can use to engage students in the mathematical content of the chapter.

Using Models

Use an electric fan and a helium balloon on a string to demonstrate how the air from the fan moves the balloon horizontally and the lift from the helium moves the balloon vertically. The third side of the triangle can be seen by the string on the balloon.

Social Studies Connection

Have students use road maps to locate several obscure towns by using the letter-number index on the map. Point out that the starting point for this system is the corner A-1. The letter of the location gives its vertical displacement from this corner, and the number gives its horizontal displacement. (This may vary, depending on the map.) The third side of the triangle is the actual distance from A-1 to the location.

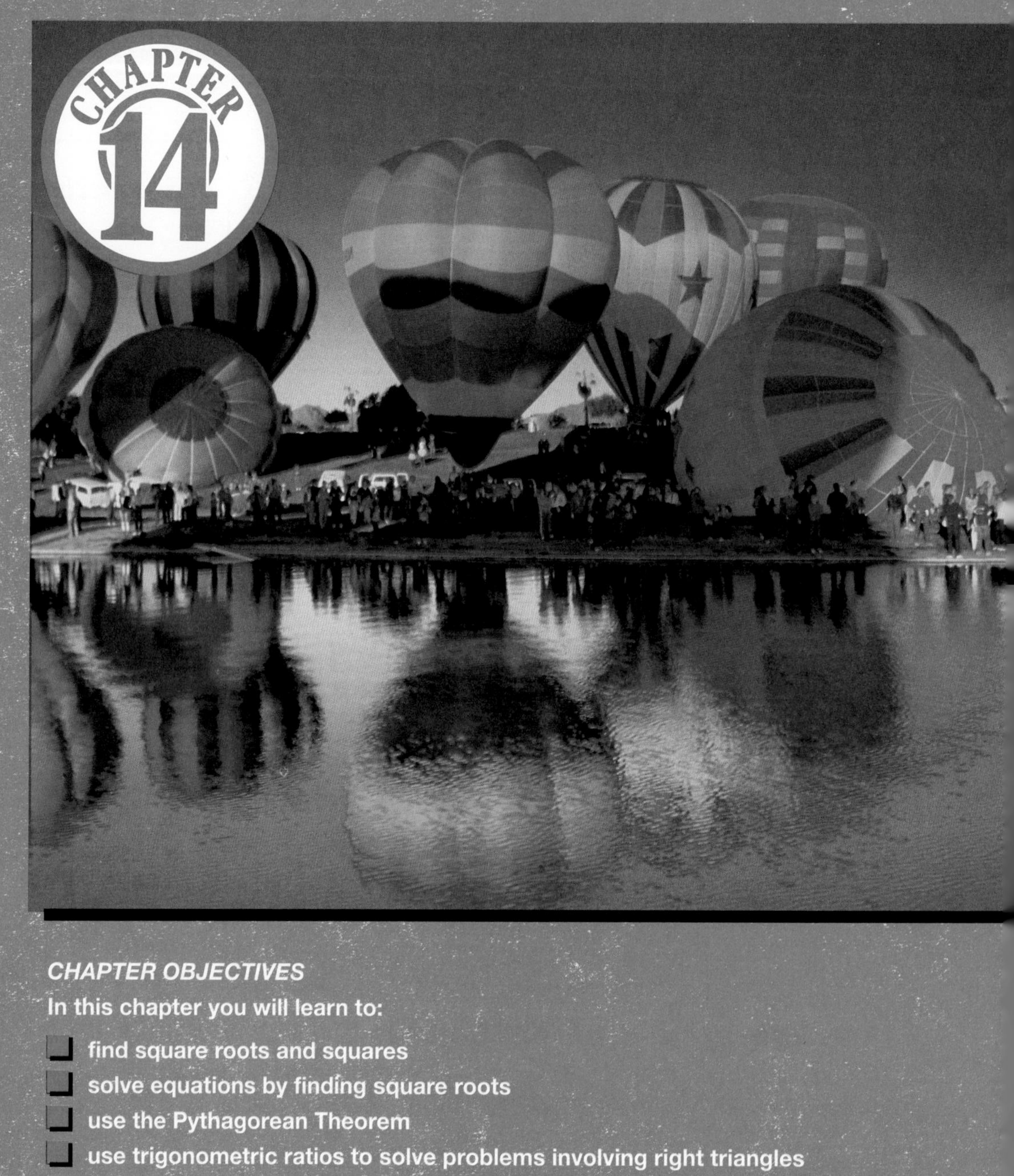

CHAPTER OBJECTIVES

In this chapter you will learn to:

- find square roots and squares
- solve equations by finding square roots
- use the Pythagorean Theorem
- use trigonometric ratios to solve problems involving right triangles
- use Venn diagrams to solve problems

Applying Algebra to Right Triangles

Hot-air balloons are fascinating to watch as they drift slowly by. A free-floating balloon flies in whatever direction the wind is blowing. The pilot can control the vertical movement of the balloon, but cannot steer it.

You probably don't think of a right triangle when you watch a balloon. However, you can use a right triangle to show the vertical motion controlled by the pilot and the horizontal motion of the wind. The third side of the triangle is the actual path of the balloon.

So the next time you watch a hot-air balloon, imagine the right triangle in the sky.

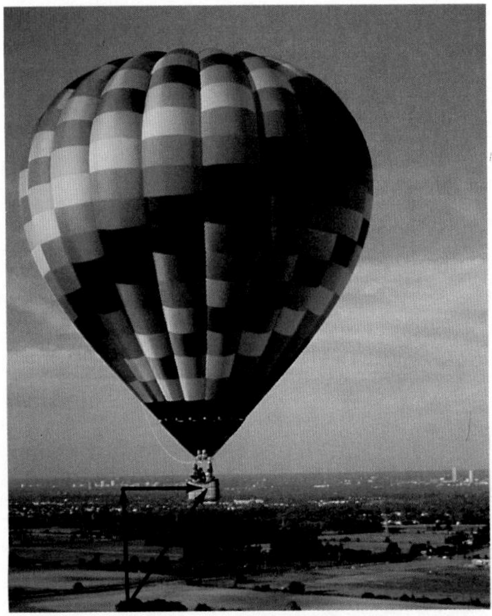

History Connection

Class Project

Do research to find how armies used balloons in the Civil War, World War I, and World War II.

Write a paragraph that tells how they were used.

History Connection

Have students use encyclopedias and books on the history of balloons or war as reference. Reports will vary but may include the following information. During all three wars, the greatest advantage of balloons was the fact that they could be used silently. During the Civil War, balloons were used primarily by the Union, and were used for observation and directing artillery fire. During World War I, balloons were again used for observation and directing artillery fire. Some became motorized and were used for bombing both land targets and submarines. During World War II, improved communications negated the need for observation balloons, but they were still used for bombing and also for protection of coastal areas and convoys.

Looking Ahead

You may want to have the following materials available to use in this chapter.

Exploration, p. 541
- compass
- straightedge

Algebra in Action, p. 553
- state road maps

5-Minute Check
(over Chapter 13)

Find the surface area of each figure described below. Round decimal answers to the nearest tenth.

1. a cylinder with a radius of 6 cm and a height of 25 cm **1168 cm²**
2. a pyramid with base 7 in. by 7 in. and slant height 12 in. **217 in.²**
3. a cone with radius 4 cm and slant height 9 cm **163.4 cm²**

Find the volume of each figure. Round decimal answers to the nearest tenth.

4. rectangular prism; length 13 cm; width 10 cm; height 4 cm **520 cm³**
5. cylinder; radius 11 in.; height 16 in. **6079 in.³**

Transparency 14-1 contains the 5-Minute Check and a teaching aid for this lesson.

1 FOCUS

The purpose of this lesson is to find squares and square roots and use them to solve problems.

Motivating the Lesson

Write the numbers 1, 4, 9, 16, 25, 39, 49, __?__ on the board and ask the students what number comes next. **64**

2 TEACH

Making and Using Lists

Write "square" and "square root" at the top of two columns on the chalkboard. As each example is done, fill in numbers in the appropriate columns.

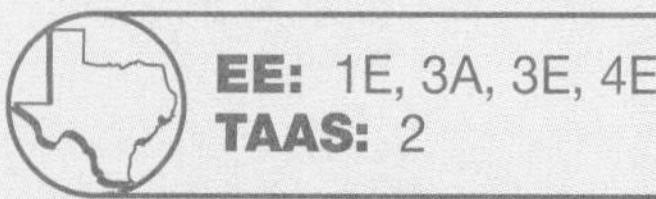

Chalkboard Examples

- *For Example 1*
  Find $\sqrt{16}$. **4**
- *For Example 2*
  Find $-\sqrt{25}$. **-5**

EE: 1E, 3A, 3E, 4E
TAAS: 2

14-1 Squares and Square Roots

Objective:
Find square roots and squares.

Key Terms:
square root
radical sign
radicand

The ability of a hang glider to glide through the air depends on its wingspan and the area of its wing. The relationship of the wingspan and the wing area is called the aspect ratio. This ratio can be expressed by the formula $R = \frac{s^2}{A}$, where R represents the ratio, s the wingspan, and A the wing area.

Suppose a glider has an aspect ratio of 2.7 and a wing area of 30 square feet. What is its wingspan?

$$R = \frac{s^2}{A}$$

$$2.7 = \frac{s^2}{30} \quad \text{Replace } R \text{ with 2.7 and } A \text{ with 30.}$$

$$30(2.7) = s^2$$

$$81 = s^2$$

$$81 = s \cdot s$$

What number multiplied by itself gives 81? Since $81 = 9 \cdot 9$, $s = 9$. The wingspan is 9 feet.

Since $9 \cdot 9 = 81$, one **square root** of 81 is 9. It is also true that $-9 \cdot (-9) = 81$. This suggests that another square root of 81 is -9.

Definition of Square Root If $x^2 = y$, then x is a square root of y.

In algebra the symbol $\sqrt{\ }$, called a **radical sign**, is used to indicate a nonnegative square root. Any expression inside a radical sign is called the **radicand.**

radical sign → $\sqrt{81}$ ← radicand

$\sqrt{81} = 9$ $\sqrt{81}$ indicates the nonnegative square root of 81.

$-\sqrt{81} = -9$ $-\sqrt{81}$ indicates the negative square root of 81.

Squaring a number and finding the square root of a number are closely related to the square.

FYI
Hang gliding has been popular since the early 1970s. The record altitude on a hang glider is 16,158 feet by Bob Calvert of Great Britain.

Bell Ringer

The Human Calculator can add fifteen 4-digit numbers in 30 seconds. A large computer can add 1.2 billion four-digit numbers in 1 second. About how long would it take the Human Calculator, working nonstop, to add 1.2 billion 4-digit numbers? **76 years, 37 days, 18 hours, 40 minutes**

The square shown at the right has sides that are 5 feet long. The area of the square is found by *squaring* 5. If you know that the area of the square is 25 square feet, then the length of a side is found by *finding the square root of* 25.

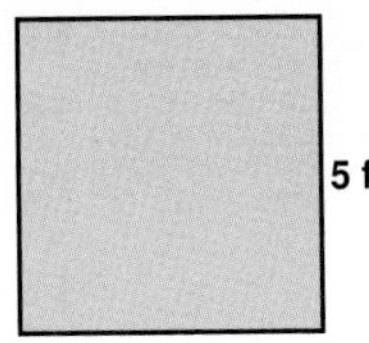

Examples

1 Find $\sqrt{9}$.

The symbol $\sqrt{9}$ represents the nonnegative square root of 9.

Since $3 \cdot 3 = 9$, $\sqrt{9} = 3$.

2 Find $-\sqrt{4}$.

The symbol $-\sqrt{4}$ represents the negative square root of 4.

Since $2 \cdot 2 = 4$, $-\sqrt{4} = -2$.

The inverse operation of the square root operation is the squaring operation. Thus, the square of either 9 or -9 is 81. The square of a number is the product of the number and itself.

$$9^2 = 9 \cdot 9 = 81$$

$$(-9)^2 = -9 \cdot (-9) = 81$$

Numbers such as 81, that are squares of whole numbers, are called *perfect squares.*

Checking for Understanding

Communicating Algebra

1. In your own words, define *square root.* See margin.
2. Explain how squaring a number is like finding the area of a square. See margin.
3. If $n^2 = 25$, then n is a __?__ of 25. square root

Guided Practice

State the square of each number.

4. 5 25   5. 8 64   6. 12 144   7. 6 36

Exercises

Independent Practice

Find each square root.

8. $\sqrt{4}$ 2   9. $\sqrt{9}$ 3   10. $\sqrt{49}$ 7   11. $\sqrt{16}$ 4

12. $\sqrt{64}$ 8   13. $\sqrt{25}$ 5   14. $\sqrt{100}$ 10   15. $-\sqrt{9}$ -3

3 PRACTICE/APPLY

Checking the Concept

After completing Exercises 4-7, have students explain how the square of each number differs from the square root of the number.

Error Analysis

Watch for students who find either the square or the square root when the other is asked for.
Prevent by modeling problems, labeling square roots and squares.

Independent Practice

Homework Assignment	
Basic	9-35 odd, 36-42, 44, 45
Average	8-34 even, 36-45
Honors	12-30 even, 32-45

Practice Masters Booklet, **p. 133**

Name __________ Date __________

Practice Worksheet 14-1

Squares and Square Roots

Find each square root.

1. $-\sqrt{4}$ −2	2. $\sqrt{81}$ 9	3. $-\sqrt{36}$ −6	4. $\sqrt{1}$ 1
5. $-\sqrt{9}$ −3	6. $\sqrt{144}$ 12	7. $-\sqrt{121}$ −11	8. $\sqrt{36}$ 6
9. $-\sqrt{49}$ −7	10. $-\sqrt{81}$ −9	11. $-\sqrt{169}$ −13	12. $\sqrt{400}$ 20
13. $\sqrt{225}$ 15	14. $-\sqrt{289}$ −17	15. $\sqrt{196}$ 14	16. $\sqrt{324}$ 18
17. $\sqrt{900}$ 30	18. $\sqrt{256}$ 16	19. $\sqrt{625}$ 25	20. $-\sqrt{196}$ −14
21. $\sqrt{361}$ 19	22. $-\sqrt{324}$ −18	23. $-\sqrt{256}$ −16	24. $-\sqrt{900}$ −30
25. $-\sqrt{625}$ −25	26. $\sqrt{961}$ 31	27. $\sqrt{289}$ 17	28. $-\sqrt{361}$ −19

Find the square of each number.

29. 5 25	30. 2 4	31. 7 49	32. 1 1
33. 3 9	34. 6 36	35. 8 64	36. 21 441
37. 4 16	38. 12 144	39. 15 225	40. 10 100
41. 20 400	42. 16 256	43. 18 324	44. 19 361
45. 24 576	46. 11 121	47. 26 676	48. 13 169
49. 31 961	50. 27 729	51. 28 784	52. 22 484

Alternate Strategies: Reteaching the Lesson

Reteaching Activity

Using Models Have students draw a dot grid, using 12 dots horizontally and 12 dots vertically. Circle as many different squares as possible. For each square, write equations representing the circled dots as a square, then as a square root. For example, if a 3 by 3 square is circled, write $3^2 = 9$, and $\sqrt{9} = 3$.

Reteaching Masters Booklet, **p. 120**

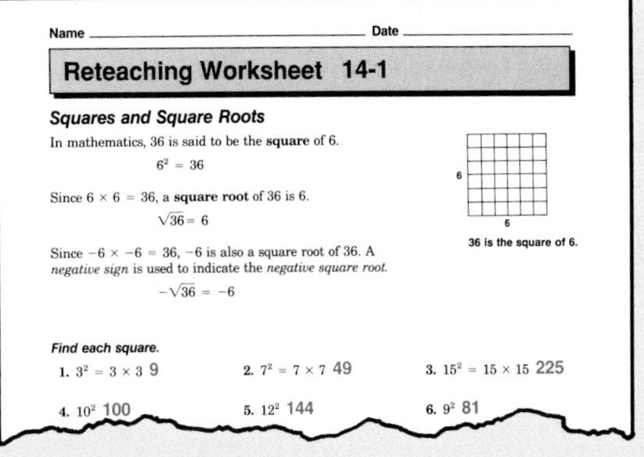

Name __________ Date __________

Reteaching Worksheet 14-1

Squares and Square Roots

In mathematics, 36 is said to be the **square** of 6.

$$6^2 = 36$$

Since $6 \times 6 = 36$, a **square root** of 36 is 6.

$$\sqrt{36} = 6$$

Since $-6 \times -6 = 36$, -6 is also a square root of 36. A *negative sign* is used to indicate the *negative square root.*

$$-\sqrt{36} = -6$$

36 is the square of 6.

Find each square.

1. $3^2 = 3 \times 3$ 9   2. $7^2 = 7 \times 7$ 49   3. $15^2 = 15 \times 15$ 225

4. 10^2 100   5. 12^2 144   6. 9^2 81

4 CLOSE

Assessment Option

Speaking Write the numbers 1-12 and also their squares on 5 × 7 index cards. Go around the room and have the students pick a card and state either its square or its square root if they pick a perfect square. If they choose 1, 4, or 9, have them give both its square and its square root.

Additional Answers

1. Sample answer: A square root is one of the two equal factors of a number.
2. Sample answer: Squaring a number is like finding the area of a square because you multiply a number by itself in both cases.

38.

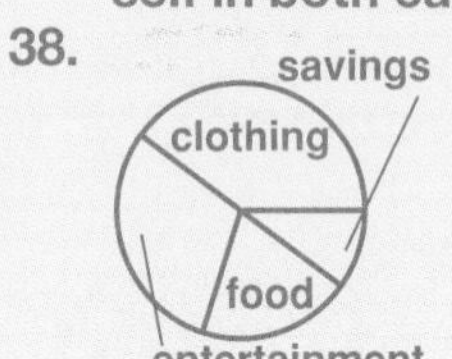

45. Sample answer: The squaring operation is the inverse of the square root operation.

Enrichment Masters Booklet, **p. 120**

Name ______________________ Date ______________

Enrichment Worksheet 14-1

Roots

The symbol $\sqrt{}$ indicates a square root. By placing a number in the upper left, the symbol can be changed to indicate higher roots.

$\sqrt[3]{8} = 2$ because $2^3 = 8$
$\sqrt[4]{81} = 3$ because $3^4 = 81$
$\sqrt[5]{100{,}000} = 10$ because $10^5 = 100{,}000$

Find each of the following.

1. $\sqrt[3]{125}$ 5
2. $\sqrt[4]{16}$ 2
3. $\sqrt[8]{1}$ 1
4. $\sqrt[3]{27}$ 3
5. $\sqrt[5]{32}$ 2
6. $\sqrt[3]{64}$ 4
7. $\sqrt[3]{1000}$ 10
8. $\sqrt[3]{216}$ 6
9. $\sqrt[6]{1{,}000{,}000}$ 10
10. $\sqrt[3]{1{,}000{,}000}$ 100
11. $\sqrt[4]{256}$ 4
12. $\sqrt[3]{729}$ 9
13. $\sqrt[6]{64}$ 2
14. $\sqrt[4]{625}$ 5
15. $\sqrt[5]{243}$ 3

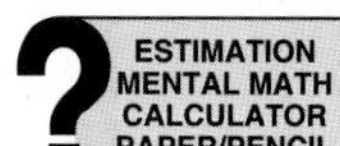

Find each square root.

16. $-\sqrt{25}$ −5
17. $-\sqrt{64}$ −8
18. $-\sqrt{16}$ −4
19. $-\sqrt{100}$ −10
20. $\sqrt{121}$ 11
21. $-\sqrt{144}$ −12
22. $\sqrt{169}$ 13
23. $-\sqrt{400}$ −20

Find the square of each number.

24. 9 81
25. 30 900
26. 25 625
27. 17 289
28. 23 529
29. 14 196
30. 40 1600
31. 34 1156

Challenge

Find each square root.

32. $\sqrt{0.04}$ 0.2
33. $\sqrt{0.16}$ 0.4
34. $\sqrt{\frac{4}{9}}$ $\frac{2}{3}$
35. $\sqrt{\frac{49}{81}}$ $\frac{7}{9}$

Mixed Review

36. Find the slope of the line that contains the points A(6, −2) and B(3, 7). (Lesson 8-8) −3
37. **Statistics** Find the lower and upper quartiles of the data 13, 16, 17, 14, 11, 9, 17, 21. (Lesson 10-4) 12; 17
38. **Personal Finance** Angie allows 40% of her income for clothing, 30% for entertainment, 20% for food, and 10% for savings. Make a circle graph of these data. (Lesson 12-2) See margin.
39. Find the perimeter of the rectangle. (Lesson 3-6) 26 m

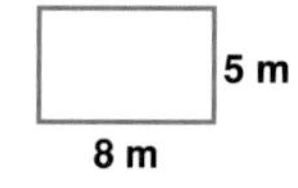

40. Find the length of the brace (x). (Lesson 12-10) 1.8 ft

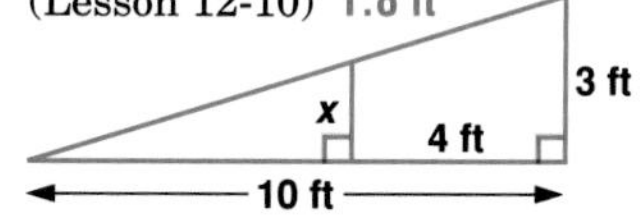

Connection

41. **Geometry** Draw a square that has an area of 64 square centimeters. What is the length of a side of the square? 8 cm

Applications

42. **Hang Gliding** Steve's hang glider has a wingspan of 15 feet and a wing area of 150 square feet. Find the aspect ratio of his hang glider. Use the formula $R = \frac{s^2}{A}$. 1.5
43. **Hang Gliding** Adventure Sports advertises a hang glider with an aspect ratio of 1.6. If its wing area is 160 square feet, what is its wingspan? 16 ft

Critical Thinking

44. Describe a realistic situation in which $\sqrt{9}$ would be the only solution of the equation $x^2 = 9$. Finding the length of the side of a square whose area is 9 square units.

Wrap-Up

45. In your own words, explain how the squaring operation is related to the square root operation. See margin.

Alternate Strategies: Extending the Lesson

Enrichment

Using Formulas The length of a skid mark can be used to find the approximate speed of the car trying to stop. The formula is $s = 13\sqrt{\ell}$, where s is speed in km per hr and ℓ is the skid mark length in meters. How fast was a car going if a skid mark was 25 meters long? 65 km/h

Cooperative Learning

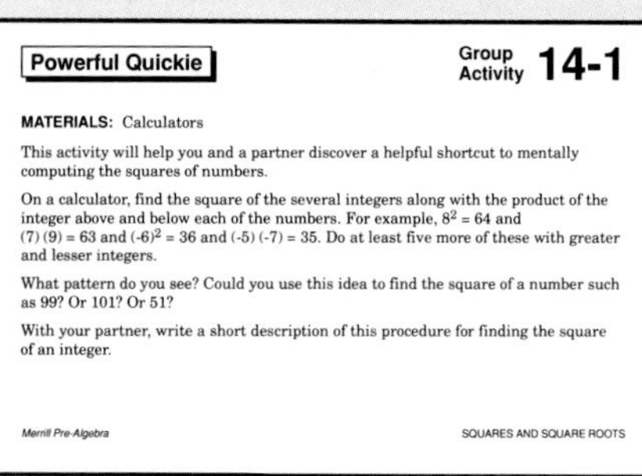

Powerful Quickie Group Activity **14-1**

MATERIALS: Calculators

This activity will help you and a partner discover a helpful shortcut to mentally computing the squares of numbers.

On a calculator, find the square of the several integers along with the product of the integer above and below each of the numbers. For example, $8^2 = 64$ and (7) (9) = 63 and $(-6)^2 = 36$ and (-5) (-7) = 35. Do at least five more of these with greater and lesser integers.

What pattern do you see? Could you use this idea to find the square of a number such as 99? Or 101? Or 51?

With your partner, write a short description of this procedure for finding the square of an integer.

Merrill Pre-Algebra SQUARES AND SQUARE ROOTS

14-2 Approximate Square Roots

Objective:
Approximate square roots.

In airshows, skydivers often compete to see who can land in the smallest square region. If a target region has an area of 250 square feet, how long is the region on each side?

Let $x =$ the length of one side of the region.

Then $x^2 = 250$. Why? $=$ **length × width $= x \cdot x$ or x^2**

$x = \sqrt{250}$ Why? **Take the square root of both sides.**

Calculator Hint

A calculator can be used to find square roots. $\sqrt{x}$ is the square root key. When this key is pressed, the calculator replaces the number in the display with its nonnegative square root.

The number 250 is not a perfect square; that is, 250 has no square root that is a whole number. However, we know that 250 is greater than 225 or 15^2 and less than 256 or 16^2. So the square root of 250 should be greater than 15 and less than 16.

$$225 < 250 < 256$$
$$15^2 < 250 < 16^2$$
$$15 < \sqrt{250} < 16$$

Since 250 is closer to 256 than to 225, the best whole number estimate for 250 would be 16. The target region is about 16 feet long on each side.

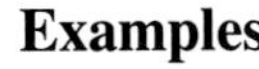

Examples

1 What is the best whole number estimate for $\sqrt{118}$?

100 and 121 are the closest perfect squares.

$$100 < 118 < 121$$
$$10^2 < 118 < 11^2$$
$$10 < \sqrt{118} < 11$$

Check: 118 $\sqrt{x}$ 10.86278

Since 118 is closer to 121 than 100, the best whole number estimate is 11. This checks with the result on the calculator.

2 What is the best integer estimate for $-\sqrt{26.79}$?

$$-36 < -26.79 < -25$$
$$-6^2 < -26.79 < -5^2$$
$$-6 < -\sqrt{26.79} < -5$$

Check: 26.79 $\sqrt{x}$ +/− −5.175906

Since −26.79 is closer to −25 than −36, the best integer estimate is −5. This checks with the result on the calculator.

FYI

The symbol $\sqrt{x}$ was first used in print by Rudolff in 1525.

Lesson Notes 14-2

5-Minute Check
(over Lesson 14-1)

Find each square root.
1. $\sqrt{196}$ **14** 2. $-\sqrt{900}$ **-30**

Find the square of each number.
3. 16 **256** 4. 21 **441**

Transparency 14-2 contains the 5-Minute Check and a teaching aid for this lesson.

1 FOCUS

The purpose of this lesson is to use estimation or a calculator to approximate square roots.

2 TEACH

Chalkboard Examples

- *For Example 1*
  What is the best whole number estimate for $\sqrt{75}$? **9**
- *For Example 2*
  What is the best integer estimate for $-\sqrt{52.38}$? **-7**

Practice Masters Booklet, **p. 134**

Name ______________ Date ______

Practice Worksheet 14-2

Approximate Square Roots

Find the best integer estimate for each of the following. Then check your estimate using a calculator.

1. $\sqrt{8}$ 3	2. $-\sqrt{12}$ −3	3. $\sqrt{55}$ 7
4. $-\sqrt{39}$ −6	5. $\sqrt{98}$ 10	6. $-\sqrt{37}$ −6
7. $\sqrt{500}$ 22	8. $-\sqrt{60}$ −8	9. $\sqrt{19}$ 4
10. $\sqrt{150}$ 12	11. $-\sqrt{70}$ −8	12. $-\sqrt{395}$ −20
13. $\sqrt{200}$ 14	14. $-\sqrt{115}$ −11	15. $\sqrt{1000}$ 32
16. $-\sqrt{40}$ −6	17. $\sqrt{1500}$ 39	18. $\sqrt{350}$ 19
19. $\sqrt{7.95}$ 3	20. $\sqrt{3.72}$ 2	21. $\sqrt{27.96}$ 5
22. $\sqrt{1.19}$ 1	23. $\sqrt{15.01}$ 4	24. $\sqrt{75.83}$ 9
25. $\sqrt{11.25}$ 3	26. $\sqrt{60.25}$ 8	27. $\sqrt{83.91}$ 9
28. $-\sqrt{75}$ −9	29. $\sqrt{26.17}$ 5	30. $\sqrt{85.07}$ 9

Bell Ringer

State the first ten perfect squares, starting with 1. **1, 4, 9, 16, 25, 36, 49, 64, 81, 100**

Reteaching Masters Booklet, **p. 121**

Name ______________ Date ______

Reteaching Worksheet 14-2

Approximate Square Roots

If the square root of a number is a whole number, the original number is called a **perfect square**. For example, 81 is a perfect square because $9 \times 9 = 81$. However, 79 and 80 are not perfect squares.

In cases where the square root of a number is not a whole number, you can estimate the square root by using the two closest perfect squares.

70 is between 64 and 81.
So, $\sqrt{70}$ is between $\sqrt{64}$ and $\sqrt{81}$ or between 8 and 9.
Since 70 is closer to 64 than to 81, $\sqrt{70}$ is closer to 8.

Circle the numbers that are perfect squares.

1. 250 2. (2500) 3. (121) 4. 112 5. (100) 6. 1000
7. (256) 8. (289) 9. 156 10. (361) 11. (400) 12.

EE: 1E, 3A, 3E
TAAS: 10,13

3 PRACTICE/APPLY

Checking the Concept

To solve Exercises 3-10, have students write the perfect squares greater and less than the number.

Independent Practice

Homework Assignment	
Basic	11-25 odd, 27-30, 32, 33
Average	12-26 even, 27-33
Honors	19-33

4 CLOSE

Assessment Option

Speaking Have each student state a whole number or a decimal. Then have the class estimate the square and the square root. Use a calculator to check the estimates.

Enrichment Masters Booklet, **p. 121**

Name ______________ Date ______________

Enrichment Worksheet 14-2

Hero's Formula

Hero of Alexandria (or Heron) was a mathematician and inventor who lived sometime between the 2nd and 3rd centuries A.D. In his work, there was a strong emphasis toward the applications of mathematics to the real world. He made discoveries in geometry and physics, and he is also believed to have invented a steam engine.

Hero's Formula, named after Hero, is a formula for finding the area of a triangle in terms of the lengths of the three sides.

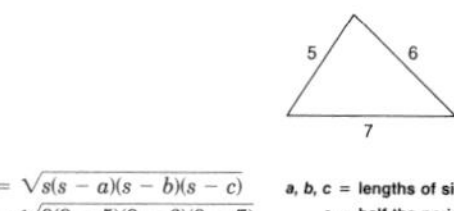

$$A = \sqrt{s(s-a)(s-b)(s-c)}$$
$$= \sqrt{9(9-5)(9-6)(9-7)}$$
$$= \sqrt{9 \times 4 \times 3 \times 2}$$
$$= 6\sqrt{6} \text{ square units}$$

a, b, c = lengths of sides
s = half the perimeter of the triangle or $\frac{1}{2}(a + b + c)$

Use Hero's Formula to find the area of each triangle.

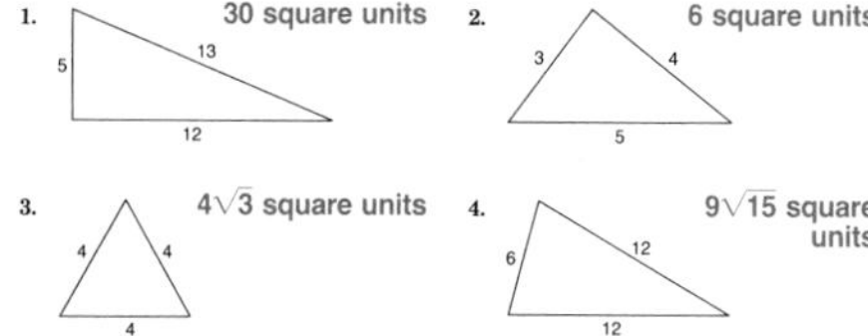

Checking for Understanding

Communicating Algebra

1. A square root is a whole number if the radicand is a __?__ . perfect square
2. After a nonnegative square root is found on a calculator, the __?__ key will give the negative square root. +/-

Guided Practice

Find the best whole number estimate for each of the following. Then check your estimate using a calculator.

3. $\sqrt{24}$ 5
4. $\sqrt{32}$ 6
5. $\sqrt{38}$ 6
6. $\sqrt{42}$ 6
7. $\sqrt{45}$ 7
8. $\sqrt{52}$ 7
9. $\sqrt{57}$ 8
10. $\sqrt{65}$ 8

Exercises

Independent Practice

Find the best integer estimate for each of the following. Then check your estimate using a calculator.

ESTIMATION
MENTAL MATH
CALCULATOR
PAPER/PENCIL

11. $\sqrt{90}$ 9
12. $\sqrt{15}$ 4
13. $-\sqrt{47}$ -7
14. $-\sqrt{89}$ -9
15. $-\sqrt{29}$ -5
16. $-\sqrt{625}$ -25
17. $\sqrt{2601}$ 51
18. $\sqrt{97}$ 10
19. $\sqrt{6.76}$ 3
20. $\sqrt{7.84}$ 3
21. $\sqrt{2.89}$ 2
22. $\sqrt{4.41}$ 2
23. $\sqrt{13.69}$ 4
24. $\sqrt{20.25}$ 4
25. $-\sqrt{62}$ -8
26. $-\sqrt{71}$ -8

Mixed Review

27. Find C(7, 3). (Lesson 11-3) 35
28. Find the area of a circle with diameter 12 feet. (Lesson 13-3) about 113 ft^2
29. Find $-\sqrt{121}$. (Lesson 14-1) -11

Applications

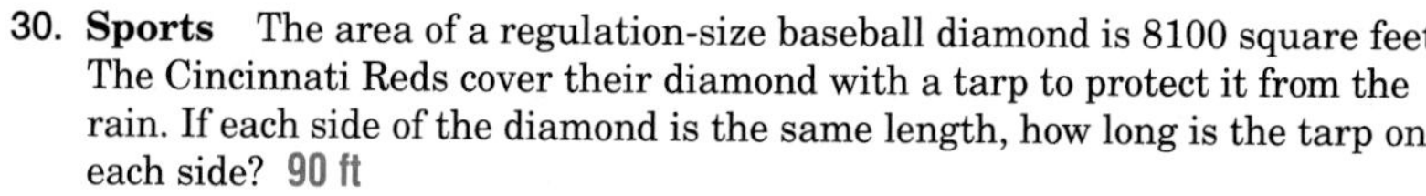

30. **Sports** The area of a regulation-size baseball diamond is 8100 square feet. The Cincinnati Reds cover their diamond with a tarp to protect it from the rain. If each side of the diamond is the same length, how long is the tarp on each side? 90 ft
31. **Construction** City code requires that a party house must allow 4 square feet for each person on the dance floor. Rocky's Dance Emporium wants to have a dance floor that is square and that is large enough for 100 people at a time. How long should it be on each side? 20 ft

Critical Thinking

32. Use your calculator to try to find the square root of -25. What is shown on the display? Why do you think this happens? an error message; cannot take the square root of a negative number

Wrap-Up

33. In your own words, explain how to find the whole number estimate for a square root. See margin.

Additional Answer

33. Sample answer: Determine the two perfect squares the number is between. The whole number estimate of the square root is the square root of the closer perfect square.

Cooperative Learning

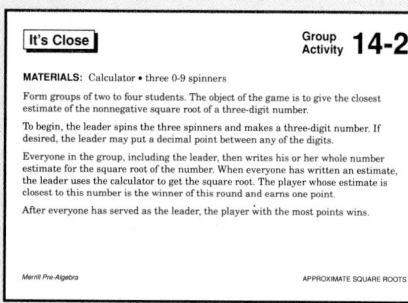

It's Close Group Activity **14-2**

MATERIALS: Calculator • three 0-9 spinners

Form groups of two to four students. The object of the game is to give the closest estimate of the nonnegative square root of a three-digit number.

To begin, the leader spins the three spinners and makes a three-digit number. If desired, the leader may put a decimal point between any of the digits.

Everyone in the group, including the leader, then writes his or her whole number estimate for the square root of the number. When everyone has written an estimate, the leader uses the calculator to get the square root. The player whose estimate is closest to this number is the winner of this round and earns one point.

After everyone has served as the leader, the player with the most points wins.

Merrill Pre-Algebra APPROXIMATE SQUARE ROOTS

14-3 Strategy: Use Venn Diagrams

Objective:
Use Venn diagrams to solve problems.

Key Term:
Venn diagram

Exquisite Interiors has 40 sample floor tiles in the shapes of various polygons. If 20 tiles are regular polygons, 14 tiles are quadrilaterals, and 5 tiles are squares, how many tiles are not regular polygons, quadrilaterals, or squares?

At first this problem may seem to be fairly easy. However, you must remember that squares are a special kind of quadrilateral and are also regular polygons.

Since 20 + 14 + 5 equals 39, why is the answer not 1?
because the 5 square tiles are also regular polygons and quadrilaterals

Explore There are 40 tiles altogether. Twenty tiles are regular polygons, 14 are quadrilaterals, and 5 are squares. You must find out how many other tiles there are.

Plan You can use a **Venn diagram** to illustrate the data. A rectangle is used to represent all the tiles. A circle is used to represent the tiles that are regular polygons and an intersecting circle is used to represent the tiles that are quadrilaterals. The intersection of the circular regions represents tiles that are both regular polygons and quadrilaterals. In other words, the intersection represents the square tiles.

Why are intersecting circles used?
to show that the categories overlap

Solve There are 5 squares, so 5 is placed in the intersection of the circular regions. The number of non-square regular polygons is 20 − 5 or 15. The number of non-square quadrilaterals is 14 − 5 or 9. There are 15 + 5 + 9 or 29 polygons represented in the circular regions. There are 40 − 29 or 11 other polygons that are neither quadrilaterals nor regular polygons.

Polygons

regular polygons	both (squares)	quadri-laterals	other
15	5	9	11

FYI
Leonhard Euler first used circles to show the relationship of sets. Later John Venn put the circles in a rectangle to form diagrams like the ones in this lesson.

Examine Look at the Venn diagram again. Add the number of polygons in each region.

$$11 + 15 + 5 + 9 = 40$$

Since the total is 40, the answer is correct.

Lesson Notes 14-3

5-Minute Check
(over Lesson 14-2)

Find the best integer estimate for each of the following. Then check your estimate using a calculator.

1. $\sqrt{153}$ **12**
2. $-\sqrt{34}$ **-6**
3. $-\sqrt{357}$ **-19**
4. $\sqrt{51.24}$ **7**
5. $-\sqrt{18.73}$ **-4**

Transparency 14-3 contains the 5-Minute Check and a teaching aid for this lesson.

1 FOCUS

The purpose of this lesson is to draw Venn diagrams representing the information in a problem and use them to solve the problem.

Motivating the Lesson

Ask students how many of them have been to the library lately. List the types of books they checked out and generate a problem related to the types.

2 TEACH

Using Questioning

For each lesson example, ask students the number of circles to be used, how the circles overlap, placement of numbers in the circles, and how the total is checked by adding numbers in the circles.

Chalkboard Examples

At a buffet, 24 people chose beef and 20 chose pork. Ten people chose both beef and pork. Each person at the buffet chose at least one of the two meats. How many people were served at the buffet? **34**

Bell Ringer

State ten radicands that would give 12 as the best whole number estimate. **Possible answers; 142, 143, 145, 144.27**

Reteaching Activity

Medicine Connection Have students use a Venn diagram to solve the following problem.
Following a severe accident, 100 patients were treated at a clinic. 58 had broken bones, and 62 had cuts. How many patients had both? **20**

EE: 1A, 1B, 1C, 1D, 1E, 2D

3 PRACTICE/APPLY

Checking the Concept

Have students solve Exercises 4-7 verbally, explaining each answer.

Error Analysis
Watch for students who don't subtract the number of items in an overlapping area from the total in the category. **Prevent by** adding the numbers in the circle to confirm the total is correct.

Independent Practice

Homework Assignment	
Basic	8-12
Average	8-12
Honors	8-12

4 CLOSE

Assessment Option

Writing Divide the class into small groups. Have each group write a problem that can be solved using Venn diagrams.

Practice Masters Booklet, **p. 135**

Name ______________ Date ______________

Practice Worksheet 14-3

Problem Solving Strategy: Use Venn Diagrams

Use a Venn diagram to solve each problem.

1. There are 90 students participating in winter sports at Whittier School. Forty-five students run track and 67 play basketball. Twenty-two students do both sports. How many students run track only? 23 students
2. At North High School, there are 413 sophomores. Seventy-five sophomores are taking typing, 115 sophomores are taking computer science, and 33 students are taking both courses. How many sophomores are taking neither typing nor computer science? 256 sophomores
3. At a banquet, 93 people chose coffee for their beverage and 47 people chose tea. Twenty-five people chose both coffee and tea. Each person chose at least one of these beverages. How many people were at the banquet? 115 people
4. One hundred fifty-seven students were surveyed in music class. Ninety-five students prefer rock-and-roll music, and one hundred eight prefer country-western music. Forty-six students prefer both rock-and-roll and country-western music. How many students prefer rock-and-roll music but not country-western music? 49 students
5. The Olde World Calzone Shoppe sells pepperoni, mushroom, and pepperoni-mushroom calzones. On Tuesday, 72 calzones were sold. Thirty-one of the calzones contained mushrooms. If 12 pepperoni-mushroom calzones were sold, how many calzones contained pepperoni? 53 calzones
6. There are two clubs at Central High School. Nineteen students are in the math club, and 25 students are in the science club. Nine students are in both the math and science clubs. How many students are in one club only? 26 students

Checking for Understanding

Communicating Algebra **Use the Venn diagrams below to complete Exercises 1-3.**

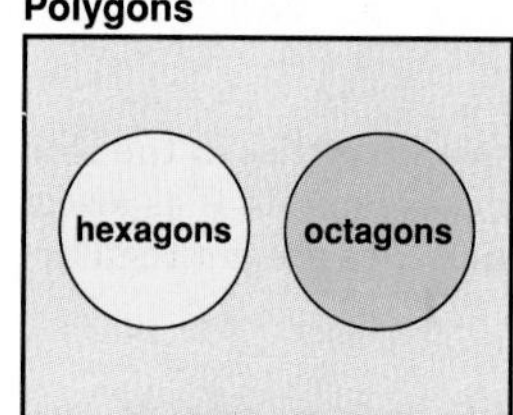

Figure 1

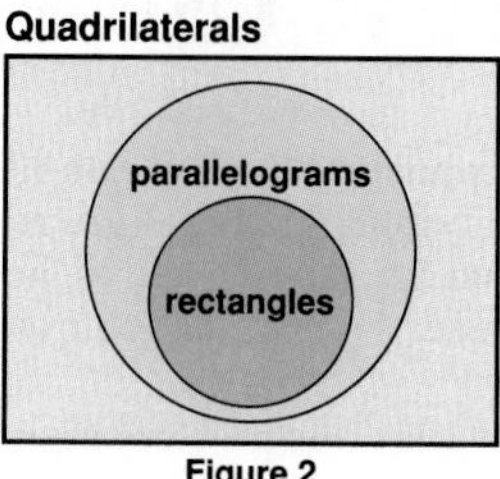

Figure 2

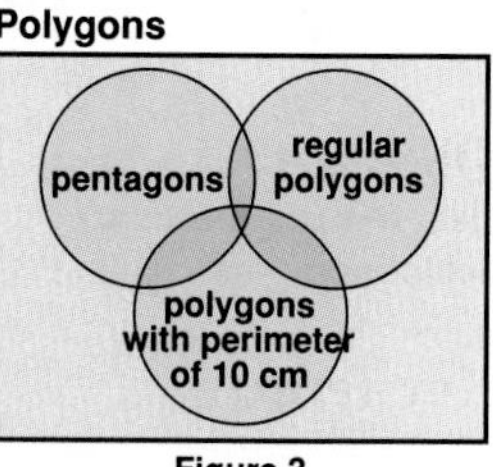

Figure 3

For Exercises 1 and 2, see margin.

1. Explain why the circular regions in Figure 1 do not intersect.
2. Explain why one circular region is contained within the other in Figure 2.
3. Write a sentence describing the polygons in the region where all three circles intersect in Figure 3. **These polygons are regular pentagons with a perimeter of 10 cm.**

Guided Practice **The Venn diagram below represents the students involved in extra activities at Valley High School.**

4. 5 students
5. 89 students
6. 5 students
7. 214 students

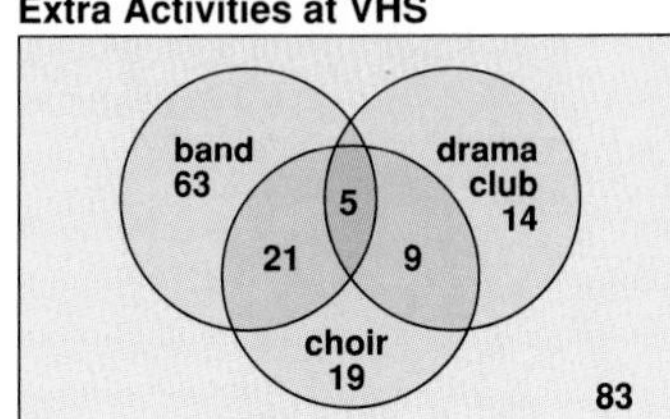

4. How many students are involved with all three of the listed activities?
5. How many students are in the band?
6. How many students are in both the drama club and the band?
7. How many students are involved in at least one extra activity?

Exercises

Independent Practice **Solve. Use any strategy.**

ESTIMATION
MENTAL MATH
CALCULATOR
PAPER/PENCIL

8. Mama Sophia's Pizzeria conducted a small survey. They asked 50 customers which pizza topping they liked better, pepperoni or sausage. Twenty-eight people liked pepperoni, 25 people liked sausage, and 8 people liked both equally. How many people did not like either pepperoni or sausage? **5 people**
9. Hattie must read a book for a book report. She read half of her book on Sunday. On Monday, she read another 30 pages. On Tuesday, she read 6 pages. On Wednesday, she read half of the remaining pages. If she has 20 pages yet to read, how many pages does the book have? **152 pages**
10. There are 26 students in a math class. The class takes a survey and finds that 14 students have pet dogs, 10 students have cats, and 5 students have birds. Four students have dogs and cats, 3 students have dogs and birds, and 1 student has a cat and a bird. If no one has all three of these animals, how many students have none of these animals? **5 students**

Critical Thinking

11. A geometry teacher drew some quadrilaterals on the chalkboard. There were 5 trapezoids, 12 rectangles, 5 squares, and 8 rhombuses. What is the least number of figures the teacher could have drawn? **20 figures**

Wrap-Up

12. Make up your own problem that can be solved using a Venn diagram. See margin.

Additional Answers

1. Because a polygon cannot be both a hexagon and an octagon.
2. Because all rectangles are special parallelograms.

12. Sample answer: A survey of 100 eighth-graders found that 67 students own cassette tapes, 35 students own compact disks, and 16 students own neither. How many own both?

Cooperative Learning

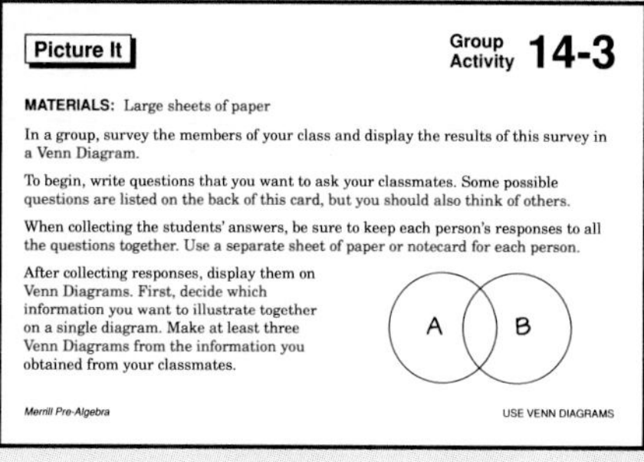
Picture It Group Activity **14-3**

MATERIALS: Large sheets of paper

In a group, survey the members of your class and display the results of this survey in a Venn Diagram.

To begin, write questions that you want to ask your classmates. Some possible questions are listed on the back of this card, but you should also think of others.

When collecting the students' answers, be sure to keep each person's responses to all the questions together. Use a separate sheet of paper or notecard for each person.

After collecting responses, display them on Venn Diagrams. First, decide which information you want to illustrate together on a single diagram. Make at least three Venn Diagrams from the information you obtained from your classmates.

A B

Merrill Pre-Algebra USE VENN DIAGRAMS

14-4 The Real Number System

Objectives:
Identify types of numbers.
Solve equations by finding square roots.
Simplify square roots.

Key Terms:
rational number
irrational number
real number

The ancient Greeks believed that all numbers could be expressed as ratios of whole numbers. This is true of most of the numbers found in previous chapters.

$\frac{3}{7}$ $\quad -15 = \frac{-15}{1}$ $\quad 0.33 = \frac{33}{100}$ $\quad 0.111\ldots = \frac{1}{9}$ $\quad \sqrt{100} = 10$

These numbers are called **rational numbers.** A rational number is any number that can be expressed as $\frac{a}{b}$, where a and b are integers and b does not equal 0. Remember that rational numbers can always be expressed by using terminating or repeating decimals.

Consider $\sqrt{2}$. $\quad \sqrt{2} = 1.4142136\ldots$ This decimal continues forever without any pattern of repeating digits.

You cannot express a number like $\sqrt{2}$ as either a terminating or a repeating decimal. This kind of number is called an **irrational number.**

Definition of Irrational Number

An irrational number is a number that cannot be expressed as $\frac{a}{b}$, where a and b are integers and b does not equal 0.

Each of the following is an irrational number.

$\sqrt{2}$ $\quad \sqrt{3}$ $\quad -\sqrt{11}$ $\quad \pi$

Examples

Determine whether each number is a rational or irrational number.

How can you show that $0.\overline{3}$ is equivalent to $\frac{1}{3}$? Explain. **1 divided by 3 is 0.333 . . . or $0.\overline{3}$.**

1 **0.33333 . . .**

The three dots indicate that the 3s keep repeating. This decimal can be expressed as $\frac{1}{3}$. So it is a rational number.

How can you show that 0.75 is equivalent to $\frac{3}{4}$? Explain. **3 divided by 4 is 0.75.**

2 **0.75**

This decimal is a terminating decimal. It can be expressed as $\frac{75}{100}$ or $\frac{3}{4}$. So it is a rational number.

3 **0.0101101110 . . .**

This decimal does not terminate, and it does not repeat. Notice that the number of 1s between the 0s is different each time. This decimal is an irrational number.

Bell Ringer

Name two advantages to using Venn diagrams. **Possible answers: represent words with pictures, easier way to sort the data.**

Lesson Notes 14-4

5-Minute Check
(over Lesson 14-3)

Solve. Use any strategy.

1. Of 30 people polled at a resort, 12 were water skiers, 19 were snow skiers, and 7 were both water and snow skiers. How many people were neither water skiers nor snow skiers? **6**
2. At Linden High School, 36 freshmen take woodworking. Twenty-five take cooking. Nine take both courses. There are 108 students in the freshman class. How many freshmen take neither woodworking nor cooking? **56**

Transparency 14-4 contains the 5-Minute Check and a teaching aid for this lesson.

1 FOCUS

The purpose of this lesson is to use irrational real numbers, as well as rational real numbers, to solve problems and simplify square roots.

Motivating the Lesson

Make a chart like the one on page 534 and omit the last column. Have students determine which sets contain each number below.
$7, -7, \frac{1}{2}, \sqrt{9}, 0, \sqrt{8}, 4.14, 3\frac{1}{3}$

2 TEACH

Using Discussion

Discuss the lesson and examples as if they were one lesson about types of numbers and a related lesson simplifying irrational numbers.

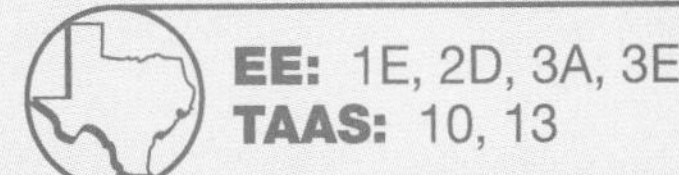

EE: 1E, 2D, 3A, 3E
TAAS: 10, 13

Chalkboard Examples

Determine whether each number is a rational or irrational number.

- *For Example 1*
  0.6666 . . . rational
- *For Example 2*
  0.62 rational
- *For Example 3*
  0.00202022202 . . . irrational
- *For Example 4*
  Solve $x^2 = \sqrt{289}$ $x = 17$ or -17
- *For Example 5*
  Solve $x^2 = \sqrt{32}$ $x \approx 5.7$ or -5.7
- *For Example 6*
  Simplify $\sqrt{700}$. $10\sqrt{7}$

The set of rational numbers and the set of irrational numbers together form the set of **real numbers.** The Venn diagram at the right shows the relationships among whole numbers, integers, rational numbers, irrational numbers, and real numbers.

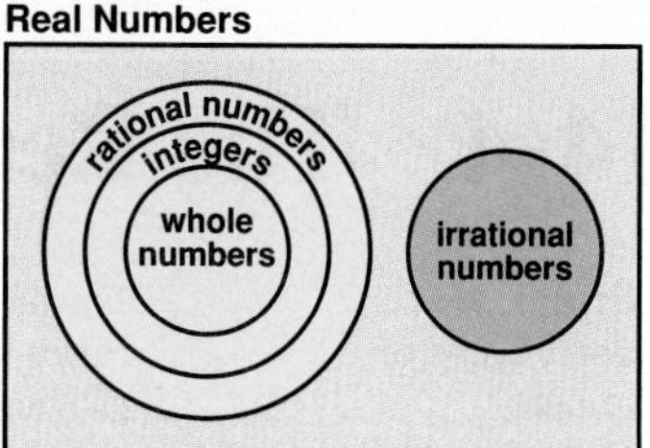

The following chart shows the sets of numbers to which several numbers belong.

Number	Whole Number	Integer	Rational	Irrational	Real
-7		✓	✓		✓
$\sqrt{15}$				✓	✓
$\sqrt{9}$	✓	✓	✓		✓
0.12121212 . . .			✓		✓
0.303303330 . . .				✓	✓
$\frac{4}{5}$			✓		✓

Throughout the text, you have solved equations that have rational number solutions. Some equations have solutions that are irrational.

You can solve some equations that involve squares by taking the square root of each side.

Physics Connection

When investigating traffic accidents, police officers often need to determine how fast a car was traveling before it skidded to a stop. The formula $s = \sqrt{30fd}$ can be used to estimate the speed. In the formula, s is the speed, d is the distance the car skidded, and f is a friction factor.

Examples

4 **Solve $x^2 = 144$.**

$x^2 = 144$

$x = \sqrt{144}$ or $x = -\sqrt{144}$ Take the square root of each side.

$x = 12$ or $x = -12$

5 **Solve $x^2 = 50$. Round your answer to the nearest tenth.**

$x^2 = 50$

$x = \sqrt{50}$ or $x = -\sqrt{50}$

50 [$\sqrt{x}$] 7.0710678

$x \approx 7.1$ or $x \approx -7.1$

Suppose you wrote a number as a product of its prime factors. Then you looked for factors that occurred twice to find the square root. Do you think the result would be the same as taking the square root of a number? Consider $\sqrt{196}$.

Alternate Strategies: Reteaching the Lesson

Reteaching Activity

Making and Using Lists Have students write the terms **whole, integer, rational, irrational,** and **real** across a piece of paper. Under each term, have students list 5 numbers that apply to that term. In cooperative groups, discuss whether each number could also be in other groups.

Reteaching Masters Booklet, p. 122

Name ______ Date ______

Reteaching Worksheet 14-4

The Real Number System

Every day we use many different kinds of numbers.

Integers are the following set of numbers.

. . . , −4, −3, −2, −1, 0, 1, 2, 3, 4, . . .

Rational numbers are numbers that can be expressed as a quotient of two integers, where the divisor is not zero.

Irrational numbers are numbers that can be named by nonterminating, nonrepeating decimals.

The set of **real numbers** includes both the rational numbers and the irrational numbers.

Name the sets of numbers to which each number belongs: the integers, the rational numbers, the irrational numbers, and/or the real numbers.

$$\sqrt{196} = \sqrt{2 \cdot 2 \cdot 7 \cdot 7}$$
$$= \sqrt{2^2 \cdot 7^2}$$
$$= \sqrt{2^2} \cdot \sqrt{7^2}$$
$$= 2 \cdot 7 \text{ or } 14$$

Check: 196 [√x] 14 ✓

The following property of square roots was used to simplify $\sqrt{196}$.

Product Property of Square Roots

In words: The square root of a product is equal to the product of the square roots of its factors.

In symbols: For any nonnegative numbers a and b, $\sqrt{a \cdot b} = \sqrt{a} \cdot \sqrt{b}$.

You can use this property to simplify irrational numbers.

Example

6 Simplify $\sqrt{200}$.

$$\sqrt{200} = \sqrt{5 \cdot 5 \cdot 2 \cdot 2 \cdot 2} \quad \text{prime factorization}$$
$$= \sqrt{5^2 \cdot 2^2 \cdot 2}$$
$$= \sqrt{5^2} \cdot \sqrt{2^2} \cdot \sqrt{2} \quad \text{product property}$$
$$= 5 \cdot 2 \cdot \sqrt{2} \text{ or } 10\sqrt{2}$$

The simplest form of $\sqrt{200}$ is $10\sqrt{2}$. $10\sqrt{2}$ is approximately 14.142 or -14.142. Use your calculator to check this result.

Checking for Understanding

4. rational, irrational numbers

Communicating Algebra

1. A repeating decimal names a(n) __?__ number. rational
2. A terminating decimal names a(n) __?__ number. rational
3. A nonterminating, nonrepeating decimal names a(n) __?__. irrational number
4. The set of real numbers is made up of __?__ and __?__.
5. The property that allows $\sqrt{4 \cdot 5}$ to be simplified to $2\sqrt{5}$ is the __?__. Product Property of Square Roots

Guided Practice

Name the sets of numbers to which each number belongs: the whole numbers, the integers, the rational numbers, the irrational numbers, and/or the real numbers. 6. integer, rational, real 7. irrational, real 8. rational, real

6. -5
7. $-\sqrt{7}$
8. $\frac{2}{3}$
9. -2.7
10. $-\sqrt{16}$

9. rational, real 10. integer, rational, real

3 PRACTICE/APPLY

Checking the Concept

After completing Exercises 6-10, have students verbalize why the numbers do not belong in sets not included in the solutions.

Error Analysis

Watch for students who assume all square roots are irrational.
Prevent by modeling several rational square roots.

Independent Practice

Homework Assignment	
Basic	11-41 odd, 46-52, 54-56
Average	12-42 even, 46-56
Honors	18-42 even, 43-56

Practice Masters Booklet, **p. 136**

Name ______________ Date ______

Practice Worksheet 14-4

The Real Number System

Name the sets of numbers to which each number belongs: the whole numbers, the integers, the rational numbers, the irrational numbers, and/or the real numbers.

1. 0 whole, integers, rational, real
2. $\frac{-1}{4}$ rational, real
3. 2.6 rational, real
4. −5.8 rational, real
5. −9 integers, rational, real
6. $\sqrt{16}$ whole, integers, rational, real
7. $\sqrt{13}$ irrational, real
8. $-\sqrt{5}$ irrational, real
9. $-\sqrt{36}$ integers, rational, real
10. 0.33 rational, real
11. 0.583333 ... rational, real
12. −0.8888 ... rational, real

Solve each equation. Round decimal answers to the nearest tenth.

13. $a^2 = 9$ $a = 3$ or $a = -3$
14. $b^2 = 25$ $b = 5$ or $b = -5$
15. $c^2 = 16$ $c = 4$ or $c = -4$
16. $d^2 = 144$ $d = 12$ or $d = -12$
17. $e^2 = 196$ $e = 14$ or $e = -14$
18. $f^2 = 100$ $f = 10$ or $f = -10$
19. $g^2 = 361$ $g = 19$ or $g = -19$
20. $h^2 = 10$ $h \approx 3.2$ or $h \approx -3.2$
21. $i^2 = 20$ $i \approx 4.5$ or $i \approx -4.5$
22. $j^2 = 45$ $j \approx 6.7$ or $j \approx -6.7$
23. $k^2 = 56$ $k \approx 7.5$ or $k \approx -7.5$
24. $l^2 = 70$ $l \approx 8.4$ or $l \approx -8.4$

Simplify.

25. $\sqrt{12}$ $2\sqrt{3}$
26. $\sqrt{18}$ $3\sqrt{2}$
27. $\sqrt{24}$ $2\sqrt{6}$
28. $\sqrt{96}$ $4\sqrt{6}$
29. $\sqrt{45}$ $3\sqrt{5}$
30. $\sqrt{75}$ $5\sqrt{3}$
31. $\sqrt{200}$ $10\sqrt{2}$
32. $\sqrt{160}$ $4\sqrt{10}$
33. $\sqrt{375}$ $5\sqrt{15}$

4 CLOSE

Assessment Option

Speaking Have each student write a rational number that can be simplified. Then have them tell how to simplify it and tell to which set of numbers his or her rational number belongs.

Additional Answers

11. whole numbers, integers, rationals, reals
12. rationals, reals
13. rationals, reals
14. rationals, reals
15. whole numbers, integers, rationals, reals
16. irrationals, reals
17. irrationals, reals
18. whole numbers, integers, rationals, reals
19. rationals, reals
20. irrationals, reals
21. rationals, reals
22. rationals, reals
56. Sample answer: Whole numbers are also integers, integers are also rational numbers, and all of them including irrational numbers are also real numbers.

Enrichment Masters Booklet, **p. 122**

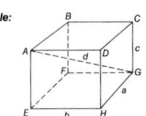

Name ______________ Date ______________

Enrichment Worksheet 14-4

Diagonals

To find the length of diagonals in cubes and rectangular solids, a formula can be applied. In the example below, the length of diagonal $\overline{AG}$ or d can be found using the formula

$$d^2 = a^2 + b^2 + c^2 \text{ or } d = \sqrt{a^2 + b^2 + c^2}$$

Example: (cube with vertices A, B, C, D, E, F, G, H; diagonal d from A to G; edges a, b, c) The diagonal, d, is equal to the square root of the sum of the squares of the length, a, the width, b, and the height, c.

Example: Find the length of the diagonal of a rectangular prism with length of 8 meters, width of 6 meters, and height of 10 meters.

$d = \sqrt{8^2 + 6^2 + 10^2}$ **Substitute the dimensions into the equation.**
$= \sqrt{64 + 36 + 100}$ **Square each value. Add.**
$= \sqrt{200}$ **Find the square root of the sum.**
$= 14.1$ m **Round the answer to the nearest tenth.**

Solve. Use $d = \sqrt{a^2 + b^2 + c^2}$. Round answers to the nearest tenth.

1. Find the diagonal of a cube with sides of 6 inches. 10.4 in.
2. Find the diagonal of a cube with sides of 2.4 meters. 4.2 m
3. Find the diagonal of a rectangular solid with length of 18 meters, width of 16 meters, and height of 24 meters. 34 m
4. Find the diagonal of a rectangular solid with length of 15.1 meters, width of 8.4 meters, and height of 6.3 meters. 18.4 m
5. Find the diagonal of a cube with sides of 34 millimeters. 58.9 mm
6. Find the diagonal of a rectangular solid with length of 8.9 millimeters, width of 6.7 millimeters, and height of 14 millimeters. 17.9 mm

Exercises

Independent Practice

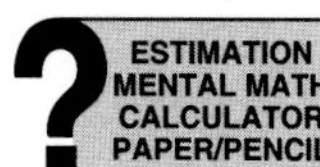

Name the sets of numbers to which each number belongs: the whole numbers, the integers, the rational numbers, the irrational numbers, and/or the real numbers. See margin.

11. 6
12. $\frac{-3}{4}$
13. 1.8
14. -4.6
15. $\sqrt{4}$
16. $\sqrt{11}$
17. $-\sqrt{10}$
18. $\sqrt{25}$
19. 0.89
20. 5.454454445 . . .
21. 0.531
22. -0.666 . . .

Solve each equation. Round decimal answers to the nearest tenth.

23. $a^2 = 49$ 7, -7
24. $b^2 = 81$ 9, -9
25. $c^2 = 4$ 2, -2
26. $d^2 = 64$ 8, -8
27. $s^2 = 121$ 11, -11
28. $n^2 = 169$ 13, -13
29. $p^2 = 1$ 1, -1
30. $t^2 = 225$ 15, -15
31. $e^2 = 28$ 5.3, -5.3
32. $g^2 = 40$ 6.3, -6.3
33. $f^2 = 11$ 3.3, -3.3
34. $y^2 = 60$ 7.7, -7.7

Simplify.

35. $\sqrt{28}$ $2\sqrt{7}$
36. $\sqrt{72}$ $6\sqrt{2}$
37. $\sqrt{54}$ $3\sqrt{6}$
38. $\sqrt{80}$ $4\sqrt{5}$
39. $\sqrt{90}$ $3\sqrt{10}$
40. $\sqrt{108}$ $6\sqrt{3}$
41. $\sqrt{128}$ $8\sqrt{2}$
42. $\sqrt{242}$ $11\sqrt{2}$

Challenge

Solve each equation.

43. $m^2 + 9 = 25$ 4, -4
44. $t^2 - 25 = 75$ 10, -10
45. $x^2 + x^2 = 50$ 5, -5

Mixed Review

46. Write the negation of $2x + 4x < 8x$. Then state whether the statement and its negation are true or false. (Lesson 2-6) $2x + 4x \geq 8x$; true; false
47. Convert 8.3 kilograms into grams. (Lesson 7-8) 8300 g
48. If 5 liters of punch costs $4.90, how much does 12 liters cost? (Lesson 9-3) $11.76
49. *True* or *false:* An equilateral triangle can never be an obtuse triangle. (Lesson 12-6) true

Find the best integer estimate for each of the following. (Lesson 14-2)

50. $\sqrt{88}$ 9
51. $-\sqrt{19.1}$ -4

Applications

52. **Sky Diving** When a sky diver jumps from an airplane, the time (t) in seconds it takes to reach a given distance can be estimated by using the formula $t = \sqrt{\frac{2s}{g}}$. In this formula, s is the free-fall distance, and g is the acceleration due to gravity, 32 ft/s^2. Sally jumps from an airplane to free-fall 2500 feet. How long will it take her to reach that distance? 12.5 seconds
53. **Meteorology** Use the formula $t^2 = \frac{d^3}{216}$ to estimate the amount of time a thunderstorm will last. In this formula, t is time in hours and d is the diameter of the storm system in miles. If a thunderstorm is 6 miles wide, find t. 1 hour

Critical Thinking

True **or** ***false.***

54. Every rational number is a real number. true
55. Every rational number is an integer. false

Wrap-Up

56. In your own words explain the Venn diagram on page 534. See margin.

Alternate Strategies: Extending the Lesson

Enrichment

Using Concept Maps Complete the following concept map, using the terms **integer, irrational, other, rational, real,** and **whole.**

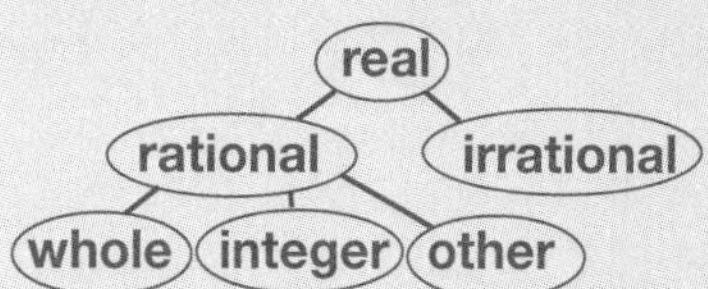

Cooperative Learning

Simply Simplified Group Activity **14-4**

MATERIALS: Calculators • 12 notecards with the radical expressions given on the back of this card • paper • pencils

The deck of "Radical" cards should be made, shuffled, and placed face down on the table.

One player turns up the top card on the card pile. All players then simplify the same radical expression. After everyone is finished, expressions are checked for accuracy using the calculator, and they are checked to be sure they are in simplified form.

The player who first arrives at the correct, simplified expression scores a point. The overall winner is the player with the most points after all cards have been used.

Merrill Pre-Algebra THE REAL NUMBER SYSTEM

14-5 The Pythagorean Theorem

Objective:
Use the Pythagorean Theorem to find the length of the side of a right triangle.

Key Terms:
hypotenuse
leg
Pythagorean Theorem

Softball has become a popular pastime in the United States. It is played on a diamond like the one shown at the right. The distance from one base to another is 60 feet. As you can see, the boundary of a softball diamond is square. When the grounds people lay out a softball diamond, they measure the distances between the bases carefully. Then they measure the diagonals to make certain the diamond is really a square. How long should a diagonal be if the diamond has been laid out correctly?

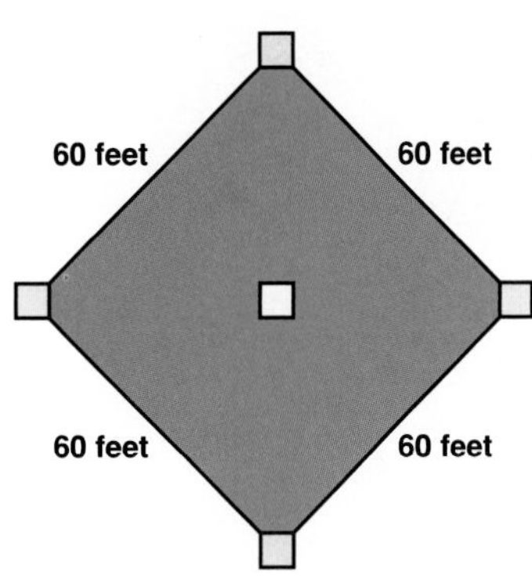

The answer to this question can be found by using a relationship involving the lengths of the sides of a right triangle that was discovered thousands of years ago. Credit for this discovery is given to a famous Greek mathematician named Pythagoras.

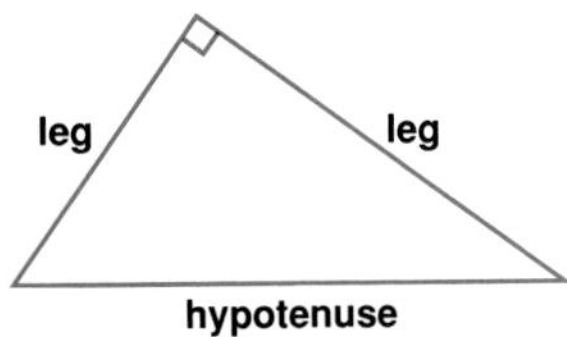

Remember that a right triangle is a triangle with one right angle. The side opposite the right angle is called the **hypotenuse**. The other two sides are called **legs**. The hypotenuse is always the longest side of a right triangle.

The relationship known as the **Pythagorean Theorem** is true for any right triangle.

Pythagorean Theorem

In a right triangle, the square of the hypotenuse is equal to the sum of the squares of the length of the legs.

In 1989, the Lady Panthers of Atlanta won the national softball tournment for girls 16 and under, slow pitch.

If a and b are the lengths of the legs of a right triangle and c is the length of its hypotenuse, an equation can be used to state the Pythagorean Theorem.

Pythagorean Theorem

$$c^2 = a^2 + b^2$$

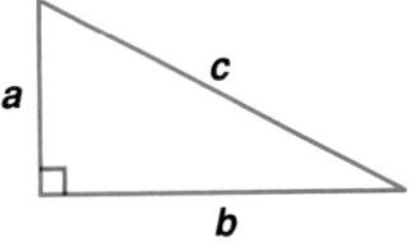

Lesson Notes 14-5

5-Minute Check
(over Lesson 14-4)

Simplify.
1. $\sqrt{160}$ $4\sqrt{10}$
2. $\sqrt{45}$ $3\sqrt{5}$
3. $\sqrt{288}$ $12\sqrt{2}$

Solve each equation. Round decimal answers to the nearest tenth.
4. $a^2 = 87$ 9.3 or -9.3
5. $x^2 = 61$ 7.8 or -7.8

Transparency 14-5 contains the 5-Minute Check and a teaching aid for this lesson.

1 FOCUS

The purpose of this lesson is to introduce the Pythagorean Theorem and use it to find the length of a side of a right triangle when the lengths of the other sides are known.

Motivating the Lesson

Show students a cone. Ask students if they can find the slant height, altitude, or radius of the base if two of these are known.

2 TEACH

Music Connection

Model the following problem. The lid on a grand piano is held open with a 28-inch prop. The prop's base is 55 inches across the piano from the lid's hinges. If the prop forms a right angle with the lid, how far from the hinges must the prop be placed? about 47 inches

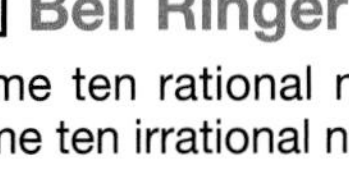

Bell Ringer

Name ten rational numbers. Then name ten irrational numbers.

EE: 1E, 3A, 3E, 4A, 4D
TAAS: 3, 11, 12

Chalkboard Examples

- *For Example 1*
  Use the Pythagorean Theorem to find the length of a diagonal of a basketball court. The court measures 29 meters long by 15 meters wide. **about 33 meters**
- *For Example 2*
  Find the length of the third side of this right triangle. $a = 12$ cm

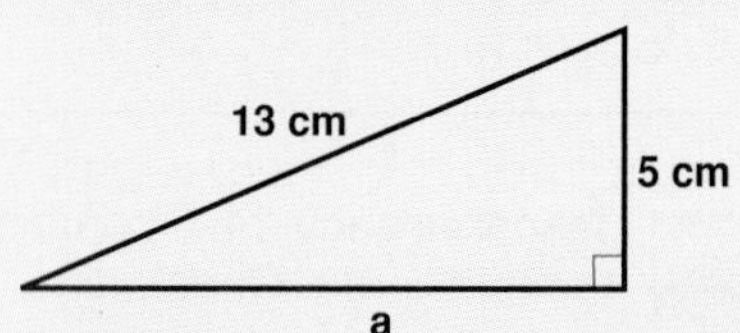

Determine whether each triangle is a right triangle.

- *For Example 3*

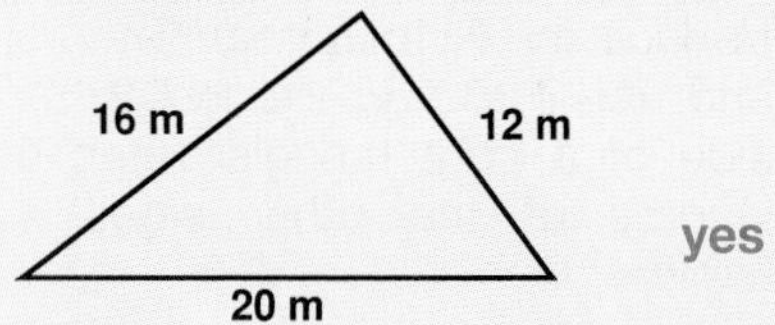

yes

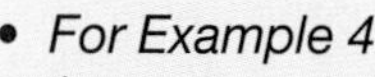

- *For Example 4*

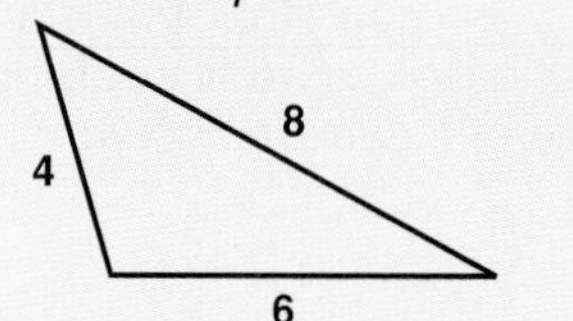

no

Why can you ignore the negative value of c in this problem? **The length of the diagonal must be a positive number.**

Example

1 **Use the Pythagorean Theorem to find the length of a diagonal of a softball diamond.**

A diagonal and two adjacent sides of a square form a right triangle. The legs of the right triangle are sides of the square and the hypotenuse of the right triangle is a diagonal of the square.

Let c represent the length of a diagonal (hypotenuse).

$c^2 = a^2 + b^2$ — Pythagorean Theorem

$c^2 = 60^2 + 60^2$ — Replace a with 60 and b with 60.

$c^2 = 3600 + 3600$

$c^2 = 7200$

$c = \sqrt{7200}$ or $c = -\sqrt{7200}$

$c \approx 85$ or $c \approx -85$ — Use a calculator.

The length of the diagonal should be about 85 feet.

The Pythagorean Theorem can be used to find the length of any side of a right triangle if the lengths of the other two sides are known.

Estimation Hint

THINK:
$60 \times 60 = 3600$
$70 \times 70 = 4900$
$\sqrt{4624}$ is between 60 and 70.

Example

2 **Find the length of the third side of the right triangle.**

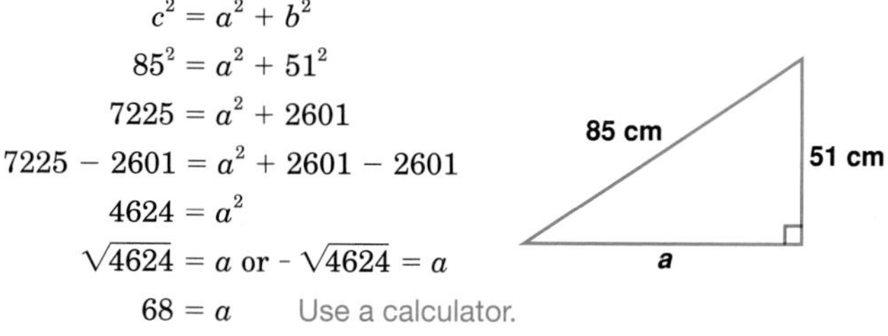

$c^2 = a^2 + b^2$

$85^2 = a^2 + 51^2$

$7225 = a^2 + 2601$

$7225 - 2601 = a^2 + 2601 - 2601$

$4624 = a^2$

$\sqrt{4624} = a$ or $-\sqrt{4624} = a$

$68 = a$ — Use a calculator.

The length of the side is 68 centimeters. — Compare with the estimate.

You can use the Pythagorean Theorem to see if a triangle is a right triangle.

Examples

Determine whether each triangle is a right triangle.

3

12 cm
9 cm
15 cm

$c^2 = a^2 + b^2$

$15^2 \stackrel{?}{=} 12^2 + 9^2$

$225 \stackrel{?}{=} 144 + 81$

$225 = 225$

The triangle is a right triangle.

Alternate Strategies: Reteaching the Lesson

Reteaching Activity

Using Models Using graph paper, have students model right triangles and determine the length of the third side if the lengths of two sides are known. Confirm by counting squares or using a calculator.

Reteaching Masters Booklet, **p. 123**

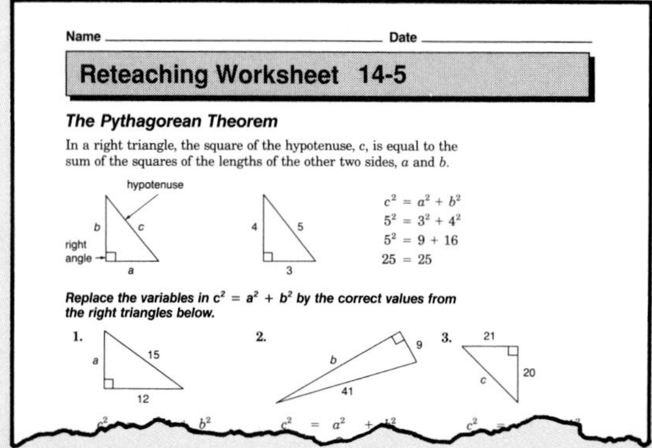

Name ______ Date ______

Reteaching Worksheet 14-5

The Pythagorean Theorem

In a right triangle, the square of the hypotenuse, c, is equal to the sum of the squares of the lengths of the other two sides, a and b.

hypotenuse; b; c; right angle; a — 4; 5; 3

$c^2 = a^2 + b^2$
$5^2 = 3^2 + 4^2$
$5^2 = 9 + 16$
$25 = 25$

Replace the variables in $c^2 = a^2 + b^2$ by the correct values from the right triangles below.

1. a; 15; 12 **2.** b; 9; 41 **3.** 21; 20; c

4

5 in. 12 in. 10 in.

$c^2 = a^2 + b^2$

$12^2 \stackrel{?}{=} 10^2 + 5^2$

$144 \stackrel{?}{=} 100 + 25$

$144 \neq 125$

The triangle is not a right triangle.

Checking for Understanding

1. hypotenuse

Communicating Algebra

1. The side opposite the right angle of a right triangle is called the __?__.
2. The Pythagorean Theorem states that __?__. See margin.
3. The Pythagorean Theorem only holds for __?__ triangles. right

Guided Practice

Identify the lengths of the hypotenuse and legs in each right triangle.

4. hypotenuse : 5 legs : 3, 4

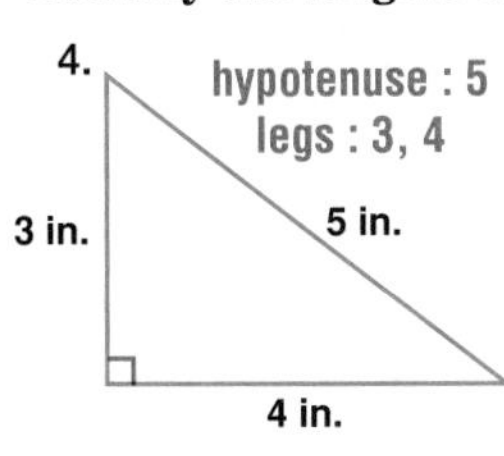

5. hypotenuse : 17 legs : 15, 8

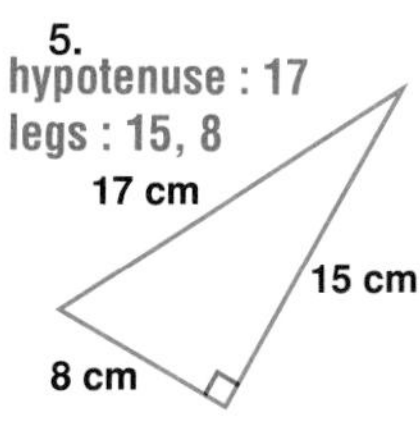

6. hypotenuse : 25 legs : 24, 7

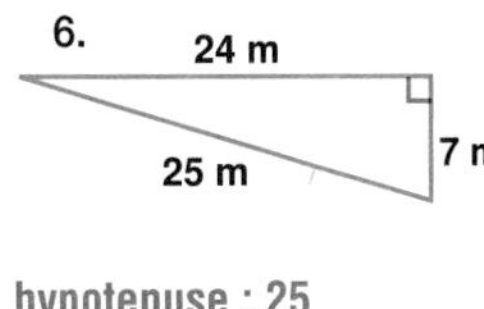

State an equation you should use to find the length of the hypotenuse of each right triangle. Then find the length of the hypotenuse.

7. $c^2 = 9^2 + 12^2$, $c = 15$

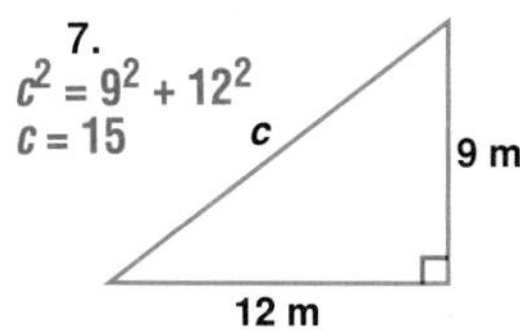

8. $c^2 = 5^2 + 12^2$, $c = 13$

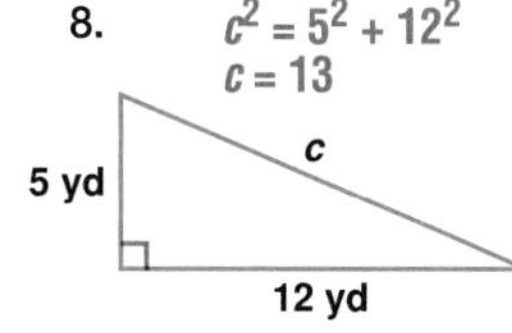

9. $c^2 = 9^2 + 40^2$, $c = 41$

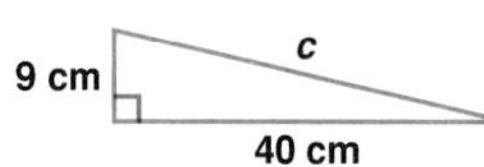

Exercises

Independent Practice

Use the Pythagorean Theorem to find the length of the hypotenuse of each right triangle. The lengths of the legs are given. Round decimal answers to the nearest tenth.

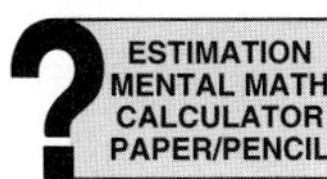

10. 6 mm, 8 mm 10 mm
11. 9 ft, 40 ft 41 ft
12. 8 m, 15 m 17 m
13. 12 in., 9 in. 15 in.
14. 24 m, 7 m 25 m
15. 5 yd, 12 yd 13 yd
16. 20 cm, 21 cm 29 cm
17. 15 in., 36 in. 39 in.
18. 16 ft, 30 ft 34 ft

Solve each equation. 21. 91, −91 24. 72, −72

19. $101^2 = a^2 + 20^2$ 99, −99
20. $89^2 = a^2 + 80^2$ 39, −39
21. $109^2 = 60^2 + b^2$
22. $85^2 = 13^2 + b^2$ 84, −84
23. $61^2 = a^2 + 60^2$ 11, −11
24. $97^2 = 65^2 + b^2$

3 PRACTICE/APPLY

Checking the Concept

Have students check Exercises 7-9 by using the lengths of the hypotenuse and one leg and confirming the length of the other leg.

Error Analysis

Watch for students who add the squares of the two known sides, no matter what two sides are given. **Prevent by** always labeling the right angle and emphasizing the difference in the hypotenuse and a leg.

Independent Practice

Homework Assignment	
Basic	11-37 odd, 39-45, 47, 48
Average	10-36 even, 39-48
Honors	18-32 even, 33-48

Practice Masters Booklet, **p. 137**

Name ____________ Date ________

Practice Worksheet 14-5

The Pythagorean Theorem

Use the Pythagorean Theorem to find the length of the hypotenuse of each right triangle. The lengths of the legs are given. Round decimal answers to the nearest tenth.

1. 5 cm, 18 cm 18.7 cm
2. 3 mm, 4 mm 5 mm
3. 6 ft, 10 ft 11.7 ft
4. 7 yd, 11 yd 13.0 yd
5. 15 in., 20 in. 25 in.
6. 6 km, 6 km 8.5 km

Solve each equation.

7. $13^2 = a^2 + 5^2$ 12
8. $29^2 = 21^2 + b^2$ 20
9. $17^2 = 8^2 + b^2$ 15
10. $25^2 = a^2 + 7^2$ 24
11. $340^2 = a^2 + 160^2$ 300
12. $500^2 = 300^2 + b^2$ 400

Find the missing measure for each right triangle. Round decimal answers to the nearest tenth.

13. b, 7 in.; c, 9 in. 5.7 in.
14. a, 5 ft; c, 10 ft 8.7 ft
15. a, 9 yd; c, 16 yd 13.2 yd
16. b, 15 cm; c, 20 cm 13.2 cm
17. a, 8 m; c, 12 m 8.9 m
18. b, 5 mm; c, 16 mm 15.2 mm

The measures of the three sides of a triangle are given. Determine if each triangle is a right triangle.

19. 8 km, 15 km, 17 km right triangle
20. 15 in., 20 in., 25 in. right triangle
21. 8 mm, 9 mm, 15 mm not a right triangle
22. 10 mi, 20 mi, 30 mi not a right triangle

Additional Answer

2. In a right triangle, the square of the hypotenuse is equal to the sum of the squares of the lengths of the legs.

Chapter 14, Quiz A (Lesson 14-1 through 14-5) is available in the Evaluation Masters Booklet, p. 124.

4 CLOSE

Assessment Option

Modeling Have students construct right triangles. Then have them construct three squares using each side of the triangle and compare the areas of the squares.

Enrichment Masters Booklet, **p. 123**

Name ______________________ Date ______________

Enrichment Worksheet 14-5

Pythagorean Theorem

Use the **Pythagorean Theorem** to find the area of the shaded region in the figure at the right.

Think of the figure as four triangles and a square.	Think of the figure as a large square.

area of the 4 triangles		area of the center square		area of large square
$4 \times \left(\frac{1}{2} \times a \times b\right)$	+	c^2		$= a^2 + a \times b + b^2 + a \times b$
$2 \times a \times b$	+	c^2		$= a^2 + b^2 + a \times b + a \times b$
$2 \times a \times b$	+	c^2		$= a^2 + b^2 + 2 \times a \times b$
$2 \times a \times b$	+	$c^2 - 2 \times a \times b$		$= a^2 + b^2$
		c^2		$= a^2 + b^2$

The relationship $c^2 = a^2 + b^2$ is true for all right triangles.

Use the Pythagorean theorem to find the area of A, B, and C in each of the following. Then, answer true or false for the statement A + B = C.

1. Squares (A 9, B 12, C 15) — A: 81, B: 144, C: 225; true

2. Equilateral Triangles (A $1.5\sqrt{3}$, 3; B $2\sqrt{3}$, 4; C $2.5\sqrt{3}$, 5) — A: $2.25\sqrt{3}$, B: $4\sqrt{3}$, C: $6.25\sqrt{3}$; true

3. Semicircles (A 3, B 4, C 5) — A: 1.125π, B: 2.000π, C: 3.125π; true

Find the missing measure for each right triangle. Round decimal answers to the nearest tenth.

25. b, 77 m; c, 85 m **36 m**
26. b, 55 cm; c, 73 cm **48 cm**
27. a, 15 ft; c, 17 ft **8 ft**
28. a, 40 in.; c, 41 in. **9 in.**
29. a, 35 km; c, 37 km **12 km**
30. b, 91 yd; c, 109 yd **60 yd**
31. b, 140 in.; c, 149 in. **51 in.**
32. a, 19 ft; c, 181 ft **180 ft**

The measures of the three sides of a triangle are given. Determine if each triangle is a right triangle.

33. 7 ft, 9 ft, 6 ft **no**
34. 5 m, 12 m, 13 m **yes**
35. 9 in., 12 in., 14 in. **no**
36. 4 m, 7 m, 5 m **no**
37. 30 cm, 24 cm, 18 cm **yes**
38. 9 cm, 40 cm, 41 cm **yes**

Mixed Review

39. Simplify $12a + 2(3a + 4)$. (Lesson 1-4) **$18a + 8$**
40. Solve $p = 82.37 - 25.5$. (Lesson 5-4) **56.87**
41. Find the volume of a rectangular prism that has length 10 cm, width 7 cm, and height 3 cm. (Lesson 13-7) **210 cm^3**
42. *True* or *false*: 82 is a perfect square. (Lesson 14-1) **false**
43. Simplify $\sqrt{56}$. (Lesson 14-4) **$2\sqrt{14}$**

Solve. Round decimal answers to the nearest tenth.

Connection

44. **Geometry** The points $R(2, 4)$ and $T(6, 1)$ are graphed on the coordinate system at the right. Find the distance between R and T. (Hint: Notice the right triangle. First find the measures of $\overline{RS}$ and $\overline{ST}$.) **5**

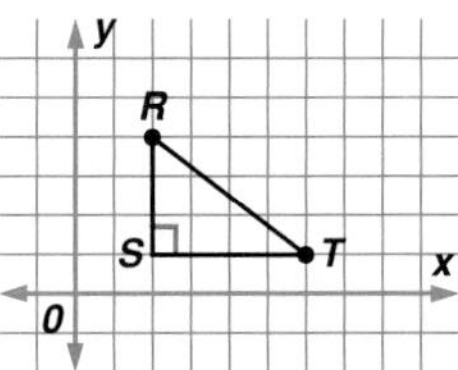

Applications

45. **Sky Diving** The radius of the canopy of a parachute is 12 feet. If the load is suspended 16 feet below, how long are the suspension lines? **20 ft**

46. **Space Travel** The parachute used by the Viking Lander on Mars had a radius of 8 meters and the payload was suspended 20 meters below the canopy. How long were the suspension lines? **21.5 m**

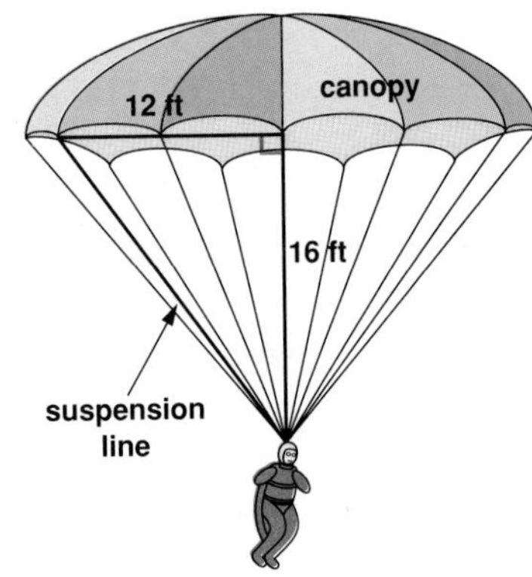

Critical Thinking

47. How is the length of a diagonal of a rectangle related to the length and the width of the rectangle? **The square of the length of a diagonal equals the square of the width plus the square of the length.**

Wrap-Up

48. Use an equation and the figure at the right to restate the Pythagorean Theorem. **$z^2 = x^2 + y^2$**

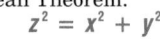

y x z

Alternate Strategies: Extending the Lesson

Enrichment

Writing Connection Have students work in groups of two to write verbal problems using the Pythagorean Theorem. Trade and solve.

Cooperative Learning

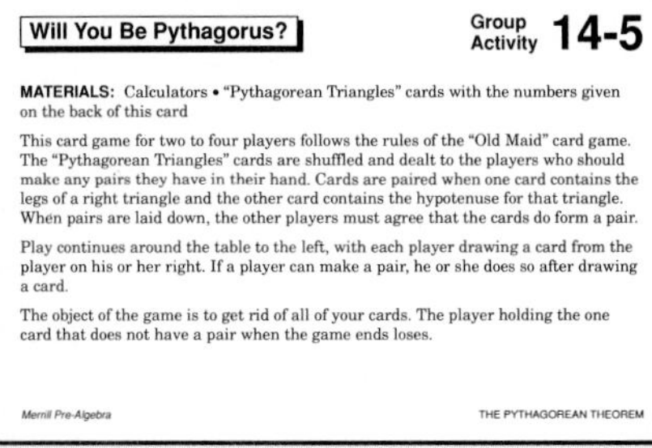

Will You Be Pythagorus? Group Activity **14-5**

MATERIALS: Calculators • "Pythagorean Triangles" cards with the numbers given on the back of this card

This card game for two to four players follows the rules of the "Old Maid" card game. The "Pythagorean Triangles" cards are shuffled and dealt to the players who should make any pairs they have in their hand. Cards are paired when one card contains the legs of a right triangle and the other card contains the hypotenuse for that triangle. When pairs are laid down, the other players must agree that the cards do form a pair.

Play continues around the table to the left, with each player drawing a card from the player on his or her right. If a player can make a pair, he or she does so after drawing a card.

The object of the game is to get rid of all of your cards. The player holding the one card that does not have a pair when the game ends loses.

Merrill Pre-Algebra THE PYTHAGOREAN THEOREM

Exploration

Graphing Irrationals

Materials: compass, straightedge

In this Exploration you will graph irrational numbers on a number line.

You know how to graph integers and rational numbers on a number line. You can also graph irrational numbers on a number line. Consider the following method for graphing $\sqrt{2}$.

▶ At 1, construct a perpendicular line segment 1 unit in length. Draw the line segment shown in color. Label it *c*.

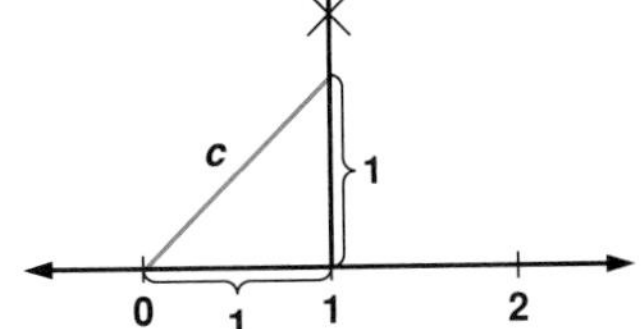

▶ The Pythagorean Theorem can be used to show that *c* is $\sqrt{2}$ units long.

$c^2 = a^2 + b^2$

$c^2 = 1^2 + 1^2$

$c^2 = 2$

$c = \sqrt{2}$

▶ Open the compass to the length of the segment shown in color. Construct a congruent segment on the number line.

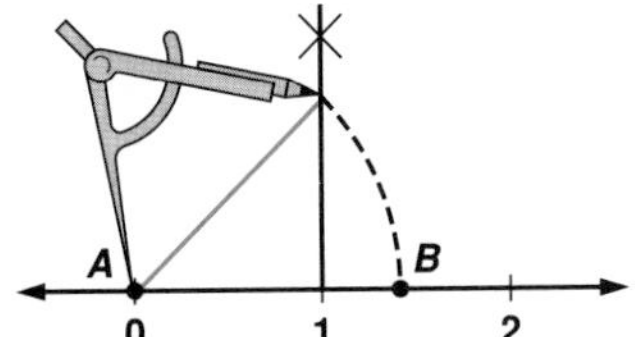

Your Turn: **Graph $\sqrt{5}$ on a number line. Think of $\sqrt{5}$ as $\sqrt{2^2 + 1^2}$.**
Graph $\sqrt{8}$ on a number line. Think of $\sqrt{8}$ as $\sqrt{2^2 + 2^2}$.
See students' work.

Analysis

1. Describe a method to graph $\sqrt{10}$. See margin.
2. Explain how the graph of $\sqrt{2}$ can be used to locate the point that represents $\sqrt{3}$. See margin.
3. Explain how to graph $-\sqrt{2}$. Construct $\sqrt{2}$ to the left of 0.
4. Can all real numbers be graphed on a number line? yes

SET-UP

Materials

- compass, straightedge

You may wish to use the Exploration worksheet provided on page 66 of the Lab Manual.

Additional Answers

1. Construct a right triangle with sides 3 units and 1 unit.
2. Use the graph of $\sqrt{2}$ as the base of a right triangle with a height of 1.

For Students Students can construct the right triangles on centimeter grid paper and use a metric ruler to measure and graph the irrational numbers if compasses are not available.

For the Overhead Projector You can use a grid and a ruler to model this exploration on the overhead.

EE: 1A, 1C, 1E, 4D

EXPLORATION

Graphing Irrational Numbers

Objective Students will use the Pythagorean Theorem to graph irrational numbers.

1 FOCUS

The purpose of this exploration is to use compass and straightedge to construct a right triangle and identify the hypotenuse as an irrational number whose length can be used to graph the irrational number.

2 TEACH

Using Manipulatives

Review the construction of a perpendicular, if necessary. Have students construct the right triangle as you model each step on the chalkboard or overhead. Ask students to estimate the value of $\sqrt{2}$ based on the graph. Students can check their estimates using a calculator.

3 PRACTICE/APPLY

Using Charts

Have students copy and complete the chart below and use it to answer Exercises 1, 2, and 4.

BASE	ALTITUDE	HYPOTENUSE
1	1	$\sqrt{2}$
1	$\sqrt{2}$	$\sqrt{3}$
1	$\sqrt{3}$	2
1	2	$\sqrt{5}$
$\sqrt{3}$	$\sqrt{3}$	$\sqrt{6}$
2	$\sqrt{3}$	$\sqrt{7}$
2	2	$\sqrt{8}$
2	$\sqrt{5}$	3

4 CLOSE

Speaking Connection

Have students use the completed chart to explain their answer to Exercise 4.

Lesson Notes 14-6

5-Minute Check
(over Lesson 14-5)

The measures of the three sides of a triangle are given. Determine if each triangle is a right triangle.

1. 15 ft, 17 ft, 8 ft **yes**
2. 9 cm, 5 cm, 12 cm **no**
3. 8 cm, 5 cm, 4 cm **no**
4. 11 in., 60 in., 61 in. **yes**
5. 5 m, 3 m, 4 m **yes**

Transparency 14-6 contains the 5-Minute Check and a teaching aid for this lesson.

1 FOCUS

The purpose of this lesson is to use the Pythagorean Theorem to solve problems involving right triangles.

Motivating the Lesson

Show students an umbrella. Measure its length then ask students the dimensions of the smallest suitcase in which it would fit.

2 TEACH

Chalkboard Examples

Mr. Birkhimer is planning to build a fence around his garden. A diagram of the garden is shown below. How much fencing does Mr. Birkhimer need to buy? **84 ft of fencing**

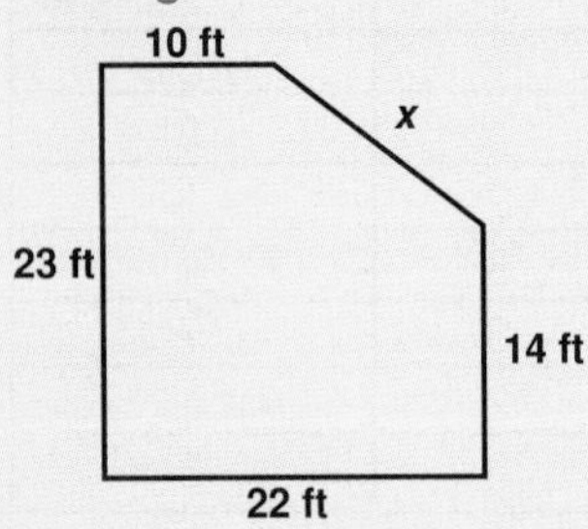

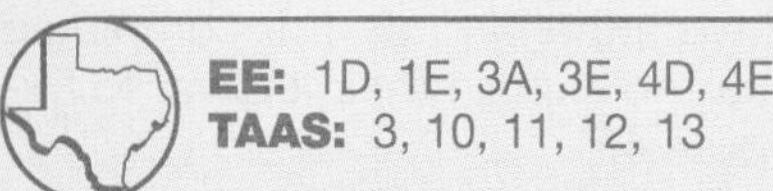

Problem Solving

14-6 Using the Pythagorean Theorem

Objective:
Solve problems using the Pythagorean Theorem.

Valerie Hayes, Vice President of Express Flying Service, is planning to build a security fence around a field to use as a holding area for small planes. A diagram of the field is shown at the right. How much fencing does Ms. Hayes need to buy?

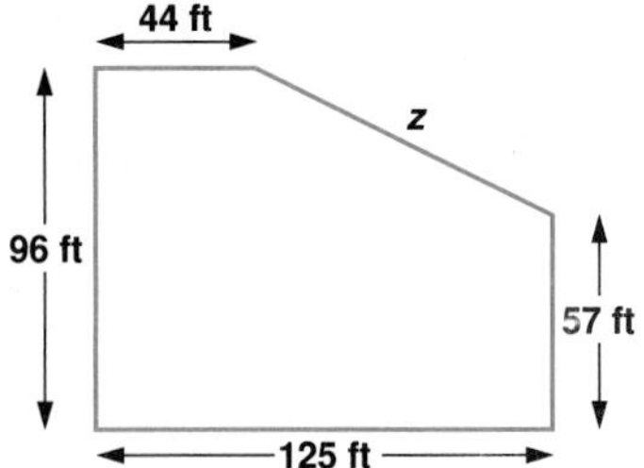

Explore *What is asked?* How much fencing is needed? *What is implied?* What is the perimeter of the field?

Plan To find the perimeter, you must find the unknown length, z. You can separate the figure into more familiar shapes as shown at the left.

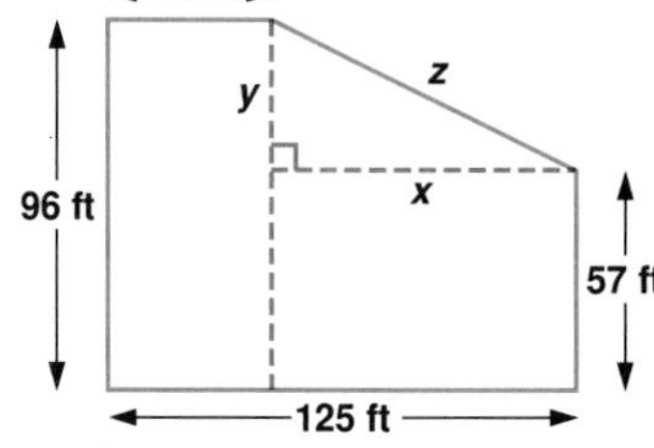

The hypotenuse of the right triangle is the side with length z. Find the measures of the legs of the right triangle and then use the Pythagorean Theorem to find the length of the hypotenuse.

Solve First find the measures of the legs.

$x = 125 - 44$ $\quad$ $y = 96 - 57$

$x = 81$ $\quad$ $y = 39$

Now apply the Pythagorean Theorem.

$z^2 = x^2 + y^2$

$z^2 = 81^2 + 39^2$ Replace x with 81 and y with 39.

$z^2 = 6561 + 1521$

$z^2 = 8082$

8082 [$\sqrt{x}$] 89.899944

$z \approx 90$

Finally, find the perimeter.

$96 + 44 + 90 + 57 + 125 = 412$

So, 412 feet of fencing is needed.

Why is the perimeter less than the perimeter of a 125 ft by 96 ft rectangle? **because the area is smaller**

Examine If the field included the corner area, its perimeter would be $2 \cdot 96 + 2 \cdot 125$ or 442 feet. The answer should be a little less than this. Thus, the answer is reasonable.

Bell Ringer

What positive number is equal to its square added to its opposite? **2**

Checking for Understanding

Communicating Algebra

1. Discuss each step that was used to solve the example. See margin.
2. Find another way to separate the irregular figure on page 542 to form rectangles and a right triangle. Then explain how your plan can be used to solve this problem. See margin.

Guided Practice

State an equation that can be used to find the answer to each question. Then solve. Round decimal answers to the nearest tenth.

3. 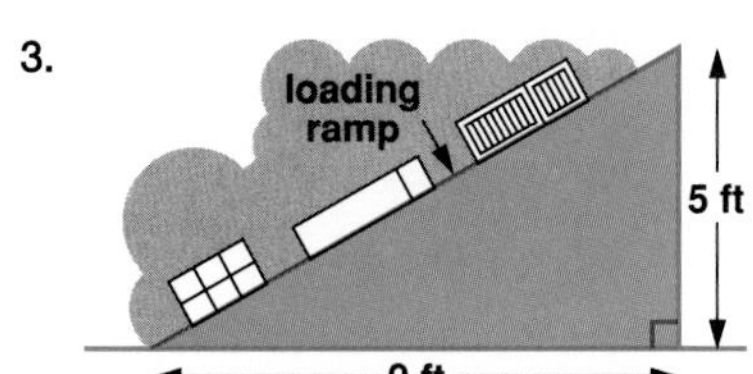

How long is the ramp? $c^2 = 5^2 + 9^2$; 10.3 ft

4. How high is the television screen?

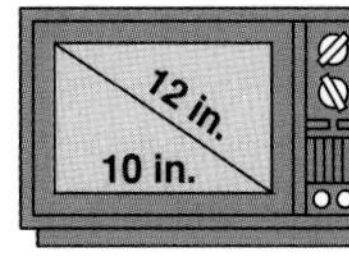

$12^2 = 10^2 + b^2$; 6.6 in.

5. 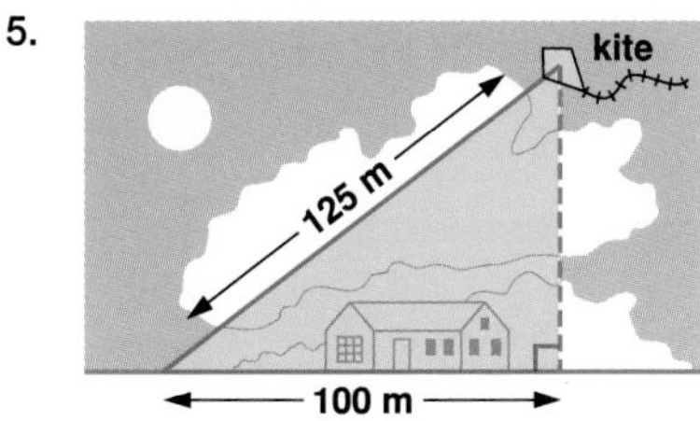

How high is the kite?
$125^2 = 100^2 + b^2$; 75 m

6. 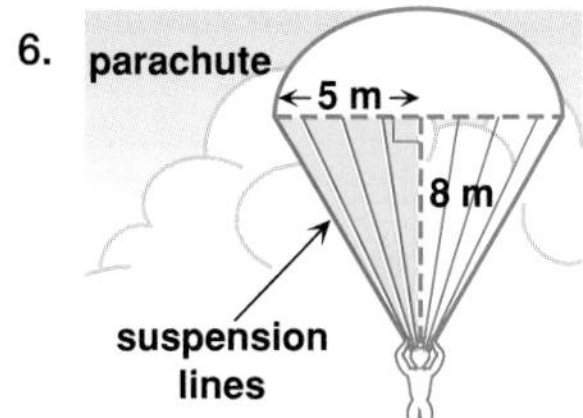

How long are the suspension lines?
$c^2 = 5^2 + 8^2$; 9.4 m

Exercises

Independent Practice

Solve. Round decimal answers to the nearest tenth.

7. 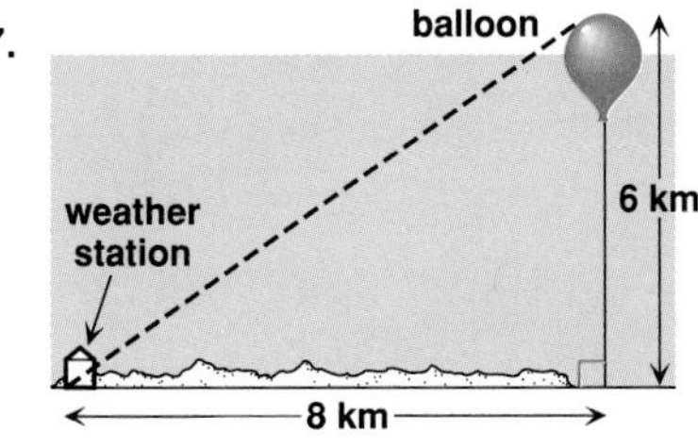

How far is the weather balloon from the weather station? 10 km

8. 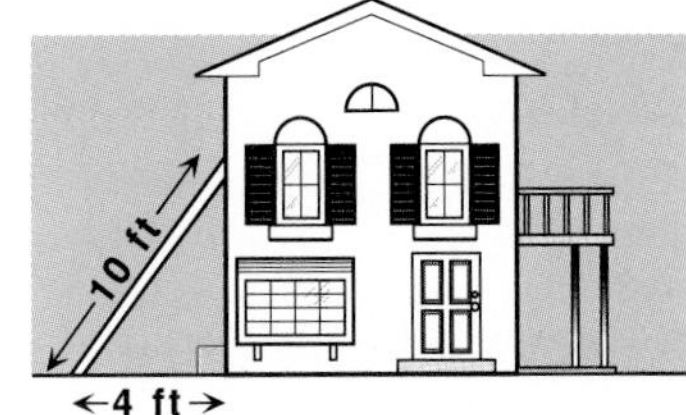

At what height does the ladder touch the house? 9.2 ft

9. The diagonal brace on a gate is 5 feet long. The height of the gate is 4 feet. How wide is the gate? 3 ft
10. The members of the Campers Club hike 7 miles east, then 3 miles south to find their overnight camping spot. How far are they from their starting point? 7.6 miles

3 PRACTICE/APPLY

Checking the Concept

Give students the option of either writing or verbalizing the equations in the solutions of Exercises 3-6.

Error Analysis

Watch for students who, when using the Pythagorean Theorem, first add the lengths of the legs then square the sum.
Prevent by listing the steps to be used for solution then verbalizing each step.

Independent Practice

Homework Assignment

Basic	7-16
Average	7-16
Honors	7-16
All	Mid-Chapter Quiz 1-10

Practice Masters Booklet, **p. 138**

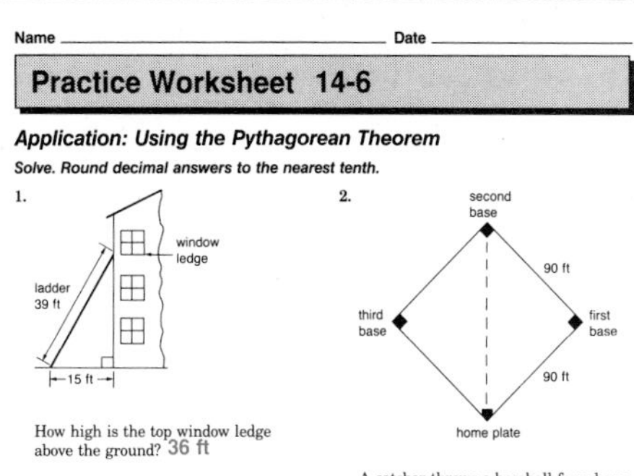
Name Date

Practice Worksheet 14-6

Application: Using the Pythagorean Theorem

Solve. Round decimal answers to the nearest tenth.

1. [figure: window ledge; ladder 39 ft; 15 ft]
How high is the top window ledge above the ground? 36 ft

2. [figure: second base; 90 ft; third base; first base; 90 ft; home plate]
A catcher throws a baseball from home plate to second base. How many feet does the ball travel? 127.3 ft

3. Mindy and Christine started from the same point. Christine traveled west at a rate of 30 miles per hour. Mindy traveled south at a rate of 40 miles per hour. How far apart were they at the end of one hour? 50 mi

4. Look at the baseball diamond in Exercise 2 above. What is the shortest distance from third base to first base? 127.3 ft

5. A helicopter flies 9 miles due west, and then 6 miles due south. How far is it from its starting point? 10.8 mi

6. A utility pole is 8 m high. A cable is stretched from the top of the pole to a point on the ground that is 5 m from the bottom of the pole. How long is the cable? 9.4 m

Alternate Strategies: Reteaching the Lesson

Reteaching Activity

Using Models Provide students with an assortment of five-sided shapes cut from construction paper. Have them find the perimeter of each by measuring four sides, dividing the shapes into rectangles and right triangles and calculating the fifth side.

Reteaching Masters Booklet, **p. 124**

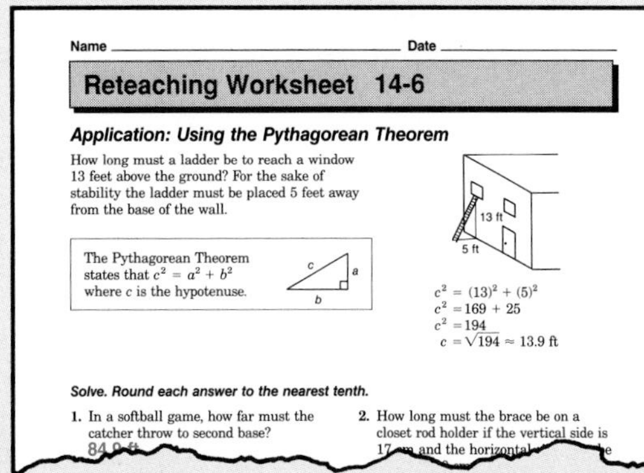
Name Date

Reteaching Worksheet 14-6

Application: Using the Pythagorean Theorem

How long must a ladder be to reach a window 13 feet above the ground? For the sake of stability the ladder must be placed 5 feet away from the base of the wall.

The Pythagorean Theorem states that $c^2 = a^2 + b^2$ where c is the hypotenuse.

[figure: 13 ft; 5 ft]

$c^2 = (13)^2 + (5)^2$
$c^2 = 169 + 25$
$c^2 = 194$
$c = \sqrt{194} \approx 13.9$ ft

Solve. Round each answer to the nearest tenth.

1. In a softball game, how far must the catcher throw to second base? 84.9 ft
2. How long must the brace be on a closet rod holder if the vertical side is 17 cm and the horizontal ...

4 CLOSE

Assessment Option

Modeling Use a compass and straightedge and graph $\sqrt{13}, \sqrt{10}$, and $\sqrt{17}$.

Additional Answers

1. Sample answer; First, the height of the triangle is found by subtracting the width of the rectangle below the triangle from the height of the other rectangle. Then, the base of the triangle is found by subtracting the width of the rectangle at the right of the triangle from the base of the figure. These two values were plugged into the Pythagorean Theorem to find the missing dimension which was added to the other dimensions to find the perimeter.
2. 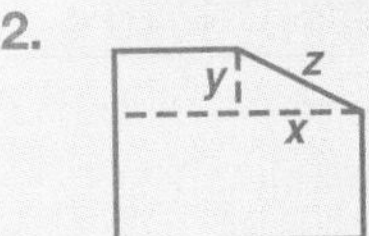

   Find the measure of the legs the same way as in the example and apply the Pythagorean Theorem.

Enrichment Masters Booklet, **p. 124**

Name ______ Date ______

Enrichment Worksheet 14-6

Using Squares and Square Roots

Solve. Use any problem solving strategy.

1. A circle has an area of 616 cm^2 and a circumference of 88 cm. Find the radius of the circle. Use $\frac{22}{7}$ for π. 14 cm
2. An airplane travels due west 65 km and then due north 72 km. How far is the plane from its starting point? 97 km
3. A cable stretches from the top of an electrical pole to an attachment on the ground 7 feet from the base of the pole. If the pole is 24 feet tall, how long is the cable? 25 ft
4. Fabric 36 inches wide is \$4.50 per yard. What is the cost of 45 square feet of fabric? \$22.50
5. A ladder 13 feet long is leaning against a building. It touches the building at a point 12 feet above the ground. How far from the building is the base of the ladder? 5 ft
6. Cindy is standing 28 feet from a point directly below her kite. How high is her kite flying if the string attached to it is 53 feet long and she is holding the string at a point 3 feet above the ground? 48 feet
7. A triangle has sides of 21 inches, 28 inches, and 29 inches. If a line indicating the height of the triangle touches the 29-inch side at a point 7 inches from the 21-inch side, what is the measure of the height? about 19.8 in.
8. The area of a rectangular field is 216 km^2 and the perimeter is 84 km. The measure of one side equals the square of the measure of the other side. Find the dimensions of the field. 6 km by 36 km

11. Luise takes a shortcut to school by walking diagonally across an empty lot. The rectangular lot is 20 meters wide and 40 meters long. How much shorter is the shortcut than a route on the sides of the lot? **15.3 m**

Mixed Review

12. *True* or *false*: If the corresponding parts of two triangles are congruent, then the two triangles are congruent. (Lesson 12-8) **true**
13. Use the Pythagorean Theorem to find the length of the hypotenuse of a right triangle that has sides 10 meters and 24 meters. (Lesson 14-5) **26 m**

Decision Making

14. For safety reasons the base of a 24-foot ladder should be at least 8 feet from the wall. Can a 24-foot ladder be used to reach a window that is 22 feet above the ground? Explain. **yes; $24^2 \overset{?}{\geq} 8^2 + 22^2 \rightarrow 576 \geq 548$**

Critical Thinking

15. When separating the drawing of the irregularly shaped field on page 542, why is it convenient to form rectangles and right triangles? **It is easiest to find the missing lengths of rectangles and right triangles.**

Wrap-Up

16. Describe some real-life problems that can be solved by using the Pythagorean Theorem. **Sample answers: building a ramp, finding the distance across a lake**

Mid-Chapter Quiz

Find each value. Round decimal answers to the nearest tenth. (Lessons 14-1, 14-2)

1. $\sqrt{36}$ **6**
2. 13^2 **169**
3. $-\sqrt{12}$ **-3.5**

Name the sets of numbers to which each number belongs: the whole numbers, the integers, the rational numbers, the irrational numbers, and/or the real numbers. (Lesson 14-4)

4. $-\sqrt{49}$ **integer, rational, real**
5. $\sqrt{6}$ **irrational, real**

Solve. Round decimal answers to the nearest tenth. (Lessons 14-4, 14-5)

6. $t^2 = 324$ **18, -18**
7. $30^2 = y^2 + 24^2$ **18, -18**
8. 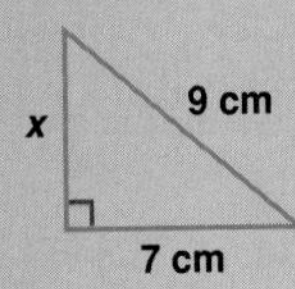

   What is the value of x? **5.7 cm**
9. 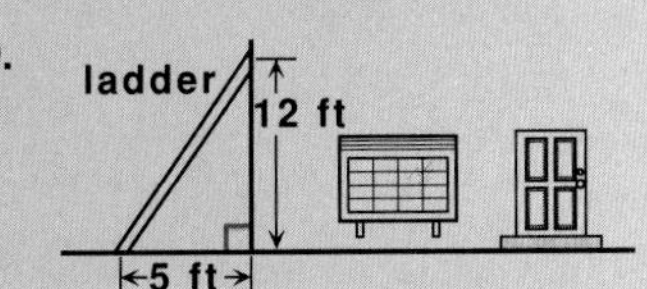

   How long is the ladder? **13 ft**
10. There are 27 students in an algebra class. Of these students, 12 students are in the school band and 9 students are in the school choir. If 5 students are in both the band and choir, how many of these students are in neither the band nor choir? (Lesson 14–3) **11 students**

Alternate Strategies: Extending the Lesson

Enrichment

Consumer Connection The size given for a television set is the diagonal length of the screen. Have students use ads for television sets and find the height and width of each screen, assuming the screen is square.

Cooperative Learning

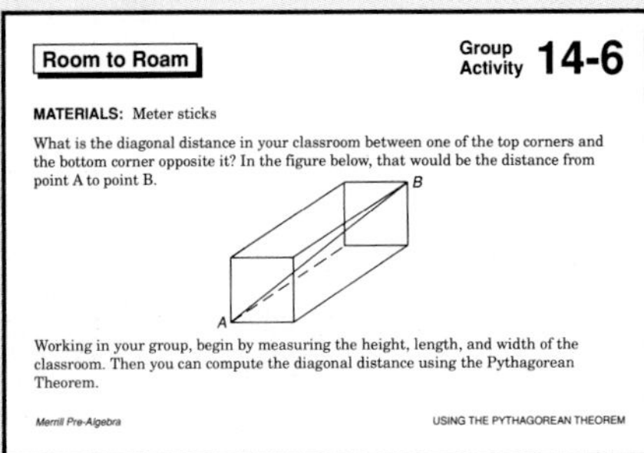

Room to Roam Group Activity **14-6**

MATERIALS: Meter sticks

What is the diagonal distance in your classroom between one of the top corners and the bottom corner opposite it? In the figure below, that would be the distance from point A to point B.

Working in your group, begin by measuring the height, length, and width of the classroom. Then you can compute the diagonal distance using the Pythagorean Theorem.

Merrill Pre-Algebra USING THE PYTHAGOREAN THEOREM

14-7 Special Right Triangles

Objective:
Find missing measures in 30° - 60° and 45° - 45° right triangles.

Suppose you draw a square *ABCD* with sides 4 cm long. Then you draw diagonal *AC*. You can use a protractor to find that $\angle CAB$, $\angle ACB$, $\angle CAD$, and $\angle ACD$ each measure 45°. The triangles formed are called 45° - 45° right triangles.

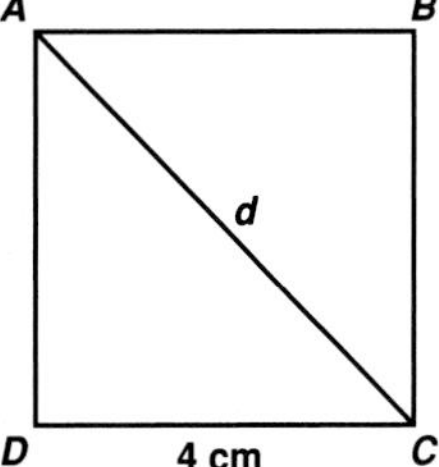

Now use the Pythagorean Theorem to find the length of diagonal *AC*.

Let d represent the measure of $\overline{AC}$.

$d^2 = (AD)^2 + (DC)^2$

$d^2 = 4^2 + 4^2$ The length of each side is 4 cm.

$d^2 = 32$

$d = \sqrt{32}$

$d = \sqrt{2 \cdot 4^2}$ or $4\sqrt{2}$ The length of the diagonal is $4\sqrt{2}$ cm.

Suppose the length of each side of the square were 5 cm. What would be the length of $\overline{AC}$? Using the Pythagorean Theorem, you find that the length is $5\sqrt{2}$ cm. These and other examples suggest that in a 45° - 45° right triangle, you can find the length of the hypotenuse by multiplying the length of a leg by $\sqrt{2}$.

Example

If the length of the hypotenuse of a 45° - 45° right triangle is $2\sqrt{2}$ cm, what is the length of each leg? **2 cm, 2 cm**

1 Find the length of $\overline{AB}$ in $\triangle ABC$.

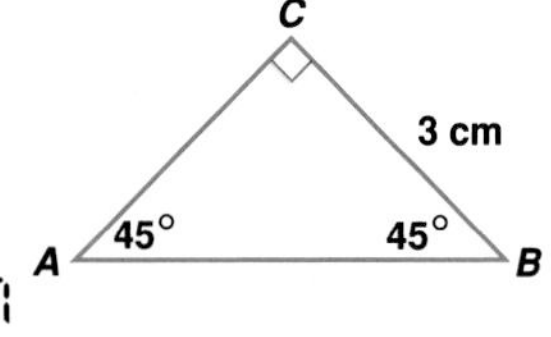

$c = a\sqrt{2}$

$c = 3\sqrt{2}$

3 [×] 2 [√x] [=] 4.2426407

The length of $\overline{AB}$ is about 4 cm.

The sides of a right triangle with a 30° angle and a 60° angle also have special relationships. In a 30° - 60° right triangle, the length of the side opposite the 30° angle is one-half the length of the hypotenuse.

$a = \frac{1}{2}c$ or $c = 2a$

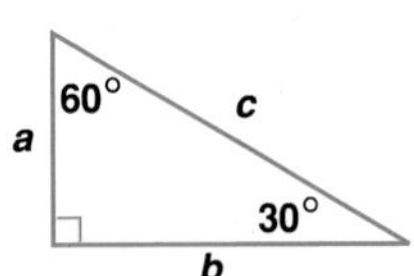

Bell Ringer

Name two jobs that would use the Pythagorean Theorem. **Possible answers; Air traffic controller, construction worker.**

Lesson Notes 14-7

5-Minute Check
(over Lesson 14-6)

Solve. Round decimal answers to the nearest tenth.

1. Ming's glider landed 20 miles east and 21 miles north of the starting point. How far is the glider from the starting point? **29 miles**
2. A fifteen-foot ladder is placed against the house. The base of the ladder is nine feet from the base of the house. How far above the ground does the ladder touch the house? **12 feet**

Transparency 14-7 contains the 5-Minute Check and a teaching aid for this lesson.

1 FOCUS

The purpose of this lesson is to study 45°-45° and 30°-60° triangles and find missing side lengths.

Motivating the Lesson

Draw a square and its diagonal on the chalkboard or overhead and ask students to describe the two triangles that are formed. **They are congruent isosceles right triangles.**

2 TEACH

Using Discussion

Draw the special right triangles on the chalkboard. Using student-generated numbers, develop the leg-hypotenuse-angle relationships.

Chalkboard Examples

- *For Example 1*
  Find the length of $\overline{CD}$ in $\triangle CDE$.

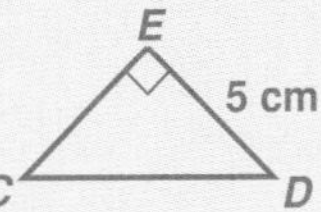

about 7 cm

EE: 1E, 3A, 3E, 4A, 4D, 4E
TAAS: 3, 11, 12

Chalkboard Examples

- *For Example 2*
  Find the length of $\overline{LM}$ in $\triangle HLM$.

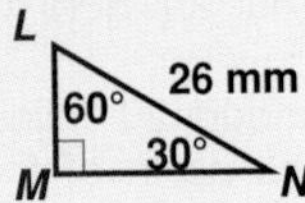

13 mm

- *For Example 3*
  Find the length of $\overline{ST}$ in $\triangle RST$.

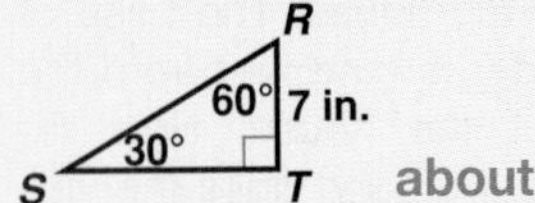

about 12 inches

3 PRACTICE/APPLY

Checking the Concept

After completing Exercises 3-6, have students find the side opposite the 60° angle in its simplest radical form.

Error Analysis

Watch for students who switch locations of the 30° and 60° labels on a 30°-60° triangle.
Prevent by reminding students that a 60° angle is twice the size of a 30° angle.

Practice Masters Booklet, **p. 139**

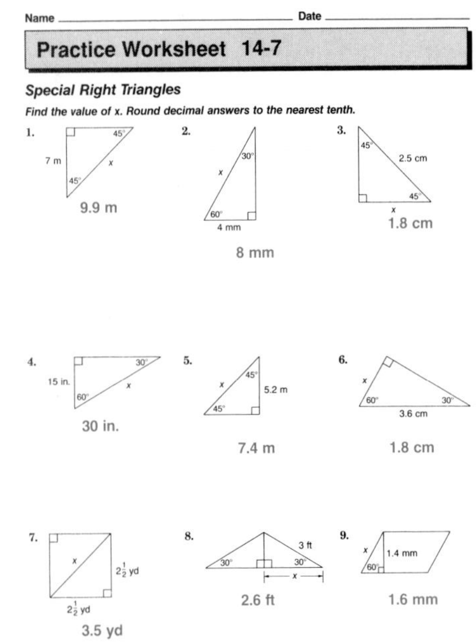

Name ________ Date ________

Practice Worksheet 14-7

Special Right Triangles

Find the value of x. Round decimal answers to the nearest tenth.

1. 7 m, 45°, 45°, x — 9.9 m
2. 30°, x, 60°, 4 mm — 8 mm
3. 45°, 2.5 cm, 45°, x — 1.8 cm
4. 15 in., 30°, 60°, x — 30 in.
5. 45°, 5.2 m, x, 45° — 7.4 m
6. x, 60°, 30°, 3.6 cm — 1.8 cm
7. x, $2\frac{1}{2}$ yd, $2\frac{1}{2}$ yd — 3.5 yd
8. 3 ft, 30°, 30°, x — 2.6 ft
9. x, 1.4 mm, 60° — 1.6 mm

Also, in a 30° - 60° right triangle, you can find the length of the side opposite the 60° angle by multiplying the length of the other leg by $\sqrt{3}$.

$$b = a\sqrt{3}$$

Examples

2 Find the length of $\overline{BC}$ in $\triangle ABC$.

B, 60°, 10 mm, a, 30°, C, A

$$a = \frac{1}{2}c$$

$$a = \frac{1}{2}(10) \quad \text{Replace } c \text{ with 10.}$$

$$a = 5$$

The length of $\overline{BC}$ is 5 mm.

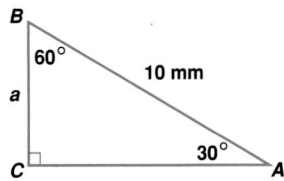

3 Find the length of $\overline{QR}$ in $\triangle PQR$.

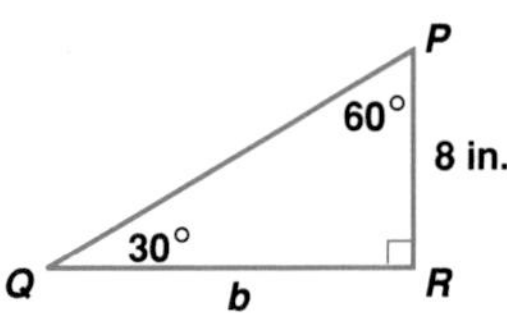

$$b = a\sqrt{3}$$

$$b = 8\sqrt{3} \quad \text{Replace } a \text{ with 8.}$$

8 [×] 3 [√x] [=] 13.856406

The length of $\overline{QR}$ is about 14 inches.

Checking for Understanding

Communicating Algebra

1. In a 30° - 60° right triangle, the length of the side opposite the 30° angle is __?__. one-half the length of the hypotenuse
2. In a 45° - 45° right triangle, the length of the hypotenuse can be found by __?__. multiplying the length of a leg by $\sqrt{2}$

Guided Practice

The length of the hypotenuse of a 30° - 60° right triangle is given. Find the length of the side opposite the 30° angle.

3. 8 in. 4 in.
4. $2\frac{1}{2}$ m $1\frac{1}{4}$ m
5. $4\frac{1}{4}$ in. $2\frac{1}{8}$ in.
6. 8.28 m 4.14 m

The length of a leg of a 45° - 45° right triangle is given. Find the length of the hypotenuse. Write your answer in simplest radical form.

7. 3 ft $3\sqrt{2}$ ft
8. 5 in. $5\sqrt{2}$ in.
9. $2\frac{1}{2}$ cm $2\frac{1}{2}\sqrt{2}$ cm
10. 14.9 mm $14.9\sqrt{2}$ mm

Exercises

Independent Practice

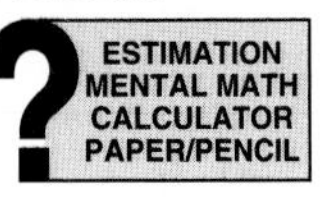

Find the value of x. Round decimal answers to the nearest tenth.

11. 4 in.

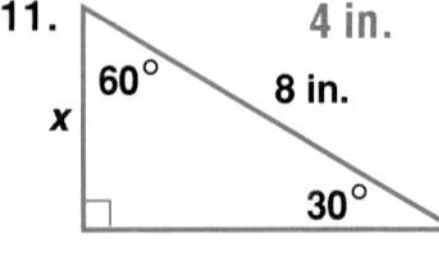

12. 7.1 ft

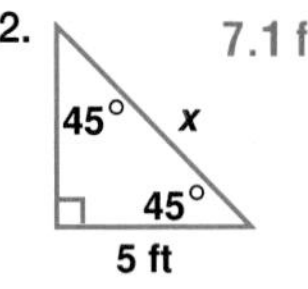

13. 9 m

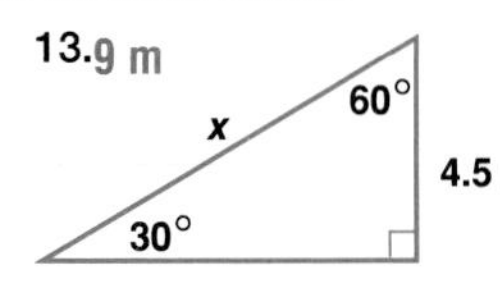

Alternate Strategies: Reteaching the Lesson

Reteaching Activity

Using Diagrams Draw the following triangles to use as reference until the concept is mastered.

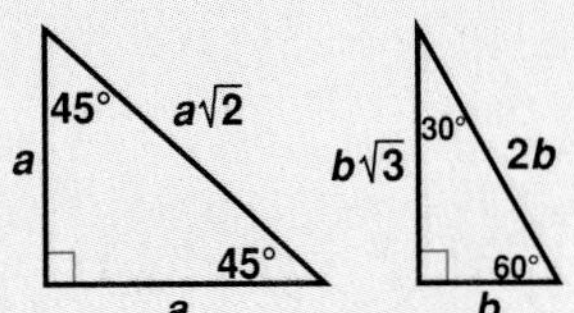

Reteaching Masters Booklet, **p. 125**

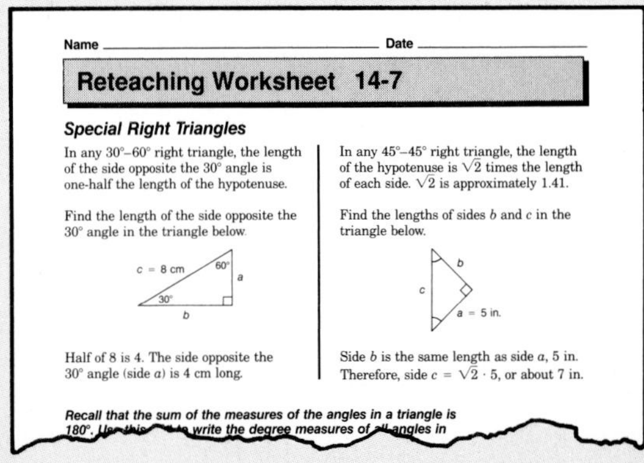

Name ________ Date ________

Reteaching Worksheet 14-7

Special Right Triangles

In any 30°–60° right triangle, the length of the side opposite the 30° angle is one-half the length of the hypotenuse.

Find the length of the side opposite the 30° angle in the triangle below.

c = 8 cm, 60°, a, 30°, b

Half of 8 is 4. The side opposite the 30° angle (side a) is 4 cm long.

In any 45°–45° right triangle, the length of the hypotenuse is $\sqrt{2}$ times the length of each side. $\sqrt{2}$ is approximately 1.41.

Find the lengths of sides b and c in the triangle below.

b, c, a = 5 in.

Side b is the same length as side a, 5 in. Therefore, side $c = \sqrt{2} \cdot 5$, or about 7 in.

Recall that the sum of the measures of the angles in a triangle is 180°. Use this ... write the degree measures of all angles in

Find the value of x. Round decimal answers to the nearest tenth.

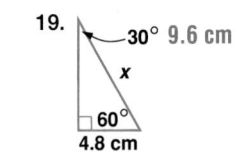

14. 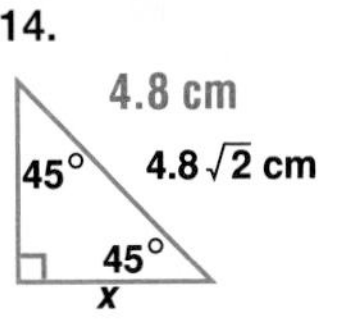

4.8 cm

15. 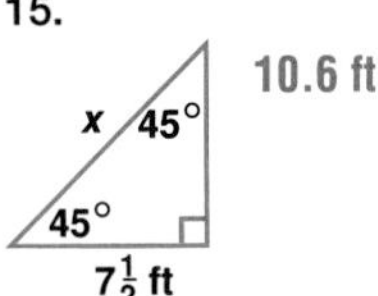

10.6 ft

16. 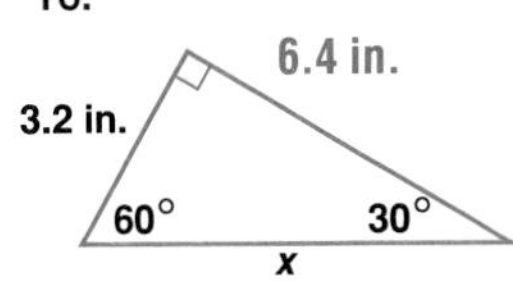

6.4 in.

17. 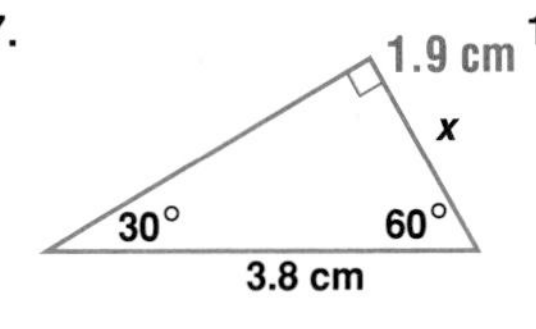

1.9 cm

18. 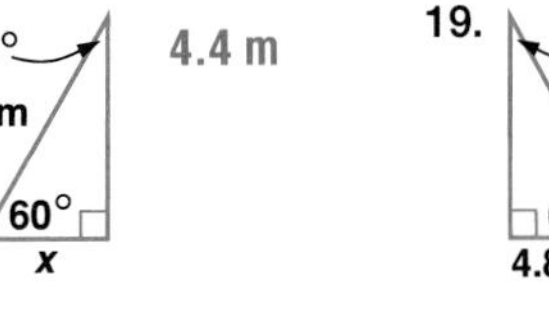

4.4 m

19. 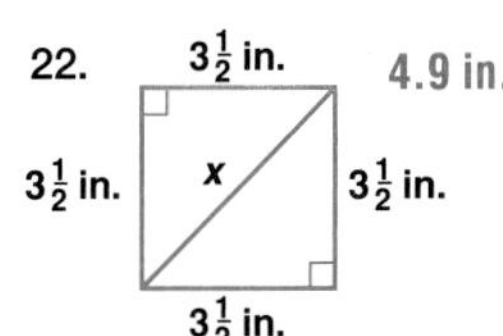

9.6 cm

20. 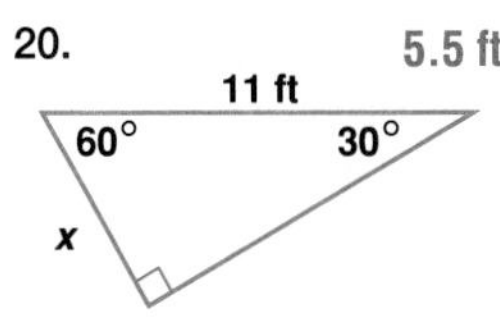

5.5 ft

21. 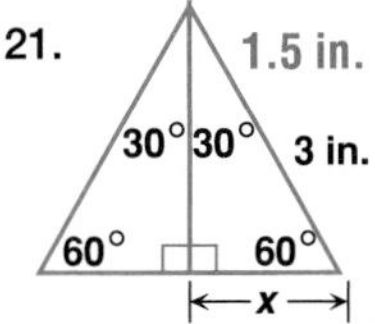

1.5 in.

22. $3\frac{1}{2}$ in. / $3\frac{1}{2}$ in. / x / $3\frac{1}{2}$ in. / $3\frac{1}{2}$ in. 4.9 in.

Mixed Review

23. Solve $x = \left(-4\frac{1}{8}\right)\left(\frac{1}{4}\right)$. (Lesson 6-3) $-1\frac{1}{32}$

24. Use the formula $V = \frac{1}{3}\pi r^2 h$ to find the volume of a circular cone that has radius 2 m and height 14 m. (Lesson 13-9) about 59 m^3

25. A big screen TV has sides of 3 feet and 4 feet. What is the length of its diagonal? (Lesson 14-6) 5 ft

Applications

26. **Sewing** In sewing, cutting on the bias means cutting on the diagonal. Ron has a square piece of material that is 2 yards on each side. What is the length of the diagonal of this piece of material? Round your answer to the nearest tenth. 2.8 yd

27. **Building** Rhonda wants to get a refrigerator into her house. She cannot lift it up the steps leading to her back door, so she decides to build a ramp. She decides to have the ramp make a 30° angle with the ground. If her back door is 2 feet above the ground, how long should Rhonda cut the boards to make the ramp? 4 ft

Critical Thinking

28. The length of the hypotenuse of a 30° - 60° right triangle is 7 feet. Find the length of the other two sides. Round answers to the nearest tenth. 3.5 ft, 6.1 ft

Wrap-Up

29. Draw a 30° - 60° right triangle. Use x as the length of the hypotenuse and label the side opposite the 30° angle in terms of x. See margin.

Independent Practice

Homework Assignment	
Basic	11-21 odd, 23-26, 28, 29
Average	12-22 even, 23-29
Honors	17-29

4 CLOSE

Assessment Option

Writing Go around the room and have each student state something that all 45°-45° right triangles have in common or something that all 30°-60° right triangles have in common. It can be as simple as they all have right angle or complex. Write each answer on the board as it is given so no answer is repeated.

Additional Answer

29.

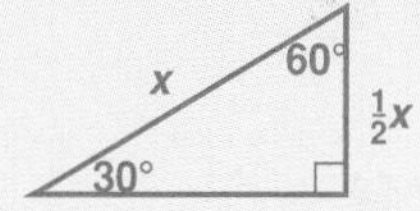

Enrichment Masters Booklet, p. 125

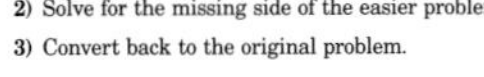
Name ______ Date ______

Enrichment Worksheet 14-7

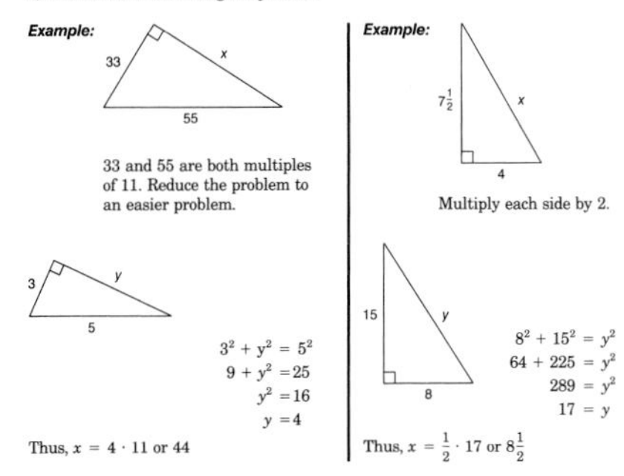
Reduced Triangle Principle

The following steps can be used to reduce the difficulty of a triangle problem by converting to easier triangle lengths.

1) Multiply or divide the three lengths of the triangle by the same number.
2) Solve for the missing side of the easier problem.
3) Convert back to the original problem.

Example: 33, x, 55. 33 and 55 are both multiples of 11. Reduce the problem to an easier problem. 3, y, 5.
$3^2 + y^2 = 5^2$
$9 + y^2 = 25$
$y^2 = 16$
$y = 4$
Thus, $x = 4 \cdot 11$ or 44

Example: $7\frac{1}{2}$, x, 4. Multiply each side by 2. 15, y, 8.
$8^2 + 15^2 = y^2$
$64 + 225 = y^2$
$289 = y^2$
$17 = y$
Thus, $x = \frac{1}{2} \cdot 17$ or $8\frac{1}{2}$

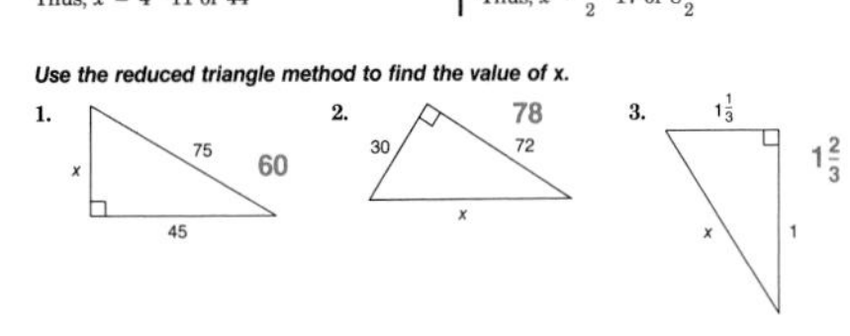
Use the reduced triangle method to find the value of x.

1. x, 75, 45   60
2. 30, 72, x   78
3. $1\frac{1}{3}$, x, 1 $1\frac{2}{3}$

Alternate Strategies: Extending the Lesson

Enrichment

Geology Connection A geologist looking for oil finds a likely rock formation that goes underground at a 30° angle. If the oil well is located 5500 feet from where the rock goes underground, how deep will the driller have to drill to hit the rock formation? about 3175 feet

Cooperative Learning

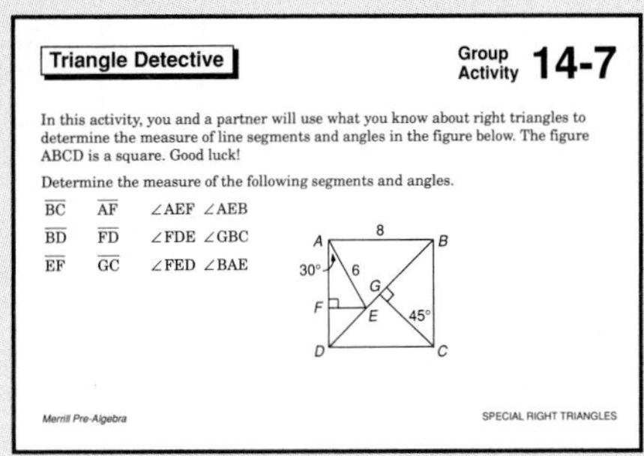
Triangle Detective

Group Activity 14-7

In this activity, you and a partner will use what you know about right triangles to determine the measure of line segments and angles in the figure below. The figure ABCD is a square. Good luck!

Determine the measure of the following segments and angles.

$\overline{BC}$	$\overline{AF}$	∠AEF ∠AEB
$\overline{BD}$	$\overline{FD}$	∠FDE ∠GBC
$\overline{EF}$	$\overline{GC}$	∠FED ∠BAE

Merrill Pre-Algebra

SPECIAL RIGHT TRIANGLES

Lesson Notes 14-8

5-Minute Check
(over Lesson 14-7)

Find the value of x. Round decimal answers to the nearest tenth.

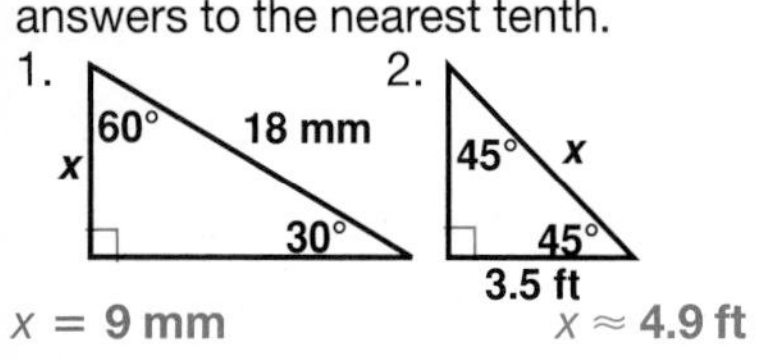

$x = 9$ mm $x \approx 4.9$ ft

Transparency 14-8 contains the 5-Minute Check and a teaching aid for this lesson.

1 FOCUS

The purpose of this lesson is to determine the tangent ratio and use it to solve problems involving right triangles. A trig table can be found on page 591.

2 TEACH

Chalkboard Examples

- *For Example 1*
  Find tan X
  $\frac{1}{2}$ or 0.5

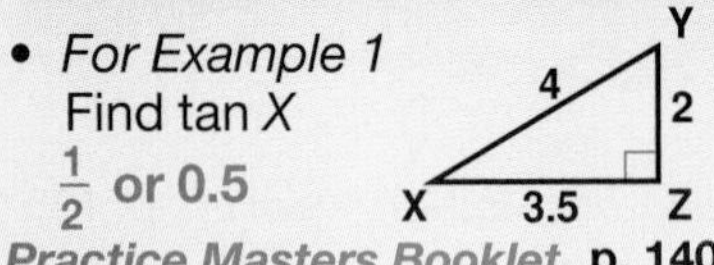

Practice Masters Booklet, **p. 140**

Name ______ Date ______

Practice Worksheet 14-8

The Tangent Ratio

Use a calculator to find each tangent ratio to the nearest ten thousandth.

1. tan 9° 0.1584	2. tan 88° 28.6363	3. tan 15° 0.2679
4. tan 40° 0.8391	5. tan 65° 2.1445	6. tan 70° 2.7475
7. tan 10° 0.1763	8. tan 48° 1.1106	9. tan 39° 0.8098
10. tan 56° 1.4826	11. tan 81° 6.3138	12. tan 76° 4.0108
13. tan 19° 0.3443	14. tan 66° 2.2460	15. tan 35° 0.7002
16. tan 27° 0.5095	17. tan 50° 1.1918	18. tan 85° 11.4301

Use a calculator to find the angle measure that corresponds to each tangent ratio. Round answers to the nearest degree.

19. tan A = 3.7321 75°	20. tan B = 0.1051 6°	21. tan C = 11.4301 85°
22. tan D = 0.3443 19°	23. tan E = 0.4663 25°	24. tan F = 0.2126 12°
25. tan S = 1.8040 61°	26. tan X = 28.6363 88°	27. tan Y = 1.0000 45°
28. tan R = 2.6051 69°	29. tan L = 0.5543 29°	30. tan K = 1.5399 57°
31. tan J = 0.0875 5°	32. tan M = 2.9042 71°	33. tan N = 5.6713 80°
34. tan P = 1.1106 48°	35. tan Q = 0.5774 30°	36. tan I = 1.7321 60°
37. tan V = 0.2309 13°	38. tan U = 1.4281 55°	39. tan Z = 8.1443 83°

14-8 The Tangent Ratio

Objective:
Find the tangent of an angle and find the measure of an angle using the tangent.

Key Term:
tangent

If you were asked to find the height of a desk or a doorway, you would probably measure it directly by using a ruler or a tape measure. However, it would be difficult to use either one of these instruments to find the height of a street lamp, a flagpole, a tree, or a lighthouse. The measure of the sides of the right triangles from special ratios can help you find heights like these. One of these ratios is called the **tangent** ratio.

Definition of Tangent

If ΔABC is a right triangle and A is an acute angle,
$$\text{tangent of } A = \frac{\text{measure of the side opposite to } \angle A}{\text{measure of the side adjacent to } \angle A}.$$

What is the equation for the tangent of ∠B?
$\tan B = \frac{b}{a}$

The abbreviation for tangent is *tan*.

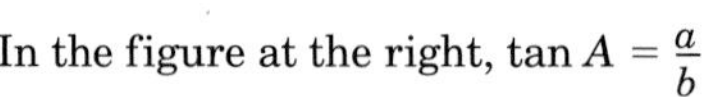

In the figure at the right, $\tan A = \frac{a}{b}$.

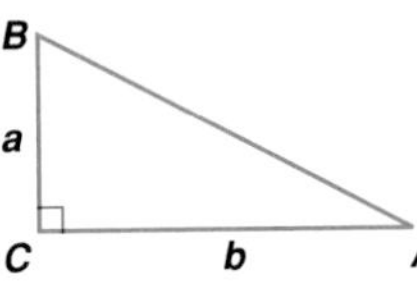

Example

1 Find tan S.

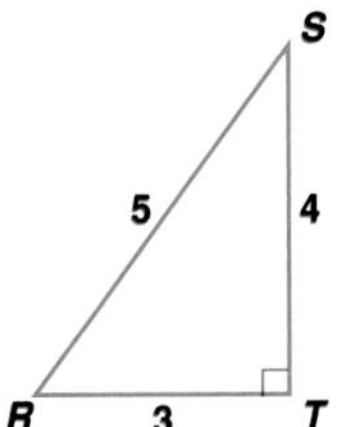

$$\tan S = \frac{\text{measure of the side opposite to } \angle S}{\text{measure of the side adjacent to } \angle S}$$

$\tan S = \frac{3}{4}$ or 0.75

So $\tan S$ is $\frac{3}{4}$ or 0.75.

A calculator can be used to find the tangent ratio for an angle with a given degree measure or to find the degree measure of an angle if the tangent ratio is known.

Examples

2 Find the tangent of 63°.

63 [TAN] 1.9626105

Therefore, $\tan 63° \approx 1.9626$.

3 Find the measure of ∠A given that tan A = 4.7030.

4.7030 [INV] [TAN] 77.995961

The measure of $\angle A$ is approximately 78°.

Bell Ringer

Name two things that all 45°-45° triangles have in common. Then name two things that all 30°-60° triangles have in common.

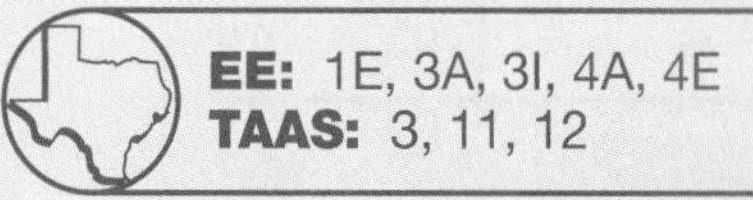

EE: 1E, 3A, 3I, 4A, 4E
TAAS: 3, 11, 12

Reteaching Masters Booklet, **p. 126**

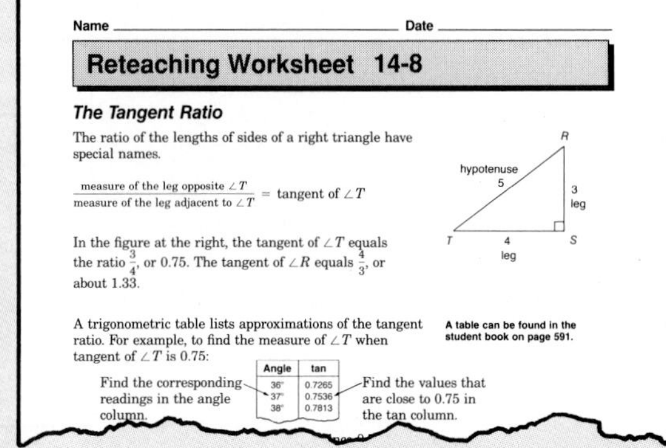

Name ______ Date ______

Reteaching Worksheet 14-8

The Tangent Ratio

The ratio of the lengths of sides of a right triangle have special names.

$\frac{\text{measure of the leg opposite } \angle T}{\text{measure of the leg adjacent to } \angle T}$ = tangent of $\angle T$

In the figure at the right, the tangent of $\angle T$ equals the ratio $\frac{3}{4}$, or 0.75. The tangent of $\angle R$ equals $\frac{4}{3}$, or about 1.33.

A trigonometric table lists approximations of the tangent ratio. For example, to find the measure of $\angle T$ when tangent of $\angle T$ is 0.75:

A table can be found in the student book on page 591.

Find the corresponding readings in the angle column.

Angle	tan
36°	0.7265
37°	0.7536
38°	0.7813

Find the values that are close to 0.75 in the tan column.

Checking for Understanding

1. Enter the degree measure. Press the tan key. The display is the tangent ratio.

Communicating Algebra

1. Describe the procedure for using a calculator to approximate a tangent ratio for an angle with a given degree measure.

Guided Practice

Write a fraction in simplest form for each tangent ratio.

2. 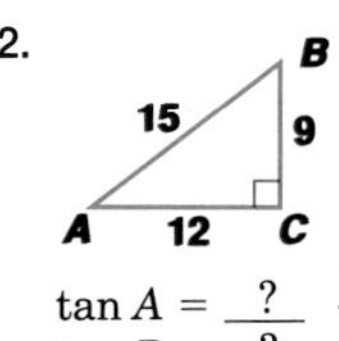

$\tan A = \underline{?}$ $\frac{3}{4}$
$\tan B = \underline{?}$ $\frac{4}{3}$

3. 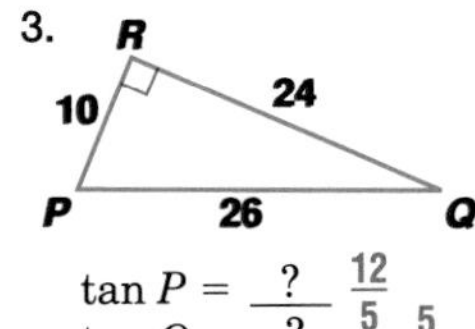

$\tan P = \underline{?}$ $\frac{12}{5}$
$\tan Q = \underline{?}$ $\frac{5}{12}$

4. 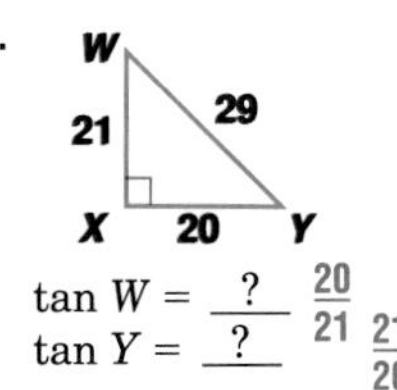

$\tan W = \underline{?}$ $\frac{20}{21}$
$\tan Y = \underline{?}$ $\frac{21}{20}$

Exercises

Independent Practice

ESTIMATION / MENTAL MATH / CALCULATOR / PAPER/PENCIL

Use a calculator to find each tangent ratio to the nearest ten thousandth.

5. tan 30° 0.5774
6. tan 45° 1.0000
7. tan 60° 1.7321
8. tan 18° 0.3249
9. tan 52° 1.2799
10. tan 74° 3.4874
11. tan 83° 8.1443
12. tan 20° 0.3640

Use a calculator to find the angle measure that corresponds to each tangent ratio. Round answers to the nearest degree.

13. $\tan A = 0.0875$ 5°
14. $\tan B = 0.2680$ 15°
15. $\tan C = 2.7380$ 70°
16. $\tan D = 0.6495$ 33°
17. $\tan P = 0.8391$ 40°
18. $\tan Q = 8.1440$ 83°

Mixed Review

19. Use a protractor to draw a 120° angle. Classify it as *acute*, *right*, or *obtuse*. (Lesson 12-1) See margin.

The length of the hypotenuse of a 30° - 60° right triangle is given. Find the length of the side opposite the 30° angle. (Lesson 14-7)

20. 10 cm 5 cm
21. $8\frac{1}{4}$ in. $4\frac{1}{8}$ in.

Applications

22. **Navigation** Refer to the picture at the right. Write an equation that relates tan 22° with the distance to the lighthouse (d) and the height of the lighthouse (h). $\tan 22° = \frac{h}{d}$

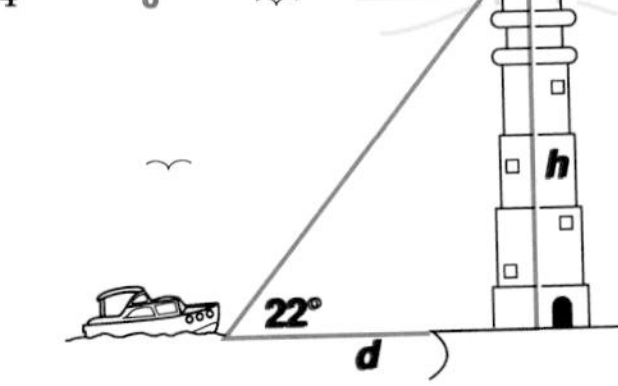

23. **Surveying** Refer to the picture at the right. Write an equation that relates tan 35° with the distance across Hidden Lake (d) and another side of the triangle. $\tan 35° = \frac{d}{c}$

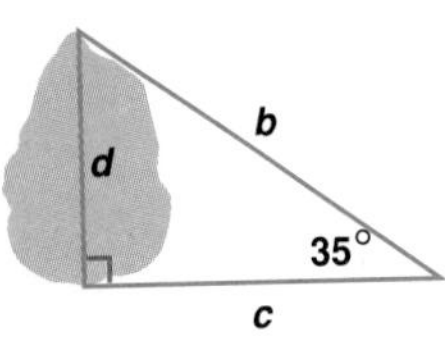

Critical Thinking

24. Write an equation that relates tan 25° with the length of the sides of the triangle at the right. Solve the equation for x. Round to the nearest tenth. $\tan 25° = \frac{x}{10}$; 4.7

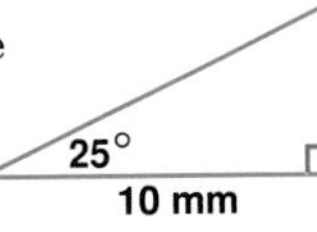

Wrap-Up

25. Draw and label a right triangle. Write an equation for the tangent of each acute angle in the right triangle. See margin.

- *For Example 2*
  Find the tangent of 28°. 0.5317
- *For Example 3*
  Find the measure of $\angle A$ given that $\tan A = 0.5774$. 30°

3 PRACTICE/APPLY

Checking the Concept

After completing Exercises 4-6, use the tangent values and a calculator to determine the angles involved.

Independent Practice

Homework Assignment	
Basic	7-23 odd, 24-27, 29, 30
Average	8-22 even, 24-30
Honors	8-14 even, 20-30

4 CLOSE

Assessment Option

Writing Write ten angle measures and then find the tangent ratio of each measure to nearest ten thousandth.

Enrichment Masters Booklet, **p. 126**

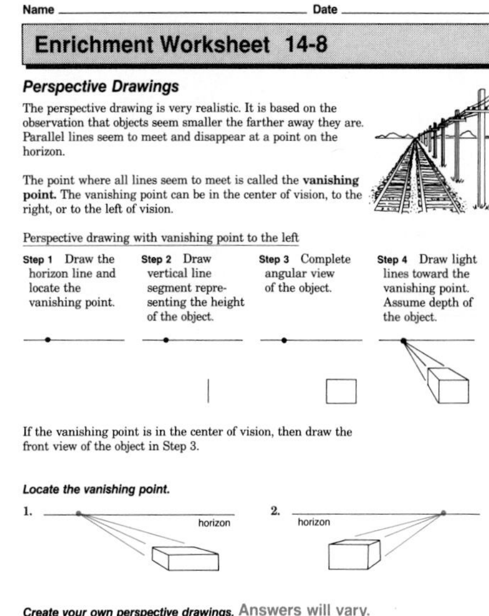

Name ______ Date ______

Enrichment Worksheet 14-8

Perspective Drawings

The perspective drawing is very realistic. It is based on the observation that objects seem smaller the farther away they are. Parallel lines seem to meet and disappear at a point on the horizon.

The point where all lines seem to meet is called the **vanishing point.** The vanishing point can be in the center of vision, to the right, or to the left of vision.

Perspective drawing with vanishing point to the left

Step 1 Draw the horizon line and locate the vanishing point.
Step 2 Draw vertical line segment representing the height of the object.
Step 3 Complete angular view of the object.
Step 4 Draw light lines toward the vanishing point. Assume depth of the object.

If the vanishing point is in the center of vision, then draw the front view of the object in Step 3.

Locate the vanishing point.

1. horizon
2. horizon

Create your own perspective drawings. Answers will vary.

Additional Answers

19. obtuse

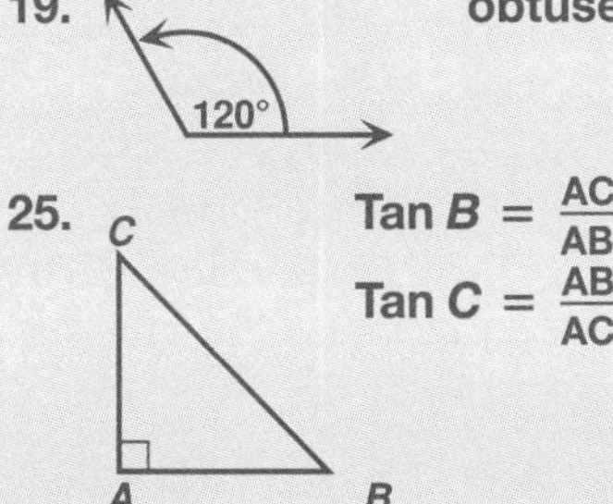

25. $\tan B = \frac{AC}{AB}$

$\tan C = \frac{AB}{AC}$

Cooperative Learning

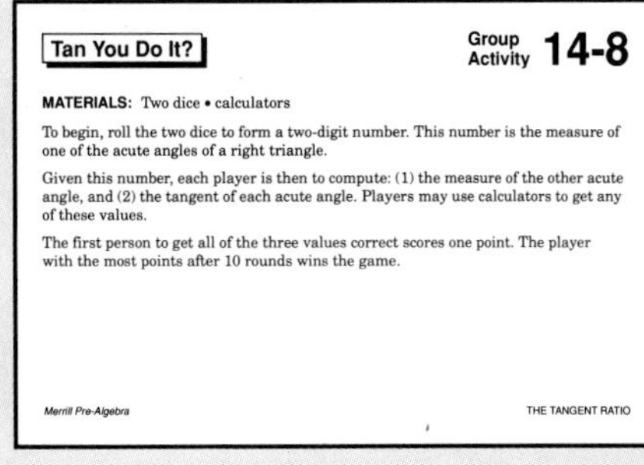

Tan You Do It? Group Activity **14-8**

MATERIALS: Two dice • calculators

To begin, roll the two dice to form a two-digit number. This number is the measure of one of the acute angles of a right triangle.

Given this number, each player is then to compute: (1) the measure of the other acute angle, and (2) the tangent of each acute angle. Players may use calculators to get any of these values.

The first person to get all of the three values correct scores one point. The player with the most points after 10 rounds wins the game.

Merrill Pre-Algebra THE TANGENT RATIO

Lesson Notes 14-9

5-Minute Check
(over Lesson 14-8)

Use a calculator to find each tangent ratio to the nearest ten thousandth.

1. tan 76° 4.0108
2. tan 59° 1.6643
3. tan 26° 0.4877

Use a calculator to find the angle measure that corresponds to each tangent ratio. Round answers to the nearest degree.

4. tan A = 0.5095 27°
5. tan B = 4.3315 77°

Transparency 14-9 contains the 5-Minute Check and a teaching aid for this lesson.

1 FOCUS

The purpose of this lesson is to define sine and cosine ratios and use them to solve problems involving right triangles.

Motivating the Lesson

Show students a picture of the Washington Monument. Ask them how they would determine its height.

2 TEACH

If students' calculators do not have trig functions, they can use the table found on page 591. You may want to instruct students on how to use the table.

Chalkboard Examples

- *For Example 1*
  Find sin A and cos A.

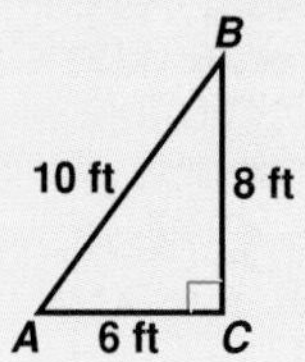

$\sin A = \frac{4}{5}$ or 0.8

$\cos A = \frac{3}{5}$ or 0.6

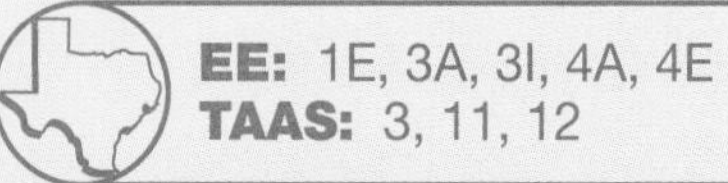

EE: 1E, 3A, 3I, 4A, 4E
TAAS: 3, 11, 12

14-9 The Sine and Cosine Ratios

Objective:
Find the sine and cosine of an angle and find the measure of an angle using the sine or cosine ratio.

The tangent ratio is a ratio that involves the measure of the legs of a right triangle. The **sine** ratio and the **cosine** ratio are two ratios that involve the length of the hypotenuse and the length of one leg. These ratios are defined below.

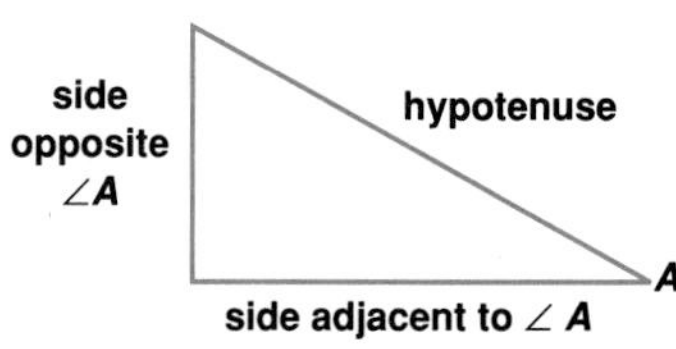

Definition of Sine and Cosine

If ΔABC is a right triangle and A is an acute angle,

sine of $\angle A = \dfrac{\text{measure of the side opposite } \angle A}{\text{measure of the hypotenuse}}$, and

cosine of $\angle A = \dfrac{\text{measure of the side adjacent to } \angle A}{\text{measure of the hypotenuse}}$.

Key Terms:
sine
cosine
trigonometry
trigonometric ratios

The abbreviation for sine is *sin*, and the abbreviation for cosine is *cos*.

In the figure at the right,

$\sin A = \frac{a}{c}$ and $\cos A = \frac{b}{c}$.

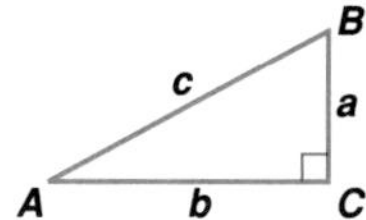

Example

1 Find sin *P* and cos *P*.

Is the sine or cosine of an angle ever greater than 1? Why? **no; The hypotenuse is always the longest side.**

$\sin P = \dfrac{\text{measure of the side opposite } \angle P}{\text{measure of the hypotenuse}}$

$\sin P = \frac{3}{5}$ or 0.6

$\cos P = \dfrac{\text{measure of the side adjacent to } \angle P}{\text{measure of the hypotenuse}}$

$\cos P = \frac{4}{5}$ or 0.8

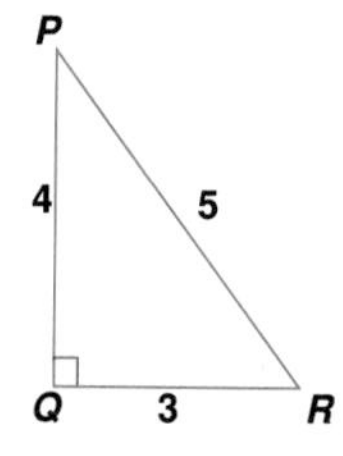

A calculator can be used to find the sine ratio or the cosine ratio for an angle with a given degree measure. It can also be used to find the degree measure of an angle if the sine ratio or the cosine ratio is known.

Bell Ringer

In your own words state the definition of tangent ratio.

Examples

How can you use a calculator to find cos 57°?
57 [COS]

2 **Find the sine of 57°.**

57 [SIN] = 0.8386706

Therefore sin 57° ≈ 0.8387.

If sin W = 0.7980, how would you use a calculator to find the measure of ∠W?
0.7980 [INV] [SIN]

3 **Find the measure of ∠D given that cos D = 0.9390.**

0.9390  [COS] 20.115708

The measure of ∠D is about 20°.

The word **trigonometry** means triangle measurement. The tangent, sine, and cosine ratios are **trigonometric ratios** because they are ratios of the measures of sides of right triangles.

- *For Example 2*
  Find the sine of 76°. 0.9703
- *For Example 3*
  Find the measure of ∠G given that cos G = 0.8746. 29°

3 PRACTICE/APPLY

Checking the Concept

After completing Exercises 5-7, have students use a calculator to find the angles.

Error Analysis
Watch for students who reverse the definitions of sine and cosine. **Prevent by** writing the formulas for reference until the concept is mastered.

Independent Practice

Homework Assignment	
Basic	9-23 odd, 25-28, 30, 31
Average	8-22 even, 25-31
Honors	8-14 even, 21-31

Practice Masters Booklet, **p. 141**

Name ______ Date ______

Practice Worksheet 14-9

The Sine and Cosine Ratios

Use a calculator to find each sine ratio or cosine ratio. Round answers to the nearest ten thousandth.

1. sin 30° 0.5000 **2.** cos 10° 0.9848 **3.** sin 45° 0.7071
4. cos 45° 0.7071 **5.** sin 50° 0.7660 **6.** cos 19° 0.9455
7. sin 60° 0.8660 **8.** cos 30° 0.8660 **9.** sin 89° 0.9998
10. cos 60° 0.5000 **11.** sin 35° 0.5736 **12.** cos 65° 0.4226
13. sin 23° 0.3907 **14.** cos 75° 0.2588 **15.** sin 15° 0.2588
16. cos 89° 0.0175 **17.** sin 56° 0.8290 **18.** cos 34° 0.8290

Use a calculator to find the angle measure that corresponds to each sine ratio or cosine ratio. Round answers to the nearest degree.

19. sin A = 0.1736 10° **20.** cos B = 0.9063 25° **21.** sin C = 0.8290 56°
22. cos D = 0.9455 19° **23.** sin E = 0.9962 85° **24.** cos F = 0.8660 30°
25. sin X = 0.5000 30° **26.** cos Y = 0.5000 60° **27.** sin Z = 0.9659 75°
28. cos S = 0.9962 5° **29.** sin T = 0.4226 25° **30.** cos R = 0.6428 50°
31. sin P = 0.9877 81° **32.** cos Q = 0.8746 29° **33.** sin N = 0.5446 33°
34. cos M = 0.9397 20° **35.** sin W = 0.8660 60° **36.** cos U = 0.4695 62°
37. sin L = 0.1219 7° **38.** cos I = 0.5446 57° **39.** sin K = 0.6293 39°

Checking for Understanding

Communicating Algebra

1. Explain the meaning of the sine ratio. See margin.
2. Explain the meaning of the cosine ratio. See margin.
3. Describe the procedure for using a calculator to approximate the cosine ratio for an angle with a given degree measure. See margin.
4. Describe the procedure for using a calculator to find the degree measure of the angle that corresponds to a given sine ratio. See margin.

Guided Practice

Write a fraction in simplest form for each sine ratio and each cosine ratio.

5. 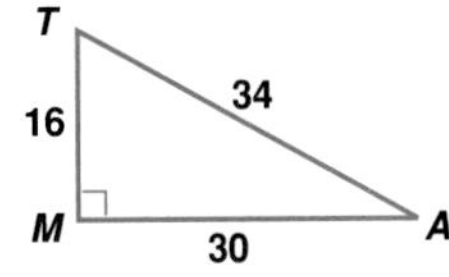

sin A = ? $\frac{8}{17}$
cos A = ? $\frac{15}{17}$
sin T = ? $\frac{15}{17}$
cos T = ? $\frac{8}{17}$

6. 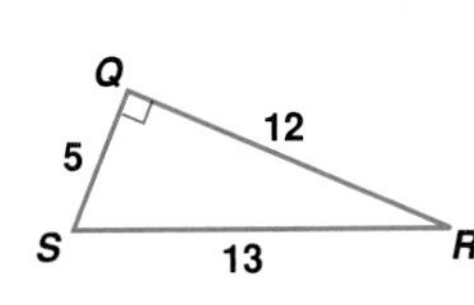

cos S = ? $\frac{5}{13}$
sin S = ? $\frac{12}{13}$
cos R = ? $\frac{12}{13}$
sin R = ? $\frac{5}{13}$

7. 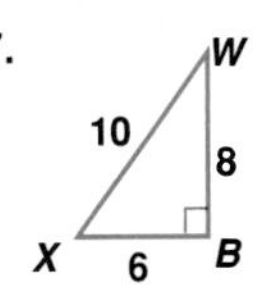

sin W = ? $\frac{3}{5}$
cos W = ? $\frac{4}{5}$
cos X = ? $\frac{3}{5}$
sin X = ? $\frac{4}{5}$

Exercises

Independent Practice

Use a calculator to find each sine ratio or cosine ratio. Round answers to the nearest ten thousandth.

8. sin 16° 0.2756 9. cos 20° 0.9397 10. cos 67° 0.3907 11. sin 54° 0.8090
12. cos 12° 0.9781 13. sin 32° 0.5299 14. sin 72° 0.9511 15. cos 48° 0.6691

Alternate Strategies: Reteaching the Lesson

Reteaching Activity

Using Models Have students use modeling clay, a pencil, and string to model the following problem. A 30-foot tower needs guy wires. What length should they be if their angle with the ground is given? Solve for several different angles.

Reteaching Masters Booklet, **p. 127**

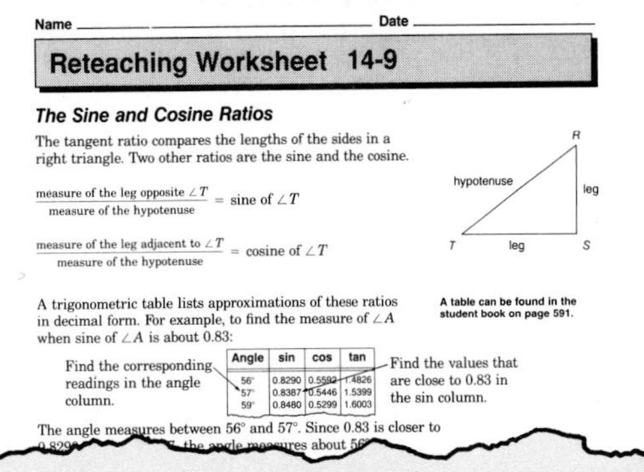

Name ______ Date ______

Reteaching Worksheet 14-9

The Sine and Cosine Ratios

The tangent ratio compares the lengths of the sides in a right triangle. Two other ratios are the sine and the cosine.

$$\frac{\text{measure of the leg opposite } \angle T}{\text{measure of the hypotenuse}} = \text{sine of } \angle T$$

$$\frac{\text{measure of the leg adjacent to } \angle T}{\text{measure of the hypotenuse}} = \text{cosine of } \angle T$$

A trigonometric table lists approximations of these ratios in decimal form. For example, to find the measure of ∠A when sine of ∠A is about 0.83:

A table can be found in the student book on page 591.

Find the corresponding readings in the angle column.

Angle	sin	cos	tan
56°	0.8290	0.5592	1.4826
57°	0.8387	0.5446	1.5399
59°	0.8480	0.5299	1.6003

Find the values that are close to 0.83 in the sin column.

The angle measures between 56° and 57°. Since 0.83 is closer to 0.829... the angle measures about 56...

4 CLOSE

Assessment Option

Writing Using the same angle measures as in the *Assessment Option* for lesson 14-8, find the sine and cosine ratio for each angle measurement using your calculator.

Additional Answers

1. The sine ratio of an acute angle of a right triangle is the ratio of the measure of the length of the leg opposite that angle to the measure of the length of the hypotenuse.
2. The cosine ratio of an acute angle of a right triangle is the ratio of the measure of the length of the leg adjacent to that angle to the measure of the length of the hypotenuse.
3. Enter the degree measure and press [COS].
4. Enter the sine ratio and press [INV] then press [COS].

31. Sample answer: Tangent equals opposite over adjacent; sine equals opposite over hypotenuse; cosine equals adjacent over hypotenuse.

Enrichment Masters Booklet, **p. 127**

Name ______________________ Date ______________

Enrichment Worksheet 14-9

The Sine Curve

Below is a table of values for sine θ.

θ	0°	45°	90°	135°	180°	225°	270°	315°	360°
$\sin\theta$	0	$\frac{\sqrt{2}}{2}$	1	$\frac{\sqrt{2}}{2}$	0	$-\frac{\sqrt{2}}{2}$	−1	$-\frac{\sqrt{2}}{2}$	0

Using these values, a graph of $y = \sin\theta$ can be drawn.

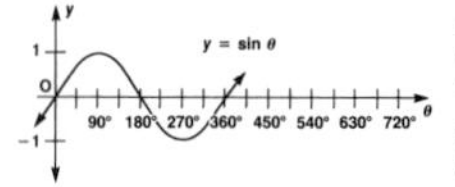

In the equation, $y = A \sin k\theta$, A is the maximum height of the curve called the **amplitude**. The period is $\frac{360°}{k}$.

In $y = \sin\theta$, $A = 1$ and $k = 1$. Therefore, the amplitude is 1 and the period is 360°.

Complete the statements below. Use the table of values. Then graph each equation.

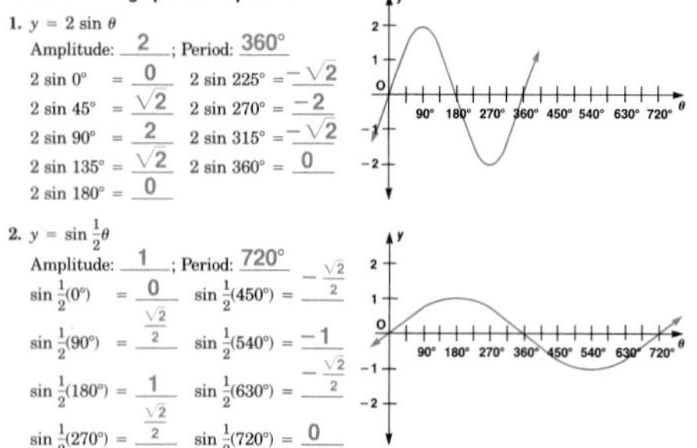

1. $y = 2\sin\theta$
   Amplitude: 2; Period: 360°
   $2\sin 0° =$ 0 $\quad 2\sin 225° =$ $-\sqrt{2}$
   $2\sin 45° =$ $\sqrt{2}$ $\quad 2\sin 270° =$ -2
   $2\sin 90° =$ 2 $\quad 2\sin 315° =$ $-\sqrt{2}$
   $2\sin 135° =$ $\sqrt{2}$ $\quad 2\sin 360° =$ 0
   $2\sin 180° =$ 0

2. $y = \sin\frac{1}{2}\theta$
   Amplitude: 1; Period: 720°
   $\sin\frac{1}{2}(0°) =$ 0 $\quad \sin\frac{1}{2}(450°) =$ $-\frac{\sqrt{2}}{2}$
   $\sin\frac{1}{2}(90°) =$ $\frac{\sqrt{2}}{2}$ $\quad \sin\frac{1}{2}(540°) =$ -1
   $\sin\frac{1}{2}(180°) =$ 1 $\quad \sin\frac{1}{2}(630°) =$ $-\frac{\sqrt{2}}{2}$
   $\sin\frac{1}{2}(270°) =$ $\frac{\sqrt{2}}{2}$ $\quad \sin\frac{1}{2}(720°) =$ 0
   $\sin\frac{1}{2}(360°) =$ 0

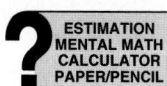

ESTIMATION / MENTAL MATH / CALCULATOR / PAPER/PENCIL

Use a calculator to find the angle measure that corresponds to each sine ratio or cosine ratio. Round answers to the nearest whole number.

16. $\sin A = 0.1392$ 8°
17. $\sin B = 0.8900$ 63°
18. $\cos T = 0.9063$ 25°
19. $\cos Q = 0.7050$ 45°
20. $\sin R = 0.5740$ 35°
21. $\cos S = 0.3250$ 71°
22. $\sin B = 0.5444$ 33°
23. $\cos D = 0.2491$ 76°
24. $\sin R = 0.9165$ 66°

Mixed Review

25. Find the quotient $\frac{m^{11}}{m^3}$. (Lesson 4-10) m^8
26. Find 32.76 cm + 4.1 cm + 13.13 cm. (Lesson 13-10) 50.0 cm
27. Use a calculator to find tan 55° to the nearest ten thousandth. (Lesson 14-8) 1.4281

Applications

For Exercises 28-30, refer to the drawing at the right.

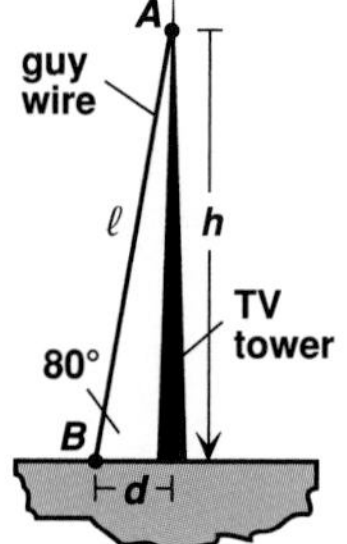

28. **Broadcasting** One end of a guy wire is attached to a television tower at point A and the other end is attached to a ground anchor at point B. Write an equation that relates the 80° angle with the length of the guy wire (ℓ) and the distance of A from the ground (h). $\sin 80° = \frac{h}{\ell}$
29. **Broadcasting** Write an equation that relates the 80° angle with the length of the guy wire (ℓ) and the distance of B from the base of the tower (d). $\cos 80° = \frac{d}{\ell}$

Critical Thinking

30. If the length of the guy wire (ℓ) is 120 feet, find h. Round your answer to the nearest tenth. 118.2 ft

Wrap-Up

31. Explain the differences among the tangent, sine, and cosine ratios. See margin.

Team Problem Solving

A large cube made up of many unit cubes is painted on all six faces. If the dimensions of the large cube are 10 × 10 × 10, how many of the unit cubes are painted on three faces? two faces? one face? no faces? Suppose the cube's dimensions are $n \times n \times n$. How many of the unit cubes are painted on three faces? two faces? one face? no faces?
8, 96, 384, 512; 8, $12(n-2)$, $6(n-2)^2$, $(n-2)^3$

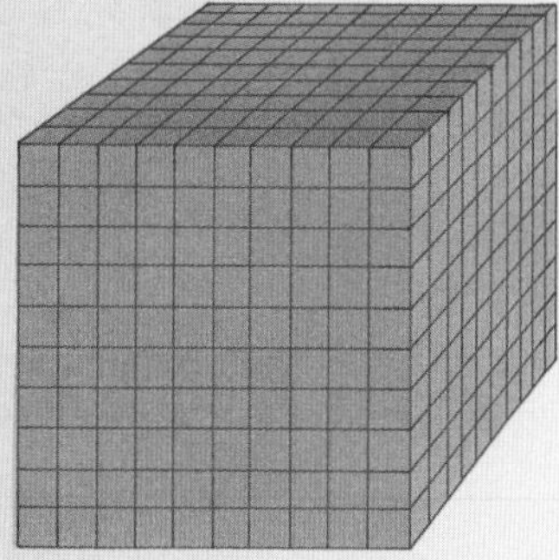

Alternate Strategies: Extending the Lesson

Enrichment

Physical Education Connection Have students assume they are in charge of installing playground equipment at a local elementary school. Have them explain how they would use the sine and cosine ratios to determine the height of the slide, the frame for the swings, and the lay out of the ball diamond.

Cooperative Learning

Make My Triangle — Group Activity **14-9**

MATERIALS: Calculators

The leader of the group secretly chooses the measure of an acute angle of a right triangle. He or she then uses a calculator to get either the sine or cosine of that angle, and announces this value to the rest of the group.

Group members are to determine: (1) the measure of the secret angle, (2) the measure of the other acute angle, (3) the sine of the other acute angle, (4) the cosine of the other acute angle, and (5) the tangent of each acute angle.

All players who correctly answer each of the above parts earn one point. The player with the most points after everyone has been the leader wins.

Merrill Pre-Algebra THE SINE AND COSINE RATIOS

Algebra in Action-Physics

Vectors

A hiker leaves camp and walks 15 kilometers due north. The hiker then walks 6 kilometers due east. To find the direction and displacement of the hiker, we can use directed segments called vectors.

A vector is a line segment which possesses both magnitude (length) and direction.

Draw a vector to represent *15 kilometers due north.*

Next, draw a vector starting at the endpoint of the first vector to represent *6 kilometers due east.*

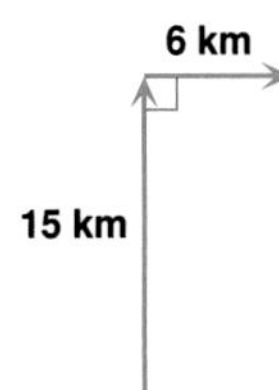

Finally, connect the starting point of the first vector with the endpoint of the second vector. This resultant vector will tell you the direction and displacement of the hiker.

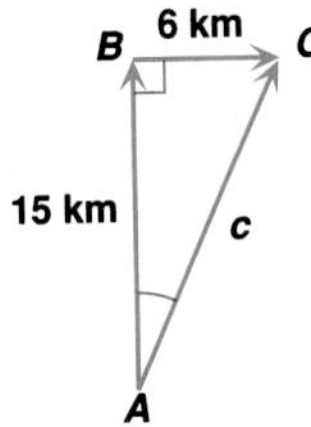

Direction:

$\tan A = \frac{6}{15}$

$\tan A = 0.4$

$A \approx 22°$

Displacement:

$a^2 + b^2 = c^2$

$6^2 + 15^2 = c^2$

$36 + 225 = c^2$

$261 = c^2$

$16 \approx c$

The direction of the hiker is about 22° northeast, and his displacement is about 16 km from the starting point.

1. A soccer player kicks the ball 12 feet to the west. Another player kicks the ball 18 feet to the north. What is the direction and displacement of the ball? Round your answer to the nearest whole number. 56° northwest; 22 ft

Applying Algebra to the Real World

Objective This optional page shows how algebra is used in the real world and also provides a change of pace.

Science Connection

Scientists observe a possible action from dormant volcanoes. One such volcano, Haleakela, is in Hawaii and is 10,000 ft. high. The peak is 30,000 ft. horizontal distance from the ocean. If a scientist stood on the beach, at what angle would she have to look to see the peak? 18.4° To climb to the peak, how far would she have to walk? 31,623 ft

Working Backwards

A pilot has to fly from his present location to a city 200 km east. He must detour around a group of thunderstorms, so he flies a path 20° NNE. When he is directly north of his destination, he flies south to get there. How far out of his way did the pilot have to fly? **Use tan 20° to find vertical displacement of 72.8 km. Use the Pythagorean Theorem to find the third side of the triangle, 212.8 km. He went 85.6 km out of the way.**

Activity

Use road maps of your state. Find your location and the location of a point of interest in another part of the state. Using the scale, find the vertical and horizontal displacements from one location to the other. Calculate the direction and displacement from one location to the other.

Lesson Notes 14-10

5-Minute Check
(over Lesson 14-9)

Use a calculator to find each sine ratio or cosine ratio. Round answers to the nearest ten thousandth.

1. sin 79° 0.9816
2. cos 30° 0.8660
3. cos 58° 0.5299
4. sin 28° 0.4695
5. cos 79° 0.1908

Transparency 14-10 contains the 5-Minute Check and a teaching aid for this lesson.

1 FOCUS

The purpose of this lesson is to determine which trigonometric ratio is needed to solve a problem and use it to solve the problem.

Motivating the Lesson

Draw a diagram of a right triangle on the chalkboard. Label the right angle and label the hypotenuse with a variable. Ask students what information is needed to solve for the variable.

2 TEACH

Use Chalkboard Examples

List each trigonometric ratio one at a time. For each, give several examples where the ratio can be used. Then mix up the examples and have students name the ratio to be used.

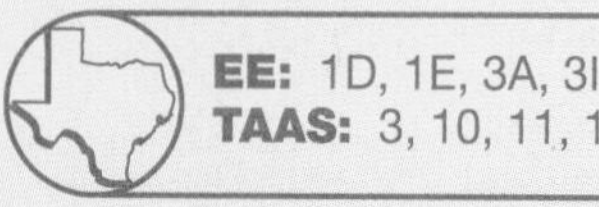

EE: 1D, 1E, 3A, 3I, 4A, 4E
TAAS: 3, 10, 11, 12, 13

Application

14-10 Using Trigonometric Ratios

Objective:
Solve problems by using the trigonometric ratios.

The Conservation District measures the distance across Hidden Valley Lake every ten years to see how much erosion has occurred. Since they cannot measure the distance directly, they use a right triangle and trigonometric ratios to find the distance.

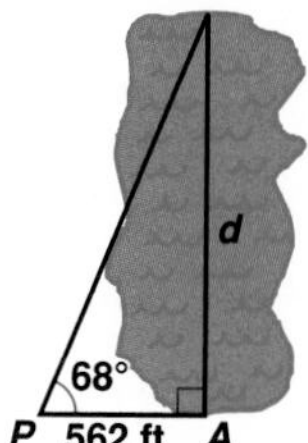

Explore Form a right triangle with the distance across the lake as one leg. Special surveying instruments can be used to find the measure of $\angle P$. You can measure the distance from A to P directly using a tape measure or other device.

Plan Look at the figure. You know the measure of one angle and the measure of the side adjacent to it.

Since the tangent ratio is the measure of the opposite side divided by the measure of the adjacent side, use the tangent ratio to solve for d, the distance across the lake.

Solve

$$\tan 68° = \frac{\text{measure of side opposite the } 68° \text{ angle}}{\text{measure of side adjacent to the } 68° \text{ angle}}$$

$$\tan 68° = \frac{d}{562}$$

$$562(\tan 68°) = d$$

562 [×] 68 [TAN] [=] 1390.9988

The distance across Hidden Valley Lake is about 1391 feet.

Examine If the angle was 60°, the distance across the lake would be $562(\sqrt{3})$, or about 973 feet. Since the angle is greater than 60° the distance should be greater than 973 feet. The answer appears to be reasonable.

The trigonometric ratios and the Pythagorean Theorem can be used to find the measure of any side or angle of a right triangle if the measure of one side and any other side or acute angle are known.

Bell Ringer

Which side of a right triangle do the sine ratio and cosine ratio both use? Hypotenuse

Examples

1 In $\triangle RST$ find the measure of $\angle R$.

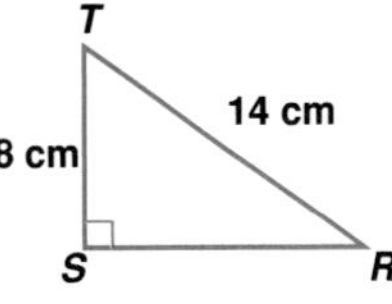

The measure of the side opposite $\angle R$ and the hypotenuse are known. Therefore the sine ratio should be used.

$$\sin R = \frac{\text{measure of side opposite } \angle R}{\text{measure of the hypotenuse}}$$

$$\sin R = \frac{8}{14}$$

$$\sin R \approx 0.5714$$

$$R \approx 34.8$$

The measure of $\angle R$ is about 34.8°.

2 In $\triangle ABC$ find the length of $\overline{AB}$.

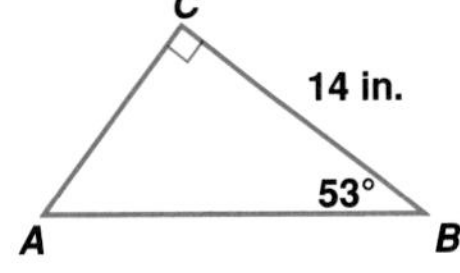

Should the length of $\overline{AB}$ be greater than or less than 14 inches? **greater than**

The measure of the side adjacent to B is known and the measure of the hypotenuse is needed. Use the cosine function.

$$\cos B = \frac{\text{measure of side adjacent to } \angle B}{\text{measure of the hypotenuse}}$$

$$\cos 53° = \frac{14}{x}$$

$x \cos 53° = 14$ Why?

$x = \frac{14}{\cos 53°}$ Why?

14 [÷] 53 [COS] [=] 23.262962

The length of $\overline{AB}$ is about 23.3 inches.

Checking for Understanding

Communicating Algebra

1. Explain how to determine which trigonometric ratio to use when solving for an unknown measure of a right triangle. **See margin.**

Guided Practice

Tell which trigonometric ratio would be the best choice for finding the value of x. Then solve for x. Round answers to the nearest tenth.

2. **sin, 12.7 ft**

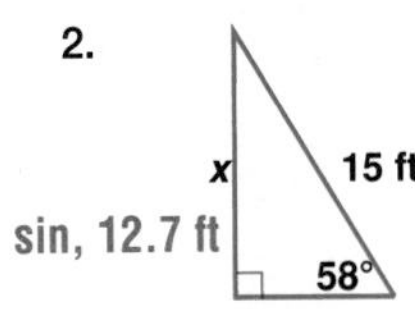

3. **cos, 35.6 cm**

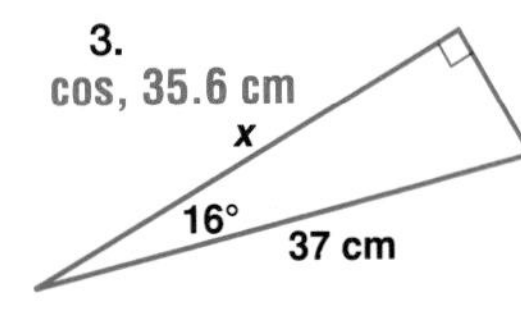

4. **tan, 12.1 m**

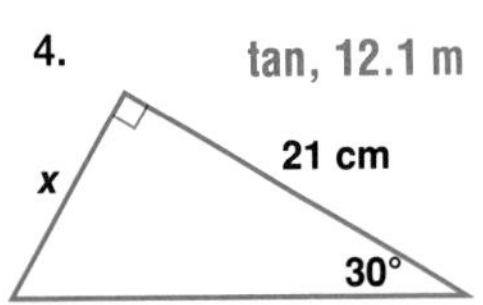

Chalkboard Examples

- *For Example 1*
  In $\triangle ABC$ find the measure of $\angle A$.

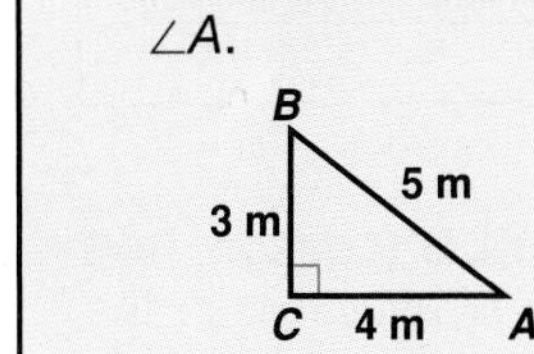

$m\angle A$ is about 53°

- *For Example 2*
  In $\triangle ABC$ find the length of $\overline{AB}$.

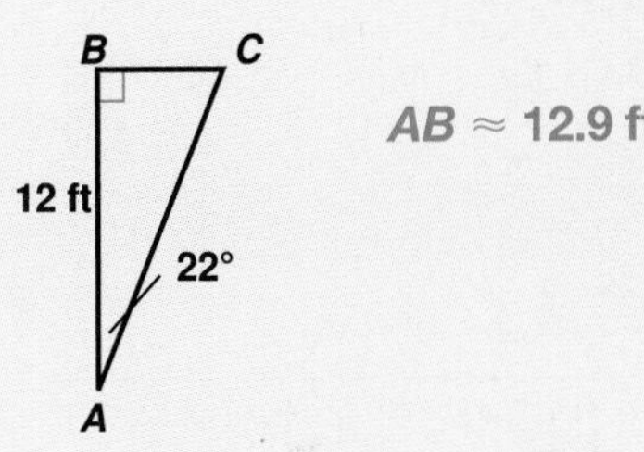

$AB \approx 12.9$ ft.

3 PRACTICE/APPLY

Checking the Concept

Allow students to use a calculator to solve Exercises 3-8.

Error Analysis

Watch for students who don't know what trigonometric ratio to use.
Prevent by drawing diagrams.

Additional Answer

1. Set up a ratio based on the information in the problem and use the trig ratio that is defined by that information.

Alternate Strategies: Reteaching the Lesson

Reteaching Activity

Using Diagrams Have each student draw a right triangle. Label any two sides or an angle and a side. Find the other angles and sides. Repeat using different information on another right triangle.

Reteaching Masters Booklet, **p. 128**

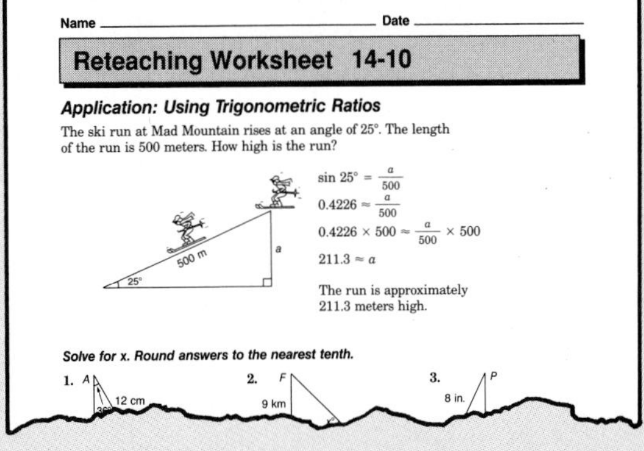

Name ______ Date ______

Reteaching Worksheet 14-10

Application: Using Trigonometric Ratios

The ski run at Mad Mountain rises at an angle of 25°. The length of the run is 500 meters. How high is the run?

500 m
25°
a

$\sin 25° = \frac{a}{500}$

$0.4226 \approx \frac{a}{500}$

$0.4226 \times 500 \approx \frac{a}{500} \times 500$

$211.3 \approx a$

The run is approximately 211.3 meters high.

Solve for x. Round answers to the nearest tenth.

1. A 12 cm
2. F 9 km
3. P 8 in.

Independent Practice

Homework Assignment	
Basic	9-22
Average	9-22
Honors	9-22

Chapter 14, Quiz B (Lesson 14-6 through 14-10) is available in the Evaluation Masters Booklet, p. 124.

Practice Masters Booklet, **p. 142**

Name ______________________ Date ______________

Practice Worksheet 14-10

Application: Using Trigonometric Ratios

Solve for y. Round answers to the nearest tenth.

1. 30 in., 25°, y — 12.7 in.
2. 16 ft, 37°, y — 12.8 ft
3. 29.4 mm, 18.1 mm, y — 38.0°
4. 72°, y, 5.6 mm — 5.9 mm
5. 11 yd, 7 yd, y — 50.5°
6. y, 63°, 4.5 cm — 2.0 cm
7. 8 mi, y, 5.8 mi — 46.5°
8. 100 m, 73°, y — 29.2 m
9. y, 55°, 10 km — 17.4 km

Tell which trigonometric ratio would be the best choice for finding the value of x. Then solve for x. Round answers to the nearest tenth.

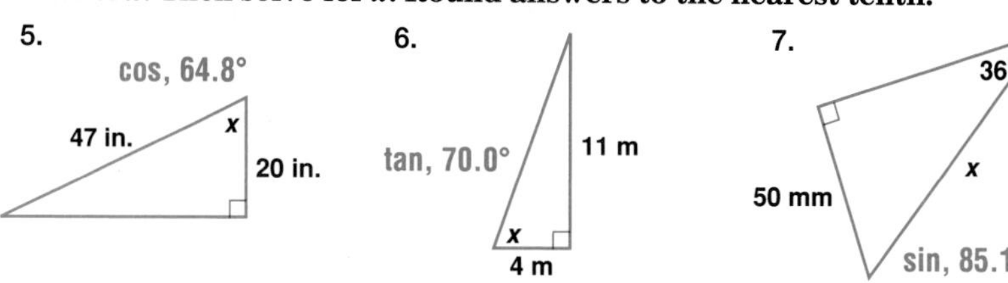

Exercises

Independent Practice

ESTIMATION
MENTAL MATH
CALCULATOR
PAPER/PENCIL

Solve for y. Round answers to the nearest tenth.

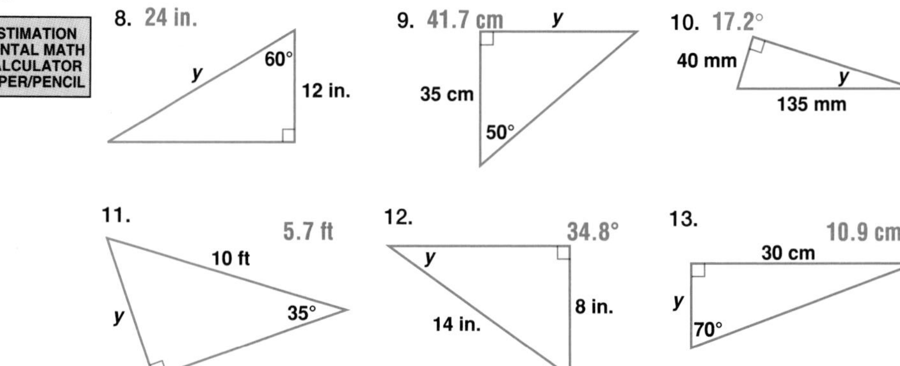

Mixed Review

14. Find the area of a parallelogram with base 8 inches and height 7 inches. (Lesson 13-1) 56 in^2

15. Use a calculator to find cos 83° to the nearest ten thousandth. (Lesson 14-9) 0.1219

Applications

Solve. Round answers to the nearest tenth.

16. **Traveling** In a sightseeing boat near the base of Horseshoe Falls at Niagara Falls, a passenger estimates the angle of elevation to the top of the falls to be 30°. If Horseshoe Falls is 173 feet high, what is the distance from the boat to the base of the falls? 299.6 ft

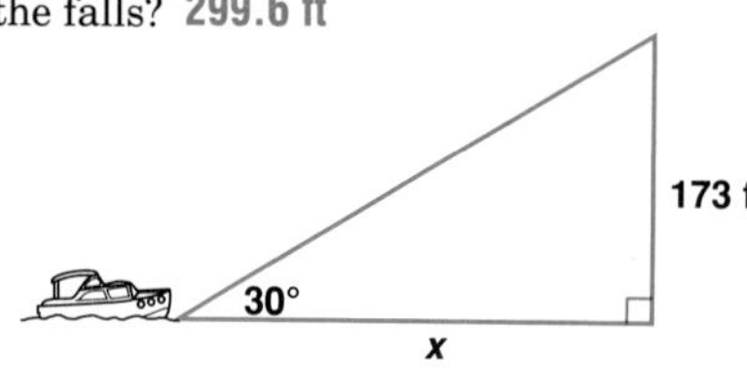

17. **Traveling** While picnicking in San Jacinto Battlefield Park, a pre-algebra student 800 feet from the base of the monument estimates the angle of elevation to the top of the monument to be 35°. From this information, estimate the height of the monument. **560.2 ft**

18. **Navigation** From a boat in the ocean, a cliff is sighted through the fog. The angle of elevation is 42° and the height of the cliff is 135 meters. How far is the boat from the cliff? **149.9 m**

19. **Building Design** A ramp is designed to help people in wheelchairs move more easily from one level to another. If a ramp 16 feet long forms an angle of 12° with the level ground, what is the vertical rise? **3.3 ft**

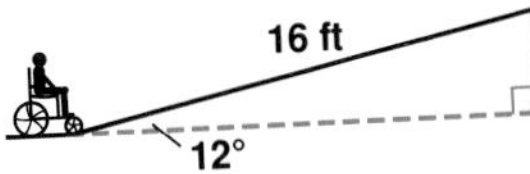

Critical Thinking

20. To *solve a triangle* means to find the measures of all the sides and all the angles of the triangle. Solve ΔABC shown at the right.

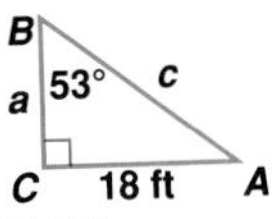

$m\angle A = 37°$, $m\angle B = 53°$, $m\angle C = 90°$, $a = 13.6$ ft, $b = 18$ ft, $c = 22.5$ ft

Wrap-Up

21. **Make Up a Problem** Write three problems about right triangles. The first problem should require the tangent ratio to find the solution. The second problem should require the sine ratio and the third problem should require the cosine ratio. **See margin.**

History

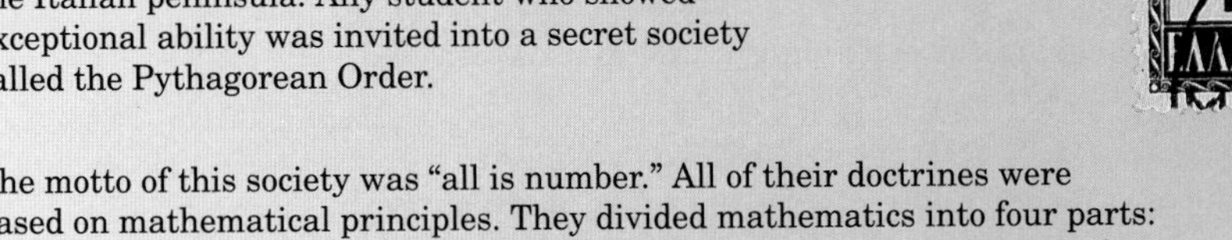

The Pythagoreans

In the sixth century B.C., the famous mathematician Pythagoras opened a school in the southern part of the Italian peninsula. Any student who showed exceptional ability was invited into a secret society called the Pythagorean Order.

The motto of this society was "all is number." All of their doctrines were based on mathematical principles. They divided mathematics into four parts: music, arithmetic, astronomy, and geometry. These four subjects became the school curriculum from the time of Plato and Aristotle up to the Renaissance.

The best known mathematical discovery of the Pythagoreans was the Pythagorean Theorem. The Babylonians and the Egyptians knew and used this right triangle property 1500 years before Pythagoras; however, Pythagoras is credited with deriving its proof.

4 CLOSE

Assessment Option

Writing Write as many ratios as you can think of that occur in a right triangle. Then draw and label a picture of a right triangle that corresponds to three of the ratios. Exchange with another student and find the desired measure.

Additional Answer

21. Sample answers: A wire rises 20 meters for every 100 meters of vertical distance. What is the measure of the angle the wire makes with the horizontal?
A tent has a center pole that is 6 feet high and a side that is 7.2 feet long. What is the measure of the angle the tent side forms with the ground?
LuAnn and Tim are flying kites in Crockett Park. When LuAnn is 30 meters from Tim, her kite forms an angle of 58° with the ground. How high is the kite?

Enrichment Masters Booklet, **p. 128**

Name ______________ Date ______

Enrichment Worksheet 14-10

Trigonometric Applications

The angle of depression is very similar to the angle of elevation. As shown in the figure below, the angle is measured looking down from the horizontal rather than looking up.

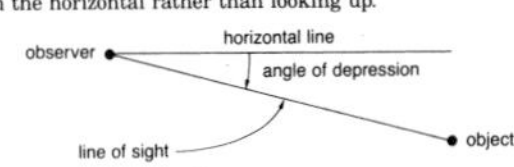

Draw a triangle to model each problem. Then solve. Round answers to the nearest tenth.

1. A lighthouse keeper is in the top of a lighthouse 95 feet above sea level. She notes that the angle of depression to a rock jutting above the water is 6°. How far is the rock from the lighthouse? **903.9 ft**

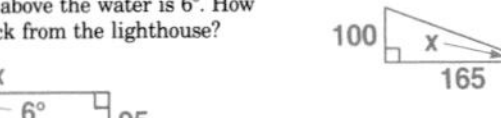

2. What is the angle of elevation of the sun when a 100-foot water tower casts a shadow 165 feet long? **31.2°**

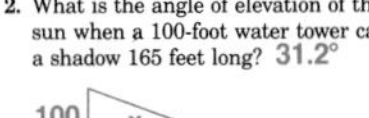

3. A disabled jet can glide at an angle of 11° with the horizontal. If it starts to glide at an altitude of 12,000 feet, can it reach a landing strip 10 miles away? **61,728 ft ≈ 11.7 mi; yes**

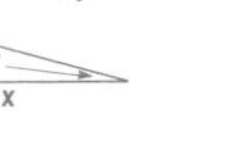

4. From a cliff 150 feet above a lake, Julio saw a boat sailing directly toward him. The angle of depression was 5°. A few minutes later, he measured it to be 11°. Find the distance the boat sailed between the two observations. **942.7 ft**

x
y
x − y
5°
11°
150

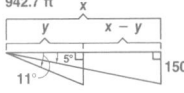

5. A horizontal road runs due east from Mount Baldy. From two points 235 meters apart on the road, the angles of elevation to the mountaintop are 43° and 30°. How high above the road is the mountaintop? **356.3 m**

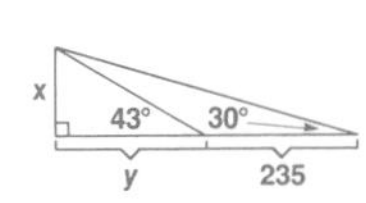

Alternate Strategies: Extending the Lesson

Enrichment

Using Cooperative Groups Have cooperative groups of students choose a topic. Have them write problems that are about the topic and use each of the trigonometric ratios to solve the problems.

Cooperative Learning

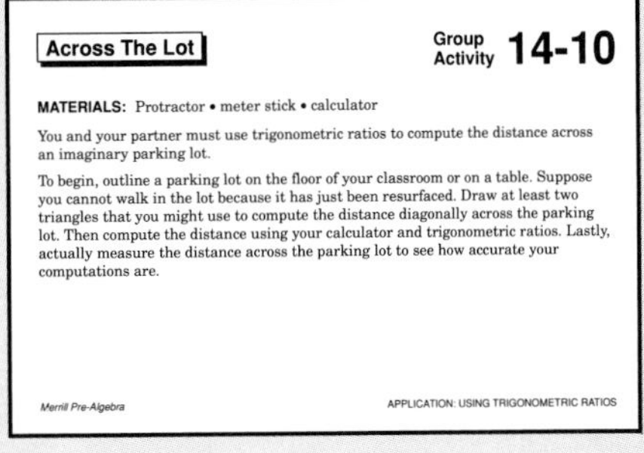

Across The Lot Group Activity **14-10**

MATERIALS: Protractor • meter stick • calculator

You and your partner must use trigonometric ratios to compute the distance across an imaginary parking lot.

To begin, outline a parking lot on the floor of your classroom or on a table. Suppose you cannot walk in the lot because it has just been resurfaced. Draw at least two triangles that you might use to compute the distance diagonally across the parking lot. Then compute the distance using your calculator and trigonometric ratios. Lastly, actually measure the distance across the parking lot to see how accurate your computations are.

Merrill Pre-Algebra APPLICATION: USING TRIGONOMETRIC RATIOS

Using the Chapter Review

The Chapter Review is a comprehensive review of the concepts presented in this chapter. This review may be used to prepare students for the Chapter Test.

Alternate Review Strategy

To provide a brief in-class review, you may wish to read the following questions to the class and require a verbal response.

1. What is the square of 9? 81
2. What is the best whole number estimate for $\sqrt{28}$? 5
3. What is a Venn diagram? It is a diagram that uses circles to represent logical relations between and operations on sets showing inclusion, exclusion, or intersection of the circles.
4. Is 2.0321312301 . . . a rational or irrational number and why? irrational; it does not terminate and it does not repeat
5. State the Pythagorean Theorem. In a right triangle, the square of the hypotenuse is equal to the sum of the squares of the length of the legs.
6. State an equation that can be used to solve this question. How long is a piece of rope that is attached to the top of a 12-foot pole and tied to a stake 9 feet from the base of the pole? $12^2 + 9^2 = x^2$
7. How long is the side opposite the 30° angle of a right triangle? one-half the length of the hypotenuse
8. How do you find the tangent of an angle B? $\frac{\text{measure of the side opposite B}}{\text{measure of the side adjacent B}}$
9. What two special ratios involve the length of the hypotenuse and the length of one leg of a right triangle? sine and cosine
10. A radio tower casts a shadow 120 meters long when the angle of elevation of the sun is 41°. How tall is the tower? 104 m

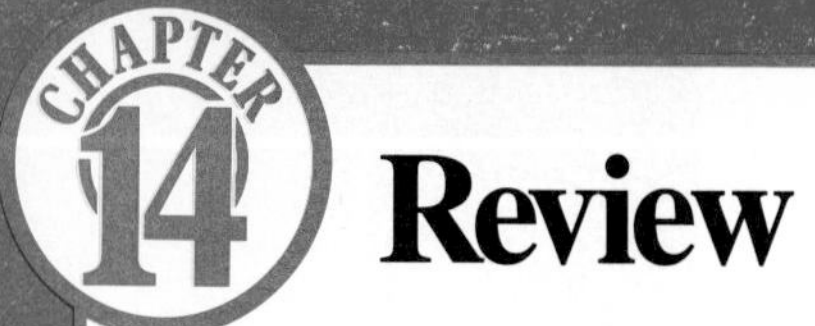

Review

Language and Concepts

Choose the correct term to complete each sentence.

1. The (square, square root) of 4 equals 16.
2. In the expression $\sqrt{25}$, the symbol $\sqrt{\ }$ is called a (radical sign, radicand).
3. The number $\sqrt{81}$ belongs to the set of (irrational, rational) numbers.
4. The longest side of a right triangle is the (hypotenuse, leg).
5. A right triangle that has a leg that is half the length of the hypotenuse is a (30° - 60°, 45° - 45°) right triangle.

Skills

Find the best integer estimate for each of the following. Then check your estimate using a calculator. (Lessons 14-1, 14-2)

6. 16^2 256
7. $\sqrt{49}$ 7
8. $-\sqrt{900}$ -30
9. $-\sqrt{39}$ -6
10. $\sqrt{9.61}$ 3

Simplify. (Lesson 14-4)

11. $\sqrt{48}$ $4\sqrt{3}$
12. $\sqrt{32}$ $4\sqrt{2}$
13. $\sqrt{300}$ $10\sqrt{3}$
14. $\sqrt{45}$ $3\sqrt{5}$

Name the sets of numbers to which each number belongs: the whole numbers, the integers, the rational numbers, the irrational numbers, and/or the real numbers. (Lesson 14-4) 15. whole number, integer, rational, real

15. 7
16. $\frac{1}{4}$
17. -2.6
18. $\sqrt{8}$

16. rational, real 17. rational, real 18. irrational, real

Use the Pythagorean Theorem to find the length of the hypotenuse of each right triangle. The lengths of the legs are given. (Lesson 14-5)

19. 12 m, 16 m 20 m
20. 14 ft, 48 ft 50 ft
21. 30 cm, 16 cm 34 cm

Find the missing measure for each right triangle. (Lesson 14-5)

22. a, 8 in.; b, 15 in. 17 in.
23. b, 63 ft; c, 65 ft 16 ft
24. a, 15 cm; c, 39 cm 36 cm

Find the value of x. Round decimal answers to the nearest tenth. (Lesson 14-7)

25. 6 m

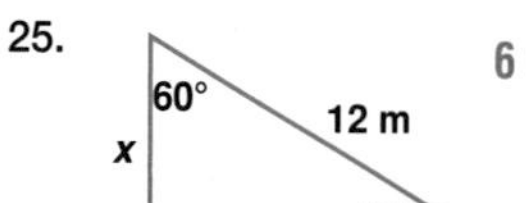

26. 9.9 ft

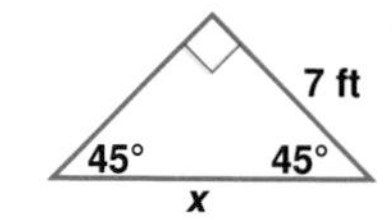

27. 3 cm

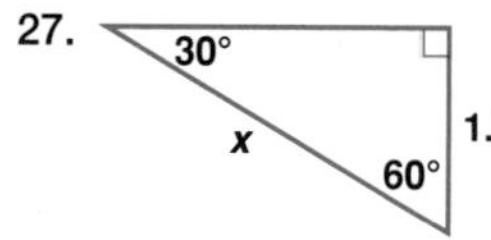

Write a fraction in simplest form for each ratio.
(Lessons 14-8, 14-9)

28. $\sin A$ $\frac{3}{5}$ 29. $\tan B$ $\frac{4}{3}$ 30. $\cos A$ $\frac{4}{5}$

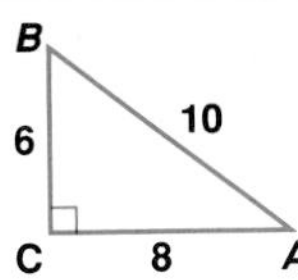

Solve for *y*. Round answers to the nearest tenth. (Lesson 14-10)

31. 35.5 in.

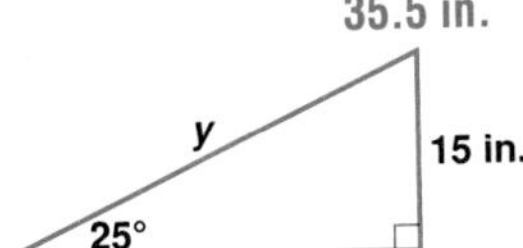

32. 56.9°

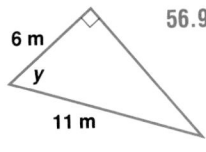

6 m
y
11 m

33. 10.5 ft

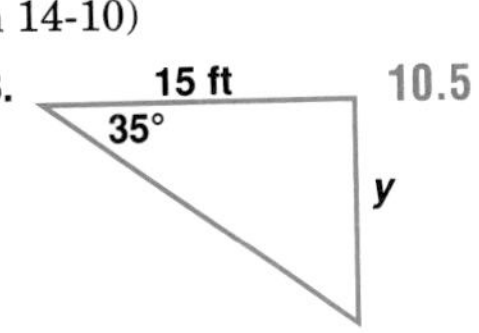

Applications and Problem Solving

Solve. Round decimal answers to the nearest tenth. (Lessons 14-3, 14-6)

34. In a recent survey of 120 students, 60 students said they play tennis and 50 students said they play softball. If 20 students play both sports, how many students do not play either tennis or softball? 30 students

35. A telephone pole is 28 feet tall. A wire is stretched from the top of the pole to a point on the ground that is 15 feet from the bottom of the pole. How long is the wire? 31.8 ft

Communicating Algebra

Write as many equations about ΔEFD as you can. $f^2 = d^2 + e^2$;

$\tan D = \frac{d}{e}$; $\tan E = \frac{e}{d}$; $\sin D = \frac{d}{f}$;

$\sin E = \frac{e}{f}$; $\cos D = \frac{e}{f}$; $\cos E = \frac{d}{f}$

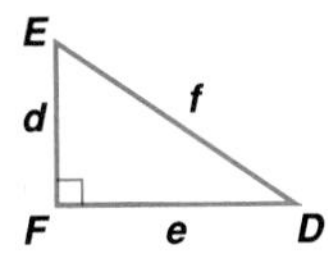

Curriculum Connection

- **History** Learn more about Pythagoras and his followers. See margin.
- **Science** Do research to find how a hot-air balloon works. See margin.

Read More About It

Lamm, Joyce. *Let's Talk About the Metric System.*

McCauley, David. *The Way Things Work.*

Pallas, Norvin. *Calculator Puzzles, Tricks, and Games.*

You may wish to use a Chapter Test (free-response format) as an additional chapter review. Two forms are provided in the Evaluation Masters Booklet as shown below.

Evaluation Masters Booklet, **p. 122**

Name ______ Date ______

Chapter 14 Test, Form 2A

1. Find the square root $\sqrt{169}$.
2. Find the square of 56.
3. Find the best integer estimate for $-\sqrt{79}$.
4. Find the best integer estimate for $\sqrt{125}$.
5. Janet has a total of 28 white, blue, and white-and-blue socks. If 8 socks are all blue and 26 socks have some blue, how many socks are all white?
6. Of the language classes offered at Knight School, 50 students take Spanish, 28 take French, and 10 take both languages. How many students take language classes altogether?
7. Solve $y^2 = 222$. Round the solution to the nearest tenth.
8. Simplify $\sqrt{80}$.
9. Use the Pythagorean Theorem to find the length of the hypotenuse of a right triangle. The lengths of the legs are 30 m and 72 m.
10. Find the missing measure of the right triangle. Round the answer to the nearest tenth. *a*, 35 ft; *b*, 42 ft
11. An insect crawls 6 inches south, 10 inches east, and 2 inches south. How many inches is it from where it began? Round the answer to the nearest tenth.

Round answers to the nearest tenth.

12. Find the length of a diagonal of a square 8 feet on each side.
13. Find the length of a diagonal of a square 3.4 cm on each side.
14. Find the length of the longer leg of a 30°–60° right triangle if the length of the hypotenuse is 14 cm.

Use a calculator to solve the problems. Round answers to the nearest thousandth.

15. Find the sine of 48°. 16. Find the tangent of 21°.

Round answers to the nearest degree.

17. Find the measure of angle *A* given that $\tan A = 0.625$.
18. Find the measure of angle *B* given that $\cos B = 0.819$.
19. Find the measure of angle *C* given that $\sin C = 0.961$.
20. Dave places a 30-foot ladder against a wall. The top of the ladder makes a 12° angle with the wall. How far from the wall is the foot of the ladder? Round to the nearest tenth.

BONUS A slope-antenna wire for shortwave radio reception is connected between the tops of two poles. One pole is 50 feet high and the other is 12 feet high. The poles are 56 feet apart. How many feet long is the wire? Round the answer to the nearest tenth.

	Answer
1.	13
2.	3136
3.	−9
4.	11
5.	2
6.	68
7.	14.9, −14.9
8.	$4\sqrt{5}$
9.	78 m
10.	54.7 ft
11.	12.8 in.
12.	11.3 ft
13.	4.8 cm
14.	12.1 cm
15.	0.743
16.	0.384
17.	32°
18.	35°
19.	74°
20.	6.2 ft
BONUS	67.7 ft

Evaluation Masters Booklet, **p. 123**

Name ______ Date ______

Chapter 14 Test, Form 2B

1. Find the square root $\sqrt{196}$.
2. Find the square of 64.
3. Find the best integer estimate for $-\sqrt{62}$.
4. Find the best integer estimate for $\sqrt{730}$.
5. Jane has a total of 22 white, blue, and white-and-blue socks. If 8 socks are all blue and 12 socks have some blue, how many socks are all white?
6. Of the language classes offered at night school, 40 students take Spanish, 16 take French, and 8 take both languages. How many students take language classes altogether?
7. Solve $y^2 = 333$. Round the solution to the nearest tenth.
8. Simplify $\sqrt{90}$.
9. Use the Pythagorean Theorem to find the length of the hypotenuse of a right triangle. The lengths of the legs are 35 m and 85 m.
10. Find the missing measure of the right triangle. Round the answer to the nearest tenth. *a*, 38 ft; *b*, 45 ft
11. An insect crawls 6 inches north, 8 inches west, and 3 inches north. How many inches is it from where it began. Round the answer to the nearest tenth.

Round answers to the nearest tenth.

12. Find the length of a diagonal of a square 12 feet on each side.
13. Find the length of a diagonal of a square 4.3 cm on each side.
14. Find the length of the longer leg of a 30°–60° right triangle if the length of the hypotenuse is 20 cm.

Use a calculator to solve the problems. Round answers to the nearest thousandth.

15. Find the sine of 56°. 16. Find the tangent of 63°.

Round answers to the nearest degree.

17. Find the measure of angle *A* given that $\tan A = 0.553$.
18. Find the measure of angle *B* given that $\cos B = 0.242$.
19. Find the measure of angle *C* given that $\sin C = 0.695$.
20. Dave places a 40-foot ladder against a wall. The top of the ladder makes a 11° angle with the wall. How far from the wall is the foot of the ladder? Round to the nearest tenth.

BONUS A slope-antenna wire for shortwave radio reception is connected between the tops of two poles. One pole is 60 feet high and the other is 8 feet high. The poles are 60 feet apart. How many feet long is the wire? Round the answer to the nearest tenth.

	Answer
1.	14
2.	4096
3.	−8
4.	27
5.	10
6.	48
7.	18.2, −18.2
8.	$3\sqrt{10}$
9.	91.9 m
10.	58.9 ft
11.	12.0 in.
12.	17.0 ft
13.	6.1 cm
14.	17.3 cm
15.	0.829
16.	1.963
17.	29°
18.	76°
19.	44°
20.	7.6 ft
BONUS	79.4 ft

Additional Answers
Communicating Algebra

History Pythagoras lived in the sixth century B.C. He was a religious teacher, mathematician, and philosopher. His followers, called Pythagoreans, followed strict rules of conduct such as observing silence, and abstaining from wine and beans.

Science Hot-air balloons rise because the air inside is heated making it lighter. To descend, the pilot of a hot-air balloon opens a vent in the balloon that allows hot air to escape.

Using the Chapter Test

This page may be used as a test or as an additional review. Two forms of a Chapter Test (multiple-choice format) are provided in the Evaluation Masters Booklet.

Evaluation Masters Booklet, pp. 118-119

Name ______________________ Date ____________

Chapter 14 Test, Form 1A

1. Find the square root $\sqrt{36}$.
   A. −18 B. 1296 C. 18 D. 6 — 1. D
2. Find the square root $-\sqrt{169}$.
   A. −13 B. 13 C. 28,561 D. 23 — 2. A
3. Find the square of 49.
   A. −7 B. 637 C. 2401 D. 7 — 3. C
4. Find the best whole number estimate for $\sqrt{51}$.
   A. 8 B. 7 C. 25 D. 102 — 4. B
5. Find the best integer estimate for $-\sqrt{123}$.
   A. −61 B. 15,129 C. −11 D. −12 — 5. C
6. Find the best integer estimate for $\sqrt{675}$.
   A. 25 B. 338 C. −26 D. 26 — 6. D
7. Harriet has a total of 36 red, blue, and red-and-blue socks. If 12 socks are all red and 20 socks have some red, how many socks are all blue?
   A. 16 B. 4 C. 12 D. 24 — 7. A
8. Of 132 music students, a total of 100 are in the band and 10 are in both band and chorus. How many students are in chorus only?
   A. 22 B. 32 C. 112 D. 42 — 8. B
9. Solve $x^2 = 96$. Round the positive solution to the nearest tenth.
   A. 48.0 B. 9.9 C. 9.8 D. 9.7 — 9. C
10. Simplify $\sqrt{50}$.
    A. $5\sqrt{2}$ B. $2\sqrt{5}$ C. $2\sqrt{25}$ D. $5\sqrt{10}$ — 10. A
11. Simplify $\sqrt{63}$.
    A. $3\sqrt{21}$ B. $7\sqrt{9}$ C. $3\sqrt{7}$ D. $9\sqrt{7}$ — 11. C
12. Use the Pythagorean Theorem to find the length of the hypotenuse of a right triangle. The lengths of the legs are 24 and 32.
    A. 28 B. 7.48 C. 56 D. 40 — 12. D

Find the missing measure for each right triangle. Round the answers to the nearest tenth.

13. a, 13; b, 15
    A. 18.3 B. 19.8 C. 28.0 D. 17.2 — 13. B
14. a, 5; c, 19
    A. 18.3 B. 19.8 C. 14.0 D. 24.1 — 14. A

Name ______________________ Date ____________

Chapter 14 Test, Form 1A (continued)

15. Rhea bikes 4 miles west, 8 miles north, and 4 miles west. How many miles is she from where she began? Round the answer to the nearest tenth.
    A. 18.3 B. 12.4 C. 16.0 D. 11.3 — 15. D
16. Find the length of a diagonal of a square 5 cm on a side.
    A. $\sqrt{5}$ cm B. $5\sqrt{2}$ cm C. $10\sqrt{2}$ cm D. $25\sqrt{2}$ cm — 16. B
17. Find the length of a diagonal of a square 4.5 cm on a side. Round the answer to the nearest tenth.
    A. 6.5 cm B. 2.1 cm C. 6.4 cm D. 9.0 cm — 17. C
18. Find the length of the shorter leg of a 30°–60° right triangle, if the length of the hypotenuse is 12 cm.
    A. 6 cm B. $6\sqrt{3}$ cm C. $12\sqrt{3}$ cm D. $6\sqrt{2}$ cm — 18. A

Use a calculator to solve each problem. Round answers to the nearest thousandth.

19. Find the tangent of 21°.
    A. 4.583 B. 87.274 C. 0.934 D. 0.384 — 19. D
20. Find the cosine of 66°.
    A. 0.407 B. 0.406 C. 0.4067 D. 8.124 — 20. A
21. Find the sine of 38°.
    A. 0.620 B. 6.164 C. 0.616 D. 0.615 — 21. C

Round answers to the nearest degree.

22. Find the measure of angle A given that $\tan A = 1.2345$.
    A. 59 B. 51 C. 50.9 D. 50 — 22. B
23. Find the measure of angle B given that $\cos B = 0.1234$.
    A. 1 B. 0.9 C. 82 D. 83 — 23. D
24. Find the measure of angle C given that $\sin C = 0.654$.
    A. 1.141 B. 41 C. 40 D. 48 — 24. B
25. Tom rests a 32-foot ladder against a wall. The top of the ladder hits the wall at a point 28 feet high. How far from the wall is the foot of the ladder? Round the answer to the nearest tenth.
    A. 8.6 B. 4.0 C. 42.5 D. 15.5 — 25. D

BONUS A slope-antenna wire for shortwave radio reception is connected between the tops of two poles. One pole is 40 feet high and the other is 10 feet high. The poles are 48 feet apart. How long is the wire? Round the answer to the nearest tenth.
A. 8.8 ft B. 56.6 ft C. 62.5 ft D. 53.9 ft — B

Test

Find the best integer estimate for each of the following.

1. $\sqrt{81}$ 9
2. 11^2 121
3. $-\sqrt{18}$ −4
4. $\sqrt{3481}$ 59

Name the sets of numbers to which each number belongs: the whole numbers, the integers, the rational numbers, the irrational numbers, and/or the real numbers. 5. whole number, integer, rational, real

5. 9
6. −1.7
7. $-\sqrt{11}$
8. $\frac{3}{8}$

6. rational, real 7. irrational, real 8. rational, real

Find the missing measure for each right triangle.

9. a, 13 m; c, 85 m 84 m
10. b, 48 cm; c, 73 cm 55 cm
11. a, 20 ft; b, 21 ft 29 ft

Write a fraction in simplest form for each ratio.

12. $\cos B$ $\frac{8}{17}$
13. $\tan A$ $\frac{8}{15}$
14. $\sin B$ $\frac{15}{17}$

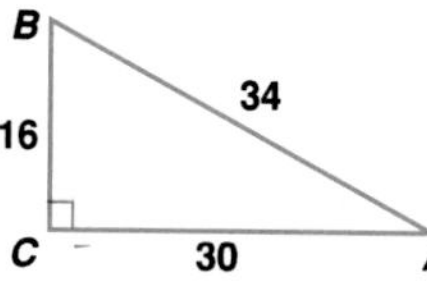

Solve for x. Round decimal answers to the nearest tenth.

15. 8.5 ft

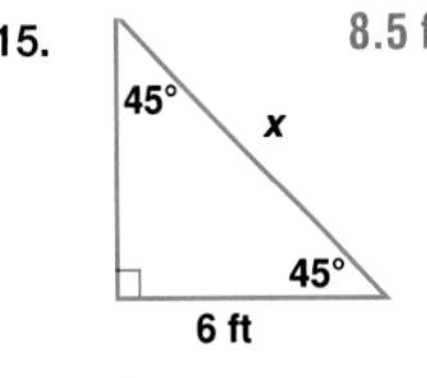

16. 7 m

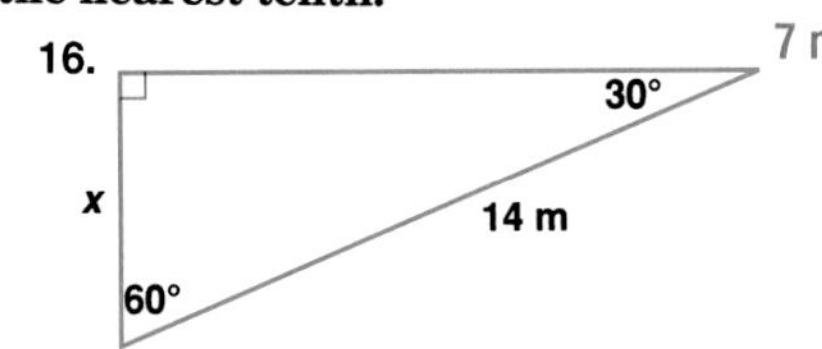

17. 9.1 in.

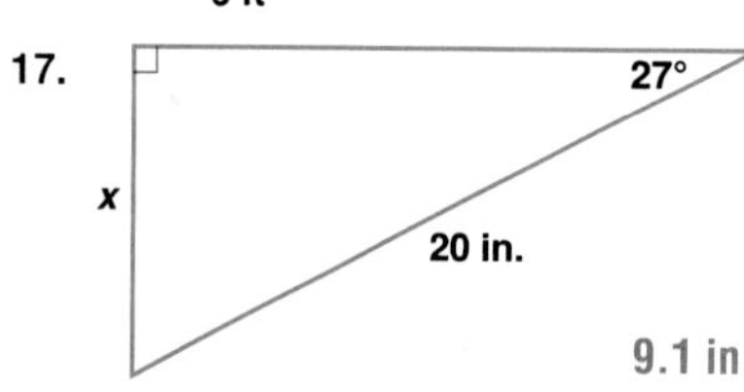

18. 22.6°

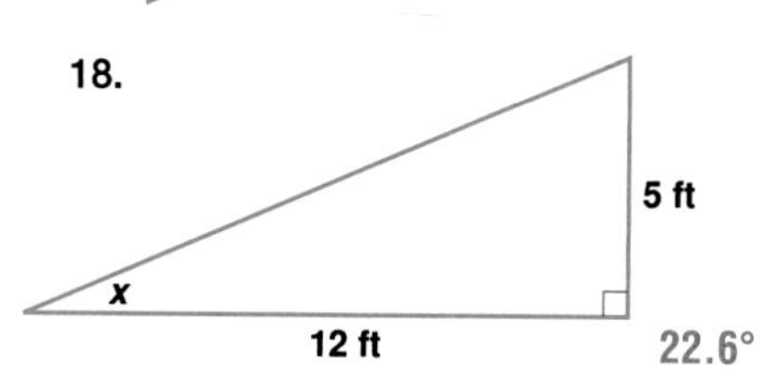

Solve.

19. There are a total of 50 triangles. Twenty triangles are right triangles and 15 are isosceles. If 7 triangles are both right and isosceles, how many are neither right nor isosceles? 22 triangles

20. Yana is standing 28 feet from a point directly below his kite. If the string attached to it is 53 feet long, how high is the kite flying? 45 ft

BONUS

The length of each side of the cube is 2 cm. Find the length of the diagonal of the cube. Round your answer to the nearest tenth. 3.5 cm

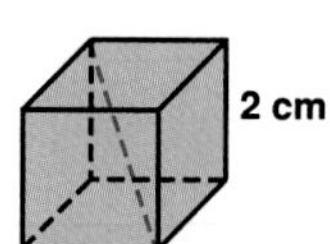

Test Generator Software is provided in both Apple and IBM formats. You may use this software to create your own tests, based on the needs of your students.

Cooperative Learning

The following activity is provided in the **Activity Masters Booklet.**

Cooperative Problem Solving, p. 45

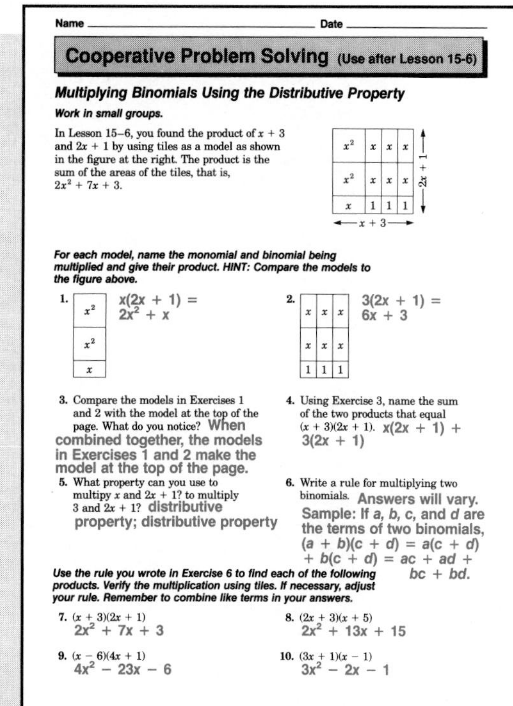

Name ______ Date ______

Cooperative Problem Solving (Use after Lesson 15-6)

Multiplying Binomials Using the Distributive Property

Work in small groups.

In Lesson 15–6, you found the product of $x + 3$ and $2x + 1$ by using tiles as a model as shown in the figure at the right. The product is the sum of the areas of the tiles, that is, $2x^2 + 7x + 3$.

For each model, name the monomial and binomial being multiplied and give their product. HINT: Compare the models to the figure above.

1. $x(2x + 1) = 2x^2 + x$
2. $3(2x + 1) = 6x + 3$
3. Compare the models in Exercises 1 and 2 with the model at the top of the page. What do you notice? When combined together, the models in Exercises 1 and 2 make the model at the top of the page.
4. Using Exercise 3, name the sum of the two products that equal $(x + 3)(2x + 1)$. $x(2x + 1) + 3(2x + 1)$
5. What property can you use to multipy x and $2x + 1$? to multiply 3 and $2x + 1$? distributive property; distributive property
6. Write a rule for multiplying two binomials. Answers will vary. Sample: If *a*, *b*, *c*, and *d* are the terms of two binomials, $(a + b)(c + d) = a(c + d) + b(c + d) = ac + ad + bc + bd$.

Use the rule you wrote in Exercise 6 to find each of the following products. Verify the multiplication using tiles. If necessary, adjust your rule. Remember to combine like terms in your answers.

7. $(x + 3)(2x + 1)$ $2x^2 + 7x + 3$
8. $(2x + 3)(x + 5)$ $2x^2 + 13x + 15$
9. $(x - 6)(4x + 1)$ $4x^2 - 23x - 6$
10. $(3x + 1)(x - 1)$ $3x^2 - 2x - 1$

Cooperative Problem Solving

Have students work in groups of two to four to discuss the following problem. A 3-digit base ten numeral can be represented as a polynomial in x with x = 10 as shown: $456_{10} = 4 \cdot 10^2 + 5 \cdot 10^1 + 6 \cdot 10$, or $456_x = 4x^2 + 5x + 6$.

If the base was changed from 10 to 2, the number 15 would be represented as: $15_{10} = 1 \cdot 2^3 + 1 \cdot 2^2 + 1 \cdot 2^1 + 1 \cdot 2$, or $x^3 + x^2 + x + 1$.

Look for a pattern and represent the number 28 in base 2, using polynomials. Answer: $x^4 + x^3 + x^2$

Interactive Bulletin Board

Logic Connection

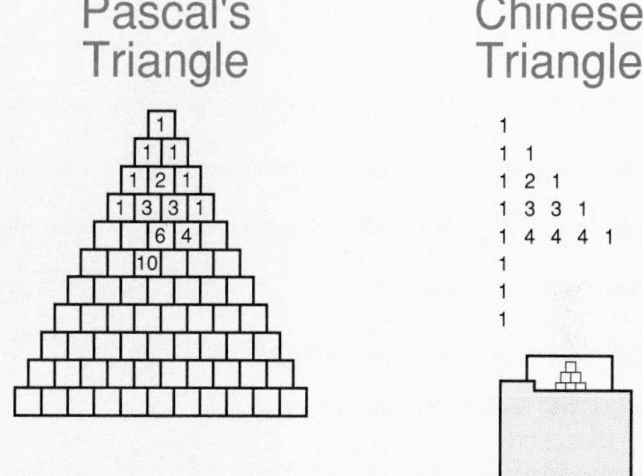

Purpose Provide practice in discovering patterns.

How to Use It Have students copy the Chinese triangle. (A chinese triangle is Pascal's triangle with the ones on the left-hand side aligned vertically). Then have students draw diagonals beginning at each one on the left-hand side and extending past the right side of the triangle. The numbers they pass through add up to sequential Fibonacci numbers. Provide blank, quarter-inch square grid triangles for students to use in their search for hidden numerical patterns. You may also want to have students color all multiples of a number to discover some of the visual patterns in Pascal's triangle.

Outside Resources

Books/Periodicals
101 Puzzles in Thought and Logic, Dover Publications, Inc.

Films/Videotapes
Classic Antics in Mathematics, AIMS Instructional Media

Software
Superplot, Edusoft

Technology

There are three pages in the ***Technology Masters Booklet*** that involve technology with concepts in this chapter. One page involves calculators and one page has a problem that can be solved using the BASIC program that is provided. Students should evaluate the information they obtain from running the program and solve a similar problem by extending the program.

Using the Chapter Opener

Transparency 15-0 is available in the Transparency Package. It provides a full-color visual and motivating activity that you can use to engage students in the mathematical content of the chapter.

Using Research

• Have students look in almanacs and newspapers to find different ways mathematics is used in baseball. Make a list. Lists might include batting averages, earned run averages, or number of errors. Also included might be the geometry of the diamond and measurements needed to lay out a diamond correctly.

• Have students use physics books or other references to find other polynomials that describe paths of moving objects. In addition to the polynomial in the Class Project, students might discover the polynomials that represent the speed a rocket needs to escape Earth's gravity, the speed needed to maintain a circular or elliptical orbit, or a description of the path of a golf ball.

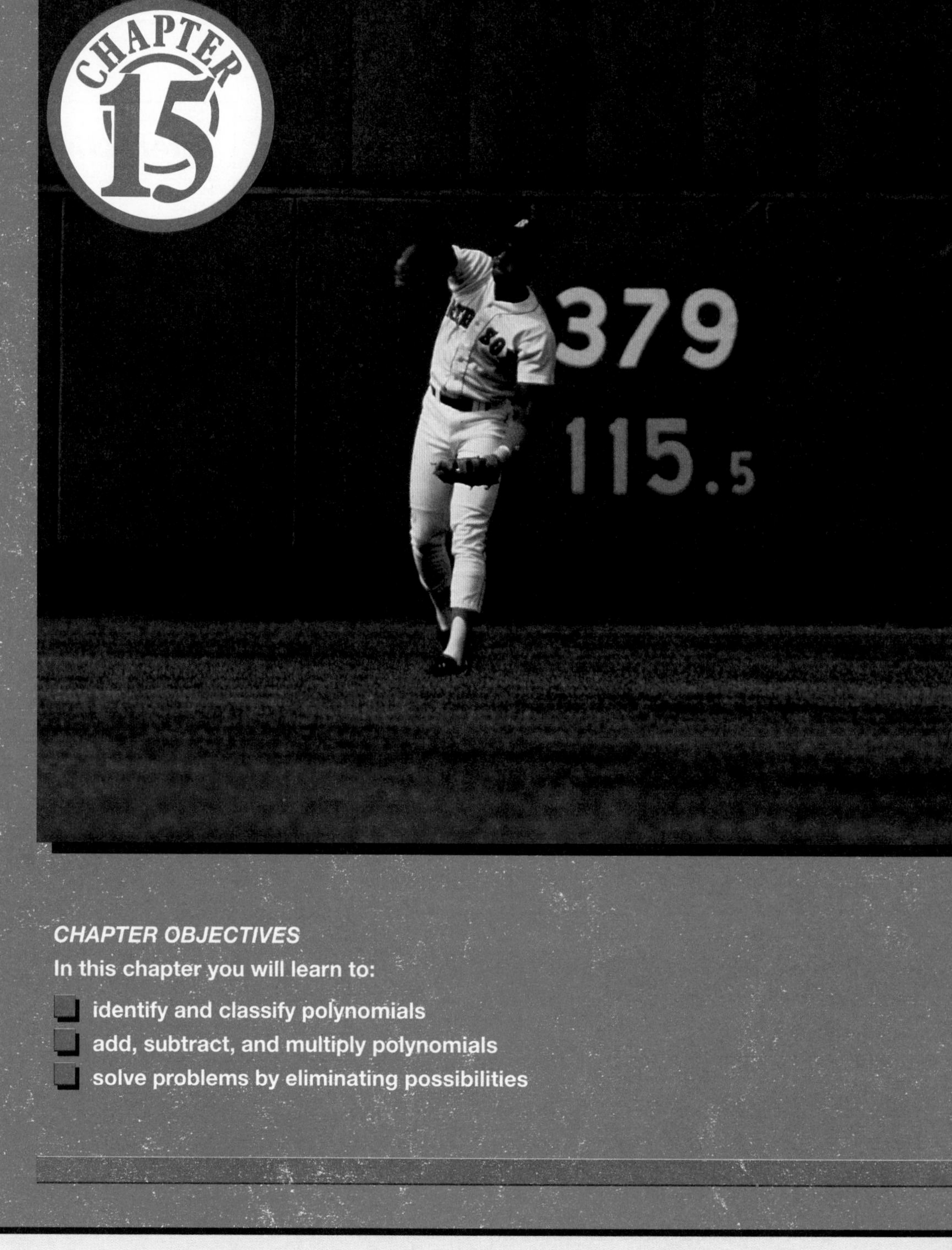

CHAPTER
15
379
115.5
CHAPTER OBJECTIVES
In this chapter you will learn to:
identify and classify polynomials
add, subtract, and multiply polynomials
solve problems by eliminating possibilities

Polynomials

There's more to mathematics in baseball than just keeping score or finding the speed at which a pitcher throws a fast ball.

Fenway Park is home to baseball's Boston Red Sox. Ninety-six meters from home plate in left field is a green wall about 18 meters high. Because it is so difficult to hit a home run over this wall, it is referred to as The Green Monster.

Mathematically, a polynomial like $x^2 - 9x + 18$ can be used to describe the speed with which the batter must hit the ball in order to clear the wall.

Class Project

Write a paragraph about Isaac Newton's contribution in the study of gravity. In your paragraph, mention the polynomial that describes the distance a falling object travels in *t* seconds.

Science Connection

Isaac Newton's contribution to the study of gravity states that the gravitational attraction between particles, including Earth and an object above Earth's surface, varies inversely as the square of the distance between them. In other words, the closer two objects are, the more attraction there is between them. The distance a falling object travels in t seconds is $vt + \frac{1}{2}gt^2$. If the object is dropped from a stationary position, $v = 0$. The acceleration due to gravity (g), is $-9.80\ m/s^2$ or $-32\ ft/s^2$.

Looking Ahead

You may want to have the following materials available to use in this chapter.

Exploration, p. 577
tiles*

Exploration, p. 583
tiles*

* You can use the Easy-to-Make manipulative provided on page 1 of the Lab Manual.

Lesson Notes 15-1

5-Minute Check
(over Chapter 14)

Simplify.
1. $\sqrt{169}$ 13
2. $-\sqrt{0.09}$ -0.3
3. $\sqrt{40}$ $2\sqrt{10}$

Find the missing measure for each right triangle. Round decimal answers to the nearest tenth.
4. b, 3 cm; c, 5 cm $a = 4$ cm
5. a, 5 ft; b, 7 ft $c = 8.6$ ft

Transparency 15-1 contains the 5-Minute Check and a teaching aid for this lesson.

1 FOCUS

The purpose of this lesson is for students to determine if an expression is a polynomial, use characteristics to classify it, and find what degree it is.

Motivating the Lesson

Use words such as monacle, bicycle, tricycle, and polyester to develop the prefixes mono-, bi-, tri-, and poly-.

2 TEACH

Using Cooperative Groups

After discussion and examples of key terms, divide students into groups of four. Write expressions on cards. For each, have a student in turn tell if it is a monomial or polynomial and name the variable, exponent(s), and degree.

EE: 1E, 3A
TAAS: 2

15-1 Polynomials

Objectives:
Identify and classify polynomials.
Find the degree of a polynomial.

Key Terms:
monomial
degree
polynomial
like term
binomial
trinomial
constant

In biology, you study animals and plants. To distinguish common characteristics, plants and animals are classified by *genus* and *species*. A common frog, for example, is identified as *Rana pipiens,* where *Rana* is the genus and *pipiens* is the species.

In mathematics, we classify expressions that have common characteristics.

Expressions such as y, 15, $-7x^2$, $\frac{x}{2}$, and $\sqrt{3}x^3y^2$ are called **monomials.** Notice that each expression consists of a *number,* a *variable,* or a *product* (not a quotient) of numbers and variables. Expressions like $2x + 3$, $\frac{4}{y^2}$, or $\sqrt{m}$ are *not* monomials. Why? $2x + 3$ is a sum; $\frac{4}{y^2}$ is a quotient; $\sqrt{m}$ is a square root.

Why is $\frac{x}{2}$ considered a product rather than a quotient? $\frac{x}{2} = \frac{1}{2}x$

Examples

State whether each expression is a monomial.

1 $\frac{4}{m}$

The expression $\frac{4}{m}$ is *not* a monomial because it contains a variable in its denominator.

2 $\frac{3}{4}x$

The expression $\frac{3}{4}x$ is a monomial because it is the product of a number and a variable.

Biology Connection

The system of naming species began over 200 years ago. Since that time, more than 1.5 million species have been named.

The **degree** of a monomial is the sum of the exponents of its variables. The following chart shows you how to find the degree of a monomial.

Monomial	Variable(s)	Exponent(s)	Degree
y	y	1	1
$-6r^2$	r	2	2
$\sqrt{3}x^3y^2$	x, y	3, 2	3 + 2 or 5
$\frac{2}{3}bc^8$	b, c	1, 8	1 + 8 or 9

Remember that $y = y^1$.

Bell Ringer

Flamingoes and alligators reside peacefully in a pond. If there are forty-four feet and thirty eyes, how many alligators are in the pond? 7

A **polynomial** is a monomial or the sum or difference of two or more monomials. Expressions such as $5x + 1$, $x^2y + x$, and $5 - 3c + 6c^2$ are polynomials. Each monomial in the polynomial is called a **term** of the polynomial.

Why are $6x^3y$ and $17x^3y$ like terms? Why are $3a^2b$ and $4ab^2$ not like terms?
$6x^3y$ and $17x^3y$ differ only by their coefficients; $3a^2b$ and $4ab^2$ differ by their variables and coefficients.

Two monomials that are the same or differ only by their coefficients, are **like terms.** For example, $6x^3y$ and $17x^3y$ are like terms; $3a^2b$ and $4ab^2$ are not. A polynomial with two *unlike* terms is a **binomial;** a polynomial with three unlike terms is a **trinomial.**

Examples

State whether each expression is a polynomial. If it is, identify it as a *monomial, binomial,* or *trinomial.*

3 $7y^3 + 4y^2 + y$

The expression $7y^3 + 4y^2 + y$ is a polynomial because it is the sum of three monomials. Since it has three unlike terms, it is a trinomial.

4 $5b - \frac{1}{b^2}$

The expression $5b - \frac{1}{b^2}$ is not a polynomial because $\frac{1}{b^2}$ is not a monomial.

You can find the degree of a polynomial by determining which term in the polynomial has the greatest degree. The degree of the polynomial is the same as that of the term with the greatest degree.

You know how to find the degree of a term, or monomial, containing variables. A monomial that does not contain a variable is called a **constant.** What do you think is the degree of a constant? Consider the constant 15.

$$15 = 15 \cdot 1$$
$$= 15 \cdot x^0 \qquad \text{Recall that } x^0 = 1.$$

So, the degree of 15 or any nonzero constant is 0.
The constant 0 has *no* degree.

Chalkboard Examples

State whether each expression is a monomial.

- *For Example 1*
  $\frac{5}{y}$ **no**
- *For Example 2*
  $\frac{2}{7}k$ **yes**

State whether each expression is a polynomial. If it is, identify it as a monomial, binomial, or trinomial.

- *For Example 3*
  $3x^4 + 8x^2 + x$ **yes, trinomial**
- *For Example 4*
  $6m - \frac{3}{x}$ **no**
- *For Example 5*
  Find the degree of each polynomial. $6x^3y^2 + 5xy + y^4$ **5**

Alternate Strategies: Reteaching the Lesson

Reteaching Activity

Act It Out Have students play a "Telling the Truth" game. Have one student write an expression on the chalkboard. The student then states, "I have a polynomial of degree (integer)". The other students determine whether the statement is true and, if it is not true, why it is false.

Reteaching Masters Booklet, p. 129

Name ____________ Date ____________

Reteaching Worksheet 15-1

Polynomials

The prefix *mono-* is from a Greek word meaning "single" or "one." A monomial has just *one* term.

The prefix *bi-* means "two." A binomial has *two* terms.

The prefix *tri-* means "three." A trinomial has *three* terms.

Each term can be a number, a variable, or a product of numbers and variables.

A term cannot be a quotient with the variable in the denominator or the square root of a variable.

Monomials
-36 x^3 $0.5y$ $\frac{-z}{10}$

Binomials
$3x + \sqrt{2}$ $-4a + b^2$ $\frac{c}{3} - \frac{d}{4}$

Trinomials
$x^2 - 3x + 4$ $4a^2b^3 + 2ab^2 - b$

Give ... ch of the following is not a m... mial.

Chapter 15 **565**

3 PRACTICE/APPLY

Checking the Concept

Give students the expressions $6x^2y + 4x^3y$ and $(6x^2y)(4x^3y)$. Ask if each expression is a monomial or a polynomial. Find and compare the degrees of the expressions.

Error Analysis
Watch for students who multiply exponents of variable factors instead of adding them. **Prevent by** writing factors in expanded form, performing the multiplication, and returning to exponential form.

Independent Practice

Homework Assignment	
Basic	21-55 odd, 56-65
Average	20-54 even, 56-65
Honors	28-31, 42-65

Practice Masters Booklet, **p. 143**

Name ______________________ Date ______________

Practice Worksheet 15-1

Polynomials

State whether each expression is a polynomial. If it is, identify it as a monomial, binomial, or trinomial.

1. $p^2 - q^2$ yes, binomial
2. $\sqrt{x+1}$ no
3. $9y$ yes, monomial
4. $ax + bx + x^3$ yes, trinomial
5. $\frac{4}{z}$ no
6. -12 yes, monomial

Find the degree of each polynomial.

7. $3x - 1$ 1
8. $2y^3$ 3
9. $3a + 2b$ 1
10. $-2t^2 + s^4$ 4
11. $4c^2 - 9c^2d^3$ 5
12. -2 0
13. $5y^6 - 2xy^3z + x^4yz^2$ 7
14. $2pq^2 - pq^3$ 4
15. $-3ka^4 - 4a^6$ 6

Evaluate each polynomial if a = 1, b = −2, c = −1, and d = −4.

16. $a^2 - 3bd$ −23
17. $b^3 - 4ad$ 8
18. $1 - b^2 + c^3$ −4
19. $2b^4 - 3ad^2$ −16
20. $\sqrt{2}bd$ $8\sqrt{2}$
21. $a^2 - a^4$ 0
22. $4abc - 5ab^2 + 3a^2b$ −18
23. $c^2 - a^2 + 1$ 1
24. $a^2 - c^2 + 1$ 1
25. $6bc^2 - 2ab + 4ab^2$ 8
26. $2b^2 - b + 3$ 13
27. $-d^2 + 3d - 1$ −29
28. $10c^3 + 5b^3 - a^2$ −51
29. $d^2 - b^2 + bd$ 20
30. $-8abc - d^3$ 48
31. $c^2 - c + 1$ 3
32. $6ac^2 - 3a + d^3$ −61
33. $a^2 - b^3 - c^4$ 8

Example

Find the degree of each polynomial.

5 $a^2 + 2ab + b^4$

First, find the degree of each term.

$a^2 \rightarrow 2$

$2ab \rightarrow 1 + 1$ or 2

$b^4 \rightarrow 4$ greatest degree

The degree of $a^2 + 2ab + b^4$ is 4.

Checking for Understanding 1., 2., 3. See margin.

Communicating Algebra

1. In your own words, define *monomial.* Write three examples of a monomial.
2. Explain how you would find the degree of the polynomial $p^3 - p^2m^2 + 4m - 1$.
3. Are $2x^3y^2$ and $5x^2y^3$ like terms? Explain why or why not.

Guided Practice

State whether each expression is a monomial.

4. $7x$ yes
5. y^2 yes
6. -8 yes
7. $-5xy$ yes
8. $3ab + c$ no
9. $\frac{2}{3}x$ yes
10. $-\frac{11xy}{7}$ yes
11. $\sqrt{mp}$ no

Find the degree of each monomial.

12. $11m$ 1
13. $-6y^3$ 3
14. 12 0
15. $\frac{a}{7}$ 1
16. $3m^2n$ 3
17. $-2p^2qr^4$ 7
18. $\frac{ab^2}{3}$ 3
19. $-b$ 1

Exercises

Independent Practice

State whether each expression is a polynomial. If it is, identify it as a *monomial, binomial,* or *trinomial.*

20. $5m$ yes, monomial
21. $2x + 1$ yes, binomial
22. $x^3 - y^3$ yes, binomial
23. $4 + 3a - 8a^3$ yes, trinomial
24. $\sqrt{d} - 5$ no
25. $\frac{3}{g}$ no
26. $\frac{e}{6}$ yes, monomial
27. $\frac{6}{x+y}$ no
28. $\frac{4ab}{c} - \frac{2d}{x}$ no
29. -17 yes, monomial
30. $5ab^2 - 2a + b^2$ yes, trinomial
31. $15n^2 + 3nt$ yes, binomial

Find the degree of each polynomial.

32. $3y^2$ 2
33. $-5x^3yz^2$ 6
34. $2x + 1$ 1 40. 3
35. $21m + 12n$ 1
36. $-3x^2 + 5m^5$ 5
37. $4x^3 + 7xy - 2xz^3$ 4
38. $18a^3b^4 - 11ab^5$ 7
39. $19n^2 + 27n^2t^2$ 4
40. $32xyz - 11x^2y + 17xz^2$
41. $a^2 + b^3 + c^{14} + d^2$ 14
42. $2xy^2z - 5xyz^5 + 6x^3$ 7
43. $3x^4y^2z + 6xy^3z - 12z^6$ 7
44. 2^2a^2 2
45. $3^3xy - 5x$ 2
46. $-5^2rs^3 - 2y^5$ 5

Evaluate each polynomial if $a = -1$, $b = 2$, $c = -3$, and $d = 4$.

47. $a^3 - 2ab$ 3
48. $b^3 - 2ac$ 2
49. $4a^5 - 2ab^2$ 4
50. $5abc + 2a^2b - 6ab^2$ 58
51. $4ab^2 - 2ab + 6bc^2$ 96
52. $5ac^2 - 2a + b^2$ -39
53. $\sqrt{2b}$ 2
54. $\sqrt{d} - b^2$ -2
55. $\sqrt{-27c} - a$ 10

Additional Answers

1. A monomial is a number, a variable, or a product of the two. Sample examples: a, 8, $42x^2y$
2. Find the term with the highest sum of exponents.
3. No. The coefficients of the two terms is not the only thing that is different.

Mixed Review

56. Solve $3.5k = 31.5$ using the inverse operation. (Lesson 1-7) **9**
57. *True* or *false:* $|5| = -5$. (Lesson 2-2) **false**
58. Name two factors of any nonzero number. (Lesson 4-1) **1 and itself**
59. Solve the inequality $b - 2.3 \le 5.9$. (Lesson 5-7) $b \le 8.2$
60. Estimate 9% of 312. (Lesson 9-6) **31.2**
61. Use the formula $A = \frac{1}{2}h(a + b)$ to find the area of a trapezoid that has bases of 13 mm and 5 mm and a height of 10 mm. (Lesson 13-2) 90 mm^2
62. Find $-\sqrt{196}$. (Lesson 14-1) **-14**

Application

63. **Architecture** Mr. Snyder, an architect, draws a floor plan for the first floor of a house. Using the measurements given, write a polynomial that represents the total area of the first floor.
$2xy + 2y^2 + 2yz$

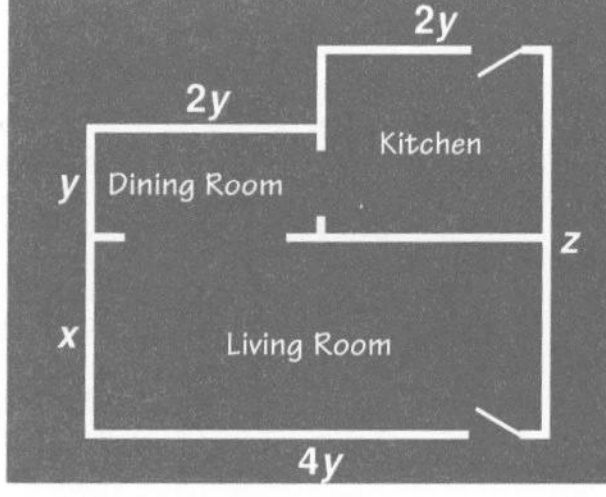

Critical Thinking

64. What is the degree of the polynomial $x^{n+2} + x^{n-3}y^3 + y^{n-1}$? $n + 2$

Wrap-Up

65. From your everyday experience, think of an example in which you classify objects. **Sample answer: clothing**

Biography: Amalie Emmy Noether

Emmy Noether was born into a distinguished German-Jewish family of mathematicians and scientists in 1882. Her interest and ability in mathematics developed when she began studying at the University of Erlangen, Germany. She went on to complete a PhD degree in 1907.

While German universities permitted women to earn degrees, job opportunities for them were limited. The best position Ms. Noether could reach in Germany was that of "unofficial associate professor." In 1933, however, when Ms. Noether came to the United States, she was appointed to an actual faculty position at Bryn Mawr College in Pennsylvania.

The focus of Emmy Noether's work in mathematics was *abstract algebra,* the study of different algebraic systems. Her work so inspired her successors that mathematicians often speak of it as the "Noether school" of mathematics.

4 CLOSE

Assessment Option

Writing Have the students write ten polynomial expressions; three monomials, three binomials, and three trinomials, and one with more than three unlike terms. Then have them write five expressions that are not polynomials.

Alternate Strategies: Extending the Lesson

Enrichment

Science Connection Have students use physics books to find formulas that involve polynomials. Have students make a list of the polynomials and the degree of each.

Cooperative Learning

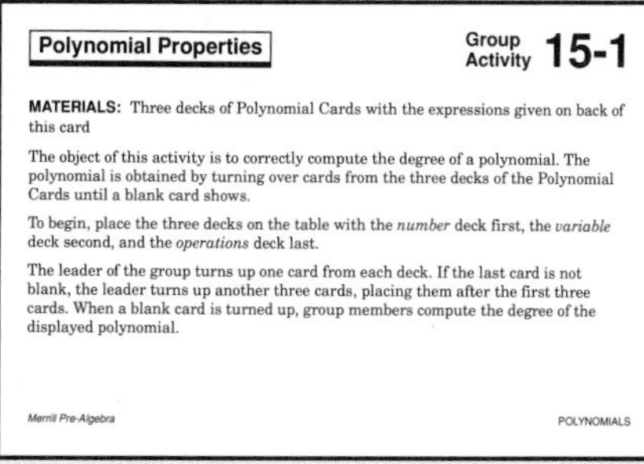

Polynomial Properties Group Activity **15-1**

MATERIALS: Three decks of Polynomial Cards with the expressions given on back of this card

The object of this activity is to correctly compute the degree of a polynomial. The polynomial is obtained by turning over cards from the three decks of the Polynomial Cards until a blank card shows.

To begin, place the three decks on the table with the *number* deck first, the *variable* deck second, and the *operations* deck last.

The leader of the group turns up one card from each deck. If the last card is not blank, the leader turns up another three cards, placing them after the first three cards. When a blank card is turned up, group members compute the degree of the displayed polynomial.

Merrill Pre-Algebra POLYNOMIALS

Enrichment Masters Booklet, **p. 129**

Name ______________ Date ______________

Enrichment Worksheet 15-1

The Summation Sign

The Greek letter Σ (sigma) is called the **summation sign.** It is used to abbreviate the writing of a series.

Consider the series $2 + 4 + 6 + 8 + 10$. It can be written as $2(1) + 2(2) + 2(3) + 2(4) + 2(5)$. Each term is 2 times a number, so $2k$ can be used to represent each term.

The sum of $2k$ from $k = 1$ to $k = 5$ can be written $\sum_{k=1}^{5} 2k$.

This symbol means that you successively replace k by each value 1, 2, 3, 4, and 5, and write the resulting numbers as an indicated sum. The variable k is called the **index**.

Example: Write the series $\sum_{t=1}^{6} (t - 1)$ as an indicated sum.

$$\sum_{t=1}^{6} (t - 1) = 0 + 1 + 2 + 3 + 4 + 5$$

Write each series as an indicated sum.

1. $\sum_{j=3}^{7} j$ $3 + 4 + 5 + 6 + 7$
2. $\sum_{k=4}^{8} (k + 2)$ $6 + 7 + 8 + 9 + 10$
3. $\sum_{t=1}^{5} \frac{1}{2}t$ $\frac{1}{2} + 1 + \frac{3}{2} + 2 + \frac{5}{2}$
4. $\sum_{x=1}^{5} x^2$ $1 + 4 + 9 + 16 + 25$
5. $\sum_{k=2}^{6} (2k + 1)$ $5 + 7 + 9 + 11 + 13$
6. $\sum_{k=1}^{5} \frac{k(k + 1)}{2}$ $1 + 3 + 6 + 10 + 15$

Use Σ to write each series. Answers may vary. Sample answers given.

7. $4 + 7 + 10 + 13$ $\sum_{k=1}^{4} (3k + 1)$
8. $6 + 10 + 14 + 18$ $\sum_{k=1}^{4} (4k + 2)$
9. $1 + 8 + 27 + 64$ $\sum_{k=1}^{4} k^3$
10. $\frac{1}{4} + \frac{2}{5} + \frac{3}{6} + \frac{4}{7}$ $\sum_{k=1}^{4} \frac{k}{k + 3}$

Lesson Notes 15-2

5-Minute Check
(over Lesson 15-1)

Find the degree of each polynomial.
1. $22x + 5y^4$ 4
2. $6x^2 + 7x + 5$ 2
3. $8m^3 + xy^4$ 5
4. $7x^3y^3 + 3x^2y + 2xy$ 6
5. $4k^5 + m^4n^3 + pr^3$ 7

Transparency 15-2 contains the 5-Minute Check and a teaching aid for this lesson.

1 FOCUS

The goal of the lesson is to apply skills learned about the properties of addition and the distributive property to adding polynomials.

Motivating the Lesson

Show the class a bowl of apples and oranges (or a picture of a bowl of apples and oranges), and ask them to describe the contents of the bowl using one number.

2 TEACH

Chalkboard Examples

- *For Example 1*
  Find $(4x^2 + 2x + 3) + (x^2 + 5x + 6)$ using tiles. $5x^2 + 7x + 9$

Find each sum.

- *For Example 2*
  $(6x + 2) + (x + 1)$ $7x + 3$
- *For Example 3*
  $(m^2 - 2mn + n^2) + (4m^2 - 6n^2)$
  $5m^2 - 2mn - 5n^2$

EE: 1C, 1E, 2E, 3A, 4B
TAAS: 2, 4

15-2 Adding Polynomials

Objective:
Add polynomials.

When an architect designs a building, she often makes a *model* of her plan. The model helps her to see whether her design is going to work. In mathematics, we can also make models. A model of a polynomial can be made by using tiles or drawings like the ones shown below.

Let [1 × 1 tile] be a 1×1 square. The square has an area of 1.

Let [1 × x tile] be a $1 \times x$ rectangle. The rectangle has an area of x.

Let [x × x tile] be an $x \times x$ square. The square has an area of x^2.

You can use these tiles to make a model of a polynomial.

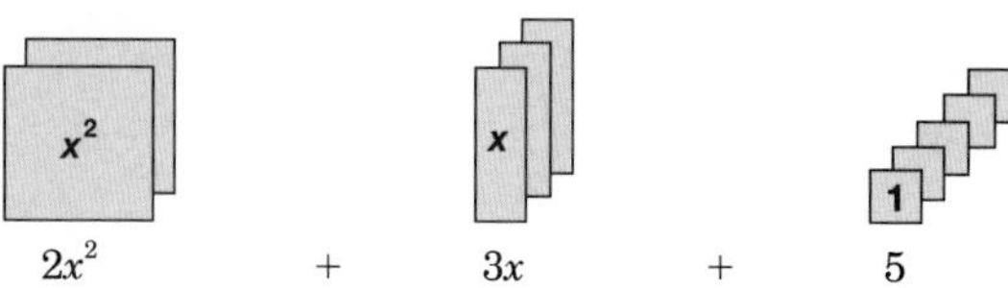

$2x^2 + 3x + 5$

Tiles can also help you to understand how to add polynomials.

Example

1 **Find $(3x^2 + x + 2) + (x^2 + 2x + 4)$ using tiles.**

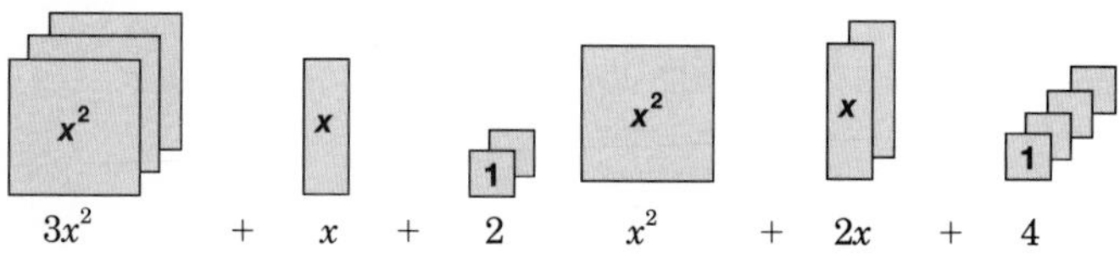

$3x^2 + x + 2 \quad x^2 + 2x + 4$

In this problem, both $3x^2$ and x^2 are represented by $x \times x$ tiles. This means they are like models, or in algebraic terms, they are like terms. Both x and $2x$ are represented by $1 \times x$ tiles. They are also like terms. Similarly, 2 and 4 are like terms.

To add these polynomials, combine the like terms.

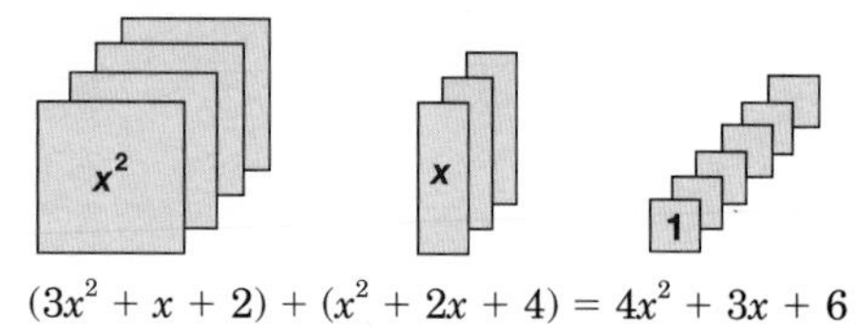

$(3x^2 + x + 2) + (x^2 + 2x + 4) = 4x^2 + 3x + 6$

Bell Ringer

What is the degree of the polynomial $6xy$? 2 of the polynomial $12xy^2z$? 4

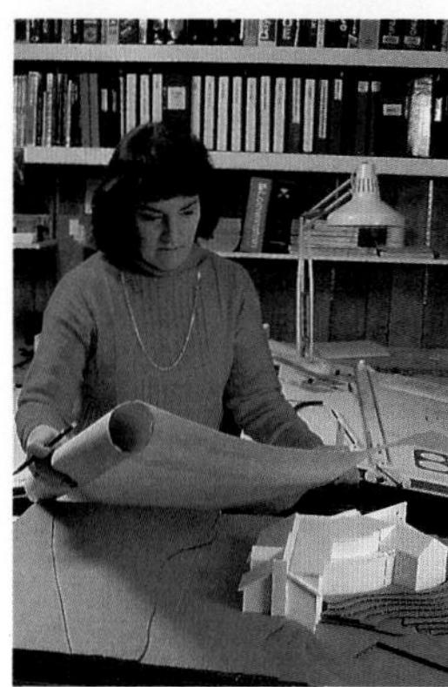

You can also add polynomials by using some of the properties discussed in earlier chapters.

Examples

Find each sum.

2 $(3x + 1) + (2x + 5)$

$= (3x + 2x) + (1 + 5)$ Associative and commutative properties of addition

$= (3 + 2)x + (1 + 5)$ Distributive property

$= 5x + 6$

3 $(2a^2 - 4ab + b^2) + (3a^2 - 5b^2)$

$= (2a^2 + 3a^2) + (-4ab) + [b^2 + (-5b^2)]$

$= (2 + 3)a^2 + (-4ab) + [1 + (-5)]b^2$

$= 5a^2 + (-4ab) + (-4b^2)$

$= 5a^2 - 4ab - 4b^2$

What properties are used to solve this problem? **comm prop of add, assoc prop of add, dist prop**

4 $(4rs^2 - r^2 - 3s^2) + (2s^2 + 5rs^2 + 7r^2)$

Sometimes it is helpful to arrange the terms in vertical columns and then add.

$$\begin{array}{r} 4rs^2 - r^2 - 3s^2 \\ + 5rs^2 + 7r^2 + 2s^2 \\ \hline 9rs^2 + 6r^2 - 1s^2 \end{array} \rightarrow 9rs^2 + 6r^2 - s^2 \quad -1s^2 = -s^2$$

Notice that like terms are aligned and added.

Checking for Understanding

Communicating Algebra

1. Identify the like terms in $x^2 + 7x + 2x^2 + x + 4$. **x^2, $2x^2$; $7x$, x**
2. Name the polynomial represented by the model at the right. **$2x^2 + 3x + 5$**

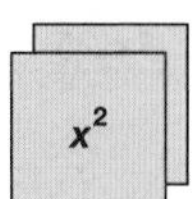

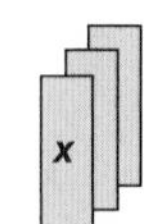

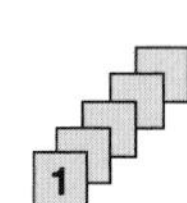

3. Draw a model of the polynomial $3x^2 + 6x + 4$. **See Solutions Manual.**

Guided Practice

Find each sum using tiles or drawings.

4. $(2x + 3) + (x + 4)$ **$3x + 7$**
5. $(5x + 1) + (3x)$ **$8x + 1$**
6. $(2x^2 + 3x + 1) + (3x^2 + x + 4)$ **$5x^2 + 4x + 5$**
7. $(3x^2 + 5x + 2) + (4x^2 + 3)$ **$7x^2 + 5x + 5$**

Exercises

Independent Practice

Find each sum.

8. $(5x - 7y) + (6x + 8y)$ **$11x + y$**
9. $(7n + 2t) + (4n - 3t)$ **$11n - t$**
10. $(7m - 2n) + (9m + 4n)$ **$16m + 2n$**
11. $(17n - 5m) + (11n - 3m)$ **11. $28n - 8m$**
12. $(2x^2 + 3) + (4x - 7)$ **$2x^2 + 4x - 4$**
13. $(5r + 5s) + (6r - 8s)$ **$11r - 3s$**

Chalkboard Examples

- *For Example 4*
  $(7xy^2 - 2x^2 - 4y^2) + (2y^2 + xy^2 + 5x^2)$ **$8xy^2 + 3x^2 - 2y^2$**

3 PRACTICE/APPLY

Checking the Concept

Have students work in pairs to solve Exercises 4-7. Have one student use tiles and the other use drawings then compare results.

Error Analysis

Watch for students who add exponents when they add coefficients to combine like terms.
Prevent by working simpler problems involving units of measurement instead of variables. Show that only the coefficient changes. Relate this to like terms using variables.

***Practice Masters Booklet,* p. 144**

Name ______ Date ______

Practice Worksheet 15-2

Adding Polynomials

Find each sum.

1. $(5w^2 + 8w) + (2w^2 + 3w)$ $7w^2 + 11w$
2. $(3x^2 - x) + (2x^2 + 3x)$ $5x^2 + 2x$
3. $(x^2 + 3x - 10) + (x^2 + 5x - 14)$ $2x^2 + 8x - 24$
4. $(3x^2 - 4x + 1) + (3x^2 - 5x + 2)$ $6x^2 - 9x + 3$
5. $(x - y) + (x + y)$ $2x$
6. $(9x + 2) + (3x - 6)$ $12x - 4$
7. $(-4a + 2b) + (7a + b)$ $3a + 3b$
8. $(4 - 3x) + (3x + 1)$ 5
9. $(3x + 6) + (2x - 2)$ $5x + 4$
10. $(3a^2 - 7a - 2) + (5a^2 - 3a - 17)$ $8a^2 - 10a - 19$
11. $(6x^2 + 7x - 2) + (3x^2 - 4x + 10)$ $9x^2 + 3x + 8$
12. $(12x^2 - 8x + 7) + (15x^2 + 4x - 1)$ $27x^2 - 4x + 6$
13. $(3x + 6y + 2) + (-9x - 2y + 8)$ $-6x + 4y + 10$
14. $(4a + 6ab - 2b) + (-5a - 2ab)$ $-a + 4ab - 2b$
15. $(9x^2 + 6x - 5) + (-2x^2 - x + 7)$ $7x^2 + 5x + 2$
16. $(-15x^2 + 5x + 2) + (3x^2 + 7)$ $-12x^2 + 5x + 9$
17. $(-2x + 3y - 4z) + (-5x + 10y)$ $-7x + 13y - 4z$
18. $(4b^2 - 3b + 7) + (-8b^2 - 5b + 16)$ $-4b^2 - 8b + 23$
19. $(6y^2 + 13y - 8) + (4y^2 - 8y + 7)$ $10y^2 + 5y - 1$
20. $(12z^2 - 8z + 17) + (21z - 8)$ $12z^2 + 13z + 9$

21. $\begin{array}{r} 2x + 4 \\ + \; x - 7 \\ \hline 3x - 3 \end{array}$
22. $\begin{array}{r} 5x - 7y \\ + 6x + 8y \\ \hline 11x + y \end{array}$
23. $\begin{array}{r} 2x + 3y \\ + 6x - 5y \\ \hline 8x - 2y \end{array}$
24. $\begin{array}{r} 7n + 2t \\ + 4n - 3t \\ \hline 11n - t \end{array}$
25. $\begin{array}{r} 3a + 6c \\ + 4a - 12c \\ \hline 7a - 6c \end{array}$
26. $\begin{array}{r} 4a^2 - 4b^2 \\ + 3a^2 + 3b^2 \\ \hline 7a^2 - b^2 \end{array}$
27. $\begin{array}{r} 24x^2 - 14xy - 3y^2 \\ + \; 6x^2 - 47xy - 63y^2 \\ \hline 30x^2 - 61xy - 66y^2 \end{array}$
28. $\begin{array}{r} 18a^2 - 9ab - 4b^2 \\ + \; 5a^2 + 3ab + 9b^2 \\ \hline 23a^2 - 6ab + 5b^2 \end{array}$

Alternate Strategies: Reteaching the Lesson

Reteaching Activity

Using Models Using construction paper, have students cut out and label several models as shown in Lesson 2. Mix these models in a container. Draw out several and write the polynomial represented. Repeat. Add the two polynomials.

***Reteaching Masters Booklet,* p. 130**

Name ______ Date ______

Reteaching Worksheet 15-2

Adding Polynomials

Monomials, binomials, and trinomials are also called **polynomials.** A polynomial can have any number of terms.

To add two or more polynomials, look for **like terms.** Like terms are those that have exactly the same variables to the same powers.

Examples

A. $\begin{array}{r} 5x + 1 \\ + 4x + 3 \\ \hline 9x + 4 \end{array}$
B. $\begin{array}{r} x + 2y + 6 \\ + 3x + y - 2 \\ \hline 4x + 3y + 4 \end{array}$
C. $\begin{array}{r} 3x + 2y + 1 \\ + 5x \qquad + 2 \\ \hline 8x + 2y + 3 \end{array}$

In Example C above, notice that there is nothing to add to the term $2y$. That is, the second polynomial does not include a term having the variable y.

Independent Practice

Homework Assignment	
Basic	9-29 odd, 30-33, 35-37
Average	8-28 even, 30-37
Honors	19-37

4 CLOSE

Assessment Option

Modeling Go around the room having the students add polynomials using tiles. Give them two or three polynomials and have the students add them together. Have the students add monomials with unlike terms as well as binomials and trinomials with unlike terms.

Enrichment Masters Booklet, **p. 130**

Name ________________ Date ________

Enrichment Worksheet 15-2

Adding Polynomials

Can you make a sentence using these words?

A FRUIT TIME LIKE AN BUT FLIES BANANA ARROW LIKE FLIES

Add the polynomials. Then find the word in the table at the right that corresponds to the sum. Read the words in order down the column to discover the hidden saying.

	Word
1. $(2x^2 + 3x^2) + (5x^2 + x^2)$ **$11x^2$**	TIME
2. $(2x^2 + 3x^3) + (5x^2 + x^2)$ **$3x^3 + 8x^2$**	FLIES
3. $(2x^2 + x) + (xy + x)$ **$2x^2 + 2x + xy$**	LIKE
4. $(x^3 + 2x^2) + (5x^3 + x)$ **$6x^3 + 2x^2 + x$**	AN
5. $(x + xy) + (x^2 + xy)$ **$x^2 + 2xy + x$**	ARROW
6. $(5x^2 + x) + (x + 2x^4)$ **$2x^4 + 5x^2 + 2x$**	BUT
7. $(xy + y^2 + x^2) + (2xy + x^2)$ **$2x^2 + 3xy + y^2$**	FRUIT
8. $(3x^2 + 2x^3) + (x^3 + x)$ **$3x^3 + 3x^2 + x$**	FLIES
9. $(x + x^2) + x^3$ **$x^3 + x^2 + x$**	LIKE
10. $(x^3 + x^3) + (x^3 + x^3)$ **$4x^3$**	A
11. $2x^{12} + 2x^{12}$ **$4x^{12}$**	BANANA

A	$4x^3$
FRUIT	$2x^2 + 3xy + y^2$
TIME	$11x^2$
LIKE	$x^3 + x^2 + x$
AN	$6x^3 + 2x^2 + x$
BUT	$2x^4 + 5x^2 + 2x$
FLIES	$3x^3 + 8x^2$
BANANA	$4x^{12}$
ARROW	$x^2 + 2xy + x$
LIKE	$2x^2 + 2x + xy$
FLIES	$3x^3 + 3x^2 + x$

Find each sum.

14. $(5m + 3n) + 8m$ **$13m + 3n$**
15. $(12x + 7y) + 8y$ **$12x + 15y$**
16. $(5x + 8y) + (-3x + 5y)$ **$2x + 13y$**
17. $(-5a - 8b) + (4a + 8b)$ **$-a$**
18. $(6x^2 + 10x + 3) + (-2x^2 + 7x - 12)$
19. $(3a + 5ab - 3b^2) + (7a + 5b^2)$

20. $\begin{array}{r} 4a + 5b - c \\ + \; 8a - 6b + c \\ \hline \mathbf{12a - b} \end{array}$

21. $\begin{array}{r} -6b^2 + 13b - 5 \\ + \; 2b^2 \quad\quad - 10 \\ \hline \mathbf{-4b^2 + 13b - 15} \end{array}$

22. $\begin{array}{r} -21y^2 + 11y - 32 \\ + \; 18y^2 - 8y + 10 \\ \hline \mathbf{-3y^2 + 3y - 22} \end{array}$

23. $\begin{array}{r} 4a + 5b - 6c \\ 3a - 7b + 2c \\ + \; 2a - b + 7c \\ \hline \mathbf{9a - 3b + 3c} \end{array}$

24. $\begin{array}{r} 2x^2 - 5x + 7 \\ x^2 - x + 11 \\ + \; 5x^2 + 7x - 13 \\ \hline \mathbf{8x^2 + x + 5} \end{array}$

25. $\begin{array}{r} -9ax^3 - 5ax^2 + 6ax \\ -3ax^3 - 6ax^2 - 7ax \\ + \; 5ax^3 \quad\quad + ax \\ \hline \mathbf{-7ax^3 - 11ax^2} \end{array}$

18. **$4x^2 + 17x - 9$** 19. **$10a + 5ab + 2b^2$**

Combine like terms. Then evaluate for $a = 3$ and $b = 7$.

26. $(2a + 5b) + (6a - 3b)$ **38**
27. $(-21a + 7b) + (18a - 3b)$ **19**
28. $(4a + 3b + 2) + (3a - 4b - 10)$ **6**
29. $(5a + 2b - 1) + (10a - 3b + 2)$ **39**

Mixed Review

30. Find the circumference of a circle that has a radius of 4 inches. (Lesson 6-13) **about 25.12 inches**
31. Find the surface area of a rectangular prism if the length is 1.2 feet, the width is 0.3 feet, and the height is 0.9 feet. (Lesson 13-4) **3.42 ft^2**
32. Solve $n^2 = 64$. (Lesson 14-4) **8, -8**
33. State whether $\frac{a + c}{5}$ is a polynomial. (Lesson 15-1) **yes**

Connection

34. **Geometry** Write and simplify an expression for the perimeter of each figure.

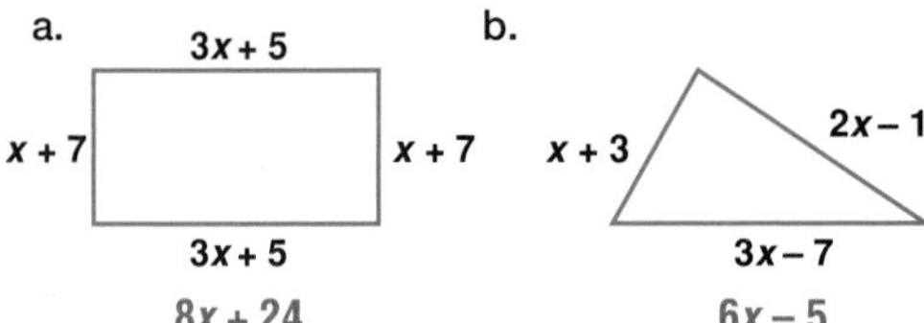

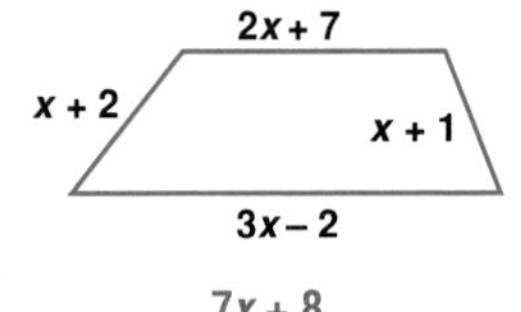

8x + 24 **6x − 5** **7x + 8**

Application

35. **Construction** A standard measurement for a window is *united inch.* You can find the united inches of a window by adding the length of the window to the width. If the length of a window is $2x - 8$ inches and the width is $x + 3$ inches, what is the size of the window in united inches? **$3x - 5$ united inches**

Critical Thinking

36. Given: $(3x - 5y) + (7x + 2y) = 10x - 3y$.
Find: $(10x - 3y) - (7x + 2y)$. **$3x - 5y$**

Wrap-Up

37. **Make Up a Problem** Write a polynomial addition problem. Add the two polynomials in three different ways (tiles, horizontal format, vertical format). **See Solutions Manual.**

Alternate Strategies: Extending the Lesson

Enrichment

Health Connections For several meals, have students chart the number of servings he or she eats from each of the four basic food groups. Using *m* for meat, *d* for dairy, *f* for fruit and vegetable, and *b* for bread and cereal, have each student write a polynomial representing each meal. Find daily and cumulative totals.

Cooperative Learning

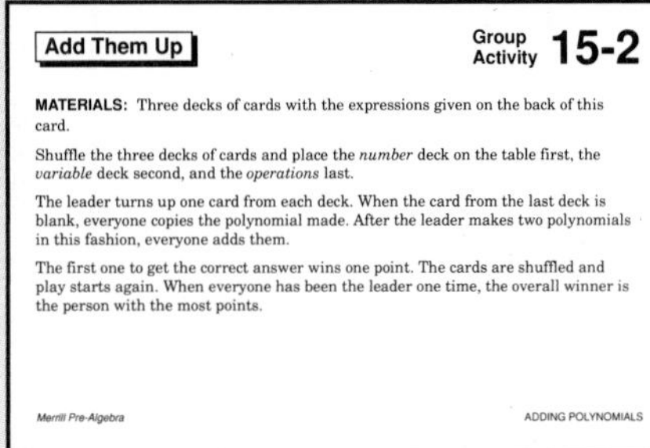

Add Them Up Group Activity **15-2**

MATERIALS: Three decks of cards with the expressions given on the back of this card.

Shuffle the three decks of cards and place the *number* deck on the table first, the *variable* deck second, and the *operations* last.

The leader turns up one card from each deck. When the card from the last deck is blank, everyone copies the polynomial made. After the leader makes two polynomials in this fashion, everyone adds them.

The first one to get the correct answer wins one point. The cards are shuffled and play starts again. When everyone has been the leader one time, the overall winner is the person with the most points.

Merrill Pre-Algebra ADDING POLYNOMIALS

15-3 Subtracting Polynomials

Objective:
Subtract polynomials.

In the last lesson, you used tiles as a model for *adding* polynomials. Now you will use tiles as a model for *subtracting* polynomials.

Example

1 Find $(2x^2 + 5x + 4) - (2x^2 + x + 2)$ using tiles.

Make a model of $2x^2 + 5x + 4$. Then remove two x^2-tiles, one x-tile, and two 1-tiles.

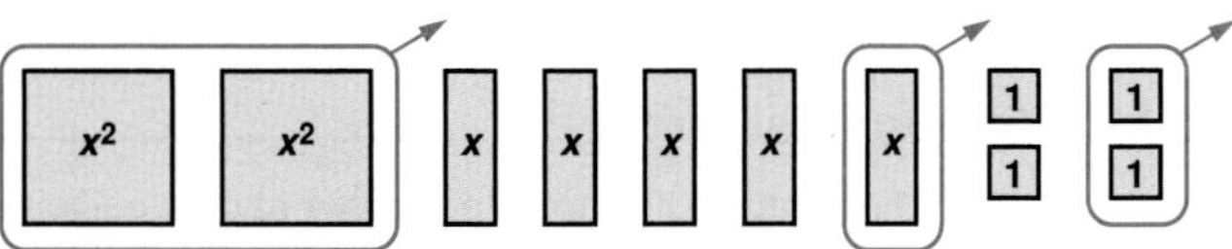

There are four x-tiles and two 1-tiles remaining.

$(2x^2 + 5x + 4) - (2x^2 + x + 2) = 4x + 2$

Remember, you can subtract two numbers by using additive inverses.

What is the additive inverse of -2? **2**

additive inverses

$7 - 2 = 5$ $\quad$ $7 + (-2) = 5$

same result

When 2 is multiplied by -1, the result is its additive inverse, -2. To find the additive inverse of a polynomial, the entire polynomial is multiplied by -1. Study the following table.

Polynomial	Multiply by -1	Additive Inverse
$-y$	$-1(-y)$	y
$4x - 3$	$-1(4x - 3)$	$-4x + 3$
$2xy + 5y$	$-1(2xy + 5y)$	$-2xy - 5y$
$2x^2 - 3x - 5$	$-1(2x^2 - 3x - 5)$	$-2x^2 + 3x + 5$

Example

Find each difference.

2 $(5x + 3) - (2x + 1)$

$= (5x + 3) + (-1)(2x + 1)$ — Add the additive inverse of $2x + 1$.

$= 5x + 3 + (-2x) - 1$ — $(-1)(2x + 1) = -2x - 1$

$= 5x + (-2x) + 3 + (-1)$ — Commutative property of addition

$= 3x + 2$ — Combine like terms.

Bell Ringer

Add the following polynomials.
$5x^2 + 6x - 4$; $7x$; $3x^2 + 8x$
$8x^2 + 21x + 4$

Lesson Notes 15-3

5-Minute Check
(over Lesson 15-2)

Find each sum.

1. $(3d + 4f) + (18d - 16f)$
   $21d - 12f$
2. $(4x^2 + 9x - 6) + (7x^2 - x - 9)$
   $11x^2 + 8x - 15$
3. $(8y^3 + 5y - 3) + (17y^2 - 5y + 10)$
   $8y^3 + 17y^2 + 7$
4. $(2m^4 + 7) + (5m^3 - 9)$
   $2m^4 + 5m^3 - 2$
5. $(6a^2 + 4a - 3) + (-4a^2 - a + 8)$
   $2a^2 + 3a + 5$

Transparency 15-3 contains the 5-Minute Check and a teaching aid for this lesson.

1 FOCUS

The purpose of this lesson is to use the additive inverse property to subtract polynomials.

Motivating the Lesson

Again show students the bowl of apples and oranges. How many apples can be removed from the bowl? How many pieces of fruit can be removed? Why do these answers differ?

2 TEACH

Using Models Use shaded or different colored tiles to show negative terms while modeling Example 2. Remind students of the zero principle when combining like terms.

EE: 1C, 1E, 2E, 3A
TAAS: 2

Chalkboard Examples

- *For Example 1*
  Find $(3y^2 + 2y + 4) - (3y^2 + y + 2)$ using tiles. $y + 2$

Find each difference.

- *For Example 2*
  $(8x + 6) - (5x + 5)$ $3x + 1$
- *For Example 3*
  $(6k^2 - 3k + 2) - (2k^2 - 4k)$
  $4k^2 + k + 2$
- *For Example 4*
  $(8x^2 - 7xy - 2y^2) - (3x^2 + xy - 5y^2)$
  $5x^2 - 8xy + 3y^2$

3 PRACTICE/APPLY

Checking the Concept

Have students check their answers to Exercises 3-8 by using the vertical format and adding additive inverses.

Practice Masters Booklet, **p. 145**

Name ______________ Date ______________

Practice Worksheet 15-3

Subtracting Polynomials

Find each difference.

1. $(7a + 2) - (5a + 1)$
   $2a + 1$
2. $(3x + 10) - (x + 10)$
   $2x$
3. $(17x + 13) - (7x - 4)$
   $10x + 17$
4. $(37y - 17) - (14y + 11)$
   $23y - 28$
5. $(2x + 3) - (3x - 1)$
   $-x + 4$
6. $(x^2 + 1) - (x^2 - 1)$
   2
7. $(x^2 + 7x + 3) - (x^2 + 7x + 3)$
   0
8. $(5r - 3s) - (7r + 5s)$
   $-2r - 8s$
9. $(14x^2 - 22) - (14x + 5)$
   $14x^2 - 14x - 27$
10. $(43xy - 43) - (19xy + 13)$
    $24xy - 56$
11. $(11x^2 + 5x) - (7x^2 + 3)$
    $4x^2 + 5x - 3$
12. $(x^2 + 3) - (6 + 4x)$
    $x^2 - 4x - 3$
13. $(15x - 3y) - (7x - 6y)$
    $8x + 3y$
14. $(18t^2 + 4t) - (16t^2 - 6t)$
    $2t^2 + 10t$
15. $(-2a^2 + 4b^2) - (5a^2 - 6b^2)$
    $-7a^2 + 10b^2$
16. $(-16x - 2y) - (-3x + 7y)$
    $-13x - 9y$
17. $(6x + 10y) - (13x - 5y + 4)$
    $-7x + 15y - 4$
18. $(-9x^2 + 7x + 7) - (6x^2 - 2x - 7)$
    $-15x^2 + 9x + 14$
19. $(4x^2 - 3x - 7) - (-5x^2 - 9x + 12)$
    $9x^2 + 6x - 19$
20. $(-8y^2 + 7y - 3) - (15y^2 - 9y + 4)$
    $-23y^2 + 16y - 7$
21. $\begin{array}{r} 6x^2 + 9x + 10 \\ -\ 3x^2 + 5x + 4 \\ \hline 3x^2 + 4x + 6 \end{array}$
22. $\begin{array}{r} 8z^2 - 5z + 11 \\ -\ 8z^2 + 2z - 8 \\ \hline -7z + 19 \end{array}$
23. $\begin{array}{r} c + 2d - e \\ -\ 3c + d + 6e \\ \hline -2c + d - 7e \end{array}$
24. $\begin{array}{r} 4u^2 + 3uv \\ -\quad - 2uv + v^2 \\ \hline 4u^2 + 5uv - v^2 \end{array}$
25. $\begin{array}{r} 10x^2y^2 + 5xy - 8 \\ -\ -5x^2y^2 - 7xy + 9 \\ \hline 15x^2y^2 + 12xy - 17 \end{array}$
26. $\begin{array}{r} 8k^2 \qquad + 3 \\ -\ 5k^2 + 3k - 5 \\ \hline 3k^2 - 3k + 8 \end{array}$
27. $(14n^2 - 8nt + 12t^2) - (-12n^2 + 15nt - 13t^2)$
    $26n^2 - 23nt + 25t^2$
28. $(54m^3 - 84m^2 - 26m) - (8m^2 - 9m - 2)$
    $54m^3 - 92m^2 - 17m + 2$

Examples

What is the additive inverse of $(x^2 - 4x)$? $-x^2 + 4x$

3 $(3x^2 - 6x + 4) - (x^2 - 4x)$

$= (3x^2 - 6x + 4) + (-x^2 + 4x)$ — Add the additive inverse of $(x^2 - 4x)$.

$= 3x^2 + (-x^2) - 6x + 4x + 4$

$= 2x^2 - 2x + 4$

4 $(7a^2 - 6ab - b^2) - (2a^2 + ab - 5b^2)$

Align like terms and add the additive inverse of the second polynomial.

$$\begin{array}{r} 7a^2 - 6ab - b^2 \\ +\ (-2a^2) + (-ab) + 5b^2 \\ \hline 5a^2 - 7ab + 4b^2 \end{array}$$

Checking for Understanding

Communicating Algebra

1. What is the sum of a number and its additive inverse? 0
2. Explain how you would find the additive inverse of $3a^2 + 4ab - b^2$.
   Multiply each term by -1.

Guided Practice

Find each difference using tiles or drawings.

3. $(5x + 2) - (2x + 1)$ $3x + 1$
4. $(4x + 7) - (x + 3)$ $3x + 4$
5. $(4x^2 + 3) - (4x^2 + 2)$ 1
6. $(3x^2 + 5x + 4) - (x^2 + 3x + 2)$
7. $(5x^2 + 4x + 2) - (4x^2 + x + 2)$
   $x^2 + 3x$
8. $(2x^2 + 6x + 2) - (x^2 + 1)$
   $x^2 + 6x + 1$

6. $2x^2 + 2x + 2$

State the additive inverse of each polynomial.

9. a $-a$
10. $-3x$ $3x$
11. $12xy$ $-12xy$
12. $x + 4$ $-x - 4$
13. $4n - 1$ $-4n + 1$
14. $5x^2 - 3$ $-5x^2 + 3$
15. $4a + 3b$
16. $m^2 + 4m + 1$
17. $5g^2 - 3g - 8$
    $-5g^2 + 3g + 8$
18. $-3d^2 + 2$
    $3d^2 - 2$
19. $6x^2 + 3xy - 2y^2$
    $-6x^2 - 3xy + 2y^2$
20. $-a^2 - ab$
    $a^2 + ab$

15. $-4a - 3b$
16. $-m^2 - 4m - 1$

Exercises

28. $d^2 - 7d - 3$ 29. $9y^2 + 11y + 5$ 30. $5z^2 + 3z + 5$
31. $4a^2 - 8ab + 6b^2$ 32. $-9x + 21y - 20$

Independent Practice

Find each difference.

21. $(7m + 3) - (3m + 1)$ $4m + 2$
22. $(3x + 5) - (2x + 9)$ $x - 4$
23. $(x + 6) - (4x + 3)$ $-3x + 3$
24. $(5x - 3) - (3x + 7)$ $2x - 10$
25. $(3x + 4y) - (2x + y)$ $x + 3y$
26. $(12a - 5b) - (3a - 9b)$ $9a + 4b$
27. $(5x^2 + 11) - (5x^2 - 6)$ 17
28. $(4d^2 - 7d + 1) - (3d^2 + 4)$
29. $(12y^2 + 6y - 1) - (3y^2 - 5y - 6)$
30. $(3z^2 + 5z + 8) - (-2z^2 + 2z + 3)$
31. $(6a^2 - 5ab + b^2) - (2a^2 + 3ab - 5b^2)$
32. $(-6x + 7y - 9) - (3x - 14y + 11)$
33. $\begin{array}{r} 5y^2 + 7y + 9 \\ -\ 2y^2 + 3y + 6 \\ \hline 3y^2 + 4y + 3 \end{array}$
34. $\begin{array}{r} 7m^2 - 6m + 13 \\ -\ 7m^2 + 3m - 5 \\ \hline -9m + 18 \end{array}$
35. $\begin{array}{r} a + 3b - c \\ -\ 2a + b + 7c \\ \hline -a + 2b - 8c \end{array}$
36. $\begin{array}{r} 3a^2 + 5ab \\ -\quad -2ab + b^2 \\ \hline 3a^2 + 7ab - b^2 \end{array}$
37. $\begin{array}{r} 11m^2n^2 + 4mn - 6 \\ -\ (-5m^2n^2) - 6mn + 17 \\ \hline 16m^2n^2 + 10mn - 23 \end{array}$
38. $\begin{array}{r} 7z^2 \qquad + 4 \\ -\ 3z^2 + 2z - 6 \\ \hline 4z^2 - 2z + 10 \end{array}$

Alternate Strategies: Reteaching the Lesson

Reteaching Activity

Writing Connection Have students choose a topic and write verbal problems similar to Exercise 50. Topics might include a walkway around a pool or yard (second degree) or differences in volume (third degree). Trade and solve by writing the polynomials and subtracting.

Reteaching Masters Booklet, **p. 131**

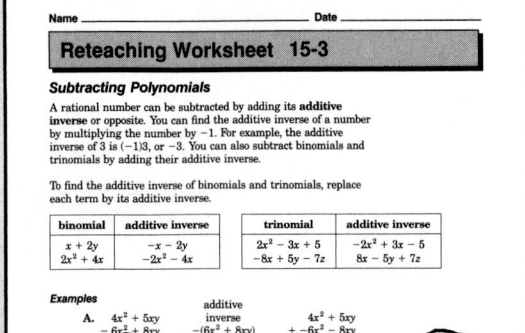

Name ______________ Date ______________

Reteaching Worksheet 15-3

Subtracting Polynomials

A rational number can be subtracted by adding its **additive inverse** or opposite. You can find the additive inverse of a number by multiplying the number by -1. For example, the additive inverse of 3 is $(-1)3$, or -3. You can also subtract binomials and trinomials by adding their additive inverse.

To find the additive inverse of binomials and trinomials, replace each term by its additive inverse.

binomial	additive inverse
$x + 2y$	$-x - 2y$
$2x^2 + 4x$	$-2x^2 - 4x$

trinomial	additive inverse
$2x^2 - 3x + 5$	$-2x^2 + 3x - 5$
$-8x + 5y - 7z$	$8x - 5y + 7z$

Examples

A. $\begin{array}{r} 4x^2 + 5xy \\ -\ 6x^2 + 8xy \end{array}$ additive inverse $-(6x^2 + 8xy)$ $\begin{array}{r} 4x^2 + 5xy \\ +\ -6x^2 - 8xy \end{array}$

Mixed Review

39. Solve $-2(3 + 4x) = 5x - 6$. (Lesson 7-4) 0
40. Name the quadrant of the graph of (-2, 9). (Lesson 8-4) quadrant 2
41. Find the surface area of the pyramid at the right. (Lesson 13-6) 105 ft^2

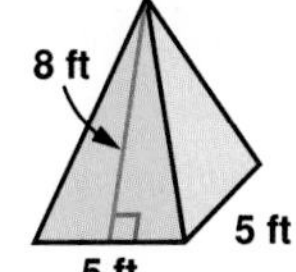

42. Use the Pythagorean Theorem to find the length of the hypotenuse of the right triangle at the right. (Lesson 14-5) 30 cm

24 cm
18 cm

43. Find the sum $(4a^2 + 7a - 2) + (3a^2 - 9a - 3)$. (Lesson 15-2) $7a^2 - 2a - 5$

Challenge

Savings Account	
Name	**Balance**
Bill	$6x + 7$
Jorge	$7x - 10$
Marinella	$12x + 3$
Angela	$4x + 27$

44. Which two savings accounts have a difference of $5x + 13$? Marinella and Jorge
45. Which two accounts have a difference of $8x - 24$? Marinella and Angela
46. Which two accounts have a difference of $3x - 37$? Jorge and Angela
47. Suppose $x = \$10$. Which account has the greatest balance? Marinella's account

Application

48. **Framing** Jose plans to mat and frame a picture. The area inside the frame is $4x^2 - 7$ square inches. The area of the picture is $2x^2 + 3$ square inches. How much matting will Jose need? $2x^2 - 10$ square inches

Critical Thinking

49. Write a polynomial subtraction problem with a difference of $3m^2 - 5m + 4$. Check your work by adding.
Sample answer: $(5m^2 + 2m + 7) - (2m^2 + 7m + 3) = 3m^2 - 5m + 4$

Wrap-Up

50. **Make Up a Problem** Write a polynomial subtraction problem. Find the difference in three different ways (tiles, horizontal format, vertical format). See Solutions Manual.

Mid-Chapter Quiz

State whether each expression is a polynomial. If it is, identify it as a *monomial, binomial,* or *trinomial.* (Lesson 15-1)

1. $4a^2$ yes; monomial
2. $-2y + 3$ yes; binomial
3. $\frac{a}{5}$ yes; monomial
4. $r^3 - s^2$ yes; binomial
5. $-\frac{3}{(x + y)}$ no
6. $7mt^2 + 3m - 2t$ yes; trinomial

Find each sum or difference. (Lessons 15-2, 15-3)

7. $(3a + 6) + (a - 1)$ $4a + 5$
8. $(7x - 2) + (-3x + 1)$ $4x - 1$
9. $(5r^2 + 4) - (2r^2 - 3)$ $3r^2 + 7$
10. $(4x + 3y) + (-7x + 3y)$ $-3x + 6y$
11. $(6n^2 - 5n + 1) - (3n - 4)$ $6n^2 - 8n + 5$
12. $(-8c^2 + 2cd - 5d^2) - (c^2 + 3cd - 4d^2)$ $-9c^2 - cd - d^2$

Error Analysis

Watch for students who multiply only the first term of a polynomial by -1 when finding an additive inverse.
Prevent by emphasizing the use of the distributive property.

Independent Practice

Homework Assignment	
Basic	21-39 odd, 41-45, 50-52
Average	24-40 even, 41-46, 50-52
Honors	30-40 even, 41-52
All	Mid-Chapter Review 1-2

4 CLOSE

Assessment Option

Speaking Model several polynomial subtraction problems. Have students state the problem that is modeled and how they would solve the problem.

Enrichment Masters Booklet, **p. 131**

Name ______ Date ______

Enrichment Worksheet 15-3

Turn Symmetry

Some geometric figures can be turned about a point and will fit point for point in their original position. This property is called **turn symmetry.** All figures can be turned 360° to fit in their original positions. Turn symmetry refers to turns less than 360°.

For example, a square has turn symmetry. It can be turned 90°, 180°, or 270° about its center of rotation and its appearance will not be changed.

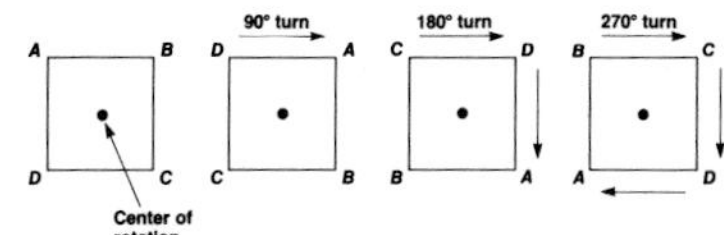

For each figure below, mark the center of rotation with a dot. Then list all possible degrees of turn symmetry so that each figure has the appearance of its original position. If a figure does not have turn symmetry, write none.

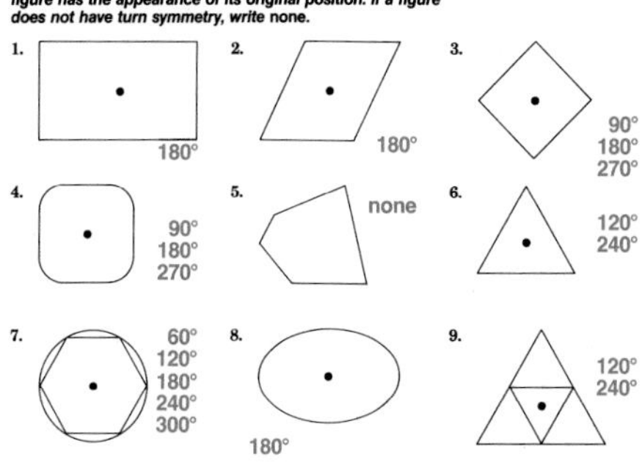

Alternate Strategies: Extending the Lesson

Enrichment

Using Critical Thinking Have students develop a model for a term of a polynomial where the power of a variable is three. The model would be a cube.

Cooperative Learning

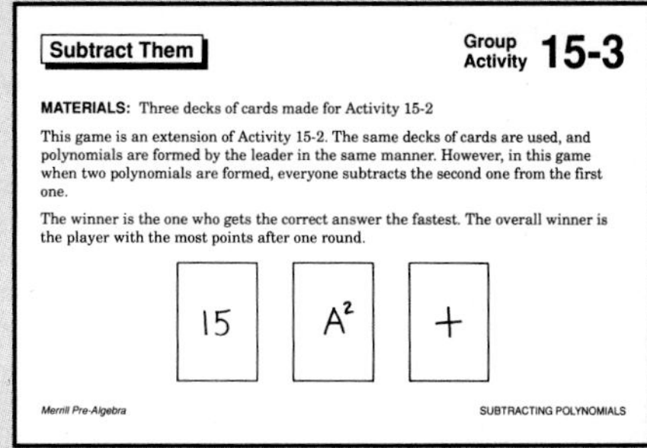

Subtract Them Group Activity **15-3**

MATERIALS: Three decks of cards made for Activity 15-2

This game is an extension of Activity 15-2. The same decks of cards are used, and polynomials are formed by the leader in the same manner. However, in this game when two polynomials are formed, everyone subtracts the second one from the first one.

The winner is the one who gets the correct answer the fastest. The overall winner is the player with the most points after one round.

Merrill Pre-Algebra SUBTRACTING POLYNOMIALS

Lesson Notes 15-4

5-Minute Check
(over Lesson 15-3)

Find each difference.

1. $(18h^2 - 16hk^2 + 4k^2) - (h^2 - 3hk^2)$
   $17h^2 - 13hk^2 + 4k^2$
2. $(3x^2 + 2xy^2 + 3y^2)$
   $- (-4x^2 - 3xy^2)$
   $7x^2 + 5xy^2 + 3y^2$
3. $(8m^2 - 13mn^2 + 12n^2)$
   $- (8m^2 - 13mn^2)$
   $12n^2$
4. $-12xy^2 + 14x^2y + 6y^2$
   $-9xy^2 + 13x^2y + 6y^2$
   $-3xy^2 + x^2y$

Transparency 15-4 contains the 5-Minute Check and a teaching aid for this lesson.

1 FOCUS

The purpose of this lesson is to develop rules for finding powers of powers, products, and monomials by applying previous knowledge of exponents and multiplication properties.

Motivating the Lesson

Show square waterproof boxes, one with sides twice as long as those of the other. Ask students how many times the contents of a full smaller box could be poured into the larger box. List student responses. Use water to test guesses.

2 TEACH

Using Calculators Give replacements for the variables in the examples and have students use calculators to evaluate. Then have students generalize their findings using variables and compare them to the rules.

EE: 1E, 3A, 3D, 4B
TAAS: 2, 4

15-4 Powers of Monomials

Objective:
Find powers of monomials.

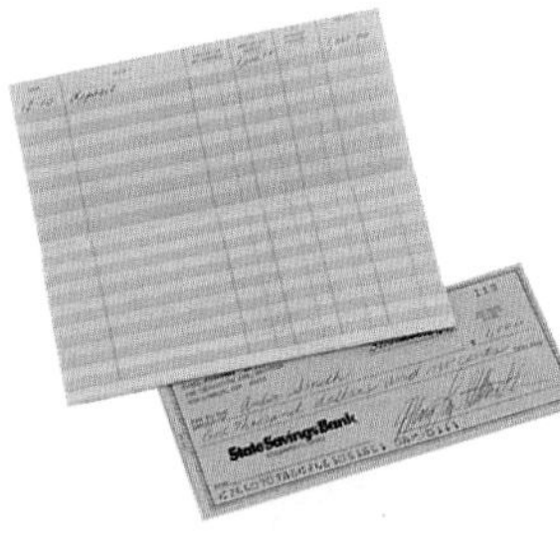

Amber opens a savings account with \$1000. It earns 4% interest every 6 months. So, in one year, the balance is (1000)(1.04)(1.04) or $(1000)(1.04)^2$. Suppose she keeps the money in the account for four years. Then the deposit is worth $1000(1.04^2)^4$. To compute this product, you need to know how to find the power of a power.

Consider the calculation for the following expressions:

$$(4^2)^3 = 4^2 \cdot 4^2 \cdot 4^2 = 4^{2+2+2} = 4^6 \qquad (x^4)^2 = (x^4)(x^4) = x^{4+4} = x^8$$

For $(4^2)^3$, how can you obtain the exponent 6 from the exponents 2 and 3? For $(x^4)^2$, how can you obtain 8 from 4 and 2? These and other similar examples suggest that you can find a *power of a power* like $(x^4)^2$ by multiplying the exponents.

Power of a Power

For any number a, and positive integers m and n,
$$(a^m)^n = a^{mn}.$$

Example

1 Simplify $(y^5)^3$.

$(y^5)^3 = y^{5 \cdot 3}$ Multiply the exponents.
$= y^{15}$

Check: $(y^5)^3 = y^5 \cdot y^5 \cdot y^5$
$= y^{5+5+5}$ or y^{15} ✓

FYI

If you put \$1000 in an account that earns 4% interest every 6 months, in ten years it will be worth $1000(1.04^2)^{10}$ or \$2191—more than twice what you started with!

To find the volume of a cube, you multiply its length, width, and height. The volume of the cube shown at the right is $x \cdot x \cdot x$ or x^3. Suppose you double its dimensions. Then its volume is $(2x)(2x)(2x)$ or $(2x)^3$.

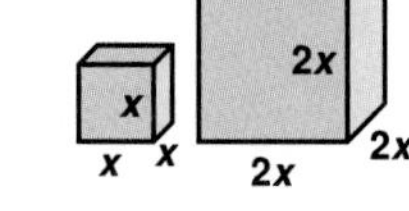

$$(2x)(2x)(2x) = (2 \cdot 2 \cdot 2)(x \cdot x \cdot x) = 2^3x^3 \text{ or } 8x^3$$ Commutative and associative properties

So, $(2x)^3 = 2^3x^3$. The exponent, 3, is applied to *both* factors. $(2x)^3$ is an example of a power of a product.

Bell Ringer

Subtract the following polynomials.
$15x^2 + 10x + 5$; $11x^2 - 11x + 4$
$4x^2 + 21x + 1$

These and other examples suggest that the power of a product is the product of the powers.

Power of a Product

For all numbers a and b and positive integer m,
$$(ab)^m = a^m b^m.$$

Example

2 **Simplify $(3xy)^3$.**

$$(3xy)^3 = (3^1x^1y^1)^3$$
$$= 3^3x^3y^3$$
$$= 27x^3y^3$$

The rules for the *power of a power* and the *power of a product* can be combined into one rule. This rule can be stated as follows.

Power of a Monomial

For all numbers a and b and positive integers m, n, and p,
$$(a^m b^n)^p = a^{mp} b^{np}.$$

Examples

3 **Simplify $(a^2b^3)^2$.**

$$(a^2b^3)^2 = (a^2)^2(b^3)^2$$
$$= a^4b^6$$

Check: $(a^2b^3)^2 = (a^2b^3)(a^2b^3)$
$= (a^2 \cdot a^2)(b^3 \cdot b^3)$
$= a^4b^6$ ✓

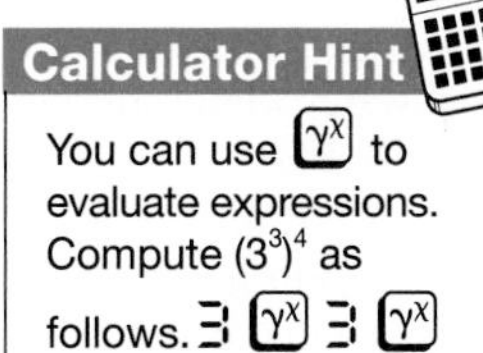

Calculator Hint

You can use y^x to evaluate expressions. Compute $(3^3)^4$ as follows. 3 y^x 3 y^x 4 = 531441.

4 **Evaluate $(-4a^3)^2$ if $a = 2$.**

$(-4a^3)^2 = (-4 \cdot 2^3)^2$ Replace a with 2.
$= -4^2 \cdot (2^3)^2$
$= 16 \cdot 2^6$
$= 16 \cdot 64$ or 1024

Check: $(-4 \cdot 2^3)^2 = (-4 \cdot 8)^2$
$= -32^2$
$= 1024$ ✓

Checking for Understanding

Communicating Algebra

1. What is the area of the square? [square labeled $3x$] 3^2x^2 or $9x^2$
2. Draw and label the dimensions of a square with an area of y^8 units. **See margin.**
3. In your own words, explain the difference between $x^3 \cdot x^2$ and $(x^3)^2$. **See margin.**
4. Suppose the dimensions of a cube are tripled. What happens to its volume? **It is multiplied by 27.**

Guided Practice

Simplify.

5. $(2^3)^2$ 64
6. $(a^5)^3$ a^{15}
7. $(3y)^2$ $9y^2$
8. $(mn^3)^3$ m^3n^9
9. $(x^2y^3)^2$ x^4y^6
10. $(-pq)^2$ p^2q^2
11. $(n^3r^2)^4$ $n^{12}r^8$
12. $(-ab^2)^3$ $-a^3b^6$

Chalkboard Examples

- *For Example 1*
  Simplify $(a^4)^2$. a^8
- *For Example 2*
  Simplify $(2mk)^4$. $16m^4k^4$
- *For Example 3*
  Simplify $(x^3y^2)^3$. x^9y^6
- *For Example 4*
  Evaluate $(-2a^2)^2$ if $a = 3$. 324

3 PRACTICE/APPLY

Checking the Concept

Have students state whether they are finding a power of a power, product, or monomial in Exercises 5-12.

Practice Masters Booklet, **p. 146**

Name ______________________ Date ______________

Practice Worksheet 15-4

Powers of Monomials

Simplify.

1. $(4^2)^3$ 4096	2. $[(-3)^2]^2$ 81	3. $(x^3)^4$ x^{12}
4. $(7d)^3$ $343d^3$	5. $(11k)^2$ $121k^2$	6. $(-2y)^3$ $-8y^3$
7. $(-6m)^4$ $1296m^4$	8. $(-l)^{10}$ l^{10}	9. $(xy)^4$ x^4y^4
10. $(rs)^6$ r^6s^6	11. $(ab^2)^4$ a^4b^8	12. $(c^3d^5)^2$ c^6d^{10}
13. $(-3x^2y^4)^3$ $-27x^6y^{12}$	14. $(2e^3f)^4$ $16e^{12}f^4$	15. $(3a^2b^3)^2$ $9a^4b^6$
16. $(4g^2h)^6$ $4096g^{12}h^6$	17. $(-2jk^3)^4$ $16j^4k^{12}$	18. $(-6pq)^4$ $1296p^4q^4$
19. $(-5x^3z^9)^3$ $-125x^9z^{27}$	20. $(-2ij)^5$ $-32i^5j^5$	21. $(4x^4y)^3$ $64x^{12}y^3$
22. $(x^7y^6)^3$ $x^{21}y^{18}$	23. $(cat)^2$ $c^2a^2t^2$	24. $(5m^2y)^2$ $25m^4y^2$
25. $(-2a^2b^3)^4$ $16a^8b^{12}$	26. $(p^{10}x^7)^4$ $p^{40}x^{28}$	27. $(-z^3y)^3$ $-z^9y^3$
28. $4p(-3p)^2$ $36p^3$	29. $2b(2ab)^3$ $16a^3b^4$	30. $3y(-2y)^3$ $-24y^4$
31. $3m(-2m)^2$ $12m^3$	32. $2e^2(-3e)^3$ $-54e^5$	33. $-2f(4fg)^2$ $-32f^3g^2$

Evaluate each expression if $x = -2$ ad $y = -3$.

34. $3xy^2$ -54	35. $4x^2y$ -48	36. $(xy)^2$ 36
37. $(-2xy^2)^2$ 1296	38. $x(y^2)^3$ -1458	39. $(2x^2)^3$ 512

Additional Answers

2.

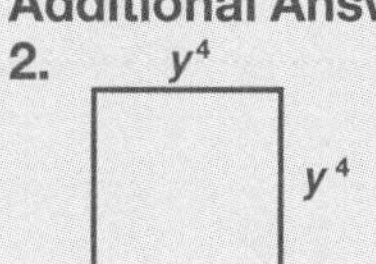

3. $x^3 \cdot x^2$ is a product of two monomials and $(x^3)^2$ is a monomial to the second power.

Reteaching Masters Booklet, **p. 132**

Name ______________________ Date ______________

Reteaching Worksheet 15-4

Powers of Monomials

To multiply two expressions with exponents, you can add the exponents. Remember to check that the expressions have the same base.

$4^2 \cdot 4^3 = 4 \cdot 4 \cdot 4 \cdot 4 \cdot 4$
$= 4^5$ $4^2 \cdot 4^3 = 4^{2+3}$

$x^2 \cdot x^3 = x \cdot x \cdot x \cdot x \cdot x$
$= x^5$ $x^2 \cdot x^3 = x^{2+3}$

To raise an exponential expression to a power, you can multiply the exponents.

$(4^2)^3 = 4^2 \cdot 4^2 \cdot 4^2$
$= 4^6$ $(4^2)^3 = 4^{2 \cdot 3}$

$(x^2)^3 = (x^2)(x^2)(x^2)$
$= x^6$ $(x^2)^3 = x^{2 \cdot 3}$

To square an expression, raise it to a power of 2. Square each expression.

1. 17^3 17^6
2. $2x^2$ $4x^4$
3. $-2x^2$ $4x^4$

Error Analysis

Watch for students who can't distinguish between multiplying powers and finding the power of a power. **Prevent by** working several similar examples of each, using expanded form. For example, use y^2y^3 and $(y^2)^3$.

Independent Practice

Homework Assignment	
Basic	13-39 odd, 41-46, 49, 50
Average	14-40 even, 41-50
Honors	29-50

Chapter 15, Quiz A (Lesson 15-1 through 15-4) is available in the Evaluation Masters Booklet, p. 133.

CLOSE

Assessment Option

Writing Have the students write in their own words, the rules for finding the power of a power and for finding the power of a product.

Enrichment Masters Booklet, **p. 132**

Name ______ Date ______

Enrichment Worksheet 15-4

Fibonacci Sequence

The first 15 terms of the **Fibonacci sequence** follow.

1, 1, 2, 3, 5, 8, 13, 21, 34, 55, 89, 144, 233, 377, 610

In addition to the fact that each term is the sum of the two previous terms, there are other interesting relationships.

Solve.

1. Find the sum of the first four terms. 7
2. Find the sum of the first five terms. 12
3. Find the sum of the first six terms. 20
4. What is the relationship between the sums and terms in the sequence? The sum is one less than the Fibonacci number after the next Fibonacci number.
5. Use your answer from Exercise 4 above to predict the sum of the first 10 terms, and of the first 12 terms. Check your answers by finding the sums. 143, 376
6. Divide each of the first 15 terms by 4. Make a list of the remainders. What pattern do you see in the remainder sequence? 1, 1, 2, 3, 1, 0, 1, 1, 2, 3, 1, 0, 1, 1, 2; The six digits 1, 1, 2, 3, 1, 0 repeat.
7. Complete the next three lines of this pattern of the sums of the squares of consecutive terms of the Fibonacci sequence.

$1^2 + 1^2 = 1 \times 2$
$1^2 + 1^2 + 2^2 = 2 \times 3$
$1^2 + 1^2 + 2^2 + 3^2 = 3 \times 5$
$1^2 + 1^2 + 2^2 + 3^2 + 5^2 = 5 \times 8$
$1^2 + 1^2 + 2^2 + 3^2 + 5^2 + 8^2 = 8 \times 13$
$1^2 + 1^2 + 2^2 + 3^2 + 5^2 + 8^2 + 13^2 = 13 \times 21$
$1^2 + 1^2 + 2^2 + 3^2 + 5^2 + 8^2 + 13^2 + 21^2 = 21 \times 34$

Exercises

Independent Practice

Simplify. 13. 5^9 or 1,953,125

13. $(5^3)^3$
14. $[(-4)^2]^2$ 16^2 or 256
15. $(m^2)^5$ m^{10}
16. $(-y^3)^6$ y^{18}
17. $(5c)^3$ $125c^3$
18. $(10y)^2$ $100y^2$
19. $(-3z)^3$ $-27z^3$
20. $(-7n)^4$ $2401n^4$
21. $(yz)^4$ y^4z^4
22. $(pq)^5$ p^5q^5
23. $(xy^3)^3$ x^3y^9
24. $(x^3y^5)^2$ x^6y^{10}
25. $(3ab^4)^3$ $27a^3b^{12}$
26. $(4x^2y^3)^2$ $16x^4y^6$
27. $(-2x^2)^3$ $-8x^6$
28. $(-3r^3)^2$ $9r^6$
29. $3x(2x)^2$ $12x^3$
30. $2b^2(-3b)^3$ $-54b^5$
31. $-3x(4xy)^2$ $-48x^3y^2$
32. $-3b(2a)^3$ $-24a^3b$

Evaluate each expression if $a = 2$ and $b = -3$.

33. $2a^2b$ -24
34. $3ab^2$ 54
35. $(ab^2)^2$ 324
36. $(-ab)^3$ 216
37. $(-2b)^2$ 36
38. $a(b^2)^3$ 1458
39. $(3b^2)^2$ 729
40. $2(3a^2)^2$ 288

Mixed Review

42. 100 pens

41. Solve $-13 + m = -5$. (Lesson 3-1) 8
42. In a sample, 20 of 80 students surveyed would choose black pens. If 400 students buy pens, how many black pens should be ordered? (Lesson 10-8)
43. Using the formula $V = \pi r^2h$, find the volume of a cylinder that has a radius of 8 cm and a height of 15 cm. (Lesson 13-8) about 3014.4 cm^2
44. The length of a leg in a $45° - 45°$ right triangle is 7 inches. Find the length of the hypotenuse. (Lesson 14-7) $7\sqrt{2}$ inches
45. Find the difference $(6x^2 + 2) - (3x^2 - 8)$. (Lesson 15-3) $3x^2 + 10$

Applications

46. **Chemistry** Some chemicals and metals such as salt and magnesium can be extracted from sea water. If a manufacturer wanted to extract salt from a cubic mile of sea water, about how many cubic feet of sea water would this be? Make an estimate by rounding 5280 feet to 5000 feet, or 5×10^3. 1.25×10^{11} ft^3
47. **Biology** It takes 4 hours for a culture with 1 bacterium to split into two, or double to two bacteria. To grow to 1024 bacteria, the culture must double ten times, or 2^{10}, which requires 40 hours. If the culture doubles another 10 times, there will be $(2^{10})^2$ bacteria.
    a. Simplify $(2^{10})^2$. 2^{20}
    b. If $2^{10} = 1024$, then we could say 2^{10} is close to 10^3. Using this information, estimate $(2^{10})^2$. 10^6 or 1,000,000

Connection

48. **Geometry** Find the volume of the rectangular prism at the right. $10x^3$

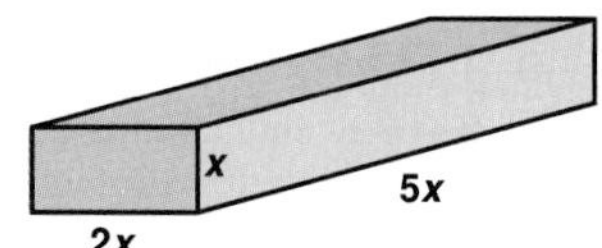

Critical Thinking

49. Are $(2^3)^4$ and $(4^3)^2$ equal? Explain why or why not. Hint: Write both expressions as a power of 2. yes; Both equal 2^{12}.

Wrap-Up

50. Using the information at the top of page 574, find the amount in Amber's savings account. $1368.57

Alternate Strategies: Extending the Lesson

Enrichment

Using Cooperative Groups Have students choose three different one-digit integers. Use one integer as a base, one as an exponent, and one as the power of the exponential term. Rearrange the integers until all possible combinations have been written. Evaluate each, compare, and summarize and explain results.

Cooperative Learning

Potent Powers Group Activity **15-4**

MATERIALS: The deck of *number* and the deck of *variable* cards made for Activity 15-1 • one 0-6 spinner

The object of this game is to be the first one to correctly find the power of a monomial.

To begin, place the two decks on the table with the *number* deck first and the *variable* deck second. The leader turns up one card from the *number* deck and one card from the *variable* deck to form a monomial.

Lastly, the leader spins the spinner. The number obtained is used for the power of the monomial. Everyone must copy the expression.

The first player to simplify the expression correctly scores one point. The winner is the one with the most points after one round.

Merrill Pre-Algebra POWERS OF MONOMIALS

Multiplying Polynomials

Materials: tiles

In this Exploration, you will use tiles as a model for multiplying a polynomial by a monomial.

Consider a rectangle with a width of x and a length of $x + 2$. What would this rectangle look like? Use the edges of an x-tile to mark off the dimensions of the rectangle. Then complete the rectangle by filling it in with tiles.

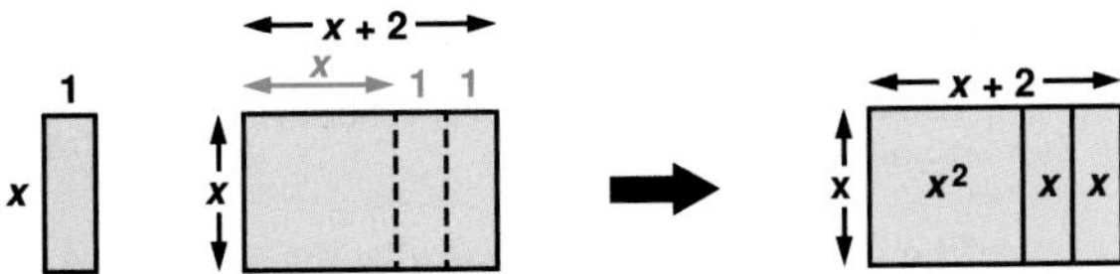

Now, find the area of the large rectangle. To find the area, add the areas of all the individual tiles that make up the large rectangle. There is one x^2-tile and two x-tiles. The area is $x^2 + x + x$ or $x^2 + 2x$.

Another way to find the area of the large rectangle is to multiply the length by the width. This would be $x(x + 2)$.

Since both $x^2 + 2x$ and $x(x + 2)$ represent the area of the same rectangle, you can say: $x(x + 2) = x^2 + 2x$.

Your Turn: Draw a model of $2x(x + 2) = 2x^2 + 4x$. See Solutions Manual.

Tell whether each statement is *true* or *false*. Justify your answer with tiles. See Solutions Manual.

1. $x(2x + 3) = 2x^2 + 3x$
2. $2x(3x + 4) = 6x^2 + 4x$

Multiply each expression using tiles.

3. $x(x + 5)$ $x^2 + 5x$
4. $2x(x + 2)$ $2x^2 + 4x$
5. $3x(2x + 1)$ $6x^2 + 3x$

Analysis

6. Suppose you have a square garden plot that measures x feet on a side. If you double the length of the plot and increase the width by 3 feet, how large will the new plot be? Write two expressions for the area of the new plot. $2x(x + 3)$, $2x^2 + 6x$
7. If the original plot was 10 feet on a side, what is the area of the new plot? 260 ft²

SET-UP

Materials

- Algebra Tiles, Lab Manual, p. 1

You may wish to use the Exploration worksheet provided on page 69 of the Lab Manual.

For Students Students can use commercial or paper tiles. Each student or group of students will need six $x \times x$ and five $1 \times x$ tiles. If there is a limited supply of tiles, students can use one of each size to trace and cut out enough tiles to model each exercise. Be sure that the length of x is always the same in each set of tiles.

For the Overhead Projector This exploration will work on the overhead with translucent or opaque tiles.

EXPLORATION: *Multiplying Polynomials*

Objective Students will be introduced to multiplication of polynomials from a geometric perspective.

1 FOCUS

This exploration allows students to apply their knowledge of the distributive property through modeling and also allows them to see that geometry can be interpreted algebraically.

2 TEACH

Using Models

Use a $1 \times x$ tile to construct several rectangles. Ask students how they would express the area of each rectangle. You may need to review the definition of like terms. Then, model the example and have students translate it into a multiplication of polynomials problem.

3 PRACTICE/APPLY

Working With a Partner

One student can model a problem, while the other records it on paper. Then, switch roles.

4 CLOSE

Using Calculators

Have students answer Exercise 7 using the information in Exercise 6. Then have them check answers to Exercise 6 by substituting 10 into the expressions they wrote for the area of the new plot.

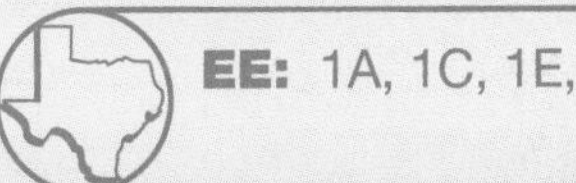

5-Minute Check
(over Lesson 15-4)

Simplify.
1. $(2^3)^2$ 64
2. $(-5rs)^3$ $-125r^3s^3$
3. $(m^2k^3y^4)^3$ $m^6k^9y^{12}$

Transparency 15-5 contains the 5-Minute Check and a teaching aid for this lesson.

1 FOCUS

The focus of this lesson is to teach the multiplication of a polynomial by a monomial using the distributive property.

2 TEACH

Chalkboard Examples

- *For Example 1*
  Find $3(4x + 5)$ $12x + 15$
- *For Example 2*
  Find $-6m(3m^2 - 1)$
  $-18m^3 + 6m$
- *For Example 3*
  Find $4ab(-2a^2 + 3a - 5)$
  $-8a^3b + 12a^2b - 20ab$

***Practice Masters Booklet,* p. 147**

Name ________________ Date ________________

Practice Worksheet 15-5

Multiplying a Polynomial by a Monomial

Find each product using the distributive property.

1. $3(2x + 3y)$ $6x + 9y$
2. $4x(6 - 5m)$ $24x - 20mx$
3. $-2a(3a + 5ab)$ $-6a^2 - 10a^2b$
4. $-7c(-4c - 6c^2)$ $28c^2 + 42c^3$
5. $10(3x - 4y)$ $30x - 40y$
6. $a^4(3a^3 + 4)$ $3a^7 + 4a^4$
7. $-p^2(2p + 3pt - 4p^2)$ $-2p^3 - 3p^3t + 4p^4$
8. $-3t(5t^3 - 4t)$ $-15t^4 + 12t^2$
9. $12xy(4xy + 6x)$ $48x^2y^2 + 72x^2y$
10. $3a^2b(4a + 3b)$ $12a^3b + 9a^2b^2$
11. $r(r^2 - 9)$ $r^3 - 9r$
12. $-2y(y + 6)$ $-2y^2 - 12y$
13. $5mp(7m - 2p)$ $35m^2p - 10mp^2$
14. $2x(4x + 3)$ $8x^2 + 6x$
15. $-2y(-5 - 3y)$ $10y + 6y^2$
16. $2xy(-4xy + 3y)$ $-8x^2y^2 + 6xy^2$
17. $2a^2b^3(3a^2b - 4ab^2)$ $6a^4b^4 - 8a^3b^5$
18. $y^2(y^2 + y - 2)$ $y^4 + y^3 - 2y^2$
19. $-3xy(5x^4 - 7y^3 + 6x^2y)$ $-15x^5y + 21xy^4 - 18x^3y^2$
20. $2x(2x^3 + 3xy - 5x)$ $4x^4 + 6x^2y - 10x^2$
21. $3p(7x - 4p)$ $21px - 12p^2$
22. $4pt(7pt + 7t)$ $28p^2t^2 + 28pt^2$
23. $3(7x + 6y + z)$ $21x + 18y + 3z$
24. $5x(7xy + 6x - 8y^2)$ $35x^2y + 30x^2 - 40xy^2$
25. $10a^2(5b^3 + 6a^2b - 8a)$ $50a^2b^3 + 60a^4b - 80a^3$
26. $4a^7(13a^2 - 7)$ $52a^9 - 28a^7$

15-5 Multiplying a Polynomial by a Monomial

Objective:
Multiply a polynomial by a monomial.

You can use tiles as a model for multiplying a polynomial and a monomial.

The figure at the right is a rectangle whose width is $2x$ and whose length is $x + 3$.

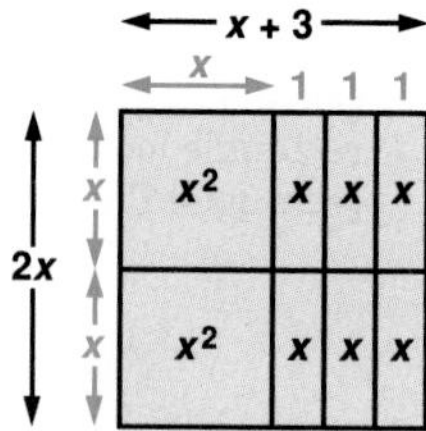

Would you get the same answer if you drew the rectangle with 2x at the top and x + 3 on the side? **yes**

The area of the rectangle is the product of the length and the width. The expression $2x(x + 3)$ represents the area of the rectangle.

The area of the rectangle is also the sum of the areas of the tiles. The area is $2x^2 + 6x$.

Therefore, $2x(x + 3) = 2x^2 + 6x$.

You can also use the distributive property to multiply a polynomial and a monomial.

Examples

1 Find $6(3x - 2)$.

$$6(3x - 2) = 6(3x) - 6(2) \quad \text{Use the distributive property.}$$
$$= 18x - 12$$

2 Find $-5y(2y^2 - 4)$.

$$-5y(2y^2 - 4) = -5y(2y^2) - (-5y)(4)$$
$$= -10y^3 - (-20y)$$
$$= -10y^3 + 20y$$

3 Find $2rs(-6r^2 + r - 7)$.

$$2rs(-6r^2 + r - 7) = 2rs(-6r^2) + 2rs(r) - 2rs(7)$$
$$= -12r^3s + 2r^2s - 14rs$$

Checking for Understanding

Communicating Algebra

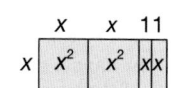

1. Use the rectangle at the right to determine the product of x and $2x + 2$. $2x^2 + 2x$

   (rectangle labels: x, x, 1 1 across the top; x at the side; tiles x^2, x^2, x, x)

2. Draw a rectangle and fill it in with tiles to represent $x(2x + 1)$. **See margin.**
3. In your own words, explain how you would use the distributive property to multiply $4k(5k - 3)$. **Multiply $4k$ and $5k$ and subtract the product of $4k$ and 3.**

Bell Ringer

What is the simplest calculator key sequence you could use to evaluate $(7^3)^2$? 7 y^x 6

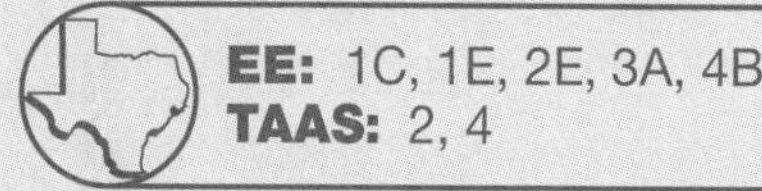

***Reteaching Masters Booklet,* p. 133**

Name ________________ Date ________________

Reteaching Worksheet 15-5

Multiplying a Polynomial by a Monomial

Sometimes the meaning of multiplication is taught by expressing larger numbers as sums.

$$\begin{array}{r} 345 \\ \times \quad 7 \\ \hline \end{array} \quad \text{is equivalent to} \quad \begin{array}{r} 300 + 40 + 5 \\ \times \qquad\qquad 7 \\ \hline 2100 + 280 + 35 \end{array}$$

If you check the sum at the right with your calculator, you will find it equals the product $7 \cdot 345$. The same idea can be used to multiply a polynomial by a monomial. First, multiply each term of the polynomial by the monomial. Then combine any like terms.

$$\begin{array}{r} 3 + 4x - 2 + y^2 \\ \times \qquad\qquad -4x^2 \\ \hline -12x^2 + (-16x^3) - (-8x^2) + (-4x^2y^2) \end{array}$$

After combining like terms, the product is $-4x^2 - 16x^3 - 4x^2y^2$.

Guided Practice

Find each product using tiles or drawings.

4. $2x(2x + 1)$ $4x^2 + 2x$
5. $x(x + 3)$ $x^2 + 3x$
6. $3x(x + 1)$ $3x^2 + 3x$
7. $x(3x + 2)$ $3x^2 + 2x$

Exercises

Independent Practice

Find each product using the distributive property.

8. $5(2x + 7)$ $10x + 35$
9. $3m(m + 9)$ $3m^2 + 27m$
10. $8b(b - 7)$ $8b^2 - 56b$
11. $x(-3x + 2)$ $-3x^2 + 2x$
12. $2x(4x^2 + 3x)$ $8x^3 + 6x^2$
13. $3a(a^3 - 2a^2)$
14. $8m(m^3 - 2m)$
15. $-3n(20n^4 - 6n^2)$
16. $-7x(-3x^2 + 6x)$
17. $7(a^2 - 2a + 3)$
18. $10(x^2 + 4x - 7)$
19. $-9(2k^3 - 3k - 6)$
20. $11(-4d^2 + 6d + 12)$
21. $x(7x^3 + 21x - 13)$
22. $a^2(-4a^4 + 3a^2 - 9)$

13. $3a^4 - 6a^3$
14. $8m^4 - 16m^2$
15. $-60n^5 + 18n^3$
16. $21x^3 - 42x^2$
17. $7a^2 - 14a + 21$
18. $10x^2 + 40x - 70$
19. $-18k^3 + 27k + 54$
20. $-44d^2 + 66d + 121$
21. $7x^4 + 21x^2 - 13x$
22. $-4a^6 + 3a^4 - 9a^2$

Mixed Review

23. **Probability** Using a tree diagram, find the number of possible outcomes: *a toss of a coin and a roll of a die.* (Lesson 11-1) **12 outcomes**

24. **Carpentry** Lauren and Miguel both measure a sheet of plywood. Lauren says the length is 3.2 m. Miguel says the length is 322 cm. Which measurement is more precise? Why? (Lesson 13-10) **322 cm; more significant digits**

25. Use a calculator to find cos 23°. Round to the nearest ten thousandth. (Lesson 14-9) **0.9205**

26. Simplify $(-3y^2)^2(2y^3)$. (Lesson 15-4) $18y^7$

Connections

27. **Geometry** The area of the rectangle at the right is $x(x + 7)$.

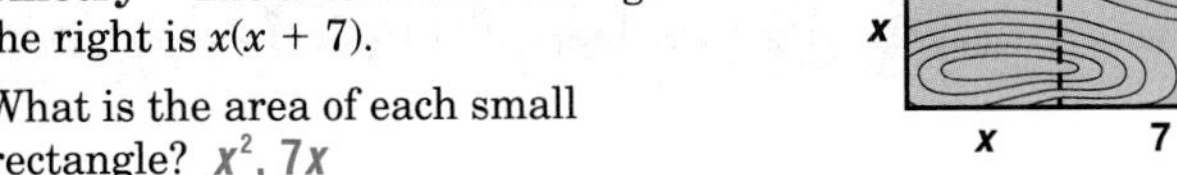

a. What is the area of each small rectangle? x^2, $7x$

b. If the areas of the two small rectangles are added, does this sum equal the area of the rectangle as a whole, $x(x + 7)$? **yes**

c. What property does this illustrate? **distributive property**

28. **Geometry** For the rectangular prism at the right, compute the area of the top, bottom, front, back, left and right sides. Then add to find the total surface area. $10m^2$, $10m^2$, $2m^2 + 6m$, $2m^2 + 6m$, $5m^2 + 15m$, $5m^2 + 15m$; $34m^2 + 42m$

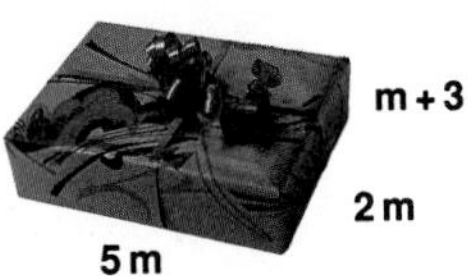

Critical Thinking

29. Find the product of $(x + 1)$ and $(x + 2)$ using tiles. Hint: You will need to use tiles having area measures of x^2, x, and 1. $x^2 + 3x + 2$

Wrap-Up

30. **Make Up a Problem** Write a multiplication problem similar to those in Exercises 4-7. Find the product using tiles and using the distributive property. **See margin.**

Additional Answers

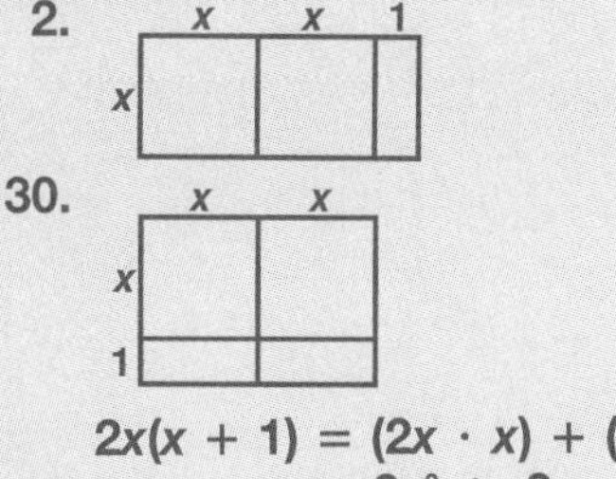

$2x(x + 1) = (2x \cdot x) + (2x \cdot 1)$
$= 2x^2 + 2x$

Cooperative Learning

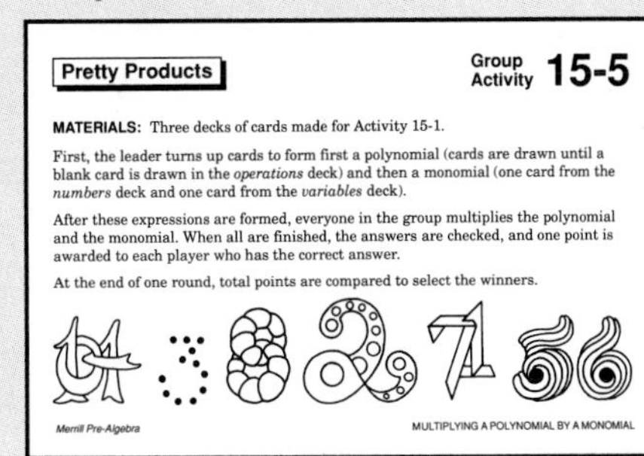

Pretty Products Group Activity **15-5**

MATERIALS: Three decks of cards made for Activity 15-1.

First, the leader turns up cards to form first a polynomial (cards are drawn until a blank card is drawn in the *operations* deck) and then a monomial (one card from the *numbers* deck and one card from the *variables* deck).

After these expressions are formed, everyone in the group multiplies the polynomial and the monomial. When all are finished, the answers are checked, and one point is awarded to each player who has the correct answer.

At the end of one round, total points are compared to select the winners.

Merrill Pre-Algebra MULTIPLYING A POLYNOMIAL BY A MONOMIAL

3 PRACTICE/APPLY

Checking the Concept

Have students check their answers to Exercises 5-8 by using the distributive property.

Error Analysis

Watch for students who are careless in determining the signs in a polynomial product.

Prevent by having students verbalize determination of the sign for each step of using the distributive property.

Independent Practice

Homework Assignment

Basic	9-21 odd, 23-30
Average	8-22 even, 23-30
Honors	15-30

4 CLOSE

Assessment Option

Speaking Write several multiplications of a polynomial by a monomial problem on the chalkboard or overhead. Have students state how to solve the problem.

Enrichment Masters Booklet, **p. 133**

Name ____________ Date ____________

Enrichment Worksheet 15-5

The Product Sign

The Greek symbol Π (pi) is called the **product sign.** It can be used to write algebraic or numeric products.

Consider the series 3 × 4 × 5 × 6. To represent it algebraically, the series can be written as

$\prod_{k=3}^{6} k$ or $\prod_{k=0}^{3} (k + 3)$

1. Can you find another way to write the product 3 × 4 × 5 × 6 using Π?
Answers may vary. Sample answer: $\prod_{k=1}^{4} (k + 2)$

Write each series as an indicated product.

2. $\prod_{k=1}^{3} k$ 1 × 2 × 3
3. $\prod_{i=4}^{7} (i - 3)^2$ 1 × 4 × 9 × 16
4. $\prod_{j=1}^{4} \frac{j}{j+1}$ $\frac{1}{2} \times \frac{2}{3} \times \frac{3}{4} \times \frac{4}{5}$
5. $\prod_{j=1}^{3} 2^j$ 2 × 4 × 8
6. $\prod_{k=10}^{11} k^2 - 5$ 95 × 116
7. $\prod_{k=2}^{5} \frac{k+1}{k-1}$ $\frac{3}{1} \times \frac{4}{2} \times \frac{5}{3} \times \frac{6}{4}$ or $3 \times 2 \times \frac{5}{3} \times \frac{3}{2}$

Use Π to write each series. Answers may vary. Sample answers given.

8. 1 × 2 × 3
$\prod_{k=1}^{3} k$
9. 1 × 4 × 9 × 16
$\prod_{k=1}^{4} k^2$
10. $\frac{1}{2} \times \frac{2}{3} \times \frac{3}{4} \times \frac{4}{5} \times \frac{5}{6}$
$\prod_{k=1}^{5} \frac{k}{k+1}$
11. 15 × 24 × 35 × 48
$\prod_{k=5}^{8} k(k - 2)$

Applying Algebra to the Real World

Objective This optional page shows how algebra is used in the real world and also provides a change of pace.

Using Discussion

Have students verbalize traits that appear frequently within their families. Do some family members not have these traits? Use this discussion to develop definitions of *dominant, recessive,* and *hybrid*. Use Punnett squares to show how two parents with brown eyes (dominant) can have a blue-eyed (recessive) child.

Using Research

Genetics is fascinating to most students. Use a biology book to find other examples of simple genetic traits and present these using Punnett squares. Mention some variations of control of a trait by a single gene. Some traits are controlled by more than one gene, such as hair color. Some are sex-linked, such as hemophilia, baldness, and color blindness, and appear predominantly in either males or females. Some traits show incomplete dominance, such as skin color, or wavy hair resulting from one parent with curly hair and one with straight hair.

Activity

Using Cooperative Groups Have each group of students investigate a different genetic disease such as hemophilia, sickle cell anemia, or cystic fibrosis. Report on symptoms, occurrence, and treatment.

Algebra in Action-Genetics

Punnett Squares

Punnett squares are used to show possible ways that genes can combine at fertilization. In a Punnett square, *dominant* genes are shown with capital letters. *Recessive* genes are shown with the lowercase of the same letter. Letters representing the parent's genes are placed on the outer sides of the Punnett square. Letters inside the boxes of the square show the possible gene combinations for their offspring.

The Punnett square at the right represents a cross between two hybrid tall pea plants. A hybrid trait is the result of a combination of a dominant and a recessive gene. The plants are tall because the dominant trait masks the recessive trait.

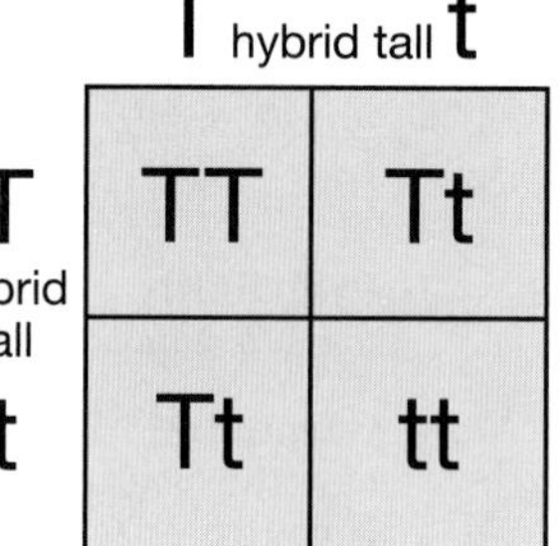

Let T represent the dominant gene for tallness.
Let t represent the recessive gene for shortness.

The gene combinations for the offspring are as follows:

- 25% of the offspring are pure tall, TT.
- 50% of the offspring are hybrid tall, Tt.
- 25% of the offspring are pure short, tt.

Notice that the Punnett square is similar to an area model.

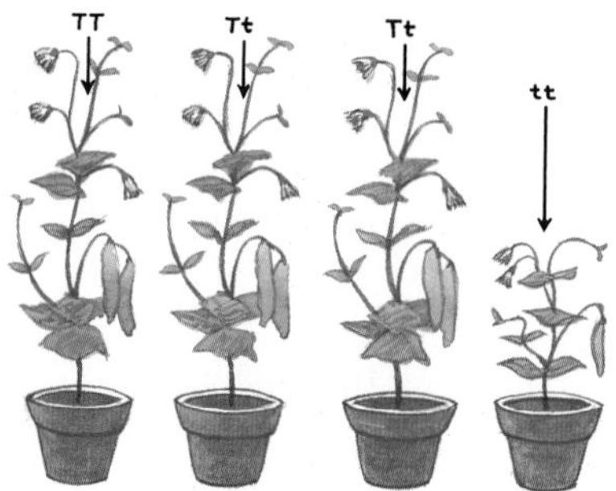

In humans, free earlobes is a dominant trait over attached earlobes. Let E represent free earlobes and e represent attached earlobes. Draw a Punnett square for each parent combination. Predict the gene combinations for the offspring. See margin.

1. EE, Ee **2.** EE, EE **3.** ee, ee **4.** Ee, ee

15-6 Multiplying Binomials

Objective:
Multiply binomials.

You can use tiles as a model for multiplying two binomials.

Consider the binomials $x + 3$ and $2x + 1$. To multiply these binomials, mark off a rectangle that has dimensions $x + 3$ and $2x + 1$.

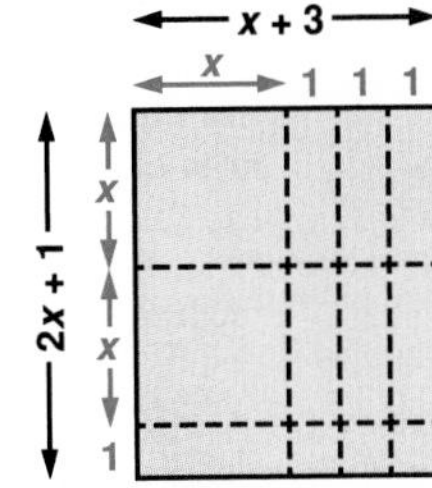

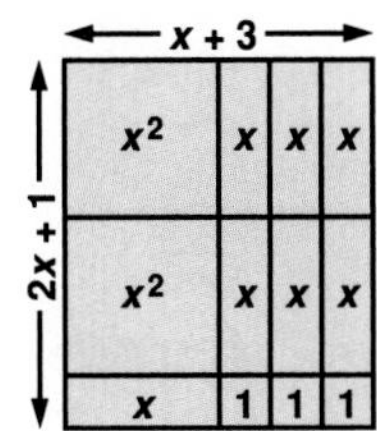

Next, fill in the rectangle with tiles.

How many terms are in $2x^2 + 7x^2 + 3$? What kind of polynomial is this? 3; trinomial

The product $(x + 3)(2x + 1)$ represents the area of the rectangle. The area is also the sum of the areas of the tiles, $2x^2 + 7x + 3$. Therefore, $(x + 3)(2x + 1) = 2x^2 + 7x + 3$.

Checking for Understanding

Communicating Algebra

1. How is multiplying two binomials the same as multiplying a binomial by a monomial? How is it different? See margin.
2. Draw a rectangle and fill it in with tiles to represent $(x + 3)(3x + 1)$. See margin.

Guided Practice

For each model, name the two binomials being multiplied and give their product.

3.

x^2	x^2	x	x
x	x	1	1
x	x	1	1

$2x + 2$, $x + 2$; $2x^2 + 6x + 4$

4.

x^2	x	x
x	1	1
x	1	1
x	1	1
x	1	1

$x + 2$, $x + 4$; $x^2 + 6x + 8$

5.

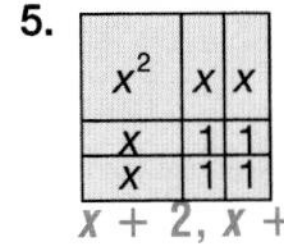

$x + 2$, $x + 2$; $x^2 + 4x + 4$

6.

x^2	x^2	x^2	x	x
x	x	x	1	1

$3x + 2$, $x + 1$; $3x^2 + 5x + 2$

Exercises

Independent Practice

Find each product using tiles or drawings.

7. $(x + 2)(x + 2)$
8. $(x + 1)(x + 5)$
9. $(2x + 1)(x + 3)$
10. $(3x + 1)(x + 2)$
11. $(x + 4)(2x + 1)$
12. $(2x + 2)(2x + 1)$
13. $(2x + 1)(3x + 2)$
14. $(3x + 3)(x + 1)$
15. $(x + 3)(3x + 2)$

7. $x^2 + 4x + 4$ 8. $x^2 + 6x + 5$ 9. $2x^2 + 7x + 3$ 10. $3x^2 + 7x + 2$ 11. $2x^2 + 9x + 4$ 12. $4x^2 + 6x + 2$ 13. $6x^2 + 7x + 2$ 14. $3x^2 + 6x + 3$ 15. $3x^2 + 11x + 6$

Lesson Notes 15-6

5-Minute Check
(over Lesson 15-5)

Find each product using the distributive property.

1. $8(4x - 3)$ $32x - 24$
2. $3y(4y^2 - 2)$ $12y^3 - 6y$
3. $-2k^2p(-7k^3 + 2k^2 + 3)$ $14k^5p - 4k^4p - 6k^2p$

Transparency 15-6 contains the 5-Minute Check and a teaching aid for this lesson.

1 FOCUS

The purpose of this lesson is to extend the models from Lesson 15-5 to include modeling the multiplication of two binomials.

2 TEACH

Chalkboard Examples

Draw a rectangle and fill it in with tiles to represent $(3x + 1)(x + 1)$.

Practice Masters Booklet, **p. 148**

Name ____________ Date ____________

Practice Worksheet 15-6

Multiplying Binomials

Find each product using tiles or drawings.

1. $(x + 1)(x + 1)$ $x^2 + 2x + 1$
2. $(x + 1)(x + 2)$ $x^2 + 3x + 2$
3. $(x + 2)(x + 3)$ $x^2 + 5x + 6$
4. $(x + 3)(x + 2)$ $x^2 + 5x + 6$
5. $(x + 3)(x + 4)$ $x^2 + 7x + 12$
6. $(x + 6)(x + 2)$ $x^2 + 8x + 12$
7. $(x + 5)(x + 4)$ $x^2 + 9x + 20$
8. $(x + 6)(x + 5)$ $x^2 + 11x + 30$
9. $(2x + 1)(x + 2)$ $2x^2 + 5x + 2$
10. $(2x + 1)(2x + 1)$ $4x^2 + 4x + 1$
11. $(x + 4)(2x + 2)$ $2x^2 + 10x + 8$
12. $(3x + 1)(x + 5)$ $3x^2 + 16x + 5$
13. $(x + 6)(3x + 2)$ $3x^2 + 20x + 12$
14. $(2x + 1)(3x + 1)$ $6x^2 + 5x + 1$

For each model, name the two binomials being multiplied and give their product.

15. 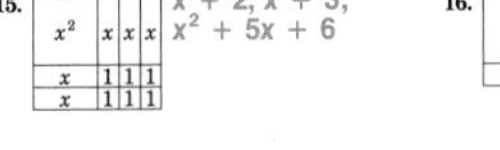
$x + 2$, $x + 3$; $x^2 + 5x + 6$

16. 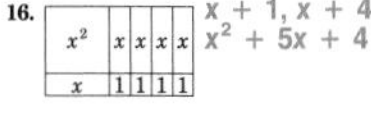
$x + 1$, $x + 4$; $x^2 + 5x + 4$

17. 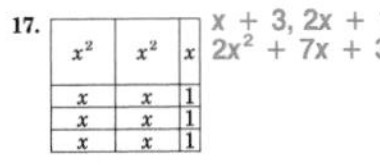
$x + 3$, $2x + 1$; $2x^2 + 7x + 3$

18. 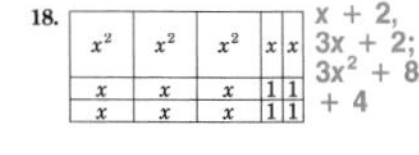
$x + 2$, $3x + 2$; $3x^2 + 8x + 4$

19. 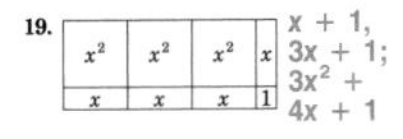
$x + 1$, $3x + 1$; $3x^2 + 4x + 1$

20. 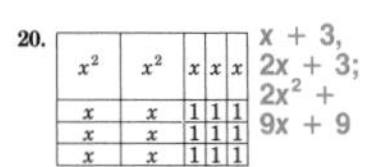
$x + 3$, $2x + 3$; $2x^2 + 9x + 9$

Reteaching Masters Booklet, **p. 134**

Name ____________ Date ____________

Reteaching Worksheet 15-6

Multiplying Binomials

Here is a different way to find the product $34 \cdot 76$.

$$\begin{aligned} 34 \cdot 76 &= (30 + 4)(70 + 6) \\ &= 30(70 + 6) + 4(70 + 6) \\ &= (30 \cdot 70) + (30 \cdot 6) + (4 \cdot 70) + (4 \cdot 6) \\ &= 2100 + 180 + 280 + 24 \end{aligned}$$

If you check the sum with your calculator, you will find it equals the product $34 \cdot 76$.

The method shown above uses the distributive property in each of two steps, the second and third lines. Notice that each term of the first quantity, $30 + 4$, is multiplied by each term of the second quantity, $70 + 6$. The same method can be used to multiply two binomials.

$$(a + b)(c + d) = ac + ad + bc + bd$$

Example: Find the product $(x + 6)(x + 2)$.

Bell Ringer

Find each product.

1. $6x(x + 1)$ $6x^2 + 6x$
2. $4(x^2 + 2x + 4)$ $4x^2 + 8x + 16$

EE: 1C, 1E, 3A
TAAS: 2

3 PRACTICE/APPLY

Checking the Concept

Have students work in pairs to solve Exercises 3-6. Take turns naming the binomials and giving their product.

Independent Practice

Homework Assignment	
Basic	7-15 odd, 16-21
Average	8-14 even, 16-21
Honors	11-21

4 CLOSE

Assessment Option

Modeling Have students work in pairs. One student models a binomial multiplication problem and the other states the two binomials and the product. Switch roles and repeat.

Enrichment Masters Booklet, **p. 134**

Name ______________ Date ______________

Enrichment Worksheet 15-6

Multiplying Binomials

Two binomials can be multiplied by using a memory device called the **FOIL** method as shown below.

To multiply two binomials, find the sum of the products of
F the first terms,
O the outer terms,
I the inner terms, and
L the last terms.

Example: Find the product $(2x + 3)(5x + 8)$.

Multiply the First terms.	$(2x + 3)(5x + 8)$ ($2x \cdot 5x$)	$10x^2$
Multiply the Outer terms.	$(2x + 3)(5x + 8)$ ($2x \cdot 8$)	$+ 16x$
Multiply the Inner terms.	$(2x + 3)(5x + 8)$ ($3 \cdot 5x$)	$+ 15x$
Multiply the Last terms.	$(2x + 3)(5x + 8)$ ($3 \cdot 8$)	$+ 24$

$(2x + 3)(5x + 8) = 10x^2 + 16x + 15x + 24$ **Combine like terms.**
$= 10x^2 + 31x + 24$

Use the FOIL method to find each product.

1. $(x + 3)(x + 5)$ $x^2 + 8x + 15$
2. $(2x + 4)(x + 7)$ $2x^2 + 18x + 28$
3. $(3x + 1)(3x + 1)$ $9x^2 + 6x + 1$
4. $(x + 4)(x + 4)$ $x^2 + 8x + 16$
5. $(2x + 1)(2x + 3)$ $4x^2 + 8x + 3$
6. $(x - 3)(x + 2)$ $x^2 - x - 6$
7. $(x + 3)(x - 2)$ $x^2 + x - 6$
8. $(x - 4)(x - 8)$ $x^2 - 12x + 32$
9. $(2x + 1)(x + 8)$ $2x^2 + 17x + 8$

Mixed Review

16. If ∠A and ∠B are complementary and the measure of ∠B is 64°, find the measure of ∠A. (Lesson 12-3) 26°
17. Find a whole number estimate for $\sqrt{97}$. (Lesson 14-2) 10
18. Find the product $3r^2(r^3 - 5r^2 + 2r)$. (Lesson 15-5) $3r^5 - 15r^4 + 6r^3$

Application

19. **Home Economics** Mrs. Baxter makes baby quilts and full-sized quilts. The baby quilts are x feet by x feet. The full-sized quilts are 3 feet wider and 4 feet longer than the baby quilts. Draw an x^2 tile to represent the baby quilt and then draw additional tiles to increase its size to a full-sized quilt. How has the area changed? Write a binomial multiplication problem to describe the area of the full-sized quilt. See Solutions Manual; increased by $7x + 12$; $(x + 3)(x + 4) = x^2 + 7x + 12$.

Critical Thinking

20. For each rectangle below, name the two binomials being multiplied. Then, name the product.

a. $(2x + 1)(x + 2) = 2x^2 + 5x + 2$
b. $(x + 2)(2x + 1) = 2x^2 + 5x + 2$

a.

x^2	x^2	x
x	x	1
x	x	1

b.

x^2	x	x
x^2	x	x
x	1	1

What do you notice about the products for **a** and for **b**? What property does this illustrate? same; commutative property

Wrap-Up

21. Find the product of $(2x + 5)(x + 1)$ using tiles. $2x^2 + 7x + 5$

Team Problem Solving

It is true that $50\frac{1}{2} + 49\frac{38}{76} = 100$.

Can you find two other addition expressions that use each of the digits 0 to 9 exactly once and equal 100? Hint: There can be more than two addends.

Sample answers: $78\frac{3}{6} + 21\frac{45}{90}$; $89 + 6\frac{1}{2} + 4\frac{35}{70}$; $90 + 8\frac{3}{6} + 1\frac{27}{54}$; $97\frac{30}{45} + 2\frac{6}{18}$; $97\frac{43}{86} + 2\frac{5}{10}$; $1 + 2\frac{35}{70} + 96\frac{4}{8}$

Additional Answers

1. The products each represent the area of a rectangle. The rectangle formed when modeling the product of two binomials is wider.

2. $3x + 1$ (across); $x + 3$ (down)

x^2	x^2	x^2	x
x	x	x	1
x	x	x	1
x	x	x	1

Cooperative Learning

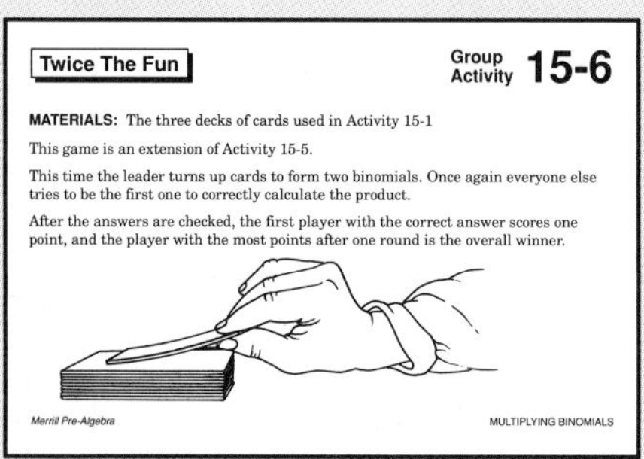

Twice The Fun — Group Activity 15-6

MATERIALS: The three decks of cards used in Activity 15-1

This game is an extension of Activity 15-5.

This time the leader turns up cards to form two binomials. Once again everyone else tries to be the first one to correctly calculate the product.

After the answers are checked, the first player with the correct answer scores one point, and the player with the most points after one round is the overall winner.

Merrill Pre-Algebra — MULTIPLYING BINOMIALS

Exploration

Factoring

Materials: tiles

In this Exploration, you will examine how to factor polynomials from a geometric perspective.

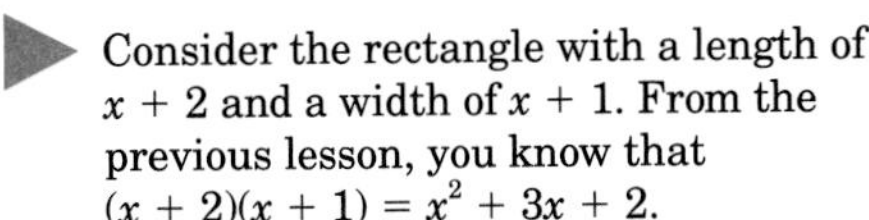

▶ Consider the rectangle with a length of $x + 2$ and a width of $x + 1$. From the previous lesson, you know that $(x + 2)(x + 1) = x^2 + 3x + 2$.

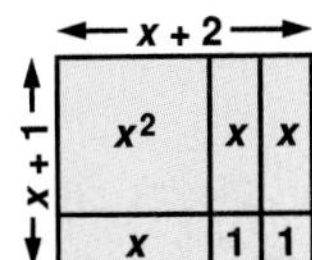

The binomials $(x + 2)$ and $(x + 1)$ are **factors** of the trinomial $x^2 + 3x + 2$.

▶ Now consider the polynomial $x^2 + 7x + 6$. Is this polynomial factorable?

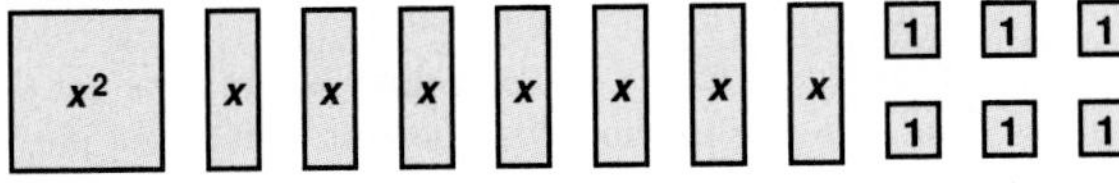

This polynomial is factorable if the tiles can be arranged into a rectangle.

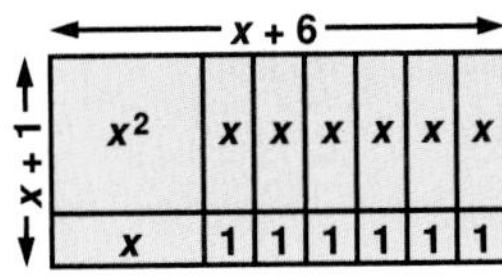

The rectangle at the right shows that $x^2 + 7x + 6$ is factorable. The factors are $(x + 1)$ and $(x + 6)$.

Your Turn: Show that $x^2 + 6x + 8$ is factorable by forming a rectangle with tiles. See margin.

Build a rectangle with the appropriate tiles or by using a drawing. Tell whether each polynomial is factorable. See Solutions Manual for drawings.

1. $x^2 + 5x + 6$ yes
2. $x^2 + 7x + 5$ no
3. $3x^2 + 8x + 5$ yes

Analysis

4. Consider the multiplication $x(x + 1)(x + 2)$. Can this multiplication be represented geometrically? If so, how? Make a drawing to explain your answer.
   Yes; make a 3-dimensional drawing. See Solutions Manual.

SET-UP

Materials

- Algebra Tiles, Lab Manual, p. 1

You may wish to use the Exploration worksheet provided on page 70 of the Lab Manual.

For Students Students can use commercial or paper tiles. Each group of students will need three $x \times x$, eight $1 \times x$, and eight 1×1 tiles. If there is a limited supply of tiles, students can use one of each size to trace and cut out enough tiles to model each exercise. Be sure that the length of x is always the same in each set of tiles.

For the Overhead Projector This exploration will work on the overhead with translucent or opaque tiles.

EXPLORATION: *Factoring*

Objective Familiarize students with a visual/geometric interpretation of factoring polynomials.

1 FOCUS

This exploration allows the student to understand the distributive property in reverse through modeling and seeing the common terms.

Motivating the Exploration

Have students work in groups of 3. Ask groups to make a list of positive integer factors whose product is 12.

2 TEACH

Using Cooperative Groups

Have the groups of 3 arrange twelve 1×1 tiles to form as many rectangles as possible. Direct the recorder for the group to list the dimensions of each rectangle as an ordered pair with the width first. Then have the groups compare the two lists.

3 PRACTICE/APPLY

Working With a Partner

One student can model a polynomial and the other determines if it is factorable by trying to arrange the model into a rectangle. Then, switch roles.

4 CLOSE

Writing Connection

Have students write an explanation to go along with their drawing in the last exercise.

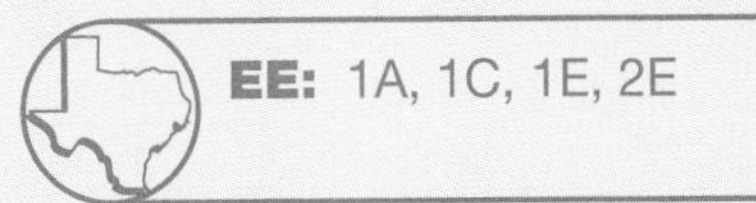

Lesson Notes 15-7

5-Minute Check
(over Lesson 15-6)

Find each product using tiles or drawings.

1. $(2x + 1)(x + 2)$ $2x^2 + 5x + 2$
2. $(3x + 1)(x + 3)$ $3x^2 + 10x + 3$
3. $(2x + 2)(2x + 5)$ $4x^2 + 14x + 10$
4. $(x + 2)(x + 1)$ $x^2 + 3x + 2$
5. $(4x + 3)(2x + 1)$ $8x^2 + 10x + 3$

Transparency 15-7 contains the 5-Minute Check and a teaching aid for this lesson.

1 FOCUS

The purpose of this lesson is to use a table to record information from a problem.

Motivating the Lesson

Read the Chalkboard Example to the class and ask how this problem differs from most other problems. **Sample answer: There are no words that indicate an operation.**

2 TEACH

Chalkboard Examples

- *For Example*
  Lyndsi, Jill, Leah, and Krista are friends. Each of them plays one of the following instruments: flute, piano, drums, and violin. Use the following information to determine who plays each instrument.

  Krista and Lyndsi are in the marching band. Lyndsi broke one of her sticks the other day at practice. Leah plays in the orchestra. Jill usually plays the accompaniment for the school singing groups.
  Lyndsi - drums
  Jill - piano
  Leah - violin
  Krista - flute

Problem Solving

15-7 Strategy: Eliminate Possibilities

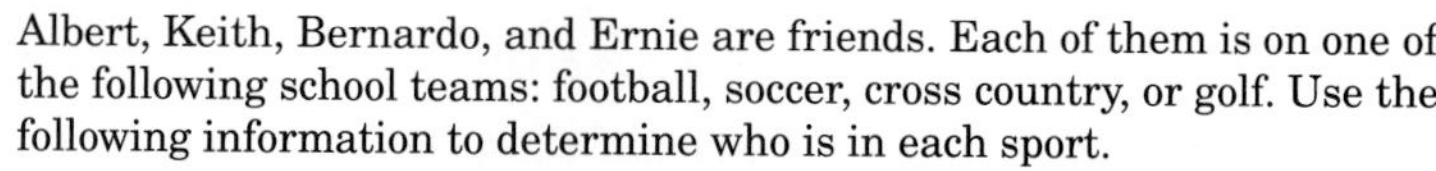

Objective:
Solve problems by eliminating possibilities.

Albert, Keith, Bernardo, and Ernie are friends. Each of them is on one of the following school teams: football, soccer, cross country, or golf. Use the following information to determine who is in each sport.

> Albert is shorter than the boy who plays soccer.
> Bernardo only likes to play games with round balls.
> Ernie has a problem with his knee and cannot run.
> Keith practices kicking a ball as part of his training.

Explore There are 4 boys and 4 sports. You must match each boy with the sport he plays by using the information from the 4 statements above.

Plan Make a chart to organize the information. Through the process of elimination, each boy can be matched with his sport.

Solve Put an x to show that Albert does not play soccer. Put 2 x's to show that Bernardo does not play football or run cross country. Put 3 x's to show that Ernie does not play football or soccer, or run cross country. Circle the box that shows that Ernie plays golf. Since only one student plays golf, put x's in the rest of the boxes in that row. Now, by the process of elimination, you can see that Bernardo plays soccer. Place an x to show that Keith does not run cross country, which means he plays football. Albert's sport, then, is cross country.

How would the problem be changed if the last statement did not exist? **You would not be able to tell what sports Keith and Albert play.**

	Albert	Keith	Bernardo	Ernie
football	X	◯	X	X
soccer	X	X	◯	X
cross country	◯	X	X	X
golf	X	X	X	◯

Albert runs cross country, Keith plays football, Bernardo plays soccer, and Ernie plays golf.

Examine Check the result against the statements. The first statement says that Albert does not play soccer, and the answer says that Albert runs cross country. There is no conflict here. Using the same method for each sentence, you can see that there are no conflicts.

Bell Ringer

Find each product using tiles or drawings.

1. $(x + 2)(2x + 3)$
2. $(3x + 3)(x + 3)$

$2x^2 + 7x + 6$
$3x^2 + 12x + 9$

EE: 1A, 1B, 1C, 1D, 1E

Reteaching Activity

Using Discussion Choose four students from the class. Place their names across the top of a chart. List four activities on the left of the chart, being certain each activity applies to only one student. Brainstorm a list of clues that would eliminate possibilities and help match each student with his or her activity.

Checking for Understanding

Guided Practice

Darla: gerbil
Amanda: cat
Norma: dog
Tara: parrot

1. Solve by eliminating possibilities:
   Darla, Amanda, Norma, and Tara are friends and each has one of the following pets: dog, cat, parrot, or gerbil. If each girl has a different pet, use the following information to match each girl with her pet.

   Norma likes to visit the girl with the gerbil.
   Tara and Amanda frequently help the girl with the dog to walk her pet.
   Darla cannot have a dog or a cat because she is allergic to them.
   Tara plans to teach her pet how to talk.

2. In problem 1, which pet did you match first? Answers may vary.
3. How did the first match help to solve the rest of problem 1? It eliminated that pet as a possibility for the other girls.

Exercises

Independent Practice

Solve. Use any strategy.

4. Cecilia, Greta, Lucy, Dustin, Pedro, Reuben, and Grant have started a band to make some extra money on weekends. The band has a lead guitar player, a rhythm guitar player, a bass guitar player, a keyboard player, a drummer, a lead singer, and a backup singer. If each person has one responsibility in the band, use the following information to match each person with his or her responsibility.

   Cecilia: lead guitar
   Greta: backup singer
   Lucy: drummer
   Dustin: lead singer
   Pedro: bass guitar
   Reuben: keyboard
   Grant: rhythm guitar

   Cecilia, Lucy, and the bass guitar player like pizza with anchovies.
   Reuben, Greta, and the lead singer like pizza with mushrooms.
   Lucy and the keyboard player are cousins.
   Pedro and Lucy do not have good singing voices.
   Grant is taller than the drummer and the bass guitar player.
   Greta does not play any guitar.
   Cecilia, Grant, and the lead singer live on the same street.
   Reuben wants to learn how to play the drums.
   The keyboard player and the drummer baked a cake to surprise Greta.
   Reuben's best friend plays the bass guitar.
   Cecilia and the drummer like to play tennis in their spare time.
   Grant and the lead guitar player are both freshmen.
   Grant, Cecilia, and the keyboard player are studying chemistry in school.

Connection

5. **Statistics** Jerry's Music Store took a survey of 100 people. Sixty-three people said they like rock, 49 said they like rap, and 24 said they like jazz. Twenty-five people like rock and rap, 5 like jazz and rap, and 14 like rock and jazz. If 3 people like all 3 types of music, how many people do not like rock, rap, or jazz? 5 people

Wrap-Up

6. Explain how to solve problems by eliminating possibilities. See margin.

3 PRACTICE/APPLY

Checking the Concept

Have students work with a partner to solve Exercises 1-3.

Error Analysis

Watch for students who make wild guesses.
Prevent by reviewing the four-step method.

Independent Practice

Homework Assignment	
Basic	4-6
Average	4-6
Honors	4-6

Chapter 15, Quiz B (Lesson 15-5 through 15-7) is available in the Evaluation Masters Booklet, p. 133.

4 CLOSE

Assessment Option

Writing Have students write the steps they would take to create a table for use in solving a problem that involves eliminating the possibilities.

Practice Masters Booklet, **p. 149**

Name ____________ Date ____________

Practice Worksheet 15-7

Problem Solving Strategy: Eliminate Possibilities

Solve by eliminating possibilities.

1. The number is odd.
   The number has two digits.
   The sum of the digits is nine.
   The product of the digits is twenty.
   The ten's digit is one less than the unit's digit.
   What is the number? 45

2. Pencils cost $0.05.
   Notebooks cost $0.30.
   Henry spent $1.40.
   How many of each did he buy if he bought the same number of pencils and notebooks? 4

3. A number is between 300 and 400. If it is divided by 2, the remainder is 1. If it is divided by 4, 6, or 8, the remainder is 3. If it is divided by 10, the remainder is 5. If it is divided by 3, 5, 7, or 9, the remainder is zero. What is the number? 315

4. Harry, Merrie, Sherrie, Larry, and Carrie live on the same street. Their houses are white, yellow, tan, green, and blue. One of them has a dog, one has a cat, one has two goldfish, one has a hamster, and one doesn't have a pet. Follow the clues to determine who lives in which house and what pet that person has.
   a. The white house is farthest to the right on the street.
   b. Larry lives between Merrie and Harry.
   c. Harry lives in the middle house which is blue.
   d. The house farthest on the left has a dog.
   e. A hamster lives in the white house.
   f. The yellow house is next to the white house and no pet lives there.
   g. Larry has a cat.
   h. Sherrie doesn't live next to Harry.
   i. The green house is to the right of the tan house.
   Merrie, tan, dog; Larry, green, cat; Harry, blue, two goldfish; Carrie, yellow, no pet; Sherrie, white, hamster

Additional Answer

6. Create a table to organize the data. Separate the data into two categories and use these categories to label the columns and rows of the table. Decide what connection you need to establish between the categories. Use logical reasoning to draw conclusions about the relationships among the data and complete the chart accordingly.

Cooperative Learning

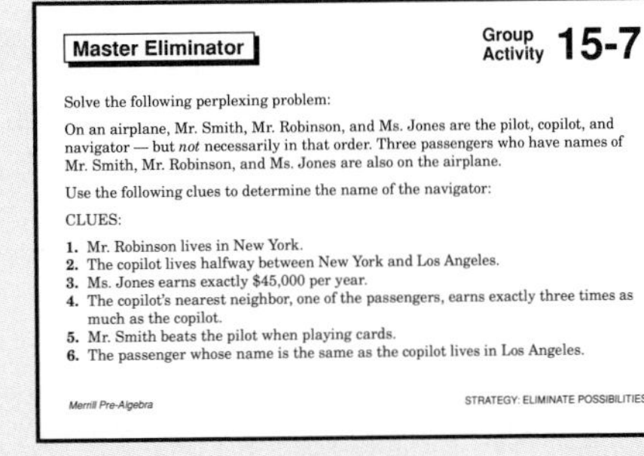

Master Eliminator — Group Activity **15-7**

Solve the following perplexing problem:

On an airplane, Mr. Smith, Mr. Robinson, and Ms. Jones are the pilot, copilot, and navigator — but *not* necessarily in that order. Three passengers who have names of Mr. Smith, Mr. Robinson, and Ms. Jones are also on the airplane.

Use the following clues to determine the name of the navigator:

CLUES:

1. Mr. Robinson lives in New York.
2. The copilot lives halfway between New York and Los Angeles.
3. Ms. Jones earns exactly $45,000 per year.
4. The copilot's nearest neighbor, one of the passengers, earns exactly three times as much as the copilot.
5. Mr. Smith beats the pilot when playing cards.
6. The passenger whose name is the same as the copilot lives in Los Angeles.

Merrill Pre-Algebra STRATEGY: ELIMINATE POSSIBILITIES

Using the Chapter Review

The Chapter Review is a comprehensive review of the concepts presented in this chapter. This review may be used to prepare students for the Chapter Test.

Alternate Review Strategy

To provide a brief in-class review, you may wish to read the following questions to the class and require a verbal response.

1. State whether $2x + \frac{3}{4}$ is a polynomial. If it is, identify it as a monomial, binomial, or trinomial. yes, binomial
2. Find the degree of the polynomial $6x^3y^2 + x^2y$. 5
3. Find the sum of $(7x + 5) + (-6x - 3)$. $x + 2$
4. Find the difference of $(4m^2 - 8) - (-2m^2 - 1)$. $6m^2 - 7$
5. State the additive inverse of $9y^2 - 5y + 2$. $-9y^2 + 5y - 2$
6. Simplify $(2r^5)^3$. $8r^{15}$
7. Evaluate $(-ab)^2$ if $a = 2$ and $b = 4$. 64
8. Find the product of $4x(2x - 3)$. $8x^2 - 12x$
9. Find the product of $(x + 8)$ and $(x + 4)$. $x^2 + 12x + 32$
10. Solve by eliminating possibilities.
    Angie, Sara, Brandon, and Nevada are neighbors and each has one of the following pets: rabbit, turtle, mouse, snake. If each child has a different pet, use the following information to match each child with a pet.
    Sara likes furry animals. Brandon and Nevada have cold-blooded pets. Brandon's pet might eat Angie's pet if the two animals were placed together in a cage.
    Angie - mouse; Sara - rabbit; Brandon - snake; Nevada - turtle

Review

Language and Concepts

Choose the correct term to complete each sentence.

1. The degree of a monomial is the (sum, product) of the exponents of its variables.
2. A (binomial, trinomial) is the sum or difference of three monomials.
3. The degree of a polynomial is the same as that of the term that has the (least, greatest) degree.
4. To subtract two polynomials, you add the (additive inverse, multiplicative inverse) of the second polynomial.
5. The (commutative property, distributive property) is used in multiplying a polynomial by a monomial.

Skills

State whether each expression is a polynomial. If it is, identify it as a *monomial, binomial,* or *trinomial.* (Lesson 15-1)

6. $3x^4 - x$
7. $\frac{4}{ax}$ no
8. ax^2 yes, monomial
9. $9b^2 + b - 1$
10. $8x - \frac{5}{3}$ yes, binomial
11. $k^3 - \frac{2}{k}$ no

6. yes, binomial
9. yes, trinomial

Find the degree of each polynomial. (Lesson 15-1)

12. $4x$ 1
13. $5a^2b$ 3
14. $3x + y^2$ 2
15. $19m^2n^3 - 14mn^4$ 5
16. $x^2 - 6xy + xy^2$ 3
17. $12rs^2 + 3r^2s + 5r^4s$ 5

Find each sum. (Lesson 15-2)

18. $(2x^2 - 5x) + (3x^2 + x)$ $5x^2 - 4x$
19. $(a^2 - 6ab) + (3a^2 + ab)$ $4a^2 - 5ab$
20. $(x^2 - 5x + 3) + (4x - 3)$ $x^2 - x$
21. $(-3y^2 + 2) + (4y^2 - 5y - 2)$ $y^2 - 5y$

Find each difference. (Lesson 15-3)

22. $(7a - 11b) - (3a + 4b)$ $4a - 15b$
23. $(6y - 8z) - (6y + 4z)$ $-12z$
24. $(3a^2 - b^2 + c^2) - (a^2 + 2b^2)$ $2a^2 - 3b^2 + c^2$
25. $(14a^2 - 3a) - (6a^2 + 5a + 17)$ $8a^2 - 8a - 17$

Simplify. (Lesson 15-4)

26. $(a^2)^3$ a^6
27. $(-2x)^3$ $-8x^3$
28. $(p^2q)^3$ p^6q^3
29. $-5c(2cd)^3$ $-40c^4d^3$
30. $4y(y^2z)^3$ $4y^7z^3$
31. $6a(-ab)^7$ $-6a^8b^7$

Find each product. (Lesson 15-5)

32. $4d(2d - 5)$ $8d^2 - 20d$
33. $x(-5x + 3)$ $-5x^2 + 3x$
34. $a^2(2a^3 + a - 5)$
35. $3y(-y^2 - 8y + 4)$ $-3y^3 - 24y^2 + 12y$
36. $-2g(g^3 + 6g + 3)$ $-2g^4 - 12g^2 - 6g$
37. $-3az(2z^2 + 4az + a^2)$ $-6az^3 - 12a^2z^2 - 3a^3z$

34. $2a^5 + a^3 - 5a^2$

Find each product using tiles. (Lesson 15-6)

38. $(x + 3)(x + 1)$ $x^2 + 4x + 3$
39. $(2x + 1)(x + 1)$ $2x^2 + 3x + 1$
40. $(3x + 2)(2x + 2)$ $6x^2 + 10x + 4$

Applications and Problem Solving

41. Solve by eliminating possibilities:
Lindsay, Lee, Anna, and Marcos formed a study group. Each one has a favorite subject that is different from the others. The subjects are art, math, music, and physics. Use the following information to match each person with his or her favorite subject.

Lindsay likes subjects where she can use her calculator.
Lee does not like music or physics.
Anna and Marcos prefer classes in the cultural arts.
Marcos plans to be a professional cartoonist.

Lindsay: physics
Lee: math
Anna: music
Marcos: art

Communicating Algebra

In your own words, explain how to add polynomials. Add like terms.

Curriculum Connection

- **Science** Research the scientific names used to classify a lion and a tiger. How are these names similar? How are these names different? *Panthera leo, Panthera tigris;* same genus name; different species name
- **Science** Find an example of a polynomial in your science book. Sample answer: $d = \frac{1}{2}gt^2$ (The distance traveled by a falling object is proportional to the square of the time of the fall.)

Read More About It

Livingston, M.C., ed. *Poems of Lewis Carroll.*

Selby, Peter H. *Practical Algebra: A Self-Teaching Guide.*

Wyler, Rose and Gerald Ames. *It's All Done with Numbers.*

You may wish to use a Chapter Test (free-response format) as an additional chapter review. Two forms are provided in the Evaluation Masters Booklet as shown below.

Evaluation Masters Booklet, **p. 131**

Name ______ Date ______

Chapter 15 Test, Form 2A

Identify each expression as a monomial, binomial, trinomial, or none of these.

1. $3x$ 2. $3 + x + x^2$ 3. $\frac{3}{x}$

Write the degree of each expression.

4. $5x$ 5. $x^2 + 3x$ 6. 12

Find each sum or difference.

7. $(3x + 2) + (5x + 3)$
8. $(6a^2 + 4) + (8a^2 - 3a + 6)$
9. $(5c^2 + 4c + 3) + (3c^2 + 4c + 5)$
10. $(2x^2 - 3x + 4) + (-6x^2 - 5x - 8)$
11. $(9y - 3) - (4y + 7)$
12. $(7y^2 - 3y + 4) - (8y^2 - 6y + 4)$
13. $(-12x^2 - 3) - (6x^2 - 4x + 8)$
14. $(5a^2 - 3a - 6) - (4a^2 + 5a + 7)$
15. Simplify $(3a)^2$.
16. Simplify $(ab^6)^4$.

Find each product using the distributive property.

17. $3(2a^2 + 4a - 3)$
18. $f^3(8f^2 - 6)$
19. $-2a^2(3a^2 - 4a + 1)$

Find each product using tiles or drawings.

20. $(4a + 3)(4a - 3)$ 21. $(-2b + 6)(2b + 6)$
22. $(3x - 4)(4x - 3)$ 23. $(-3c + 7)(-3c + 7)$

24. Alice, Betty, and Carl collect stuffed animals. Alice has 8 more than Carl and Betty has 2 less than Carl. Write a polynomial to express how many animals Alice and Betty have together.

25. When 18 people were asked to choose their favorite of the colors red, blue, and yellow, twice as many chose red as chose yellow and three times as many preferred blue as preferred yellow. How many people chose yellow?

BONUS Simplify $(3a - 4)(2a - 6) - (2a - 6)$.

1. monomial
2. trinomial
3. none of these
4. 1
5. 2
6. 0
7. $8x + 5$
8. $14a^2 - 3a + 10$
9. $8c^2 + 8c + 8$
10. $-4x^2 - 8x - 4$
11. $5y - 10$
12. $-y^2 + 3y$
13. $-18x^2 + 4x - 11$
14. $a^2 - 8a - 13$
15. $9a^2$
16. a^4b^{24}
17. $6a^2 + 12a - 9$
18. $8f^5 - 6f^3$
19. $-6a^4 + 8a^3 - 2a^2$
20. $16a^2 - 9$
21. $-4b^2 + 36$
22. $12x^2 - 25x + 12$
23. $9c^2 - 42c + 49$
24. $2c + 6$
25. 3

$6a^2 - 28a + 30$

Evaluation Masters Booklet, **p. 132**

Name ______ Date ______

Chapter 15 Test, Form 2B

Identify each expression as a monomial, binomial, trinomial, or none of these.

1. $3x - 7$ 2. $\frac{3}{x}$ 3. $x^2 + x + 2$

Write the degree of each expression.

4. 5 5. $6xy^4z^3$ 6. $a^2 + a$

Find each sum or difference.

7. $(2x + 4) + (3x + 3)$
8. $(7a^2 - 4) + (8a^2 - 3a + 6)$
9. $(5c^2 + 6c + 3) + (2c^2 + 4c + 5)$
10. $(5x^2 + 3x + 4) + (-6x^2 - 5x + 8)$
11. $(8y - 3) - (4y - 7)$
12. $(4y^2 - 3y - 4) - (8y^2 + 6y + 4)$
13. $(-18x^2 - 5) - (6x^2 - 4x + 8)$
14. $(5a^2 + 3a + 6) - (4a^2 - 5a - 7)$
15. Simplify $(6b)^2$.
16. Simplify $(ab^6)^2$.

Find each product using the distributive property.

17. $5(2c^2 + 4c - 3)$
18. $g^3(9g^3 - 8)$
19. $-2b^2(3b^2 - 5b - 1)$

Find each product using tiles or drawings.

20. $(4a + 3)(3a - 4)$ 21. $(-2d + 6)(2d + 8)$
22. $(3x - 4)(3x + 4)$ 23. $(-2s + 5)(-2s + 5)$

24. Alex, Bill, and Diane collect tropical fish. Alex has 8 fewer than Diane and Bill has 2 more than Diane. Write a polynomial to express how many fish Alex and Bill have together.

25. When 18 people were asked to choose their favorite of the colors red, blue, and yellow, twice as many chose blue as chose yellow and six times as many preferred red as preferred yellow. How many people chose yellow?

BONUS Simplify $(3a - 4)(2a + 6) - (2a + 6)$.

1. binomial
2. none of these
3. trinomial
4. 0
5. 8
6. 2
7. $5x + 7$
8. $15a^2 - 3a + 2$
9. $7c^2 + 10c + 8$
10. $-x^2 - 2x + 12$
11. $4y - 4$
12. $-4y^2 - 9y - 8$
13. $-24x^2 + 4x - 13$
14. $a^2 - 8a - 13$
15. $36b^2$
16. a^2b^{12}
17. $10c^2 + 20c - 15$
18. $9g^6 - 8g^3$
19. $-6b^4 + 10b^3 + 2b^2$
20. $12a^2 - 7a - 12$
21. $-4d^2 - 4d + 48$
22. $9x^2 - 16$
23. $4s^2 - 20s + 25$
24. $2d - 6$
25. 2

$6a^2 + 8a - 30$

Using the Chapter Test

This page may be used as a test or as an additional review. Two forms of a Chapter Test (multiple-choice format) are provided in the Evaluation Masters Booklet.

Evaluation Masters Booklet, **pp.127-128**

Name ________________ Date ________

Chapter 15 Test, Form 1A

1. Choose the expression which is not a monomial.
   A. $\frac{4}{5}$ B. $\frac{4}{x}$ C. $3x^2y$ D. 5 — 1. B
2. Write the degree of $3ab^6$.
   A. 18 B. 9 C. 6 D. 7 — 2. D
3. Identify the expression $x^2 + 2x + 4$.
   A. monomial B. binomial C. trinomial D. constant — 3. C
4. Write the degree of $ax^2 + xy + 3y^2$.
   A. 1 B. 2 C. 3 D. 4 — 4. C

Find each sum or difference.

5. $(9f^2 + 4f - 6) + (f^2 - 2f - 2)$
   A. $10f^2 + 2f - 8$ B. $10f^2 + 2f - 4$ C. $10f^2 + 2f + 8$ D. $9f^2 + 2f + 2$ — 5. A
6. $(-2x^2 - 2x - 6) + (-x^2 + 2x - 6)$
   A. $2x + 12$ B. $-3x^2 - 4x - 12$ C. $3x^2 - 4x - 12$ D. $-3x^2 - 12$ — 6. D
7. $(5a^2 + 3a + 2) + (6a^2 - 5a + 6)$
   A. $11a^2 - 2a + 8$ B. $11a^2 + 2a + 8$ C. $11a^2 + 8a + 8$ D. $11a^2 - 2a - 4$ — 7. A
8. $(2x^2 - 7x - 3) - (5x^2 - 9)$
   A. $3x^2 - 7x - 12$ B. $-3x^2 - 7x + 6$ C. $3x^2 - 7x - 6$ D. $-3x^2 - 7x - 12$ — 8. B
9. $(-3z^2 + 4z + 7) - (8z^2 + 4z - 3)$
   A. $-11z^2 + 4$ B. $-11z^2 - 8z + 10$ C. $5z^2 + 8z + 4$ D. $-11z^2 + 10$ — 9. D
10. $(4w^2 + 3w + 6) - (3w^2 + 4w + 7)$
    A. $w^2 - w - 1$ B. $w^2 + 7w + 13$ C. $w^2 - w + 1$ D. $-w^2 - w + 1$ — 10. A
11. $(10y^2 + 4y - 3) - (6y^2 - 8y + 12)$
    A. $4y^2 - 12y - 15$ B. $4y^2 + 12y + 9$ C. $4y^2 + 12y - 15$ D. $4y^2 - 4y + 9$ — 11. C
12. Simplify $(3^2)^3$.
    A. 216 B. 18 C. 27 D. 729 — 12. D
13. Simplify $(-2^3)^2$.
    A. −36 B. 36 C. 64 D. −64 — 13. C
14. Simplify $(xy^3)^4$.
    A. x^4y^{12} B. xy^7 C. $4xy^{12}$ D. xy^{12} — 14. A
15. Simplify $(-2x^4)^3$.
    A. $8x^{12}$ B. $-8x^{12}$ C. $-8x^7$ D. $-6x^{12}$ — 15. B

Name ________________ Date ________

Chapter 15 Test, Form 1A (continued)

Find each product using the distributive property.

16. $-2(4x^2 - 8x - 6)$
    A. $-8x^2 - 16x - 12$ B. $-8x^2 - 16x + 12$ C. $-8x^2 + 16x + 12$ D. $-8x^2 + 16x - 12$ — 16. C
17. $3a(4a^2 + 2a - 3)$
    A. $12a^3 + 6a^2 - 9a$ B. $12a^2 + 6a - 9$ C. $7a^3 + 6a^2 - 9a$ D. $12a^3 + 5a^2 - 9$ — 17. A
18. $-4b(20b^4 - 6b^2)$
    A. $-80b^5 - 10b^3$ B. $-80b^5 - 2b^3$ C. $-80b^5 + 10b^3$ D. $-80b^5 + 24b^3$ — 18. D
19. $8x(-4x^2 + 6x - 5)$
    A. $-32x^3 + 48x^2 + 40x$ B. $32x^3 + 48x + 40$ C. $-32x^3 + 48x^2 - 40x$ D. $32x^2 + 48x - 40$ — 19. C

Find each product using tiles or drawings.

20. $(x + 2)(x + 4)$
    A. $x^2 + 8$ B. $2x + 6$ C. $2x + 8$ D. $x^2 + 6x + 8$ — 20. D
21. $(3m + 4)(2m - 7)$
    A. $6m^2 - 29m - 28$ B. $6m^2 - 13m - 28$ C. $6m^2 + 13m + 28$ D. $6m^2 + 13m - 28$ — 21. B
22. $(2x - 3)(2x + 3)$
    A. $4x^2 - 9$ B. $4x^2 - 12x + 9$ C. $4x^2 - 6$ D. $4x^2 + 9$ — 22. A
23. Tom has 5 more baseball cards than John. Mike has 3 fewer cards than John. How many cards do Tom and Mike have altogether?
    A. $2j - 2$ B. $2j + 2$ C. $j - 8$ D. $2j + 8$ — 23. B
24. Mary made 5 doll-carriage blankets. Each blanket is x inches wide and $(x + 6)$ inches long. Find the combined area of the blankets.
    A. $10x + 6$ B. $5x^2 + 30$ C. $5x^2 + 30x$ D. $5x + 30$ — 24. C
25. Minnie's Fruit Store asked people their favorite fruits. There were 10 votes for apple, 7 for banana, and 5 for grape. However, 1 voted for both apple and banana, 1 voted for both grape and banana, 1 voted for both apple and grape, and 2 voted for all three fruits. Find the smallest number of people who could have been asked.
    A. 25 B. 27 C. 15 D. 17 — 25. C

BONUS Simplify $3x^2(2x + 3) + 4x^2(2x - 3)$.
A. $27x^3$ B. $14x^3 - 3x^2$ C. $14x^2 - 3x$ D. $14x^3 + 3x^2$ — B

Test

State whether each expression is a polynomial. If it is, identify it as a *monomial*, *binomial*, or *trinomial*.

1. $-\frac{3}{y}$ no
2. $4x^2 + 5x + 1$ yes; trinomial
3. x^2y yes; monomial
4. $rs^3 - \frac{3}{r}$ no
5. $\frac{3a^5b^4}{7}$ yes; monomial
6. $1 - 4mt + 2m^2t^3$ yes; trinomial

Find the degree of each polynomial.

7. $4x^2 + 3$ 2
8. $-9ab^3$ 4
9. $12ct^2 + 9c^3t^2$ 5
10. $\frac{r^2s^4}{3}$ 6

Find each sum or difference.

11. $(-4a^2 + 3) - (3a^2 - 7)$ $-7a^2 + 10$
12. $(7x - 6y) + (-4x + y)$ $3x - 5y$
13. $(10b^2 - 7bc) - (5b^2 - 4bc)$ $5b^2 - 3bc$
14. $(-5n^2 - 6n) - (-5n^2 + 4n + 2)$ $-10n - 2$
15. $$\begin{array}{r} 6x^2 - 5x + 4 \\ \underline{+ (-2x^2) - 4x - 8} \\ 4x^2 - 9x - 4 \end{array}$$
16. $$\begin{array}{r} 9w^2 + 5w - 8 \\ \underline{- 6w^2 + 8w - 9} \\ 3w^2 + 13w - 17 \end{array}$$

Simplify.

17. $(ab^3)^3$ a^3b^9
18. $2(-3x^2)^3$ $-54x^6$
19. $(3x^2y^3)^2$ $9x^4y^6$

Find each product.

20. $2x(3x^2 + 1)$ $6x^3 + 2x$
21. $5a^3(-3a^2 - 8a + 2)$ $-15a^5 - 40a^4 + 10a^3$
22. $-4rs(1 - 3r + r^3s^2)$ $-4rs + 12r^2s - 4r^4s^3$

Find each product using tiles or drawings.

23. $(2x + 1)(x + 2)$ $2x^2 + 5x + 2$
24. $(x + 1)(3x + 4)$ $3x^2 + 7x + 4$

Solve.

25. If the length of a window is $7x + 4$ inches and the width is $3x - 11$ inches, what is the size of the window in united inches? (Remember: United inches equals the length of the window plus the width.) $10x - 7$ united inches

BONUS

Factor the polynomial $2x^2 + 9x + 4$. $(2x + 1)(x + 4)$

Test Generator Software is provided in both Apple and IBM formats. You may use this software to create your own tests, based on the needs of your students.

Academic Skills Test

Cumulative, Chapters 1-15

1. A clock has a diameter of 14 inches. Which expression shows the length of trim needed to circle the edge of the clock? (Use $\pi \approx \frac{22}{7}$.)

   A $\frac{22}{7} \times 7^2$ C $\frac{22}{7} \times 28$

   (B) $\frac{22}{7} \times 14$ D Not Here

2. Which is the solution of the system of equations $x + y = 4$ and $y = -3x$?

   A (-6, 2)
   B (1, 3)
   (C) (2, -6)
   D (3, 1)

3. The price of a CD player Lois wants to buy is listed at $139.99. If the sales tax rate is 6%, a reasonable estimate for the total cost is—

   A $0.80 C $140
   B $8.00 (D) $150

4. Julio is 6 feet tall. At 10:00 he casts a shadow 4 feet long. At the same, the flagpole casts a shadow 42 feet long. How tall is the flagpole?

   (A) 63 feet C 28 feet
   B 44 feet D Not Here

5. What is the area of the triangle?

   A 480 cm^2
   B 360 cm^2
   (C) 240 cm^2
   D 74 cm^2

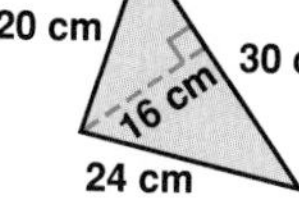

6. A cylindrical can is 12 cm tall and the ends each have a diameter of 10 cm. Which expression can be used to find the area the can label covers?

   (A) $3.14 \times 10 \times 12$
   B $3.14 \times 5 \times 5 \times 12$
   C $2(3.14 \times 5^2) + 3.14 \times 10 \times 12$
   D $3.14 \times 5^2 + 2(3.14 \times 10 \times 12)$

7. Jane's kite is flying directly over a spot 120 feet from where she is standing. The kite string is 130 feet long. How high is the kite?

   A 500 feet
   B 177 feet
   C 125 feet
   (D) 50 feet

   130 ft
   120 ft

8. In a right triangle, the tangent ratio is the measure of the leg opposite an angle to the measure of the leg adjacent to the angle. What is the tangent ratio of angle *D*?

   A $\frac{3}{5}$
   B $\frac{4}{5}$
   (C) $\frac{4}{3}$
   D $\frac{5}{3}$

   D, E, F; 15 in.; 9 in.; 12 in.

9. Which is equivalent to $(7x^2 + 3y) - (3x^2 + 5y)$?

   (A) $4x^2 - 2y$ C $4x^4 - 2y^2$
   B $4x^2 + 8y$ D $4x^4 + 8y^2$

10. Which is equivalent to $(-2x)^3$?

    (A) $-8x^3$ C $-2x^3$
    B $8x^3$ D $2x^3$

A Cumulative Review (free-response format) and Cumulative Test (multiple-choice format) are also provided in the Evaluation Masters Booklet as shown at the right.

Test Item	1	2	3	4	5	6	7	8	9	10
Lesson Number	6-11	8-10	9-8	12-10	13-1	13-5	14-6	14-8	15-3	15-4
TAAS Objective	11	2	13	11	4	4	3	3	2	2

Using the Academic Skills Test

This test familiarizes students with a standardized format while testing skills and concepts presented up to this point.

Evaluation Masters Booklet, p. 134

Name ______ Date ______

Cumulative Review, Chapters 1-15

1. Evaluate ab, if $a = 3$ and $b = 5$. (Lesson 1–2) — 1. 15
2. Simplify $|-5| + |3|$. (Lesson 2–1) — 2. 8
3. Find the perimeter of a rectangle with a length of 8 m and width of 3 m. (Lesson 3–6) — 3. 22 m
4. Find LCM of 16 and 24. (Lesson 4–7) — 4. 48
5. Solve $y - 4.7 = 8.3$. (Lesson 5–7) — 5. 13
6. Express $\frac{3}{8}$ as a decimal. (Lesson 6–1) — 6. 0.375
7. Solve $-5y - 12 = -72$. (Lesson 7–2) — 7. 12
8. Find the slope of the line that contains $A(3, 6)$ and $B(1, 1)$. (Lesson 8–8) — 8. $\frac{5}{2}$
9. A $39.95 radio is on sale for 25% off. Find the discount to the nearest cent. (Lesson 9–8) — 9. $9.99
10. Find the median of 65, 65, 66, 68, and 70. (Lesson 10–2) — 10. 66
11. Find the value C(7, 3). (Lesson 11–3) — 11. 35
12. Two dice are rolled. Find the probability that the sum will be greater than 5. (Lesson 11–5) — 12. $\frac{13}{18}$
13. Angles *A* and *B* are complementary. The measure of angle *A* is 37°. Find $m\angle B$. (Lesson 12–3) — 13. 53°
14. In $\triangle ABC$, $m\angle A = 70°$ and $m\angle B = 75°$. Find $m\angle C$. (Lesson 12–6) — 14. 35°
15. Find the area of the trapezoid with base (a) of 20 cm, base (b) of 12 cm, and height of 10 cm. (Lesson 13–2) — 15. 160 cm^2
16. Find the area of a circle with a radius of 9 in. Use $\pi \approx 3.14$. (Lesson 13–3) — 16. 254.34 in^2
17. Find the volume of a circular cone with a radius of 8 mm and a height of 15 mm. Use $\pi \approx 3.14$. (Lesson 13–9) — 17. 1004.8 mm^3
18. Find the best whole number estimate for $\sqrt{200}$. (Lesson 14–2) — 18. 14
19. Simply $\sqrt{88}$. (Lesson 14–4) — 19. $2\sqrt{22}$
20. Find the missing measure for the right triangle: a, 16 m; b, 18 m. Round to the nearest tenth. (Lesson 14–5) — 20. 24.1 m
21. Find the sum $(6a - 9c) + (2a + 4c)$. (Lesson 15–2) — 21. $8a - 5c$
22. Find the difference $(9m + 5) - (-3m + 8)$. (Lesson 15–3) — 22. $12m - 3$
23. Simplify $(-y^2)^7$. (Lesson 15–4) — 23. $-y^{14}$
24. Find the product $-3x(-5x + 3)$. (Lesson 15–5) — 24. $15x^2 - 9x$
25. Find the product $(x + 5)(x - 5)$. (Lesson 15–6) — 25. $x^2 - 25$

Evaluation Masters Booklet, p. 135

Name ______ Date ______

Cumulative Test, Chapters 1-15

1. Evaluate ab, if $a = 2$ and $b = 3$.
   A. 6 B. 23 C. 5 D. 8 — 1. A
2. Find the perimeter of a rectangle having length 6 m and width 5 m.
   A. 65 m B. 30 m C. 22 m D. 11 m — 2. C
3. Find the LCM of 18 and 32.
   A. 576 B. 288 C. 4 D. 2 — 3. B
4. Solve $y - 3.8 = 2.6$.
   A. 6.4 B. −1.2 C. −6.4 D. 1.2 — 4. A
5. Express $\frac{1}{8}$ as a decimal.
   A. $0.\overline{8}$ B. 1.8 C. 8.0 D. 0.125 — 5. D
6. Solve $-8x - 4 = -36$.
   A. −4 B. −5 C. 4 D. 5 — 6. C
7. Find the slope of the line that contains $A(2, 4)$ and $B(1, 2)$.
   A. $-\frac{1}{2}$ B. $\frac{1}{2}$ C. −2 D. 2 — 7. D
8. A $19.95 book is on sale for 20% off. Find the discount to the nearest cent.
   A. $19.75 B. $3.99 C. $15.96 D. $4.00 — 8. B
9. Find the value of P(6,3).
   A. 216 B. 18 C. 9 D. 120 — 9. D
10. Two dice are rolled. Find the probability that the sum will be 5.
    A. $\frac{1}{9}$ B. $\frac{1}{6}$ C. $\frac{5}{36}$ D. $\frac{1}{3}$ — 10. A
11. Angles *A* and *B* are complementary and $m\angle A = 40°$. Find $m\angle B$.
    A. 120° B. 40° C. 140° D. 50° — 11. D
12. In $\triangle ABC$, $m\angle A = 42°$ and $m\angle B = 65°$. Find $m\angle C$.
    A. 65° B. 107° C. 130° D. 73° — 12. D
13. Find the area of a circle with a radius of 6 inches. Use $\pi \approx 3.14$.
    A. 452.16 in^2 B. 37.68 in^2 C. 113.04 in^2 D. 18.84 in^2 — 13. C
14. Find the volume of a cone having a radius of 10 mm and a height of 12 mm. Use $\pi \approx 3.14$.
    A. 376.8 mm^3 B. 3768 mm^3 C. 1256 mm^3 D. 120 mm^3 — 14. C
15. Find the best whole number estimate for $\sqrt{123}$.
    A. 12 B. 62 C. 10 D. 11 — 15. D
16. Simplify $\sqrt{75}$. A. $5\sqrt{15}$ B. $5\sqrt{3}$ C. $3\sqrt{5}$ D. 37.5 — 16. B
17. Find the sum $(3a - 6b + c) + (2a + 6b - 4c)$.
    A. $6a - 4$ B. $5a + 5c$ C. $5a - 3c$ D. $5a + 12b$ — 17. C
18. Find the difference $(8m + 6) - (-2m - 4)$.
    A. $6m - 2$ B. $6m + 2$ C. $10m + 2$ D. $10m + 10$ — 18. D
19. Find the product $-3x(3x - 2)$.
    A. $-9x^2 + 6$ B. $-9x^2 - 6x$ C. $-9x^2 + 6x$ D. $-9x^2 - 6$ — 19. C
20. Find the product $(x + 3)(x + 3)$.
    A. $x^2 + 9$ B. $x + 9$ C. $x^2 + 3x + 6$ D. $x^2 + 6x + 9$ — 20. D

Mathematical Symbols

Symbol	Meaning
$\div$	divide
$\cdot$	times
$=$	is equal to
$-$	negative
$+$	positive
$\pm$	positive or negative
$\neq$	is not equal to
$>$	is greater than
$<$	is less than
$\ngtr$	is not greater than
$\nless$	is not less than
$\geq$	is greater than or equal to
$\leq$	is less than or equal to
$^\circ$	degrees
$\perp$	is perpendicular to
$\parallel$	is parallel to
$\approx$	is approximately equal to
$\cong$	is congruent to
$\sim$	is similar to
$\sqrt{}$	nonnegative square root
$\%$	percent
π	pi
$\overleftrightarrow{AB}$	line AB
$\overline{AB}$	line segment AB
$\overrightarrow{AB}$	ray AB
$\triangle ABC$	triangle ABC
$\angle ABC$	angle ABC
$m\,\overline{AB}$	measure of line segment AB
$m\angle ABC$	measure of angle ABC

Metric System

Prefixes

kilo-	hecto-	deka-	no prefix	deci-	centi-	milli-
thousands	hundreds	tens	ones	tenths	hundredths	thousandths

Length
1 centimeter (cm) = 10 millimeters (mm)
1 meter (m) = 100 centimeters
1 meter = 1000 millimeters
1 kilometer (km) = 1000 meters

Area
1 square centimeter (cm^2) = 100 square millimeters (mm^2)
1 square meter (m^2) = 10,000 square centimeters

Volume
1 cubic centimeter (cm^3) = 1000 cubic millimeters (mm^3)

Capacity
1 liter (L) = 1000 milliliters (mL)

Mass
1 gram (g) = 1000 milligrams (mg)
1 kilogram (kg) = 1000 grams

Time
1 minute (min) = 60 second (s)
1 hour (h) = 60 minutes
1 day (d) = 24 hours
1 year = 365 days

Formulas

$C = \pi d$ or $2\pi r$	circumference of a circle
$A = \ell w$	area of a rectangle
$A = bh$	area of a parallelogram
$A = \frac{1}{2}bh$	area of a triangle
$A = \pi \cdot r \cdot r$ or πr^2	area of a circle
$I = p \cdot r \cdot t$	interest
$d = r \cdot t$	distance
$A = \frac{1}{2}(a + b)$	area of a trapezoid
$V = Bh$	volume of a prism or cylinder
$V = \frac{1}{3}Bh$	volume of a pyramid or cone
$c^2 = a^2 + b^2$	Pythagorean Theorem
$C = \frac{5}{9}(F - 32)$	Fahrenheit to Celsius
$F = \frac{9}{5}C + 32$	Celsius to Fahrenheit

Trigonometric Ratios

Angle	sin	cos	tan	Angle	sin	cos	tan
0°	0.0000	1.0000	0.0000	45°	0.7071	0.7071	1.0000
1°	0.0175	0.9998	0.0175	46°	0.7193	0.6947	1.0355
2°	0.0349	0.9994	0.0349	47°	0.7314	0.6820	1.0724
3°	0.0523	0.9986	0.0524	48°	0.7431	0.6691	1.1106
4°	0.0698	0.9976	0.0699	49°	0.7547	0.6561	1.1504
5°	0.0872	0.9962	0.0875	50°	0.7660	0.6428	1.1918
6°	0.1045	0.9945	0.1051	51°	0.7771	0.6293	1.2349
7°	0.1219	0.9925	0.1228	52°	0.7880	0.6157	1.2799
8°	0.1392	0.9903	0.1405	53°	0.7986	0.6018	1.3270
9°	0.1564	0.9877	0.1584	54°	0.8090	0.5878	1.3764
10°	0.1736	0.9848	0.1763	55°	0.8192	0.5736	1.4281
11°	0.1908	0.9816	0.1944	56°	0.8290	0.5592	1.4826
12°	0.2079	0.9781	0.2126	57°	0.8387	0.5446	1.5399
13°	0.2250	0.9744	0.2309	58°	0.8480	0.5299	1.6003
14°	0.2419	0.9703	0.2493	59°	0.8572	0.5150	1.6643
15°	0.2588	0.9659	0.2679	60°	0.8660	0.5000	1.7321
16°	0.2756	0.9613	0.2867	61°	0.8746	0.4848	1.8040
17°	0.2924	0.9563	0.3057	62°	0.8829	0.4695	1.8807
18°	0.3090	0.9511	0.3249	63°	0.8910	0.4540	1.9626
19°	0.3256	0.9455	0.3443	64°	0.8988	0.4384	2.0503
20°	0.3420	0.9397	0.3640	65°	0.9063	0.4226	2.1445
21°	0.3584	0.9336	0.3839	66°	0.9135	0.4067	2.2460
22°	0.3746	0.9272	0.4040	67°	0.9205	0.3907	2.3559
23°	0.3907	0.9205	0.4245	68°	0.9272	0.3746	2.4751
24°	0.4067	0.9135	0.4452	69°	0.9336	0.3584	2.6051
25°	0.4226	0.9063	0.4663	70°	0.9397	0.3420	2.7475
26°	0.4384	0.8988	0.4877	71°	0.9455	0.3256	2.9042
27°	0.4540	0.8910	0.5095	72°	0.9511	0.3090	3.0777
28°	0.4695	0.8829	0.5317	73°	0.9563	0.2924	3.2709
29°	0.4848	0.8746	0.5543	74°	0.9613	0.2756	3.4874
30°	0.5000	0.8660	0.5774	75°	0.9659	0.2588	3.7321
31°	0.5150	0.8572	0.6009	76°	0.9703	0.2419	4.0108
32°	0.5299	0.8480	0.6249	77°	0.9744	0.2250	4.3315
33°	0.5446	0.8387	0.6494	78°	0.9781	0.2079	4.7046
34°	0.5592	0.8290	0.6745	79°	0.9816	0.1908	5.1446
35°	0.5736	0.8192	0.7002	80°	0.9848	0.1736	5.6713
36°	0.5878	0.8090	0.7265	81°	0.9877	0.1564	6.3138
37°	0.6018	0.7986	0.7536	82°	0.9903	0.1392	7.1154
38°	0.6157	0.7880	0.7813	83°	0.9925	0.1219	8.1443
39°	0.6293	0.7771	0.8098	84°	0.9945	0.1045	9.5144
40°	0.6428	0.7660	0.8391	85°	0.9962	0.0872	11.4301
41°	0.6561	0.7547	0.8693	86°	0.9976	0.0698	14.3007
42°	0.6691	0.7431	0.9004	87°	0.9986	0.0523	19.0811
43°	0.6820	0.7314	0.9325	88°	0.9994	0.0349	28.6363
44°	0.6947	0.7193	0.9657	89°	0.9998	0.0175	57.2900
45°	0.7071	0.7071	1.0000	90°	1.0000	0.0000	∞

Extra Practice

SET 1A *(Lessons 1-1, 1-2)* Evaluate expressions using order of operations.

Example

Evaluate $3x - (5y + c)$ if $x = 8, y = 2$, and $c = 6$.

$3x - (5y + c) = 3 \cdot 8 - (5 \cdot 2 + 6)$

$= 3 \cdot 8 - (10 + 6)$ Multiply inside parentheses first.

$= 24 - 16$ Substitute 24 for $3 \cdot 8$ and 16 for $10 + 6$.

$= 8$ Substitute 8 for $24 - 16$.

Evaluate each expression.

1. $7 + 8 + 12 \div 4$ 18
2. $12 + 20 \div 4 - 5$ 12
3. $36 \div 9 + 7 - 6$ 5
4. $(25 \cdot 3) + (10 \cdot 3)$ 105
5. $(40 \cdot 2) - (6 \cdot 11)$ 14
6. $40 \cdot (6 - 2)$ 160
7. $\frac{96 - 11}{11 + 6}$ 5
8. $\frac{84 + 12}{13 + 11}$ 4
9. $\frac{3 \cdot 3 + 3}{3 \cdot 3 - 3}$ 2

Evaluate each expression if $a = 4$, $b = 2$, and $c = 3$.

10. $ab - bc$ 2
11. $4a + b \cdot b$ 20
12. $9 \cdot c - ab$ 19
13. $4a - (b + c)$ 11
14. $4(a + b) - c$ 21
15. $6a + 6b$ 36
16. $5a + 6 - 8c$ 2
17. $36 - 12c$ 0
18. $7a - (2b + c)$ 21
19. $\frac{6(a + b)}{3c}$ 4
20. $\frac{4ac}{b}$ 24
21. $\frac{3(a + b)}{c - 1}$ 9

SET 1B *(Lessons 1-3, 1-4)* Use properties of whole numbers to simplify expressions.

Example

Simplify $p + 2(r + 8p)$.

$p + 2(r + 8p) = p + 2r + 2 \cdot 8p$ Distributive property

$= p + 2r + 16p$ Substitution property of equality

$= p + 16p + 2r$ Commutative property of addition

$= (1 + 16)p + 2r$ Distributive property

$= 17p + 2r$ Substitution property of equality

Simplify each expression. 9. $12a + 10b$ 12. $11a + 4y + 5f$

1. $3a + 7a$ $10a$
2. $9c + 7c$ $16c$
3. $13a + 5a$ $18a$
4. $21c + 10c$ $31c$
5. $30x + 20x$ $50x$
6. $24y + 16y$ $40y$
7. $10a + 30a - 7d$ $40a - 7d$
8. $16b + 17b + b$ $34b$
9. $5a + 10b + 7a$
10. $5(x + y) + 3y$ $5x + 8y$
11. $9(a + 2) + 14a$ $23a + 18$
12. $3a + 4y + 8a + 5f$
13. $3(b + 8) + 9b$ $12b + 24$
14. $2(3 + x) + 5(3 + 2y)$ $21 + 2x + 10y$
15. $5(r + s) + 4(2r + 3s)$ $13r + 17s$

SET 1C *(Lessons 1-5, 1-7, 1-10)* Solve equations and inequalities.

Example

Using inverse operations, solve $48 = 6x$.

$48 = 6x$

$48 \div 6 = x$ Write the related division sentence.

$8 = x$ Substitute 8 for $48 \div 6$.

Solve each equation from the given set of numbers.

1. $y - 4 = 7$; {10, 11, 12} 11
2. $x + 34 = 56$; {12, 22, 32} 22
3. $20 \div a = 5$; {4, 6, 8} 4
4. $39 = 3b$; {11, 12, 13} 11

Solve each equation by using inverse operations.

5. $4 + x = 16$ 12
6. $37 = z + 22$ 15
7. $8 = 12 - a$ 4
8. $r - 19 = 3$ 22
9. $4x = 24$ 6
10. $48b = 192$ 4
11. $99 = 3x$ 33
12. $p \div 7 = 4$ 28
13. $12 = \frac{x}{3}$ 36

State whether each inequality is true for the given value.

14. $2r - 12 \leq 5; r = 11$ F
15. $26 > 3n + 2; n = 3$ T
16. $6s - 18 > 0; s = 3$ F
17. $7 + 4b < 25; b = 4$ T

SET 1D *(Lessons 1-8, 1-9)* Translate verbal phrases into algebraic expressions.

Example

Write an algebraic expression for *four years older than Bart.*

Let y represent the number of years.

The words *years older* suggest addition.

The expression is $y + 4$.

Translate each phrase into an algebraic expression.

1. the sum of x and 5 $x + 5$
2. y multiplied by 12 $12y$
3. 58 less than s $s - 58$
4. twice a certain number $2n$
5. quotient of 63 and y $63 \div y$
6. the difference of x and 6 $x - 6$
7. 3 less pieces of pizza than Sandra $s - 3$
8. twice the distance that Pat ran $2p$
9. four more points than Ed $p + 4$
10. 5 times the cost of a pen $5c$

Translate each algebraic expression into a verbal phrase. See margin.

11. $x - 12$
12. $9s$
13. $5y - 2$
14. $4(m + 3)$
15. $\frac{a - 5}{3}$
16. $7 + \frac{c}{2}$
17. $9 + 2k$
18. $\frac{6}{5g}$

SET 2A (Lesson 2-1) Graph integers on a number line.

Example

Graph {-3, -1, 0, 4} on a number line.

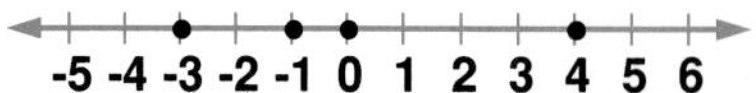

Name the coordinates of the points that are graphed.

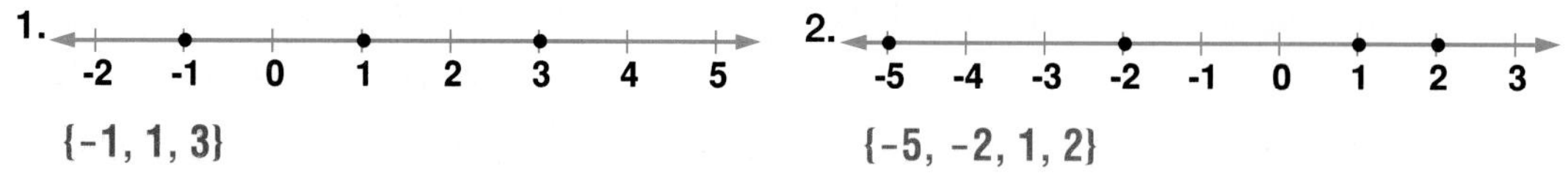

1. {-1, 1, 3}
2. {-5, -2, 1, 2}

Graph each set of numbers on a number line. See Solutions Manual.

3. {0, 4, 5}
4. {1, 7, 9}
5. {-1, 2, 4}
6. {-4, -3, -1}
7. {-3, -1, 1, 3}
8. {-2, 0, 4, 5}
9. {-1, -2, -6}
10. {5, -1, 3}
11. {-4, 0, -5}

SET 2B (Lesson 2-2) Compare and order integers.

Example

Use the integers graphed on the number line to write two inequalities.

Since -2 is to the left of 3, write $-2 < 3$.

Since 3 is to the right of -2, write $3 > -2$.

Use the integers graphed on each number line to write two inequalities.

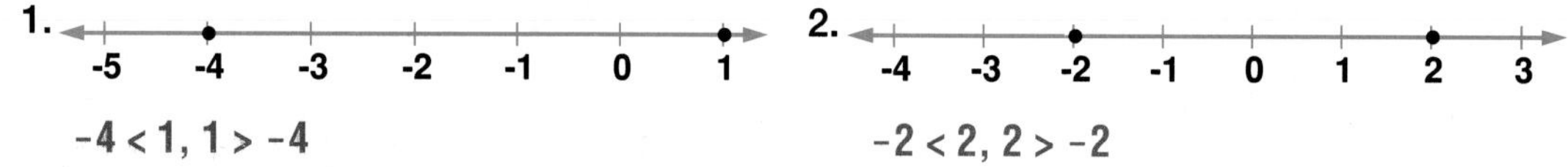

1. $-4 < 1$, $1 > -4$
2. $-2 < 2$, $2 > -2$

Replace each ■ with <, >, or = .

3. 12 ■ 4 $>$
4. -5 ■ 3 $<$
5. -9 ■ -7 $<$
6. |-5| ■ 2 $>$

Order the numbers in each set from least to greatest.

7. {8, -2, 0}
   {-2, 0, 8}
8. {3, -4, -1}
   {-4, -1, 3}
9. {-2, -9, 5, 2}
   {-9, -2, 2, 5}

SET 2C *(Lessons 2-3, 2-4, 2-5, 2-7, 2-8)* Compute with integers.

Example

Simplify the expression $32ab - (-11ab)$.

$32ab - (-11ab) = 32ab + 11ab$ Subtract $-11ab$ by adding its additive inverse.

$= (32 + 11)ab$ Use the distributive property.

$= 43ab$ Substitute 43 for 32 + 11.

Solve each equation. 2. 12 6. -180 7. -40

1. $x = 13 + (-12)$ 1
2. $y = -2 + (-4) + 18$
3. $-3 - 12 = p$ -15
4. $r = -8 \cdot 4$ -32
5. $11 - 3 = t$ 8
6. $w = (10)(-3)(6)$
7. $r = 1 + (-43) + 2$
8. $h = (-4)(-2)(0)$ 0
9. $v = \frac{-54}{9}$ -6
10. $(-4)(7)(3) = x$ -84
11. $z = \frac{78}{-2}$ -39
12. $\frac{-344}{-86} = b$ 4

Simplify each expression. 14. $-23m$ 17. $19ab$

13. $-3a + 7a$ $4a$
14. $9m + (-32m)$
15. $-2x - 8x$ $-10x$
16. $-14 \cdot (6x)$ $-84x$
17. $14ab + 5ab$
18. $(5y)(13z)$ $65yz$
19. $(-8a)(-b)$ $8ab$
20. $4(-5)(-2xy)$ $40xy$

Evaluate each expression if $a = 2$, $b = -5$, and $c = 14$.

21. $-18 + b$ -23
22. $a - b - c$ -7
23. $3ab$ -30
24. $-15b$ 75
25. $\frac{c}{-7}$ -2

SET 3A *(Lessons 3-1, 3-2, 3-3, 3-4)* Solve equations using the properties of equality.

Example

Solve $17 = \frac{d}{-9}$.

$17 = \frac{d}{-9}$

$17 \cdot (-9) = \frac{d}{-9} \cdot (-9)$ Multiply each side by -9.

$-153 = d$

Solve each equation.

1. $f + 14 = 19$ 5
2. $p + (-3) = 11$ 14
3. $y - 28 = -23$ 5
4. $-16 = -7 - r$ 9
5. $-13a = -91$ 7
6. $9b = -144$ -16
7. $5 + x = -14$ -19
8. $18 = -2y$ -9
9. $15 - (-4) = d$ 19
10. $\frac{a}{-4} = 7$ -28
11. $-19 = \frac{f}{5}$ -95
12. $4 = \frac{c}{-116}$ -464
13. $-12b = 144$ -12
14. $18 = t - (-4)$ 14
15. $14c = -154$ -11
16. $t - 25 = -13$ 12
17. $\frac{x}{-6} = 15$ -90
18. $\frac{b}{-120} = -5$ 600

SET 3B (Lessons 3-5, 3-6) Apply equation-solving techniques to solve problems involving formulas.

Example

Solve $I = \frac{V}{R}$, if $R = 13$ ohms and $I = 50$ amperes.

$I = \frac{V}{R}$

$50 = \frac{V}{13}$ Replace I with 50 and R with 13.

$50 \times 13 = \frac{V}{13} \times 13$ Multiply each side by 13.

$650 = V$ The voltage is 650 volts.

Solve. Use the given formula.

1. $s = g + c$, if $s = 199$ and $g = 174$ **25**
2. $f = t - h$, if $t = 108$ and $h = 12$ **96**
3. $d = rt$, if $d = 130$ and $t = 5$ **26**
4. $s = g + c$, if $s = 135$ and $c = 13$ **122**
5. $I = \frac{V}{R}$, if $V = 210$ and $R = 7$ **30**
6. $I = \frac{V}{R}$, if $I = 33$ and $R = 12$ **396**
7. $d = rt$, if $d = 1200$ and $t = 24$ **50**
8. $f = t - h$, if $f = 89$ and $t = 126$ **37**
9. $s = g + c$, if $g = 167$ and $c = 23$ **190**
10. $d = rt$, if $d = 275$ and $r = 25$ **11**

SET 3C (Lessons 3-7, 3-8) Solve inequalities.

Example

Solve $-6d \leq 42$.

$-6d \leq 42$

$\frac{-6d}{-6} \geq \frac{42}{-6}$ Divide each side by -6 and reverse the order symbol.

$d \geq -7$

Solve each inequality.

1. $w + 8 < 16$ **$w < 8$**
2. $r - 4 > -7$ **$r > -3$**
3. $a + (-3) \geq 9$ **$a \geq 12$**
4. $x - (-5) > 14$ **$x > 9$**
5. $10 \leq -5 + b$ **$15 \leq b$**
6. $-6z < 18$ **$z > -3$**
7. $-16 \geq -8b$ **$2 \leq b$**
8. $-46 \leq 23a$ **$-2 \leq a$**
9. $y - 11 < -3$ **$y < 8$**
10. $\frac{s}{-4} < 12$ **$s > -48$**
11. $-9 \geq \frac{k}{3}$ **$-27 \geq k$**
12. $\frac{r}{-13} \leq -30$ **$r \geq 390$**
13. $a + (-27) > 3$ **$a > 30$**
14. $24 < 6d$ **$4 < d$**
15. $47a \leq 423$ **$a \leq 9$**
16. $\frac{s}{3} < 19$ **$s < 57$**
17. $r - (-3) > -16$ **$r > -19$**
18. $\frac{n}{-5} \leq 116$ **$n \geq -580$**
19. $3 - c \geq 18$ **$-15 \geq c$**
20. $-4m < -120$ **$m > 30$**
21. $4 + d < -8$ **$d < -12$**

SET 4A *(Lessons 4-1, 4-4)* Find factors of numbers and monomials.

Example

Factor $30a^2b$ completely.

$$30a^2b = 2 \cdot 15 \cdot a^2 \cdot b$$

$$= 2 \cdot 3 \cdot 5 \cdot a \cdot a \cdot b$$

Factor each number or monomial completely. Factors are shown with exponents for your convenience.

1. 5 5
2. 16 2^4
3. 22 $2 \cdot 11$
4. 35 $5 \cdot 7$
5. 92 $2^2 \cdot 23$
6. 27 3^3
7. 34 $2 \cdot 17$
8. 42 $2 \cdot 3 \cdot 7$
9. 50 $2 \cdot 5^2$
10. 56 $2^3 \cdot 7$
11. $6cd^2$
12. $21x$ $3 \cdot 7 \cdot x$
13. $19abc$
14. $14x^3y$
15. $9a^3$ $3^2 \cdot a^3$
16. $18r^2s^3$
17. $74m^2k$
18. 112 $2^4 \cdot 7$
19. $44p^3q^3$
20. 273

11. $2 \cdot 3 \cdot c \cdot d^2$ 13. $19 \cdot a \cdot b \cdot c$ 14. $2 \cdot 7 \cdot x^3 \cdot y$

16. $2 \cdot 3^2 \cdot r^2 \cdot s^3$ 17. $2 \cdot 37 \cdot m^2 \cdot k$ 19. $2^2 \cdot 11 \cdot p^3 \cdot q^3$ 20. $3 \cdot 7 \cdot 13$

SET 4B *(Lessons 4-5, 4-6, 4-7)* Use prime factorization to find the GCF and LCM.

Example

Use prime factorization to find the LCM for 14 and 20.

$14 = 2 \cdot 7$

$20 = 2 \cdot 2 \cdot 5$

The greatest power of 2 is 2^2.

The greatest power of 5 is 5.

The greatest power of 7 is 7. The LCM is $2^2 \cdot 5 \cdot 7$ or 140.

Find the GCF for each set of numbers or expressions.

1. 12, 18 6
2. 14, 63 7
3. 112, 144 16
4. $15k$, $35k^2$ $5k$
5. $33r$, 121 11
6. $6ab$, $12ab$, $14ab$ $2ab$
7. $4xy$, $16x$ $4x$
8. $-7z$, $49z^2$ $7z$
9. $18ab$, $9a$, $45ab^2$ $9a$
10. 8, $-28k$ 4
11. $-13z$, $39yz$, $52y$ 13
12. $-16w$, $-28w^3$ $4w$

Find the LCM for each set of numbers.

13. 3, 12 12
14. 4, 14 28
15. 6, 21 42
16. 7, 9 63
17. $20k$, $30k^2$ $60k^2$
18. $8cd$, $36cd$ $72cd$
19. 6, 8, $12x$ $24x$
20. $4r$, 14, $35r^2$ $140r^2$
21. $4pq$, $6p^2$ $12p^2q$
22. $5c$, 35 $35c$
23. $7ab$, $11a$ $77ab$
24. $12x^3$, $16xy$ $48x^3y$

SET 4C *(Lesson 4-8)* Use the LCM to write equivalent fractions.

Example

Which is larger, $\frac{4}{15}$ or $\frac{3}{10}$?

Write $\frac{4}{15}$ and $\frac{3}{10}$ as equivalent fractions with the same denominator.

The LCM of 15 and 10 is $2 \cdot 3 \cdot 5$ or 30.

Find equivalent fractions with the LCM as the denominator.

$\frac{4}{15} = \frac{■}{30} \rightarrow \frac{4}{15} = \frac{8}{30}$ $\quad \frac{3}{10} = \frac{■}{30} \rightarrow \frac{3}{10} = \frac{9}{30}$

Since $\frac{9}{30} > \frac{8}{30}$, then $\frac{3}{10} > \frac{4}{15}$.

Replace each ● with <, >, or = to make a true statement.

1. $\frac{1}{3}$ ● $\frac{3}{8}$ <
2. $\frac{4}{6}$ ● $\frac{9}{12}$ <
3. $\frac{5}{12}$ ● $\frac{2}{5}$ >
4. $\frac{1}{4}$ ● $\frac{2}{9}$ >
5. $\frac{7}{8}$ ● $\frac{10}{12}$ >
6. $\frac{7}{9}$ ● $\frac{3}{4}$ >
7. $\frac{5}{6}$ ● $\frac{15}{18}$ =
8. $\frac{3}{11}$ ● $\frac{2}{5}$ <
9. $\frac{5}{6}$ ● $\frac{20}{24}$ =
10. $\frac{5}{16}$ ● $\frac{1}{3}$ <
11. $\frac{4}{5}$ ● $\frac{9}{12}$ >
12. $\frac{13}{15}$ ● $\frac{15}{18}$ >

SET 4D *(Lessons 4-2, 4-9, 4-10)* Multiply and divide powers.

Example

Simplify $\frac{(-a)^5}{(-a)^2}$.

$$\frac{(-a)^5}{(-a)^2} = (-a)^{5-2}$$
$$= (-a)^3$$
$$= -a^3$$

Simplify. Assume no denominator equals zero.

1. $7^3 \cdot 7^2$ 7^5
2. $n^5 \cdot n^2$ n^7
3. $(3x^3)(6x)$ $18x^4$
4. $(-4x^5y)(8x^2)$ $-32x^7y$
5. $(ab^3)(8a^2b^2)$ $8a^3b^5$
6. $x^3(xy^5)$ x^4y^5
7. $\frac{a^7}{a^6}$ a
8. $\frac{c^7}{c^3}$ c^4
9. $\frac{(-4)^4}{(-4)^3}$ -4
10. $\frac{c^{50}}{c^{47}}$ c^3
11. $\frac{m^9}{m^9}$ 1
12. $(ab^2)(4a^2b)$ $4a^3b^3$
13. $\frac{(-2)^6}{(-2)^4}$ $(-2)^2$ or 4
14. $\frac{n^{19}}{n^3}$ n^{16}
15. $(-3r^2)(-4r)$ $12r^3$
16. $k^3(m^2k^3)$ m^2k^6

SET 5A *(Lessons 5-1, 5-2, 5-3, 5-4, 5-5, 5-6)* Add and subtract rational numbers.

Example

Solve $t = 4\frac{7}{8} - 7\frac{1}{3}$.

$t = 4\frac{7}{8} - 7\frac{1}{3}$

$= 4\frac{21}{24} - 7\frac{8}{24}$ The LCD of 8 and 3 is 24.

$= 4\frac{21}{24} + \left(-7\frac{8}{24}\right)$ Subtract $7\frac{8}{24}$ by adding its inverse, $-7\frac{8}{24}$.

$= 4\frac{21}{24} + \left(-6\frac{32}{24}\right)$ Rename $-7\frac{8}{24}$ as $-6\frac{32}{24}$.

$= -2\frac{11}{24}$

Estimate each sum or difference to the nearest whole number.

1. $7.4 + 5.86$ **13**
2. $3.55 - 0.82$ **3**
3. $2.7 + 3.1 + 4.6$ **11**
4. $11.5 - 2.7$ **9**

Solve each equation. Write each solution in simplest form.

5. $\frac{7}{3} + \frac{2}{3} = a$ **3**
6. $\frac{5}{12} - \frac{2}{12} = x$ **$\frac{1}{4}$**
7. $h = \frac{15}{8} + \frac{-4}{8}$ **$\frac{11}{8}$**
8. $48.6 - 3.04 = p$ **45.56**
9. $-13.8 - 22.3 = s$ **-36.1**
10. $x = -5.8 + 16.12$ **10.32**
11. $3\frac{3}{5} + \frac{7}{10} = s$ **$4\frac{3}{10}$**
12. $b = -4\frac{1}{6} + 2\frac{1}{8}$ **$-2\frac{1}{24}$**
13. $t = -33.3 + 9.51$ **-23.79**

SET 5B *(Lesson 5-7)* Solve equations and inequalities with rational numbers.

Example

Solve the inequality $n - 13.53 > 5.48$.

$n - 13.53 > 5.48$

$n - 13.53 + 13.53 > 5.48 + 13.53$ Add 13.53 to each side.

$n > 19.01$

Any number greater than 19.01 is a solution.

Solve each equation or inequality. Write the solutions in simplest form.

1. $a - 5.6 = 4.9$ **10.5**
2. $8.2 + b = 2.4$ **-5.8**
3. $p + 7 = 1.1$ **-5.9**
4. $c + 1\frac{3}{5} = 2$ **$\frac{2}{5}$**
5. $\frac{3}{8} + z = 4\frac{1}{4}$ **$3\frac{7}{8}$**
6. $g - \frac{4}{9} = -\frac{1}{3}$ **$\frac{1}{9}$**
7. $x - 1\frac{3}{5} = -5\frac{1}{10}$ **$-3\frac{1}{2}$**
8. $s + \frac{1}{3} = 6\frac{1}{5}$ **$5\frac{13}{15}$**
9. $x + 3.1 = 1.6$ **-1.5**
10. $a + 4.2 > 6.9$ **$a > 2.7$**
11. $1.3 + d \leq 0.5$ **$d \leq -0.8$**
12. $4.8 - y < 9$ **$y < -4.2$**
13. $p + \frac{3}{4} > 5\frac{1}{4}$ **$p > 4\frac{1}{2}$**
14. $s - \frac{1}{9} > -4\frac{2}{3}$ **$s > -4\frac{5}{9}$**
15. $n + 4\frac{7}{8} \geq 6\frac{1}{6}$ **$n \geq 1\frac{7}{24}$**

SET 5C *(Lesson 5-9)* Find terms of an arithmetic sequence.

Example

Use the expression $a + (n - 1)d$ to find the eighth term in the arithmetic sequence 5, 9, 13, 17, ...

$a + (n - 1)d = 5 + (8 - 1)4$	The first term: $a = 5$
$= 5 + (7)4$	The number of terms: $n = 8$
$= 5 + 28$	The common difference: $d = 4$
$= 33$	The eighth term is 33.

Write the next three terms of each sequence. 2. 63, 127, 255 4. 5.9, 7.1, 8.3

1. 3, 6, 9, . . . 12, 15, 18
2. 1, 3, 7, 15, 31, . . .
3. 10, 5, 0, -5, . . .
4. 1.1, 2.3, 3.5, 4.7, . . .
5. 1, 4, 9, 16, . . . 25, 36, 49
6. -6, -5, -3, 0, 4, . . .
7. 2.4, 4.6, 6.8, 9.0, . . .
8. 7, 4, 1, -2, . . . -5, -8, -11
9. 109, 120, 131, 142, . . .

7. 11.2, 13.4, 15.6 3. -10, -15, -20 6. 9, 15, 22 9. 153, 164, 175

Find the twelfth term in each arithmetic sequence.

10. 5, 7, 9, 11, . . . 27
11. 0, 8, 16, 24, . . . 88
12. 4, 1, -2, -5, . . . -29
13. 199, 187, 175, 163, . . . 67
14. -12, -10, -8, -6, . . . 10
15. 48, 39, 30, 21, . . . -51

SET 5D *(Lesson 5-10)* Convert within the customary system.

Example

9 lb 3 oz -2 lb 15 oz	➧	8 19 ~~9~~ lb ~~3~~ oz -2 lb 15 oz 6 lb 4 oz

Since 15 oz is greater than 3 oz, rename 9 lb 3 oz as 8 lb 19 oz. Then subtract.

Add or subtract.

1. 8 ft 9 in. + 3 ft 5 in. = 12 ft 2 in.
2. 11 gal 3 qt − 10 gal 1 qt = 1 gal 2 qt
3. 4 lb 9 oz + 5 lb 8 oz = 10 lb 1 oz
4. 8 ft 2 in. − 4 ft 7 in. = 3 ft 7 in.
5. 2 gal 2 qt + 9 gal 2 qt = 12 gal
6. 12 lb − 1 lb 7 oz = 10 lb 9 oz
7. 1 yd 2 ft + 8 yd 1 ft = 10 yd
8. 10 ft 1 in. − 5 ft 10 in. = 4 ft 3 in.

SET 6A *(Lessons 6-1, 6-11, 6-12)* Compare and order rational numbers expressed as fractions and decimals.

Example

Replace the ● with <, >, or = to make a true sentence.

$-\frac{5}{8}$ ● -0.7

-0.625 ● -0.7 Express $-\frac{5}{8}$ as a decimal.

Since $-0.625 > -0.7$, $-\frac{5}{8} > -0.7$.

Replace each ● with <, >, or = to make a true sentence.

1. 9.3 ● 9.33 <
2. -4.2 ● -5.1 >
3. 1.05 ● -1.1 >
4. -18.2 ● -18.9 >
5. $\frac{8}{9}$ ● $\frac{13}{15}$ >
6. $\frac{2}{3}$ ● $\frac{5}{8}$ >
7. $-\frac{1}{4}$ ● $-\frac{2}{7}$ >
8. $-\frac{3}{4}$ ● $-\frac{9}{12}$ =
9. $8\frac{3}{5}$ ● $8\frac{2}{3}$ <
10. $2\frac{3}{8}$ ● 2.4 <
11. -7.5 ● $-7\frac{1}{3}$ <
12. $-13\frac{5}{8}$ ● -13.7 >
13. 645 ● 6.45×10^2 =
14. -3.05 ● $-3\frac{1}{20}$ =
15. $-\frac{5}{12}$ ● $-\frac{8}{18}$ >
16. $9\frac{2}{3}$ ● 9.6×10^{-1} >

SET 6B *(Lessons 6-2, 6-3, 6-4, 6-5, 6-6, 6-7)* Multiply and divide rational numbers.

Example

Solve $x = 6\frac{2}{3} \div \left(-1\frac{2}{3}\right)$.

$x = 6\frac{2}{3} \div \left(-1\frac{2}{3}\right)$

$x = \frac{20}{3} \div \left(-\frac{5}{3}\right)$ Rewrite the mixed numbers as fractions.

$x = \frac{20}{3} \cdot \left(-\frac{3}{5}\right)$ Dividing by $-\frac{5}{3}$ is the same as multiplying by $-\frac{3}{5}$.

$x = \frac{\overset{4}{\cancel{20}}}{\underset{1}{\cancel{3}}} \cdot \left(-\frac{\overset{1}{\cancel{3}}}{\underset{1}{\cancel{5}}}\right)$

$x = -4$

Solve each equation. Write each solution in simplest form. 6. -10.07 7. -1.82

1. $y = \frac{1}{4} \cdot \frac{8}{9}$ $\frac{2}{9}$
2. $t = -\frac{3}{4}\left(\frac{2}{5}\right)$ $-\frac{3}{10}$
3. $b = -3\left(-5\frac{1}{3}\right)$ 16
4. $a = \left(-\frac{3}{7}\right)^2$ $\frac{9}{49}$
5. $z = (1.4)(3)$ 4.2
6. $c = (-1.9)(5.3)$
7. $p = (0.7)(-2.6)$
8. $g = (-0.05)(-8.02)$ 0.401
9. $x = \frac{8}{9} \div \frac{2}{3}$ $\frac{4}{3}$
10. $d = -2\frac{1}{5} \div \frac{4}{5}$ $-\frac{11}{4}$
11. $r = 6 \div \left(-\frac{1}{3}\right)$ -18
12. $w = -7\frac{1}{2} \div \left(-1\frac{2}{3}\right)$ $\frac{9}{2}$
13. $h = 1.44 \div 8$ 0.18
14. $y = 22.5 \div 2.5$ 9
15. $m = -9.54 \div (-5.3)$ 1.8
16. $k = -0.027 \div 0.45$ -0.06

SET 6C *(Lessons 6-8, 6-13)* Solve equations and inequalities with rational numbers.

Example

Solve $\frac{a}{-3.2} < -2.6$.

$\frac{a}{-3.2} < -2.6$

$(-3.2)\frac{a}{-3.2} > (-3.2)(-2.6)$ Multiply each side by -3.2. Remember to reverse the order symbol.

$a > 8.32$ Any number greater than 8.32 is a solution.

Solve each equation or inequality. Check your solution.

1. $3a = 2.1$ **0.7**
2. $-\frac{1}{2}n = 3$ **-6**
3. $\frac{x}{1.5} = -6.2$ **-9.3**
4. $\frac{3}{5}y = -1\frac{1}{10}$ **$-1\frac{5}{6}$**
5. $\frac{n}{3} > -2.4$ **$n > -7.2$**
6. $-\frac{2}{3}a \leq \frac{1}{6}$ **$a \geq -\frac{1}{4}$**
7. $\frac{1}{3}b \leq 0.45$ **$b \leq 1.35$**
8. $-3.5k = 0.28$ **0.08**
9. $\frac{n}{1.6} \geq -4.3$ **$n \geq -6.88$**
10. $\frac{5}{8}x = -\frac{3}{4}$ **$-1\frac{1}{5}$**
11. $-\frac{2}{3}m \geq -7$ **$m \leq 10\frac{1}{2}$**
12. $-0.33d < -8.25$ **$d > 25$**
13. $-10\frac{1}{2}r \leq 1\frac{3}{4}$ **$r \geq \frac{1}{6}$**
14. $-5.5t > -0.11$ **$t < 0.02$**
15. $\frac{5}{6}c = -2\frac{1}{9}$ **$-2\frac{8}{15}$**
16. $9y > 3\frac{3}{5}$ **$y > \frac{2}{5}$**

SET 6D *(Lesson 6-10)* Find terms of a geometric sequence.

Example

Use the expression $ar^{(n-1)}$ to find the eighth term of the sequence 64, 32, 16, 8, . . .

The first term: $a = 64$

The common ratio: $r = \frac{1}{2}$

The number of terms: $n = 8$

$$ar^{(n-1)} = 64 \cdot \left(\frac{1}{2}\right)^{(8-1)}$$
$$= 64 \cdot \left(\frac{1}{2}\right)^{7}$$
$$= 64 \cdot \frac{1^7}{2^7}$$
$$= 64 \cdot \frac{1}{128}$$
$$= \frac{1}{2}$$

The eighth term is $\frac{1}{2}$.

Write the next three terms of each sequence.

1. 3, 6, 12, 24, . . . **48, 96, 192**
2. -2, 6, -18, 54, . . . **-162, 486, -1458**
3. 9, 3, 1, $\frac{1}{3}$, . . . **$\frac{1}{9}, \frac{1}{27}, \frac{1}{81}$**
4. 2500, 500, 100, 20, . . . **$4, \frac{4}{5}, \frac{4}{25}$**
5. $\frac{1}{2}$, -2, 8, -32, . . . **128, -512, 2048**
6. 144, 72, 36, 18, . . . **$9, 4\frac{1}{2}, 2\frac{1}{4}$**

Use the expression $ar^{(n-1)}$ to find the seventh term of each sequence.

7. 1, 4, 16, 64, . . . **4096**
8. 3, -9, 27, -81, . . . **2187**
9. 729, 243, 81, 27, . . . **1**
10. 32, 16, 8, 4, . . . **$\frac{1}{2}$**
11. 96, -48, 24, -12, . . . **$1\frac{1}{2}$**
12. $\frac{1}{8}, \frac{1}{4}, \frac{1}{2}$, 1, . . . **8**

SET 7A (Lessons 7-2, 7-3, 7-4, 7-7) Write and solve two-step equations and problems.

Example

Solve $3x + 7 = -2 + 8x$.

$3x + 7 = -2 + 8x.$

$3x - 8x + 7 = -2 + 8x - 8x$ Subtract $8x$ from each side.

$-5x + 7 = -2$

$-5x + 7 - 7 = -2 - 7$ Subtract 7 from each side.

$-5x = -9$

$\frac{-5x}{-5} = \frac{-9}{-5}$ Divide each side by -5.

$x = \frac{9}{5}$

Solve each equation.

1. $4y + 9 = 13$ **1**
2. $5s - 7 = -23$ **-6**
3. $-3 = 18 - x$ **21**
4. $\frac{z}{4} + 17 = 9$ **-32**
5. $-4 = \frac{d + 5}{9}$ **-41**
6. $\frac{x - 7}{-6} = 4$ **-17**
7. $9x - 3 = 4x + 12$ **3**
8. $17d = 8d - 3$ **$-\frac{1}{3}$**
9. $a + 11 = 21 - a$ **5**
10. $13y + 11 = -5y + 35$ **$1\frac{1}{3}$**
11. $4b = -b - 85$ **-17**
12. $30c + 14 = 19c - 8$ **-2**
13. $3x + 1 = 4x - 11$ **12**
14. $11x - 18 = 3x + 6$ **3**
15. $-5 - x = 3x + 5$ **$-\frac{5}{2}$**

SET 7B (Lessons 7-5, 7-6) Solve multi-step equations and inequalities.

Example

Solve $y - 23 < -8 + 4y$.

$y - 23 < -8 + 4y$

$y - 4y - 23 < -8 + 4y - 4y$ Subtract $4y$ from each side.

$-3y - 23 < -8$

$-3y - 23 + 23 < -8 + 23$ Add 23 to each side.

$-3y < 15$

$\frac{-3y}{-3} > \frac{15}{-3}$ Divide each side by -3 and reverse the order symbol.

$y > -5$

Solve each equation or inequality.

1. $3(b + 1) = 4b - 1$ **4**
2. $-5(1 - x) = 3x + 2$ **$3\frac{1}{2}$**
3. $11(c - 2) = 3(c + 6)$ **5**
4. $\frac{2}{3}n + 8 = \frac{1}{3}n - 1$ **-27**
5. $3(s + 1) - 8 = 5(s - 3)$ **5**
6. $2(2r + 5) + 1 = 5 - 2(3 - r)$ **-6**
7. $3k - 8 > 16$ **$k > 8$**
8. $-4a + 7 \leq 13$ **$a \geq -1.5$**
9. $6a + 9 < -4a + 29$ **$a < 2$**
10. $9q + 3 \leq 7q - 25$ **$q \leq -14$**
11. $-2(f + 8) > -4$ **$f < -6$**
12. $-13 \leq \frac{d}{11} - 9$ **$-44 \leq d$**

SET 7C *(Lesson 7-8)* Convert within the metric system.

Example

1200 cm = ■ km

Smaller units to larger units means fewer units.

First, divide by 100.	Next, divide by 1000.	
1200 ÷ 100 = 12	12 ÷ 1000 = 0.012	
1200 cm = 12 m	12 m = 0.012 km	So, 1200 cm = 0.012 km.

Complete.

1. 8 km = ■ m 8000
2. 16 g = ■ kg 0.016
3. 56 L = ■ mL 56,000
4. 4300 mg = ■ g 4.3
5. 2.5 L = ■ mL 2500
6. 55 cm = ■ m 0.55
7. 0.2 km = ■ cm 20,000
8. 6700 mL = ■ L 6.7
9. 4800 cm = ■ m 48
10. 31 g = ■ kg 0.031
11. 0.5 L = ■ mL 500
12. 36,000 mg = ■ kg 0.036
13. 9.4 kg = ■ g 9400
14. 43,000 cm = ■ km 0.43
15. 970 mL = ■ L 0.97
16. 0.8 km = ■ mm 800,000
17. 7.9 m = ■ km 0.0079
18. 98 cm = ■ mm 980

SET 8A (Lessons 8-1, 8-2) Graph the solution of equations and inequalities on a number line.

Example

Solve $-4r + 5 < 13$ and graph the solution.

$-4r + 5 < 13$

$-4r + 5 - 5 < 13 - 5$ Subtract 5 from each side.

$-4r < 8$

$\frac{-4r}{-4} > \frac{8}{-4}$ Divide each side by -4.

$r > -2$

Solve each equation and graph the solution. See Solutions Manual.

1. $3x + 5 = 2$
2. $4a - 1 = 11$
3. $-3 + b = 5$
4. $2x - 4 = 3x + 1$
5. $\frac{c}{-4} = -1$
6. $-1.5g = 6$

Solve each inequality and graph the solution. See Solutions Manual.

7. $a - 4 < -2$
8. $3d + 1 > 7$
9. $3.5r \geq 14$
10. $2z + \frac{1}{4} \geq \frac{3}{4}$
11. $3c - 1 \leq 4c + 2$
12. $-\frac{1}{2}t < -2$

SET 8B (Lessons 8-3, 8-4, 8-5, 8-6, 8-11) Graph equations and inequalities in the coordinate plane.

Example

Graph $y < 3x + 4$.

Find four solutions for the equation $y = 3x + 4$. Then graph the line. Remember: Since this line is not part of the solution, use a dashed line.

The graph of $y < 3x + 4$ is the region *below* the boundary line. Shade this region.

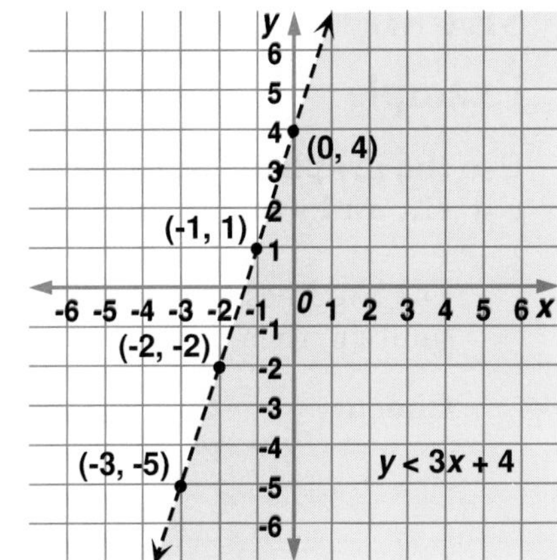

Graph each equation. See Solutions Manual.

1. $y = 3x + 2$
2. $y = -\frac{1}{3}x$
3. $y = -2x - 5$
4. $y = -x$
5. $x + y = 2$
6. $x - y = 1$

Graph each inequality. See Solutions Manual.

7. $y < x - 1$
8. $y > 2x + 2$
9. $y \geq -3$
10. $y < -3x + 5$
11. $y \leq \frac{1}{2}x - 7$
12. $y \geq -x - 6$

SET 8C *(Lessons 8-8, 8-9)* Use slope and intercepts to graph equations.

Example

Find the coordinates of the points of the x-intercept and the y-intercept for $y = 2x + 4$.

Find the y-intercept.
Let $x = 0$ and solve for y.

$y = 2(0) + 4$
$y = 4$

The y-intercept is 4.
The ordered pair is (0,4).

Find the x-intercept.
Let $y = 0$ and solve for x.

$0 = 2x + 4$
$0 - 4 = 2x + 4 - 4$
$-4 = 2x$
$-2 = x$

The x-intercept is -2.
The ordered pair is (-2,0).

Find the slope of the line that contains each pair of points.

1. A(3,2), B(5,8) **3**
2. R(-1,1), S(2,7) **2**
3. X(2,9), Y(-7,6) $\frac{1}{3}$
4. L(-1,-3), M(-3,1) **-2**
5. C(7,-3), D(-1,1) $-\frac{1}{2}$
6. G($\frac{1}{2}$,-1), H($-\frac{1}{2}$,5) **-6**

Graph each equation using the x-intercept and the y-intercept. **See Solutions Manual.**

7. $y = x + 3$
8. $y = 2x - 8$
9. $y = -5x - 10$
10. $y = -7x - 2$
11. $y = \frac{1}{3}x - 4$
12. $y = 6 - 3x$

SET 8D *(Lesson 8-10)* Solve systems of linear equations by graphing.

Example

Use the graph at the right to solve $y = -2x$ and $y = x + 3$.

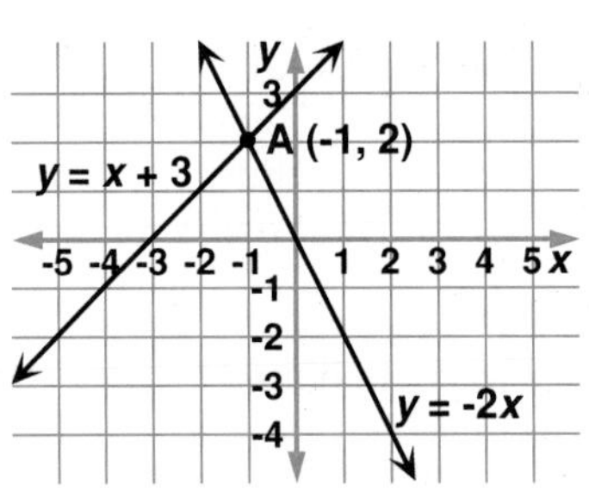

The two lines intersect at A(-1,2). The solution, then, is the ordered pair (-1,2).

Check:

$y = -2x$	$y = x + 3$
$2 = -2(-1)$	$2 = -1 + 3$
$2 = 2$ ✓	$2 = 2$ ✓

Use a graph to solve each system of equations. **See Solutions Manual for graphs.**

1. $y = 2x - 1$
   $y = x + 1$ **(2,3)**
2. $y = x - 3$
   $y = 2x$ **(-3,-6)**
3. $y = -x + 2$
   $y = 5x - 10$ **(2,0)**
4. $y = \frac{1}{2}x$
   $y = 3x + 5$ **(-2,-1)**
5. $y = -4x + 15$
   $y = x$ **(3,3)**
6. $x + y = 5$
   $2x - y = -8$ **(-1,6)**
7. $y = x + 7$
   $y = -3x - 9$
   (-4,3)
8. $y = -5x$
   $y = 2x + 14$
   (-2,10)
9. $-2x - y = 5$
   $3x - y = 0$
   (-1,-3)

SET 9A (Lessons 9-1, 9-5) Write equivalent expressions for ratios, decimals, and percents.

Example

Express $\frac{7}{9}$ as a percent. Round to the nearest tenth.

7 ÷ 9 = 0.777777

$\frac{7}{9} \approx 0.777 \rightarrow 77.7\%$

Express each ratio as a fraction in simplest form.

1. 5 out of 80 $\frac{1}{16}$
2. 18 to 3 $\frac{6}{1}$
3. 36 to 144 $\frac{1}{4}$
4. 108:9 $\frac{12}{1}$

Express each decimal or fraction as a percent. Round to the nearest tenth.

5. 0.07 7%
6. 0.305 30.5%
7. 1.98 198%
8. 0.003 0.3%
9. $\frac{2}{5}$ 40%
10. $\frac{3}{8}$ 37.5%
11. $\frac{7}{4}$ 175%
12. $\frac{11}{12}$ 91.7%

Express each percent as a fraction in simplest form.

13. 42% $\frac{21}{50}$
14. 5% $\frac{1}{20}$
15. $87\frac{1}{2}\%$ $\frac{7}{8}$
16. 112% $\frac{28}{25}$

SET 9B (Lessons 9-2, 9-3, 9-4) Use ratios and proportions to solve problems.

Example

What number is 75% of 185?

$\frac{P}{B} = \frac{r}{100} \rightarrow \frac{P}{185} = \frac{75}{100}$ Replace *B* with 185 and *r* with 75.

$P \cdot 100 = 75 \cdot 185$ Find the cross products.

75 × 185 ÷ 100 = 138.75

$P = 138.75$ 138.75 is 75% of 185.

Solve each proportion.

1. $\frac{7}{8} = \frac{a}{64}$ 56
2. $\frac{3}{5} = \frac{m}{65}$ 39
3. $\frac{9}{4} = \frac{r}{36}$ 81
4. $\frac{1.8}{5.4} = \frac{14.4}{p}$ 43.2

Write a proportion that could be used to solve for each variable. Then solve.

5. 12 ounces at $1.40
   18 ounces at *x* dollars
   $\frac{12}{1.40} = \frac{18}{x}$; $2.10
6. 16 by 20 inches reduced to *x* by 8 inches $\frac{16}{20} = \frac{x}{8}$; 6.4 inches
7. $\frac{1}{4}$-inch represents 1 mile
   6 inches represents *y* miles
   $\frac{\frac{1}{4}}{1} = \frac{6}{y}$; 24 miles

Use a proportion to solve each problem.

8. What is 30% of 270? 81
9. Find 80% of 72. 57.6
10. 18 is what percent of 90? 20%
11. 60 is what percent of 240? 25%

SET 9C *(Lessons 9-6, 9-7)* Solve equations involving percents.

Example

17 is what percent of 68?

17 = R · 68 — Write in $P = R \cdot B$ form.

$17 = 68R$ — Solve for R.

$\frac{17}{68} = \frac{68R}{68}$ — Divide each side by 68.

17 ÷ 68 = 0.25

$0.25 = R$

$25\% = R$

Solve.

1. 192 is what percent of 240? 80%
2. Find 5% of $95.00. $4.75
3. 50 is 40% of what number? 125
4. 57 is 60% of what number? 95
5. Find 18% of 230. 41.4
6. 120 is what percent of 160? 75%
7. What is 20% of $52.00? $10.40
8. $630 is 35% of how many dollars? $1800
9. 9 is 1% of what number? 900
10. 96 is what percent of 600? 16%

SET 9D *(Lessons 9-8, 9-10)* Solve problems involving percents.

Example

Find the percent of change from $150 to $162.

$162 - 150 = 12$ — Find the amount of increase.

$\frac{12}{150} = \frac{r}{100}$ — Write the percent proportion.

$12 \cdot 100 = 150r$ — Find the cross products.

$1200 = 150r$ — Divide each side by 150.

1200 ÷ 150 = 8

$r = 8$ The percent of increase is 8%.

Find the discount or interest to the nearest cent.

1. $10 hat, 35% off $3.50
2. $38 jeans, 20% off $7.60
3. $185 bike, 25% off $46.25
4. $5000 at 6% for 6 months $150
5. $450 at $5\frac{3}{4}$% for 8 months $17.25
6. $8.99 CD, 15% off $1.35

Find the percent of change in the prices below. Round to the nearest whole percent.

7. old: $25.00 new: $23.00 8%
8. old: $62.00 new: $78.50 27%
9. old: $118.00 new: $99.98 15%
10. old: $34.80 new: $56.60 63%
11. old: $1900.00 new: $1590.00 16%
12. old: $95.99 new: $105.25 10%

SET 10A *(Lesson 10-1)* Gather and record data.

Example

What percent of the sample have fewer than 2 pets?

Number of Pets	Tally	Frequency
0	𝍸 I	6
1	𝍸 IIII	9
2	𝍸 𝍸 I	11
3	𝍸	5
4 or more	II	2

6 + 9 or 15 people have fewer than 2 pets.
The number of people surveyed is 33.

$\frac{15}{33} = 0.4545\ldots$

About 45% of the sample have fewer than 2 pets.

1. See Solutions Manual.

The number of magazine subscriptions sold by each student is given below.

21	50	29	42
36	23	38	51
28	42	22	19
55	34	31	39
22	28	30	35
37	37	29	44
46	52	24	28

1. Make a frequency table for the set of data.
2. What is the lowest number of subscriptions sold? 19
3. What is the highest number of subscriptions sold? 55
4. What is the frequency of selling exactly 28 subscriptions? 3
5. Each student who sells 50 or more subscriptions receives a prize. How many students receive a prize? 4 students
6. What percent of the students sold over 40 subscriptions? 29%
7. Make a histogram of the set of data. See Solutions Manual.

SET 10B *(Lessons 10-2, 10-4)* Describe data using measures of central tendency and measures of variation.

Example

Given the set of data 4, 9, 6, 1, 4, 3, 8, 3, 4, 5, find the interquartile range.

First, order the scores. 1, 3, 3, 4, 4, 4, 5, 6, 8, 9

The median is $(4 + 4) \div 2 = 4$.
The upper quartile is 6. The lower quartile is 3.
The interquartile range is $6 - 3$ or 3.

Use the set of temperature data below to answer each of the following.

65	53	68	45
59	59	67	62
52	64	62	68
42	64	71	59

1. What is the mode? 59
2. What is the mean? 60
3. What is the median? 62
4. What is the range of temperatures? 29
5. What are the upper and lower quartiles? 66; 56
6. What is the interquartile range? 10

SET 10C (Lessons 10-3, 10-5, 10-6) Display data using stem-and-leaf, box-and-whisker, and scatter plots.

Example

Make a stem-and-leaf plot of these test score data: 88, 79, 93, 75, 59, 72, 71, 99, 78, 83, 81, 83, 79, 94, 79, 52. Then, determine the range.

5	2 9
6	
7	1 2 5 8 9 9 9
8	1 3 3 8
9	3 4 9

The range is 99 − 52 or 47.

1., 4. See Solutions Manual.

The ages of people visiting the zoo are listed at the right.

10	32	33	16	17	55
52	9	8	11	22	67
28	30	37	12	5	3
3	7	47	28	41	6
26	14	2	30	82	52

1. Construct a stem-and-leaf plot.
2. What is the age range? 80
3. What age range seemed most represented? 0-9
4. Construct a box-and-whisker plot.
5. Are there any outliers? If so, what are they? yes; 82

Zoo admission prices are $4.00 for adults (over 18), $2.00 for students (ages 5-18), and free for children under age 5. See Solutions Manual.

6. Draw a scatter plot of the ages listed above and their admission prices.
7. What type of relationship, positive, negative, or none, is shown by the scatter plot? positive

---

SET 10D (Lessons 10-8, 10-9) Use statistics to predict and recognize misleading statistics.

Example

Use the sample data on bus fares to predict how many people in a city of 100,000 would be willing to pay up to $1.50 per ride.

Amount Willing to Pay for Bus Ride	
up to $0.75	50
up to $1.00	160
up to $1.50	220
up to $2.00	70

The sample size is 500.
50 + 160 + 220 or 430 people are willing to pay up to $1.50.

$\frac{430}{500} \cdot 100{,}000 = 86{,}000$ 86,000 people would be willing to pay up to $1.50.

Use the bus fare data above to answer each of the following.

1. How many people in a city of 600,000 would be willing to pay up to $1.00 per bus ride? 252,000 people
2. How many people in a city of 1,500,000 would be willing to pay up to $1.50 per bus ride? 1,290,000 people

SET 11A *(Lessons 11-1, 11-2)* Count outcomes.

Example

A quiz has three true-false questions and two multiple-choice questions. If each multiple-choice question has four choices, how many outcomes are possible?

Number of outcomes for each true-false question: 2
Number of outcomes for each multiple-choice question: 4

3 true-false questions		2 multiple-choice questions	
$\overbrace{2 \times 2 \times 2}$	$\times$	$\overbrace{4 \times 4} = 128$	There are 128 possible outcomes.

Find the number of possible outcomes.

1. Each spinner is spun once. 12 outcomes

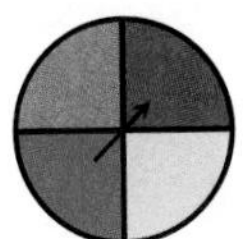
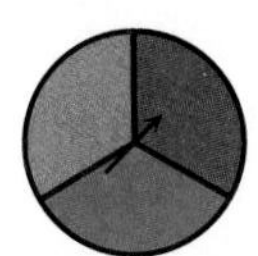

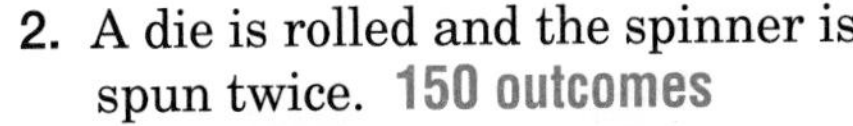

2. A die is rolled and the spinner is spun twice. 150 outcomes

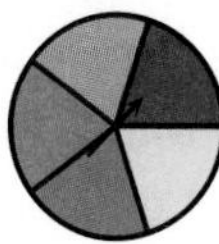

3. Marilyn has a choice of toast, muffin, or bagel with a choice of tea or coffee. 6 outcomes
4. A quiz has six multiple-choice questions. Each question is answered with a, b, c, or d.
5. Glen has 5 shirts, 3 pairs of pants, and 2 belts. Any combination of outfits matches.
6. A quiz has two true-false questions and three multiple-choice questions. Each multiple-choice question has five choices. 500 outcomes

---

4. 4096 outcomes 5. 30 outcomes

SET 11B *(Lesson 11-3)* Find permutations and combinations.

Example

How many three letter "words" can be made from the letters W, S, O, and R?

Order is important, so you want to find the number of *permutations* of 4 things taken 3 at a time.

$P(4,3) = 4 \cdot 3 \cdot 2 = 24$ There are 24 three-letter words that can be made from W, S, O, and R.

Find each value.

1. $7!$ 5040
2. $\frac{6!3!}{5!0!}$ 36
3. $P(5,2)$ 20
4. $C(7,3)$ 35
5. $C(9,6)$ 84

Answer each question.

6. How many ways can you select 5 magazines off a shelf of 8 magazines? 56 ways
7. How many 4-place numbers can be formed with the digits 2, 3, 4, and 5 if no digit is used more than once in a number? 24 numbers
8. How many ways can 3 students be selected from a committee of 9 students to attend a school board meeting? 84 ways
9. How many ways can first, second, and third place prizes be awarded to twelve different entries in a baking contest? 1320 ways

SET 11C (Lessons 11-4, 11-6, 11-7, 11-8) Find probabilities of simple events and of compound events.

Example

A card is drawn from the cards at the right. Find P(5 or odd).

These events are not mutually exclusive.

Therefore, P(5 or odd) = P(5) + P(odd) − P(5 and odd).

1 2 3 4 5 6

$= \frac{1}{6} + \frac{3}{6} - \frac{1}{6} \cdot \frac{3}{6}$

$= \frac{4}{6} - \frac{3}{36}$

$= \frac{24}{36} - \frac{3}{36}$ Rename $\frac{4}{6}$ as $\frac{24}{36}$.

$= \frac{21}{36}$ or $\frac{7}{12}$

In one bag, there are 4 blue marbles, 5 red marbles, and 3 green marbles. In another bag, there are 2 white marbles and 6 yellow marbles.

1. You select one marble at random from the second bag. Find P(white). $\frac{2}{8}$ or $\frac{1}{4}$
2. You select one marble at random from the first bag. Find P(blue or green). $\frac{7}{12}$
3. You select one marble at random from each bag. Find P(red and white). $\frac{5}{48}$
4. You select one marble at random from each bag. Find P(red and black). 0
5. You select two marbles from the first bag without replacing the first one. Find the probability of selecting a red marble and then a blue marble. $\frac{20}{132}$ or $\frac{5}{33}$

SET 12A (Lesson 12-1) Use some basic terms of geometry.

Example

Use the figure at the right to find $m\angle PQR$.

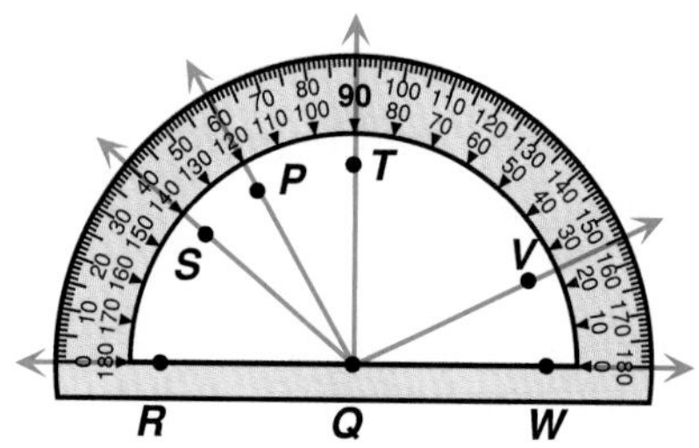

$m\angle PQR = 120°$ Use the scale that begins with 0 at $\overrightarrow{QR}$.

Use the figure above to find each measure. Classify each angle as *acute, right,* or *obtuse.*

1. $m\angle VQW$ 25; acute
2. $m\angle TQW$ 90°; right
3. $m\angle SQW$ 140°; obtuse
4. $m\angle SQR$ 40°; acute
5. $m\angle VQR$ 155° obtuse

Use the figure at the right to name an example of each term. Sample answers given for Exercises 6-8.

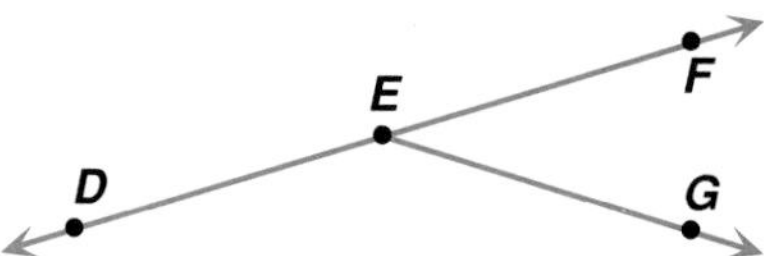

6. point *E*
7. line segment $\overline{DF}$
8. ray $\overrightarrow{EG}$
9. acute angle $\angle FEG$
10. line $\overleftrightarrow{DF}$
11. obtuse angle $\angle DEG$

SET 12B *(Lesson 12-2)* Construct a circle graph.

Example

An angle of a circle graph represents 20%. Find the measure of the angle. Draw the angle on a circle graph.

$\frac{20}{100} \times 360 = 72$ Rename 20% as $\frac{20}{100}$.

There are 360° in a circle.

The measure of the angle is 72°.

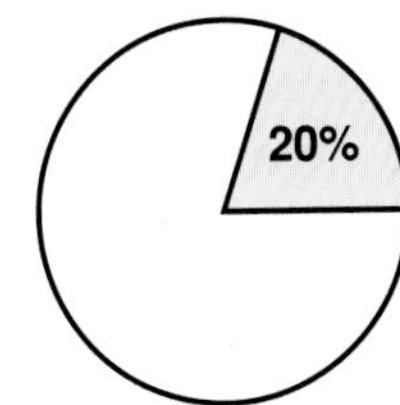

Make a circle graph to display each set of data. See Solutions Manual.

1.

Davis Family Monthly Expenditures	
Housing	$800
Taxes	$600
Food	$350
Clothing	$200
Insurance	$150
Savings	$100

2.

Items Donated for Food Drive	
Canned Goods	169
Pasta	86
Cereal	70
Peanut Butter	42
Condiments	18

SET 12C *(Lessons 12-3, 12-4)* Identify the relationships of intersecting and parallel lines.

Example

In the diagram at the right, ℓ is parallel to m. The measure of $\angle 2$ is 38°. Find $m\angle 7$.

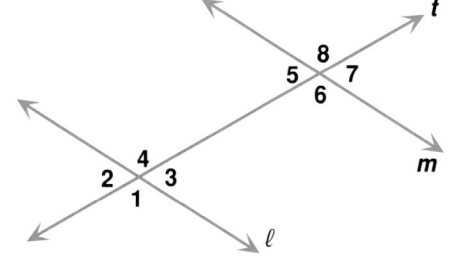

$\angle 2$ and $\angle 7$ are alternate exterior angles.

$m\angle 2 = m\angle 7$ Corresponding angles are congruent.

$m\angle 7 = 38°$

The measure of $\angle 7$ is 38°.

Angles C and D are complementary. Find $m\angle C$ when $m\angle D$ has each measure.

1. 60° **30°**
2. 75° **15°**
3. 28° **62°**
4. 5° **85°**

Angles X and Y are supplementary. Find $m\angle X$ when $m\angle Y$ has each measure.

5. 140° **40°**
6. 45° **135°**
7. 95° **85°**
8. 9° **171°**

Refer to the diagram in the Example above. If the measure of $\angle 2$ is 38°, find the measure of each angle below.

9. $\angle 1$ **142°**
10. $\angle 3$ **38°**
11. $\angle 4$ **142°**
12. $\angle 5$ **38°**
13. $\angle 6$ **142°**
14. $\angle 8$ **142°**

SET 12D *(Lessons 12-5, 12-6, 12-8, 12-9, 12-10)* Identify properties of congruent and similar triangles.

Example

Find the value of x.

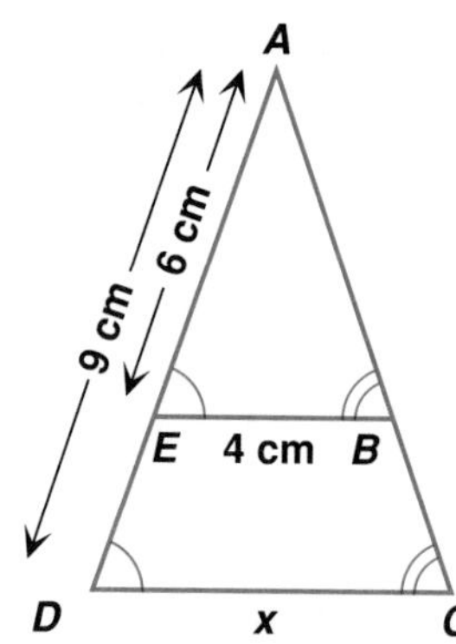

$\angle A \cong \angle A$, $\angle D \cong \angle E$, $\angle B \cong \angle C$
So, $\triangle AEB \cong \triangle ADC$ because their corresponding angles are congruent.

$\frac{m\overline{AE}}{m\overline{AD}} = \frac{m\overline{EB}}{m\overline{DC}}$ Corresponding sides of similar triangles are congruent.

$\frac{6}{9} = \frac{4}{x}$

$6 \cdot x = 9 \cdot 4$ Cross multiply.

$6x = 36$

$x = 6$ Divide each side by 6.

If $\triangle JKL \cong \triangle DGW$, name the part congruent to each angle or segment given.

1. $\angle K$ $\angle G$
2. $\overline{WG}$ $\overline{LK}$
3. $\angle D$ $\angle J$
4. $\overline{KL}$ $\overline{GW}$
5. $\overline{DG}$ $\overline{JK}$

Solve.

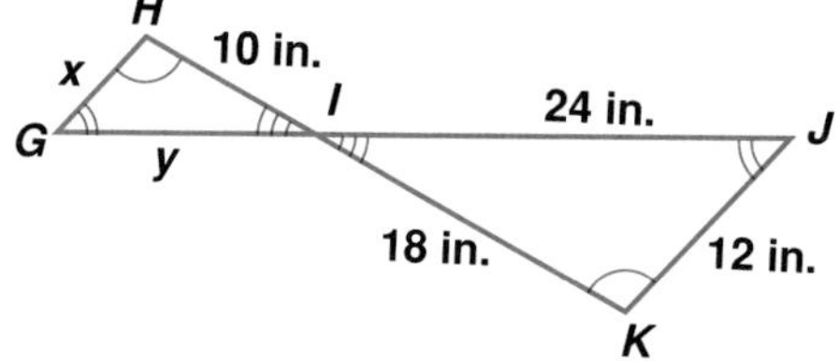

6. Find the value of x. $6\frac{2}{3}$ in.
7. Find the value of y. $13\frac{1}{3}$ in.

SET 12E *(Lessons 12-11, 12-12)* Classify and draw polygons.

Example

Find the sum of the measures of the angles of a heptagon.

$n = 7$ The number of sides is 7.

$(n - 2)180 = (7 - 2)180$ Replace n with 7.

$= 5 \cdot 180$

$= 900$ The sum of the measures of the angles of a heptagon is 900°.

Classify each quadrilateral.

1. 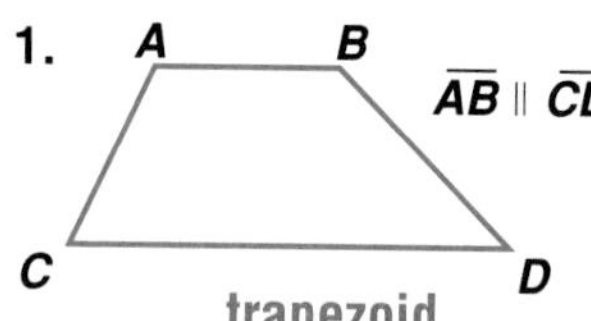

trapezoid

2. 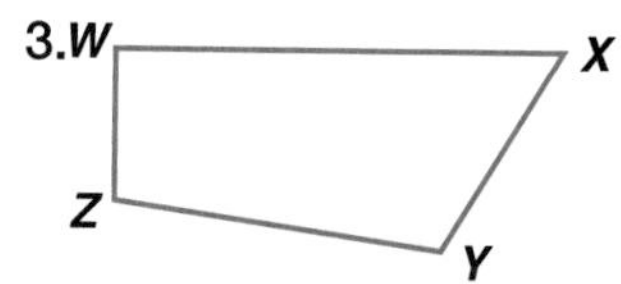

rhombus

3. W X Z Y
quadrilateral

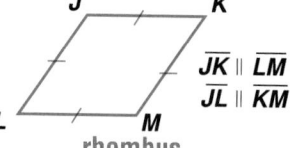

Classify each polygon. Then find the sum of the measures of the angles of each polygon.

4. G F H
triangle; 180°

5. 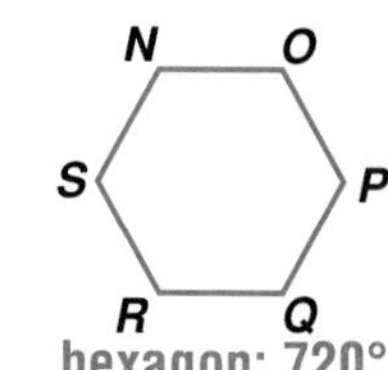

hexagon; 720°

6. 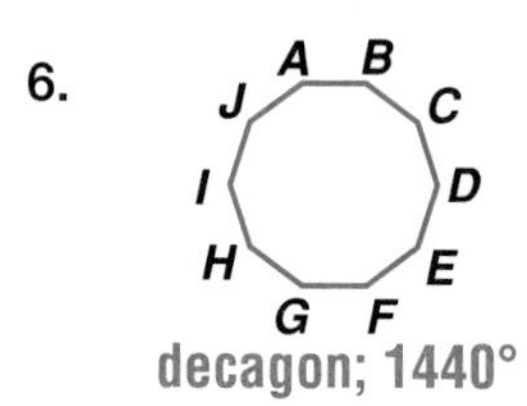

decagon; 1440°

SET 13A *(Lessons 13-1, 13-2, 13-3)* Find the area of polygons and circles.

Example

Find the area of a circle that has a diameter of 10 inches. Round your answer to the nearest whole number.

$A = \pi r^2$

$A = \pi \cdot 5^2$ The radius, r, is one-half the diameter, or 5 inches.

$A \approx 78.5$ The area is about 79 square inches.

Find the area of each region shown or described below. Round to the nearest whole number.

1\. 2. 3.

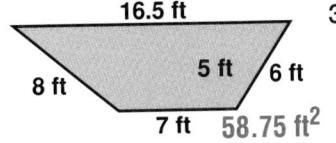

201 mm²

4. triangle: base, 6 cm; height, 11 cm **33 cm²**
5. parallelogram: base, 4.5 in.; height, 3 in. **13.5 in.²**
6. circle: radius, 7 ft **154 ft²**
7. circle: diameter, 15.4 m **186 m²**

SET 13B *(Lessons 13-4, 13-5, 13-6)* Find the surface area of prisms, cylinders, pyramids, and cones.

Example

Find the surface area of the circular cone shown at the right. Round to the nearest hundredth.

Area of base: Area of curved surface:

$A = \pi r^2$ $A = \pi rs$

$A = \pi \cdot 3^2$ $A = \pi \cdot 3 \cdot 5$

$A \approx 28.27$ $A \approx 47.12$

total surface area = (area of base) + (area of curved surface)

= 28.27 + 47.12

= 75.39 The surface area is about 75.39 ft².

Find the surface area for each figure below. Round to the nearest hundredth.

1\. **248 in²**

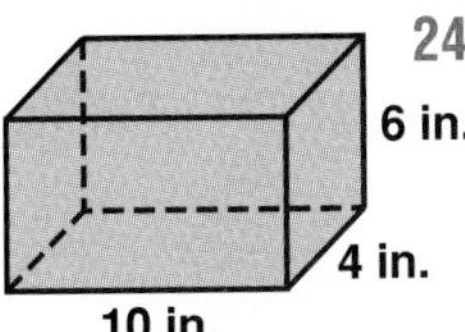

2\. **600 ft²**

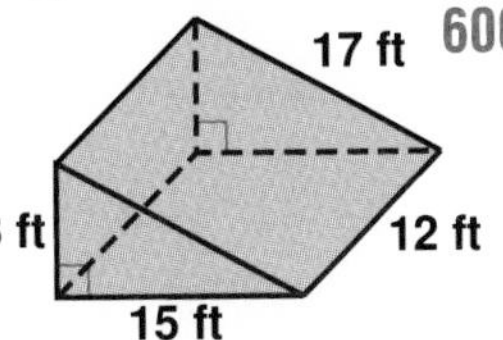

3\. **267.04 cm²**

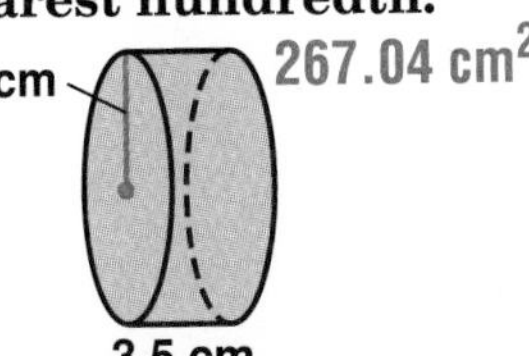

4\.

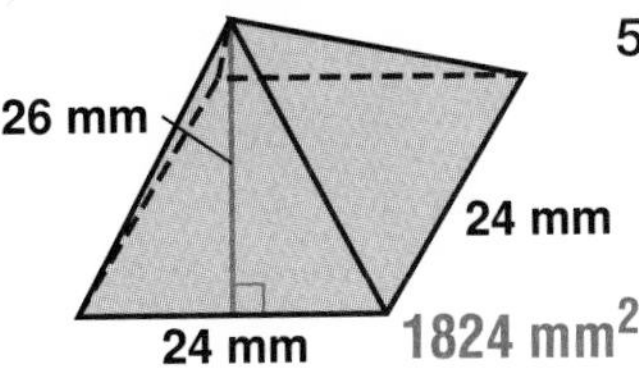

1824 mm²

5\.

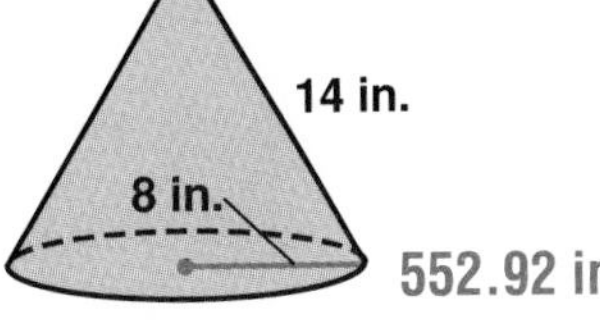

552.92 in²

6\.

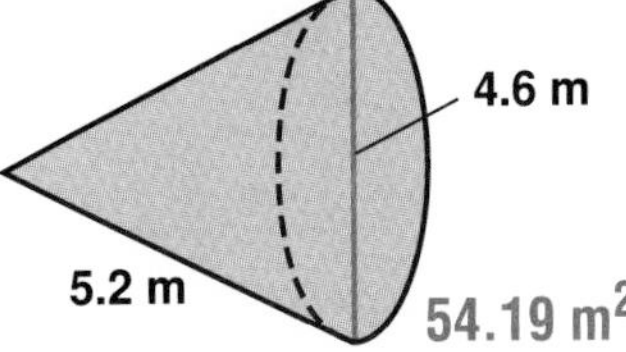

54.19 m²

SET 13C *(Lessons 13-7, 13-8, 13-9)* Find the volume of prisms, cylinders, pyramids, and cones.

Example

Find the volume of the pyramid.

$V = \frac{1}{3}Bh$ Formula for volume of a pyramid

$V = \frac{1}{3}\ell wh$ Replace B with ℓw.

$V = \frac{1}{3} \cdot 4 \cdot 3 \cdot 7$ Replace ℓ with 4, w with 3, and h with 7.

$V = 28$

The volume is 28 cm^3.

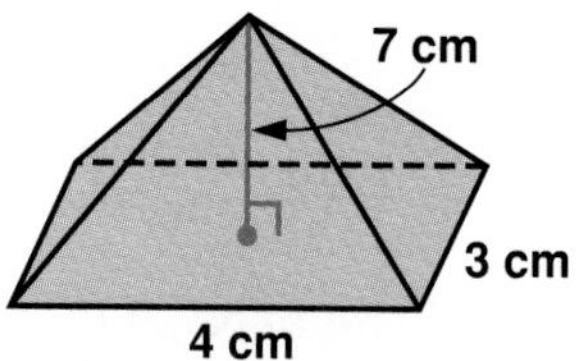

Find the volume of each figure below. Round to the nearest hundredth.

1.
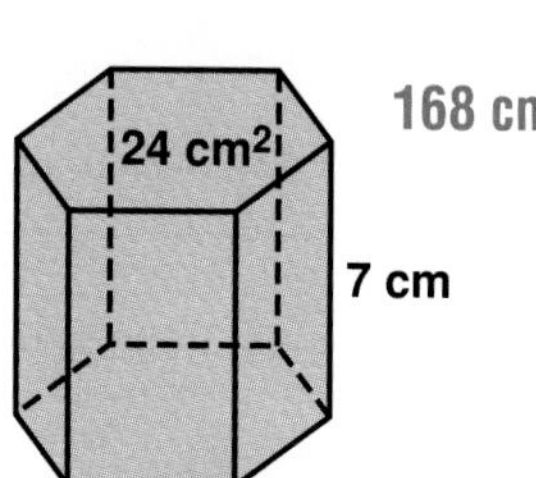

168 cm^3

2.
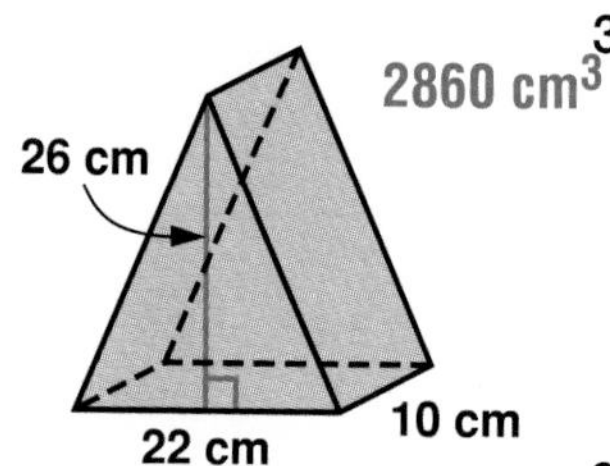

2860 cm^3

3.
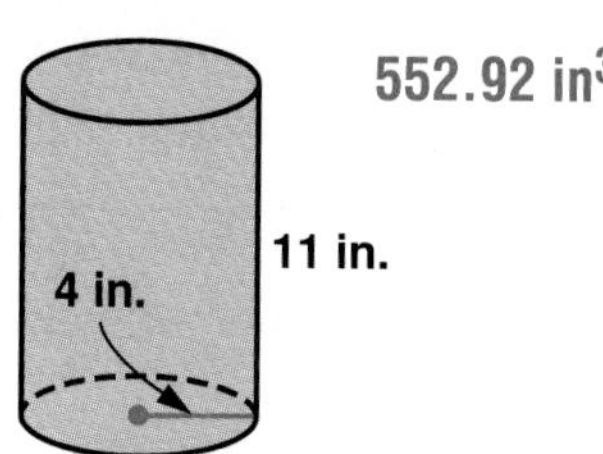

552.92 in^3

4.
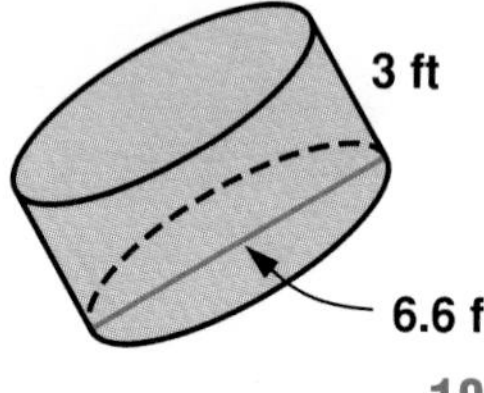

102.64 ft^3

5.
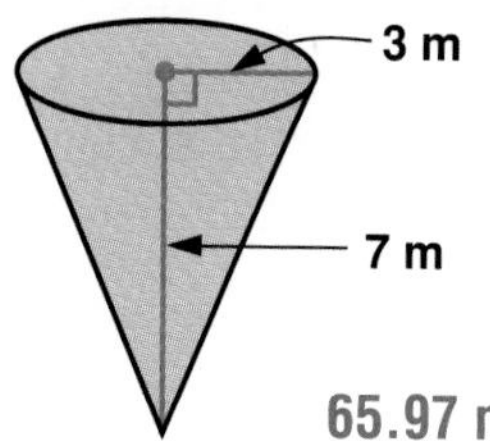

65.97 m^3

6.
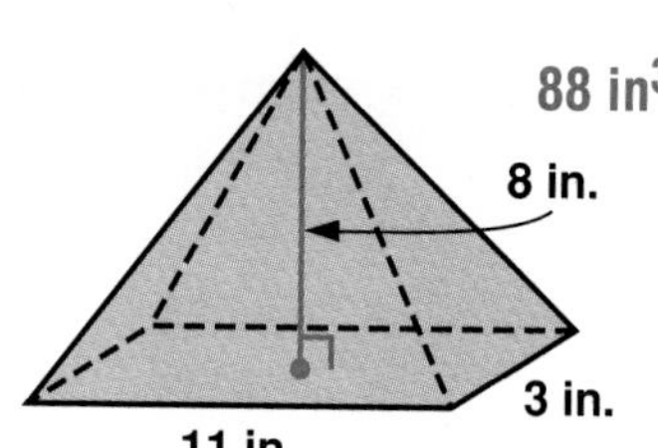

88 in^3

SET 14A *(Lessons 14-1, 14-2)* Find square roots and squares.

Example

What is the best integer estimate for $-\sqrt{38.4}$?

$-49 < -38.4 < -36$

$-7^2 < -38.4 < -6^2$

$-7 < -\sqrt{38.4} < -6$

Check:

38.4 [√x] [+/−] -6.196773

Since -38.4 is closer to -36 than -49, the best integer estimate is -6. This checks with the result on the calculator.

Find the square of each number.

1. 4 **16**
2. 11 **121**
3. 15 **225**
4. 24 **576**
5. 30 **900**
6. 35 **1225**

Find each square root. If the number is not a perfect square, find the best integer estimate for each square root. Then check your estimate using a calculator.

7. $\sqrt{36}$ **6**
8. $\sqrt{81}$ **9**
9. $\sqrt{196}$ **14**
10. $-\sqrt{289}$ **-17**
11. $\sqrt{21}$ **5**
12. $-\sqrt{85}$ **-9**
13. $\sqrt{7.3}$ **3**
14. $-\sqrt{484}$ **-22**
15. $-\sqrt{1600}$ **-40**
16. $\sqrt{1.99}$ **1**
17. $-\sqrt{62}$ **-8**
18. $\sqrt{74.1}$ **9**
19. $\sqrt{625}$ **25**
20. $-\sqrt{88.8}$ **-9**
21. $\sqrt{8100}$ **90**

SET 14B *(Lesson 14-4)* Solve equations by finding square roots.

Example

Solve $a^2 = 62$. Round your answer to the nearest tenth.

$a^2 = 62$

$a = \sqrt{62}$ or $a = -\sqrt{62}$ Find the square root of each side.

$a \approx 7.9$ or $a \approx -7.9$

Solve each equation. Round decimal answers to the nearest tenth.

1. $x^2 = 16$ **±4**
2. $y^2 = 36$ **±6**
3. $c^2 = 144$ **±12**
4. $k^2 = 225$ **±15**
5. $m^2 = 324$ **±18**
6. $d^2 = 441$ **±21**
7. $r^2 = 2500$ **±50**
8. $p^2 = 34$ **±5.8**
9. $b^2 = 89$ **±9.4**
10. $h^2 = 55$ **±7.4**
11. $j^2 = 119$ **±10.9**
12. $n^2 = 120$ **±11.0**
13. $t^2 = 37$ **±6.1**
14. $q^2 = 361$ **±19**
15. $s^2 = 167$ **±12.9**
16. $a^2 = 111$ **±10.5**

SET 14C *(Lessons 14-5, 14-6)* Use the Pythagorean Theorem.

Example

Find the length of the third side of the right triangle.

$c^2 = a^2 + b^2$ Pythagorean Theorem

$34^2 = 16^2 + b^2$ Replace c with 34 and a with 16.

$1156 = 256 + b^2$

$1156 - 256 = 256 - 256 + b^2$ Subtract 256 from each side.

$\sqrt{900} = b^2$

$\sqrt{900} = b$ or $-\sqrt{900} = b$

$30 = b$ or $-30 = b$

The length of the side is 30 meters.

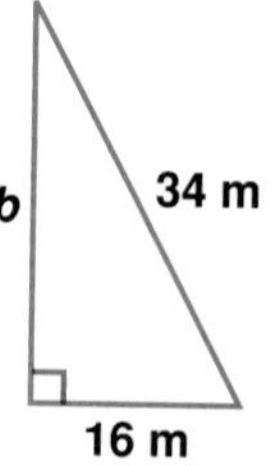

Find the missing measure for each right triangle. Round decimal answers to the nearest tenth.

1. 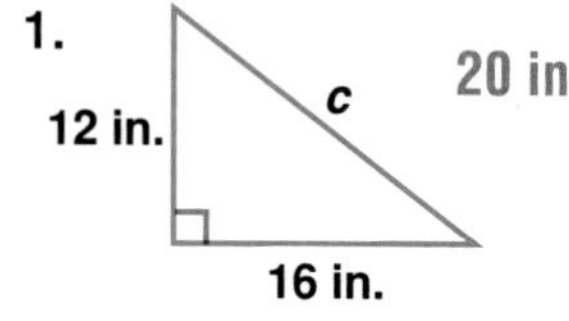

20 in.

2. 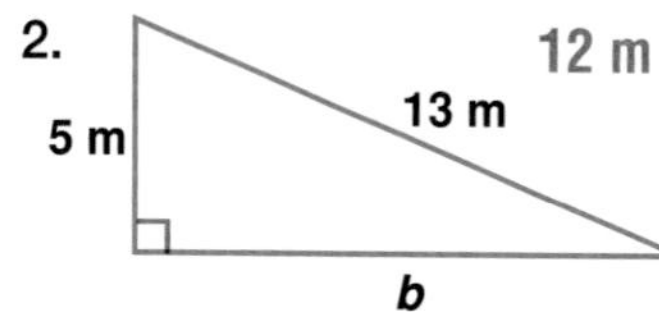

12 m

3. 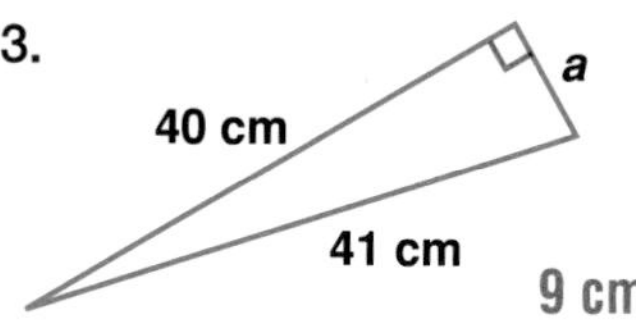

9 cm

4. a, 7 m; b, 24 m **25 m**
5. a, 18 in.; c, 30 in. **24 in.**
6. b, 10 ft; c, 20 ft **17.3 ft**
7. a, 3 cm; c, 9 cm **8.5 cm**
8. b, 8 m; c, 32 m **31.0 m**
9. a, 36 ft; b, 42 ft **55.3 ft**
10. a, 30 km; b, 45 km **54.1 km**
11. a, 32 yd; c, 65 yd **56.6 yd**
12. b, 11 cm; c, 19 cm **15.5 cm**

SET 14D *(Lessons 14-7, 14-8, 14-9, 14-10)* Use trigonometric ratios to solve problems involving right triangles.

Example

Solve for *x*. Round your answer to the nearest tenth.

The measure of the side adjacent to P is known and the measure of the hypotenuse is needed. Use the cosine function.

$\cos P = \dfrac{\text{measure of the side adjacent to } \angle P}{\text{measure of the hypotenuse}}$

$\cos 30° = \dfrac{12}{x}$

$x \cos 30° = 12$ Multiply each side by x.

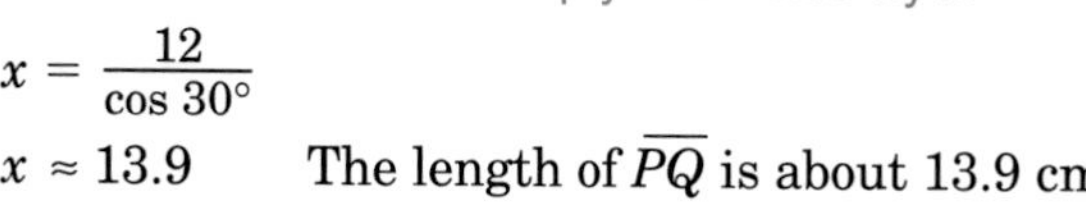

$x = \dfrac{12}{\cos 30°}$

$x \approx 13.9$ The length of $\overline{PQ}$ is about 13.9 cm.

R
12 cm
30°
P x Q

Solve for *y*. Round answers to the nearest tenth.

1. **6.3 ft**
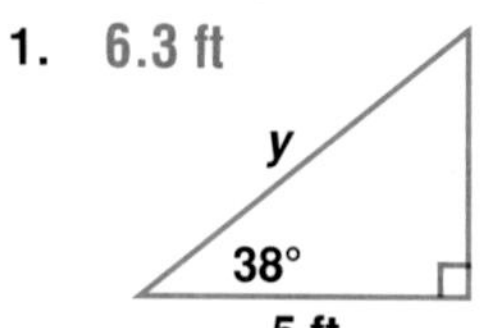

2. **20.8 m**
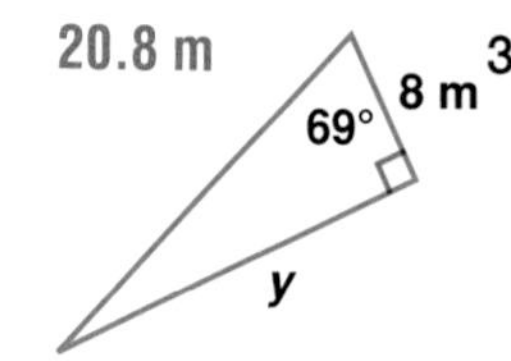

3. **7.7 cm**
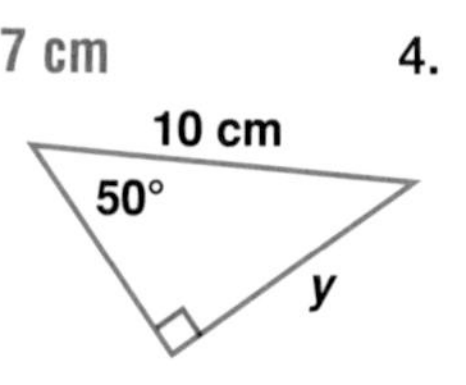

4. **8.4 in.**
12 in.
55°
y

SET 15A (*Lesson 15-1*) Identify and classify polynomials.

Example

State whether $5a^2 - \frac{a}{4}$ is a polynomial. If it is, identify it as a *monomial, binomial,* or *trinomial.*

The expression $5a^2 - \frac{a}{4}$ is a polynomial because it is the sum of two monomials. Since it has two unlike terms, it is a binomial.

State whether each expression is a polynomial. If it is, identify it as a *monomial, binomial,* or *trinomial.* 7. yes; trinomial

1. x^2 yes; monomial
2. $5a - 3$ yes; binomial
3. $5 - 4d + d^2$ yes; binomial
4. $\frac{9}{r^2}$ no
5. $\frac{t^5}{7}$ yes; monomial
6. $\sqrt{11ab}$ no
7. $4pq^2 - pq + 9p$
8. $\frac{2}{a} + 9$ no
9. $\frac{r^3 - s}{3}$ yes; binomial
10. $\frac{2}{3} - 4k^2$ yes; binomial
11. $\frac{5n}{m} + \frac{2a}{5}$ no
12. -41 yes; monomial

Find the degree of each polynomial.

13. $4x$ 1
14. $a^2 - 6$ 2
15. $11r + 5s$ 1
16. $3y^2 + 4y - 2$ 2
17. $9cd^3 - 5$ 4
18. $-5p^3 + 8q^2$ 3
19. $w^2 + 2x - 3y^3 - 7z$ 3
20. $\frac{x^3}{6} - x$ 3
21. $-17n^2p - 11np^3$ 4

SET 15B (*Lessons 15-2, 15-3, 15-4, 15-5, 15-6*) Add, subtract, and multiply polynomials.

Example

Find $-5x(2x^2 - 3x + 1)$.

$$-5x(2x^2 - 3x + 1) = (-5x)(2x^2) - (-5x)(3x) + (-5x)(1) \quad \text{Use the distributive property.}$$
$$= -10x^3 + 15x^2 - 5x$$

Find each sum, difference, or product. 14. $7r^3 - 21r^2 + 49r$ 15. $6x^2 + 8x + 2$

1. $(3a + 4) + (a + 2)$ $4a + 6$
2. $(8m - 3) + (4m + 1)$ $12m - 2$
3. $(5x - 3y) + (2x - y)$ $7x - 4y$
4. $(3n + 2) - (n + 1)$ $2n + 1$
5. $(-3c + 2d) - (7c - 6d)$ $-10c + 8d$
6. $(8p^2 - 2p + 3) + (-3p^2 - 2)$ $5p^2 - 2p + 1$
7. $(4x^2 + 1) - (3x^2 - 4)$ $x^2 + 5$
8. $(5a - 4b) - (-a + b)$ $6a - 5b$
9. $(6c^3 + 3) - (3c^3 - 1)$ $3c^3 + 4$
10. $(-11r^2 + 3s) + (5r^2 - s)$ $-6r^2 + 2s$
11. $4n(5n - 3)$ $20n^2 - 12n$
12. $-3x(4 - x)$ $-12x + 3x^2$
13. $6m(-m^2 + 3)$ $-6m^3 + 18m$
14. $7r(r^2 - 3r + 7)$
15. $(2x + 2)(3x + 1)$
16. $(x + 4)(3x + 1)$ $3x^2 + 13x + 4$
17. $\begin{array}{r} 3a^2 + 5a + 1 \\ +\ 2a^2 - 3a - 6 \\ \hline 5a^2 + 2a - 5 \end{array}$
18. $\begin{array}{r} 6x^2 - 4x + 11 \\ -\ 5x^2 + 5x - 4 \\ \hline x^2 - 9x + 15 \end{array}$
19. $\begin{array}{r} 8n^2 + 3mn \\ -\ 4n^2 + 2mn - 9 \\ \hline -4n^2 + mn + 9 \end{array}$

Glossary

absolute value of a number (55) The number of units the number is from zero on the number line.

acute angle (440) Any angle that measures between 0° and 90°.

acute triangle (457) A triangle having three acute angles.

addition property for inequalities (110) For any numbers a, b, and c: 1. If $a > b$, then $a + c > b + c$. 2. If $a < b$, then $a + c < b + c$.

addition property of equality (92) For any numbers a, b, and c, if $a = b$, then $a + c = b + c$.

additive identity property (66) For any number a, $a + 0 = a$.

additive inverse (66) The sum of a number and its additive inverse is zero. For example, the additive inverse of 65 is -65.

adjacent angles (446) Two angles are adjacent if they have a common side and the same vertex, but they do *not* overlap.

algebraic expression (9) A combination of variables, numbers, and at least one operation.

algebraic fraction (144) Fractions with variables in the numerator and/or denominator.

alternate interior angles (449) In the figure, transversal t intersects lines l and m. $\angle 3$ and $\angle 5$, and $\angle 4$ and $\angle 6$ are alternate interior angles.

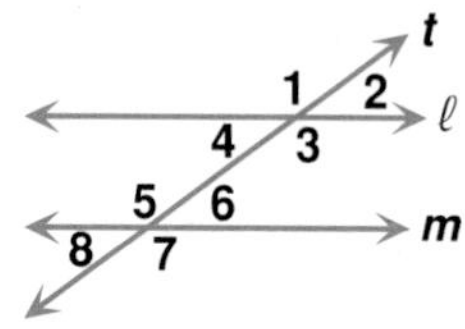

angle (439) Two rays with a common endpoint form an angle.

angle bisector (453) A ray through the interior of an angle that divides the angle into two congruent angles.

area (106, 484) The number of square units needed to cover a surface.

arithmetic sequence (190) A sequence in which the difference between any two consecutive terms is the same.

associative property of addition (22, 174) For any numbers a, b, and c, $(a + b) + c = a + (b + c)$.

associative property of multiplication (22, 220) For any numbers a, b, and c, $(a \cdot b) \cdot c = a \cdot (b \cdot c)$.

bar notation (169) In repeating decimals the line or bar placed over the digits that repeat. For example, $2.\overline{63}$ indicates that the digits 63 repeat.

base (131) In 10^3, the base is 10. The base is used as a factor as many times as given by the exponent (3). That is, $10^3 = 10 \times 10 \times 10$.

base (334) In a percent proportion, the number to which the percentage is compared.

base (484–485, 488) The base of a rectangle, a parallelogram, or a triangle is any side of the figure. The bases of a trapezoid are the parallel sides.

base (495) The bases of a prism are the two parallel congruent sides.

BASIC (21) One type of computer language. BASIC stands for **B**eginner's **A**ll-purpose **S**ymbolic **I**nstruction **C**ode.

binomial (565) A polynomial with two unlike terms.

bisect (452) To divide something into two congruent parts.

boundary (315) A line that separates a plane into two regions.

box-and-whisker plot (378) A diagram that summarizes data using the median, the upper and lower quartiles, and the extreme values. A box is drawn around the quartile value and whiskers extend from each quartile to the extreme data points.

brackets (16) A grouping symbol [ ].

capacity (195) The amount of liquid or dry substance a container can hold.

Celsius (260) The temperature scale of the metric system.

center of a circle (243) The given point from which all points on the circle are the same distance.

change in *x* (305) The horizontal change of a line in a coordinate plane.

change in *y* (305) The vertical change of a line in a coordinate plane.

circle (243) The set of all points in a plane that are the same distance from a given point called the center.

circle graph (442) A type of statistical graph used to compare parts of a whole.

circular cone (502) A shape in space that has a circular base and one vertex.

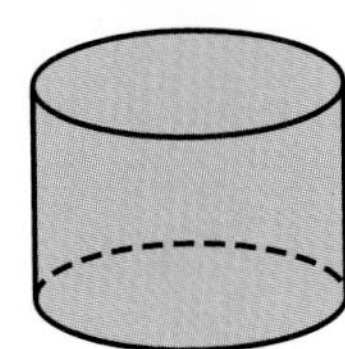

circular cylinder (498) A shape in space that has two parallel and congruent circular bases.

circumference (243) The distance around a circle.

closure property of addition (174) For all rational numbers x and y, $x + y$ is a rational number.

closure property of multiplication (220) For all rational numbers x and y, $x \cdot y$ is a rational number.

combination (408) An arrangement or listing in which order is *not* important.

common difference (190) The difference between any two consecutive terms in an arithmetic sequence.

common factor (140) A number that is a factor of two or more numbers.

common multiple (146) A number that is a multiple of two or more numbers.

common ratio (233) The ratio between any two successive terms in a geometric sequence.

commutative property of addition (22, 174) For any numbers a and b, $a + b = b + a$.

commutative property of multiplication (22, 220) For any numbers a and b, $a \cdot b = b \cdot a$.

compass (452) An instrument used for drawing circles or parts of circles.

complementary angles (446) Two angles are complementary if the sum of their measures is 90°.

composite number (136) Any whole number greater than one that has more than two factors.

compound statement (116) One statement formed by connecting two simple statements with words such as *and*, *or*, *if*, *then*, and *if and only if*.

computer program (139) A series of statements that gives directions to a computer.

congruent (446, 461) Congruent figures match or fit exactly and have the same size and shape.

conjunction (116) Two statements connected by the word *and*.

constant (565) A monomial that does not contain a variable.

coordinate of a point (54, 284) A number associated with the point on a number line.

coordinate system (293) Two perpendicular number lines form a coordinate system.

corresponding angles (449) Corresponding angles are angles that hold the same position on two different parallel lines cut by a transversal.

cosine (550) If $\triangle ABC$ is a right triangle and A is an acute angle,

$$\text{cosine of } \angle A = \frac{\text{measure of the side adjacent to } \angle A}{\text{measure of the hypotenuse}}.$$

cross products (327) In the proportion $\frac{3}{6} = \frac{4}{8}$, the cross products are 8×3 and 4×6.

customary units (195) Units of measure frequently used in the United States. The customary units of length are inches, feet, yards, and miles. The customary units of weight are ounces, pounds, and tons. The customary units of capacity are fluid ounces, cups, pints, quarts, and gallons.

data (362) Numerical information gathered for statistical purposes.

decagon (474) A polygon having ten sides.

deductive reasoning (231) A process of reasoning where a rule is used to make a conclusion or a decision.

degree (439) The most common unit of measure for angles.

degree of a monomial (564) The sum of the exponents of the variables of the monomial.

demographics (362) The numbers that describe the characteristics of a population.

density property (242) Between any two rational numbers there is at least one other rational number.

dependent events (421) Two or more events in which the outcome of one event does affect the outcome of the other event(s).

diagonal (475) A line segment that joins two nonconsecutive vertices of a polygon.

diameter (243) The distance across a circle through its center.

discount (349) The amount deducted from the original price.

disjunction (117) Two statements connected by the word *or*.

distributive property (25, 220) For any numbers a, b, and c, $a(b + c) = ab + ac$ and $(b + c)\,a = ba + ca$.

divisible (128) A number is divisible by another if, upon division, the remainder is zero.

division (36) For all numbers a, b, and c, with $b \neq 0$, $\frac{a}{b} = c$ if $bc = a$.

division property of equality (95) For any numbers a, b, and c, with $c \neq 0$, if $a = b$, then $\frac{a}{c} = \frac{b}{c}$.

empty set (265) A set with no elements.

equation (30) A mathematical sentence that contains the equals sign, $=$.

equilateral triangle (474) A triangle having three congruent sides.

equivalent equations (89) Two or more equations with the same solution. For example, $x + 3 = 5$ and $x = 2$ are equivalent equations.

evaluate (19) To find the value of an expression by replacing variables with numerals.

experimental probability (417) An estimated probability based on the relative frequency of positive outcomes occurring during an experiment.

exponent (131) In 10^3, the exponent is 3. The exponent tells how many times the base, 10, is used as a factor.

$$10^3 = 10 \times 10 \times 10.$$

exterior angles (449) In the figure, transversal t intersects lines l and m. $\angle 1$, $\angle 2$, $\angle 7$, and $\angle 8$ are exterior angles.

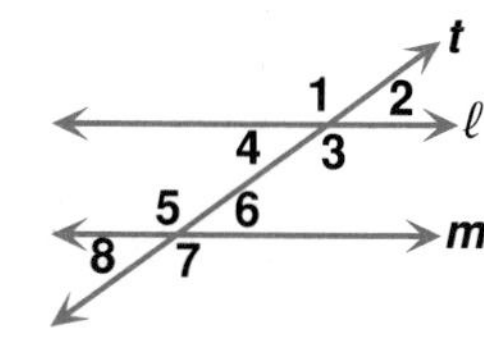

face (495) A face of a prism is any surface that forms a side or a base of the prism.

factor (128) If two or more numbers are multiplied together, then each number is a factor of the product.

factorial (407) The expression $n!$ is the product of all counting numbers beginning with n and counting backwards to 1.

Fahrenheit (260) The customary temperature scale of the United States.

Fibonacci numbers (194) Numbers listed in the Fibonacci sequence.

Fibonacci sequence (194) A list of numbers in which the first two numbers are both 1 and each number that follows is the sum of the previous two numbers, 1, 1, 2, 3, 5, 8, . . .

formula (101) An equation that states a rule for the relationship between certain quantities.

frequency table (363) A chart that indicates the number of values in each interval.

Fundamental Counting Principle (403) If event M can occur in m ways and is followed by event N that can occur in n ways, then the event M followed by event N can occur in $m \cdot n$ ways.

geometric sequence (233) A sequence in which the ratio between any two successive terms is the same.

gram (218, 276) The basic unit of mass in the metric system.

graph of a point (284, 293) A dot marking a point that represents a number on a number line or an ordered pair on a coordinate plane.

greatest common factor (GCF) (140) The greatest of the common factors of two or more numbers.

height (484–485) The height of a rectangle, a parallelogram, a triangle, or a trapezoid is the length of its altitude.

heptagon (474) A polygon having seven sides.

hexagon (474) A polygon having six sides.

histogram (364) A bar graph whose bars are next to each other to show how the data are distributed.

hypotenuse (537) In a right triangle, the side opposite the right angle is called the hypotenuse.

identity property of addition (22, 174) For any number a, $a + 0 = a$.

identity property of multiplication (22, 220) For any number a, $a \cdot 1 = a$.

independent events (418) Two or more events in which the outcome of one event does *not* affect the outcome of the other event(s).

inductive reasoning (231) A process of reasoning where a rule is made after seeing several examples.

inequality (46) Any sentence containing $>$, $<$, $\neq$, $\leq$, $\geq$.

integers (54) The whole numbers and their opposites.

$\ldots, {}^{-}3, {}^{-}2, {}^{-}1, 0, 1, 2, 3, \ldots$

interest (350) The amount charged or paid for the use of money.

interior angles (449) In the figure, transversal t intersects lines l and m. $\angle 3$, $\angle 4$, $\angle 5$, and $\angle 6$ are interior angles.

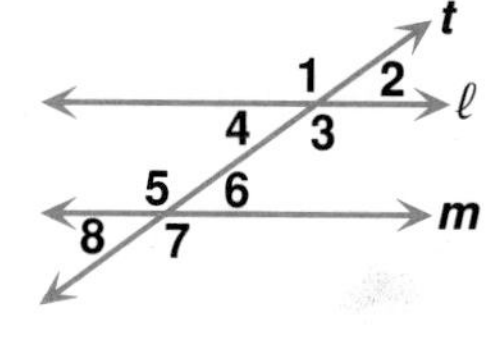

interquartile range (374) The range of the middle half of the data.

inverse operations (35) Operations that undo each other, such as addition and subtraction.

inverse property of addition (174) For every rational number a, $a + ({}^{-}a) = 0$.

inverse property of multiplication (219) For every nonzero number $\frac{a}{b}$, where $a, b \neq 0$, there is exactly one number $\frac{b}{a}$ such that $\frac{a}{b} \cdot \frac{b}{a} = 1$.

irrational numbers (533) Numbers that cannot be expressed as $\frac{a}{b}$, where a and b are integers and b does not equal 0.

kilogram (276) One thousand grams. A pair of shoes has a mass of about 1 kilogram.

kilometer (275) One thousand meters.

lateral surface (501) The lateral surface of a prism, cylinder, pyramid, or cone is all the surface of the figure except the base or bases.

least common denominator (LCD) (149) The least common multiple of the denominators of two or more fractions.

least common multiple (LCM) (146) The least of the nonzero common multiples of two or more numbers.

leg (537) A leg of a right triangle is either of the two sides that form the right angle.

length (195) The measure of how long it is from one end to the other end of something.

like terms (26, 565) Expressions that contain the same variables, such as $3ab$ and $7ab$.

line (438) A never-ending straight path. A representation of line CD ($\overleftrightarrow{CD}$) is shown below.

line segment (438) Two endpoints and the straight path between them. A representation of line segment ST ($\overline{ST}$) is shown below.

linear equation (300) An equation for which the graph is a straight line.

liter (218, 276) The basic unit of capacity in the metric system.

logic (70) The study of formal reasoning.

lower quartile (375) The median of the lower half of a set of numbers.

mass (276) The amount of matter an object contains.

mean (367) The sum of the numbers in a set of data divided by the number of pieces of data.

measures of central tendency (367) Numbers or pieces of data that can represent the whole set of data.

median (368) In a set of data, the median is the number in the middle when the data are organized from least to greatest.

meter (218, 275) The basic unit of length in the metric system.

metric system (218) A system of measurement using the basic units: meter for length, gram for mass, and liter for capacity.

midpoint (452) A point on a line segment that divides the line segment into two congruent line segments.

mode (367) The number or item that appears most often in a set of data.

monomial (129, 558) An expression that is either a constant, a variable, or a product of numbers and variables.

multiple of a number (146) The product of the number and any whole number.

multiplication property of equality (98) For any numbers a, b, c, if $a = b$, then $ac = bc$.

multiplicative inverse (219) A number times its multiplicative inverse is equal to 1. The multiplicative inverse of $\frac{3}{4}$ is $\frac{4}{3}$.

multiplicative property of zero (22) For any number a, $a \cdot 0 = 0 \cdot a = 0$.

mutually exclusive events (424) Two or more events such that no two events can happen at the same time.

negation (70) If a statement is represented by p, then not p is the negation of that statement.

negative integers (54) Whole numbers to the left of zero on the number line or numbers less than 0.

$$^-1, ^-2, ^-3, \ldots$$

null set (265) A set with no elements.

obtuse angle (440) Any angle that measures between 90° and 180°.

obtuse triangle (457) A triangle having one obtuse angle.

octagon (474) A polygon having eight sides.

open sentence (30) A sentence containing at least one variable. The sentence is neither true nor false.

opposites (66) Two integers are opposites if their sum is zero.

ordered pair (290) A pair of numbers in which the order is specified.

origin (293) The point of intersection of the x-axis and y-axis in a coordinate system.

outcome (400) One possible result of a probability event. For example, 4 is an outcome when a die is rolled.

outliers (378) Data that are more than 1.5 times the interquartile range from the quartiles.

parallel lines (449) Lines in the same plane that do not intersect.

parallelogram (472) A quadrilateral with two pairs of parallel sides.

parentheses (16) A grouping symbol ( ).

pentagon (474) A polygon having five sides.

percent (334) A ratio with a denominator of 100. For example, 7% and $\frac{7}{100}$ names the same number.

percent proportion (334)

$$\frac{\text{Percentage}}{\text{Base}} = \text{Rate or } \frac{P}{B} = \frac{r}{100}$$

percentage (334) In a percent proportion, a number that is compared to another number called the base.

perfect square (527) A rational number whose square root is a rational number.

perimeter (105) The distance around a geometric figure.

permutation (407) An arrangement or listing in which order is important.

perpendicular lines (446) Intersecting lines that form right angles.

pi (π) (243) The ratio of the circumference of a circle to the diameter of a circle. Approximations for π are 3.14 and $\frac{22}{7}$.

plane (438) A flat surface that has no boundaries. A plane can be named by three noncollinear points of the plane.

point (438) A specific location in space.

polygon (474) A simple closed figure in a plane formed by three or more line segments.

polynomial (565) A monomial or the sum or difference of two or more monomials.

positive integers (54) Whole numbers to the right of zero on the number line or numbers greater than 0.

power (131) A number that can be written using an exponent.

precision (515) The precision of a measurement depends on the unit of measure. To improve the precision of a measurement, a measuring instrument that provides smaller units of measure should be chosen.

prime factorization (136) Every composite number can be expressed as the product of prime numbers. For example, the prime factorization of 63 is $3 \times 3 \times 7$.

prime number (136) A prime number is a whole number greater than 1 that has exactly two factors, 1 and itself.

principal (350) The amount of an investment or a debt.

prism (495) A figure in space that has two parallel and congruent bases in the shape of polygons.

probability (411) The probability of a certain outcome is the ratio of the number of ways the certain outcome can occur to the number of possible outcomes.

product property of square roots (535) For any nonnegative numbers a and b,

$$\sqrt{a \cdot b} = \sqrt{a} \cdot \sqrt{b}$$

property of proportions (327) If $\frac{a}{b} = \frac{c}{d}$ then $ad = bc$. If $ad = bc$, then $\frac{a}{b} = \frac{c}{d}$.

proportion (327) A sentence that states that two ratios are equivalent.

protractor (440) An instrument used to measure angles.

pyramid (501) A figure in space with three or more triangular faces and a base in the shape of a polygon.

Pythagorean Theorem (537) In a right triangle, the square of the hypotenuse is equal to the sum of the squares of the length of the legs.

quadrant (293) One of the four regions into which two perpendicular number lines separate the plane.

quadrilateral (471) A polygon having four sides.

radical sign (526) The symbol used to indicate a nonnegative square root. $\sqrt{\ }$

radicand (526) Any expression inside a radical sign.

radius (243) The distance from the center of a circle to any point on the circle.

range (374) The difference between the least and greatest numbers in a set of numbers.

rate (320) A ratio of two measurements having different units.

rate (334) In a percent proportion, the ratio of a number to 100.

rate of interest (350) The percent charged or paid for the use of money.

ratio (143, 324) A comparison of two numbers. The ratio of 2 to 3 can be stated as 2 out of 3, 2 to 3, 2:3, or $\frac{2}{3}$.

rational numbers (166, 533) Numbers of the form $\frac{a}{b}$ where a and b are integers and $b \neq 0$.

ray (439) A part of a line that extends indefinitely in one direction.

real numbers (534) Irrational numbers together with rational numbers form the set of real numbers.

reciprocal (219) Another name for a multiplicative inverse.

rectangle (472) A parallelogram with all angles congruent.

rectangular prism (495) A prism with rectangles as bases.

regular polygon (474) A polygon having all sides congruent and all angles congruent.

relative frequency (417) The fraction of the events that have positive outcomes.

repeating decimal (169) A decimal whose digits repeat in groups of one or more. Examples are 0.181818 . . . and 0.83333. . . .

rhombus (472) A parallelogram with all sides congruent.

right angle (440) An angle that measures 90°.

right triangle (457) A triangle having a right angle.

sample (363) A randomly selected group chosen for the purpose of collecting data.

sample space (411) The set of all possible outcomes.

scatter plot (383) A graph that shows the general relationship between two sets of data.

scientific notation (237) A way of expressing a number as the product of a number that is at least 1 but less than 10 and a power of 10.

sequence (190) A list of numbers in a certain order.

side (474) A side of a polygon is any of the line segments that form the polygon.

significant digits (515) The digits that are recorded when a measurement is made. These digits indicate the precision of the measurement.

similar figures (465) Figures having the same shape.

simulation (429) The process of acting out a problem.

sine (550) If $\triangle ABC$ is a right triangle and A is an acute angle,

$$\text{sine of } \angle A = \frac{\text{measure of the side adjacent to } \angle A}{\text{measure of the hypotenuse}}.$$

slant height (501) The length of the altitude of a lateral face of a regular pyramid.

slope (305) The slope of a line is the ratio of the change in y to the corresponding change in x.

$$\text{slope} = \frac{\text{change in } y}{\text{change in } x}$$

solution (30) A replacement for a variable for which a true sentence results. The solution for $y = 8 + 9$ is 17.

square (472) A parallelogram with all sides congruent and all angles congruent.

square (527) The product of a number and itself.

square pyramid (501) A pyramid with a square base.

square root (526) One of the two equal factors of a number. A square root of 144 is 12 since $12^2 = 144$.

standard form (131) The standard form for seven hundred thirty nine is 739.

statement (70) Any sentence that is either true or false, but not both.

statistics (363) The study of collecting, analyzing, and presenting data.

stem-and-leaf plot (371) A system used to condense a set of data where the greatest place value of the data forms the stem and the next greatest place value forms the leaves.

straightedge (452) Any object that can be used to draw a straight line.

substitution property of equality (19) For all numbers a and b, if $a = b$, then a may be replaced by b.

subtraction (35) For all numbers a, b, and c, $a - b = c$ and $a - c = b$ if $b + c = a$.

subtraction property for inequalities (110) For any numbers a, b, and c:

1. If $a > b$, then $a - c > b - c$.
2. If $a < b$, then $a - c < b - c$.

subtraction property of equality (89) For any numbers a, b, and c, if $a = b$, then $a - c = b - c$.

supplementary angles (446) Two angles are supplementary if the sum of their measures is 180°.

surface area (495) The sum of the areas of all the surfaces (faces) of a 3-dimensional figure.

system of equations (311) A set of equations with the same variables.

tangent (548) If $\triangle ABC$ is a right triangle and A is an acute angle,

$$\text{tangent of } \angle A = \frac{\text{measure of the side opposite to } \angle A}{\text{measure of the side adjacent to } \angle A}.$$

term (26, 565) A number, a variable, or a product of numbers and variables.

term of a sequence (190) A number in a sequence.

terminating decimal (169) A decimal whose digits end. Examples are 0.25 and 0.125.

tessellation (477) A repetitive pattern of polygons that fit together with no holes or gaps.

transversal (449) A line that intersects two lines to form eight angles.

trapezoid (472) A quadrilateral with exactly one pair of parallel sides.

tree diagram (400) A diagram used to show the total number of possible outcomes in a probability experiment.

triangle (456) A polygon having three sides.

triangular prism (496) A prism with triangles as bases.

trigonometric ratios (551) Ratios that involve the measures of the sides of right triangles. The tangent, sine, and cosine ratios are three trigonometric ratios.

trigonometry (551) The study of triangle measurement.

trinomial (565) A polynomial with three unlike terms.

unit rate (320) A rate with a denominator of 1.

upper quartile (375) The median of the upper half of a set of numbers.

variables (19) Placeholders in mathematical expressions or sentences.

variation (374) The divergence in the values of a set of data.

Venn diagram (531) A diagram consisting of circles inside a rectangle which is used to show the relationships of sets.

vertex (439) A vertex of an angle is the common endpoint of the rays forming the angle.

vertex (456, 474) A vertex of a polygon is a point where two sides of the polygon intersect.

vertex (501) The vertex of a pyramid is the point where all the faces except the base intersect.

vertical angles (446) Congruent angles formed by the intersection of two lines. In the figure, the vertical angles are $\angle 1$ and $\angle 3$; $\angle 2$ and $\angle 4$.

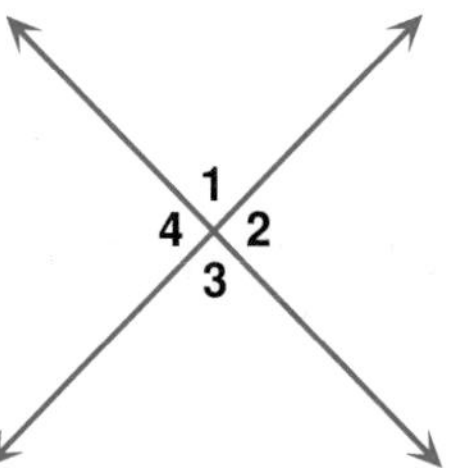

volume (506) The number of cubic units needed to fill a space.

***x*-axis** (293) The horizontal line of the two perpendicular number lines in a coordinate plane.

***x*-coordinate** (293) The first number of an ordered pair.

***x*-intercept** (305) In a linear equation, the value of x when y is *0*.

***y*-axis** (293) The vertical line of the two perpendicular number lines in a coordinate plane.

***y*-coordinate** (293) The second number of an ordered pair.

***y*-intercept** (308) In a linear equation, the value of y when x is 0.

Selected Answers

Chapter 1 The Language of Algebra

Page 17 Lesson 1-1
5. division; 48 **7.** division; 1 **9.** addition; 20 **11.** addition; 17 **13.** subtraction; 7 **15.** addition; 3 **17.** 47 **19.** 0 **21.** 16 **23.** 14 **25.** 16 **27.** 27 **29.** 2 **31.** 94 **33.** 72 **35.** 189 **37.** false **39.** true **41.** false **43.** $(18 + 4) \times 3 = 66$ **45.** $24 \div 2 - (4 + 8) = 0$ **47.** $50 \times 6 + 8 \times 12$; \$396

Pages 20–21 Lesson 1-2
5. 3 **7.** 25 **9.** 16 **11.** 15 **13.** 10 **15.** 73 **17.** 18 **19.** 20 **21.** 36 **23.** 8 **25.** 20 **27.** 30 **29.** 4 **31.** 19 **33.** 64 **35.** 12 **37.** division **38.** subtraction **39.** 26 **40.** true **41.** $8 \cdot 7$; (8)(7)

Page 24 Lesson 1-3
5. commutative property of addition **7.** multiplicative property of zero **9.** associative property of multiplication **11.** identity property of multiplication **13.** commutative property of multiplication **15.** multiplicative property of zero **17.** associative property of multiplication **19.** multiplicative property of zero **21.** commutative property of addition **23.** commutative property of addition **25.** 40 **27.** 130 **29.** 200 **31.** $12 + 9$ **33.** $2z + 7$ or $7 + z \cdot 2$ **35.** $(12 + 15) + x$; $27 + x$ **37.** $n(6 \cdot 5)$; $30n$ **39.** $(3 \cdot 2)z$; $6z$ **41.** $(5 \cdot 4)x$; $20x$ **43.** 149 **44.** subtraction **45.** 16 **46.** $ab \div 2$ **47.** 17 **48.** 9 **49.** Sample answer: wash dishes, dry dishes

Pages 27–28 Lesson 1-4
5. $8 \cdot 5 + 8 \cdot 9$ **7.** $5 \cdot 11 + 5 \cdot 12$ **9.** $5x + 5y$ **11.** $8(3 + 6)$ **13.** $9(x + y)$ **15.** $3(x + 2y)$ **17.** $8x$ **19.** $13k + 23$ **21.** $38x + 45$ **23.** $22a + 8$ **25.** $3y + 23$ **27.** $15f + 8g + 7q$ **29.** $33y + 35$ **31.** $22b + 42$ **33.** $14x + 18y$ **35.** $3y + 5y$ **37.** $2 \times 7 + 1 \times 7 + 1.25$ **39.** 184 **41.** 156 **43.** 430 **45.** 240 **46.** 24 **47.** $2 \times a \times b$; $2 \cdot a \cdot b$ **48.** 6 **49.** $x + (5 + 1)$ **50.** multiplicative property of zero **51.** $12z$

Page 31 Lesson 1-5
5. 3 **7.** 29 **9.** 2 **11.** 3 **13.** 6 **15.** 14 **17.** 5 **19.** 24 **21.** 9 **22.** commutative property of addition **23.** $10m + 1$ **24.** $11y + 21$ **25.** 180 ft^2

Page 34 Lesson 1-6
3. 30; 31 **5.** 33 **7.** 6 quarters **9.** 11 2-point; 8 1-point

Page 34 Mid-Chapter Quiz
1. 33 **2.** 50 **3.** 2 **4.** 3 **5.** 144 **6.** $x + 12$ **7.** $15x$ **8.** $12x$ **9.** 29 **10.** 10

Pages 37–38 Lesson 1-7
5. $21 = 36 - 15$ or $15 = 36 - 21$ **7.** $14 = 11 + 3$ **9.** $c = 6 + 18$ **11.** $b \div 6 = 7$ or $b \div 7 = 6$ **13.** $28 = 4 \cdot 7$ **15.** $a = 7 \cdot 19$ **17.** 12 **19.** 24 **21.** 20 **23.** 3 **25.** 135 **27.** 12 **29.** 7 **31.** 0.83 **33.** 19.98 **35.** 3.77 **37.** 1 **38.** $5(x + y)$ **39.** $30y$ **40.** $53c + 6$ **41.** 9 **42.** $7 + x = 7$ **49.** 96 **51.** 2.5 m/s

Pages 41–42 Lesson 1-8
5. $w + 4$ **7.** $t - 9$ **9.** $11 + x$ **11.** $6 + z$ **13.** $20 - r$ **15.** $80 + x$ **17.** $n \div 7$ **19.** $z \cdot 6$ **21.** $j + 10$ **23.** $a + 300$ **25.** $2f$ **27.** $3n - 8$ **29.** the sum of a number and three **31.** the product of 9 and a number **33.** two times the sum of a number and three **35.** 0 **36.** $48a + 30$ **37.** 4 **38.** 26 **39.** true **41.** Sandy Koufax **43.** $k + 2$

Pages 44–45 Lesson 1-9
3. $2x = 6$ **5.** $x + 4 = 12$ **7.** $x - 5 = 7$ **9.** $x - 42 = 60$ **11.** $x - 9 = 15$; \$24 **13.** $x - 18 = 72$; 90 games **15.** $35x = 175$; \$5 **17.** $x + 61 = 117$; 56 home runs **18.** 45 **19.** $2n$ **20.** three times the sum of a number and two **21.** no

Page 47 Lesson 1-10
5. false **7.** true **9.** open **11.** false **13.** true **15.** false **17.** true **19.** true **21.** false **23.** less than **25.** equal to **27.** greater than **28.** 9 **29.** $18 \div y$ **30.** $x - 6 = 15$ **31.** $4t = 56$; 14 seconds **33.** $s < 200{,}000$

Pages 48–49 Chapter 1 Review
1. solved **3.** multiply **5.** $x \leq 2$ **7.** 18 **9.** 11 **11.** 133 **13.** 15 **15.** 15 **17.** 15 **19.** identity of addition **21.** identity property of multiplication **23.** distributive property **25.** $7 + x$ **27.** $5a + 10$ **29.** $14a + 12$ **31.** 5 **33.** 36 **35.** 5 **37.** 129 **39.** 36 **41.** 32 **43.** $5b$ **45.** $n \div 6$ **47.** true **49.** false

Chapter 2 Integers

Pages 55–56 Lesson 2-1
7. -4, -3, -2, -1, 0 **9.** 3 **11.** 16
13. **15.**

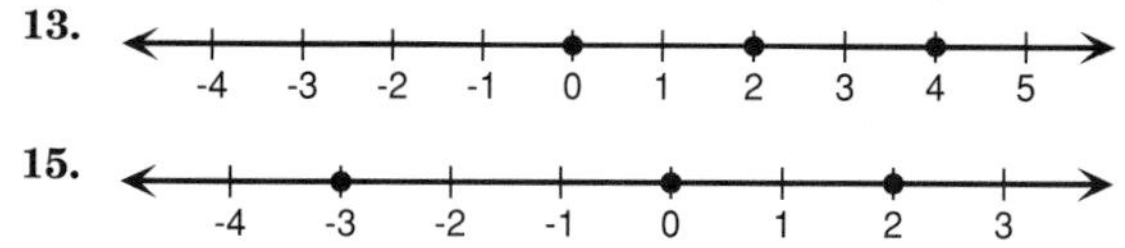

17. 15 **19.** 0 **21.** 5 **23.** 39 **24.** 19 **25.** 7 **26.** 3 **27.** $x + 23 = 41$; \$18 **29.** 1 **31.** -1 **33.** fraction, decimal **35.** -6, 120

Pages 57–58 Lesson 2-2
7. $-5 < -2$ **9.** less than **11.** greater than **13.** greater than **15.** less than **17.** {-3, 0, 10} **19.** {-8, -4, -3, 0} **21.** $144 > 135$ or $135 < 144$ **23.** 16 **25.** 8
24.

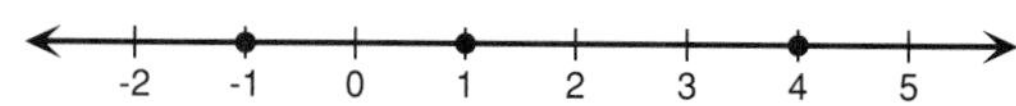

Pages 61–62 Lesson 2-3
5. negative **7.** positive **9.** 4 **11.** 15 **13.** 16 **15.** -18 **17.** 15 **19.** 26 **21.** -29 **23.** 16 **25.** -15 **27.** 24 **29.** 5 **31.** 1 **33.** -26 **35.** -27 **37.** -40 + (-23.95); -63.95 **39.** 16 + (-25); -9 **41.** 150 + (-275); -125

43. never **45.** $24y + 30$ **46.** $|-3|$ means that -3 is 3 units from zero on the number line. **47.** $3 < 8$ **48.** $30 < 31$ **49.** $n \div 3$ **51.** -123°C

Page 64 Lesson 2-4
3. positive **5.** negative **7.** positive **9.** -26 **11.** 6 **13.** -31 **15.** -26 **17.** 63 **19.** $-16x$ **21.** $-7y$ **23.** $-20d$ **25.** $-29f$ **27.** 1 **29.** -5 **31.** -71 **33.** false **34.** Sample answers: 0, 2 **35.** 15 **36.** negative **37.** $100 + (-15.95) + 18 + (-52.87)$; \$49.18

Pages 67–68 Lesson 2-5
5. -6 **7.** 13 **9.** $-b$ **11.** $-cd$ **13.** $5x$ **15.** $7 + (-13) = x$ **17.** $-17 + (-9) = b$ **19.** $-18 + 16 = y$ **21.** -8 **23.** -6 **25.** 5 **27.** -18 **29.** -38 **31.** -15 **33.** -80 **35.** 0 **37.** 26 **39.** -5 **41.** -55 **43.** 6 **45.** $-10a$ **47.** $-29ab$ **49.** $-45d$ **51.** $41y$ **53.** 32 **54.** 21 **55.** 28 **56.** positive **57.** 6 **58.** $-11x$ **59.** -8 **61.** -3 **63.** -\$1475

Page 71 Lesson 2-6
5. true **7.** $3(11 - 5) = 8$; false; true **9.** false **11.** false **13.** true **15.** Mozart was a poet; true; false **17.** $3y - 2y \neq 1$; false; true **19.** $45 \leq 2(16 - 9)$; true; false **21.** -25 **22.** -4

Pages 74–75 Lesson 2-7
3. negative **5.** positive **7.** negative **9.** negative **11.** negative **13.** negative **15.** 66 **17.** -162 **19.** 68 **21.** -850 **23.** -270 **25.** -126 **27.** -48 **29.** 12 **31.** $-4b$ **33.** $-15x$ **35.** $30y$ **37.** $35yz$ **39.** $-3ab$ **41.** $40x$ **43.** 6 **44.** {-6, -2, 3} **45.** $22y$ **46.** -40 **47.** Some horses are not brown.

Page 75 Mid-Chapter Quiz
1. 2 **2.** 7 **3.** 5 **4.** greater than **5.** greater than **6.** greater than **7.** -11 **8.** -14 **9.** 6 **10.** -8 **11.** -45 **12.** 15

Pages 77–78 Lesson 2-8
3. negative **5.** positive **7.** negative **9.** positive **11.** negative **13.** negative **15.** 7 **17.** -12 **19.** 6 **21.** 3 **23.** -7 **25.** 49 **27.** -4 **29.** 10 **31.** 4 **33.** -12 **35.** -4 **37.** -3 **39.** 2 **40.** 166 pages **41.** 0 **42.** true **43.** negative **44.** $-36x$ **45.** -50 students

Pages 80–81 Lesson 2-9
3. 111°F **5.** -4 **7.** 6194 m **9.** 630 ft **11.** 8th floor **13.** positive **14.** -38

Pages 82–83 Chapter 2 Review
1. g **3.** a **5.** b **7.** 2 **9.** 3 **11.** 59 **13.** greater than **15.** less than **17.** -8 **19.** -8 **21.** -5 **23.** 7 **25.** -5 **27.** -7 **29.** $-4a$ **31.** $-16c$ **33.** 136 **35.** -5 **37.** -6 **39.** 2 **41.** 1 **43.** 48 **45.** Violins are not members of the string family. **47.** 17°F

Chapter 3 Solving One-Step Equations

Pages 90–91 Lesson 3-1
5. -8 **7.** -38 **9.** -3 **11.** -75 **13.** -93 **15.** -19 **17.** -35 **19.** 43 **21.** 22 **23.** -25 **25.** -13 **27.** -38 **29.** 20 **31.** -23 **33.** $x + 850 = 10{,}935$; \$10,085 **34.** 15 **35.** $24k + 3$ **36.** -7, -2, 9 **37.** -20 **38.** positive **39.** 18 degrees

Pages 93–94 Lesson 3-2
5. $x - 9 = 15$ **7.** $p + 7 = -18$ **9.** $18 = t - 4$ **11.** $p + 17 = 2$ **13.** $m - 8 = -15$ **15.** -1 **17.** 79 **19.** -23 **21.** 34 **23.** -4 **25.** -74 **27.** -36 **29.** 76 **31.** -36 **33.** $x - 150 = 300$; \$450 **34.** 12 more than 3 times x **35.** 131 **36.** -22 **37.** no **38.** $g = 19$ **39.** $x + 34 = 21$; -13° **45.** -700

Pages 96–97 Lesson 3-3
5. -4 **7.** 8 **9.** -9 **11.** 4 **13.** -8 **15.** -13 **17.** -13 **19.** 19 **21.** -4 **23.** -4 **25.** -3 **27.** -5 **29.** -15 **31.** 48 pounds **33.** false **34.** 9 **35.** -52 **36.** 13 **37.** $y - 19 = 14$ **38.** -9 **39.** 14 in. **41.** 3 hours

Pages 99–100 Lesson 3-4
7. 12; 36 **9.** -16; -64 **11.** -7; -161 **13.** 13; -208 **15.** -98 **17.** -156 **19.** 126 **21.** 147 **23.** -210 **25.** -704 **27.** -408 **29.** -2889 **31.** -2535 **33.** -1704 **35.** 21,204 **37.** -148, 973 **39.** Add 3 and 4. **40.** $45 < 55$ **41.** $x + 2900 = 5140$; 2240 feet **42.** 3 **43.** -7 **44.** -5 **45.** about 36 million gallons; about 900,000 barrels **47.** 3 weeks

Pages 102–103 Lesson 3-5
5. 240 miles **7.** 400 mph **9.** 221 **11.** \$40 **13.** 160 **15.** 30 **16.** 6 **17.** -6 **18.** 70 **19.** 8.5 gallons **21.** 53 mph **23.** 1376 meters or about 1.4 kilometers

Page 103 Mid-Chapter Quiz
1. -182 **2.** -37 **3.** 643 **4.** -15 **5.** -8 **6.** 57 **7.** 4 **8.** -13 **9.** -35 **10.** 143 **11.** -405 **12.** 245 **13.** c

Pages 107–108 Lesson 3-6
5. 8 mi; 4 m^2 **7.** 16 cm; 15 cm^2 **9.** 28 ft; 33 ft^2 **11.** 26 m; 36m^2 **13.** 322 yd; 4128 yd^2 **15.** 15 cm **17.** 10 rs **18.** -532 **19.** $r = d \div 2$ **20.** 6 hours **23.**

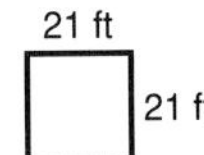

25. 84 ft

Pages 111–112 Lesson 3-7
5. $m > -1$ **7.** $16 < t$ **9.** $k \geq -15$ **11.** $y < 17$ **13.** $m > -5$ **15.** $z > 22$ **17.** $b < 2$ **19.** $w < -4$ **21.** $y > 27$ **23.** $z < 39$ **25.** $t > -1$ **27.** $r < -49$ **29.** $k < -16$ **31.** $x \geq -25$ **33.** $p \geq 19$ **35.** $x > 15$ **37.** $x \geq 13$ **39.** identity for multiplication **40.** Some integers are not even. **41.** -7 **42.** 105 hours **43.** 16 miles **44.** 72 square feet **45.** $6909 + x < 7687$; 778 teams

Pages 114–115 Lesson 3-8
5. 6; no **7.** -4; yes **9.** 9; no **11.** -6; yes **13.** $y > 13$ **15.** $z < 13$ **17.** $r \geq -18$ **19.** $x \geq 4$ **21.** $w \geq -146$ **23.** $m > 168$ **25.** $p \geq -168$ **27.** $h < 360$ **29.** $r \leq -18$ **31.** $n \geq -17$ **33.** $400 \geq a$ **35.** $x \leq -102$ **37.** $7x > -56$; $x > -8$ **39.** 3 **40.** 10 **41.** 135 square yards **42.** $-6 < p$ **43.** $s \leq 19$ **45.** $x \leq 300 + 30$

Page 118 Lesson 3-9
3. false **5.** false **7.** $0 \leq n \leq 10$ **9.** false **11.** true **13.** true **15.** true **17.** $3 < p \leq 11$ **19.** $-13 < m < (-6)$ **20.** false **21.** $-12ab$ **22.** no **23.** $30 \leq t \leq 85$

Pages 120–121 Lesson 3-10
3. $x + 4 = 16$ **5.** $\frac{x}{7} = 49$ **7.** $21x \leq -84$ **9.** $4x > 76; x > 19$
11. $\frac{x}{8} > 72; x > 576$ **13.** $3x = 75; \$25$ **15.** $3x < 36; x < 12$
17. $x + 17 = 75$; 58 boxes **18.** $f \geq (-27)$ **19.** $-4 < s < (-2)$

Pages 122–123 Chapter 3 Review
1. h **3.** d **5.** b **7.** j **9.** 5 **11.** -4 **13.** -26
15. -12 **17.** 110 **19.** 288 **21.** 3 mph **23.** 72 mm
25. 80 ft **27.** 7500 yd^2 **29.** $a > 2$ **31.** $m < 40$
33. $c < (-6)$ **35.** $d < 84$ **37.** $k \geq 84$ **39.** false **41.** true
43. $5x = 60$; 12 times **45.** $\frac{x}{5} = 4; \$20$

Chapter 4 Factors and Fractions

Pages 129–130 Lesson 4-1
5. yes **7.** yes **9.** 2 **11.** 2, 3, 6 **13.** yes **15.** no
17. yes **19.** no **21.** 3891 **23.** 183 **25.** 120 **27.** 1
29. 1 and the number **30.** 22 **31.** 5 **32.** 72 **33.** true
34. -7 **35.** 7 mph **36.** $t > 60$ **37.** 1600, 2000

Pages 132–133 Lesson 4-2
7. $m \cdot m$ **9.** $a \cdot a \cdot a \cdot a \cdot a$ **11.** 2^3 **13.** 1^4 **15.** 6^3 **17.** t^5
19. a^3 **21.** false **23.** true **25.** 81 **27.** 48 **29.** 250
31. 64 **33.** 121 **35.** 78, 125 **37.** 7 **38.** 19
39. $0.3 \leq b < 1.6$ **40.** true **41.** yes
42. $2 + 3 + 4 + 5 = 14$, so 3 is not a factor **47.** s^3

Page 135 Lesson 4-3
5. 30 people **7.** 15 handshakes **9.** $(4 + 3) \times 6 + 3 = 45$

Pages 137–138 Lesson 4-4
3. composite **5.** prime **7.** 2 **9.** 7 **11.** $3 \cdot 3 \cdot 7$
13. $2 \cdot 7 \cdot 7$ **15.** $2 \cdot 3 \cdot 5$ **17.** 7^2 **19.** $2^2 \cdot 7$ **21.** $-1 \cdot 2 \cdot 13$
23. $2^4 \cdot 5$ **25.** $-1 \cdot 2^4 \cdot 17$ **27.** $2^2 \cdot 7 \cdot x^2 \cdot y$
29. $-1 \cdot 2^3 \cdot 3^2 \cdot a \cdot b^3$ **31.** $2 \cdot 3 \cdot 7 \cdot x \cdot y^2$ **33.** $2 \cdot 3 \cdot 5 \cdot 7 \cdot a \cdot b^3$
35. $\{-6, -2, 0, 3\}$ **36.** 66 **37.** 8^3 **38.** 4

Pages 141–142 Lesson 4-5
5. 4 **7.** 10 **9.** $12ab$ **11.** $9a$ **13.** -1 **15.** 12 **17.** 14
19. 12 **21.** 5 **23.** 72 **25.** 3 **27.** $14k$ **29.** $13m^2$
31. 9 **33.** $8y$ **35.** 6 **37.** $6m$ **38.** $-19xy$ **39.** 30 cm
40. $78 > m$ **41.** no **42.** 108 **43.** 14 miles
45. 7 years old

Pages 144–145 Lesson 4-6
3. $\frac{7}{8}$ **5.** $\frac{9}{10}$ **7.** yes **9.** no, $\frac{5}{7}$ **11.** no, $\frac{17}{20}$
13. no, $\frac{1}{2y}$ **15.** no, $\frac{z}{2}$ **17.** $\frac{1}{5}$ **19.** $\frac{3}{4}$ **21.** $\frac{3}{5}$
23. $\frac{1}{3}$ **25.** $\frac{2}{3}$ **27.** $\frac{5}{7}$ **29.** $\frac{1}{2}$ **31.** $\frac{6}{7}$ **33.** $\frac{5}{8}$
35. $\frac{9}{22}$ **37.** $\frac{4m}{5}$ **39.** $\frac{3s}{10}$ **41.** $\frac{7}{13}$ **43.** $\frac{k^2}{3}$
45. The GCF of 10 and 15 is not 5. **46.** -22 **47.** 17
48. composite **49.** 2 **51.** $\frac{4}{7}$

Page 145 Mid-Chapter Review
1. no **2.** yes **3.** yes **4.** no **5.** 15 **6.** 1 **7.** $\frac{41}{56}$
8. -4 **9.** 28 **10.** $2^3 \cdot 5$ **11.** $3 \cdot 5^2$
12. $-1 \cdot 2^2 \cdot 3^2 \cdot 5$ **13.** $2 \cdot 7 \cdot 11 \cdot a^2 \cdot b \cdot c^2$ **14.** 18
15. $5x$ **16.** 12 **17.** $12xy$

Pages 147–148 Lesson 4-7
3. 0, 12, 24, 36 **5.** 0, 30, 60, 90 **7.** 10 **9.** 72 **11.** 60
13. yes **15.** yes **17.** yes **19.** no **21.** yes **23.** yes
25. 30 **27.** 24 **29.** 90 **31.** 35 **33.** 84 **35.** 288
37. $84y$ **39.** $48xy$ **41.** $24k$ **43.** 84 **45.** -45 **46.** false
47. 11 amps **48.** $3 \cdot 3 \cdot 5 \cdot a \cdot a \cdot b \cdot b \cdot b$ **49.** 13 **51.** 60 in.

Pages 150–151 Lesson 4-8
3. 10 **5.** 8 **7.** a^2 **9.** $25a^2$ **11.** less than **13.** less than **15.** 8 **17.** 35 **19.** $120a$ **21.** $24k^2m$
23. greater than **25.** greater than **27.** greater than
29. greater than
31. -2 -1 0 1 2 3 4
32. $-33 < x$ **33.** false
34. 9 **35.** yes **36.** $\frac{7r}{s^2}$ **37.** $\frac{1}{2}$

Pages 153–154 Lesson 4-9
5. $8 \cdot 4 = 32$ **7.** $32 \cdot 4 = 128$ **9.** $9 \cdot 81 = 729$ **11.** y^9
13. 3^{10} **15.** 8^6 **17.** m^4 **19.** $12a^5$ **21.** $-15x^6$
23. $-20x^5y$ **25.** a^3b^4 **27.** m^7b^2 **29.** $7^4 \cdot 4^5$ **31.** 13
32. 11 **33.** $8a$ **34.** false **35.** 63

Pages 157–158 Lesson 4-10
5. $64 \div 4 = 16$ **7.** $625 \div 625 = 1$ **9.** y^2 **11.** x^{-1} or $\frac{1}{x}$
13. $(-2)^1$ or -2 **15.** $(-7)^2$ **17.** a^4 **19.** c^0 or 1
21. m^4 **23.** y^0 or 1 **25.** 1 **27.** $\frac{1}{10^2}$ **29.** $\frac{1}{x}$ **31.** $\frac{t^3}{s^2}$
32. false **33.** 48 ft^2 **34.** $\frac{x}{4} \geq 9$ **35.** $\frac{1}{7}$ **36.** 36
37. $\frac{3}{11}$ **38.** $36r^2$ **39.** $\frac{21}{82} \neq \frac{1}{4}$ **41.** 10^{-2} has a negative exponent. **43.** 2 **45.** 10^6 or 1 million

Pages 160–161 Chapter 4 Review
1. true **3.** false, $\frac{2}{3}$ **5.** true **7.** false, prime **9.** true
11. yes **13.** yes **15.** 2, 3, 6 **17.** 2, 3, 5, 6, 10 **19.** 4^2
21. 3^3 **23.** 48 **25.** 250 **27.** $-1 \cdot 2 \cdot 5^2$
29. $2^3 \cdot 5^2 \cdot a \cdot a \cdot b$ **31.** 16 **33.** 12 **35.** $6a^2b$ **37.** $\frac{a}{4}$
39. $\frac{9x}{5y}$ **41.** 42 **43.** $48ab$ **45.** less than **47.** less than
49. $6x^5$ **51.** x^6y^4 **53.** y^0 or 1 **55.** $\frac{1}{4^2}$ **57.** 3 hours

Chapter 5 Rational Numbers

Page 168 Lesson 5-1
5. Rational **7.** Rational **9.** equal to **11.** Irrational, Rational **13.** Whole, Irrational, Rational
15. $\frac{2}{1}$, $\frac{4}{2}$

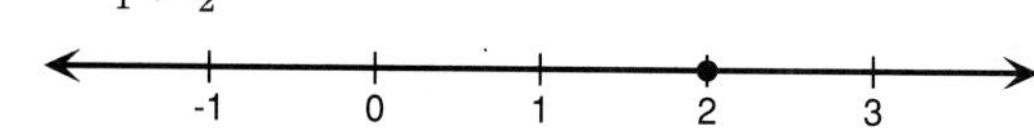

17. -3, $\frac{-6}{2}$

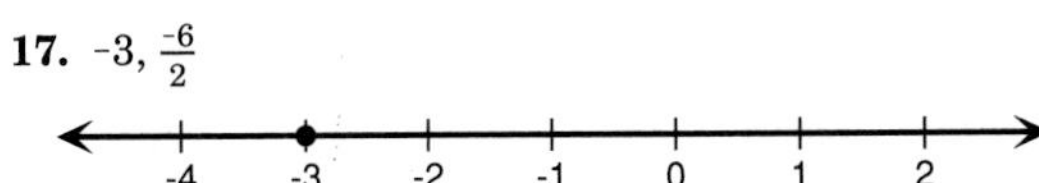

19. greater than **21.** greater than **23.** less than **25.** -23 **26.** 6 or more hours **27.** prime **28.** $-21m^5$

29. $\frac{11}{16}$-inch

Page 171 Lesson 5-2

11. 7 **13.** 53 **15.** 408; 51 **17.** 100 **19.** $\frac{1}{2}$ **21.** $\frac{8}{25}$

23. $\frac{21}{25}$ **25.** $\frac{49}{50}$ **27.** $-\frac{33}{50}$ **29.** $-2\frac{13}{50}$ **31.** $-9\frac{16}{25}$

33. $5\frac{31}{100}$ **35.** $-\frac{93}{125}$ **37.** $1\frac{51}{100}$ **39.** $-\frac{281}{500}$ **41.** $\frac{243}{500}$

43. $9\frac{313}{500}$ **45.** $\frac{1}{3}$ **47.** $1\frac{4}{9}$ **49.** $\frac{4}{33}$ **51.** $\frac{5}{33}$

53. $2\frac{5}{11}$ **56.** $8 + x$ **57.** $u = \frac{t}{w}$ **58.** 28 **59.** $\frac{4}{-5}, -\frac{4}{5}$

60. false **61.** $\frac{23}{1000}$-inch

Page 173 Lesson 5-3

3. 7 **5.** 12 **7.** 40 **9.** $45 **11.** 33, no **13.** 40, yes **15.** 6.0 **17.** 24.7 **19.** 95.5 **21.** 49.6 **23.** $3 **25.** $6 **27.** no **30.** $9^3 + 2$

31.

32. $-\frac{17}{50}$ **33.** 2 + 4 + 1 + 2 = 9; yes

Pages 175–176 Lesson 5-4

5. 2.31 **7.** 4.22 **9.** 88.55 **11.** Commutative Property of Addition **13.** Closure Property of Addition **15.** 104.77 **17.** 8.61 **19.** 0.2051 **21.** 2.7 **23.** -8.81 **25.** -6.48 **27.** $7.3s - 4$ **29.** $14.29w$ **31.** $3.08y$ **33.** 5.18 **35.** 9.08

37. 13.72 **38.** $k \leq 11$ **39.** 128 **40.** $3\frac{1}{5}$ **41.** 24.6 **42.** 23 miles **43.** $4c$ **45.** -$21.49

Pages 178–179 Lesson 5-5

5. $\frac{7}{8}$ **7.** $\frac{7}{17}$ **9.** $\frac{12}{25}$ **11.** $\frac{8}{9}$ **13.** $\frac{2}{13}$ **15.** $1\frac{1}{3}$

17. $1\frac{7}{18}$ **19.** $1\frac{1}{3}$ **21.** $\frac{7}{10}$ **23.** $3\frac{1}{2}n$ **25.** $9x$ **27.** $-t$

29. false **30.** 8 **31.** 100 **32.** -23.4 **33.** $18.41d$

35. $21\frac{1}{4}$ inches

Page 179 Mid-Chapter Review

1. equal to **2.** less than **3.** greater than **4.** greater than **5.** $\frac{3}{5}$ **6.** $\frac{7}{20}$ **7.** $-2\frac{2}{5}$ **8.** $\frac{2}{3}$ **9.** $1\frac{5}{9}$

10. $20 **11.** 30 **12.** 32 **13.** 13.4 **14.** 18.4 **15.** -0.7

16. 2 **17.** $\frac{1}{2}$ **18.** 4

Page 182 Lesson 5-6

3. 8, $\frac{5}{8}$ **5.** 14, $\frac{3}{7}$ **7.** 8, $\frac{1}{8}$ **9.** 12, $\frac{1}{3}$ **11.** 7

13. 38 **15.** $1\frac{9}{14}$ **17.** $\frac{1}{2}$ **19.** $-8\frac{1}{2}$ **21.** $-4\frac{1}{4}$

23. $4\frac{6}{7}$ **25.** $3\frac{1}{4}$ **27.** $-1\frac{1}{5}$ **29.** $5\frac{19}{20}$ **30.** 21.34

31. -12.74 **32.** $1\frac{2}{7}$ **33.** $3\frac{1}{2}$ **34.** $\frac{1}{10}$ **35.** $8\frac{3}{4}$ inches

Pages 186–187 Lesson 5-7

5. -7.9 **7.** -9.2 **9.** -15 **11.** $a < 5$ **13.** 8.4 **15.** $-4\frac{1}{2}$

17. 14 **19.** -21 **21.** $4\frac{1}{8}$ **23.** $5\frac{1}{2}$ **25.** $a > 3\frac{1}{2}$

27. $n < -4.3$ **29.** $f \geq -10.1$ **31.** $p > -3.5$ **33.** $a \geq -\frac{1}{2}$

35. $f \geq 8\frac{1}{4}$ **37.** $x \leq -4.2$ **39.** $b = 3.78$ **40.** -5

41. 8 ft **42.** -16 **43.** $-2\frac{3}{5}$ **44.** $-2\frac{3}{4}$ **45.** 2.93

46. $\frac{11}{15}$ **47.** $-\frac{5}{12}$ **48.** $1\frac{5}{56}$ **49.** $2\frac{1}{2} + x \geq 5\frac{1}{3}$; $2\frac{5}{6}$ lb

51. 269.5 + x = 298.2; 28.7 miles **53.** 44.2°

Page 189 Lesson 5-8

3. 123,454,321 and 12,345,654,321 **5.** red **7.** 15, 20, 26; 9th **9.** no **11.** 4 games won so far

Pages 192–193 Lesson 5-9

5. 11, 13, 15 **7.** 89, 84, 79 **9.** 78, 74, 70 **11.** 7.45, 7.6, 7.75 **13.** no **15.** yes **17.** 19, 23, 27 **19.** 16, 20, 24 **21.** 9.01, 10.13, 11.25 **23.** 26, 37, 50 **25.** 125, 216, 343 **27.** 0; 3 **29.** 78 **31.** -8 **32.** 72

33. $z \geq -1\frac{3}{5}$ **34.** at least $5\frac{3}{4}$ yards **35.** $810

Pages 196–197 Lesson 5-10

5. 2 **7.** 8800 **9.** 12,000 **11.** 8 **13.** 6600 **15.** 12 yd **17.** 11 lb 4 oz **19.** 7 gal **21.** 3 lb 11 oz **23.** 16 ft

25. 2400 pounds **27.** 2 ft 5 in. **28.** $p < -35$ **29.** $\frac{1}{3^2}$

30. $3\frac{7}{8}$ **31.** -10, -16, -23

Pages 198–199 Chapter 5 Review

1. *e* **3.** *h* **5.** *a, b, c, d, e* **7.** less than **9.** equal to

11. $\frac{17}{20}$ **13.** $\frac{2}{25}$ **15.** $-2\frac{9}{25}$ **17.** $\frac{3}{11}$ **19.** $7 **21.** $3

23. $16 **25.** 140 **27.** Commutative Property of Addition **29.** Closure Property of Addition **31.** 1.11 **33.** 5.8

35. -5.5 **37.** 24 **39.** 14 **41.** 1 **43.** $2\frac{1}{4}$ **45.** $\frac{1}{6}$

47. $8\frac{19}{40}$ **49.** Add 9 to each side. **51.** 32, 35, 38; yes

53. 8 gal 1 qt **55.** 7 yd 2 ft **57.** 212 yd

Chapter 6 Multiplying and Dividing Patterns

Pages 206–207 Lesson 6-1

11. $-0.\overline{3}$ **13.** 0.125 **15.** $-0.1\overline{6}$ **17.** $-2.8\overline{3}$ **19.** 1.7 **21.** 0.7 **23.** -0.375 **25.** $0.\overline{1}$ **27.** $0.3\overline{8}$ **29.** 0.4375 **31.** $2.\overline{5}$ **33.** $0.\overline{5}$ **35.** $0.5\overline{1}$ **37.** 2.5625 **39.** 0.775 **41.** 0.8888888 **43.** .89 **44.** no **45.** $m^2n^5p^3$ **46.** true

47. 26.5 **48.** $\frac{6}{7}$ **49.** $b < 4\frac{1}{8}$ **51.** $1.625 or $1.63

Page 210 Lesson 6-2

3. 35 ÷ 7; 5 **5.** $\frac{1}{3} \times 6$; 2 **7.** $\frac{1}{2} \times 10$; 5 **9.** 4 **11.** $6

13. 4 **15.** 3 **17.** 8 **19.** 10 **21.** 20 **23.** 7 **24.** -0 **25.** 3.375 **27.** less than

Pages 213–214 Lesson 6-3

5. positive **7.** positive **9.** $\frac{3}{5}$ **11.** $-\frac{5}{3}$ **13.** $-\frac{11}{5}$ **15.** 15

17. $-\frac{3}{2}$ **19.** $-\frac{35}{2}$ **21.** -3 **23.** -4 **25.** 10 **27.** $-\frac{133}{18}$

29. $\frac{1}{4}$ **31.** $\frac{25}{64}$ **33.** $\frac{16}{25}$ **35.** $\frac{9}{8}$ **37.** $\frac{4}{9}$ **39.** -4

41. $-1\frac{2}{3}$ **43.** -12 **44.** $\frac{a^2}{3b^2}$ **45.** $-2\frac{11}{25}$ **46.** $15.5d$
47. -5.46 **48.** 4 **49.** $1\frac{1}{4}$ cups

Pages 217–218 Lesson 6-4

9. 108.60 **11.** 357.24 **13.** 14.08 **15.** 59 **17.** 20.88 **19.** 36.54 **21.** -0.588 **23.** 1160 **25.** 127.9 **27.** -30.5 **29.** 3.015 **31.** 172.97 **33.** 5.13 **35.** 2.7824 **37.** 81.095406 **39.** 0.01564 **41.** 20 **43.** -15 **45.** 004 **47.** $18b^2$ **48.** $3\frac{5}{6}$ **49.** 53.5 inches **50.** 3 **51.** $-6\frac{3}{7}$ **52.** $\frac{3}{4}$ **53.** 67, 567 pesos **55.** $3.2 billion

Page 221 Lesson 6-5

5. no **7.** yes **9.** $-\frac{9}{8}$ **11.** $\frac{5}{4}$ **13.** -1 **15.** $\frac{y}{x}$ **17.** Closure Property of Multiplication **19.** Inverse Property of Multiplication **21.** Distributive Property **23.** 14 **25.** 68 **27.** $3\frac{1}{8}$ **29.** $12\frac{1}{2}$ **30.** true **31.** -4 **32.** -0.312 **33.** 41.41

Pages 223–224 Lesson 6-6

5. $\frac{5}{6} \cdot \frac{11}{10}$; $\frac{11}{12}$ **7.** $\frac{13}{15} \cdot \frac{1}{6}$; $\frac{13}{90}$ **9.** $\frac{13}{5} \cdot \frac{7}{27}$; $\frac{91}{135}$ **11.** $\frac{68}{9} \cdot \frac{-1}{8}$; $\frac{-17}{18}$ **13.** -4 **15.** $\frac{10}{3}$ **17.** $\frac{21}{16}$ **19.** $-\frac{9}{2}$ **21.** -10 **23.** 6 **25.** $\frac{5}{2}$ **27.** 6 **29.** $-\frac{25}{4}$ **31.** $-\frac{3}{2}$ **33.** $\frac{1}{2}$ **35.** $\frac{81}{256}$ **37.** 54 **38.** 44.0 **39.** $54.70 **40.** $-\frac{4}{13}$ **41.** $\frac{3}{5}$ **43.** $2\frac{1}{4}$ inches

Pages 226–227 Lesson 6-7

7. 2.4 **9.** 90 **11.** .009 **13.** 80 **15.** -31 **17.** 3.21 **19.** 20 **21.** -15 **23.** 5 **25.** 2.1 **27.** 1.6 **29.** 39.0 **31.** 20 **32.** $9y$ **33.** Distributive Property **35.** 24 table tops

Page 227 Mid-Chapter Review

1. 0.6 **2.** 14 **3.** $8 \times 3 + 8 \times \frac{1}{4}$ **4.** 20 **5.** 0.0072 **6.** $-\frac{1}{2}$ **7.** $\frac{16}{81}$ **8.** -4.5 **9.** $\frac{9}{16}$

Page 230 Lesson 6-8

3. 20 **5.** $4 < c$ **7.** $-\frac{18}{25}$ **9.** 1.65 **11.** $t < -\frac{25}{22}$ **13.** -0.5 **15.** -13.6 **17.** -0.3 **19.** -1.08 **21.** $r \geq -1\frac{1}{9}$ **23.** $h < -2.3$ **25.** $x \geq -8$ **27.** 32 **28.** $f < 1.5$ **29.** $-\frac{3}{8}$ **30.** 4.38 **31.** about $\frac{2}{5}$ **33.** 50; 60

Page 232 Lesson 6-9

5. deductive **7.** inductive **9.** deductive **11.** 20, 25 **13.** 1,000, 10,000

Page 235 Lesson 6-10

5. no **7.** yes; $\frac{1}{2}$ **9.** yes; $\frac{1}{2}$ **11.** 17, 23, 30 **13.** 19, 23, 27 **15.** $-3\frac{1}{2}, -5\frac{1}{2}, -7\frac{1}{2}$ **17.** $\frac{5}{16}, -\frac{5}{32}, \frac{5}{64}$ **19.** 40 **21.** 2 **22.** 6.11 **23.** $f < -\frac{8}{21}$ **25.** $2881.20

Page 239 Lesson 6-11

3. 1.59; 10^2 **5.** 1.800; 10^3 **7.** 8.5; 10^{-1} **9.** 5.93; 10^{-5} **11.** 520,000 **13.** -61,000 **15.** -0.005765 **17.** 239,000 **19.** 0.00005 **21.** 5.04×10^{-1} **23.** 9.7×10^4 **25.** 6.23×10^{-3} **27.** 8.92×10^{-6} **29.** 3.0×10^{-4} **31.** 4 **32.** no **33.** $t < -0.92$ **34.** inductive **35.** 2.997928 EE 10

Pages 241–242 Lesson 6-12

5. -5.049 **7.** $1\frac{3}{5}$ **9.** 1.2×10^4 **11.** less than **13.** greater than **15.** greater than **17.** less than **19.** less than **21.** less than **23.** equal to **25.** greater than **27.** greater than **28.** $21x^2$ **29.** $1\frac{1}{8}$ **30.** no **31.** 2.4×10^{-2} **33.** Mets

Pages 244–245 Lesson 6-13

5. $24 \cdot 3.14$ **7.** $2 \cdot 2\frac{1}{2} \cdot \frac{22}{7}$ **9.** $18 \cdot 3.14$ **11.** $2 \cdot 1.3 \cdot 3.14$ **13.** 34.54 mm **15.** 198 ft **17.** 51.496 km **19.** 88 yd **21.** -7.0×10^3 **22.** $-\frac{2}{3}$ **23.** 45.4 **25.** about 7962 mi

Pages 246–247 Chapter 6 Review

1. repeating **3.** reciprocals **5.** inverse **7.** 4.75 **9.** $0.\overline{2}$ **11.** 10 **13.** 130 **15.** $-2\frac{1}{4}$ **17.** 3 **19.** $-3\frac{1}{2}$ **21.** 0.2 **23.** 175 **25.** $2\frac{1}{4}$ **27.** -0.8 **29.** 6.8 **31.** $a \leq -18$ **33.** -25 **35.** no **37.** yes; 12, 3, $\frac{3}{4}$ **39.** 6.5×10^4 **41.** 2.1×10^{-3} **43.** equal to **45.** greater than **47.** 37.68 cm **49.** 88 ft **51.** deductive

Chapter 7 Solving Equations and Inequalities

Pages 252–253 Lesson 7-1

1. 12 **3.** 12 **5.** 36 exercises **7.** 216 pages **9.** 25 bacteria

Pages 257–258 Lesson 7-2

9. Add 7; -2 **11.** Subtract 4; 98 **13.** Add 19; 144 **15.** Multiply by -5; -9 **17.** -4 **19.** -12 **21.** 17 **23.** -15 **25.** -12 **27.** 132 **29.** 84 **31.** 168 **33.** -19 **35.** -231 **37.** 252 **39.** 33 **41.** 10 **43.** 16 **45.** $20 + 2c = -30$ **47.** $\frac{e}{4} - 5 = 7$ **48.** $15 \div 3$ **49.** true **50.** 12.6 **51.** 12 ft 6 in. **52.** 0.72 **53.** $\frac{4}{9}$ **54.** $\frac{7}{12}$ **55.** 50 chips

Pages 260–261 Lesson 7-3

3. Let x = number of years; $4800 - 35x = 4520$; 8 years **5.** $50 + 15s = 170$; 8 scoops **7.** $1.10 + 1.40m = 12.30$; 8 miles **9.** $95 = 2t - 15$; 55 **11.** 7.5 **12.** $3(n + 5) = 27$

Pages 265–266 Lesson 7-4

5. $5d + 15$ **7.** subtract $2k$ from each side; subtract 10 from each side; -31 **9.** subtract $5y$ from each side; add 6 to each side; 6 **11.** subtract $2p$ from each side; subtract 8 from each side; 2 **13.** 53 **15.** -21 **17.** 3 **19.** 3.5 **21.** $\varnothing$ **23.** -2.5 **25.** all numbers **27.** 15 **29.** 10 **31.** 1.5 **33.** -2 **35.** 2 **37.** false **38.** $\frac{5}{11}$ **39.** inductive reasoning **40.** -11 **41.** 12 years

Page 266 Mid-Chapter Review

1. 10 **2.** 13 **3.** 2 **4.** -20 **5.** 4 **6.** 5 **7.** 24 caps **8.** Let n = number; $3 + 2n = -9$; -3

Page 268 Lesson 7-5

3. -6 **5.** 1.5 **7.** -16 **9.** $\frac{35}{2}$ or $17\frac{1}{2}$ **11.** -4 **13.** 2

15. -1 **17.** 2 **19.** -3 **21.** 63 **23.** 10 **25.** 7 hours **26.** 3.36×10^{-4} **27.** 5 **29.** $2y - 682{,}742$

Page 271 Lesson 7-6
3. $x > 2$ **5.** $y > -6$ **7.** $-1 > y$ **9.** $a > 11$ **11.** $g \leq 7$ **13.** $z < -93$ **15.** $t > -4$ **17.** $y < 6$ **19.** $1.17 < t$ **21.** $-11 \geq k$ **23.** $m < -2$ **25.** $x > -50$ **27.** $x < 0.25$ **29.** $y > -5$ **31.** $3n - 5 > 16$ **33.** $\frac{1}{2}m - 5 > 16$ **34.** 36 **35.** $w \leq 13.2$ **36.** about 4 **37.** true **38.** -8 **39.** 6 **40.** 3 **41.** $2(3.49) + s \leq 10; s \leq 3.02$

Page 274 Lesson 7-7
3. $8x + 10 \geq 60$ **5.** $55c + 35 \leq 400$ **7.** $12n - \frac{1}{20}n < 3250$ **9.** $3n + n \leq 120$; $90 **11.** $250(24) + 1200 \leq x$; $7200 **13.** -1.2 **14.** $-5 > b$ **15.** $x \geq 4$

Pages 276–277 Lesson 7-8
5. 2 **7.** 9400 **9.** 3 **11.** 5 **13.** 60,000 **15.** 3000 **17.** 5000 **19.** 2 **21.** 0.018 **23.** 7.3 **25.** 0.053 **27.** 2 **29.** 0.25 **31.** 10,600 **33.** 11,000 **35.** -7, -10, -13 **36.** $5\frac{1}{6}$ **37.** $2 > y$ **38.** $n + (n + 2) \geq 12$ **39.** $p \leq 238$ **41.** 65 cm, 55 cm

Pages 278–279 Chapter 7 Review
1. multiply **3.** ∅ **5.** greater than or equal to **7.** -18 **9.** -8 **11.** -0.6 **13.** -9 **15.** 56 **17.** -1 **19.** 2 **21.** -3 **23.** all numbers **25.** $m < 4$ **27.** $6 \leq x$ **29.** $-3.2 < z$ **31.** 500 **33.** 2.9 **35.** 700 **37.** 100 boxes **39.** $\frac{c}{2} + 30 = 150$; $240 **41.** $8x - 2 < 15; x < \frac{17}{8}$

Chapter 8 Graphing Equations and Inequalities

Page 285 Lesson 8-1
7. -2 **9.** 3 **11.** $\frac{5}{3}$ **13.** -8 **15.** 5 **17.** -6 **19.** 4 **21.** -2 **23.** a **25.** $(12 + 7) + m$ **26.** 81 **27.** $6x + 11 \leq 35$

Pages 287–288 Lesson 8-2
7. $x < 1$ **9.** $x \leq 0$ **11.** $x > -2$ **15.** $x < 4.0$

13. $a \leq 0$;

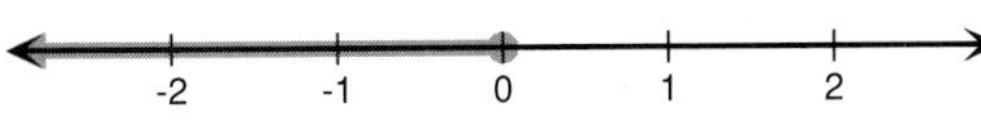

17. $y \leq 2$

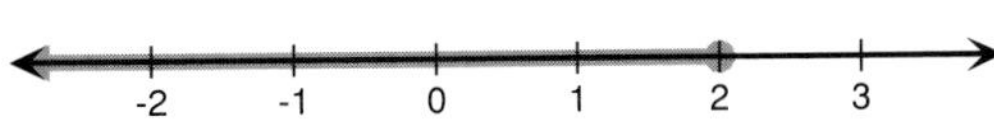

19. $x > 0.5$ **23.** $m < -3$
21. $c > -4$

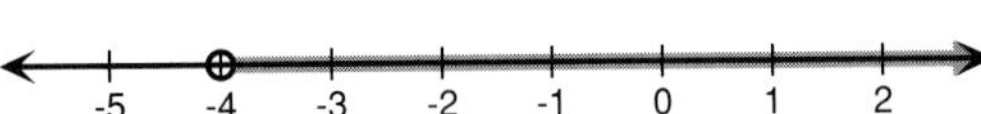

25. $r < 1$

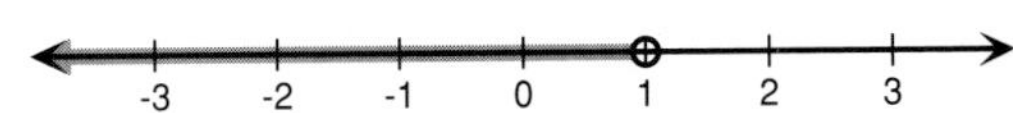

27. $x > -6$ **30.** 5 **31.** false **32.** $110

29.

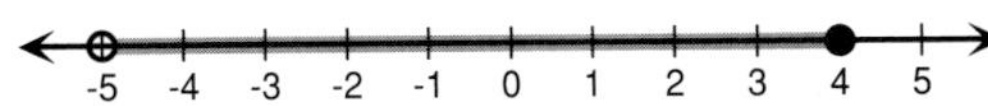

33. -6 **35.** $x < 9.3$

Pages 291–292 Lesson 8-3
5. no **7.** yes **9.** (1, 0) **11.** Z **13.** F **15.** L **17.** C **19.** Y **21.** (4, 1) **23.** (8, 3) **25.** (5, 6) **27.** (9, 8) **29.** (6, 0) **31.** (0, 9) **32.** $-22ab$ **33.** -8 **34.** 1 **35.** $x > -2$ **37.** triangle

Page 295 Lesson 8-4
5. $\frac{1}{2}$; -5; quadrant 4 **7.** -1; -4.7; quadrant 3 **9.** -2.25; 0; none **11.** 0; 0; none **25.** three

13.–23.

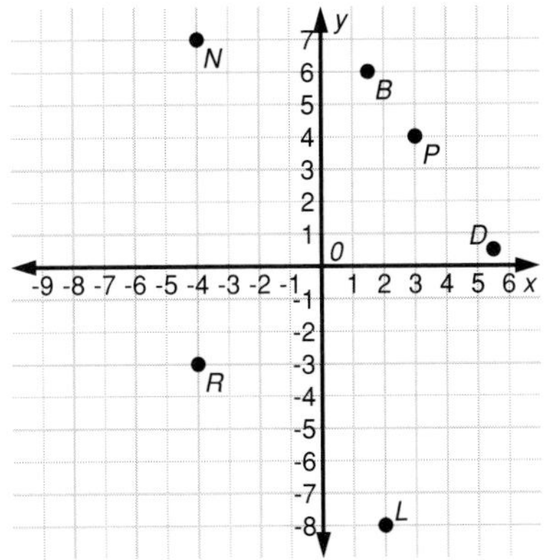

27. one **28.** -12 **29.** $2 \cdot 2 \cdot 7 \cdot a \cdot a \cdot b \cdot b \cdot b$ **30.** 5.875 **31.** $m \geq -14$ **33.** triangle

Pages 297–298 Lesson 8-5
5. (-3, 2), (0, 5), (4, 9), (9, 14) **7.** (2, 2), (-1, -13), (0, -8), (4, 12) **9.** (0, 3.2), (1, 4.2), (-1, 2.2), (-2, -1.2) **11.** (0, 0), (1, 2), (-1, -2), (2, 4) **13.** (0, 0), (1, 6), (-1, -6), (2, 12) **15.** (0, -3), (1, -1), (-1, -7), (2, 1) **17.** (0, 3), (1, -2), (-1, 8), (2, -7) **19.** (0, 5), $(1, 5\frac{1}{2})$, (2, 6), (-2, 4) **21.** (0, 1), $(1, 1\frac{2}{3})$, (3, 3), (-3, -1) **23.** (0, 6), (1, 5), (-1, 7), (6, 0) **25.** (0, 5), (1, 3), (-1, 7), (2, 1) **27.** (4, 0), (1, -3), (5, 1), (-2, -6) **29.** (1, -1), (-1, 1), (4, -4), (0, 0) **31.** (1, 10.75), (0, 8.5), (2, 13), (-2, 4) **33.** $r < -55$ **34.** $k < -10$ **35.** 3

36.–37.

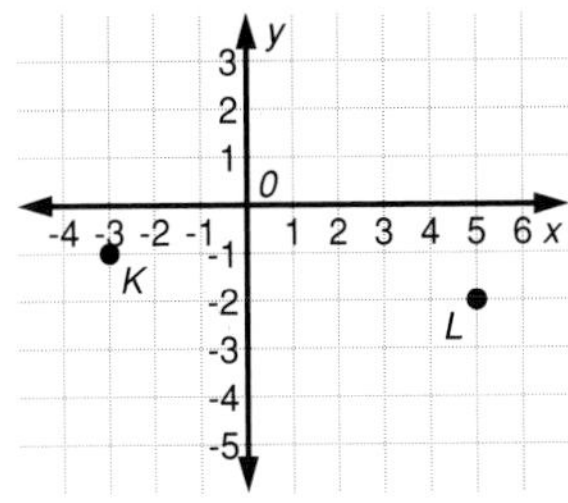

39. (-2, -5), (0, -1), (2, 3)

41. (45, 45), (30, 60), (10, 80), (70, 20), (55, 35)

Pages 300–301 Lesson 8-6

5.

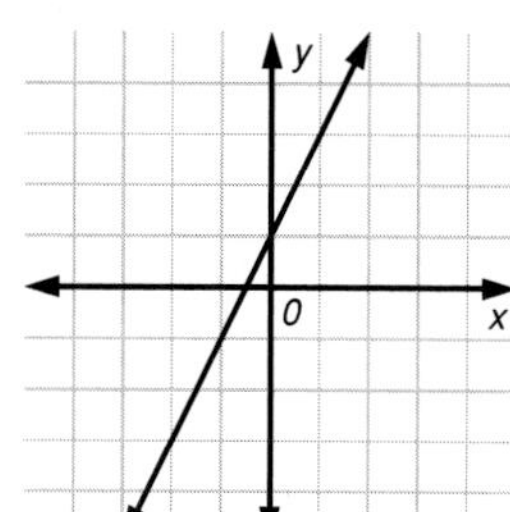

9.

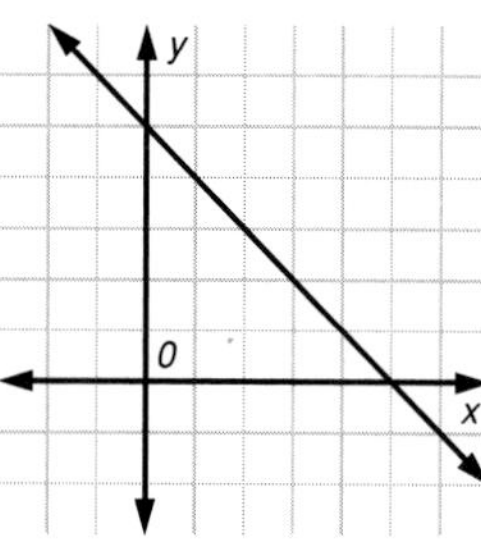

13.

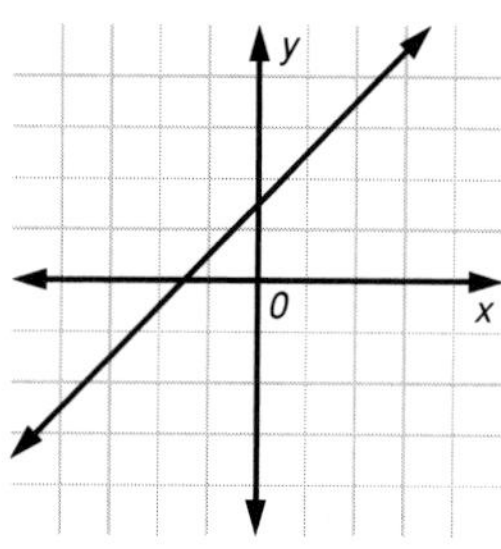

17.

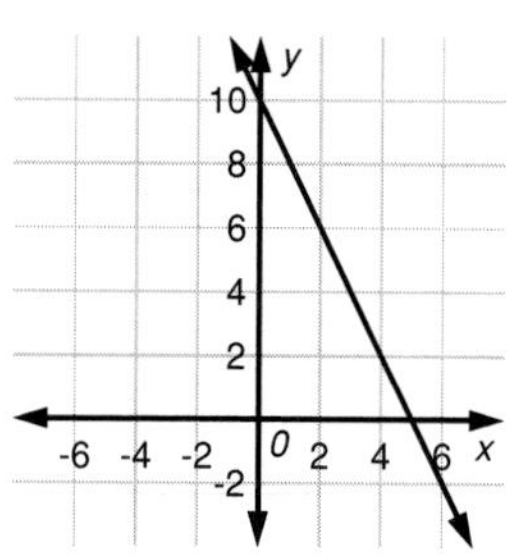

23. $x = y + 3$ **25.** $a + b = 0$ **26.** $\frac{3}{11}$ **27.** $\frac{3 + x}{5} = 11$

28. (0, 1), (1, -2), (-1, 4), (2, -5) **29.** 6

31.

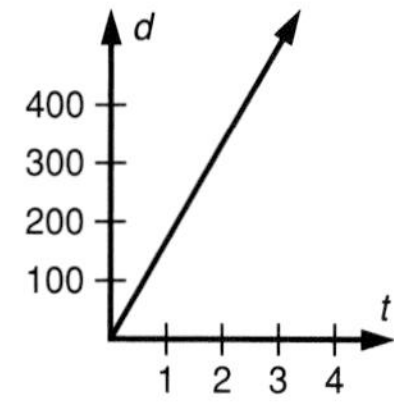

Pages 301 Mid-Chapter Quiz

1.

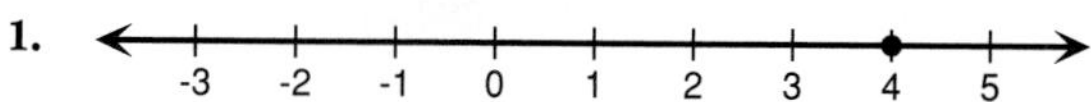

3.

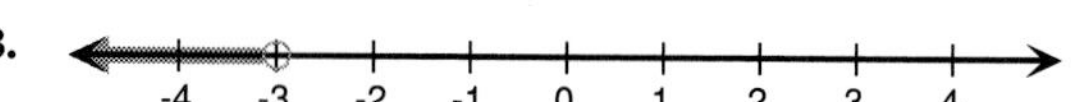

5.–7.

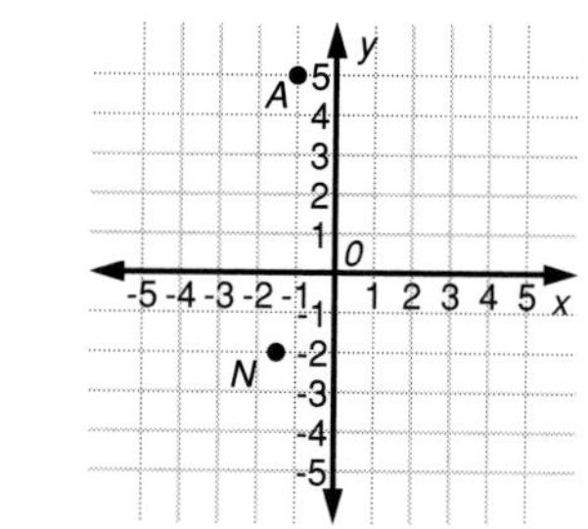

9.

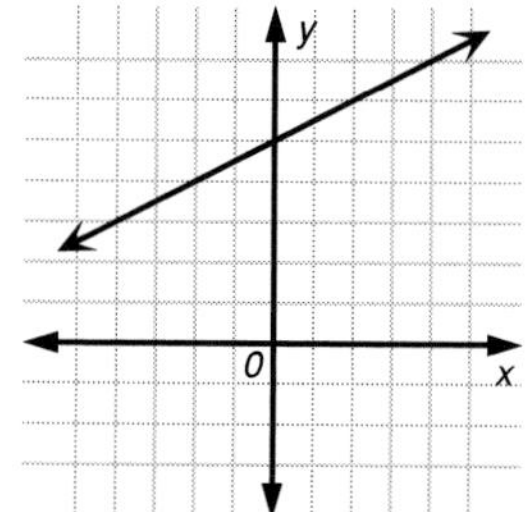

Pages 303–304 Lesson 8-7

7. $\left(\frac{1}{2}, 25\right)$, (2, 100) **9.** 156 lb **11.** $4 per hour; $24

Pages 306–307 Lesson 8-8

5. $-\frac{3}{4}$ **7.** $\frac{1}{3}$ **9.** 0 **11.** 1 **13.** $2\frac{2}{3}$ **15.** $\frac{3}{8}$ **17.** $-\frac{1}{2}$

19. $9x^3$ **20.** $2m + c$ **21.** 10 **29.** 0.1

22.

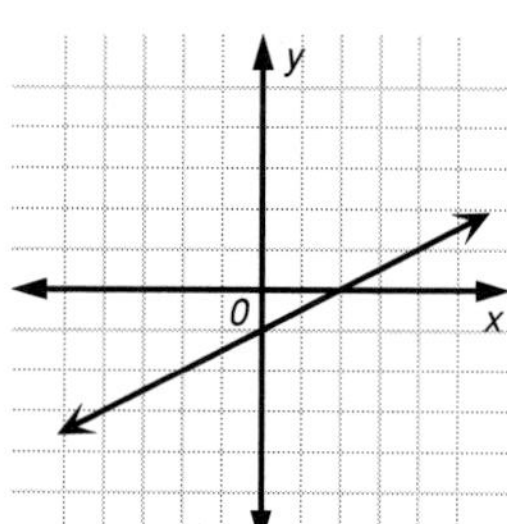

31. a. Oct. 25 b. 5 weeks c. Aug. 30

Pages 309–310 Lesson 8-9

5. 3, -3 **7.** -2, -2 **9.** $\frac{4}{3}$, -4 **11.** $\frac{1}{3}$, $-\frac{2}{3}$ **13.** 0.6, -4.2

15. 1, -1 **17.** $-\frac{3}{2}$, 3 **19.** 2, 10 **21.** 6, 3 **23.** 9.3
25. $-\frac{7}{8}$

24.

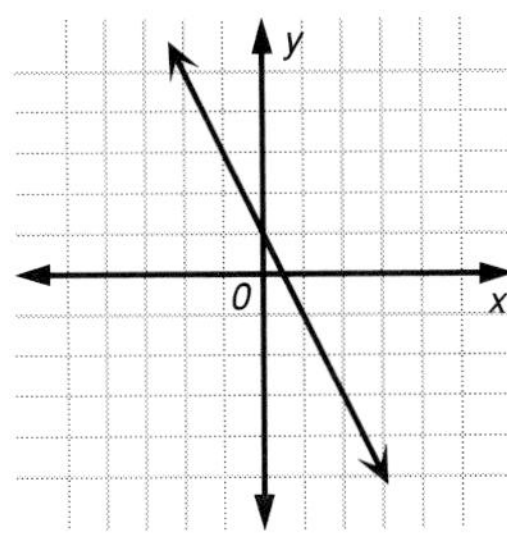

Pages 312–313 Lesson 8-10
5. (-2, 2) **7.** (-6, -3) **9.** (3.5, 1) **11.** (4.5, 0)
13. (-1, -3) **15.** (3, -2) **17.** (-1, -1) **19.** (0, 0)
21. (-1, 2) **23.** $\left(\frac{1}{2}, 2\right)$ **24.** 2 **25.** $\frac{1}{2}$ **27.** (300, 1500)

26.

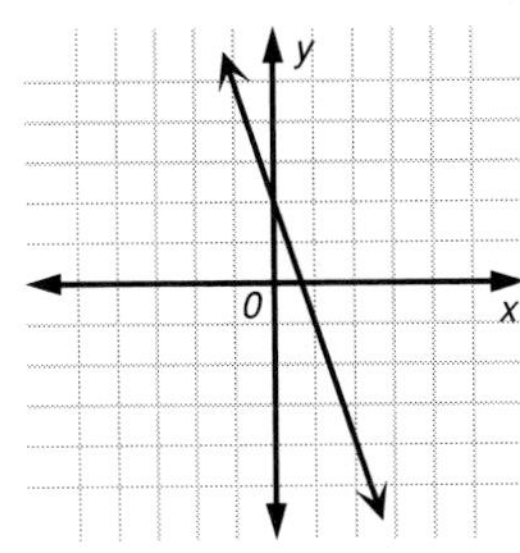

Pages 316–317 Lesson 8-11
7.

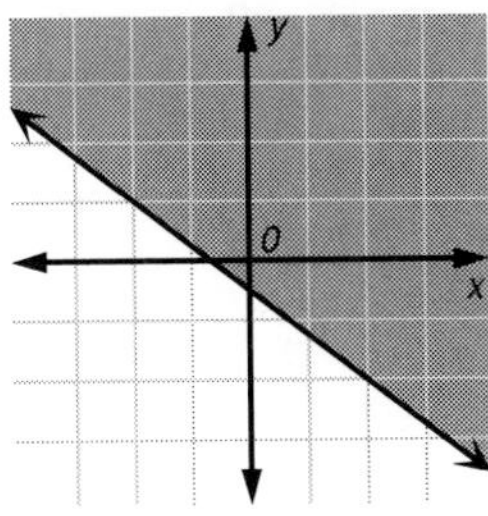

9.

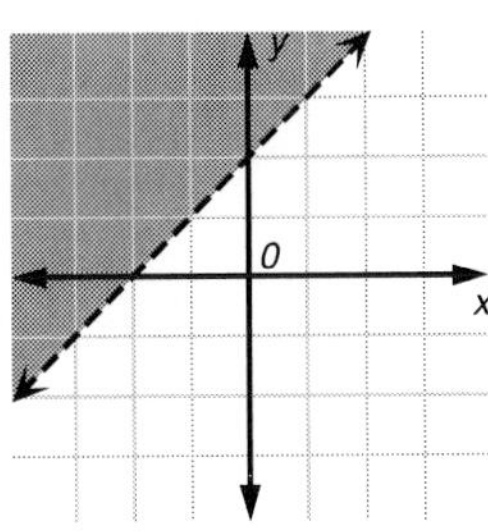

13.

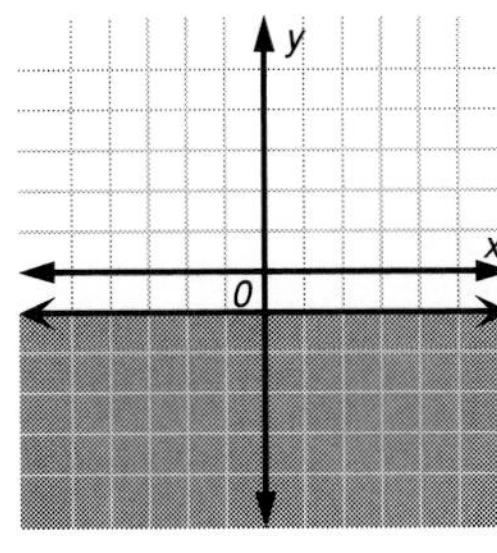

17.

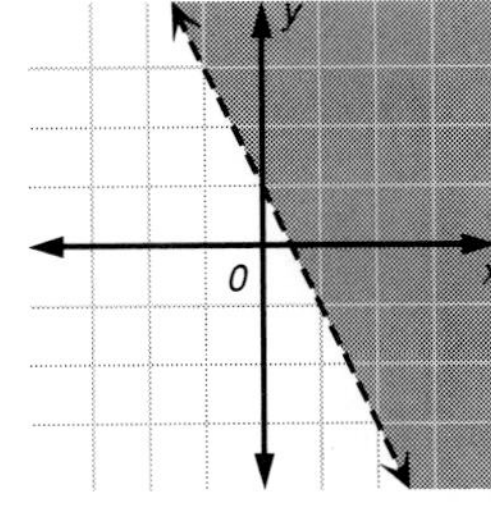

21. $\frac{2}{3}$ **22.** -3; -3

23. (2, -6)

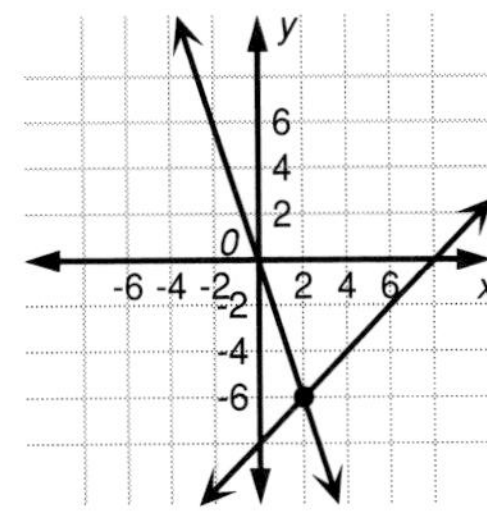

Pages 318–319 Chapter 8 Review
1. c **3.** e **5.** a **7.** i **9.** j **11.** -4 **13.** -9
15. $x \geq -5$ **17.** $x \leq 1$ **19.** $a \geq -2$ **21.** $x \geq -6$

23.–25

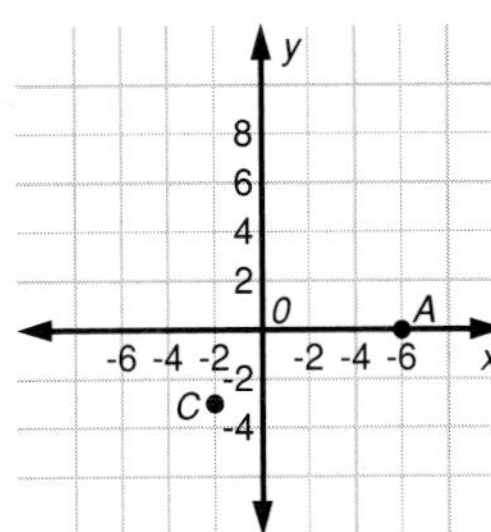

27. (0, 0), $\left(1, \frac{3}{2}\right)$, (2, 3), (-2, -3)

29. (0, -3), (1, 2), (2, 7), (-1, -8) **35.** -6

31.

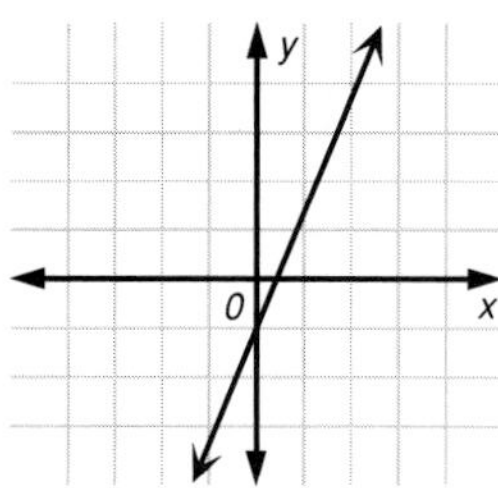

37. $\frac{2}{5}$

39.

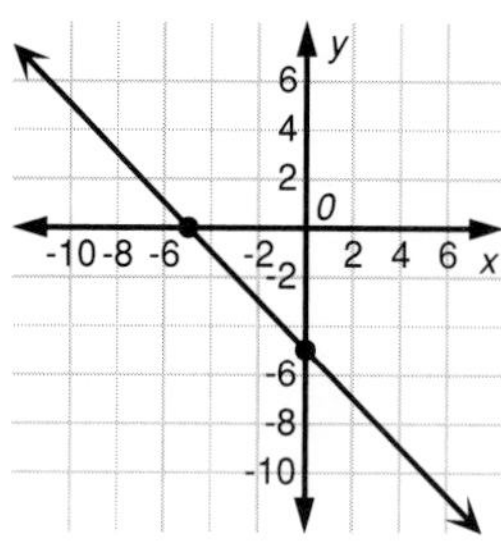

45.

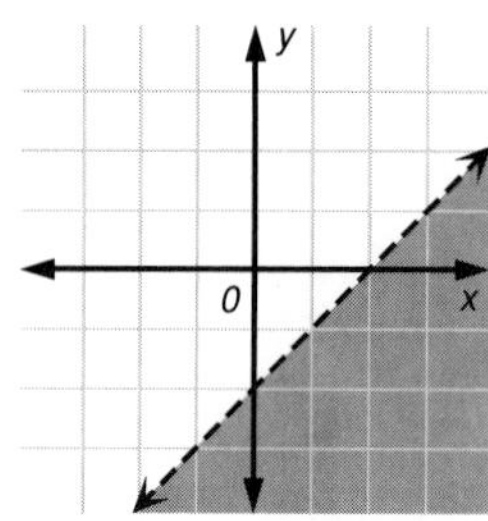

49. 83° F

Chapter 9 Proportion and Percent

Page 325 Lesson 9-1

3. $\frac{5}{7}$ **5.** $\frac{28}{1}$ **7.** $\frac{3}{5}$ **9.** $\frac{100 \text{ miles}}{4 \text{ hours}}$ **11.** $\frac{1}{11}$ **13.** $\frac{3}{1}$ **15.** $\frac{7}{13}$ **17.** $\frac{33}{40}$ **19.** $\frac{4}{1}$ **21.** $\frac{9}{5}$ **23.** 35.2 mph **25.** $7/ticket **27.** 2.4 inches/hour **29.** $250/employee **31.** sample anwer: $n + 1 = 8$ **32.** 80¢ **35.** $0.18/ounce

Pages 328–329 Lesson 9-2

7. ≠ **9.** = **11.** 18 **13.** 2 **15.** ≠ **17.** ≠ **19.** ≠ **21.** = **23.** = **25.** ≠ **27.** 36 **29.** 1 **31.** 3.5 **33.** 16 **35.** 2.1 **37.** 5.1 **38.** 21 **39.** 7 **40.** x represents the x coordinate and y represents the y coordinate. **41.** $\frac{4}{3}$ **42.** $\frac{37 \text{ calories}}{\text{gram}}$ **43.** 2 **45.** 11 **47.** 4.5 cups **49.** 9.5 gallons

Pages 332–333 Lesson 9-3

5. $\frac{40}{3} = \frac{25}{x}$; $1.875 **7.** $\frac{20}{30} = \frac{25}{x}$; 37.5 cm **9.** $\frac{\frac{1}{4}}{1} = \frac{3}{x}$; 12 ft **11.** $\frac{250}{2} = \frac{x}{5}$; 625 bushels **13.** $\frac{15}{21} = \frac{20}{x}$; 28 cm **15.** false **16.** sample answer: (0, -3), (1, -1), (2, 1), (3, 3) **17.** $\frac{1.5 \text{ inches}}{\text{hour}}$ **18.** 1.5 **19.** 22.5 pounds **21.** 135 cm **23.** 1.5 pounds

Pages 336–337 Lesson 9-4

5. 4% **7.** 35% **9.** c **11.** b **13.** 25.92 **15.** 40 **17.** 12.5% **19.** 87.5% **21.** 375% **23.** 24 **25.** 60 **27.** 65% **29.** $24 **30.** 4, -4 **31.** true **32.** 15 **33.** $66\frac{2}{3}$% **35.** $151.68 **37.** $3.25

Pages 340–341 Lesson 9-5

5. 36% **7.** 47.5% **9.** 31% **11.** 90% **13.** $\frac{3}{5}$ **15.** $\frac{8}{25}$ **17.** 0.28 **19.** 0.8 **21.** 81% **23.** 113% **25.** 40.7% **27.** 309.3% **29.** 20% **31.** 225% **33.** 62.5% **35.** 58.3% **37.** $\frac{14}{25}$ **39.** $\frac{73}{100}$ **41.** $\frac{2}{3}$ **43.** $\frac{1}{6}$ **45.** 0.82 **47.** 0.41 **49.** 0.485 **51.** 0.334 **53.** 12.5% **55.** 53% **57.** 18.75% **59.** 98 **60.** 38 **61.** -23 **63.** $\frac{1}{5}$ **64.** 3 **65.** 20% **66.** 120 **67.** $\frac{2}{3}$ **69.** yes; $0.7 < 0.75$

Pages 343–344 Lesson 9-6

5. 75% **7.** 25% **9.** 67% **11.** c **13.** c **15.** $\frac{1}{4}$ **17.** $\frac{2}{3}$ **19.** $\frac{1}{3}$ **21.** $\frac{1}{20}$ **23.** $1\frac{1}{2}$ **25.** $\frac{1}{3}$ **27.** $\frac{1}{2}$ **29.** $\frac{1}{100}$ **31.** 20 **33.** 60 **35.** $5.50 **37.** 100 **39.** 25% **41.** $33\frac{1}{3}$% **43.** 20% **45.** inductive **46.** $\frac{5}{8}$ **47.** $c > 2$ **48.** 20 **49.** 82.7% **50.** $\frac{19}{50}$ **51.** Texas: 33%; Montana: 20%; Kansas: 17%; Nebraska: 17%; New Mexico: 15% **53.** $3

Page 345 Mid-Chapter Quiz

1. $\frac{5}{3}$ **2.** $\frac{3}{5}$ **3.** $\frac{9}{11}$ **4.** $1.28/gallon **5.** 0.75 pound/week **6.** 6 **7.** 9 **8.** 2 **9.** 2.8 pounds **10.** $1\frac{2}{3}$ gallons **11.** 9 **12.** 37.5% **13.** 88% **14.** $33\frac{1}{3}$% **15.** 87.5% **16.** 0.2; $\frac{1}{5}$ **17.** 0.008, $\frac{1}{125}$ **18.** 1.1, $\frac{11}{10}$ **19.** 9 **20.** $2

Pages 347–348 Lesson 9-7

5. $15 = 0.03 \cdot B$; 50 **7.** $18 = R \cdot 60$; 30 **9.** $16 = R \cdot 64$; 25 **11.** $P = 0.31 \cdot 14$; 4.34 **13.** 25% **15.** $242.80 **17.** 62.5% **19.** $6540 **21.** 125 **23.** 50% **25.** $c \geq 18$ **26.** 2 **27.** 125% **28.** $15 **29.** $48,700 **31.** 6%

Pages 350–351 Lesson 9-8

5. $10.50 **7.** $174.38 **9.** $7.53 **11.** $650 **13.** $945 **15.** $21 **17.** 25% **19.** 15% **20.** 24 **22.** 20 **23.** $68.64 **25.** $1068.52 **27.** $34.09

Pages 352–353 Lesson 9-9

3. 12 ways **5.** 35 cards **7.** $153.90 **9.** $255

Page 355 Lesson 9-10

5. 25% **7.** 6% **9.** 14% **11.** 7% **13.** 24% **15.** 8% **17.** 4% **19.** $\frac{1}{2}$ **20.** 20% **21.** 20% **22.** about 36% **23.** 1% **25.** 20%

Pages 356–357 Chapter Review

1. ratio **3.** proportion **5.** 882 **7.** $\frac{2}{3}$ **9.** $\frac{1}{2}$

11. 50 mph **13.** 4 **15.** 0.4 **17.** \$200.25 **19.** 87.5% **21.** 40% **23.** 106% **25.** 105% **27.** 121% **29.** 0.33 **31.** 0.235 **33.** 50% **35.** 30% **37.** 200 **39.** 40 **41.** 2.50% **43.** 5 **45.** \$7.50; \$42.50 **47.** \$1.20; \$2.39 **49.** \$31.25 **51.** 20% decrease

Chapter 10 Statistics and Graphs

Pages 364–365 Lesson 10-1

5. blue **7.** 45 **9.** no intervals, not numerical **11.** true **13.** 27% **15.** no **17.** 27 **19.** 6 **21.** 22 **23.** The test scores range from 27 to 40, with 35 being the most common score. **24.** first floor **25.** (3, 1) **26.** $\frac{115 \text{ revolutions}}{10 \text{ seconds}}$ **27.** 7% increase

Pages 369–370 Lesson 10-2

5. 2.6; 2.6 and 1.5; 2.7 **7.** 4.7; 4.7; 4.76 **9.** 105; 78; 100.4 **11.** 56.6; 55; 55 **13.** 126; 127; 121 and 130 **15.** 0.9; 0.9; none **17.** 159.5 **19.** lower **21.** no effect **23.** no effect **25.** 157.2; 155; 155 **27.** -13°F **28.** 2.5 **29.** 6 cups **30.** 34% **31.** 119 **32.** 77 **33.** 69.7; 70; 68 and 70 **35.** *a.* 2; 4 *b.* 8; 8

Page 373 Lesson 10-3

7. 6, 7, and 8 **9.** 0 and 0

11.
0 | 8 8 9
1 | 1 2 4 5 7
2 | 5 7 8 9 9 9
3 | 0 1 6 9
4 | 0 1

13. 8 **15.** kind of museum **19.** (0, 1), (2, 0), (4, -1), (-2, 2) **20.** $87\frac{1}{2}$% **21.** 7; 7; 3 **23.** clustered

Pages 376–377 Lesson 10-4

3. 24 **5.** 27, 6 **7.** 62 **9.** 22 **11.** 81 **13.** 67 **15.** 22 **17.** 79 **19.** 82, 72 **23.** Mary's is greater. **25.** Tanya; her scores are closer to her median most of the time; Mary's scores vary more game by game. **26.** -8 **27.** 14; 35; $\frac{40}{100}$

28.
6 | 1 8
7 | 5 7 8 8
8 | 1 3 8
9 | 0 2 5

29. a. close b. Wichita's is greater. c. San Francisco and Wichita have about the same average temperature, but Wichita's temperatures vary more.

Pages 380–381 Lesson 10-5

5. 35 **7.** 20 **9.** no **11.** 70 **13.** 80 **15.** 25 **17.** 17.5 and 117.5; no **19.** 15 or 16 **21.** 8 and 40 **23.** extremes, quartiles, and medians; all values **25.** $(\frac{3}{2}, 0)$, (0, 3) **26.** \$140.25 **27.** 12; 10

Pages 381 Mid-Chapter Quiz

1.

Scores	Tally	Frequency
16–20	~~||||~~	5
21–25	~~||||~~ ||||	9
26–30	~~||||~~ ~~||||~~ |	11

2. 24; 22; 21

3.
1 | 7 7 7 8 9
2 | 1 1 1 1 1 1 2 2 5 7 7 8 8 9 9 9
3 | 0 0 0 0

4. 13; 8

5.

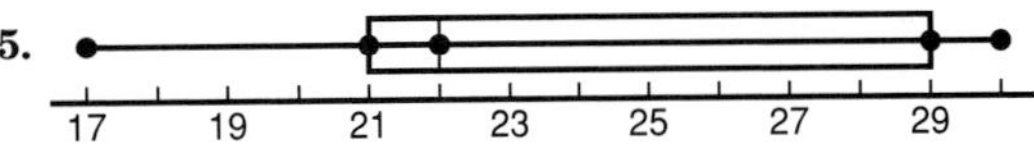

Pages 384–385 Lesson 10-6

3. none **5.** positive **7.** positive **9.** negative **11.** none **13.** above most of the points **15.** no **17.** science **19.** $\frac{2x}{9}$ **20.** 56; 41; 15 **21.** 111; 185

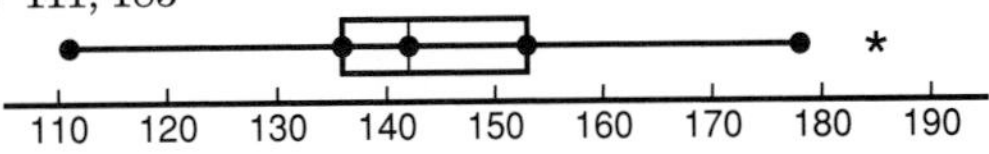

23. If there is a negative relationship between the doses of the antibiotic and the severity of disease, the antibiotic is probably effective.

Page 387 Lesson 10-7

1. 400 **3.** 24 **5.** 116 pages **7.** 77 pieces **9.** \$24 **11.** \$35.32 **13.** 204 squares

Pages 389–390 Lesson 10-8

3. 50 **5.** $\frac{3}{10}$ **7.** 80 **9.** about 315 **11.** 53 girls; yes; randomly taken **13.** 112 small, 217 medium, 80 large, 16 extra large **15.** 29,400 fillers **18.** $1\frac{1}{2}$ **19.** 24 **20.** positive

Pages 392–393 Lesson 10-9

7. different scale **9.** the first graph, because the monthly sales don't appear to be rising as quickly **11.** \$34,700; median **13.** sports; mode **15.** 9.32×10^4 **16.** 4.6; 4.3; none **17.** 700 cans **19.** \$82,000; median; \$150,000 is much larger than the other four prices.

Pages 394–395 Chapter 10 Review

1. mode **3.** can **5.** 25 **7.** 11–12 **11.** 4.4; 4.3; none **13.** 29 **15.** 13 **17.** 14 **19.** 9 **21.** 0, 27 **23.** positive **25.** 120 lockers

Chapter 11 Probability

Pages 401–402 Lesson 11-1

5. 4 outcomes **7.** 2 outcomes **9.** 12 outcomes **11.** 9 outcomes **13.** 18 outcomes **15.** 10 outcomes **17.** -96 **18.** $\frac{1}{5}$ **19.** mode **21.**

V < R, W, G
W < R, W, G
S < R, W, G

Pages 404–405 Lesson 11-2
5. $4 \times 2 \times 4$ **7.** $2 \times 2 \times 2 \times 2$ or 2^4 **9.** $5 \times 6 \times 4$
11. 12 outcomes **13.** 18 dinners **15.** 27 dinners
17. 1024 outcomes **19.** 32,768 outcomes **20.** 3.45
21. 27% **22.** 8 outcomes **23.** 18 days

Page 409 Lesson 11-3
5. combination **7.** combination **9.** permutation
11. 720 **13.** 20 **15.** 10 **17.** 3,628,800 **19.** 12
21. 1680 **23.** 252 **25.** 1 "word" **26.** 7 **27.** $13.50
28. 72 outcomes **29.** 24 orders **31.** 45 line segments

Pages 412–413 Lesson 11-4
5. $\frac{1}{2}$ **7.** If Monday: 1. If not Monday: 0. **9.** $\frac{1}{2}$ **11.** 0
13. $\frac{3}{8}$ **15.** $\frac{1}{12}$ **17.** $\frac{1}{2}$ **19.** $\frac{3}{4}$ **21.** $\frac{1}{3}$ **23.** 1 **25.** $\frac{1}{12}$
27. 0 **29.** Sample answers: 1, 1, 1; 1, 2, 3; 6, 5, 4
31. The probability of tossing a coin and getting heads is 1 out of 2. **33.** $\frac{22}{25}$ **34.** $t \geq 3$ **35.** 25% **36.**

5	1 4 8 8
6	3 4 6 7 9
7	0 1

37. 42 **39.** $\frac{1}{5}$

Pages 415–416 Lesson 11-5
3. $\frac{1}{6}$ **5.** $\frac{1}{4}$ **7.** 100 stamps **9.** $2.88 **11.** 11; 10; 10
12. $\frac{7}{15}$

Pages 419–420 Lesson 11-6
3. $\frac{1}{21}$ **5.** $\frac{1}{42}$ **7.** $\frac{1}{20}$ **9.** $\frac{1}{20}$ **11.** $\frac{3}{20}$ **13.** $\frac{2}{5}$ **15.** $\frac{1}{3}$
17. $\frac{1}{4}$ **19.** $\frac{1}{4}$ **21.** $\frac{1}{4}$ **23.** $\frac{1}{7}$ **25.** $\frac{8}{21}$ **26.** false
27. 25¢/doughnut **28.** $\frac{21}{36}$ or $\frac{7}{12}$ **29.** $\frac{4}{27}$

Page 420 Mid-Chapter Quiz
1. *SO, SA, CO, CA, PO, PA* **2.** 54 outcomes **3.** 120
4. 210 **5.** 126 **6.** $\frac{3}{7}$ **7.** 0 **8.** $\frac{8}{49}$

Pages 422–423 Lesson 11-7
3. $\frac{2}{9}$ **5.** $\frac{1}{6}$ **7.** $\frac{1}{9}$ **9.** $\frac{1}{12}$ **11.** $\frac{1}{36}$ **13.** $\frac{1}{21}$ **15.** $\frac{1}{21}$ **17.** $\frac{2}{195}$
19. $\frac{1}{130}$ **21.** $\frac{5}{78}$ **23.** $\frac{4}{3705}$ **25.** $\frac{1}{1560}$ **27.** $-2x$
28. positive **29.** 15 **30.** $\frac{1}{6}$ **31.** $\frac{9}{49}$

Pages 426–427 Lesson 11-8
3. yes **5.** no **7.** yes **9.** $\frac{1}{6}$ **11.** $\frac{2}{3}$ **13.** $\frac{33}{49}$ **15.** $\frac{2}{7}$
17. $\frac{7}{10}$ **19.** $\frac{2}{3}$ **21.** $\frac{11}{15}$ **23.** 1

24.

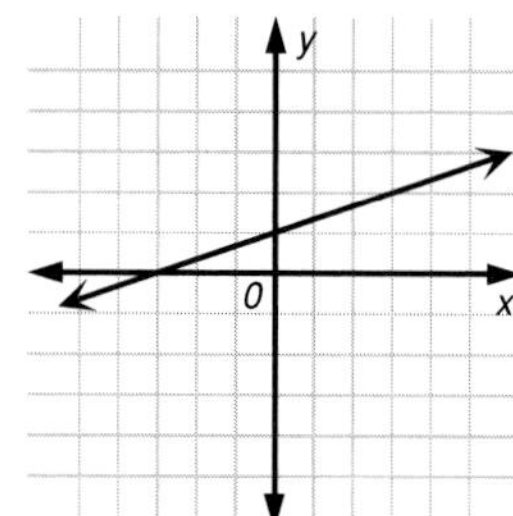

25. 3 hours **26.** $\frac{1}{3}$ **27.** 0.85

Page 431 Lesson 11-9
9. Use a die and let a roll of 1 be a no show. **13.** 3000 fish

Pages 432–433 Chapter 11 Review
1. event **3.** probability **5.** are not **7.** 6 outcomes
9. 1296 outcomes **11.** 1 **13.** 56 **15.** 1716 ways
17. $\frac{2}{5}$ **19.** $\frac{1}{10}$ **21.** $\frac{1}{25}$ **23.** 0 **25.** $\frac{1}{9}$

Chapter 12 Applying Algebra to Geometry

Pages 440–441 Lesson 12-1
5. $\overleftrightarrow{AE}$ **7.** $\overrightarrow{CD}$ **9.** $\angle DCE$ **11.** 24° **13.** line **15.** plane
17. point **19.** 140°; obtuse **21.** 25°; acute **23.** 50°; acute **25.** 90°; right

27. C D

29. S T

31. E F

33. G H **35.** acute **37.** right

39. obtuse **40.** false **41.** true **42.** $\frac{2}{5}$ **43.** *HHH, HHT, HTH, HTT, THH, THT, TTH, TTT* **44.** $\frac{7}{12}$
45. The three "pods" determine a plane.

Pages 443–444 Lesson 12-2
5. $33\frac{1}{3}$% **6.** acute

7.

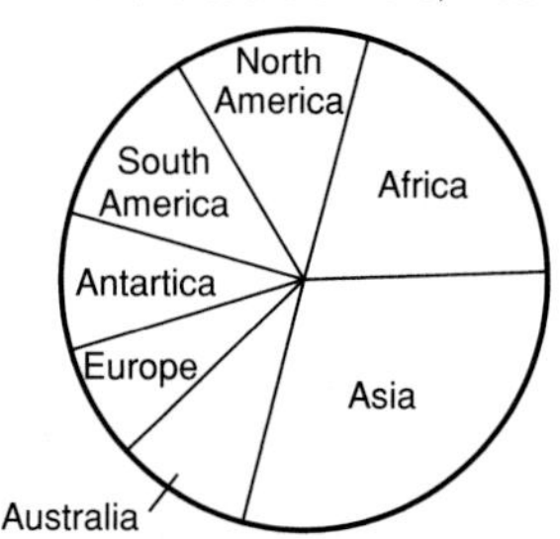

Pages 447–448 Lesson 12-3
5. 150° **7.** 100° **9.** 60° **11.** 40° **13.** 40° **15.** 155°
17. 85°; 95° **19.** 54°; 126° **21.** 31°; 59° **22.** $7x = -28$
23. 19 points **24.** 720 **25.** 56 **27.** 74°; 16°

Page 451 Lesson 12-4
5. $\angle AFG$; $\angle BFG$; $\angle CGF$; $\angle DGF$ **7.** $\angle BFG$, $\angle CGF$; $\angle AFG$, $\angle DGF$ **9.** $\angle EFA$, $\angle FGC$; $\angle BFE$, $\angle DGF$; $\angle AFG$, $\angle CGH$; $\angle BFG$, $\angle DGH$ **11.** 58° **13.** 122° **15.** 122°
16. $\frac{1}{6}$ **17.** 74°; 164°

Pages 454–455 Lesson 12-5
31. $2\frac{2}{3}$ feet

32.

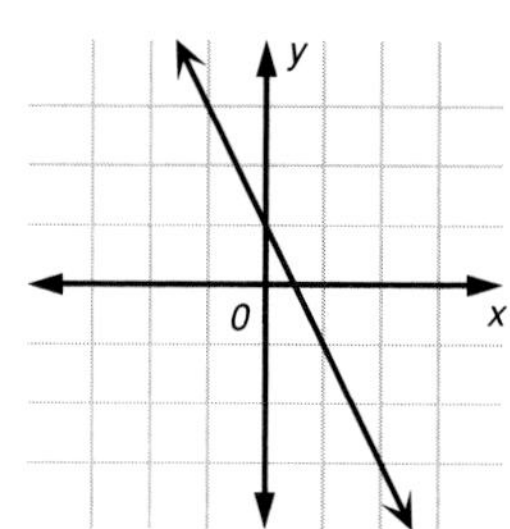

33.

6	6 6 6 7 9
7	0 0 1 1 2 2 4

34. 64°

Pages 457–458 Lesson 12-6
3. 69°; acute **5.** 117°; obtuse **7.** 50°; right **9.** 85° **11.** 25° **13.** 85° **14.** $\frac{14}{33}$ **17.** 45°; 55° **19.** 119°

Page 458 Mid-Chapter Quiz
6. about 61° **7.** $m\angle A = 50°$; $m\angle B = 40°$ **8.** $m\angle F = 100°$; $m\angle G = 80°$ **9.** 34° **10.** 146° **11.** 34° **12.** 146° **13.** 146°

Page 460 Lesson 12-7
3. hypothesis: If it is warm; conclusion: then it is summer **5.** hypothesis: If a month has 31 days; conclusion: then it is January **7.** hypothesis: If the sun is shining; conclusion: then it is morning **9.** If the animal is a cow, then it has four legs.; false; true **11.** If two lines are perpendicular, then they form right angles.; true; true **12.** 20; 40 **13.** 99° **15.** no **17.** no

Page 463 Lesson 12-8
5. $\angle B$ **7.** $\overline{ED}$ **9.** $\angle C$ **11.** *DEF* **13.** *BAE* **15.** $\overline{GH}$ **17.** $\angle H$ **19.** 15% **20.** 216 **21.** If an angle measures less than 90°, it is an acute angle.

Page 467 Lesson 12-9
5. $\overline{RN}$ **7.** $\frac{m\overline{PQ}}{m\overline{ST}}$; $\frac{m\overline{PR}}{m\overline{SU}}$; $\frac{m\overline{UT}}{m\overline{RQ}}$ **9.** 3 cm **11.** 4.5 m **12.** 0 **13.** no; Sides are not congruent.

Pages 469–470 Lesson 12-10
3. $\frac{4}{5} = \frac{8}{x}$; 10 km **5.** $\frac{3}{5} = \frac{4.5}{x}$; 7.5 cm **6.** uneven intervals on x-axis or y-axis; no labels on the axes **7.** 2.7 ft **9.** Cleveland to Atlanta: 25 cm; New York to Atlanta: 32.5 cm **11.** 2.6 ft **13.** $10\frac{2}{3}$ m

Pages 472–473 Lesson 12-11
5. 60° **7.** parallelogram **9.** quadrilateral **11.** square **13.** 150° **15.** 100° **17.** sometimes **19.** never **21.** always **22.** -19 **23.** $2 \cdot 7 \cdot 7$ **24.** 20° **25.** 16 ft **27.** 108°

Pages 475–476
5. quadrilateral; not regular **7.** 720° **9.** 1440° **11.** 8640° **13.** 90 ft **15.** 66.8 m **17.** 0.6; 0.45; 0.4 **18.** $\frac{1}{12}$ **20.** true **21.** 120°

Pages 478–479 Chapter Review
1. b **3.** g **5.** a **7.** i **13.** $\angle KIJ$; $\angle ECD$ **15.** $\angle KIJ$, $\angle FIC$; $\angle BCD$, $\angle FCI$ **17.** $\angle KIJ$, $\angle JIF$; $\angle ACH$, $\angle HCE$ **19.** $\overline{BH}$ **21.** $\angle JIF$, $\angle ICE$; $\angle HFG$, $\angle FCE$ **25.** 42° **27.** $\angle Y$ **29.** $\overline{XZ}$ **31.** 18 ft **33.** 720° **35.** 12.5 ft **37.** If Mrs. Clark lives in a city, Mrs. Clark lives in Boston.; true; false

Chapter 13 Measuring Area and Volume

Pages 486–487 Lesson 13-1
7. 5 cm; 4 cm; $5 \cdot 4$; 20 cm^2 **9.** 20 cm; 17 cm; $\frac{1}{2} \cdot 20 \cdot 17$; 170 cm^2 **13.** 555 mm^2 **15.** 544 m^2 **17.** 85 m^2 **19.** 216 cm^2 **21.** 35 in^2 **23.** $3\frac{1}{8}$ in^2 **25.** 4 **26.** false **27.** 4^5 or 1024 outcomes **28.** obtuse **29.** 15 roses

Pages 489–490 Lesson 13-2
5. 15 m, 5 m, 6 m; 60 m^2 **7.** 20 mm, 12 mm, 12 mm; 192 mm^2 **9.** 300 in^2 **11.** 70 ft^2 **13.** 29.484 m^2 **14.** 4.401×10^7 **15.** 126° **16.** 28 in^2 **17.** 137,500 ft^2 **19.** 9875 ft^2

Page 493 Lesson 13-3
3. $3 \cdot 3 \cdot \pi$; 28.3 cm^2 **5.** $3.5 \cdot 3.5 \cdot \pi$; 38.5 mi^2 **7.** 7543 ft^2 **9.** 804 cm^2 **11.** 154 yd^2 **13.** 85 km^2 **15.** 58 sec **16.** 39 cm^2 **17.** 4 bags

Pages 496–497 Lesson 13-4
7. $2(5 \cdot 2) + 2(8 \cdot 2) + 2(8 \cdot 5)$; 132 in^2 **9.** $2(3.5 \cdot 3.5) + 2(3.5 \cdot 12) + 2(3.5 \cdot 12)$; 192.5 m^2 **11.** 200 mm^2 **13.** -76 **14.** $\frac{1}{2}$ **15.** about 154 cm^2 **17.** 360 ft^2 **19.** no; The surface area could not be more than the area of the paper.

Pages 499–500 Lesson 13-5
5. $2(\pi \cdot 9^2) + 2 \cdot \pi \cdot 9 \cdot 54$; about 3563 in^2 **7.** 3167 m^2 **9.** 434 ft^2 **11.** \$0.09/pound **12.** 310 cm^2 **13.** hypothesis: If a polygon has six sides; conclusion: then it is a hexagon **15.** 17 *g*

Pages 503–504 Lesson 13-6
5. circular cone; 2 surfaces **7.** 799.4 m^2 **9.** 51.6 ft^2 **11.** 115.5 ft^2 **13.** 1.75, 1.88, 2.01 **14.** 7.5 m **15.** about 534 cm^2

Page 504 Mid-Chapter Quiz
1. 20 cm^2 **2.** 600 yd^2 **3.** 1256.6 in^2 **4.** 166 mm^2 **5.** 402.1 in^2 **6.** 208 m^2 **7.** 81 cm^2 **8.** 47.1 in^2

Pages 507–508 Lesson 13-7
5. cube; $4 \cdot 4 \cdot 4$; 64 ft^3 **7.** 216 cm^3 **9.** 336 cm^3 **11.** 1200 ft^3 **13.** 62.5 cm^3 **15.** 255 cm^3 **17.** 8, 8, 11 **18.** about 75 m^2 **19.** 198 sugar cubes

Pages 509–510 Lesson 13-8
3. $\pi \cdot 3 \cdot 3 \cdot 5$; 141.3 yd^3 **5.** $\pi \cdot 14 \cdot 14 \cdot 10$; 6157.5 in^3 **7.** 301.6 ft^3 **9.** 1017.9 m^3 **11.** 7.7 m^3 **13.** 6 **15.** $m > 88$ **16.** $\angle A$ **17.** 48 in^3 **19.** about 1275

Pages 513–514 Lesson 13-9
3. $\frac{1}{3} \cdot 12 \cdot 10 \cdot 15$; 600 in^3 **5.** $\frac{1}{3} \cdot \frac{1}{2} \cdot 4 \cdot 8 \cdot 12$; 64 in^3 **7.** 150.8 m^3 **9.** 10,053.1 cm^3 **11.** 1357.2 cm^3 **13.** 50 cm^3 **15.** 1885.0 m^3 **16.** $\frac{11}{12}$ **17.** 540° **18.** about 2614 in^3 **19.** about 6.3 in^3

Pages 516–517 Lesson 13-10
5. 4; 0.01 ft **7.** 1; 0.001 kg **9.** 4; 0.0001 m **11.** 62 mm; 64 mm **13.** 18.1 m; 18.3 m **15.** 2.9 m; 3.1 m **17.** 9 ft; 11 ft **19.** 7.1 L **21.** 84.47 m **23.** 8.0 km **25.** 171 kg **27.** 35 m^2 **28.** $\angle 2$, $\angle 6$; $\angle 3$, $\angle 7$ **29.** 56 in^3 **31.** 0.0004 mm; 0.40 mm; 0.4 mm; 40 mm

Page 519 Lesson 13-11
1. 100 cm **5.** 3.2 m^3 **7.** 27 diagonals **9.** 181 posts **11.** about 754.0 ft^2

Pages 520-521 Chapter Review
1. square centimeter **3.** surface area **5.** altitude **7.** precision **9.** 82.5 in^2 **11.** 221 m^2 **13.** 254.3 mi^2

15. 2840 m^2 **17.** $3\frac{3}{8} \text{ ft}^2$ **19.** 7665 cm^2 **21.** 9.4 m^2
23. 3325 in^3 **25.** 2770.9 ft^3 **27.** 504 m^3 **31.** 1 **33.** 5
35. 8.0 m^2

Chapter 14 Applying Algebra to Right Triangles

Pages 527–528 Lesson 14-1
5. 64 **7.** 36 **9.** 3 **11.** 4 **13.** 5 **15.** -3 **17.** -8 **19.** -10 **21.** -12 **23.** -20 **25.** 900 **27.** 289 **29.** 196 **31.** 1156 **33.** 0.4 **35.** $\frac{7}{9}$ **36.** -3 **37.** 12; 17 **39.** 26 cm **40.** 1.8 ft **41.** 8 cm **43.** 16 ft

Page 530 Lesson 14-2
3. 5 **5.** 6 **7.** 7 **9.** 8 **11.** 9 **13.** -7 **15.** -5 **17.** 51 **19.** 3 **21.** 2 **23.** 4 **25.** -8 **27.** 35 **28.** about 113 ft^2 **29.** -11 **31.** 20 ft

Page 532 Lesson 14-3
5. 89 students **7.** 214 students **9.** 152 pages

Pages 535–536 Lesson 14-4
7. irrational, real **9.** rational, real **11.** whole numbers, integers, rational numbers, real numbers **13.** rational numbers, real numbers **15.** whole numbers, integers, rational numbers, real numbers **17.** irrational numbers, real numbers **19.** rational numbers, real numbers **21.** integers, rational numbers, real numbers **23.** 7, -7 **25.** 2, -2 **27.** 11, -11 **29.** 1, -1 **31.** 5.3, -5.3 **33.** 3.3,-3.3 **35.** $2\sqrt{7}$ **37.** $3\sqrt{6}$ **39.** $3\sqrt{10}$ **41.** $8\sqrt{2}$ **46.** $2x + 4x \geq 8x$; true; false **47.** 8300 g **48.** $11.76 **49.** true **50.** 9 **51.** -4 **53.** 1 hour

Pages 539–540 Lesson 14-5
5. 17 cm; 8 cm, 15 cm **7.** $c^2 = 9^2 + 12^2$; 15 m **9.** $c^2 = 9^2 + 40^2$; 41 cm **11.** 41 ft **13.** 15 in. **15.** 13 yd **17.** 39 in. **19.** 99, -99 **21.** 91, -91 **23.** 11, -11 **25.** 36 m **27.** 8 ft **29.** 12 km **31.** 51 in. **33.** no **35.** no **37.** yes **39.** $18a + 8$ **40.** 56.87 **41.** 210 cm^3 **42.** false **43.** $2\sqrt{14}$ **45.** 20 ft

Pages 543–544 Lesson 14-6
3. $c^2 = 5^2 + 9^2$; 10.3 ft **5.** $125^2 = 100^2 + b^2$; 75 m **7.** 10 km **9.** 3 ft **11.** 15.3 m **12.** true **13.** 26 m

Page 544 Mid-Chapter Quiz
1. 6 **2.** 169 **3.** -3.5 **4.** integer, rational, real **5.** irrational, real **6.** 18, -18 **7.** 18, -18 **8.** 5.7 cm **9.** 13 ft **10.** 11 students

Pages 546–547 Lesson 14-7
3. 4 in. **5.** $2\frac{1}{8}$ in. **7.** $3\sqrt{2}$ ft **9.** $2\frac{1}{2}\sqrt{2}$ cm **11.** 4 in. **13.** 9 m **15.** 10.6 ft **17.** 1.9 cm **19.** 9.6 cm **21.** 1.5 in. **23.** $-1\frac{1}{32}$ **24.** about 59 m^3 **25.** 5 ft **27.** 4 ft

Page 549 Lesson 14-8
3. $\frac{12}{5}$; $\frac{5}{12}$ **5.** 0.5774 **7.** 1.7321 **9.** 1.2799 **11.** 8.1443 **13.** 5° **15.** 70° **17.** 40° **19.** obtuse **20.** 5 cm **21.** $4\frac{1}{8}$ in. **22.** $\tan 22° = \frac{h}{d}$

Pages 551-552 Lesson 14-9
5. $\frac{8}{17}, \frac{15}{17}, \frac{15}{17}, \frac{8}{17}$ **7.** $\frac{3}{5}$; $\frac{4}{5}$; $\frac{3}{5}$; $\frac{4}{5}$ **9.** 0.9397 **11.** 0.8090 **13.** 0.5299 **15.** 0.6691 **17.** 63° **19.** 45° **21.** 71° **23.** 76° **25.** m^8 **26.** 50.0 cm **27.** 1.4281 **29.** $\cos 80° = \frac{d}{l}$

Pages 555–557 Lesson 14-10
3. cosine; 35.6 cm **5.** cosine; 64.8° **7.** sine; 85.1 mm **9.** 41.7 cm **11.** 5.7 ft **13.** 10.9 cm **14.** 56 in^2 **15.** 0.1219 **17.** 560.2 ft **19.** 3.3 ft

Pages 558–559 Chapter 14 Review
1. square **3.** rational **5.** 30°-60° **7.** 7 **9.** -6 **11.** $4\sqrt{3}$ **13.** $10\sqrt{3}$ **15.** whole number, integer, rational, real **17.** rational, real **19.** 20 m **21.** 34 cm **23.** 16 ft **25.** 6 m **27.** 3 cm **29.** $\frac{4}{3}$ **31.** 35.5 in. **33.** 10.5 ft **35.** 31.8 ft

Chapter 15 Polynomials

Pages 566–567 Lesson 15-1
5. yes **7.** yes **9.** yes **11.** no **13.** 3 **15.** 1 **17.** 7 **19.** 1 **21.** yes; binomial **23.** yes; trinomial **25.** no **27.** no **29.** yes; monomial **31.** yes; binomial **33.** 6 **35.** 1 **37.** 4 **39.** 4 **41.** 14 **43.** 7 **45.** 2 **47.** 3 **49.** 4 **51.** 96 **53.** 2 **55.** 10 **56.** 9 **57.** false **58.** 1 and itself **59.** $b \leq 8.2$ **60.** 31.2 **61.** 90 mm^2 **62.** -14 **63.** $2xy + 2y^2 + 2yz$

Pages 569–570 Lesson 15-2
5. $8x + 1$ **7.** $7x^2 + 5x + 5$ **9.** $11n - t$ **11.** $28n - 8m$ **13.** $11r - 3s$ **15.** $12x + 15y$ **17.** $-a$ **19.** $10a + 5ab + 2b^2$ **21.** $-4b^2 + 13b - 15$ **23.** $9a - 3b + 3c$ **25.** $-7ax^3 - 11ax^2$ **27.** 19 **29.** 39 **30.** about 25.12 inches **31.** 3.42 ft^2 **32.** 8, -8 **33.** yes **35.** $3x - 5$ inches

Pages 572–573 Lesson 15-3
3. $3x + 1$ **5.** 1 **7.** $x^2 + 3x$ **9.** $-a$ **11.** $-12xy$ **13.** $-4n + 1$ **15.** $-4a - 3b$ **17.** $-5g^2 + 3g + 8$ **19.** $-6x^2 - 3xy + 2y^2$ **21.** $4m + 2$ **23.** $-3x + 3$ **25.** $x + 3y$ **27.** 17 **29.** $9y^2 + 11y + 5$ **31.** $4a^2 - 8ab + 6b^2$ **33.** $3y^2 + 4y + 3$ **35.** $-a + 2b - 8c$ **37.** $16m^2n^2 + 10mn - 23$ **39.** 0 **40.** quadrant 2 **41.** 105 ft^2 **42.** 30 cm **43.** $7a^2 - 2a - 5$

Page 573 Mid-Chapter Quiz
1. yes; monomial **2.** yes; binomial **3.** yes; monomial **4.** yes; binomial **5.** no **6.** yes; trinomial **7.** $4a + 5$ **8.** $4x - 1$ **9.** $3r^2 + 7$ **10.** $-3x + 6y$ **11.** $6n^2 - 8n + 5$ **12.** $-9c^2 - cd - d^2$

Pages 575–576 Lesson 15-4

5. 64 **7.** $9y^2$ **9.** x^4y^6 **11.** $n^{12}r^8$ **13.** 5^9 or 1,953,125 **15.** m^{10} **17.** $125c^3$ **19.** $-27z^3$ **21.** y^4z^4 **23.** x^3y^9 **25.** $27a^3b^{12}$ **27.** $-8x^6$ **29.** $12x^3$ **31.** $-48x^3y^2$ **33.** -24 **35.** 324 **37.** 36 **39.** 729 **41.** 8 **42.** 100 pens **43.** 3014.4 cm^2 **44.** $7\sqrt{2}$ inches **45.** $3x^2 + 10$ **47.** a. 2^{20} b. 10^6 or 1,000,000

Page 579 Lesson 15-5

5. $x^2 + 3x$ **7.** $3x^2 + 2x$ **9.** $3m^2 + 27m$ **11.** $-3x^2 + 2x$ **13.** $3a^4 - 6a^3$ **15.** $-60n^5 + 18n^3$ **17.** $7a^2 - 14a + 21$ **19.** $-18k^3 + 27k + 54$ **21.** $7x^4 + 21x^2 - 13x$ **23.** 12 outcomes **24.** 322 cm; more significant digits **25.** 0.9205 **26.** $18y^7$ **27.** a. x^2; $7x$ b. yes c. distributive property

Pages 581–582 Lesson 15-6

3. $2x + 2$; $x + 2$; $2x^2 + 6x + 4$ **5.** $x + 2$; $x + 2$; $x^2 + 4x + 4$ **7.** $x^2 + 4x + 4$ **9.** $2x^2 + 7x + 3$ **11.** $2x^2 + 9x + 4$ **13.** $6x^2 + 7x + 2$ **15.** $3x^2 + 11x + 6$ **16.** 26° **17.** 10 **18.** $3r^5 - 15r^4 + 6r^3$ **19.** increased by $7x + 12$; $(x + 3)(x + 4) = x^2 + 7x + 12$

Page 585 Lesson 15-7

1. Darla: gerbil, Amanda: cat, Norma: dog, Tara: parrot
3. It eliminated the pet as a possibility for the other girls.
5. 5 people

Pages 586–587 Chapter 15 Review

1. sum **3.** greatest **5.** distributive property **7.** no **9.** yes; trinomial **11.** no **13.** 3 **15.** 5 **17.** 5 **19.** $4a^2 - 5ab$ **21.** $y^2 - 5y$ **23.** $-12z$ **25.** $8a^2 - 8a - 17$ **27.** $-8x^3$ **29.** $-40c^4d^3$ **31.** $-6a^8b^7$ **33.** $-5x^2 + 3x$ **35.** $-3y^3 - 24y^2 + 12y$ **37.** $-6az^3 - 12a^2z^2 - 3a^3z$ **39.** $2x^2 + 3x + 1$ **41.** Lindsay: physics, Lee: math, Anna: music, Marcos: art

Index

M

P

Photo Credits

Cover: Richard DeWeese Advertising Photography

vii, ix, xi, xiii, Aaron Haupt/Glencoe; **1,** Studiohio; **3(t),** Doug Martin; **3(b),** Ted Rice; **4,** Bud Fowle Photography; **12,** Doug Martin; **15,** Al Tielemans/DUOMO; **19,** David M. Dennis; **22,** National Portrait Gallery; **25, 26,** Doug Martin; **30, 31,** First Image; **33,** Vic Bider/The Stock Market; **34,** First Image; **38,** Bob Gomel/The Stock Market; **39,** Larry M. Roberts; **41,** DUOMO; **45,** Charles Krebs/The Stock Market; **46,** E.R. Degginger; **47,** First Image; **49,** Doug Martin; **50,** E.R. Degginger; **52,** Edi Ann Otto; **53,** Phil Degginger; **54,** NASA; **56,** file photo; **58,** Tim Courlas/COSI; **60,** California Institute of Technology; **62(t),** Daniel A. Erickson; **62(b),** U.S. Naval Institute; **66,** Paul Nesbit; **70,** First Image; **73,** William D. Popejoy; **74,76,** First Image; **77,** Studiohio; **78,** Ruth Bogart; **79,** Tim Courlas; **80,** Jeff Smith/The Image Bank; **81,** Geri Murphy; **83,** Edi Ann Otto; **84,** Bud Fowle Photography; **86, 87,** Kenji Kerins; **89,** David Dennison; **92,** Doug Martin; **95,** Bud Fowle Photography; **97(t),** Tim Courlas; **97(b),** Bob Daemmrich; **98,** Doris DeWitt/TSW; **101,** Tim Courlas; **102,** Pictures Unlimited; **104,** Sylvain Legrand/Agence Vandystadt/Photo Researchers; **105,** Doug Martin; **108(l),** Gay Bumgarner/TSW; **108(r),** Bud Fowle Photography; **110(t),** Bud Fowle Photography; **110(b),** Randy Schieber; **113,** Hank deLespinasse/The Image Bank; **115,** Ken Van Dyne; **116,** Stan Osolinski/The Stock Market; **117,** Mitchell Funk/The Image Bank; **119,** Doug Martin; **121,** Randy Schieber; **123,** Kenji Kerins; **124,** C.L. Chryslin/The Image Bank; **126, 127,** Kenji Kerins; **128,** John Kelly/The Image Bank; **130,** Studiohio; **131,** Ted Rice; **134,** ITTC Productions/The Image Bank; **135,** Leonard Kamsler Photography; **136,** Studiohio; **138,** Jana Schneider/The Image Bank; **139,** Bud Fowle Photography; **140,** First Image; **142,** Bud Fowle Photography; **143,** First Image; **145,** William E. Ferguson; **146,** Bud Fowle Photography; **148,** Alvin Staffan; **149,** Doug Martin; **152, 153,** Studiohio; **154(l),** Historical Pictures Service, Inc.; **154(r),** Garry Gay/The Image Bank; **155,** P & G Bowater/The Image Bank; **158,** LLNL/Science Source/Photo Researchers; **159,** TSW; **161,** Kenji Kerins; **162,** Doug Martin; **164,** Paul J. Sutton/DUOMO; **165,** Mitchell Layton/DUOMO; **166,** Bud Fowle Photography; **169,** Chuck Muhlstock/FPG; **171,** Randy Schieber; **172(t),** E.R. Degginger; **172(b),** Edward Bower/The Image Bank; **174-182,** Studiohio; **185,** Anne Rippy/The Image Bank; **187,** Studiohio; **188,** Elaine Comer; **189-191,** Studiohio; **192,** First Image; **193,** Studiohio; **194(t),** First Image; **194(b),** Doug Martin; **195,** Bud Fowle Photography; **199,** Paul J. Sutton/DUOMO; **202,** Phil Degginger; **204,** AIRSCAN™ Thermogram by Daedalus Enterprises, Inc., courtesy National Geographic; **205,** First Image; **207,** Roger K. Burnard; **209,** First Image; **210,** Geri Murphy; **211,** David Frazier; **213,** Roy Morsch/The Stock Market; **215,** David Woods/The Stock Market; **217,** Department of Defense; **219(l),** First Image; **219(r),** Steve Lissau; **222,** First Image; **227,** Ed Bock/The Stock Market; **228(l),** David Frazier; **228(r),** Randy Schieber; **231-235,** First Image; **237(t),** Fred E. Mang, Jr./National Park Service; **237(b),** Susan Leach; **238,** First Image; **239,** file photo; **240,** Al Tielemans/DUOMO; **241,** Bryan Yablonsky/DUOMO; **243,** David Sailors/The Stock Market; **244(t),** First Image; **244(b),** Pictures Unlimited; **247,** Phil Degginger; **250,** Joseph Nettis/Photo Researchers; **251,** Doug Martin; **252,** First Image; **253, 255(t),** Randy Schieber; **255(b), 256,** First Image; **258,** Tim Courlas; **259(t),** Kenji Kerins; **259(b),** Tim Courlas; **261,** Paul Steel/The Stock Market; **263,** Studiohio; **264,** Randy Schieber; **267,** Tim Courlas; **270,** Doug Martin; **271,** Studiohio; **272(t),** David Madison/DUOMO; **272(b),** Jerry Wahler/Photo Researchers; **274,** Michael Philip Manheim/The Stock Market; **276,** Tim Courlas; **277,** NASA; **279,** Joseph Nettis/Photo Researchers; **280,** First Image; **282,** Aaron Haupt; **285,** C.L. Chryslin/The Image Bank; **286,** First Image; **287,** Steve Lissau; **288,** Leo Mason/The Image Bank; **289,** Dominique Sarraute/The Image Bank; **290(t),** Historical Pictures Service, Inc.; **290(b),** Aaron Haupt; **292,** Historical Pictures Service, Inc.; **296,** James Westwater; **299,** Walter Bibikow/The Image Bank; **303,** Aaron Haupt; **304,** Tim Courlas; **308,** E.R. Degginger; **315,** Roger K. Burnard; **317,** Cobalt Productions; **319,** Aaron Haupt; **322,** Ruth Dixon; **324,** Studiohio; **326,** Art Resources/Scala; **327,** Susan Biddle/The White House; **329,** Doug Martin; **330,** Kenji Kerins; **331(t),** Kenji Kerins; **331(b),** Steve Vidler/Leo deWys, Inc.; **332,** Pictures Unlimited; **333,** NASA; **335,** First Image; **336,** Bud Fowle Photography; **342, 343,** Doug Martin; **345,** Thomas Braise/The Stock Market; **346, 347,** Doug Martin; **349, 351,** Kenji Kerins; **352,** Mary Lou Uttermohlen; **353, 354,** Kenji Kerins; **357,** Ruth Dixon; **360,** Ralph Mercer/TSW; **361,** Historical Pictures Service, Inc./Victor Company Trademark; **362,** Luria/FPG; **364,** First Image; **366,** Doug Martin; **367,** Tim Courlas; **368,** Doug Martin; **369,** Studiohio; **372;** Rick Rickman/DUOMO; **374,** Steve Vidler/Leo deWys, Inc.; **376, 378,** Doug Martin; **382,** Studiohio; **383,** Bob Daemmrich; **386(t),** Pictures Unlimited; **386(b),** Susan Rhoades-Martin; **388,** Pictures Unlimited; **390,** First Image; **393,** Aaron Haupt; **395,** Ralph Mercer/TSW; **398,** Bud Fowle Photography; **401,** First Image;

402, Mary Lou Uttermohlen; **404,** Elaine Comer-Shay; **405,** Bud Fowle Photography; **406,** Doug Martin; **407,** David Frazier; **408(l),** Mitchell Layton/DUOMO; **408(r),** John Scheiber/The Stock Market; **409,** Bud Fowle Photography; **410,** Light Source; **411,** David Brownell/The Image Bank; **413,** Light Source; **414,** Historical Pictures Service, Inc.; **415, 417,** Mary Lou Uttermohlen; **423,** D. Luria/FPG; **424,** Doug Martin; **425,** David Madison/DUOMO; **426,** Studiohio; **429,** Randy Schieber; **430,** Doug Martin; **431,** Roy Morsch/The Stock Market; **433,** Bud Fowle Photography; **436,** Courtesy Chrysler Corporation, Dodge Stealth R/T; **437,** Andrew Sacks/TSW; **438,** Agricultural Research Service, USDA(PN4132); **442,** NASA; **444,** Elizabeth Hathon/The Stock Market; **445,** Photobank/Arnie Rosner/Focus Stock Photo; **450,** Steve Lissau; **459,** Randy Trine; **461,** Sharon Kurgis; **465,** Gabe Palmer/The Stock Market; **471,** Pictures Unlimited; **474,** file photo; **479,** Andrew Sacks/TSW; **482,** Doug Armand/TSW; **483,** J. Paul Kennedy/The Stock Market; **488,** Diamond Rose Photography; **492,** Light Source; **493,** file photo; **494, 495,** Light Source; **500,** Tim Courlas; **501,** The Telegraph Colour Library/FPG; **502,** Mary Lou Uttermohlen; **506,** Doug Martin; **509,** First Image; **514(t),** Mary Lou Uttermohlen; **514(b),** Bob Thomason/TSW; **515,** Doug Martin; **517,** Tim Courlas; **518,** Steve Ross/Leo deWys, Inc.; **521,** Doug Armand/TSW; **524,** The Telegraph Colour Library/FPG; **525,** Ron Rovtar; **526,** Steve Lissau; **528,** Paul Brown; **529(t),** Greg Miller; **529(b), 530,** Bud Fowle Photography; **536,** Ed Shay; **538, 542,** Doug Martin; **547,** Bud Fowle Photography; **548,** David Frazier; **551,** Bud Fowle Photography; **554,** Edna Douthat; **556,** Henry T. Kaiser/Leo deWys, Inc.; **557(t),** Gwen Fidler; **557(b),** Bud Fowle Photography; **559,** The Telegraph Colour Library/FPG; **562,** Al Tielemans/DUOMO; **563,** Andrew Popper/DUOMO; **564,** Lynn Stone; **565,** David M. Dennis; **567,** Historical Pictures Service, Inc.; **568,** Mary Lou Uttermohlen; **569,** Doug Martin; **574,** Mary Lou Uttermohlen; **579,** Gerard Photography; **582,** Doug Martin; **584,** Mary Lou Uttermohlen; **585,** Doug Martin; **587,** Al Tielemans/DUOMO